WITHDRAWN

A COMPREHENSIVE TREATISE ON INORGANIC AND THEORETICAL CHEMISTRY

VOLUME XII

U, Mn, Ma and Re, Fe (Part I)

The complete work

A COMPREHENSIVE TREATISE ON INORGANIC AND THEORETICAL CHEMISTRY

In Sixteen Volumes. With Diagrams.

SUPPLEMENT TO MELLOR'S COMPREHENSIVE TREATISE ON INORGANIC AND THEORETICAL CHEMISTRY

Other volumes in preparation

By the same author

MODERN **IN**ORGANIC CHEMISTRY

A COMPREHENSIVE TREATISE ON

INORGANIC
AND THEORETICAL
CHEMISTRY

BY

J. W. MELLOR, D.Sc., F.R.S.

VOLUME XII

WITH 320 DIAGRAMS

LONGMANS

LONGMANS, GREEN AND CO LTD
48 Grosvenor Street, London W.1

*Associated companies, branches and representatives
throughout the world*

FIRST PUBLISHED . . . 1932
REPRINTED BY NOVOGRAPHIC PROCESS
1942, 1947, 1953, 1957, 1961 AND 1965

Printed in Great Britain by
Lowe and Brydone (Printers) Limited, London, N.W.10

Dedicated

TO THE

PRIVATES IN THE GREAT ARMY
OF WORKERS IN CHEMISTRY

THEIR NAMES HAVE BEEN FORGOTTEN

THEIR WORK REMAINS

PREFACE

I AM greatly obliged to my friends Messrs. L. S. Theobald, B.Sc., A.R.C.S., A. T. Green, F.Inst.P., A.I.C., and F. H. Clews, M.Sc., A.I.C., for reading the proofs of this and preceding volumes.

J. W. M.

CONTENTS

CHAPTER LXIII

URANIUM

CHAPTER LXIV

MANGANESE

CHAPTER LXV

MASURIUM AND RHENIUM

CHAPTER LXVI

IRON

ABBREVIATIONS

aq. = aqueous

atm. = atmospheric or atmosphere(s)

at. vol. = atomic volume(s)

at. wt. = atomic weight(s)

$T^°$ or $°K$ = absolute degrees of temperature

b.p. = boiling point(s)

$\theta^°$ = centigrade degrees of temperature

coeff. = coefficient

conc. = concentrated or concentration

dil. = dilute

eq. = equivalent(s)

f.p. = freezing point(s)

m.p. = melting point(s)

mol(s) = $\begin{cases} \text{gram-molecule(s)} \\ \text{gram-molecular} \end{cases}$

mol(s). = $\begin{cases} \text{molecule(s)} \\ \text{molecular} \end{cases}$

mol. ht. = molecular heat(s)

mol. vol. = molecular volume(s)

mol. wt. = molecular weight(s)

press. = pressure(s)

sat. = saturated

soln. = solution(s)

sp. gr. = specific gravity (gravities)

sp. ht. = specific heat(s)

sp. vol. = specific volume(s)

temp. = temperature(s)

vap. = vapour

In the **cross references** the first number in clarendon type is the number of the volume; the second number refers to the chapter; and the succeeding number refers to the "§," section. Thus **5.** 38, 24 refers to § 24, chapter 38, volume 5.

The oxides, hydrides, halides, sulphides, sulphates, carbonates, nitrates, and phosphates are considered with the basic elements; the other compounds are taken in connection with the acidic element. The double or complex salts in connection with a given element include those associated with elements previously discussed. The carbides, silicides, titanides, phosphides, arsenides, etc., are considered in connection with carbon, silicon, titanium, etc. The intermetallic compounds of a given element include those associated with elements previously considered.

The use of **triangular diagrams** for representing the properties of three-component systems was suggested by G. G. Stokes (*Proc. Roy. Soc.*, **49.** 174, 1891). The method was immediately taken up in many directions and it has proved of great value. With practice it becomes as useful for representing the properties of ternary mixtures as squared paper is for binary mixtures. The principle of triangular diagrams is based on the fact that in an equilateral triangle the sum of the perpendicular distances of any point from the three sides is a constant. Given any three substances *A*, *B*, and *C*, the composition of any possible combination of these can be represented by a point in or on the triangle. The apices of the

ABBREVIATIONS

triangle represent the single components A, B, and C, the sides of the triangle represent binary mixtures of A and B, B and C, or C and A; and points within the triangle, ternary mixtures. The compositions of the mixtures can be represented in percentages, or referred to unity, 10, etc. In Fig. 1, pure A will be represented by a point at the apex marked A. If 100 be the

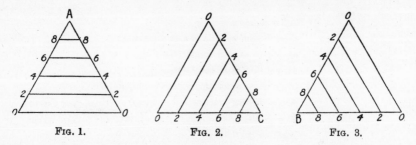

FIG. 1. FIG. 2. FIG. 3.

standard of reference, the point A represents 100 per cent. of A and nothing else; mixtures containing 80 per cent. of A are represented by a point on the line 88, 60 per cent. of A by a point on the line 66, etc. Similarly with B and C—Figs. 3 and 2 respectively. Combine Figs. 1, 2, and 3 into one diagram by superposition, and Fig. 4 results. Any point in this

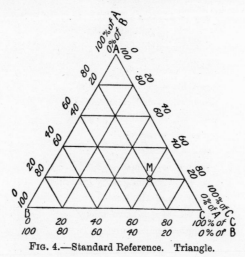

FIG. 4.—Standard Reference. Triangle.

diagram, Fig. 4, thus represents a ternary mixture. For instance, the point M represents a mixture containing 20 per cent. of A, 20 per cent. of B, and 60 per cent. of C.

CHAPTER LXIII

URANIUM

§ 1. The History of Uranium

THE black mineral called **pitchblende** from Joachimsthal in Bohemia and Johann-georgenstadt in the Erzgebirge of Saxony was recognized by the early mineralogists, but they were puzzled with its classification. In 1727, F. E. Brückmann [1] called it *Schwarz Beckerz*; J. G. Wallerius, *Beckblände*, or *pseudogalena picca*—that is, a pitchy zinc blende; and I. Eques a Born, *Pechblende*, or *pseudogalena nigra compacta*. J. G. Wallerius, I. Eques a Born, and M. T. Brünnich classed the mineral among the zinc ores; but A. G. Werner transferred it to the iron ores, and called it *Pech-blende*, or *Eisenpecherz*; and later, A. G. Werner suggested that the mineral might contain the metallic radical tungsten or wolfram. In August, 1786, M. H. Klaproth [2] read a paper: *Chemische Untersuchungen des Uranerzes*, in which he showed that the mineral partly dissolves in aqua regia, and that the cold, clear soln. when treated with alkalies deposits a yellow oxide. A soln. of the precipitated oxide in sulphuric acid gave crystals of a lemon-yellow sulphate; in nitric acid, crystals of greenish nitrate; in hydrochloric acid, yellowish-green crystals of the chloride; in vinegar, topaz-yellow crystals of the acetate; and in phosphoric acid, amorphous, yellowish-white flocculi of the phosphate. He thus proved that " the mineral does not belong to the ores of zinc, to those of iron, nor yet to those of tungsten or wolfram, and, in general, to none of the metallic substances hitherto known; but, on the contrary, it consists of an *eigenthumliche, selbständige, metallische Substanz*. Consequently, its former designations pitchblende, pitchironstone, etc., are no longer applicable, and must be replaced by another more appropriate name. I have chosen that of *uranite*, as a kind of memorial that the chemical discovery of this new element happened in the epoch of the astronomical discovery of the planet Uranus." At the beginning of his memoir M. H. Klaproth said :

The ancient philosophers, who considered our globe as the centre of the material universe; and the sun on the contrary, merely as a planet destined, like the others, to a periodical circumvolution round the earth, flattered themselves that they had discovered a great mystery of nature, in the agreement of the seven celestial bodies which they assumed for planets, with the seven metals known in those times. In consequence of the various hypotheses which they founded on this supposed mystery, they allotted to each metal a certain planet, by whose astral effluvia its generation and maturation were to be promoted. In like manner they took from these planets their names and symbols, to designate the metals subordinated to them. However, as the above number of metals has long since been increased by later researches; and as the discovery of new planets has not kept pace with that of metals, the metals newly discovered have been deprived of the honour of receiving their names from the planets, like the older ones.

M. H. Klaproth called the element **uranium**—after the planet Uranus, at that time the *dernier cri* of celestial exploration. J. G. Leonhardi [3] suggested naming it *klaprothium*, in honour of its discoverer. The etymology of the term uranium was discussed by P. Diergart, and H. von Freudenberg.

In 1789, M. H. Klaproth found uranium in *green mica*, the *mica viridis* of I. Eques a Born. A. G. Werner had named the mineral *torberite*—after Torber Bergman—or **torbernite**—the latinized form Torbernus as written by T. Bergman himself. Objections were raised to naming minerals after persons, and A. G. Werner substituted the term *chalcolite*—from χαλκός, copper—signifying, as he said, a cupriferous mineral, in allusion to T. Bergman's analysis indicating that the mineral is muriated copper and clay. After M. H. Klaproth had shown that the mineral contains uranium and not copper as the dominant base, A. G. Werner, and D. L. G. Karsten dropped the term chalcolite, and called it *uranium mica*—*Uranglimmer*. M. H. Klaproth called it *uranites spathosus* ; A. Breithaupt, *uranphyllite*, and *cuprouranite* ; A. Aikin, *uranite* ; whilst W. H. Miller, and J. D. Dana kept the old term of A. G. Werner, *tobernite*.

M. H. Klaproth heated a mixture of yellow uranium oxide with a reducing agent, and obtained a black powder which he considered to be metallic uranium. He said :

I triturated 120 grains of the yellow oxide to a paste with linseed oil, and caused the oil gently to burn on a sherd. There remained 85 grains of a heavy black powder which I exposed in a well-secured charcoal crucible to the medium heat of a porcelain kiln. . . . The metallized oxide of pitchblende forms a heavy, loosely coherent mass which by friction between the fingers can be divided into a dark brown powder possessed of a metallic lustre.

This result was confirmed by J. B. Richter,[4] C. F. Bucholz, A. Schönberg, L. R. Lecanu and M. Serbat, J. A. Arfvedson, and J. J. Berzelius between the years 1792 and 1823. This is strange. E. M. Péligot, in his *Recherches sur l'urane* (1841), pointed out that a mistake had been made. The supposed uranium was really the lowest oxide, UO_2—or possibly a mixture of that oxide with uranium—derived from yellow uranium oxide by reduction with carbon. E. M. Péligot obtained elemental uranium by reducing the tetrachloride with sodium. The history of uranium has been discussed by J. L. C. Zimmermann.[5]

REFERENCES.

[1] F. E. Brückmann, *Magnalia Dei in Subterraneis, oder Unterirdische Schatzkammer aller Königreiche und Länder*, Helmstadt, 1. 204, 1727 ; J. G. Wallerius, *Mineralogia*, Stockholm, 249, 1747 ; M. T. Brünnich, *Forsög til mineralogie*, Tronthjem, 1777 ; I. Eques a Born, *Lythophylacium Bornianum*, Pragae, 133, 1772 ; A. G. Werner, *Berg. Journ.*, 1. 612, 1789.

[2] M. H. Klaproth, *Mém. Acad. Berlin*, 273, 1789 ; 160, 1792 ; *Beiträge zur chemischen Kenntnis der Mineralkörper*, Berlin, 2. 197, 1797 ; London, 477, 1801 ; *Crell's Ann.*, ii, 387, 1789.

[3] J. G. Leonhardi, in P. J. Macquer, *Chymisches Wörterbuch*, Leipzig, 6. 597, 1809 ; M. H. Klaproth, *Schriften Ges. Berlin*, 273, 1789 ; 160, 1792 ; *Crell's Ann.*, ii, 387, 1789 ; *Beiträge zur chemischen Kenntniss der Mineralkörper*, Berlin, 2. 217, 1797 ; London, 492, 1801 ; I. Eques a Born, *Lythophylacium Bornianum*, Pragae, 1. 42, 1772 ; A. G. Werner, *Berg. Journ.*, 2. 376, 1789 ; *Versuch einer Mineralogie*, Leipzig, 1. 217, 1780 ; *Handbuch der Mineralogie*, Leipzig, 1. 55, 308, 1803 ; D. L. G. Karsten, *Ueber Herrn Werners Verbesserungen in der Mineralogie auf Veranlassung der freimüthigen Gedanken*, Berlin, 43, 1793 ; T. Bergman, *De minerarum docimasia humida*, Upsala, 1780 ; *Opuscula physica et chemica*, 2. 431, 1782 ; London, 2. 446, 1788 ; P. Diergart, *Chem. Ztg.*, 23. 103, 1900 ; H. von Freudenberg, *Journ. prakt. Chem.*, (2), 61. 497, 1900 ; A. Breithaupt, *Berg. Hütt. Ztg.*, 24. 302, 1865 ; *Kurze Charakteristik des Mineralsystems*, Freiburg 1820 ; W. H. Miller, *Introduction to Mineralogy*, London, 517, 1852 ; A. Aikin, *Manual of Mineralogy*, London, 1814 ; J. D. Dana, *A System of Mineralogy*, New York, 856, 1892.

[4] J. B. Richter, *Ueber die neueren Gegenstände der Chymie*, Breslau, 1. 1, 1791 ; 9. 36, 1798 ; *Gehlen's Journ.*, 4. 402, 1805 ; C. F. Bucholz, *ib.*, 4. 17, 134, 1805 ; *Beiträge zur Erweiterung und Berichtigung der Chemie*, Erfurt, 1. 62, 1799 ; J. A. Arfvedson, *Svenska Akad. Handl.*, 404, 1822 ; *Ann. Phil.*, 7. 253, 1824 ; *Pogg. Ann.*, 1. 245, 1824 ; *Schweigger's Journ.*, 44. 8, 1825 ; J. J. Berzelius, *ib.*, 44. 191, 1825 ; *Pogg. Ann.*, 1. 359, 1824 ; *Svenska Akad. Handl.*, 152, 1823 ; *Ann. Phil.*, 9. 266, 1825 ; A. Schönberg, *De conjunctione chemica ejusque rationibus*, Upsalæ, 18, 1813 ; *Schweigger's Journ.*, 15. 285, 1815 ; E. M. Péligot, *Compt. Rend.*, 12. 735, 1841 ; 22. 487, 1846 ; 42. 73, 1856 ; *Ann. Chim. Phys.*, (3), 5. 5, 1842 ; (3), 20. 329, 1847 ; *Journ. Pharm. Chim.*, (2), 27. 522, 1841 ; *Liebig's Ann.*, 41. 141, 1841 ; 43. 258, 1842 ; *Journ. prakt. Chem.*, (1), 24. 442, 1841 ; (1), 38. 112, 1846 ; L. R. Lecanu and M. Serbat, *Quart. Journ. Science*, 17. 139, 1824 ; *Journ. Pharm. Chim.*, (2), 9. 141, 1823 ; L. R. Lecanu, *ib.*, (2), 11. 279, 1825.

[5] J. L. C. Zimmermann, *Liebig's Ann.*, 213. 285, 1882 ; 216. 22, 1883.

§ 2. The Occurrence of Uranium

Uranium does not occur native, but it occurs in a few scarce minerals, and is sparsely distributed in the earth's crust. According to F. W. Clarke and H. S. Washington,[1] the average proportion of uranium in the igneous rocks of the earth's crust is 8×10^{-5} per cent.; J. H. L. Vogt estimated $n \times 10^{-8}$ per cent. They added that, in general, uranium is nearly as abundant as copper. W. Vernadsky gave $0 \cdot 0_5 3$ per cent. for the proportion of uranium, and $0 \cdot 0_4 5$ for the atomic proportion of uranium in the earth's crust. W. and J. Noddack and O. Berg gave 7×10^{-8} for the absolute abundance of uranium in the earth's crust. The general subject was discussed by H. S. Washington, W. Lindgren, G. Tammann, E. Herlinger, A. von Antropoff, O. Hahn, W. and J. Noddack and O. Berg, J. Joly, V. G. Khlopin and M. A. Pasvik, and R. A. Sonder.

H. A. Rowland,[2] C. E. St. John, M. N. Saha, and C. C. Hutchins and E. L. Holden classed uranium with the elements whose presence in the sun is doubtful. J. N. Lockyer attributed to uranium the lines 3931·0, 3943·0, and 3965·8 in the solar spectrum, but the measurements of B. Hasselberg made this doubtful. He found that 75 per cent. of the principal uranium lines are absent from the solar

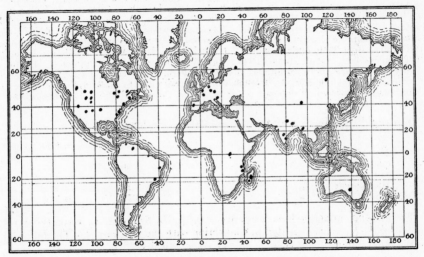

Fig. 1.—The Geographical Distribution of Uranium Ores.

spectrum. Against this, G. Meyer and H. Greulich found that if less than 7 per cent. of uranium be present, the spectrum of uranium is obscured by the spectral lines of the other metals. The relatively large proportion of iron in the sun is sufficient to account for the observations of B. Hasselberg without accepting the inference that uranium is absent from the sun. J. N. Lockyer reported uranium lines in the spectra of the colder stars. This, and the reports of H. von Sieliger and H. Kienle are doubtful. E. Paneth and co-workers found in 17 meteorites an average of $2 \cdot 3 \times 10^{-6}$ grm. per gram.

The geographical distribution of uranium ores is illustrated by Fig. 1.[3] The main localities are as follow :

Europe.—Virtually all the pitchblende of the **British Isles** [4] is obtained from Cornwall— Redruth, Providence, Wheal Gorland, South Basset, Wheal Edwards, and St. Day. A little has been reported in Devon. Uranium minerals occur near Limoges, and at Symphonen, near Autun, in **France.** There is also a small deposit near Vielsalm, in **Belgium,** and one in Bergell.[5] There is a deposit in **Portugal,**[6] east and west of Vizeu. There is a deposit in **Turkey** near Adrianople. Uranium minerals have been found in **Russia** [7]—Lotsmanskaja, near Ekaterinoslav ; Khutor Golowin, near Shitomit ; Wolf

Island, Lake Omega ; Carelia, Arctic Coast—*vide infra*, Asia. The ore also occurs near Moss, Annerod, Elvestad, Huggenäskilen, Skraatrop, and Arendal in **Norway**.[8] Deposits have been reported in **Germany**[9]—Saxon Voigtland, Schwarzwald, Falkenstein, and Steinig, and in the Siebengebirge. In **Saxony**—Freiburg, Dippoldeswalde, Niederschlag, Schneeberg, Johanngeorgenstadt, Breitenbrunn, Gottesburg, Marienberg, Eibenstock, and Neustädtel. In **Bohemia**—Joachimsthal, Pribram, Zinnwald, and Neudeck ; at Wölsenberg, Bavaria ; and at Rezbanya in **Hungary**.

Asia.—There is an occurrence of mendeléeffite, etc., near Sludjanka in Transbaikalia, **Siberia** ; [10] and in **Turkestan**, at Tjaja Mujun, Prialaj Mountains, Ferghaua. Deposits in **India**[11] have been reported in Bengal ; Pichhli and Banekhap in Gaya District, and Rapur Taluq, Nellore district, Madras ; on Abraki Pahar, east of Banekhap, Central India ; and in Ceylon. There is also a deposit in Burma,[12] and autunite occurs at the Beau Site, Caoson, Nguyen-Binh, and Pia Quac, Cuobang ; south of Andijan, Siberia ; [13] and in the islands of **Japan**.[14]

Africa.—There are deposits of uranium minerals at Katanga, **Belgian Congo**,[15] and at Morogoro district, Tanganyika Territory.[16]

Madagascar.[17]—Betafo.

America.[18]—Uranium deposits have been reported in **Canada**—Villeneuve Mica Mines, Ottawa Co., Quebec (pitchblende) ; Hybla, Hastings Co. ; Peterborough Co. (uraconite) ; Mica Lake, Berthier Co., Quebec (samarskite) ; Lake Pieds des Monts, Charleroix Co. (pitchblende) ; Kearney Sound, Toronto ; Pary Sound, and Butt, Georgian Bay, Ontario (pitchblende). Uranium ores have been reported from many parts of the **United States**.[19] There are small deposits in Arizona ; Connecticut—Middletown, Glastonburg, and Branchville ; North Carolina—Mitchell and Alexander Co. ; South Carolina—Marietta ; Colorado— Black Hawke near Central City, Long Park, Jimtown, Placesville, and Quartz Hill, Gilpin Co. ; South Dakota—Bald Mountain District, Black Hills ; Massachusetts—Chesterfield ; Montana—Pola Mesa, north of La Sal ; Nevada—Wabuska ; New Mexico—Tyrone, and White Signal mining district, Grant Co. ; New Hampshire—Acworth ; Texas—Llano Co. ; Utah—Silver Reef, Mammoth Mine in the Tintic District, Moal, East of the San Rafel swell, and 25 miles south-east of Green River ; and Wyoming—Lusk (uranophane). Uranium also occurs in **Venezuela**[20]—Montanas Negras ; in **Peru**,[21] near Quisque ; and in Placer de Guadaloupe, Chihuahua, **Mexico** ; in Minas Geraes, **Brazil** ; and in **Salvador**, Central America.

Australasia.[22]—Uranium deposits occur at Mount Painter, Radium Hill, Olasy, South Australia ; and Wodgina, West Australia.

The world's production of uranium minerals is, in long tons, approximately :

						1919	1920
United Kingdom	.	.	.	.	.	—	60
Czechoslovakia	.	.	.	.	.	10	75
Portugal	.	.	.	.	.	1,358	430
Madagascar	.	.	.	.	.	10	5
United States	.	.	.	.	.	12,954	31,318

The uranium minerals have been discussed by B. Szilard,[23] C. Baskerville, etc. Many of these have been treated in connection with the rare earths. The following are the more important of them arranged alphabetically :

Ampangabeite, a hydrated uranyl tantalocolumbate with 19·4 per cent. UO_2. **Anneroedite** is a pyrocolumbate of uranium, yttrium, cerium, and calcium ; it has roughly about 16 per cent. UO_2—*vide* columbium. **Autunite** is also called uranite, and lime-uranium mica. In the idealized case, it can be represented by $Ca(UO_2)_2(PO_4)_2.8H_2O$, and approximates 55 to 62 per cent. UO_2. **Becquerelite**, $(Pb,UO_2)O.2H_2O$. **Betafite**, a hydrated uranium columbatotitanate with 27·15 per cent. UO_3. **Blomstrandite** is a uranium columbatotantalate with about 23 per cent. UO_2—*vide* rare earths. **Braggite** is a variety of fergusonite. **Brannerite**, a complex titanate, $2RO.R_2O_3.3RO_2.3UO_3.18TiO_2.4H_2O$, containing rare earths, 10·3 per cent. UO_2, and 33·5 per cent. UO_3. **Bröggerite** is a variety of uraninite, or pitchblende, approximating 76 to 79 per cent. $UO_2.UO_3$. **Carnotite** in the idealized case approximates $K_2O.2UO_3.V_2O_5.3H_2O$, approximating 62 to 65 per cent. UO_2—*vide* vanadium. **Chalcolite**—a synonym of torbernite. **Chinkolobwite**, $12UO_3.5SiO_2.14H_2O$. **Clarkeite**, $(Na_2Ca,Pb)O.3UO_3.3H_2O$. **Cleveite**, a variety of uraninite with about 66 per cent. $UO_2.UO_3$. **Coracite** is a calcium uranyl uranate approximating 59 per cent. UO_3. **Cuproautunite**, $CuO.2UO_3.P_2O_5.10H_2O$, a cupriferous torbernite. **Cuprouranite**, one of the names for uraninite. **Curite**, $PbO.5UO_3.4H_2O$; **Cyrtolite**, altered zircon. **Dewindtite**, $Pb(UO_2)_2.(PO_4)_2.3H_2O$. **Dumontite**, $2PbO.3UO_3.P_2O_5.5H_2O$. **Ebigite**—*vide* uranothallite. **Eliasite**, or pittinite, is a variety of gummite approximating $(Pb,Ca,Ba)U_3SiO_{12}.6H_2O$, and approximates 61 to 67 per cent. UO_3. **Euxenite** is a titanocolumbate of yttrium, erbium, cerium, thorium, and uranium with 4 to 16 per cent. UO_2—*vide* rare earths. **Fergusonite**, including bragite and tyrite, is a metacolumbate tantalate of yttrium and other rare earths, calcium, and uranium ; and it contains 1 to 8 per cent. UO_2—*vide* rare earths. **Flutherite** is uranothallite. **Fouthmarierite** approximates $PbO.4UO_3.5H_2O$. **Fritzcheite**, $(U,Mn,V)PO_4.H_2O$. **Gilpinite** is a complex sulphate, $(Cu,Fe,Na_2)O.UO_3.SO_3.4H_2O$, the same as phannite. **Gummite**, including pittinite, is a decomposition product of pitchblende with 61 to 75 per cent. UO_3. **Hatchettolite** is a uranium columbatotantalate with up to about 16 per cent. UO_2—*vide* rare earths. **Ianthinite** is $2UO_3.7H_2O$. **Johannite** is a uranium sulphate containing some copper, and approximates 67 per cent. UO_2. **Lambertite** is a form of uranophane. **Kasolite** is $Pb(UO_2)(SiO_4).H_2O$. **Liebigite** is a hydrated calcium uranyl carbonate approximating uranothallite ; and to $CaCO_3.(UO_2)CO_3.20H_2O$. It has about 38 per cent. UO_3. **Mackintoshite** is a uranothorium silicate with about 22 per cent. UO_2—*vide* rare earths. **Maitlandite** is $2(Pb,Ca)O.3ThO_2.4UO_2.8SiO_2.23H_2O$. **Medjidite** is a variety of uranochalcite and calcium uranyl sulphate. **Mendeléeffite** is a hydrated titanocolumbate containing 23·5 per cent. U_3O_8, 15 per cent. of CaO, together with some lead, iron, and rare earths. **Nægite** is a silicate approximating 28·27 per cent. U. **Nasturan**, a variety of pitchblende. **Nivenite** is a decomposition product of nasturan with about 67 per cent. U_2O_5; and **nohlite**, a decomposition product of samarskite with about 14 per cent. UO_2. **Parsonite** is $Pb_2(UO_2)(PO_4)_2.H_2O$. **Phosphuranylite** is a uranyl phosphate, $(UO_2)_3(PO_4)_2.6H_2O$, with 71 to 78 per cent. UO_3. **Pilbarite** approximates $PbO.UO_3.ThO_2.2SiO_2.4H_2O$ with about 27·09 per cent. UO_3—*vide* rare earths. **Pitchblende**—also called uraninite, and nasturan—is approximately U_3O_8, with some lead uranate, and contains 75 to 85 per cent. of UO_2. It also contains rare earths, etc. **Pittinite** is a decomposition product of pitchblende. **Polycrase** is a columbatotantalate of ytterium earths with 0·5 to 20 per cent. UO_2—*vide* rare earths. **Priorite** is $UO_2.UO_3$ with about 3·24 per cent. of thoria—*vide* rare earths. **Randite** is a calcium uranyl carbonate with about 32 per cent. UO_2; and **rauvite**, a calcium uranyl vanadate, $CaO.2UO_3.6V_2O_5.20H_2O$—*vide* vanadium. **Renardite** is $PbO.4UO_3.P_2O_5.9H_2O$. **Rogersite** is the same as nohlite. **Rutherfordine** is a carbonate of uranyl, lead, etc., with about 69·5 per cent. U. This is not rutherfordite, a cerium variety of fergusonite—*vide* rare earths. **Samarskite**—and yttrioilmenite—is a complex columbatotantalate of yttrium, uranium, cerium, iron, etc., containing 10 to 15 per cent. UO_3—*vide* rare earths. **Samiresite** is a titanatocolumbate of lead, uranium, etc., with 21·2 per cent. of UO_2. **Schoepite** is $UO_3.2H_2O$. **Schröckingite** is a uranium carbonate with calcium sulphate. **Sklodowskite** approximates $MgO.2UO_3.2SiO_2.7H_2O$. **Soddite** is $12UO_3.5SiO_2.14H_2O$. **Stassite** is $4PbO.8UO_3.3P_2O_5.12H_2O$. **Thorianite** is an oxide of thorium, uranium, zirconium, lead, iron, and rare earths containing 4·1 to 10·4 per cent. U—*vide* thorium. **Thorogummite** is a hydrated uranyl thorium silicate containing about 22 per cent. UO_3—*vide* rare earths, and thorium. **Toddite** is a variety of columbite with some manganese and iron replaced by uranium; it contains about 11 per cent. of U_3O_8. **Torberite**, or torbernite, is also called chalcolite, cuprouranite, and uranium mica. It is a hydrated uranyl copper phosphate with 56 to 62 per cent. UO_3, and approximates $Cu(UO_2)_2(PO_4)_2.8H_2O$. **Trögerite** is a hydrated uranyl arsenate approximating $(UO_2)_3(AsO_4)_2.12H_2O$, and it contains about 64 per cent. UO_3—*vide* arsenates. **Tyrite** is fergusonite. **Tysonite** is a hydrated basic sulphate of uranium, calcium, copper, and iron, containing 60 to 80 per cent. U. **Tyuyamuyunite** is $CaO.2UO_3.V_2O_5.nH_2O$. **Ulrichite** is a plumbiferous trioxide of uranium. **Uraconite** contains uranium sulphate and approximates 66 to 71 per cent. of U_3O_8. **Uraninite**, and **uranotemnite** are the same as pitchblende—**uranite**—*vide* uranite. **Uranium ochre** is uraconite. **Uranmolybdate** is a uranium trimolybdate. **Uranochalcite**, or uranium green, is a hydrated calcium uranyl sulphate with 30 to 36 per cent. of U_3O_8. **Uranocircite** is a barium uranyl phosphate, $Ba(UO_2)_2(PO_4)_2.8H_2O$, with about 47 per cent. U. **Uranophane** is related to uranotile and approximates $CaO.2UO_3.2SiO_2.6H_2O$, having 53 to 67 per cent. UO_3. **Uranopilite** is a calcium uranyl sulphate with about 77 per cent. UO_3. **Uranopitchblende**—*vide* pitchblende. **Uranosphærite** is a hydrated bismuth uranate, $(BiO)_2U_2O_7.3H_2O$, with about 50 per cent. UO_3. **Uranospinite** is a calcium uranyl arsenate, $Ca(UO_2)_2(AsO_4)_2.8H_2O$, with about 49 per cent. U—*vide* arsenates. **Uranothallite**, also called flutherite, is a hydrated calcium uranyl carbonate, $2CaCO_3.U(CO_3)_2.10H_2O$, approximating 31 to 32 per cent. U. **Uranothorite**, thorite with a high proportion of uranium. **Uranotile** is a hydrated calcium uranyl silicate with about 66·75 per cent. UO_3. **Vietinghofite**, a ferruginous derivative of samarskite with about 9 per cent. UO_3. **Voglianite** resembles zippeite, with 12 per cent. U_3O_8. **Voglite** is a copper uranium carbonate, $(UO_2)Cu(CO_3)_2.10H_2O$, with about 35 per cent. U. **Walpurgite** is a basic bismuth uranyl arsenate, $(UO_2)_3Bi_{10}(OH)_{24}(AsO_4)_4$, with about 16·5 per cent. U—*vide* arsenates. **Yttroersite** is a titanate of yttrium, thorium, and uranium with about 2·22 per cent. U—*vide* rare earths. **Yttrogummite** is the end-product of the decomposition of cleveite, and has about 20 per cent. UO_3—*vide* rare earths. **Yttrotantalite** is a columbatotantalate of yttrium, cerium, etc., with 0·8 to 5 per cent. UO_3—*vide* columbium. **Zeunerite** is a copper uranyl arsenate, $Cu(UO_2)_2(AsO_4)_2.8H_2O$, with about 56 per cent. UO_3—*vide* arsenates **Zippeite** is a basic uranyl sulphate with 13 to 17 per cent. U_3O_8—*vide* voglianite. **Zirkelite** contains about 1·3 per cent. uranium.

Many other minerals have uranium as an accessory constituent. K. A. Hofmann and F. Zerban [24] reported 0·31 per cent. U_3O_8 in *œschynite*; E. Rimann, in *boden-*

benderite; G. P. Tschernik, 0·03 per cent. U in *cerite*; M. E. Pennington, and B. Szilard, 0·48 per cent., and H. V. Ellsworth, 11 per cent. U_3O_8 in *columbite*. D. Mawson described *davidite*—named after T. W. E. David—as a titanium-iron mineral carrying rare earths and uranium. From the imperfect description it might be a variety of ilmenite. F. Zambonini found 9·87 per cent. UO_2 in *delorenzite*; H. Lange, 2·03 per cent. UO_2 in a red Greenland *fluorspar*; F. Katzer, 5 per cent. UO_2, and B. Szilard, 0 to 4 per cent. U in *hjelmite*; F. Katzer, 0·43 per cent. UO_3 in *kochelite*; B. Szilard, 1·3 to 1·6 per cent. U in *microlite*; K. A. Hofmann and F. Zerban, 0·9 per cent. U_3O_8 in *monazite*; F. Katzer, 1 to 10 per cent. UO_3, and K. A. Hofmann and F. Zerban, 1 per cent. U_3O_8 in *orangite*; G. P. Tschernik, traces of uranium in *orthite*; O. Hauser, 0·1 per cent. U, and B. Szilard, 0·9 per cent. U in *risorite*; B. Szilard, 0·3 to 0·5 per cent. U in *rowlandite*; J. W. Mallet, F. Katzer, and B. Szilard, up to about 3·26 per cent. U in *sipylite*; F. Katzer, and B. Szilard, 1 to 10 per cent. UO_3 in *thorite*; F. Katzer, and B. Szilard, about 4 per cent. UO_3, and K. A. Hofmann and F. Zerban, 0·5 to 3·5 per cent. U_3O_8 in *xenotime*; B. Szilard, up to 10 per cent. U in *yttrialite*; W. E. Hidden and C. H. Warren found a small proportion of uranium in *yttrocrasite*, a titanate of yttrium, thorium, and uranium; H. V. Ellsworth, and T. L. Walker and A. L. Parsons, in *ellsworthite*; H. V. Ellsworth, *lyndochite*; H. V. Ellsworth, *thucholite*; D. Guimaraes, *eschewegite*;

d F. P. Venable observed a little uranium in *zircon*; B. Jezek, and A. Krejci, in *pisekite*; and K. Kimura, in *hagatalite*. Traces of uranium—and up to 2 to 3 per cent.—have been reported in the *kolm*, a variety of bituminous coal, of Sweden. C. Winkler [25] found that kolm contains 0·06 to 7 per cent. U_3O_8. G. Nordenskjöld observed that the ash from a bed of carbonaceous sedimentary rock contained 2 to 3 per cent. of U_3O_3. F. Katzer also reported examples of coal-ash containing 2 to 3 per cent. of U_3O_8; and an anthrasitic carbon inclusion in pegmatite with 35·43 per cent. Carnotite and vanadium minerals in Utah are associated with the carbonaceous plant residues in the sandstones. A. P. Forjas, and H. de Carvalho reported uranium in the mineral waters of Corredoura, and Caria, Portugal.

REFERENCES.

[1] F. W. Clarke and H. S. Washington, *Proc. Nat. Acad.*, **8.** 112, 1922; *The Composition of the Earth's Crust*, Washington, 21, 1924; H. S. Washington, *Trans. Amer. Inst. Min. Eng.*, **39.** 735, 1908; *Proc. Nat. Acad.*, **1.** 574, 1915; *Journ. Washington Acad.*, **14.** 435, 1924; *Journ. Franklin Inst.*, **190.** 777, 1920; *Bull. Nat. Research Council*, **2.** ii, 30, 1926; *Amer. Journ. Science*, (4), **38.** 90, 1914; (5), **9.** 351, 1925; (5), **12.** 272, 1926; W. Lindgren, *Econ. Geol.*, **18.** 419, 1923; *Mineral Deposits*, New York, 14, 1913; G. Tammann, *Zeit. anorg. Chem.*, **131.** 96, 1923; **134.** 269, 1924; E. Herlinger, *Fortschr. Min.*, **12.** 253, 1927; A. von Antropoff, *Sitzber. Nat. Hist. Ver. Rheinlande*, 1, 1926; O. Hahn, *Naturwiss.*, **14.** 159, 1926; W. and J. Noddack, *ib.*, **17.** 747, 1920; W. and J. Noddack and O. Berg, *ib.*, **13.** 568, 1925; J. Joly, *The Surface History of the Earth*, Oxford, 1925; V. G. Khlopin and M. A. Pasvik, *Trav. Rad. Acad. U.R.S.S.*, **3.** 105, 1928; C. E. St. John, *Astrophys. Journ.*, **70.** 160, 1930; E. Paneth, *Zeit. Elektrochem.*, **34.** 645, 1928; E. Paneth, D. Urry and W. Koeck, *Nature*, **125.** 490, 1930; H. Giebler, *Astron. Nach.*, 191, 1912; F. Küstner, *ib.*, 194, 1913; J. H. L. Vogt, *Zeit. prakt. Geol.*, **6.** 226, 315, 1898; **7.** 10, 274, 1899; **14.** 223, 1906; W. Vernadsky, *Essai de minéralogie descriptive*, St. Petersburg, **1.** 121, 740, 1914; *La geochimie*, Paris, 16, 1924; A. E. Fersman, *Bull. Acad. St. Petersburg*, (6), **6.** 367, 1912; R. A. Sonder, *Zeit. anorg. Chem.*, **192.** 257, 1930.

[2] H. A. Rowland, *Johns Hopkins Univ. Circ.*, 85, 1891; *Chem. News*, **63.** 133, 1891; *Amer. Journ. Science*, (3), **41.** 243, 1891; C. C. Hutchins and E. L. Holden, *ib.*, (3), **34.** 454, 1887; *Phil. Mag.*, (5), **24.** 328, 1887; M. N. Saha, *ib.*, (6), **40.** 808, 1920; J. N. Lockyer, *ib.*, (5), **6.** 161, 1879; *Compt. Rend.*, **86.** 317, 1878; *Proc. Roy. Soc.*, **27.** 279, 1878; **62.** 52, 1897; B. Hasselberg, *Svenska Akad. Handl.*, **45.** 5, 1910; G. Meyer and H. Greulich, *Phys. Zeit.*, **22.** 583, 1921; E. Paneth, D. Urry and W. Koeck, *Nature*, **125.** 490, 1930; C. E. St. John, *Astrophys. Journ.*, **70.** 160, 1930; J. and W. Noddack, *Naturwiss.*, **17.** 757, 1920.

[3] F. L. Hess, *Eng. Min. Journ.*, **121.** 94, 1926; L. Moser, *Oesterr. Chem. Ztg.*, **26.** 67, 1923; A. Haenig, *Oesterr. Zeit. Berg. Hütt.*, **56.** 177, 1908.

[4] F. W. Rudler, *A Handbook to a Collection of the Minerals of the British Islands*, London, 81, 1905; K. L. Kithel and J. A. Davis, *Bull. U.S. Bur. Mines*, 103, 1913; H. G. Dines, *Mining Mag.*, **42.** 213, 1930.

[5] H. Hirschi, *Schweiz. Min. Mitt.*, **5.** 429, 1925.

[6] L. Duparc, *Arch. Science. Phys.*, **5.** 79, 1923; *Tschermak's Mitt.*, (2), **38.** 100, 1925; A. Pereira-Forjaz, *Compt. Rend.*, **164.** 102, 1917.

[7] O. Hauser and H. Herzfeld, *Centr. Min.*, 756, 1910 ; G. P. Tschernik, *Bull. Acad. Russ.*, **16.** 505, 1922 ; F. de Hautpick, *Mining Journ.*, **92.** 10, 38, 64, 91, 122, 132, 185, 207, 237, 295, 1911 ; K. A. Nenadkevich, *Bull. Acad. St. Petersburg*, (6), **20.** 767, 1926 ; P. K. Grigoreff, *Bot. Geol. Komitäts*, 1, 1925 ; A. Labunzoff, *ib.*, 113, 1925 ; S. Kurbatoff, *Bull. Acad. St. Petersburg*, (6), **20.** 315, 1925 ; A. Fersman, *ib.*, (2), **20.** 775, 1926 ; *Compt. Rend. Acad. Russia*, 147, 1925 ; N. Leschenko, *Nechr. Berg. inst. Jekater.*, **19.** 171, 1926.

[8] H. Länge, *Zeit. Naturwiss.*, **82.** 7, 1910 ; G. P. Tschernik, *Bull. Acad. St. Petersburg*, (6), **3.** 1203, 1909 ; P. Schei, *Nyt Mag.*, **43.** 137, 1905.

[9] C. Schniffner, *Uranmineralien in Sachsen*, Freiberg i. Sa., 1911 ; J. Step and F. Becke, *Sitzber. Akad. Wien*, **113.** 589, 1904 ; F. Babanek, *Oesterr. Zeit. Berg. Hütt.*, **32.** 1, 21, 61, 1924 ; W. A. Yoder, *Bull. Dept. Trade U.S.A.*, 91, 1924 ; R. d'Andrimont, *Bull. Soc. Géol. Belg.*, **31.** 1, 1904 ; F. Henrich, *Zeit. angew. Chem.*, **37.** 667, 1924.

[10] S. P. Alexandroff, *Gornyi Zhurnal Moscow*, **118.** 415, 1922 ; S. M. Kurbatoff, *Bull. Acad. Leningrad*, **19.** 315, 1925.

[11] G. H. Tipper, *Rec. Geol. Sur. India*, **50.** 255, 1919 ; C. Friedel and E. Cumenge, *Compt. Rend.*, **128.** 532, 1899 ; *Bull. Soc. Min.*, **22.** 26, 1899 ; E. Gleditsch, *Compt. Rend.*, **148.** 1451, 1909 ; *Radium*, **6.** 165, 1909 ; W. F. Hillebrand and F. L. Ransome, *Amer. Journ. Science*, (4), **10.** 138, 1900 ; B. B. Boltwood, *ib.*, (4), **18.** 97, 1904 ; E. P. Adams, *ib.*, (4), **19.** 321, 1905 ; T. Crook and G. S. Blake, *Min. Mag.*, **15.** 171, 1910 ; R. B. Moore and K. L. Kithil, *A Preliminary Report on Uranium, Vanadium, and Radium*, Washington, 1913 ; C. V. R. Dunstan, *Rep. Min. Sur. Ceylon*, 1, 1904 ; *Nature*, **69.** 510, 1904 ; V. S. Dubey and A. Holmes, *ib.*, **123.** 794, 1929 ; V. S. Dubey, *ib.*, **126.** 807, 1930.

[12] G. Tschernik, *Bull. Acad. St. Petersburg*, (6), **3.** 1203, 1909.

[13] K. A. Nenadkevitsch, *Bull. Acad. St. Petersburg*, (6), **3.** 185, 1909.

[14] S. Kozu and W. Watanabe, *Proc. Pan-Pacific Science Congr.*, **3.** i, 839, 1928.

[15] M. G. Buttenbach, *Min. Scient. Press.*, **123.** 636, 1921 ; A. L. Hacquaert, *Natuurwet, Tijds.*, **8.** 131, 1926 ; C. W. Davis, *Amer. Journ. Science*, (5), **11.** 201, 1926 ; A. Schoep, *Bull. Soc. Geol. Belg.*, **32.** 345, 1923 ; **33.** 87, 1923 ; *Compt. Rend.*, **173.** 1186, 1921 ; **174.** 1066, 1922 ; *Ann. Musée Congo Belg.*, **1.** 2, 1930.

[16] W. Marckwald, *Centr. Min.*, 761, 1906 ; *Landw. Jahrb.*, **38.** v, 423, 1909 ; P. Krusch, *Zeit. prakt. Geol.*, **19.** 83, 1911.

[17] A. Lacroix, *Bull. Soc. Min.*, **33.** 321, 1910 ; **35.** 233, 1912 ; *Compt. Rend.*, **154.** 1040, 1912 ; *Minéralogie de Madagascar*, Paris, **2.** 131, 1922 ; *Bull. Econ. Madagascar*, **17.** 48, 1920 ; *Les industries minérales nonmétallifères à Madagascar*, Paris, 1920 ; G. F. King, *Eng. Min. Journ.*, **111.** 14, 1921 ; Y. Briére, *Compt. Rend.*, **182.** 641, 1926.

[18] W. F. Hillebrand, *Bull. U.S. Geol. Sur.*, 90, 1892 ; Anon., *Canadian Min. Journ.*, **40.** 772, 830, 1919 ; *Eng. Min. Journ.*, **108.** 841, 1919 ; C. W. Knight, *Rept. Ontario Bur. Mines.* 28, 1922.

[19] R. C. Coffin, *Radium, Uranium and Vanadium Deposits of Southwestern Colorado*, Denver, 1921 ; W. E. Hidden and J. B. Mackintosh, *Amer. Journ. Science*, (3), **38.** 480, 1889 ; E. S. Larsen, F. L. Hess and W. T. Schaller, *Amer. Min.*, **11.** 155, 1926 ; F. L. Hess and R. C. Wells, *Journ. Franklin Inst.*, **189.** 225, 1920 ; F. I. Leach, *Eng. Min. Journ.*, **109.** 989, 1920 ; F. L. Hess, *ib.*, **114.** 272, 1922 ; *Bull. U.S. Geol. Sur.*, 530, 1913 ; E. T. Wherry, *ib.*, 580, 1914 ; H. Fleck and S. W. French, *Colorado School Mines Quart.*, **3.** 2, 1907 ; S. C. Lind and C. H. Davis, *Science*, (2), **49.** 441, 1919 ; Anon., *Min. Scient. Press.*, **118.** 429, 1919 ; *Eng. Min. Journ.*, **106**, 57, 1918 ; F. F. Curran, *ib.*, **96.** 1165, 1223, 1923 ; S. Fischer, *Trans. Amer. Electrochem. Soc.*, **25.** 361, 1923 ; F. Rickard, *Min. Scient. Press.*, **106.** 851, 1913 ; W. C. Kerr, *Amer. Journ. Science*, (3), **14.** 496, 1877 ; F. A. Genth, *Amer. Chem. Journ.*, **1.** 87, 1879 ; *Chem. News*, **40.** 210, 1879 ; R. B. Moore and K. L. Kithil, *Bull. U.S. Bur. Mines*, 70, 1913.

[20] A. P. Mora, *Bol. Riqueza Publica Venezuela*, **3.** 695, 1892.

[21] E. Weckworth, *Mining Journ.*, **85.** 523, 1909.

[22] L. K. Ward, *Rev. Mining Operations South Australia*, 19, 1913 ; *Mining Journ.*, **103.** 1134, 1913 ; S. Radcliffe, *ib.*, **92.** 27, 268, 1911 ; *Austral. Mining Standard*, **71.** 238, 1924 ; T. Crook and G. S. Blake, *Min. Mag.*, **15.** 271, 1911 ; H. J. L. Brown, *Occurrence of Uranium Ores in South Australia*, Adelaide, 1911 ; *Bull. Dept. Mines S. Australia*, 10, 1911 ; J. Plummer, *Min. Scient. Press.*, **100.** 292, 1910 ; E. S. Simpson, *Bull. West Australia Geol. Sur.*, 59, 1914.

[23] B. Szilard, *Radium*, **6.** 233, 1909 ; F. Katzer, *Oesterr. Zeit. Berg. Hütt.*, **57.** 313, 1909 ; C. Baskerville, *Eng. Min. Journ.*, **87.** 203, 1909 ; W. Lindgren, *Econ. Geol.*, **18.** 419, 1923 ; F. B. Notestein, *ib.*, **13.** 50, 1918 ; C. W. Blomstrand, *Journ. prakt. Chem.*, (2), **29.** 191, 1884 ; C. A. Viol, *Science*, (2), **49.** 227, 1919 ; R. B. Moore, *ib.*, (2), **49.** 227, 1919.

[24] K. A. Hofmann and F. Zerban, *Ber.*, **36.** 3093, 1903 ; F. Zambonini, *Zeit. Kryst.*, **45.** 76, 1908 ; G. P. Tschernik, *Journ. Russ. Phys. Chem. Soc.*, **29.** 215, 292, 1897 ; *Ann. Géol. Min. Russ.*, **5.** 196, 1902 ; *Proc. Russ. Min. Soc.*, **45.** 285, 1909 ; M. E. Pennington, *Journ. Amer. Chem. Soc.*, **18.** 38, 1896 ; D. Mawson, *Trans. Roy. Soc. South Australia*, **30.** 191, 1906 ; F. Katzer, *Oesterr. Zeit. Berg. Hütt.*, **57.** 313, 1909 ; K. Kimura, *Japan. Journ. Chem.*, **2.** 82, 1925 ; A. Krejci, *Casopiz Min. Geol. Prag.*, **1.** 2, 1923 ; B. Jezek, *ib.*, **1.** 69, 1923 ; B. Szilard, *Radium*, **6.** 233, 1909 ; D. Guimaraes, *Bol. Inst. Brasileiro*, **2.** 1, 1926 ; J. W. Mallet, *Amer. Journ. Science*, (3), **14.** 397, 1877 ; W. E. Hidden and C. H. Warren, *ib.*, (4), **22.** 515, 1906 ; R. D. Hall and E. F. Smith, *Proc. Amer. Phil. Soc.*, **44.** 177, 1905 ; T. L. Walker and A. L. Parsons, *Univ. Toronto Geol. Studies*, **16.** 13, 1923 ; F. P. Venable, *Chem. News*, **64**, 315, 1891 ; H. Lange, *Zeit. Naturwiss.*,

82. 23, 1910 ; O. Hauser, *Zeit. anorg. Chem.*, **60**. 230, 1908 ; F. W. Clarke, *Bull. U.S. Geol. Sur.*, 419, 1910 ; H. V. Ellsworth, *Amer. Min.*, **11**. 332, 1926 ; **12**. 48, 212, 368, 1927 ; **13**. 419, 1928 ; E. Rimann, *Bol. Acad. Nac. Ciencias*, **31**. 5, 1929.

²⁵ G. Nordenskjöld, *Compt. Rend.*, **120**. 859, 1895 ; C. Winkler, *Oefvers. Akad. Förh.*, 495, 505, 1901 ; F. Katzer, *Oesterr. Zeit. Berg. Hütt.*, **57**. 313, 1909 ; A. P. Forjas, *Compt. Rend.*, **189**, 703, 1929 ; H. de Carvalho, *ib.*, **191**. 95, 1930.

§ 3. The Extraction of Uranium from its Ores

The chief sources of uranium are pitchblende, also called uraninite, and carnotite. The early workers, J. A. Arfvedson,[1] and G. C. Wittstein, following M. H. Klaproth, extracted uranium by digesting powdered pitchblende with nitric acid, or aqua regia, evaporating the soln. to dryness ; extracted the soluble matter with hydrochloric acid ; precipitated arsenic, lead, etc., with hydrogen sulphide ; treated the filtrate with nitric acid and then with ammonium carbonate ; boiled the soln. and digested the precipitated uranium, zinc, and cobalt oxides with cold dil. hydrochloric acid, which leaves the uranium oxide as an insoluble residue. J. Persoz boiled the nitric acid soln. with copper oxide or lead oxide and dissolved the precipitated uranium and iron oxides in dil. nitric acid ; the soln. was boiled with mercuric oxide, and the copper and mercury precipitated by hydrogen sulphide : the uranium salt alone remains in soln. J. J. Ebelmen, and E. M. Péligot roasted the ore, and washed it with hydrochloric acid before digesting it with nitric acid. L. R. Lecanu and M. Serbat opened the ore by fusion with nitre ; and A. Werner by fusion with sodium hydrosulphate, or with hot sulphuric acid. Modifications were used by F. Wöhler, H. Hermann, I. Wertheim, A. Laugier, G. A. Quesneville, J. B. Richter, W. T. Brande, and C. F. Bucholz. These processes are only of historical interest.

At the present time the main purpose in treating uranium ores is the extraction of radium, and uranium salts are produced as a by-product. Starting with pitchblende, a complex ore containing variable proportions of uranium—say 65 to 85 per cent. UO_3—and also compounds of copper, silver, zinc, thallium, rare earths, lead, arsenic, antimony, bismuth, vanadium, columbium, tantalum, molybdenum, tungsten, manganese, iron, cobalt, nickel, alumina, magnesia, lime, silica, sulphur, and selenium—the ore is first concentrated, and then roasted in a reverberatory furnace, to remove sulphur, arsenic, and other volatile impurities. Sodium carbonate or sulphate, or a mixture of sodium carbonate and nitrate, is added to the roasted ore and the mixture fused in the reverberatory furnace. This converts uranium into sodium uranate, and sodium vanadate, molybdate, tungstate, and arsenate are formed. These salts pass into soln. when the cold product is extracted with hot water. The residue is the starting point for the extraction of radium. It can be digested with dil. sulphuric acid, which takes up any uranium as uranyl sulphate. The excess of acid is removed by evaporation, and the residue extracted with water. The residue consists of silica, lead sulphate, and basic bismuth sulphate and arsenate. The two extracts are treated with an excess of sodium carbonate to precipitate the basic carbonates of iron, aluminium, nickel, and cobalt, while the uranium remains in soln. as sodium uranyl carbonate. The liquid is boiled. The clear liquid can then be neutralized with dil. sulphuric acid, boiled, and evaporated, when sodium diuranate, $Na_2U_2O_7.6H_2O$, separates as a heavy yellow precipitate. If ammonium carbonate be employed in place of sodium carbonate, or if the soln. of sodium uranyl carbonate is boiled with ammonium sulphate, ammonium diuranate is produced. If uranium oxide, U_3O_8, is desired, the ammonium salt is calcined. The above procedure, more or less modified, was described by A. Patera,[2] C. Giseke, E. Vysoky, L. Kessler, C. Mann, F. Pisani, R. Arendt and W. Knop, A. T. Elliott, E. F. Anthon, and K. A. Hofmann and E. Strauss. A. L. D. d'Adrian removed the iron as volatile chloride before separating the other metals ; R. E. Pearson and E. N. Craig described an electrolytic process.

In order to obtain uranyl nitrate, the oxide is dissolved in nitric acid and the soln. crystallized, or the roasted ore may be dissolved in nitric acid and the soln. evaporated to dryness. The residue is digested with water, and the filtered soln. allowed to crystallize, as in the processes of E. M. Péligot, and J. J. Ebelmen. H. N. McCoy and G. C. Ashman, and E. Wilke-Dörfurt purified the uranyl nitrate by recrystallization from water ; and H. C. Bolton also found that in order to get rid of vanadium it is necessary to recrystallize uranyl nitrate from water. F. Giolitti and G. Tavanti allude to the difficulty in removing alkalies from uranyl nitrate, and they succeeded in purifying the salt by dissolving the oxide in nitric acid, converting the soln. into one of ammonium uranate, precipitating by the addition of ammonia, calcining the product, etc.

The uranium can be extracted from carnotite by fusing the powdered mineral with potassium hydrosulphate, and extracting the cold product with water, as recommended by G. Gin, J. H. Haynes, H. Schlundt, R. W. Stimson, and R. B. Moore and K. L. Kithil. The soln. on crystallization furnishes the double sulphates of vanadium and uranium ; these are reduced by zinc and sulphuric acid, and the vanadium precipitated from the soln. by the addition of ammonia and ammonium carbonate. When the soln. is boiled, ammonium diuranate is precipitated. In K. B. Thews's process, the ore containing vanadium, uranium, and radium or any of these metals is ground and mixed with two or three times its weight of water. The mixture is heated until the water boils and a reducing agent, such as hydrogen, and an acid solvent, such as an organic acid, e.g. oxalic acid, or a mineral acid, e.g. hydrochloric acid, are added. The soln. is removed from the gangue and worked up for the metals in any suitable way. In place of hydrogen other reducing agents, such as carbon monoxide or formaldehyde, may be used, or if excess of hydrochloric acid be used, a metal such as zinc may be added and the hydrogen generated in situ. For the processes of K. B. Thews and F. J. Heinle, and C. L. Parsons and co-workers, vide the extraction of vanadium. P. Misciattelli examined the separation of uranium and thorium by the ether extraction of soln. of the mixed nitrates.

The phosphatic uranium minerals are not usually treated for uranium. In the recovery of uranium from laboratory residues, when it is worth while, analogous processes can be used to those which have been suggested for the extraction of uranium from phosphatic minerals. W. Jani [3] boiled the soln. in sulphuric acid, mixed with a little nitric acid, with sodium hydroxide ; suspended the washed precipitate in a soln. of sodium carbonate ; and saturated the soln. with carbon dioxide. The uranium passes into soln., from which it can be recovered in the usual way. F. Strohmer fused for half an hour a mixture of the phosphate with four times its weight of sodium and potassium carbonates along with some powdered carbon. After treating with hot water and washing until free from soda, the residue is dissolved in hydrochloric acid containing a little nitric acid ; and the iron and uranium are precipitated by ammonia, and separated by ammonium carbonate. An analogous process was used by G. Werther, and by C. F. Mohr. W. Knop recommended adding to the hydrochloric acid soln. of the phosphate a mixture of potassium ferrocyanide and glue, and decomposing the precipitated uranium ferrocyanide with sodium hydroxide ; W. Heintz treated the nitric acid soln. with tin, so as to precipitate stannic phosphate, etc., leaving uranyl nitrate in soln. ; E. Reichardt treated the hydrochloric or nitric acid soln. with ferric chloride, then with an excess of sodium carbonate, and filtered the uranium salt soln. from the ferric phosphate and hydroxide ; and G. C. Laube, A. Gawalowsky, and E. Reichardt precipitated the phosphate by means of magnesia mixture.

REFERENCES.

[1] M. H. Klaproth, Mém. Acad. Berlin, 273, 1789 ; 160, 1792 ; Beiträge zur Chemischen Kenntniss der Mineralkörper, Berlin, 2. 197, 1797 ; London, 477, 1801 ; Crell's Ann., ii, 387, 1789 ; J. B. Richter, Ueber die neueren Gegenstände der Chymie, Breslau, 1. 1, 1791 ; 9. 36, 1798 ;

Gehlen's Journ., **4**. 402, 1805 ; J. A. Arfvedson, *Svenska Akad. Handl.*, 404, 1822 ; *Ann. Phil.*, **7**. 253, 1824 ; *Pogg. Ann.*, **1**. 245, 1824 ; *Schweigger's Journ.*, **44**. 8, 1825 ; C. F. Bucholz, *Gehlen's Journ.*, **4**. 17, 134, 1805 ; *Beiträge zur Erweiterung und Berichtigung der Chemie*, Erfurt, **1**. 62, 1799 ; E. M. Péligot, *Compt. Rend.*, **12**. 735, 1841 ; **22**. 487, 1846 ; **42**. 73, 1856 ; *Ann. Chim. Phys.*, (3), **5**. 5, 1842 ; (3), **20**. 329, 1847 ; *Journ. Pharm. Chim.*, (2), **27**. 522, 1841 ; *Liebig's Ann.*, **41**. 141, 1841 ; **43**. 258, 1842 ; *Journ. prakt. Chem.*, (1), **24**. 442, 1841 ; (1), **38**. 112, 1846 ; L. R. Lecanu and M. Serbat, *Quart. Journ. Science*, **17**. 139, 1824 ; *Journ. Pharm. Chim.*, (2), **9**. 141, 1823 ; G. C. Wittstein, *Repert. Pharm.*, **63**. 231, 1844 ; J. Persoz, *Ann. Chim. Phys.*, (2), **58**. 202, 1835 ; J. J. Ebelmen, *ib.*, (3), **5**. 189, 1842 ; I. von Haller, *Jahrb. geol. Reichsanst. Wien*, **4**. 557, 1853 ; I. Wertheim, *Ber. Vers. deut. Naturf*, 193, 1843 ; *Ann. Chim. Phys.*, (3), **11**. 49, 1844 ; *Journ. prakt. Chem.*, (1), **29**. 207, 1842 ; A. Werner, *ib.*, (1), **12**. 381, 1837 ; *Dingler's Journ.*, **68**. 465, 1838 ; F. Wöhler, *Pogg. Ann.*, **64**. 94, 1845 ; *Praktische Uebungen in der chemischen Analyse*, Göttingen, 156, 1861 ; G. A. Quesneville, *Journ. Pharm. Chim.*, (2), **15**. 494, 1829 ; A. Laugier, *ib.*, (2), **9**. 145, 1825 ; W. T. Brande, *Quart. Journ. Science*, **14**. 86, 1823 ; H. Hermann, *Ueber einige Uranverbindungen*, Göttingen, 1861.

² A. Patera, *Sitzber. Akad. Wien*, **5**. 353, 1849 ; **11**. 842, 1853 ; *Dingler's Journ.*, **132**. 36, 1854 ; **141**. 371, 1856 ; *Journ. prakt. Chem.*, (1), **46**. 182, 1849 ; (1), **51**. 122, 1850 ; (1), **61**. 379, 1854 ; (1), **69**. 118, 1856 ; C. Giseke, *ib.*, (1), **55**. 445, 1852 ; *Arch. Pharm.*, (2), **69**. 150, 1852 ; *Dingler's Journ.*, **124**. 355, 1852 ; E. F. Anthon, *ib.*, **156**. 207, 1860 ; E. Vysoky, *ib.*, **155**. 305, 1860 ; **181**. 448, 1866 ; *Oesterr. Zeit. Berg. Hütt.*, **7**. 277, 1859 ; **14**. 185, 1866 ; L. Kessler, *Journ. Pharm. Chim.*, (3), **31**. 182, 1857 ; C. Mann, *Oesterr. Zeit. Berg. Hütt.*, **23**. 2, 1875 ; K. A. Hofmann and E. Strauss, *Ber.*, **33**. 3126, 1900 ; R. Arendt and W. Knop, *Journ. prakt. Chem.*, (1), **70**. 385, 1857 ; E. M. Péligot, *Compt. Rend.*, **12**. 735, 1841 ; **22**. 487, 1846 ; **42**. 73, 1856 ; *Ann. Chim. Phys.*, (3), **5**. 5, 1842 ; (3), **20**. 329, 1847 ; *Journ. Pharm. Chim.*, (2), **27**. 522, 1841 ; *Liebig's Ann.*, **41**. 141, 1841 ; **43**. 258, 1842 ; *Journ. prakt. Chem.*, (1), **24**. 442, 1841 ; (1), **38**. 112, 1846 ; J. J. Ebelmen, *Ann. Chim. Phys.*, (3), **5**. 189, 1842 ; E. Wilke-Dörfurt, *Wiss. Veroffent. Siemens-Konzern*, **1**. 143, 1920 ; H. C. Bolton, *Amer. Chemist*, **5**. 363, 1875 ; *Bull. Soc. Chim.*, (2), **27**. 295, 1877 ; F. Giolitti and G. Tavanti, *Gazz. Chim. Ital.*, **38**. ii, 239, 1908 ; H. N. McCoy and G. C. Ashman, *Amer. Journ. Science*, (4), **26**. 521, 1908 ; G. Gin, *Atti Congress Int. Chim. Appl. Roma*, **6**. ii, 294, 1906 ; *Zeit. angew. Chem.*, **19**. 896, 1906 ; *Trans. Amer. Electrochem. Soc.*, **16**. 393, 1909 ; R. W. Stimson, *Brit. Pat. No.* 320845, 1928 ; J. H. Haynes, *Mines Minerals*, **30**. 139, 1909 ; R. W. Moore, *Trans. Amer. Electrochem. Soc.*, **43**. 317, 1923 ; R. B. Moore and K. L. Kithil, *A Preliminary Report on Uranium, Vanadium, and Radium*, Washington, 1905 ; C. L. Parsons, *Journ. Ind. Eng. Chem.*, **9**. 466, 1917 ; C. L. Parsons, R. B. Moore, S. C. Lind and O. C. Schaefer, *The Extraction and Recovery of Radium, Uranium, and Vanadium from Carnotite*, Washington, 30, 1915 ; *Bull. U.S. Bur. Mines*, 104, 1915 ; F. Pisani, *Compt. Rend.*, **52**. 106, 1861 ; A. T. Elliott, *U.S. Pat. No.* 1471332, 1471514, 1923 ; A. L. D. d'Adrian, *ib.*, 1434485, 1922 ; K. B. Thews, *ib.*, 1495538, 1924 ; *Continental Met. Chem. Engg.*, **1**. 45, 1926 ; K. B. Thews and F. J. Heinle, *Journ. Ind. Eng. Chem.*, **15**. 1159, 1923 ; H. Schlundt, *Journ. Phys. Chem.*, **20**. 485, 1916 ; R. E. Pearson and E. N. Craig, *Canadian Pat. No.* 225966, 1922 ; P. Misciattelli, *Atti Accad. Lincei*, (6), **7**. 1019, 1928.

³ W. Jani, *Chem. News*, **23**. 220, 1871 ; T. J. Savery, *ib.*, **48**. 251, 1883 ; F. Strohmer, *Zeit. anal. Chem.*, **17**. 84, 1878 ; *Dingler's Journ.*, **225**. 561, 1877 ; G. Werther, *Journ. prakt. Chem.*, (1), **43**. 321, 1848 ; W. Heintz, *Liebig's Ann.*, **151**. 216, 1869 ; G. C. Laube, *Zeit. angew. Chem.*, **2**. 575, 1889 ; W. Knop, *Chem. Centr.*, (2), **10**. 161, 1865 ; E. Reichardt, *Zeit. anal. Chem.*, **8**. 116, 1869 ; **13**. 310, 1874 ; A. Gawalowsky, *ib.*, **15**. 292, 1876 ; C. F. Mohr, *Lehrbuch der chemisch-analytischen Titrirmethode*, Braunschweig, 391, 1862.

§ 4. The Isolation of Uranium

As previously indicated, up to the time of E. M. Péligot [1] (1841), observers had mistaken uranium dioxide for the element. They obtained what they considered to be the element by reducing the ordinary oxide with carbon. This serves to show that the carbon reduction process under the conditions which they worked does not proceed far enough. H. Moissan showed that although the uranium oxides are not reduced to the metal by carbon at the highest temp. obtainable with ordinary combustion furnaces, the metal is readily obtained by the carbon reduction process in the electric furnace. H. C. Greenwood found that complete reduction occurs only when the temp. exceeds 1500°.

According to H. Moissan, if a mixture of 500 grms. of uranium tritaoctoxide and 40 grms. of sugar charcoal is rammed into a carbon crucible, the whole is reduced in about 12 minutes in the electric carbon tube furnace ; and on cooling, a metallic ingot, weighing 350 grms., and possessing a bright fracture, is obtained. The metal contains very little carbon ; but if the heating be too long, the metal takes up carbon readily, yielding a highly carburized metal, and ultimately the

U_2C_3-carbide. To prevent the action of nitrogen on the metal it is best to work with the carbon tube of the electric furnace closed at one end. H. Moissan added that uranium containing 0·1 to 0·5 per cent. of carbon may be superficially refined by heating the fragments in a brasque of green uranium oxide for several hours in a forge furnace. To ensure success the crucible containing the uranium oxide and metal must be placed inside a second crucible containing a finely powdered titaniferous brasque, otherwise the metal produced is yellow, and is covered with nitride. J. Aloy also obtained the metal by a similar process. H. Lohmann said that carbon may be removed by heating the metal to a temp. near to its m.p. in vacuo or in a current of neutral gas. Carbon is vaporized without any oxidizing or reducing agents being present.

J. Aloy found that the oxide is reduced by powdered aluminium in the thermite process. The reaction is very vigorous. He said that it is better to use UO_2 than U_3O_8, and he obtained a product with 96–97 per cent. U. A. Stavenhagen and E. Schuchard used 30 grms. of a mixture of a mol of UO_3 with 2 mols of aluminium and 20 c.c. of liquid air. The reaction goes smoothly and brilliantly—J. Aloy added that the product contained a relatively high proportion of aluminium. According to F. Giolitti and G. Tavanti, when a mixture of this oxide with excess of powdered aluminium is thrown on to the surface of fused aluminium maintained at a vivid red-heat, not alloys of aluminium and uranium, mixed with alumina, as stated by H. Moissan, but a mixture of uranous oxide, alumina, and aluminium is obtained. When, however, a mixture of ferric oxide with 10 per cent. of the oxide U_3O_8 is intimately mixed with more than sufficient aluminium filings to reduce both the oxides, and the reaction started by means of barium dioxide and aluminium, the oxide of uranium is reduced to metallic uranium. J. W. Marden and H. C. Rentschler, and J. Aloy also reduced the oxide by heating it with magnesium; and E. K. Rideal obtained uranium of 98 to 99 per cent. purity by heating in an atm. of hydrogen, in a magnesia-tube, in an electric furnace, a mixture of 80 per cent. of uranium oxide and 20 per cent. of magnesium powder compressed into rods. The finely-divided " uranium black " was pyrophoric, and the hydrogen was displaced by carbon dioxide in the apparatus before the product was exposed to air. The excess of magnesium was removed by washing with dil. acetic acid. If the oxide be reduced by a mixture of sodium and magnesium in the presence of calcium chloride in a steel cylinder at a bright red-heat, E. K. Rideal obtained a greyish-black powder containing 99·4 to 99·6 per cent. of uranium with traces of iron. A. Burger, H. Kuzel and E. Wedekind, and A. S. Cachemaille found that uranium trioxide is reduced by the vapour of calcium in vacuo; and W. Jander, and J. W. Marden obtained uranium by heating uranium oxide with metallic calcium in a welded iron crucible embedded in charcoal for 40 minutes at 950°–1250°. The resulting mass is then treated with ammonium chloride soln. to remove the unchanged calcium, and the residual powder is levigated, when a light black powder is separated which consists of highly oxidized uranium. The remaining powder contains particles of iron, which can be separated by a magnet, and the residue is then passed through a sieve, which retains coarse, impure powder and gives a fine black powder containing about 97·2 per cent. U, 2·5 per cent. Fe, and 0·3 per cent. O, the yield being about 66 per cent. of the theoretical. If the crucible is prepared with a thick lining of lime, a product is obtained containing 99·9 per cent. U, and not more than 0·09 per cent. O, but the yield is only 27 per cent. of the theoretical. J. F. Goggin and co-workers found that the yield in the reduction of the oxide by calcium is small. The Electric Furnaces and Smelters, Ltd., reduced the oxide by heating it in admixture with calcium carbide and a silicide—e.g. ferrosilicon.

E. M. Péligot reduced uranium tetrachloride admixed with potassium chloride and sodium, and covered with potassium chloride, in a porcelain crucible, contained in a graphite crucible, packed with dry powdered carbon, and the temp. rapidly raised to redness. The cold product was lixiviated with water, and there remained a grey powder with a few metallic globules. E. M. Péligot first reduced the tetrachloride with potassium in a platinum crucible, and found that the uranium was contaminated with platinum. J. L. C. Zimmermann also reduced the tetrachloride with sodium. D. Lely and L. Hamburger heated the tetrachloride with sodium in an exhausted steel vessel, and rendered the metal compact by heating it in an alundum tube in an exhausted vessel. W. I. Baragiola used a similar process. R. W. Moore distilled the tetrachloride in a current of chlorine, and the sodium in vacuo, and cut it in pieces under dry benzene. The mixture was heated in a steel bomb in vacuo, and the product extracted first with absolute alcohol to remove excess of sodium, then with water to remove sodium chloride, and finally with 2 per cent. acetic acid. The heavy brownish residue of metallic uranium was washed with acetone and dried in vacuo. A yield of 90 per cent. of the theoretical quantity of metal containing 99·8 per cent. uranium was readily obtained. The powder was very pyrophoric, but it can be pressed into discs in a hydraulic press in an atm. of nitrogen, when it is no longer pyrophoric. These discs may be melted by the arc in an atm. of rarefied argon to bright, steel-grey, ductile, metallic buttons which readily tarnish on exposure to the air. J. W. Marden also reduced the chloride by sodium with calcium chloride as a flux in a closed vessel. A. Roderburg added that when the uranium chloride is reduced by sodium in a porcelain vessel, the uranium is contaminated with aluminium and silicon; and when in iron vessels, with iron. Nickel, magnesia, graphite, or silver vessels are rapidly destroyed; and nickel-steel is more resistant than other steels. M. A. Hunter and A. Jones obtained 99 per cent. uranium by reducing the anhydrous chloride with sodium in a steel-bomb. J. W. Marden reduced the uranium halide or potassium uranium fluoride by means of calcium in the presence of calcium chloride; pressed the powdered metal into a desired shape and heated it until it was homogeneous and ductile. J. W. Marden and H. C. Rentschler observed that uranium readily alloys with metals, and interacts with lime and magnesia refractories, but thoria crucibles give good results. J. F. Goggin and co-workers found that a good yield of very pure fused uranium is obtained by the reduction of uranium chloride with a 10 per cent. excess of metallic calcium; the operation is carried out in an alundum crucible placed inside a nichrome-wound reduction bomb which is placed inside a steel cylinder from which the air is exhausted. The product obtained by this method was a hard, brittle metal containing 0·57 per cent. Fe, 0·09 per cent. C, and 0·03 per cent. O when commercial calcium was used, but a much purer product, containing only 0·01 per cent. Fe, was obtained by the use of resublimed calcium. The ingot showed fine crystalline markings, had a silvery lustre and convex surface, and appeared to be sound. E. M. Péligot stated that the tetrachloride is reduced to the metal by aluminium, but H. Hermann found that the vapour of the tetrachloride is not reduced to uranium by that metal. E. Botolfsen reduced the oxide with calcium in vacuo, and removed the calcium and calcium oxide by 2 per cent. acetic acid. J. W. Marden reduced uranium ammonium chloride with aluminium. H. Moissan preferred to reduce sodium uranium hexachloride, Na_2UCl_6. 300 grms. of the double chloride and 100 grms. of freshly-cut sodium were introduced in alternate layers into a strong iron cylinder, which was closed with a screw stopper. The cylinder was heated for 25 minutes over a brightly-burning wood fire. The heat of the reaction raised the vessel to a white-heat in a few minutes. After cooling, the cylinder was opened, and the powdery contents first treated with alcohol at 96° in order to remove the excess of sodium, then washed quickly with cold, previously boiled water, and finally with alcohol and ether. This process was also employed by W. G. Mixter. J. Aloy similarly reduced the lithium or potassium salt with alkali metal.

H. Hermann found that the potassium salt is not reduced to uranium by zinc in the presence of sodium chloride. According to A. Commaille, magnesium deposits the hydrated uranic oxide from aq. soln. of uranium oxalate; S. Kern obtained a similar result with the nitrate in aq. soln. ; and G. Gore obtained no reduction by adding silicon to the molten fluoride.

L. Schicht found that the electrolysis of acetic soln. of uranium salts reduces the uranic to uranous salts, and from neutral soln. a little uranium (possibly the oxide) is formed; a similar result was obtained with alkaline soln. containing acetic, citric, or tartaric acid, or sugar. G. Gore obtained no uranium by the electrolysis of an aq. soln. of the fluoride, nor by the electrolysis of the molten fluoride. C. Luckow obtained a little uranium by the electrolysis of a neutral salt soln. E. F. Smith obtained only the uranosic oxide by the electrolysis of aq. soln. of the acetate, formate, and nitrate.

H. Moissan observed that fused sodium uranium hexachloride can be easily electrolyzed, and spongy uranium, often containing small crystals, is deposited at the cathode. A potential difference of 8 to 10 volts and a current of 50 amps. was employed. The bath is kept liquid by the heating action of the current itself. The double chloride was contained in a cylindrical porcelain vessel, and electrodes of carbon were used. The vessel was closed by a ground porcelain plate, carrying the two electrodes and a glass tube through which was passed, above the fused chloride, a current of hydrogen free from nitrogen. When quite cold the contents of the vessel were quickly treated with ice-cold water, and washed with alcohol—finely divided uranium decomposes water at ordinary temp. With iron electrodes, silver white, fine-grained alloys of iron and uranium are produced. These alloys can be filed with ease. R. E. Pearson and E. N. Craig passed a current through a sulphuric acid cell with pasty uranium oxide in the cathode chamber, and obtained uranium. J. Aloy also found that during the electrolysis, the uranium alloys with iron, aluminium, cadmium, and platinum electrodes. F. H. Driggs and W. C. Lilliendahl obtained the metal by the electrolysis of potassium uranous fluoride in a molten mixture of sodium and calcium chlorides, using a carbon crucible as anode and a molybdenum wire as cathode. The Wolfram-lampen A.G. found that soln. of salts in conducting organic solvents—e.g. acetone —which exert no oxidizing action, give, on electrolysis, deposits of uranium on nickel, platinum, etc. J. Ferée electrolyzed an aq. soln. of uranous chloride using a mercury cathode, and obtained uranium amalgam. When this is distilled in vacuo, it furnishes *pyrophoric uranium*. R. M. Keeney obtained alloys with aluminium and iron electrolytically and found that iron alloys with over 20 per cent. of uranium were pyrophoric, and more markedly so with higher proportions of uranium.

The process of H. Kuzel [2] for obtaining colloidal chromium, molybdenum, and tungsten (*q.v.*) has not been followed closely for **colloidal uranium**. T. Svedberg prepared the **isobutylalcosol** by the electric dispersion method—**3**. 23, 10. H. Agulhon and T. Robert also prepared colloidal uranium by the electrical dispersion process.

REFERENCES.

[1] E. M. Péligot, *Ann. Chim. Phys.*, (3), **5**. 5, 1842 ; (3), **12**. 549, 1844 ; (3), **22**. 329, 1848 ; (4), **17**. 368, 1869 ; *Journ. Pharm. Chim.*, (2), **27**. 522, 1841 ; *Compt. Rend.*, **12**. 735, 1841 ; **22**. 487, 1846 ; **42**. 73, 1856 ; H. Moissan, *ib.*, **116**. 347, 1433, 1893 ; **122**. 1088, 1302, 1896 ; **142**. 425, 1906 ; *Ann. Chim. Phys.*, (7), **8**. 141, 1896 ; (7), **9**. 264, 1896 ; *Le four électrique*, Paris, 233, 1897 ; London, 162, 1904 ; *Bull. Soc. Chim.*, (3), **11**. 11, 1894 ; (3), **17**. 266, 1897 ; (3), **35**. 944, 1906 ; J. Ferée, *ib.*, (3), **25**. 622, 1901 ; J. Aloy, *ib.*, (3), **23**. 368, 1900 ; (3), **25**. 153, 344, 1901 ; *Ann. Chim. Phys.*, (7), **24**. 412, 1901 ; *Recherches sur l'uranium et ses composés*, Toulouse, 1901 ; A. Burger, *Reduktion durch Calcium*, Basel, 19, 1907 ; Wolfenlampen A.G., *German Pat.*, *D.R.P.* 237014, 1910 ; Electric Furnaces and Smelters, Ltd., *French. Pat. No.* 427537, 1911 ;. *Rev. Mét.*, **8**. 876, 1911 ; R. E. Pearson and E. N. Craig, *Canadian Pat. No.* 221041, 1922 ; H. C. Greenwood, *Journ. Chem. Soc.*, **93**. 1492, 1908 ; F. Giolitti and G. Tavanti, *Gazz. Chim. Ital.*, **38**. ii, 239, 1908 ; A. Stavenhagen, *Ber.*, **32**. 3065, 1899 ; A. Stavenhagen and E. Schuchard, *ib.*, **35**. 909, 1902 ; J. L. C. Zimmermann, *ib.*, **13**. 348, 1882 ; **15**. 847, 1182, 1882 ; **17**. 2739, 1884 ; *Liebig's Ann.*, **213**. 1, 1882 ; **216**. 14, 1883 ; **232**. 310, 1886 ; E. K. Rideal, *Journ. Soc. Chem. Ind.*, **33**. 673, 1914 ; *Das Elektrochemische Verhalten des Urans und einiger Uranverbindungen*, Bonn, 1913 ; A. Fischer and E. K. Rideal, *Zeit. anorg. Chem.*, **81**. 170, 1913 ; W. Jander,

ib., **138**. 321, 1924 ; D. Lely and L. Hamburger, ib., **87**. 209, 1914 ; A. Roderburg, ib., **81**. 122, 1913 ; W. G. Mixter, ib., **78**. 231, 1912 ; Amer. Journ. Science, (4), **34**. 141, 1912 ; W. I. Baragiola, Schweiz. Apoth. Ztg., **53**. 477, 1913 ; R. W. Moore, Trans. Amer. Electrochem. Soc., **43**. 317, 1923 ; J. W. Marden and H. C. Rentschler, ib., **43**. 326, 1923 ; U.S. Pat. No. 1648962, 1927 ; Brit. Pat. No. 220944, 1924 ; Canadian Pat. No. 305418, 1930 ; J. W. Marden, ib., 246147, 1926 ; 1728940, 1728942, 1929 ; U.S. Pat. No. 1646734, 1648954, 1927 ; K. B. Thews, ib., 1495538, 1927 ; H. Kuzel and E. Wedekind, Met. Chem. Engg., **12**. 260, 1914 ; H. Hermann, Ueber einige Uran-verbindungen, Göttingen, 1861 ; J. F. Goggin, J. J. Cronin, H. C. Fogg and C. James, Journ. Ind. Eng. Chem., **18**. 114, 1926 ; F. H. Driggs and W. C. Lilliendahl, ib., **22**. 516, 1930 ; F. H. Driggs, Eng. Min. Journ., **130**. 119, 1930 ; R. M. Keeney, Eng. Min. Journ., **106**. 405, 1918 ; Min. Ind., **26**. 720, 1917 ; **27**. 737, 1918 ; A. S. Cachemaille, Brit. Pat. No. 238663, 239742, 1924 ; H. Lohmann, ib., 157780, 1921 ; M. A. Hunter and A. Jones, Trans. Amer. Electrochem. Soc., **44**. 23, 1923 ; E. Botolfsen, Tids. Kemi Bergvesen, **9**. 66, 1929 ; Bull. Soc. Chim., (4), **45**. 626, 1929 ; A. Commaille, Compt. Rend., **63**. 556, 1866 ; Chem. News, **14**. 188, 1866 ; S. Kern, ib., **33**. 236, 1876 ; L. Schicht, ib., **41**. 280, 1880 ; Berg. Hütt. Ztg., **39**. 121, 1880 ; G. Gore, Electrochemistry, London, 97, 1906 ; C. Luckow, Zeit. anal. Chem., **19**. 1, 1880 ; E. F. Smith, Ber., **13**. 751, 1880.
    [2] H. Kuzel, Austrian Pat. No. 2572, 2573, 1906 ; German Pat., D.R.P. 186980, 194348, 197379, 1905 ; 199962, 1907 ; T. Svedberg, Ber., **38**. 3616, 1905 ; **39**. 1705, 1906 ; Die Methoden zur Herstellung kolloiden Lösungen anorganischer Stoffe, Dresden, 488, 1920 ; H. Agulhon and T. Robert, Compt. Rend., **158**. 349, 1914.

§ 5. The Physical Properties of Uranium

D. I. Mendeléeff [1] discussed some analogies in the **colour** of chromium, molybdenum, tungsten, and uranium. E. M. Péligot described the uranium which he prepared as a grey powder ; and H. Moissan observed that the powder is liable to form a nitride which produces a yellow film on the metal. E. K. Rideal described the metal which he prepared as a greyish-black powder. H. Moissan found that when prepared by the carbon reduction process uranium furnishes an ingot with a bright fracture. When the metal is of a high degree of purity it is white, with a fainter bluish tinge than iron, and can be polished like iron. If the metal has a yellow tinge, some nitride is present. R. W. Moore said that by fusing the metal in vacuo, it can be cast into small ingots and then has the appearance of polished iron. J. F. Goggin and co-workers found that the ingot of uranium shows fine crystalline markings and has a silvery lustre ; H. Moissan stated that when prepared by electrolysis fairly large, well-defined crystals may be formed on the cathode. J. C. McLennan and R. W. McKay found that the **X-radiograms** of uranium indicated a body-centred, cubic lattice with $a=3.43$ A.

E. M. Péligot gave 18·33 to 18·40 for the **specific gravity** of the metal ; J. L. C. Zimmermann, 18·485 at 13°/4° in vacuo. J. Aloy said that a sample obtained by the aluminothermic process had a sp. gr. 16·5—the sample was presumably contaminated with aluminium. J. C. McLennan and R. W. McKay obtained 19·6 for the density from the X-radiograms. J. L. C. Zimmermann calculated the **atomic volume** to be 12·84. E. Donath and J. Mayrhofer made some observations on this subject. C. del Fresno discussed the at. vol., and W. Biltz and K. Meisel estimated it to be 12·6 at absolute zero. E. J. Cuy estimated the **atomic radius** of U···· to be 1·22 A.; H. G. Grimm, V. M. Goldschmidt, L. Pauling, E. Herlinger, and E. T. Wherry also studied the at. radius of uranium, from which it follows that the value for quadrivalent uranium atoms is 0·97 to 1·05 A. P. Vinassa studied the mol. number. H. Moissan observed that uranium is easily filed ; it does not mark glass ; and when it has taken up a little carbon from the crucible, it can be tempered. R. W. Moore found that the metal is very **ductile ;** some buttons of the metal were rolled cold from a thickness of 5 mm. to small sheets about 0·375 mm. thick. D. Lely and L. Hamburger found uranium to be less malleable than thorium. P. W. Bridgman found the **compressibility** of uranium at 30° to be $\delta v/v_0 = -10^{-7}(9.66 - 2.5 \times 10^{-5}p)p$, and at 75°, $\delta v/v_0 = -10^{-7}(9.55 - 2.2 \times 10^{-5}p)p$, where p denotes the press. in kgrms. per sq. cm. for values of p between 1 and 12,000. The compressibility, β, at 30° is 0.0_6966 ;

and $\delta\beta/\beta\delta p=0\cdot0_552$. L. H. Adams found that $\delta\beta=-0\cdot05$. J. Laissus discussed the **diffusion** of uranium in iron.

E. Donath gave $0\cdot0249$ for the **specific heat** at $0°$; and J. L. C. Zimmermann, $0\cdot0276$ at $0°$. A. Blümcke found $0\cdot0280$ for the sp. ht. between $0°$ and $98°$, and $6\cdot66$ for the atomic heat; whilst J. Dewar gave $0\cdot0138$ for the sp. ht. at $-223°$, and $3\cdot29$ for the at. ht. H. Fritz made some observations on the relation of the sp. ht. to some of the other properties of the metal. H. Moissan found that uranium melts less easily than platinum, chromium, and molybdenum, but more easily than tungsten and vanadium. J. Maydel discussed some relations of the sp. ht. W. Guertler and M. von Pirani gave $1850°$ for the **melting point** ; A. Fischer and E. K. Rideal found that a specimen with $0\cdot4$ per cent. of carbon melted in vacuo between $1300°$ and $1400°$. W. R. Mott gave $1600°$ for the m.p. According to H. Moissan, uranium may be distilled in an electric furnace and the vapour furnishes small metallic spheres free from carbon. E. Botolfsen observed that uranium does not sublime in a high vacuum below its m.p. According to H. Moissan, the **boiling point** of uranium is above that of iron. W. R. Mott estimated the b.p. to be $3500°$. W. G. Mixter gave $303\cdot9$ Cals. for the **heat of oxidation** to UO_3 ; and for the heat of oxidation to U_3O_8, $\frac{1}{3}$ of $895\cdot5$ Cals. per gram-atom. E. D. Eastman calculated $10\cdot5$ for the **entropy** of uranium; G. N. Lewis and co-workers gave $11\cdot1$; W. Herz, $15\cdot37$; and B. Bruzs, $24\cdot1$ at the m.p. $2100°$ K. R. D. Kleeman discussed the internal and free energies of uranium ; and W. Herz, the entropy.

V. Henri,[2] and J. C. Ghosh and B. N. Mitter found that the **extinction coefficients** of mixtures of uranyl salts and organic acids are greater than the sum of the extinction coeff. taken separately ; and this was cited as evidence of the formation of unstable intermediate compounds. A. Müller discussed the colour. A. Dorabialska studied the radiant energy.

Uranium salts do not show a **flame spectrum,** nor yet a simple spark spectrum ; and W. Huggins [3] found that uranium oxide in the oxyhydrogen flame shows only the continuous spectrum characteristic of red-hot solids. The **spark spectrum** is produced if a condenser is in the circuit. R. Thalén first made a drawing of the spark spectrum, and later gave some measurements of the spectral lines. The spectral lines are exceptionally numerous, but as shown by E. Formanek, and A. S. Russell and R. Rossi, none is distinctive enough to serve for the detection of small quantities of uranium spectroscopically. The more important lines in the spark spectrum are 5528, 5494, 5482, 5480, 5478, and 5475 in the green, and 4473, 4362, and 4341 in the indigo-blue. The spark spectrum was examined in more detail by J. N. Lockyer, E. Demarçay, G. Meyer and H. Greulich, O. Lohse, F. Exner and E. Haschek, A. Hagenbach and H. Konen, J. H. Pollok, C. E. Gissing, and J. M. Eder and E. Valenta. G. Meyer and H. Greulich found that the spectral lines are masked by those of other metals unless the uranium is present in considerable concentration—say 7 per cent. C. Porlezza and A. Donati discussed the electroscopic detection of uranium. E. J. Allin examined the underwater spark spectrum. H. Nagaoka and T. Futagami examined the spectral lines due to the transformation products of uranium. The **arc spectrum** was examined by J. N. Lockyer, F. Exner and E. Haschek, C. C. Kiess and W. F. Meggers, K. W. Meissner, J. M. Eder and E. Valenta, E. Z. Stowell, and B. Hasselberg ; the **ultra-violet spectrum,** by R. J. Lang, H. Nagaoka and T. Futagami, F. Exner and E. Haschek, and O. Lohse ; and the **ultra-red spectrum,** by C. C. Kiess and W. F. Meggers. W. W. Coblentz found uranium oxide gives a continuous spectrum in the ultra-red with hazy maxima at $2\cdot8\mu$ and $3\cdot4\mu$. The anomalous *dispersion* was discussed by H. Ebert ; and the effect of *pressure* by W. J. Humphreys. The *Stark effect* was studied by H. Nagaoka and Y. Sugiura. No **series spectrum** has been detected ; C. C. Kiess and W. F. Meggers, and P. G. Nutting discussed the structure of the lines ; and J. C. McLennan and co-workers, the relation between the electronic structure and the spectrum. H. Nagaoka and T. Futagami compared the spectra of thorium, helium, and uranium. J. C. McLennan and E. Cohen studied the **absorption spectrum** of the vapour of uranium. E. T. Wherry detected uranium in minerals from their absorption spectra.

Numerous researches have been made on the absorption spectrum of soln. of uranium salts. These include observations by J. H. Gladstone,[4] G. G. Stokes, H. C. Sorby, W. Böhlendorff, E. Hagenbach, S. Kato, J. M. Hiebendaal, H. Oeffinger, H. Morton and H. C. Bolton, H. Kayser, etc. All the uranium salts, solid or in soln., show an absorption spectrum. The exact position of the bands is usually dependent on the temp. With a rise of temp. the bands are usually displaced towards the red. Thus, H. Bremer found for one of the bands of uranyl sulphate, 4906 (20°), 4909 (40°), 4915 (60°), and 4992 (80°), and with another band, 4738 (20°), 4741 (40°), 4743 (60°), and 4745 (80°); whilst for one of the bands of uranyl nitrate, 4859 (20°), 4868 (40°), 4870 (60°), and 4872 (80°), and for another band, 4696 (20°), 4702 (40°), 4706 (60°), and 4708 (80°). Similar results were obtained with some double sulphates, and with the acetate. H. Morton and H. C. Bolton made similar observations with respect to the double salts—sulphate, carbonate, and oxalate. J. M. Hiebendaal, on the contrary, observed that temp. had no perceptible influence on the position of the bands. H. C. Jones and J. S. Guy found that the uranyl bands become more diffuse with rise of temp. ; and H. C. Jones and W. W. Strong, and M. Cantone studied this subject. For the effect of low temp., *vide infra*, phosphorescence spectra.

H. Morton and H. C. Bolton found that solid *uranyl fluoride* exhibited the bands λ=4930, 4770, 4661, 4480, 4310, and 4180 ; the aq. soln., 4780, 4620, 4460, 4330, 4195, and 4055 ; the soln. in hydrofluoric acid, 4820, 4665, 4480, 4340, and 4200 ; and *potassium uranyl fluoride*, 4880, 4800 to 4720, 4630 to 4580, and 4490 ; M. Cantone, and E. L. Nichols and E. Merritt also examined *ammonium uranyl fluoride*. According to H. Morton and H. C. Bolton, solid *uranyl chloride* has absorption bands for λ=4920, 4750, 4620, 4480, 4340, and 4220 ; and H. Becquerel studied the pleochroism of the salt. E. Formanek found for the aq. soln., six absorption bands : 4913, 4748, and, with dil. soln., 4572, 4430, 4289, and 4146, as well as a dark one in the violet. E. Deussen gave 4900, 4755, 4580, 4410, 4285, and 4140 with the bands 4025, 3925, 3800, and 3710 in the extreme violet and ultra-violet. Observations were also made by H. Oeffinger, O. Knoblauch, and H. Morton and H. C. Bolton. J. Formanek's results are illustrated by I, Fig. 2. A conc. soln. of uranyl chloride in hydrochloric acid shows only a small band at 4925, but with dilution, the bands 4975, 4630, 4442, 4289, and 4150 appear— II, Fig. 2. According to J. Formanek, when a soln. of a uranyl salt—say the chloride—is reduced by zinc and hydrochloric acid, there are three stages in the process. In the first stage there are eight bands, *viz.* 6500, 6718, 6304, 5497, 4961, 4844, 4566, and 4307—III, Fig. 2 ; the first and second are also shown by very dil. soln. As reduction proceeds, new bands—6367, 6165, 6030, 5782, 5231, 5065, and 4514—appear, so that the whole spectrum has twelve bands—IV, Fig. 2. As the reduction proceeds further, the liquid becomes dirty green, and the third stage appears with no new bands, but the intensity of single bands is altered— V, Fig. 2 , 6500 and 6718 are weakened, while 6367, 6165, and 5231 are strengthened. The presence of iron, cobalt, nickel, chromium, aluminium, and zinc does not disturb the phenomena. H. C. Jones and W. W. Strong also studied the effect of reducing agents on a soln. of uranyl salts in different solvents ; and of oxidizing agents—hydrogen dioxide, and nitric acid—on uranous salt soln. E. Deussen also examined the absorption spectra of soln. of uranyl chloride in alcohol, and glycerol ; and H. C. Jones and W. W. Strong examined the absorption spectra of uranyl chloride in methyl, ethyl, propyl, isopropyl, butyl, and isobutyl alcohols, ether, methyl and ethyl esters, formamide, glycerol, acetone, and on aq. soln. in the presence of calcium, zinc, and aluminium chloride. According to A. Müller, the colour of uranyl salts is, in general, yellow, but the presence of hydroxyl or keto-groups, particularly in the α- or ortho-positions, displaces the colour strongly towards the red.   The benzene nucleus also acts strongly in displacing the colour towards the red end of the spectrum, particularly when the uranyl group is directly connected with phenolic oxygen.   H. L. Howes, and H. Morton and H. C. Bolton examined the absorption spectra of the double salts : *ammonium uranyl chloride*, and *potassium uranyl chloride*, when solid, and in soln. ; and H. L. Howes, *rubidium* and *cæsium uranyl chlorides*.   E. Becquerel also studied soln. of the potassium salt.   H. Becquerel studied the pleochroism of the crystals.   H. C. Jones and W. W. Strong also studied the absorption spectra of soln. of *uranyl bromide*.

E. Deussen found for aq. soln. of *uranyl sulphate* absorption bands for $\lambda=4885$, 4725, 4560, 4410, 4310, 4180, 4060, and 3950.   Observations were also made by W. Böhlendorff, J. W. Hiebendaal, H. Bremer, N. Titlestad, M. Cantone, H. C. Jones and J. S. Guy, H. C. Jones and W. W. Strong, and E. L. Nichols and H. L. Howes, and H. Morton and H. C. Bolton gave for neutral aq. soln. the bands 4955, 4750, 4580, (4475), 4340, 4210, and 4100 ; and for acidic soln., 4890, 4780, (4520), 4370, 4320, 4210, and 4090.   E. Deussen also examined soln. in alcohol, and in glycerol ; and H. C. Jones and W. W. Strong, in conc. sulphuric acid.   J. Moir gave for soln. of uranyl sulphate in sulphuric acid, bands with the centres at 5650, 5410, 5140, and 4920.   H. L. Howes examined the spectra of soln. of this salt.   H. Morton and H. C. Bolton found for aq. soln. of *ammonium diuranyl sulphate* bands at

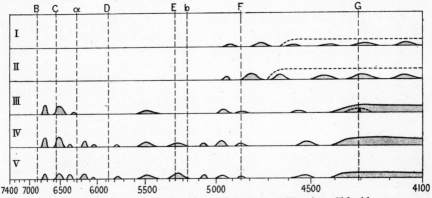

Fig. 2.—Absorption Spectra of Solutions of Uranium Chloride.

4875, 4720, 4575, (4480), 4330, and 4210 ; *ammonium uranyl sulphate*, at 4935, 4800, 4620, 4450, 4330, 4240, and 4100 ; *sodium uranyl sulphate*, at 4875, 4775, 4580, 4440, 4335, and 4180 ; *potassium uranyl sulphate*, at 4790, 4540, 4370, 4230, 4100 ; and *rubidium uranyl sulphate*, at 4885, 4805, 4645, 4475, 4325, 4205, and 4050. M. Cantone also examined ammonium uranyl sulphate ; E. L. Nichols and E. Merritt, potassium uranyl sulphate ; and E. L. Nichols and H. L. Howes, ammonium, potassium, and rubidium uranyl sulphates, as well as *cæsium uranyl sulphate*. H. Morton and H. C. Bolton also found absorption bands with soln. of *thallous uranyl sulphate* at 4905, 4630, 4480, 4295 ; and with *magnesium uranyl sulphate*, at 4790, 4540, 4370, 4230, and 4100.   These soln. show similar spectra, indicating that the double salts are all decomposed in aq. soln. ; this is supported by the fact that the solid salts also show different spectra.   Solid potassium uranyl sulphate has bands at 4805, 4690, 4520, and 4340.   H. L. Howes also examined the spectra of soln. of this salt at different temp.   H. Morton and H. C. Bolton found for *ammonium uranyl carbonate*, bands at 4630, 4450, 4350, 4240, 4125, and 4030 ; *potassium uranyl carbonate*, at 4655, 4450, 4350, 4235, 4130, and 4035 ; and *sodium uranyl carbonate*, at 4665, 4510, 4355, 4250, 4120, and 4045.   H. Oeffinger also made observations on uranyl carbonate.   H. Becquerel studied the pleochroism of *uranyl nitrate*.   J. Moir gave for the centres of the bands of solid uranyl nitrate $\lambda=5600$, 5350, 5100, and 4850.   H. Morton and H. C. Bolton found for the absorption bands in aq. soln. 4880, 4720, 4550, 4400, 4280, 4160, and 4040 ; J. Formanek, 4867, 4705, 4545, 4425, 4290, and 4150—I, Fig. 3 ; and E. Deussen, 4860, 4720, 4540, 4380, 4290, 4150, 4020, 3870, 3790, and 3690. Observations were also made by W. Böhlendorff, O. Knoblauch, E. Hagenbach, J. M. Hiebendaal, H. Oeffinger, H. Bremer, J. C. Ghosh and B. N. Mitter, L. J. Boardman, V. R. von Kurelec, G. H. Dieke and A. C. S. van Heel, F. E. E. Germann, H. L. Howes, H. C. Jones and J. S. Guy, M. Cantone, and E. L. Nichols and E. Merritt. According to J. Formanek, the absorption spectrum in soln. of ethyl alcohol has bands at 4830, 4657, 4500, 4350, 4214, and 4085—II, Fig. 3. J. M. Hiebendaal also examined alcoholic soln. ; H. Morton and H. C. Bolton, soln. in alcohol, ether, glycerol, and acetic ether ; E. Deussen, soln. in methyl and ethyl alcohols, acetone, and glycerol ; and H. C. Jones and W. W. Strong, of soln. of uranyl nitrate in methyl, ethyl, and propyl alcohols, acetone, methyl ester, and nitric acid. Observations on *uranyl phosphate* were made by H. C. Sorby, C. Horner, and E. L. Nichols and E. Merritt. H. Morton and H. C. Bolton gave for solid monouranyl phosphate, 4825, 4700, 4580, 4405, and 4290 ; for the aq. soln., 5060, 4775, 4615, 4480, 4345, and 4240 ; for aq. soln. of diuranyl phosphate, 4870, 4720, 4580, 4425, 4280, and 4170 ; and for aq. soln. of *calcium uranyl phosphate*, 4820, 4675, 4520, 4350, 4220, and 4110. H. W. Vogel made some observations on *uranyl hydroxide* ; M. Cantone, on *ammonium uranate* ; J. Moir found that autunite, or *calcium uranyl phosphate*, has bands

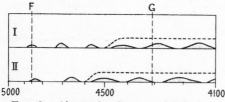

FIG. 3.—Absorption Spectra of Solutions of Uranyl Nitrate.

with centres at 5750, 5540, 5290, and 5080 ; *uranyl metaphosphate* in solid metaphosphoric acid, 5900, 5600, 5420, 5150, and 4950 ; and *uranyl sodium metaphosphate* in microcosmic salt lead, 6020, 5620, 5430, and 5170. The crystals of *autunite* and of *torbernite* were examined by F. Rinne. H. Kahler studied the band spectra of crystals containing *uranium oxide*. E. Deussen, H. Morton and H. C. Bolton, W. Böhlendorff, H. Oeffinger, O. Knoblauch, H. C. Jones and J. S. Guy, H. C. Jones and W. W. Strong, V. Henri and M. Landau, M. Cantone, E. H. Harvey, E. L. Nichols and E. Merritt, J. Moir, and H. Bremer studied *uranyl acetate* and its double salts ; H. Morton and H. C. Bolton, *uranyl formate* ; E. Deussen, H. Morton and H. C. Bolton, V. Henri and M. Landau, and W. Böhlendorff, *uranyl oxalate* and its double salts ; H. Oeffinger, *uranyl citrate, uranyl tartrate,* and *potassium uranyl cyanide* ; and A. Mazzucchelli and co-workers, a number of organic salts. J. Formanek observed that uranyl salts react with alkanna tincture ; for if a neutral soln. of uranyl chloride or nitrate be added to tincture of alkanna, the liquid becomes green, and there is then a strong absorption band at 6870, and a feeble one at 6315. This is characteristic of uranium.

H. Morton and H. C. Bolton found that solid *uranous fluoride* has absorption bands at 5890, 5530 to 5210, 5020 to 4700, and 4400, and with maxima at 6670, 5455, 5280, 4840, and 4770, whilst *potassium uranous fluoride* has maxima at 6600, 6340, 6140, 5940, 5370, 5240, 4910, and 4760. The absorption spectra of soln. of *uranous chloride* were examined by H. Oeffinger, A. Mazzucchelli and O. G. d'Alceo, and J. L. C. Zimmermann. E. Becquerel found for the solid salt bands at $\lambda=6940^*$, 6850, 6720, 6550, 6310, 6110*, 5850, 5760, 5650, 5610*, 5570*, and 5485, with broad bands at 5190, 4940, and 4780 ; and with aq. soln., for $\lambda=7056$, 6570*, 6530*, 6450, 6310, 6110, 5880, 5540*, 5500*, 4995 (broad), 4960*, and 4740*— where the * indicates strong bands. H. C. Jones and W. W. Strong examined soln. of uranous chloride in methyl ester, in methyl, ethyl, propyl and isopropyl alcohols, acetone, ether, and glycerol ; and in the presence of aluminium chloride and various acids ; and T. R. Merton, soln. in acetone, acetonitrile, ethyl acetoacetate, ethyl alcohol, and acetophenone. H. C. Jones and W. W. Strong also studied the absorption spectrum of *uranous bromide*. H. Oeffinger, A. Mazzucchelli and O. G. d'Alceo examined the absorption spectra of aq. soln. of *uranous sulphate*, and J. M. Hiebendaal, of alcoholic soln. E. Becquerel found for the solid salt bands at 6900, 6720 ?*, 6650*, 6550, 6450, 6310, 6150, 6100, 5890, 5530*, 5490*, 5400, and 5000; and for aq. soln., at 7056, 6570*, 6530*, 6450, 6310, 5530*, 5490*, and 4980 (broad). H. W. Vogel made observations on *uranous nitrate*; H. Oeffinger, L. C. Beard and O. M. Reiff, and H. C. Jones and W. W. Strong, on *uranous acetate*; and A. Mazzucchelli and co-workers, on a number of organic salts.

The absorption spectrum of the canary-yellow *glass* coloured by uranium was found by E. Hagenbach to furnish bands between 5110 and 4860, 4700 and 4600, and at 4500; H. W. Vogel said that the bands are similar to those with uranyl nitrate, but are displaced a little more towards the red. O. Lubarsch observed, with thin layers, bands between 5070 and 4840, and 4710 and 4620, and with thick layers, bands between 6520 and 6460, 6230 and 6150, and 5930 and 5870; these he referred to uranous oxide. The absorption spectrum of uranium glass was studied by J. B. Burke, C. Camichel, R. A. Houstoun, J. Becquerel, M. Luckiesh, E. L. Nichols and E. Merritt, T. Dreisch, R. C. Gibbs, E. Graviola and P. Pringsheim, F. G. Wick, W. T. Anderson and L. F. Bird, etc.

Uranyl salts in soln. exhibit a greenish fluorescence. E. Becquerel [5] found the **fluorescence** or **phosphorescence spectrum** of uranyl chloride to have bands of wave-lengths 6230, 5955, 5685, 5433, 5176, and 4980; uranyl sulphate, 6620, 6262, 5955, 5690, 5418, 5170, and 4945; uranyl nitrate, 6544, 6180, 5810, 5860, 5590, 5325, 5090, and 4920; and uranyl acetate, 6525, 6180, 5860, 5590, 5325, 5090, and 4920. The bands for the nitrate and acetate occupy nearly the same parts of the spectrum, but with the chloride and sulphate the bands are near the red end. According to E. L. Nichols and H. L. Howes, the phosphorescence spectrum of uranyl sulphate, $UO_2SO_4.3H_2O$, consists of eight equidistant bands, the first and eighth of which disappear at the temp. of liquid air. The remaining bands are resolved into groups of narrow line-like bands, the homologous members of which form series having constant frequency intervals, ranging from 85·7 in cæsium uranyl sulphate to 83·0 in potassium uranyl sulphate. The fluorescence groups are distinguished by a strong pair of bands about eight frequency units apart and several weak bands some of which are doublets. There is a shift of all bands towards the violet, with increasing mol. wts., of about fifteen frequency units in passing from the spectrum of uranyl sulphate to that of cæsium uranyl sulphate.

G. G. Stokes noticed that the phosphorescence spectrum and the absorption spectrum of uranyl salts slightly overlapped. H. Morton and H. C. Bolton also noted coincidences in the positions of several fluorescence and absorption bands of the uranyl salts; and H. and J. Becquerel and H. K. Onnes also noted coincidences in the narrowed bands at low temp. E. L. Nichols and E. Merritt found that in the case of potassium uranyl sulphate, the bands 4760 and 4920 of the absorption spectrum coincide with those of the phosphorescence spectrum; and they are reversible, in that the bands may appear as absorption or luminescence bands according to the conditions under which they are observed. This reversibility was first described by H. Becquerel in 1885 with soln. of uranyl nitrate. H. L. Howes also mentioned the reversibility of the 5080 and 4880 bands of the double uranyl chlorides. When uranyl salts are crystallized in violet light, they exhibit a green luminosity of sufficient persistence to be observed in a phosphoroscope, but the same phenomenon cannot be detected thus in soln. of these salts. J. Perrin said that fluorescence and phosphorescence are not to be distinguished by the greater or lesser persistence of emission, but by the action of a change of temp. and of infra-red radiation; and that the luminosity of uranyl salts should be regarded as a true fluorescence. Of soln. of uranyl salts, that of the sulphate in water containing an excess of sulphuric acid shows the greatest fluorescence. The fluorescence of the sulphate is considerably greater in sulphuric acid soln., being only one-fourth or one-fifth that of the solid salt. The average life of the luminosity is about 5×10^{-4} sec. The luminosity is regarded as a "prolonged fluorescence" analogous to the brief fluorescence of dyes such as fluorescein, the persistence of luminosity of which is of a much smaller magnitude. Fluorescence of the uranyl salts is considerably reduced by the addition of various substances such as halide salts, organic acids, etc. Mere traces of hydrochloric acid or of alcohol greatly diminish the fluorescence of the sulphate when dissolved in sulphuric acid. J. Perrin observed that the presence of eosin lowers the fluorescence of uranium ; and M. Privault, that quinol inhibits the photochemical oxidation and the fluorescence of uranium. R. Coustal found the permanent luminescence of crystalline solids to be independent of time, temp., and previous insolation ; that ultra-red radiations are without effect ; but it is most intense when the ultra-violet fluorescence is greatest. The permanent luminescence is an effect of radioactivity.

H. Becquerel, and J. Becquerel found that at low temp. the bands of the uranyl phosphorescent spectrum, like those of the absorption spectrum, become sharp, so that the simple diffuse bands of uranyl nitrate at ordinary temp. become, in liquid air, intense narrow double bands between which other weaker bands appear. Potassium uranyl sulphate and especially the chloride give groups of bands, which, in liquid air, are resolved into fine intense bands arranged similarly in each spectrum. It is assumed that the phosphorescence is localized in the uranyl radicle. H. and J. Becquerel and H. K. Onnes found that the bands which are characteristic of the uranyl salts at the ordinary temp., and undergo subdivision at the temp. of liquid air, are transformed into groups of much finer lines at the temp. of liquid hydrogen. At the same time the emission maxima are displaced towards the smaller wavelengths. Since the displacement is relatively small when the temp. falls from that of liquid air to that of liquid hydrogen, it is possible that the bands approach asymptotically a limiting position as the temp. is lowered. It is concluded that the difference between the frequencies of two successive homologous bands is practically constant, and this holds for all series of homologous bands of the same salt. For different uranyl salts the values of this constant differ but slightly from one another. In structure the uranyl salt bands resemble the band spectra of gases. At the temp. of solid hydrogen a strong magnetic field has no influence even on the narrow bands. The phosphorescence of the uranyl salts is quite different in character from that of other classes of phosphorescent substances, and in no way depends on the presence of traces of impurities. The transfer of electrons under the photo-electric influence of the absorbed light appears to be a process which is entirely confined to the uranium atom, or at least to the uranyl group. Observations on the phosphorescent spectra of uranyl salts were also made by E. L. Nichols, E. L. Nichols and E. Merritt, J. Moir, R. M. Müller, E. Goldstein, E. Wiedemann and G. C. Schmidt, O. Lommel, M. Cantone, S. J. Wawiloff and V. L. Levschin, S. J. Wawiloff, H. C. Jones and W. W. Strong. H. Becquerel observed similar phenomena with glass coloured by uranium oxide. O. Lommel also studied the phosphorescence of glass. L. de Boisbaudran observed that alumina is not made fluorescent by uranium salts. H. and J. Becquerel and H. K. Onnes found that the fluorescence spectra consist of three to eight regularly spaced groups, lying between bluish-green and red. Each group consists of about five components, which are separated on cooling and whose number then is augmented by numerous less regularly appearing lines. The distance in the scale of frequencies between homologous components is constant over the whole of the fluorescence spectrum of one definite substance. The absorption spectra, too, show a regular structure. The constant frequency interval between homologous components here has another, invariably smaller, value than in the fluorescence. When one considers the spectra of one substance one gets the impression that every series of fluorescence lines is prolonged towards the violet in a corresponding absorption series. F. Perrin and R. Delorme discussed the duration of the fluorescence of uranyl salts. S. J. Wawiloff and V. L. Levschin observed that the luminosity of a soln. of uranyl sulphate in sulphuric acid continues for 10^{-5} to

10^{-4} sec. after illumination, and fades approximately exponentially. A rise of temp., or the addition of water, shortens the duration of luminosity. A. C. S. van Heel studied the various spectra of uranyl compounds in terms of the theory of transitions from various energy states or levels. E. L. Nichols and M. K. Slattery studied the photo or cathodic luminescence produced by traces of uranium in various salts—sodium and potassium phosphates, borax, and sodium and calcium fluorides.

The **triboluminescence** of oxides and sulphides has been discussed by A. Karl ; [6] and of uranium salts, by J. A. Siemssen. The salts appear luminous when shaken or struck in the dark.

The high frequency or **X-ray spectrum** of uranium has the absorption limit 0·1075 for the K-series, which was studied by W. Duane and co-workers,[7] J. Schrör, M. de Broglie, B. Walter, H. R. Robinson and C. L. Young, G. Réchou, E. Frimann, J. E. Mack and J. M. Cork, and by M. Siegbahn and E. Jönsson. The L-series has lines $\alpha_2\alpha^1$, 0·92014 ; $\alpha_1\alpha$, 0·90833 ; $\beta_1\beta$, 0·71807 ; $\beta_2\gamma$, 0·75268 ; $\gamma_1\delta$, 0·61283 ; 1ϵ, 1·06477 ; η, 0·8029 ; $\beta_5\zeta$, 0·72413 ; $\gamma_2\theta$, 0·6044 ; $\beta_4\upsilon$, 0·7454 ; $\beta_3\phi$, 0·7084 ; $\gamma_3\chi$, 0·597 ; and $\gamma_4\psi$, 0·5738, with the absorption limits 0·7214, 0·5918, and 0·5685. The L-series was studied by M. de Broglie, J. Zahradnicek, A. Sandström, J. H. Williams, S. Idei, D. Coster, E. Hjalmar, A. Dauvillier, G. L. Clark, S. K. Allison, H. R. Robinson and C. L. Young, H. R. Robinson, H. Hirata, S. K. Allison and V. J. Andrew, J. Schrör, H. Brauns, and M. Siegbahn. The M-series includes α_1, 3·916 ; α, 3·9014 ; β, 3·7083 ; γ, 3·4714 ; δ, 2·943 ; and ϵ, 2·813, or M_1, 3·491, M_2, 3·326, and M_3, 2·873. They were studied by G. Wentzel, F. R. Hirsh, E. Lindberg, H. R. Robinson and C. L. Young, and D. Coster. The N-series, studied by V. Dolejsek, includes N_7P_1, 8·594 ; N_7P_2, 8·700 ; N_7O_3, 10·080 ; N_6O_2, 9·876 ; N_6O_5, 12·856 ; N_5O_1, 12·777 ; and N_5O_2, 12·702. The N-series, the O-series, and the P-series were also studied by H. R. Robinson and C. L. Young. W. Herz gave $3·13 \times 10^6$ for the **vibration frequency.** T. E. Aurén found that the relative at. absorption coeff. for X-rays is 1123 when that of lead is 569, and that of water, unity. S. J. M. Allen studied this subject. S. J. M. Allen, W. Duane and co-workers, and E. C. Stoner and L. H. Martin made observations on the absorption of X-rays by uranium ; and R. W. James and G. W. Brindley, on the scattering of X-rays. H. R. Robinson and A. M. Cassie studied the secondary X-rays from a target of uranium oxide bombarded by a beam of K-rays ; H. B. Wahlin, the emission of positive ions by the heated metal.

In 1804, A. F. Gehlen [8] found that an ethereal soln. of uranium chloride is decomposed in sunlight, and J. Fiedler, in a dissertation with the motto : *Nihil luce obscurius*—Nothing is darker (*i.e.* less known) than light—said that uranic chloride in the presence of organic substances is reduced to uranous chloride. A. E. Becquerel, and P. L. Chastaing observed that alcoholic soln. of uranyl nitrate, in light, deposit green uranous oxide, and J. J. Ebelmen observed a similar thing with alcoholic soln. of uranyl sulphate. H. C. Bolton observed that uranyl salt soln. in the presence of glycerol are reduced by light ; A. St. V. Niépce, and E. Boivin observed the same thing in the presence of tartaric acid ; C. J. Burnett, and A. St. V. Niépce, in the presence of paper. Many organic uranyl salts are reduced in light—*e.g.* A. St. V. Niépce and L. Corvisart, W. C. Holmes, W. Seekamp, C. J. Burnett, and D. von Monckhoven found this to be the case with uranyl oxalate and its double salts ; A. St. V. Niépce and L. Corvisart, and L. L. Bonaparte, R. E. Liesegang, with the acetate, citrate, formate, tartrate, aconitate, etc. ; and G. Courtois, with aq. soln. of uranyl propionate, butyrate, lactate, quinate, salicylate, oxalate, and tartrate are stable in the dark but not in light ; whilst soln. of the acetate, formate, benzoate, glycollate, and citrate decompose in darkness and in light. G. Wisbar found that in light the presence of uranyl salts induces the decomposition of glutaric and succinic acids ; W. C. Pierce and co-workers, malonic acid ; W. G. Leighton and G. S. Forbes, and H. Fay, acetic, propionic, isobutyric, oxalic, malonic, tartaric, and succinic acids ; J. C. Ghosh and B. N. Mitter, these acids and in addition lactic, glycollic, and mandelic acids; T. Pavolini, hydroxy-acids; R. Luther and J. Plotnikoff, R. H. Müller, W. P. Jorissen, and W. P. Jorissen and L. T. Reicher, oxalic acid—P. F. Bacon, W. T. Anderson and F. W. Robinson, J. E. Moss and A. W. Knapp, P. F. Büchi, and E. Baur proposed the photolysis of oxalic acid in the presence of uranyl salts as a standard for measurement; E. Baur, and E. C. Hatt, formic acid; H. von Euler, acetic acid; J. Plotnikoff, hydriodic acid; H. Kunz-Krause and P. Manicke, iodic acid; J. C. Ghosh and J. Mukherjee, leucomalachite; J. Aloy and A. Valdiguié, dextrose, methylene-blue, aldehydes, the lower fatty alcohols, olefinic hydrocarbons—amylene, acetylenic hydrocarbons, cyclohexenes, toluenes, xylenes, cymene, chloroform, bromoform, iodoform, aliphatic ethers, aliphatic aldehydes, aromatic aldehydes (slow), ketones (slow), fatty acids—while the sat. hydrocarbons, cyclohexanes, benzene, phenols, amines, amides, and the phenolic ethers do not react; A. J. Allmand and L. Reeve, lactic acid; and D. Berthelot and H. Gaudechon, maleic, fumaric, pyruvic, and lactic acids. C. Neuberg observed the following changes occur in the presence of uranium salts, in sunlight: alcohols to aldehydes; poly-alcohols to hydroxy-aldehydes or ketones; acids to aldehydes or keto-compounds, sometimes with fewer carbon atoms than the original substance; monosaccharides to osones; disaccharides undergo inversion; polysaccharides and glucosides are hydrolyzed; amino-acids undergo deamidisation and lose carbon dioxide, yielding aldehydes with a smaller number of carbon atoms than the original substance; glycerides are partly hydrolyzed; and peptones and proteins are partly hydrolyzed. D. Berthelot and H. Gaudechon observed that apart from salts of uranium, neither the fluorescent nor radioactive substances experimented with accelerated photochemical reactions. The accelerating influence of the uranium salts is limited to a special class of reactions, namely, the decomposition of open-chain acids, especially dibasic or complex acids. These are reactions which occur spontaneously in ultra-violet light, and under the influence of the catalyst they take place in visible light. The catalyst thus lowers the vibration frequency of the photochemical reaction, in the same way as an ordinary catalyst lowers the temp. of a chemical reaction. P. L. Chastaing, and J. M. Eder observed that blue and violet light are most active in promoting these photolytic reactions; and, in agreement, N. Titlestad showed that light of wave-length between 4840 and 4230 is most active. According to J. Aloy and E. Rodier, when, under the influence of light, uranyl salts are converted into uranous salts in the presence of the acid entering into the constitution of the salt and a readily oxidizable substance such as alcohol, the reaction which occurs is as follows: $UO_2Cl_2 + 2HCl + C_2H_5.OH = UCl_4 + CH_3.CHO + 2H_2O$. Two mols. of acid are necessary for each mol. of uranyl salt. In this way uranous fluoride, chloride, bromide, iodide, and sulphate have been prepared, and an aq. soln. of the nitrate. If an insufficient amount of acid is present, basic salts are obtained. If the reaction is allowed to proceed further, a black precipitate of uranous hydroxide is obtained.

E. Baur and co-workers found that the reactions are accelerated by substances which destroy fluorescence; when all the uranyl salt has been reduced, fluorescence ceases. Consequently, the two phenomena appear to be connected. When light is absorbed by a soln. of a uranium salt, the uranyl ion undergoes a reversible change from the "dark" condition into the "light" condition; when the reverse action takes place, the light energy absorbed is given off again in the form of fluorescence. The addition of certain substances, such as chlorine or iodine ions, ferric and vanadyl salts, vanadic acid, and quadrivalent uranium salts, extinguishes the fluorescence. The same substances also destroy the Becquerel effect. In the sexivalent stage the uranium absorbs light energy, forming octovalent and tervalent uranium: $5U^{VI} + Light \rightarrow 3U^{VIII} + 2U^{III}$. If any substance is present with which the activated uranium can react, it does so, and reduction occurs; but if not, the reaction is reversed, and the uranium reverts to the "dark" condition, and fluorescence occurs. The reverse reaction is prevented by the presence of substances which destroy fluorescence—*e.g.* reducing agents like oxalic acid, potassium iodide, and uranous salts which react with octovalent uranium; or oxidizing agents like ferric salts which react with the tervalent uranium. E. C. Hatt said the hypothesis that the light produces compounds of higher and lower valency is rendered probable by the fact that the insolated soln. have an oxidizing action on potassium iodide and a reducing action on potassium permanganate. In the photolysis of uranyl formate, the liberation of carbon dioxide and hydrogen is supposed to be due to the octovalent uranium; and the reaction dies down through the accumulation of sexavalent uranium, which acts as an extinguisher. In the photolytic decomposition of oxalic acid by uranyl sulphate, the octovalent uranium produces carbon dioxide, and tervalent uranium, carbon monoxide, while sexavalent uranium is re-formed. The products of the reaction are found to be formic acid, carbon dioxide, and carbon monoxide. The amount of formic acid formed is very small, and it is held that it must remain small, because it is used up as fast as it is produced in reducing the uranyl-ion to uranous-ion. The gas evolved contains a slight excess of carbon dioxide above that required for the simple stoichiometric relationship $CO_2 : CO$. The formation of formic acid is regarded as a cathodic reduction of carbon dioxide, thus: $CO_2 + 2H^{\cdot} + 2\ominus = H.CO_2H$. The hydrogen reported to be formed in the photolysis of oxalic acid was shown by E. Baur and A. Rebmann to be carbon monoxide derived from glyoxylic acid present as an impurity. In the photolysis of uranyl acetate two reactions occur: (i) the photocatalytic decomposition into methane and carbon dioxide observed by H. Fay; and (ii) the non-catalytic oxidation of acetate-ions to ethane and carbon dioxide by uranyl salts, which only occurs in acetic acid soln. with a sufficient concentration of acetate-ions. The photolysis is favoured by the presence of free acetic acid, but is restricted by chloride ions and mercuric ions to some extent, and almost entirely by ferric salts or formic acid. The reaction cannot be regarded as a unimolecular decomposition of a uranyl acetate complex by light, but as an action of an activated uranyl complex on the surrounding molecules by an interchange of electrons. The process is an oxidation-reduction reaction and is therefore akin to electrolysis. Thus, in the electrolytic decomposition of acetate, acetyl peroxide and atomic hydrogen are the respective anodic and cathodic products, which then interact and form methane and carbon dioxide. Since the photolytic oxidation of acetic acid to ethane and carbon dioxide, and of glyoxylic acid to carbon monoxide and carbon dioxide, can be reproduced electrochemically only by the use of a considerable potential difference, it is concluded that the energy quantum absorbed by the uranyl complex must also have such a value as would suffice, not only for the production of oxygen, but also for the formation of peroxides, observed by A. Bach, and F. L. Usher and J. H. Priestley. In the photolysis of carbon dioxide in the presence of a uranyl salt, F. L. Usher and J. H. Priestley observed that formic acid is produced, with formaldehyde probably acting as an intermediate product, but E. Baur did not accept the observation. W. R. G. Atkins and H. H. Poole, M. Plotnikoff, and R. H. Müller made observations on the subject.

E. Baur found that the potential at a platinum electrode immersed in a soln. containing both uranous and uranyl salts is less positive in sunlight than in darkness; consequently, if two platinum electrodes are immersed in a soln. of the mixed salts so that one electrode is in darkness while the other is exposed to a bright light, the cell can be made to furnish a current—**Becquerel effect.** The displacement of the potential is considerable, and takes place more or less rapidly according to the nature of the salts employed. N. Titlestad immersed platinum electrodes in a soln. containing both uranous and uranyl sulphates, and the potential difference is measured when one electrode is illuminated and the other kept in darkness. In darkness, the e.m.f. of uranous-uranyl cells is represented by the equation: $E = e + RT/2F . \log_e [UO_2^{\cdot\cdot}][H^{\cdot}]^4/U^{\cdot\cdot\cdot\cdot}$, corresponding with the chemical change: $UO_2^{\cdot\cdot} + 4H^{\cdot} \rightarrow U^{\cdot\cdot\cdot\cdot} + 2H_2O + 2F$. e is 0·404 volt more positive than the normal hydrogen electrode. Illumination displaces the potential towards the negative side, but this effect is observed only with smooth electrodes. The displacement of potential is approximately proportional to the logarithm of the light intensity. Some results are illustrated by Fig. 4 for light of relative intensities 4, 1, and 0·25 with soln. containing 75 mols of uranous sulphate and 25 mols of uranyl sulphate, at 25°. The initial velocity of the displacement of equilibrium on illumination is proportional to the intensity of the light. The velocity of displacement is practically independent of external circumstances, but the velocity of return increases with increasing concentration and temp., and with diminution in the sulphuric acid concentration. From these results it follows that the law of mass action does not apply to such cells. Small amounts of alcohol affect the light potentials slightly. On repeated illumination, the electrodes become slightly more positive. According to A. Samsonoff, uranous salts alone give no photoelectric current, and with uranyl salts the presence of traces of uranous salts is necessary for the effect. In the photoelectric cells indicated above it is assumed that the ions which result from the removal of electrons by the action of the light diffuse to the electrodes at different rates. The maximum effect is obtained when the incident light corresponds with the region of maximum absorption. In the continual action of the light rays, fatigue effects are exhibited, and when the light is removed, after-effects are observed. It is supposed that the photoelectric effect is not a consequence of, but rather the preliminary stage in, the chemical changes which occur under the influence of the light. The assimilation of carbon dioxide by plants is supposed to be accompanied in the same way by a previous formation of electrically charged mols. G. Trümpler found that the photochemical effect with uranous and uranyl salt soln. may show negative or positive effects according to the conditions; the former is attributed to the formation of quinquevalent uranium, and the latter to the presence of octovalent uranium in the illuminated region. Both stages are formed by the action of light on the uranyl salt. The negative effect is weakened by the presence of iodine, hydriodic acid, vanadium sulphate, vanadyl sulphate, hydrochloric acid, ferric sulphate, and ferrous sulphate. The positive effect is weakened by the presence of sulphur dioxide, uranous sulphate, and oxalic acid. All the substances which have a weakening action of the positive or negative Becquerel effect also reduce the fluorescence of uranyl sulphate soln. The fluorescence of these soln. is also decreased by an increase in the temp. H. Schiller studied the Becquerel effect with the uranium formates and oxalates; T. Pavolini, and A. Goldmann also studied the photoelectric effect; and S. J. Wawilow and W. L. Lewschin, the photoluminescence.

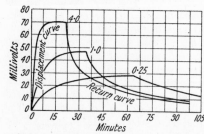

FIG. 4.—The Effect of Light of Different Intensities on the Photoelectric Effect.

H. Müller [9] found that the exposure of uranium to intense α-rays produced no effect on the induced radioactivity. A. Nodon found that the photogenic radiations emitted by the sun can penetrate metals of high valency, like lead or uranium, but not those of low valency, like magnesium, zinc, aluminium, or iron. M. de Broglie examined the α-ray spectrum. S. Maracineanu observed that after exposure to sunlight the activity of uranium oxide shows marked variations, which may amount to as much as 50 per cent. of the total activity. If the uranium oxide is exposed simultaneously to sunlight and to bombardment by the α-particles from polonium, the variations after exposure are more frequent than for sunlight alone. J. Thibaud studied the β-ray spectra and the photoelectric effect; J. Lifschitz and S. M. Hooghoudt, the Becquerel effect with soln. of uranyl salts; B. Gudden, the range of the α-particles from uranium; W. M. Cohn, the luminosity in cathode rays; F. Lotze, the pleochroic uranium haloes. For the **radioactivity of uranium,** *vide* radium, **4.** 26, 126.

C. Benedicks [10] said that the sp. **electrical resistance** of uranium is less than that of bismuth, being about $62 \cdot 0 \times 10^{-6}$ ohms at $18°$. P. W. Bridgman found the resistance to be $0 \cdot 000076$ ohm at $0°$. This is high for a metal, being of the order of the resistance of liquid mercury and of bismuth. The temp. coeff. of the resistance between $0°$ and $100°$ is $0 \cdot 00230$. The resistance was found to decrease under press., as is normal for most metals. The average press. coeff. over the range 0 to 12,000 kgrms. per sq. cm. was $-0 \cdot 0_5 436$. A. Schulze made some observations on this subject. W. Meissner and B. Voigt, and J. C. McLennan and co-workers measured the electrical conductivity at low temp.; and W. Meissner and B. Voigt obtained for the ratio r of the resistance R_0 at $0°$ to the resistance R at the observed temp. when the value at $0°$ is $0 \cdot 0_2 6811$ ohm :

	$0 \cdot 16°$	$-186 \cdot 20°$	$-195 \cdot 47°$	$-252 \cdot 59°$	$-268 \cdot 80°$	$-271 \cdot 59°$
r	1	$0 \cdot 7001$	$0 \cdot 6844$	$0 \cdot 5867$	$0 \cdot 5445$	$0 \cdot 5400$

According to C. Dittrich, the difference between the μ_{32} and μ_{1024} conductivities of soln. of uranyl chloride, nitrate, or sulphate is abnormally high presumably because ionization occurs in stages; the conductivity increases appreciably with time owing to hydrolysis. The formation of acid H'-ions by hydrolysis is demonstrated by the effect of the soln. on the inversion of sugar. Some uranyl salts—*e.g.* the oxalate—show a diminished conductivity on exposure to light owing to the photolysis of the soln. The **transport number** of the uranyl-ion is 56 at $25°$. Uranyl salts of weak acids have a marked tendency to form complex ions. This is shown by the fact that the sp. conductivities of the mixed sodium and uranyl salts are in most cases less than those of the sodium salts themselves : in the case of the oxalate, tartrate, and citrate, the specific conductivity of the mixture decreases with increasing concentration of the uranyl salt. Migration experiments confirm the formation of complex ions, because whilst in mixed soln. of uranyl and sodium oxalates the uranium is transported to the anode, it goes to the cathode in a mixed soln. of uranyl and sodium chlorides. The direction seems to depend also on the concentration. The solubility of uranyl oxalate is increased by the addition of sodium oxalate—a further proof that a complex ion is formed. The mixture of uranyl nitrate with sodium salts of organic acids is in most cases accompanied by an absorption of heat.

H. Moissan, as indicated above, obtained uranium by the **electrolysis** of molten sodium uranium hexachloride. According to C. Luckow, E. F. Smith and co-workers, and E. F. Kern, the electrolysis of soln. of uranium salts does not furnish the metal under ordinary conditions, but the cathode product is a hydrated oxide in various stages of oxidation. The fact is employed for the electrolytic separation of uranium from uranyl salts, the hydrated oxide being converted by heat to the U_3O_8-oxide before weighing. F. W. O. de Coninck and M. Camo observed that in the electrolysis of soln. of uranyl nitrate containing traces of nitric acid, a deposit is not formed, or rather the deposit initially produced is dissolved in the acid. If 6 to 8 per cent. soln. of the nitrate are electrolyzed, black, pulverulent, pyrophoric uranium monoxide is formed, and it oxidizes to the orange hydrate, $UO_3.H_2O$, when dried in the water-oven. If a weaker current is employed, the canary-yellow hydrate, $U_2O_3.2H_2O$, and the orange-coloured hydrate, $U_2O_3.H_2O$, are formed. With some soln. a current of about one amp. gives a mixture of the yellow and orange hydrates; with others the black oxide, U_4O_5, is obtained, along with one of its hydrates which is violet. The latter in a dry atm. slowly changes into the yellow hydrate. The black oxide, U_4O_5, is very stable, and is thus distinguished from the monoxide; it does not oxidize at $100°$, and when strongly heated in hydrogen is reduced to the monoxide. According to C. A. Pierlé, in aq. soln. with low current density, uranyl salts deposit, in the first place, hydrated uranic oxide, $UO_3.H_2O$, which is changed as the electrolysis proceeds to a black oxide of varying composition. With higher current density, uranyl sulphate is reduced to uranous sulphate, but in the presence of free acid the deposit obtained is small in amount and poorly adherent, although metallic in appearance. In neutral or alkaline soln., the deposit formed is a mixture of black and yellow oxides. The use of a diaphragmed cell does not change the character of the deposits. The deposit obtained when alkaline uranyl tartrate or citrate soln. are electrolyzed is an oxide much richer in uranium than that deposited from soln. acidified with tartaric or citric acid. Soln. of potassium uranyl fluoride, whether acid, alkaline, or neutral, form a deposit containing fluorine ; in acid soln. the deposit is $UF_4.6H_2O$; neutral and alkaline soln. give a deposit containing uranium tetrafluoride and uranium oxide. Deposits obtained from neutral soln. of potassium uranyl cyanide consist of pure potassium uranate. When acidified with hydrocyanic acid, the deposit is the yellow hydrated oxide contaminated with a little of the black oxide.

C. A. Pierlé added that the black deposit formed when uranyl salt soln. are electrolyzed is not $U_3O_8.2H_2O$, as reported by E. F. Smith, but rather $U_3O_{10}.2H_2O$, which has a potential different from that of U_3O_8. C. A. Pierlé found that the electrical conductivity of non-aqueous soln. of uranyl salts is a function of the water present, and the deposits formed are oxides contaminated with organic matter. Anhydrous pyridine dissolves anhydrous uranium tetrachloride to form conducting soln. ; these, on electrolysis, deposit a compound containing uranium and pyridine on the cathode. Soln. of uranium tetrachloride in acetone do not yield metallic uranium on electrolysis ; the soln. is a good conductor of electricity. The deposit obtained replaces mercury from mercurous sulphate. Uranium tetrachloride reacts with anhydrous acetone, forming $\beta\beta$-dichloropropane. During electrolysis, hydrogen is evolved. R. Groves and A. S. Russell studied the electrodeposition of uranium on mercury. U. Sborgi found the **electrochemical equivalent** of uranium, from soln. of the tetrachloride, to correspond with the at. wt. 240.

W. Muthmann and F. Fraunberger found that the **electrode potential** of a fresh surface of uranium in contact with N-KCl is -0.46 volt. Unlike the case of chromium, molybdenum, and tungsten, they observed no evidence of the **passivity** of uranium. U. Sborgi examined the anodic behaviour of uranium ; in some cases a little carbon dioxide was evolved—it was derived from the presence of a small proportion of carbon as impurity in the metal. The anode dissolved in sulphuric acid and sulphates, nitric acid and nitrates, hydrochloric acid and chlorides, bromides, acetates, and chlorate. In iodides separation of the halogen was also observed. In all the experiments except three the metal dissolved as though it had the valency four, but in some cases allowance has to be made for the evolved gas. In two experiments with sulphates and in one with nitrates the results indicated a valency of six. In phosphates and in alkalies the electrode was covered with a yellow deposit, and the current fell to a minimum ; when the deposit was mechanically removed at frequent intervals, the result agreed with the valency four. There was no evidence of uranium becoming passive. A. Günther-Schulze discussed the electrolytic valve action. A. Fischer and E. K. Rideal found that with an alcoholic soln. of uranium tetrachloride, the potential for $U/U^{....}$ is 0.30 volt, and when this is calculated for aq. soln. from the difference for copper in aq. and alcoholic soln., the electrode potential becomes 0.23 volt. This allocates uranium's place in the electrochemical series between copper and hydrogen. This cannot be right, because uranium decomposes water and reduces soln. of stannous chloride. Its potential must therefore approach that of a baser metal, and they added that it probably lies between -0.4 and 0.2 volt. P. Herasymenko found the reduction potential of uranyl salts $U^{VI}=U^V$ for 10-fold dilution to be -0.056 volt. Powdered oxides fixed on to platinum with gelatine were found by C. A. Pierlé to have the following potentials : $U_3O_8/UO_2(NO_3)_2$, 14.3 grms. per litre$=0.776$ volt ; $UO_3.H_2O/UO_2(NO_3)_2=-0.860$; black oxide from aq. uranyl salts $/UO_2(NO_3)_2=-0.6872$ volt ; uranium 91.49 per cent. $/UO_2(NO_3)_2=-0.093$ volt. Uranous oxide, UO_2, gives a single potential identical with that obtained for the green oxide, U_3O_8. W. Ogawa noted that uranium activated galena as a radio-detector. E. Z. Stowell studied the behaviour of uranium as cathode in the oscillating arc; and M. Haitinger, the intensity of the ultra-violet rays from a uranium arc light.

H. Moissan [11] said that uranium is not magnetic when it is free from iron, but more precise measurements show that it is probably slightly paramagnetic. K. Honda found a specimen with 0·23 per cent. of iron had a **magnetic suscepti-bility** of $4·34 \times 10^{-6}$; and M. Owen gave $3·26 \times 10^{-6}$ mass unit. S. Meyer gave $0·21 \times 10^{-6}$ for the atomic magnetization (gram-atom per litre). P. Pascal found that the mol. magnetic susceptibility of the uranium ion decreases proportionally with an increase in its degree of oxidation, thus, the value for $U(SO_4)_2$ is 320×10^{-5}, and for $UO_2(SO_4)_2$, $-5·57 \times 10^{-5}$. S. Freed and C. Kasper studied the magnetic susceptibility of uranyl ions. D. M. Bose and H. G. Bhar found that the suscepti-bilities of salts of sexivalent uranium are diamagnetic.

REFERENCES.

[1] P. Vinassa, *Gazz. Chim. Ital.*, **28**. 178, 1928; E. M. Péligot, *Ann. Chim. Phys.*, (3), **5**. 5, 1842; (3), **12**. 549, 1844; (3), **22**. 329, 1848; (4), **17**. 368, 1869; *Journ. Pharm. Chim.*, (2), **27**. 522, 1841; *Compt. Rend.*, **12**. 735, 1841; **22**. 487, 1846; **42**. 73, 1856; J. Laissus, *Rev. Mét.*, **25**. 50, 1928; H. Moissan, *Compt. Rend.*, **116**. 347, 1433, 1893; **122**. 1088, 1302, 1896; **142**. 425, 1906; *Ann. Chim. Phys.*, (7), **8**. 141, 1896; (7), **9**. 264, 1896; *Le four électrique*, Paris, 233, 1897; London, 162, 1904; *Bull. Soc. Chim.*, (3), **11**. 11, 1894; (3), **17**. 266, 1897; (3), **35**. 944, 1906; J. C. McLennan and R. W. McKay, *Trans. Roy. Soc. Canada*, (3), **24**. 1, 1930; V. M. Goldschmidt, *Skr. Norske Vid. Akad.*, 2, 1926; E. T. Wherry, *Amer. Min.*, **14**. 54, 1929; R. W. Moore, *Trans. Amer. Electrochem. Soc.*, **43**. 317, 1923; E. K. Rideal, *Journ. Soc. Chem. Ind.*, **33**. 673, 1914; *Das elektrochemische Verhalten des Urans und einiger Uranverbindungen*, Bonn, 1913; A. Fischer and E. K. Rideal, *Zeit. anorg. Chem.*, **81**. 170, 1913; J. F. Goggin, J. J. Cronin, H. C. Fogg and C. James, *Journ. Ind. Eng. Chem.*, **18**. 114, 1926; J. Aloy, *Bull. Soc. Chim.*, (3), **23**. 368, 1900; (3), **25**. 153, 344, 1901; *Ann. Chim. Phys.*, (7), **24**. 412, 1901; *Recherches sur l'uranium et ses composés*, Toulouse, 1901; J. L. C. Zimmermann, *Ber.*, **13**. 348, 1882; **15**. 847, 1182, 1882; **17**. 2739, 1884; *Liebig's Ann.*, **213**. 1, 1882; **216**. 14, 1883; **232**. 310, 1886; D. Lely and L. Hamburger, *Zeit. anorg. Chem.*, **87**. 209, 1914; J. Maydel, *ib.*, **178**. 113, 1929; **186**. 289, 1930; W. Biltz and K. Meisel, *ib.*, **198**. 791, 1931; W. G. Mixter, *ib.*, **78**. 231, 1912; *Amer. Journ. Science*, (4), **34**. 141, 1912; E. D. Eastman, *Journ. Amer. Chem. Soc.*, **45**. 80, 1923; L. Pauling, *ib.*, **49**. 765, 1927; G. N. Lewis, G. E. Gibson and W. M. Latimer, *ib.*, **44**. 1008, 1922; E. J. Cuy, *ib.*, **49**. 201, 1927; W. R. Mott, *Trans. Amer. Electrochem. Soc.*, **34**. 255, 1918; E. Donath and J. Mayrhofer, *Ber.*, **16**. 1592, 1883; E. Donath, *ib.*, **12**. 742, 1879; H. Fritz, *ib.*, **17**. 2160, 1884; H. G. Grimm, *Zeit. phys. Chem.*, **122**. 177, 1926; A. Blümcke, *Wied. Ann.*, **23**. 173, 1884; W. Herz, *Zeit. anorg. Chem.*, **177**. 116, 1928; **180**. 284, 1929; C. del Fresno, *Anal. Fis. Quim.*, **24**. 707, 1926; J. Dewar, *Proc. Roy. Soc.*, **89**. A, 158, 1913; W. Guerther and M. von Pirani, *Zeit. Metallkunde*, **11**. 1, 1919; D. I. Mendeléeff, *Liebig's Ann. Suppl.*, **8**. 184, 1872; P. W. Bridgman, *Proc. Amer. Acad.*, **58**. 166, 1923; B. Bruzs, *Journ. Phys. Chem.*, **31**. 681, 1927; L. H. Adams, *Journ. Washington Acad.*, **17**. 529, 1927; R. D. Kleeman, *Journ. Phys. Chem.*, **31**. 1669, 1927; E. Botolfsen, *Tids. Kemi Bergvesen*, **9**. 66, 1929; *Bull. Soc. Chim.*, (4), **45**. 626, 1929; E. Herlinger, *Zeit. Kryst.*, **80**. 465, 1931.

[2] V. Henri, *Compt. Rend.*, **158**. 181, 1914; J. C. Ghosh and B. N. Mitter, *Journ. Indian Chem. Soc.*, **4**. 353, 1927; A. Müller, *Zeit. anorg. Chem.*, **109**. 235, 1920; A. Dorabialska, *Rocz. Chem.*, **9**. 494, 1929; G. I. Polrowsky, *Zeit. Physik*, **41**. 493, 1927.

[3] R. Thalén, *Om spectralanalys*, Upsala, 1866; *Nova Acta Upsala*, (3), **6**. 9, 1868; *Ann. Chim. Phys.*, (4), **18**. 202, 385, 1869; W. Huggins, *Phil. Mag.*, (4), **40**. 302, 1870; *Proc. Roy. Soc.*, **18**. 546, 1870; A. S. Russell and R. Rossi, *ib.*, **87**. A, 478, 1912; J. N. Lockyer, *ib.*, **27**. 279, 1878; *Compt. Rend.*, **86**. 317, 1878; *Phil. Trans.*, **178**. 561, 1881; R. J. Lang, *ib.*, **224**. A, 371, 1924; E. Demarçay, *Spectres électriques*, Paris, 1895; F. Exner and E. Haschek, *Wellen-längentabellen für spectralanalytische Untersuchungen auf Grund der ultravioletten Funkenspectren der Elemente*, Leipzig, 1902; *Wellenlängentabellen für spectralanalytische Untersuchungen auf Grund der ultravioletten Bogenspectren der Elemente*, Leipzig, 1904; *Die Spectren der Elemente bei normalen Druck*, Leipzig, 1912; J. M. Eder and E. Valenta, *Atlas typischer Spectren*, Wein, 1911; *Sitzber. Akad. Wien*, **119**. 519, 1910; A. Hagenbach and H. Konen, *Atlas der Emissions-spectren*, Jena, 1905; C. E. Gissing, *Spark Spectra of the Metals*, London, 1910; B. Hasselberg, *Svenska Akad. Handl.*, **45**. 5, 1910; O. Lohse, *Sitzber. Akad. Berlin*, 179, 1897; *Publ. Obs. Potsdam*, **12**. 109, 1902; J. H. Pollok, *Proc. Roy. Soc. Dublin*, **9**. 331, 1909; W. J. Humphreys, *Astrophys. Journ.*, **6**. 169, 1897; P. G. Nutting, *ib.*, **23**. 64, 1906; H. Ebert, *Astron. Nachr.*, **162**. 193, 1903; E. Formanek, *Die qualitative Spektralanalyse anorganischer und organischer Korper*, Berlin, 145, 1905; G. Meyer and H. Greulich, *Phys. Zeit.*, **22**. 583, 1921; C. C. Kiess and W. F. Meggers, *Bull. Bur. Standards*, **16**. 51, 1920; K. W. Meissner, *Ann. Physik*, (4), **50**.

713, 1916 ; H. Kayser, *Handbuch der Spectroscopie*, Leipzig, **6**. 732, 1912 ; W. W. Coblentz, *Bull. Bur. Standards*,·**5**. 173, 1908; *Supplementary Investigations of Infra-red Spectra*, Washington, 112, 1908 ; C. Porlezza and A. Donati, *Ann. Chim. Applicata*, **16**. 622, 1926 ; J. C. McLennan, A. B. McLay and H. G. Smith, *Proc. Roy. Soc.*, **112**, A, 76, 1926 ; J. C. McLennan and E. Cohen, *Trans. Roy. Soc. Canada*, (3), **20**. 365, 1926 ; E. J. Allin, *ib.*, (3), **21**. 231, 1927 ; H. Nagaoka and T. Futagami, *Proc. Imp. Acad. Tokyo*, **2**. 7, 318, 390, 533, 1926 ; H. Nagaoka and Y. Sugiura, *Science Papers Inst. Phys. Chem. Research*, **2**. 139, 1924 ; E. T. Wherry, *Amer. Min.*, **14**. 299, 323, 1929 ; E. Z. Stowell, *Phys. Rev.*, (2), **37**. 1452, 1931.

⁴ H. Becquerel, *Ann. Chim. Phys.*, (6), **14**. 170, 1888 ; E. Becquerel, *ib.*, (4), **27**. 539, 1872 ; *Compt. Rend.*, **75**. 296, 1872 ; **101**. 205, 1885 ; V. Henri and M. Landau, *ib.*, **158**. 181, 1914 ; C. Camichel, *ib.*, **140**. 139, 1905 ; **141**. 185, 1905 ; W. Böhlendorff, *Studien zur Absorptionsspectralanalyse*, Erlangen, 1890 ; H. Bremer, *Einfluss der Temperatur gefärbter Lösungen auf die Absorptionsspectren derselben*, Erlangen, 1890 ; E. Deussen, *Wied. Ann.*, **66**. 1128, 1898 ; O. Knoblauch, *ib.*, **43**. 738, 1891 ; J. M. Hiebendaal, *Onderzoek over eenige absorptiespectra*, Utrecht, 1873 ; H. Oeffinger, *Ueber die Lichtabsorptionen der Uransalze*, Tübingen, 1866 ; H. W. Vogel, *Praktische Spectralanalyse irdischer Stoffe*, Berlin, 1889 ; *Sitzber. Akad. Berlin*, 409, 1878 ; *Ber.*, **8**. 1523, 1875 ; **11**. 913, 1363, 1878 ; W. J. Russell and W. Lapraik, *B.A. Rep.*, 576, 1886 ; J. Formanek, *Die qualitative Spektralanalyse anorganischer und organischer Körper*, Berlin, 145, 1905 ; J. H. Gladstone, *Journ. Chem. Soc.*, **10**. 79, 1858 ; W. N. Hartley, *ib.*, **83**. 221, 1903 ; E. Hagenbach, *Pogg. Ann.*, **146**. 65, 232, 375, 508, 1872 ; O. Lubarsch, *ib.*, **153**. 420, 1874 ; C. Horner, *Chem. News*, **29**. 66, 1874 ; H. Morton and H. C. Bolton, *ib.*, **28**. 47, 113, 167, 233, 244, 257, 268, 1873 ; *Monit. Scient.*, (3), **4**. 24, 305, 1874 ; *Amer. Chemist*, **3**. 361, 401, 1873 ; **4**. 1, 41, 81, 1874 ; E. Nichols, *Phys. Rev.*, (1), **2**. 302, 1895 ; L. J. Boardman, *ib.*, (2), **20**. 552, 1922 ; W. T. Anderson and L. F. Bird, *ib.*, (2), **32**. 293, 1928 ; G. G. Stokes, *Phil. Trans.*, **142**. 463, 1852 ; H. C. Sorby, *Nature*, **1**. 588, 1870 ; *Phil. Mag.*, (4), **39**. 65, 450, 1870 ; *Proc. Roy. Soc.*, **17**. 511, 1869 ; **18**. 197, 1870 ; J. B. Burke, *ib.*, **76**. A, 165, 1905 ; J. L. C. Zimmermann, *Liebig's Ann.*, **213**. 285, 1882 ; H. Kayser, *Handbuch der Spectroscopie*, Leipzig, **3**. 418, 1905 ; A. Mazzucchelli and O. G. d'Alceo, *Atti Accad. Lincei*, (5), **21**. ii, 850, 1912 ; (5), **22**. i, 41, 1913 ; A. Mazzucchelli and U. Perret, *ib.*, (5), **22**. ii, 445, 1913 ; T. R. Merton, *Proc. Roy. Soc.*, **87**. A, 138, 1912 ; *Journ. Chem. Soc.*, **105**. 23, 1914 ; W. W. Strong, *Phys. Zeit.*, **11**. 668, 1910 ; H. C. Jones and W. W. Strong, *Phil. Mag.*, (6), **19**. 566, 1910 ; *Amer. Chem. Journ.*, **45**. 1, 1911 ; *The Absorption Spectra of Solutions*, Washington, 43, 57, 81, 1911 ; *A Study of the Absorption Spectra of Solutions*, Washington, 85, 1910 ; H. C. Jones and J. S. Guy, *The Absorption Spectra of Solutions*, Washington, 14, 24, 1913 ; *Amer. Chem. Journ.*, **49**. 1, 1913 ; H. L. Howes, *Phys. Rev.*, (2), **11**. 66, 1918 ; E. L. Nichols, H. L. Howes and F. G. Wick, *ib.*, (2), **14**. 201, 1919 ; E. L. Nichols and H. L. Howes, *ib.*, (2), **14**. 293, 1919 ; E. L. Nichols and E. Merritt, *ib.*, (1), **33**. 354, 1911 ; (2), **3**. 457, 1914 ; (2), **9**. 113, 1917 ; *Studies in Luminescence*, Washington, 19, 1912 ; S. Kato, *Science Papers Inst. Phys. Chem. Research, Tokyo*, **13**. 7, 49, 1930 ; F. E. E. Germann, *Journ. Amer. Chem. Soc.*, **44**. 1466, 1922 ; *Phys. Rev.*, (2), **19**. 623, 1922 ; J. Moir, *Trans. Roy. Soc. South Africa*, **8**. 51, 1919 ; **10**. 33, 1921 ; M. Cantone, *Rend. Accad. Napoli*, (3), **13**. 149, 1907 ; J. Becquerel, *Phys. Zeit.*, **8**. 929, 1907 ; R. A. Houstoun, *Ann. Physik*, (4), **21**. 525, 1906 ; N. Titlestad, *Zeit. phys. Chem.*, **72**. 257, 1910 ; M. Luckiesh, *Journ. Franklin Inst.*, **184**. 73, 227, 1917 ; R. C. Gibbs, *Phys. Rev.*, (1), **28**. 361, 1909 ; H. Kahler, *ib.*, (2), **25**. 717, 1925 ; F. Rinne, *Centr. Min.*, 618, 708, 712, 1901 ; E. Graviola and P. Pringsheim, *Zeit. Physik*, **43**. 384, 1927 ; T. Dreisch, *ib.*, **40**. 714, 1927 ; V. R. von Kurelec, *Biochem. Zeit.*, **180**. 65, 1927 ; A. Müller, *Zeit. anorg. Chem.*, **109**. 235, 1919 ; G. H. Dieke and A. C. S. van Heel, *Versl. Akad. Amsterdam*, **34**. 652, 1925 ; F. G. Wick, *Proc. Amer. Acad.*, **58**. 557, 1923 ; J. C. Ghosh and B. N. Mitter, *Journ. Indian Chem. Soc.*, **4**. 353, 1928 ; L. C. Beard and O. M. Reiff, *Journ. Ind. Eng. Chem.—Anal.*, **3**. 280, 1931 ; E. H. Harvey, *Journ. Amer. Pharm. Assoc.*, **20**. 643, 1931.

⁵ E. Becquerel, *Ann. Chim. Phys.*, (4), **27**. 539, 1872 ; *Compt. Rend.*, **88**. 1237, 1879 ; J. Perrin, *ib.*, **182**. 929, 1926 ; **184**. 1097, 1927 ; M. Privault, *ib.*, **184**. 1120, 1927 ; L. de Boisbaudran, *ib.*, **105**. 347, 1887 ; M. de Broglie, *ib.*, **174**. 939, 1922 ; M. and L. de Broglie, *ib.*, **173**. 527, 1921 ; H. Becquerel, *ib.*, **101**. 1252, 1885 ; **144**. 459, 671, 1907 ; J. Becquerel, *ib.*, **152**. 511, 1911 ; H. and J. Becquerel and H. K. Onnes, *ib.*, **150**. 647, 1910 ; *Comm. Phys. Lab. Leiden*, 110, 111, 1909 ; *Proc. Acad. Amsterdam*, **12**. 76, 1909 ; G. G. Stokes, *Phil. Trans.*, **142**. 463, 1852 ; G. H. Dieke and A. C. S. van Heel, *Proc. Akad. Amsterdam*, **28**. 953, 1925 ; *Versl. Akad. Amsterdam*, **34**. 652, 1925 ; A. C. S. van Heel, *ib.*, **28**. 955, 1925 ; *Comm. Phys. Lab. Leiden*, Suppl. 55, B, 1925 ; H. Morton and H. C. Bolton, *Chem. News*, **28**. 47, 113, 167, 233, 244, 257, 268, 1873 ; *Monit. Scient.*, (3), **16**. 24, 305, 1874 ; *Amer. Chemist*, **3**. 361, 401, 1873 ; **4**. 1, 41, 81, 1874 ; E. L. Nichols and E. Merritt, *Phys. Rev.*, (1), **33**. 354, 1911 ; E. L. Nichols and H. L. Howes, *ib.*, (2), **14**. 293, 1919 ; H. L. Howes, *ib.*, (2), **11**. 66, 1918 ; E. L. Nichols and M. K. Slattery, *Journ. Amer. Opt. Soc.*, **12**. 449, 1926 ; E. L. Nichols, *Science*, (2), **55**. 157, 1922 ; J. Moir, *Trans. Roy. Soc. South Africa*, **8**. 51, 225, 1919 ; E. L. Nichols and E. Merritt, *Studies in Luminescence*, Washington, 1912 ; H. Brauns, *Zeit. wiss. Photochem.*, **25**. 235, 1928 ; H. C. Jones and W. W. Strong, *A Study of the Absorption Spectra of Solutions*, Washington, 119, 1910 ; M. Cantone, *Rend. Accad. Napoli*, (3), **13**. 149, 1907 ; E. Goldstein, *Sitzber. Akad. Berlin*, 818, 1900 ; O. Lommel, *Wied. Ann.*, **3**. 113, 1878 ; E. Wiedemann and G. C. Schmidt, *ib.*, **54**. 604, 1895 ; **56**. 201, 1895 ; *Zeit. phys. Chem.*, **18**. 529, 1895 ; F. Perrin, *Ann. Physique*, (10), **12**. 169, 1929 ; F. Perrin and R. Delorme, *Journ. Phys. Radium*, (6), **10**. 177, 1929 ; *Compt. Rend.*, **186**. 428, 1928 ; R. Coustal, *ib.*, **187**.

1139, 1928; S. J. Wawiloff and V. L. Levschin, *Naturwiss.*, **15**. 899, 1927; *Zeit. Physik*, **35**. 920, 1926; **44**. 539, 1927; **48**. 397, 1928; S. J. Wawiloff, *ib.*, **50**. 52, 1928; R. M. Müller, *Proc. Roy. Soc.*, **121**. A, 313, 1928.

⁶ J. A. Siemssen, *Chem. Ztg.*, **43**. 267, 1919; **46**. 450, 1922; A. Karl, *Compt. Rend.*, **146**. 1104, 1908.

⁷ M. Siegbahn, *Ber. deut. phys. Ges.*, **18**. 150, 278, 1916; *Jahrb. Rad. Elektron.*, **13**. 296, 1916; M. Siegbahn and E. Jönsson, *Phys. Zeit.*, **20**. 251, 1919; M. Siegbahn and E. Frimann, *ib.*, **17**. 17, 61, 1916; *Phil. Mag.*, (6), **32**. 39, 1916; T. E. Aurén, *ib.*, (6), **33**. 471, 1917; A. Dauvillier, *Journ. Phys. Rad.*, **3**. 221, 1922; *Compt. Rend.*, **172**. 915, 1350, 1921; **173**. 35, 647, 1921; M. and L. de Broglie, *ib.*, **173**. 527, 1921; M. de Broglie, *ib.*, **169**. 962, 1919; **170**. 585, 1920; **174**. 939, 1922; G. Réchou, *ib.*, **180**. 1107, 1925; V. Dolejsek, *Nature*, **109**. 582, 1922; *Zeit. Physik*, **10**. 129, 1922; **21**. 111, 1924; A. Sandström, *ib.*, **65**. 632, 1930; **66**. 784, 1930; E. Hjalmar, *ib.*, **15**. 65, 1923; B. Walter, *ib.*, **30**. 357, 1924; E. Frimann, *ib.*, **39**. 813, 1926; E. Lindberg, *ib.*, **50**. 82, 1928; **54**. 632, 1929; W. Duane, H. Fricke and W. Stenström, *Proc. Nat. Acad.*, **6**. 607, 1920; D. Coster, *Compt. Rend.*, **172**. 1176, 1921; *Phys. Rev.*, (2), **18**. 218, 1921; (2), **19**. 20, 1922; *Zeit. Physik*, **4**. 178, 1921; J. Zahradnicek, *ib.*, **60**. 712, 1930; H. R. Robinson and C. L. Young, *Proc. Roy. Soc.*, **128**. A, 92, 1930; S. J. M. Allen, *Phys. Rev.*, (2), **27**. 266, 1926; (2), **28**. 907, 1926; J. E. Mack and J. M. Cork, *ib.*, (2), **30**. 741, 1927; S. K. Allison, *ib.*, (2), **31**. 916, 1928; (2), **32**. 1, 1928; (2), **33**. 1087, 1090, 1929; (2), **34**. 7, 176, 1929; S. K. Allison and V. J. Andrew, *ib.*, (2), **38**. 441, 1931; J. H. Williams, *ib.*, (2), **37**. 1431, 1692, 1931; F. R. Hirsh, *ib.*, (2), **38**. 914, 1931; S. Idei, *Science Rep. Tohoku Univ.*, **19**. 559, 1930; A. Sandström, *Zeit. Physik*, **66**. 784, 1930; H. B. Wahlin, *ib.*, (2), **37**. 467, 1931; G. Wentzel, *Naturwiss.*, **10**. 369, 1922; E. C. Stoner and L. H. Martin, *Proc. Roy. Soc.*, **107**. A, 312, 1925; H. Hirata, *ib.*, **105**. A, 40, 1924; H. R. Robinson and A. M. Cassie, *ib.*, **113**. A, 282, 1926; H. R. Robinson, *Phil. Mag.*, (6), **50**. 241, 1925; J. Schrör, *Ann. Physik*, (4), **80**. 297, 1925; G. L. Clark, *Journ. Amer. Chem. Soc.*, **46**. 379, 1924; H. Brauns, *Zeit. wiss. Photochem.*, **25**. 325, 1927; W. Herz, *Zeit. anorg. Chem.*, **177**. 116, 1928; T. Pavolino, *Giorn. Farm. Chim.*, **79**. 310, 1930; R. W. James and G. W. Brindley, *Zeit. Kryst.*, **78**. 470, 1931.

⁸ A. F. Gehlen, *Gehlen's Journ.*, **3**. 566, 1806; A. E. Becquerel, *La lumière*, Paris, 1868; L. L. Bonaparte, *Journ. prakt. Chem.*, (1), **30**. 308, 1843; *Journ. Chim. Méd.*, **8**. 676, 1842; H. Kunz-Krause and P. Manicke, *Ber. deut. pharm. Ges.*, **32**. 209, 1922; A. St. V. Niépce and L. Corvisart, *Compt. Rend.* **49**. 370, 1859; A. St. V. Niépce, *ib.*, **46**. 448, 489, 1858; *Phot. Mitt.*, **4**. 206, 1867; W. Seekamp, *Liebig's Ann.*, **122**. 115, 1862; **133**. 253, 1865; **278**. 373, 1893; G. Wisbar, *ib.*, **262**. 232, 1891; J. C. Schnauss, *Arch. Pharm.*, (3), **2**. 41, 1873; *Chem. Ztg.*, **16**. 842, 1892; W. C. Holmes, *Amer. Dyestuff Rep.*, **13**. 188, 197, 1924; H. C. Bolton, *Amer. Journ. Science*, (2), **48**. 206, 1869; R. H. Müller, *Proc. Roy. Soc.*, **121**. A, 313, 1928; C. J. Burnett, *Phil. Mag.*, (4), **20**. 50, 1860; *Liverpool and Manchester Journ. Phot.*, (2), **1**. 183, 1857; J. J. Ebelmen, *Ann. Chim. Phys.*, (3), **5**. 209, 1842; L. Vanino and E. Zumbusch, *Journ. prakt. Chem.*, (2), **82**. 193, 1910; P. L. Chastaing, *Ann. Chim. Phys.*, (5), **11**. 145, 1877; *Étude sur la part de lumière dans les actions chimiques, et particulier dans les oxydations*, Paris, 1877; J. Plotnikoff, *Zeit. phys. Chem.*, **58**. 214, 1907; R. Luther and J. Plotnikoff, *ib.*, **61**. 513, 1908; E. C. Hatt, *ib.*, **92**. 513, 1918; C. Dittrich, *Die Uranylsalze vom physikalischchemischen Standpunkt aus betrachtet*, Leipzig, 1899; *Zeit. phys. Chem.*, **29**. 461, 1899; N. Titlestad, *ib.*, **72**. 257, 1910; G. Trümpler, *ib.*, **90**. 385, 1915; H. Schiller, *ib.*, **80**. 641, 1912; W. P. Jorissen and L. T. Reicher, *ib.*, **31**. 142, 1899; W. P. Jorissen, *Zeit. angew. Chem.*, **12**. 521, 1899; J. C. Ghosh and B. N. Mitter, *Journ. Indian Chem. Soc.*, **4**. 353, 1927; J. C. Ghosh and J. Mukherjee, *ib.*, **4**. 343, 1927; H. Fay, *Amer. Chem. Journ.*, **18**. 269, 1896; A. Bach, *Compt. Rend.*, **116**. 1145, 1893; D. Berthelot and H. Gaudechon, *ib.*, **152**. 262, 1911; **157**. 333, 1913; J. B. Senderens, *ib.*, **149**. 213, 1909; J. Perrin, *ib.*, **182**. 929, 1926; J. Aloy and A. Valdiguié, *ib.*, **176**. 1229, 1923; *Bull. Soc. Chim.*, (4), **33**. 572, 1923; (4), **37**. 1135, 1925; (4), **39**. 792, 1926; J. Aloy and E. Rodier, *ib.*, (4), **31**. 246, 1922; G. Courtois, *ib.*, (4), **33**. 1173, 1923; M. Abelous, J. Aloy and A. Valdiguié, *Compt. Rend. Soc. Biol.*, **96**. 1385, 1927; R. F. Bacon, *Philippine Journ. Science*, **2**. 129, 1907; J. E. Moss and A. W. Knapp, *Brit. Journ. Actinotherapy*, **2**. 37, 1927; H. von Euler, *Ber.*, **37**. 3411, 1904; P. Prätorius and F. Korn, *ib.*, **43**. 2744, 1910; E. Baur, *Zeit. Elektrochem.*, **25**. 102, 1919; **34**. 595, 1928; *Schweiz. Chem. Ztg.*, **2**. 40, 1918; *Zeit. phys. Chem.*, **63**. 683, 1908; **72**. 323, 1910; **80**. 668, 1912; **100**. 36, 1922; **111**. 315, 1924; *Helvetica Chim. Acta*, **1**. 186, 1918; E. Baur and A. Rebmann, *ib.*, **5**. 221, 1922; F. L. Usher and J. H. Priestley, *Proc. Roy. Soc.*, **78**. 318, 1906; J. Fiedler, *De lucis effectibus chemicis in corpora anorganica*, Uratislaviæ, 1835; M. Plotnikoff, *Chem. Ztg.*, **55**. 318, 1931; W. R. G. Atkins and H. H. Poole, *Proc. Roy. Dublin Soc.*, **19**. 321, 1929; T. Pavolini, *Ind. Chimica*, **5**. 1107, 1930; A. J. Allmand and L. Reeve, *Journ. Chem. Soc.*, 2834, 1926; E. Boivin, *Monit. Photogr.*, **17**. 165, 1878; R. E. Liesegang, *Arch. Phot.*, **6**. 1, 1865; D. von Monckhoven, *Phot. Mitt.*, **16**. 129, 1880; J. M. Eder, *Ueber die chemischen Wirkungen des farbigen Lichtes*, Halle, 1879; *Phot. Corresp.*, **16**. 218, 1880; C. Neuberg, *Biochem. Zeit.*, **13**. 305, 1908; A. Samsonoff, *Zeit. wiss. Photochem.*, **9**. 12, 1910; **11**. 33, 1912; A. Goldman, *Ann. Physik*, (4), **27**. 449, 1908; W. C. Pierce, A. Leviton and W. A. Noyes, *Journ. Amer. Chem. Soc.*, **51**. 80, 1929; W. G. Leighton and G. S. Forbes, *ib.*, **52**. 3139, 1930; P. F. Büchi, *Zeit. phys. Chem.*, **111**. 269, 1924; E. L. Nichols, *Science*, (2), **55**. 157, 1922; W. T. Anderson and F. W. Robinson, *Journ. Amer. Chem. Soc.*, **47**. 718, 1925; S. J. Wawilow and W. L. Lewschin, *Zeit. Physik*, **48**. 397, 1928.

⁹ H. Müller, *Sitzber. Akad. Wien*, **135**. 563, 1926; J. Lifschitz and S. B. Hooghoudt, *Zeit.*

phys. Chem., **128**. 87, 1927 ; F. Lotze, *Centr. Min.*, 87, 1928 ; M. de Broglie, *Compt. Rend.*, **174**. 939, 1922 ; S. Maracineanu, *ib.*, **181**. 774, 1925 ; A. Nodon, *ib.*, **174**. 1061, 1922 ; J. Thibaud, *Journ. Phys. Rad.*, **6**. 82, 1925 ; B. Gudden, *Zeit. Physik*, **26**. 110, 1924 ; W. M. Cohn, *ib.*, **72**. 392, 1931.

    [10] W. Meissner and B. Voigt, *Ann. Physik*, (5), **7**. 892, 1930 ; P. W. Bridgman, *Proc. Amer. Acad.*, **58**. 151, 1923 ; P. Herasymenko, *Chem. Listy*, **19**. 172, 1925 ; A. Schulze, *Zeit. Metallkunde*, **15**. 155, 1925 ; W. Muthmann and F. Fraunberger, *Sitzber. Bayer. Akad.*, **34**. 214, 1904 ; C. Benedicks, *Internat. Journ. Metallog.*, **7**. 225, 1915 ; U. Sborgi, *Atti. Accad. Lincei*, (5), **21**. i, 135, 1912 ; *Gazz. Chim. Ital.*, **42**. ii, 144, 1912 ; *Zeit. Elektrochem.*, **13**. 115, 1913 ; C. Luckow, *Zeit. anal. Chem.*, **19**. 18, 1880 ; E. F. Smith, *Ber.*, **13**. 751, 1880 ; *Amer. Chem. Journ.*, **1**. 329, 1879 ; L. G. Kollock and E. F. Smith, *Journ. Amer. Chem. Soc.*, **23**. 607, 1901 ; E. F. Smith and D. L. Wallace, *ib.*, **20**. 279, 1898 ; E. T. Wherry and E. F. Smith, *ib.*, **29**. 806, 1907 ; E. F. Kern, *ib.*, **23**. 685, 1901 ; A. Fischer and E. K. Rideal, *Zeit. anorg. Chem.*, **81**. 170, 1913 ; E. K. Rideal, *Journ. Soc. Chem. Ind.*, **33**. 673, 1914 ; *Das elektrochemische Verhalten des Urans und einiger Uranverbindungen*, Bonn, 1913 ; A. Günther-Schulze, *Ann. Physik*, (4), **65**. 223, 1921 ; H. Moissan, *Compt. Rend.*, **122**. 1088, 1896 ; C. A. Pierlé, *Journ. Phys. Chem.*, **23**. 517, 1919 ; *Journ. Ind. Eng. Chem.*, **12**. 60, 1920 ; F. W. O. de Coninck and M. Camo, *Bull. Acad. Belg.*, 321, 1901 ; C. Dittrich, *Zeit. phys. Chem.*, **29**. 449, 1899 ; *Die Uranylsalze vom physikalischchemischen Standpunkt aus betrachtet*, Leipzig, 1899 ; J. C. McLennan, L. E. Howlett and J. O. Wilhelm, *Trans. Roy. Soc. Canada*, (3), **23**. 287, 1930 ; W. Ogawa, *Journ. Japan. Soc. Chem. Ind.*, **31**. 486, 1928 ; E. Z. Stowell, *Phys. Rev.*, (2), **37**. 1452, 1931 ; M. Haitinger, *Mikrochemie*, (2), **3**. 430, 1931 ; R. Groves and A. S. Russell, *Journ. Chem. Soc.*, 2805, 1931.

    [11] S. Freed and C. Kasper, *Journ. Amer. Chem. Soc.*, **52**. 4671, 1930 ; H. Moissan, *Compt. Rend.*, **116**. 347, 1433, 1893 ; **122**. 1088, 1302, 1896 ; **142**. 425, 1906 ; *Ann. Chim. Phys.*, (7), **8**. 141, 1876 ; (7), **9**. 264, 1896 ; *Le four électrique*, Paris, 233, 1897 ; London, 162, 1904 ; *Bull. Soc. Chim.*, (3), **11**. 11, 1894 ; (3), **17**. 266, 1897 ; (3), **35**. 944, 1906 ; M. Owen, *Ann. Physik*, (4), **37**. 657, 1912 ; K. Honda, *ib.*, (4), **32**. 1044, 1910 ; S. Meyer, *Monatsh.*, **20**. 369, 1899 ; *Wied. Ann.*, **68**. 324, 1899 ; P. Pascal, *Compt. Rend.*, **147**. 742, 1908 ; D. M. Bose and H. G. Bhar, *Zeit. Physik*, **48**. 716, 1928.

§ 6. The Chemical Properties of Uranium

Uranium is fairly reactive chemically ; and in many of its properties it resembles iron. H. Moissan [1] found that **argon** has no action on the metal at a high temp. F. Fischer and F. Schrötter observed no reaction when uranium is electrically disintegrated under liquid argon. A. Sieverts and E. Bergner observed that neither argon nor **helium** shows a measurable solubility in uranium. No compound with **hydrogen** has been prepared ; but A. Sieverts and E. Bergner found that 100 grms. of metal at 1100° and 760 mm. absorb 1·6 mgrms. of hydrogen. G. Hägg studied the mol. vol. E. M. Péligot found that the metal is stable at ordinary temp. in dry **air**. J. Férée's pyrophoric uranium has been discussed above ; G. Chesneau found that the sparks detached from uranium by friction with hard steel instantly ignite mixtures of methane and air, so that the temp of the sparks cannot be less than 1000° ; they also ignite alcohol, benzene, or light petroleum which has been poured on cotton. Sparks detached from steel by flint ignite none of these vapours and gases. J. L. C. Zimmermann found that the metal is slowly oxidized by exposure to ordinary atm. air ; and R. W. Moore added that it is considerably tarnished after a few days' exposure to air. J. Aloy observed that in moist air the surface of the metal becomes dull or matte. E. M. Péligot found that when the metal is feebly heated in air it burns with a brilliant white flame, and swells up to form uranium tritaoctoxide, and J. L. C. Zimmermann added that the ignition temp. in air or **oxygen** is between 150° and 170° ; H. Moissan said that it ignites in oxygen at 170°. The ignition temp. must depend on the state of subdivision of the metal. A. Burger made observations on this subject. E. M. Péligot found that if the powder be strewn through the flame, it burns showing brilliant sparks ; whilst H. Moissan observed that if molten uranium be dropped on to porcelain, or if fragments are shaken up in a glass vessel, brilliant sparks are produced owing to the combustion of a small amount of metal. There results, but with far greater brilliancy, a phenomenon analogous to that of the combustion of iron particles which catch fire by simple friction in the air.

E. M. Péligot said that uranium does not decompose cold water, but H. Moissan observed that if finely powdered, the metal slowly decomposes cold water, but more quickly at 100°; reduced iron also decomposes boiling water. Uranium which has been previously fused quickly acquires a layer of oxide when in contact with water, and the action is considerably quickened if carbon dioxide be present. D. Lely and L. Hamburger noticed that uranium is stable towards water and alkali-lye; and J. L. C. Zimmermann found that uranium is not perceptibly attacked by soln. of potassium or sodium hydroxide.

According to H. Moissan, electrolytic uranium catches fire in **fluorine,** burning brilliantly to produce a green volatile fluoride. O. Ruff and A. Heinzelmann found that the tetrafluoride which is formed is accompanied by a small proportion of hexafluoride. E. M. Péligot also said that finely-divided uranium burns in **chlorine** with the evolution of much light and heat to form the tetrachloride. J. L. C. Zimmermann gave 150° for the ignition temp. in chlorine, and added that a layer of chloride forming on the surfaces of the grains protects the interior from chlorination; but H. Moissan gave 180° for the ignition temp. in chlorine, and added that the reactions with chlorine and with the other halogens are all complete. J. L. C. Zimmermann gave approximately 240° for the ignition temp. in **bromine,** and added that the metal burns without incandescence and is partially converted to the tetrabromide; while H. Moissan gave 210° for the ignition temp. in bromine vapour, and added that the combustion proceeds with incandescence. J. L. C. Zimmermann found that **iodine** vapour attacks uranium with difficulty, forming the tetraiodide; whilst H. Moissan gave 260° for the temp. at which the iodide is formed with incandescence. J. Aloy observed that electrolytic uranium is easily attacked by iodine. Uranium is attacked by **hydrogen chloride** at a dull red-heat, forming a stable chloride; and by **hydrogen iodide** at a red-heat. E. M. Péligot, and D. Lely and L. Hamburger found uranium to be soluble in dil. **hydrochloric acid,** forming uranous chloride and evolving hydrogen. J. L. C. Zimmermann found that in the cold, conc. and dil. hydrochloric acid of sp. gr. 1·19 and 1·11 attack uranium; the hydrogen is given off turbulently with the more conc. acid, and a hyacinth-red soln. of the trichloride is formed, which becomes a green soln. of the tetrachloride when shaken in air.

E. M. Péligot observed that boiling **sulphur** unites with uranium with incandescence; J. L. C. Zimmermann said that when uranium burns in sulphur vapour, the black disulphide is formed; and H. Moissan found that the reaction takes place at 500° to form a black sulphide which is slowly attacked by hydrochloric acid, giving off hydrogen sulphide. Uranium also combines with **selenium** with incandescence. E. M. Péligot, and D. Lely and L. Hamburger observed that uranium is dissolved by dil. **sulphuric acid,** giving off hydrogen and forming the uranous salt. J. L. C. Zimmermann found that dil. sulphuric acid, of sp. gr. 1·15, dissolves uranium slowly in the cold, and more rapidly when warm, forming uranous salt and hydrogen; conc. sulphuric acid, of sp. gr. 1·85, when heated forms sulphur dioxide with the finely-divided metal, but the metal which has been previously melted is attacked only slowly. M. G. Levi and co-workers found that the reaction with a soln. of **potassium persulphate** is fairly rapid, forming a yellow soln. and giving off a gas; the reaction is slower with a soln. of **ammonium persulphate.**

H. Moissan reported that uranium has a great affinity for **nitrogen,** and unless great care be taken to avoid the action of this gas during the preparation of the metal a certain amount of nitride will be formed. I. Zschukoff said that the two elements interact at 1000°. W. P. Jorissen and A. P. H. Trivelli observed that nitrogen is evolved when uranium is exposed to cathode rays. The nitrogen is derived from the presence of 0·94 per cent. of nitrogen in the metal—probably as nitride. Powdered uranium reacts with **ammonia** above a dull red-heat with incandescence, hydrogen is evolved, and a black powder is formed. J. L. C. Zimmermann observed no perceptible action with aq. ammonia. F. Haber used uranium as a catalyst in the synthesis of ammonia (*q.v.*). F. Emich observed that when uranium is heated in **nitric oxide** it burns very brilliantly to the trita-trioxide. E. M. Péligot found that with dil. **nitric acid,** nitric oxide is evolved and uranyl nitrate formed ; and J. L. C. Zimmermann showed that the metal which has been previously melted is only slowly attacked by warm nitric acid of sp. gr. 1·305 ; but the powdered metal is vigorously attacked, forming nitric oxide and uranyl nitrate. Red, fuming nitric acid attacks the powdered metal vigorously in the cold, but the fused metal is attacked very slowly.

H. Moissan noted the ready formation of carbide when the metal is heated with **carbon.** J. L. C. Zimmermann noted that **acetic acid** of sp. gr. 1·065 has no perceptible action. C. Beindl mentioned uranium as a catalyst in the synthesis of hydrocyanic acid from nitrogen, hydrogen, and carbon monoxide. A. Korczynsky, and O. Schmidt discussed its use as a hydrogenation catalyst for organic substances. Uranium displaces the metals, in part even in the cold, from soln. of **copper sulphate, silver nitrate, gold chloride, mercuric nitrate, stannous chloride,** and **platinum tetrachloride**—with **mercuric chloride** a mixture of mercury and mercurous chloride is formed.

Some reactions of analytical interest.—Green soln. of quadrivalent uranium salts are readily oxidized to sexavalent uranyl salts ; and yellow uranyl salts are readily reduced to green quadrivalent uranium salts—say when warmed with zinc and sulphuric acid. No precipitation occurs when soln. of either type of salt is treated with **hydrochloric acid** and then with **hydrogen sulphide.** Quadrivalent uranium salt soln. with **ammonium sulphide** rapidly darken in colour, and when boiled give a black precipitate ; whilst uranyl salt soln. precipitate brown uranyl sulphide which is soluble in dil. acids and in soln. of ammonium carbonate. Quadrivalent uranium salt soln. with alkali-lye or aq. ammonia give a voluminous pale green precipitate of the hydroxide, insoluble in excess—the precipitate rapidly oxidizes in air ; uranyl salt soln. give yellow precipitates of the uranates—the precipitation is hindered by tartaric or citric acid, and hydroxylamine chloride, and in the case of aq. ammonia it is favoured by ammonium chloride. The precipitate is soluble in soln. of ammonium carbonate. **Mercuric oxide** precipitates the uranium completely from soln. of uranyl salts mixed with ammonium chloride. Quadrivalent uranium salt soln. give a pale green precipitate with **alkali carbonates or hydrocarbonates ;** the precipitate is soluble in an excess of the hydrocarbonate, and it is readily oxidized, while a soln. of **ammonium carbonate** produces a similar precipitate, soluble in excess. Uranyl salt soln. with these reagents give orange-yellow precipitates of the alkali uranyl carbonate which is soluble in an excess of the precipitant. Quadrivalent uranium is precipitated from soln. of its salts by **barium carbonate ;** and similarly with uranyl salt soln. Quadrivalent uranium salt soln. with **potassium ferrocyanide** give a yellowish-green precipitate which on oxidation becomes reddish-brown ; uranyl salt soln. give a reddish-brown precipitate, or in dil. soln., a brownish-red coloration which becomes yellow when treated with potassium hydroxide. Quadrivalent uranium salt soln. with **potassium ferricyanide** give a yellowish-green precipitate which quickly oxidizes to a reddish-brown substance ; **hydrofluoric acid** forms an insoluble fluoride. Uranyl salt soln. with **sodium hydrophosphate** give a precipitate of yellowish-white uranyl phosphate, or, in the presence of ammonium acetate, ammonium uranyl phosphate. Uranyl salt soln. give a precipitate of a peruranate with **hydrogen dioxide,** and with **sodium dioxide ;** the precipitate is soluble in an excess of the alkali dioxide. V. Auger [2] found that uranyl salts are not precipitated by **cupferron,** but if reduced to uranous salts by zinc and acid, precipitation occurs. J. A. Siemssen found that **ethylenediamine** with uranyl salt soln. gives a yellow crystalline precipitate. Uranyl salt soln., particularly the nitrate, colour **turmeric paper** brown ; and, according to H. J. H. Fenton, give a brown colour with **dioxymaleic acid.** J. H. de Boer discussed the violet coloration with **alizasinesulphonic acid.**

The physiological action of uranium salts.—G. C. Gmelin,[3] A. Rabuteau, and C. le Conte showed that uranium salts are poisonous to the animal organism. B. Fischer and C. Hartwich say that uranium is included in the official lists of poisons in Germany and Russia, and that it is approximately as toxic as arsenic. J. Woroschilsky's observations on mammals, birds, frogs, and worms show that however administered uranium is a very poisonous metal. C. le Conte said that the most characteristic symptom of poisoning by uranium is the high sugar content of urine. R. H. Chittenden and M. T. Hutchinson showed that uranium salts have a marked inhibitory influence on the activity of digestive ferments; and R. H. Chittenden and A. Lambert showed that in experiments with uranyl nitrate on rabbits uranium is an irritant poison, and like other metallic irritants produces gastro-intestinal irritation of more or less intensity. But it is not in any sense a rapid poison, and the injection of a fatal dose is not followed by any noticeable effects for some time. The action of a small amount (0·15 grm.) seems to be as rapid and pronounced as that of a larger quantity (1 grm.). The first noticeable symptom is muscular weakness ; the salt checks digestion, but apparently increases proteïd metabolism to a slight extent : it increases the output of carbonic anhydride, raises the body temp., and finally leads to emaciation. In the kidney, a condition of acute nephritis and destruction of the renal tissue is found, like that produced in poisoning by arsenic, mercury, and phosphorus. Albuminuria is severe and constant. With small doses the volume of urine is increased, but when toxic action is pronounced there may be partial or even complete suppression of that secretion. The production of glycosuria generally occurs after that of albuminuria, but it is a very constant and characteristic symptom. The urine, in cases of uranium poisoning, invariably contains a large amount of crystallized calcium oxalate. In chronic poisoning by uranium, the nervous symptoms (loss of sight and of co-ordinating power) sometimes predominate, according to J. Woroschilsky, F. Cartier, D. E. Jackson and F. C. Mann, and R. Fleckseder, owing to the coagulating action of uranium salts, observed by N. Kowalewsky, A. Müller, and B. Szilard, on albumin. Conc. soln. of uranium salts corrode the mucous membrane, transforming the walls of the stomach into a dead film of uranic albuminate. The subcutaneous injection of a non-corrosive uranium salt produces glycosuria, with fatty degeneration of the walls of the blood-vessels and fatty changes in the liver and kidneys, so that the animal wastes and dies. The subcutaneous injection of 0·5 to 2·0 mgrm. of UO_3 per kilogram will kill a cat, dog, or rabbit. The nitrate or acetate introduced by the mouth produces gastroenteritis and nephritis, with hæmorrhages in the substance of the kidney.

O. Loew found that dil. soln. of uranium nitrate—say 0·1 per cent.—increased the yields of peas and oats, stimulating the production of straw and seed. Soln. with 0·2 per cent. of the salt poisoned young pea-plants in three days. J. Stoklasa found that with *melilotus albus*, the addition of an optimum quantity of 2·5 kgrms. per hectare of soil, had a favourable effect on the total yield of dry matter. There was no indication of any toxic effect with 20 kgrms. per hectare. C. Acqua observed that when plants are grown in soln. containing traces of uranyl nitrate, root growth is rapidly arrested owing to the penetration of uranium into the nuclei of the meristem. It can be seen there in the form of a yellow substance, probably the yellow oxide. The chromatin of these nuclei is found to have disappeared, so that karyokinetic division is no longer possible. According to P. Becquerel, there is an optimum dose with uranium salts which favours the maximum growth of the bacillus and above which they begin to exert a toxic effect. A dose of 1 in 2500 has a marked inhibitory influence. H. Agulhon and T. Robert found that colloidal uranium of cònc. 1·2 : 10,000,000 to 6 : 100,000, prepared by electrical dispersion, has a much greater effect in increasing the activity of the pyocyanic bacillus than has powdered uranium. Although colloidal uranium is capable of accelerating the formation of pyocyanin for a race which produces it normally, it is incapable of producing the chromogenic function in cultures of races which are devoid of this function. H. Bechhold, and M. Neisser and U. Friedemann discussed the coagulating action of uranium salts on bacteria. W. Sigmund discussed the relation between the at. wt. and the degree of ionization on the physiological action of soln. of salts.

Some uses of uranium.—Very few of the applications of uranium at present known are of great industrial importance.[4] Uranium has been tried in the manufacture of lamp-filaments and gas-mantles ; [5] in the manufacture of iron alloys ; [6] in photometry ; [7] in photography for toning, etc. ; [8] as a dye or stain for textiles, leather, and wood ; [9] in medicine in the form of *Uranwein* for *diabetes mellitus* ; [10] as a colouring agent—*uranium yellow*—in the form of ammonium or sodium diuranate, for glasses, glazes, and enamels ; [11] as a reagent for phosphates, etc., in analysis ; and as a catalytic agent in chemical processes.[12]

REFERENCES.

[1] A. Sieverts and E. Bergner, *Ber.*, **45**. 2576, 1912 ; G. Hägg, *Zeit. phys. Chem.*, **12**. B, 33, 1931 ; H. Moissan, *Compt. Rend.*, **116**. 347, 1433, 1893 ; **122**. 1088, 1302, 1896 ; **142**. 425, 1906 ; *Ann. Chim. Phys.*, (7), **8**. 141, 1896 ; (7), **9**. 264, 1896 ; *Le four électrique*, Paris, 233, 1897 ; London, 162, 1904 ; *Bull. Soc. Chim.*, (3), **11**. 11, 1894 ; (3), **17**. 266, 1897 ; (3), **35**. 944, 1906 ; J. Aloy, *Recherches sur l'uranium et ses composés*, Toulouse, 1901 ; *Ann. Chim. Phys.*, (7), **24**. 412, 1901 ; *Bull. Soc. Chim.*, (3), **23**. 368, 1900 ; (3), **25**. 153, 344, 1901 ; J. L. C. Zimmermann, *Ber.*, **13**. 348, 1882 ; **15**. 847, 1182, 1882 ; **17**. 2739, 1884 ; *Liebig's Ann.*, **213**. 1, 1882 ; **216**, 14, 1883 ; **232**. 310, 1886 ; E. M. Péligot, *Ann. Chim. Phys.*, (3), **5**. 5, 1842 ; (3), **12**. 549, 1844 ; (3), **22**. 329, 1848 ; (4), **17**. 368, 1869 ; *Journ. Pharm. Chim.*, (2), **27**. 522, 1841 ; *Compt. Rend.*, **12**. 735, 1841 ; **22**. 487, 1846 ; **42**. 73, 1856 ; R. W. Moore, *Trans. Amer. Electrochem. Soc.*, **43**. 317, 1923 ; O. Schmidt, *Zeit. phys. Chem.*, **118**. 193, 1925 ; F. Emich, *Monatsh.*, **15**. 375, 1894 ; G. Chesneau, *Compt. Rend.*, **122**. 471, 1896 ; J. Férée, *Bull. Soc. Chim.*, (3), **25**. 622, 1901 ; A. Korczynsky, *ib.*, (4), **29**. 283, 1921 ; C. M. A. Bignon and L. M. Bullier, *German Pat., D.R.P.* 77166, 1893 ; *French Pat. No.* 234223, 1893 ; *Zeit. angew. Chem.*, **7**. 655, 1894 ; F. Haber, *German Pat., D.R.P.* 259996, 1913 ; F. Haber, *ib.*, 229126, 1909 ; I. Zschukoff, *Ann. Inst. Anal. Phys. Chim.*, **3**. 14, 1926 ; M. G. Levi, E. Miglorini and G. Ercolini, *Gazz. Chim. Ital.*, **38**. i, 583, 1908 ; O. Ruff and A. Heinzelmann, *Ber.*, **42**. 492, 1909 ; A. Burger, *Reduktion durch Calcium*, Basel, 1907 ; D. Lely and L. Hamburger, *Zeit. anorg. Chem.*, **87**. 209, 1914 ; C. Beindl, *U.S. Pat. No.* 1492193, 1492194, 1924 ; F. Fischer and F. Schrötter, *Ber.*, **43**. 1442, 1910 ; W. P. Jorissen and A. P. H. Trivelli, *Chem. Weekbl.*, **8**. 59, 1911.

[2] J. A. Siemssen, *Chem. Ztg.*, **35**. 139, 1911 ; H. J. H. Fenton, *Journ. Chem. Soc.*, **93**. 1064, 1908 ; J. H. de Boer, *Chem. Weekbl.*, **21**. 404, 1924 ; V. Auger, *Compt. Rend.*, **170**. 995, 1920.

[3] G. C. Gmelin, *Schweigger's Journ.*, **43**. 110, 1825 ; *Edin. Med. Journ.*, **3**. 324, 1827 ; C. le Conte, *Gaz. Méd. Paris*, 196, 1854 ; *Compt. Rend. Soc. Biol.*, **5**. 171, 1853 ; R. H. Chittenden and A. Lambert, *Biol. Zeit.*, **25**. 513, 1889 ; *Studies Physiol. Lab. Yale Univ.*, **3**. 1, 1889 ; R. H. Chittenden and M. T. Hutchinson, *ib.*, **2**. 55, 1889 ; J. Woroschilsky, *Chem. Ztg.*, **14**. 1002. 1890 ; R. Fleckseder, *Arch. Exp. Path.*, **56**. 54, 1906 ; D. E. Jackson and F. C. Mann, *Amer. Journ. Physiol.*, **26**. 381, 1910 ; *Indiana Univ. Stud.*, **8**. 2, 1911 ; O. Loew, *Bull. Agric. Coll. Tokyo*, **5**. 173, 1902 ; J. H. Bechhold, *Zeit. phys. Chem.*, **48**. 385, 1904 ; M. Neisser and U. Friedemann, *Zeit. angew. Chem.*, **17**. 833, 1904 ; N. Kowalewsky, *Zeit. anal. Chem.*, **24**. 551, 1885 ; B. Szilard, *Journ. Chim. Phys.*, **5**. 495, 636, 1907 ; A. Müller, *Zeit. anorg. Chem.*, **57**. 311, 1908 ; W. Sigmund, *Jahresb. Staatsrealschule Karolinenthal*, **26**. 1, 1902 ; H. Agulhon and T. Robert, *Compt. Rend.*, **158**. 349, 1914 ; J. Stoklasa, *ib.*, **156**. 153, 1913 ; P. Becquerel, *ib.*, **156**. 164, 1913 ; C. Acqua, *Atti Accad. Lincei*, (5), **22**. ii, 390, 1913 ; F. Cartier, *Thérap. Gaz.*, 766, 1891 ; *Glycosuries toxiques et en particulier intoxication par le nitrate d'urane*, Paris, 1891 ; B. Fischer and C. Hartwich, *Handbuch der pharmazeutische Praxis*, Berlin, **2**. 1070, 1903 ; A. Rabuteau, *Élémens de toxicologie et de médecine légale, appliquées à l'empoisonnement*, Paris, 1888.

[4] Anon., *Metal Ind.*, **20**. 9, 1922.

[5] E. Ruhstrat, *German Pat., D.R.P.* 238380, 1910 ; H. Kuzel, *ib.*, 192290, 194348, 194707, 1905 ; F. J. Planchon, *ib.*, 194896, 1907 ; A. Lottermoser, *Chem. Ztg.*, **32**. 311, 1908 ; L. Vanino and J. Gans, *Journ. prakt. Chem.*, (2), **71**. 196, 1905 ; W. Schmidt-Dumont, *Journ. Gasbeleucht.*, **39**. 697, 1897.

[6] A. Haenig, *Oesterr. Zeit. Berg. Hütt.*, **56**. 177, 196, 208, 221, 1908.

[7] R. F. Bacon, *Philippine Journ. Science*, **2**. 129, 1907 ; D. van Monckhoven, *Phot. Mitt.*, **16**. 129, 1880 ; J. M. Eder, *Phot. Corr.*, **16**. 218, 1880.

[8] J. C. Schnauss, *Chem. Ztg.*, **16**. 842, 1892 ; A. Stieglitz, *Anthony's Phot. Bull.*, **23**. 47, 1892 ; *Phot. Arch.*, **33**. 52, 1892 ; R. Namias, *Bayr. Ind. Gewerbebl.*, **26**. 529, 1894 ; A. Lumière and A. Seyewetz, *Monit. Scient.*, (4), **19**. 101, 1905 ; C. T. Roche, *Phot. Wochenbl.*, **14**. 5, 1888 ; A. St. V. Niépce, *Compt. Rend.*, **46**. 448, 489, 1858.

[9] E. Odernheimer, *German Pat., D.R.P.* 72523, 1892 ; *Färber Ztg.*, **5**. 17, 1894 ; A. Werner, *Bull. Soc. Mulhouse*, **62**. 542, 1892.

[10] M. Pesqui, *Pharm. Ztg.*, **46**. 837, 1901.

[11] M. H. Klaproth, *Beiträge zur chemischen Kenntnis der Mineralkörper*, Berlin, **2**. 214,

1797 ; London, **1**. 489, 1801 ; W. Stein, *Die Glasfabrikation*, Braunschweig, 57, 1862 ; H. Benrath, *Die Glasfabrikation*, Braunschweig, 287, 1875 ; G. Bontemps, *Guide du verrier*, Paris, 98, 362, 546, 1848 ; H. Schnurpfeil, *Das Glas in seiner verschiedenen Farbentechnik*, Stuttgart, 12, 24, 28, 31, 69, 72, 1911 ; H. Schwarz, *Verh. Ver. Bef. Gewerbfl.*, **66**. 213, 1887 ; A. Salvetat, *Decoration von Thonwaaren*, Wien, 15, 1871 ; C. Lauth and G. Dutailly, *Bull. Soc. Chim.*, (3), **1**. 246, 1888 ; F. H. Riddle, *Trans. Amer. Cer. Soc.*, **8**. 210, 1906 ; L. H. Minton, *ib.*, **9**. 771, 1907 ; J. R. Lorah, *Journ. Amer. Cer. Soc.*, **10**. 813, 1927 ; A. Holl, *Keramos*, **9**. 5, 1930.
     [12]. F. Haber, *German Pat.*, *D.R.P.* 259996, 1913 ; *Zeit. Elektrochem.*, **16**. 244, 1910 ; *Chem. Ztg.*, **34**. 345, 1910 ; J. W. Swan and J. A. Kendall, *Brit. Pat. No.* 3500, 1895 ; C. Beindl, *U.S. Pat. No.* 1492193, 1492194, 1924.

§ 7. The Valency and Atomic Weight of Uranium

The early investigations of A. Schönberg,[1] J. A. Arfvedson, and J. J. Berzelius on the at. wt. of uranium are only of historical interest, because the dioxide was mistaken for the element. After the recognition of the true nature of the element by E. M. Péligot, in 1841, and his subsequent determination of the equivalent, it was assumed that the at. wt. was about 120, and the valency is 3. In 1872, D. I. Mendeléeff [2] pointed out that there is no place in the periodic table for a tervalent element of at. wt. 120, and he emphasized the resemblance in the properties of chromium, molybdenum, tungsten, and uranium considered as a family group. He therefore suggested that the at. wt. be doubled so that uranium could be placed below tungsten in the periodic table. He also represented the oxides of the element, by analogy with the other elements of the family, by the formulæ UO_2, U_3O_8, and UO_3, implying that the element can be quadrivalent and sexavalent. The position of uranium in the periodic table, and comparisons of the properties of uranium with those of other members of the family group were made by F. W. O. de Coninck, S. M. Losanitsch, H. E. Roscoe, A. von Grosse, W. Muthmann, H. Rossi, E. J. Mills, J. L. C. Zimmermann, O. F. von der Pfordten, M. M. Gerber, and G. Alibegoff. Isomorphism has very little to say about the relations of uranium with the other members of the family group. J. L. C. Zimmermann's determinations of the vapour density of uranium tetrachloride and tetrabromide, O. Ruff and A. Heinzelmann's determination of the vapour density of the hexafluoride, and L. Rügheimer's determination of the mol. wt. of the tetrachloride from its effect on the b.p. of bismuth trichloride favour the doubled at. wt., 240. Similarly with the sp. ht. rule ; with U. Sborgi's determination of the electrochemical eq. of soln. of uranium tetrachloride ; and with the high frequency or X-ray spectrum. The mass of evidence mounts to the altitude of proof that the at. wt. of uranium, in agreement with the prognostications of D. I. Mendeléeff, approximates 240 ; and that uranium is a member of the chromium, molybdenum, and tungsten family of elements.

The observations of O. Ruff and A. Heinzelmann on the vapour density of uranium hexafluoride establish the *sexavalency* of uranium ; and since ammoniacal soln. furnish ammonium uranate, in which the trioxide, UO_3, appears as the anhydride of uranic acid, it is highly probable that uranium is sexavalent in this oxide, as well as in the uranyl derivatives, $UO_2(NO_3)_2$, etc. The existence of uranium pentachloride corresponds with a *quinquevalent* uranium, but the evidence is not unequivocal. The *quadrivalency* of uranium in the tetrachloride and tetrabromide has been established by the mol. wt. determination of J. L. C. Zimmermann, and L. Rügheimer, by the existence of the dioxide and disulphide, and by the isomorphism of thorium and uranium dioxides observed by W. F. Hillebrand, and of the disulphates observed by W. F. Hillebrand and W. H. Melville. A. Rosenheim and co-workers obtained a complex with pyrocatechol and quadrivalent uranium, namely $2\{(NH_4)_2[U(C_6H_4O_2)_3]\}C_6H_4O_2.8H_2O$. The *tervalency* of uranium is in agreement with the existence of the trihalides ; and the *bivalency* with the existence of the difluoride, monoxide, and monosulphide—but the evidence is here not decisive. It is an open question whether uranium is *octovalent* in the tetroxide, UO_4, of P. G. Melikoff and L. Pissarjewsky.

Although the earlier attempts to determine the at. wt. of uranium were vitiated by the erroneous assumption that uranium dioxide was the metal, this does not affect the analytical data. The methods of purifying uranium, however, were not good, so that although the data can be adapted to the new knowledge about the nature of the element, the results of J. J. Berzelius,[3] J. A. Arfvedson, and R. F. Marchand are unsatisfactory. C. F. Rammelsberg's observations on the analysis of uranium tetrachloride vary so widely that they are best omitted when computing the general mean. There remain J. J. Ebelmen's determination of the ratio $UO_2(C_2O_4).H_2O : UO_2$ from which is calculated 238 for the at. wt. of uranium ; and his determination of the ratio $3UO_2 : U_3O_8$ gives 240. J. L. C. Zimmerman's value for the ratio $3UO_2 : U_3O_8$ gives the at. wt. 239·6 ; and his value for the ratio $Na(UO_2)(C_2H_3O_2)_3 : Na_2U_2O_7$ gives 240·2 ; I. Wertheim obtained 240 from the same ratio. E. M. Péligot obtained 240 from the ratio $CO_2 : U_3O_8$, and F. W. O. de Coninck 238·4 from the same ratio. P. Lebeau calculated the at. wt. 238·5 from the ratio $U(OH)_4(NO_3)_2 : UO_2$. J. Aloy obtained 239·4 from the ratio $N : UO_2$ prepared by igniting the nitrate, measuring the resulting nitrogen, and reducing the uranium tritaoctoxide. O. Hönigschmid and W. E. Schilz calculated 238·136 from the ratio $UCl_4 : 4Ag$, and 238·142 from the ratio $UCl_4 : 4AgCl$. T. W. Richards and B. S. Merigold calculated 238·4 from the ratio $UBr : 4AgBr$, and with the same ratio O. Hönigschmid calculated 238·09 to 238·18 ; and O. Hönigschmid and S. Horovitz, 238·05 to 238·17. From the ratio $UBr_4 : 4Ag$, T. W. Richards and B. S. Merigold calculated 238·4 ; O. Hönigschmid, 238·11 to 238·18 ; and O. Hönigschmid and S. Horovitz, 238·06 to 238·17. F. W. Clarke calculated 238·977 as the best representative value or the general mean of the results available up to 1910 ; and J. Meyer, 238·2 for the results available up to 1921. The International Table gives 238·2 for the best representative value. The at. wt. of uranium was discussed by A. S. Russell, and S. Meyer.

The **atomic number** of uranium is 92. Uranium is the last in the list of elements arranged according to their increasing at. wts. Thorium has the at. number 90 ; and the gap 91 is filled with the isotopes, protactinium and brevium. P. Vinassa discussed the molecular numbers. O. Hahn[4] discussed the **isotopes** of uranium ; F. W. Aston was unable to measure the mass spectrum of uranium in order to determine the isotopes. Both thorium and uranium are regarded as elements whose nuclei are so complex that they are only partially stable, that is, they are very slowly undergoing a process of degradation into simpler forms. The **electronic structure** on N. Bohr's system is : (2) for the K-shell ; (2, 6) for the L-shell ; (2, 6, 10) for the M-shell ; (2, 6, 10, 14) for the N-shell ; (2, 6, 10) for the O-shell ; (2, 6, 4) for the P-shell ; and (2) for the Q-shell. This subject was discussed by W. D. Harkins, C. D. Niven, P. D. Foote, J. D. M. Smith, and J. N. Frers. The spontaneous **atomic disintegration** of uranium has been discussed in connection with the radioactivity of uranium—**4**. 26, 10 and 11. Ordinary uranium is there shown to be a mixture of two isotopes, designated uranium-I and uranium-II, with the respective at. wts. 238·2 and 234·2. The one is spontaneously passing into the other by way of the intermediate stages uranium-X and uranium-X_2— vide **4**. 26, 10 and 11. The uranium-X, and helium in the form of α-rays, represent the products of the first stage in the spontaneous decay of uranium proper. E. Rutherford and J. Chadwick,[5] and H. Müller obtained negative results in the attempt to disintegrate the atom by bombardment with α-rays. The subject was discussed by G. I. Podrowsky. According to A. Gaschler, the radioactive transformation of uranium into uranium-X can be accelerated by an intense electric discharge. He said :

In a narrow vertical tube of fused quartz an electrode of tungsten was 15 cm. above a thin layer of uranium oxide resting on mercury in which was embedded the second tungsten electrode. The oxide was freed from all radio-active constituents before it was used. After frequent electrical discharges of 0·3 or 0·4 ampère had passed for thirty hours from one electrode to the other, definite and growing radio-activity manifested itself by the presence of β-rays and γ-rays. Moreover, the radio-active material was separated by chemical means and its half-period when measured proved to be that of uranium-X. The β-ray and γ-ray activity of the uranium oxide freed from the mercury varied between 1·4 and 20 times the radio-activity of an equally large amount of uranium oxide in equilibrium with its decay products, and increased proportionally to the energy applied and to the time.

REFERENCES.

[1] A. Schönberg, *De conjunctione chemica ejusque rationibus*, Upsaliæ, 18, 1813 ; *Schweigger's Journ.*, **15**. 285, 1815 ; J. A. Arfvedson, *Svenska Akad. Handl.*, 404, 1822 ; *Ann. Phil.*, **7**. 253, 1824 ; *Pogg. Ann.*, **1**. 245, 1824 ; *Schweigger's Journ.*, **44**. 8, 1825 ; J. J. Berzelius, *ib.*, **44**. 191, 1825 ; *Pogg. Ann.*, **1**. 359, 1824 ; *Svenska Akad. Handl.*, 152, 1823 ; *Ann. Phil.*, **9**. 266, 1825 ; E. M. Péligot, *Compt. Rend.*, **12**. 735, 1841 ; **22**. 487, 1846 ; **42**. 73, 1856 ; *Ann. Chim. Phys.*, (3), **5**. 5, 1842 ; (3), **20**. 329, 1847 ; *Journ. Pharm. Chim.*, (2), **27**. 522, 1841 ; *Liebig's Ann.*, **41**. 141, 1841 ; **43**. 258, 1842 ; *Journ. Prakt. Chem.*, (1), **24**. 442, 1841 ; (1), **38**. 112, 1846.

[2] D. I. Mendeléeff, *Liebig's Ann. Suppl.*, **8**. 178, 1872 ; *Chem. News*, **41**. 39, 1880 ; *Journ. Russ. Phys. Chem. Soc.*, **13**. 517, 1881 ; *Ber.*, **14**. 2821, 1881 ; S. M. Losanitsch, *Ghlas Srpslea Kralevska Akad. Belgrade*, **69**. 139, 1905 ; G. Alibegoff, *Liebig's Ann.*, **233**. 177, 1886 ; J. L. C. Zimmermann, *ib.*, **204**. 204, 1880 ; **216**. 1, 1882 ; W. Muthmann, *ib.*, **238**. 108, 1887 ; O. F. von der Pfordten, *ib.*, **222**. 137, 1883 ; L. Rügheimer, *ib.*, **364**. 45, 1909 ; F. W. O. de Coninck, *Rev. Gén. Chim. Pure Appl.*, **5**. 377, 1902 ; H. E. Roscoe, *Journ. Chem. Soc.*, **27**. 933, 1874 ; *Ber.*, **7**. 1131, 1874 ; O. Ruff and A. Heinzelmann, *ib.*, **42**. 495, 1909 ; *Zeit. anorg. Chem.*, **72**. 63, 1910 ; U. Sborgi, *Zeit. Elektrochem.*, **19**. 115, 1913 ; *Atti Accad. Lincei*, (5), **21**. i, 135, 1912 ; *Gazz. Chim. Ital.*, **42**. ii, 144, 1912 ; W. F. Hillebrand, *Zeit. anorg. Chem.*, **3**. 343, 1893 ; *Bull. U.S. Geol. Sur.*, 113, 1893 ; W. F. Hillebrand and W. H. Melville, *Amer. Chem. Journ.*, **14**. 1, 1892 ; P. G. Melikoff and L. Pissarjewsky, *Ber.*, **30**. 2902, 1897 ; A. von Grosse, *Zeit. phys. Chem.*, **10**. 3, 395, 1930 ; A. Rosenheim, B. Raibmann and G. Schendel, *Zeit. anorg. Chem.*, **196**. 160, 1931 ; E. Donath, *Ber.*, **12**. 742, 1879 ; E. J. Mills, *Phil. Mag.*, (5), **18**. 393, 1884 ; H. Rossi, *Beiträge zur Kenntnis des vierwertigen Urans*, München, 1902 ; M. M. Gerber, *Chem. News*, **43**. 242, 1881.

[3] J. J. Berzelius, *Schweigger's Journ.*, **44**. 191, 1825 ; *Pogg. Ann.*, **1**. 359, 1824 ; *Svenska Akad. Handl.*, 152, 1823 ; *Ann. Phil.*, **9**. 266, 1825 ; J. A. Arfvedson, *Svenska Akad. Handl.*, 404, 1822 ; *Ann. Phil.*, **7**. 253, 1824 ; *Pogg. Ann.*, **1**. 245, 1824 ; *Schweigger's Journ.*, **44**. 8, 1825 ; E. M. Péligot, *Compt. Rend.*, **12**. 735, 1841 ; **22**. 487, 1846 ; **42**. 73, 1856 ; *Ann. Chim. Phys.*, (3), **5**. 5, 1842 ; (3), **20**. 329, 1847 ; *Journ. Pharm. Chim.*, (2), **27**. 522, 1841 ; *Liebig's Ann.*, **41**. 141, 1841 ; **43**. 258, 1842 ; *Journ. prakt. Chem.*, (1), **24**. 442, 1841 ; (1), **38**. 112, 1846 ; C. F. Rammelsberg, *Pogg. Ann.*, **55**. 318, 1842 ; **56**. 125, 1843 ; **59**. 9, 1843 ; **66**. 91, 1845 ; *Journ. prakt. Chem.*, (1), **29**. 324, 1842 ; R. F. Marchand, *ib.*, (1), **23**. 497, 1841 ; T. W. Richards and B. S. Merigold, *Proc. Amer. Acad.*, **37**. 365, 1902 ; *Zeit. anorg. Chem.*, **31**. 235, 1902 ; *Chem. News*, **85**. 177, 186, 201, 207, 222, 229, 249, 1902 ; I. Wertheim, *Ber. Vers. deut. Naturf.*, 193, 1843 ; *Ann. Chim. Phys.*, (3), **11**. 49, 1844 ; *Journ. prakt. Chem.*, (1), **29**. 209, 1843 ; J. J. Ebelmen, *ib.*, (1), **27**. 385, 1842 ; *Ann. Chim. Phys.*, (3), **5**. 189, 1842 ; A. S. Russell, *Nature*, **114**. 717, 1924 ; J. L. C. Zimmermann, *Liebig's Ann.*, **232**. 299, 1886 ; J. Aloy, *Recherches sur l'uranium et ses composés*, Toulouse, 1901 ; *Bull. Soc. Chim.*, (3), **27**. 260, 1902 ; *Ann. Chim. Phys.*, (7), **24**. 418, 1901 ; *Compt. Rend.*, **132**. 551, 1901 ; P. Lebeau, *ib.*, **154**. 1612, 1808, 1912 ; **155**. 163, 1912 ; *Bull. Soc. Chim.*, (4), **11**. 488, 1912 ; F. W. O. de Coninck, *Bull. Acad. Belg.*, 1041, 1907 ; 163, 1477, 1908 ; *Ann. Chim. Phys.*, (7), **28**. 5, 1903 ; *Compt. Rend.*, **147**. 1477, 1908 ; **152**. 711, 1179, 1911 ; **155**. 1511, 1912 ; O. Hönigschmid, *ib.*, **158**. 2004, 1914 ; *Zeit. Elektrochem.*, **20**. 452, 1914 ; *Monatsh.*, **36**. 355, 1915 ; O. Hönigschmid and S. Horovitz, *ib.*, **37**. 185, 1916 ; O. Hönigschmid and W. E. Schilz, *Zeit. anorg. Chem.*, **170**. 145, 1928 ; W. E. Schilz, *Eine Revision des Atomgewichtes des Urans. Analyse des Uranochlorids*, München, 1927 ; F. W. Clarke, *A Recalculation of the Atomic Weights*, Washington, 373, 1910 ; *Chem. News*, **63**. 77, 1891 ; *Amer. Chem. Journ.*, **3**. 273, 1880 ; J. Meyer in R. Abegg, *Handbuch der anorganischen Chemie*, Leipzig, **4**. i, (2), 882, 1921 ; S. Meyer, *Mitt. Inst. Radiumforsch.*, 226, 1928.

[4] O. Hahn, *Zeit. anorg. Chem.*, **147**. 16, 1925 ; J. D. M. Smith, *Journ. Chem. Soc.*, 2029, 1927 ; N. Bohr, *Nature*, **112**. Suppl., 1923 ; J. N. Frers, *Zeit. anorg. Chem.*, **186**. 145, 1930 ; C. D. Niven, *Phil. Mag.*, (7), **3**. 1314, 1927 ; F. W. Aston, *ib.*, (6), **49**. 1191, 1925 ; F. Soddy, *ib.*, (4), **38**. 483, 1919 ; P. D. Foote, *Nature*, **114**. 789, 1924 ; P. Vinassa, *Gazz. Chim. Ital.*, **58**. 178, 1928 ; W. D. Harkins, *Phys. Rev.*, (2), **38**. 1270, 1931.

[5] A. Gaschler, *Nature*, **116**. 396, 1925 ; E. Rutherford and J. Chadwick, *ib.*, **113**. 457, 1924 ; *Proc. Phys. Soc.*, **36**. 417, 1924 ; W. G. Guy and A. S. Russell, *Journ. Chem. Soc.*, **123**. 2618, 1923 ; H. Müller, *Sitzber. Akad. Wien*, **135**. 563, 1926 ; G. I. Podrowsky, *Zeit. Physik*, **57**. 560, 1929.

§ 8. The Intermetallic Compounds of Uranium

J. W. Marden and H. C. Rentschler [1] said that uranium readily alloys with metals—*vide supra*, uranium. Definite alloys of uranium with the alkali metals have not been reported, although A. Colani referred to alloys with sodium and potassium formed when uranous chloride is heated with an excess of these elements. H. Moissan [2] prepared some alloys of **copper** and uranium. Alloys with silver and gold have not been reported. A similar remark applies to alloys of uranium with the metals of the alkaline earths, beryllium, and cadmium. J. W. Marden obtained alloys with **zinc** by reducing mixtures of uranium oxide and zinc chloride by calcium. A. Colani referred to a binary alloy formed when uranous chloride is heated with an excess of **magnesium.** G. Tammann and J. Hinnüber [3] found that **mercury** dissolves 0·00014 per cent. of uranium at ordinary temp. J. Férée obtained an alloy with mercury—that is, *uranium amalgam*—by electrolyzing an aq. soln. of uranous chloride using a mercury cathode—*vide supra*, pyrophoric uranium. According to A. S. Russell and co-workers, uranium is deposited on zinc, tin, copper, or mercury when the liquid amalgam is shaken with an acidified soln.

A. Colani referred to the formation of a binary alloy when uranous chloride is heated with an excess of aluminium. L. Guillet prepared alloys with aluminium by the aluminothermite process. He used uranium oxide which he prepared from ammonium uranate. The ignition mixture consisted of barium dioxide and aluminium (4 : 1), which was ignited with a match. H. Moissan prepared the alloys by adding a mixture of aluminium powder and uranium oxide to molten aluminium ; part of the aluminium burns, and there is such an energetic development of heat that the oxide is reduced, and the metal alloys with the rest of the aluminium. J. Aloy prepared alloys by the electrolysis of molten potassium uranium hexachloride with an aluminium cathode. P. A. Heller found that the production of aluminium-uranium alloys by the thermite method gives a very poor yield, but satisfactory results may be obtained by reducing a mixture of uranyl fluoride and uranium tetrafluoride (formed by adding U_3O_8 to hydrofluoric acid) by means of metallic calcium in the presence of aluminium, the operation being conducted in an iron bomb. By this method an alloy containing 62·8 per cent. U, 34·8 per cent. Al, 1·4 per cent. Ca, 0·5 per cent. C, and 0·25 per cent. Si was obtained. L. Guillet considers that two intermetallic compounds are formed. **Uranium hemitrialuminide,** U_2Al_3, is obtained by the thermite process from a mixture of 110 grms. of aluminium and 390 grms. of uranium oxide. The cubic crystals are very hard. The compound is stable in air, but readily oxidizes when heated. At 450° to 500°, chlorine forms red needles of the pentachloride, and at a higher temp., uranium tetrachloride—including, of course, aluminium trichloride. Water forms a film of green oxide on the alloy ; and acids attack it readily. A mixture of 135 grms. of aluminium and 365 grms. of uranium oxide, by the thermite process, furnishes **uranium trialuminide,** UAl_3, in fine acicular, silver-white crystals. The sp. gr. is 5·32 at 20°. Their chemical properties resemble those of the hemitrialuminide.

H. Moissan prepared alloys of uranium and **titanium** by the method he employed for alloys with aluminium. A. Colani referred to a binary alloy with tin when an excess of that metal is heated with uranous chloride. J. A. Heany obtained an alloy with **vanadium.** H. Moissan, J. A. Heany, and A. Stavenhagen and E. Schuchard obtained an alloy with **molybdenum ;** and A. Stavenhagen and E. Schuchard the quaternary alloy U–Cr–Mo–Ti. J. W. Marden and H. C. Rentschler, and H. Moissan, alloys with **tungsten.** The Westinghouse Lamp Co. obtained uranium-tungsten alloys by shaking up a mixture of the finely-divided metals in a soln. of paraffin oil in ether, and then sintering them together.

REFERENCES.

[1] J. W. Marden and H. C. Rentschler, *Trans. Amer. Electrochem. Soc.*, **43**. 326, 1923; A. Colani, *Ann. Chim. Phys.*, (8), **12**. 59, 1907.
[2] H. Moissan, *Bull. Soc. Chim.*, (3), **15**. 1283, 1896; *Compt. Rend.*, **122**. 1302, 1896; J. W. Marden, *U.S. Pat. No.* 1728940, 1728942, 1929; A. Colani, *Ann. Chim. Phys.*, (8), **12**. 59, 1907.
[3] J. Férée, *Bull. Soc. Chim.*, (3), **25**. 622, 1901; A. S. Russell, *Nature*, **127**. 273, 1931; R. Groves and A. S. Russell, *Journ. Chem. Soc.*, 2805, 1931; L. Guillet, *Bull. Soc. Enc. Nat. Ind.*, **101**. 254, 1902; J. Aloy, *Recherches sur l'uranium et ses composés*, Paris, 1901; *Ann. Chim. Phys.*, (7), **24**. 412, 1901; A. Colani, *ib.*, (8), **12**. 59, 1907; Westinghouse Lamp Co., *U.S. Pat. No.* 1567219, 1925; J. A. Heany, *ib.*, 1759454, 1930; P. A. Heller, *Metall Erz.*, **19**. 397, 1922; H. Moissan, *Compt. Rend.*, **113**. 2, 1891; **122**. 1302, 1896; A. Stavenhagen and E. Schuchard, *Ber.*, **35**. 909, 1902; J. W. Marden and H. C. Rentschler, *Trans. Amer. Electrochem. Soc.*, **43**. 326, 1923; G. Tammann and J. Hinnüber, *Zeit. anorg. Chem.*, **160**. 249, 1927.

§ 9. Uranium Dioxide and the Lower Oxides

The chief oxides of uranium are the dioxide, UO_2, and the trioxide, UO_3, with the intermediate oxide, U_3O_8. There are a few other less well-defined oxides which have been reported. C. Wagner and W. Schottey [1] discussed the system : uranium-oxygen. F. W. O. de Coninck and M. Camo found that the electrolysis of a 6 to 8 per cent. soln. of uranyl nitrate yields a black, pulverulent, pyrophoric oxide—possibly *uranium monoxide—vide supra*, the electrolysis of uranium salts. A similar substance was obtained by reducing the pentoxide with hydrogen at a high temp. These conclusions lack confirmation. The pale green soln. obtained by reducing uranyl salts with zinc gives a pale green precipitate when treated with alkali-lye, and the hyacinth-red soln. containing tervalent uranium also gives a pale green precipitate with alkali-lye. These products are supposed by A. Guyard to contain *uranium dihydroxide*. The conclusion is not supported by the observations of O. Follenius, A. Belohoubek, H. Hermann, and J. L. C. Zimmermann. According to E. M. Péligot, if a soln. of uranyl dichloride is reduced with zinc and hydrochloric acid, the hyacinth-red soln. contains uranium trichloride, and gives a brown precipitate—probably **uranium trihydroxide,** $U(OH)_3$—when treated with aq. ammonia. This rapidly oxidizes to green tetrahydroxide, and thence to ammonium uranate. J. L. C. Zimmermann discussed these observations. A. Rosenheim and H. Löbel also regarded the brown precipitate obtained by adding aq. ammonia to hydrochloric acid soln. of uranium trichloride to be uranium trihydroxide. Not infrequently reference is made in literature to **uranium sesquioxide, or hemitrioxide,** U_2O_3 when, presumably, the trioxide is meant, and the old at. wt. 120 has been used. F. W. O. de Coninck and M. Camo said that they prepared the lemon-yellow *dihydrate*, $U_2O_3.2H_2O$, and the orange *hydrate*, $U_2O_3.H_2O$, and also black *uranium hemipentoxide*, U_2O_5, by the electrolysis of soln. of uranyl nitrate as indicated above. The chemical individuality of these electrolytic products has not been established.

The observations of M. H. Klaproth,[2] J. B. Richter, C. F. Bucholz, J. J. Berzelius, and A. Schönberg on the preparation of uranium by heating an intimate mixture of uranium oxide and carbon can be employed for the preparation of **uranium dioxide,** or **uranous oxide,** UO_2. The properties of the old uranium are properties of uranium dioxide. J. Aloy found that uranium dioxide is formed in the electric arc furnace when the temp. is not high enough to produce the carbide. P. Jolibois and R. Bossuet found that to convert uranosic oxide into the dioxide by simple dissociation, it must be heated at $2000°$ in vacuo—*vide infra*, uranosic oxide. W. Biltz and H. Müller recommended heating the uranosic oxide at $900°$ in hydrogen, when the product is brown ; if a dense form of uranosic oxide is used, the product is dark brownish-violet. By heating the uranosic oxide in vacuo, W. Biltz and H. Müller, unlike E. Friederich and L. Sittig, could not get nearer UO_2 than $UO_{2.15}$. Uranium dioxide was obtained by J. L. C. Zimmermann by heating the tritaoctoxide in an indifferent gas—carbon dioxide or nitrogen; and A. Ditte showed that the transformation proceeds quickly if the oxide be moistened with a few drops of hydrofluoric acid, and that the trioxide in the presence of the vapour of hydrogen fluoride forms the dioxide. I. Wertheim heated a mixture of uranium tritaoctoxide and oxalic acid; J. J. Berzelius, and F. W. O. de Coninck, uranyl oxalate; and F. W. O. de Coninck, uranyl bromide, sulphite, or sulphate out of contact with air. J. A. Arfvedson, A. Laugier, and L. R. Lecanu obtained the dioxide by heating to redness uranosic oxide in a current of hydrogen. P. Jolibois and R. Bossuet said that the reaction commences at 625° and is completed at 650°. O. F. von der Pfordten, and P. Sabatier and J. B. Senderens similarly heated the trioxide to redness in hydrogen gas and obtained the dioxide; J. Aloy, uranyl hydroxide; F. W. O. de Coninck, uranium trioxide, or uranyl sulphate, chloride, or bromide; E. M. Péligot, and P. Lebeau, uranyl nitrate; J. J. Ebelmen, and H. Hermann, uranous sulphate; E. M. Péligot, and J. J. Ebelmen, the oxalate; and J. A. Arfvedson, potassium uranyl chloride—and washing out the potassium chloride and undecomposed salt with water. E. M. Péligot added that the oxide should be allowed to remain in hydrogen until the containing vessel is cold, owing to the pyrophoric properties of the dioxide, but J. J. Ebelmen said that if the temp. be cherry-red, the dioxide, after cooling in hydrogen, is stable in air; E. M. Péligot heated potassium uranyl chloride in the absence of air; and F. Wöhler heated the alkali salt with an excess of ammonium chloride, and washed the soluble matters from the resulting uranium dioxide. E. F. Smith and J. M. Matthews heated to whiteness for about 6 hrs. uranium tritaoctoxide mixed with a large excess of ammonium chloride in a porcelain crucible packed with charcoal in a larger fireclay crucible. A. Colani obtained the dioxide by passing steam in a current of carbon dioxide over heated sodium uranium hexachloride, and extracted the cold product with water. F. W. O. de Coninck heated uranyl chloride with powdered magnesium, aluminium, lime, or baryta out of contact with air, and washed the cold product with water. H. Rose melted uranyl phosphate with six parts of a mixture of equal proportions of sodium carbonate and potassium cyanide, and extracted the cold mass with water; uranium dioxide remained. J. J. Ebelmen reduced the hemipentoxide by heating it with sulphur; and H. Hermann reduced the hemipentoxide, and also sodium uranate, with sulphur and ammonium chloride, and he also heated uranosulphate with potassium pentasulphide at 200° in a closed crucible; in each case the products were washed with water. H. Hermann also reduced the tritaoctoxide and the trioxide by heating them in a current of carbon dioxide laden with the vapour of carbon disulphide. F. W. O. de Coninck obtained this oxide as a black powder by the electrolysis of a soln. of uranyl nitrate—*vide supra*.

K. A. Hofmann and K. Höschele prepared fine, black, cubic crystals of uranium dioxide by fusing together one part of sodium diuranate and 4 parts of magnesium chloride; and W. F. Hillebrand, by fusing uranium tritaoctoxide with borax for a long time. Amorphous uranium dioxide is similarly converted into the crystalline variety by fusion with borax.

A. Samsonoff prepared **colloidal uranium dioxide** by electrolyzing a soln. of uranyl chloride; it appears as a black precipitate at the cathode. The precipitate is soluble in water, giving a dark-coloured soln. which shows the presence of ultra-microscopic particles. A very dil. soln. has a yellow tinge, and the absorption spectrum indicates that neither a uranous nor a uranyl salt is present. In an electric field the soln. becomes decolorized at the anode, and precipitation takes place at the cathode. On addition of electrolytes, coagulation phenomena character-istic of the positive colloids are observed. The same substance is also obtained in the reduction of uranyl chloride by zinc or copper in dil. acid soln. Uranous chloride acts as a protector, and increases the stability of the colloidal soln. E. M. Péligot found that when alkali-lye or aq. ammonia is added to a soln. of a uranous salt, a reddish-brown gelatinous precipitate of the hydrated dioxide is formed. The flocculent precipitate becomes black and compact when boiled. When the precipitate is dried in vacuo it approximates to the *monohydrate*, $UO_2.H_2O$. This rapidly oxidizes in air, and dissolves in acids to form uranous salts. J. Aloy obtained a black *dihydrate*, $UO_2.2H_2O$, or, possibly, **uranous hydroxide**, $U(OH)_4$, by the action of hot alkali-lye on crystalline uranous sulphate. The product when thoroughly washed can be kept for several days without perceptible change. When heated it passes into the green tritaoctoxide. It is soluble in dil. acids.

Uranium dioxide has been variously described as forming a black, crystalline powder (F. Wöhler); iron-grey needles (C. F. Bucholz); black, lustrous scales (E. M. Péligot); reddish-brown powder when free from nitrogen and chlorine (E. F. Smith and J. M. Matthews); reddish crystals which are transparent under the microscope (A. Colani); metallic powder consisting of microscopic, regular octahedra (J. A. Arfvedson); and E. M. Péligot, and J. Aloy, as a black, or brown, pyrophoric powder. E. Friederich and L. Sittig found that blue and brown forms are produced when uranosic oxide is heated over 1000° in nitrogen and hydrogen respectively. F. W. O. de Coninck observed that a brick-red variety is produced when uranyl bromide is heated in air; it is said to be very stable at high temp., and to pass into the black variety without loss of oxygen when it is heated in hydrogen. For the **colour** of the oxide, *vide infra*, uranium trioxide. L. Pauling discussed the crystal structure. W. F. Hillebrand, and A. Schoep found that the octahedral or cubic crystals are isomorphous with those of cerium and thorium dioxides. V. M. Goldschmidt and L. Thomassen found that the **X-radiograms** of uranium, thorium, and cerium dioxides correspond with a face-centred, cubic lattice with the oxygen atoms arranged probably on the calcium fluoride type. The edges of the unit cube are 5·47 A. for uranium dioxide, 5·41 A. for thorium dioxide, and 5·41 A. for cerium dioxide—*vide infra*, pitchblende. A. E. van Arkel gave $a=5·48$ A. W. Biltz and H. Müller made some observations on this subject. E. J. Cuy estimated the interatomic distances in the crystal to be 2·37 A. M. H. Klaproth gave 6·44 for the **specific gravity**; J. B. Richter, 6·94; C. F. Bucholz, 9·0; and J. J. Ebelmen, 10·15. A. Raynaud gave 8·2 for the sp. gr. of the dioxide prepared at 300°–320°. W. F. Hillebrand found that the crystals had a sp. gr. between 10·95 and 11·0 at ordinary temp., and referred to water at 4°. W. Biltz, and W. Biltz and H. Müller gave 10·82 at 25°/4° for the sp. gr. of the oxide which had been heated to 1300°; 24·97 for the **molecular volume**, and 6·15 for the at. vol. of the oxygen—*vide infra*, uranium trioxide, and uranosic oxide. H. V. Regnault gave 0·0619 for the **specific heat**. O. Ruff and O. Goecke found that the oxide has a **melting point** of 2196° in an atm. of nitrogen. E. Friederich and L. Sittig gave 2500°–2600° for the m.p. of the blue and brown dioxides. The great stability of this oxide misled the earlier investigators into the belief that they were dealing with a veritable element. For the **volatilization** of the dioxide, *vide infra*, uranium trioxide. E. Friederich and L. Sittig observed that when the dioxide, is heated on tungsten filaments in hydrogen or in nitrogen complete volatilization occurs in a few minutes. W. G. Mixter found the **heat of formation** to be $U+O_2=UO_2+256$ Cals.; and **heat of oxidation**, $UO_2+O=UO_3+34·2$ Cals. J. O. Perrine observed no fluorescence with **ultra-violet light**. J. Vrede studied the dioxide as a detector of **electromagnetic waves**. M. K. Slattery found that a trace of the dioxide added to many salts—*e.g.* sodium or lithium fluoride—renders them fluorescent in ultra-violet light. E. Friederich and L. Sittig found that when the powdered oxide is pressed into rods and then heated to 1000°, the sp. **electrical resistance** at room temp. of the blue dioxide is 30×10^3 ohms per sq. mm., and that of the brown dioxide is $26·5 \times 10^6$ ohms per sq. mm. M. le Blanc and H. Sachse gave for the sp. conductivity, K, of uranium dioxide:

20°	50°	100°	150°	200°	300°	400°	500°
K 2·4×10⁻⁴	4·0×10⁻⁴	1·0×10⁻³	5·0×10⁻³	1·0×10⁻²	2·5×10⁻²	4·0×10⁻²	7·0×10⁻²

C. A. Pierlé found the **electrode potential** of the black oxide is the same as for the green uranium tritaoctoxide (*q.v.*).   R. Luther and A. C. Michie found that uranous salts are strong reducing agents even in acid soln. ; the oxidation by atm. oxygen is accelerated by iron salts, platinum black, and especially by copper salts.   The difference of potential between a platinized platinum electrode and a soln. of uranous and uranyl salts in sulphuric acid is given by $\epsilon = \epsilon_o + (RT/2F) \log [UO_2{}^{\cdot\cdot}][H^{\cdot}]^4/[U^{\cdot\cdot\cdot\cdot}]$, where ϵ_o is 0·419 volt more positive than the normal calomel electrode, or 0·696 volt more positive than the normal hydrogen electrode—*vide supra*, uranous sulphate. The **magnetic susceptibility** of this oxide, $7·51 \times 10^{-6}$, is greater than that of the metal or of any of the higher oxides.   S. Freed and C. Kasper studied the subject.

According to J. L. C. Zimmermann, the dioxide, unlike uranium trioxide, has strongly basic properties, readily forming uranous salts with acidic radicles. O. Schmidt studied the adsorption of **argon.**   Some of the modes of preparation show that it is not reduced when heated in **hydrogen.**   F. W. O. de Coninck found that when the red forms are heated in hydrogen they pass into the black variety with the loss of only a trace of oxygen.   C. F. Rammelsberg said that when prepared by the hydrogen reduction process, the dioxide is contaminated with occluded hydrogen.   H. von Wartenberg and co-workers found that uranium dioxide cannot be reduced by hydrogen at a press. of about 5 atm. and up to 2500°. E. M. Péligot found that when uranium dioxide is prepared at a low temp. it oxidizes very easily with incandescence when heated in **air,** and that it is pyrophoric, forming the green tritaoctoxide—this was shown by the analyses of J. A. Arfvedson, J. J. Berzelius, R. F. Marchand, E. M. Péligot, J. J. Ebelmen, and E. F. Smith and J. M. Matthews.   The varieties prepared at higher temp. do not oxidize so readily. The powdered variety may glow when heated to a high enough temp. and swell up as the tritaoctoxide is formed.   This glowing was observed by C. F. Bucholz, J. A. Arfvedson, L. R. Lecanu, and E. D. Clarke ; P. Sabatier and J. B. Senderens observed that with a sample they prepared, the oxidation was effected without glowing ; and J. Aloy found that a sample prepared at a high temp. was oxidized at a red-heat rather slowly.   P. Jolibois and R. Bossuet said that the oxidation of the dioxide in **oxygen** proceeds very rapidly, the action commencing at about 185°. E. D. Clarke found that the oxide burns vigorously with sparking when it is heated in the oxyhydrogen blowpipe flame.   H. V. Regnault found that when the oxide is heated to redness in **water** vapour, the tritaoctoxide and hydrogen are formed. According to F. W. O. de Coninck, an 11 vol. soln. of **hydrogen dioxide** slowly converts the dioxide into the monohydrate, which then oxidizes to the trioxide.

E. M. Péligot found that at a red-heat **chlorine** converts the dioxide into uranyl chloride, and that when mixed with carbon, chlorine converts it into uranium tetrachloride—H. E. Roscoe said the pentachloride ; H. Hermann found that a mixture of the dioxide and carbon heated in **bromine** vapour furnishes uranium tetrabromide.   E. M. Péligot found that **hydrogen chloride** does not attack the red-hot dioxide ; and the dioxide does not dissolve in boiling dil. **hydrochloric acid ;** but J. Aloy found that a little dioxide is dissolved.   A. Colani said that dissolution continues slowly and continuously over a long period of time at a rate varying with the mode of preparation of the oxide ; and A. Raynaud, that it requires 3100 grms. of hydrochloric acid of sp. gr. 1·17 to dissolve a gram of the oxide at 17°, and 4650 grms. of **hydrobromic acid** of sp. gr. 1·52 to dissolve the same amount of dioxide.   The solubility is a little greater in the boiling acids. L. R. Lecanu observed very little action when the dioxide is heated to redness with **sulphur,** and J. J. Ebelmen said there is no reaction.   J. A. Arfvedson found that **hydrogen sulphide** produces no change at a red-heat.   F. Bourion found that **sulphur monochloride** converts the dioxide at 230° to 250° into uranium tetrachloride.   E. M. Péligot said that boiling dil. **sulphuric acid** has no action on the dioxide, but it dissolves in the conc. acid—O. F. von der Pfordten, H. Rose, and J. J. Ebelmen found that a green soln. of uranous and uranyl sulphates is formed. A. Raynaud found that it requires 2200 grms. of sulphuric acid of sp. gr. 1·79 to dissolve a gram of the dioxide at 17°.   The solubility is greater in the boiling acid.

A. Colani added that while only a small amount goes into soln., a considerable amount is converted into insoluble sulphate. O. Schmidt studied the adsorption of **nitrogen,** and of **ammonia.** G. Gore found that the dioxide is slightly attacked by liquid ammonia, and H. Rose, that it is insoluble in a soln. of **ammonium chloride.** According to P. Sabatier and J. B. Senderens, **nitrous oxide** at 450° has no action, but at 500° oxidation occurs; **nitric oxide** at 500° acts vigorously; and **nitrogen peroxide** at 500° forms a basic nitrate. F. W. O. de Coninck found that dil. **nitric acid** hydrates the dioxide in the cold, and when warmed the dioxide is dissolved, forming, according to A. Raynaud, uranyl nitrate. It is also soluble in **aqua regia.** A. Raynaud added that the solubility in nitric acid and in aqua regia increases slowly and regularly between 0° and 20°, more rapidly between 20° and 50°, and shows very little change from 50° to 100°. The solubility of the dioxide in acids, in a given time, varies greatly with the previous thermal history of the dioxide. H. C. Greenwood found that when the dioxide is heated with **carbon** in vacuo, a reaction begins at 1490°, and carbon monoxide is formed; E. Tiede and E. Birnbräuer gave 1600°. O. Heusler found that the equilibrium between uranium dioxide and carbon can be represented by log $p = 12 \cdot 09 - 19100T^{-1}$ between 1480° and 1801°. The heat consumed by the evolution of a mol of carbon monoxide is 87·3 Cals. O. Schmidt studied the adsorption of **carbon monoxide, carbon dioxide, methane, ethane, and ethylene.** A. Michael and A. Murphy observed that when the dioxide is heated at 250° with **carbon tetrachloride** in a sealed tube a little uranium tetrachloride is formed; and H. Hermann showed that at a red-heat **carbon disulphide** forms $UO_2.2US_2$, but a mixture of carbon dioxide and disulphide vapour has no action. P. Sabatier and A. Mailhe found that **formic acid,** in contact with heated uranium dioxide, is catalytically transformed into carbon dioxide and water. A. Raynaud found that it requires over 12,000 grms. of **acetic acid** to dissolve a gram of the dioxide at 17°. The solubility is rather greater in boiling acid.

P. Plantamour found that **potassium** at the temp. of vaporization does not react with the dioxide. According to E. F. Smith and O. L. Shinn, and J. J. Ebelmen, uranium dioxide resembles molybdenum dioxide in reducing ammoniacal soln. of **silver salts :** $UO_2 + 2Ag + 2OH' = UO_3 + 2Ag + H_2O$. F. Isambert also found that hydrated uranium dioxide acts on a neutral soln. of silver nitrate, first precipitating silver oxide : $4AgNO_3 + UO_2 = 2Ag_2O + U(NO_3)_4$; and the green soln. soon turns yellow as the oxide is reduced to silver with the formation of a yellow uranyl salt : $U(NO_3)_4 + 2Ag_2O = UO_2(NO_3)_2 + 2AgNO_3 + 2Ag$.

R. Salvadori found that when a soln. of hydrazine hydrate and uranyl nitrate is boiled for 20 minutes, a green precipitate of **hydrazine uranite,** $(N_2H_5)_2O.7UO_2$. $6H_2O$, is formed. H. Debray fused cupric uranyl phosphate with sodium carbonate, and washed out the sodium phosphate from the cold product; there remained crystals of **copper tetrauranite,** CuU_4O_7, resembling aventurine. K. A. Hofmann and K. Höschele obtained a deep blue substance approximating **cerium uranite,** $UO_2.2CeO_2$, in cubic crystals by heating a mixture of 5 parts of cerous sulphate and 2 parts of uranyl sulphate with an excess of magnesium chloride in a covered crucible for about 15 hrs. The blue *dihydrate* was obtained by adding ammonia or dil. alkali-lye to a mixed soln. of 30 grms. of uranyl nitrate and 45 grms. of cerous nitrate.

REFERENCES.

[1] F. W. O. de Coninck and M. Camo, *Bull. Acad. Belg.*, 321, 1901; A. Guyard, *Bull. Soc. Chim.*, (2), **1.** 89, 1863; J. L. C. Zimmermann, *Liebig's Ann.*, **216.** 12, 1883; O. Follenius, *Zeit. anal. Chem.*, **11.** 179, 1872; A. Belohoubek, *ib.*, **16.** 104, 1877; H. Hermann, *Ueber einige Uranverbindungen*, Göttingen, 1861; E. M. Péligot, *Ann. Chim. Phys.*, (3), **5.** 20, 1842; A. Rosenheim and H. Löbel, *Zeit. anorg. Chem.*, **57.** 234, 1908; H. Löbel, *Ueber Halogenverbindungen des Urans*, Berlin, 1907; C. Wagner and W. Schottey, *Zeit. phys. Chem.*, **11.** B, 163, 1930.

[2] M. H. Klaproth, *Mém. Acad. Berlin*, 273, 1789; 160, 1792; *Beiträge zur chemischen Kenntnis der Mineralkörper*, Berlin, **2.** 197, 1797; London, 477, 1801; *Crell's Ann.*, ii, 387, 1789; *Schriften Ges. Berlin*, 273, 1789; J. B. Richter, *Ueber die neueren Gegenstände der Chymie,*

Breslau, **1**. 1, 1791 ; **9**. 36, 1798 ; *Gehlen's Journ.*, **4**. 402, 1805 ; H. E. Roscoe, *Journ. Chem. Soc.*, **27**. 933, 1874 ; *Ber.*, **7**. 1131, 1874 ; C. F. Bucholz, *Gehlen's Journ.*, **4**. 17, 134, 1805 ; *Beiträge zur Erweiterung und Berichtigung der Chemie*, Erfurt, **1**. 62, 1799 ; J. A. Arfvedson, *Svenska Akad. Handl.*, 404, 1822 ; *Ann. Phil.*, **7**. 253, 1824 ; *Pogg. Ann.*, **1**. 245, 1824 ; *Schweigger's Journ.*, **44**. 8, 1825 ; J. J. Berzelius, *ib.*, **44**. 191, 1825 ; *Pogg. Ann.*, **1**. 359, 1824 ; *Svenska Akad. Handl.*, 152, 1823 ; *Ann. Phil.*, **9**. 2d6, 1825 ; A. Schönberg, *De conjunctione chemica ejusque rationibus*, Upsaliæ, 18, 1813 ; *Schweigger's Journ.*, **15**. 285, 1815 ; E. M. Péligot, *Compt. Rend.*, **12**. 735, 1841 ; **22**. 487, 1846 ; **42**. 73, 1856 ; *Ann. Chim. Phys.*, (3), **5**. 5, 1842 ; (3), **20**. 329, 1847 ; *Journ. Pharm. Chim.*, (2), **27**. 522, 1841 ; *Liebig's Ann.*, **41**. 1841 ; **43**. 258, 1842 ; *Journ. prakt. Chem.*, (1), **24**. 442, 1841 ; (1), **38**. 112, 1846 ; H. Hermann, *Ueber einige Uranverbindungen*, Göttingen, 1861 ; H. Rose, *Ansführliches Handbuch der analytischen Chemie*, Braunschweig, **2**. 523, 1851 ; J. Aloy, *Recherches sur l'uranium et ses composés*, Toulouse, 1901 ; *Ann. Chim. Phys.*, (7), **24**. 412, 1901 ; *Bull. Soc. Chim.*, (3), **23**. 368, 1900 ; (3), **25**. 153, 344, 1901 ; P. Sabatier and J. B. Senderens, *ib.*, (3), **13**. 870, 1895 ; *Compt. Rend.*, **114**. 1431, 1892 ; **120**. 618, 1895 ; *Ann. Chim. Phys.*, (7), **7**. 348, 1896 ; A. Ditte, *ib.*, (6), **1**. 342, 1884 ; *Compt. Rend.*, **91**. 117, 1880 ; P. Sabatier and A. Mailhe, *ib.*, **152**. 1212, 1911 ; F. Isambert, *ib.*, **80**. 1087, 1875 ; P. Lebeau, *ib.*, **155**. 163, 1912 ; H. Debray, *ib.*, **52**. 44, 1861 ; *Ann. Chim. Phys.*, (3), **61**. 451, 1860 ; F. W. O. de Coninck, *ib.*, **135**. 900, 1902 ; **152**. 711, 1179, 1911 ; **155**. 1511, 1912 ; *Bull. Acad. Belg.*, 448, 1904 ; 1041, 1907 ; 163, 993, 1908 ; 744, 1909 ; *La chimie de l'uranium*, Paris, 1911 ; *Ann. Chim. Phys.*, (7), **28**. 5, 1903 ; (8), **3**. 500, 1904 ; F. W. O. de Coninck and M. Camo, *Bull. Acad. Belg.*, 321, 1901 ; F. W. O. de Coninck and A. Raynaud, *Bull. Soc. Chim.*, (4), **11**. 1037, 1912 ; A. Raynaud, *ib.*, (4), **11**. 802, 1912 ; *Compt. Rend.*, **154**. 1480, 1912 ; P. Jolibois and R. Bossuet, *ib.*, **174**. 386, 1922 ; E. D. Clarke, *The Gas Blowpipe*, London, 76, 1819 ; W. F. Hillebrand, *Bull. U.S. Geol. Sur.*, 60, 1888 ; 78, 1889 ; 90, 1892 ; 113, 1893 ; *Amer. Journ. Science*, (3), **36**. 295, 1888 ; (3), **40**. 384, 1890 ; (3), **42**. 390, 1891 ; *Chem. News*, **64**. 221, 230, 244, 255, 279, 290, 303, 1891 ; *Zeit. anorg. Chem.*, **3**. 243, 1893 ; E. F. Smith and O. L. Shinn, *ib.*, **7**. 47, 1894 ; *Journ. Amer. Chem. Soc.*, **16**. 569, 1894 ; E. F. Smith and J. M. Matthews, *ib.*, **17**. 687, 1895 ; G. Gore, *Proc. Roy. Soc.*, **20**. 441, 1872 ; **21**. 140, 1873 ; A. Colani, *Compt. Rend.*, **137**. 382, 1903 ; **155**. 1249, 1912 ; *Recherches sur les composés uraneux*, Paris, 1907 ; *Ann. Chim. Phys.*, (8), **12**. 59, 1907 ; H. V. Regnault, *ib.*, (3), **1**. 129, 1841 ; (2), **62**. 358, 1836 ; J. J. Ebelmen, *ib.*, (3), **5**. 189, 1842 ; F. Bourion, *ib.*, (8), **21**. 58, 1910 ; J. Vrede, *Phys. Zeit.*, **31**. 323, 1930 ; M. K. Slattery, *Journ. Amer. Opt. Soc.*, **19**. 175, 1929 ; P. Plantamour, *Journ. prakt. Chem.*, (1), **23**. 230, 1841 ; R. F. Marchand, *ib.*, (1), **23**. 497, 1841 ; I. Wertheim, *ib.*, (1), **29**. 211, 1843 ; *Ann. Chim. Phys.*, (3), **11**. 49, 1844 ; *Ber. Vers. deut. Naturf.*, 313, 1843 ; F. Wöhler, *Liebig's Ann.*, **41**. 345, 1842 ; O. F. von der Pfordten, *ib.*, **222**. 142, 1883 ; J. L. C. Zimmermann, *ib.*, 213, 1, 1882 ; **216**. 14, 1883 ; **232**. 273, 1886 ; *Ber.*, **13**. 348, 1882 ; **15**. 847, 1182, 1882 ; **17**. 2739, 1884 ; O. Ruff and O. Goecke, *Zeit. angew. Chem.*, **24**. 1459, 1911 ; O. Ruff, *Ber.*, **34**. 3509, 1901 ; K. A. Hofmann and K. Höschele, *ib.*, **48**. 20, 1915 ; E. Wedekind and C. Horst, *ib.*, **48**. 105, 1915 ; C. A. Pierlé, *Journ. Phys. Chem.*, **23**. 517, 1919 ; A. Michael and A. Murphy, *Amer. Chem. Journ.*, **44**. 365, 1910 ; L. Pauling, *Journ. Amer. Chem. Soc.*, **49**. 765, 1927 ; S. Freed and C. Kasper, *ib.*, **52**. 4671, 1930 ; H. C. Greenwood, *Journ. Chem. Soc.*, **93**. 1483, 1908 ; C. F. Rammelsberg, *Sitzber. Akad. Berlin*, 100, 1885 ; *Pogg. Ann.*, **59**. 5, 1843 ; A. Samsonoff, *Zeit. Koll.*, **8**. 96, 1911 ; O. Schmidt, *Zeit. phys. Chem.*, **133**. 263, 1928 ; L. R. Lecanu, *Journ. Pharm. Chim.*, (2), **11**. 279, 1825 ; L. R. Lecanu and M. Serbat, *ib.*, (2), **9**. 141, 1823 ; *Quart. Journ. Science*, **17**. 139, 1824 ; A. Laugier, *Journ. Pharm. Chim.*, (2), **9**. 145, 1823 ; C. L. Parsons, *Journ. Ind. Eng. Chem.*, **9**. 466, 1917 ; V. M. Goldschmidt and L. Thomassen, *Videnskapsselskapets Skrifter*, 5, 1923 ; W. G. Mixter, *Amer. Journ. Science*, (4), **34**. 141, 1912 ; *Zeit. anorg. Chem.*, **78**. 221, 1912 ; A. Schoep, *Bull. Soc. Chim. Belg.*, **32**. 274, 345, 1923 ; **33**. 87, 1923 ; **49**. 188, 1927 ; *Compt. Rend.*, **173**. 1186, 1921 ; **174**. 1066, 1922 ; *Natuurwet. Tijds.*, **9**. 1, 1927 ; R. Luther and A. C. Michie, *Zeit. Elektrochem.*, **14**. 826, 1908 ; H. von Wartenberg, J. Broy and R. Reinicke, *ib.*, **29**. 214, 1923 ; W. Biltz and H. Müller, *Zeit. anorg. Chem.*, **163**. 257, 1927 ; W. Biltz, *ib.*, **193**. 321, 1930 ; O. Heusler, *ib.*, **154**. 353, 1926 ; E. Friederich and L. Sittig, *ib.*, **145**. 127, 1925 ; E. Friederich, *Zeit. Physik*, **31**. 813, 1925 ; E. Tiede and E. Birnbräuer, *ib.*, **87**. 129, 1914 ; J. O. Perrine, *Phys. Rev.*, (2), **22**. 48, 1922 ; R. Salvadori, *Atti Accad. Lincei*, (5), **21**. ii, 455, 1912 ; A. E. van Arkel, *Physica*, **4**. 286, 1924 ; E. J. Cuy, *Journ. Amer. Chem. Soc.*, **49**. 201, 1927 ; M. le Blanc and H. Sachse, *Ber. Sächs. Akad.*, **82**. 153, 1930.

§ 10. Uranium Oxides between the Dioxide and Trioxide

According to E. M. Péligot,[1] by calcining uranium tritaoctoxide, or uranyl nitrate, and rapidly cooling the product, **uranium hemipentoxide,** or simply pentoxide, U_2O_5, is formed. F. Wöhler, and B. Drenckmann obtained it by rapidly heating uranium dioxide in air, and rapidly cooling the product ; F. Janda, by heating ammonium diuranate in a graphite crucible ; F. W. O. de Coninck, by rapidly heating uranyl sulphate to redness ; and F. W. O. de Coninck and M. Camo, by the electrolysis of a soln. of uranyl nitrate—*vide supra*. A. Colani obtained it as a by-product in preparing uranium tetrachloride. It is sometimes represented as U_4O_5, but this formula is based on the halved at. wt. C. F. Rammelsberg represented it by $UO_2(UO_2)O$, but A. Remelé, and C. F. Rammelsberg regarded its individuality as doubtful. J. J. Ebelmen, A. Colani, and J. L. C. Zimmermann regarded it as a mixture of the dioxide and the tritaoctoxide. C. Stähling found that the green oxide of uranium hydrates slowly on exposure to air, but not so with the black oxide formed by calcination; and he suggests that the black oxide is uranium hemipentoxide. The hydration explains how the radioactivity of the green oxide but not of the black oxide changes in air. P. Lebeau, and P. Jolibois and R. Bossuet consider that the black oxide is U_3O_8, and that there is no evidence of the formation of an intermediate oxide. A. Colani observed no evidence of its formation in his study of the dissociation press. of uranium tritaoctoxide, $U_3O_8 \rightleftharpoons 3UO_2 + O_2$; but R. Schwarz obtained indications of its existence; and he added that by igniting the higher oxide in a stream of carbon dioxide in an electric furnace at 1122°, a black residue was obtained corresponding approximately in composition with the formula U_2O_5; traces of nitride were produced when nitrogen was employed. The contrary results of J. L. C. Zimmermann were vitiated by his use of a platinum crucible over a gas flame, which permitted reduction. Uranium hemipentoxide is described as a black powder which is stable in air. E. M. Péligot, and F. W. O. de Coninck and M. Camo found that it is transformed into the dioxide when heated in hydrogen; it dissolves in acids to form a mixed soln. of uranous and uranyl salts. A. Colani added that acetic acid extracts uranium trioxide, and leaves the dioxide; and the slow evaporation of the soln. in sulphuric acid gives uranyl sulphate.

The calcination of powdered uranium furnishes **uranium tritaoctoxide,** U_3O_8, a compound analyzed by J. J. Berzelius,[2] J. A. Arfvedson, R. F. Marchand, J. J. Ebelmen, E. M. Péligot, etc. C. F. Rammelsberg represented it by the formula $UO_2.2(UO_2)O$; or **uranosic oxide,** $UO_2.2UO_3$. It can be regarded as **uranyl uranate,** $(UO_2)_2UO_4$; or, according to the suggestion of J. L. C. Zimmermann, favoured by P. Groth, as **uranous uranate,** $U(UO_4)_2$, since it contains both quadrivalent and sexavalent uranium atoms:

$$\begin{matrix} O \\ O \end{matrix} \hspace{-4pt} \searrow\hspace{-6pt}\nearrow U \hspace{-4pt}\begin{matrix} \searrow O \searrow \\ \nearrow O \nearrow \end{matrix} U \begin{matrix} \searrow O \searrow \\ \nearrow O \nearrow \end{matrix} U \hspace{-4pt}\begin{matrix} \diagdown O \\ \diagup O \end{matrix}$$

The chemical properties are more in accord with the assumption that it is uranosic oxide, $UO_2.2UO_3$, rather than that it is either uranyl uranate, $(UO_2)_2UO_4$, or uranous uranate, $U(UO_4)_2$. The early workers found that this oxide is produced when any of the uranium oxides or hydrated oxides, or any of the uranium salts with a volatile base or acid, is calcined at a red-heat in air—*e.g.* uranyl nitrate, ammonium uranyl carbonate, ammonium uranate, etc. H. Moissan recommended uranyl nitrate; and W. F. O. de Coninck, uranyl sulphate. A. Colani recommended a temp. exceeding 900°; H. N. MacCoy and G. C. Ashman, 700°—*vide infra* for the conditions of stability. P. Jolibois and R. Bossuet found that the uranium trioxide passes into uranosic oxide at 502°, and that the action is irreversible; the only product obtained when the dioxide is heated in oxygen is uranosic oxide. The dissociation press. of uranosic oxide at 900° is approximately the same as the partial press. of the oxygen in air, and E. Friederich and L. Sittig added that it is not advisable to heat the oxide over 1100°, in accord with R. Schwarz's recommendation, but by slowly cooling the oxide in air, any dissociated uranosic oxide may take up oxygen. They therefore recommended preparing uranosic oxide by heating one of the other oxides in oxygen at 900°–1000°. Brown uranium dioxide prepared below 600° began to assume the dark green colour of mixtures of U_3O_8 and UO_2 when warmed to 600°, and it ultimately passes into the green oxide. If kept from the flame gases, uranosic oxide can be prepared below 800°. It is then coloured moss-green; whereas if prepared over 800° the colour is nearly black— *vide infra,* uranium trioxide. H. V. Regnault obtained uranosic oxide by passing steam over the red-hot dioxide. The extraction of the oxide from pitchblende has been previously discussed. The commercial oxide is impure. E. Donath recommended preparing the oxide by reducing uranyl acetate to uranium dioxide by heating it in hydrogen, treating the product with nitric acid, and calcining the resulting nitrate ; and F. Giolitti and G. Tavanti, by adding 300 c.c. of conc. ammonia to a soln. of 100 grms. of sodium uranyl acetate in 4 litres of water and 50 c.c. of hydrochloric acid, washing the precipitate ten times with a 2 per cent. soln. of ammonium chloride, and then dissolving it in hydrochloric acid. The precipitation with ammonia and the washing are repeated twice, and the product is finally calcined. J. L. C. Zimmermann recommended the following process :

The commercial oxide is dissolved in hydrochloric acid, sat. with hydrogen sulphide, and allowed to stand for a long time. The filtrate from arsenic sulphide, etc., is treated with an excess of ammonia and ammonium carbonate, and ammonium sulphide added to the warm soln. The filtrate is mixed with an excess of hydrochloric acid, and boiled to drive out the dissolved carbon dioxide, and the uranium precipitated as uranyl sulphide by the addition of ammonia and ammonium sulphide. The soln. is warmed on a water-bath to decompose the ammonium sulphide ; and the mixture of uranium sulphide and sulphur is well washed with water, and heated over a blast-burner. The resulting uranosic oxide is dissolved in nitric acid, and uranyl nitrate is crystallized from the filtrate. This salt is dissolved in ether, and the filtrate evaporated to dryness on the water-bath, and calcined. The treatment on the resulting uranosic oxide can be repeated once more.

A. N. Pilkoff discussed the subject ; and E. Wilke-Dörfurt made the following observations on the preparation of the tritaoctoxide, from cleveite residues used for the extraction of helium. A soln. of the nitrate which had been purified from the rare earth metals and thorium by oxalic acid, and from extraneous heavy metals by hydrogen and ammonium sulphides, yields an oxide, which is not free from alkali. The presence of the latter is attributed to co-precipitation of uranate, and not to adsorption, and can therefore be avoided by the reduction of the uranium. By suitable regulation of the action of ammonium sulphide, it is possible to precipitate uranous instead of uranyl sulphide, and this substance does not show any tendency to retain alkali ; the latter, if absorbed, can be removed by double precipitation, and avoided by working with smaller quantities. The sulphide is readily converted into uranous chloride, which is transformed through the hydroxide into the nitrate ; the latter is oxidized by nitric acid to uranyl nitrate, which is purified by being crystallized from water, and then converted into the oxide, U_3O_8, in which the presence of traces of alkali cannot be detected spectroscopically. The frequently-recommended crystallization of uranyl nitrate from ether is not desirable, since, on the one hand, the product so obtained is not free from alkali, and, on the other, the explosive tendency of the ethereal soln. renders it unsuitable for working with very valuable material. C. L. Parsons obtained the oxide on a large scale.

J. J. Berzelius, and J. A. Arfvedson added ammonia to soln. of uranosic oxide in acids, and obtained a precipitate ranging in colour from dark green to purple-brown. The soln. behaves like a mixture of uranous and uranyl salts ; the precipitate, in the absence of definite proof, has been regarded as **hydrated uranosic oxide.** C. F. Rammelsberg treated uranium tetrachloride with ammonia, and obtained a precipitate which takes up oxygen, forming, as he thought, the *hexahydrate,* $U_3O_8.6H_2O$, when dried in vacuo over conc. sulphuric acid. According to J. J. Ebelmen, violet-brown flakes are obtained when a soln. of uranyl oxalate is exposed to sunlight—*vide supra.* J. Aloy obtained a similar product with a 90 per cent. alcoholic soln. of uranyl acetate or an aq soln. of uranyl acetate mixed with ether ; J. Zehenter obtained a similar product by the action of light on uranyl acetate without the presence of alcohol or ether. J. Aloy and co-workers observed that a soln. of any uranyl salt in the presence of a readily oxidizable organic substance—*e.g.* alcohol, ether, or glucose—when exposed to light or ultra-violet rays yields a violet precipitate containing some of the acid present in the original salt. This acid can be removed by washing with boiling water. The precipitate was considered to be the *dihydrate,* $U_3O_8.2H_2O$. J. Aloy and E. Rodier represented the violet product of the action of light on uranium salts by $UO_2(OH).O.U(OH)_2.$ $O.UO_2(OH)$. A similar product is obtained, without the action of light, whenever uranous and uranic salts are present in neutral or feebly acid soln. at the requisite temp. The evidence of the chemical individuality of these hydrates is not decisive.

Uranosic oxide usually appears as a dark green powder—hence it is sometimes called *green oxide of uranium*. According to A. Remelé, the **colour** depends on its mode of preparation, ranging from black through dark olive-green to green—*vide infra*, uranium trioxide; but, in any case, J. L. C. Zimmermann found that the streak on biscuit porcelain is always green. A. Staehling thought that the black and green oxides are allotropic forms of uranosic oxide—*vide infra*. P. Lebeau found that both have the same ultimate composition, and that the black oxides are stable in air and can be heated at 1000° under atm. press. without decomposition; whilst the green oxides, prepared at temp. below 800°, contain varying amounts of uranium trioxide and can undergo change when exposed to moist air, the uranium trioxide present undergoing hydration. V. M. Goldschmidt and L. Thomassen, and W. Biltz and H. Müller found that the crystal structure deduced from the X-radiogram of uranosic oxide is irregular—*vide infra*, pitchblende. C. J. B. Karsten gave 7·31 for the **specific gravity,** and J. J. Ehelmen, 7·31. W. F. Hillebrand gave for the sp. gr. at 19·1° to 30·3°/4°, and the **molecular volumes** of the oxides UO_n:

n	2·417	2·201	2·051	2·022	2·005
Sp. gr.	10·15	10·98	10·83	10·82	10·95
Mol. vol.	27·28	24·90	25·02	25·01	24·69

The results of W. Biltz and H. Müller are indicated below in connection with uranium trioxide; and similarly also with the **volatilization** of uranosic oxide. M. L. Phillips studied the radiation of light from uranium oxide. E. Donath obtained 0·07979 for the **specific heat** near ordinary temp.; and A. S. Russell 0·0616 between 0° and −77°, and 0·0428 between −77° and −190°; or 0·0429 at −134°, 0·0616 at −39°, and 0·0710 at 22°, with the corresponding values for the **molecular heat** 36·15, 51·96, and 59·85 respectively. E. M. Péligot observed a loss of 0·7 to 1·0 per cent. of oxygen when uranosic oxide is vigorously calcined, and it passes into the pentoxide; but C. F. Rammelsberg found that it is stable at temp. high enough to enable uranium to be quantitatively determined in this form. P. Jolibois and R. Bossuet found that with 3 hrs.' heating in vacuo, at 1000°, uranosic oxide only lost a very small fraction of its oxygen. J. L. C. Zimmermann said that uranosic oxide is stable at a red-heat only in oxygen gas; a little oxide is lost if it be heated in air to redness and rapidly cooled; and W. F. Hillebrand showed that if it is heated under molten borax, uranium dioxide is formed. J. L. C. Zimmermann observed that the reaction $U_3O_8 \rightleftharpoons 3UO_2 + O_2$ is reversible, and that equilibrium is very slowly attained. A. Colani found that the **dissociation pressure** p mm. is:

	625°	745°	850°	940°	990°	1055°	1125°	1165°
p	15	29	108	157	208	248	281	315

and by extrapolation, $p = 760$ mm. between 1400° and 1500°. This shows how the higher oxide passes into the dioxide when heated in an inert gas, or in the presence of fused borax. C. Zengelis observed a discoloration on silver suspended over a layer of the oxide in a closed vessel, indicating a slight vaporization at ordinary temp. P. Jolibois and R. Bossuet found that uranous oxide lost only a very small fraction of oxygen when heated for 3 hrs. at 1000° in vacuo; and to convert the tritaoctoxide completely into the dioxide required a temp. of 2000° in vacuo. W. Biltz and H. Müller represented the effect of heat at different temp. and press. on uranosic oxide by curves resembling Fig. 5. Uranium trioxide (*q.v.*) is not formed. Observations were also made by G. F. Hüttig, and C. Wagner and W. Schottky. C. Staehling discussed the radioactivity of the uranium oxides—**4.** 26, 11; and A. L. Helfgott, the radiation. W. G. Mixter gave for the **heat of formation**

$3U+4O_2=U_3O_8+845\cdot2$ Cals. ; and for the heat of formation from uranium dioxide 78 Cals.—W. Biltz and H. Müller calculated 117 Cals. from the equilibrium constant of the reaction : $U_3O_8+2H_2=2H_2O+3UO_2$. C. Staehling observed that the freshly-calcined oxides lost from 1 to 30·7 per cent. of their radioactivity when kept for about five years, and half the activity was lost during the first six months. The loss was greatest with the green oxide and least with the black oxide. If the oxide be converted into nitrate, and calcined for uranosic oxide the original activity is restored, but it immediately commences to diminish as before. The activity can be restored by simple calcination. During the process of restoration, the oxide undergoes loss in weight, due, for the most part, to the removal of moisture. The black oxide which shows little loss in activity also shows little loss in weight or alteration in activity on calcination. The green oxide on exposure to the air in thin layers undergoes hydration as well as a loss in activity, the hydration presumably diminishing the superficial density of the uranium atoms. The black oxides obtained by calcination at high temp. do not hydrate and show little or no decrease in radioactivity. These are supposed to show that the black oxide is probably an allotropic modification of the green oxide. A. Dorabialska, and

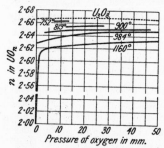

E. Wiegand studied the radiation of heat from the oxide. J. O. Perrine observed no **fluorescence** with ultra-violet light ; M. L. Phillips, the radiation from the oxide ; and E. L. Nichols and D. T. Wilber, no flame phosphorescence. W. P. Jorissen and W. E. Ringer found that 100 mgrms. of uranosic oxide, after an hour's exposure to **cathode rays** and cooling, weighed 71·2 mgrms. The radioactivity was also increased about 30 per cent. H. N. MacCoy and G. C. Ashman recommended thin films of uranosic oxide as a standard for α-ray activity. The radioactivity was studied by W. P. Widdowson and A. S. Russell, B. B. Boltwood, etc.—*vide* **4**. 26, 2. F. Behounek

FIG. 5.—Action of Heat on Uranosic Oxide.

observed no increase in the **radioactivity** of uranosic oxide by exposure to sunlight. The subject was studied by S. Maracineanu. D. K. Goralevitsch recommended U_3O_8 as a standard for radioactivity. The subject was studied by A. B. Verigo. G. Kirsch and H. Pettersson studied the reflection of α-particles. J. Vrede studied uranosic oxide as a detector of electromagnetic waves. According to F. Streintz, the **electrical conductivity** of the compressed powder is negligibly small. E. Friederich and L. Sittig compressed the powder into rods, heated them in oxygen at 1000°, and found the sp. resistance to be 42×10^6 to 45×10^6 ohms per sq. mm. at ordinary temp., and about one-tenth this value at 300°. M. le Blanc and H. Sachse gave for the sp. conductivity, K :

	20°	50°	100°	150°	200°	300°	400°	500°
K	10^{-7}	$2\cdot5\times10^{-7}$	$9\cdot0\times10^{-7}$	$3\cdot0\times10^{-6}$	$1\cdot5\times10^{-5}$	$1\cdot3\times10^{-4}$	$7\cdot0\times10^{-4}$	$2\cdot4\times10^{-3}$

C. A. Pierlé found that the **electrode potential** of uranosic oxide, against a soln. of 14·3 grms. of uranyl nitrate per litre, is 0·776 volt, the same as that of uranous oxide. L. Andrieux found that the electrolysis of a soln. of uranosic oxide in fused magnesium, calcium, or lithium pyroborate and fluoride yields uranium boride, UB^4. Uranosic oxide is paramagnetic ; and K. Honda gave for the **magnetic susceptibility** $4\cdot34\times10^{-6}$, while E. Wedekind and C. Horst gave $0\cdot95\times10^{-6}$.

J. A. Arfvedson, and P. Jolibois and R. Bossuet said that the only product obtained by heating uranosic oxide in **hydrogen** is uranium dioxide ; and P. Jolibois and R. Bossuet found that the action commences at 625°, and the reduction can be completed at 650°. W. Biltz and H. Müller represented the equilibrium condition $K=p_{H_2O}/p_{H_2}$, in the reaction : $U_3O_8+2H_2\rightleftharpoons2H_2O+3UO_2$, by 14·5 at 545°. E. Newbery and J. N. Pring observed that at about 2000°, in contact with hydrogen at 150 atm. press., uranium tritaoctoxide is reduced to the dioxide. According to P. Jolibois and R. Bossuet, uranosic oxide is not oxidized to the trioxide when heated in **oxygen,** so that the reaction $6UO_3 = 2U_3O_8 + O_2$ which occurs at 502° is not reversible—*vide infra,* uranium trioxide. Uranosic oxide is insoluble in **water.** J. A. Arfvedson stated that uranosic oxide which has been heated to redness dissolves very slowly and sparingly in dil. **hydrochloric acid,** and H. Rose added that when it is digested with hydrochloric acid, uranium trioxide is mainly extracted. G. J. Fowler and J. Grant found that when uranosic oxide is heated with **potassium chlorate,** oxygen comes off at 390°, chlorine is also evolved, and potassium uranate is formed. J. J. Ebelmen said that **sulphur** at a red-heat reduces uranosic oxide to uranium dioxide. F. Bourion found that **sulphur mono-chloride** and uranosic oxide in a sealed tube at 230° to 250° form uranium tetra-chloride. J. A. Arfvedson found that the oxide which has been heated to redness dissolves slowly and sparingly in dil. **sulphuric acid,** but it dissolves more readily, and completely in boiling conc. sulphuric acid. F. Isambert observed that uranosic oxide dissolves in nitric acid to form uranyl nitrate. According to O. F. von der Pfordten, uranosic oxide does not exist in acid soln., but rather as a mixture of the uranous and uranyl salts. C. F. Bucholz found that uranosic oxide is reduced to uranium dioxide by **carbon** at a red-heat. R. Schwarz said that when the oxide is heated in a current of **carbon dioxide** at 1120°, it yields the hemipentoxide. H. Hermann found the dioxide is obtained with a mixture of the vapour of **carbon disulphide** and carbon dioxide—and with carbon disulphide alone $UO_2.2US_2$ is formed. A. Michael and A. Murphy found that uranium pentachloride is formed when uranosic oxide is heated for many hrs. with **carbon tetrachloride** in a sealed tube at 250°. H. C. Bolton said that **citric acid** in the presence of potassium nitrate dissolves powdered pitchblende. F. W. O. de Coninck said that the reaction which occurs when uranosic oxide is heated with **calcium oxalate** can be represented : $2CaC_2O_4 + U_3O_8 = 2CaCO_3 + 2CO_2 + 3UO_2$—*vide supra,* uranium dioxide. P. Sabatier and A. Mailhe studied its action as a catalyst in reducing **ethyl alcohol** to ethylene. According to J. L. Gay Lussac and L. J. Thénard, **potassium** or **sodium** at a red-heat reduces uranosic oxide to the dioxide. J. Aloy, and E. K. Rideal obtained a similar product by heating uranosic oxide with **magnesium.** D. Balareff found that **barium oxide** reacts vigorously with uranium tritaoctoxide below 300° with the evolution of much heat. A. Ditte observed that the **alkali fluorides** and **thallous fluoride** form yellow, crystalline plates of a complex salt. F. Isambert found that uranosic oxide very slowly separates silver from a soln. of **silver nitrate.**

C. A. Pierlé found that the black deposit formed when uranium salts are electrolyzed is not $U_3O_8.2H_2O$, as stated by E. F. Smith, but rather a dihydrated *uranium tritadecoxide,* $U_3O_{10}.2H_2O$, and its potential against a soln. of 14 grms. of uranyl nitrate per litre is -0.6872 volt, whereas with uranosic oxide the potential is -0.776 volt. According to J. L. C. Zimmermann, an impure hydrated form of *uranium heptitacosioxide,* U_7O_{20}, or $UO_2.6UO_3$, or $U_3O_8.4UO_3$, is produced by allowing uranyl sulphide to stand under a soln. of ammonium sulphide for a couple of months in the absence of air. The chocolate-brown precipitate is washed with air-free water, dried at 100°, extracted with carbon disulphide to remove the sulphur, and dried at 100°. It contains traces of probably uranyl sulphide, and of an ammonium salt. The black powder is soluble in mineral acids, with the evolution of a small amount of hydrogen sulphide and the formation of a yellowish-green soln. It is not affected by a soln. of ammonium sulphide ; it is partly soluble in a soln. of ammonium carbonate ; it is not affected by alkali-lye ; and potassium permanganate is decolorized by its soln. in sulphuric acid. When heated in a tube, water and a little ammonia are given off, at 270° the colour becomes brick-red, and at a high temp. greenish-black.

Reference was made to **pitchblende,** or **uraninite,** in connection with the history of uranium ; and, in allusion to the radioactive elements which it contains, it has been said that " pitchblende is a perfect museum of chemical rarities." It occurs as a mineral in Bohemia, Saxony, Hungary, Cornwall, Norway, Turkey, United States, Bengal, East Africa, Quebec, etc. It usually occurs massive, botryoidal, granular, or with a columnar or curved lamellar structure. Crystalline forms are rare. It may be coloured black and resemble pitch—hence the name pitchblende—or it may have a grey, green, or brown tinge. The streak is brownish-black, grey, or olive-green. F. von Kobell [3] applied the term *nasturan*—from ναστός, dense—to a compact variety which was virtually free from thoria and the rare earths. Of the crystalline varieties, there are : *uranniobite* of R. Hermann which comes from Norway, occurring in octahedral crystals of sp. gr. 9·0 to 9·7 ; **bröggerite** of C. W. Blomstrand—named after W. C. Brögger—which comes from Anneröd, Norway, where it occurs in octahedral crystals. Analyses of bröggerite were given by W. Riss, G. Tschernik, W. Elsholz, G. Kirsch, W. F. Hillebrand, C. W. Blomstrand, and K. A. Hofmann and W. Heidepriem. The sp. gr. given by the same observers ranges from 5·96 to 11·59—average 8·73. C. W. Blomstrand gave $6U^{IV}R^{II}(U^{VI}O_6)$. $U_3^{IV}(U^{VI}O_6)_2$; and W. E. Hidden, $3RO.UO_3$. The **cleveite** of A. E. Nordenskjöld—named after P. T. Cleve—comes from Arendal, Norway, where it occurs in cubic (dodecahedral and octahedral) crystals of sp. gr. 7·50. It was analyzed by A. E. Nordenskjöld, W. E. Hidden and J. B. Mackintosh, and W. Elsholz. The formula approximates $6RO.2UO_3.3H_2O$. The crystals were described by F. Müllbauer, and A. E. Nordenskjöld ; and occluded gases by M. W. Travers, W. Ramsay, and H. Deslandres. The *nivenite* of W. E. Hidden and J. B. Mackintosh—named after W. Niven—occurs in Llano Co., Texas, in velvety black masses with an indistinct crystallization, of sp. gr. 8·01 and hardness 5·5. Nivenite is more quickly attacked by sulphuric acid than other varieties.

Analyses were reported by the early workers M. H. Klaproth, C. F. Rammelsberg, J. J. Ebelmen, R. Hermann, C. H. Pfaff, A. Becker and P. Jannasch, W. Steinkuhler, C. W. Knight, H. Hirschi, T. L. Walker, F. Hecht and E. Körner, C. von Hauer, J. D. Whitney, F. A. Genth, W. R. Criper, P. Krusch, W. Elsholz, K. Nenadkevich, C. B. Comstock, and T. Scheerer ; and more recent analyses by J. Lorenzen, P. K. Grigoreff, W. E. Hidden and J. B. Mackintosh, C. W. Davis, W. Marckwald, J. Step, A. Schoep, P. Schei, Y. Brière, T. H. Laby, G. Kirsch, G. P. Tschernik, K. A. Hofmann and W. Heidepriem, H. V. Ellsworth, J. S. de Lury and H. V. Ellsworth, R. C. Wells, A. E. Nordenskjöld, F. W. Clarke, and W. F. Hillebrand. The proportion of UO_3 ranges from 14·00 to 59·3 per cent. ; UO_2, 19·89 to 70·99 ; ThO_2, 1·65 to 9·79 ; rare earths—$CeO_2.La_2O_3$, and Y_2O_3—up to 12·67 per cent. ; PbO_2, 3·07 to 11·31 ; CaO, 0·08 to 1·04 ; MgO, up to 0·30 ; ZnO, up to 0·44 ; MnO, up to 0·09 ; Na_2O, up to 0·31 ; H_2O, 0·43 to 4·28 ; Fe_2O_3, 0·09 to 1·26 ; Cb_2O_5, up to 0·96 ; ZrO_2, up to 0·2 ; SiO_2, up to 0·90 ; Al_2O_3, up to 0·20 ; P_2O_5, up to 0·22 ; As_2O_5, up to 2·34 ; Bi_2O_3, up to 0·75 ; SO_3, up to 0·19 ; F, up to 0·04 ; as well as up to 2·63 per cent. of nitrogen (helium). The helium was discussed by W. Ramsay and co-workers, J. N. Lockyer, W. A. Tilden, N. A. Langlet, etc. ; the zirconium and hafnium content, by O. Free ; the thallium contents, by S. Wleugel ; and the polonium and radium contents and the radioactivity, as well as the lead contents, by M. and P. Curie and G. Bémont, A. Debierne, G. F. Barker, R. C. Wells, B. B. Boltwood, T. L. Walker, G. Bardet, O. Mügge, V. M. Goldschmidt, F. Kolbeck and P. Ulrich, G. Kirsch, H. V. Ellsworth, A. Becker and P. Jannasch, C. W. Davis, F. Giesel, O. Behrendsen, etc.—*vide* **4**. 26, 3. The radioactivity and age of the mineral was discussed by A. E. Fersman—*vide* **4**. 26, 3. R. J. Moss discussed the helium content. J. K. Marsh estimated the rare earth content of uraninites.

G. Kirsch suggested that there are two distinct minerals—one an oxide, UO_2, and the other a uranate, U_2O_5 or U_3O_8, which are represented by radioactive transformation pseudomorphs. The cubic oxide is called *ulrichite*—after C. Ulrich —while bröggerite and cleveite are regarded as altered varieties containing thoria or the rare earths. Its sp. gr. is 7·5 and hardness 6. Massive pitchblende is cryptocrystalline and probably rhombic. B. Szilard said that just as thorianite contains 65 to 74 per cent. of thorium and 4 to 11 per cent. of uranium, so uraninite contains 65 to 74 per cent. of uranium, and 4 to 11 per cent. of thorium ; and just as thorium hydroxide dissolves in a soln. of thorium nitrate, so does uranium hydroxide dissolve in a soln. of thorium nitrate ; in the former case, on evaporation, a substance similar in composition to thorianite is obtained, whilst in the latter a yellow substance similar to uraninite is formed. Salts of thorium and uranium dissolve not only the hydroxides named above, but also the hydroxides of the rare earth metals and of nearly all those metals occurring in thorianite and uraninite ; the compounds obtained with yttrium, iron, lead, and zirconium have characteristic properties. All are amorphous. B. Szilard suggested that thorianite and uraninite are formed in nature by processes analogous to that just described. C. W. Blomstrand said that the natural uranates may be taken as a type built up in accord with the formula $3RO.UO_3$, in which the uranium trioxide uniformly appears as an ortho-acid, while the basic portion of the molecule is composed principally of uranous oxide, a portion of which is replaced by lead or some kindred metal. C. W. Blomstrand regarded uraninite as a derivative of sexibasic orthouranic acid, $U(OH)_6$, in which hydrogen is replaced by quadrivalent uranium :

$$U\!\!\underset{O}{\overset{O}{\underset{\diagdown}{\diagup}}}\!\!U\underset{O}{\overset{O}{\diagup}}U\underset{O}{\overset{O}{\diagdown}}U\!\!\underset{O}{\overset{O}{\underset{\diagup}{\diagdown}}}\!\!U$$

True pitchblende or uraninite is considered to be represented best by the formula $7UO_2.PbO.5UO_2$, i.e. $U_7Pb(UO_5)_5$, or by $UPbUO_6.2U_3(UO_6)_3$. There are two forms of the thorouraninites—(i) bröggerite, $UO_2.RO.UO_3$, i.e. $URUO_6$, or $6URUO_6.U_3(UO_6)_2$; and (ii) cleveite, $UO_2.4RO.2UO_3.4H_2O$, or $UR_4(UO_6)_2.4H_2O$. W. F. Hillebrand, however, showed that the generalized or idealized formula, $U_3{}^{IV}(U^{VI}O_6)_2$, or $(UO_2)_3(UO_3)_2$, of C. W. Blomstrand is not of general application. A. Schoep found that the uraninite of Katanga, Belgian Congo, has the formula $(UO_2)_3(UO_3)_2$, and he suggested that originally uraninite was uranium dioxide, and thorianite, thorium dioxide—both minerals being isomorphous and analogous in composition. The trioxide, UO_3, found with uraninite is an oxidation product of the original dioxide, UO_2. The hypothesis was supported by W. Biltz and H. Müller. The irreversibility of the reaction : $U_3O_8+O=3UO_3$ under certain conditions does not invalidate this argument—vide infra, uranium trioxide. The alteration and weathering of uraninite was discussed by A. L. Hacquaert, and H. V. Ellsworth.

The crystals of uraninite are usually octahedra or dodecahedra, but rarely cubes. H. S. Spence, R. van Aubel, and R. Brauns described the crystals. According to V. M. Goldschmidt and L. Thomassen, the X-radiograms of pitchblende, bröggerite, cleveite, and thorianite correspond with a regular, face-centred lattice, the edges being 5·56 A. for thorianite, 5·47 A. for bröggerite, and 5·47 A. for cleveite. They correspond with isomorphous mixtures of the three oxides and also of lead dioxide. The crystalline substance in thorianite and bröggerite has a uniform arrangement, with a distortion of the single points, as if the crystal were composed of sub-parallel planes. The subject was studied by A. Hadding and R. van Aubel. Cleveite yields uranosic oxide on ignition. Bröggerite, after ignition, shows the uranous oxide structure.

The crystal substance in pitchblende is present in a finely divided state (10^{-4} to 10^{-7} cm.). The uranium atoms form face-centred cubes with edges 5·42 A. to 5·45 A. It is supposed that, as the ground lattice of these minerals is uranous oxide, the excess of oxygen corresponding with uranic oxide is present in solid soln. This case is analogous to the occurrence of yttrium fluoride in calcium fluoride. W. Biltz and H. Müller made some observations on this subject. The sp. gr. of the analyzed amorphous specimens range from 6·40 to 9·73 ; the crystalline varieties from about 9·0 to 9·7. J. J. Saslawsky studied the mol. vol. ; and W. Steinkuhler, and H. Schneiderhöhn, the hardness, which is about 5·5. R. Cusack gave 1188° for the m.p. This was corrected by A. L. Fletcher to 1238°, who also observed specimens softening at 1220°, flowing slowly at 1265° to 1330°, and rapidly at 1380° to 1440°. W. C. Brögger said that the ratio of the axes of the heat conductivity curve is $1:1\cdot00389$, corresponding with cubic crystallization. J. Verhaeghe studied the arc spectrum; and A. de Gramont, the spark spectrum. E. Wartmann said that the mineral is slightly conducting; and F. Beijerinck, and R. D. Harvey, that it is a non-conductor; and E. T. Wherry added that the crystals make a poor radio-detector. The mineral is not attracted by a magnet, but F. von Kobell said that it is attracted after it has been calcined. Pitchblende is not easily attacked by hydrochloric acid, but it forms a yellow soln. with nitric acid. It is also soluble in sulphuric acid.

Some complex carbonates (q.v.) are alteration products of uraninite. The *Uranokker* of A. G. Werner,[4] the *lichtes Uranpecherz* of J. K. Freiesleben, the *uranisches Gummierz* and the *Urangummi* of A. Breithaupt, the *Phosphorgummite* of R. Hermann, and the **gummite** of J. D. Dana are alteration products of uraninite of very variable composition. A. L. Hacquaert discussed pseudomorphs of gummite and uranophane after uraninite. These minerals contain, according to the analyses of C. M. Kersten, F. Ragsky, R. Hermann, H. von Foullon, F. A. Genth, and H. Buttgenbach, 61·33 to 75·20 per cent. UO_3; 2·51 to 5·57, PbO; 0·36 to 8·64, Fe_2O_3; 0·05 to 1·92, Mn_2O_3; 2·05 to 6·00, CaO; 0·09 to 2·20, MgO; up to 1·08, BaO; 4·26 to 5·13, SiO_2; and 9·41 to 11·86, H_2O. The *uranisches Pittinerz* of A. Breithaupt, or the *pittinite* of R. Hermann, is a variety of gummite; as are also the *eliasite* of R. Hermann; the *yttrogummite* of A. E. Nordenskjöld; the *thorogummite* of W. E. Hidden and J. B. Mackintosh; the *chlorothorite* of W. E. Hidden; the *coracite* of J. L. le Conte, J. D. Whitney, and F. A. Genth; and the *soddite*, $12UO_3.5SiO_2.14H_2O$—named after F. Soddy—and *chinkolobwite*, $12UO_3.5SiO_2.14H_2O$—named from the locality, *Chinkolobwe*—from Katanga, Belgian Congo, described by A. Schoep. Soddite occurs in dull yellow, rhombic prisms, with the axial ratios $a:b:c=0\cdot7959:1:1\cdot6685$. The refractive indices are $\beta=1\cdot64$ and $\gamma=1\cdot68$. V. Billiet gave $a=1\cdot645$, and $\beta=1\cdot662$. According to A. Schoep, the sp. gr. is 4·627, and the hardness 2. Chinkolobwite occurred as a felted mass of canary-yellow needles on a specimen of soddite, and the rectangular prismatic crystals have the refractive indices $\beta=1\cdot635$, and $\gamma=1\cdot646$, with a negative optical character. There is also **sklodowskite**—named after Mme. Curie-Sklodowska—a hydrated magnesium uranium silicate, $MgO.2UO_3.2SiO_2.7H_2O$. It occurs in pale yellow, rhombic prisms, which have the axial ratios $a:b:c=0\cdot3114:1:1\cdot0554$; the (100)-cleavage is perfect. V. Billiet gave for the indices of refraction $a=1\cdot613$, $\beta=1\cdot635$, and $\gamma=1\cdot657$. A. Schoep found that the sp. gr. is 3·54; the optical character is negative; and the pleochroism, colourless to yellow. N. A. Yajnik and S. J. Kohli studied the radioactivity of uranium ochre.

REFERENCES.

[1] C. F. Rammelsberg, *Sitzber. Akad. Berlin*, 100, 1885; *Pogg. Ann.*, 59. 5, 1241, 1843; A. Remelé, *ib.*, 124. 126, 1865; 125. 237, 1865; *Compt. Rend.*, 58. 716, 1864; *Monit. Scient.*, (2), 1. 469, 1864; *Zeit. anal. Chem.*, 4. 371, 1865; *Compt. Rend.*, 58. 716, 1864; C. Stähling, *ib.*, 173. 1463, 1921; P. Lebeau, *ib.*, 174. 338, 1922; P. Jolibois and R. Bossuet, *ib.*, 174. 386, 1922; J. L. C. Zimmermann, *Liebig's Ann.*, 232. 273, 1885; F. Wöhler, *ib.*, 41. 345, 1842; B. Drenckmann, *Zeit. ges. Naturwiss.*, 17. 126, 1861; F. Janda, *Oesterr. Zeit. Berg. Hütt.*, 49. 325, 340, 1901; F. W. O. de Coninck and M. Camo, *Bull. Acad. Belg.*, 321, 1901; F. W. O. de Coninck, *ib.*, 993, 1908; *Ann. Chim. Phys.*, (7), 28. 5, 1903; A. Colani, *Recherches sur les composés uraneux*, Paris, 1907; *Ann. Chim. Phys.*, (8), 12. 59, 1907; J. J. Ebelmen, *ib.*, (3), 5. 189, 1842; E. M. Péligot, *ib.*, (3), 5. 5, 1842; R. Schwarz, *Helvetica Chim. Acta*, 3. 330, 1920.

[2] C. F. Rammelsberg, *Sitzber. Akad. Berlin*, 100, 1885; H. V. Regnault, *Ann. Chim. Phys.*, (2), 62. 358, 1836; P. Sabatier and A. Mailhe, *ib.*, (8), 20. 289, 1910; F. Bourion, *ib.*, (8), 21. 58, 1910; A. Colani, *ib.*, (8), 12. 59, 1907; *Compt. Rend.*, 137. 382, 1903; 155. 1249, 1912; *Recherches sur les composés uraneux*, Paris, 1907; F. Behounek, *Phys. Zeit.*, 31. 215, 1930; S. Maracineanu, *Compt. Rend.*, 183. 345, 1926; 184. 1547, 1927; 185. 122, 1927; 186. 746, 1928; H. Moissan, *Ann. Chim. Phys.*, (7), 9. 264, 1896; *Bull. Soc. Chim.*, (3), 17. 267, 1897; *Compt. Rend.*, 122. 1088, 1896; C. Staehling, *ib.*, 169. 1036, 1919; A. Ditte, *ib.*, 91. 167, 1880; F. Isambert, *ib.*, 80. 1087, 1875; P. Jolibois and R. Bossuet, *ib.*, 174. 386, 1922; P. Lebeau, *ib.*, 174. 388, 1922; 173. 1468, 1921; D. K. Goralevitsch, *Journ. Russ. Phys. Chem. Soc.*, 62. 843, 1930; F. W. O. de Coninck, *Recherches de l'uranium*, Paris, 1911; *Bull. Acad. Belg.*, 222, 1901; F. W. O. de Coninck and A. Raynaud, *Bull. Soc. Chim.*, (4), 9. 301, 1911; A. L. Helfgott, *Zeit. Physik*, 49. 555, 1928; J. L. C. Zimmermann, *Liebig's Ann.*, 213. 288, 1882; 216. 24, 1883; 232. 273, 1885; O. F. von der Pfordten, *ib.*, 222. 140, 1883; G. Kirsch and H. Pettersson, *Sitzber. Akad. Wien*, 134. 491, 1925; A. Remelé, *Compt. Rend.*, 58. 716, 1864; *Monit. Scient.*, (2), 1. 469, 1864; *Zeit. anal. Chem.*, 4. 379, 1865; *Pogg. Ann.*, 124. 114, 1865; 125. 209, 1865; *Journ. prakt. Chem.*, (1), 93. 316, 1864; (1), 97. 193, 1866; E. Newbery and J. N. Pring, *Proc. Roy. Soc.*, 92. A, 276, 1916; H. C. Bolton, *Chem. News*, 37. 168, 1878; *Ann. New York Acad.*, 1. 1, 1879; 2. 1, 1882; *Min. Mag.*, 1. 136, 1877; 4. 181, 1882; *Ber.*, 13. 726, 1880; *B.A. Rep.*, 505, 1880; *Proc. Amer. Assoc.*, 31. 271, 1883; C. L. Parsons, *Journ. Ind. Eng. Chem.*, 9. 466, 1917; J. J. Berzelius, *Schweigger's Journ.*, 44.

191, 1825; *Pogg. Ann.*, **1**. 359, 1824; *Svenska Akad. Handl.*, 152, 1823; *Ann. Phil.*, **9**. 266, 1825; R. F. Marchand, *Journ. prakt. Chem.*, (1), **23**. 497, 1841; H. Rose, *Ausführliches Handbuch der analytischen Chemie*, Braunschweig, **2**. 523, 1851; M. H. Klaproth, *Mém. Acad. Berlin*, 273, 1789; 160, 1792; *Beiträge zur chemischen Kenntniss der Mineralkörper*, Berlin, **2**. 197, 1797; London, 477, 1801; *Crell's Ann.*, ii, 387, 1789; *Schriften Ges. Berlin*, 273, 1789; 160, 1792; C. F. Bucholz, *Gehlen's Journ.*, **4**. 17, 134, 1805; *Beiträge zur Erweiterung und Berichtigung der Chemie*, Erfurt, **1**. 62, 1799; J. A. Arfvedson, *Svenska Akad. Handl.*, 404, 1822; *Ann. Phil.*, **7**. 253, 1824; *Pogg. Ann.*, **1**. 245, 1824; *Schweigger's Journ.*, **44**. 8, 1825; E. M. Péligot, *Compt. Rend.*, **12**. 735, 1841; **22**. 487, 1846; **42**. 73, 1856; *Ann. Chim. Phys.*, (3), **5**. 5, 1842; (3), **20**. 329, 1847; *Journ. Pharm. Chim.*, (2), **27**. 522, 1841; *Liebig's Ann.*, **41**. 141, 1841; **43**. 258. 1842; *Journ. prakt. Chem.*, (1), **24**. 442, 1841; (1), **38**. 112, 1846; W. F. Hillebrand, *Bull. U.S. Geol. Sur.*, 60, 1888; 78, 1889; 90, 1892; 113, 1893; *Amer. Journ. Science*, (3), **36**. 295, 1888; (3), **40**. 384, 1890; (2), **42**. 390, 1891; *Chem. News*, **64**. 221, 230, 244, 255, 279, 290, 303, 1891; *Zeit. anorg. Chem.*, **3**. 243, 1893; A. Dorabialska, *Rocz. Chem.*, **9**. 494, 1929; J. Vrede, *Phys. Zeit.*, **31**. 323, 1930; J. J. Ebelmen, *Ann. Chim. Phys.*, (3), **5**. 189, 1842; H. Hermann, *Ueber einige Uranverbindungen*, Göttingen, 1861; J. Aloy, *Recherches sur l'uranium et ses composés*, Toulouse, 1901; *Ann. Chim. Phys.*, (7), **24**. 412, 1901; *Bull. Soc. Chim.*, (3), **23**. 368, 1900 (3), **25**. 153, 344, 1901; J. Aloy and E. Rodier, *ib.*, (4), **27**. 101, 1920; J. Aloy and A. Valdiguié, *Compt. Rend.*, **176**. 1229, 1923; J. L. Gay Lussac and L. J. Thénard, *Recherches physicochimiques*, Paris, **1**. 262, 1811; G. J. Fowler and J. Grant, *Journ. Chem. Soc.*, **57**. 275, 1890; M. L. Phillips, *Journ. Franklin Inst.*, **206**. 537, 1928; P. Groth, *Chemische Krystallographie*, Leipzig, **1**. 116, 1906; F. Streintz, *Ann. Physik*, (4), **9**. 854, 1902; K. Honda, *ib.*, (4), **32**. 1044, 1910; W. P. Widdowson and A. S. Russell, *Phil. Mag.*, (6), **46**. 915, 1923; W. P. Jorissen and W. E. Ringer, *Chem. Weèkbl.*, **4**. 242, 476, 1907; B. B. Boltwood, *Amer. Journ. Science*, (4), **25**. 269, 1908; C. J. B. Karsten, *Schweigger's Journ.*, **65**. 394, 1832; E. Wilke-Dörfurt, *Wiss. Veroffeutl. Siemens-Konzern*, **1**. 143, 1920; E. Donath, *Ber.*, **12**. 742, 1879; E. Wedekind and C. Horst, *ib.*, **48**. 105, 1915; J. Zehenter, *Monatsh.*, **21**. 235, 1900; J. O. Perrine, *Phys. Rev.*, (2), **22**. 48, 1923; M. L. Phillips, *ib.*, (2), **32**. 832, 1928; F. Giolitti and G. Tavanti, *Gazz. Chim. Ital.*, **38**. ii, 239, 1908; E. L. Nichols and D. T. Wilber, *Phys. Rev.*, (2), **17**. 707, 1921; H. N. MacCoy and G. C. Ashman, *Amer. Journ. Science*, (4), **26**. 530, 1908; W. G. Mixter, *ib.*, (4), **34**. 141, 1912; *Zeit. anorg. Chem.*, **78**. 231, 1912; D. Balareff, *ib.*, **136**. 216, 1924; A. Michael and A. Murphy. *Amer. Chem. Journ.*, **44**. 365, 1910; E. Newbery and J. N. Pring, *Proc. Roy. Soc.*, **92**. A, 276, 1916; A. S. Russell, *Phys. Zeit.*, **13**. 59, 1912; C. A. Pierlé, *Journ. Phys. Chem.*, **23**. 517, 1919; ·R. Schwarz, *Helvetica Chim. Acta*, **3**. 330, 1920; E. K. Rideal, *Journ. Soc. Chem. Ind.*, **33**. 673, 1914; *Das elektrochemische Verhalten des Urans und einiger Uranverbindungen*, Bonn, 1913; A. Fischer and E. K. Rideal, *Zeit. anorg. Chem.*, **81**. 170, 1913; W. Biltz and H. Müller, *ib.*, **163**. 257, 1927; E. Friederich and L. Sittig, *ib.*, **145**. 127, 1925; E. Friederich, *Zeit. Physik*, **31**. 813, 1925; L. Sittig, *Herstellung bei hohen Temperaturen beständiger Nitride*, Berlin, 1922; E. F. Smith, *Amer. Chem. Journ.*, **1**. 329, 1879; V. M. Goldschmidt and L. Thomassen, *Videnskapsselskapets Skrifter*, 5, 1923; G. F. Hüttig, *Fortschr. Phys. Chem.*, **18**. 5, 1924; C. Zengelis, *Zeit. phys. Chem.*, **50**. 219, 1904; C. Wagner and W. Schottky, *ib.*, **11**. B, 163, 1930; L. Andrieux, *Ann. Chim. Phys.*, (10), **12**. 423, 1929; *Recherches sur l'électrolyse des oxydes métallique dessous dans l'anhydride borique ou dans les borates fondus*, Paris, 1929; A. B. Verigo, *Bull. Acad. U.S.S.R.*, 519, 1929; E. Wiegand, *Zeit. Physik*, **30**. 40, 1924; A. N. Pilkoff, *Journ. Russ. Chem. Soc.*, **1**. 133, 1931; M. le Blanc and H. Sachse, *Ber. Sächs. Akad.*, **82**. 153, 1930.

³ M. H. Klaproth, *Mém. Acad. Berlin*, 273, 1789; 160, 1792; *Beiträge zur chemischen Kenntnis der Mineralkörper*, Berlin, **2**. 197, 1797; London, 477, 1801; *Crell's Ann.*, ii, 387, 1789; *Schriften Ges. Berlin*, 273, 1789; P. K. Grigoreff, *Bot. Geol. Komit.*, 1, 1925; J. K. Marsh, *Phil. Mag.*, (7), **7**. 1005, 1929; C. F. Rammelsberg, *Handbuch der Mineralchemie*, Leipzig, 175, 1860; *Pogg. Ann.*, **59**. 35, 1843; T. Scheerer, *ib.*, **72**. 561, 1847; **77**. 570, 1847; R. van Aubel, *Compt. Rend.*, **185**. 586, 1927; J. J. Ebelmen, *Ann. Chim. Phys.*, (3), **5**. 498, 1843; W. Steinkuhler, *Bull. Soc. Chim. Belg.*, **32**. 233, 1923; H. V. Ellsworth, *Rep. Geol. Survey*, *Dept. Mines Canada*, D, 1921; R. Hermann, *Journ. prakt. Chem.*, (1), **76**. 326, 1859; C. W. Blomstrand, *ib.*, (2), **7**. 60, 1873; (2), **29**. 191, 1884; *Geol. För. Förh. Stockholm*, **7**. 94, 1881; C. H. Pfaff, *Schweigger's Journ.*, **35**. 326, 1822; T. L. Walker, *Univ. Toronto Geol. Stud.*, 17, 1924; ·O. Free, *Phil. Mag.*, (7), **1**. 950, 1926; C. von Hauer, *Jahrb. geol. Reichsanst. Wien*, **4**. 197, 1853; J. D. Whitney, *Phil. Mag.*, (3), **37**. 153, 1850; *Amer. Journ. Science*, (2), **7**. 434, 1849; F. A. Genth, *ib.*, (2), **23**. 421. 1857; C. B. Comstock, *ib.*, (3), **19**. 220, 1880; W. E. Hidden and J. B. Mackintosh, *ib.*, (3), **38**, 481, 1889; J. L. le Conte, *ib.*, (2), **3**. 117, 173, 1847; C. W. Davis, *ib.*, (5), **11**. 201, 1926; W. F. Hillebrand, *ib.*, (3), **36**. 295, 1888; (3), **40**. 384, 1890; (3), **42**. 390, 1891; *Chém. News*, **64**. 221, 230, 244, 255, 279, 290, 303, 1891; *Bull. U.S. Geol. Sur.*, 60, 1888; 78, 1889; 90, 1892; 113, 1893; F. W. Clarke, *ib.*, 220, 1903; J. Lorenzen, *Nyt Mag.*, **28**. 249, 1884; P. Schei, *ib.*, **43**. 137, 1905; R. Cusack, *Proc. Irish Acad.*, (3), **4**. 399, 1897; A. L. Fletcher, *Scient. Proc. Roy. Dublin Soc.*, (2), **13**. 643, 1913; J. D. Dana, *A System of Mineralogy*, New York, 889, 1892; F. von Kobell, *Neues Jahrb. Min.*, 403, 1834; *Die Mineralnamen*, München, 84, 1853; A. Schoep, *Bull. Soc. Geol. Belg.*, **32**. 345, 1923; **33**. 87, 1923; **50**. 215, 1927; *Compt. Rend.*, **173**. 1186, 1921; **174**. 1066, 1922; *Bull. Soc. Min.*, **47**. 147, 1924; *Bull. Soc. Chim. Belg.*, **32**. 274, 1923; W. Marckwald, *Landw. Jahrb.*, **38**. v, 423, 1909; *Centr. Min.*, 761, 1906; R. Brauns, *ib.*, 689, 1911; E. Wartmann, *Mém. Soc. Genève*, **12**. 1, 1853; F. Beijerinck, *Ueber das Leitungsvermögen der Mineralien*

für Elektricität, Stuttgart, 1897; *Neues Jahrb. Min. B.B.*, **11**. 403, 1897; K. A. Hofmann and W. Heidepriem, *Ber.*, **34**. 914, 1901; J. Step, *Sitzber. Akad. Wien*, **113**. 585, 1904; R. D. Harvey, *Econ. Geol.*, **23**. 778, 1928; W. Ramsay, *Proc. Roy. Soc.*, **58**. 65, 81, 1895; **59**. 325, 1896; W. Ramsay and M. W. Travers, *ib.*, **60**. 443, 1897; M. W. Travers, *ib.*, **64**. 130, 1898; J. N. Lockyer, *ib.*, **58**. 67, 113, 116, 192, 193, 1895; **59**. 4, 1895; **59**. 342, 1896; **60**. 133, 1896; W. A. Tilden, *ib.*, **59**. 218, 1896; N. A. Langlet, *Oefvers. Akad. Stockholm*, **52**. 211, 1895; M. and P. Curie and G. Bémont, *Compt. Rend.*, **127**. 175, 1215, 1898; B. Szilard, *ib.*, **143**. 1145, 1906; **145**. 463, 1907; A. Debierne, *ib.*, **129**. 593, 1899; G. F. Barker, *Amer. Journ. Science*, (4), **16**. 163, 1903; B. B. Boltwood, *ib.*, (4), **23**. 77, 1907; S. Wleugel, *Zeit. Kryst.*, **4**. 520, 1880; W. R. Criper, *Mem. Geol. Sur. India*, **34**. 11, 1902; P. Krusch, *Zeit. prakt. Geol.*, **19**. 83, 1911; W. Elsholz, *Ueber die Uranoxyde in den Pechblenden*, Berlin, 1916; F. Giesel, *Ber.*, **36**. 342, 1903; W. C. Brögger, *Neues Jahrb. Min.*, ii, 170, 1884; J. J. Saslawsky, *Zeit. Kryst.*, **59**. 195, 1924; G. Bardet, *ib.*, **42**. 183, 1906; F. Müllbauer, *ib.*, **61**. 321, 1925; H. Scheiderhöhn, *Anleitung zur mikroskopischen Bestimmung und Untersuchungen von Erzen und Aufbreitungsprodukten besonders im auffallenden Licht*, Berlin, 263, 1922; F. Kolbeck and P. Uhlrich, *Centr. Min.*, 207, 1904; O. Behrendsen, *Phys. Zeit.*, **3**. 572, 1902; A. de Gramont, *Bull. Soc. Min.*, **18**. 171, 1895; Y. Brière, *ib.*, **52**. 85, 1929; R. J. Moss, *Trans. Roy. Dublin Soc.*, (2), **8**. 139, 1904; G. Tschernik, *Bull. Acad. St. Petersburg*, (6), **3**. 1203, 1909; W. Riss, *Mitt. Inst. Radiumforsch.*, 162, 1924; H. Deslandres, *Compt. Rend.*, **120**. 1112, 1895; A. E. Nordenskjöld, *Geol. För. Förh. Stockholm*, **4**. 20, 1878; *Neues Jahrb. Min.*, 406, 1878; H. V. Ellsworth, *Amer. Min.*, **13**. 442, 1928; **15**. 455, 1930; R. C. Wells, *ib.*, **15**. 470, 1930; H. S. Spence, *ib.*, **15**. 474, 1930; A. Hadding and R. van Aubel, *Compt. Rend.*, **188**. 716, 1929; T. H. Laby, *Proc. Roy. Soc. New South Wales*, **43**. 28, 1909; V. M. Goldschmidt, *Zeit. Kryst.*, **44**. 545, 1908; V. M. Goldschmidt and L. Thommassen, *Videnskapsselskapets Skrifter*, 5, 1923; A. L. Hacquaert, *Natuurwetenschap. Tijd.*, **9**. 34, 1927; W. Biltz and H. Müller, *Zeit. anorg. Chem.*, **163**. 257, 1927; G. Kirsch, *Mitt. Inst. Radiumforsch.*, 150, 1922; *Tschermak's Mitt.*, (2), **38**. 223, 1925; E. T. Wherry, *Amer. Min.*, **10**. 28, 1925; J. G. Fairchild, *ib.*, **14**. 265, 1929; F. Hecht and E. Körner, *Monatsh.*, **49**. 438, 444, 460, 1928; A. Becker and P. Jannasch, *Jahrb. Rad. Elektron.*, **12**. 1, 1915; C. W. Knight, *Ann. Rep. Ontario Bur. Mines*, **28**. 94, 1919; H. Hirschi, *Mitt. Schweiz. Min. Petr.*, **1**. 310, 1921; **3**. 240, 1923; **4**. 64, 1924; **5**. 173, 248, 429, 1925; K. Nenadkevich, *Bull. Acad. U.R.S.S.*, (6), **20**. 767, 1926; A. E. Fersman, *ib.*, (6), **20**. 775, 1926; J. Verhaeghe, *Bull. Acad. Belg.*, (5), **14**. 18, 1928; W. E. Hidden, *Trans. New York Acad.*, **8**. 185, 1889; R. Zückert, *Mitt. Preuss. Geol. Landesanst.*, ii, 900, 1930; J. S. de Lusy and H. V. Ellsworth, *Amer. Min.*, **16**. 569, 1931; H. V. Ellsworth, *ib.*, **16**. 576, 1931; R. C. Wells, *ib.*, **15**. 470, 1930.

[4] A. G. Werner, *Letztes Mineralsystem*, Freiberg, 26, 1817; J. K. Freiesleben, *Geognostische Arbeiten*, Freiberg, 1818; A. Breithaupt, *Uebersicht des Mineralsystems*, Freiberg, 60, 1830; *Vollständige Charakteristik des Mineralsystems*, Dresden, 218, 1832; *Vollständiges Handbuch der Mineralogie*, Dresden, **3**. 901, 1847; H. Buttgenbach, *Ann. Soc. Géol. Belg.*, **44**. 5, 1922; A. L. Hacquaert, *ib.*, **50**. c, 15, 1927; *Natuurwet. Tijd.*, **9**. 34, 1927; N. A. Yajnik and S. J. Kohli, *Proc. Asiatic Soc. Bengal*, **18**. 73, 1922; A. L. Fletcher, *Scient. Proc. Roy. Dublin Soc.*, (2), **13**. 443, 1913; W. Haidinger, *Jahrb. geol. Reichsanst. Wien*, **3**. 124, 1853; H. von Foullon, *ib.*, **33**. 1, 1883; R. Hermann, *Journ. prakt. Chem.*, (1), **76**. 322, 1859; C. M. Kersten, *Schweigger's Journ.*, **66**. 18, 1832; F. Ragsky, *Pogg. Ann. Ergbd.*, **4**. 348, 1854; F. A. Genth, *Amer. Chem. Journ.*, **1**. 89, 1879; *Amer. Journ. Science*, (2), **23**. 421, 1857; J. D. Whitney, *ib.*, (2), **7**. 433, 1849; J. L. le Conte, *ib.*, (2), **3**. 117, 173, 1847; W. E. Hidden and J. B. Mackintosh, *ib.*, (3), **38**. 480, 1889; W. E. Hidden, *Trans. New York Acad.*, **8**. 185, 1889; A. E. Nordenskjöld, *Geol. För. Förh. Stockholm*, **4**. 31, 1878; A. Schoep, *Bull. Soc. Geol. Belg.*, **32**. 345, 1923; **33**. 87, 1923; *Bull. Soc. Chim. Belg.*, **32**. 274, 1923; *Compt. Rend.*, **173**. 1186, 1921; **174**. 1066, 1922; **179**. 413, 1924; *Natuurwet. Tijd.*, **9**. 25, 30, 1927; V. Billiet, *ib.*, **7**. 112, 1926; J. D. Dana, *A System of Mineralogy*, New York, 889, 1892.

§ 11. Uranium Trioxide and its Hydrates

J. J. Ebelmen [1] prepared **uranium trioxide,** or **uranic oxide,** UO_3, by heating uranyl hydroxide to 300°—the product appears from the analysis to contain some uranosic oxide. He also obtained it by raising the temp. of ammonium uranyl carbonate very gradually to 300°, and holding it there for a long time; and O. Brunck said that this salt is best heated at a temp. not exceeding 300°, and in a current of air, until the exit gases no longer turn red litmus blue. The product contains traces of ammonia. H. Lienau heated about 50 grms. of ammonium uranate in a flask, on an oil-bath at 250°, for 30 hrs.; F. W. O. de Coninck heated uranyl sulphate to dull redness and obtained the trioxide; and E. M. Péligot, and F. W. O. de Coninck heated uranyl nitrate at 250° until no acid vapours are given off. P. Lebeau, V. A. Jacquelain, R. de Forcrand, and O. Brunck showed that the trioxide prepared from the nitrate is always contaminated with basic nitrate, even when heated for a long time at 350°. P. Lebeau said that the product

can be obtained free from nitrate if the oxide obtained at a low temp. be heated
in oxygen gas for a long time at 500°—but the trioxide then contains traces of
uranosic oxide. G. F. Hüttig and E. von Schröder, and W. Biltz and H. Müller
prepared hydrated uranium peroxide by treating a soln. of 20 grms. of uranyl
nitrate in 200 c.c. of water with 3 to 10 per cent. hydrogen dioxide, washing, and
drying the precipitate at 60° to 70°. The sulphur-yellow powder was heated in an
atm. of oxygen in an electric furnace at 350° for 3 to 4 hrs., and then from 30 to
60 min. at 400°. The product was cooled in a desiccator. The colour of the
oxide is orange.

Analyses by W. Biltz and H. Müller correspond with UO_3; the observed ratio
U : O ranges from 1 : 2·97 to 1 : 3·07. If the at. wt. of uranium is taken to be
120, the formula is U_2O_3. According to E. M. Péligot, and C. F. Rammelsberg,
the formula is $(UO_2)O$, where the bivalent radicle UO_3 is called *uranyl*, and accordingly uranium trioxide can be regarded as *uranyl oxide*, $(UO_2)O$. This is supported
by the difficulty in preparing the hexahalides—uranium sexavalent—and the ease
with which the uranyl salts—$UO_2(NO_3)_2$, UO_2SO_4, UO_2Cl_2, UO_2F_2, etc.—can be
prepared. Uranium trioxide is an orange-yellow powder; J. J. Ebelmen said
brick-red. According to F. W. O. de Coninck, when crystalline uranium nitrate
is rapidly calcined, it yields a red modification of the trioxide, which is supposed
to be a polymeride, $(UO_3)_2$, of the orange variety. The orange variety is formed
by the slow thermal decomposition of the nitrate and it is partially transformed
into the red variety if kept at a red-heat for some time. If the red form is kept
for 40 hrs. at a dull red-heat, or at a high temp., it is converted into a brown oxide,
but it does not give the green uranosic
oxide if heated to redness in a closed
platinum crucible. R. de Forcrand
also prepared what he regarded as a
polymeride of the trioxide by heating
uranyl nitrate at 500° to 600°.
Attempts to determine the mol. wts.
have not been successful. So far as
the available evidence is concerned the
difference in colour may represent
nothing more than a difference in the

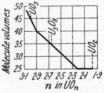

Fig. 6.—Molecular
Volumes of the
Uranium Oxides.

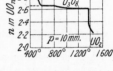

Fig. 7.—The Thermal
Decomposition of
Uranium Trioxide.

grain-size of the two products. V. M. Goldschmidt and L. Thomassen, and
W. Biltz and H. Müller examined X-radiograms of uranium trioxide, and found
it to be amorphous—*vide infra*. W. Biltz, and W. Biltz and H. Müller measured
the **specific gravity** and **molecular volume** of the oxides, at 25°/4°, between
$UO_{3·069}$ and $UO_{1·992}$, and calculated the mol. vol. of the contained oxygen. The
results are plotted in Fig. 6. The following is a selection from the results, for
UO_n:

n	3·069	2·920	2·666	2·537	2·454	2·333	2·262	2·000	1·992
Sp. gr.	6·039	7·074	8·301	8·776	9·384	9·756	10·90	10·75	10·80
Mol. vol.	47·57	40·28	33·83	33·44	29·58	28·24	25·17	25·21	25·03
Vol. O	11·4	9·45	7·9	7·9	6·95	6·65	5·5	6·3	6·2

G. Beck gave 7·29 for the sp. gr., and 39·2 for the mol. vol. D. Balareff discussed
the mol. vol. L. Elsner stated that when uranium oxide is heated in a porcelain
oven, there is evidence of some **volatilization ;** and W. Biltz and H. Müller observed
that in a quartz bulb $UO_{2·61}$ gave a faint sublimate at 1214° and 1·0 mm. press. ;
$UO_{2·46}$, a faint sublimate at 1240° and 1·4 mm. ; $UO_{2·30}$, a very faint one at 1160°
and 0·3 mm. ; and $UO_{2·20}$, a faint one at 1240° and 0·02 mm. In another set of
experiments at 1300°±20°, over about 10 hrs., and about 1 mm. press., 0·036 per
cent. sublimed from $UO_{2·000}$; 0·6 per cent. from $UO_{2·3}$; and 4·0 per cent. from
$UO_{2·667}$. The sublimate approximated $UO_{2·15}$. The evolution of oxygen from
the solid thus favoured sublimation—the residue from the UO_2 remained unchanged, the other left a residue approximating $UO_{2·17}$. J. J. Ebelmen, and

F. W. O. de Coninck discussed the decomposition of uranium trioxide : $6UO_3$ $=2U_3O_8+O_2$. According to O. Brunck, the oxygen which is evolved contains a perceptible quantity of ozone. At a constant press. of 10 mm. of oxygen, W. Biltz and H. Müller obtained the results indicated in Fig. 7 and they noted that the colour of UO_3 is pale orange-yellow, and as it passes into $UO_2._9$, the colour becomes greyish-brown with a greenish tinge, and the X-radiogram shows the presence of U_3O_8 on passing to $UO_2._8$, the green tinge becomes more marked, until with $UO_2._{67}$ the colour is moss-green or olive-green ; on attaining $UO_2._6$, the colour darkens, and becomes almost black with $UO_2._2$, and the X-radiogram shows the presence of U_3O_8, as well as of UO_2 ; on passing to $UO_2._1$ and UO_2, the colour becomes black or dark brown, and the X-radiogram of UO_2 alone appears. W. Biltz and H. Müller measured the **dissociation pressure** of the oxides between UO_3 and U_3O_8. The results are illustrated by Fig. 8. The observed dissociation press. are not equilibrium press., although in some cases they may approach that state. A. Fischer and co-workers observed the decomposition of uranium trioxide in air between 470° and 580° to form uranosic oxide ; and P. Jolibois and R. Bossuet

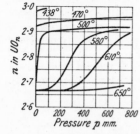

observed breaks at 360° when the trioxide is heated at 30° and at 710 mm. press. ; D. Balareff observed that in vacuo, at 502°, the formation of uranosic oxide is rapid, and the change from uranosic oxide to the trioxide is irreversible. P. Lebeau observed that a preparation of uranosic oxide kept for about five years acquires a brownish-green surface film of hydrated trioxide ; and that the greyish-black uranosic oxide obtained by heating the oxalate at 350° becomes brownish-orange and increases in weight when heated for 12 hrs. in air at 350° ; if the uranosic oxide has been heated to 800°, it is inactive and is dead-burned.

Fig. 8.—Dissociation Pressure of Uranium Oxides.

W. Biltz and H. Müller made analogous experiments which showed that finely-divided uranosic oxide can be oxidized, and that the oxidation of uranosic oxide to the trioxide in geological processes is rendered probable.

W. G. Mixter found that the **heat of formation,** $(U,3O)=303·9$ Cals. ; $(UO_2,O)=34·2$ Cals. ; and $U_3O_8+O=3UO_3+16·2$ Cals. R. de Forcrand gave 19·803 Cals. for the heat of soln. of the trioxide in dil. nitric acid. A. Wehnelt classed uranium as an " inactive oxide " as far as the **emission of electrons** is concerned when it is fixed on a platinum disc and used as the cathode of a discharge tube. M. L. Phillips studied the radiations from the incandescent oxide. F. Behounek observed no increase in the radioactivity of the trioxide on exposure to sunlight ; the subject was studied by S. Maracineanu. M. le Blanc and H. Sachse found the sp. **electrical conductivity** of the trioxide to be over $5×10^{-8}$ at 400°. According to E. Wedekind and C. Horst, the trioxide is paramagnetic, and the **magnetic susceptibility** $1·08×10^{-6}$ unit. The subject was discussed by W. Biltz and C. Fendius, who observed 293 Cals. for the heat of formation.

V. Kohlschütter and K. Vogdt attributed the retention of gases like **helium, nitrogen,** and **nitrous oxide** to the water present in the oxide. The subject was discussed by C. Friedheim—*vide infra*, hydroxylamine uranate. P. Sabatier and J. B. Senderens, and H. Hermann observed that when heated in **hydrogen,** it is reduced to a lower oxide. G. Gore found that dry **hydrogen chloride** forms a yellow product soluble in water ; F. O. von der Pfordten, that **acids** form yellow soln. Conc. **hydrobromic acid** was found by R. Sendtner to dissolve hydrated uranium trioxide, forming a soln. of uranyl bromide ; but **hydriodic acid** acts as a reducing agent. A. W. Cronander found that when the trioxide is heated in a sealed tube with **phosphorus pentachloride,** the complex $PCl_5.UCl_5$ is formed—*vide infra*. V. Kohlschütter found that **hydrogen sulphide** reduces neutral, alkaline, or feebly acidic soln. R. Sendtner found that hydrated uranium trioxide dissolves in dil. **selenic acid**, forming a soln. of uranyl selenate ; and in **selenious acid**, forming a soln.

of uranyl selenite. H. Moissan found that when uranium trioxide mixed with **carbon** is heated in the electric furnace at 3000°, it is reduced to the metal ; O. Brunck, that it is reduced to uranosic oxide when heated in **carbon dioxide**; H. Hermann, that **carbon disulphide** vapour mixed with carbon dioxide reduced it to the dioxide ; and H. E. Quantin, that **carbon tetrachloride,** or a mixture of chlorine and carbon monoxide, at a high temp., forms a mixture of uranyl dichloride and uranium hexachloride ; but A. Michael and A. Murphy said that in a sealed tube at 250°, carbon tetrachloride and uranium dioxide form uranium pentachloride, and P. Camboulives, that carbon tetrachloride at 360° forms the tetra- and pentachlorides. L. Kahlenberg and H. W. Hillyer found that the trioxide is insoluble in a boiling, aq. soln. of **potassium tartrate ;** and W. Gibbons, that it is soluble in **oleic acid.** G. Rauter found that when heated with **silicon tetrachloride** in a sealed tube, the trioxide forms chlorine, uranium tetrachloride, uranyl chloride, and silica.

T. Graham prepared a **colloidal solution** of hydrated uranium trioxide by adding alkali-lye to a soln. of uranyl nitrate or chloride in the presence of sugar ; the salts and alkali were removed from the deep orange soln. by dialysis. The soln. was fairly stable, and it was coagulated by electrolytes. B. Szilard obtained the colloidal soln., containing a little electrolyte, by the gradual addition of uranyl hydroxide to a dil. soln. of uranyl nitrate as long as the former is dissolved ; the soln. thus obtained is orange-yellow in colour and very stable. The uranyl hydroxide here employed was obtained by exposing to light a mixture of uranyl acetate and ether and thoroughly washing the resulting precipitate. F. Mylius and R. Dietz also prepared the colloid by precipitating the chlorine from an aq. soln. of uranyl chloride, by means of silver oxide, and afterwards dialyzing the soln. The colloidal soln. so prepared has an astringent taste, reddens litmus, and when heated deposits dihydrated uranium trioxide. V. A. Kargin also prepared the hydrosol. B. Moore and T. A. Webster found that a dil. soln. of the colloid is a powerful catalyst in the synthesis of formic acid by exposing an aq. soln. of carbon dioxide to sunlight. K. C. Sen discussed the peptization of the hydrated oxide by sugars.

In the electrometric titration of 100 c.c. of a soln. of $0.00833M$-uranyl nitrate in $0.0149N$-HNO_3, H. T. S. Britton obtained the results summarized in Fig. 9. There is a slight inflexion in the curve with 14·9 c.c. of alkali, due to the presence of sexivalent uranium nitrate in the soln. With 45 c.c. of alkali the composition of the solute is $U(NO_3)_{2.38}(OH)_{3.62}$, and the soln. then becomes deeper yellow but clear ; with 55·8 c.c. of alkali, when the solute has the composition $U(NO_3)_{1.08}(OH)_{4.92}$, a yellow precipitate separates—*i.e.* when p_H is nearly 4·2. The deepening of the colour of the highly basic soln. is attributed to a gradual increase in the size of the basic particles of the solute, since the uranium hydroxide is held in soln. in a state closely akin to that of a colloid. The hydrion conc. of the soln. when 48 c.c. of alkali has been added is $10^{-3.7}$; the soln. then contains the proportions

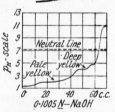

FIG. 9.—Electrometric Titration of Uranyl Nitrate Soln. with Sodium Hydroxide.

of uranium and nitrate present in uranyl nitrate, but is much deeper in colour than that obtained by dissolving uranyl nitrate crystals. The explanation of this difference probably lies in the fact that uranyl nitrate is crystallized from strongly acid soln. On soln. in water, it tends to revert to a state which is probably colloidal, as shown by the changes in colour and in conductivity which C. Dittrich found that it undergoes on standing and especially at high temp. If the increase in conductivity which takes place on standing is due to the formation of particles which are essentially colloidal, these particles must be capable of some kind of ionization. There seems to be very little support for the belief that uranyl salt soln. contain the uranyl-cation ; none is to be found in conductivity measurements, which show that the increases in conductivity with dilution of soln. of the nitrate, chloride, and sulphate are anomalous. Precipitation is complete when 64 c.c. of alkali has been added, as compared with 64·7 c.c. which are required for the complete formation of uranic hydroxide. Hence the precipitate is uranic hydroxide containing a very small quantity of undecomposed nitrate. Dilute acid soln. of uranium nitrate or uranyl salt soln. themselves, when gently heated, undergo some profound change ; the colour becomes deeper and the reverse change on cooling takes place very slowly. They become alkaline to phenolphthalein when the theoretical amount of alkali is added, but a precipitate separates only when an appreciable excess of alkali has been added or the soln. has been boiled for some time. The opalescence of the alkaline colloidal soln. depends on the temp. to which the original soln. has been heated. The deep yellow soln. formed by gentle heating are almost clear, whereas those which have been boiled become visibly colloidal. If not too great an excess of alkali is added, the resulting colloidal soln. remains quite stable for several days. They are coagulable on addition of 1 or 2 c.c. of sat. potassium chloride soln. Heating thus appears to cause some change in the state of aggregation of the particles of uranium hydroxide, or more likely of highly basic salt, which are probably in equilibrium with free nitrate ions and are thereby enabled to enter into reaction with alkalies, so that the uranium hydroxide complexes remain in colloidal soln. P. Jolibois and R. Bossuet found that the precipitate obtained by the addition of soda-lye to a soln. of uranyl nitrate is not the diuranate, but the hydroxide associated with 1·2 to 8·0 per cent. of adsorbed alkali.

The observations of G. F. Hüttig and E. von Schröder on the vap. press. of hydrated uranium trioxide with an excess of water are summarized in Fig. 10, in the form of a dehydration curve. This shows that three hydrates can exist under these conditions. Observations were also made by A. Fischer and E. K. Rideal. At a little over 160°, the *hemihydrate*, $UO_3.\frac{1}{2}H_2O$, or $2UO_3.H_2O$, or **pyrouranic acid, or diuranic acid**, $H_2U_2O_7$, exists. This hydrate loses its water at 300°, forming uranium trioxide. According to L. Pissarjewsky, the heat of neutralization of a mol of pyrouranic

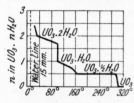

Fig. 10.—Dehydration Curve of Hydrated Uranium Trioxide.

acid by sodium hydroxide is 17·859 Cals. The *monohydrate*, $UO_3.H_2O$, or **uranyl hydroxide,** $UO_2(OH)_2$, or **uranic acid,** H_2UO_4, appears at about 96° on the dehydration curve of G. F. Hüttig and E. von Schröder, Fig. 10. J. J. Ebelmen obtained it as an orange-yellow product by heating the higher hydrate in vacuo at 100° ; and B. Drenckmann, by keeping it at 160° ; and R. de Forcrand, at 80°. It was also obtained by F. J. Malaguti, and C. F. Bucholz by drying the higher hydrate at 100°. F. J. Malaguti prepared it as an amorphous, lemon-yellow powder by heating an alcoholic soln. of uranyl nitrate for some time at a temp. below its b.p., and washing the precipitate. J. J. Berzelius, C. F. Bucholz, and J. Aloy heated uranyl nitrate on a sand-bath so long as nitrous fumes were evolved, and extracted soluble salts from the residue by repeatedly boiling it with water. J. Riban obtained crystals by heating a 2 per cent. soln. of uranyl acetate for 100 hrs. in a sealed tube at 175°. J. Aloy obtained this hydrate by exposing dihydrated uranium dioxide to air ; and also by heating the violet hydrate or uranosic oxide with water at 100° until it is completely converted into the yellow hydrate ; F. W. O. de Coninck, by the action of cold hydrogen dioxide on uranium dioxide ; C. Dittrich, by decomposing uranyl nitrate on a hot sand-bath and then boiling the product with water ; J. Zehenter, by exposing to air the violet precipitate obtained by the insolation of a soln. of uranyl acetate—the violet hydroxide soon passes into the yellow, monohydrated uranium trioxide ; and A. Mailhe, by digesting precipitated copper hydroxide with a soln. of uranyl nitrate. F. W. O. de Coninck and M. Camo electrolyzed a soln. of uranyl nitrate with a current of less than 1 amp., and obtained the orange monohydrate. S. J. Diachkowsky prepared

colloidal uranyl hydroxide by the hydrolysis of uranates and dialysis in running water. Dehydration leads to coagulation of the hydrosol resulting in the precipitation of a hydrate of uranic acid. When hydration is complete, the precipitate formed on coagulation corresponds with $Na_2U_2O_7$. In either case on treatment with water a colloidal soln. is again formed. The whole synthesis can be represented :
$$nNa_2U_2O_7 \rightleftharpoons [Na_2U_2O_7.H_2UO_4]_{n-1} \rightleftharpoons [H_2O(UO_3)_2UO_2(OH)_2]_n \rightleftharpoons [UO_2(OH)_2]_{n+1},$$ the equilibrium being disturbed if sodium diuranate or uranic acid is removed from the sphere of reaction. The particles are negatively charged and their velocity in an electric field corresponds with a charge of 1.984×10^{-8} e.s.u. The density of the sol is 7.45, and the size of the particles varies from 1.144×10^{-15} to one amicron, showing that the system is polydisperse. Hydrochloric acid, barium chloride, and aluminium chloride coagulate the sol ; and with aluminium chloride the sign of the charge changes. K. C. Sen discussed the retardation in the peptization of the colloid by the presence of sugar.

J. Aloy said that he obtained the hydrate in yellow, microscopic, rhombic plates ; and J. Riban, in yellow, six-sided prisms or plates. According to F. W. O. de Coninck and M. Camo, the sp. gr. is 5.926 at 15°. J. J. Ebelmen found that the monohydrate loses its water completely at 300° ; F. J. Malaguti, that one-third of the water is lost at 400°, and all at a higher temp. Oxygen is given off at the same time, forming uranosic oxide, etc. G. F. Hüttig and E. von Schröder's observations on this subject are summarized in Fig. 10. G. F. Hüttig gave for the heat of formation of the hydrates, $(UO_3,\frac{1}{2}H_2O)=13.29$ Cals. ; $(UO_3,H_2O)=23.4$ Cals. ; $(UO_3,1\frac{1}{2}H_2O)=31.74$ Cals. ; and $(UO_3,2H_2O)=39.24$ Cals. R. de Forcrand gave 14.846 Cals. for the heat of soln. of the monohydrate in dil. nitric acid. According to J. Aloy, the heat of neutralization of $UO_3.H_2O+HCl$, etc., with $0.5N$-soln. of the acids is with hydrochloric acid, 8.4 Cals. ; with hydrobromic acid, 8.8 Cals. ; with nitric acid, 8.4 Cals. ; with sulphuric acid, 9.5 Cals. ; and with acetic acid, 7.5 Cals. According to C. A. Pierlé, the electrode potential of the hydrate, $UO_3.H_2O$, against a soln. of 14.3 grms. of uranyl nitrate per litre, is -0.860 volt. J. Aloy observed that it is reduced to uranium dioxide when heated in hydrogen, and that it is easily soluble in dil. acids. F. W. O. de Coninck found that the hydrate reacts with calcium oxalate, at a red-heat, in accord with : $CaC_2O_4+UO_3.H_2O$ $=CaCO_3+CO_2+UO_2+H_2O$.

J. J. Ebelmen prepared the *dihydrate*, $UO_3.2H_2O$, or *hydrated uranic acid*, $H_2UO_4.H_2O$, by exposing a soln. of uranyl oxalate to sunlight until the violet-brown precipitate is yellow, and then drying it in air ; and by boiling a soln. of ammonium uranyl carbonate until it falls as a yellow precipitate, or, according to B. Drenckmann, by allowing a soln. to stand for 9 months with a limited access of air ; J. Aloy, by the slow oxidation in air of the violet hydrate of uranosic oxide ; B. Drenckmann, by heating a mixture of potassium chlorate and uranosic oxide up to the m.p., and when cold, boiling the product repeatedly with water ; F. Mylius and R. Dietz, by boiling the colloidal soln. ; J. Aloy, by heating uranosic oxide with water ; F. W. O. de Coninck, by heating uranium dioxide with hydrogen dioxide ; and P. Lebeau, by evaporating a soln. of uranyl nitrate at ordinary temp. over sulphuric acid, and then extracting the residue with ether. The dihydrate appears as a lemon-yellow powder ; and J. Aloy obtained it in rhombic, rectangular plates and prisms. According to H. Rose, the dihydrate reddens moist litmus paper—*vide supra*, colloidal uranium trioxide. T. L. Walker described a lemon-yellow mineral from Kasolo, Katanga, Belgian Congo, which he called **schoepite**—after A. Schoep. Its composition was found by A. Schoep to approximate $UO_3.2H_2O$; the rhombic crystals have the axial ratios $a:b:c=0.426:1:0.875$. The sp. gr. is 5.685. The (001)-cleavage is perfect ; there is no pleochroism. V. Billiet found that the indices of refraction are $\alpha=1.690$, $\beta=1.714$, and $\gamma=1.735$. It is optically negative. A. Schoep said that **becquerelite**—*vide infra*, lead uranate —is a similar mineral from the same locality, and that the axial ratios of the rhombic crystals are $a:b:c=0.5537:1:0.5938$, with a perfect cleavage parallel to (001), and a less marked cleavage parallel to (101). Becquerelite contains over 5 per cent. of lead oxide as impurity, whilst schoepite rarely contains 1 per cent. The two minerals show that the dihydrate, $UO_3.2H_2O$, is dimorphous. Becquerelite loses half its water at 150° and the remainder at 500°, whilst schoepite loses half its water at 110° and all at 325°—*vide infra*, fourmarierite. S. C. Lind and C. W. Davis described a mineral which they called *lambertite*—after R. Lambert— and which occurred at Silver Cliff Hill, Lusk, Wyoming. It is said to be hydrated uranium trioxide, but E. S. Larsen and co-workers found that lambertite is nothing but *uranophane*, $CaO.2UO_3.2SiO_3.6H_2O$. According to J. J. Ebelmen, and B. Drenckmann, the dihydrate is stable in air, and it does not absorb carbon dioxide from the atm.; and it loses a mol. of water at 100° to 160°, and at 300° passes into uranium trioxide—*vide supra*, the monohydrate. G. F. Hüttig and E. von Schröder's observations on this subject are summarized in Fig. 10. R. de Forcrand gave 12·375 Cals. for the heat of soln. in dil. nitric acid. A. Schoep described a mineral found in the cavities of a specimen of uraninite from Katanga, Belgian Congo. The mineral was called **ianthinite**—from $\iota\alpha\nu\theta\iota\nu\sigma\varsigma$, violet coloured. It forms acicular rhombic crystals with the axial ratios $a:b:c=2\cdot5938:1:—$. The cleavage is micaceous and the colour violet-black with a brownish-violet streak. The pleochroism is strong, a, colourless, b, dark violet, and c, violet. The indices of refraction are $a=1\cdot674$, $\beta=1\cdot90$, and $\gamma=1\cdot92$. V. Billiet gave 1·64, 1·92, and 1·90 respectively. Its composition approximates to the *hemiheptahydrate*, $2UO_3.7H_2O$.

Uranium trioxide is amphoteric. All the hydrates dissolve in acids to form yellow soln. of *uranyl salts*; whilst with inorganic and organic bases uranium trioxide forms *uranates*. W. R. E. Hodgkinson and F. K. S. Lowndes observed that when the hydrate is heated with potassium chlorate, chlorine is given off and potassium diuranate is formed. M. E. Chevreul found that uranic acid reddens litmus as acids do, but affects hematine-blue as do salifiable bases.

REFERENCES.

[1] J. J. Berzelius, *Berzelius' Jahresb.*, 24. 118, 1845; *Schweigger's Journ.*, 44. 191, 1825; *Pogg. Ann.*, 1. 359, 1824; *Svenska Akad. Handl.*, 152, 1823; *Ann. Phil.*, 9. 266, 1825; C. F. Bucholz, *Gehlen's Journ.*, 4. 17, 134, 1805; *Beiträge zur Erweiterung und Berichtigung der Chemie*, Erfurt, 1. 62, 1799; L. Elsner, *Die chemisch-technischen Mittheilungen*, Berlin, 36, 1858; *Journ. prakt. Chem.*, (1), 90. 257, 1866; B. Szilard, *Journ. Chim. Phys.*, 5. 488, 1907; H. Lienau, *Beiträge zur Kenntnis der Uranylsalze*, Berlin, 44, 1898; H. Hermann, *Ueber einige Uran-verbindungen*, Göttingen, 1861; J. Aloy, *Recherches sur l'uranium et ses composés*, Toulouse, 1901; *Ann. Chim. Phys.*, (7), 24. 412, 1901; *Bull. Soc. Chim.*, (3), 23. 368, 1900; (3), 25. 153, 344, 1901; *Compt. Rend.*, 122. 1542, 1896; C. Dittrich, *Die Uranylsalze vom physikalisch-chemischen Standpunkte aus betrachtet*, Leipzig, 1899; *Zeit. phys. Chem.*, 29. 467, 1899; E. M. Péligot, *Ann. Chim. Phys.*, (3), 12. 549, 1844; J. J. Ebelmen, *ib.*, (3), 5. 199, 1842; F. J. Malaguti, *ib.*, (3), 9. 463, 1843; W. Gibbons, *Pharm. Journ.*, (3), 13. 737, 1883; *Monit. Scient.*, (3), 25. 908, 1883; *Arch. Pharm.*, 221. 621, 1883; F. W. O. de Coninck, *Bull. Acad. Belg.*, 222, 1901; 363, 448, 1904; 993, 1908; *Compt. Rend.*, 148. 1462, 1909; F. W. O. de Coninck and A. Raynaud, *Bull. Soc. Chim.*, (4), 9. 301, 1911; F. W. O. de Coninck and M. Camo, *Bull. Acad. Belg.*, 321, 1901; A. Michael and A. Murphy, *Amer. Chem. Journ.*, 44. 365, 1910; C. F. Rammelsberg, *Sitzber. Akad. Berlin*, 100, 1885; C. Friedheim, *Ber.*, 38. 2352, 1905; V. Kohlschütter and K. Vogdt, *ib.*, 38. 1419, 2992, 1905; V. Kohlschütter, *Liebig's Ann.*, 314, 311, 1901; G. Rauter, *ib.*, 270. 254, 1892; R. Sendtner, *ib.*, 195. 325, 1879; H. Moissan, *Monit. Scient.*, (4), 9. 623, 1895; *Compt. Rend.*, 115. 1031, 1892; H. E. Quantin, *ib.*, 106. 1074, 1888; P. Camboulives, *ib.*, 150. 175, 1910; R. de Forcrand, *ib.*, 156. 1954, 1913; P. Lebeau, *ib.*, 154. 1808, 1912; M. L. Phillips, *Phys. Rev.*, (2), 32. 832, 1928; L. Kahlenberg and H. W. Hillyer, *Amer. Chem. Journ.*, 16. 94, 1894; G. Gore, *Phil. Mag.*, (4), 29. 541, 1865; *Proc. Roy. Soc.*, 14. 204, 1865; A. Wehnelt, *Ann. Physik*, (4), 14. 425, 1904; O. Brunck, *Zeit. anorg. Chem.*, 10. 245, 1895; G. F. Hüttig, *Zeit. angew. Chem.*, 35. 391, 1922; G. F. Hüttig and E. von Schröder, *Zeit. anorg. Chem.*, 121. 243, 1922; G. Beck, *ib.*, 174. 31, 1928; W. Biltz, *ib.*, 109. 132, 1919; 193. 321, 1930; W. Biltz and C. Fendius, *ib.*, 176. 49, 1928; W. Biltz and H. Müller, *ib.*, 163. 257, 1927; V. A. Kargin, *ib.*, 198. 79, 1931; P. Sabatier and J. B. Senderens, *Bull. Soc. Chim.*, (3), 13. 870, 1895; *Compt. Rend.*, 120. 618, 1895; J. Riban, *ib.*, 93. 1141, 1881; *Bull. Soc. Chim.*, (2), 33. 157, 1880; H. Rose, *Ausführliches Handbuch der analytischen Chemie*, Braunschweig, 2. 523, 1851; W. R. E. Hodgkinson and F. K. S. Lowndes, *Chem. News*, 58. 309, 1888; 59. 63, 1889; J. Zehenter, *Monatsh.*, 21. 235,

1900; B. Drenckmann, *Zeit. ges. Naturwiss.*, **17**. 131, 1861; P. Jolibois and R. Bossuet, *Compt. Rend.*, **174**. 1625, 1922; F. Mylius and R. Dietz, *Ber.*, **34**. 2774, 1901; H. Ley, *ib.*, **33**. 2659, 1900; T. Graham, *Phil. Trans.*, **151**. 183, 1861; *Phil. Mag.*, (4), **23**. 204, 290, 368, 1862; *Journ. Chem. Soc.*, **15**. 216, 1862; *Chem. News*, **4**. 86, 1861; *Proc. Roy. Soc.*, **11**. 243, 1862; B. Moore and T. A. Webster, *ib.*, **87**. B, 163, 1913; A. Mailhe, *Action d'un oxyde ou d'un hydrate métallique sur les solutions des sels des autres métaux*, Toulouse, 1902; H. T. S. Britton, *Journ. Chem. Soc.*, **127**. 2148, 1925; C. A. Pierlé, *Journ. Phys. Chem.*, **23**. 517, 1919; L. Bruner, *Zeit. phys. Chem.*, **32**. 133, 1900; M. E. Chevreul, *Ann. Phil.*, **12**. 144, 1818; *Bull. Philomath.*, 20, 1818; W. G. Mixter, *Amer. Journ. Science*, (4), **34**. 141, 1912; *Zeit. anorg. Chem.*, **78**. 231, 1912; K. C. Sen, *ib.*, **174**. 61, 1928; *Journ. Indian Chem. Soc.*, **4**. 117, 131, 1927; V. A. Jacquelain, *Chem. Centr.*, (1), **16**. 193, 1845; S. J. Diachkowsky, *Ukraine Chem. Journ.*, **2**. 340, 1926; L. Pissarjewsky, *Zeit. anorg. Chem.*, **24**. 108, 1900; D. Balareff, *ib.*, **134**. 75, 1924; *Journ. prakt. Chem.*, (2), **102**. 283, 1921; V. M. Goldschmidt and L. Thomassen, *Videnskapsselskapets Skrifter*, 5, 1923; E. K. Rideal, *Journ. Soc. Chem. Ind.*, **33**. 673, 1914; *Das elektrochemische Verhalten des Urans und einiger Uranverbindungen*, Bonn, 1913; A. Fischer and E. K. Rideal, *Zeit. anorg. Chem.*, **81**. 170, 1913; V. Billiet, *Natuurwet. Tijds.*, **7**. 112, 1927; A. Schoep, *Ann. Musée Congo Belg.*, **1**. 43, 1930; *Bull. Soc. Chim. Belg.*, **33**. 88, 578, 1924; *Bull. Soc. Chim.*, (4), **49**. 310, 1927; *Natuurwet. Tijds.*, **7**. 97, 1926; **9**. 1, 1927; *Bull. Soc. Min.*, **46**. 9, 1923; S. C. Lind and C. W. Davis, *Science*, (2), **49**. 441, 1919; E. S. Larsen, F. L. Hess and W. T. Schaller, *Amer. Min.*, **11**. 155, 1926; T. L. Walker, *ib.*, **8**. 67, 1923; A. W. Cronander, *Oefvers. Akad. Stockholm*, **27**. 57, 1870; *Ber.*, **6**. 1466, 1873; *Bull. Soc. Chim.*, (2), **19**. 499, 1873; F. Behounek, *Phys. Zeit.*, **31**. 215, 1930; S. Maracineanu, *Compt. Rend.*, **183**. 345, 1926; **184**. 1547, 1927; **185**. 122, 1927; **186**. 746, 1928; E. Wedekind and C. Horst, *Ber.*, **48**. 105, 1915; F. O. von der Pfordten, *Liebig's Ann.*, **222**. 142, 1883; M. le Blanc and H. Sachse, *Ber. Sächs. Akad.*, **82**. 153, 1930.

§ 12. The Normal Uranates, or Monouranates

Uranic acid, H_2UO_4, behaves as a dibasic acid, forming salts of the type R_2UO_4; and, like the other acids of the same family of elements, it forms more acid salts, $R_2O.nUO_3$, in which n may be 2, 3, 4, 5, and 6. With the exception of pyrouranic acid, or diuranic acid, $H_2U_2O_7$, the corresponding acids are unknown. The acid salts are probably constituted like the corresponding molybdic and tungstic salts; but they have not yet been investigated. Only salts of the more electropositive metals have been prepared.

Normal *ammonium uranate*, $(NH_4)_2UO_4$, has not been prepared, although acid salts are known. K. A. Hofmann[1] prepared anhydrous **hydroxylamine uranate,** $(NH_3OH)_2UO_4$, as a golden-yellow, amorphous powder, by heating the ammine— *vide infra*—with glycerol at 100°. The product is washed with alcohol and ether. The *monohydrate*, $(NH_3OH)_2UO_4.H_2O$, is formed by allowing the ammine to remain for some hours in contact with water at ordinary temp., or by treating the ammine with hot water, or by treating it with acetic acid. K. A. Hofmann obtained it by digesting uranic acid or uranyl nitrate with an excess of an aq. soln. of hydroxylamine; and V. Kohlschütter and K. Vogdt, by adding hydroxylamine hydrochloride to the orange precipitate produced by adding alkali-lye to a soln. of a uranyl salt. H. Gubler modified the process, and also added dil. aq. ammonia to a soln. of 50 grms. of uranyl nitrate in 200–300 c.c. of water, with constant stirring until the uranium is all precipitated as ammonium uranate. A soln. of 14–15 grms. of hydroxylamine hydrochloride in 50 c.c. of water is then added; and after standing half an hour, the precipitate is filtered, and washed twice with alcohol, and ether. There is generally a dark decomposition product formed in these processes. The hydroxylamine uranate obtained by V. Kohlschütter and K. Vogdt appeared in yellowish-green crystals; whilst that prepared by K. A. Hofmann appeared in yellow, elongated plates, pointed at both ends at an angle of 120°. When heated the salt decomposes with a slight explosion, producing a greenish-black powder. V. Kohlschütter and K. Vogdt said that when slowly heated at 125°, it decomposes into water and ammonia, which pass away, and into nitrogen and nitrous oxide, which remain practically entirely dissolved in the uranic acid, and escape on dissolving the residue in dil. acids. Uranium oxide only exercises this power of retaining indifferent gases so long as it contains traces of water, the real solvents being hydrates of uranium trioxide. It is suggested that the water present plays an important part in the retention of such gases as helium in uranium minerals. On the other hand, C. Friedheim suggested that the product obtained by heating hydroxylamine uranate at 125° is not a solid soln. of nitrogen and nitrous oxide in uranic acid, but that the decomposition proceeds: $UO_2(O.NH_3OH)_2$ $\rightarrow UO_2 : (O.NH_3)_2 : O$. Hydroxylamine uranate is known to behave as an acid, and the compound obtained by the action of heat may be regarded as an anhydride, so that the residue after heating consists of this anhydride mixed with a certain amount of uranic acid. The action of sulphuric acid on the anhydride is to yield uranyl sulphate and $(HO.NH_3)_2O$. This latter loses water, yielding the anhydride of hydroxylamine, $(NH_2)_2O$, which immediately decomposes into nitrogen, nitrous oxide, ammonia, hydrogen, and water. The hydrogen is probably used up in reducing uranium trioxide. H. Gubler said that the salt does not explode at 100° when out of contact with oxygen; but if heated to 100° in a current of oxygen, uranic acid remains as a residue, while hydroxylamine is given off, and this decomposes into steam and an equal vol. of nitrogen and nitrous oxide. If the temp. exceeds 100°, some ammonia is formed as well; but if no oxygen is present and the water vapour is removed by a current of inert gas, steam, ammonia, and hydrogen are formed. K. A. Hofmann found that the salt readily reduces Fehling's soln. V. Kohlschütter and K. A. Hofmann added that the brownish-black substance which is formed when hydroxylamine uranate is dehydrated at 125° is **uranium pentoxynitride**, UO_5N, a substance which liberates a mixture of nitrogen and nitrous oxide when treated with cold dil. acids, uranic acid passing into soln. According to K. A. Hofmann, **hydroxylamine diamminouranate**, $(NH_3OH)_2UO_4.2NH_3$, is obtained by adding 100 c.c. of 7 per cent. aq. ammonia to an aq. soln. of 20 grms. of uranyl nitrate and 10 grms. of hydroxylamine hydrochloride. The product is washed successively with dil. ammonia, alcohol, and ether. The constitution is represented by the formula $UO_2(O.NH_3.O.NH_4)_2$. The amminouranate is a lustrous, canary-yellow, crystalline powder consisting of microscopic, rhombic tablets; it is stable at the ordinary temp., loses ammonia when heated at 73°, and decomposes with a slight explosion when heated to 178°–180° in a capillary tube. It reduces Fehling's soln. at the ordinary temp., and when cautiously heated to 120° is converted into uranic acid, H_2UO_4. The ammonia is readily expelled when the salt is treated with water as indicated above; the uranic acid is not reduced when the salt is boiled with soda-lye. These facts are taken to confirm the above formula. When the amminouranate is treated with 2 mols. of acetic acid, it yields ammonium acetate and hydroxylamine uranate; with an excess of acetic acid, it yields a double salt of uranyl acetate and hydroxylamine acetate, which crystallizes in yellow, lustrous prisms.

According to V. Kohlschütter and K. A. Hofmann, **potassium hydroxylamine hydrouranate**, $(NH_3OH)(NH_3OK)UO_4.H_2O$, is obtained by dissolving 10 grms. of uranyl nitrate and 15 grms. of hydroxylamine hydrochloride in 100 c.c. of water, and adding a 10 per cent. soln. of potash-lye until the yellow, flocculent precipitate at first formed is redissolved; reddish-yellow cubes separate slowly from the liquid, precipitation being hastened by adding alcohol. The substance disintegrates to a yellow powder when heated, and has an ammoniacal smell; it is sparingly soluble in water, and is oxidized slowly by Fehling's soln. Turmeric is coloured brown by dil. soln. When the potassium compound is digested with water which has been sat. with carbon dioxide, the colour changes to green and hydroxylamine uranate is produced. The corresponding **sodium hydroxylamine hydrouranate**, $(NH_3OH)(NH_3ONa)UO_4.H_2O$, is obtained in minute prismatic crystals in a similar manner; and the mother-liquor deposits **sodium hydroxylamine uranate**, $(NH_3ONa)_2UO_4.6H_2O$, in orange-red rosettes of prisms, and dissolves in its water of crystallization when heated; it is readily soluble in water, and vigorously reduces Fehling's soln.

A. Ditte[2] prepared **lithium uranate**, Li_2UO_4, by fusing together a mixture of lithium chloride and uranosic oxide, and extracting the cold product with water.

J. L. C. Zimmermann prepared lithium uranate by heating a mixture of lithium and ammonium chlorides with uranyl chloride at a high temp. The product, when cold, is washed with cold water. Whilst potassium and sodium chlorides under similar conditions give the diuranates, lithium chloride forms the normal salt. Lithium uranate is far more easily decomposed by hot water than the corresponding sodium or potassium salts; lithium and uranyl hydroxides are produced. G. Tammann and W. Rosenthal prepared lithium uranate by heating mol. proportions of lithium carbonate and uranium trioxide to 600°. The reaction begins at 380°. B. Drenckmann obtained **sodium uranate,** Na_2UO_4, by heating sodium diuranate with a large excess of sodium chloride; A. Ditte, by heating uranosic oxide with sodium carbonate or chloride with or without sodium chlorate; T. Poleck, by boiling the yellow soln. of sodium perdiuranate, obtained by fusing a uranyl salt with sodium dioxide; and L. Michel, by heating uranium molybdate with sodium chloride. J. L. C. Zimmermann converted the amorphous salt into crystals by fusing it with sodium chloride. A. Ditte said that the salt forms greenish-yellow plates, and L. Michel, reddish-yellow, doubly refracting, rhombic prisms with a cleavage on the (110)-face, and the optic axial angle $2E=59°$. W. G. Mixter gave for the heat of formation, $(UO_3,Na_2O)=96\cdot1$ Cals.; $(UO_2,Na_2O_2)=110\cdot9$ Cals.; and $U_3O_8+Na_2O_2+2Na_2O=3Na_2UO_4+285\cdot1$ Cals. A. Ditte added that the salt is insoluble in water, and freely soluble in acids. A. Ditte prepared normal **potassium uranate,** K_2UO_4, as in the case of the sodium salt, namely, by fusing together a mixture of potassium chloride and uranosic oxide; if the mixture in a platinum crucible be heated from below, the uranate separates as a crystalline crust at the surface, and can be washed free from chlorides by water. H. Grandeau obtained it by fusing a mixture of uranyl phosphate and potassium sulphate; J. L. C. Zimmermann, by fusing a mixture of 6 parts of uranyl chloride, 16 parts of ammonium chloride, and 4 parts of potassium chloride; and O. Brunck, by heating together a mixture of uranium trioxide and potassium chlorate. The products washed free from soluble matters furnish, according to H. Grandeau, orange-yellow, pseudo-hexagonal plates. The crystals are rhombic, with the optic axial angle $2E=110°$, approximately. A. Ditte obtained **rubidium uranate,** Rb_2UO_4, by fusing rubidium chloride and uranosic oxide as in the case of the potassium salt. G. Tammann and W. Rosenthal found that a mixture of mol. proportions of copper oxide, or of silver oxide, and uranium trioxide begins to react, forming brown **copper uranate,** $CuUO_4$, at 340°, and brown **silver uranate,** Ag_2UO_4, at 150° respectively.

F. W. O. de Coninck prepared **calcium uranate,** $CaUO_4$, as a dark red precipitate, by adding ammonia to a mixed soln. of uranyl chloride and calcium chloride: $UO_2Cl_2+CaCl_2+4NH_3+2H_2O=CaUO_4+4NH_4Cl$, and A. Ditte, by heating a mixture of uranosic oxide and calcium chloride—free from oxide. G. Tammann and W. Rosenthal found that the formation of calcium uranate begins at 160° when a mixture of mol. proportions of the constituent oxides is heated. According to A. Ditte, the greenish-yellow plates are insoluble in water, but soluble in dil. acids. If heated to redness for a long time the colour deepens, and the compound dissolves less readily in dil. acids. By using processes analogous to those employed for calcium uranate, F. W. O. de Coninck, and A. Ditte prepared **strontium uranate,** $SrUO_4$; also **barium uranate,** $BaUO_4$. J. A. Hedvall and N. von Zweigbergh observed that a mixture of barium dioxide and uranium trioxide begins to give off oxygen at 250°. G. Tammann and W. Rosenthal found that the normal uranates begin to form when a mixture of mol. proportions of uranium trioxide and strontium oxide is heated to 125°, and with barium oxide the reaction begins at 240°. No **beryllium uranate** was observed by heating a mixture of mol. proportions of the constituent oxides to 600°; but yellow **magnesium uranate,** $MgUO_4$, was obtained. A. Ditte also prepared magnesium uranate. I. Wertheim found that **zinc uranate,** $ZnUO_4$, is deposited on a sheet of zinc immersed in a soln. of uranyl nitrate; and it is deposited when zinc uranyl acetate is treated with baryta-water. M. Kohn observed that when a boiling conc. soln. of uranyl nitrate is treated with basic zinc carbonate, and the yellow precipitate is washed successively with water, alcohol, and ether, the product consists of hydrated uranium trioxide contaminated with zinc oxide.   G. Tammann and W. Rosenthal found that the formation of zinc uranate begins when a mixture of mol. proportions of the constituent oxides is heated to 200° ; with orange-yellow **cadmium uranate,** $CdUO_4$, the reaction begins at 425° ; with orange-yellow **mercuric uranate,** $HgUO_4$, at 175° ; and with yellow **aluminium uranate,** $Al_2(UO_4)_3$, at 450°.   C. Renz found that **indium uranate** is precipitated from a soln. of an indium salt when it is treated with a soln. of sodium uranate ; and H. C. Bolton obtained a yellow precipitate of **thallous uranate,** resembling the alkali uranates, when thallous hydroxide is added to a soln. of a uranyl salt.   G. Tammann and W. Rosenthal observed that **cerium uranate** is not formed when an equimolar mixture of cerium and uranium trioxides is heated to 600°.

The canary-yellow or orange-yellow crystalline crusts found on the pitchblende from Kasolo, Katanga, Belgian Congo, were called by A. Schoep **becquerelite**—after H. Becquerel.   The minute rhombic crystals have the axial ratios $a : b : c$ $=0.5537 : 1 : 0.5938$, and are like schoepite, $UO_3.2H_2O$, but contain a higher proportion of lead.   S. G. Gordon, re-orienting the measurements, obtained $a : b : c$ $=0.432 : 1 : 0.874$, virtually the same as schoepite.   When dried at 100° becquerelite corresponds with a kind of **lead uranate,** or it may be the hydrated trioxide with some uranyl replaced by lead, namely, $(UO_2.Pb)O$, $2H_2O$—*vide supra*, schoepite. The crystals of becquerelite may be twinned after the aragonite type ; the (001)- and (110)-cleavages are perfect ; the indices of refraction $a=1.75$, and $\gamma=1.77$; the optical character is negative ; and the pleochroism ranges from colourless to deep yellow.   V. Billiet gave 1.750, 1.88, and 1.87 for the indices of refraction of the rhombic crystals.   G. Tammann and W. Rosenthal observed that a mixture of mol. proportions of lead oxide and uranium trioxide begins to react at 375°, forming lead uranate.   Normal lead uranate, $PbUO_4$, was prepared by I. Wertheim, and C. F. Rammelsberg by calcining lead acetate and a uranium salt at a dull red-heat.   J. Zehenter said that the reddish-brown mass consists of microscopic needles. It becomes black when heated to bright redness.   The salt is insoluble in water, potash-lye, aq. ammonia, alcohol and ether ; sparingly soluble in cold acetic acid ; and freely soluble in nitric acid and hot acetic acid.   According to K. C. Bailey, lead uranate is insoluble in boiling distilled water, or in a boiling soln. of sodium chloride, but in both cases some lead salt passes into soln. when the system is exposed to a-rays.   The reaction was discussed by A. Holmes.   J. Melon found that the composition of the rhombic crystals is $PbO.5UO_3.10H_2O$, and V. Billiet found the indices of refraction to be $\beta=1.92$ and $\gamma=1.94$.   C. S. Ross, E. P. Henderson and E. Posnjak described a mineral from Spruce Vine, Carolina, which they called **clarkeite**—after F. W. Clarke.   Its composition approximates $(Na_2,Ca,Pb)O.3UO_3.3H_2O$.   It is reddish-brown and massive ; without cleavage, and with a conchoidal fracture.   It is considered to be a direct alteration product of uraninite, gummite and uranophane being later products.

For **vanadium uranate,** *vide* uranyl vanadate.   V. A. Kargin studied the complex salts formed by uranium trioxide with vanadium pentoxide.   G. Tammann and W. Rosenthal observed that green vanadium uranate, $V_2(UO_4)_3$, begins to form at 290° when a mixture of mol. proportions of the constituent oxides is heated ; with **chromium uranate,** $Cr_2(UO_4)_3$, the reaction begins at 230° ; with **manganous uranate,** $MnUO_4$, at 450° ; and the brown **ferric uranate,** $Fe_2(UO_4)_3$, is formed at 600°.   J. A. Arfvedson passed ammonia into a soln. containing ferric and uranyl salts, and heated the precipitate in hydrogen.   He called the product *iron uranate*.   It appears to be a mixture of iron and uranium oxides.   G. Tammann and W. Rosenthal found that **cobalt uranate,** $CoUO_4$, is formed when an equimolar mixture of the constituent oxides is heated to 600°—the reaction begins at 230° ; in the formation of **nickel uranate,** $NiUO_4$, the reaction begins at 340°.

REFERENCES.

[1] K. A. Hofmann, *Zeit. anorg. Chem.*, **15**. 75, 1897 ; **16**. 463, 1898 ; H. Gubler, *Beiträge zur Kenntnis des Hydroxylamins*, Basel, 1908 ; V. Kohlschütter and K. A. Hofmann, *Liebig's Ann.*, **307**. 321, 1899 ; V. Kohlschütter and K. Vogdt, *Ber.*, **38**. 1419, 2992, 1905 ; C. Friedheim, *ib.*, **38**. 2352, 1905.

[2] A. Ditte, *Compt. Rend.*, **95**. 990, 1882 ; J. A. Arfvedson, *Svenska Akad. Handl.*, 404, 1822 ; *Ann. Phil.*, **7**. 253, 1824 ; *Pogg. Ann.*, **1**. 245, 1824 ; *Schweigger's Journ.*, **44**. 8, 1825 ; J. Melon, *Ann. Soc. Géol. Belg.*, **47**. 200, 1925 ; J. L. C. Zimmermann, *Ber.*, **14**. 140, 1881 ; *Liebig's Ann.*, **213**. 290, 1882 ; H. Buttgenbach, *Ann. Soc. Géol. Belg.*, **47**. 31, 1924 ; B. Drenckmann, *Zeit. ges. Naturwiss.*, **17**. 113, 1861 ; T. Poleck, *Ber.*, **27**. 1051, 1891 ; C. Renz, *ib.*, **34**. 2765, 1901 ; *Beiträge zur Kenntnis des Indiums und Thalliums*, Breslau, 1902 ; L. Michel, *Bull. Soc. Min.*, **13**. 72, 1890 ; W. G. Mixter, *Amer. Chem. Journ.*, (4), **34**. 141, 1912 ; *Zeit. anorg. Chem.*, **78**. 231, 1912 ; H. Grandeau, *Ann. Chim. Phys.*, (6), **8**. 224, 1886 ; *Compt. Rend.*, **95**. 921, 1882 ; **100**. 1134, 1885 ; F. W. O. de Coninck, *ib.*, **148**. 1769, 1909 ; O. Brunck, *Zeit. anorg. Chem.*, **10**. 246, 1895 ; M. Kohn, *ib.*, **50**. 315, 1906 ; G. Tammann and W. Rosenthal, *ib.*, **156**. 20, 1926 ; J. A. Hedvall and N. von Zweigbergk, *ib.*, **108**. 119, 1919 ; H. C. Bolton, *Amer. Chemist*, **2**. 456, 1872 ; S. G. Gordon, *Amer. Min.*, **10**. 38, 1925 ; A. Schoep, *Compt. Rend.*, **174**. 1240, 1922 ; *Bull. Soc. Chim. Belg.*, **33**. 88, 1924 ; *Bull. Soc. Min.*, **46**. 9, 1923 ; **47**. 147, 1924 ; *Naturwet. Tijds.*, **7**. 97, 1927 ; V. Billiet, *ib.*, **7**. 112, 1927 ; C. F. Rammelsberg, *Sitzber. Akad. Berlin*, 882, 1882 ; I. Wertheim, *Ber. Vers. deut. Naturf.*, 193, 1843 ; *Ann. Chim. Phys.*, (3), **11**. 49, 1844 ; *Journ. prakt. Chem.*, (1), **29**. 207, 1842 ; J. Zehenter, *Monatsh.*, **25**. 210, 1904 ; W. Vernadsky, *Compt. Rend.*, **176**. 993, 1923 ; K. C. Bailey, *Phil. Mag.*, (7), **4**. 404, 1927 ; A. Holmes, *ib.*, (7), **4**. 1242, 1927 ; C. S. Ross, E. P. Henderson and E. Posnjak, *Amer. Min.*, **16**. 213, 1931 ; V. A. Kargin, *Zeit. anorg. Chem.*, **198**. 79, 1931.

§ 13. The Polyuranates

According to J. A. Arfvedson,[1] **ammonium diuranate,** $(NH_4)_2U_2O_7$, is obtained as a hydrated yellow powder when uranyl nitrate or chloride is treated with an excess of aq. ammonia. A. J. Carson and T. H. Norton prepared the salt in a similar way, and dried the product at 100°. They said that there is a marked difference between the observed and theoretical proportions of uranium with the uranates of ammonium, and of methyl-, dimethyl-, trimethyl-, ethyl-, diethyl-, triethyl-, isobutyl-, and phenyl-ammonium—the ethyl-ammonium salt approaches nearest to the theoretical value. Ammonium diuranate is the ammonium uranate of commerce, where it, as well as the sodium salt, is known as *uranium yellow.* A. Patera, and E. Vysoky described the preparation of the two uranium yellows. The ammonium salt is obtained commercially by boiling a soln. of sodium uranyl carbonate with ammonium sulphate, or by boiling sodium diuranate with a conc. soln. of ammonium chloride. Ammonium diuranate is a deep yellow powder which, according to J. A. Arfvedson, can be dried at 100° without change, but at a higher temp. it is resolved into nitrogen, ammonia, water, and uranosic oxide ; if it is heated with ammonium chloride, F. Stolba found that an appreciable quantity of uranium volatilizes with the ammonium salt. J. J. Berzelius said that it is very sparingly soluble in water, but it is not soluble in water containing ammonium chloride, and J. A. Arfvedson said that it is insoluble in aq. ammonia. These facts are sometimes utilized in the analytical separation of uranium ; the salt cannot be freed from ammonia by boiling it with water. E. M. Péligot observed that the diuranate is soluble in a soln. of ammonium carbonate, forming ammonium uranyl carbonate.

H. von Unruh obtained anhydrous **sodium diuranate,** $Na_2U_2O_7$, by adding sodium to an ethereal soln. of uranyl nitrate, $6Na+2UO_2(NO_3)_2.6H_2O =4NaNO_3+3H_2+3H_2O+Na_2U_2O_7$. I. Wertheim obtained the anhydrous salt by heating the hydrated salt obtained commercially by A. Patera, E. F. Anthon, F. Stolba, L. Kessler, K. A. Hofmann and E. Strauss, and F. J. Metzger and M. Heidelberger, as indicated in connection with the extraction of uranium from its ores. J. L. C. Zimmermann obtained it by a process similar to that which he employed for normal lithium uranate. It is isomorphous with the corresponding potassium salt. F. Stolba, and A. Patera obtained the *hexahydrate* by adding an excess of sodium hydroxide to a soln. of a uranyl salt, and drying the washed precipitate in air. A. Lancien obtained it by boiling uranyl molybdate in soda-lye for a long time. The light yellow *uranium yellow* of commerce—*vide supra*, the ammonium salt—is obtained by decomposing a soln. of sodium uranyl carbonate with sulphuric acid ; and the *orange-yellow*, by decomposing a uranyl salt with an excess of sodium hydroxide. According to F. J. Metzger and M. Heidelberger, sodium uranate, of the composition $Na_2U_2O_7$, may actually be precipitated, but on washing with water to remove the excess of alkali, it gradually undergoes partial hydrolysis, so that pure sodium uranate, obtained by adding sodium hydroxide to a soln. of uranyl nitrate, has the composition $Na_4U_5O_{17}$, and A. Patera's precipitate the composition $Na_9U_{10}O_{35}$. J. A. Arfvedson prepared **potassium diuranate**, $K_2U_2O_7$, by treating a soln. of a uranyl salt with an excess of potashlye, and calcining the washed product at a red-heat. P. Jolibois and R. Bossuet found that the precipitate from uranyl nitrate soln. with soda-lye is not the diuranate, the precipitate contains no nitrate, and 1·2 to 8 per cent. of adsorbed alkali. H. T. S. Britton also showed that the precipitate is probably uranium hydroxide. J. J. Berzelius obtained the diuranate by melting uranium trioxide with an excess of potassium carbonate, and extracting the cold mass with water ; and also by calcining potassium uranyl carbonate, and I. Wertheim, by calcining potassium uranyl acetate, and extracting the products with water. J. L. C. Zimmermann, and A. Lancien obtained it by processes analogous to those used for the sodium salt. The colour varies from brick-red to orange-yellow according to the mode of preparation. J. L. C. Zimmermann described it as a crystalline powder with the crystals probably rhombic and isomorphous with those of the sodium salt. The salt becomes dark red when heated, but the original colour is restored on cooling. J. L. C. Zimmermann, and F. W. O. de Coninck observed that the salt is insoluble in water and freely soluble in acids. According to A. Patera, if the precipitated salt is dried at 100°, the *trihydrate* is formed ; and, according to F. Stolba, if dried in air, at ordinary temp., the *hexahydrate*. L. Fernandes obtained a complex with gallic acid.

C. F. Rammelsberg obtained a brick-red precipitate by adding aq. ammonia to a mixed soln. of uranyl nitrate and an excess of silver nitrate. A. Guyard, and G. Alibegoff obtained **silver diuranate**, $Ag_2U_2O_7$, by the action of freshly-precipitated silver oxide on a soln. of uranyl nitrate ; G. Alibegoff, by the action of potassium uranate on fused silver nitrate ; and I. Wertheim, by boiling uranyl silver acetate with water. The orange-red product is decomposed by hydrochloric acid. J. Aloy said that a basic silver uranate is produced when uranic acid is digested with a soln. of silver nitrate. A. Ditte prepared **calcium diuranate**, CaU_2O_7, by heating a mixture of uranosic oxide and calcium chlorate, and fusing the product with sodium or calcium chloride so as to convert the amorphous salt into greenish-yellow plates. A. Ditte prepared **strontium diuranate**, SrU_2O_7, by an analogous process. According to a communication by " J.," the brownish-red product is sparingly soluble in water and soluble in acids, including oxalic acid. J. A. Arfvedson added barium chloride and an excess of ammonia to a boiling soln. of uranyl chloride, washed the product with boiling water, and obtained what was presumably **barium diuranate**, BaU_2O_7, which J. J. Berzelius obtained by adding barium chloride to a soln. of ammonium diuranate ; and J. J. Berzelius, and O. B. Kühn, by adding an excess of baryta-water to a soln. of uranyl nitrate. I. Wertheim used uranyl acetate with an insufficient amount of baryta-water to precipitate all the uranium ; the idea was to avoid the formation of barium carbonate ; he also obtained the diuranate by heating barium uranyl acetate to redness. A. Ditte prepared the salt by heating uranosic oxide with barium chlorate ; and J. Zehenter, by heating barium uranyl acetate between 300° and a red-heat. The yellowish-red crystalline powder is decomposed by hydrogen at a red-heat. I. Wertheim obtained **magnesium diuranate**, MgU_2O_7, as a yellowish-brown powder, by calcining magnesium uranyl acetate ; and J. J. Berzelius, by adding ammonia to a mixed soln. of uranyl nitrate and magnesium nitrate. K. A. Hofmann and K. Höschele obtained magnesium diuranate, $Mg_3U_2O_9$, by fusing anhydrous magnesium chloride with uranic acid. J. A. Arfvedson obtained **lead diuranate,** PbU_2O_7, by adding aq. ammonia to a mixed soln. of lead and uranyl nitrates ; I. Wertheim, by boiling freshly-precipitated lead carbonate with a soln. of uranyl nitrate, and then with the acetate ; J. Persoz, by adding uranyl nitrate to a soln. of lead acetate ; and J. Zehenter, by boiling a dil. soln. of lead uranyl acetate in a reflux apparatus, whereby golden-yellow crystals of the hemipentahydrate, $PbU_2O_7.2\frac{1}{2}H_2O$, are formed—they become anhydrous on ignition. The yellowish-red or brownish-red salt which has been heated is sparingly soluble in acetic acid. J. Zehenter represented it by the formula :

$$Pb\left\langle\begin{array}{c}O.UO_2\\O.UO_2\end{array}\right\rangle O$$

A. Weisbach found a mineral near Schneeberg, Saxony, occurring in half globular, aggregated forms, made up of minute, acutely terminated crystals of **bismuthyl diuranate,** $(BiO)_2U_2O_7.3H_2O$, or $Bi_2O_3.2UO_2.3H_2O$, according to the analysis of C. Winkler. The mineral was called **uranosphærite.** Its colour is orange-yellow to brick-red ; its sp. gr., 6·36 ; and its hardness, 2·3. A. L. Fletcher said that small particles soften at 1170°, and large particles melt at 1320°.

B. Drenckmann[2] prepared **sodium triuranate,** $Na_2O.3UO_3$, by heating a mixture of uranyl sulphate and sodium chloride, and washing the residue with water. The hygroscopic golden-yellow powder consists of rhombic crystals of sp. gr. 6·912. It becomes silver-grey when heated to a high temp. It is insoluble in water, but freely soluble in dil. acids. J. Zehenter obtained **barium triuranate,** $BaU_3O_{10}.4\frac{1}{2}H_2O$, by boiling a soln. of barium uranyl acetate. The yellow crystalline mass loses $2\frac{1}{2}H_2O$ at 140°, and the remaining 2 mols. at low redness.

According to N. A. Orloff, **neodymium triuranate,** $Nd_2(U_3O_{10})_3.18H_2O$, is formed as a yellow crystalline precipitate on heating on a water-bath neodymium hydroxide with a soln. of uranyl acetate ; and similarly with **praseodymium triuranate,** $Pr_2(U_3O_{10})_3.18H_2O$. The corresponding **aluminium triuranate** is not formed in this way. J. Zehenter obtained **lead triuranate,** PbU_3O_{10}, by calcining lead triuranyl acetate. The reddish-brown microscopic prisms are insoluble in water, potash-lye, aq. ammonia, and cold acetic acid ; but soluble in nitric acid and hot acetic acid. The constitution is represented :

$$UO_2\left\langle\begin{array}{c}O.UO_2.O\\O.UO_2.O\end{array}\right\rangle Pb$$

According to H. Gubler,[3] if uranyl acetate be dissolved in a little very dil. hydrochloric acid, filtered, mixed with an excess of ammonia, and the gelatinous precipitate dried on a porous tile, there is produced pale orange-yellow **ammonium tetrauranate,** $(NH_4)_2O.4UO_3.7H_2O$. J. Zehenter obtained **potassium tetrauranate,** $K_2O.4UO_3.5H_2O$, by evaporating an aq. soln. of potassium uranyl acetate, with the frequent addition of water, until the soln. is no longer acid. The yellow crystalline powder resembles the hexauranate in its properties. It loses about 2 mols. of water at 110°, and the rest at dull redness. A. Schoep described a reddish-brown mineral from Belgian Congo, and he called it **fourmarierite**—after P. Fourmariér. It occurs in rhombic crystals with axial ratios $a : b : c = 0.8832 : 1 : 0.8115$. The mineral is dichroic, and has a perfect cleavage perpendicular to the inclined axis. Its chemical composition approximates $PbO.4UO_3.5H_2O$, **lead tetrauranate,** but since the proportion of lead varies, he prefers to write it $(Pb,UO_2)O.H_2O$— *vide infra,* becquerelite and schoepite, which can also be represented by this formula. Its sp. gr. is 6·046 ; hardness, 3 to 4 ; and index of refraction > 1.754—V. Billiet gave 1·94–1·92 for the rhombic crystals. No water is lost at 100°, but all the water and some oxygen are lost at 350°. Some specimens contain up to 0·67 per cent. tellurium trioxide, and a little ferric oxide is usually present.

According to J. Zehenter,[4] when an aq. soln. of sodium uranyl acetate is boiled, an orange-yellow powder of **sodium pentauranate,** $Na_2O.5UO_3.5H_2O$, is deposited. The *pentahydrate* consists of rounded granules and six-sided plates. When heated, the yellow powder becomes brownish-yellow, and then dirty grey. It loses most of its water of crystallization over conc. sulphuric acid, or in vacuo, or at 100°; the remainder is driven off at a red-heat. It is insoluble in water, alcohol, aq. ammonia, and potash-lye, but freely soluble in hydrochloric, sulphuric, and nitric acids, and less soluble in hot acetic acid. F. Stolba reported a *dodecahydrate* to be formed by adding sodium hydroxide, not in excess, to a soln. of uranyl sulphate, and drying the precipitate in air. J. Zehenter found that **barium pentauranate,** $BaU_5O_{17}.8H_2O$, is formed in golden yellow crystals by heating a soln. of barium uranyl acetate on a water-bath and replacing the water evaporated from time to time. The crystals lose $4\frac{1}{2}H_2O$ at 140°, and the remainder at dull redness. A. Schoep reported a reddish-brown mineral occurring in acicular crystals, and also massive at Kasolo, Katanga, Belgian Congo; as translucent, reddish-brown, acicular crystals on torbernite; or else in compact, earthy masses consisting of minute needles. The mineral is called **curite**—after P. Curie—and the analysis corresponds with **lead pentauranite,** $2PbO.5UO_3.4H_2O$. The axial ratios of the rhombic crystals are $a : b : c = 0.9553 : 1 : 0.6535$, and the (100)- and (110)-cleavages are good. V. Billiet gave 2·12, and 2·07 for the index of refraction of the rhombic crystals. The sp. gr. is 7·192 at 17°; the hardness, 4 to 5; the index of refraction, >1.74. V. Billiet gave $\beta = 2.07$, and $\gamma = 2.12$. A. Schoep observed that when heated, the mineral becomes dark brown; it is soluble in cold nitric acid and in hot hydrochloric acid. J. Zehenter obtained the salt $4PbO.5UO_3.4H_2O$, by heating a dil. soln. of lead uranyl acetate on a water-bath, replacing from time to time the water as it evaporates. The slow evaporation of the soln. furnishes a golden-yellow, micro-crystalline powder resembling lead uranate in its general properties. It becomes anhydrous at dull redness. W. Vernadsky and C. Chamié considered curite to be an alteration product of pitchblende.

According to J. Zehenter,[5] ammonium uranyl acetate in aq. soln. decomposes in a short time, or at once on heating or evaporation, forming **ammonium hexauranate,** $(NH_4)_2O.6UO_3.10H_2O$, as a yellow powder, which consists of microscopic granules and six-sided plates. It loses 6 mols. of water at 120°, and at a higher temp. ammonia and water are given off, leaving uranosic oxide. The salt is insoluble in hot or cold water and in alkali-lye, but is freely soluble in hydrochloric, sulphuric, and acetic acids. According to R. Salvadori, when a 50 per cent. soln. of hydrazine hydrate is added to an aq. soln. of uranyl nitrate, **hydrazine pentauranate,** $(N_2H_5)_2O.5UO_3.8H_2O$, is precipitated. It loses almost all its nitrogen at 100°. B. Drenckmann prepared **potassium hexauranate,** $K_2O.6UO_3.6H_2O$, by heating over a blast gas-flame a mixture of potassium chloride and uranyl sulphate containing an excess of sulphuric acid, and the whole being covered by a layer of potassium chloride. The product was slowly cooled and boiled with water. The residue dried in vacuo furnished a hygroscopic yellow powder of the *hexahydrate*, which under the microscope was seen to consist of rhombic prisms. The salt loses all its water at 300°–400° and becomes brick-red; and at a higher temp. it becomes dark silver-grey and loses oxygen. J. Zehenter obtained the *decahydrate* by boiling for some hours a 1 per cent. soln. of potassium uranyl acetate. The yellow crystalline powder loses 5 mols. of water at 110°, and the remainder between 300° and dull redness. It is very sparingly soluble or insoluble in hot and cold water, alkali-lye, alcohol, and ether, and freely soluble in hot acetic acid and in dil. hydrochloric, sulphuric, and nitric acids.

J. Zehenter [6] prepared **barium heptauranate,** $Ba_2U_7O_{23}.11H_2O$, in yellow, microscopic, hexagonal leaflets, by boiling a soln. of barium uranyl acetate for 4 to 5 hrs. in a flask fitted with a reflux apparatus. The crystals lose $2\frac{1}{2}$ mols. of water at 110°, and the remainder at dull redness.

J. Zehenter prepared **lead enneauranate,** $Pb_5U_9O_{32}.10H_2O$, by boiling a soln.

of lead uranyl acetate in a flask fitted with a reflux condenser. The reddish-yellow precipitate consists of microscopic crystals. The mineral **tyuyamuyunite** is a **calcium uranatovanadate,** $CaO.2UO_3.V_2O_5.nH_2O$. It is radioactive, and, according to I. D. Kurbatoff,[7] occurs in Tyuya Muyun. V. A. Kargin prepared **uranyl vanadate,** $UO_3.2V_2O_5$, from a mixture of the hydrosols of the component oxides.

REFERENCES.

[1] A. J. Carson and T. H. Norton, *Amer. Chem. Journ.*, **10.** 219, 1888 ; J. A. Arfvedson, *Svenska Akad. Handl.*, 404, 1822 ; *Ann. Phil.*, **7.** 253, 1824 ; *Pogg. Ann.*, **1.** 245, 1824 ; *Schweigger's Journ.*, **44.** 8, 1825 ; J. J. Berzelius, *ib.*, **44.** 191, 1825 ; *Pogg. Ann.*, **1.** 359, 1824 ; *Svenska Akad. Handl.*, 152, 1823 ; *Ann. Phil.*, **9.** 266, 1825 ; E. M. Péligot, *Compt. Rend.*, **12.** 735, 1841 ; **22.** 487, 1846 ; **42.** 73, 1856 ; *Ann. Chim. Phys.*, (3), **5.** 5, 1842 ; (3), **20.** 329, 1847 ; *Journ. Pharm. Chim.*, (2), **27.** 522, 1841 ; *Liebig's Ann.*, **41.** 141, 1841 ; **43.** 258, 1842 ; *Journ. prakt. Chem.*, (1), **24.** 442, 1841 : (1), **38.** 112, 1846 ; I. Wertheim, *Ber. Vers. deut. Naturf*, 193, 1843 ; *Ann. Chim. Phys.*, (3), **11.** 49, 1844 ; *Journ. prakt. Chem.*, (1), **29.** 207, 1842 ; E. F. Anthon, *Dingler's Journ.*, **156.** 207, 1860 ; L. Kessler, *Journ. Pharm. Chim.*, (3), **31.** 182, 1857 ; C. F. Rammelsberg, *Sitzber. Akad. Berlin*, 100, 1885 ; F. Stolba, *Zeit. anal. Chem.*, **3.** 74, 1864 ; A. L. Fletcher, *Scient. Proc. Roy. Dublin Soc.*, (2), **13.** 443, 1913 ; E. Vysoky, *Oesterr. Zeit. Berg. Hütt.*, **7.** 277, 1859 ; **14.** 185, 1866 ; *Dingler's Journ.*, **155.** 305, 1860 ; **181.** 448, 1866 ; A. Patera, *ib.*, **132.** 36, 1854 ; **141.** 371, 1856 ; *Sitzber. Akad. Wien*, **5.** 353, 1849 ; **11.** 842, 1853 ; *Journ. prakt. Chem.*, (1), **61.** 379, 1854 ; (1), **69.** 118, 1856 ; C. Winkler, *ib.*, (2), **7.** 5, 1873 ; " J.," *Oesterr. Zeit. Zucker Ind.*, **25.** 443, 1896 ; A. Ditte, *Compt. Rend.*, **95.** 990, 1882 ; J. L. C. Zimmermann, *Ber.*, **14.** 440, 1881 ; *Liebig's Ann.*, **213.** 290, 1882 ; G. Alibegoff, *ib.*, **233.** 117, 1886 ; O. B. Kühn, *ib.*, **41.** 337, 1842 ; K. A. Hofmann and K. Höschele, *ib.*, **47.** 238, 1914 ; A. Lancien, *Bull. Scien. Pharmacol.*, **15.** 132, 1908 ; H. von Unruh, *Einwirkung von trocknem Ammoniak auf wasserfreie Uranylsalze*, Rostock, 1909 ; K. A. Hofmann and E. Strauss, *Ber.*, **33.** 3126, 1900 ; F. J. Metzger and M. Heidelberger, *Journ. Amer. Chem. Soc.*, **31.** 1040, 1909 ; J. Aloy, *Recherches sur l'uranium et ses composés*, Paris, 1901 ; H. T. S. Britton, *Journ. Chem. Soc.*, **127.** 2148, 1925 ; A. Guyard, *Bull. Soc. Chim.*, (2), **1.** 95, 1864 ; F. W. O. de Coninck, *Bull. Acad. Belg.*, 709, 1903 ; A. Weisbach, *Jahrb. Berg. Hütt. Sachs*, 119, 1873 ; *Neues Jahrb. Min.*, 315, 1873 ; J. Zehenter, *Monatsh.*, **25.** 197, 1904 ; J. Persoz, *Ann. Chim. Phys.*, (2), **56.** 335, 1834 ; P. Jolibois and R. Bossuet, *Compt. Rend.*, **174.** 1625, 1922 ; L. Fernandes, *Gazz. Chim. Ital.*, **53.** 514, 1923.

[2] B. Drenckmann, *Zeit. ges. Naturwiss.*, **17.** 113, 1861 ; N. A. Orloff, *Chem. Ztg.*, **31.** 1119, 1907 ; J. Zehenter, *Monatsh.*, **25.** 210, 1904.

[3] H. Gubler, *Beiträge zur Kenntnis des Hydroxylamins*, Basel, 1908 ; J. Zehenter, *Monatsh.*, **21.** 235, 1900 ; A. Schoep, *Bull. Soc. Chim. Belg.*, **33.** 558, 1924 ; V. Billiet, *Naturwet. Tijds.*, **7.** 112, 1927.

[4] J. Zehenter, *Monatsh.*, **21.** 235, 1900 ; **25.** 210, 1924 ; F. Stolba, *Zeit. anal. Chem.*, **3.** 74, 1864 ; V. Billiet, *Naturwet. Tijds.*, **7.** 112, 1927 ; W. Vernadsky and C. Chamié, *Compt. Rend.*, **178.** 1726, 1924 ; A. Schoep, *ib.*, **173.** 1186, 1921 ; *Bull. Soc. Chim. Belg.*, **33.** 558, 1924 ; *Ann. Soc. Géol. Belg.*, **49.** 188, 310, 1927 ; *Naturwet. Tijds.*, **9.** 1, 1927.

[5] J. Zehenter, *Monatsh.*, **21.** 235, 1900 ; B. Drenckmann, *Zeit. ges. Naturwiss.*, **17.** 134, 1861 ; R. Salvadori, *Atti Accad. Lincei*, (5), **21.** ii, 455, 1912.

[6] J. Zehenter, *Monatsh.*, **25.** 197, 1904.

[7] I. D. Kurbatoff, *Compt. Rend. U.R.S.S. Acad.*, 452, 1930 ; I. D. Kurbatoff, N. A. Karzhavina and N. A. Samoils, *ib.*, 69, 1930 ; V. A. Kargin, *Zeit. anorg. Chem.*, **198.** 79, 1931.

§ 14. Uranium Peroxides, and the Peruranates

Attempts by B. Drenckmann [1] to oxidize uranium to a higher oxide than the trioxide by passing chlorine into a soln. of potassium hydroxide with potassium uranate in suspension were not successful, nor did the treatment of potassium uranate with chlorous acid give any better result. A. Guyard said that when hydrated uranium trioxide or an alkali uranate is boiled with a soln. of silver nitrate, a black, insoluble crystalline powder of uranium pentoxide is formed : $4AgNO_3+K_2U_2O_7=Ag_2O.2UO_5+2AgNO_2+2KNO_2$; but this has not been confirmed. T. Fairley failed to prepare an oxide higher than the trioxide by treating acidic, neutral, or alkaline soln. of the uranate with hypochlorites, permanganates, or ozone ; but he found that the addition of hydrogen dioxide to a slightly acid soln. of uranyl nitrate or acetate produces a precipitate, which, after collecting, and washing successively with alcohol and ether, and drying in a desiccator, or at 100°, forms a yellowish-white, hygroscopic powder with the composition of dihydrated **uranium tetroxide,** $UO_4.2H_2O$. A similar product was obtained by G. Alibegoff, and L. Pissarjewsky. G. Alibegoff said that when the *dihydrate* is heated in oxygen, it begins to decompose at 125°, and the decomposition is rapid at 140° ; it first forms uranium trioxide, and above 140°, uranosic oxide. O. Brunck found that the salt loses no water in a current of carbon dioxide at 150°, but above 150°, water and oxygen are given off, and orange-yellow uranium trioxide is formed—no ozone could be detected. T. Fairley found that the compound glows below a red-heat, leaving a green uranosic oxide. A. Mazzucchelli found that the precipitation is hindered by the presence of chlorides, sulphates, acetates, oxalates, and tartrates owing to the tendency of the tetroxide to form soluble complex salts. No precipitation occurs in the presence of alkalies or alkaline earths owing to the formation of soluble peruranates. L. Pissarjewsky gave for the heat of formation $(UO_3,O) = -6.151$ Cals. ; and $UO_3.H_2O + O + H_2O = UO_4.2H_2O - 6.151$ Cals. According to A. Mazzucchelli and C. Barbero, the electrolytic potentials of a soln. of a mol of uranium trioxide in 20 litres of $N\text{-}H_2SO_4$ in the presence of the necessary amount of hydrogen dioxide to form the tetroxide, against $N\text{-}H_2SO_4$ after 1, 3, and 15 hrs., are with large or small platinum electrodes respectively -0.788, -0.793, and -0.802 volt ; with gold electrodes respectively -0.902, -0.893, and -0.893 volt. The dihydrate is slightly soluble in water. A. Mazzucchelli said that the compound precipitated by hydrogen dioxide from uranyl acetate has a solubility of 0.0061 grm. per litre at 20°, and 0.0084 grm. per litre at 90°. The dihydrate is soluble in a soln. of ammonium chloride. The dihydrate is soluble in cold, and more so in warm, conc. hydrochloric acid, with the evolution of chlorine—a mixture with conc. hydrochloric acid dissolves gold ; alkali-lye decomposes the dihydrate, with the separation of an alkali uranate and the formation of a soln. of a peruranate : $3UO_4 + 2K_2O = 2UO_3 + K_4UO_8$. In acidic liquids the dihydrate is decomposed by hypochlorites and permanganates, with the evolution of oxygen ; it does not decompose hydrogen dioxide.

T. Fairley said that if the precipitate is dried in air, it furnishes the tetrahydrate, $UO_4.4H_2O$, which loses half its water at 100° ; but G. Alibegoff could not prepare a tetrahydrate of definite composition. T. Fairley also reported the formation of the anhydrous tetroxide, UO_4, as a crystalline precipitate, almost white, by adding a soln. of uranyl nitrate to a mixture of hydrogen dioxide and a large excess of sulphuric acid, and allowing the soln. to stand for a week or more. G. Alibegoff could not prepare the anhydrous tetroxide in this way, or by dehydrating the dihydrate.

T. Fairley suggested $(UO_3)_2UO_6$ for the composition of the tetroxide, and he based his opinion on the decomposition of the hydrate by alkalies—*vide infra*. The peruranates were regarded as compounds with the composition $(R_2O)_2UO_6$, or $R_2O.UO_3.UO_6$. L. Pissarjewsky found the ratio of uranium to active oxygen in the tetroxide is 1 : 1, so that the formula can be written :

$$\begin{array}{ccc}
\mathrm{(HO)_2} \!\!\diagdown & & \diagup \mathrm{O} \\
& \!\!\!\!\mathrm{U} & \\
\mathrm{O} \!\!\diagup & & \diagdown \mathrm{O}
\end{array}
\qquad \text{or} \qquad
\begin{array}{cc}
\mathrm{(HO)_4} \!\!\equiv\!\! \mathrm{U} & \!\!\!\diagup \mathrm{O} \\
& \diagdown \mathrm{O}
\end{array}$$

according to G. Alibegoff. L. Pissarjewsky represented the anhydrous oxide :

$$\begin{array}{cc}
\mathrm{O} \!\!\diagdown & \diagup \mathrm{O} \\
\!\!\!\!\mathrm{U} & \\
\mathrm{O} \!\!\diagup & \diagdown \mathrm{O}
\end{array}
\qquad\qquad
\begin{array}{cc}
\mathrm{O} \!\!\diagdown & \\
\!\!\!\!\mathrm{U}\!=\!\mathrm{O} & \\
\mathrm{O} \!\!\diagup &
\end{array}$$

Peruranic oxide $\qquad\qquad\qquad$ Uranium trioxide

G. F. Hüttig and E. von Schröder prepared the *hemienneahydrate*, $UO_4.4\tfrac{1}{2}H_2O$, by dissolving 20 grms. of uranyl nitrate in water, and filtering the soln. to remove traces of basic nitrate. The filtrate was mixed with a little 3 per cent. hydrogen dioxide until a precipitate began to form, and continuing the precipitation by adding a more conc. soln. of hydrogen dioxide. The sulphur-yellow precipitate was filtered by suction and washed until the nitrate was removed. The product was allowed to stand for 10 hrs. at room temp., and another 10 hrs. at 35° until it was dried. The yield was about 15 grms. The dehydration curve of a mixture of this hydrate with water is shown in Fig. 11. The hemienneahydrate first appears. It can be regarded as $UO_4.5H_2O$, or $2UO_3.2H_2O_2.7H_2O$, or, by analogy with the persulphuric acids, $2H_2UO_5.7H_2O$, or **permonouranic acid.** The loss of water on a rising temp. is attended by the loss of oxygen, and at about 54° the *trihydrate*, $UO_{3.5}.3H_2O$, appears. It can be regarded as $2UO_3.H_2O_2.5H_2O$, or, by analogy with the persulphuric acids, as $H_2U_2O_8.5H_2O$, or **per-diuranic acid.** As the temp. rises to 163°, more oxygen and water are given off, and the hemihydrated trioxide appears—*vide* Fig. 11. These observations give no support to the hypothesis that a definite tetroxide exists. On the other hand, A. Rosenheim and H. Daehr prepared the amorphous salt by adding, drop by drop, a 30 per cent. soln. of hydrogen dioxide to a 10 per cent., boiling soln. of uranyl nitrate. The amorphous precipitate, washed with boiling water and dried in air, corresponded with the trihydrate, but

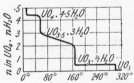

Fig. 11.—Dehydration Curve of Hydrated Uranium Tetroxide.

when dried to constant weight at 100°, it furnished the *dihydrate*, $UO_4.2H_2O$. By using a 2 per cent. soln. of uranyl oxalate and ammonium uranyl oxalate and a 30 per cent. soln. of hydrogen dioxide, yellowish-white crystals of the trihydrate were formed, and when these were dried at 100°, the dihydrate was produced.

P. G. Melikoff and L. Pissarjewsky showed that the alkali peruranates can be resolved by aluminium hydroxide into alkali peroxides and uranium tetroxide—*vide infra*. This reaction favours the assumption that the alkali peruranates are constituted $(R_2O_2)_2UO_4$, or $(R_2O_2)UO_4$; and this is also in agreement with the fact that while carbon dioxide has no action on uranic acid, it converts insoluble peruranates into the metal hydrocarbonate, hydrogen dioxide, and free peruranic acid. Alkali-lye partially reduces the peroxide to the trioxide and an alkali peroxide is formed. This again is in agreement with the assumption that the alkali peruranates are not salts of a peruranic acid, but rather additive compounds of the tetroxide with the metal peroxides. L. Pissarjewsky measured the electrical conductivity of soln. of peruranic acid, and also measured the catalysis of soln. of hydrogen dioxide by this acid. From this he inferred that the sodium salt Na_4UO_8, or $(Na_2O_2)_2UO_4$, is the salt of a weak **peruranic acid** with the constitution $UO(HO_2)_3.OH$, or $H_4(O_2)_3UO_2$. R. Sieverts and E. L. Müller discussed the formation of peruranic acid by the action of hydrogen dioxide on soln. of uranyl nitrate, and uranic acid.

T. Fairley, and P. G. Melikoff and L. Pissarjewsky prepared **ammonium per-diuranate,** $\{(NH_4)_2O_2\}(UO_4)_2.8H_2O$, by adding hydrogen dioxide and an excess of ammonia to a soln. of uranyl nitrate, and precipitating the salt with alcohol. The orange-yellow crystalline product can be dried in vacuo ; it is less decomposable than the sodium or potassium salts. The dry salt glows like tinder when heated, forming a mixture of uranium trioxide with a lower oxide. The salt is freely soluble in water, and the aq. soln. gives precipitates with most metallic salt soln. Nearly all the salts of this type give off ozonized oxygen when treated with conc. sulphuric acid. Alkali-lye forms a precipitate of alkali uranate and a soln. of alkali peruranate. A. Mazzucchelli and C. Barbero found that the potentials of soln. of a mol of the salt in 20 litres after 1, 3, and 15 hrs. with a large platinum electrode against $0.1N$-KCl are respectively -0.557, -0.530, and -0.501 volt ; with a small platinum electrode, respectively, -0.540, -0.534, and -0.501 volt ; and with a gold electrode, respectively, -0.529, -0.509, and -0.427 volt.

F. W. O. de Coninck fused a mixture of uranyl chloride and alkali in a current of air, and obtained red **sodium permonouranate,** Na_2UO_5 ; and J. Aloy obtained the *pentahydrate*, $Na_2UO_5.5H_2O$, by adding hydrogen dioxide to a soln. of uranyl nitrate, adding some alcohol to the mixture, and stirring up with sodium hydroxide free from carbonate. The precipitate gradually dissolves and a red crystalline mass is deposited. It is washed with methyl alcohol. The compound slowly loses oxygen at ordinary temp., and rapidly at 100°. It is decomposed by water, forming an insoluble uranate; with hydrochloric acid it forms chlorine; and with nitric acid no gas is given off, and uranium oxide is formed. P. G. Melikoff and L. Pissarjewsky obtained **lithium perdiuranate,** $Li_2O_2(UO_4)_2.8H_2O$, in pale yellow, short, isotropic prisms, by the action of lithium hydroxide and hydrogen dioxide on a soln. of uranyl nitrate, followed by precipitation with alcohol. The crystals are cubic or tetragonal. It behaves towards acids and hydrated alumina like the sodium salt. The salt is unstable, and readily forms a red acid uranate. The salt, **lithium peruranate,** $(Li_2O_2)_2UO_4$, was also obtained in red crystals which give off oxygen in the desiccator. According to T. Fairley, and P. G. Melikoff and L. Pissarjewsky, **sodium peruranate,** $(Na_2O_2)_2UO_4.8H_2O$—L. Pissarjewsky gave $9H_2O$—is obtained by adding hydrogen dioxide to a soln. of uranic or peruranic acid in soda-lye, and precipitating by the addition of alcohol. O. Kassner obtained it by the action of sodium dioxide on a soln. of uranyl nitrate, and the addition of alcohol, which precipitates the salt in yellow crystals. According to T. Fairley, the salt slowly separates from the soln. without the addition of alcohol; and if only a small proportion of alkali is present, the addition of alcohol first precipitates a deep red oil, which gradually crystallizes, and which T. Fairley represented by the formula $Na_2O.UO_3.UO_6.6H_2O$, i.e. **sodium perdiuranate,** $Na_2O_2(UO_4)_2.6H_2O$. The perdiuranate is considered to be derived from a pyrouranic acid, thus :

$$
\begin{array}{ccc}
NaO.O\diagdown & & \diagup ONa \\
& \diagup U\!-\!O\!-\!U\diagdown & \\
O\diagup \wedge & & \wedge \diagdown O \\
O.O & & O.O
\end{array}
$$

The salt was also prepared by O. Kassner. According to T. Fairley, the golden-yellow needles and plates of $(Na_2O_2)_2UO_4.8H_2O$ are slowly decomposed on exposure to air—absorbing carbon dioxide and giving off oxygen. The crystals are isotropic, belonging to the cubic system. According to T. Fairley, a mol of the salt loses three gram-atoms of oxygen and three-fourths of its water when heated. It is soluble in water and sparingly soluble in alcohol. When treated with normal sulphuric acid, L. Pissarjewsky symbolized the reaction : $(Na_2O_2)_2UO_4+3H_2SO_4$ $=2Na_2SO_4+UO_2SO_4+3H_2O+3O+36.5$ Cals. Dil. sulphuric acid, hydrochloric acid, acetic acid, and succinic acid split off hydrogen dioxide. T. Fairley said that in the presence of hydrochloric acid gold is dissolved, indicating that chlorine has been liberated ; an acidified soln. of potassium permanganate, sodium hypochlorite, or other unstable oxidizing agent liberates 3 gram-atoms of oxygen. The aq. soln. is completely decomposed by boiling ; and when boiled with aq. ammonia, tabular crystals separate out. P. G. Melikoff and L. Pissarjewsky found that when a soln. of the sodium salt is repeatedly shaken up with hydrated alumina, until the filtrate contains no more hydrogen dioxide, the filtrate contains two-thirds of the quantity of hydrogen dioxide which would have been formed by the action of sulphuric acid, and peruranic acid is simultaneously formed as a precipitate containing one-third the proportion of hydrogen dioxide just indicated. The filtrate contains sodium aluminate. Hence, hydrated alumina has broken the peruranate down into sodium dioxide and uranium tetroxide. This agrees with the formula indicated above :

$$
\begin{array}{c}
(NaO.O)_2\diagdown \\
(NaO)_2\diagup
\end{array}\!U\!\!\begin{array}{c}\diagup O \\ \diagdown O\end{array}
$$

although they prefer the less likely formula $(NaO.O)(NaO)UO<O_2.Na_2O_2$. From conductivity measurements, L. Pissarjewsky inferred that the salt is strongly hydrolyzed in soln. to form hydrogen dioxide and sodium hydroxide. The soln. of one-fourth of a mol of Na_4UO_8 in v litres has the conductivity :

v	.	8	16	32	64	128	256	512	1024
λ	.	76.26	91.95	111.16	132.92	148.05	151.12	150.21	149.49

As in the case of the sodium salt, F. W. O. de Coninck prepared **potassium per-monouranate**, K_2UO_5; and J. Aloy, by a process analogous to that used for $Na_2UO_5.5H_2O$, obtained the *trihydrate*, $K_2UO_5.3H_2O$, with properties similar to those of the sodium salt. T. Fairley prepared **potassium peruranate**, $(K_2O_2)_2UO_4.10H_2O$, by adding hydrogen dioxide to a soln. of uranic or peruranic acid in potash-lye, and precipitating the salt by alcohol. The orange-yellow salt is less stable than the corresponding sodium or ammonium salt. Its properties are similar to those of the sodium salt. P. G. Melikoff and L. Pissarjewsky found that when a soln. of the sodium salt is treated with a soln. of copper sulphate, **copper peruranate**, $(CuO_2)_2UO_4.nH_2O$, is precipitated as a dark green gelatinous mass; calcium chloride similarly furnishes **calcium peruranate**, $(CaO_2)_2.UO_4.10H_2O$, in rhombic crystals; and with barium chloride, **barium peruranate**, $(BaO_2)_2UO_4.8H_2O$, is formed as an orange-coloured crystalline powder. If a suspension of the barium salt in water be treated with carbon dioxide, hydrogen dioxide and barium hydro-carbonate are formed and free peruranic acid, which with carbon dioxide is slightly decomposed into hydrogen dioxide, etc. The decomposition is attended by a sharp colour change from orange to yellow. Sulphuric acid also forms hydrogen dioxide. If barium chloride be added to a soln. of the ammonium salt, **barium perdiuranate**, $BaO_2(UO_4)_2.9H_2O$, is formed in yellow isotropic crystals; carbon dioxide furnishes two-thirds the proportion of hydrogen dioxide obtained by the action of sulphuric acid. F. W. O. de Coninck reported **barium permonouranate**, $BaUO_4$, to be formed as in the analogous case of the potassium salt; and similarly with **calcium per-monouranate**, $CaUO_4$. P. G. Melikoff and L. Pissarjewsky obtained lead uranato-peruranate, $PbUO_4.(PbO)_2UO_4$, from soln. of sodium peruranate and lead acetate. The reaction here is different from those previously considered; and this constitu-tion is inferred from the action of dil. acetic acid, which forms lead acetate and peruranic acid but no hydrogen dioxide. The dark orange-yellow product consists of isotropic crystals—cubic or tetragonal. With sulphuric acid, hydrogen dioxide is formed; with the dioxides of lead, manganese, cobalt, and nickel, there is a turbulent evolution of oxygen; and with barium and cadmium dioxides, oxygen is given off after long standing. As in the case of the copper salt, when a soln. of nickel sulphate is added to one of the sodium salt, a greenish-yellow gelatinous precipitate of **nickel peruranate**, $(NiO)_2UO_4$, is formed.

REFERENCES.

[1] B. Drenckmann, *Zeit. ges. Naturwiss.*, **17**. 153, 1861; T. Fairley, *Journ. Chem. Soc.*, **31**. 133, 1877; O. Kassner, *Arch. Pharm.*, **232**. 226, 1894; G. Alibegoff, *Liebig's Ann.*, **233**. 117, 1886; J. L. C. Zimmermann, *ib.*, **232**. 324, 1886; A. Mazzucchelli and C. Barbero, *Atti Accad. Lincei*, (5), **16**. ii, 35, 109, 1906; A. Mazzucchelli and F. Bimbi, *ib.*, (5), **16**. ii, 576, 1907; A. Maz-zucchelli, *ib.*, (5), **15**. ii, 429, 494, 1906; (5), **17**. ii, 30, 1910; *Gazz. Chim. Ital.*, **40**. ii, 241, 1910; L. Pissarjewsky, *Journ. Russ. Phys. Chem. Soc.*, **35**. 42, 1903; *Zeit. anorg. Chem.*, **18**. 59, 1898; **24**. 108, 1903; P. G. Melikoff and L. Pissarjewsky, *Ber.*, **30**. 2902, 1897; **31**. 632, 1898; *Zeit. anorg. Chem.*, **19**. 405, 1899; A. Sieverts and E. L. Müller, *ib.*, **173**. 297, 1928; O. Brunck, *ib.*, **10**. 246, 1895; G. F. Hüttig and E. von Schröder, *ib.*, **121**. 243, 1922; A. Rosenheim and H. Daehr, *ib.*, **181**. 177, 1929; H. Daehr, *Zur Kenntnis der Peruransäure und Peruranate*, Berlin, 1928; A. Guyard, *Bull. Soc. Chim.*, (2), **1**. 95, 1863; J. Aloy, *ib.*, (3), **27**. 734, 1902; (3), **29**. 292, 1903; *Recherches sur l'uranium et ses composés*, Paris, 1901; F. W. O. de Coninck, *Bull. Acad. Belg.*, 692, 1909; *Compt. Rend.*, **148**. 1769, 1909.

§ 15. Uranium Fluorides and Oxyfluorides

F. Giolitti and G. Agamennone [1] are reported to have said that on adding an excess of hydrofluoric acid to the liquid obtained by the electrolysis of an aq. soln. of uranyl chloride acidified with hydrochloric acid, a green precipitate of **uranium difluoride**, $UF_2.2H_2O$, is formed. A. Sieverts pointed out that this conclusion is really based on a misprint in the analysis; the actual product was $UO_2F_2.2H_2O$—*vide infra*.

H. Moissan observed that when uranium is acted on by fluorine, the chief product is **uranium tetrafluoride,** or **uranous fluoride,** UF_4. H. C. Bolton obtained it by the action of hydrofluoric acid on hydrated uranium dioxide ; and H. Hermann, by the action of that acid on uranium dioxide. H. C. Bolton also said that it can be prepared by the action of dil. hydrofluoric acid on green uranosic oxide, when a green precipitate of the tetrafluoride and a yellow soln. of uranyl fluoride are produced; this corresponds with the equation: $U_3O_8+8HF=UF_4+2UO_2F_2+4H_2O$. A. Ditte, on the contrary, said that the tetrafluoride, or rather a hexafluoride, remains in soln. and the green powder is uranyl fluoride ; he represented the reaction : $U_3O_8+18HF=2(UF_6.2HF)+UO_2F_2+6H_2O+H_2$. A. Smithells noted that considerable heat is evolved during the reaction, and found that A. Ditte's statement is doubly wrong, for (i) the yellow soln. contains uranyl fluoride, as indicated by H. C. Bolton, and (ii) no hydrogen is liberated during the reaction. Some uranium oxydifluoride is also formed—*vide infra.* H. C. Bolton also found that the tetrafluoride is produced when a soln. of uranyl fluoride is reduced with stannous chloride. According to O. Ruff and A. Heinzelmann, fluorine reacts with uranium pentachloride at $-40°$ in accord with the equation : $2UCl_5+5F_2 =UF_4+UF_6+5Cl_2$. The two fluorides can be separated by fractional distillation. When uranium carbide is treated with fluorine, only the tetrafluoride is formed. H. C. Bolton said that the *monohydrate,* $UF_4.H_2O$, is obtained as a green powder when hydrofluoric acid is added to an aq. soln. of uranium tetrachloride and the green voluminous precipitate is dried in vacuo or at $100°$. H. C. Bolton described the tetrafluoride as a green amorphous powder. O. Ruff and A. Heinzelmann said that when heated out of contact with air, it melts at about $1000°$. According to H. C. Bolton, the tetrafluoride is attacked by dry hydrogen at a red-heat, giving off hydrogen fluoride and leaving a reddish-brown residue which is insoluble in water and is scarcely attacked by acids. It has been suggested that this residue is a *subfluoride,* but this is a mere guess. The tetrafluoride is unstable ; it oxidizes in air at ordinary temp., and when warmed in air it is converted into uranyl fluoride ; at a higher temp. it passes into uranosic oxide without melting. H. Hermann found that the tetrafluoride is insoluble in water ; it is very slightly soluble in dil. acids. When heated with sulphuric acid, the hydrogen fluoride is expelled; and it is easily and vigorously attacked by hot, conc. nitric acid. N. A. Orloff found that a soln. of uranium tetrafluoride in oxalic acid furnishes a dark green liquid with a violet fluorescence, and it deposits a complex *ammonium uranous oxalatofluoride,* $UF_4.2(NH_4)_2C_2O_4.4H_2O$. The low solubility of the tetrafluoride suggested to F. Giolitti a method of determining uranium by converting its salts into the quadrivalent stage, and then precipitating with hydrofluoric acid. H. C. Bolton added that boiling alkali-lye converts the tetrafluoride into uranous hydroxide.

H. C. Bolton found that while a soln. of formic or oxalic acid produces no precipitate in a soln. of potassium uranyl fluoride, if the acidified soln. be placed in direct sunlight, a green precipitate gradually falls, and if the action be prolonged, the soln. becomes colourless and retains only a trace of uranium. When the precipitate is washed, and dried at $100°$, it forms a green, impalpable powder of **potassium uranous pentafluoride,** KUF_5, or $UF_4.KF$. If heated in air, the salt fuses, gives off hydrogen fluoride, and leaves a residue of potassium uranate ; but if heated in a closed tube, the salt fuses, gives off hydrogen fluoride, and leaves a black residue cf uranium dioxide suspended in fused potassium fluoride. It is decomposed when heated in hydrogen. The salt is quite insoluble in water and dil. acids ; it dissolves with difficulty in boiling, conc. hydrochloric acid ; but it is more easily decomposed by conc. sulphuric acid, which drives out hydrogen fluoride, forming a green soln. of uranyl sulphate. When heated with a soln. of alkali-lye, it forms a black precipitate of uranium dioxide and alkali fluoride passes into soln. A. Smithells observed that when potassium hydrofluoride and green uranosic oxide are fused together, the hydrofluoric acid of the acid salt is liberated, and acts on the oxide producing uranous fluoride, UF_4, and β-uranium oxyfluoride, UO_2F_2. In the early stages of the fusion, the former unites with potassium fluoride to form the double salt $UF_4.KF$, whilst one molecule of UO_2F_2 and three of KF form the uranyl fluoride. By further heating, the uranous fluoride is converted into the uranyl fluoride, whilst the result of prolonged fusion of the latter is the insoluble crystalline compound, which is also obtained by using the normal instead of the acid potassium salt, and which contains no fluorine—*vide infra*, A. Ditte's sodium and potassium uranyl hexafluorides. H. C. Bolton prepared **sodium uranous pentafluoride** in a manner similar to that employed for the corresponding potassium salt. It resembles the potassium salt, but is rather more soluble, since the soln. is green, not colourless after a long exposure. The salt was not analyzed.

F. Giolitti and G. Agamennone found that if an aq. soln. of uranyl formate is exposed to sunlight for a couple of days, the soln. becomes green, and when it is treated with hydrofluoric acid, a bluish-green powder of **uranium oxydifluoride**, $UOF_2.2H_2O$, is formed. The same salt was produced by the electrolytic reduction of a soln. of uranium trioxide in an excess of hydrofluoric acid. The action of hydrofluoric acid on uranosic oxide proceeds in accord with $U_3O_8+6HF=UOF_2+2UO_2F_2+3H_2O$—*vide supra*. The uranous oxyfluoride separates as a fine green powder, whilst the uranyl fluoride remaining in soln. separates as a yellow mass on evaporation. A heavy green powder, presumably uranium tetrafluoride, is also deposited. Green **ammonium uranium oxytrifluoride**, $NH_4F.UOF_2$, was obtained by electrolyzing a soln. of ammonium uranyl carbonate in an excess of hydrofluoric acid. When the green product is heated, ammonium fluoride is given off.

O. Ruff and A. Heinzelmann prepared **uranium hexafluoride**, UF_6, in three ways. As indicated above, fluorine reacts with uranium pentachloride at $-40°$, forming the tetra- and hexa-fluorides. The hexafluoride is distilled off, and chlorine and silicon tetrafluoride which may be present are removed by the passage of a rapid current of air. The hexafluoride is also produced by the action of dry hydrogen fluoride on uranium pentachloride, whereby a complex $UF_5.nHF$ is formed, which breaks up on distillation into uranium tetra- and hexafluorides. It is difficult to separate the hydrogen fluoride from uranium hexafluoride, so that this process is not so useful. Uranium carbide with fluorine alone furnishes uranium tetrafluoride, but in the presence of chlorine, at $-70°$, the hexafluoride is produced. Uranium hexafluoride forms glistening, colourless or pale yellow, hygroscopic, monoclinic **crystals** of **specific gravity** 4·68 at 20·7°, and **molecular volume** 75·4. The **vapour density** at 448° is 11·7 when the calculated value for the mol. wt. $UF_6=352·8$ is 12·16, so that the vapour consists of single molecules. N. V. Sidgwick discussed the electronic structure. O. Ruff and A. Heinzelmann found that the **melting point** of the hexafluoride is 69·2°, at which temp. the vap. press. is about 2 atm. The compound sublimes without melting, at room temp. and under a diminished press. The **vapour pressure** at 0° is 48 mm.; at 20°, 129 mm.; at 37°, 298·2 mm.; at 41°, 406·1 mm.; at 45°, 410·1 mm.; at 48°, 521·2 mm.; and at 56·2°, 764·6 mm. R. Lorenz and W. Herz made observations on this subject. O. Ruff and A. Heinzelmann found that the **boiling point** is 56·2°; and the calculated mean latent **heat of vaporization** between 42° and 57° is 29·4 cals. per gram of the hexafluoride, or 10,360 cals. per mol. The salt is very hygroscopic, and it fumes in air. It is reduced to the tetrafluoride by **hydrogen** at ordinary temp. Dry **air**, and **oxygen** have no action. The hexafluoride reacts vigorously with **water**, forming a yellowish-green soln., which with ammonia forms ammonium fluoride and uranate. Uranium hexafluoride does not react chemically with **chlorine** or **bromine**, but liquid chlorine and liquid bromine dissolve some of the hexafluoride; **iodine** has no action. The hexafluoride reacts with **sulphur**, forming uranium disulphide and tetrafluoride and a gaseous sulphur fluoride. The hexafluoride is easily soluble in dil. **sulphuric acid**; and it is almost insoluble in dry **carbon disulphide**, but there is a slow reaction, attended by the formation of the tetrafluoride; the reaction with moist carbon disulphide is vigorous, and a gas, smelling like sulphur monochloride, is given off. The hexafluoride does not react with **nitrogen**; gaseous **ammonia** colours green the soln. in tetrachloroethane—a substance containing ammonia, fluorine, and quadrivalent uranium is formed ; the soln. in tetrachloroethane is coloured bluish-green by **nitric oxide;** it is decomposed by **nitric acid;** it is reduced by **phosphorus** in the cold, and by **arsenic** when warmed, forming uranium tetrafluoride and phosphorus pentafluoride or arsenic trifluoride respectively. A soln. of the salt in tetrachloroethane gives a rose-coloured precipitate with **arsenic trichloride,** soluble in excess. Amorphous **carbon** also reduces the hexafluoride to the tetrafluoride ; **carbon dioxide** has no action, and so also with **carbon monoxide.** The hexafluoride reacts slowly with **chloroform,** with **nitrobenzene,** and vigorously with **alcohol,** and with **ether,** forming hydrogen and uranyl fluorides ; and with **benzene, toluene,** or **xylene** it reacts with a hissing noise, forming hydrogen fluoride, with the separation of carbon—the resulting reduced uranium salt which is formed gives off hydrogen when treated with acids. Symmetrical **tetrachloroethane** is the best solvent. The hexafluoride is insoluble in **paraffin** oil, but reacts slowly, with the separation of carbon ; it is slowly reduced to the tetrafluoride when warmed with **silicon,** and silicon tetra-fluoride is formed ; it attacks **glass** if traces of moisture are present, forming silicon tetrafluoride. The hexafluoride at ordinary temp. forms a white crust on **sodium,** and if warmed, the reaction is attended by incandescence ; **copper,** and **silver** are feebly attacked if warmed ; **gold** is not attacked, cold or warm ; **zinc, mercury, aluminium, tin, lead,** and **iron** lose their lustre at ordinary temp., and are strongly attacked if warm ; and **platinum** is not attacked, cold or warm.

As indicated above, there are discrepancies in the conclusions of different workers on the action of hydrofluoric acid on uranosic oxide. A. Ditte said that with an excess of the conc. acid, the action is slow at ordinary temp., and rapid at 50°. The yellow soln. is said to deposit yellow crystals of **uranium dihydroctofluoride,** $UF_6.2HF$, which melt when heated in a closed platinum crucible, slowly giving off hydrogen fluoride ; if air has access, uranium dioxide and undecomposed uranium hexafluoride are formed. Hydrogen dioxide has no action. A. Smithells did not confirm A. Ditte's observation. O. Ruff and A. Heinzelmann said that a complex $UF_5.nHF$ is formed by the action of dry hydrogen fluoride on uranium pentachloride.

J. J. Berzelius found that when the yellow soln. of uranium trioxide in hydro-fluoric acid is evaporated, it furnishes a white, amorphous, pulverulent crust, which creeps up the sides of the containing vessel. The dried product dissolves readily in water, and in alcohol. H. C. Bolton showed that the product is hydrated **uranyl fluoride,** $UO_2F_2.nH_2O$, which when reduced with tin and hydrochloric acid furnishes uranium tetrafluoride. As indicated above, uranyl fluoride is one product of the action of hydrofluoric acid on uranosic oxide, and as shown by A. Smithells, and F. Giolitti and G. Agamennone, it is obtained by evaporating the filtered soln. A. Ditte also prepared it by the action of hot, conc. hydrofluoric acid on uranium dioxide. A. von Unruh also obtained it by repeatedly evaporating on a water-bath a soln. of uranyl acetate with hydrofluoric acid. W. S. Andrews obtained a fluorescent uranyl fluoride by mixing soln. of 50 grms. uranyl nitrate in 200 c.c. of water, and 75 grms. ammonium fluoride in 110 c.c. of water. The precipitate can be washed with cold water, but it is soluble in water. It is brightly fluorescent under the ultra-violet rays from an iron spark, and it is weakly responsive to excitation by X-rays. F. Giolitti and G. Agamennone could not obtain uranyl fluoride by calcining uranous oxyfluoride, $UOF_2.2H_2O$. A. Smithells obtained a white crystalline sublimate by rapidly heating uranium tetrafluoride in a closed platinum crucible and cooling after five minutes. He called the product α-uranyl fluoride to distinguish it from the yellow hygroscopic crystalline plates which he called β-uranyl fluoride obtained by evaporating the filtered soln. of uranosic oxide in hydrofluoric acid in vacuo over sulphuric acid and calcium oxide. The analyses of A. Ditte, and A. Smithells agree with the formula UO_2F_2 ; and F. Giolitti and G. Agamennone represented the product obtained on evaporating the hydrofluoric acid soln. as a *dihydrate*, $UO_2F_2.2H_2O$—*vide supra,* dihydrated uranium difluoride. Both forms produce a yellow soln. with water ; give the complex salt $3KF.UO_2F_2$

when treated with potassium fluoride ; and form uranosic oxide when calcined in air. A. von Unruh said that uranyl fluoride is insoluble in ether, and amyl alcohol. He also found that liquid ammonia acts on uranyl fluoride, forming a deep orange-red powder of **uranyl tetramminodifluoride**, $UO_2.F_2.4NH_3$, which is more stable than the corresponding chloride or bromide. Gaseous ammonia acts on uranyl fluoride to form **uranyl triamminodifluoride**, $UO_2F_2.3NH_3$, as an orange-yellow powder. When either of these ammines is warmed, it forms yellow **uranyl diammino-difluoride**, $UO_2F_2.2NH_3$. F. Olsson studied complex fluorides with organic bases.

A. Ditte said that if uranyl fluoride is heated to bright redness in a closed platinum crucible the white sublimate is **uranium oxytetrafluoride**, UOF_4. It forms a snow-white mass of acicular crystals. It melts at a red-heat, and volatilizes. When heated in air it forms uranium dioxide ; and it gives a yellow soln. with water. A. Smithells found that A. Ditte's uranium oxytetrafluoride does not exist ; it is identical with white or α-uranyl fluoride. A. Ditte reported that when uranosic oxide is fused with alkali fluorides a series of insoluble alkali uranyl hexafluorides, $4RF.UO_2F_2$, is formed, but, as indicated below, A. Smithells observed that the products are ordinary alkali diuranates. A. Ditte also said that if uranosic oxide be fused with potassium hydrofluoride, instead of potassium fluoride, the product is different. He said that if, as soon as the mass is just fused, it be allowed to cool, it appears of a bright green colour, and on treatment with water gives a yellow soln. and an insoluble green powder resembling uranous fluoride. If, however, the fusion of the mass be continued, the green colour is gradually changed to a pale yellow, and at this stage treatment with water effects almost complete soln. On still further heating, the colour becomes tinged with orange, until finally, after prolonged fusion, the crucible contains the crystalline compound $4KF.UO_2F_2$. The yellow soln. obtained by lixiviating the fused masses, freed from insoluble substances by filtration, were left at rest after being slightly conc., or were evaporated on a water-bath. In both cases small but very well-defined transparent crystals were obtained. These crystals were said by A. Ditte to be **potassium uranium oxyoctofluoride**, $4KF.UOF_4.nH_2O$, where n is either $1\frac{1}{2}$ or 3, according to the temp. at which they are deposited. A. Smithells showed that the crystals are potassium uranyl pentafluoride, $3KF.UO_2F_2$, described below. A. Ditte added that by adding potash-lye to the yellow soln. obtained by treating uranosic oxide with hydrofluoric acid the same products are obtained, and that by dissolving them in water containing potassium hydrofluoride, and recrystallizing them at 50° to 60°, a monohydrate, $4KF.UOF_4.H_2O$, is produced. These statements do not agree with the observations of J. J. Berzelius, and H. C. Bolton ; and A. Smithells showed that (i) the yellow soln. obtained by acting on uranosic oxide with hydrofluoric acid is uranyl fluoride ; (ii) that when an excess of hydrofluoric acid is present and potassium hydroxide is added, potassium uranyl pentafluoride, indicated below, is formed ; and (iii) when this salt is dissolved in water containing not more than 13 per cent. of potassium hydrofluoride, triclinic potassium diuranyl enneafluoride is formed. Similar remarks probably apply to A. Ditte's **rubidium uranium oxyoctofluoride**, $4RbF.UOF_4.6H_2O$, prepared like the potassium salt.

J. J. Berzelius showed that uranyl fluoride forms yellow, soluble, crystalline compounds with the alkali fluorides. H. C. Bolton prepared **ammonium uranyl pentafluoride**, $(NH_4)_3UO_2F_5$, by evaporating a soln. of ammonium uranate in hydrofluoric acid over conc. sulphuric acid. H. Bürger used ammonium diuranate. H. Baker prepared the salt by adding ammonium fluoride to a soln. of uranyl nitrate, when the salt is precipitated in tetragonal crystals, probably isomorphous with the corresponding potassium salt, and of sp. gr. 3·186 at 20°. H. C. Bolton said that the salt is freely soluble in water, and according to H. Bürger, 100 grms. of a sat. soln. at 27° has 10·11 grms. of the salt ; and 20·70 grms. at 81·3°. A. Miolati and U. Alvisi found that the electrical conductivity, λ, of soln. of one-third of a mol, $(NH_4)_3UO_2F_5$, in v litres of water, is as follows :

v .	32	64	128	256	512	1024	∞
λ .	96·99	104·00	109·6	115·6	119·3	126·1	133·1

The difference in the electrolytic conductivities $\lambda_{1024}-\lambda_{32}=29\cdot1$, and $\mu_\infty=133\cdot1$ indicates that stable complexes are formed : $(NH_4)_3UO_2F_5 \rightleftharpoons 3NH_4 + (UO_2F_5)'''$. H. C. Bolton said that the salt is less soluble in hydrofluoric acid than in water, and insoluble in alcohol. When heated out of contact with air, ammonium fluoride is volatilized ; and when exposed to air, green uranosic oxide is formed.

According to H. C. Bolton, potassium fluoride causes in a soln. of uranium nitrate a heavy crystalline lemon-yellow precipitate, which, by washing with cold water and recrystallization from hot water, can be obtained pure. It is well in the preparation of this salt to add an excess of potassium fluoride, as the salt is soluble in uranium nitrate. H. Baker added that by crystallizing the salt thus prepared from pure water or from a soln. of acid potassium fluoride (containing not more than 13 per cent.), tabular triclinic crystals are always formed. But by crystallization from a nearly sat. soln. of potassium hydrofluoride, a salt separates in minute tetragonal crystals. Furthermore, by adding potassium fluoride to a soln. of uranium nitrate in quantity insufficient to produce a permanent precipitate, or by recrystallizing either of the preceding salts from water containing a little uranium nitrate, monoclinic crystals are obtained : so that three distinct potassium uranyl oxyfluorides exist. H. C. Bolton, and H. Baker obtained the tetragonal **potassium uranyl pentafluoride**, $3KO.UO_2F_2$, as indicated above ; also by adding potassium fluoride to a soln. of freshly-precipitated potassium diuranate in hydrofluoric acid ; and by the crystallization of a mixed soln. of potassium fluoride and uranyl fluoride. A. Smithells obtained it by evaporating a soln. of potassium fluoride or hydrofluoride and uranyl fluoride, and by fusing potassium hydrofluoride with uranosic oxide—*vide supra*. H. C. Bolton tried unsuccessfully to prepare this salt by heating to redness for more than an hour a mixture of potassium uranyl sulphate with sodium fluoride and sulphate as a flux. The greater part of the potassium uranyl sulphate remained unchanged, with the exception of a little sodium uranate which was formed near the surface of the mass. Potassium uranyl pentafluoride is dimorphous. H. C. Bolton described (i) the yellow, tabular crystals which he prepared by cooling hot, conc. soln. and which are monoclinic prisms with the axial ratios $a:b:c$ $=1.375:1:3.477$, and $\beta=99°\ 40'$; and he also obtained (ii) twinned tetragonal crystals, with the axial ratio $a:c=1:2.0815$, by the spontaneous evaporation of a cold soln. H. Baker gave $a:c=0.992$, and found penetration twinning and trilling. The sp. gr. of the tetragonal form is 4.263. The crystals are only slightly fluorescent. H. C. Bolton observed that when the salt is heated in a closed vessel, it melts to a red liquid which freezes to a yellow mass ; if heated while exposed to air, fluorine is given off, and potassium diuranate is formed. A. Miolati and U. Alvisi found that the electrical conductivity, λ, of soln. of one-third of a mol of $K_3UO_2F_5$, in v litres is as follows :

v .	32	64	128	256	512	1024	∞
λ .	97.67	104.8	109.6	115.1	119.2	127.3	133

The difference in the electrical conductivities of soln. of the salt $\lambda_{1024}-\lambda_{32}=29.6$ corresponds with that of a tribasic uranylfluoric acid : $K_3UO_2F_5 \rightleftharpoons 3K^{\cdot}+(UO_2F_5)'''$. H. C. Bolton observed that when the salt is heated in dry hydrogen, it forms uranium tetrafluoride, uranium dioxide, and potassium fluoride. At 21°, 100 parts of water dissolve 12.5 parts of the salt. The aq. soln. reddens litmus and is not decomposed by boiling, and H. Baker added that the solubility of the salt in a soln. of potassium hydrofluoride is less than in water, and the original salt can be crystallized from its soln. in this menstruum—*vide infra*. H. C. Bolton found that the salt is completely decomposed by warm, conc. sulphuric acid. When ammonia is added to the aq. soln., a precipitate of ammonium diuranate is formed ; barium chloride gives a voluminous white precipitate ; lead acetate, an orange-yellow precipitate, very soluble in acids ; and calcium chloride, a white precipitate difficult to filter. Oxalic or formic acid and a soln. of this salt, when exposed to sunlight, form potassium uranous pentafluoride. A soln. of potassium uranyl pentafluoride gives no precipitate with salts of copper, silver, zinc, mercury, iron, or platinum ; and ammonium or sodium carbonate does not decompose the boiling soln. When the pentafluoride is fused with sodium carbonate there are formed sodium uranate and fluoride. The salt is insoluble in alcohol, and ether ; and alcohol added to an aq. soln. precipitates the salt. As indicated above, a soln. of potassium uranyl pentafluoride gives a precipitate with barium chloride, which, when washed, and dried at 100°, forms orange-yellow **barium uranyl pentafluoride**, $Ba_3(UO_2F_5)_2.2H_2O$. It gives off water and hydrogen fluoride without melting when heated out of contact with air ; it is very sparingly soluble in hot water ; it is freely soluble in acids, and the soln. precipitates barium sulphate when treated with sulphuric acid, and ammonium uranate when treated with ammonia. The corresponding **calcium uranyl pentafluoride**, $Ca_3(UO_2F_5)_2.nH_2O$, and **lead uranyl pentafluoride**, $Pb_3(UO_2F_5)_2.nH_2O$, appear to be produced in an analogous manner—*vide supra*.

H. Baker found that when potassium uranyl pentafluoride is crystallized from water, or from a soln. containing not more than 13 per cent. of potassium hydro-fluoride, six-sided plates—rarely prisms—of **potassium diuranyl enneafluoride**, $K_5(UO_2)_2F_9$, are formed. The triclinic crystals have the axial ratios $a:b:c$ $=0.6222:1:0.568$, and $a=72°38'$; $\beta=116°23'$, and $\gamma=111°57'$. The sp. gr. is 4.379 at $20°$. The crystals are markedly fluorescent ; and they can be recrystallized unchanged from water. The zirconium salt $Na_5Zr_2F_{13}$ is analogous. H. Baker obtained **potassium diuranyl heptafluoride**, $K_3(UO_2)_2F_7$, from a soln. of uranyl fluoride mixed with insufficient potassium fluoride to form a precipitate ; and by recrystallizing either of the preceding potassium salts from a soln. containing uranyl fluoride. The monoclinic prisms have the axial ratios $a:b:c$ $=0.918:1:0.978$, and $\beta=114°0'$. The sp. gr. is 4.108 at $20°$. The green fluor-escence is very marked. The salt separates unchanged from its soln. in hot water.

H. C. Bolton evaporated in a desiccator, over sulphuric acid, a soln. of uranyl nitrate and sodium fluoride, or a soln. of sodium uranate in hydrofluoric acid, and obtained tabular or prismatic crystals of **sodium uranyl trifluoride**, $Na(UO_2)F_3$. $4H_2O$. The monoclinic crystals have the axial ratios $a:b:c=1.0270:1:0.5222$, and $\beta=94°51'$. The crystals lose half their water at $100°$; they melt when heated, forming sodium diuranate. The salt is not so stable as the potassium salts, but behaves similarly. When the aq. soln. is heated, or when an attempt is made to recrystallize the salt from its aq. soln., sodium fluoride crystallizes out separately.

A. Ditte described **potassium uranyl hexafluoride**, $K_4(UO_2)F_6$, as a result of fusing uranosic oxide with potassium fluoride mixed with a little carbonate, or by dissolving uranosic oxide in molten potassium hydrofluoride, and precipitating with potassium carbonate. The yellow, six-sided plates are stable in air at a red-heat ; hydrogen reduces a little of the salt at a red-heat ; when heated with ammonium chloride in hydrogen, uranium dioxide and potassium chloride are formed ; it is insoluble in hot and cold water and soluble in acids. A. Ditte similarly obtained **rubidium uranyl hexafluoride**, $Rb_4(UO_2)F_6$; **sodium uranyl hexafluoride**, $Na_4(UO_2)F_6$; and **lithium uranyl hexafluoride**, $Li_4(UO_2)F_6$. A. Smithells showed that in all probability A. Ditte erred in some way, for the products obtained are in all cases diuranates, and not fluorides at all.

According to S. Lordkipanidze, when an aq. soln. of sodium uranyl trifluoride is treated with hydrogen dioxide, and the intense yellow soln. is evaporated on a water-bath at $60°$ to $70°$, a yellow, granular salt, **sodium uranium peroxyfluoride**, $NaF.UO_4.5H_2O$, is formed. It loses four mols. of water at $100°$. Again, if an excess of hydrogen dioxide is added to an aq. soln. of potassium uranyl pentafluoride, the intense yellow liquid deposits, after standing some time, yellow, pulverulent **potassium uranium peroxyfluoride**, $KF.UO_3F_2.3(KF.UO_4).4H_2O$.

REFERENCES.

[1] F. Giolitti, *Gazz. Chim. Ital.*, **34**. ii, 166, 1904 ; F. Giolitti and G. Agamennone, *Atti Accad. Lincei*, (5), **14**. i, 114, 165, 1905 ; A. Miolati and U. Alvisi, *ib.*, (5), **6**. 376, 1897 ; H. C. Bolton, *On the Fluorine Compounds of Uranium*, Berlin, 1866 ; *Sitzber. Akad. Berlin*, 299, 1866 ; *Bull. Soc. Chim.*, (2), **2**. 450, 1866 ; H. Bürger, *Beiträge zur Kenntnis der Uranyldoppelsalze*, Bonn, 1904 ; H. Hermann, *Ueber einige Uranverbindungen*, Göttingen, 1861 ; J. J. Berzelius, *Pogg. Ann.*, **1**. 34, 1824 ; *Lehrbuch der Chemie*, Dresden, **3**. 1099, 1845 ; A. Ditte, *Compt. Rend.*, **91**. 115, 1880 ; *Ann. Chim. Phys.*, (6), **1**. 338, 1884 ; H. Moissan, *ib.*, (7), **9**. 264, 1896 ; *Bull. Soc. Chim.*, (3), **17**. 270, 1897 ; *Compt. Rend.*, **122**. 1088, 1896 ; *Le four électrique*, Paris, 238, 1897 ; London, 165, 1904 ; O. Ruff and A. Heinzelmann, *Zeit. anorg. Chem.*, **71**. 69, 1911 ; *Ber.*, **42**. 495, 1909 ; R. Lorenz and W. Herz, *Zeit. anorg. Chem.*, **43**. 336, 1924 ; F. Olsson, *ib.*, **187**. 112, 1930 ; A. Sieverts, *ib.*, **170**. 191, 1928 ; A. von Unruh, *Einwirkung von Ammoniak auf wasserfreie*

Uranylsalze, Rostock, 1909 ; H. Baker, *Liebig's Ann.*, **202**. 240, 1880 ; *Journ. Chem. Soc.*, **35**. 763, 1879; A. Smithells, *ib.*, **43**. 125. 1883 ; N. V. Sidgwick, *ib.*, **125**. 2672, 1924; N. A. Orloff, *Journ. Russ. Phys. Chem. Soc.*, **35**. 1247, 1903 ; S. Lordkipanidze, *ib.*, **32**. 283, 1900 ; F. Stolba, *Zeit. anal. Chem.*, **3**. 72, 1864 ; W. S. Andrews, *Amer. Min.*, **7**. 19, 1922.

§ 16. Uranium Chlorides

According to E. M. Péligot,[1] if uranium tetrachloride is heated, at the temp. approaching volatilization, in dry hydrogen so long as hydrogen chloride is given off, **uranium trichloride**, UCl_3, is formed. H. Löbel added that the hydrogen should be thoroughly dried and be free from all traces of oxygen. C. F. Rammelsberg obtained the trichloride by heating the tetrachloride in ammonia, but in that case, added E. Uhrlaub, the product will contain some nitride. J. L. C. Zimmermann obtained what he regarded as a soln. of the salt by reducing uranyl salts with zinc and hydrochloric acid, or, according to F. Stolba, with lead and hydrochloric acid. A. Rosenheim and H. Löbel prepared a soln. of the trichloride in a large excess of hydrochloric acid by the electrolytic reduction of a soln. of uranium trioxide in hydrochloric acid of sp. gr. 1·12, using a layer of mercury as cathode. To complete the reduction, the soln. must be cooled to 0° towards the end of the electrolysis. In the presence of traces of dissolved mercury or platinum, the reduction stops at quadrivalent uranium, due, it is supposed, to the fact that these substances facilitate the liberation of hydrogen. A. Rosenheim and H. Löbel observed that the trichloride forms dark red, hygroscopic needles. K. Someya discussed the colour of tervalent uranium ions. W. Biltz, and W. Biltz and C. Fendius gave 5·440 for the sp. gr. at 25°/4° ; 83·4 for the mol. vol. ; and for the heat of formation $(U, \frac{3}{2}Cl_2)$ =213 Cals. E. M. Péligot found it to be freely soluble in water ; and the purple soln. quickly decomposes, giving off hydrogen and forming a red deposit of uranium oxide and a green soln. of uranium tetrachloride. The aq. soln. are therefore very unstable, and A. Rosenheim and H. Löbel observed that the purple soln. in hydrochloric acid is more stable than the aq. soln., and that water and most reagents decompose the acid soln. of the trichloride. The soln. of the trichloride in acetic acid is red. J. L. C. Zimmermann measured the absorption spectrum of soln. of the trichloride.

E. M. Péligot [2] observed that uranium burns brilliantly in chlorine, forming **uranium tetrachloride**, or **uranous chloride**, UCl_4 ; he prepared the salt by passing dry chlorine over an intimate mixture of uranous oxide and carbon at a red-heat. The red vapours of the uranium tetrachloride condense near to the hot zone. C. F. Rammelsberg used uranosic oxide, and H. Löbel, uranium trioxide. H. E. Roscoe said that any of the oxides of uranium or uranyl chloride can be employed, and that octahedral crystals of the tetrachloride are deposited nearest to the hot zone, and farther away the pentachloride is deposited in black, needle-shaped crystals mixed with a brown powder. W. E. Schilz, C. F. Rammelsberg, H. Löbel, and A. Roderburg employed this process ; whilst H. Moissan passed chlorine over red-hot uranium carbide. A. Colani observed that the production of the pentachloride is avoided if uranium dioxide be employed in place of the trioxide or of uranosic oxide ; and H. E. Roscoe found that the pentachloride is converted into the tetrachloride if it be heated in a current of carbon dioxide. As shown by E. Demarçay, and L. Meyer, the metal oxides can be chlorinated by passing the vapour of carbon tetrachloride over the red-hot oxide. This process was employed by A. Colani for uranium tetrachloride. P. Camboulives passed the vapour of carbon tetrachloride over uranium trioxide at 300° ; and A. Michael and A. Murphy heated a mixture of uranium dioxide and carbon tetrachloride in a sealed tube at 250°. A. Colani, C. Matignon and F. Bourion, H. Löbel, F. Bourion, D. Lely and L. Hamburger, and J. F. Goggin and co-workers prepared the tetra-chloride by heating uranosic oxide, or uranium trioxide in a current of the vapour of sulphur monochloride, alone or mixed with chlorine. A. Colani said that if the sulphur monochloride is associated with an excess of sulphur, the reaction does not proceed so easily as in the converse case. R. W. Moore recommended the following procedure :

The uranium oxide is placed in quartz or porcelain boats inserted in a 5 cm. porcelain tube heated in an electrical resistance furnace. An empty boat is placed at one end of the porcelain tube, and re-distilled sulphur monochloride is allowed to flow into this boat drop by drop from a tube connected with a separatory funnel. The other end of the tube projecting beyond the furnace is closed by a rubber stopper with a large outlet tube opening under sulphur monochloride contained in a bottle. The furnace is inclined downwards towards the outlet end so as to allow the outflow of any sulphur monochloride condensing in the cool end of the tube. The tube is heated to 200°–300°, and the dropping-in of the sulphur monochloride is commenced. The temp. is gradually raised to 500°, and maintained there for 3 or 4 hrs. The uranium oxide is converted into a greenish, coarsely crystalline mass, which absorbs moisture slowly. The temp. is not high enough either to melt or to sublime the tetrachloride. The product is preserved in sealed tubes. Some oxide is still present and the product is purified by sublimation. A hard glass tube about 4 cms. in diameter is bent ; thus the inlet is arranged so that it can be filled with chlorine dried by bubbling through sulphur monochloride. The crude tetrachloride is placed at the lowest part of the bend ; and the outlet is closed by a stopper carrying a small tube leading to the exit. The tetrachloride is heated to bright redness while a moderate current of chlorine is passed through the tube. The dark red vapours of the tetrachloride condense in greenish crystals close to the hot zone. A fluffy yellow substance is deposited in the cooler part of the tube. It appears to be a complex of sulphur monochloride and uranium tetrachloride, because, on replacing the current of chlorine by nitrogen, and heating the part of the tube containing these crystals, they decompose into sulphur monochloride and uranium tetrachloride. The uranium tetrachloride is sealed in tubes or bottles containing dry nitrogen.

J. Aloy said that uranium tetrachloride is formed when a soln. of uranosic oxide or uranyl hydroxide in hydrochloric acid, mixed with alcohol, is exposed to sunlight and the product precipitated by adding ether. The reduction of soln. of uranyl chloride in the presence of ether, in sunlight, was first noticed by A. F. Gehlen, in 1806. R. Arndt and W. Knop also obtained a soln. of the tetrachloride by boiling for 15 mins. a soln. of uranyl chloride and hydrochloric acid with copper and a trace of hydrochloroplatinic acid. The cold soln., after filtration, was treated with hydrogen sulphide to remove copper, and the filtrate boiled to remove hydrogen sulphide. The soln. of uranium tetrachloride was treated with ammonia, and the precipitated uranous hydroxide dissolved in hydrochloric acid. J. Aloy and G. Auber, and V. Kohlschütter and H. Rossi recommended sodium hyposulphite as reducing agent.

As observed by E. M. Péligot, and H. Löbel, uranium tetrachloride forms lustrous, dark green, octahedral crystals belonging to the cubic system, when produced by sublimation in a slow current of chlorine, but, added R. Sendtner, with a fast current of chlorine the sublimate is a green, crystalline powder. H. Hansen found the X-radiogram agrees with a cubic lattice with $a=14.57$ A., and 24 mols. per cube. W. E. Schilz gave 4·73 for the sp. gr. at 4°/4° ; O. Hönig-schmid and W. E. Schilz, 4·725 at 25°/4°, W. Biltz and C. Fendius, 4·854 at 25°/4°, and for the mol. vol., 78·3. J. L. C. Zimmermann observed that the vapour is red, and that the vapour density is 13·33 when the value calculated for UCl_4 is 13·21 ; and from the effect of the tetrachloride on boiling bismuth trichloride, L. Rügheimer and K. L. Gonder obtained a mol. wt. of 373, corresponding closely with 380·3 required for UCl_4. W. Biltz and C. Fendius gave for the heat of formation $(U,2Cl_2)=251$ Cals. E. Becquerel, and T. R. Merton investigated the absorption spectrum—vide supra. W. Hampe found that the molten chloride conducts the electric current and is at the same time electrolyzed. As indicated above, the tetrachloride is reduced to the trichloride when it is heated in hydrogen. A. Voigt and W. Biltz found the sp. electrical conductivity at 570° to be 0·34, and at 620°, 0·48. H. G. Grimm, and G. von Hevesy discussed the m.p. and electrical conductivity. E. M. Péligot noted that the crystals fume in moist air, and they are very deliquescent, forming an emerald-green soln. The salt is freely soluble in water, dissolving with a hissing noise, the evolution of heat, and the formation of a dark emerald-green liquid. R. Arndt and W. Knop also observed that a soln. of the salt is fairly stable in the cold, but if ferrous chloride is present as impurity, the uranium is soon oxidized to the quinquevalent stage. H. Löbel said that the salt in aq. soln. is completely hydrolyzed, so that, as E. M. Péligot observed, it does not then form complex salts with alkali chlorides, but it does so in non-hydrolyzing solvents. According to E. M. Péligot, when the aq. soln. is evaporated, hydrochloric acid is given off, and there is formed a residue of hydrated uranous oxide which yields a soln. with water ; and when evaporated in vacuo, there remains a deliquescent residue not uranium tetrachloride ; J. J. Berzelius also observed that the boiling aq. soln. gives off hydrochloric acid, forming hydrated uranous oxide— J. Aloy said that the black precipitate formed in the boiling soln. has the composition $UCl_4.5UO_2.10H_2O$; and R. Arndt and W. Knop, that when the dark green soln. is dropped into boiling water, it is decolorized and hydrated uranous oxide is precipitated. The tetrachloride was found by H. Kunheim to be converted into uranosic oxide when heated to redness in water-vapour. H. Hermann showed that dry hydrogen sulphide transforms it into uranium disulphide and hydrogen chloride ; and A. Colani added that the hydrides of the metalloids readily react with the tetrachloride with double decomposition at a red-heat ; and with oxygen compounds it reacts in the dry way, forming uranium dioxide and a chloride— e.g. with tungsten trioxide, arsenic trioxide, etc. W. Peters found that the dehydrated salt absorbs dry ammonia to form **uranium triamminotetrachloride,** $UCl_4.3NH_3$, and the ammonia is retained in vacuo. C. F. Rammelsberg said that an excess of sodium thiosulphate precipitates from an aq. soln. of uranium tetrachloride a mixture of sulphur and a basic uranous sulphite, while some sulphur dioxide is given off. A. Remelé said that almost neutral soln. of uranous salts give precipitates free from uranium when treated with ammonium and sodium thiosulphates. E. Uhrlaub observed that when heated in ammonia gas, uranium nitride is formed, but C. F. Rammelsberg observed that, at ordinary temp., uranium tetrachloride absorbs 5·44 parts of ammonia gas, with the development of heat. This is a little more than is required for *uranous amminotetrachloride*, $UCl_4.NH_3$. H. Löbel observed that uranium tetrachloride forms a pale green soln. with alcohol, with partial alcoholysis. The alcoholysis is hindered by saturating the soln. with hydrogen chloride, and complex organic chlorides can be obtained with the liquid. The tetrachloride also forms pale green soln. with acetone, acetic ester, and benzoic ester ; but it is insoluble in ether, chloroform, and benzene. T. R. Merton also noted that uranium tetrachloride is soluble in ethyl alcohol, acetone, acetonitrile, ethyl acetoacetate, and acetophenone. The reduction of uranyl salt soln. in the presence of many organic substances has been previously discussed. J. E. Abelous and co-workers found that the insolation for several hours of common sugars— sucrose, glucose, levulose, and lactose—in 2 per cent. soln. caused no appreciable change, but if 25 c.c. of the soln. contains 2 c.c. of a 2 per cent. soln. of a uranyl salt, the yellow soln. becomes green by exposure to a bright light—in the case of uranyl acetate, a violet precipitate is formed. Levulose and sucrose react most rapidly ; aldehydes, particularly formaldehyde, are amongst the products of the reaction. Inulin is more readily attacked by this treatment than is starch or glycogen. As previously indicated, E. M. Péligot, H. Hermann, and others found that the tetrachloride is reduced to the metal by sodium, potassium, aluminium, etc. ; and A. Colani observed that binary compounds with potassium, sodium, magnesium, aluminium, tin, and antimony are formed when these metals are heated with uranium tetrachloride. Complex salts with tin, titanium, and thorium tetrachlorides could not be prepared by H. Löbel. All the uranous salt soln. are strong reducing agents—e.g. soln. of gold and silver salts give precipitates of the metal, potassium permanganate soln. are rapidly decolorized, ferric salts are converted into ferrous salts, etc.—*vide supra*, analytical reactions of uranium.

J. Aloy prepared **lithium uranous hexachloride,** $2LiCl.UCl_4$, by passing the vapour of uranium tetrachloride over the alkali chloride at a dull red-heat; the alkali salt gradually melts as the uranium tetrachloride is absorbed. Similarly with the sodium and potassium salts. These salts are pale green when first prepared, but are very hygroscopic, and rapidly darken as they absorb moisture from the air. They are very soluble in acetic acid, and dissolve also in water, with development of heat, giving a strongly acid soln. which oxidizes slowly in the air at ordinary temp., and more rapidly when heated. The soln. are decomposed by water, so that when evaporated in vacuo over sulphuric acid, crystals of alkali chloride are deposited and a green, uncrystallizable mass is left behind. Alcohol gives a green soln., which also rapidly oxidizes and becomes yellow. H. Moissan, A. Colani, and J. Aloy prepared **sodium uranous hexachloride,** $2NaCl.UCl_4$, by passing the vapour of the tetrachloride over sodium chloride at dull redness; A. Colani added that a great excess of the sodium salt is an advantage. The apple-green crystals melt at about 390°, and very little vapour is given off. The salt is very hygroscopic and decomposes like uranium tetrachloride in the presence of water, in which the salt is freely soluble. It is also decomposed by alcohol. The preparation and properties of **potassium uranous hexachloride,** $2KCl.UCl_4$, are indicated in connection with the lithium salt; and similarly with **rubidium uranous hexachloride,** Rb_2UCl_6, and **cæsium uranous hexachloride,** Cs_2UCl_6. J. Aloy prepared **calcium uranous hexachloride,** $CaCl_2.UCl_4$, by the method employed for the lithium salt, but especial care must be taken to dry the chloride before the heating, which must not be taken too far. Similarly also **with strontium uranous hexachloride,** $SrCl_2.UCl_4$, and with **barium uranous hexachloride,** $BaCl_2.UCl_4$. The complex salts with the alkaline earth metals are of a deeper green colour than those with the alkali metals; but like the latter, they are decomposed by water, and cannot be obtained crystalline by evaporating the aq. soln. in vacuo. H. Löbel also prepared complex salts with pyridine and quinoline.

H. E. Roscoe[3] prepared **uranium pentachloride,** UCl_5, simultaneously with the tetrachloride, by passing an excess of dry chlorine over a moderately heated mixture of charcoal with any of the oxides of uranium or uranyl chloride. The pentachloride exists in two distinct forms, according as it is produced slowly or quickly. When the current of chlorine is slow, the pentachloride of uranium forms long, dark, needle-shaped crystals, which reflect light with a green, metallic lustre, but appear of a ruby-red colour when viewed by transmitted light. If the rate at which the chlorine passes be rapid, the pentachloride is deposited in the form of a light, brown, mobile powder. The octahedral crystals of the tetrachloride are always deposited in quantity in that part of the tube nearest to the heated mixture; then the black, needle-shaped crystals of pentachloride are formed, mixed with more or less of the brown powder, which is generally carried for a considerable distance along the tube. According to A. Michael and A. Murphy, P. Camboulives, and F. Bourion, the pentachloride is also formed along with the tetrachloride when the uranium oxides are chlorinated by heating them in the vapour of carbon tetrachloride or sulphur monochloride. V. Pimmer employed an analogous process. O. Ruff and A. Heinzelmann recommended converting the mixture of uranium pentachloride and tetrachloride wholly into the pentachloride by sealing it with liquid chlorine in a glass tube; heating the vessel protected by an iron tube; afterwards cooling the vessel to liquefy the excess of chlorine, and then allowing the chlorine to escape by evaporation. H. E. Roscoe said that the pentachloride forms black needles and a brown powder, and added that it cannot be volatilized without partial decomposition, either when heated alone or in an atm. of chlorine or of carbon dioxide, uranium tetrachloride and free chlorine being formed. This dissociation begins in an atm. of carbon dioxide at a temp. of 120° and is completed at 235°, since the percentage of chlorine contained in the residue is four-fifths that required for the tetrachloride. The tetrachloride, when similarly heated, loses no chlorine. V. Pimmer said that the dissociation proceeds very slowly even at the ordinary temp. of a room, and volatilization occurs at 70° under 7 mm. press. The vapour density is then about half that required for the pentachloride, showing that the compound is dissociated : $2UCl_5 \rightleftharpoons 2UCl_4 + Cl_2$. The effect of the pentachloride on the b.p. of ether agrees with a mol. wt. 248·4—when the theoretical value for UCl_5 is 415·75 ; the results with chloroform, acetic acid, and ethyl alcohol show that chemical action occurs. V. Pimmer estimated that the m.p. of the pentachloride is above 300°.

According to H. E. Roscoe, the pentachloride is extremely hygroscopic, yielding on exposure to the *air* for a few minutes a yellowish-green liquid. When thrown into *water*, the pentachloride hisses as it passes into soln., giving off fumes of hydrochloric acid. V. Pimmer said that the green soln. smells both of chlorine and of hydrochloric acid ; and if only a small proportion of water is employed, the liquid blackens, in consequence of the formation of uranous hydroxide. H. E. Roscoe observed that when the pentachloride is heated to redness in dry *ammonia*, a black nitride is formed. A. W. Cronander heated uranium trioxide in a sealed tube with an excess of *phosphorus pentachloride* for 3 or 4 days, and obtained yellowish-red **uranium phosphodecachloride,** $UCl_5.PCl_5$. The product is decomposed by water : $2(UCl_5.PCl_5) + 9H_2O = UP_2O_7 + UO_2Cl_2 + 18HCl$. V. Pimmer, and H. Löbel found that uranium pentachloride forms a green soln. with *ethyl alcohol* which becomes yellow when it is boiled. H. Löbel said that the pentachloride is insoluble in dry *ether, benzene, nitrobenzene,* and *ethylene bromide* ; sparingly soluble in *carbon tetrachloride,* and *chloroform,* forming yellow soln. ; soluble in *ethyl benzoate* and the soln. becomes brown ; and soluble in *acetone* and *trichloroacetic acid,* and the soln. becomes brown when heated. The best solvents observed were *ethyl acetate* and *benzonitrile,* but the b.p. of these solvents is lowered, not raised, by the pentachloride, showing that some chemical action has taken place. V. Pimmer's observations with soln. in ether, chloroform, acetic acid, and ethyl alcohol are indicated above. According to V. Pimmer, the green soln. in *ethyl acetate* becomes yellow when boiled ; the dark yellow soln. in *benzaldehyde* does not appear to change when boiled ; *acetone* forms a green soln. ; *glycerol* forms a green soln. at 50° ; *benzyl alcohol* dissolves traces of the salt, forming a green soln. ; *carbon disulphide* decomposes uranium pentachloride, and the smell of sulphur monochloride gradually develops without dissolution ; *nitrobenzene* dissolves traces ; *benzonitrile* forms a yellow soln. ; warm *xylidine,* and *p-toluidine* dissolve some pentachloride ; whilst the pentachloride is insoluble in *benzene, aniline, ligroin, pyridine, quinoline, ethyl sulphide,* and *amyl sulphide.* H. Löbel added that many *organic oxy-compounds* dissolve the pentachloride, primarily forming addition products, which—particularly the hydroxy-compounds—rapidly decompose into uranous compounds, or pass into oxychlorides with the evolution of hydrogen chloride.

H. Löbel [4] left uranium pentachloride for many days in contact with liquid chlorine in a sealed tube, in the presence of various possible catalytic agents, but did not obtain **uranium hexachloride,** UCl_6, analogous to the hexafluoride. A. Michael and A. Murphy heated uranium trioxide or uranosic oxide with carbon tetrachloride for many hours in a sealed tube, and G. M. Ross heated uranous oxide in a sealed tube with sulphur monochloride, and obtained a green, non-volatile solid with the composition of the hexachloride. It decomposes when warmed, and with water forms uranyl chloride. The evidence for the individuality of the hexachloride is not altogether satisfactory.

REFERENCES.

¹ E. M. Péligot, *Ann. Chim. Phys.,* (3), **5.** 20, 1842 ; E. Uhrlaub, *Ueber die Verbindungen einiger Metalle mit Stickstoff,* Göttingen, 1859 ; *Pogg. Ann.,* **103.** 134, 1858 ; C. F. Rammelsberg, *ib.,* **55.** 318, 1842 ; H. Löbel, *Ueber Halogenverbindungen des Urans,* Berlin, 1907 ; A. Rosenheim and H. Löbel, *Zeit. anorg. Chem.,* **57.** 234, 1908 ; W. Biltz, *ib.,* **193.** 321, 1930 ; W. Biltz and C. Fendius, *ib.,* **172.** 385, 1928 ; **176.** 49, 1928 ; C. Fendius, *Zur Volumchemie und Verwandtschaftslehre der Uran-, Wolfram-, und Molybdänchloride,* Leipzig, 1928 ; J. L. C. Zimmermann, *Liebig's Ann.,* **213.** 300, 1882 ; F. Stolba, *Listy Chem.,* **11.** 225, 1887 ; K. Someya, *Zeit. anorg. Chem.,* **161.** 46, 1927 ; *Science Rep. Tohoku Univ.,* **16.** 411, 1927.

² E. M. Péligot, *Compt. Rend.*, **12**. 735, 1841 ; **22**. 487, 1846 ; **42**. 73, 1856 ; *Ann. Chim. Phys.*, (3), **5**. 5, 1842 ; (3), **20**. 329, 1847 ; *Journ. Pharm. Chim.*, (2), **27**. 522, 1841 ; *Liebig's Ann.*, **41**. 141, 1841 ; **43**. 258, 1842 ; *Journ. prakt. Chem.*, (1), **24**. 442, 1841 ; (1), **38**. 112, 1846 ; H. E. Roscoe, *Journ. Chem. Soc.*, **27**. 933, 1874 ; T. R. Merton, *ib.*, **105**. 23, 1914 ; C. F. Rammelsberg, *Pogg. Ann.*, **55**. 318, 1842 ; A. Remelé, *ib.*, **125**. 237, 1865 ; H. Rose, *ib.*, **116**. 352, 1862 ; *Ausführliches Handbuch der analytischen Chemie*, Braunschweig, **2**. 523, 1851 ; H. Löbel, *Ueber Halogenverbindungen des Urans*, Berlin, 1907 ; A. Rosenheim and H. Löbel, *Zeit. anorg. Chem.*, **57**. 234, 1908 ; A. Colani, *Recherches sur les composés uraneux*, Paris, 1907 ; *Ann. Chim. Phys.*, (8), **12**. 59, 1907 ; F. Bourion, *ib.*, (8), **11**. 58, 1910 ; C. Matignon and F. Bourion, *ib.*, (8), **5**. 127, 1905 ; *Compt. Rend.*, **138**. 631, 1904 ; P. Camboulives, *ib.*, **150**. 175, 1910 ; E. Becquerel, *ib.*, **101**. 1254, 1885 ; E. Demarçay, *ib.*, **104**. 111, 1887 ; A. Michael and A. Murphy, *Amer. Chem. Journ.*, **44**. 384, 1910 ; W. Hampe, *Chem. Ztg.*, **12**. 106, 1888 ; J. Aloy, *Recherches sur l'uranium et ses composés*, Paris, 1901 ; *Ann. Chim. Phys.*, (7), **24**. 412, 1901 ; *Bull. Soc. Chim.*, (3), **21**. 264, 613, 1899 ; J. Aloy and G. Auber, *ib.*, (4), **1**. 569, 1907 ; H. Moissan, *ib.*, (3), **17**. 266, 1897 ; *Ann. Chim. Phys.*, (7), **9**. 264, 1896 ; *Compt. Rend.*, **122**. 1088, 1896 ; L. Meyer, *Ber.*, **20**. 681, 1887 ; W. Peters, *ib.*, **42**. 4826, 1909 ; V. Kohlschütter and H. Rossi, *ib.*, **34**. 1472, 1901 ; H. Rossi, *Beiträge zur Kenntnis des vierwertigen Urans*, München, 1902 ; H. Hermann, *Ueber einige Uranverbindungen*, Göttingen, 1861 ; E. Uhrlaub, *Ueber die Verbindungen einiger Metalle mit Stickstoff*, Göttingen, 1859 ; *Pogg. Ann.*, **103**. 134, 1858 ; H. Kunheim, *Ueber Einwirkung des Wasserdampfes auf Chlormetalle bei hoher Temperatur*, Göttingen, 1861 ; J. L. C. Zimmermann, *Ber.*, **14**. 1938, 1881 ; *Liebig's Ann.*, **213**. 320, 1882 ; **216**. 8, 1883 ; L. Rügheimer and K. L. Gonder, *ib.*, **364**. 45, 1908 ; R. Sendtner, *ib.*, **195**. 325, 1879 ; *Ueber einige Verbindungen des Urans*, Erlangen, 1877 ; R. Arndt and W. Knop, *Journ. prakt. Chem.*, (1), **70**. 385, 1857 ; R. W. Moore, *Trans. Amer. Electrochem. Soc.*, **43**. 317, 1923 ; D. Lely and L. Hamburger, *Zeit. anorg. Chem.*, **87**. 209, 1914 ; A. Roderburg, *ib.*, **81**. 122, 1913 ; A. Voigt and W. Biltz, *ib.*, **133**. 277, 1924 ; W. Biltz, *ib.*, **133**. 306, 1924 ; **193**. 321, 1930 ; W. Biltz and C. Fendius, *ib.*, **172**. 385, 1928 ; **176**. 49, 1928 ; C. Fendius, *Zur Volumchemie und Verwandtschaftslehre des Uran-, Wolfram-, und Molybdänchloride*, Leipzig, 1928 ; A. F. Gehlen, *Gehlen's Ann.*, **3**. 569, 1806 ; J. F. Goggin, J. J. Cronin, H. C. Fogg and C. James, *Journ. Ind. Eng. Chem.*, **18**. 114, 1926 ; J. J. Berzelius, *Schweigger's Journ.*, **44**. 191, 1825 ; *Pogg. Ann.*, **1**. 359, 1824 ; *Svenska Akad. Handl.*, 152, 1823 ; *Ann. Phil.*, **9**. 266, 1825 ; J. E. Abelous, J. Aloy and A. Valdiguié, *Compt. Rend. Soc. Biol.*, **96**. 1385, 1927 ; H. Hansen, *Zeit. phys. Chem.*, **8**. B, 1, 1930 ; *Ueber Koordinationseigenschaften von Halogenides in der Nähe der Flüchtigkeitsgrenze mit Strukturuntersuchungen an Halogeniden X₄*, Kiel, 1930 ; W. E. Schilz, *Eine Revision des Atomgewichts des Urans. Analyse des Uranochlorids*, München, 1927 ; O. Hönigschmid and W. E. Schilz, *Zeit. anorg. Chem.*, **170**. 145, 1928 ; H. G. Grimm, *Zeit. Elektrochem.*, **34**. 430, 1928 ; G. von Hevesy, *ib.*, **34**. 463, 1928.

³ H. E. Roscoe, *Journ. Chem. Soc.*, **27**. 933, 1874 ; H. Löbel, *Ueber Halogenverbindungen des Urans*, Berlin, 1907 ; A. Rosenheim and H. Löbel, *Zeit. anorg. Chem.*, **57**. 234, 1908 ; A. W. Cronander, *Oefvers. Akad. Stockholm*, **27**. 56, 1870 ; *Ber.*, **6**. 1466, 1873 ; *Bull. Soc. Chim.*, (2), **19**. 499, 1873 ; O. Ruff and A. Heinzelmann, *Ber.*, **42**. 492, 1909 ; A. Michael and A. Murphy, *Amer. Chem. Journ.*, **44**. 384, 1910 ; P. Camboulives, *Compt. Rend.*, **150**. 175, 1910 ; F. Bourion, *Ann. Chim. Phys.*, (8), **21**. 58, 1910 ; V. Pimmer, *Zur Charakterisierung des Uranpentachlorids*, Zürich, 65, 1904.

⁴ H. Löbel, *Ueber Halogenverbindungen des Urans*, Berlin, 1907 ; A. Michael and A. Murphy, *Amer. Chem. Journ.*, **44**. 384, 1910 ; G. M. Ross, *Bull. Colorado School Mines*, **5**. 38, 1909 ; *Met.*, **7**. 7. 1910.

§ 17. Uranium Oxychlorides

J. Aloy [1] prepared **uranous dioxytetrachloride,** $UO_2.UCl_4.H_2O$, as a pale green, soluble crystalline mass, by evaporating an aq. soln. of uranium tetrachloride at a low temp., in vacuo, dissolving the product in alcohol, adding ether to the alcoholic soln., washing the precipitate with ether, and drying it in vacuo. N. A. Orloff prepared **sodium uranous dioxyhexachloride,** $Na_2UCl_6.UO_2.6H_2O$, in greenish-yellow crystals, by evaporating an aq. soln. of uranous chloride and sodium uranate. N. A. Orloff obtained **uranous tetroxytetrachloride,** $2UO_2.UCl_4.13H_2O$, by the action of light on a soln. of uranyl chloride in 2 parts of ether and 1 part of alcohol. It forms green soln. with water, and alcohol. When the *tridecahydrate* is dried over sulphuric acid it forms the *monohydrate*. If it be dried at 100°, **uranous octoxytetrachloride,** $4UO_2.UCl_4$, is formed ; it gives dark brown soln. with water, and with alcohol. J. J. Berzelius observed that if an aq. soln. of uranium tetrachloride be concentrated by heat, it furnishes a black powder ; and J. Aloy obtained in a similar way a product with the composition **uranous decoxytetrachloride,** $5UO_2.UCl_4.10H_2O$. He also obtained it by allowing uranous hydroxide and a soln. of uranium tetrachloride in air-free water to act on one another for some days in a closed flask. The product when dried is black ; and it can be kept in air a long time without becoming yellow.

According to E. M. Péligot,[2] dry chlorine unites with uranium dioxide at a red-heat to form an orange-yellow vapour, which condenses, forming yellow crystals of **uranyl chloride,** UO_2Cl_2. If the uranium dioxide contains any uranosic oxide, uranium trioxide remains behind on dissolving the compound in water. F. P. Venable and D. H. Jackson chlorinated uranosic oxide at 500° by a mixture of chlorine and carbon monoxide. A. von Unruh observed that when uranyl acetate, dissolved in amyl alcohol, is evaporated with hydrochloric acid until all the acetic acid is expelled, then 4 to 6 times with water to remove the excess of hydrochloric acid, and the soln. freed from water by boiling, there are formed green, fluorescent plates of the anhydrous salt. F. W. O. de Coninck added a soln. of barium chloride, drop by drop, to a conc., freshly prepared, aq. soln. of uranyl sulphate, filtered off the precipitated barium sulphate, and evaporated the soln. on a water-bath to obtain uranyl chloride. The early workers obtained a soln. of the salt by dissolving uranyl hydroxide in hydrochloric acid, or by oxidizing a soln. of uranium dioxide or uranosic oxide in hydrochloric acid, by means of nitric acid, or by exposure to air. According to M. H. Klaproth, the evaporation of the yellow soln. furnishes efflorescent, oblique, four-sided plates ; L. R. Lecanu obtained very deliquescent needles ; and J. A. Arfvedson, an uncrystallizable, deliquescent syrup. J. Aloy reported that a soln. of uranyl chloride in hydrochloric acid, saturated at 15°, furnishes crystals of **uranyl hydrotrichloride,** $UO_2Cl_2.HCl.2H_2O$, when cooled to $-10°$, and added that the crystals lose hydrogen chloride when exposed to air ; but F. Mylius and R. Dietz showed that a soln. of uranium trioxide in conc. hydrochloric acid forms yellowish-green, doubly refracting, hygroscopic prisms of the *trihydrate,* $UO_2Cl_2.3H_2O$, or $H_4UO_5.2HCl$, when evaporated in a desiccator over sulphuric acid. When these crystals are heated above 100°, they give off water, hydrogen chloride, and chlorine. F. W. O. de Coninck said that if an aq. soln. of uranyl chloride be evaporated over sulphuric acid, it furnishes crystals of the *monohydrate,* $UO_2Cl_2.H_2O$, but F. Mylius and R. Dietz showed that if a sat. aq. soln. be evaporated, the syrupy liquid furnishes flattened needles of **uranyl hydroxychloride,** $HUO_3Cl.2H_2O$, or $UO_2(OH)Cl.2H_2O$, or $H_4UO_5.HCl$. This salt loses its water of crystallization at 150°, and its aq. soln. scarcely reddens blue litmus. Silver oxide precipitates the whole of the chlorine from its aq. soln., leaving a colloidal soln. of uranic acid (*q.v.*). F. W. O. de Coninck observed no evidence of the formation of $UO_2Cl(OH)$ in his study of soln. of uranyl chloride. F. Mylius and R. Dietz suggested that both the trihydrated uranyl chloride and dihydrated uranyl hydroxychloride are addition products of uranic acid, H_4UO_5, with two and one mol. of hydrogen chloride respectively.

E. M. Péligot said that anhydrous uranyl chloride is yellow, deliquescent, and crystalline. F. Mylius and R. Dietz found the sp. gr. of the viscid aq. soln. to be 2·74, so that ordinary glass and quartz will float in the liquid. F. W. O. de Coninck found between 13·1° and 16·3°, for soln. with :

UO_2Cl_2	.	1	2	4	6	8	10 per cent.
Sp. gr.	.	1·0056	1·0112	1·0215	1·0313	1·0418	1·0517

E. M. Péligot found that the salt is readily fusible, but apparently not very volatile. F. W. O. de Coninck said that the salt melts at the beginning of a red-heat. The absorption spectrum was measured by H. C. Jones and W. W. Strong, H. L. Howes, etc.—*vide supra*, physical properties of uranium. H. M. Vernon estimated the ionization from the colours. According to C. Dittrich, the mol. wt. calculated from the lowering of the f.p., $\theta°$ of dil. soln. when the theoretical value for UO_2Cl_2 is 341·1, the ionization factor, i, and the degree of ionization, α, for soln. with M mols per litre, are :

M	.	.	1	2	4	8	16
$\theta°$	.	.	2·926°	1·338°	0·651°	0·331°	0·170°
Mol. wt.	.	.	130·5	129·4	127·1	122·2	117·6
i	.	.	2·60	2·62	2·69	2·80	2·90
a	.	.	0·81	0·83	0·85	0·90	0·95

I. Lifschitz and S. B. Hooghoudt studied the Becquerel effect. The aq. soln. is acidic to litmus and congo-red, and the observations of F. Mylius and R. Dietz show that the soln. is hydrolyzed—*vide supra*. W. Hampe found that the molten anhydrous salt conducts the electric current, with the separation of black uranium dioxide. W. Hittorf also observed that the aq. soln. is decomposed by electrolysis into uranium dioxide and chlorine. C. Dittrich gave for the electrical conductivity, λ, of soln. with half a mol in v litres of water at 25° :

v	.	4	8	16	32	64	128	256	512	1024
λ	.	89·8	89·3	96·6	104·3	111·3	118·5	127·4	136·4	147·0

where $\lambda_{1024}-\lambda_{32}=42\cdot7$, corresponding with a two-stage ionization process. The results of L. G. Winston and H. C. Jones at 0° to 35°, and of A. P. West and H. C. Jones at 35°, 50°, and 65°, are :

v	.	.	4	8	32	128	512	1024	2048	4096
λ {	0°	.	101·45	110·48	133·05	148·39	155·98	161·02	168·42	174·98
	25°	.	180·45	206·01	246·12	279·00	296·56	311·92	328·24	348·16
	35°	.	214·70	246·51	297·84	339·40	360·44	383·88	405·98	433·68

a {	0°	.	58·0	63·1	76·0	84·8	89·1	92·0	96·3	100·0
	25°	.	51·8	59·2	70·7	80·2	85·2	89·6	94·3	100·0
	35°	.	49·5	56·8	68·7	78·2	83·1	88·5	93·6	100·0

v	.	.	2	4	16	64	250	1024
λ {	35°	.	117·8	135·4	161·1	182·8	202·8	223·7
	50°	.	146·8	170·5	203·2	234·9	262·6	292·3
	65°	.	178·1	207·3	252·9	293·2	326·4	370·8

v	.	.	4	8	32	128	1024	4096
a {	35°	.	0·5136	0·5795	0·6947	0·7820	0·8974	100·00
	65°	.	0·4441	0·5173	0·6447	0·7451	0·8929	100·00

The maxima on the polarization curves of uranyl salt soln. were discussed by M. Shikata, E. B. Sanigar, W. Podrouzek, and P. Herasymenko ; and the electro-reduction of soln. of these salts by the mercury dropping cathode, by P. Herasymenko.

F. W. O. de Coninck observed that when thoroughly dried, anhydrous uranyl chloride is stable in a dry atmosphere ; and that an aq. soln., if air be excluded, slowly deposits, in light, a small quantity of uranic hydroxide, $UO_3.2H_2O$, which after some time partially redissolves. The decomposition is faster in the presence of air ; and when the aq. soln. is boiled. F. Mylius and R. Dietz found that the trihydrate is deliquescent, and that it can be heated to 100° without change, but at a higher temp. water, hydrogen chloride, and chlorine are given off, and the brownish-black substance which remains, after the salt has been heated over 400°, contains uranium trioxide. F. W. O. de Coninck found that when heated in *hydrogen*, the salt is reduced to the dioxide ; and when heated in *air*, chlorine is given off and uranosic oxide is formed. The anhydrous salt is freely soluble in *water*. At 18°, F. Mylius and R. Dietz found that 100 parts of water dissolve 746 parts of the trihydrate, and that the solubility increases with a rise of temp. The sat. soln. is yellowish-green. According to F. W. O. de Coninck, anhydrous uranyl chloride is slowly dissolved by conc. *hydrochloric acid* ; in the cold, *hydrogen sulphide* converts it into uranium dioxide, sulphur, and hydrogen chloride, and when heated, uranyl sulphate is formed ; *sulphuric acid* drives out hydrogen chloride to form uranyl sulphate ; and cold *selenic acid*, of sp. gr. 1·4, dissolves uranyl chloride, and when heated, chlorine is given off and uranyl selenite is formed. J. Persoz observed that uranyl salt soln. are reduced by *trithionic acid*. E. P. Lewis found that

uranium salts become phosphorescent when exposed to activated nitrogen.
A. Rosenheim and F. Jacobsohn found that liquid *ammonia* forms a grey mass
when it acts on anhydrous uranyl chloride ; F. F. Regelsberger did not obtain an
ammine by the action of ammonia gas on an alcoholic soln. of the anhydrous
chloride ; an unstable **uranyl tetramminochloride,** $UO_2Cl_2.4NH_3$, is formed by the
action of ammonia on solid uranyl chloride, and if ammonia acts on the complex
with ether, **uranyl diamminochloride,** $UO_2Cl_2.2NH_3$, is formed. W. Peters found
that the dehydrated salt absorbs ammonia to form **uranyl hexamminodichloride,**
$UO_2Cl_2.6NH_3$, and this compound, in vacuo, forms the diammine. According to
J. M. Ordway, aq. ammonia added to a soln. of uranyl chloride gives a precipitate
which again dissolves until half the hydrochloric acid is neutralized. F. W. O. de
Coninck observed that cold *nitric acid* forms a yellow liquid, and when heated,
chlorine and nitrous fumes are evolved and uranyl nitrate is formed ; an excess of
nitric acid forms the acid salt. R. Böttger said that *phosphorus* does not reduce
uranyl salt soln. J. Lifschitz obtained a complex with *hydroxymethylene camphor*.
F. Mylius and R. Dietz found that the trihydrate is soluble in *alcohol*, and in *ether*.
F. F. Regelsberger, E. Rimbach, C. G. Williams, A. R. Leeds, and H. Grossmann
and B. Schück observed that uranyl chloride forms crystalline compounds with
organic bases, ether, etc. The action of light on soln. of uranyl salts in the presence
of alcohol, etc., was discussed in connection with the physical properties of uranium.
J. Aloy and A. Valdiguié found that uranyl salts act catalytically by the simultaneous
oxidation and reduction of dextrose and methylene-blue when soln. are exposed
to sunlight in the absence of oxygen ; G. Berger examined the photochemical
decomposition of formic acid. P. Walden, and H. Grossmann studied the effect
of uranyl salt soln. on the rotatory power of soln. of sugar, and other optically
active hydroxyl compounds. H. J. H. Fenton observed that uranyl salts give a
red or brown coloration with dihydroxymaleic acid. S. Hakomori observed that
sexivalent uranium salts form complexes with tartaric acid. E. F. Rousseau said
that salts of uranium exposed to solar or ultra-violet radiation store the ultra-
violet energy and produce photocatalytic effects in the sterilization or activation
of ferments. A. Pil found that uranyl salt soln. do not coagulate a gelatin sol
unless a trace of an alkali halide be also present. R. Rascanu prepared complex
salts with pyridine, quinoline, 2-methylquinoline, antipyrine, pyramidon, and
phenacetin.

E. M. Péligot observed that when uranyl chloride is heated with *potassium*,
potassium chloride and uranium dioxide are formed ; K. Seubert and A. Schmidt
found that when heated with *magnesium* some uranium is formed ; and F. W. O. de
Coninck found that when heated with *zinc* dust or *iron* filings, it is reduced to
uranium dioxide, but not by *copper* turnings. N. W. Fischer found that copper
forms cuprous chloride and reduces a hydrochloric acid soln. of a uranyl salt to the
uranous stage, and R. Arndt and W. Knop said that the action is facilitated by heat
in the presence of a little platinic salt. V. Kohlschütter and H. Rossi found that
uranyl salts are reduced by copper. J. L. C. Zimmermann observed that in sulphuric acid soln. uranyl salts are reduced by zinc only to the quadrivalent or uranous
stage. N. W. Fischer found that hydrochloric acid soln. of uranyl salts are reduced
to the uranous stage by zinc, *cadmium, tin, lead*, iron, or *cobalt*. The reaction with
zinc was studied by I. Wertheim. The reduction of uranyl salt soln. to uranous
salts by magnesium was observed by T. L. Phipson, A. Commaille, S. Kern, and
G. A. Maack ; and by *aluminium*, by G. A. Maack. Molten *alkali hydroxide* forms
alkali diuranate and a small proportion of normal uranate. When uranyl chloride is
heated with *calcium hydroxide*, uranosic oxide and some calcium uranate are formed ;
if-air is excluded, dark grey uranium dioxide is produced and at a higher temp. dark
reddish-brown uranium dioxide is formed. An excess of *calcium oxide* in air forms
yellow calcium uranate, green or yellowish-green calcium diuranate, and very little
uranosic oxide. When anhydrous uranyl chloride is heated with *barium hydroxide*,
barium uranate and very little uranosic oxide are formed ; with *barium oxide*, at

a high temp., the main product is orange-yellow barium diuranate—*strontium oxide* acts in a similar manner.   E. M. Péligot observed that complex salts are formed with the *alkali chlorides*.

According to F. W. O. de Coninck, the aq. soln. gives no precipitate with *hydrochloric acid*, hot or cold; *alkali-lye* gives an orange precipitate; aq. *ammonia*, a pale yellow precipitate, insoluble in excess; *methylamine*, a dark yellow precipitate, insoluble in excess; *sodium hydrocarbonate*, no precipitate; *alkali carbonate*, a pale yellow gelatinous precipitate, insoluble in excess; *sodium hydrophosphate*, a yellow gelatinous precipitate, insoluble in excess; *ammonium hydrosulphide*, a pale brown precipitate which in a few hours becomes reddish-brown; *hydrogen sulphide*, a small brown precipitate; *cobalt nitrate*, and *copper sulphate* give no change in 24 hrs.; *potassium cyanide*, a pale yellow precipitate, insoluble in excess; and with *potassium ferrocyanide and ferricyanide*, dark reddish-brown precipitates, insoluble in excess.   For other reactions, *vide supra*, some reactions of analytical interest.

Uranyl chloride forms a series of complex salts of the general formula $2RCl.UO_2Cl_2$, or $R_2(UO_2)Cl_4$.   E. Rimbach found that crystals of **ammonium uranyl tetrachloride**, $(NH_4)_2(UO_2)Cl_4.2H_2O$, are obtained from a soln. of a mol of uranyl chloride and 2 mols of ammonium chloride in conc. hydrochloric acid, after concentration to a syrupy liquid.   E. M. Péligot previously obtained this salt from a soln. of uranium trioxide and ammonium chloride in hydrochloric acid, or from a soln. of ammonium uranate in that acid.   The rhombohedral crystals are very deliquescent and freely soluble in water.   The solubility data shown in Table I indicate that the salt is decomposed by water, the soln. is richer in uranyl chloride, and the solid is a mixture of ammonium chloride and undecomposed ammonium uranyl tetrachloride.   The corresponding **tetramethylammonium uranyl tetrachloride**, $2N(CH_3)_4Cl.UO_2Cl_2$, and **tetraethylammonium uranyl chloride**, $2N(C_2H_5)_4Cl.UO_2Cl_2$, as indicated in Table I, are not decomposed in aq.

TABLE I.—THE SOLUBILITY OF THE ALKALI AND AMMONIUM URANYL TETRACHLORIDES.

Complex salt	Temp.	100 parts of solution contain				Atomic or mol. ratios in solution
		UO_2	R	Cl	Total	$UO_2 : R : Cl$
$2NH_4Cl.UO_2Cl_2$	15°	40·67	3·51	19·15	—	1 : 1·59 : 3·59
$2N(CH_3)_4Cl.UO_2Cl_2$	29·8°	19·86	—	10·44	41·19	1 : — : 4·02
	80·7°	20·21	—	10·51	41·66	1 : — : 3·98
$2N(C_2H_5)_4Cl.UO_2Cl_2$	27·1°	15·04	—	7·80	37·17	1 : — : 3·97
	80·7°	15·11	—	7·81	37·30	1 : — : 3·96
$2KCl.UO_2Cl_2$	0·8°	38·57	3·86	13·59	—	1 : 0·69 : 2·69
	17·5°	37·36	5·27	14·50	—	1 : 0·96 : 2·96
	41·5°	35·27	7·39	15·92	—	1 : 1·44 : 3·44
	60·0°	34·19	9·14	17·25	—	1 : 1·85 : 3·85
	78·5°	35·26	9·95	18·24	—	1 : 1·95 : 3·95
$2RbCl.UO_2Cl_2$	24·8°	27·12	16·68	13·85	57·71	1 : 1·96 : 3·90
	80·3°	30·69	19·13	15·86	65·79	1 : 1·98 : 3·95
$2CsCl.UO_2Cl_2$	29·75°	22·12	22·37	—	56·24	1 : 2·06 : —

soln.   **Methylammonium uranyl tetrachloride**, $2NH_3(CH_3)Cl.UO_2Cl_2$; **dimethyl-ammonium uranyl tetrachloride**, $2NH_2(CH_3)_2Cl.UO_2Cl_2$; and **trimethylammonium uranyl tetrachloride**, $2NH(CH_3)_3.UO_2Cl_2$, were also prepared.   H. Grossmann and B. Schück prepared **ethylenediamine uranyl chloride**, $C_2H_6(NH_2)_2(UO_2)Cl_4.2H_2O$, in yellow, hygroscopic, prismatic crystals, melting at 219°.   Attempts by E. Rimbach to prepare **hydroxylamine uranyl tetrachloride,** $2NH_4OCl.UO_2Cl_4$, in aq. soln. were not successful; and in the attempts to make **hydrazine uranyl tetrachloride,** reduction always occurred. J. Aloy prepared **sodium uranyl tetrachloride,** $Na_2(UO_2)Cl_4$, by passing the vapour of uranyl chloride over heated sodium chloride, and similarly with **potassium uranyl tetrachloride,** $K_2(UO_2)Cl_4$. The golden-yellow crystals melt at a red-heat without vaporizing; the salt is freely soluble in water, and in dil. alcohol. E. M. Péligot prepared the *dihydrate,* $K_2(UO_2)Cl_4$. $2H_2O$, from a soln. of the components, using an excess of potassium chloride; J. J. Berzelius recommended using soln. with at least 15 per cent. of hydrochloric acid. E. Rimbach, and H. Bürger used an excess of uranyl chloride. J. A. Arfvedson added that if potassium chloride is not present in excess, the double salt crystallizes from the soln. with difficulty; but since both salts crystallize from the soln. at the same time, the crystals of the double salt must be picked out from those of potassium chloride. E. M. Péligot prepared the salt from a soln. of potassium uranate in a large excess of hydrochloric acid. The yellowish-green, four or six-sided plates were shown by C. F. Rammelsberg, and F. de la Provostaye to be triclinic pinacoids with the axial ratios $a : b : c = 0.607 : 1 : 0.560$, and $a = 80°\ 41'$, $\beta = 77°\ 42'$, and $\gamma = 91°\ 18'$. J. A. Arfvedson found that the hydrated salt loses its water at a temp. a little above 100°, and the anhydrous compound melts at the beginning of a red-heat. When heated above this temp. it is partially decomposed, with the evolution of chlorine; and at a still higher temp. E. M. Péligot observed that fused potassium chloride is formed, with scaly crystals of uranium dioxide in suspension. H. Becquerel studied the absorption spectrum. J. A. Arfvedson found that when heated in hydrogen the salt is decomposed. E. M. Péligot observed that the salt is freely soluble in water; and E. Rimbach, and H. Bürger found the solubility data indicated in Table I. The results show that at low temp. the complex salt is resolved by water into its components, so that a greater proportion of uranyl chloride passes into soln. The ground-mass is then a mixture of potassium chloride and potassium uranyl chloride, in agreement with E. M. Péligot's observation that on evaporating the aq. soln., potassium chloride crystallizes out, while uranyl chloride remains in soln. E. Rimbach observed that at about 60° the soln. and solid have the same composition, showing that *das Salz ist von da an untersetzt in Wasser löslich*—or, possibly, that the solubilities of the components are the same. J. Aloy said that the heat of soln. of a mol of the salt in 1000 to 2500 mols of water at 18° to 20° is 2 Cals. J. J. Berzelius found that the salt is reduced with vivid incandescence when it is heated with potassium; uranium dioxide and potassium chloride are formed. J. O. Perrine observed no ultra-violet fluorescence in the X-rays. E. Rimbach, and H. Bürger prepared **rubidium uranyl tetrachloride,** $Rb_2(UO_2)Cl_4.2H_2O$, in yellowish-green crystals, as in the analogous case of the potassium salt. The solubility data, Table I, show that the salt is not decomposed by water, from which solvent it can be crystallized unchanged. H. L. Wells and B. B. Boltwood prepared **cæsium uranyl tetrachloride,** $Cs_2(UO_2)Cl_4$, in rhombic plates, by passing hydrogen chloride into a well-cooled, conc. soln. of 10 to 50 grms. of cæsium chloride and 10 to 50 grms. of uranyl chloride; and by evaporating a soln. of 15 to 50 grms. of cæsium chloride and 15 to 50 grms. of uranyl chloride. E. Rimbach, and H. Bürger obtained it by evaporating a soln. of 2 mols of cæsium chloride and one mol of uranyl chloride. The solubility data are shown in Table I; like the rubidium salt, the cæsium salt is not decomposed in aq. soln. H. L. Wells and B. B. Boltwood said that the salt is decomposed when calcined, forming uranosic oxide. J. O. Perrine observed no ultra-violet fluorescence in the X-rays.

REFERENCES.

[1] J. J. Berzelius, *Schweigger's Journ.*, **44.** 191, 1825; *Pogg. Ann.*, **1.** 359, 1824; *Svenska Akad. Handl.*, 152, 1823; *Ann. Phil.*, **9.** 266, 1825; J. Aloy, *Recherches sur l'uranium et ses composés*, Paris, 1901; *Bull. Soc. Chim.*, (3), **21.** 613, 1899; N. A. Orloff, *Journ. Russ. Phys. Chem. Soc.*, **34.** 375, 1902; **35.** 513, 1903.

² E. M. Péligot, *Compt. Rend.*, **12.** 735, 1841 ; **22.** 487, 1846 ; **42.** 73, 1856 ; *Ann. Chim. Phys.*, (3), **5.** 5, 1842 ; (3), **20.** 329, 1847 ; *Journ. Pharm. Chim.*, (2), **27.** 522, 1841 ; *Liebig's Ann.*, **41.** 141, 1841 ; **43.** 258, 1842 ; *Journ. prakt. Chem.*, (1), **24.** 442, 1841 ; (1), **38.** 112, 1846 ; F. W. O. de Coninck, *Recherches sur le nitrate d'uranium*, Montpellier, 1901 ; *Ann. Chim. Phys.*, (8), **3.** 500, 1904 ; *Bull. Acad. Belg.*, 709, 1903 ; 836, 1904 ; 743, 836, 1909 ; *Compt. Rend.*, **147.** 1477, 1908 ; **148.** 1769, 1909 ; *La chimie de l'uranium*, Paris, 1911 ; F. W. O. de Coninck and M. Camo, *Bull. Acad. Belg.*, 321, 1901 ; K. Seubert and A. Schmidt, *Liebig's Ann.*, **267.** 239, 1892 ; F. Mylius and R. Dietz, *Ber.*, **34.** 2774, 1901 ; E. Rimbach, *ib.*, **37.** 461, 1904 ; F. F. Regels-berger, *Ueber einiger ammoniakalische Verbindungen des Uran*, Würzburg, 1883 ; *Liebig's Ann.*, **227.** 119, 1885 ; E. F. Rousseau, *Brit. Pat. No.* 226534, 1924 ; M. H. Klaproth, *Mém. Acad. Berlin*, 273, 1789 ; 160, 1792 ; *Beiträge zur chemischen Kenntnis der Mineralkörper*, Berlin, **2.** 197, 1797 ; London, 477, 1801 ; *Crell's Ann.*, ii, 387, 1789 ; J. A. Arfvedson, *Pogg. Ann.*, **1.** 245, 1824 ; *Schweigger's Journ.*, **44.** 8, 1825 ; L. R. Lecanu, *Journ. Pharm. Chim.*, (2), **11.** 279, 1825 ; W. Hittorf, *Pogg. Ann.*, **106.** 337, 513, 1859 ; A. Rosenheim and F. Jacobsohn, *Zeit. anorg. Chem.*, **50.** 297, 1906 ; H. Grossmann and B. Schück, *ib.*, **50.** 21, 1906 ; H. C. Jones and W. W. Strong, *Phys. Zeit.*, **10.** 499, 1909 ; *Amer. Chem. Journ.*, **43.** 97, 1910 ; A. P. West and H. C. Jones, *ib.*, **44.** 536, 1910 ; L. G. Winston and H. C. Jones, *ib.*, **46.** 368, 1911 ; J. M. Ordway, *Amer. Journ. Science*, (2), **26.** 208, 1858 ; H. L. Wells and B. B. Boltwood, *ib.*, (3), **50.** 249, 1895 ; *Zeit. anorg. Chem.*, **10.** 183, 1895 ; J. Aloy, *Recherches sur l'uranium et ses composés*, Paris, 1901 ; *Compt. Rend.*, **122.** 1541, 1896 ; *Bull. Soc. Chim.*, (3), **25.** 153, 1901 ; J. Aloy and A. Valdiguié, *ib.*, (4), **33.** 572, 1923 ; J. J. Berzelius, *Pogg. Ann.*, **1.** 366, 1824 ; *Schweigger's Journ.*, **44.** 191, 1825 ; H. Bürger, *Beiträge zur Kenntnis der Uranyldoppelsalze*, Bonn, 1904 ; C. F. Rammelsberg, *Handbuch der krystallographischen Chemie*, Berlin, 215, 1855 ; I. Lifschitz and S. B. Hooghoudt, *Zeit. phys. Chem.*, **146.** 145, 1930 ; F. de la Provostaye, *Ann. Chim. Phys.*, (3), **6.** 165, 1842 ; H. Becquerel, *ib.*, (6), **14.** 170, 1888 ; W. Hampe, *Chem. Ztg.*, **12.** 106, 1888 ; H. C. Bolton, *On the Fluorine Compounds of Uranium*, Göttingen, 40, 1866 ; *Sitzber. Akad. Berlin*, 299, 1866 ; *Bull. Soc. Chim.*, (2), **2.** 450, 1866 ; C. Dittrich, *Die Uranylsalze vom physikalischchemischen Standpunkte aus betrachtet*, Leipzig, 1899 ; *Zeit. phys. Chem.*, **29.** 465, 1899 ; A. von Unruh, *Einwirkung von trochenen Ammoniak auf wasserfreie Uranylsalze*, Rostock, 1909 ; C. G. Williams, *Journ. prakt. Chem.*, (1), **69.** 355, 1856 ; *Trans. Roy. Soc. Edin.*, **21.** 377, 1857 ; A. R. Leeds, *Journ. Amer. Chem. Soc.*, **3.** 134, 1882 ; F. P. Venable and D. H. Jackson, *ib.*, **42.** 2531, 1920 ; *Journ. Elisha Mitchell Soc.*, **35.** 87, 1920 ; N. W. Fischer, *Pogg. Ann.*, **9.** 265, 1827 ; **16.** 126, 1829 ; *Das Verhältniss der chemischen Verwandtschaft zur galvanischen Electricität in Versuchen dargestellt*, Berlin, 1830 ; I. Wertheim, *Ber. Vers. deut. Naturf.*, 193, 1843 ; *Ann. Chim. Phys.*, (3), **11.** 49, 1844 ; *Journ. prakt. Chem.*, (1), **29.** 227, 1843 ; R. Arndt and W. Knop, *ib.*, (1), **70.** 385, 1857 ; T. L. Phipson, *Proc. Roy. Soc.*, **13.** 217, 1864 ; A. Commaille, *Bull. Soc. Chim.*, (2), **6.** 257, 1866 ; S. Kern, *Chem. News*, **33.** 236, 1876 ; G. A. Maack, *Untersuchungen über das Verhalten des Magnesiums und Aluminiums zu den Salzlösungen verschiedener Metalle*, Göttingen, 1862 ; R. Böttger, *Chem. Centr.*, (3), **9.** 208, 1878 ; *Polyt. Notiz.*, **33.** 30, 1878 ; J. L. C. Zimmer-mann, *Liebig's Ann.*, **213.** 300, 1882 ; M. Shikata, *Trans. Faraday Soc.*, **21.** 53, 1925 ; P. Hera-symenko, *ib.*, **24.** 257, 267, 1928 ; *Chem. Listy*, **19.** 5, 1925 ; J. Persoz, *Ann. Chim. Phys.*, (3), **20.** 315, 1847 ; P. Walden, *Ber.*, **30.** 2889, 1897 ; W. Peters, *ib.*, **42.** 4826, 1909 ; V. Kohlschütter and H. Rossi, *ib.*, **34.** 1472, 1901 ; H. Grossmann, *Zeit. Ver. Zuckerind.*, 1058, 1905 ; H. M. Vernon, *Chem. News*, **66.** 104, 114, 141, 152, 1892 ; A. Pil, *Natuurw. Tids.*, **7.** 17, 1925 ; H. L. Howes, *Phys. Rev.*, (2), **6.** 192, 1915 ; J. O. Perrine, *ib.*, (2), **22.** 48, 1923 ; G. Berger, *Rec. Trav. Chim. Pays-Bas*, **44.** 47, 1925 ; J. Lifschitz, *ib.*, **41.** 627, 1922 ; H. J. H. Fenton, *Journ. Chem. Soc.*, **93.** 1064, 1908 ; E. P. Lewis, *Nature*, **111.** 599, 1923 ; S. Hakomori, *Science Rep. Tohoku Univ.*, **16.** 841, 1927 ; E. B. Sanigar, *Rec. Trav. Chim. Pays-Bas*, **44.** 549, 1925 ; W. Podrouzek, *ib.*, **44.** 592, 1925 ; R. Rascanu, *Ann. Science Univ. Jassy*, **16.** 32, 459, 1930.

§ 18. The Uranium Bromides and Iodides

G. Alibegoff,[1] and J. L. C. Zimmermann obtained **uranium tribromide,** UBr₃, by the action of hydrogen on uranium tetrabromide heated to near its m.p. The reduction could not be carried further than the tribromide. The dark brown, needle-like crystals of the tribromide prepared by G. Alibegoff are very hygroscopic. The vap. density could not be determined. When molten the salt is dark green. It dissolves in water with a hissing noise and the development of much heat. The soln. furnishes a characteristic absorption spectrum. When the violet soln. is allowed to stand exposed to air, or when it is shaken in air, it becomes dirty brown, then dirty green, and finally emerald-green characteristic of uranous salt soln., depositing a reddish powder. H. Löbel reduced electrolytically a dil. soln. of uranic acid in hydrobromic acid, when the yellow soln. becomes green, and finally red. The addition of sulphuric acid produces a brown, crystalline precipitate, which, becoming green, gives off hydrogen. A cold, sat. soln. of potassium sulphate gives a precipitate similar to that obtained with a soln. of the trichloride.

J. L. C. Zimmermann prepared **uranium tetrabromide** or **uranous bromide,** UBr_4, by passing bromine vapour along with a current of carbon dioxide or nitrogen over a heated mixture of carbon and uranium dioxide or uranosic oxide. A similar process was employed by H. Hermann, and A. Colani. A. von Unruh said that the product is a mixture of uranyl and uranous bromides. T. W. Richards and B. S. Merigold also prepared the salt in this manner, and added that it can be purified by sublimation in a dry atm. of bromine or nitrogen and rigorously excluding all traces of air or oxygen. A. Colani obtained the tetrabromide at a temp. above its m.p. but below its temp. of vaporization. According to C. F. Rammelsberg, the dark green soln. of hydrated uranous oxide in hydrobromic acid, when evaporated over sulphuric acid, deposits dark green crystals, and dries to a highly deliquescent mass. Analyses agree with the *octohydrate*, $UBr_4.8H_2O$, but this has not been confirmed. When the aq. soln. is heated, it gives off hydrogen bromide and deposits a black powder which he thought to be uranous oxide. J. L. C. Zimmermann said that the anhydrous salt, during its preparation, collects as a sublimate of dark brown or black plates—H. Hermann said fine needles. J. L. C. Zimmermann found that when the salt is heated in an inert gas, it melts and gives off a brown vapour which condenses as a sublimate of the original salt. T. W. Richards and B. S. Merigold found the sp. gr. to be 4·838 at 21°. J. L. C. Zimmermann observed that the vap. density 19·46 agrees with the theoretical value 19·36 required for UBr_4. H. Hermann reported that in contact with air the anhydrous salt fumes, and rapidly deliquesces to a dark emerald-green liquid ; it dissolves in water with a hissing noise, forming a green soln. which exhibits the characteristic reactions of the uranous salts. The green, aq. soln. of the tetrabromide is even less stable than that of the tetrachloride ; it readily gives off hydrogen bromide, and oxidizes to the yellow uranyl bromide. A. von Unruh said that the tetrabromide is insoluble in alcohol, and R. Sendtner, insoluble in ether. J. L. C. Zimmermann heated the tetrabromide with bromine in a sealed tube at 230° for a long time, but observed no change, and no sign of the formation of the **uranium pentabromide,** UBr_5.

J. Aloy passed the vapour of the tetrabromide, in a current of carbon dioxide, over red-hot sodium bromide, and obtained a dark green mass of **sodium uranous hexabromide,** Na_2UBr_6, and similarly with **potassium uranous hexabromide,** K_2UBr_6. These salts are fusible, freely soluble in water, and the aq. soln. on evaporation does not yield the double salt. They resemble the corresponding hexachlorides, but the colour is a darker green.

According to H. Hermann, the anhydrous **uranyl bromide,** UO_2Br_2, is obtained simultaneously with uranium tetrabromide when the latter is obtained by passing bromine vapour over a mixture of carbon and uranosic oxide. Uranyl bromide is rather more volatile than uranium tetrabromide. R. Sendtner extracted with ether the mixture of uranyl and uranous bromides obtained by heating uranium dioxide in a current of bromine vapour. The ethereal soln. when evaporated in vacuo furnishes fluorescent, yellowish-green needles of uranyl bromide. A. von Unruh prepared the anhydrous salt by treating the heptahydrate with amyl alcohol, decanting off the water, and boiling the soln. J. B. Berthemot boiled uranium dioxide with bromine-water, or dissolved uranium trioxide in hydrobromic acid, and obtained, on evaporation, a yellow liquid which deposited yellow needles of the *heptahydrate*, $UO_2Br_2.7H_2O$. R. Sendtner obtained the salt in a similar manner ; and C. F. Rammelsberg said that the green mixture of uranium tetrachloride and potassium bromate soon becomes yellow owing to the liberation of bromine and the formation of this salt. A. von Unruh prepared the tetrahydrate repeatedly by evaporating a soln. of uranyl acetate and hydrobromic acid on a water-bath, then with water, and finally evaporating the aq. soln. in vacuo over sulphuric acid. The flat, yellow needles of the heptahydrate, said J. B. Berthemot, have a strong, styptic taste ; and when they are dried at a high temp., they assume an orange colour, and give off hydrogen bromide, while at a red-heat they evolve bromine and form uranosic oxide. H. C. Jones and W. W. Strong measured the absorption spectra of a soln. of the salt. The crystals are very deliquescent, and, according to F. W. O. de Coninck, give off hydrogen bromide to form hydrated uranium dioxide. R. Sendtner said that the salt is freely soluble in water and in alcohol; and, added A. von Unruh, in ether. The aq. soln. hydrolyzes and deposits hydrated uranium trioxide. F. W. O. de Coninck observed that the reactions of the aq. soln. are characteristic of those of the uranyl salts—*vide supra*, uranyl chloride. If dry ammonia be passed into a dry ethereal soln. of uranyl bromide, a complex salt, $UO_2Br_2(NH_3)_2.(C_2H_5)_2O$, is deposited, and if this salt be exposed to a current of dry air, almost all the ether is driven off and egg-yellow **uranyl diamminobromide,** $UO_2Br_2.2NH_3$, is formed; and the same compound is formed when dry ammonia is passed into a dry amyl alcohol soln. of uranyl bromide, the precipitate washed with dry ether and alcohol, and dried in a current of warm air. If the product be allowed to stand in an atm. of dry ammonia for a long time, it passes into **uranyl triamminobromide,** $UO_2Br_2.3NH_3$. By treating the diammine or the anhydrous salt with liquid ammonia, deep orange-red, amorphous **uranyl tetramminobromide,** $UO_2Br_2.4NH_3$, is formed, but it is stable only below 5°. R. Rascanu prepared complex salts with antipyrine, and phenacetin.

According to R. Sendtner, if a soln. of ammonium diuranate be dissolved in an excess of hydrobromic acid, and the soln. concentrated by evaporation, it furnishes yellowish-brown, rhombic plates of **ammonium uranyl tetrabromide,** $(NH_4)_2(UO_2)Br_4.2H_2O$, which are so deliquescent that they are difficult to dry. The salt is freely soluble in water. The salt cannot be recrystallized from water. The corresponding **potassium uranyl tetrabromide,** $K_2(UO_2)Br_4.2H_2O$, was prepared in a similar way.

H. Löbel could not prepare a soln. of **uranium triiodide,** UI_3, by the electrolytic process which he employed for the trichloride and tribromide. According to C. F. Rammelsberg, hydrated uranium dioxide forms a dark green soln. of **uranium tetraiodide,** UI_4, when dissolved in hydriodic acid. If the soln. be evaporated spontaneously, it turns brown, and gives off free iodine, leaving a black, crystalline mass which contains some tetraiodide and forms a reddish-brown soln. with water. R. Sendtner found that if the soln. be extracted with ether, and the yellow, ethereal liquid be evaporated, it is decomposed. Neither H. Hermann nor R. Sendtner could obtain an iodide by the action of iodine vapour on a red-hot mixture of carbon and uranium dioxide; nor did R. Sendtner succeed in producing an iodide by passing hydrogen iodide over the heated dioxide. A. Colani could not obtain the pure tetraiodide by the action of hydrogen iodide on uranium tetrachloride, but M. Guichard found that by heating a mixture of iodine and uranium in a sealed tube at 500°, anhydrous uranium tetraiodide collects as a crystalline sublimate. The black, needle-like crystals have a sp. gr. 5·6 at 15°; the m.p. is about 500°; and volatilization occurs between 500° and 600° in vacuo. The tetraiodide is reduced when heated in hydrogen; when kept in dry air, it acquires a superficial crust of iodine crystals, and oxygen is absorbed; it inflames at a low temp. in dry oxygen or dry air, forming green uranosic oxide; in moist air it rapidly deliquesces to a brown liquid containing free iodine, and in a few hours, in the presence of an excess of water, forms a yellow liquid, which when heated precipitates green hydrated uranium trioxide. The salt dissolves in water to form a green, acidic soln. which gives the characteristic reactions of uranous salts. When the tetraiodide is treated in the cold with chlorine, it is decomposed, yielding uranium tetrachloride and iodine trichloride.

A. von Unruh observed that **uranyl iodide,** UO_2I_2, cannot be prepared like the corresponding chloride and bromide, since neither iodine vapour nor hydrogen iodide reacts with a red-hot mixture of uranium dioxide and carbon; nor did J. Aloy obtain definite results by the action of iodine vapour on uranium dioxide at various temp. A. von Unruh obtained a soln. of uranyl iodide by the action of hydriodic acid on uranyl acetate, which decomposes into uranium dioxide, iodide, and hydrogen iodide when it is warmed on a water-bath to drive off the acetic acid.

If, however, the soln. be evaporated in vacuo over sulphuric acid, it suffers only partial decomposition, and after some days deposits crystals of the salt. J. Aloy prepared the salt by adding a slight excess of a soln. of barium iodide in dry ether to an ethereal soln. of uranyl nitrate, and evaporating the red soln. in vacuo. The red, crystalline mass deliquesces in air, and it decomposes with the separation of iodine. The yellow, aq. soln. does not yield uranyl iodide on evaporation, since it decomposes into hydriodic acid, iodine, etc. The salt is freely soluble in alcohol, ether, and benzene. A. von Unruh obtained a soln. of the salt by adding an excess of uranium trioxide to freshly-prepared hydriodic acid, agitating the filtered soln. with amyl alcohol, removing the aq. layer in a separatory funnel, and boiling the amyl alcohol soln. to eliminate water. The yellow liquid soon becomes brown. G. Truttwin prepared a soln. of uranyl iodide by double decomposition in alcoholic soln. A. von Unruh prepared yellow **uranyl diamminoiodide,** $(UO_2)I_2.2NH_3$, by passing dry ammonia into a dry, ethereal soln. of uranyl iodide, and removing ether from the precipitated $UO_2I_2.2NH_3.(C_2H_5)_2O$, in vacuo, or in a current of dry air ; and also by passing dry ammonia into the dry amyl alcohol soln. of uranyl iodide, washing the precipitate with ether, and removing the ether in a current of dry air. If the product be kept in an atm. of dry ammonia, it forms orange-red **uranyl triamminoiodide,** $UO_2I_2.3NH_3$; and if treated with liquid ammonia, it forms **uranyl tetramminoiodide,** $UO_2I_2.4NH_3$, which is very unstable, for it quickly decomposes at a temp. above 5°. G. Truttwin prepared **bismuth uranyl iodide,** $UO_2I_2.BiI_3$.

REFERENCES.

[1] G. Alibegoff, *Liebig's Ann.*, **233**. 117, 1886 ; J. L. C. Zimmermann, *ib.*, **216**. 5, 1883 ; *Ber.*, **14**. 1934, 1881 ; G. Truttwin, *German Pat.*, *D.R.P.* 420391, 1924 ; C. F. Rammelsberg, *Pogg. Ann.*, **55**. 77, 1842 ; H. Hermann, *Ueber einige Uranverbindungen*, Göttingen, 1861 ; H. Löbel, *Ueber Halogenverbindungen des Urans*, Berlin, 1907 ; A. Rosenheim and H. Löbel, *Zeit. anorg. Chem.*, **57**. 234, 1908 ; J. Aloy, *Recherches sur l'uranium et ses composés*, Paris, 1901 ; *Bull. Soc. Chim.*, (3), **21**. 264, 1899 ; *Ann. Chim. Phys.*, (7), **24**. 412, 1901 ; J. B. Berthemot, *ib.*, (2), **44**. 394, 1830 ; A. Colani, *Recherches sur les composés uraneux*, Paris, 1907 ; *Compt. Rend.*, **137**. 382, 1903 ; *Ann. Chim. Phys.*, (8), **12**. 50, 1907 ; *Compt. Rend.*, **137**. 382, 1903 ; R. Sendtner, *Liebig's Ann.*, **195**. 325, 1879 ; *Ueber einige Verbindungen des Urans*, Erlangen, 1877 ; A. von Unruh, *Einwirkung von Ammoniak auf wasserfreie Uranylsalze*, Rostock, 1909 ; F. W. O. de Coninck, *Bull. Acad. Belg.*, 1025, 1902 ; *La chimie de l'uranium*, Paris, 1911 ; *Compt. Rend.*, **135**. 900, 1902 ; H. Moissan, *ib.*, **122**. 1089, 1896 ; *Bull. Soc. Chim.*, (3), **17**. 267, 1897 ; M. Guichard, *ib.*, (4), **3**. 11, 1908 ; *Compt. Rend.*, **145**. 807, 921, 1907 ; H. C. Jones and W. W. Strong, *Phys. Zeit.*, **10**. 499, 1909 ; *Amer. Chem. Journ.*, **43**. 97, 1910 ; T. W. Richards and B. S. Merigold, *Proc. Amer. Acad.*, **37**. 365, 1902 ; *Chem. News*, **85**. 177, 1902 ; *Zeit. anorg. Chem.*, **31**. 235, 1902 ; R. Rascanu, *Ann. Science Univ. Jassy*, **16**. 32, 459, 1930.

§ 19. Uranium Sulphides and Oxysulphides

J. L. C. Zimmermann [1] said that uranium has not a great affinity for sulphur. G. Alibegoff obtained what he regarded as **uranium monosulphide,** US, by heating to redness uranium hemitrisulphide in a current of hydrogen for 30 to 70 hrs. The black, amorphous powder glows when heated in air, and it behaves towards acids like **uranium hemitrisulphide,** or **uranium sesquisulphide,** U_2S_3, which he prepared by heating uranium tribromide in a current of hydrogen sulphide. The greyish-black, needle-like crystals are pseudomorphs after the tribromide. When the hemitrisulphide is exposed to air, it gives off hydrogen sulphide ; when heated in air, it glows and forms uranosic oxide ; dil. and conc. hydrochloric and nitric acids are without action ; fuming nitric acid oxidizes it with incandescence ; aqua regia oxidizes it quietly ; and bromine and hydrochloric acid attack it a little. E. Beutel and A. Kutzelnigg observed no anodic deposition of sulphide from thiosulphate soln.

According to E. M. Péligot, uranium unites with incandescence with sulphur at its b.p., forming **uranium disulphide,** or **uranous sulphide,** US_2. H. Hermann found that at a red-heat, hydrogen sulphide decomposes uranium tetrachloride quietly and without incandescence, forming uranium disulphide and hydrogen chloride. A. Colani obtained it by heating sodium uranous hexachloride in hydrogen sulphide : the sodium salt is better than uranium tetrachloride because it is less volatile ; the reaction begins at 500°, and progresses better at a higher temp. A high temp. is necessary for the production of good crystals. When the apparatus has cooled, the product is quickly washed with cold, air-free water, when the disulphide remains. A. Colani also prepared the disulphide by double decomposition of a sulphide of magnesium, aluminium, antimony, or tin with sodium uranous hexachloride in an atm. of hydrogen. Stannous sulphide gave the best results. The product contains a little hemitrisulphide ; and if air be not rigorously excluded, some dioxysulphide may be formed. C. F. Rammelsberg dropped an aq. soln. of uranium tetrachloride in an excess of ammonium sulphide and obtained a black precipitate, which when washed and dried proved to be a mixture of uranium hydroxide and sulphur. A. Colani described uranium disulphide as a black or iron-grey, crystalline powder. H. Hermann obtained black, four-sided columns by heating the powder with borax at a white-heat. According to P. Groth, the tetragonal plates have the axial ratio $a : c = 1 : 0.6152$. The streak on porcelain is grey. A. Colani said that the disulphide does not decompose or melt between 1000° and 1100° ; but M. Picon found that the disulphide is decomposed or dissociated at 1200° to 1300°. H. Hermann found that it is slowly oxidized by moist *air*, forming hydrogen sulphide and a yellow basic uranyl sulphide ; when heated in air, sulphur dioxide is evolved and uranosic oxide is formed. A. Colani added that if the powder is projected into a flame, it burns in sparks. Cold *water* reacts very slowly ; water vapour acts energetically at a red-heat, forming uranium dioxide, hydrogen sulphide, and sulphur. H. Hermann found that the disulphide is vigorously decomposed by *chlorine* without incandescence ; dil., cold or boiling *hydrochloric acid* is almost without action ; the cold, conc. acid dissolves the disulphide, forming the tetrachloride without the separation of sulphur. A. Colani added that the action is slow with the dil. acid, faster with the conc. acid, especially when warmed. H. Hermann said that *nitric acid* oxidizes it to uranyl sulphate, and A. Colani added that uranyl nitrate, sulphuric acid, and sulphur are formed. A. Verneuil found that the addition of one-thousandth part of uranium disulphide alters the character of the phosphorescence of calcium sulphide.

H. Rose [2] prepared **uranium dioxytetrasulphide**, $U_3O_2S_4$, or $UO_2.2US_2$, but its composition was established by H. Hermann. The former prepared it by heating uranosic oxide and the latter by heating uranium dioxide or ammonium uranate in the vapour of carbon disulphide alone, or carried along by a current of carbon dioxide —the same product is obtained if the uranium dioxide be at a red-heat or at a white-heat, but at the higher temp. some free carbon and sulphur are formed. J. A. Arfvedson observed that this compound is formed along with a little uranium disulphide when hydrogen sulphide is passed over heated uranosic oxide ; L. R. Lecanu, and J. J. Ebelmen, when uranosic oxide or uranium dioxide is heated with sulphur, or, according to H. Hermann, sulphur and ammonium chloride ; and H. Hermann, by heating uranyl sulphate in hydrogen sulphide or with potassium pentasulphide, or by heating sodium uranate mixed with sulphur and ammonium chloride. According to H. Rose, and H. Hermann, the greyish-black or yellowish-black powder smells of hydrogen sulphide when triturated in a mortar ; and it burns when heated in air to form uranosic oxide. Uranium dioxytetrasulphide is slowly oxidized by chlorine-water ; and a mixture of potassium chlorate and hydrochloric acid inflames the powder. J. J. Berzelius observed that it is only slightly attacked by dil. hydrochloric acid ; but H. Hermann added that it is soluble in conc. hydrochloric acid, forming uranous chloride without the separation of sulphur. J. J. Berzelius observed that cold nitric acid dissolves the dioxytetrasulphide with the separation of sulphur, whilst H. Hermann added that the fuming acid decomposes it with incandescence.

J. Milbauer obtained **uranyl sulphide,** UO_2S, in black, tetragonal, acicular crystals, by fusing together 12 parts of dry potassium thiocyanate, 3 parts of uranosic oxide, and 5 parts of sulphur. W. W. Coblentz found that uranyl sulphide exhibits no photoelectric sensitivity. An impure form was prepared by H. Hermann by adding ammonium sulphide to an aq. or alcoholic soln. of a uranyl salt. The complete precipitation of the uranyl sulphide occurs only after the warm mixture has stood for some time with a very small excess of ammonium sulphide. The olive-green precipitate is then crystalline and easily filtered. When the brown precipitate is washed with air-free water, it is hydrolyzed to uranium dioxide ; and, added A. Remelé, if washed in air, it forms yellow uranyl hydroxide. A. Remelé found that the precipitate from the alcoholic soln. can be washed with alcohol without decomposition, and after drying in vacuo over potassium hydroxide, one preparation contained 18 per cent. H_2O, 1·7 per cent. ammonium sulphide, and 80·3 per cent. UO_2S. Uranyl sulphide oxidizes in air at 180° to 240°, forming uranosic oxide. It forms with water a brown soln., which is decolorized by exposure to air, and uranyl hydroxide is precipitated. A brown liquid is also formed when uranyl sulphide is treated with aq. alcohol, but not with absolute alcohol, and when the brown soln. is boiled for some hours it becomes green, though the brown coloration returns as the soln. cools. Uranyl sulphide forms a green soln. of uranous chloride when treated with conc. hydrochloric acid, in the absence of air, and sulphur is deposited ; dil. acids also dissolve it, with the separation of two-thirds to three-fourths of the sulphur and the evolution of a little hydrogen sulphide. It is also soluble in acetic acid and in a soln. of ammonium carbonate. P. Berthier found that precipitated uranyl sulphide dissolves in sulphurous acid, and when the yellow soln. is boiled, hydrated oxide is precipitated ; and A. Remelé found that sulphur dioxide converts the precipitate into uranium dioxide. G. Buchner observed that uranyl sulphide dissolves in a soln. of sodium pyrophosphate. According to A. Remelé, alkali hydroxides decompose uranyl sulphide, forming alkali uranate ; whilst sodium, potassium, and barium sulphides appear to form very unstable complex salts. A. Remelé obtained a green precipitate of impure **barium uranyl sulphide,** $6BaS.UO_2S.nH_2O$, by adding barium nitrate to a soln. of uranyl sulphide in ammonium sulphide, rapidly washing with cold water and drying in vacuo. A brown salt was obtained by adding an excess of an aq. soln. of barium sulphide to an alcoholic soln. of uranyl nitrate, washing with alcohol, and drying in vacuo.

J. J. Berzelius observed that precipitated uranyl sulphide dissolves in an excess of a soln. of ammonium sulphide to form a dark brown liquid. A. Remelé found that if freshly-precipitated uranyl sulphide is warmed with an excess of ammonium sulphide at about 40° or 50°, it is transformed into a mixture of uranium dioxide and sulphur ; it is, however, more stable in the presence of a small proportion of a metal sulphide. Uranyl sulphide precipitated from alcoholic soln. is not decomposed by boiling it with an excess of a soln. of ammonium sulphide, nor is it reddened when allowed to stand in contact with a cold soln. of ammonium sulphide, whereas A. Patera showed that uranyl sulphide precipitated by ammonium sulphide from aq. soln. of a uranyl salt becomes dark red when allowed to stand in the cold in contact with an excess of ammonium sulphide for 12 to 24 hrs. The red product was called **uranium-red** by A. Remelé. L. E. Rivot said that the change proceeds more quickly if the ammonium sulphide employed contains a little uranyl sulphide in soln. ; and A. Remelé observed that a soln. of sulphides of potassium, sodium, or barium sulphide does not produce the red colour. J. L. C. Zimmermann found that a cold soln. of potassium hydrosulphide does not transform uranyl sulphide into the red compound ; whilst ammonium hydrosulphide and calcium hydrosulphide do not form the red compound in cold or hot soln. ; rather do they decompose the uranyl sulphide into uranium dioxide and sulphur ; on the other hand, a warm soln. of barium hydrosulphide does produce uranium-red. J. J. Berzelius observed that if hydrogen sulphide be passed for a long time into water with an alkali uranate in suspension, the precipitate is orange-red ; and H. Hermann, that if a soln. of a uranyl salt be treated with an excess of ammonia, followed by hydrogen sulphide, a red colour is produced, but if a uranyl salt soln. be treated with hydrogen sulphide and then with ammonia, a brown colour is produced. A. Remelé observed that if a uranyl salt soln. be treated with ammonium sulphide and hydrogen sulphide be passed into the liquid, uranium-red is formed. According to J. L. C. Zimmermann, a black and a red substance are produced when precipitated uranyl sulphide is left for a long time in contact with a cold soln. of ammonium sulphide. If the ammonium sulphide contains thiosulphate—formed by the action of atm. oxygen on the sulphide—the red body is produced, but in the absence of thiosulphate, the black body alone is formed. The black substance is considered to be a complex uranium oxide, $U_3O_8.2UO_3$, whereas the red substance consists of an oxygen compound which, in addition to sulphur, contains a base—sodium, potassium, ammonium, or barium—as well as uranyl sulphide. J. L. C. Zimmermann also made uranium-red by treating a soln. of uranyl nitrate, acetate, or sulphate with freshly-prepared potassium hydrosulphide and keeping the liquid warm. V. Kohlschütter thus summarizes his observations on uranium-red:

(1) Alkaline, neutral, and even slightly acidic soln. of uranic acid are reduced by hydrogen sulphide. (2) In the presence of alkali-lye the reduction may be retarded if the action of hydrogen sulphide on the alkali uranate takes place in a soln. containing an excess of uranyl sulphate or nitrate. (3) Under these conditions an orange-yellow compound is produced, yielding the blood-red substance " uranium-red " when treated with alkali-lye. (4) Uranium-red contains uranium, sulphur, and alkali metal in the proportions $5 : 2 : 5$. (5) All the uranium is present as trioxide. (6) One of the atoms of the alkali metal is more loosely combined than the others. When this is removed, the yellow intermediate compound is produced ; it is feebly acid, and contains uranium, sulphur, and alkali in the proportions $5 : 2 : 4$. (7) Treatment with dil. hydrochloric acid eliminates one-half the sulphur from this compound in the form of hydrogen sulphide and the remainder as the free element ; this suggests that uranium-red contains a disulphide residue which acts as the carrier of the loosely attached atom of the alkali metal. (8) In the uranium-alkali residue, $5UO_3.2R_2O$, the four alkali atoms may be replaced by the alkaline earths without altering the chemical character of the compound ; the five mols. of uranic acid are therefore grouped in one complex, which takes part, as such, in reactions.

V. Kohlschütter's results are summarized in the following formulæ :

$$\begin{matrix} HO \\ HS.S \end{matrix} \Big\rangle U{\equiv}(O.UO_2.OR)_4 \qquad\qquad \begin{matrix} HO \\ RS.S \end{matrix} \Big\rangle{\equiv}U(O.UO_2.OR)_4$$

Parent Acid.   Uranium-red.

V. Kohlschütter obtained **potassium uranium hydroxyhydrodisulphotetraruranate**, $HS.S.U(OH)(O.UO_2.OK)_4$, or $2K_2O.5UO_3.H_2S_2$, by passing a current of carbon dioxide or hydrogen sulphide into water with freshly prepared uranium-red in suspension ; or by the protracted washing of the uranium-red with water. It is converted back into uranium-red by treatment with dil. potash-lye. *Potassium uranium-red*, or **potassium uranium hydroxydisulphotetra-uranate**, $2K_2O.KHS_2.5UO_3.5H_2O$, or $KS.S.U(OH)(O.UO_2.OK)_4.5H_2O$, was obtained by the following process :

Agitate 140 c.c. of potash-lye (containing 11 grms. of potassium hydroxide per litre) with 100 c.c. of a soln. of uranyl nitrate (50 grms. per litre) ; pass a vigorous current of hydrogen sulphide through the product until the orange-red precipitate is formed ; pass a vigorous current of air, by suction ; agitate the moist cake with a soln. of potassium carbonate heated on a water-bath for half an hour ; wash the product by suction, with water made feebly alkaline ; dry it on a porous tile ; and finally wash the product successively with alcohol, carbon disulphide, and ether.

V. Kohlschütter also prepared *sodium uranium-red*, or **sodium uranium hydroxydisulphotetraruranate,** but he did not analyze it ; **ammonium uranium hydroxyhydrodisulphotetraruranate**, $2(NH_4)_2O.5UO_3.H_2S_2.NH_3.4H_2O$, or $HS.S.$ $U(OH)(O.UO_2.ONH_4)_4.4H_2O$, was obtained as well as the corresponding *ammonium uranium-red*, or **ammonium uranium hydroxydisulphotetraruranate**, $(NH_4)S.S.$ $U(OH)(O.UO_2.ONH_4)_4.nH_2O$. A. Patera found that the corresponding products with the alkalies and alkaline earths in place of ammonia can be obtained by boiling the ammonium salt with salts of the alkalies or alkaline earths. R. Salvadori found that if hydrogen uranate is treated with hydrogen sulphide in the presence of an excess of uranyl nitrate or sulphate, an orange-yellow precipitate of **hydrazine uranium hydroxyhydrodisulphotetrauranate,** $2(N_2H_5)_2O.5UO_3.H_2S_2.6H_2O$, is formed. When the hydrogen sulphide is removed, and an excess of hydrazine hydrate is added, *hydrazine uranium-red*, or **hydrazine uranium hydroxydisulpho-tetrauranate,** $2(N_2H_5)_2O.5UO_3.HS_2(N_2H_5).4H_2O$, is formed. The substance decomposes a little above 100°. In the air it slowly loses one mol. of hydrazine. The compound remaining readily absorbs a mol. of ammonia, becoming blood-red. Hydrazine uranium-red is also obtained when "uranium-red" is treated with hydrazine. V. Kohlschütter prepared **barium uranium hydroxyhydrodisulpho-tetrauranate,** $2BaO.5UO_3.H_2S_2.10H_2O$, and found that it loses half its water at 165°. *Barium uranium-red*, or **barium uranium hydroxydisulphotetrauranate,** was obtained by V. Kohlschütter in an impure state ; and similarly with *strontium uranium-red*, or **strontium uranium hydroxydisulphotetrauranate,** and with *calcium uranium-red*, or **calcium uranium hydroxydisulphotetrauranate.** According to V. Auger and J. N. Longinescu, the red uranium compounds are amorphous salts of a *sulphouranic acid*, $H_6U_5S_2O_{16}$, or $H_{10}U_{16}S_4O_{31}$, which plays the part of quinquevalent or quadrivalent anion respectively for the red potassium and ammonium salts, and for the orange and red barium salts.

REFERENCES.

[1] G. Alibegoff, *Liebig's Ann.*, **233**. 117, 1886 ; H. Hermann, *Ueber einige Verbindungen*, Göttingen, 1861 ; A. Colani, *Ann. Chim. Phys.*, (8), **12**. 59, 1907 ; *Recherches sur les composés uraneux*, Paris, 1907 ; *Compt. Rend.*, **137**. 382, 1903 ; A. Verneuil, *ib.*, **103**. 600, 1886 ; *Bull. Soc. Chim.*, (2), **46**. 302, 1886 ; P. Groth, *Chemische Krystallographie*, **1**. 158, 1906 ; C. F. Rammelsberg, *Pogg. Ann.*, **55**. 318, 1842 ; **56**. 125, 1842 ; **59**. 1, 1843 ; *Ber.*, **5**. 1002, 1872 ; E. M. Péligot, *Compt. Rend.*, **12**. 735, 1841 ; **22**. 487, 1846 ; **42**. 73, 1856 ; *Ann. Chim. Phys.*, (3), **5**. 5, 1842 ; (3), **20**. 329, 1847 ; *Journ. Pharm. Chim.*, (2), **27**. 522, 1841 ; *Liebig's Ann.*, **41**. 141, 1841 ; **43**. 258, 1842 ; *Journ. prakt. Chem.*, (1), **24**. 442, 1841 ; (1), **38**. 112, 1846 ; M. Picon, *Compt. Rend.*, **189**. 96, 1929 ; J. L. C. Zimmermann, *Liebig's Ann.*, **216**. 5, 1883 ; *Ber.*, **14**. 1934, 1881 ; E. Beutel and A. Kutzelnigg, *Monatsh.*, **58**. 295, 1931.

[2] H. Rose, *Gilbert's Ann.*, **73**. 139, 1823 ; H. Hermann, *Ueber einige Verbindungen*, Göttingen, 1861 ; J. J. Berzelius, *Schweigger's Journ.*, **44**. 191, 1825 ; *Pogg. Ann.*, **1**. 359, 1824 ; *Svenska Akad. Handl.*, 152, 1823 ; *Ann. Phil.*, **9**. 266, 1825 ; L. R. Lecanu, *Journ. Pharm. Chim.*, (2), **11**. 279, 1825 ; J. A. Arfvedson, *Svenska Akad. Handl.*, 404, 1822 ; *Ann. Phil.*, **7**. 253, 1824 ; *Pogg. Ann.*, **1**. 245, 1824 ; *Schweigger's Journ.*, **44**. 8, 1825 ; J. J. Ebelmen, *Ann. Chim. Phys.*, (3), **5**. 189, 1842 ; P. Berthier, *Ann. Chim. Phys.*, (2), **50**. 369, 1832 ; A. Remelé, *Compt. Rend.*, **58**. 716, 1864 ; *Monit. Scient.*, (2), **1**. 469, 1864 ; *Les Mondes*, **6**. 459, 1864 ; *Ber.*, **39**. 96, 1864 ; *Pogg. Ann.*, **124**. 114, 1865 ; **125**. 209, 1865 ; *Zeit. anal. Chem.*, **4**. 371, 1865 ; *Journ. prakt. Chem.*, (1), **93**. 316, 1864 ; (1), **97**. 193, 1866 ; A. Patera, *ib.*, (1), **51**. 122, 1850 ; A. Röhrig, *ib.*, (3), **37**. 239, 1888 ; J. L. C. Zimmermann, *Liebig's Ann.*, **204**. 204, 1880 ; V. Kohlschütter, *ib.*, **314**. 311, 1901 ; J. Milbauer, *Zeit. anorg. Chem.*, **42**. 448, 1904 ; R. Salvadori, *Atti Accad. Lincei*, (5), **21**. ii, 455, 1912 ; L. E. Rivot, *Docimasie*, Paris, **3**. 167, 1864 ; W. W. Coblentz, *Scient. Papers Bur. Standards*, **18**. 586, 1922 ; *Various Photoelectric Investigations*, Washington, 596, 1922 ; G. Buchner, *Arch. Pharm.*, (3), **21**. 118, 1883 ; V. Auger and J. N. Longinescu, *Compt. Rend.*, **182**. 970, 1926.

§ 20. The Uranium Sulphates

A. Rosenheim and H. Loebel [1] prepared a sulphate of tervalent uranium the composition of which is probably **uranium hydrodisulphate,** or **hydrosulphatosulphate,** $UH(SO_4)_2$, or $U(HSO_4)(SO_4)$, or maybe $U(HSO_4)_3$. A soln. of uranium trichloride was obtained in a large excess of hydrochloric acid, by the electrolytic reduction of a soln. of uranium trioxide in hydrochloric acid of sp. gr. 1·12, with a mercury cathode, cooling the soln. to 0° towards the end of the reduction. When this soln. is mixed with fairly conc. sulphuric acid, both cooled to 0°, deep brown crystalline leaflets of this sulphate separate out. They are washed with anhydrous acetic acid. The salt can be kept under the mother-liquor for some hours out of contact with air ; on drying, it quickly forms uranous sulphate, $U(SO_4)_2$. Water oxidizes it to uranous sulphate, with the evolution of hydrogen. E. Müller and A. Flath, and

D. T. Ewing and E. F. Eldridge studied the electrometric titration of soln. of uranous sulphate with potassium permanganate or dichromate.

The existence of anhydrous **uranium disulphate,** or **uranous sulphate,** $U(SO_4)_2$, has not been established, although a product with this composition was obtained by F. Giolitti and G. Bucci [2] by heating the octohydrate at 300°. Hydrates with $\frac{1}{2}$, $1\frac{1}{2}$, 2, 3, 4, 5, 6, 7, 8, and $9H_2O$ have been reported either as stages in the drying of the higher hydrates or as definite products of crystallization from soln. of the salt. The individualities of the di-, tetra-, octo- and enneahydrates have alone been established, though the evidence is based on only a partial study of the equilibrium conditions—*vide infra,* Fig. 12. F. Giolitti and G. Liberi said that many of the phenomena presented by the uranous sulphates are almost certain indications that in these salts the sulphuric acid residue does not form ions by itself, but constitutes part of certain complex ions, which contain also uranium. This explains the large number of different salts obtained, the complexity of their formulæ, and the fact that uranous sulphates of identical composition often exhibit divergent crystalline forms and other physical and chemical properties. G. N. Wyrouboff came to a similar conclusion.

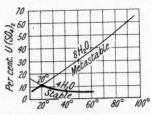

FIG. 12.—Solubility Curves of the Tetra- and Octohydrates of Uranous Sulphate.

V. Kohlschütter obtained the *dihydrate,* $U(SO_4)_2.2H_2O$, in grey needles, by adding conc. sulphuric acid to the sulphuric acid soln. of the *tetrahydrate,* $U(SO_4)_2.4H_2O$. J. J. Ebelmen prepared the tetrahydrate by dissolving uranosic oxide in an excess of hot conc. sulphuric acid, and evaporating the soln. in vacuo. The mother-liquor contains uranyl sulphate. It is better, however, before evaporating the soln., to mix it with a little alcohol and expose it in a closed flask to sunlight. V. Kohlschütter obtained this salt by triturating uranous oxalate with conc. sulphuric acid, pouring the mush into alcohol, and washing the crystals successively with alcohol and ether. F. Giolitti and G. Bucci exposed to direct sunlight a mixture of a gram of uranyl sulphate, 12 grms. of water, 6 grms. of alcohol, and 3·12 to 4·68 grms. of sulphuric acid, or a gram of uranyl sulphate, 6 grms. of 95 per cent. alcohol and 0·9 grm. of sulphuric acid. J. Aloy and G. Auber added in small portions at a time powdered or a conc. soln. of sodium hyposulphite to a 5 to 10 per cent. soln. of uranyl sulphate until a precipitate begins to form. This is dissolved by adding a few drops of sulphuric acid, and the green soln. treated with its own vol. of 90 per cent. alcohol. The precipitate is washed with dil. aq. alcohol, dissolved in dil. sulphuric acid, and the soln. evaporated at a moderate heat—a 60 per cent. yield was obtained. The tetrahydrate appears as a pale green powder, or else in dark green, rhombic, bipyramidal crystals, which, according to W. F. Hillebrand and W. H. Melville, are isomorphous with the corresponding hydrate of thorium sulphate, $Th(SO_4)_2.4H_2O$, and have the axial ratios $a : b : c = 0.7563 : 1 : 0.3805$. L. Fernandes found that the tetrahydrates $U(SO_4)_2.4H_2O$ and $Zr(SO_4)_2.4H_2O$ are isomorphous and form mixed crystals over the range 99·14 to 10·3 per cent. of the zirconium salt; the crystals are also isomorphous with the corresponding compounds of cerium and thorium. J. J. Ebelmen added that the crystals are stable in air. V. Kohlschütter supposed that a second form of the tetrahydrate exists, $2U(SO_4)_2.8H_2O$, or $U_2(SO_4)_4.8H_2O$, which is produced by evaporating the soln. in dil. sulphuric acid; but F. Giolitti and G. Bucci could not verify this—*vide infra.*

N. A. Orloff obtained the *octohydrate,* $U(SO_4)_2.8H_2O$, by exposing to sunlight for some hours a soln. of uranyl sulphate in alcohol in the presence of some sulphuric acid; whilst F. Giolitti and G. Bucci recommended a soln. containing a gram of uranyl sulphate, 4 grms. of water, 2 grms. of 95 per cent. alcohol, and 0·863 grm. of sulphuric acid. G. N. Wyrouboff mixed uranyl sulphate or a soln. of uranosic oxide in conc. sulphuric acid with alcohol, and stirred the warm soln. for 2 or

3 hrs.   The product is then dissolved in dil. sulphuric acid, and the uranous sulphate precipitated by alcohol.   The product is heated to 200°, and when cold dissolved in water, and allowed to crystallize at ordinary temp. over sulphuric acid.   The green crystals, said F. de la Provostaye, are stable in air.   According to G. N. Wyrouboff, the monoclinic prisms are isomorphous with the crystals of the corresponding thorium sulphate, $Th(SO_4)_2.8H_2O$, and have the axial ratios $a : b : c = 0.7190 : 1 : 0.5692$, and $\beta = 93°\ 24'$.   F. de la Provostaye thought the crystals were rhombic.   R. J. Meyer and H. Nachod prepared the octohydrate by the electrolytic reduction of a standard soln. of uranyl sulphate containing 2 mols of conc. sulphuric acid per mol of the crystalline salt, and precipitating the soln. with alcohol, or else evaporating it at 75° or over sulphuric acid.   If the soln. be evaporated at 93° to 95°, the tetrahydrate is formed, and it is also produced by gradually adding conc. sulphuric acid to the soln. between 0° and 70° until precipitation ceases.   The precipitation of the two hydrates from soln. thus depends on acidity.   The octohydrate is irreversibly converted into the tetrahydrate at 68°; it is less soluble in $0.1N\text{-}H_2SO_4$ than in water; whilst below 55°, the tetrahydrate is the more soluble, indicating the presence of complex ions.   The solubility curves for the two hydrates in sulphuric acid soln.—vide supra, Fig. 12—intersect at 26°, but this is not a transition point; both hydrates are stable in soln. between 15° and 92°.   The depression of the f.p. shows that the tetrahydrate has twice the mol. wt. of the octohydrate in $\frac{1}{8}N$- to $\frac{1}{32}N$-soln. in $0.1N\text{-}H_2SO_4$.   For the octohydrate (mol. wt. 574) the mol. wts. are 66.2 and 51.0 respectively for soln. with 2.687 and 0.336 per cent. $U(SO_4)_2$; and for the tetrahydrate the mol. wts. are 119 and 78 respectively for soln. with 2.687 and 0.336 per cent. $U(SO_4)_2$.

F. Giolitti and G. Liberi reported the *pentahydrate*, $U(SO_4)_2.5H_2O$, as a pale green incrustation produced by the interaction of uranyl sulphate, water, 95 per cent. alcohol, and sulphuric acid, in the respective proportions by weight : 1, 4, 0.5, and 8 ; as well as the *hexahydrate*, $U(SO_4)_2.6H_2O$, in mammillary masses of pale green crystals, by the action of these constituents in the respective proportions by weight : 1, 4, 0.9, and 8 ; and 1, 4, 1.86, and 6.   E. M. Péligot prepared crystals of the *enneahydrate*, $U(SO_4)_2.9H_2O$, by heating a mixture of uranium tetrachloride and sulphuric acid so as to drive off the hydrochloric acid, and allowing the green product to crystallize from an aq. soln.   C. F. Rammelsberg obtained this hydrate by crystallization from a soln. of uranium dioxide in boiling conc. sulphuric acid, and he showed that the product obtained by E. M. Péligot, and thought to be the octohydrate, is really the enneahydrate.   G. N. Wyrouboff added that the enneahydrate is formed only from a feeble acidified soln., and he obtained it by treating a cold soln. of uranyl sulphate with sodium thiosulphate, and dissolving the precipitate in dil. sulphuric acid.   The soln. is treated with alcohol, and the precipitate dissolved in the least possible quantity of dil. sulphuric acid.   The soln. is allowed to crystallize over sulphuric acid.   The green, monoclinic prisms were found by C. F. Rammelsberg to be isomorphous with the corresponding thorium sulphate, $Th(SO_4)_2.9H_2O$, and to have the axial ratios $a : b : c = 0.5970 : 1 : 0.6555$, and $\beta = 97°\ 49'$.   At first C. F. Rammelsberg mistook twinned monoclinic crystals for rhombic crystals. The (100)-cleavage is complete ; and the (011)-cleavage is clear.   G. Beck gave 4.60 for the sp. gr. of $U(SO_4)_2$, and 94.1 for the mol. vol.; he also gave 78 cals. for the heat of formation from the oxides.

G. N. Wyrouboff observed that the crystals of the enneahydrate lose a mol. of water when exposed to air ; and C. F. Rammelsberg found that when the crystals are heated, water is slowly evolved—five-sixths of the total water is expelled at 200° ; at 230°, 7 mols. are given off, and at a red-heat all the water along with some sulphuric acid is expelled ; at a higher temp. all the sulphur trioxide is expelled and uranosic oxide remains.   F. Giolitti and G. Bucci showed that the octohydrate loses a mol. of water when kept in a desiccator for 60 hrs., and when kept for 31 hrs., at a press. of 19 to 20 mm., 4 mols. of water are lost ; and the remainder very slowly. The rate at which water is lost when the octohydrate is kept in a desiccator over sulphuric acid furnishes a dehydration curve which has breaks corresponding with the *heptahydrate*, $U(SO_4)_2.7H_2O$; the *trihydrate*, $U(SO_4)_2.3H_2O$; and the *dihydrate*, $U(SO_4)_2.2H_2O$. When the octohydrate is heated in the absence of air, it passes into the tetrahydrate at about 90°, and into the anhydrous salt at about 300°, and at a higher temp. uranosic oxide is formed. At 100°, in a water-oven, the dihydrate is formed in 8 hrs.—and only another 0·52 per cent. of water is lost in 8 hrs. more. G. N. Wyrouboff found that the octohydrate loses $6\frac{1}{2}$ mols. of water at 120° and $7\frac{1}{2}$ at 200°. The salt always loses some sulphuric acid when the attempt is made to dehydrate it completely. F. Giolitti and G. Bucci found that the tetrahydrate quickly loses a mol. of water when under 19 to 20 mm. press., forming the trihydrate. The tetrahydrate behaves very like the octohydrate when it is heated. J. J. Ebelmen reported that normal uranyl sulphate is formed when hydrated uranous sulphate is heated in air. F. W. O. de Coninck observed that if uranous sulphate be gradually heated, the upper layer at a dull red-heat forms uranyl sulphate, while the layer underneath loses sulphur trioxide to form uranium dioxide, which passes partly into uranosic oxide and partly into what he regarded as uranium hemipentoxide. G. Beck gave 78 Cals. for the heat of formation of $U(SO_4)_2$. H. Becquerel studied the absorption spectrum. Uranous sulphate, even in acidic soln., is a strong reducing agent—*e.g.* it precipitates gold and silver from soln. of their salts—*vide supra*, uranous chloride. R. Luther and A. G. Michie found that the reducing action is accelerated catalytically by the presence of copper salts, and to a less degree by platinum black and by iron salts. The oxidation-reduction potential, taken as a measure of the oxidizing or reducing power of a soln., was determined by H. N. McCoy and H. H. Bunzel for a soln. of uranyl and uranous salts with an immersed platinum electrode, for $E=E_0+0.0298 \log_{10} ([UO_2]/[U]E_0$ was found to be 0·615 volt, in the presence of $0.125M$-H_2SO_4, when the value for iron in neutral soln. is 0·987 volt, and for $0.05M$-HCl soln., 0·984 volt. The lower value for uranium than for iron is in accord with the greater velocity of oxidation of uranous salts by air than is the case with ferrous salts. R. Luther and A. C. Michie found that a soln. of uranous and uranyl salts in sulphuric acid is 0·697 volt more positive than the normal hydrogen electrode—*vide supra*, uranium dioxide.

When the hydrated salt is heated in hydrogen, J. J. Ebelmen observed that it is converted into the dioxide. The tetra- and octohydrates, as indicated above, are stable in air, but the enneahydrate loses a mol. of water. The aq. soln. rapidly absorbs oxygen from the air, forming a yellow liquid. F. W. O. de Coninck, E. M. Péligot, J. J. Ebelmen, and V. Kohlschütter said that the tetrahydrate dissolves in water, but is quickly hydrolyzed, with the separation of a basic salt ; the degree of hydrolysis depends on the temp. ; if the mixture be exposed to air, the precipitate gradually passes into soln. as oxidation occurs. F. W. O. de Coninck said that 100 grms. of the sat. aq. soln. at 9·1° has 15·67 grms. $U(SO_4)_2$; at 11·3°, 15·96 grms. ; and at 13°, 16·02 grms. The soln. in darkness slowly deposits a basic salt. According to F. Giolitti and G. Bucci, the solubilities of the tetrahydrate and octohydrate expressed as S grms. of $U(SO_4)_2$ per 100 grms. of sat. soln. are :

	12°	24°	37°	48·2°	63°	18°	25·5°	37°	48·2°	67°	93°
S	16·0	9·8	8·3	8·1	7·3	10·7	13·32	19·98	28·72	36·8	63·2

$U(SO_4)_2.4H_2O$ $U(SO_4)_2.8H_2O$

Soln. of the octohydrate are stable between 18° and 105°. The separation of the tetrahydrate is very sluggish, and the exact temp. of the transformation has not been determined. At a temp. below 18° or 20° the octohydrate is the stable form in which uranous sulphate crystallizes from its aq. soln., because its solubility is then less than that of the tetrahydrate ; but above, say, 20° the octohydrate is the metastable form and the tetrahydrate the stable form. The transformation of the octohydrate into the tetrahydrate occurs between 68° and 87°, and hence takes place when the octohydrate is in a metastable state. Below 25° the sat. soln. is liable to deposit a basic salt as a product of the hydrolysis. F. W. O. de Coninck found the sp. gr. of aq. soln. of uranous sulphate containing p per cent. of salt between $15 \cdot 6°$ and $18 \cdot 3°$:

p	1	2	4	6	8	10 per cent.
Sp. gr.	1·0058	1·0107	1·0218	1·0320	1·0429	1·0539

The soln. on electrolysis behaves like a soln. of uranyl sulphate (q.v.). E. M. Péligot found that when the normal salt is treated with an excess of water, **uranous oxysulphate,** $UOSO_4.2H_2O$, is formed as an insoluble precipitate. F. Giolitti and G. Bucci observed that when the octohydrate is treated with a large proportion of cold water, it is mostly dissolved, but about 25 per cent. is converted into a green powder of the oxysulphate—the amount so converted depends on the temp. If the octohydrate be acted upon by a small proportion of water, the basic salt at first formed slowly dissolves, forming a soln. of the normal salt. J. J. Ebelmen found that soln. of uranyl sulphate in dil. alcohol may deposit this basic salt when exposed to sunlight ; and a soln. of uranosic oxide in sulphuric acid may deposit this salt when it is boiled; on cooling, however, the precipitate may re-dissolve. C. F. Rammelsberg obtained the same basic salt by adding ammonia, cautiously, to a soln. of the octohydrate—if too much ammonia be added, uranous hydroxide is formed. The *dihydrate* is a pale green powder, almost insoluble in water. J. J. Ebelmen found that with a large proportion of water, especially boiling water, the salt blackens and sulphuric acid is formed. F. Giolitti and G. Liberi also obtained the *pentahydrate*, $UOSO_4.5H_2O$, as a pale green powder. According to F. W. O. de Coninck, water can convert the normal octohydrate into **uranous hexoxytetrasulphate,** $U_5O_6(SO_4)_4.8H_2O$, or $UO_2.4UOSO_4.8H_2O$, which is less soluble in acids than is the case with the oxysulphate. F. Giolitti and G. Liberi reported **uranous trioxypentasulphate,** $U_4O_3(SO_4)_5.32H_2O$, or $3UOSO_4.U(SO_4)_2.$ $32H_2O$, as a pale green powder ; when the *dotricontahydrate* is dried in air, it furnishes the *icosihydrate*, $3UOSO_4.U(SO_4)_2.20H_2O$; the *pentadecahydrate*, $3UOSO_4.U(SO_4)_2.15H_2O$; and the *decahydrate*, $3UOSO_4.U(SO_4)_2.10H_2O$.

J. J. Ebelmen found the tetrahydrate to be very soluble in dil. hydrochloric acid, but much less soluble in the conc. acid. F. W. O. de Coninck observed that 100 parts of the acid diluted with four vols. of water dissolve 17·24 parts of the octohydrate at $9 \cdot 2°$, and 17·42 parts at $9 \cdot 7°$; and that the sp. gr. of a soln. of p per cent. of the salt in hydrochloric acid of sp. gr. 1·046, between $16°$ and $18 \cdot 4°$, are as follow :

p	1	2	3	4	5
Sp. gr.	1·0525	1·0572	1·0619	1·0667	1·0714

At $15 \cdot 1°$, 100 parts of hydrobromic acid, diluted with 4 vols. of water, dissolve 25 parts of the octohydrate. J. J. Ebelmen observed that the hydrated salt is freely soluble in dil. sulphuric, but less soluble in the conc. acid. R. J. Meyer and H. Nachod found for the solubility, S grms. of $U(SO_4)_2$ per 100 grms. of soln., of the octohydrate in $0 \cdot 1N\text{-}H_2SO_4$:

	15·5°	20·0°	30·4°	40·0°	60·0°	92·0°
S	6·61	8·78	13·89	18·50	29·93	(6·61)

where the bracketed number refers to the formation of a less soluble polymer of the tetrahydrate. The solubility data for the tetrahydrate are :

	22·7°	25·0°	30·4°	40·0°	50·0°	80·0°
S	13·68	12·62	10·92	8·98	8·32	6·93

The results are plotted in Fig. 13, where the dotted lines refer to the data of F. Giolitti and G. Bucci for aq. soln., Fig. 12. F. W. O. de Coninck found that 100 parts of sulphuric acid, diluted with 4 vols. of water, dissolve 15·5 parts of the octohydrate at 10° ; and that soln. with p per cent. of the octohydrate in sulphuric acid of sp. gr. 1·14, between 17·4° and 18·7°, have the following sp. gr. :

p . .	1	2	3	4	5
Sp. gr. . .	1·0525	1·0572	1·0619	1·0667	1·0714

V. Kohlschütter found that the soln. in dil. sulphuric acid is readily oxidized ; and F. Giolitti and G. Bucci observed that uranous sulphate dissolved in 10 per cent. sulphuric acid is not hydrolyzed. C. F. Rammels-berg showed that the soln. of the salt in very dil. sulphuric or hydrochloric acid becomes turbid when heated, but clarifies again on cooling. If conc. hydrochloric or sulphuric acid be added to the aq. soln., the salt is precipitated without having changed chemically. V. Kohlschütter poured a mush of uranous oxalate and conc. sulphuric acid into just enough water for dissolution, and found that the soln. solidifies in a short time, and after washing the product with absolute alcohol, by suction, there remained what appeared to be **uranous dihydro-pentasulphate**, $2U(SO_4)_2.H_2SO_4$, or $U_2H_2(SO_4)_5$.

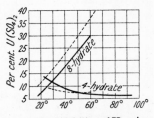

Fig. 13.—Solubility of Uranium Sulphate in Sulphuric Acid.

F. Giolitti and G. Bucci reported **uranous dihydrotrisulphate**, $U(SO_4)_2.H_2SO_4.10H_2O$, or $UH_2(SO_4)_3.10H_2O$, to be formed as a pale green powder, by the interaction, in sunlight, of a mixture of 42 grms. of uranyl sulphate, 168 grms. of water, 336 grms. of alcohol, and 41 grms. of sulphuric acid.

F. W. O. de Coninck reported that 100 parts of selenic acid of sp. gr. 1·4, diluted with 4 vols. of water, dissolve 21·46 parts of the salt at 10·7°, and 21·88 parts at 11·4° ; 100 parts of nitric acid, diluted with 4 vols. of water, dissolve 18·08 parts of the salt at 10·3°, and 18·5 parts at 11·2° ; 100 parts of 94 per cent. alcohol, diluted with 4 vols. of water, dissolve 12·19 parts of the salt at 9·6°, and 12·5 parts at 10·4° ; 100 parts of acetic acid, $CH_3COOH.H_2O$, diluted with 4 vols. of water, dissolve 24·4 parts of the salt at 15·5° ; and the solubility in glycol at 14·8° is 3·15 per cent. C. F. Rammelsberg's observation on the action of ammonia on the aq. soln. of the salt is indicated above. G. N. Wyrouboff found that the aq. soln. when treated with barium chloride and warmed gives a precipitate of a uranous salt and a liquid containing sulphuric acid, consequently he inferred that soln. contains a complex salt ; and this conclusion is in agreement with that of F. Giolitti and G. Bucci, cited above. F. W. O. de Coninck stated that platinum tetrachloride has no action on a very dil. soln. of the salt either in diffused daylight or in darkness ; but in direct sunlight the uranous sulphate is oxidized to uranyl sulphate, which then hydrolyzes to form a basic salt.

C. F. Rammelsberg reported that a soln. of ammonium and uranous sulphates furnishes dark green needles of **ammonium uranous tetrasulphate**, $(NH_4)_4U(SO_4)_4$. The salt is freely soluble in water ; and when heated, the soln. deposits a basic salt ; with potash-lye the salt gives off ammonia and forms uranous hydroxide. V. Kohlschütter reported **ammonium uranous hexasulphate**, $(NH_4)_6U(SO_4)_6.3H_2O$, to be formed by evaporating a soln. of uranous sulphate in a conc. soln. of ammonium sulphate mixed with just enough sulphuric acid to prevent turbidity. The dark green pyramids soon decompose ; **potassium uranous trisulphate**, $K_2U(SO_4)_3.2H_2O$, forms green plates. C. F. Rammelsberg represented the salt as a monohydrate and said that it is slightly soluble in water.

J. J. Ebelmen,[3] and A. von Unruh obtained anhydrous **uranyl sulphate**, $(UO_2)SO_4$, by heating one of the hydrates to 300°, and F. W. O. de Coninck, by heating the hydrate to 175°. According to A. C. Schultz-Sellack, the anhydrous salt is formed by evaporating a soln. of the salt in conc. sulphuric acid. The amber-yellow crystals do not effloresce ; they can be heated to dull redness without decomposition ; and, according to J. J. Ebelmen, when exposed to air they take up about 3 mols. of water. K. Brückner found that at a red-heat, in sulphur vapour, a mixture of uranous and uranosic oxides is formed. J. A. Arfvedson dissolved uranosic oxide in hot, conc. sulphuric acid, diluted the soln. with water, and oxidized the solute by the addition of nitric acid. J. J. Ebelmen evaporated a soln. of uranyl nitrate with sulphuric acid to dryness, expelled the excess of acid by heat, dissolved the residue in water, and evaporated the soln. to a syrupy consistency. When the soln. is allowed to stand for some time, it deposits crystals of the *trihydrate*, $(UO_2)SO_4.3H_2O$. F. W. O. de Coninck triturated uranyl sulphate with potassium or sodium hydrosulphate in a porcelain mortar, and as in some of W. Spring's experiments, the solids interact; on extracting the product with water and crystallizing, the trihydrate is produced. H. Lescoeur obtained the *monohydrate*,

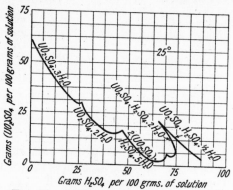

Fig. 14.—Equilibrium Curves of the Ternary System : $UO_2SO_4-H_2SO_4-H_2O$ at 25°.

$(UO_2)SO_4.H_2O$, by adding an equal vol. of conc. sulphuric acid to a sat. soln. of uranyl sulphate ; and also by heating the trihydrate to 160°—*vide infra*—while F. W. O. de Coninck found that the trihydrate passes into the monohydrate between 110° and 115°. The monohydrate takes up 2 mols. of water on exposure to air, reforming the trihydrate. J. J. Ebelmen, and C. F. Bucholz represented the trihydrate by $(UO_2)SO_4.3\frac{1}{2}H_2O$, but E. M. Péligot showed that $(UO_2)SO_4.3H_2O$ is the correct formula. A. Colani's results for the system $UO_2SO_4-H_2SO_4-H_2O$ at 25° are summarized in Fig. 14. The curves are plotted from data of which the following are selected. The concentrations are expressed in grams per 100 grms. of solution.

| UO_2SO_4 . | . | 61·18 | 58·96 | 28·65 | 15·77 | 17·03 | 17·74 | 3·81 | 7·09 |
| H_2SO_4 (free) | . | 0 | 1·64 | 26·99 | 43·45 | 40·19 | 47·75 | 67·40 | 72·49 |

| | $UO_2SO_4.3H_2O$ | | $UO_2SO_4.2H_2O$ | | $UO_2SO_4.H_2SO_4.5H_2O$ | |

| UO_2SO_4 . | . | 7·09 | 6·74 | 16·90 | 19·65 | 17·76 | 7·81 | 3·77 |
| H_2SO_4 (free) | . | 72·49 | 75·33 | 71·14 | 68·93 | 71·52 | 82·86 | 89·62 |

| | $UO_2SO_4.H_2SO_4.2H_2O$ | | $UO_2SO_4.H_2SO_4.\frac{1}{2}H_2O$ | |

C. F. Bucholz described the crystals of the trihydrate as yellow prisms. P. F. Reinsch said that under the microscope the crystals appear dark bluish-yellow with a green shimmer, forming groups resembling asters. F. W. Clarke gave 3·280 for the sp. gr. at 16·5°/4°. G. Beck gave 5·24 for the sp. gr. and 69·9 for the mol. vol. of $UO_2(SO_4)$. According to J. J. Ebelmen, the crystals of the trihydrate slowly lose about a mol. of water and effloresce on exposure to air ; they lose 2 mols. of water at 100°, and the third mol. begins to escape at 150°, and all is expelled at 300° ; and C. F. Bucholz added that when calcined in air, uranosic oxide is formed. F. W. O. de Coninck said that at 105° to 110°, 2 mols. of water are given off ; at a higher temp. a little sulphuric acid is lost ; at a dull red-heat some uranium trioxide is formed ; at bright redness, uranium dioxide ; and with continued calcination uranosic oxide is formed. H. Lescoeur found that the vap. press., p mm., of $(UO_2)SO_4.nH_2O$, is :

| n | . | Sat. soln. | 2·75 | 2·3 | 1·7 | 1·3 | 1·1 | 1·0 |
| p | . | 10·8 | 11·0 | 9·8 | 9·7 | 9·2 | 4·5 | <2 |

A. H. Pareau also made some observations on this subject.   G. Beck gave 50 Cals.

for the heat of formation. P. Pringsheim and M. Yost studied the Raman effect; and C. Ouellet, the photolysis of soln. containing uranyl sulphate. J. J. Ebelmen observed that when the salt is heated to redness in hydrogen, water and sulphur dioxide are first given off, then hydrogen sulphide and sulphur, and finally uranium dioxide, free from sulphur remains. F. W. O. de Coninck represented the reaction: $(UO_2)SO_4 + 2H_2 = UO_2 + SO_2 + 2H_2O$. The trihydrate is freely soluble in water. According to C. F. Bucholz, 100 parts of water at ordinary temp. dissolve 166 parts of salt, and boiling water, 222 parts of salt; whilst J. J. Ebelmen said that 100 parts of water at 21° dissolve 212·7 parts of salt, and boiling water, 357 parts; and F. W. O. de Coninck found that 100 parts of water at 13·2° dissolve 18·86 parts of salt; at 14·1°, 19·37 parts; at 15°, 20·20 parts; and at 15·5°, 20·40 parts. F. W. O. de Coninck found that aq. soln. of p per cent. of the salt, between 10° and 15·6° have the following sp. gr.:

p	1	2	4	6	8	10	12
Sp. gr.	1·0062	1·0113	1·0229	1·0338	1·0442	1·0557	1·0669

C. Dittrich measured the lowering of the f.p. of water, $\theta°$, of soln. with n mols of the salt per litre, and hence calculated the mol. wt. and degree of dissociation, a:

n	0·5	0·25	0·125	0·0625	0·03125
$\theta°$	0·968°	0·479°	0·256°	0·134°	0·074°
Mol. wt.	430·0	390·7	347·8	324·5	290·3°
a	0·14	0·06	0·05	0·13	0·26

These data show that in dil. soln. the sulphate is less ionized than the chloride or nitrate. F. W. O. de Coninck gave 5·5 Cals. for the heat of soln. at 17·3°; and J. Aloy, 5·1 Cals. for a mol of the trihydrate in 100 to 2500 mols of water at 18° to 20°. G. Beck gave 50 Cals. for the heat of formation from the oxide. F. W. O. de Coninck gave 1·365 for the index of refraction of an 8 per cent. soln., and 1·371 for a 10 per cent. soln. The absorption spectrum was studied by H. C. Jones and W. W. Strong; and the Becquerel effect, by I. Lifschitz and S. B. Hooghoudt. For the fluorescence, *vide supra*, the physical properties of uranium. H. M. Vernon estimated the degree of ionization from the colour. C. Dittrich gave for the conductivity, λ mho, of a soln. of an eq., *i.e.* half the mol UO_2SO_4, in v litres at 25°:

v	4	8	16	32	64	128	256	512	1024
λ'	17·1	20·5	25·5	32·0	41·5	53·2	67·7	85·2	103·4

As in the case of the chloride and nitrate, the difference $\lambda_{1024} - \lambda_{32} = 71·4$ is unusually high. This is taken to mean that the ionization occurs in stages. C. Dittrich found that the migration velocity of the uranyl ion, in aq. soln. at 25°, is 56. The values for the eq. conductivity, λ, by H. C. Jones and co-workers, and the percentage ionization, a, are:

v		8	32	128	512	1024	2048	4096
	35°	158·81	201·03	158·21	333·38	377·29	428·71	484·32
λ	50°	179·79	223·69	288·77	381·83	436·95	512·04	597·28
	65°	197·94	240·24	309·93	416·68	488·19	582·85	694·01
a	35°	32·79	41·51	53·31	68·83	77·90	88·52	100·00
	65°	28·52	34·62	44·66	60·04	70·34	83·98	100·00

The results of L. G. Winston and H. C. Jones between 0° and 35° are:

v		8	32	128	512	1024	2048	4096
	0°	78·13	100·65	128·62	157·54	175·68	191·68	203·33
λ	25°	120·82	156·80	203·02	257·69	296·95	332·57	373·65
	35°	136·43	176·52	229·42	295·20	343·01	391·00	446·33
	0°	38·4	49·5	63·2	77·5	86·4	94·2	100·0
a	25°	32·3	42·0	54·3	69·0	79·5	89·0	100·0
	35°	30·6	39·6	51·4	66·2	76·9	87·6	100·0

F. W. O. de Coninck found that when soln. of uranyl sulphate are electrolyzed in a U-tube, cooled by immersion in water, there is first deposited on the negative electrode the yellow, hydrated oxide, $U_2O_3.2H_2O$, and finally a greenish precipitate consisting of the oxide and a small proportion of a basic sulphate. A. S. Russell and D. C. Evans found that metals more electropositive than mercury, except cobalt, go into soln. as sulphates, without the accompaniment of mercury, when the amalgams are shaken with uranyl sulphate soln. The order is not that of the electrode potentials of the metals in the free state, being : Zn, Mn, Cd, Tl, Sn, Pb, Cu, Cr, Fe, Bi, Co, Hg, Ni. S. Freed and C. Kasper studied the magnetic susceptibility of the salt.

C. Dittrich found that the conductivity increases as the soln. ages with time, probably owing to hydrolysis. Thus, L. R. Lecanu noted that the soln. is acidic to litmus. L. Bruner studied the hydrolysis of the salt. A number of basic salts has been reported. N. Athanasesco reported **uranyl trioxysulphate,** $(UO_2)_4O_3SO_4.7H_2O$, as a dirty yellow mass of microscopic needles, to be formed by heating a 15 per cent. soln. of uranyl sulphate at 250°. The water is expelled only at a high temp., and some of it is constitutional water. J. M. Ordway found that the addition of barium carbonate to cold, aq. soln. of uranyl sulphate withdraws about two-thirds of the sulphate, and this corresponds with the formation of **uranyl dioxysulphate,** $(UO_2)_3O_2SO_4.nH_2O$. Barium chloride, nitrate, or acetate also furnishes basic uranyl salts. N. Athanasesco obtained the *dihydrate*, $(UO_2)_3O_2SO_4.2H_2O$, by heating a 3 per cent. aq. soln. of uranyl sulphate at 250°. The lemon-yellow, micro-crystalline powder is insoluble in and undecomposed by water. The mineral **uraconite,** from Joachimsthal, Bohemia, described by J. F. Vogl as *Uranocker,* and by F. S. Beudant under the name *uraconite,* is an amorphous, lemon-yellow or orange, scaly or earthy, amorphous powder with a composition approximating the *tetradecahydrate,* $(UO_2)_3O_2SO_4.14H_2O$. A. L. Fletcher noted that softening begins at 1050°, and fusion at 1070°. J. M. Ordway treated an aq. soln. of uranyl sulphate with ammonia until half the acid radicle was neutralized, and obtained a white precipitate approximating **uranyl oxysulphate,** $(UO_2)_2OSO_4.nH_2O$.

A nur ber of more or less basic sulphates has been described as minerals. J. F. John described *Uranvitriol,* from Joachimsthal, and Johanngeorgenstadt, which W. Haidinger named **johannite**—after Archduke Johann of Austria. C. U. Shepard also obtained it from Middletown, Connecticut. The analysis reported by J. F. Vogl indicates 67·72 per cent. U_3O_8; 20·02, SO_3; 5·99, CuO; 0·20, FeO; and 5·59, H_2O. Its colour is emerald-green or apple-green; the crystals are flattened, and are arranged in concentric druses or reniform masses. The pleochroism is strong—a is colourless, b pale yellow, and c greenish-yellow or canary-yellow. B. Jezek referred the mineral to the monoclinic system, but E. S. Larsen and H. Berman said the optical properties do not permit this orientation, since the extinction is not parallel to the b-axis. E. S. Larsen and G. V. Brown described a hydrated uranium sulphate, containing some copper, iron, and sodium, from Gilpin County, Colorado, and Cornwall, England, and they called it *gilpinite.* E. S. Larsen and H. Berman consider that the physical properties of gilpinite and johannite are so much alike that the two minerals can be considered to be the same species. The chemical analyses of both agree better with $(Cu,Fe,Na_2)O.UO_3SO_3.4H_2O$ than with $CuO.3UO_3.3SO_3.4H_2O$; the minerals are triclinic, with the axial ratios $a : b : c = 1·218 : 1 : 0·6736$, and $a = 69°\ 24'$, $\beta = 124°\ 56'$, and $\gamma = 132°\ 56'$. The optic axial angle $2V$ is nearly 90° for Na-light. The mineral shows polysynthetic twinning in two directions, and resembles that of plagioclase. B. Jezek gave 3·307 for the sp. gr. E. S. Larsen and H. Berman found that the indices of refraction are $a = 1·572$ to 1·577, $\beta = 1·592$ to 1·597, and $\gamma = 1·611$ to 1·616. The subject was also discussed by E. S. Larsen and G. V. Brown. The sp. gr. is 3·19, and the hardness 2·0 to 2·5. H. Dauber described lemon-yellow crystals of a hydrated basic sulphate from Joachimsthal, Bohemia, containing 79·9 per cent. UO_3; 4·0, SO_3; and 14·3, H_2O. A basic uranium sulphate from Joachimsthal, Bohemia, was called by J. F. John *verwitterter Uranvitriol;* by F. X. M. Zippe, *Uranblüthe;* by W. Haidinger, **zippeite**—after F. X. M. Zippe; and by M. Adam, *dauberite*—after H. Dauber. It occurs in sulphur-yellow, lemon-yellow, or orange-yellow delicate needles, acicular rosettes, or warty crusts of hardness 3. A. L. Fletcher gave 1250° for the fusion temp. E. S. Larsen gave for the indices of refraction of zippeite $a = 1·630$, and $\beta = 1·70$; and $a = 1·630$, $\beta = 1·689$, and $\gamma = 1·739$; and F. Slavik gave $\mu = 1·634$ to 1·645. The analyses reported by J. F. Vogl have 62·04 to 67·86 per cent. U_3O_8; 13·06 to 17·36, SO_3; 0·17, Fe_2O_3; 0·61, CaO; and 15·23 to 17·69, H_2O. J. F. Vogl described a basic sulphate from Joachimsthal, Bohemia, which J. D. Dana called **voglianite.** It occurs in green, globular and nodular, earthy coatings and has the analysis: 79·50 to 79·60, U_3O_8; 12·13 to 12·34, SO_3; 0·12 to 0·36, FeO; 2·24, CuO; 0·05 to 1·66, CaO; and 5·25 to 5·49, H_2O. The mineral was also described by F. Slavik.

F. W. O. de Coninck found that 100 parts of ordinary conc. hydrochloric acid at 128° dissolve 29·4 parts of uranyl sulphate, and at 13·6°, 30·76 parts; 100 parts of hydrobromic acid, of sp. gr. 1·21, at 11·2°, 16·4 parts; and at 12·9°, 16·9 parts; and 100 parts of sulphuric acid, of sp. gr. 1·138, at 12·7°, 23·25 parts, and at 14°, 24·39 parts. If the acid be diluted 1 : 4, 100 parts dissolve 27·02 parts of the salt at 15·3°, but the salt is less soluble in more conc. acid. He gave for the sp. gr. of p per cent. of uranyl sulphate in sulphuric acid of sp. gr. 1·168, between 20·6° and 22·7°, $p=1$, 1·1738; $p=2$, 1·1775; $p=3$, 1·1830; $p=4$, 1·1872; and $p=5$, 1·1918. J. J. Berzelius, and A. C. Schultz-Sellack obtained an acid salt corresponding with uranyl pyrosulphate from sulphuric acid soln.; and with a hot, conc. soln., J. J. Berzelius obtained uranyl trisulphate, $(UO_2)S_3O_{10}$. E. M. Péligot, and B. Drenckmann also obtained acid salts. G. N. Wyrouboff reported **uranyl dihydrotrisulphate,** $2(UO_2)SO_4.H_2SO_4.5H_2O$, to be formed by evaporating at 60° a soln. of a mol of uranyl sulphate in 5 mols of sulphuric acid. The pseudotetragonal cubes are very fluorescent, and deliquescent; and they lose 2 mols. of water at 110°. A. C. Schultz-Sellack, and E. M. Péligot obtained **uranyl dihydrosulphate,** $(UO_2)SO_4.H_2SO_4$. $(UO_2)(HSO_4)_2$, by the slow evaporation of a soln. of uranyl sulphate in hot, moderately conc. sulphuric acid at about 200°. The greenish-yellow, fluorescent crystals are very deliquescent. F. W. O. de Coninck found that 100 parts of selenic acid, of sp. gr. 1·4, at 15·3°, dissolve 27·03 parts of uranyl sulphate.

A. von Unruh exposed anhydrous uranyl sulphate for 24 hrs. in an atm. of ammonia, and kept the product in a desiccator until it no longer smelt of ammonia, or until it had a constant weight; the yellow powder consists of **uranyl triamminosulphate,** $(UO_2)SO_4.3NH_3$; if it be gently warmed, it forms **uranyl diamminosulphate,** $(UO_2)SO_4.2NH_3$; and if it, or anhydrous uranyl sulphate, be digested with liquid ammonia, a deep orange powder of **uranyl tetramminosulphate,** $(UO_2)SO_4.4NH_3$, is formed. According to F. W. O. de Coninck, 100 parts of ordinary conc. nitric acid dissolve 8·93 parts at 10·8°, and at 12·3°, 9·26 parts of uranyl sulphate; if the acid be diluted with its own vol. of water, 100 parts dissolve 17·8 parts of salt at 15·4°, and 18·28 parts at 16·4°; while 100 parts of aqua regia, made from equal vols. of nitric and hydrochloric acids, at 15·4°, dissolve 17·86 parts of the salt.

According to C. F. Bucholz, 100 parts of absolute alcohol at ordinary temp. dissolve 4 parts of uranyl sulphate, and boiling alcohol, 5 parts; and F. W. O. de Coninck found that 100 parts of 85 per cent. alcohol dissolve 2·63 parts of the salt at 16·7°, and 2·59 parts at 15·8°. C. F. Bucholz, and J. J. Ebelmen observed that a soln. of uranyl sulphate mixed with alcohol and exposed to direct sunlight precipitates the whole of the uranium as uranous sulphate; F. Giolitti and G. Bucci obtained different products from mixed soln. of different proportions of uranyl sulphate, water, alcohol, and sulphuric acid; and F. W. O. de Coninck found that when aq. alcoholic soln. of uranyl sulphate are exposed to light, a mixture of uranous sulphate with a small quantity of basic uranyl sulphate is deposited. The filtrate, on exposure to violet or blue light, forms at first a hydrated uranosic oxide, and eventually the black oxide, U_4O_5. F. W. O. de Coninck said that uranyl sulphate is sparingly soluble in organic acids—e.g. conc. formic and acetic acids. W. T. Anderson and F. W. Robinson found that the photochemical decomposition of oxalic acid in the presence of a soln. of uranyl sulphate is a reaction of zero order, not greatly influenced by temp., and possesses the characteristics desired in an efficient chemical radiometer for use in the ultra-violet. The reaction was investigated by F. C. Hymas. R. H. Müller studied the decomposition of lactic acid in the presence of uranyl sulphate. The solubility in glycol is 1·15 per cent. at 15°. If uranyl sulphate is dissolved in a small quantity of water, mixed with an excess of ethylene glycol, and exposed to sunlight for 2 hrs., the liquid becomes quite green, and in $2\frac{1}{2}$ hrs. uranous sulphate is precipitated. In glycerol no such action takes place, and even after fifteen months' exposure only a slight green coloration is obtained. This reaction serves to distinguish between ethylene glycol and glycerol. F. W. O. de Coninck observed that uranyl sulphate and calcium carbonate interact when covered with water, or when a mixture of the two salts is fused, triturated in a mortar, or compressed ; and from 19·97 to 29·33 per cent. of calcium carbonate is converted into sulphate. For J. M. Ordway's observations on the action of barium carbonate, etc., *vide supra*. O. Hahn found that the precipitation of uranyl sulphate in the presence of uranium-X is not in harmony with K. Fajan's rule, but is in accord with the rule that an element is precipitated from its soln., however dilute, with a crystallizing precipitate when it is built into the crystal lattice of the precipitate and thus forms mixed crystals with the ions of the crystallizing precipitate. If this is not the case, the element remains in the filtrate, no matter how sparingly soluble its compound with the oppositely charged component of the lattice in the particular solvent may be. F. C. Hymas, W. T. Anderson and F. W. Robinson, and W. C. Pierce and co-workers studied the effect of uranyl sulphate on the photochemical decomposition of malonic, and oxalic acids. R. Rascanu prepared a complex with antipyrine.

J. A. Arfvedson, and E. M. Péligot evaporated a mixed soln. of uranyl and ammonium sulphates and obtained **ammonium uranyl disulphate,** $(NH_4)_2UO_2(SO_4)_2.2H_2O$, on evaporating the soln. for crystallization. C. F. Rammelsberg said that the crystals appear to be isomorphous with those of sodium manganese sulphate, and sodium magnesium sulphate. F. de la Provostaye described the crystals (of the dihydrate) as monoclinic prisms with the axial ratios $a:b:c=1·428:1:1·226$, and $\beta=102°$. P. Groth suggested that the compound may be triclinic and isomorphous with the $K_2Mn(SO_4)_2.2H_2O$ series, but G. Carobbi could find no evidence in support of this. H. Morton and H. C. Bolton said that the salt loses all its water and forms *ammonium diuranyl trisulphate,* $(NH_4)_2(UO_2)_2(SO_4)_3$, when it is heated ; the transformation is attended by changes in the fluorescence and absorption spectra. At a higher temp., the salt passes into uranosic oxide. J. A. Arfvedson said that the salt is freely soluble in water ; and E. M. Péligot, sparingly soluble. E. Rimbach, and F. W. O. de Coninck also prepared the dihydrate, $(NH_4)_2(UO_2)(SO_4)_2.2H_2O$, by evaporating a soln. of eq. proportions of the component salts in vacuo. A. Colani obtained the dihydrate under the conditions indicated in Fig. 15.

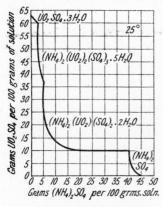

FIG. 15.—Equilibrium Diagram for the System : $(NH_4)_2SO_4$–UO_2SO_4–H_2O.

F. W. Clarke found that the greenish, strongly fluorescent crystals have a sp. gr. 3·0131 at 21·5°/4° ; they are stable in air and in water. J. Meyer and E. Kasper reported **ammonium uranyl disulphate,** $(NH_4)_4H_2[UO_4(SO_4)_2].3H_2O$, and **ammonium potassium uranyl trisulphate,** $(NH_4)_2K_4[UO_3(SO_4)_3]$; and E. Rimbach, unstable **ammonium uranyl trisulphate,** $(NH_4)_4(UO_2)(SO_4)_3.2H_2O$, to be formed like the corresponding potassium salt—*vide infra*. A. Colani obtained **ammonium diuranyl trisulphate,** $(NH_4)_2(UO_2)_2(SO_4)_3.5H_2O$, under the conditions indicated in Fig. 15.   The following is a selection from the data :

| UO_2SO_4 . | 61·18 | 61·28 | 61·32 | 47·25 | 35·70 | 16·46 | 10·00 | 1·89 | 0 |
| $(NH_4)_2SO_4$ | 0 | 0·25 | 0·38 | 2·00 | 4·15 | 7·46 | 40·65 | 42·13 | 43·25 |

$UO_2SO_4.3H_2O$ $(NH_4)_2(UO_2)(SO_4)_3.5H_2O$ $(NH_4)_2(UO_2)(SO_4)_2.2H_2O$ $(NH_4)_2SO_4$

E. Rimbach, and H. Bürger obtained **hydroxylamine diuranyl trisulphate,** $(NH_4O)_2SO_4.2UO_2SO_4.5H_2O$, from a soln. of eq. proportions of the component salts. The salt is difficult to crystallize on account of its large solubility. It can be obtained from aq. soln. in warty masses of crystals, or precipitated from its aq. soln. as a crystalline powder by means of alcohol. It gives no evidence of being decomposed by water. H. Grossmann and B. Schück prepared yellow, six-sided crystals of **ethylenediamine uranyl disulphate,** $C_2H_6(NH_2)_2(UO_2)(SO_4)_2.4H_2O$, which decompose at 285°; and G. Canneri obtained **guanidine uranyl disulphate,** $(C_5H_5N_3)_2.H_2SO_4.(UO_2)SO_4.6H_2O$.

F. W. O. de Coninck and E. Chauvenet prepared **lithium uranyl disulphate,** $Li_2(UO_2)(SO_4)_2.4H_2O$, by evaporating, at a low temp., an aq. soln. of equimolar proportions of the component salts; and F. W. O. de Coninck obtained **sodium uranyl disulphate,** $Na_2(UO_2)(SO_4)_2.3H_2O$, by well triturating a mixture of a mol of uranyl hydroxide with 2 mols of sodium hydrosulphate, and treating the product with water. A. Colani prepared this salt as well as **sodium uranyl trisulphate,** $Na_4(UO_2)(SO_4)_3.3H_2O$; and the equilibrium curves of the ternary system $Na_2SO_4-UO_2SO_4-H_2O$ at 25° are shown in Fig. 16. The following is a selection from the data:

UO₂SO₄ .	61·18	61·67	61·31	40·96	32·65	31·50	29·79	1·56	0
Na₂SO₄ .	0	1·32	6·03	14·56	25·10	25·53	25·72	20·41	20·70

$UO_2SO_4.3H_2O$ $Na_2(UO_2)(SO_4)_2.3H_2O$ $Na_4(UO_2)(SO_4)_3.3H_2O$ $Na_2SO_4.10H_2O$

J. A. Arfvedson, J. J. Berzelius, E. M. Péligot, J. J. Ebelmen, E. Rimbach, and H. Bürger prepared **potassium uranyl disulphate,** $K_2(UO_2)(SO_4)_2.2H_2O$, by

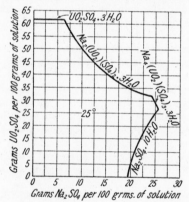

FIG. 16.—Equilibrium Diagram for the System: $Na_2SO_4-UO_2SO_4-H_2O$.

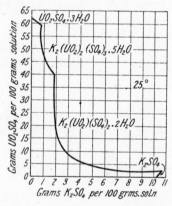

FIG. 17.—Equilibrium Diagram for the System: $UO_2SO_4-K_2SO_4-H_2O$.

crystallization from a soln. of the component salts; E. Rimbach, and H. Bürger, from a sulphuric acid soln. of potassium uranyl trisulphate (q.v.); B. Drenckmann, by evaporating a conc. sulphuric acid soln. of 2 mols of potassium hydrosulphate and a mol of uranyl nitrate until all the nitric acid is driven off, dissolving the residue in hot, conc. sulphuric acid, and cooling the soln. slowly—finally by a freezing mixture; and F. W. O. de Coninck, by triturating uranyl hydroxide with a large excess of potassium hydrosulphate. J. Meyer and E. Kasper gave the formula $KH_5[UO_4(SO_4)_2]$, as well as $K_2H_4[UO_4(SO_4)_2].2H_2O$, for their preparations. G. Carobbi found no evidence in support of P. Groth's suggestion that the crystals of the hexahydrate are triclinic and isomorphous with those of the (Mg,Fe,Zn,Co,Ni)-$(K,Rb,Cs,Tl,NH_4)_2(SO_4)_2.6H_2O$ series. A *trihydrate* was also formed by the process last described. F. de la Provostaye said that the lemon-yellow crystals of the *dihydrate* are monoclinic; they have a greenish fluorescence and are stable in air. A. Colani's study of the ternary system: $K_2SO_4-UO_2SO_4-H_2O$ at 25° is summarized in Fig. 17. The following is a selection from the data:

UO_2SO_4	.	61·18	61·25	61·50	59·29	39·73	9·91	2·39	0·91	0
K_2SO_4	.	0	0·23	0·45	0·51	1·77	2·69	11·17	10·69	10·40

$UO_2SO_4.3H_2O$ $\quad$ $K_2(UO_2)_2(SO_4)_3.5H_2O$ $\quad$ $K_2(UO_2)(SO_4)_2.2H_2O$ $\quad\quad$ K_2SO_4

According to F. W. Clarke, the dihydrate has a sp. gr. 3·363 at 19·1°/4°. This salt is of historical interest, since in 1896 H. Becquerel first detected the phenomenon of radioactivity in the crystals of this salt. J. J. Ebelmen said that the dihydrate loses all its water at 120°, and J. J. Berzelius added that it fuses at a red-heat, and on cooling, it appears greenish-yellow, but, according to J. J. Ebelmen, the salt is not chemically changed. At 22°, 100 parts of water were found by J. J. Ebelmen to dissolve 11·11 parts of salt, and boiling water, 19·61 parts. According to E. Rimbach, and H. Bürger, 100 parts of soln. contain 10·41 parts of salt at 25°, and 23·13 parts at 70·5°; in both cases, soln. and solid have the same composition, and the salt can be recrystallized many times from water without perceptible change. J. J. Ebelmen found that both aq. ammonia and a soln. of ammonium·sulphide precipitate hydrated uranium trioxide from the aq. soln. The precipitate is contaminated with adsorbed alkali. J. J. Berzelius found that alcohol does not dissolve the double salt, and precipitates it from its aq. soln. ; whilst J. A. Arfvedson added that alcohol extracts some uranyl sulphate from the double salt. According to E. Rimbach, a hot soln. of uranyl sulphate with an excess of potassium sulphate, say in the mol. proportion 1 : 3, furnishes crystals of **potassium uranyl trisulphate,** $K_4(UO_2)(SO_4)_3.2H_2O$, which are decomposed in aq. soln. into $K_4(UO_2)(SO_4)_3$ $\rightleftharpoons K_2SO_4 + K_2(UO_2)(SO_4)_2$. The equilibrium is displaced from right to left, and conversely with a falling temp. In sat. soln., the soln. is richer in potassium sulphate than the excess of solid. When the salt is recrystallized from a sulphuric acid soln., the decomposition is complete, and crystals of the disulphate are formed. A. Colani prepared **potassium diuranyl trisulphate,** $K_2(UO_2)_2(SO_4)_3.5H_2O$; and J. Meyer and E. Kasper, **potassium uranyl trisulphate,** $K_2H_4[UO_3(SO_4)_3].6H_2O$. E. Rimbach prepared crystals of **rubidium uranyl disulphate,** $Rb_2(UO_2)(SO_4)_2.2H_2O$, from a soln. of equimolar proportions of the component salts. The crystals resemble those of the potassium salt ; they can be recrystallized from aq. soln. ; but the salt is not so soluble as the corresponding potassium salt. E. Rimbach said that **rubidium uranyl trisulphate,** $Rb_4(UO_2)(SO_4)_3.2H_2O$, can be obtained like the corresponding potassium salt, but it is far less stable. J. O. Perrine observed no ultra-violet fluorescence in the X-rays. F. W. O. de Coninck prepared **cæsium uranyl disulphate,** $Cs_2(UO_2)(SO_4)_2.2H_2O$, as in the case of the corresponding sodium salt.

For **copper uranyl sulphate,** *vide supra,* Johannite. J. L. Smith reported what he regarded as a hydrated **calcium uranyl sulphate,** occurring as a mineral near Adrianople, Turkey, and at Joachimsthal, Bohemia. He called it **medjïdite**— after the Sultan Abdul Medjid. It occurs as a dark; amber-yellow incrustation on pitchblende. Its hardness is 2·5. A. Breithaupt also described nodular crusts of green acicular crystals associated with the pitchblende of Joachimsthal, Bohemia, and he called the mineral *uranochalzit,* or **uranochalcite.** Its hardness is 2·0 to 2·5 ; and its analysis : U_3O_8, 36·14 per cent. ; SO_3, 20·03 ; FeO, 0·14 ; CuO, 6·55 ; CaO, 10·10 ; and H_2O, 27·16. A. L. Fletcher gave 970° for the softening temp., and fusion occurs at 1110° to 1170°. The molten mineral attacks platinum, A. Weisbach described a uranium ochre occurring in yellow, flattened, acicular crystals as a velvety incrustation on the uraninite of Johanngeorgenstadt, Bohemia. The mineral is called **uranopilite.** The analysis corresponds with $CaO.8UO_3.2SO_3.25H_2O$. The sp. gr. is 3·75 to 3·97. F. W. O. de Coninck and E. Chauvenet obtained crystals of **magnesium uranyl disulphate,** $Mg(UO_2)(SO_4)_2.$ $5H_2O$, from a soln. of equimolar proportions of the component salts. According to M. Kohn, yellow rhombic crystals of **thallous uranyl disulphate,** $Tl_2(UO_2)(SO_4)_2.$ $3H_2O$, are produced when a hot, conc. soln. of equimolar proportions of the component salts in dil. sulphuric acid is allowed to cool. Supersaturated soln. of the

double salt are readily obtained. The water of crystallization is given off at 100°.
J. O. Perrine observed no ultra-violet fluorescence in the X-rays.

REFERENCES.

[1] A. Rosenheim and H. Loebel, *Zeit. anorg. Chem.*, **57**. 234, 1908 ; H. Loebel, *Ueber Halogenverbindungen des Urans*, Berlin, 1907 ; D. T. Ewing and E. F. Eldridge, *Journ. Amer. Chem. Soc.*, **44**. 1484, 1922 ; E. Müller and A. Flath, *Zeit. Elektrochem.*, **29**. 500, 1923.
[2] F. Giolitti and G. Bucci, *Zeit. Elektrochem.*, **12**. 823, 1906 ; *Gazz. Chim. Ital.*, **35**. ii, 151, 162, 1905 ; F. Giolitti and G. Liberi, *ib.*, **36**. ii, 443, 1906 ; L. Fernandes, *ib.*, **55**. 290, 1925 ; *Atti Accad. Lincei*, (6), **2**. 182, 1925 ; V. Kohlschütter, *Ber.*, **34**. 3619, 1901 ; N. A. Orloff, *Journ. Russ. Phys. Chem. Soc.*, **34**. 381, 1902 ; W. F. Hillebrand and W. H. Melville, *Bull. U.S. Geol. Sur.*, 90, 1892 ; *Amer. Chem. Journ.*, **14**. 1, 1891 ; F. W. O. de Coninck, *Bull. Acad. Belg.*, 483, 1901 ; 94, 161, 1902 ; 275, 1905 ; 993, 1908 ; *Recherches de l'uranium*, Paris. 1911 ; *Ann. Chim. Phys.*, (7), **28**. 5, 1903 ; F. de la Provostaye, *ib.*, (3), **5**. 48, 1842 ; J. J. Ebelmen, *ib.*, (3), **5**. 190, 1842 ; G. N. Wyrouboff, *Bull. Soc. Min.*, **32**. 342, 1909 ; J. Aloy and G. Auber, *Bull. Soc. Chim.*, (4), **1**. 569, 1907 ; E. M. Péligot, *Compt. Rend.*, **12**. 735, 1841 ; **22**. 487, 1846 ; **42**. 73, 1856 ; *Ann. Chim. Phys.*, (3), **5**. 5, 1842 ; (3), **20**. 329, 1847 ; *Journ. Pharm. Chim.*, (2), **27**. 522, 1841 ; *Liebig's Ann.*, **41**. 141. 1841 ; **43**. 258, 1842 ; *Journ. prakt. Chem.*, (1), **24**. 442, 1841 ; (1), **38**. 112, 1846 ; C. F. Rammelsberg, *Zeit. Kryst.*, **15**. 640, 1889 ; *Sitzber. Akad. Berlin*, 603, 1886 ; *Pogg. Ann.*, **55**. 318, 1842 ; **56**. 125, 1842 ; **59**. 1, 1843 ; *Ber.*. **5**. 1003, 1872 ; **19**. 603, 1886 ; R. Luther and A. C. Michie, *Zeit. Elektrochem.*, **15**. 1, 1909 ; H. Becquerel, *Compt. Rend.*, **101**. 1254, 1885 ; H. N. McCoy and H. H. Bunzel, *Journ. Amer. Chem. Soc.*, **31**. 367, 1909 ; R. J. Meyer and H. Nachod, *Liebig's Ann.*, **440**. 186, 1924 ; J. Meyer and E. Kasper, *Zeit. anorg. Chem.*, **155**. 49, 1926 ; G. Beck, *ib.*, **174**. 31, 1928.
[3] C. Dittrich, *Die Uranylsalze vom physikalischchemischen Standpunkte aus betrachtet*, Leipzig, 1899 ; *Zeit. phys. Chem.*, **29**. 465, 1899 ; A. S. Russell and D. C. Evans, *Journ. Chem. Soc.*, **127**. 2221, 1925 ; J. J. Berzelius, *Pogg. Ann.*, **1**. 359, 1824 ; *Schweigger's Journ.*, **44**. 191, 1825 ; J. A. Arfvedson, *ib.*, **44**. 8, 1825 ; *Pogg. Ann.*, **1**. 245, 1824 ; E. M. Péligot, *Compt. Rend.*, **12**. 735, 1841 ; **22**. 487, 1846 ; **42**. 73, 1856 ; *Ann. Chim. Phys.*, (3), **5**. 5, 1842 ; (3), **20**. 329, 1847 ; *Journ. Pharm. Chim.*, (2), **27**. 522, 1841 ; *Liebig's Ann.*, **41**. 141, 1841 ; **43**. 258, 1842 ; *Journ. prakt. Chem.*, (1), **24**. 442, 1841 ; (1), **38**. 112, 1846 ; C. F. Bucholz, *Gehlen's Journ.*, **4**. 17, 134, 1805 ; *Beiträge zur Erweiterung und Berichtigung der Chemie*, Erfurt, **1**. 62, 1799 ; B. Drenckmann, *Zeit. ges. Naturwiss.*, **17**. 126, 1861 ; W. Spring, *Bull. Acad. Belg.*, 290, 1904 ; F. W. O. de Coninck and E. Chauvenet, *ib.*, 151, 182, 1905 ; 50, 1908 ; F. W. O. de Coninck, *ib.*, 222, 349, 1901 ; 94, 161, 1902 ; 275, 360, 1905 ; *Recherches de l'uranium*, Paris, 1911 ; *Ann. Chim. Phys.*, (7), **28**. 5, 1903 ; F. de la Provostaye, *ib.*, (3), **5**. 51, 1842 ; (3), **6**. 165, 1842 ; J. J. Ebelmen, *ib.*, (3), **5**. 190, 1842 ; J. Aloy, *Compt. Rend.*, **122**. 1541, 1896 ; N. Athanasesco, *ib.*, **103**. 271, 1886 ; H. Becquerel, *ib.*, **122**. 420, 501, 1896—*vide* **4**. 26, 1 ; F. Perrin, *ib.*, **182**. 929, 1926 ; F. Giolitti and G. Bucci, *Gazz. Chim. Ital.*, **35**. ii, 151, 1905 ; A. H. Pareau, *Wied. Ann.*, **1**. 39, 57, 1877 ; **2**. 144, 1877 ; L. R. Lecanu, *Journ. Pharm. Chim.*, (2), **11**. 279, 1825 ; P. F. Reinsch, *Zeit. Kryst.*, **9**. 561, 1884 ; F. W. Clarke, *Amer. Chem. Journ.*, **5**. 240, 1883 ; A. P. West and H. C. Jones, *ib.*, **44**. 508, 1910 ; L. G. Winston and H. C. Jones, *ib.*, **46**. 368, 1911 ; S. F. Howard and H. C. Jones, *ib.*, **48**. 526, 1912 ; H. C. Jones and W. W. Strong, *ib.*, **43**. 97, 224, 1910 ; *Phys. Zeit.*, **10**. 499, 1909 ; H. Lescoeur, *Ann. Chim. Phys.*, (7), **4**. 213, 1895 ; *Recherches sur la dissociation des hydrates salins et des composés analogues*, Lille, 1888 ; J. M. Ordway, *Amer. Journ. Science*, (2), **26**. 208, 1858 ; J. L. Smith, *ib.*, (2), **5**. 337, 1848 ; K. Brückner, *Monatsh.*, **27**. 49, 1906 ; A. C. Schultz-Sellack, *Ueber die wasserhaltigen und wasserfreien Salze der Schwefelsäure*, Göttingen, 1868 ; *Ber.*, **4**. 13, 1871 ; E. Rimbach, *ib.*, **37**. 461, 1904 ; J. F. Vogl, *Gängverhältnisse und Mineralreichthum Joachimsthals*, Teplitz, 95, 1857 ; G. N. Wyrouboff, *Bull. Soc. Min.*, **32**. 340, 1909 ; A. von Unruh, *Einwirkung von trocknem Ammoniak auf wasserfreie Uranylsalze*, Rostock, 1909 ; M. Kohn, *Zeit. anorg. Chem.*, **59**. 111, 1908 ; G. Beck, *ib.*, **174**. 31, 1928 ; J. Meyer and E. Kasper, *ib.*, **155**. 49, 1926 ; H. Grossmann and B. Schück, *ib.*, **50**. 21, 1906 ; F. S. Beudant, *Traité élémentaire de minéralogie*, Paris, **2**. 672, 1832 ; M. Adam, *Tableau minéralogique*, Paris, 64, 1869 ; A. Weisbach, *Neues Jahrb. Min.*, ii, 258, 1882 ; H. Dauber, *Pogg. Ann.*, **92**. 251, 1854 ; W. Haidinger, *Edin. Journ. Science*, **3**. 306, 1830 ; *Pogg. Ann.*, **20**. 472, 1830 ; *Handbuch der bestimmenden Mineralogie*, Wien, 510, 1845 ; J. F. John, *Chemische Untersuchungen mineralischer, vegetabilischer, und animalischer Substanzen*, Berlin, **5**. 254, 1821 ; F. Slavik, *Rosp. Ceske Akad.*, **26**. 60, 1917 ; *Bull. Acad. Bohème*, **22**. 32, 1918 ; F. X. M. Zippe, *Verh. Ges. Böhm.*, 81, 1824 ; A. Breithaupt, *Vollständiges Handbuch der Mineralogie*, Dresden, 173, 1841 ; L. Bruner, *Zeit. phys. Chem.*, **32**. 133, 1900 ; C. U. Shepard, *A Treatise on Mineralogy*, New Haven, 70, 1857 ; J. D. Dana, *A System of Mineralogy*, New York, 978, 1892 ; H. Bürger, *Beiträge zur Kenntnis der Uranyldoppelsalze*, Bonn, 1904 ; R. H. Müller, *Biochem. Zeit.*, **178**. 77, 1926 ; H. Morton and H. C. Bolton, *Chem. News*, **28**. 47, 113, 167, 233, 244, 257, 268, 1873 ; *Monit. Scient.*, (2), **16**. 24, 305, 1874 ; *Amer. Chemist*, **3**. 361, 401, 1873 ; **4**. 1, 41, 81, 1874 ; A. L. Fletcher, *Scient. Proc. Roy. Dublin Soc.*, (2), **13**. 443, 1913 ; F. C. Hymas, *Journ. Soc. Chem. Ind.*, **50**. 81, T, 1931 ; I. Lifschitz and S. B. Hooghoudt, *Zeit. phys. Chem.*, **146**. 145, 1930 ; C. F. Rammelsberg, *Ber.*, **5**. 1005, 1872 ; O. Hahn, *ib.*, **59**. B, 2014, 1926 ; K. Fajan, *ib.*, **46**. 3486, 1913 ; H. M. Vernon, *Chem. News*, **66**. 104, 141, 152, 1892 ; E. S. Larsen, *Bull. U.S. Geol. Sur.*, 679, 1921 ; E. S. Larsen

and G. V. Brown, *Amer. Min.*, **2**. 75, 1917; E. S. Larsen and H. Berman, *ib.*, **11**. 1, 1926; B. Jezek, *Bull. Acad. Bohème*, **19**. 21, 1915; A. Colani, *Compt. Rend.*, 185, 273, 1927; *Bull. Soc. Chim.*, (4), **43**. 754, 1928; P. Groth, *Chemische Krystallographie*, Leipzig, **2**. 483, 1908; G. Carobbi, *Atti Accad. Lincei*, (5), **33**. i, 228, 1924; *Gazz. Chim. Ital.*, **55**. 406, 1924; W. T. Anderson and F. W. Robinson, *Journ. Amer. Chem. Soc.*, **47**. 718, 1925; W. C. Pierce, A. Leviton and W. A. Noyes, *ib.*, **51**. 80, 1929; W. C. Pierce, *ib.*, **51**. 2731, 1929; S. Freed and C. Kasper, *ib.*, **52**. 4671, 1930; G. Canneri, *Gazz. Chim. Ital.*, **55**. 611, 1925; J. O. Perrine, *Phys. Rev.*, (2), **22**. 48, 1923; P. Pringsheim and M. Yost, *Zeit. Physik*, **58**. 1, 1929; C. Ouellet, *Helvetica Chim. Acta*, **14**. 936, 1931; R. Rascanu, *Ann. Science Univ. Jassy*, **16**. 32, 459, 1930; F. C. Hymas, *Journ. Soc. Chem. Ind.*, **50**. 81, T, 1931.

§ 21. Uranium Carbonates

When an alkali carbonate is added to a soln. of a uranous salt, H. Rose,[1] C. F. Rammelsberg, E. M. Péligot, and J. L. C. Zimmermann observed that a whitish-green, voluminous precipitate is formed. It is sparingly soluble in a sat. soln. of an alkali carbonate, more soluble in a soln. of an alkali hydrocarbonate, and freely soluble in a soln. of ammonium carbonate. The precipitate is more or less hydrolyzed **uranous carbonate,** but C. F. Rammelsberg found that when washed and dried it is uranous hydroxide. The precipitate darkens when warmed owing to oxidation. The addition of ammonium carbonate to a uranous salt soln. was found by J. L. C. Zimmermann to give a whitish-green precipitate, soluble in excess. According to C. F. Rammelsberg, when the soln. of the precipitate in ammonium carbonate is allowed to evaporate, carbon dioxide is given off, and uranous hydroxide is first deposited, then ammonium diuranate; and J. A. Arfvedson found that when the soln. is heated, uranosic oxide free from carbonate is precipitated. Although uranous carbonate has not been prepared, the soln. of the precipitates just indicated in a soln. of ammonium carbonate is assumed to contain **ammonium uranous carbonate,** and in the case of the alkali carbonates, **alkali uranous carbonate.** E. M. Péligot obtained a precipitate of uranous hydroxide by adding calcium carbonate to a soln. of a uranous salt; and H. Rose, and J. L. C. Zimmermann found that all the uranium is so precipitated by the addition of barium carbonate.

J. J. Ebelmen found that alkali carbonates precipitate from soln. of uranyl salts a yellow alkali uranyl carbonate which is soluble in an excess of the precipitant, and it is more soluble in soln. of the alkali hydrocarbonates than in soln. of the normal carbonates. Alkali hydroxides precipitate alkali uranates from the soln. in alkali carbonates. A soln. of the precipitate produced by ammonium carbonate in an excess of that salt deposits, when boiled, hydrated uranium trioxide. J. N. von Fuchs observed that the addition of calcium carbonate to a soln. of a uranyl salt precipitates the uranium, and H. Rose found that with barium carbonate the precipitation is complete. J. M. Ordway made some observations on this subject —*vide supra*, basic uranyl sulphates. J. J. Ebelmen, and B. Drenckmann found that uranyl hydroxide attracts no carbon dioxide from atm. air. L. R. Lecanu, and E. M. Péligot believed that **uranyl carbonate,** $(UO_2)CO_3$, remained when ammonium uranyl carbonate is heated, but the observations of J. J. Ebelmen on the action of heat on this salt make this doubtful. According to W. T. Brande, hydrated uranium trioxide dissolves in an aq. soln. of carbon dioxide, and when the liquid is heated, the hydrated oxide is precipitated free from carbon dioxide. T. Parkman observed that the unwashed precipitate obtained by adding the least possible quantity of sodium carbonate to a soln. of uranyl nitrate contains $UO_3 : CO_2$ in the proportions 3 : 2; and with sodium carbonate and soln. of uranyl sulphate, in the proportions 3 : 1. These precipitates were supposed to be mixtures of alkali diuranate and uranyl carbonate. F. W. O. de Coninck added potassium carbonate to a soln. of uranyl nitrate, and obtained a precipitate with 17 per cent. of carbon dioxide, but after the precipitate had been washed it appeared to be a mixture of carbonate and oxide. K. Seubert and M. Elten obtained a complex basic salt whose analysis agreed with **uranyl decahydroxytri-**

carbonate, $5(UO_2)(OH)_2.3(UO_2)CO_3.6H_2O$, by mixing 10 grms. uranyl nitrate, with 5·7 grms. sodium carbonate in 20 c.c. of water. The orange precipitate was washed with alcohol. At the present time normal uranyl carbonate, $(UO_2)CO_3$, has not been isolated, and the different products which have been reported are stages in the hydrolysis : $UO_2CO_3+H_2O=UO_2(OH)_2+CO_2$. W. Marckwald found a kind of ochre as an alteration product of the uraninite of the Uruguru Mountains, East Africa, which he called **rutherfordite**—after E. Rutherford. For rutherfordite, *vide* **5**. 38, 3. The analysis corresponds with normal uranyl carbonate, $(UO_2)CO_3$. The yellow mineral is strongly radioactive, and has a sp. gr. 4·82.

Several complex uranyl carbonates have been obtained. J. J. Berzelius, L. R. Lecanu, E. M. Péligot, and W. Delffs obtained **ammonium uranyl tricarbonate,** $(NH_4)_4(UO_2)(CO_3)_3.2H_2O$, by dissolving ammonium diuranate in a warm, aq. soln. of ammonium carbonate and allowing the lemon-yellow filtrate to crystallize— assisted, maybe, by spontaneous evaporation. J. J. Ebelmen recommended digesting an excess of ammonium diuranate with a soln. of ammonium carbonate at 60° to 70°, filtering the soln. while warm, and allowing it to cool slowly. The undissolved ammonium uranate can be treated with the mother-liquor. E. Burcker added a mixture of aq. ammonia and ammonium carbonate to a soln. of uranyl nitrate until the precipitate first formed redissolved, and allowed the soln. to crystallize. According to F. Giolitti and V. Vecchiarelli, a soln. containing an excess of ammonia together with a mol of uranyl nitrate and 3 mols of ammonium carbonate deposits this salt in the form of lemon-yellow, transparent prisms which, according to F. de la Provostaye belong to the monoclinic system. W. Keferstein gave for the axial ratios $a:b:c=0·9635:1:0·8670$, and $\beta=99°\ 17'$; the (001)-cleavage is nearly complete. The sp. gr. is 2·773. According to J. J. Ebelmen, the salt can be preserved in stoppered bottles, but when opened, there is a smell of ammonium carbonate ; the salt is also stable in air containing a little vapour of ammonium carbonate, but in open air the salt is slowly decomposed and acquires an orange tinge. L. R. Lecanu, and E. M. Péligot thought that when the salt is heated uranyl carbonate is first formed, and then green uranosic oxide ; but J. J. Ebelmen showed that kept at 100° there is a considerable loss in weight in a few hours ; and between 200° and 250° there is a rapid evolution of water and ammonium carbonate, and the residue has an orange colour. The last portions of ammonium carbonate are expelled with difficulty, but if kept at 300° for a long time, brick-red uranium trioxide remains. If heated in a closed vessel, the salt leaves uranium dioxide, which is pyrophoric, taking fire in air as it oxidizes to green uranosic oxide. F. Giolitti and V. Vecchiarelli added that the salt loses ammonia at the ordinary temp., and more readily on heating to, say, 100°. The ratio $NH_3:CO_2$ always remains the same, 4 : 3, so that it must be assumed that the salt splits up completely with two parts $(UO_2)O$ and $CO_2.2(NH_4)_2CO_3$. The complex character of the salt is shown by the changes in the absorption spectrum which occur when ammonium carbonate is added to a soln. of uranyl nitrate ; by the cryoscopic measurements, which corre- spond with a decreasing mol. wt., ultimately reaching 90 ; and by the electrical conductivity, which also indicates an increasing and ultimately complete ionization. While J. J. Berzelius said that the salt is insoluble in water, J. J. Ebelmen found that 100 parts of water dissolve about 20 parts of the salt at 15°, and at 18·6° F. Giolitti and V. Vecchiarelli, 16·56 parts. The salt readily dissolves in a soln. of ammonium carbonate, and J. A. Arfvedson found that when the soln. is boiled, ammonium carbonate is given off, and the liquid becomes turbid as hydrated uranyl oxide is precipitated, but some uranium remains in soln., and, according to J. J. Ebel- men, and B. Drenckmann, the precipitate retains about 2 per cent. of adsorbed ammonia, but no carbon dioxide. E. M. Péligot supposed the precipitate to be ammonium diuranate. According to F. Giolitti and V. Vecchiarelli, the decom- position of the soln. by heat is very similar to that of the dry salt. The sat. soln., after being heated to 94° and cooled, deposits yellow needles of, probably, a basic ammonium uranyl carbonate ; and when the liquid is treated with ammonia, ammonium uranate is precipitated. According to H. Schlundt and R. B. Moore, when an excess of hot $4N$-$(NH_4)_2CO_3$ is added to a nearly sat. soln. of uranyl nitrate, both uranium and uranium-X dissolve completely, but on cooling crystals of ammonium uranyl tricarbonate separate, while the whole of the uranium-X remains in soln. The radioactivity of the double carbonate increases after a time, a maximum being attained at the end of about twelve days. A similar increase takes place when the substance is gently heated. In both cases the increase in activity is accompanied by a slight deepening of the yellow colour of the crystals. The phenomenon appears to be due to the decomposition which the substance undergoes, the removal of ammonia, carbon dioxide, and water resulting in a diminution of the retardation of the particles which are emitted by the active element contained in the compound. The increase in the activity is proportional to the loss of weight, a similar effect being observed when thin layers of uranyl acetate and nitrate are gently heated. According to F. Giolitti and V. Vecchiarelli, when a conc. soln. of 5 mols. of ammonium carbonate is mixed with 2 mols. of uranyl nitrate, at 50° to 55°, the liquid, on cooling, deposits a bright yellow, crystalline mass of **ammonium diuranyl pentacarbonate,** $2(UO_2)CO_3.3(NH_4)_2CO_3.4H_2O$, which is soluble in water; this salt is said to be probably identical with one previously reported by E. M. Péligot. When alcohol is added to the mother-liquor, it deposits a bright yellow powder with a composition $(NH_4)_{18}(UO_2)_8(CO_3)_{17}.nH_2O$. It is soluble in water, but there is nothing to indicate that it is a chemical individual.

According to J. J. Ebelmen, uranyl hydroxide, precipitated by a soln. of sodium carbonate, dissolves in an excess of the precipitant, forming a yellow soln. containing a complex salt. If a soln. of sodium uranate in a warm, aq. soln. of sodium hydrocarbonate be evaporated, it furnishes a yellow crystalline crust of **sodium uranyl tricarbonate,** $Na_4(UO_2)(CO_3)_3$; and E. F. Anthon obtained it as a yellow crystalline powder by evaporating an aqua regia extract of pitchblende to dryness, extracting the product with water, adding an excess of sodium carbonate to the soln., and evaporating the liquid. W. Jani also obtained it by passing carbon dioxide through a soln. of sodium carbonate with sodium diuranate in suspension, and evaporating the filtered soln. E. F. Anthon found that the lemon-yellow powder loses water when heated, and it becomes brick-red and loses carbon dioxide before a red-heat is attained, but after heating for half an hour, at a red-heat, some carbonate still remains. W. Jani said that when the salt is heated, it acquires a pale brick-red colour, and water then extracts sodium carbonate from the cold mass, leaving a residue of sodium diuranate. E. F. Anthon reported that the salt dissolves slowly in water, and a soln., sat. at 15°, has a sp. gr. 1·61. According to J. Aloy, potassium uranate, and, according to J. J. Ebelmen, and M. E. Chevreul, precipitated uranyl hydroxide dissolve in an aq. soln. of potassium carbonate, but more readily in a soln. of the hydrocarbonate, forming a yellow liquid from which **potassium uranyl tricarbonate,** $K_4(UO_2)(CO_3)_3$, separates in yellow crystals or as a crystalline crust. J. J. Ebelmen, however, said that uranyl hydroxide precipitated by potash-lye is not soluble in a soln. of potassium carbonate, although it is readily dissolved by a soln. of the hydrocarbonate. J. Aloy also prepared this salt by treating a neutral soln. of a uranyl salt, say the acetate, with a small excess of potassium cyanide, dissolving the precipitate by adding sufficient potassium carbonate, and concentrating the soln. for crystallization. The lemon-yellow, hexagonal, bipyramidal crystals were found by J. Aloy to be stable in air. J. J. Ebelmen found that at 300° the salt is decomposed, forming orange-yellow potassium uranate; and, according to J. J. Berzelius, there remains a mixture of potassium diuranate and carbonate after the salt has been heated to redness. According to J. J. Ebelmen, 100 parts of water at 15° dissolve 7·4 parts of the salt, and more is dissolved at a high temp. One part of the salt in 333 parts of water gives a deep yellow soln.; or 1 : 1332-soln. is pale yellow; a 1 : 5328-soln. has a yellow tinge; and a 1 : 10656-soln. is colourless—the most dil. soln. is made turbid by potash-lye, and in a few hours deposits orange-yellow flakes of potassium diuranate. Boiling water free from alkali, dissolves the salt with partial decomposition and the separation of potassium diuranate ; and a cold, very dil. soln. also deposits the uranate if an excess of potassium carbonate be not present. Potash-lye precipitates all the uranium in the soln. as potassium diuranate, even if a large excess of potassium carbonate be present. Acids, not in excess, produce the same yellow precipitate as is formed when potassium carbonate is added to a soln. of a uranyl salt. J. Aloy found that the salt is freely soluble in an aq. soln. of potassium carbonate ; and J. J. Ebelmen added that it is insoluble in alcohol. According to J. A. Hedvall, a large number of metallic ions give a precipitate with soln. of the alkali uranyl carbonates, but analytical results, the visible evolution of carbon dioxide, and the gradual colour change due to hydrolysis show that most of these products even shortly after precipitation cannot be regarded as definite compounds. Least hydrolysis occurs when the potassium uranyl carbonate in not too dilute a soln. is precipitated in the cold by addition of excess of the metallic salt soln. ; the precipitate is rapidly washed with water and allowed to dry in the air. Thus, *silver salts* give a yellow precipitate ; *mercurous salts*, a yellow precipitate—initially white and finally greyish-yellow ; *mercuric salts*, a red precipitate ; *cupric salts*, an apple-green precipitate, becoming yellowish-green ; *lead salts*, a white precipitate, becoming yellow ; *zinc and cadmium salts*, a pale yellow precipitate ; *manganous and aluminium salts*, no precipitate ; *ferrous salts*, a dark green precipitate ; *cobalt and nickel salts*, a pale yellow precipitate, becoming brownish-yellow ; *magnesium and calcium salts*, no precipitate ; *strontium salts*, a small, pale yellow precipitate ; and *barium salts*, a pale yellow precipitate.

J. A. Hedvall prepared **silver uranyl carbonate,** $Ag_4(UO_2)(CO_3)_3$, in yellow flocks, which form a crystalline powder. It darkens in colour even when kept in the dark, owing to the uranium radiation. It begins to give off carbon dioxide at 145°. According to J. F. Vogl, a calcium uranyl carbonate occurs as an incrustation on the uraninite of Joachimsthal, Bohemia. According to analyses reported by J. F. Vogl, A. Schrauf, and H. von Foullon, its composition corresponds with **calcium uranyl tetracarbonate,** $Ca_2(UO_2)(CO_3)_4.10H_2O$. A. Weisbach called it flutherite, and A. Schrauf, **uranothallite.** The siskin-green mineral occurs in minute crystals, united in scaly or granular aggregates. A. Schrauf gave for the axial ratios of the rhombic crystals $a : b : c = 0.601 : 1 : 0.358$. The (100)-cleavage is imperfect. A. Brezina gave $0.9539 : 1 : 0.7826$ for the axial ratios, using better developed crystals than those used by A. Schrauf. The hardness is 2·5 to 3·0. J. L. Smith described another mineral from the uraninite deposits near Adrianople, Turkey, and he called it **liebigite**—after J. von Liebig. J. F. Vogl also described a similar mineral from Johanngeorgenstadt, Bohemia. The analysis corresponds with **calcium uranyl dicarbonate,** $Ca(UO_2)(CO_3)_2.20H_2O$. The apple-green, mamillary concretions or thin coatings show a cleavage in one direction. The hardness is 2·0 to 2·5. E. S. Larsen represented the formula of liebigite by $CaO.UO_3.2CO_2.20H_2O$, and he considered that liebigite and uranothallite are possibly the same mineral species. The optical axial angles $2E = 65°$; and $2V = 42°$; and the indices of refraction are $\alpha = 1.500$, $\beta = 1.503$, and $\gamma = 1.537$. The cleavage is normal to a. In addition to the *icosihydrate*, liebigite, C. Blinkoff reported that the *decahydrate*, $CaCO_3.(UO_2)CO_3.10H_2O$, is formed by the action of carbon dioxide at 10 atm. press. on a suspension of 10 grms. of calcium uranate in 800 c.c. of water for two years. The compound is decomposed when boiled with water. If half the proportion of water is employed, the basic salt, **calcium tetrauranyl tricarbonate,** $2CaO.4UO_3.3CO_2.22H_2O$, is formed in pale yellow, tetragonal plates which are decomposed by water. A. Schrauf described a greenish or yellow mineral occurring in six-sided, rhombic plates on the uraninite of Joachimsthal, Bohemia. It was named **schröckingerite**—after Baron Schröckinger —and is regarded as a hydrated uranyl carbonate containing a little lime and sulphate. G. A. König described a canary-yellow incrustation on the granite at Franckford, Pennsylvania. He called it **randite**—after T. D. Rand. The analysis is UO_3, 31·63 per cent.; CO_2, 29·34; CaO, 32·50; and H_2O, 6·53. J. F. Vogl described a **copper calcium uranyl carbonate** from the Elias mine, Joachimsthal, Bohemia. W. Haidinger called it **voglite**—after J. F. Vogl. It occurs in emerald-green or grass-green aggregates of rhomboidal scales. The analysis is UO_3, 37·00 per cent.; CO_2, 26·41; CaO, 14·09; CuO, 8·40; and H_2O, 13·90. C. Blinkoff reported **strontium diuranyl dicarbonate**, $SrO.2UO_3.2CO_2.10H_2O$, to be formed by treating a soln. of 10 grms. of uranyl nitrate with strontium hydroxide, suspending the washed precipitate in 200 c.c. of water, and leaving the mixture for a long time in contact with carbon dioxide under press.—*vide supra*, calcium uranyl carbonate. The salt is decomposed by boiling water. J. A. Hedvall prepared **barium uranyl carbonate**, $Ba_2(UO_2)(CO_3)_3.6H_2O$, in yellow microscopic plates, by the action of a barium salt on a soln. of potassium uranyl carbonate. It loses water slowly at ordinary temp., and more quickly at 50°, changing in colour from bright yellow to lemon-yellow. Above 350° much carbon dioxide is given off, and the colour becomes orange-yellow. C. Blinkoff obtained **barium diuranyl dicarbonate**, $BaO.2UO_3.2CO_2.5H_2O$, in a similar way. In addition to the *pentahydrate*, he obtained an *octohydrate* by using twice as much water for the preparation of the salt. H. Behrens and P. D. C. Kley obtained **thallous uranyl tricarbonate**, $Tl_4(UO_2)(CO_3)_3$, as a crystalline precipitate on adding thallous nitrate to an ammoniacal soln. of sodium uranyl carbonate. The crystalline precipitate is very sparingly soluble in water, so that the formation of this salt is recommended for the micro-detection of uranium—one part in 5000 can be so detected.

B. Menes prepared **ammonium uranium tetracarbonate**, $(NH_4)_2[U(CO_3)_4].6H_2O$, by adding uranyl sulphate to a warm, sat. soln. of ammonium carbonate through which carbon dioxide is passed. The *guanidinium salt*, $(CN_3H_6)_2[U(CO_3)_4].10H_2O$, was also prepared.

REFERENCES.

[1] B. Menes, *Ueber Komplexverbindungen des vierwertigen Urans*, Berlin, 1929; W. T. Brande, *Quart. Journ. Science*, **14**. 86, 1823; L. R. Lecanu, *Journ. Pharm. Chim.*, (2), **11**. 279, 1825; E. Burcker, *ib.*, (4), **27**. 347, 1878; T. Parkman, *Amer. Journ. Science*, (2), **34**. 326, 1862; J. L. Smith, *ib.*, (2), **5**. 336, 1848; (2), **11**. 259, 1851; F. W. O. de Coninck, *Bull. Acad. Belg.*, 363, 1904; B. Drenckmann, *Zeit. ges. Naturwiss.*, **17**. 126, 1861; E. M. Péligot, *Compt. Rend.*, **12**. 735, 1841; **22**. 487, 1846; **42**. 73, 1856; *Ann. Chim. Phys.*, (3), **5**. 5, 1842; (3), **20**. 329, 1847; *Journ. Pharm. Chim.*, (2), **27**. 522, 1841; *Liebig's Ann.*, **41**. 141, 1841; **43**. 258, 1842; *Journ. prakt. Chem.*, (1), **24**. 442, 1841; (1), **38**. 112, 1846; J. J. Ebelmen, *Ann. Chim. Phys.*, (3), **5**. 209, 1842; F. de la Provostaye, *ib.*, (3), **6**. 163, 1842; K. Seubert and M. Elten, *Zeit. anorg. Chem.*, **4**. 79, 1893; J. A. Hedvall, *ib.*, **146**. 225, 1925; W. Keferstein, *Pogg. Ann.*, **59**. 275, 1856; W. Delffs, *ib.*, **55**. 229, 1842; H. Schlundt and R. B. Moore, *Phys. Zeit.*, **9**. 81, 1908; E. F. Anthon, *Dingler's Journ.*, **156**. 207, 288, 1860; J. Aloy, *Recherches sur l'uranium et ses composés*, Toulouse, 1901; *Ann. Chim. Phys.*, (7), **24**. 412, 1901; M. E. Chevreul, *Ann. Phil.*, **12**. 144, 1818; *Bull. Philomath.*, 20, 1818; F. Giolitti and V. Vecchiarelli, *Gazz. Chim. Ital.*, **35**. ii, 170, 1905; J. J. Berzelius, *Schweigger's Journ.*, **44**. 191, 1825; *Pogg. Ann.*, **1**. 359, 1824; *Svenska Akad. Handl.*, 152, 1823; *Ann. Phil.*, **9**. 266, 1825; J. A. Arfvedson, *Svenska Akad. Handl.*, 404, 1822; *Ann. Phil.*, **7**. 253, 1824; *Pogg. Ann.*, **1**. 245, 1824; *Schweigger's Journ.*, **44**. 8, 1825; C. Blinkoff, *Beiträge zur Kenntnis kondensierter Uranylverbindungen*, Bern, 1906; W. Marckwald, *Centr. Min.*, 761, 1906; A. Schrauf, *Tschermak's Mitt.*, (1), **3**. 137, 1873; *Zeit. Kryst.*, **6**. 410, 1882; G. A. König, *ib.*, **3**. 596, 1899; *Proc. Acad. Philadelphia*, 408, 1878; T. D. Rand, *ib.*, 274, 1880; J. F. Vogl, *Jahrb. geol. Reichsanst. Wien*, **4**. 221, 1853; A. Weisbach, *Synopsis Mineralogica*, Freiberg, 48, 1875; W. Haidinger, *Handbuch der bestimmenden Mineralogie*, Wien, 223, 1845; H. Rose, *Ausführlichs Handbuch der analytischen Chemie*, Braunschweig, **2**. 523, 1851; *Pogg. Ann.*, **116**. 252, 1862; C. F. Rammelsberg, *ib.*, **55**. 318, 1842; **56**. 125, 1842; **59**. 1, 1843; *Ber.*, **5**. 1003, 1872; J. L. C. Zimmermann, *Liebig's Ann.*, **216**. 10, 1883; J. N. von Fuchs, *Schweigger's Journ.*, **62**. 184, 1831; E. Plate in L. Gmelin and K. Kraut, *Handbuch der anorganischen Chemie*, Heidelberg, **2**. ii, 411, 1897; W. Jani, *Chem. News*, **23**. 220, 1871; A. Brezina, *Verh. geol. Reichsanst. Wien*, 269, 1883; *Ann. Nat. Hist. Hofmuseums*, **5**. 495, 1883; H. von Foullon, *ib.*, **5**. 1883; *Verh. geol. Reichsanst. Wien*, 269, 1883; H. Behrens and P. D. C. Kley, *Mikrochemische Analyse*, Leipzig, **1**. 150, 1915; E. S. Larsen, *Amer. Min.*, **2**. 87, 1917; J. M. Ordway, *Amer. Journ. Science*, (2), **26**. 208, 1858.

§ 22. Uranium Nitrates

J. J. Ebelmen,[1] and F. Isambert treated uranous oxide or hydroxide with silver nitrate, and obtained what was considered to be **uranous nitrate,** $U(NO_3)_4$, but the silver oxide which was formed oxidized the product to uranyl nitrate. J. Aloy and G. Auber obtained a green soln. by the action of sodium hydrosulphite on uranyl nitrate, but the uranous nitrate could not be isolated.

C. F. Bucholz,[2] H. Kuhn, H. Lescoeur, B. Drenckmann, L. R. Lecanu, and E. M. Péligot obtained **uranyl nitrate,** $(UO_2)(NO_3)_2.6H_2O$, by evaporating for crystallization a soln. of uranosic oxide or uranium trioxide in dil. nitric acid. F. Janda recommended an acid of sp. gr. 1·321. F. W. O. de Coninck obtained a soln. of the salt by the metathetical reaction between soln. of silver nitrate and uranyl chloride. T. J. Savery obtained a soln. as a product of the action of tin and nitric acid on uranyl phosphate or ammonium uranyl phosphate. The *hexahydrate* is obtained by crystallization from the aq. soln. The hexahydrate is the ordinary form which is understood when speaking of uranyl nitrate. The conditions of stability are indicated in Fig. 18. It is prepared directly from uranite, as indicated in connection with the extraction of uranium. The commercial salt generally contains small proportions of impurities—according to F. Giolitti and G. Tavanti, particularly alkali. Methods for the purification of the salt were given by J. Aloy, and F. W. O. de Coninck. C. Dittrich purified the salt by passing hydrogen sulphide into a soln. of the commercial salt ; added ammonia and ammonium carbonate in excess to the filtrate, and then added ammonium sulphide. The uranyl salt soln. is evaporated from the precipitate, and the filtrate boiled with hydrochloric acid to remove carbon dioxide. Ammonia and ammonium sulphide are added to precipitate uranyl sulphide ; the mixture is boiled for an hour. The black mixture of sulphur and uranium dioxide is washed first with warm water, and then with warm water containing some ammonium sulphide. The product is calcined in air, and the uranosic oxide dissolved in nitric acid, and the soln. crystallized. The salt is further purified by repeated crystallization, as recommended by H. N. McCoy and G. C. Ashman. F. E. E. Germann found that the heating and cooling curves of soln. of uranyl nitrate show the existence of this hydrate. It is formed spontaneously below −35°, and does not exist above −20°. A. Colani measured the solubility of uranyl nitrate in nitric acid, and expressing concentrations in grams per 100 grms. of soln. at 25°, obtained :

HNO_3	0	12·35	28·67	30·15	46·12	53·71	60·38	68·83
$UO_2(NO_3)_2$	56·08	40·36	29·65	37·90	37·18	27·49	23·65	22·49
		$6H_2O$			$3H_2O$		$2H_2O$	

The results are plotted in Fig. 18. In addition to the hexa- and dihydrates, the conditions of stability of the *trihydrate*, $UO_2(NO_3)_2.3H_2O$, are shown in the diagram. E. Kordes gave −18·1° for the eutectic temp. R. de Forcrand obtained indications of the existence of a *tetracosihydrate*, $(UO_2)(NO_3)_2.24H_2O$, in his study of the heating and cooling curves of sat. soln. F. W. O. de Coninck said that at 100° the hexahydrate passes into the *tetrahydrate*, $(UO_2)(NO_3)_2.4H_2O$, and that the tetrahydrate passes into the hexahydrate in moist air. H. Lescoeur found that the hexahydrate at 85° loses water and nitric acid, leaving a mixture of what is probably uranium trioxide and the trihydrate. E. M. Péligot found that the hexahydrate forms the trihydrate in vacuo. J. Aloy exposed the hexahydrate in vacuo or to a current of dry air at 0° ; P. Lebeau dried the hexahydrate at ordinary temp. and press. in a desiccator over conc. sulphuric acid or calcium oxide for 5 or 6 days ; and A. von Unruh heated the hexahydrate at 200° for some hours, and also passed a current of dry air over the addition product with ether. A. C. Schultz-Sellack reported that if a soln. of uranyl nitrate in nitric acid be evaporated and cooled, yellow fluorescent needles of the trihydrate are formed— the evaporation may be conducted in vacuo over conc. sulphuric acid, and potassium hydroxide ; but B. Drenckmann said that the hexahydrate alone is formed under these conditions. A. Ditte, however, obtained the trihydrate from a soln. of uranyl nitrate in monohydrated nitric acid. G. N. Wyrouboff obtained the trihydrate by evaporating a neutral soln. at 65° and drying the crystals at the same temp. The trihydrate was found by G. N. Wyrouboff to furnish yellow triclinic crystals with the axial ratios $a : b : c = 1 \cdot 7753 : 1 : 1 \cdot 4104$, and $\alpha = 85° 35'$, $\beta = 94° 12'$, and $\gamma = 81° 44'$. A. C. Schultz-Sellack said that the crystals do not effloresce in vacuo, but they take up water on exposure to air, passing into the hexahydrate. The m.p. is 120° ; A. F. Waseléeff gave 121·5°. A. Ditte found that 100 parts of monohydrated nitric acid dissolve 39 parts of the trihydrate at 14°. A. F. Waseléeff obtained the *dihydrate*, $(UO_2)(NO_3)_2.2H_2O$, by crystallization from conc. nitric acid of sp. gr. 1·502—with strongly acid soln. the hexahydrate is formed. M. Markétos also obtained it by dehydrating the hexahydrate in vacuo, and he said that the dihydrate is the equilibrium product under these conditions. P. Lebeau obtained the dihydrate by exposing to a current of dry air at ordinary temp. the crystals obtained by evaporating a soln. of the hexahydrate in ether, and dried with calcium nitrate. The conditions of stability are shown in Fig. 18. The pale yellow crystals of the

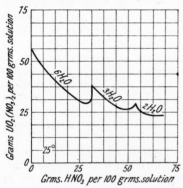

dihydrate were found by A. F. Waseléeff to be strongly fluorescent, and to melt at 179·3°. According to P. Lebeau, the salt decomposes in moist air at 115°, forming nitric acid and the hydrate $UO_3.2H_2O$. It dissolves in fuming nitric acid, and the soln. furnishes well-defined crystals. The percentage solubility in dry ether is 52·39 at 7° and 54·25 at 10°. A. F. Waseléeff, and P. Lebeau said that the *hemitrihydrate* probably does not exist. A. von Unruh reported a *monohydrate* to be formed in soln. by shaking the ethereal soln. for some hours with dry calcium chloride ; and J. Aloy, by heating the trihydrate at 100° in a current of dry air—if the temp. exceeds 100°, some nitrate is decomposed. R. de Forcrand's experiments on the dehydration of the hexa-

Fig. 18.—The Solubility of Uranyl Nitrate in Nitric Acid.

hydrate give no indications of the existence of the monohydrate as a chemical individual. M. Markétos found that if the hexahydrate be heated to 170° to 180° in a current of carbon dioxide charged with the vapour of nitric acid, by bubbling the gas through nitric acid of sp. gr. 1·4 mixed with sulphuric acid of sp. gr. 1·843, a yellow powder of *anhydrous* uranyl nitrate is formed. A. von Unruh showed that the anhydrous salt cannot be obtained by heating the hexa-hydrate, or from the ether complex $(UO_2)(NO_3)_2.2(C_2H_5)_2O$, but an ethereal soln. can be obtained by treating an ethereal soln. of the trihydrate with sodium, calcium chloride, or copper sulphate. If the hexahydrate is employed, the water of crystallization settles to the bottom as a conc. aq. soln. of the uranyl salt, and if sodium is added, the alkali uranate is formed, and if calcium oxide is added, calcium uranate. If the hexahydrate be dissolved in amyl alcohol, and decanted from the aqueous layer which separates out, the anhydrous solid cannot be obtained from the amyl alcohol soln. either by evaporation or by keeping it in vacuo ; and when heated on an oil-bath, the amyl alcohol is oxidized to valeric acid, and uranosic oxide, and nitrous fumes are formed. According to P. Lebeau, the anhydrous salt is a yellow amorphous powder, readily soluble in water, and it reacts violently with ether. It decomposes at 200°, forming uranosic oxide and uranium trioxide. E. Späth obtained a different variety of the anhydrous salt by heating the dinitroxyl compound—*vide infra*—to 164°.

The hexahydrate forms lemon-yellow prisms having a greenish tinge. B. Drenckmann found that neutral soln. give tabular crystals, and acidic soln., prisms. F. de la Provostaye found that the rhombic bipyramidal crystals have the axial ratios $a : b : c = 0.8737 : 1 : 0.6088$. Measurements were also reported by C. C. Haberle, J. Schabus, W. J. Grailich, and C. F. Rammelsberg. E. Quercigh studied the habit of the crystals separating from different solvents. L. Pauling and R. G. Dickinson found that the X-radiogram of the rhombic bipyramidal crystals of hexahydrated uranyl nitrate corresponds with a space-lattice having four mols of $UO_2(NO_3)_2.6H_2O$ per unit cell, with $a_{100} = 13.15$ A., $a_{010} = 8.2$ A., and $a_{001} = 11.42$ A. Observations on this subject were also made by G. L. Clark. J. Schabus said that the crystals are pleochroic, with a pale greenish-yellow, b greenish-yellow, and c lemon-yellow. A. des Cloizeaux gave for the optic axial angles with red and blue rays, $2E = 68° 15'$ and $69° 15'$ respectively, and $2V = 44° 5'$ and $44° 27'$ respectively; and W. J. Grailich gave $2E = 68° 5'$ for red light. C. H. D. Bödeker gave 2.807 for the sp. gr. of the hexahydrate. A. F. Waseléeff gave for the sp. gr., D, of aq. soln. with p per cent. of the anhydrous nitrate :

p	.	.	2.80	10.92	20.05	29.77	39.73	49.92	54.77
D	.	.	1.33597	1.34417	1.35412	1.36758	1.38272	1.39889	1.41155
μ	.	.	1.0257	1.1035	1.1983	1.3247	1.4669	1.6506	1.7536

F. W. O. de Coninck also found for the sp. gr. of aq. soln. with :

p	.	1	2	4	6	8	10	12	14	16
D	.	1.0049	1.0096	1.0187	1.0281	1.0378	1.0462	1.0550	1.0643	1.0718

H. Lescoeur found the vap. press. of the hexahydrate to be negligible at 15°. At the m.p., 60°, the vap. press. of the sat. soln. is 12.2 mm.; that of the dry hexahydrate is 11.7 mm.; that of the molten hexahydrate, 11.8 mm.; and that of the 3.4 hydrate, less than 3 mm. E. Löwenstein found that with sulphuric acid of conc. C per cent. H_2SO_4, the losses in weight in t days, expressed in mols of water per mol of the hexahydrate, were :

C	.	30	40	50	60	70	80	90	97
t	.	10	10	10	20	20	30	30	30
Loss		0	0	0	2.94	2.99	3.97	4.01	4.00

With C below 20, the salt is hygroscopic. For the vap. press. of water corresponding with the different values of C, vide sulphuric acid. G. Tammann observed that the lowering of the vap. press. of water for soln. with 14.49, 34.62, and 46.40 grms. $UO_2(NO_3)_2$ per 100 grms. of water were, respectively, 13.1, 34.9, and 49.3 mm.

L. R. Lecanu observed that the hexahydrate remains unaltered in air between 15° and 20°; but, added C. F. Bucholz, it effloresces to a yellow powder in a dry, warm atm.; and E. M. Péligot observed that the trihydrate is formed when the salt is kept in vacuo. F. W. O. de Coninck said that if kept in air for 3 or 4 days the salt may have the eq. of 6 to 8 mols. of water. Various more or less discordant statements about the dehydration of the hexahydrate are indicated in connection with the reputed hydrates. C. F. Bucholz found that when the salt is heated, it melts in its water of crystallization, giving off water and acid. A. F. Waseléeff gave 60.2° for the m.p. of the salt, and J. M. Ordway, 59.5°; at 118° the liquid begins to boil, when about 4 mols. of water and some acid are given off. When the liquid is cooled, E. M. Péligot observed that it forms transparent prisms, which, when exposed to air, rapidly absorb water and become opaque. At a higher temp. the molten liquid, said C. F. Bucholz, becomes reddish-yellow, ultimately forming uranosic oxide; but, according to J. J. Berzelius, with the intermediate formation of a basic salt, and J. A. Arfvedson said that some uranyl nitrite is formed as the salt loses oxygen, and it decomposes into nitrogen oxides and uranosic oxide without the intermediate formation of uranium trioxide. F. W. O. de Coninck reported that 2 mols. of water are lost when the hexahydrate is kept for a few hours at 100°; 2 mols. more water are lost between 115° and 130°; and the remainder above 170°. The product fuses between 82° and 105° according to the proportion of contained water and loses some nitric acid; at about 255° nitrous fumes are given off, and at a higher temp. a red modification of uranium trioxide is formed (q.v.). The various reports on the dehydration phenomena are not all concordant. The observations of C. Dittrich on the lowering of the f.p., $\theta°$; the calculated mol. wt. when the theoretical value for $UO_2(NO_3)_2$ is 395·4; the factor i; and the degree of ionization, a, of n normal soln. of uranyl nitrate—$\frac{1}{2}UO_2(NO_3)_2$ per litre—are:

n	1	0·5	0·25	0·125	0·0625
θ	2·967°	1·339°	0·646°	0·329°	0·168°
Mol. wt.	153·4	151·6	148·9	142·5	137·8
i	2·57	2·60	2·65	2·77	2·87
a	0·78	0·80	0·82	0·88	0·94

Consequently the nitrate is almost completely ionized in $\frac{1}{16}N$-soln. F. W. O. de Coninck gave 0·946 for the sp. ht. of a 10 per cent. soln.; and C. Dittrich found the sp. ht. of $\frac{1}{2}N$- and $\frac{1}{4}N$-soln. of uranyl nitrate to be respectively 0·892 and 0·956. R. de Forcrand gave for the heat of formation of uranyl nitrate, $(UO_2,3O_2,N_2)_{solid}$ $=67·25$ Cals.; and for $(UO_2,3O_2,N_2,Aq.)=86·25$ Cals. R. de Forcrand gave for the heat of soln. of UO_3 in dil. nitric acid, 19·803 Cals.; $UO_3.H_2O$, 14·846 Cals.; and $UO_3.2H_2O$, 12·375 Cals. J. Aloy gave $-3·7$ Cals. for the heat of soln. of a mol of the trihydrate in 1000 to 2500 mols of water at 18° to 20°; and F. W. O. de Coninck $-3·8$ Cals. for the heat of soln. of the trihydrate in water at 17° to 18°. R. de Forcrand also gave for the heats of hydration for the solid hydrates from solid, liquid, and gaseous water: $UO_2(NO_3)_2 \rightarrow UO_2(NO_3)_2.H_2O+5·70$, 7·13, and 16·79 Cals. respectively; $UO_2(NO_3)_2.H_2O \rightarrow UO_2(NO_3)_2.2H_2O+5·39$, 6·82, and 16·48 Cals. respectively; $UO_2(NO_3)_2.2H_2O \rightarrow UO_2(NO_3)_2.3H_2O+2·27$, 3·70, and 13·36 Cals. respectively; and $\frac{1}{2}UO_2(NO_3)_2.3H_2O \rightarrow \frac{1}{2}UO_2(NO_3)_2.6H_2O+0·94$, 2·27, and 11·93 respectively. The subject was discussed by W. Biltz. R. de Forcrand, and M. Markétos also gave for the heats of soln., Q_s, of the anhydrous salt and its hydrates, $UO_2(NO_3)_2.nH_2O$:

n	0	1	2	3	6
Q_s { R. de Forcrand.	19·00	11·87	5·05	1·35	$-5·45$ Cals.
{ M. Markétos .	16·00	—	5·42	2·00	$-4·76$ Cals.

The optical character of the crystals of the hexahydrate is positive. V. von Lang gave for the mean index of refraction $\beta=1·4950$ for red, 1·4967 for yellow, 1·4991 for green, and 1·5023 for blue light. F. W. O. de Coninck gave $\mu=1·338$, 1·348, and 1·364 for the indices of refraction of 8, 10, and 12 per cent. soln. respectively. A. F. Waseléeff's measurements of μ at 17°/17° are indicated above. The absorption and fluorescence spectra were described by E. Hagenbach, H. Becquerel, H. C. Jones and W. W. Strong, etc.—*vide supra*, the physical properties of uranium. The absorption spectrum of aq. soln. was examined by

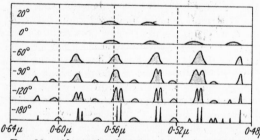

FIG. 19.—Absorption Spectra of Aqueous Solutions of Uranyl Nitrate.

E. L. Nichols and E. Merritt at temp. between 20° and $-185°$, and various changes were observed. H. L. Howes found that the spectra of aq. soln. showed the results indicated in Fig. 19. F. E. E. Germann explained the results by assuming that they are produced by the hexa- and tetracosihydrates and various mixtures of the two dependent on the conc. of the soln. and on the rate of cooling. J. C. Ghosh and B. N. Mitter also studied this subject—*vide supra*. V. R. von Kurelec examined the spectrum in various non-aqueous solvents; and B. K. Mukerji and N. R. Dhar, the photosensitization of aq. soln. H. M. Vernon estimated the ionization from the colour.

J. Becquerel observed that the greenish-yellow fluorescence of the nitrate does not increase as the temp. is lowered to −190°; the converse statement applies to most fluorescent substances. A. Bornträger found that the dry crystals become luminescent when rubbed with the hand. A. S. Herschel found that the crystals exhibit a greenish-yellow triboluminescence, for they emit flashes of light when mechanically shaken or crushed; W. N. Iwanoff also noticed that slight detonations occurred when some crystals which had been kept in a stoppered bottle in the dark for three years were being weighed out. L. W. Andrews also noticed the detonation of some crystals in which the water of crystallization had been replaced by ether. W. Eichhorn observed the triboluminescence but no detonations when old crystals were shaken in a flask. A. Müller obtained only mild detonations in the case of a few specimens crystallized from ether, never when crystallized from water or prepared in the absence of free nitric acid; and he assumed that the effect may be due to the decomposition of an unstable compound of a lower oxide of nitrogen with a uranium-ether addition compound. X-rays had no perceptible effect on the crystallization of uranyl nitrate. J. A. Siemssen observed that a specimen of uranyl nitrate kept for 21 years in a stoppered bottle showed only a feeble triboluminescence in comparison with the effect produced by other specimens; and a specimen of sodium uranate which was not triboluminescent furnished uranyl nitrate with a fairly strong triboluminescence. H. Longchambon found that the spectrum of the triboluminescence of uranyl nitrate is the line spectrum of nitrogen complicated by the secondary effects of fluorescence.

G. L. Clark, and L. Pauling and R. G. Dickinson examined the action of secondary L-rays of uranium. E. K. Rideal and R. G. W. Norrish found that uranyl nitrate soln. have different potentials in light and in darkness. E. Shpolsky observed that the presence of uranyl nitrate or acetate inhibits the photochemical reaction in Eder's soln. H. Greinacher showed that the raising of the temp. by the radioactive transformations of the uranium, etc., amounts to 0·01°—vide radioactivity. J. Korczyn discussed the β-rays of the salt; J. C. Jacobsen, the action of γ-rays on the salt; and D. M. Bose and H. G. Bhar, the magnetic susceptibility.

According to F. W. O. de Coninck, aq. soln. of uranyl nitrate undergo photolysis, being slowly decomposed by diffused sunlight; but if the soln. are acidified by hydrochloric or acetic acid, they are very stable. Soln. of uranyl nitrate in commercial methyl or ethyl alcohol are readily decomposed by diffused sunlight, and a black uranium oxide is deposited. As indicated in connection with the general physical properties of uranium, C. F. Bucholz observed that ethereal soln. are decomposed in sunlight, forming ethyl nitrate, uranosic oxide, and a green liquid. P. Chastaing noticed that while red light and yellow light are without action on the alcoholic soln., violet light at once reduces the uranyl salt, forming aldehyde and acetic acid. H. Fay observed that a soln. of tartaric acid and uranyl nitrate gradually assumes a deep green colour when exposed to sunlight, a light green salt of uncertain character being subsequently deposited; the production of the latter is greatly promoted by heat, but in no case has gas been evolved—vide supra, the physical properties of uranium. H. M. Vernon attempted to estimate the degree of ionization from the change in the colour of the soln. when diluted with water, and when warmed.

C. Dittrich measured the electrical conductivity, λ, of aq. soln. of an eq. of uranyl nitrate—$\frac{1}{2}UO_2(NO_3)_2$—in v litres of water at 25°, and found:

v .	4	8	16	32	64	128	256	512	1024	2048	4096
λ .	74·09	81·42	88·23	94·34	100·8	107·6	115·0	122·7	131·5	140·7	151·8

Measurements were also made at 25° by H. Ley, and L. G. Winston and H. C. Jones, whilst A. P. West and H. C. Jones, and S. F. Howard and H. C. Jones obtained for higher temp. the following results for the conductivities, λ, and the computed percentage degrees of ionization, α :

v		4	8	32	128	512	1024	2048	4096
λ	35°	157·89	177·97	216·65	249·88	285·11	304·61	318·91	349·78
	50°	199·01	226·59	279·42	327·08	376·95	404·71	422·85	467·92
	65°	245·03	277·69	345·77	406·32	476·52	514·08	538·35	596·77
α	35°	45·14	50·88	61·94	71·44	81·51	87·09	91·17	100·00
	65°	41·06	46·53	57·94	68·09	79·85	86·14	90·21	100·00

L. G. Winston and H. C. Jones obtained :

v		4	8	32	128	512	1024	2048	4096
λ	0°	74·91	83·44	97·22	110·14	116·33	123·14	128·92	136·77
	25°	132·91	150·57	180·64	207·89	224·95	241·47	255·38	274·50
	35°	158·84	181·20	219·38	254·21	277·35	298·63	317·44	343·09
α	0°	54·8	61·0	71·1	80·5	85·0	90·0	94·2	100·00
	25°	48·4	54·9	65·8	75·8	82·0	88·0	93·1	100·00
	35°	46·3	52·8	63·9	74·1	80·8	87·1	92·5	100·00

The value of $\lambda_{1024} - \lambda_{32}$ in C. Dittrich's measurements is 37·16. This difference is unusually high for a normal salt of a bivalent anion. This is attributed to hydrolytic changes. L. R. Lecanu noticed that the moist salt reddens blue litmus ; and C. Dittrich's observations on the effect of uranyl nitrate on the inversion of sugar show that the degree of hydrolysis of $\frac{1}{10}N$-soln. of uranyl nitrate at 65° is 0·0361, meaning that at this temp. 0·036 of each eq. of uranyl nitrate in soln. is hydrolyzed ; at lower temp. the degree of hydrolysis will be smaller. L. Bruner studied the hydrolysis of the salt. The conductivity curve in C. Dittrich's measurements does not approach a constant value with increasing dilution, as would be the case if the process of ionization were simply that symbolized : $UO_2(NO_3)_2 \rightleftharpoons UO_2^{\cdot\cdot} + 2NO_3'$, although L. Gomez showed by taking the difference between each value of λ and the next succeeding one at double the dilution, the difference decreases until the dilution $v=64$. From this point the difference increases progressively. This is attributed to the progressive ionization of the salt, in accord with $UO_2(NO_3)_2 \rightleftharpoons UO_2(NO_3)^{\cdot} + NO_3'$, followed by $UO_2(NO_3)^{\cdot} \rightleftharpoons UO_2^{\cdot\cdot} + NO_3'$, with hydrolysis when the dilution exceeds $v=64$. Again, by extrapolation of the cryoscopic data, indicated above, the apparent mol. wt. at infinite dilution is almost exactly one-third the real mol. wt. This is in agreement with the scheme : $UO_2(NO_3)_2 \rightleftharpoons UO_2^{\cdot\cdot} + 2NO_3'$. With increasing conc., the ratio of the apparent to the real mol. wt. approaches the value 2·5, so that even in conc. soln. the salt is ionized to a considerable extent, possibly in accord with the equation : $2UO_2(NO_3)_2 \rightleftharpoons U_2O_4^{\cdots\cdot} + 4NO_3'$. The values of the degree of ionization, calculated on the assumption that the salt is a simple ternary electrolyte, are thus uncertain. L. Gomez measured the transport numbers for the anions at conc. between 0·0024 and 0·074 mol per litre. The resulting curve is typical of that of a ternary electrolyte, and shows a minimum at a conc. of 0·015 mol per litre, indicating a maximum conc. of the $[UO_2(NO_3)]'$-ion. At conc. beyond 0·07 mol, the transport number approaches unity, and the metallic radicle now forms part of the anion. At conc. lower than 0·01 mol the presence of UO_2'' is indicated. The addition of ammonia to a uranyl salt soln. precipitated the compound $(NH_4)_2U_2O_7$. This indicates the probable presence of the anion U_2O_7'' in the soln. F. W. O. de Coninck and M. Camo found that a black pyrophoric oxide is a product of the electrolysis of a soln. of uranyl nitrate. C. A. Pierlé measured the potentials of various uranium oxides (q.v.) against soln. of uranyl nitrate. H. Stadelmann examined the deposits obtained by dipping a carbon and a metal rod, electrically connected, into a soln. of uranyl nitrate. S. Bodforss studied the electrometric titration of a soln. of a uranyl salt in the presence of acetic acid by a soln. of a phosphate ; in presence of a small amount of a quadrivalent uranium salt, the equilibrium $UO_2^{\cdot\cdot} + 4H^{\cdot} - 2\ominus \rightleftharpoons U^{\cdots\cdot} + 2H_2O$ is set up and the potential E

of the soln. with respect to a platinum electrode is given by the formula $E = E_0 + RT/2F . \log_e [UO_2{}^{..}][H^.]^4/[U^{....}]$. If the hydrogen-ion concentration remains constant, the potential is altered only when an excess of uranyl salt has been added. I. Lifschitz and S. B. Hooghoudt studied the Becquerel effect with soln. of uranyl salts. V. von Lang observed that the dimagnetism of crystals of the hexahydrate is strongest parallel to the a-axis of the crystals, and weakest parallel to the b-axis.

V. N. Ipatéeff and B. Muromtzeff found that hydrogen at 250 atm. press. and at 200° to 300° gives UO_3, U_3O_8, or UO_2—according to temp.—when it acts on a soln. of uranyl nitrate. According to C. F. Bucholz, the hexahydrate deliquesces in a moist atm., and cold water dissolves about half its weight of the salt, forming a greenish-yellow soln. F. W. O. de Coninck obtained a similar result between 12·9° and 14·2°. A. F. Waseléeff found the solubility, S, in grams of the hexahydrate per 100 grms. of sat. soln. to be :

	−18·1°	−12·1°	−2·2°	0°	12·3°	25·6°	36·7°	45·2°	71·8°
S	54·9	58·0	62·1	63·0	67·4	72·8	78·1	83·0	86·3

The eutectic point is at −18·1° and corresponds with the ratio $UO_2(NO_3)_2 : 28·9H_2O$ The freezing points of soln., with S grms. of the hexahydrate per 100 grms. of soln., are as follow :

	−1·6°	−2·1°	−2·9°	−4·4°	−6·0°	−7·9°	−11·2	−18·1
S	13·8	15·6	21·9	30·0	33·4	41·4	47·5	54·9

The curve for these results is the ice line, Fig. 20. The hydrolysis of the salt has just been discussed. J. J. Berzelius observed that when aq. soln. of uranyl nitrate are boiled, and the filtrate evaporated, there remains a sticky mass of a basic salt, **uranyl oxynitrate,** of unknown composition. J. M. Ordway said that half the ammonia required for precipitating the uranium can be added before precipitation begins, and the soln. may then contain a basic salt. G. Rousseau and G. Tite observed that if a soln. of uranyl nitrate be heated with marble in a sealed tube at 180° to 200° for 24 hrs., a yellow, microcrystalline, basic uranyl nitrate is formed. A. Ditte heated uranyl acetate with monohydrated nitric acid, and obtained a yellow crystalline powder supposed to be basic uranyl nitrate. It is insoluble in water. J. W. Thomas found that hydrogen chloride acts on the trihydrate with the evolution of heat, forming uranyl chloride, etc. F. W. O. de Coninck found that uranyl nitrate is

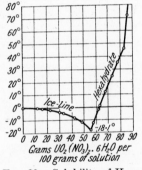

FIG. 20.—Solubility of Hexa-hydrated Uranium Nitrate.

soluble in hydrochloric acid. It is also soluble in hydrobromic acid, and soln. of 1, 2, 3, 4, and 5 per cent. of uranyl nitrate in hydrobromic acid, of sp. gr. 121, have the respective sp. gr. 1·2122, 1·2168, 1·2198, 1·2250, and 1·2305. Uranyl nitrate is freely soluble in sulphuric acid, and soln. of 1, 2, 3, 4, and 5 per cent. of the nitrate in sulphuric acid, of sp. gr. 1·138, have the respective sp. gr. 1·1427, 1·1450, 1·1511, 1·1540, and 1·1576. F. J. Faktor found that sodium thiosulphate precipitates uranyl thiosulphate from soln. of uranyl nitrate. H. Rose said that when the salt is mixed with ammonium chloride and heated, uranosic oxide is formed. A. von Unruh obtained **uranyl diamminonitrate,** $UO_2(NO_3)_2.2NH_3$, as a yellow amorphous powder, by keeping in vacuo the diammino-complex with ether, and by passing ammonia into a soln. of uranyl nitrate in amyl alcohol—freed from water by boiling. The yellow flakes can be dried in vacuo over sulphuric acid. If the diammine be kept in an atm. of ammonia, it forms **uranyl triamminonitrate,** $UO_2(NO_3)_2.3NH_3$; and if in liquid ammonia, **uranyl tetramminonitrate,** $UO_2(NO_3)_2.4NH_3$. When treated with hydrazine hydrate, R. Salvadori obtained hydrazine uranates (*q.v.*). C. C. Palit and N. R. Dhar found that the presence of uranium nitrate favoured the dissolution of mercury in nitric acid. T. Curtius and A. Darapsky found that sodium azide colours the soln. deep red, and after boiling some time uranyl hydroxide is deposited. According to E. Späth, when 22·5 grms. of dihydrated uranyl nitrate are dissolved in 30 c.c. of fuming nitric acid of sp. gr. 1·52, and the well-cooled soln. treated with a mixture of 20 grms. of nitrogen pentoxide and an excess of liquid nitrogen peroxide—12 c.c.—a light yellow precipitate of **uranyl dinitroxylnitrate,** $UO_2(NO_3)_2.2NO_2$, is formed. It is decomposed by water into uranyl nitrate and nitrogen peroxide; and at 163° to 165° it forms anhydrous uranyl nitrate, not the same as that prepared by M. Markétos. F. W. O. de Coninck found that soln. of 1, 2, 3, 4, and 5 per cent. of uranyl nitrate in nitric acid, of sp. gr. 1·053, have the respective sp. gr. 1·1585, 1·1614, 1·1663, 1·1698, and 1·1751. J. J. Berzelius, J. J. Ebelmen, E. M. Péligot, B. Drenckmann, and A. C. Schultz-Sellack were unable to prepare an acid salt of uranyl nitrate. L. R. Lecanu observed that the salt fuses when heated on charcoal, and then detonates like nitre. E. V. Alexeevsky and A. I. Avgastinik studied the adsorption of soln. of uranyl nitrate by charcoal. C. F. Bucholz found that 100 parts of absolute ethyl alcohol dissolve 333 parts of uranyl nitrate; and F. W. O. de Coninck observed that at 12·7° to 13°, 100 parts of ethyl alcohol dissolve 3·33 parts of the salt; whilst 100 parts of methyl alcohol dissolve 4·35 parts of nitrate at 10·6° to 11·5°; and that soln. of 1, 2, 3, 4, and 5 per cent. of uranyl nitrate in methyl alcohol have the respective sp. gr. 0·8902, 0·8938, 0·9003, 0·9068, and 0·9108. Uranyl nitrate is also soluble in propyl and isobutyl alcohols, but less soluble in amyl alcohol. C. F. Bucholz found that uranyl nitrate is freely soluble in ether; P. Misciattelli compared the solubilities of the thorium and uranium nitrates in ether; and he studied the ternary system $UO_2(NO_3)_2$–H_2O–$(C_2H_5)_2O$ at 0° and 20°. For the system at 0° (Fig. 21), with non-saturated soln., the compositions of the aq. and ethereal layers were:

Aqueous layer			Ethereal layer		
Ether	Water	Nitrate	Ether	Water	Nitrate
11·6	88·40	—	99·00	1.00	—
9·79	77·74	12·47	98·53	1·60	0·31
7·05	73·50	19·38	97·49	0·96	1·55
9·48	66·56	25·09	86·46	6·95	6·58
6·48	65·00	38·52	87·85	3·02	9·13
5·50	66·50	38·00	67·50	6·50	26·00

whilst the compositions of the saturated soln. were:

Aqueous layer			Ethereal layer			Solid phase
Ether	Water	Nitrate	Ether	Water	Nitrate	
—	—	—	78·00	—	22·00	$UO_2(NO_3)_2$
—	—	—	68·00	7·00	24·50	
4·15	47·47	48·38	45·15	10·29	44·56	
5·00	46·30	48·70	41·17	13·56	45·27	$UO_2(NO_3)_2.6H_2O$
—	30·60	69·40	—	—	—	

The results are summarized in Fig. 21; and those for 20° in Fig. 22. O. Guempel also studied the ternary system: uranyl nitrate–ether–water; and F. W. O. de Coninck stated that 100 parts of ether dissolve 6·25 parts of the salt at 10·6° to 11·5°; whilst 100 parts of acetone, at 11·9° to 12·2°, dissolve 1·6 parts of the salt; 100 parts of formic acid, at 10·6° to 11·5°, 18·6 parts; and 100 parts of acetic acid, at 10·6° to 11·5°, 5·43 parts. Soln. of 1, 2, 3, 4, 5, 6, and 7 per cent. of uranyl nitrate in acetic acid, of sp. gr. 1·055, have the respective sp. gr. 1·0387, 1·0434, 1·0469, 1·0505, 1·0564, 1·0626, and 1·0662. L. Vanino said that when solid uranyl nitrate is heated with acetic anhydride, nitrogen oxides are evolved and uranyl acetate is formed. F. W. O. de Coninck found that uranyl nitrate is soluble in ethyl acetate, sparingly soluble in turpentine, and insoluble in petroleum and in the aromatic hydrocarbons—benzene, toluene, and xylene, as well as in carbon disulphide.

The data are not always concordant : thus, according to A. W. Postans, uranyl nitrate dissolves in all proportions in glycerol, whilst F. W. O. de Coninck said that it is insoluble. E. Shpolsky studied the inhibition of the photochemical reaction with Eder's soln. ; and G. G. Rao and N. R. Dhar, the catalytic action in the photosynthesis of formaldehyde from alkali hydrocarbonates. W. Thomson and F. Lewis studied the action of uranium nitrate on indiarubber. R. Rascanu prepared complex salts with pyridine, quinoline, 2-methylquinoline, antipyrine, pyramidon, and phenacetin.

According to P. Jolibois and R. Bossuet, when sodium hydroxide is added to a dil. aq. soln. of uranyl nitrate, precipitation commences only when an equimolar proportion of the alkali has been added ; from this stage up to the addition of two mols, a precipitate is obtained, and if this is filtered off and the filtrate is boiled, a further precipitate is deposited. Either precipitate contains 1·5 per cent. or more of sodium hydroxide, which is not removed by washing. If more than two mols of alkali are added, precipitation is complete and the precipitate contains still

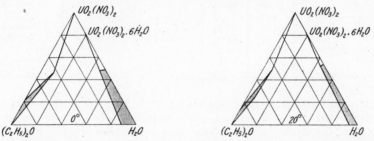

FIGS. 21 and 22.—The Ternary System : $UO_2(NO_3)_2$–$(C_2H_5)_2O$–H_2O at 0° and 20°.

higher percentages of alkali. Radioactivity measurements on the different pre cipitates show that the intensity of radiation is proportional to the amount of radium present. The first precipitate which is formed contains a very important proportion of the uranium-X, the oxide of which is apparently less basic than that of uranium. D. I. Mendeléeff said that uranyl nitrate readily forms complex salts with the alkali nitrates ; but, according to R. J. Meyer and F. Wendel, not with the nitrates of the bivalent metals, although A. Lancien reported unstable salts with the nitrates of cadmium, nickel, and rhodium.

R. J. Meyer and F. Wendel prepared **ammonium uranyl trinitrate,** $NH_4(UO_2)(NO_3)_3$, by crystallization from a soln. of equimolar proportions of the component nitrates in nitric acid of sp. gr. 1·4 ; or by crystallizing a soln. with an excess of potassium nitrate over sulphuric acid and potassium hydroxide. A. Colani found that the anhydrous salt separates from an equimolar mixture of the com ponent nitrates in cold nitric acid of sp. gr. 1·33, and it is readily decomposed by water. The crystals were found by H. Steinmetz to be trigonal prisms, with the axial ratio $a : c = 1 : 10027$, and to have the (110)-cleavage perfect. The salt appears to be dimorphous, because E. Rimbach reported that the product obtained from a soln. of ammonium diuranate in an excess of conc. nitric acid contains both trigonal crystals and rhombic bipyramids, which, according to A. Sachs, have the axial ratios $a : b : c = 0·7003 : 1 : 1·1419$, with the optic axial angle $2H = 44° 41'$. The greenish-yellow crystals are hygroscopic. E. Rimbach's, and H. Bürger's observa tions on the solubility of the salt are summarized in Table II, which shows that at a low temp. the salt is decomposed in aq. soln., but as the temp. reaches about 60°, the salt is not decomposed. As a result, below 60°, the solid phase is a mixture of uranyl nitrate and of ammonium uranyl trinitrate, and the soln. contains more ammonium nitrate than corresponds with the double salt. A. Colani said that **ammonium uranyl tetranitrate,** $(NH_4)_2UO_2(NO_3)_4$, separates in slowly deliquescent crystals which are decomposed by water. H. Grossmann and B. Schück prepared

TABLE II.—THE SOLUBILITY OF THE AMMONIUM AND ALKALI URANYL TRINITRATES

Complex salt	Temp.	100 parts of solution contain				Atomic or mol. ratios in solution $UO_2 : R : NO_3$
		UO_2	R	NO_3	Total	
$NH_4(UO_2)(NO_3)_3$	0·5°	29·71	2·93	—	—	1 : 1·47 : 3·47
	13·5°	32·35	3·42	—	—	1 : 1·58 : 3·58
	24·9°	36·46	3·54	—	68·89	1 : 1·47 : 3·46
	35·0°	42·07	3·44	—	—	1 : 1·22 : 3·22
	59·0°	44·37	2·90	—	—	1 : 0·98 : 2·98
	80·7°	44·95	2·98	—	78·77	1 : 1·00 : 3·00
$K(UO_2)(NO_3)_3$	0·5°	31·98	1·72	—	—	1 : 0·37 : 2·37
	13·0°	33·40	2·74	—	—	1 : 0·57 : 2·57
	25·0°	37·07	4·01	23·47	64·46	1 : 0·76 : 1·60
	45·0°	42·18	5·16	—	—	1 : 0·84 : 2·84
	59·0°	41·65	6·03	—	—	1 : 1·00 : 3·00
	80·6°	43·71	6·38	—	80·03	1 : 3·01 : 1·01
$Rb(UO_2)(NO_3)_3$	25·0°	35·41	4·65	19·74	59·60	1 : 0·44 : 1·40
	80·0°	34·66	11·01	—	69·49	1 : 0·01 : 3·01
$Cs(UO_2)(NO_3)_3$	16·1°	31·39	6·59	—	55·39	1 : 0·43 : —

ethylenediamine uranyl nitrate, $C_2H_4(NH_2)_2.2HNO_3.UO_2(NO_3)_2.2H_2O$, in greenish-yellow, four-sided, columnar crystals, which melt at about 215° and are strongly fluorescent. The double uranyl nitrate acts on a photographic plate, whilst the double sulphate and chloride have no action on it ; on the other hand, the electroscope is affected about equally by the nitrate and the sulphate. A. Colani said that the complex nitrates of uranyl and potassium and sodium nitrates do not crystallize from aq. soln. in the cold. R. J. Meyer and F. Wendel were unable to prepare *lithium uranyl nitrate* or *sodium uranyl nitrate* ; but they prepared **potassium uranyl trinitrate,** $K(UO_2)(NO_3)_3$, as in the case of the ammonium salt, from a soln. of the component salts. The rhombic, bipyramidal crystals were found by H. Steinmetz to have the axial ratios $a : b : c=0·854 : 1 : 0·6792$, with a well-marked (010)-cleavage. The crystals of the salt prepared by E. Rimbach from a soln. of potassium diuranate in a large excess of nitric acid were also rhombic bipyramids, which, according to A. Sachs, have the axial ratios $a : b : c=0·7015 : 1 : 1·1560$, and the optic axial angle $2H=44° 34'$ for Na-light. The greenish-yellow fluorescent crystals are very hygroscopic. E. Rimbach, and H. Bürger found the solubilities indicated in Table II, and the results show that below 60° the salt is dissociated like the ammonium salt, but above that temp. the solid phase and solute have the same composition. W. Marckwald studied the radioactivity of the salt. R. J. Meyer and F. Wendel, and E. Rimbach prepared **rubidium uranyl trinitrate,** $Rb(UO_2)(NO_3)_3$, as in the case of the ammonium salt. A. Sachs gave for the axial ratio of the trigonal prisms, $a : c=1 : 1·0074$, and $a=96° 56'$. The (110)-cleavage is complete. The salt is less deliquescent than the potassium salt. The solubility data, Table II, by E. Rimbach, and H. Bürger show that somewhere below 80° the salt decomposes into its components, but above that temp. the solid phase and solute have the same composition. J. O. Perrine observed no ultraviolet fluorescence in the X-rays. E. Rimbach, H. Bürger, and R. J. Meyer and F. Wendel prepared **cæsium uranyl trinitrate,** $Cs(UO_2)(NO_3)_3$, as in the case of the ammonium salt. The trigonal crystals were found by A. Sachs to have the axial ratio $a : c=1 : 1·0117$, and $a=96° 48'$. They are isomorphous with those of the potassium salt. The effect of water is indicated in Table II. According to F. W. O. de Coninck, when silver nitrate is added to a soln. of uranyl chloride and the filtrate evaporated to dryness, there remains **silver uranyl nitrate,** mixed with uranyl nitrate, and a red basic nitrate. J. O. Perrine observed no ultra-violet fluorescence in the X-rays. A. Lancien obtained **cadmium uranyl nitrate,** $Cd(UO_2)(NO_3)_4.30H_2O$, in yellow needles which lose 10 mols. of water in vacuo over sulphuric acid. J. O. Perrine observed no ultra-violet fluorescence with **mercury uranyl nitrate** in the X-rays. R. J. Meyer and F. Wendel prepared **thallous uranyl trinitrate,** $Tl(UO_2)(NO_3)_3$, by evaporating over sulphuric acid and potassium hydroxide a soln. of equimolar parts of the component nitrates in nitric acid of sp. gr. 1·4. The yellow crystals are not perceptibly fluorescent, and they are decomposed by moist air into their component salts. W. Marckwald found the radioactivity of the salt to be smaller than that of the potassium salt.

REFERENCES.

[1] J. J. Ebelmen, *Ann. Chim. Phys.*, (5), **5**. 209, 1842 ; F. Isambert, *Compt. Rend.*, **80**. 1087, 1875 ; J. Aloy and G. Auber, *Bull. Soc. Chim.*, (4), **1**. 569, 1907.

[2] C. C. Haberle, *Gehlen's Journ.*, **4**. 146, 1834 ; C. Dittrich, *Die Uranylsalze von physikalisch-chemischen Standpunkte aus betrachtet*, Leipzig, 1899 ; *Zeit. phys. Chem.*, **29**. 465, 1899 ; H. Ley, *ib.*, **30**. 193, 1899 ; *Ber.*, **33**. 2658, 1900 ; L. Bruner, *ib.*, **32**. 133, 1900 ; F. W. O. de Coninck, *Recherches de l'uranium*, Paris, 1911 ; *Bull. Acad. Belg.*, 222, 1901 ; 992, 1908 ; 743, 1909 ; *Compt. Rend.*, **131**. 1206, 1303, 1900 ; **132**. 90, 204, 1901 ; *Bull. Soc. Chim.*, (4), **17**. 422, 1915 ; F. W. O. de Coninck and M. Camo, *Bull. Acad. Belg.*, 321, 1901 ; J. J. Ebelmen, *Ann. Chim. Phys.*, (3), **5**. 209, 1842 ; F. de la Provostaye, *ib.*, (3), **5**. 48, 1842 ; H. C. Jones and W. W. Strong, *Phys. Zeit.*, **10**. 499, 1909 ; *Amer. Chem. Journ.*, **43**. 97, 224, 1900 ; A. P. West and H. C. Jones, *ib.*, **44**. 508, 1910 ; S. F. Howard and H. C. Jones, *ib.*, **48**. 526, 1912 ; L. G. Winston and H. C. Jones, *ib.*, **46**. 403, 1911 ; H. Fay, *ib.*, **18**. 283, 1896 ; L. Gomez, *Anal. Fis. Quim.*, **17**. 24, 1919; A. F. Waseléeff, *Journ. Russ. Phys. Chem. Soc.*, **42**. 570, 1910 ; **43**. 1183, 1911 ; F. J. Faktor, *Pharm. Post.*, **34**. 485, 1901 ; W. N. Iwanoff, *Chem. Ztg.*, **36**. 297, 1912 ; W. Eichhorn, *ib.*, **38**. 139, 1914 ; A. Müller, *ib.* **40**. 38, 1916 ; **41**. 439, 1917 ; J. A. Siemssen, *ib.*, **43**. 267, 1919 ; **46**. 450, 1922 ; A. Bornträger, **11**. 223, 1896 ; L. Vanino, *ib.*, **35**. 1005, 1911 ; F. Giolitti and G. Tavanti, *Gazz. Chim. Ital.*, **38**. ii, 239, 1908 ; H. N. McCoy and G. C. Ashman, *Amer. Journ. Science*, (4), **26**. 521, 1908 ; J. M. Ordway, *ib.*, (2), **26**. 208, 1858 ; (2), **27**. 14, 1859 ; J. Becquerel, *Compt. Rend.*, **152**. 511, 1911 ; M. Markétos, *ib.*, **155**. 210, 1912 ; P. Jolibois and R. Bossuet, *ib.*, **174**. 168, 1922 ; H. Longchambon, *ib.*, **176**. 691, 1923 ; R. Lespieau, *ib.*, **125**. 1094, 1897 ; R. de Forcrand, *ib.*, **156**. 1004, 1207, 1954, 1913 ; *Ann. Chim. Phys.*, (9), **3**. 5, 1915 ; O. Guempel, *Bull. Soc. Chim. Belg.*, **38**. 443, 1929 ; I. Lifschitz and S. B. Hooghoudt, *Zeit. phys. Chem.*, **146**. 145, 1930 ; E. Shpolsky, *Nature*, **126**. 647, 1930 ; P. Lebeau, *Compt. Rend.*, **152**. 439, 1911 ; **155**. 163, 1912 ; *Bull. Soc. Chim.*, (4), **9**. 297, 1911 ; A. Colani, *ib.*, (4), **39**. 1243, 1926 ; (4), **43**. 194, 1928 ; *Compt. Rend.*, **185**. 1475, 1927 ; C. C. Palit and N. R. Dhar, *Journ. Phys. Chem.*, **30**. 1125, 1926 ; C. F. Rammelsberg, *Die neuesten Forschungen in der krystallographischen Chemie*, Leipzig, 58, 1857 ; J. Schabus, *Bestimmung der Krystallgestalten in chemischen Laboratorien erzeugter Producte*, Wien, 1853 ; C. H. D. Bödeker, *Die Beziehungen zwischen Dichte und Zusammensetzung bei festen und liquiden Stoffen*, Leipzig, 1860 ; A. S. Herschel, *Nature*, **60**. 29, 1899 ; E. K. Rideal and R. G. W. Norrish, *Proc. Roy. Soc.*, **103**. A, 342, 1923 ; W. J. Grailich, *Sitzber. Akad. Wien*, **27**. 41, 1857 ; V. von Lang, *ib.*, **31**. 120, 1858 ; **32**. 61, 1858 ; V. R. von Kurelec, *Biochem. Zeit.*, **180**. 65, 1927 ; E. Hagenbach, *Pogg. Ann.*, **146**. 395, 1872 ; H. Rose, *ib.*, **74**. 571, 1848 ; A. W. Postans, *Pharm. Journ.*, (3), **13**. 752, 1883 ; J. Korczyn, *Sitzber. Akad. Wien*, **133**. 225, 1925 ; A. des Cloizeaux, *Ann. Mines*, (5), **14**. 358, 1858 ; H. Becquerel, *Compt. Rend.*, **101**. 1252, 1885 ; *Ann. Chim. Phys.*, (6), **14**. 170, 1888 ; A. Ditte, *ib.*, (5), **18**. 337, 1879 ; *Compt. Rend.*, **89**. 576, 641, 1879 ; G. Rousseau and G. Tite, *ib.*, **115**. 175, 1892 ; J. Aloy, *ib.*, **122**. 1541, 1896 ; *Recherches sur l'uranium et ses composés*, Toulouse, 1901 ; *Ann. Chim. Phys.*, (7), **24**. 412, 1901 ; H. Lescoeur, *ib.*, (7), **4**. 213, 1895 ; *Recherches sur la dissociation des hydrates salins, et des composés analogues*, Lille, 1888 ; F. Janda, *Oesterr. Zeit. Berg. Hütt.*, **49**. 325, 340, 1901 ; G. N. Wyrouboff, *Bull. Soc. Min.*, **32**. 349, 1896 ; A. C. Schultz-Sellack, *Ueber die wasserhaltigen und wasserfreien Salze der Schwefelsäure*, Göttingen, 1868 ; *Zeit. Chem.*, (2), **6**. 646, 1870; A. von Unruh, *Einwirkung von trocknem Ammoniak auf wasserfreie Uranylsalze*, Rostock, 1909 ; E. Löwenstein, *Ueber Hydrate deren Dampfspannung sich kontinuierlich mit der Zusammensetzung ändert*, Göttingen, 1909 ; *Zeit. anorg. Chem.*, **63**. 69, 1909 ; E. Kordes, *ib.*, **168**. 177, 1927 ; H. Grossmann and B. Schück, *ib.*, **50**. 21, 1906 ; E. Späth, *Monatsh.*, **33**. 853, 1912 ; R. Salvadori, *Atti Accad. Lincei*, (5), **21**. ii, 455, 1912 ; A. Lancien, *Bull. Sci. Pharmacol.*, **18**. 213, 1912 ; E. Quercigh, *Riv. Min. Crist. Ital.*, **44**. 6, 1915 ; D. M. Bose and H. G. Bhar, *Zeit. Physik*, **48**. 716, 1928 ; L. W. Andrews, *Journ. Amer. Chem. Soc.*, **34**. 1686, 1912 ; G. L. Clark, *ib.*, **46**. 372, 1924 ; F. E. E. Germann, *ib.*, **44**. 1466, 1922 ; *Phys. Rev.*, (2), **19**. 623, 1922 ; H. L. Howes, *ib.*, (2), **9**. 192, 1915 ; E. L. Nichols and E. Merritt, *ib.*, (2), **3**. 457, 1914 ; (2), **9**. 113, 1917 ; B. Drenckmann, *Zeit. ges. Naturwiss.*, **17**. 134, 1861 ; H. Bürger, *Beiträge zur Kenntnis der Uranyldoppelsalze*, Bonn, 1904 ; P. Misciattelli, *Atti Accad. Lincei*, (6), **7**. 1019, 1928 ; *Gazz. Chim. Ital.*, **60**. 839, 882, 1930 ; E. V. Alexeevsky and A. I. Avgastinik, *Journ. Russ. Phys. Chem. Soc.*, **61**. 131, 1929 ; S. Bodforss, *Svenska Kemi Tids.*, **37**. 296, 1925 ; E. Rimbach, *Ber.*, **37**. 461, 1904 ; R. J. Meyer

and F. Wendel, *ib.*, **36**. 4055, 1903 ; V. N. Ipatéeff and B. Muromtzeff, *ib.*, **63**. B, 160, 1930 ;
W. Marckwald, *ib.*, **39**. 201, 1906 ; C. F. Bucholz, *Gehlen's Journ.*, **4**. 17, 134, 1805 ; *Beiträge zur
Erweiterung und Berichtigung der Chemie*, Erfurt, **1**. 62, 1799 ; E. M. Péligot, *Compt. Rend.*, **12**.
735, 1841 ; **22**. 487, 1846 ; **42**. 73, 1856 ; *Ann. Chim. Phys.*, (3), **5**. 5, 1842 ; (3), **20**. 329, 1847 ;
Journ. Pharm. Chim., (2), **27**. 522, 1841 ; *Liebig's Ann.*, **41**. 141, 1841 ; **43**. 258, 1842 ; *Journ.
prakt. Chem.*, (1), **24**. 442, 1841 ; (1), **38**. 112, 1846 ; L. R. Lecanu, *Journ. Pharm. Chim.*, (2), **11**.
279, 1825 ; J. A. Arfvedson, *Svenska Akad. Handl.*, 404, 1822 ; *Ann. Phil.*, **7**. 253, 1824 ; *Pogg.
Ann.*, 1. 245, 1824 ; *Schweigger's Journ.*, **44**. 8, 1825 ; J. J. Berzelius, *ib.*, **44**. 191, 1825 ; *Pogg.
Ann.*, 1. 359, 1824 ; *Svenska Akad. Handl.*, 152, 1823 ; *Ann. Phil.*, **9**. 266, 1825 ; L. Pauling and
R. G. Dickinson, *Journ. Amer. Chem. Soc.*, **46**. 1615, 1924 ; P. Chastaing, *Étude sur la part de
lumière dans les actions chimiques, et particulier dans les oxydations*, Paris, 1877 ; *Ann. Chim.
Phys.*, (5), **11**. 145, 1877 ; J. W. Thomas, *Journ. Chem. Soc.*, **33**. 371, 1878 ; *Chem. News*, **37**.
246, 1878 ; H. M. Vernon, *ib.*, **66**. 104, 114, 141, 152, 1892 ; T. J. Savery, *ib.*, **48**. 251, 1883 ;
T. Curtius and A. Darapsky, *Journ. prakt. Chem.*, (2), **61**. 408, 1900 ; H. Steinmetz in P. Groth,
Chemische Krystallographie, Leipzig, **2**. 152, 1908 ; H. Stadelmann, *Verh. Ges. Naturfor. Arzte
Würzburg*, **2**. 262, 1904 ; G. Tammann, *Mém. Acad. St. Petersburg*, (7), **35**. 1, 1887 ; H. Kühn,
Liebig's Ann., **41**. 337, 1842 ; D. I. Mendeléeff, *ib.*, **168**. 61, 1873 ; J. O. Perrine, *Phys. Rev.*,
(2), **22**. 48, 1923 ; H. Greinacher, *Ann. Physik*, (4), **24**. 79, 1907 ; A. Sachs, *Zeit. Kryst.*, **38**. 497,
1904 ; C. A. Pierlé, *Journ. Phys. Chem.*, **23**. 517, 1919 ; W. Biltz, *Zeit. anorg. Chem.*, **109**. 132,
1919 ; J. C. Ghosh and B. N. Mitter, *Journ. Indian Chem. Soc.*, **4**. 353, 1928 ; B. K. Mukerji and
N. R. Dhar, *ib.*, **5**. 411, 1928 ; G. G. Rao and N. R. Dhar, *Journ. Phys. Chem.*, **35**. 1418, 1424,
1931 ; J. C. Jacobsen, *Zeit. Physik*, **70**. 145, 1931 ; W. Thomson and F. Lewis, *Proc. Manchester
Lit. Phil. Soc.*, **4**. 266, 1891 ; *Chem. News*, **64**. 169, 1891 ; R. Rascanu, *Ann. Science Univ.
Jassy*, **16**. 32, 459, 1930.

§ 23. The Uranium Phosphates

A. Colani,[1] and G. Werther prepared **uranous orthophosphate,** $U_3(PO_4)_4$, by
treating a soln. of uranous tetrachloride with normal sodium phosphate. The
voluminous precipitate, when washed, dried, and heated to redness in hydrogen
chloride carried along by a current of carbon dioxide, forms a dark green powder
consisting of minute crystals with hexagonal surfaces. This salt behaves chemically
like other uranous phosphates, but is more readily attacked by acids, particularly
nitric acid. P. Chastaing said that if an excess of a soln. of uranous chloride is
treated with sodium metaphosphate, the green *trihydrate*, $U_3(PO_4)_4.3H_2O$, is formed.
According to A. Colani, **uranous oxyphosphate,** $U_2O(PO_4)_2$, is obtained when
uranyl orthophosphate or pyrophosphate is heated to dark redness in hydrogen ; if
the heating be continued too long, some phosphorus is lost as phosphine. The
oxyphosphate is also obtained by heating the pyrophosphate in the hottest part of a
porcelain oven. The former process yields a dark green, microcrystalline powder,
the latter, larger crystals. The salt is easily attacked by boiling nitric acid. With
alkali chlorides, in a dry atmosphere, it forms uranium dioxide and complex phosphates. P. Chastaing said that the green *trihydrate*, $U_2O(PO_4)_2.3H_2O$, is formed by
precipitating a soln. of uranous chloride with normal sodium pyrophosphate, and the
tetrahydrate, $U_2O(PO_4)_2.4H_2O$, by treating the soln. of uranous chloride with normal
sodium orthophosphate. J. Aloy and G. Auber obtained uranous phosphates
by the double decomposition of an alkali phosphate with a soln. of uranous sulphate,
or by reducing uranyl phosphate with sodium hyposulphite. C. F. Rammelsberg,
and J. Aloy said that an excess of sodium hypophosphate precipitates all the
uranium from a soln. of uranous chloride as **uranous hydrophosphate,**
$U(HPO_4)_2.2H_2O$. The product is very sparingly soluble in dil. hydrochloric acid,
but freely soluble in the conc. acid, and the phosphate is re-precipitated on adding
water. R. Arendt and W. Knop also obtained the *dihydrate* by treating a hydrochloric acid soln. of uranous chloride with phosphoric acid ; and P. Chastaing, by
adding an excess of sodium metaphosphate to a soln. of uranous chloride.
C. F. Rammelsberg found that potash-lye extracts the phosphoric acid, but not so
aq. ammonia. J. Aloy said that the precipitate from uranous oxalate is the
pentahydrate, $U(HPO_4)_2.5H_2O$, or $UO_2.P_2O_5.6H_2O$, and it can be obtained in
microscopic crystals stable in air, insoluble in sulphuric and hydrochloric acids of
medium concentration, but freely soluble in conc. hydrochloric acid, forming a blue
soln., and decomposed by alkali-lye, forming uranous hydroxide.

C. F. Rammelsberg obtained **uranous pyrophosphate,** $UP_2O_7.3H_2O$, by treating a soln. of uranous chloride with normal sodium pyrophosphate. The *trihydrate* loses all its water when heated in a current of carbon dioxide. A. Colani prepared it by reducing amorphous uranyl metaphosphate in hydrogen at a dull red-heat; the amorphous powder can be crystallized by heating it in a current of hydrogen chloride carried along by carbon dioxide. A. Colani also made the pyrophosphate by passing the vapour of phosphoryl monochloride in a current of carbon dioxide over uranous oxide at a red-heat—uranosic oxide can be used at a bright red-heat; it can also be obtained similarly from uranyl pyrophosphate or orthophosphate; a small amount of a volatile compound of uranium, phosphorus, and chlorine is formed. The pyrophosphate is also formed by heating one of the other uranous phosphates, with the exclusion of air, in a current of carbon dioxide, at the softening temp. of porcelain—with metaphosphate a part remains undecomposed. The pyrophosphate is also produced by heating a mixture of uranous metaphosphate with five times its weight of potassium chloride, at a dull red-heat, in a current of dry carbon dioxide, and afterwards washing the cold product to remove soluble salts.

P. Hautefeuille and J. Margottet prepared **uranous metaphosphate,** $U(PO_3)_4$, or $UO_2.2P_2O_5$, by melting uranium trioxide or uranyl metaphosphate with four times its weight of metaphosphoric acid—A. Colani used orthophosphoric acid; and K. R. Johnson dissolved uranyl sulphate in metaphosphoric acid at 316°. The emerald-green plates, said P. Hautefeuille and J. Margottet, are isomorphous with the metaphosphates of aluminium, chromium, and iron, and, according to A. Colani, with thorium metaphosphate, with which they form mixed crystals. The sp. gr. is 3·9, but K. R. Johnson gave 3·818 for the sp. gr. and 149 for the mol. vol. The salt does not melt in the blowpipe flame. The crystals are stable in air. A. Colani found that at a high temp., in hydrogen, uranium dioxide, phosphine, and phosphorus are formed. P. Hautefeuille and J. Margottet found that the salt is insoluble in water and acids, and A. Colani added that the metaphosphate is not dissolved by conc. and boiling hydrochloric, sulphuric, or nitric acid; if heated for 24 hrs. with 50 per cent. phosphoric acid in an evacuated and sealed glass tube, at 175° to 200°, a green soln. of a uranous salt is formed, and the soln. deposits fine green needles. With molten alkali hydroxides, oxygen is taken up from the atmosphere to form alkali phosphate and uranate; fused alkali carbonates in an atm. of carbon dioxide and at a red-heat form alkali phosphate and uranium dioxide—if air has access, the dioxide forms a uranate; and with fused alkali or alkaline earth chlorides, green crystalline products are formed. Boiling, conc. alkali-lye attacks the metaphosphate superficially, forming alkali phosphate and a protective black film of uranium dioxide.

According to A. Colani, when equal weights of sodium metaphosphate or, better, sodium pyrophosphate, and uranium dioxide are heated with a large excess of sodium chloride, or when equimolar parts of normal sodium and uranous pyrophosphates are heated with a large excess of sodium chloride, emerald-green crystals of **sodium uranous diphosphate,** $Na_2U(PO_4)_2$, are formed. This salt is also formed, with not such good results, by the general mode of preparation, namely, by heating an intimate mixture of the alkali phosphate with an excess of uranous oxide in a platinum Rose's crucible through which carbon dioxide is passed; the fused mixture is cooled very slowly, so as to cause the double phosphate to crystallize well and thus become separated from the excess of oxide used. The rhombic, bipyramidal crystals have the axial ratios $a : b : c = 0.6766 : 1 : 0.4006$. The salt is freely soluble in nitric acid, and the green liquid, when heated, or on standing at ordinary temp. for some time, becomes yellow and gives off nitrous fumes. It forms a yellow soln. with conc. hydrochloric acid which when treated with water gives a gelatinous precipitate of uranous phosphate. By heating a mixture of sodium uranous hexachloride with sodium pyrophosphate, or by heating sodium pyrophosphate with an excess of uranium tetrachloride, or by fusing uranium dioxide with sodium metaphosphate in the presence of sodium chloride, dark green crystals of **sodium uranous triphosphate,**

$NaU_2(PO_4)_3$, are formed. The monoclinic prisms have the axial ratios $a:b:c$ $=2\cdot5605:1:1\cdot1918$, and $\beta=101°$ 3′. Again, if normal sodium pyrophosphate is fused with uranium dioxide, dark green rhombic crystals of **sodium uranous octophosphate,** $Na_{12}U_3(PO_4)_8$, are formed; they have the axial ratios $a:b:c$ $=0\cdot5758:1:0\cdot2157$. The general method of preparation just indicated, using potassium metaphosphate, furnishes green crystals of **potassium uranous diphosphate,** $K_2U(PO_4)_2$. The rhombic crystals have the axial ratios $a:b:c$ $=0\cdot3711:1:0\cdot3902$. The chemical behaviour is the same as that of the corresponding sodium salt. If a mixture of potassium uranous hexachloride with the calculated quantity of normal potassium pyrophosphate be heated with an excess of potassium chloride, dark green, probably triclinic, plates of **potassium uranous triphosphate,** $KU_2(PO_4)_3$, are formed. Uranium dioxide heated with a mixture of normal potassium pyrophosphate and twice the weight of potassium chloride furnishes dark green plates of **potassium uranous octophosphate,** $K_{12}U_3(PO_4)_8$. They are soluble in acids. By melting uranous metaphosphate with five times its weight of calcium chloride, green, pleochroic crystals of **calcium uranous diphosphate,** $CaU(PO_4)_2$, are formed. The monoclinic crystals have the axial ratio $a:b:c$ $=1\cdot508:1:1\cdot124$, and $\beta=93°$ 29′. The green, pleochroic crystals of **strontium uranous diphosphate,** $SrU(PO_4)_2$, prepared in a similar manner, are rhombic and have the axial ratios $a:b:c=1\cdot474:1:1\cdot165$. The method employed for the calcium salt applies also to **barium uranous diphosphate,** $BaU(PO_4)_2$, which can also be prepared by fusing a mixture of one part of sodium uranous hexachloride, 3 parts of barium pyrophosphate, and 10 parts of anhydrous barium chloride. The salt appeared in thin green plates, too small for crystallographic measurement.

According to G. Werther,[2] when a soln. of 3 mols of uranyl nitrate, containing some free nitric acid, is mixed with a soln. of 2 mols of normal sodium phosphate, a yellow, pulverulent precipitate is produced from which acetic acid extracts only a little sodium uranyl acetate. The product is a hydrated mixture of normal **uranyl orthophosphate,** $(UO_2)_3(PO_4)_2.nH_2O$, with uranyl hydrophosphate, $UO_2(HPO_4).nH_2O$. If more sodium phosphate be added, the precipitate also contains sodium uranyl phosphate. The product forms a yellowish-green mass when ignited. F. A. Genth described a mineral from Mitchell Co., North Carolina, and he called it **phosphouranylite.** It occurs as a deep lemon-yellow, pulverulent incrustation on other uranium minerals; and the powder consists of microscopic rectangular plates. The analysis agrees with hydrated **uranyl orthophosphate,** $(UO_2)_3(PO_4)_2.6H_2O$, after deducting the 4·4 per cent. of lead oxide associated with the mineral.

The *trihydrate* of **uranyl hydrophosphate,** $UO_2(HPO_4).3H_2O$, was prepared by G. Werther, and H. Lienau by the addition of sodium dihydrophosphate to an acidic soln. of uranyl nitrate. It forms a sulphur-yellow, crystalline powder; and it can also be regarded as a pyro-salt, $(UO_2)_2P_2O_7.7H_2O$. Tetrahydrated uranyl pyrophosphate, $(UO_2)_2P_2O_7.4H_2O$—*vide infra*—can be represented as a *hemitrihydrate* of uranyl hydrophosphate, namely, $2(UO_2)(HPO_4).3H_2O$. According to L. Bourgeois, if 5 grms. of ammonium dihydrophosphate and 18 grms. of uranyl nitrate be mixed in aq. soln., a precipitate is formed; this is washed by decantation, mixed with 500 grms. of water and enough hydrochloric acid to dissolve nearly all the precipitate, boiled, and the filtered liquid allowed to stand for some days. Yellow, tetragonal crystals of the *tetrahydrate,* $(UO_2)HPO_4.4H_2O$, are formed, having the axial ratio $a:c=1:1\cdot7284$. H. Debray, and L. Bourgeois found that the salt becomes crystalline when heated in hydrogen chloride. This tetrahydrate also can be regarded as a pyro-salt, $(UO_2)_2P_2O_7.9H_2O$. A. Laugier, and G. Werther added phosphoric acid to a soln. of uranyl acetate, and obtained a crystalline precipitate of the *hemienneahydrate,* $(UO_2)(HPO_4).4\frac{1}{2}H_2O$; G. Werther also obtained it by treating a soln. of uranyl nitrate with sodium dihydrophosphate, or with insufficient normal sodium phosphate for the complete precipitation of the uranium; H. St. C. Deville added a soln. of acid calcium phosphate to an excess of uranyl nitrate soln.

at 50° to 60°; and W. Heintz found that a soln. of uranyl nitratophosphate in hot water gradually deposits the hemienneahydrate of uranyl hydrophosphate. The greenish-yellow salt forms microscopic, right-angled plates; it is insoluble in water, and the soln. in nitric acid furnishes a nitratophosphate. G. Werther said that the air-dried salt loses one-fifth of its total water at 60°; and W. Heintz, that it loses three-fifths of its total combined water at 110°. This hydrate can be regarded as a pyro-salt, $(UO_2)_2P_2O_7.10H_2O$. H. Lienau reported a *heptahydrate*, $(UO_2)(HPO_4).7H_2O$, by adding lithium dihydrophosphate to an acidic soln. of uranyl nitrate. It can be regarded as a pyro-salt, $(UO_2)P_2O_7.15H_2O$. G. Werther boiled uranium trioxide with a little phosphoric acid, and obtained the hemitrihydrate, indicated above, as a yellow precipitate; while the mother-liquor, evaporated over sulphuric acid, slowly deposited lemon-yellow crystals of **uranyl dihydrophosphate**, $(UO_2)(H_2PO_4)_2.3H_2O$, a salt which can also be regarded as a pentahydrated metaphosphate, $UO_2(PO_3)_2.5H_2O$. When the salt is heated to 100°, it loses two-fifths of its water; at 110° to 120°, it loses 11·1 per cent.; and at 160°, 13·3 per cent., *i.e.* nearly four-fifths. The remaining water is given off at a red-heat. The salt is decomposed by water, forming an insoluble basic salt and a soluble acidic salt. It is soluble in phosphoric acid, forming a soln. which gives an ammonium salt when treated with ammonia. All the uranyl orthophosphates were found by G. Werther to decompose when melted with carbonized sodium potassium tartrate; and by H. Rose, with sodium carbonate and potassium cyanide, forming alkali phosphate and uranium dioxide.

According to R. Arendt and W. Knop, and A. Kitchin, **uranyl pyrophosphate**, $(UO_2)_2P_2O_7$, is formed by heating the hydrophosphate to redness. A. Girard obtained it by pouring an excess of a soln. of normal sodium pyrophosphate into an aq. soln. of uranyl nitrate—the precipitate gradually becomes crystalline—and heating the product to 100°. P. Chastaing also obtained it from the basic metaphosphate by leaving it in contact with the mother-liquor for some time. The yellow precipitate loses 11 per cent. of water, *i.e.* 5 mols. at 100°. According to A. Girard, the pyrophosphate is insoluble in water, alcohol, and ether, but soluble in nitric acid, and the soln. when treated with alkali-lye gives a precipitate of the original salt. It dissolves in a soln. of sodium pyrophosphate, but not in a soln. of sodium hydrophosphate. P. Chastaing regarded the precipitate produced with a soln. of normal sodium pyrophosphate and a uranyl salt as a *tetrahydrate*, $(UO_2)_2P_2O_7.4H_2O$; and G. Werther obtained this hydrate as a pale yellow, amorphous precipitate by treating uranium trioxide with dil. phosphoric acid, and washing the product with water. It loses about 3 mols. of water at 120°, and the remainder at a red-heat. It is dark yellow when hot, and pale yellow when cold. This salt can be regarded as hemitrihydrated uranyl hydrophosphate, $2(UO_2)(HPO_4).3H_2O$. Similarly, as indicated above, the *heptahydrate* of uranyl pyrophosphate is also $(UO_2)(HPO_4).3H_2O$; the *enneahydrate* is also $(UO_2)(HPO_4).4H_2O$; the *decahydrate* is also $(UO_2)(HPO_4).4\frac{1}{2}H_2O$; and the *pentadecahydrate* is also $(UO_2)(HPO_4).7H_2O$.

C. F. Rammelsberg boiled uranyl dihydrophosphate with nitric acid, and heated the product to redness. There remained **uranyl metaphosphate**, $UO_2(PO_3)_2$. P. Chastaing digested uranium trioxide and metaphosphoric acid in equimolar proportions, and obtained a yellow product which he regarded as a kind of basic salt, *uranyl oxymetaphosphate*, $4UO_3.3P_2O_5$; and the yellow precipitate produced by the action of metaphosphoric acid on uranyl acetate he regarded as a decahydrate—possibly enneahydrate. It loses very little water at 100°, but at 110° it forms a heptahydrate. If allowed to stand in contact with its mother-liquor, it passes into the pyrophosphate, $(UO_2)_2P_2O_7.4H_2O$. According to J. B. Richter, if uranyl phosphate or carbonate be dissolved in phosphoric acid, and the soln. evaporated, an acidic salt is formed as an amorphous, sticky mass, and H. Rose obtained a similar product from a soln. of uranium trioxide in phosphoric acid. P. Chastaing said that the mother-liquor remaining after the separation of $4UO_3.3P_2O_5$ from a soln. of uranium trioxide in phosphoric acid contains *uranyl tetraphosphate*, $UO_3.2P_2O_5$.

R. Arendt and W. Knop added uranyl acetate to a hot soln. of a phosphate and an excess of an ammonium salt, acidified with acetic acid, and obtained **ammonium uranyl phosphate.** H. Lienau prepared this salt, of the composition $(NH_4)(UO_2)PO_4.3H_2O$, by gradually adding a cold aq. soln. of 2 mols of ammonium dihydrophosphate and 2 mols of nitric acid to a soln. of 2 mols of uranyl nitrate. The crystalline precipitate is insoluble in water and acetic acid, but soluble in all the mineral acids, in oxalic acid, and in a soln. of alkali carbonate. A. Kitchin's method for the determination of uranyl salts is based on precipitation of the ammonium salt in the presence of acetic acid and ammonium acetate. The volumetric titration of phosphates with uranium salt soln. and potassium ferrocyanide as indicator was employed by C. Pincus—also by F. Sutton, H. Neubauer, R. Arendt and W. Knop, K. Broockmann, A. E. Haswell, C. Mohr, V. Edwards, G. Guérin, O. Abesser, W. Jani and M. Märcker, E. Kessel, C. Leconte, H. Rheineck, A. Pavec, W. Strecker and P. Schiffer, and A. Vozarik. In O. S. Pulman's method the uranium phosphate is reduced by zinc and acid to the uranous form, and titrated back to the uranyl salt by standard potassium permanganate. L. Barthe prepared **methylamine uranyl phosphate,** $(CH_3)NH_3(UO_2)PO_4$, as a pale yellow colloid, by saturating an aq. soln. of phosphoric acid with the amine, and adding uranyl acetate drop by drop. The precipitate, when dried in vacuo, becomes horny. It is stable, and is not decomposed at 100°. Similarly with **ethylamine uranyl phosphate,** $(C_2H_5)NH_3(UO_2)PO_4$, and with **trimethylamine uranyl phosphate,** $(CH_3)_3NH(UO_2)PO_4$. H. Lienau found that in attempting to prepare **lithium uranyl phosphate** by this process, heptahydrated uranyl hydrophosphate is formed, and the trihydrate was produced in attempting to prepare the **sodium uranyl phosphate.** G. Werther mixed soln. of uranyl nitrate and an excess of normal sodium phosphate, and obtained a dark yellow precipitate which dissolves in a large excess of the sodium phosphate soln., but it does not dissolve in water ; acetic acid extracts sodium diuranate. G. Werther represented the composition of the precipitate by $Na_2(UO_2)_5(PO_4)_4.6H_2O$, but seems to have regarded it as a mixture. L. Ouvrard found that fused normal sodium pyrophosphate or orthophosphate dissolves much uranium trioxide and obtained dendritic, yellow, monoclinic crystals of $Na_4(UO_2)(PO_4)_2$. G. G. Stokes examined the fluorescent properties of mixtures of uranyl and sodium phosphates. L. Ouvrard fused a mixture of uranium trioxide and normal potassium pyrophosphate, and obtained a sulphur-yellow powder of **potassium uranyl phosphate,** $K(UO_2)PO_4$, consisting of microscopic rhombic crystals. H. Grandeau prepared a similar salt by heating uranyl phosphate with an excess of potassium sulphate. H. Lienau obtained the *trihydrate*, $K(UO_2)PO_4.3H_2O$, by the method he employed for the ammonium salt. L. Ouvrard reported yellow prisms of $K_4(UO_2)(PO_4)_2$, to be formed by melting together uranium trioxide and normal potassium phosphate.

A. Rosenheim obtained **lithium uranyl pyrophosphate,** $Li_2[UO_2P_2O_7]$, as a crystalline precipitate by treating uranyl sulphate or nitrate with a conc. soln. of the alkali phosphate, and boiling the mixture. B. Menes prepared **lithium uranium pyrophosphate,** $Li_2H_2[U_2(P_2O_7)_3].30H_2O$, by treating a soln. of uranium sulphate with one of lithium pyrophosphate. J. Persoz treated a soln. of a uranyl salt with normal sodium pyrophosphate and obtained a precipitate soluble in excess ; when the soln. is evaporated, it furnishes a gummy mass. G. Buchner found that the soln. gives no precipitate when treated with ammonium sulphide ; and that uranyl sulphide readily dissolves in a soln. of sodium pyrophosphate, and the soln. remains clear when boiled for a long time. All this points to the formation of a complex salt. L. Ouvrard prepared sulphur-yellow, monoclinic prisms of **sodium uranyl pyrophosphate,** $Na_2(UO_2)P_2O_7$, by fusing a mixture of uranium trioxide and sodium metaphosphate. According to P. Pascal, when a soln. of sodium pyrophosphate, saturated with uranyl pyrophosphate is treated with alcohol, a yellow powder of the complex salt, $Na_6(UO_2)[(UO_2)_2(P_2O_7)_3].nH_2O$, is precipitated. It quickly passes into $Na_2(UO_2)_2P_2O_7.H_2O$, which is insoluble in water. The f.p. of uranyl pyrophosphate in sodium pyrophosphate rises to a maximum corresponding with $3Na_4P_2O_7.(UO_2)_2P_2O_7$, and then descends to a minimum at $2Na_4P_2O_7.(UO_2)_2P_2O_7$, up to which stage the characteristic reactions of uranyl salts are not obtainable. If this soln. is evaporated and the gummy residue treated with alcohol, a very soluble, hygroscopic powder having the constitution $Na_8[(UO_2)_2(P_2O_7)_3].6H_2O$ is obtained. A. Rosenheim obtained the sodium salt by the method he used for the lithium salt. B. Menes also prepared **sodium uranium pyrophosphate,** $Na_4[U_2(P_2O_7)_3].14H_2O$, by the action of a soln. of uranium sulphate on one of sodium pyrophosphate. No precipitates are obtained with ammonium and potassium salts. L. Ouvrard prepared **potassium uranyl pyrophosphate,** $K_2(UO_2)P_2O_7$, by melting uranium trioxide with potassium metaphosphate. The yellow, rhombic, dichroic, doubly refracting crystals have a sp. gr. 4·2 at 20°. A. Rosenheim and T. Triantaphyllides could not prepare complex uranic pyrophosphates analogous to those of chromic, molybdic, and manganic pyrophosphates.

The history of the mineral **torbernite**—*torberite, cupro-uranite, chalcolite, uranium-mica,* or *uranite*—has been previously discussed. The mineral is found at Joachimsthal and Zinnwald in Bohemia; at Johanngeorgenstadt, Eibenstock, and Schneeberg, in Saxony; at Reichenbach, Baden; at Tincroft, Wheal Buller, and other parts of Cornwall; Katanga, Belgian Congo; etc. Analyses by G. Werther, F. Pisani, A. H. Church, F. L. Hess, A. Pereira-Forjaz, V. Dürrfeld, W. Steinkuhler, C. Winkler, J. J. Berzelius, A. Frenzel, W. Gregor, M. H. Klaproth, R. Phillips, etc. The results correspond with **copper uranyl phosphate,** $Cu(UO_2)_2(PO_4)_2.8H_2O$. Y. Bucholz found that the Cornish mineral contains 12 not $8H_2O$. C. Winkler observed that arsenic acid may in part replace the phosphoric acid. F. Henrich, and J. Hoffmann discussed the radium content of the mineral. H. Debray obtained the octohydrate by adding uranyl nitrate to a soln. of copper carbonate in phosphoric acid, and allowing the liquid to stand for some time, best at 50° to 60°. Pale green plates are gradually deposited. Torbernite occurs in foliated or micaceous aggregates, and in square, thick or thin plates, and more rarely in pyramids. The colour is green in various shades which have been referred to as emerald-, leek-, apple-, siskin-, and grass-green. A. Schrauf gave for the axial ratio of the tetragonal crystals $a : c$ $=1 : 2·9361$; the (001)-cleavage is micaceous and perfect; the laminæ are brittle. A. F. Hallimond gave 1 : 2974. The optical character is negative. T. L. Walker found that the corrosion figures have monoclinic symmetry; but F. Rinne obtained corrosion figures with cold acid, indicating normal tetragonal symmetry. The crystals were also described by A. Lévy, P. A. Dufrénoy, E. Mallard, J. F. L. Hausmann, R. P. Greg and W. G. Lettsom, F. Hessenberg, W. Phillips, N. von Kokscharoff, C. F. Naumann, A. Schrauf, T. L. Walker, F. Rinne, and A. F. Hallimond. A. Breithaupt said that the sp. gr. ranges from 3·329 to 3·372. In general, the sp. gr. of torbernite ranges from 3·33 to 3·60; and the hardness, from 2·0 to 2·5. N. L. Bowen found torbernite occurring in Spain and in Cornwall. W. Steinkuhler gave for Cornish torbernite the sp. gr. 3·68 at 17°, and the hardness 2; while for a specimen from Katanga he gave the sp. gr. 3·84 to 3·951 at 17°. The mean index of refraction of the Cornish specimen was 1·594 to 1·600, and for the Katanga specimen, 1·600 to 1·618. B. Stoces found for some Bohemian torbernites μ ranging from 1·610 to 1·628. According to A. F. Hallimond, the torbernite from Gunnislake, Cornwall, is metatorbernite, differing from torbernite in having the axial ratio $a : c=1 : 2·97$, sp. gr. 3·22, and refractive indices $\omega=1·592$, and $\epsilon=1·582$. The sp. gr. of metatorbernite is 3·683 to 3·700; the refractive indices $\omega=1·623$ and $\epsilon=1·625$; and the axial ratio $a : c=1 : 2·28$. A. H. Church said that the octohydrated mineral loses no water in dry air or in vacuo; but at 100° it loses 6 mols., and the remainder at a red-heat; Y. Bucholz said that the dodecahydrate loses 4 mols. of water in a desiccator; at 95°, it loses another mol.; at 148° to 156°, it loses another 4 mols.; at 220°, another 2 mols. are given off; and the **last mol.** is expelled at a red-heat. According to F. Rinne, the tetragonal, negative, doubly refracting mineral loses some water at 60° to 65°, passing into a tetragonal *meta-torbernite* with a positive and feeble double refraction; and by the loss of more water at 100°, it passes into a series of rhombic meta-forms which resemble very closely autunite or lime-uranite. A. G. Bergman measured the vap. press. of the crystalline hydrate, and obtained the curves shown in Fig. 24, for $Ca(UO_2)(PO_4)_2.8H_2O$, $Cu(UO_2)_2(PO_4)_2.8H_2O$, and $Co(UO_2)_2(PO_4)_2.8H_2O$. E. Jannettaz found the ratio of the heat conductivities, a/γ, to be 1·5. F. Rinne found that the absorption spectrum between 510 and 440$\mu\mu$ shows five bands which are also characteristic of autunite. T. W. Case observed no evidence of photo-electric conductivity. H. Debray said that the mineral is not altered by heating it with water up to 200°; and when melted with sodium carbonate it forms copper uranite. H. von Foullon studied the products formed during the weathering of pitchblende. The *octohydrate*, the first product of the dehydration of the dodeca-hydrate, torbernite, was called by F. Rinne, and A. F. Hallimond **metatorbernite-I**, and the second product metatorbernite-II. When torbernite loses water, either in a desiccator or when heated, it changes to metatorbernite, acquiring another crystalline form and other optical properties. When torbernite is kept over sulphuric acid of different concentrations and at various temp., the points fall on one or other side of the transition

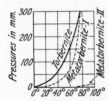

FIG. 23.—Transition Curve of Torbernite.

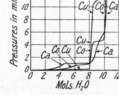

FIG. 24.—Vapour Pressures of Calcium and Cobalt Uranyl Phosphates.

curve of torbernite. When torbernite of sp. gr. 3·219 is heated under water for several hours at 100°, the sp. gr. changes to 3·67, and the loss in weight corresponds with the transition from the dodecahydrate to the octohydrate, Fig. 23. A morphotropic relation exists between the crystals of the two substances, and the extra 4 mols. of water are held in layers that alternate with basal layers having the constitution of metatorbernite. The mol. vol. of the extra water corresponds with a sp. gr. of 1·2. A. F. Hallimond thus contrasted the properties of torbernite and of metatorbernite :

		$a : c$	Sp. gr.	ω	ϵ
Torbernite		1:2·97	3·22	1·592	1·582
Metatorbernite	artificial .	—	3·67	—	—
	natural . .	1:2·28	3·68	1·623	1·625

The mineral **autunite** is a variety of uranium-mica, or chalcolite, and J. J. Berzelius showed that it is *le sel à base de chaux, où l'oxide d'urane joue le rôle d'acide.* Accordingly, it has been called *lime-uranite*, and by A. Breithaupt, *calcouranite.* W. H. Miller called it autunite from its occurrence at St. Symporien, near Autun. It also occurs near Limoges, and Aoubert, Puy-de-Dôme ; at Siebengebirge, Johanngeorgenstadt, Eibenstock, Steinbruch, Fuchsbau, and Falkenstein ; Lurisia, Italy ; Beira Alta, Portugal ; near Lake Omega, Russia ; near South Basset, Wheal Edwards, and St. Day, Cornwall ; Maharitza, Madagascar ; Tongking, China ; at Middletown, and Branchville, Connecticut ; Chesterfield, Massachusetts ; Acworth, New Haven ; Schnylkill, near Philadelphia ; in Mitchell Co. and Alexander Co., North Carolina ; Black Hills, South Dakota ; at Silver Reef, Utah ; etc. Analyses by C. Winkler, G. Lincio, F. Henrich, A. H. Church, A. Pereira-Forjaz, A. F. Hallimond, A. Laugier, J. J. Berzelius, F. Pisani, E. M. Péligot, E. Jannetaz, E. Boutée, and A. Lacroix are in agreement with **calcium uranyl phosphate,** $Ca(UO_2)_2(PO_4)_2.8H_2O$. Some varieties have 10 or 12 mols. of water. The colour of the mineral is lemon-yellow or sulphur-yellow. The mineral occurs in foliated aggregates with a micaceous structure, and in thin tabular crystals nearly tetragonal in form, and with angles deviating but slightly from those of torbernite. A. des Cloizeaux gave for the axial ratios of the rhombic crystals $a:b:c$ $=0.9875:1:2.8517$. The (001)-cleavage is complete and basal; the laminæ are brittle. A. Brezina considered autunite from Johanngeorgenstadt to be monoclinic, with the axial ratios $a:b:c=0.3463:1:0.3525$, and $\beta=90°\ 30'$. The crystals were examined by W. Phillips, and G. Lincio. According to A. des Cloizeaux, the optical character is negative. The optic axial angle $2E$ is 60° 57' at 17°; 57° 32' at 47°; 56° 36' at 71.5°; 55° 8' at 81°; and 54° 10' at 91°. F. Rinne also found that $2E$ falls with a rise of temp., and this much more rapidly than is indicated by the data of A. des Cloizeaux; indeed, F. Rinne found that $2E$ is zero at 75°. Even at 50° the polarization colours begin to shade off, and at 75° the crystal is isotropic; above 75° the mineral begins to lose water and passes into a new, probably rhombic, form—*meta-autunite*—which is stable up to 300°. The pleochroism is feeble; the optical character is negative. The sp. gr. is 3.05 to 3.19, and the hardness is 2.0 to 2.5. A. G. Bergman measured the vap. press. of the crystalline hydrate, and the results are illustrated by Fig. 24. A. des Cloizeaux found that the mean index of refraction is $\beta=1.572$. A. Michel-Lévy and A. Lacroix gave for the indices of refraction $\alpha=1.577$, $\beta=1.575$, and $\gamma=1.553$. F. Rinne observed that the absorption spectrum between 510 and $440\mu\mu$ shows five distinct bands. F. Kohlbeck and P. Uhlich, E. Gleditsch, W. Marckwald and A. S. Russell, A. Muguet and J. Seroin, G. Lincio, etc., examined the radioactive properties of the mineral.

W. T. Schaller was able to replace sodium, potassium, barium, manganese, and lead for calcium in artificial autunite. J. G. Fairchild obtained artificial autunite by allowing soln. of uranium and calcium nitrates to mix slowly with phosphoric acid by diffusion through a large vol. of water. The first precipitate is amorphous, but large plates of artificial autunite were obtained when the system is left undisturbed for a month. If the soln. be treated with sodium chloride, calcium uranyl phosphate is no longer obtained, but a sodium autunite is precipitated. The same result is obtained by mixing soln. of calcium chloride and phosphoric acid in the proportions required for dicalcium phosphate, and adding this to a nearly boiling soln. of sodium chloride (150 grms. per 500 c.c.). This was mixed with 3.7 grms. of uranyl nitrate dissolved in a little water, so that the proportions were those needed to form $CaO.2UO_3.P_2O_5.8H_2O$. A small excess of the uranium salt does no harm. As the hot soln. slowly cools to the temp. of the room, yellow, 8-sided plates separate out. The degree of acidity of the soln. controls the size of the crystals. The analysis—P_2O_5, 16.13; UO_3, 64.90; CaO, 1.10; Na_2O, 5.62; and H_2O, 13.22— corresponds with sodium autunite; and the crystals have the indices of refraction $\omega=1.605$ and ϵ is nearly the same. If this product be digested in a soln. of calcium chloride, of sp. gr. 1.25, 4- and 8-sided plates of **calcium autunite,** $CaO.2UO_3.P_2O_5.nH_2O$, are formed. The indices of refraction are $\omega=1.600$ and $\epsilon=1.590$. When calcium autunite is digested in a half sat. soln. of sodium chloride on the steam bath for 2 days, **sodium autunite** is formed in uniaxial plates with $\omega=1.583$ and $\epsilon=1.566$. If the sodium autunite is digested with a conc. soln. of potassium chloride, **potassium autunite** is formed in 8-sided plates with $\omega=1.575$ and $\epsilon=1.553$; with a soln. of barium chloride, **barium autunite** is formed, analogous with uranocircite, in uniaxial plates, with polysynthetic twinning, and having $\omega=1.613$ and $\epsilon=1.604$. A soln. of manganese chloride furnished **manganese autunite** in lamellæ with diagonal twinning, and having $\omega=1.60$; copper chloride similarly furnishes **copper autunite,** with $\omega=1.608$; nickel chloride gives greenish-yellow **nickel autunite ;** cobalt chloride gives pinkish-brown **cobalt autunite ;** magnesium chloride gives **magnesium autunite** in plates with $\omega=1.48$; lead chloride gives a non-homogeneous product, but **lead autunite** is formed when the mixed nitrates of uranyl, calcium, and lead are allowed to react slowly with a $0.01M$-soln. of phosphoric acid through a vol. of 4 litres of water. The birefringent plates have $\omega=1.625$.

A. F. Hallimond called a related yellow mineral from Basset, Cornwall, **bassetite**. It was analyzed by A. H. Church. The monoclinic mineral has the axial ratios $a : b : c = 0.3473 : 1 : 0.3456$, and $\beta = 89° \ 17'$; the (001)- and (100)-cleavages are good; the sp. gr. is 3·10; the optical character is negative; the optic axial angle $2E = 110°$; the indices of refraction are $\beta = 1.574$, and $\gamma = 1.580$; and the pleochroism, β, is deep yellow, and γ, pale yellow. Another related mineral from Gedruth, Cornwall, was called **uranospathite**; it is pseudotetragonal and rhombic, with $a : b : c = 1 : 1 : -$. It occurs in yellow or pale green tabular crystals, with $2V = 69°$; the cleavages (001) and (100) are good; the sp. gr. is 2·50; the indices of refraction, $\beta = 1.510$, and $\gamma = 1.521$; and the pleochroism, α, is pale yellow, and $\beta = \gamma$ is deep yellow.

C. Blinkoff prepared **calcium uranyl hydrophosphate**, $Ca(UO_2)(HPO_4)_2.nH_2O$, by heating uranyl nitrate with an excess of conc., aq. soln. of calcium hydrophosphate; at 50° to 60°, crystals of the *tetrahydrate* are formed; at 100°, the *trihydrate*; and at 250°, in a sealed tube, the *dihydrate*. According to C. Blinkoff, calcium uranyl phosphate is not produced by H. Lienau's method employed for the ammonium salt; nor is it obtained by mixing soln. of uranyl acetate and calcium acetate, or from an acetic acid soln. of calcium uranate and phosphoric acid. If, however, a nitric acid soln. of calcium phosphate mixed with an aq. soln. of uranyl nitrate, in the proportions $CaO : UO_3 = 1 : 2$, be heated in a sealed tube at 200° for a couple of days, yellow tetragonal plates of a basic salt, **calcium uranyl dioxytetraphosphate**, $3CaO.5UO_3.2P_2O_5.16H_2O$, or $Ca_3(UO_2)_5O_2(PO_4)_4.16H_2O$, are formed. C. Blinkoff added the calculated quantity $(UO_2 : PO_4 = 1 : 1)$ of phosphoric acid to a soln. of strontium uranate in acetic acid containing a few drops of nitric acid, and obtained a basic salt, **strontium uranyl oxytetraphosphate**, $2SrO.5UO_3.2P_2O_5.24H_2O$, or $Sr_2(UO_2)_5O(PO_4)_4.24H_2O$. If no nitric acid be used, and the soln. be much diluted before the addition of phosphoric acid, **strontium uranyl dihydrotetraphosphate**, $SrO.4UO_3.2P_2O_5.21H_2O$, or $Sr(UO_2)_4H_2(PO_4)_4.20H_2O$, is formed. A. Weisbach obtained yellowish-green crystals of a mineral resembling autunite from Falkenstein in Saxon Voigtland. He called it **uranocircite**. The analysis corresponds with **barium uranyl phosphate**, $Ba(UO_2)_2(PO_4)_2.8H_2O$, so that it is a *baryta-uranite*, or a *baryta-autunite*. The rhombic crystals have the (001)-cleavage perfect, and the (100)- and (010)-cleavages are distinct. The optic axial angle $2E = 15°$ to 20°. The sp. gr. is 3·53. According to A. H. Church, the mineral loses $6H_2O$ in vacuo over sulphuric acid, and the remaining $2H_2O$ is lost at a red-heat. P. Gaubert found that at 150° the mineral passes into a *meta-uranocircite*, analogous to meta-autunite. While uranocircite represents the octohydrate, C. Blinkoff prepared the *decahydrate*, $Ba(UO_2)_2(PO_4)_2.10H_2O$, in yellow plates, by adding phosphoric acid to a very dil. soln. of barium uranate in acetic acid; and the *tridecahydrate*, $Ba(UO_2)_2(PO_4)_2.13H_2O$, by adding the calculated quantity of phosphoric acid to a soln. of barium uranate in acetic acid to which a few drops of nitric acid had been added.

As previously indicated, the mineral phosphouranylite contains 4·4 per cent. of lead oxide. A. Schoep reported a radioactive mineral from Kasola, Katanga, Belgian Congo, as a canary-yellow powder, which under the microscope is seen to consist of rectangular scales—probably tetragonal. The mineral was named **dewindtite**—after J. Dewindt. The analysis, after deducting impurities, corresponds with **lead diuranyl phosphate**, $4PbO.8UO_3.3P_2O_5.12H_2O$, or possibly $Pb(UO_2)_2(PO_4)_2.3H_2O$. Its sp. gr. is 4·08, and the index of refraction exceeds 1·74. V. Billiet gave for the indices of refraction $\alpha = 1.762$ and $\beta = 1.763$. A. Schoep also found in the same locality a golden-yellow radioactive mineral which he named **stasite**—after J. S. Stas. It has the same composition as dewindtite, but consists of minute prisms with square terminations, and an index of refraction over 1·74. The cleavage is perfect in one direction, and the sp. gr. is 5·03. The evidence for the dimorphism of these minerals is doubtful. Another radioactive mineral from the same locality was called **parsonite**—after A. L. Parsons. Its analysis, after deducting presumed impurities, corresponds with **lead uranyl phosphate,** $Pb_2(UO_2)(PO_4)_2.H_2O$. The colour is pale brown ; the structure is earthy—minutely crystalline to compact ; the tabular crystals are monoclinic or triclinic ; the sp. gr. is 6·23. V. Billiet gave 1·85 for the α index of refraction of the monoclinic crystals. A. Schoep obtained a similar radioactive mineral from Chinkolobwe, Belgian Congo. It was named **dumontite**—after A. Dumont. It forms transparent, ochre-yellow, biaxial, elongated prisms—probably rhombic—with the index of refraction over 1·78. It is strongly pleochroic—α, pale yellow; β, deep yellow. The analysis agrees with $2PbO.3UO_3.P_2O_5.5H_2O$. All the water is expelled at about 300°, and oxygen is lost at 500°. V. Billiet gave $\alpha=1·88$ and $\gamma=1·89$ for the indices of refraction of the rhombic crystals. A. Schoep also described **renardite**—named after A. F. Renard—from the Kasola mine, Katanga. Its composition corresponds with $PbO.4UO_3.P_2O_5.9H_2O$. It occurs in minute, yellow, flat, rectangular prisms belonging to the rhombic system, with $a:c=1:0·8327$; the (100)-cleavage is perfect; the indices of refraction $\alpha=1·715$, $\beta=1·736$, and $\gamma=1·73$; and the sp. gr. is just over 4. The pleochroism α is colourless and β and γ are yellow. The mineral fuses on charcoal to a black scoriaceous mass; and it is readily soluble in hot nitric or hydrochloric acid. In the latter case, lead chloride is deposited as the soln. cools.

A. Breithaupt described a mineral observed on the uranium minerals of Autun, France ; Steinig, Saxon Voigtland ; Neuhammer, Bohemia ; and Johanngeorgenstadt, Saxony. The mineral resembles autunite in the four-sided rhombic plates, nearly tetragonal. Its colour is reddish-brown or hyacinth-red, and it is considered to be **manganese uranyl phosphate,** or mangano-uranite. It was called **fritzscheite**—after C. L. Fritzsche. The sp. gr. is 3·504, and the hardness 2·0 to 2·5.

P. Pascal prepared **silver, barium, and lead uranylhexametaphosphates,** $M_4[UO_2(PO_3)_6]$. They are obtained by fusing the alkali trimetaphosphate at about 700°, and chilling the fused mass rapidly. The product forms the complexes indicated when treated with salts of the corresponding metals.

A. W. Cronander prepared *uranium phosphodecachloride,* $UCl_5.PCl_5$—*vide supra.* A. Colani treated metaphosphoric acid with uranium tetrachloride at a dull red-heat, and obtained **uranous tetrachlorophosphate,** $U_3(PO_4)_4.UCl_4$; and also by the action of uranium tetrachloride on uranous pyrophosphate. The green rhombic crystals have the axial ratios $a:b:c=0·8376:1:0·3737$. Twinning occurs about the (101)-plane ; and the (101)- and (100)-cleavages are complete. The salt is sparingly soluble in hydrochloric acid, but readily soluble in nitric acid, and aqua regia. J. Aloy obtained **uranous tetrachlorohydrophosphate,** $U(HPO_4)_2.UCl_4$, in green crystals, from a soln. of uranous hydrophosphate in conc. hydrochloric acid.

W. Heintz allowed a mixture of nitric acid and uranyl hydrophosphate to stand in the cold, and obtained aggregates of yellow microscopic prisms of **uranyl nitratophosphate,** $2UO_3.N_2O_5.P_2O_5.16H_2O$. The salt melts when heated, and gives off nitrous fumes and water. It is soluble in warm water, and the soln. deposits the hydrophosphate $(UO_2)(HPO_4).4\frac{1}{2}H_2O$. The salt is soluble in nitric, hydrochloric, and sulphuric acids ; acetic acid does not form a clear soln. in the cold.

REFERENCES.

[1] P. Chastaing, *Bull. Soc. Chim.,* (2), **34.** 20, 1880 ; J. Aloy and G. Auber, *ib.,* (4), **1.** 570, 1907 ; J. Aloy, *Recherches sur l'uranium et ses composés,* Paris, 1901 ; *Ann. Chim. Phys.,* (7), **24.** 412, 1901 ; A. Colani, *ib.,* (8), **12.** 59, 1907 ; *Recherches sur les composés uraneux,* Paris, 1907 ; C. F. Rammelsberg, *Pogg. Ann.,* **55.** 318, 1842 ; **56.** 125, 1842 ; **59.** 1, 1843 ; *Sitzber. Akad. Berlin,* 447, 1872 ; *Ber.,* **5.** 1003, 1872 ; K. R. Johnson, *ib.,* **22.** 976, 1889 ; G. Werther, *Sitzber. Akad. Berlin,* 230, 1848 ; *Journ. prakt. Chem.,* (1), **43.** 321, 1848 ; R. Arendt and W. Knop, *ib.,* (1), **70.** 385, 1857 ; L. Troost, *Compt. Rend.,* **101.** 210, 1885 ; P. Hautefeuille and J. Margottet, *ib.,* **96.** 849, 1883.

[2] A. W. Cronander, *Oefvers. Akad. Stockholm,* **27.** 57, 1870 ; *Ber.,* **6.** 1466, 1873 ; *Bull. Soc. Chim.,* (2), **19.** 499, 1873 ; P. Chastaing, *Bull. Soc. Chim.,* (2), **34.** 20, 1880 ; L. Bourgeois, *ib.,* (3), **19.** 733, 1897 ; *Bull. Soc. Min.,* **21.** 32, 1898 ; E. Jannetaz, *Compt. Rend.,* **114.** 1352, 1892 ;

Bull. Soc. Min., **10**. 17, 1877 ; A. Lacroix, *ib.*, **31**. 218, 245, 259, 1908 ; E. Boutée, *ib.*, **28**. 243. 1905 ; P. Gaubert, *ib.*, **27**. 222, 1904 ; H. Lienau, *Beiträge zur Kenntnis der Uranylsalze*, Berlin, 25, 1898 ; A. Girard, *Compt. Rend.*, **34**. 22, 1852 ; P. Hautefeuille and J. Margottet, *ib.*, **96**. 1144, 1883 ; A. Muguet and J. Seroin, *ib.*, **171**. 1005, 1920 ; A. Pereira-Forjaz, *ib.*, **164**. 102, 1917 ; C. Leconte, *ib.*, **29**. 55, 1849 ; A. Schoep, *Bull. Soc. Chim. Belg.*, **34**. 347, 1925 ; *Bull. Soc. Géol. Belg.*, **33**. 190, 1924 ; *Bull. Soc. Min.*, **48**. 77, 1925 ; **51**. 1, 247, 1928 ; *Compt. Rend.*, **176**. 171, 1923 ; **174**. 623, 765, 1922 ; **176**. 171, 1923 ; **179**. 693, 1924 ; F. Pisani, *ib.*, **52**. 817, 1861 ; A. Michel-Lévy and A. Lacroix *ib.*, **106**. 777, 1888 ; P. Pascal, *ib.*, **157**. 932, 1913 ; **177**. 1298, 1923 ; E. Gleditsch, *ib.*, **149**. 267, 1909 ; *Le Radium*, **8**. 256, 1911 ; L. Ouvrard, *Recherches sur l'action des phosphates alcalins sur quelques oxydes metalliques*, Paris, 1888 ; *Compt. Rend.*, **110**. 1333, 1890 ; L. Barthe, *ib.*, **152**. 1396, 1911 ; *Koll. Zeit.*, **11**. 246, 1913 ; B. Menes, *Ueber Komplexverbindungen des vierwertigen Urans*, Berlin, 1929 ; G. Werther, *Sitzber. Akad. Berlin*, 230, 1848 ; *Journ. prakt. Chem.*, (1), **43**. 322, 1848 ; C. Pincus, *ib.*, (1), **76**. 104, 1859 ; C. Winkler, *ib.*, (2), **7**. 10, 1873 ; (2), **16**. 91, 1877 ; R. Arendt and W. Knop, *ib.*, (1), **70**. 385, 1857 ; A. Kitchin, *Chem. News*, **27**. 119, 1873 ; F. Sutton, *ib.*, **1**. 97, 122, 1860 ; G. G. Stokes, **7**. 147, 1863 ; *Proc. Roy. Soc.*, **11**. 166, 1862 ; *Phil. Trans.*, **152**. 599, 1862 ; C. Bödeker, *Liebig's Ann.*, **117**. 195, 1860 ; W. Heintz, *ib.*, **151**. 216, 1869 ; W. Steinkuhler, *Bull. Soc. Chim. Belg.*, **32**. 253, 270, 1923 ; O. Abesser, W. Jani and M. Marcker, *Zeit. anal. Chem.*, **12**. 239, 1873 ; C. R. Fresenius, *ib.*, **10**. 204, 1871 ; H. Debray, *Compt. Rend.*, **52**. 44, 1861 ; *Ann. Chim. Phys.*, (5), **61**. 419, 1861 ; J. Persoz, *ib.*, (3), **20**. 315, 1847 ; H. Grandeau, *Compt. Rend.*, **100**. 1134, 1885 ; *Ann. Chim. Phys.*, (6), **8**. 223, 1886 ; J. J. Ebelmen, *ib.*, (3), **5**. 189, 1842 ; A. Laugier, *ib.*, (2), **24**. 239, 1823 ; H. St. C. Deville, *ib.*, (3), **61**. 446, 1861 ; E. Starkenstein, *Biochem. Zeit.*, **32**. 235, 1911 ; C. F. Rammelsberg, *Sitzber. Akad. Berlin*, 447, 1872 ; H. Rose, *Ausführliches Hand-buch der analytischen Chemie*, Braunschweig, **2**. 523, 1851 ; E. M. Péligot, *Compt. Rend.*, **12**. 735, 1841 ; **22**. 487, 1846 ; **42**. 73, 1856 ; *Ann. Chim. Phys.*, (3), **5**. 5, 1842 ; (3), **20**. 329, 1847 ; *Journ. Pharm. Chim.*, (2), **27**. 522, 1841 ; *Liebig's Ann.*, **41**. 141, 1841 ; **43**. 258, 1842 ; *Journ. prakt. Chem.*, (1), **24**. 442, 1841 ; (1), **38**. 112, 1846 ; M. H. Klaproth, *Mém. Acad. Berlin*, 273, 1789 ; 160, 1792 ; *Beiträge zur chemischen Kenntnis der Mineralkörper*, Berlin, **2**. 197, 1797 ; London, 477, 1801 ; *Crell's Ann.*, ii, 387, 1789 ; J. B. Richter, *Ueber die neueren Gegenstände der Chymie*, Breslau, **1**. 1, 1791 ; **9**. 36, 1798 ; *Gehlen's Journ.*, **4**. 402, 1805 ; A. Colani, *Ann. Chim. Phys.*, (8), **12**. 127, 1907 ; *Recherches sur les composés uraneux*, Paris, 1907 ; J. Aloy, *Recherches sur l'uranium et ses composés*, Toulouse, 1901 ; *Ann. Chim. Phys.*, (8), **24**. 412, 1901 ; V. Billiet, *Naturwet. Tijds.*, **7**. 112, 1927 ; G. Buchner, *Arch. Pharm.*, (3), **21**. 118, 1883 ; C. Blinkoff, *Beiträge zur Kenntnis kondensierter Uranylverbindungen*, Bern, 16, 1906 ; A. F. Hallimond, *Min. Mag.*, **17**. 221, 326, 1916 ; **19**. 43, 1920 ; A. Weisbach, *Jahrb. Berg. Hütt.*, 48, 1877 ; *Neues Jahrb. Min.*, 315, 1873 ; 406, 1877 ; F. Sandberger, *ib.*, i, 250, 1886 ; A. Frenzel, *ib.*, 946, 1873 ; W. Marckwald and A. S. Russell, *Jahrb. Rad. Elektron.*, **8**. 457, 1911 ; A. des Cloizeaux, *Ann. Mines.*, (5), **11**. 261, 1857 ; (5), **14**. 339, 1858 ; *Ann. Chim. Phys.*, (6), **8**. 226, 1886 ; J. J. Berzelius, *Pogg. Ann.*, **1**. 383, 1824 ; *Schweigger's Journ.*, **44**. 191, 1825 ; *Ann. Phil.*, **9**. 266, 1825 ; *Svenska Akad. Handl.*, 152, 1823 ; *Nouveau système de minéralogie*, Paris, 295, 1819 ; A. H. Church, *Journ. Chem. Soc.*, **28**. 109, 1875 ; *Chem. News*, **12**. 183, 1865 ; *Min. Mag.*, **1**. 234, 1877 ; R. Phillips, *Ann. Phil.*, (2), **5**. 57, 1823 ; W. Phillips, *Trans. Geol. Soc.*, **3**. 112, 1816 ; *An Elementary Introduction to Mineralogy*, London, 267, 1823 ; W. Gregor, *ib.*, (1), 5. 281, 1815 ; *Phil. Trans.*, **95**. 331, 1805 ; H. von Foullon, *Jahrb. geol. Reichsanst. Wien*, **33**. 1, 1883 ; J. Hoff-mann, *Zeit. prakt. Geol.*, **12**. 123, 172, 1904 ; G. Lincio, *Atti Accad. Torino*, **48**. 959, 1913 ; A. Schrauf, *T'schermak's Mitt.*, (1), **2**. 181, 1872 ; F. A. Genth, *Amer. Chem. Journ.*, **1**. 92, 1879 ; F. L. Hess, *Bull. U.S. Geol. Sur.*, 750, 1924 ; F. Rinne, *Centr. Min.*, 618, 708, 712, 1901 ; F. Kohl-beck and P. Uhlich, *ib.*, 206, 1904 ; Y. Bucholz, *ib.*, 362, 1903 ; A. Breithaupt, *Berg. Hütt. Ztg.*, **24**. 302, 1815 ; W. T. Schaller, *Amer. Min.*, **13**. 111, 1928 ; F. Henrich, *Ber.*, **55**. B, 1212, 1922 ; A. Rosenheim and T. Triantaphyllides, *ib.*, **48**. 582, 1915 ; A. Rosenheim, *ib.*, **153**. 126, 1926 ; A. Brezina, *Zeit. Kryst.*, **3**. 273, 1879 ; V. Dürrfeld, *ib.*, **51**. 279, 1912 ; T. W. Case, *Phys. Rev.*, (2), **9**. 305, 1917 ; J. F. L. Hausmann, *Handbuch der Mineralogie*, Göttingen, **2**. 1104, 1847 ; F. Hessenberg, *Mineralogische Notizen*, Frankfurt, **6**. 41, 1863 ; R. P. Greg and W. G. Lettsom, *Manual of the Mineralogy of Great Britain and Ireland*, London, 384, 1858 ; P. A. Dufrénoy, *Traité de minéralogie*, Paris, 1860 ; B. Stoces, *Rozp. Ceske Akad.*, **27**. 27, 1918 ; A. Lévy, *Descrip-tion d'une collection de minéraux formée par M. Henri Heuland*, Londres, **3**. 329, 1837 ; A. G. Berg-man, *Journ. Russ. Phys. Chem. Soc.*, **56**. 177, 1925 ; N. von Kokscharoff, *Materialien zur Minera-logie Russlands*, St. Petersburg, **5**. 35, 1866 ; E. Mallard, *Traité de minéralogie*, Paris, 517, 1852 ; W. H. Miller, *Introduction to Mineralogy*, London, 519, 1852 ; N. L. Bowen, *Amer. Journ. Science*, (4), **48**. 195, 1919 ; T. L. Walker, *ib.*, (4), **6**. 41, 1898 ; O. S. Pulman, *ib.*, (4), **16**. 229, 1903 ; *Zeit. anorg. Chem.*, **37**. 113, 1903 ; W. Strecker and P. Schiffer, *Zeit. anal. Chem.*, **50**. 495, 1911 ; E. Kessel, *ib.*, **8**. 164, 1869 ; H. Neubauer, *Archiv. Wiss. Heilkunde*, **4**. 228, 1893 ; K. Broockmann, *Rep. anal. Chem.*, **1**. 212, 1881 ; A. E. Haswell, *ib.*, **2**. 251, 1882 ; C. Mohr, *Zeit. anal. Chem.*, **19**. 150, 1880 ; *Chem. News*, **45**. 248, 1882 ; A. Vozarik, *Zeit. physiol. Chem.*, **76**. 433, 1912 ; G. Guérin, *Chem. News*, **8**. 175, 1882 ; *Rep. anal. Chem.*, **3**. 157, 1883 ; H. Rheineck, *Dingler's Journ.*, **200**. 383, 1870 ; V. Edwards, *Chem. News*, **59**. 159, 1889 ; A. Pavec, *Listy's Chemiké*, **1**. 313, 1875 ; J. G. Fairchild, *Amer. Min.*, **14**. 265, 1929 ; C. F. Naumann, *Elemente der Mineralogie*, Leipzig, 603, 1898.

CHAPTER LXIV

MANGANESE

§ 1. The History of Manganese

THE mineral commonly called *pyrolusite* has been known from ancient times. It was used then, as it is now, for bleaching glass ; this it does by disguising in some way the green or yellow colour produced by iron oxides present as impurities in the raw materials, etc. Indeed, it is the references to the use of this mineral for decolorizing glass which enable the specific mineral to be traced through writings from the first century up to the present time. In the first century of our era, Dioscorides, in his Περὶ ῞γλης ᾽Ιατρικῆς (**5**. 93), referred to the μάγνης λίθος as a mineral which had the power of attracting iron ; and Pliny, in his *Historiœ naturalis* (**36**. 25, 66), to the *magnes* or *lapis magnes*—that is, the loadstone, or magnetic oxide of iron. Pliny said :

What is there endowed with more marvellous properties than the *magnes* ? In which of her departments has Nature displayed greater waywardness ? What is there in existence more inert than a piece of rigid stone ? And yet, behold ! Nature has endowed the stone with both sense and hands. What is there more stubborn than iron ? Yet the iron allows itself to be attracted under the mysterious and invisible influence of the *magnes*, for the iron springs towards it, and is held fast by its embraces.

Pliny then described five different kinds of *lapis magnes*, and he classed them as male and female. The male varieties were said to be more red than black ; and he added that the fourth kind, found near Alexandria, in Troas, is black, of the female sex, and consequently has no attractive power ; while the fifth kind comes from Magnesia, in Asia, is white, and has no attractive power. Pliny here seems to get confused in his classification. Pliny also said that in Ethiopia there is *hœmatites magnes*, a mineral of blood-red colour. The *hœmatites* has not the same property of attracting iron as *lapis magnes*. In the second century of our era, C. Galen [1] described bloodstone as *magnites*. In describing the manufacture of glass, Pliny said that " in the course of time, as human industry is ingenious in discovering, *lapis magnes* began to be employed as one of the ingredients of glass, from the impression that a magnet could attract glass as well as iron." Whether or not *lapis magnes* was first used in glass-making from the application of a wrong hypothesis, it is more probable, said J. Beckmann, that the early glass-makers tried various minerals for colouring glass ; and they must have soon found that one kind of *lapis magnes*, according as it is used in greater or less quantity, imparts to glass many beautiful shades of colour—violet, red, and dark brown. They probably also found that when a very small proportion of this kind of *lapis magnes* was added, the glass became colourless. In this way the glass-makers were able to make glass vessels which, in the words of Pliny, were " entirely colourless and transparent, and as nearly as possible resembled rock crystals "—*Maximus tamen honos in candido translucentibus, quam proxima crystalli similitudine*. The evidence is thus fairly clear that some varieties of pyrolusite, on account of their external resemblance to the magnetic minerals, were classed with the *lapis magnes*. Pliny added that, on the authority of Nicander, the term *magnes* comes from the name

139

of the person who was the first to discover the mineral on Ida, for when Magnes was taking his herds to pasture he found that the nails of his shoes and the iron ferrule of his staff adhered to the ground. Pliny said that the *lapis magnes* was also called *sidera*, as well as *heraclion*. The former term no doubt comes from the Greek σίδηρος, iron, and the latter from Heraclea in Lydia or Thessaly. The term *magnesia* can also be referred to the locality, Magnesia, where the fifth variety of *lapis magnes* occurred. According to L. Delâtre, the term is derived from μάγγανον, meaning a delusion or mystification, in allusion to the brittle and unstable (oxidizable) nature of the metal which it furnished. Writers in the Middle Ages came to use the term *lapis magnes* or *lapis magnesius* for the magnetic variety, and *magnesia* for the non-magnetic mineral of a similar appearance. Thus, the tenth-century Arabian writer Avicenna, in his *Canon medicinæ* (Venetiis, **1**. 356, 1608), has a chapter entitled *De magnete*, and another entitled *De magnesia*, and he definitely distinguishes between the magnetic and the non-magnetic minerals ; while the thirteenth-century Albertus Magnus, in his *De mineralibus*, said that *magnesia*, which some call *magnosiam*, is a black mineral frequently used in glass-making. The use of the mineral in glass-making was mentioned by Roger Bacon, Basilius Valentinus, C. Leonardus, B. P. de Vargas, R. Boyle, M. Mercatus, A. Neri, and many others. V. Biringuccio said that the mineral *manganese* which is found at the mountain of Viterbo, Tuscany, as well as in Germany, is the colour of iron-slag. He added that no metal can be obtained from it by fusion, but it imparts a fine azure colour to glass ; and when put into molten glass, the glass is cleansed, even if it were green or yellow. In a hot fire it gives off a vapour like lead, and turns into ashes. G. Agricola made similar remarks about the use of *magnes* in glass.

About this time the word came to be written in many ways—H. Cardanus, and M. Mercatus used *manganensis*, C. Leonardus, *manganesum*, and V. Biringuccio, *manganese*. In addition, D. G. F. C. Fuchs said that the terms *manganesia*, *magnesie*, *mégalaise*, *magalaise*, *magne*, *magnesia vitriariorum*, *magnesium*, *magalœa sitiens*, and *ferrum nigricans spledens Wolstersdorfi* were employed. O. Vogel discussed the origin of the term " manganese."

Paracelsus spoke of the *magnesia* of the philosophers, but did not refer to its use in glass-making—*vide* **4**. 29, 1. As indicated in connection with magnesium, the term *magnesia alba* was applied to the magnesian earth in contrast with *magnesia nigra* applied to the mineral now under discussion. The term *Braunstein* appears in Basilius Valentinus' *Letztes Testament*, where the word is used for the ferruginous earths employed by potters for painting ; C. Schwenkfeld used the word in a similar connection. A. Cæsalpinus referred to *lapis manganensis* as *ferrum mineralisatum*, *minera fuliginea*, *manus inquinante, quœ sparsim striis conuergentibus constat* ; and nearly a century later the Swedish mineralogist J. G. Wallerius included with *brunsten* the varieties *magnesia solida*, *magnesia striata*, *magnesia squamosa*, and *magnesia tessulate*, used in tempering the colour of glass. S. A. Forsius called the mineral *manganaise gris*, and C. von Linnæus, *molybdenum magnesii*. W. Haidinger called the different varieties of these earths **pyrolusite**—from πῦρ, fire ; λούειν, to wash, in allusion to their use for discharging the yellow and green colour from glass, and they were whimsically called *sapo vitriariorum*, or *le savon des verriers*, by J. B. L. Romé de l'Isle.

The mineralogists of the eighteenth century did not make much progress in establishing *Braunstein* as a specific mineral, for this term, as well as the several variants of *lapis magnes*, was applied to common iron ores, and sometimes to pyrites. Observations on the mineral were made by J. C. V. de Bomare,[2] F. E. Brückmann, F. A. Cartheuser, G. de Courtivron, J. A. Cramer, C. E. Gellert, E. F. Geoffroy, C. A. Gerhard, J. F. Henkel, B. C. J. von Hermann, J. Hill, P. J. Hjelm, J. C. Ilsemann, J. H. G. von Justi, V. Kräutermann, J. G. Lehmann, H. Maret, L. B. G. de Morveau, J. T. A. Peithner, M. Pomet, J. B. L. Romé de l'Isle, M. B. Valentini, J. G. Wallerius, J. F. Westrumb, J. L. Woltersdorf, and

J. J. Woyt. A. Libavius erred in classifying the mineral with the antimony ores ; and C. von Linnæus, with molybdenum ores. J. H. Pott showed that the iron contained in the mineral is an accidental and not an essential constituent, and he obtained a number of salts from the mineral, but he did not recognize that he had in hand the salts of a new metal. In common with J. W. Baumer, S. Rinman, G. A. Scopoli, C. F. G. H. Westfield, A. G. Werner, G. de Courtivron, and C. A. Gerhard, J. H. Pott regarded *Braunstein* as one of the alumina earths. A. Cronstedt supposed that the mineral contained essentially tin ; and B. G. Sage inferred that it is a mineralized mixture of cobalt and zinc. In 1770, J. G. Kaim extracted a regulus by heating a mixture of pyrolusite and black flux at a high temp., but this observation does not appear to have been followed up.

In 1774, C. W. Scheele,[3] in his memoir : *Om Brunsten eller Magnesia*, showed that *Braunstein* is the oxide of a peculiar metal, for in its reactions with acids and various other reagents it gives results exhibited by the oxide of no other metal. He said that *Braunstein* contains a calx which resembles lime in many respects, and he even tried to find if the one can be converted into the other, but with negative results. He showed that the mineral has a strong attraction for phlogiston— meaning that it readily gives off oxygen—and forms colourless salts. Soln. of manganese which did not contain phlogiston—meaning the oxidized salts—were coloured. As a result of his experiments to discover the constituent parts of *Braunstein*, C. W. Scheele said : " I have not yet been able to produce the metal or confirm by synthesis what I have learnt by analysis." T. Bergman pointed out that although the new metal had not been isolated, its existence had been *incontestablement établie* by C. W. Scheele. J. G. Gahn isolated the metal in 1774. A report of the investigation does not appear to have been published. C. W. Scheele must have been closely connected with the work, and he supplied J. G. Gahn with materials. This is shown by the following excerpt from a letter from C. W. Scheele to J. G. Gahn :

Upsala, den 16 Mai 1774.
Hochgeehrter Herr !
I am sending herewith some *depurirten Braunstein*, in which, I think, it will be difficult to detect any iron. I should have sent it by the previous post, but I had none ready. I have tested your *reducirten Braunstein*, and find that it is a *Braunsteinerde* united with a little iron and much phlogiston. Your experiment therefore gives me great satisfaction, and I am eager to know what will be the result of treating this purified pyrolusite in your furnace. I trust that you will send me a little of the regulus as soon as possible.
Ich bin Dero dienstschuldigster Diener,
C. W. Scheele.

The " reduced pyrolusite," " regulus," and the " pyrolusitic ore united with a little iron and much phlogiston " obviously refer to J. G. Gahn's isolation of the manganese. Immediately afterwards T. Bergman obtained what he called *magnesium*, or *magnesium regulinum*. These observers do not appear to have known that J. G. Kaim, four years earlier, had obtained a regulus from *Braunstein*. In the English translation of T. Bergman's memoir, the metal is called *manganese*. There was some confusion about this time in the nomenclature. The metal was also called *Braunsteinkönig*, or *Braunstein regulus*, and *Braunstein metal*. M. H. Klaproth at first used the term *Braunsteinkalk*, and this appeared in the English translation as *oxide of manganese*; and soon afterwards (1807) M. H. Klaproth himself adopted *manganese* for the name of the element. The term *manganese* was advocated by P. K. Buttmann, and it quickly came into general use—*vide* magnesium, **4**. 29, 1. M. F. Brünnich, R. Kirwan, and C. G. Hagen at first regarded manganese as a semi-metal—*Halbmetall*. The observations of J. G. Gahn, and T. Bergman were subsequently confirmed by P. de la Peyrouse, L. B. G. de Morveau, H. T. Scheffer, R. Kirwan, S. Rinman, J. C. Ilsemann, F. A. C. Gren, P. J. Hjelm, J. J. Bindheim, and J. F. John. The development of our knowledge of the individual compounds is indicated in connection with the descriptions of them.

REFERENCES.

¹ C. Leonardus, *Speculum lapidum*, Parisiis, 71, 1610 ; H. Cardanus, *De subtilitate*, Lugduni, 294, 1580 ; M. Mercatus, *Metallotheca*, Romæ, 148, 1717 ; J. Beckmann, *Beyträge zur Geschichte der Erfindungen*, Leipzig, 4. 401, 1799 ; London, 2. 235, 1846 ; Paracelsus, *The Hermetic and Alchemical Writings*, London, 1. 117, 1894 ; V. Biringuccio, *Pirotechnica*, Venezia, 36, 1540 ; L. Delâtre, *La langue française dans ses rapports avec la Sanscrit et avec les autres langues indo-européenes*, Paris, 1. 316, 1854 ; P. Larousse, *Grand dictionnaire universel*, Paris, 10. 1066, 1873 ; D. G. F. C. Fuchs, *Geschichte des Braunsteins*, Jena, 9, 1791 ; Roger Bacon, *De alchemia*, in J. J. Manget, *Bibliotheca chemica curiosa*, Genevæ, 1. 614, 1702 ; Basilius Valentinus, *Letztes Testament*, Strassburg, 1751 ; G. Agricola, *De re metallica*, Basileæ, 471, 1546 ; London, 585, 1912 ; A. Neri, *L'arte vetraria*, Firenze, 1612 ; C. Schwenkfeld, *Stirpium et fossilium Silesiœ catalogus*, Lipsiæ, 381, 1600 ; A. Cæsalpinus, *De metallicis*, Romæ, 1596 ; J. G. Wallerius, *Mineralogia*, Stockholm, 268, 1747 ; S. A. Forsius, *Mineralographia*, Stockholm, 1772 ; C. von Linnæus, *Systema naturæ*, Lugduni Batavorum, 1735 ; W. Haidinger, *Edin. Journ. Science*, 4. 41, 1826 ; 9. 304, 1828 ; *Isis*, 2. 681, 1826 ; *Trans. Roy. Soc. Edin.*, 11. 136, 1827 ; *Pogg. Ann.*, 11. 374, 1827 ; 14. 199, 1828 ; J. B. L. Romé de l'Isle, *Cristallographie*, Paris, 3. 89, 1783 ; B. P. de Vargas, *De re metallica*, Madrid, 1569 ; R. Boyle, *Experiments and Observations touching Colours*, London, 1664 ; C. Galen, *Opera—de simplicibus medicamentis*, Basel, 93, 1531 ; O. Vogel, *Stahl Eisen*, 36. 68, 1916.

² J. W. Baumer, *Naturgeschichte des Mineralreichs*, Gotha, 1. 270, 1763 ; S. Rinman, *Vet. Akad. Handl. Stockholm*, 26. 241, 1765 ; *Försök till jermetshistoria*, Stockholm, 1782 ; G. A. Scopoli, *Principia mineralogiœ systematicœ*, Prague, 70, 1772 ; C. F. G. H. Westfield, *Mineralogische Abhandlungen*, Göttingen, 16, 1767 ; A. G. Werner, in A. Cronstedt, *Mineralogie*, Stockholm, 251, 1758 ; A. Cronstedt, *Versuch einer Mineralogie*, Leipzig, 113, 1780 ; C. A. Gerhard, *Beiträge zur Chemie und Geschichte der Mineralogie*, Francofurti, 1. 246, 1773 ; *Crell's Chem. Ann.*, i, 56, 1785 ; A. Libavius, *De natura metallorum*, Francofurti, 1597 ; P. J. Hjelm, *Vet. Akad. Handl. Stockholm*, 39. 82, 1778 ; *Crell's Die neuesten Entdeckungen in der Chemie*, 5. 164, 1782 ; B. C. J. von Hermann, *Versuch einier mineralogischen Beschreibung des uralischen Erzgebirges*, Berlin, 1. 2, 1788 ; *Crell's Chem. Ann.*, 3. 196, 1789 ; L. B. G. de Morveau, *Nouv. Mém. Acad. Dijon*, 2. 90, 1783 ; J. F. Westrumb, *Kleine physikalisch chemische Abhandlungen*, Leipzig, 2. 199, 1788 ; *Crell's Chem. Ann.*, 4. 298, 1787 ; J. C. Ilsemann, *Crell's Die neuesten Entdeckungen in der Chemie*, 1. 350, 1781 ; G. de Courtivron, *L'art des forges*, Paris, 1761 ; F. E. Brückmann, *Magnalia Dei in subterraneis*, Helmstädt, 1. 77, 1727 ; J. J. Woyt, *Gazophylaceum medicophysicum*, Leipzig, 4. 535, 1743 ; M. B. Valentini, *Muscæum muscæorum*, Frankfurt a. M., 1. 40, 1714 ; M. Pomet, *Aufrichtiger Materialist und Specerenhändler*, Leipzig, 749, 1717 ; E. F. Geoffroy, *Tractatus de materia medica*, Paris, 1741 ; J. F. Henkel, *Pyritologia*, Leipzig, 87, 1747 ; J. A. Cramer, *Elementa artis docimasticœ*, Leyden, 201, 1730 ; J. T. A. Peithner, *Erste Gründe der Bergwerksurssenschaften*, Prag, 8, 1769 ; J. Hill, *The History of Fossils*, London, 1748 ; C. E. Gellert, *Anfangsgründe der metallurgischen Chemie*, Leipzig, 48, 1750 ; J. L. Woltersdorf, *Systema minerale*, Berlin, 31, 1748 ; J. C. V. de Bomare, *Traité de minéralogie*, Paris, 1762 ; J. H. G. von Justi, *Grundriss des gessamten Mineralreichs*, Göttingen, 1765 ; H. Maret, *Elémens de chimie théorique et pratique*, Dijon, 1777 ; F. A. Cartheuser, *Elementa mineralogiœ systematice disposita*, Francofurti, 72, 1755 ; J. G. Lehmann, *Kurzer entwurfeiner Mineralogie*, Leipzig, 129, 1769 ; B. G. Sage, *Élémens de minéralogie docimastique*, Paris, 1772 ; J. B. L. Romé de l'Isle, *Essai de cristallographie*, Paris, 1772 ; V. Kräutermann, *Historisch medicinisches Regnum minerale*, Frankfurt, 118, 1717 ; J. G. Wallerius, *Mineralogia*, Stockholm, 268, 1747 ; C. von Linnæus, *Systema Natura*, Lugduni Batavorum, 1735 ; M. T. Brünnich, *Mineralogie*, Copenhagen, 301, 1781 ; R. Kirwan, *Elements of Mineralogy*, London, 1784 ; C. G. Hagen, *Lehrbuch der Apothekerkunst*, Regiomont, 489, 1786 ; T. Bergman, *Sciagraphia regni mineralis*, Lipsiæ, 1782 ; J. H. Pott, *Lithogeognosia*, Potsdam, 2. 74, 1751 ; *Observationum et animadversionum chymicarum*, Berolini, 79, 1739 ; *Crell's Archiv.*, 3. 290, 296, 1786 ; *Misc. Berol. Soc. Scient.*, 6. 40, 1740 ; J. G. Kaim, *Dissertatio de metallis dubiis*, Wien, 48, 1770.

³ C. W. Scheele, *Svenska Akad. Handl.*, 35. 89, 177, 1774 ; *Abhand. Akad. Stockholm*, 36. 95, 183, 1774 ; *Opuscula chemica et physica*, Lipsiæ, 1. 227, 1788 ; London, 53, 1901 ; *Crell's Die neuesten Entdeckungen in der Chemie*, 1. 112, 140, 1781 ; *Nachgelassene Briefe und Aufzeichmunzen*, Stockholm, 120, 1892 ; J. G. Kaim, *Dissertatio de metallis dubiis*, Wien, 48, 1770 ; T. Bergman, *De mineris ferri albis*, Upsala, 1774 ; *Opuscula physica et chemica*, Lipsiæ, 2. 184, 1792 ; London, 2. 203, 1798 ; M. H. Klaproth, *Beiträge zur chemischen Kenntniss der Mineralkörper*, Berlin, 2. 239, 1797 ; 4. 137, 1807 ; London, 1. 510, 1801 ; P. K. Buttmann, *Ueber die Benennung einiger Mineralien bei den Alten, besonders den Magnet und den Basalt*, Berlin, 1808 ; *Gehlen's Journ.*, 6. 582, 1808 ; J. G. Gahn, in T. Bergman, *De mineris ferri albis*, Upsala, 1774 (*vide supra*) ; P. de la Peyrouse, *Journ. Phys.*, 16. 156, 1780 ; L. B. G. de Morveau, *ib.*, 16. 157, 348, 1780 ; H. T. Scheffer, *Kemiska föreläsninger rörande salter, jordarter, vatten, fetmir, metaller och färgning*, Upsala, 1775 ; R. Kirwan, *Elements of Mineralogy*, London, 1784 ; S. Rinman, *Försök till jernets historia*, Stockholm, 1782 ; J. C. Ilsemann, *Crell's Die neuesten Entdeckungen in der Chemie*, 1. 358, 1781 ; F. A. C. Gren, *ib.*, 1. 371, 1781 ; P. J. Hjelm, *ib.*, 5. 164, 1782 ; *Vet. Akad. Handl. Stockholm*, 49. 141, 1788 ; *Crell's Chem. Ann.*, 2. 159, 1787 ; J. J. Bind-

heim, *ib.*, **7**. 33, 1789 ; **8**. 120, 1789 ; J. F. John, *Ann. Phil.*, **2**. 172, 263, 1813 ; **3**. 413, 1813; *Gehlen's Journ.*, **3**. 452, 1807 ; **4**. 436, 1807 ; M. F. Brünnich, *Mineralogie*, Copenhagen, 301, 1777 ; C. G. Hagen, *Lehrbuch der Apothekerkunst*, Regiomont, 489, 1786.

§ 2. The Occurrence of Manganese

Manganese itself does not occur native, but it is widely diffused in small quantities as oxide, silicate, and carbonate, and less frequently as sulphide, phosphate, tungstate, columbate, etc. Manganese is about the fifteenth in the list of the most abundant elements in the earth's crust. F. W. Clarke [1] estimated that the known igneous rocks of the earth's crust contain 0·125 per cent. of Mn ; shales and sandstones contain traces ; while the limestones of the earth's crust contain 0·05 per cent. MnO. The known terrestrial matter in the earth's lithosphere contains 0·09 per cent. of Mn ; H. S. Washington gave 0·07 per cent. F. W. Clarke and H. S. Washington gave 0·10 per cent. Mn for the average composition of the known igneous rocks, whilst J. H. L. Vogt gave 0·075 per cent. Manganese is less abundant than titanium or hydrogen, and more abundant than sulphur, carbon, copper, and nickel. W. Vernadsky gave 0·028 for the percentage amount of manganese in the earth's crust, and 0·09 for the percentage atomic proportion of manganese. W. and J. Noddack and O. Berg gave 7×10^{-2} for the absolute abundance of manganese in the earth ; and A. von Antropoff gave for the atomic percentages 0·36 in stellar atmospheres ; 0·035 in the earth's crust ; and 0·06 in the whole earth. The subject was discussed by H. S. Washington, O. Hahn, J. Joly, V. M. Goldschmidt, G. Tammann, E. Herlinger, P. Niggli, H. von Klüber, and R. A. Sonder.

Manganese also occurs in extra-terrestrial bodies. H. A. Rowland [2] included manganese in his list of elements whose presence had been established in the sun. Reports of spectroscopic observations on the manganese lines in the solar and stellar spectra were made by J. N. Lockyer, S. A. Mitchell, S. Albrecht, P. W. Merrill and C. G. Burwell, C. Young, C. G. Abbot, F. J. M. Stratton, H. von Klüber, H. N. Russell, C. H. Payne, E. P. Waterman, P. W. Merrill, J. Stebbins, W. C. Rufus, C. D. Shane, G. E. Hale and co-workers, F. McClean, A. J. Angström, and A. Cornu. W. W. Morgan studied the manganese lines of α-Andromedæ. In 1804, M. H. Klaproth [3] observed the occurrence of manganese in meteorites from Siena, Lissa, Smolenski, and Stannern, and since that time numerous analyses have been reported in which the manganese ranges up to 5·77 per cent., as F. Koch found to be the case with a meteorite from Mocs. G. Berg, and E. Herlinger reported an average of 0·22 per cent. in stoney meteorites ; and O. C. Farrington, an average of 0·03 per cent. in all available analyses of meteorites. J. and W. Noddack's estimates of the percentage composition, and of the atomic distribution relative to oxygen unity, are :

Earth's crust.	Igneous rocks.	Meteoric iron.	Troilite.	Atomic distribution.
$8 \cdot 0 \times 10^{-4}$	$2 \cdot 05 \times 10^{-3}$	$3 \cdot 0 \times 10^{-4}$	$4 \cdot 6 \times 10^{-4}$	$1 \cdot 6 \times 10^{-3}$

F. Zambonini found manganese occurring in mineral vesbine from Vesuvian lava. The manganese minerals occur in igneous, metamorphic, and sedimentary rocks. They also occur in mineral veins traversing these rocks, as original minerals formed at the same time as the enclosing rock, or as *secondary* minerals formed by the chemical alteration of pre-existing minerals in the rocks or veins or by the introduction from without of manganese salts in soln. Secondary manganese minerals are also formed by the weathering of these minerals when they are exposed at the surface. The oxides of manganese occur in metamorphic rocks and in veins, but rarely in igneous rocks—O. A. Derby [4] described such a case. The carbonates occur in all except the igneous rocks. The silicates are characteristic of metamorphic rocks ; they also occur in igneous rocks, rarely in mineral veins, and seldom if ever in sedimentary rocks ; the titanosilicates are found in igneous and metamorphic rocks ; the columbates, tantalates, and tungstates are found in veins in igneous rocks ; while the phosphates, arsenates, and antimonates occur in both igneous veins and metamorphic rocks. The formation of manganese deposits has been discussed by R. Beck and W. H. Weed, J. Bellinger, G. Bertrand, G. Bischof, F. W. Clarke, L. Demaret, C. F. Drake, W. H. Emmons, L. L. Fermor, E. Fuchs and L. de Launay, G. de Geer, E. C. Harder, S. Iimori, C. A. Moreing, R. A. F. Penrose, G. Rother, H. Lasch, A. W. Stelzner and A. Bergeat, G. A. Thiel, J. H. L. Vogt, T. L. Watson, G. Berg, etc.

Manganese and iron are dissolved from crystalline rocks, going into soln. as sulphate or carbonate, and being re-deposited as carbonate, oxide, or hydroxide; and E. C. Sullivan showed that the manganese is dissolved by carbonated water or dil. sulphuric acid more readily than iron. V. Vincent made some observations on the solubility of different forms of manganese in carbonated water. Manganese dissolved as carbonate, sulphate, or phosphate is precipitated by oxidation generally in the form of pyrolusite, as hydrated psilomelane, wad, or as hydrated hemitrioxide. The colloidal or gel precipitate readily adsorbs barium, potassium, and other salts; and as shown by A. Gorgeu, it may slowly crystallize. This deposition is exemplified by the dendritic infiltrations which occur in many rocks, as illustrated by Fig. 1 by L. L. Fermor, which shows the dendrites of manganese

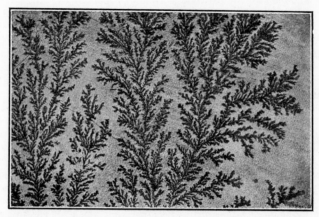

Fig. 1.—Dendritic Infiltration of Manganese Oxide on Sandstone (Central India).

oxide on some sandstone in Central India; and by the black coating which may be found covering river pebbles, or surrounding manganiferous springs. H. Leitmeier discussed dendritic formations. W. A. Tarr discussed the rhythmic banding of manganese dioxide in a tuff. G. A. Thiel found that manganese is deposited from very dil. soln. of manganese sulphate or hydrocarbonate (32 to 200 parts Mn per million), with or without peat solution or ferrous sulphate, when kept in contact for several months at the ordinary temp. with various minerals and rocks in a powdered form. Magnesium carbonate, either as a mineral or as a rock constituent, is the most active agent for precipitating manganese from such solutions. Iron carbonate and calcium carbonate produce partial precipitation from carbonate solutions, but have no effect on sulphate soln. in association with humic acid. Silicates are very inactive. The nodules of manganese dioxide are found as nodular concretions made up of concentric layers—thin on the outside but thicker in the interior. Many contain fragments of pumice-stone, sharks' teeth, mollusc shells, coral, etc., as nuclei. The deep-sea nodules were found by the Challenger expedition in the deep-sea red-clay at depths of about 2220 fathoms, and they were especially abundant between Hawaii and Japan. The Gazelle expedition found the manganese nodules in many parts of the Pacific Ocean, and particularly near Cook Island; while C. Chun found manganiferous iron nodules in the South Atlantic Ocean at a depth of 6700 metres. A. H. Church called the nodules *pelagite*, and they have been also called *halobolite*. Similar nodules were found by N. Andrussoff in the Black Sea, and by J. Y. Buchanan in the shallow waters of Lock Fyne, Scotland, but, as shown by J. Murray, they are more characteristic of the deeper ocean abysses. Similar nodular forms of terrestrial origin were recorded by M. Thresh, and W. M. Doherty. J. Murray and R. Irvine suggested that the manganese nodules are derived from the subaqueous decomposition of volcanic debris ; but C. W. von Gümbel attributes their formation to submarine spring waters holding manganese in soln., which is precipitated by contact with sea-water. J. Y. Buchanan assumed that organic matter reduced the sulphates of sea-water to sulphides, which precipitated the iron and manganese as sulphides, which were subsequently oxidized, but R. Irvine and J. Gibson showed that sea-water would decompose the sulphide to form soluble manganese hydrocarbonate. J. B. J. D. Boussingault, and L. Dieulafait supposed that the manganese oxide is formed by the oxidation of the carbonate in soln. at the surface, and that the precipitated oxide subsides to the sea-bottom. The sedimentary deposits may be formed in many ways. Bog, swamp, and sinter deposits, as wad, are common, and have been described by F. R. Mallet, L. L. Fermor, G. Bischof, H. Lasch, and J. H. L. Vogt. As in the case of hydrated iron oxide (*q.v.*), bacteria play an important part in the deposition of hydrated manganese oxide. Pipes and meters serving manganiferous water acquire a thin layer of yellowish iron oxide on the walls; and over this is a layer of a mixture of manganese and iron oxides. The subject was discussed by C. Zapffe.

Curiously enough, although the manganese and iron are dissolved from the rocks by the same reagents, they may be partially separated when the re-deposition occurs. The separation is not complete, for nearly all limonites contain some manganese, and nearly all psilomelanes contain some iron. C. R. Fresenius found that the warm carbonate waters of Weisbaden deposit the iron as hydroxide, leaving the manganese in soln. as hydrocarbonate. The manganese is thus carried by the water further than the iron. E. C. Sullivan also found that almost all the iron is precipitated by calcium carbonate from a mixed soln. of ferrous and manganese sulphates before manganese is deposited. This is in agreement with the thermochemical argument of L. Dieulafait. F. P. Dunnington also proved that acidic soln. of ferrous sulphate formed by the oxidation of pyrites, etc., can dissolve manganese oxides, forming, under favourable conditions, ferric sulphate and hydroxide. The soln. of ferrous sulphate, in contact with manganese carbonate, is rapidly oxidized by air, forming manganese sulphate, ferric hydroxide, and carbon dioxide. When the mixed iron and manganese sulphates come in contact with limestone, the two iron sulphates react, forming carbon dioxide, ferric hydroxide, and calcium sulphate, while in the absence of air the manganese sulphate has very little action on calcium carbonate, although in the presence of air, manganese oxide is gradually formed. Consequently, when a soln. of the mixed sulphates percolates through limestone, the iron will be precipitated and the manganese will remain in soln. until the soln. in contact with calcium carbonate is exposed to air. G. A. F. Molengraaff made observations on the manganese nodules.

From the thermochemical relations : $2FeO + O = Fe_2O_3 + 26 \cdot 6$ Cals., and $2FeO + 2CO_2 = 2FeCO_3 + 10 \cdot 0$ Cals. ; and $2MnO + O_2 = 2MnO_2 + 21 \cdot 4$ Cals., and $2MnO + 2CO_2 = 2MnCO_3 + 13 \cdot 6$ Cals., it is probable that when oxygen and carbon dioxide in excess are in contact with weathering silicate rocks, the oxides Fe_2O_3 and MnO_2 and not the carbonates will be formed ; while if the gases are not in excess, Fe_2O_3 and $MnCO_3$, not MnO_2 and $FeCO_3$, will be formed. Ferrous carbonate —spathic iron ore—will be formed under reducing conditions. Other things being equal, if minerals are formed from aq. soln., that which has the greatest heat of formation should preponderate over the others. Of the common manganese compounds :

	MnS	MnO	MnCO₃	MnO₂
(Heats of formation) .	$22 \cdot 6$	$47 \cdot 4$	$54 \cdot 2$	$58 \cdot 1$ Cals.

pyrolusite, MnO_2, might be expected to preponderate over the others. As a matter

of fact, this mineral is the most abundant ore of manganese, while manganese
sulphide with its small heat of formation is comparatively rare.   There is need for
more care than usual in applying thermochemical data to geological problems,
because minerals may be formed under very different conditions—temperature and
pressure—from those which obtained when the data were determined.

The geographical distribution of manganese [5] is illustrated by the map, Fig. 2.
The main localities are as follow :

Europe.   The manganese ores of the **United Kingdom** [6] are derived mainly from deposits
in Wales—Carnarvonshire and Merionethshire—where rhodochrosite predominates ; and
from Launceston, Cornwall, and Brentor, Devon, where the chief ores are pyrolusite and
rhodonite.   A little wad is obtained in Derbyshire.   The manganese ores in Scotland have
been worked only on a small scale ; and in Ireland there are occurrences at Sutton, Co.
Dublin, and a few other unimportant localities.   The chief occurrences of manganese ore
in **France** [7] are at the Cabesses mine, Dept. Ariège, and mines in the department of Saône-
et-Loir.   The former ceased work in 1904, and the output from the latter is small.   The
production of manganese ore in **Portugal** [8] is small.   The workable deposits of manganese
ore ·in **Spain** [9] are the carbonate in Seville, Ciudad Real, Huelva, Gerona, and Oviedo.
In **Italy** [10] deposits of manganese ore occur in Liguria, Tuscany, etc. ; on Monte Argentario ;
Carrara ;   Rapolano ;   the   Island   of   Elba ;   Turin ;   Pralorgnan ;   Piedmont ;   and

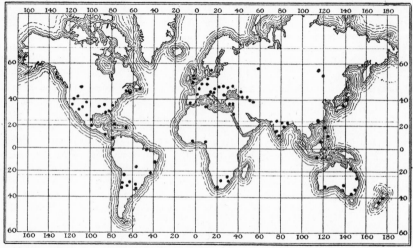

FIG. 2.—The Geographical Distribution of Manganese Ores.

Gambetesa.   The ore is usually somewhat siliceous.   There are also deposits in Sardinia,
and at Iglesias, on San Pietro Island, off Sardinia.   Deposits of manganese ore occur in
Greece [11] on the islands of Milo and Andros, but the output is small.   There are also the
Kassandra mines of Salonika.   In **Turkey** [12] there are deposits in Aidin, Pirga, and
Surmenéh.   Occurrences have been reported in **Yugoslavia** [13]; **Albania** [14] ; near Brosteni,
Sucéva, and at the Arschitya mine near Jakobeny, **Roumania** [15] ; and Wandenlitzen in
Carinthia [16] ; in the old **Austria-Hungary**,[17] including Bosnia and Herzegovina, the chief
producing centres are Bukovina and Carinthia.   Deposits also occur in Carniola, Bohemia,
Istria, and Styria.   In **Bulgaria** [18] there are deposits at Jamboli, Bela, and Dobra Nadejda.
Nearly all the manganese ore produced in **Germany** [19] comes from the neighbourhood of
Coblentz ; and there are manganiferous iron ore deposits near Siegen and Nassau.   In
Belgium [20] manganiferous iron ore is mined in the province of Liège.   In **Sweden** [21] the
chief producing districts are Undenäs, West Gothland, Wermland, and Jönköpings.   The
ore obtained is pyrolusite and manganite, hausmannite and braunite, and carbonate and
silicate accompanying iron ores.   The bulk of the world's output is obtained from
Russia.[22]   The Georgian deposits are estimated by D. Zereteli to contain 220×10^6 tons,
while 73×10^6 tons have already been extracted—principally from the Tschiaturi mine.
There are also extensive deposits in the Union of Socialist Soviet Republics—notably in the
Nikopol and Gaisinsk districts, the Urals, Siberia, and North Caucasia.

Asia.   A. Gaudry [23] described the manganese deposits of **Cyprus.**   In **Asia Minor** [24]
there is a deposit of ore, chiefly psilomelane and manganite, near Surmeneh, on the Black
Sea.   A large proportion of the world's supply of manganese ore comes from **India**.[25]   The
deposits of economic value are thus divided by L. L. Fermor : (i) those associated with a

series of manganiferous intrusives, notably in Vizagapatam, Madras ; (ii) those associated with the Dharwar rocks, in Gangpur, Panch Mahals, Jhabua, Balaghat, Bhandra, Chindwara, and Nagpur ; and (iii) those occurring as lateroid replacements on the outcrops of the Dharwar rocks in Singhbhum, Jubbulpore, Bellary, Sandur, Chitaldrug, Kadur, Shimoga, and Tumkur, and in Goa of Portuguese India. There is a small deposit at Ampitiya in Ceylon.[26]

A. A. Sankoff [27] described the deposits in Kara-Tschaguir, **Fergana**. In **Borneo** [28] manganese occurs at Gunong Bessi and in Bandjermassin. Deposits occur in Pengasih and Nanggolau, **Java** ; there is a deposit of manganese ore in the **Federated Malay States**, at Tambun ; and in the **Philippines**,[29] in Nagpartion, and on the island of Masbate. The deposits in **China** [30] were described by V. K. Ting. There are numerous deposits of manganese ore in **Japan** [31]—in Hokkaido, Aomori, Kitayama, Akita, etc.

Africa. Large manganese deposits occur in **Morocco** [32] ; in **Tunis**,[33] near Ain-Mulares ; in **Algeria**,[34] at Soukahras and Tebessa ; and in the **Sinai** [35] peninsula—Um Bogma Hills, Gebel Um Rinna ; Wadi Kharig, Wadi Baba, Wadi Naseb, Wadi Abu Hamata, Bir Um Hand, Abu Zenima, Wadi Um Sakran, etc. In what was German **East Africa** manganese ore occurs in the Unaka district and in the Kipengele Hills. There is also a deposit in British East Africa ; in **Somaliland** [36] ; and in Portuguese **Angola**.[37] Manganese ores occur in the Katanga of the **Belgian Congo** [38] ; and on the **Gold Coast** [39] at Dagwina in the Wassaw district. A. E. Kitson described the deposits as of three types : (i) Manganese-bearing argillaceous phyllites and fine mica-schists, with subordinate siliceous phyllites. These rocks are only slightly altered, and the manganese oxide is in the form in which it was originally deposited in the sediments. (ii) Spessartite (manganese garnet)—quartz rock, with or without rhodonite (manganese silicate), associated with biotite-paragneiss, biotite-schist, amphibolite, etc. These are highly altered forms of the first group. (iii) Segregation deposits formed by surface concentration of manganese oxide during the weathering of rocks of the first and second types. The special economic importance of the manganese deposits is dependent upon the degree of concentration that has taken place. These deposits occur in numerous districts in the Gold Coast Colony, Ashanti, and the Northern Territories. Owing to folding of the sediments they are visible at many places from the Birrim River, near Dixcove, on the coast to the north-west corner of the Northern Territories, for a distance of some 440 miles. The largest deposit occurs at Insuta-Dagwin, Gold Coast. There are also deposits near Zuaragu, Wa, and Kalimbi Hill. A small deposit of lateritic manganese ore occurs near Somabula in **Rhodesia**,[40] and there is a deposit on **St. Helena**. According to R. Dent, an old pyrolusite mine occurs on Chowa, Kafu-lamadzi (the place of iron), east of Broken Hill ; and he suggested that the mines were worked in prehistoric times. In **South Africa** [41] there are deposits in the Cape Province—Hout's Bay, Constantia Nek, Kogel Bay, near Worcester, near Wellington, French Hoek, and Caledon. In the Transvaal there are deposits near Pretoria ; and in Natal, in the Vryheid district, Nyalisa, Bellevue, Kruisfontein, and Baviaan's Kranz.

North America. There are deposits of manganese ore in several provinces of **Canada** [42] —e.g. near Kaslo, British Columbia ; near New Ross, and at the Tenny Cape Mines, Hants Co., in Nova Scotia ; at Markhamville, Jordan Mountain, and Dawson Settlement in New Brunswick ; in the Nestapoca chain of islands, and on the Amherst Island in Quebec ; on Cypress Hill, Alberta ; and at Manuels, Topsail, Long Pond, Chepel Cove, and Briguo on Conception Bay, Newfoundland. In the **United States** [43] there are deposits in *California* in the Franciscan formation of the Coast Ranges, in the Sierra Nevadas, in the counties of Inyo, San Bernadino, San Joaquin, and Alameda. In *Virginia* there is a large deposit at Crimora, and in many other localities. In *Georgia* the commercially valuable deposits are limited to the northern part of the state. In *Arkansas* there are deposits in the Ouachita Mountains, and in the Batesville field in Independence and Izard counties. In *Montana* there are deposits of manganiferous iron ore in Western Butte and at Philipsburg. In *Idaho* there are deposits in Bannock Co. In *Colorado* there are deposits north-west of Leadville. In *Nevada* deposits occur in the Ely and Siegal districts of White Pine Co. In *Utah* there are several deposits near Monroe, Sevier Co. ; Manning Canyon, near Marysville ; near Junction, Piute Co. ; and near Pahreah, Kane Co. There are deposits at Tombstone in *Arizona* ; at Silver City, Kingston, and Lake Valley in New Mexico ; at Jewel Cave, *South Dakota* ; near Whitfield, in the Chilhowee Mountain Range, near Morristown, and near Sweetwater, *Tennessee* ; in Iron, Reynolds, and Madison counties in *Missouri* ; near Lehigh in *Oklahoma* ; in Cleburne, Cherokee, Blount, and Etowah counties in *Alabama* ; in the south-west of *North Carolina* ; in a belt extending from New Market, Greenwood Co., to McCormick, Abbeville Co. ; and in Chester and Greeneville counties, *South Carolina* ; Glenmore, *West Virginia* ; near Harper's Ferry, Keyser's Ridge, and Bear Creek, and in Montgomery and Frederick counties, *Maryland* ; South Wallingford, and the Brandon and Chittenden areas of *Vermont* ; at Ironton, and on the Broad Mountain and in the Philadelphia and Chester counties, in *Pennsylvania* ; near Clinton, *New Jersey* ; and manganiferous iron ore is mined in the Lake Superior iron district. In **Mexico** [44] manganese ore has been reported in the districts of Acattan and Tepexi, near Coxcatlan, Guerrero ; Sierrita de Tepeyahualco, Puebla ; at Pachua and Real del Monta, Hildalgo, and Tetela del Oro.

In the **West Indies** [45] there are three groups of deposits in *Cuba* : the Christo, the

Ponupo, and the Cauto, north of Santiago ; and in the San Maestro range.   There are deposits at Coteaux in *Hayti* ; at Marshall's Hall, Portland, in *Jamaica* ; and on *St. Thomas Island.*

In **Costa. Rica** [46] there is a manganese ore mine at Playarreal.   There are several deposits on the Atlantic coast of **Panama.**

South America.   Fully 95 per cent. of the manganese ore produced in **Brazil** [47] comes from the Miguel-Burnier, Ouro Preto, and Lafayette districts of Minas Geraes.   Manganese ore has also been found in the states of Bahia, Parana, Santa Catharina, and Matto Grosso. In **Chile** [48] there are ores in a limestone-chert formation in the Carrizal district ; ores embedded in sandstone, shale, and limestone in Las Canas, La Liga, Arrayan, and Corral Quemada ; and veins in volcanic flows in Acules and Los Chorros.   Manganiferous iron ore occurs in **Uruguay.**[49]   In **Argentine** [50] iron ores have been reported in San Luiz. In **Colombia** there are deposits on the Caribbean coast extending easterly for 30 miles from Puerto-Bello ; and at Madinga, Gulf of San Blas.

Australasia.   In **Australia** [51] there are deposits in the Gladstone district of *Queensland,* also in the Rockhampton, Maryborough, Hodgkinson, Ipswich, and Darling Downs districts. Manganese ore has been reported in considerable quantities in different localities in *New South Wales*, chiefly in the Bathurst and Bendemeer districts ; in *Victoria*, at East Gippsland, and at Heathcote, Bendigo district ; in *South Australia*, Gordon and the Pernatly Lagoon ; there are unworked deposits at Zeehan, in *Tasmania.*   Good quality manganese ore has been reported in many places in *West Australia.*   In **New Zealand** [52] manganese ore has been found at Tikiora, Bay of Islands ; Parua Bay, near Whangarei ; Waiheke Island ; Pahiki Island, Hauraki Gulf ; the vicinity of Wellington ; Taieri Mouth, Otago ; etc.

Over a thousand well-defined minerals have been recognized in the earth's crust. Of these, nearly 150 contain manganese as an essential constituent, and many more contain smaller proportions.   There are also many minerals which contain only traces of manganese, and these small proportions may have a remarkable effect on the colour of the mineral.   W. N. Hartley and H. Ramage [53] discussed the occurrence of manganese in common minerals.   Manganese, indeed, is one of nature's pigments.   L. L. Fermor quotes the following examples :

As a very good example of this, *winchite* may be mentioned ; this is practically a variety of tremolite, a colourless mineral, but contains small quantities of manganese, iron, and alkalies, in addition to the usual constituents.   The winchite, instead of being white or colourless, is blue or lavender in the hand-specimen, and shows very beautiful pleochroism, under the microscope, in shades of lilac and blue.   In the same way *blandfordite* is a pyroxene containing a certain quantity of manganese and alkalies ; in the hand-specimen it is of a deep crimson colour, whilst under the microscope it shows a beautiful pleochroism, in shades of blue, carmine, and lilac, as has been noticed for any known mineral.   Similarly the manganese-micas show various shades of pink, delicate green, orange, and lilac-brown, in thin scales examined under the microscope.   As other examples of the effect on the colour of a mineral may be mentioned the manganese-epidote, *piedmontite*, and the manganese-sphene, *greenovite*.

The mineral oxides are usually different shades of black or grey ; the other manganese minerals may be coloured blue, pink, lilac, crimson, yellow, orange, green, and brown.   The colours may be modified by other constituents, *e.g.* alkalies favour the violet and blue.   L. L. Fermor said that a comparison of the composition and colour of similar minerals shows that red, pink, lavender, and allied tints are peculiar to manganese.   In some Indian rose-quartzes the manganese can be extracted by boiling dil. sulphuric acid.   M. Berthelot also attributed the colour of amethyst (*q.v.*) to manganese.   The following is a list of the manganese minerals. It includes the oxides, manganates, sulphides, sulphates, chlorides, carbonates, silicates, titanosilicate, columbates, tantalates, phosphates, arsenates, antimonates, borates, and tungstates :

Agnolite, $H_2Mn_3(SiO_3)_4 + H_2O$.   **Alabandite**, MnS, manganese monosulphide.   **Allactite**, $Mn_3As_2O_8.4Mn(OH)_2$, manganese arsenate.   **Allochroite**, manganiferous variety of andradite, $3CaO.Al_2O_3.3SiO_2$.   **Altered mica**, *see* caswellite.   **Alurgite**, a manganese-mica. **Ankerite**, $(Ca,Mg,Fe,Mn)CO_3$.   **Anthochroite**, manganiferous diopside.   **Apjohnite** (bosjemanite), $MnSO_4.Al_2(SO_4)_3 + 24H_2O$, manganese aluminium sulphate.   **Aplome**, manganiferous variety of andradite, $3CaO.Al_2O_3.3SiO_2$.   **Ardennite**, aluminium-manganese vanadiosilicate.   **Arfvedsonite** (manganiferous), sodium-calcium, ferrous iron metasilicate with manganese.   **Arseniopleite**, calcium-manganese arsenate.   **Arsenoklasite**, $(Mn_3(AsO_4)_2.2Mn(OH)_2$.   **Asbolite**, wad with a large percentage of cobalt.   **Asteroite**, variety of manganhedenbergite.   **Astochite**, $(Mg,Mn,Ca)SiO_3$ and $(Na,K,H)_2SiO_3$.

Astrophyllite, $(Na,K)_4(Fe,Mn)_4Ti(SiO_4)_4$. **Atopite**, $Ca_2Sb_2O_7$ often with Mn. **Axinite**, $(Ca,Mn,Fe)_7Al_4B_2(SiO_4)_8$. **Babingtonite**, $(Ca,Fe,Mn)SiO_3$ with $Fe_2(SiO_3)_3$. **Bäckströmite**, $Mn(OH)_2$. **Barkevikite**, manganese-amphibole near glaucophane. **Barysilite**, $Pb_3Si_2O_7$ with Mn, Ca, and Mg. **Beldongrite**, $6Mn_3O_5.Fe_2O_3.8H_2O$. **Bementite**, $2MnSiO_3.H_2O$. **Berzeliite**, $(Ca,Mg,Mn)_3As_2O_8$. **Bixbyite**, $FeO.MnO_2$. **Blandfordite**, a manganiferous pyroxene. **Bog manganese**, manganese oxides with oxides of iron, barium, aluminium, silicon, and sometimes nickel and cobalt. **Bosjemanite**, *see* apjohnite. **Brackebushite**, $(Pb,Fe,Mn)_3V_2O_8.H_2O$? **Brandtite**, $Ca_2MnAs_2O_8+2H_2O$. **Braunite**, $3Mn_2O_3.MnSiO_3$. **Brostenite**, $2MnO_2.(Mn,Zn)O.2H_2O$. **Bushmanite**, $(Mn,Mg)Al_2(SO_4)_4+24H_2O$—*vide* apjohnite. **Bustamite**, $(Mn,Ca)SiO_3.nCaCO_3$, manganese-calcium metasilicate. **Calcimangite**, *see* manganocalcite. **Carpholite**, $H_4MnAl_2Si_2O_{10}$. **Caryinite**, $(Pb,Mn,Ca,Mg)_3As_2O_3$? **Caryopilite**, $4MnO.3SiO_2.3H_2O$. **Caswellite** (altered mica), Ca,Mg,Mn,Fe,Al silicate. **Cesarolite**, $PbO.3MnO_3.H_2O$. **Chalcophanite**, $(Mn.Zn)O.2MnO_2.2H_2O$, a decomposition product of franklinite. **Childrenite**, $(Fe,Mn)Al(OH)_2PO_4+2H_2O$. **Chloromanganokalite**, $4KCl.MnCl_2$. **Chondrarsenite**, $Mn_3As_2O_8.3Mn(OH)_2$, basic manganese arsenate. **Columbite-tantalite**, $(Fe,Mn)(Nb,Ta)_2O_6$, iron-manganese columbate and tantalate. **Corondite**, $R''(Mn_3O_7)''$, where R denotes Mn, Pb, etc. **Crednerite**, $3CuO.2Mn_2O_3$. **Danalite**, $(Be,Ge,Zn,Mn)_7Si_3O_{12}S$. **Dannemorite**, iron-manganese amphibole. **Dentrite**, a branching form of wad. **Dickinsonite**, chiefly (Mn,Fe,Na) hydrated phosphate. **Dietrichite**, $(Zn,Fe,Mn)Al_2(SO_4)_4+24H$. **Dysluite**, $(Zn,Fe,Mn)O.(Al,Fe)_2O_3$, zinc-manganese-iron graphite (spinel). **Edenite** (manganiferous), aluminous calcium-magnesium amphibole with manganese. **Eosphorite**, $(Mn,Fe)Al(OH)_2PO_4+2H_2O$. **Fairfieldite** (leucomanganite), $(Mn,Ca)_3(PO_4)_2.2H_2O$. **Fauserite**, $2MnSO_4.MgSO_4.15H_2O$, or $(Mn,Mg)SO_4.6H_2O$. **Ferrorhodonite**, $(Mn,Fe)SiO_3$, manganese-iron metasilicate. **Ferrostibian**, hydrated antimonate of Mn and Fe. **Fillowite**, $3R_3P_2O_8+H_2O$ with $R=Mn$, Fe, Ca, and Na_2. **Flinkite**, $MnAsO_4.2Mn(OH)_2$, manganese arsenate. **Fluorite** (manganiferous), CaF_2 with manganese. **Fowlerite**, $(Mn,Zn,Fe,Ca)SiO_3$, manganese-zinc metasilicate. **Franklinite**, $(Fe,Zn,Mn)O.(Fe,Mn)_2O_3$. **Friedelite**, $H_7(MnCl)Mn_4Si_4O_{16}$ (Groth); $H_7(MnCl)Mn_4(SiO_4)$ (Palache). **Gamsigradite**, manganese-hornblende. **Ganomalite**, $Pb_3Si_2O_7$. $(Ca,Mn)_2SiO_4$. **Ganophyllite**, $6H_2O.7MnO.Al_2O_3.8SiO_2$, manganiferous zeolite. **Graphtonite**, $(Fe,Mn,Ca)_3P_2O_8$. **Glauchroite**, $CaMnSiO_4$. **Greenovite**, a manganiferous sphene, $CaTiSiO_5$. **Groroilite**, a variety of bog manganese. **Gudmundite**, $FeSbS$. **Halobolite**, similar to pelagite, found in the deep sea. **Hancockite**, $H_2(Pb,Ca,Sr,Mn)_4(Al,Fe,Mn)_6Si_6O_{26}$. **Harstigite**, $H_7(Ca,Mn)_{12}Al_3Si_{10}O_{40}$. **Hauerite**, MnS_2, manganese disulphide. **Hausmannite**, Mn_3O_4, or $2MnO.MnO_2$. **Hellandite**, $Ca_2R''_3(R''O)_3(SiO_4)_2$ with $R''=Ce$, Di, La, Al, Fe, Mn. **Helvite**, $(Be,Mn,Fe)_7Si_3O_{12}S$, or $3(Be,Mn,Fe)_2SiO_4.(Mn,Fe)S$. **Hemafibrite**, $Mn_3As_2O_8.3Mn(OH)_2$ $+2H_2O$. **Hematolite**, $(Al,Mn)AsO_4.4Mn(OH)_2$. **Hematostibiite**, $Mn_3Sb_2O_{13}$? **Hetaerolite**, $ZnO.Mn_2O_3.H_2O$(?), a zinc-bearing hausmannite. **Hexagonite**, tremolite containing a little manganese. **Hielmite**, stanno-tantalate of V, Fe, Mn, and Ca. **Hollandite**, $m(Ba,Mn)_2MnO_5+nFe_4(MnO_5)_3$. **Hornblende** (manganiferous). **Hortonolite**, $(Fe,Mg,Mn)_2SiO_4$, manganiferous olivines. **Hübnerite**, near wolframite, but containing 20–25 per cent. MnO. **Hureaulite**, manganese phosphate. **Hydrorhodonite**, alteration product from rhodonite to serpentine. **Ilesite**, $(Mn,Zn,Fe)SO_4+4H_2O$. **Ilvaite** (manganiferous), calcium-iron silicate with manganese. **Inesite**, $2(Mn,Ca).SiO_3.H_2O$, manganiferous zeolite. **Jacobsite**, $(Mn,Mg)O.(Fe,Mn)_2O_3$. **Jeffersonite**, manganese-zinc pyroxene. **Juddite**, a manganiferous amphibole. **Kempite**, $MnCl_2.3MnO_2.2H_2O$. **Kaneite**, Mn_5As_4, manganese arsenide. **Kentrolite**, $2PbO.Mn_2O_3.2SiO$. **Keramohalite**, *see* apjohnite. **Knebelite**, $(Fe,Mn)_2SiO_4$. **Kutnohorite**, a ferruginous manganiferous dolomite. **Lampadite** (lepidophacite). **Lamprophyllite**, contains Na, Fe, Mn, Ti, and SiO_2. **Landesite**, $3Fe_2O_3$. $20MnO.8P_2O_5.27H_2O$. **Langbanite**, $m(Sb_2O_3)nFe_2O_3.Mn''(Mn'',Si)O_3$. **Lavenite** $(Na_4,Ca_2,Mn_2,Zr)(SiZr)O_{32}$. **Lepidophacite**, *see* lampadite. **Leucomanganite**, *see* fairfieldite. **Leucophœnicite**, $H_2(Mn,Zn,Ca)_7SiO_{14}$. **Lithiophilite**, $Li(Mn,Fe)PO_4$, lithium-manganese-iron phosphate. **Loseyite**, a basic carbonate of zinc and manganese, $2(Zn,Mn)CO_3.5(Zn,Mn)(OH)_2$. **Luckite**, $(Fe,Mn)SO_4+4H_2O$. **Mallardite**, $MnSO_4.7H_2O$, manganese sulphate. **Manganandalusite**, manganiferous andalusite (Al_2SiO_5). **Manganapatite**, $[(Ca,Mn)F]Ca_4(PO_4)_3$, apatite with manganese replacing calcium to 10·5 per cent. MnO. **Manganbrucite**, brucite $(MgO.H_2O)$ with considerable manganese oxide. **Manganchlorite**, clinochlore $(H_8Mg_5Al_2Si_3O_{18})$ with 2·3 per cent. MnO. **Mangandiaspore**, a manganiferous diaspore. **Mangandolomite**, $(Ca,Mg,Mn)CO_3$. **Manganese-humite**, *see* leucophœnicite. **Mangan-grossularite**, $3(Ca.Mn)O.Al_2O_3.3SiO_2$. **Manganhedenbergite**, hedenbergite $(CaFe(SiO_3)_2)$, calcium-iron pyroxene, with 6·5 per cent. manganese. **Manganite**, $Mn_2O_3.H_2O$. **Manganocalcite** (calcimangite, spartaite), $(Ca,Mn)CO_3$, calcite $(CaCO_3)$ with varying amounts of manganese. **Manganocolumbite-manganotantalite**, $(Mn,Fe)(Nb,Ta)_2O_6$, manganese-iron columbate and tantalate. **Manganoferrite**, $(Fe,Mn)_3O_4$. **Manganolangbeinite**, $K_2Mn_2(SO_4)_3$. **Manganomagnetite** (manganmagnetite), magnetite (Fe_2O_4) with 4 to 6 per cent. manganese. **Manganophyllite**, biotite with considerable manganese. **Manganosiderite** (mangansiderite) $(Fe,Mn)CO_3$. **Manganosite**, MnO. **Manganostibiite**, basic manganese antimonate. **Manganopectolite**, pectolite $(HNaCa_2(SiO_3)_3)$ with 4 per cent. of MnO. **Mangan-vesuvianite**, silicate of Ca, Al, Fe, with Mn. **Marjatskite**, manganese-glauconite. **Masonite**, manganesian chloritoid. **Natrophilite**,

$NaMnPO_4$. Sodium-manganese phosphate. **Neotocite,** hydrated iron-manganese silicate. **Neptunite,** $R'_2R''TiSO_4O_{12}$, with $R'=Na,K$, and $R''=Fe,Mn$. **Oligonite,** see manganosiderite. **Ottrelite,** $H_2(Fe,Mn)Al_2Si_2O_9$. **Partschinite,** $(Mn,Fe)_3Al_2Si_3O_{12}$. **Pelagite,** $MnO_2.Fe_2O_3$ with SiO_2,Al_2O_3, and H_2O in mechanical admixture; found in the deep sea. **Peloconite,** see wackenrodite. **Piedmontite,** epidote $(HCa_2(Al,Fe)_3Si_3O_{13})$ with 5 to 15 per cent. Mn_2O_3. **Pinakiolite,** $3MgO.B_2O_3+MnO.Mn_2O_3$, manganese-magnesium borate. **Plumbomanganite,** $3MnS.PbS$. **Polianite,** MnO_2, like pyrolusite chemically, but of different crystallographic form. **Psilomelane,** $MnO_2(Mn,K_2,Ba)O$. nH_2O, or H_4MnO_5. **Purpurite,** $(Fe,Mn)_2O_3.P_2O_5.H_2O$. **Pyrochroite,** $Mn(OH)_2$, white manganese hydrate. **Pyrolusite,** MnO_2. **Pyrophanite,** $MnTiO_3$. manganese titanate. **Pyrosmalite,** $H_7[(Fe,Mn)Cl](Fe,Mn)_4Si_4O_{16}$. **Pyroxmangite,** $(Mn,Fe)SiO_3$. **Quenselite.** $2PbO.Mn_2O_3.H_2O$. **Rancierte** (or rancierite), $Mn_3O_4.2H_2O$. **Reddingite,** $(Mn,Fe)_3(PO_4)_2$, $3H_2O$. **Reissacherite,** a variety of bog manganese with a high percentage of water. **Retzian,** basic arsenate of yttrium earths, manganese, and calcium. **Rhodochrosite,** $MnCO_3$. **Rhodonite,** $MnSiO_3$, manganese metasilicate. **Richterite,** $(K_2,Na_2,Mg,Ca,Mn)_4$-$(SiO_3)_4$, sodium-magnesium-manganese amphibole. **Ræpperite,** zinc-bearing tephroite, manganiferous olivines. **Roscoelite,** vanadium mica sometimes with Mn. **Romanechite,** $(Ba,Mn)O.3MnO_2.H_2O$. **Rothoffite** (polyadelphite), manganese-calcium-iron garnet; manganiferous andradite $(Ca_3Fe_2(SiO_4)_3$; (polyadelphite $(Ca,Mn)_3,(Fe,Al)_2Si_3O_{12})$. **Salmite,** manganesian chloritoid. **Sarkinite,** $Mn(OH)_2.Mn_3As_2O_8$. **Scacchite,** $MnCl_2$. **Schefferite,** $6CaMgSi_2O_6.MgFeSi_2O_6.Mn_2Si_2O_6$, manganese pyroxene. **Seamanite,** $3MnO.(B_2O_5.P_2O_5)$. $3H_2O$. **Senaite,** $(Fe,Pb)O.2(Ti,Mn)O_2$. **Serandite,** a hydrated silicate of manganese associated with sodium, calcium, and potassium silicates. **Silfbergite,** see dannemorite. **Sitaparite,** $9Mn_2O_3.4Fe_2O_3.MnO_2.3CaO$. **Skemmatite,** $3MnO_2.Fe_2O_3.6H_2O$. **Soda-berzeliite,** $(Ca,Mn,Na_2)_3As_2O_8$. **Spandite,** $3(Ca,Mn)O.(Al,Fe)_2O_3.3SiO_2$. **Spartaite,** see manganocalcite. **Spessartite,** $Mn_3Al_2(SiO_4)_3$, manganese-aluminium garnet. **Staurolite** (manganiferous), $H_2O.2FeO.5Al_2O_3.4SiO_2$ with manganese. **Stainierite,** $(Co,Fe,Al)_2O_3.H_2O$. **Stibiatil,** Sb_2O_5,Mn_2O_3 and FeO. **Strigovite,** $H_4(Fe,Mn)_2(Fe,Al)_2Si_2O_{11}$. **Sussexite,** $H(Mn,Zn,Mg)BO_3$. **Synadelphite,** $2(Al,Mn)AsO_4.5Mn(OH)_2$, manganese arsenate. **Szmikite,** $MnSO_4.H_2O$, manganese sulphate. **Tephroite,** Mn_2SiO_4, manganese olivine. **Triplite,** $R_3P_2O_3.RF_2$ with $R=Fe$ and Mn. **Triploidite,** $(Mn,Fe)P_2O_8.(Mn,Fe)(OH)_2$. **Trimerite,** $(Mn,Ca)_2SiO_4.Be_2SiO_4$. **Triphylite,** $Li(Fe,Mn)PO_4$, lithium-iron-manganese phosphate. **Troostite,** $(Zn,Mn)_2SiO_4$. **Urbanite,** $(Ca,Mg,Mn)SO_4+2NaFe''(SiO_3)_2$. **Varvicite,** an impure pyrolusite derived from the alteration of manganite. **Violan,** manganiferous diopside. **Vredenburgite,** $3Mn_3O_4$. $2Fe_2O_3$. **Wackenrodite** (peloconite), bog manganese with a considerable percentage of lead. **Wad,** impure mixture of manganese oxides; includes bog manganese, asbolite, and lampadite. **Wenzelite,** $Mn_3(PO_4)_2.5H_2O$. **Willemite** (manganiferous), $(Zn,Mn)_2SiO_4$; troostite and tephrowillemite are varieties of willemite rich in manganese. **Winchite,** a blue manganiferous amphibole. **Withamite,** epidote with small quantity of Mn. **Wolframite,** $(Fe,Mn)WO_4$, iron-manganese tungstate. **Xantharsenite,** near chrondrarsenite, but contains more water. **Youngite,** $mZnS.nPbS.oMnS$. **Zincite** (manganiferous), $(Zn,Mn)O$.

It will be observed that manganese minerals may be associated with other minerals as isomorphous mixtures—e.g. in *sphalerite,* or *zinc blende,* $(Zn,Cd,Fe,Mn)S$; *zincite,* or *red zinc oxide,* $(Zn,Mn)O$; ferriferous or manganiferous *smithsonite,* or *calamine,* $(Zn,Fe,Mn,Mg,Ca)CO_3$; *manganocalcite,* $(Mn,Ca)CO_3$; *ankerite,* $5(Ca,Fe,Mn)(CO_3)_2.4Ca,Mg(CO_3)_2$; *botryogen,* $(Mg,Fe,Mn,Ca)_5(FeOH)_4(SO_4)_9.36H_2O$; *monimolite,* $(Pb,Fe,Mn)_3(SbO_4)_2$; *caryinite,* $(Mn,Ca,Pb,Mg)_3(AsO_4)_2$; *ottrelite* and *phyllite,* $(Al,Fe)_2(Fe,Mn,Ca,Mg)H_2Si_2O_9$; *ganophyllite,* $Pb_3(Ca,Mn)_2Si_3O_{11}$; *sphenoclase,* $(Ca,Mg,Fe,Mn)_6Al_2Si_6O_{21}$; etc. C. Benedicks [54] described a manganiferous garnet; J. Krenner, and K. Schlossmacher, a manganiferous *spinel*; etc.

According to G. Forchhammer,[55] manganese occurs in very many silicates as a tinctorial agent—*vide supra*—and in all iron ores. L. L. Fermor suggested that the iron-manganese ores be classified as follows: (i) *manganese ores* with 40 to 63 per cent. Mn, and 0 to 10 per cent. Fe; (ii) *ferruginous manganese ores* with 25 to 60 per cent. Mn, and 10 to 30 per cent. Fe; (iii) *manganiferous iron ores* with 5 to 30 per cent. Mn, and 30 to 56 per cent. Fe; and (iv) *iron ores* with 0 to 5 per cent. Mn and 45 to 70 per cent. Fe. E. C. Harder has described the so-called **manganiferous iron ores,** which are mixtures of manganese and iron oxides in varying proportions—*e.g.* from less than one to more than 40 per cent. Mn. The iron is in the form of limonite or hæmatite, and the manganese is in the form of psilomelane or pyrolusite—rarely as carbonate. The high and medium grades are used for making spiegeleisen and ferromanganese, while the lower grade ore, with a small proportion of manganese, is used for making iron. There also occur **manganiferous silver ores** in the oxidized portions of the silver deposits of Western United States. The black, amorphous ore consists of manganese and iron oxides and it carries silver chloride, and lead carbonate or an altered sulphide. The iron is present probably as limonite, and the manganese as wad. The iron oxide generally predominates over the manganese oxide, though at Butte the iron oxide is " almost entirely absent." Ores with a high proportion of silver and lead are smelted for these metals only when the manganese and iron oxides are valuable aids in fluxing. Ores with a low proportion of silver and lead, but with a high proportion of manganese and iron oxides, may be used for making spiegeleisen, ferromanganese, or iron alone when the proportion of manganese oxide is small. Ores too low in silver and lead for direct smelting, and too low in iron and manganese for making spiegeleisen or ferromanganese, are used as fluxes, when iron and manganese pass into the slag, while the silver and lead may be recovered in the smelting. Some **manganiferous zinc ores** contain franklinite, willemite, zincite, tephroite, or rhodonite along with iron and manganese oxides—*e.g.* the zinc ores of New Jersey. The ore is roasted to recover the zinc oxide, and the residuum is used for making spiegeleisen.

The commercial manganese ores are divided into three classes : the high-grade ores, bearing 35 per cent. or more of metallic manganese ; manganiferous iron ores, with 10 to 35 per cent. manganese ; and ferruginous ores, with 5 to 10 per cent. manganese. Manganese ores are quoted at so much per cent. per long ton. During 1924, the price of ore ranged from 1s. 9¾d. to 2s. 0d. per unit. The world's production in metric tons approximates :

1888	1896	1903	1910	1920	1924	1929
153,954	238,542	723,669	1,901,983	1,746,000	2,251,000	2,868,700

The production by countries is as follows :

	1888	1924	1928
Australasia	2,349	4,798	170
Bosnia, etc.	4,000	79,113	—
Brazil	—	159,229	359,651
British India . . .	—	815,894	994,118
Canada . . .	1,203	530	—
Czechoslovakia . . .	—	79,133	108,441
Chile	24,746	4,243	—
China	—	38,500	43,332
Cuba	1,581	23,436	2,440
Dutch East Indies . .	—	8,482	24,452
Egypt	—	150,194	137,502
France	7,676	3,680	3,108
Germany	—	317	211
Gold Coast	—	237,160	339,883
Greece	385	5,726	1,080
Holland	1,107	—	—
Italy	1,652	12,189	10,274
Japan	—	7,585	17,720
Porto Rico . . .	—	4,698	1,547
Portugal . . .	5,638	—	—
Roumania	—	4,698	31,267
Russia and Georgia . .	48,653	499,799	710,300
Spain	2,830	20,840	13,704
Sweden	6,089	10,885	15,790
Tunis and Algeria . .	—	3,220	3,676
Turkey . . .	669	—	—
United Kingdom . . .	13,054	2,496	239
United States . . .	29,198	57,422	47,612
Other countries . . .	3,114	—	2,144

D. A. Wells [56] found manganese to be present in nearly all igneous and metamorphic rocks. H. Moissan found that the pigment of the design on the wall of the grotto at La Mouthe is black on account of the presence of manganese oxide. Some objects found in the grotto are covered with a black deposit of manganese dioxide. F. W. Clarke estimated that the *limestone* of the earth's crust contains an average of 0·05 per cent. MnO. E. J. Chapman found manganese to be present in many limestones ; W. Crum, A. Vogel, and L. Dieulafait, in *marbles*. The term *cipolin marbles* is applied to concretionary masses of limestone found in the lower parts of beds of gneiss, sometimes in large quantities, sometimes in isolated lenti- cular masses, and which are evidently contemporaneous with the rocks by which they are enclosed.   L. Dieulafait detected manganese in over a thousand specimens of these marbles from different parts of the world.   Water from the Atlantic Ocean, Indian Ocean, Red Sea, and the Mediterranean Sea, when allowed to stand in bottles for a month, furnishes a sediment containing manganese oxide ; this oxide is pro- duced by the oxidation of the manganous carbonate in soln.   Calcium carbonate is also formed.   Hence, the calcareous mud from the bottom of the ocean forms chalk which contains manganese oxide.   Indeed, fifty specimens of chalk from the Paris basin were found to contain more than fifty times as much manganese as the coloured marbles of the Pyrenees and Italy.   L. Raab reported manganese in *chromite* ore and in *magnetite* ; R. Böttger, in *graphite* and *iodine* ; L. Picciardi, in the *volcanic ash* from Ætna ; and B. Platz found potassium permanganate in the masonry of a blast furnace.   The purest of *clays* nearly always contain traces of manganese, while the ferruginous clays contain quite appreciable amounts. L. Az- éma observed the presence of manganese in various coloured clays.   F. B. Guthrie and L. Cohen found 0·254 per cent. Mn_2O_3 in some sterile *soils*. A. Contino found 0·03 to 0·48 per cent. Mn_3O_4 in various soils—sandy, volcanic, clay, and calcareous.   P. de Sornay found 0·027 to 0·409 per cent. Mn in Mauritius soils ; O. M. Shedd found 0·005 to 0·331 per cent. MnO in the surface soils of Kentucky, and 0·002 to 0·260 per cent. in the subsoils. J. S. McHargue, G. Bertrand, A. Leclerc, and J. J. Skinner and M. X. Sullivan made observations on this subject.

C. W. Scheele observed the presence of manganese in commercial *alkali salts* and *potassium hydroxide* ; R. Böttger, in *potassium chlorate* ; J. Volhard, in *sodium hydroxide, red-lead*, and most *iron salts*, but not in ammonium ferric alum ; and R. Wegscheider, in *barium carbonate*.

G. Forchhammer [57] observed that sea-water contains manganese in soln.   As indicated above, L. Dieulafait inferred that the manganese is present as manganous carbonate, and when the water is allowed to stand for a month, the carbonate at the surface in contact with air is converted into oxide, and precipitated ; at the same time, the calcium hydrocarbonate is converted into insoluble carbonate, so that a sediment of mixed calcium carbonate and manganese oxide is formed.   The observations of J. Murray and co-workers, J. Y. Buchanan, C. W. von Gümbel, etc., on the formation of manganese oxide nodules in deep seas, etc., have been previously discussed.   The manganese minerals readily undergo decomposition and pass into soln. when they are exposed to the action of surface waters ; and hence manganese finds its way into the rivers and seas.   J. Murray estimated that one cubic mile of average river-water contains in soln. 5703 tons of manganese hemitrioxide, and that 6524 cubic miles of river-water are annually discharged into the sea.   This means that 37,000,000 tons of the oxide, or nearly 26,000,000 tons of manganese, are brought every year by rivers into the oceans.   This process has been going on for untold ages, so that a large proportion of manganese salts might be expected to be present in sea-water.   This is not the case, for the manganese is deposited from sea-water and is found in the mud, etc., which deep-sea explorations have shown to be formed at the bottom of the ocean.   D. A. Wells, and B. M. Lersch reported manganese to be present in numerous spring-waters.   Thus, C. R. Fresenius reported it in the waters of Niederselters, Driburg, Langenschwalbach, Pyrmont, Ems, Homburg, and Wiesbaden ; J. Bouquet found traces in the waters of Vichy ; P. Berthier, St. Nectaire ; J. Löwe, Krouthal, Nassau ; C. Bromeis, at Nauheim ; J. J. Berzelius, H. Göttl, and F. Ragsky, Carlsbad ; G. Wolf, Gastein ; A. von Planta, Ragaz-Pfäfers ; E. Ludwig, Srebremica, Bosnia ; and Karlsbrunn, Austrian Silesia ; M. Gläser and W. Kalmann, and R. Nasini and co-workers, Roncegno, Southern Tyrol ; C. F. Eichleiter, Orsola, Southern Tyrol ; A. Goldberg, Bad Elster, Saxony ; E. Bechi, Acqua delle piazzuole des Arnotals ; C. A. H. von

Wolzogen - Kühr, Amsterdam ; S. de Luca, Pozzuoli, Italy ; G. Lunge and R. E. Schmidt, St. Lorenzquelle, Leuk, Switzerland ; A. Carnot, Aveyron, France ; F. Jadin and A. Astruc, Vichy, Luxeuil, and Bussang in the Vosges, the Alps, Montagne Noire, the plain of Languedoc, and Boulou, France ; C. H. Bothamley, Harrogate and Askern, Yorkshire ; B. A. Burrell, Knaresborough, Yorkshire ; T. E. Thorpe, Cheltenham, England ; and C. du Ponteil, Hot Lake, White Island, New Zealand ; E. H. S. Bailey and F. B. Porter, a trace in the artesian well of Abilene, Kansas ; W. P. Mason, Missouri Springs, Missouri ; A. H. Wiebe, Mississippi river ; W. F. Hillebrand, Shoal Creek, Missouri ; Mountain View Mine, Montana ; and La Junta, Colorado ; J. K. Haywood, F. A. Gooch and J. E. Whitfield, Hot Springs of Arkansas, and the Excelsior Geyser, Yellowstone National Park ; M. B. Harden, Rockbridge Alum Spring, Virginia ; and F. G. Novy, salt springs of Texas. S. Yoshimura studied the variation in the manganese content of the water of Takasuka-Numa, Saitama, during periods of stagnation, and circulation. M. Weibull found 23 mgrms. MnO per litre of water from Lund, Sweden ; the quantity of other mineral matters present was not particularly large. *Chrenothrix manganifera* was present in the water and caused the manganese to be deposited in the water-pipes to such an extent as to block them. The formation from which the water came consisted principally of gneiss in which were veins of diorite containing 8·2 per cent. of manganous oxide. C. A. H. von Wolzogen-Kühr found 0·3 parts of manganese per million in the water of the Oranjekom and canals of Amsterdam, and 0·1 per cent. in the mud. The oxidation of manganese compounds by the oxygen of the air does not occur with an acidity of $p_H=8\cdot1$; and manganese bacteria can oxidize dissolved manganese not only in alkaline soln., $p_H=10$, but also in acidic soln., $p_H=4$ to 5. Manganese has also been reported as a common constituent in the deposits from various springs, etc. Thus, H. Braconnot observed it with the springs of Luxeuil, Vosges ; C. M. Kersten, in a mine-water at Freyberg ; E. F. Leuchs observed a large mass of hydrated manganese oxide in the water channel of Nürnberg ; R. W. Townsend, in the discharge from a spring at 44° near Cape of Good Hope ; C. M. Kersten, at Carlsbad ; E. H. S. Bailey, in the city water-pipes of Hutchinson, Arkansas Valley ; R. Woy, O. Materne, and E. von Raumer reported cases of obstruction in service water-pipes by manganiferous deposits.

G. Forchhammer [58] found that manganese is present in the ashes of the *Zostera marina*, and E. J. Maumené observed manganese in the ashes of the *Fucus serratus*. C. W. Scheele found manganese to be present in wood ashes, and a little in the ashes of thyme—*Thymus serpillum* ; G. Forchhammer, in the ashes of the *Padina pavonia* ; T. J. Herapath, in the ashes of the radish, turnip, beetroot, and carrot ; E. O. von Lippmann, the vinasse from a beet-sugar factory ; T. Richardson, sugarcane ; W. F. Salm-Hortsdar, oats ; J. von Liebig, tea and coffee ; R. Böttger, and A. Domergue and C. Nicolas, in tea—0·022 to 0·065 per cent. ; L. L. Fermor, bamboo ; F. A. Flückiger, and E. F. von Gorup-Besanez, the water-chestnut— *Trapa natans* ; G. Campani, wood, corn, and tobacco ; R. Böttger, beech, box, and cork ; F. P. Dunnington, corn ; J. E. de Vrij, beech-nuts ; J. A. Trillat, in vegetables ; M. Balland, in potatoes ; and J. S. McHargue, in the pericarp and germ of rice, barley, wheat, tomatoes, oranges, and lemons. Observations were also made by A. Hafner and H. Krist, and W. P. Headden. N. Passerini found 0·068 per cent. of manganese in dried *Lupinus albus* ; the different parts of the plant, dried at 100°, contained the following proportions of ash, and the indicated percentages of manganese in the ash—the first column for legumes refers to those separated from the middle of the plant, and the second column to those from the ends :

	Leaves.	Legumes.		Stems.	Branches.	Seeds.	Roots.	Nodules.
Ash .	8·267	3·726	3·280	2·286	2·021	2·102	3·910	10·400
Mn_2O_3	12·436	7·080	5·927	4·580	4·231	2·190	1·536	0·377

Unlike P. Pichard, F. Jadin and A. Astruc did not find manganese to be most concentrated in the parts of a tree which are in vegetative activity, provided the percentages are not calculated on the weight of ash, but on the dried organs. In that case, more manganese is present in old leaves than in young leaves. They also found more manganese in the aerial portions than in the roots. G. Bertrand and M. Rosenblatt found that in one group of plants, the manganese content of the leaves is at a maximum at the commencement of the leaf formation, and then diminishes with age, the rate of diminution differing with the group. In another group, the manganese content increases very rapidly with age to a maximum, and then diminishes. In another group, the manganese content increases continuously with age. D. H. Wester found manganese present in various flowers, free from dust and selected in dry weather ; and also in the seeds of 48 species of plants. C. C. McDonnell and R. C. Roark found little difference in the stem and flowers—open and closed—of the *Chrysanthemum cinerariæfolium*. According to J. S. McHargue, the proportion of manganese present in the hazel nut varies considerably in different parts of the same seed, and the seed coat surrounding the kernel contains a much larger proportion than the kernel or the outer coats. There is a close connection between the amount of manganese and the presence of oxydases in plant tissues, and it is therefore considered probable that the accumulation of manganese in the seed-coat bears an important relation to the vital processes in the formation and germination of seeds. L. E. Westman and R. M. Rowat found that in the *Rhamnus purshiana* (cascara sagrada) the proportion of manganese in the inner third of the bark is about twice as great as in the outer third. When the powdered drugs of the *Rhamnaceæ* family are extracted with water, approximately one-fourth of the manganese goes into solution. G. Bertrand and M. Rosenblatt found that with the *Nicotina rustica* and *Lilium lancefolium* those organs in which chemical changes are the most intense contain the highest percentages of manganese. The seeds contain a high proportion of manganese, doubtless for the use of the future seedling.

E. J. Maumené found manganese to be present in potatoes, wheat, rye, barley, rice, sorrel, beans, sugar beet, carrot, lentils, peas, asparagus, different kinds of fruit, fodder, cocoa, coffee, and tea ; but more in lemons, oranges, onions, and garlic. G. Bertrand and M. Rosenblatt found manganese in those plants in which E. J. Maumené found none. Hence, *the presence of manganese is general in all the organs and species of plants so far examined.* G. Bruni and C. Pelizzola found manganese dioxide in raw caoutchouc. F. Jadin and A. Astruc also found manganese in the ash of lucerne, sainfoin, vetches, clover, potatoes, mangolds, poplar leaves, chestnut, rice, maize, barley, oats, .bran, and meadow-hay. J. S. Jones and D. E. Bulles found 42 mgrms. per kilogram of air-dried vetch ; 33 in red-clover ; 68 in Alsike clover ; 32 in lucerne ; 33 in field-peas ; 27 in sweet clover ; and 34 in white clover. More was present in the leaves than in the other parts. H. Marcelet observed no relation between the proportion of arsenic and manganese in sea-water plants. L. E. Westman and R. M. Rowat found manganese in the ash of many laxative drugs—alder buckthorn bark, cascara sagrada, cassia bark, podophyllen root, senna leaves, rhubarb root, *Rhamnus californica* bark, liquorice root, jalap root, wahoo bark, cassia pulp, and Barbadoes aloes ; and J. S. McHargue, in spear grass. E. J. Maumené found 0·0001 to 0·0020 grm. per litre in thirty-one wines of different European and African vintages. O. Prandi and A. Civetta found that wines contain 0·53 to 1·65 parts of manganese per million ; the wines of better quality usually contain the highest proportion. G. Massol observed that mistelles —fortified musts—contain from 0 to 0·010 grm. MnO per litre. A. Hilger, and L. Rössler found 0·3 to 0·8 per cent. of manganese in the ash obtained from wines ; L. Medicus found bilberry wine specially rich in manganese ; and A. Alessi observed manganese in some residues in ancient wine-glasses. J. Kachler found that the manganese is present as manganese oxalate in the cambial sap of the pine ; and G. Campani observed that it is present in plant-ashes as oxide, silicate, or phosphate. G. Guérin found that when wood-sawdust is macerated for two or three days with a one per cent. soln. of potassium hydroxide, a deep brown liquid is obtained, and when this is acidified with hydrochloric acid, a bulky, flocculent precipitate is produced. This precipitate can be washed with very dil. hydrochloric acid, redissolved in ammonia, reprecipitated by acid, washed and dried. It is a pale brown powder, which, when obtained from the beech, had the composition, C, 52·762 ; H, 5·04 ; N, 4·60 ; S, 0·666 ; P, 1·297 ; Mn, 0·402 per cent. According to G. Bertrand, all manganese salts have the property of bringing about the oxidation by atmospheric oxygen of solutions of quinol, pyrogallol, and para-amidophenol, guaiacum, and similar substances. The soln. acquires a colour which depends on the nature of the carbon compound, whilst the intensity of the coloration depends on the nature of the acid in combination with the manganese. Oxidation is much more energetic with salts such as the succinate, gluconate, or salicylate than with the chloride, sulphate, or nitrate. He inferred that the oxydases are special compounds of manganese in which the acid radical, of a proteid character and varying with the particular ferment, has just sufficient activity to keep the metal in soln., whilst the metal is the real carrier of oxygen. The subject was discussed by A. Villiers, A. Livache, and J. S. McHargue.

Animals feed on plants, directly or indirectly, and the presence of manganese might therefore be expected in animal tissues. G. Forchhammer [59] found manganese in sea-organisms. L. N. Vauquelin, and J. McCrae detected manganese in hair ; J. J. Berzelius, in bone ; A. Béchamp, in the liver ; H. Oidtmann, in the human liver and spleen ; J. S. McHargue, in the liver, kidney, and pancreas. P. Pichard found less manganese in animals than in plants ; less in bones than in flesh ; less in flesh than in an egg ; and less in the white of egg than in the yolk ; E. Pollacci, in the human milk and the milk of house animals ; E. J. Maumené, in urine, bones, hair, and the fæces of man ; F. von Oefele, in the excrement of man ; and E. N. Horsford, in the normal urine of man. J. S. McHargue found colostrum to be richer in manganese than ordinary milk. The tissues of cod-liver, fish roe, and the yolks of eggs are rich in manganese, whilst purified cod-liver oil and the whites of eggs contain negligibly small amounts. E. J. Maumené observed no manganese in human blood, but a contrary result was obtained by E. Cottereau, B. du Buisson, N. A. E. Millon, and A. Riche, for they found 1 to 5 mgrms. per kilogram in the blood of human beings and animals ; while G. Bertrand and F. Medigreceanu found that human blood does not contain more than 0·02 mgrm. per litre ; and the amount in the blood of horses, oxen, pigs, rabbits, ducks, and hens is about the same, whilst that in sheep does not exceed 0·06 mgrm. per litre. Most of the manganese occurs in the plasma ; the element is not present in hæmoglobin. P. Carles said that the human blood contains a trace of manganese, but the metal is not present in the blood of oxen, rabbits, fowls, or ducks. Somewhat larger quantities are present in the liver and kidneys, and still more is present in the hair and nails. G. Campani found manganese in the serum and blood corpuscles of the ox. E. J. Maumené, and M. E. Chevreul found manganese in mutton-fat. J. S. McHargue considers that manganese is contained in those plant and animal tissues richest in *vitamins*, and a relationship exists between this element and the vital factors contained in these tissues. H. C. Bradley found 0·6 to 1·2 per cent. of manganese in the tissues and eggs of fresh-water clams, unio, and anodonta —the manganese is most abundant in the gills and mantle. This element is said to be necessary for vital activity, since mussels cannot live in lakes poor in manganese and in the crenothrix and diatoms which contain large amounts of manganese and which form the food of mussels. G. Bertrand and F. Medigreceanu found manganese from hundredths to tenths of a mgrm. in 100 grms. of the digestive, respiratory, and genito-urinary organs, glands with internal secretion, muscular, nervous and osseous tissue, skin and teeth, adipose tissue, eyes, and finally the bile, milk, or eggs of typical animals of the three classes, mammals, birds, and fishes—but not in the white of birds' eggs. For similar organs of the same species the variation in manganese content is very slight from one animal to another, and is but little greater amongst different species of the same class. The difference is, however, more marked from class to class, birds having a higher manganese content than mammals. Amongst the more important organs or tissues, the manganese content is highest in the uterus of birds (0·786–2·20 mgrms. per 100 grms.), the lowest value occurring in the muscular and nervous tissues and the lungs. The grey matter of ox brain has a higher manganese content than the white matter ; the heart and the muscles of the tongue than the muscles of the trunk and limbs. Milk is very poor in manganese, although slightly richer than blood. They found that of the invertebrata the gastropod molluscs and the lamellibranchia are the most abundantly supplied with manganese. The animal kingdom as a whole is, however, very poor in manganese as compared with the vegetable kingdom. J. Cotte observed manganese in various sponges, particularly in the gemmules. H. M. Fox and H. Ramage found manganese in nineteen species of polychaetes ; it was widely distributed in the molluscs, being found in all the organs of the land gastropods ; it was found in many organs of the marine gastropods, but was absent from *Haliotis*. E. F. Hopkins found that manganese is necessary for the growth of *Chlorella*.

REFERENCES.

[1] F. W. Clarke, *The Data of Geochemistry*, Washington, 29, 1924 ; *Chem. News*, **61**. 414, 1890 ; F. W. Clarke and G. Steiger, *Journ. Washington Acad.*, **4**. 57, 1914 ; F. W. Clarke and H. S. Washington, *Proc. Nat. Acad.*, **8**. 112, 1922 ; *The Composition of the Earth's Crust*, Washington, 1924 ; H. S. Washington, *Trans. Amer. Inst. Min. Eng.*, **39**. 735, 1908 ; *Bull. Nat. Research Council*, **2**. ii, 30, 1926 ; *Journ. Franklin Inst.*, **190**. 777, 1920 ; *Amer. Journ. Science*, (4), **38**. 90, 1914 ; (5), **9**. 351, 1925 ; (5), **12**. 272, 1926 ; *Journ. Washington Acad.*, **14**. 435, 1924 ; V. M. Goldschmidt, *Videnskapsselskapets Schrift.*, 11, 1922 ; 3, 1923 ; *Zeit. Elektrochem.*, **28**. 411, 1922 ; *Der Stoffwechsel der Erde*, Kristiania, 1922 ; E. Herlinger, *Fortschr. Min.*, **12**. 253, 1927 ; A. von Antropoff, *Sitzber. Nat. Hist. Ver. Rheinlande*, 1, 1926 ; O. Hahn, *Naturwiss.*, **14**. 159, 1926 ; W. and J. Noddack and O. Berg, *ib.*, **13**. 568, 1925 ; J. Joly, *The Surface History of the Earth*, Oxford, 1925 ; G. Tammann, *Zeit. anorg. Chem.*, **131**. 96, 1923 ; **134**. 269, 1924 ; P. Niggli, *Geochemie und Konstitution der Atomkerne*, Helsingfors, 50, 1928 ; *Die leichtflüchtigen Bestandteile im Magma*, Leipzig, 5, 1920 ; *Naturwiss.*, **9**. 463, 1921 ; R. A. Sonder, *Zeit. anorg. Chem.*, **192**. 257, 1930 ; *Zeit. Kryst.*, **57**. 611, 1923 ; J. H. L. Vogt, *Zeit. prakt. Geol.*, **6**. 225, 314, 377, 413, 1898 ; **7**. 10, 274, 1899 ; **14**. 223, 1906 ; W. Vernadsky, *Essai de minéralogie descriptive*, St. Petersburg, **1**. 121, 740, 1914 ; *La geochimie*, Paris, 16, 1924 ; *Centr. Min.*, 758, 1912 ; A. E. Fersman, *Bull. Acad. St. Petersburg*, (6), **6**. 367, 1912 ; H. von Klüber, *Das Vorkommen der chemischen Elemente im Kosmos*, Leipzig, 1931.

[2] H. A. Rowland, *Johns Hopkins Univ. Arc.*, 85, 1891 ; *Amer. Journ. Science*, (3), **41**. 243, 1891 ; *Chem. News*, **63**. 133, 1891 ; *Preliminary Table of Solar Spectrum Wave-lengths*, Chicago, 1898 ; J. N. Lockyer, *Phil. Trans.*, **163**. 253, 1873 ; F. McClean, *Monthly Notices Astron.*, **52**. 22, 1891 ; A. J. Angström, *Recherches sur le spectre solaire*, Upsala, 1868 ; A. Cornu, *Compt. Rend.*, **86**. 313, 530, 1878 ; *Ann. École Norm.*, (2), **9**. 21, 1880 ; *Journ. École Polyt.*, **53**. 175, 1883 ; R. Wildt, *Zeit. Physik*, **54**. 856, 1929 ; S. A. Mitchell, *Astrophys. Journ.*, **71**. 1, 1930 ; S. Albrecht, *ib.*, **72**. 65, 1930 ; P. W. Merrill and C. G. Burwell, *ib.*, **71**. 285, 1930 ; C. Young, *The Sun*, London, 1892 ; C. G. Abbot, *The Sun*, London, 1912 ; F. J. M. Stratton, *Astronomical Physics*, London, 1925 ; H. von Klüber, *Das Vorkommen der chemischen Elemente im Kosmos*, Leipzig, 1931 ; H. N. Russell, *Astrophys. Journ.*, **63**. 1, 1926 ; *Mount Wilson Contr.*, 383, 1929 ; C. H. Payne, *Proc. Nat. Acad.*, **11**. 192, 1925 ; *Stellar Atmospheres*, Cambridge, 1925 ; C. H. Payne and C. P. Chase, *Circ. Harvard Coll. Observatory*, 300, 1927 ; E. P. Waterman, *Bull. Lick Observatory*, 243, 1913 ; J. Stebbins, *ib.*, 43, 1903 ; C. D. Shane, *ib.*, 10, 1920 ; P. W. Merrill, *Astrophys. Journ.*, **56**. 457, 1922 ; **58**. 195, 1923 ; **63**. 13, 1926 ; W. W. Morgan, *ib.*, **73**. 104, 1931 ; W. C. Rufus, *Publ. Astron. Obs. Univ. Michigan*, **2**. 103, 1915 ; G. E. Hale, F. Ellermann and J. A. Parkhurst, *Publ. Yerkes Obs.*, **2**. 253, 1903.

[3] J. N. Lockyer, *Proc. Roy. Soc.*, **43**. 117, 1887 ; M. H. Klaproth, *Abhand. Akad. Berlin*, 24, 1803 ; *Gilbert's Ann.*, **13**. 338, 1803 ; *Beiträge zur chemischen Kenntniss der Mineralkörper*, Berlin, **5**. 245, 1810 ; P. A. von Holger, *Zeit. Physik*, **5**. 6, 1823 ; **7**. 138, 1830 ; **8**. 283, 1830 ; **9**. 327, 1831 ; J. J. Berzelius, *Pogg. Ann.*, **33**. 33, 129, 136, 1834 ; E. H. von Baumhauer, *ib.*, **66**. 491, 500, 1845 ; A. Duflos, and N. W. Fischer, *ib.*, **72**. 480, 1847 ; A. Duflos, *ib.*, **74**. 65, 1849 ; C. Bergmann, *ib.*, **78**. 412, 1849 ; H. Lasch, *Tschermak's Mitt.*, (2), **40**. 294, 1930 ; J. Auerbach, *Sitzber. Akad. Wien*, **49**. 497, 1864 ; *Pogg. Ann.*, **118**. 347, 1863 ; C. F. Rammelsberg, *ib.*, **62**. 453, 1844 ; **74**. 444, 1849 ; *Sitzber. Akad. Berlin*, 245, 1844 ; V. de Luynes, *Ann. Muséum Hist. Nat.*, (4), **5**. 164, 1844 ; W. S. Clark, *On metallic Meteorites*, Göttingen, 1852 ; *Liebig's Ann.*, **82**. 367, 1852 ; E. Cohen, *Meteoritenkunde*, Stuttgart, **1**. 55, 1894 ; W. Crookes, *Phil. Trans.*, **217**. A, 411, 1918 ; F. Behrend and G. Berg, *Chemische Geologie*, Stuttgart, 1927 ; O. C. Farrington, *Publ. Field Museum Geol.*, **3**. 213, 1910 ; J. and W. Noddack, *Naturwiss.*, **18**. 757, 1920 ;

N. S. Manross, *Liebig's Ann.*, **81**. 253, 1852 ; C. A. Joy, *Amer. Journ. Science*, (2), **37**. 247, 1864 ; *Liebig's Ann.*, **86**. 43, 1853 ; E. Uricoechea, *ib.*, **91**. 252, 1853 ; M. Böcking, *ib.*, **96**. 246, 1855 ; *Neues Jahrb. Min.*, 304, 1856 ; E. Pugh, *Liebig's Ann.*, **98**. 358, 1856 ; E. P. Harris, *ib.*, **100**. 183, 1859 ; F. Wohler, *Sitzber. Akad. Wien*, **8**. 504, 1852 ; C. U. Shepard, *Amer. Journ. Science*, (2), **15**. 4, 366, 1853 ; (2), **17**. 332, 1854 ; (3), **21**. 119, 1881 ; C. Jackson, *ib.*, (2), **36**. 261, 1863 ; (2),**43**. 281, 1867 ; (3), **4**. 496, 1872 ; J. L. Smith, *ib.*, (2), **38**. 386, 1864 ; J. W. Mallet, *ib.*, (3), **2**. 13, 1871 ; (3), **28**. 287, 1884 ; (3), **33**. 59, 1887 ; F. A. Genth, *ib.*, (3), **12**. 73, 1876 ; J. R. Santos, *ib.*, **15**. 338, 1878 ; L. G. Eakins, *ib.*, (3), **32**. 313, 1886 ; J. E. Whitfield, *ib.*, (3), **33**. 500, 1887 ; D. Fisher and C. G. Allmendingen, *ib.*, (3), **34**. 383, 1887 ; K. Supler, *Ber. Ver. Naturf. Ges. Freiburg*, **1**. 257, 1858 ; P. Kuhlberg, *Arch. Naturkunde Dorpat*, **4**. 27, 1865 ; G. Darlington, *Phil. Mag.*, (4), **10**. 13, 1855 ; P. Grigorieff, *Zeit. deut. geol. Ges.*, **32**. 419, 1880 ; F. Koch, *Tschermak's Mitt.*, (2), **5**. 243, 1882 ; W. Will, *Neues Jahrb. Min.*, ii, 179, 1889 ; E. Johanson, *Arb. Naturf. Ver. Riga*, (2), **7**. 51, 1891 ; C. Friedheim, *Sitzber. Akad. Berlin*, 204, 1888 ; F. Zambonini, *Amer. Min.*, **12**. 1, 1927 ; G. Berg, *Metallwirtschaft*, **9**. 1, 1930 ; *Vorkommen und Geochemie der mineralischen Rohstoffe*, Leipzig, 1929 ; E. Herlinger, *Fortschr. Min.*, **12**. 253, 1927.

⁴ O. A. Derby, *Amer. Journ. Science*, (4), **12**. 18, 1901 ; (4), **25**. 213, 1908 ; F. P. Dunnington, *ib.*, (3), **36**. 175, 1888 ; C. R. Fresenius, *Liebig's Ann.*, **75**. 172, 1850 ; E. C. Sullivan, *Bull. U.S. Geol. Sur.*, 312, 1907 ; *Econ. Geol.*, **1**. 67, 1905 ; G. A. Thiel, *ib.*, **19**. 108, 1924 ; **20**. 301, 1925 ; *Amer. Journ. Science*, (5), **7**. 457, 1924 ; R. A. F. Penrose, *Ann. Rep. Arkansas Geol. Sur.*, **1**. 1, 1890 ; *Journ. Geol.*, **1**. 275, 356, 1893 ; E. C. Harder, *Bull. U.S. Geol. Sur.*, 427, 1910 ; C. A. Moreing, *Trans. Amer. Inst. Min. Met. Eng.*, **2**. 250, 1894 ; T. L. Watson, *Trans. Amer. Inst. Min. Eng.*, **34**. 207, 1904 ; C. F. Drake, *ib.*, **28**. 191, 1898 ; W. H. Emmons, *ib.*, **42**. 3, 1911 ; J. H. L. Vogt, *Zeit. prakt. Geol.*, **14**. 217, 1906 ; J. Bellinger, *ib.*, **11**. 237, 1903 ; L. Dieulafait, *Compt. Rend.*, **96**. 718, 1883 ; **101**. 609, 644, 674, 1885 ; V. Vincent, *ib.*, **162**. 259, 1916 ; G. Bertrand, *Rev. Gen. Chim.*, **8**. 205, 1905 ; A. Gorgeu, *Bull. Soc. Min.*, **13**. 21, 1890 ; **16**. 96, 133, 1898 ; *Bull. Soc. Chim.*, (3), **9**. 496, 650, 1893 ; M. Thresh, *Essex Naturalist*, **12**. 137, 1902 ; W. M. Doherty, *Rept. Australasian Assoc.*, 339, 1898 ; L. L. Fermor, *The Manganese Deposits of India*, Calcutta, **1**. 22, 1909 ; *Rec. Geol. Sur. India*, **37**. 82, 1909 (I am indebted to the Director of the Geological Survey of India for Fig. 1) ; F. R. Mallet, *ib.*, **12**. 99, 1879 ; **16**. 116, 1883 ; F. W. Clarke, *The Data of Geochemistry*, Washington, 559, 1924 ; W. Lindgren, *Mineral Deposits*, New York, 251, 1913 ; J. Murray, *Challenger Reports—Deep-sea Deposits*, London, 341, 1891 ; *Proc. Roy. Soc. Edin.*, **9**. 255, 1876 ; J. Murray and R. Irvine, *Trans. Roy. Soc. Edin.*, **37**. 721, 1895 ; R. Irvine and J. Gibson, *Proc. Roy. Soc. Edin.*, **18**. 54, 1890 ; J. Y. Buchanan, *ib.*, **18**. 17, 1890 ; *Trans. Roy. Soc. Edin.*, **36**. 482, 1891 ; *Chem. News*, **44**. 253, 1881 ; J. B. J. D. Boussingault, *Ann. Chim. Phys.*, (5), **27**. 289, 1882 ; C. W. von Gümbel, *Sitzber. Akad. München*, **8**. 197, 1878 ; *Forschungsreise der S.M.S. Gazelle*, Berlin, **2**. 33, 1890 ; *Neues Jahrb. Min.*, 869, 1878 ; G. Bischof, *Lehrbuch der chemischen und physikalischen Geologie*, Bonn, **1**. 540, 1863 ; London, **3**. 522, 1859 ; A. W. Stelzner and A. Bergeat, *Die Erzlagerstätten*, Leipzig, 239, 1914 ; 571, 1906 ; E. Fuchs and L. de Launay, *Traité des gîtes minéraux et métallifères*, Paris, **2**. 1, 1893 ; G. Rother, *Centr. Min.*, 223, 1914 ; R. Beck and W. H. Weed, *The Nature of Ore Deposits*, New York, 104, 535, 1905 ; L. Demaret, *Ann. Mines Belg.*, **10**. 809, 1905 ; A. H. Church, *Min. Mag.*, **1**. 50, 1876 ; C. Chun, *Aus dem Tiefen des Weltmeeres : Schilderungen von der deutschen Tiefsee Expedition*, Jena, 150, 1900 ; N. Andrussoff, *Guide des excursions du VII Congrès Geol. Internat.*, **29**. 13, 1897 ; G. A. F. Molengraaff, *Proc. Akad. Amsterdam*, **18**. 415, 1915 ; W. A. Tarr, *Journ. Geol.*, **26**. 610, 1918 ; H. Leitmeier, *Koll. Zeit.*, **4**. 280, 1909 ; F. Cornu and H. Leitmeier, *ib.*, **4**. 285, 1909 ; F. Cornu and M. Lazarevic, *ib.*, **4**. 295, 1909 ; G. de Geer, *Geol. För. Förh. Stockholm*, **6**. 42, 1884 ; S. Iimori, *Bull. Japan Chem. Soc.*, **2**. 270, 1927 ; *Science Papers Phys. Chem. Research Tokyo*, **7**. 253, 1927 ; F. von Sandberger, *Sitzber. bayer. Akad.*, 191, 1891 ; G. Schreckenthal, *Chem. Erde*, **6**. 51, 1930 ; H. Lasch, *Tschermak's Mitt.*, (2), **40**. 294, 1930 ; G. Berg, *Metallwirtschaft*, **9**. 1, 1930 ; *Vorkommen und Geochemie der mineralischen Rohstoffe*, Leipzig, 1929 ; C. Zapffe, *Ean. Geol.*, **26**. 799, 1931.

⁵ A. H. Curtis, *Manganese Ores*, London, 1919 ; H. Schneiderhöhn, *Ber. Fachausschüsse Ver. deut. Eissenhüttenleute*, **7**. 1, 1926 ; O. R. Kuhn, *Iron Trade Rev.*, **69**. 425, 432, 1921 ; C. R. Elicott, *Blast Furnace*, **6**. 252, 1918 ; Anon., *Mining Mag.*, **14**. 251, 1916 ; *Bull. Imp. Inst.*, **17**. 406, 1919 ; M. Scheffer, *Glückauf*, **49**. 2056, 2111, 2151, 1913 ; E. Priwoznik, *Oesterr. Zeit. Berg. Hütt.*, **49**, 582, 1911 ; H. Schüphaus, *Stahl Eisen*, **32**. 794, 1912 ; J. P. Rowe, *Mining World*, **32**. 1127, 1909 ; C. Hardy, *Eng. Min. Journ.*, **121**. 89, 1926 ; A. Hänig, *Berg. Hütt. Jahrb.*, **57**. 121, 1909 ; M. Lecomte-Denis, *Le manganese*, Paris, 1909 ; F. Lohmann, *Internat. Bergwirtschaft*, **22**. 283, 1929 ; E. Krenkel, *Naturwiss.*, **18**. 554, 1930 ; Anon., *Journ. Soc. Arts*, **60**. 825, 1912.

⁶ H. Dewey and C. E. N. Bromehead, *Tungsten and Manganese Ores of Great Britain*, London, 1916 ; Anon., *Mining Journ.*, **81**. 828, 1907 ; E. Halse, *Trans. North England Inst. Min. Mech. Eng.*, **36**. 103, 1887 ; H. de la Beche, *Report on the Geology of Cornwall, Devon, and West Somerset*, London, 609, 1839 ; A. H. Curtis, *Manganese Ores*, London, 23, 1919 ; Anon., *Mining Mag.*, **14**. 149, 1916 ; E. Halse, *Trans. Fed. Inst. Min. Eng.*, **3**. 940, 1892 ; **4**. 167, 1893.

⁷ E. Fuchs and L. de Launay, *Traité des gîtes minéraux et métallifères*, Paris, **2**. 13, 1893 ; A. Lacroix, *Bull. Soc. Min.*, **23**. 251, 1900 ; E. L. Gruner, *Ann. Mines*, (4), **18**. 61, 1850 ; A. Gorgeu, *Bull. Soc. Chim.*, (3), **9**. 650, 1893 ; (3), **16**. 96, 133, 1895 ; F. Klockmann, *Zeit. prakt. Geol.*, **8**. 265, 1900 ; M. Beaugey, *Bull. Soc. Géol. France*, **17**. 297, 1889 ; C. A. Moreing, *Trans. Inst. Min. Met.*, **2**. 250, 1894 ; B. Mühlbach, *Zeit. Berg. Hütt. Salinenwesen*, **58**. 3, 182, 1910 ; A. Carnot, *Ann. Mines*, (9), **4**. 189, 1893.

⁸ J. Birkinbine, *Min. Resources U.S. Geol. Sur.*, 149, 1901 ; F. Johnson, *Trans. Inst. Min. Met.*, **3**. 275, 1895 ; J. A. Jones, *ib.*, **3**. 263, 1895.
⁹ Anon., *Mining Journ.*, **119**. 717, 1917 ; E. Fuchs and L. de Launay, *Traité des gîtes minéraux et métallifères*, Paris, **2**. 22, 1893 ; R. A. Jones, *Mining Journ.*, **62**. 1058, 1125, 1892 ; *Trans. Inst. Min. Met.*, **3**. 263, 1895 ; F. Johnson, *ib.*, **3**. 275, 1895 ; P. de Rubies and J. Dorronsoro, *Anal. Fis. Quim.*, **27**. 778, 1929 ; J. Head, *Journ. Iron Steel Inst.*, **50**. ii, 139, 1896 ; C. Sundenheim, *Amer. Manf.*, **60**. 226, 1896 ; R. W. Barrington, *Mineral Ind.*, **5**. 420, 1897 ; F. Klockmann, *Glückauf*, **33**. 433, 1897 ; J. Hereza, *Revista Min.*, **53**. 50, 1902 ; C. Doetsch, *Mining Journ.*, **71**. 1529, 1901 ; R. Pibz, *Zeit. prakt. Geol.*, **22**. 373, 1914 ; W. Hoyer, *Zeit. prakt. Geol.*, **19**. 407, 1911 ; H. Michael, *ib.*, **16**. 129, 1908.
¹⁰ A. W. Stelzner and A. Bergeat, *Die Erzlagerstätten*, Leipzig, 253, 1904 ; H. B. de Saussure, *Voyage dans les Alpes*, Neuchatel, **3**. 229, 1796 ; E. Fuchs and L. de Launay, *Traité des gîtes minéraux et métallifères*, Paris, **2**. 9, 1893 ; E. Manzella, *Atti Congresso Naz. Chim.*, 1199, 1926 ; G. Tonietti, *Mining Journ.*, **84**. 459, 1908 ; E. Halse, *Trans. North England Inst. Min. Mech. Eng.*, **34**. 145, 1885 ; G. Castelli, *Rass. Mineraria*, **63**. 101, 1925 ; L. Edlmann, *ib.*, **55**. 1, 1921 ; G. Pariente, *ib.*, **55**. 4, 1921 ; M. Priehäusser, *Zeit. prakt. Geol.*, **17**. 396, 1909 ; C. Rimatori, *Atti Accad. Lincei*, (5), **10**. ii, 226, 1901 ; F. Millosevich, *ib.*, (5), **15**. ii, 317, 1905.
¹¹ A. W. Stelzner and A. Bergeat, *Die Erzlagerstätten*, Leipzig, 253, 1904 ; A. H. Curtis, *Manganese Ores*, London, 73, 1919 ; D. A. Wray, *Mining Mag.*, **32**. 329, 1925.
¹² L. Dominian, *Eng. Min. Journ.*, **78**. 184, 1905 ; M. Simon, *Ann. Mines*, (10), **13**. 269, 1908.
¹³ F. Slavik, *Journ. Croatian Nat. Hist. Soc.*, **32**. 1, 1920 ; G. Behaghel, *Die Eisen- und Manganerz Osteuropas*, Leipzig, 1922.
¹⁴ F. Nowack, *Montan. Rund.*, **16**. 695, 1924 ; Z. Szentpetery, *Asvanytaranak Ertesitöje*, **4**. 95, 214, 1917 ; D. A. Wray, *Mining Mag.*, **32**. 329, 1925.
¹⁵ V. C. Butureau, *Ann. Univ. Jassy*, **5**. 87, 1908 ; **6**. 7, 1909 ; P. Poni, *ib.*, **1**. 15, 1900 ; M. Savul, *ib.*, **12**. 136, 1924 ; *Ann. Mines*, (10), **18**. 262, 1911 ; R. von Mogilnicki, *Berg. Hütt. Jahrb.*, **65**. 27, 1917.
¹⁶ R. Canaval, *Jahrb. Nat. Hist.*, **28**. 357, 1909 ; *Geol. Centr.*, **13**. 507, 1900 ; G. Rother, *Centr. Min.*, 223, 1914.
¹⁷ B. Walter, *Beitrag zur Kenntnis der Erzlagerstätten Bosniens*, Wien, 44, 1887 ; *Jahrb. geol. Reichsanst. Wien*, **26**. 373, 1876 ; H. Quiring, *Zeit. prakt. Geol.*, **27**. 133, 1919 ; **28**. 117, 1920 ; L. K. Moser, *Verh. geol. Reichsanst, Wien*, 380, 1903 ; J. Lowag, *Oesterr. Zeit. Berg. Hütt.*, **50**. 73, 90, 1902 ; J. Pocsubay, *Montan. Ztg.*, **9**. 153, 1902 ; E. Priwoznik, *Berg. Hütt. Jahrb.*, **50**. 434, 1902 ; Anon., *Stahl Eisen*, **41**. 1117, 1921 ; R. von Mogilnicki, *Hütt. Jahrb.*, **65**. 27, 1917 ; H. Philipp, *Bergbau*, **32**. 24, 1919 ; **33**. 22, 1920 ; A. Hofmann and F. Slavik, *Bull. Acad. Bohème*, 1, 1909 ; F. Katzer, *Berg. Hütt. Zeit.*, **54**. 203, 1906 ; F. Kossmat, *Mitt. geol. Ges. Wien*, 364, 1909 ; *Verh. geol. Reichsanst.*, 337, 1905 ; F. Kossmat and C. von John, *Zeit. prakt. Geol.*, **13**. 305, 1905 ; C. von John and C. F. Eichleiter, *Jahrb. geol. Reichsanst.*, **53**. 502, 1904 ; H. K. Scott, *Journ. Iron Steel Inst.*, **94**. ii, 288, 1916 ; A. H. Curtis, *Manganese Ores*, London, 69, 1919 ; A. Hofmann, *Bull. Acad. Bohème*, 10, 1909 ; V. Zsivny, *Banyaszati és Kohaszati Lapok*, 466, 1910 ; J. Krenner, *ib.*, **41**. 165, 1908 ; *Math. Termes Ertesite*, **36**. 548, 1918 ; Anon., *Iron Coal Trades Rev.*, **78**. 50, 1909 ; F. Slavik, *Casopis Narod. Mus.*, **102**. 112, 1928 ; H. Drucker, *Oesterr. Ungar. Montan. Met. Ztg.*, 27, 1907 ; T. Naske, *Stahl Eisen*, **28**. 543, 1908 ; P. Rozlozsnik, *Jahresb. Ungar. Geol. Anstalt*, 95, 1908 ; M. Scheffer, *Glückauf*, **49**. 2056, 2111, 2151, 1913.
¹⁸ A. H. Curtis, *Manganese Ores*, London, 71, 1919 ; G. Schmid, *Zeit. prakt. Geol.*, **29**. 43, 1921 ; A. Muzet, *Bull. Soc. Ind. Min.*, **15**. 113, 1910 ; H. K. Scott, *Trans. Inst. Min. Met.*, **22**. 597, 1913.
¹⁹ A. Schneider, *Neues Jahrb. Min.*, i, 19, 1890 ; M. Hüser, *Glückauf*, **34**. 529, 1898 ; G. Jüngst, *ib.*, **43**. 993, 1907 ; W. Pothmann, *Zur Frage der Eisen- und Manganerzversorgung der deutschen Industrie*, Jena, 1920 ; Anon., *Mining Journ.*, **117**. 215, 1917 ; A. Butts, *Min. Ind.*, **25**. 495, 1916 ; F. Jovic, *Iron Age*, **99**. 496, 1917 ; Anon., *Journ. Board Trade*, **103**. 343, 1919 ; *Stahl Eisen*, **37**. 388, 1917 ; F. H. Wilcox, *Trans. Amer. Inst. Min. Eng.*, **56**. 412, 1917 ; A. W. Stelzner and A. Bergeat, *Die Erzlagerstätten*, Leipzig, 239, 571, 1906 ; R. Delkeskamp, *Zeit. prakt. Geol.*, **9**. 356, 1901 ; J. Bellinger, *ib.*, **11**. 68, 237, 1903 ; W. Witte, *Die Eisen und Manganerzlagerstätte bei Oberrosbach, Prov. Oberhessen*, Berlin, 1926 ; *Neues Jahrb. Min. B.B.*, **53**. 271, 1928 ; F. Beyschlag, *Zeit. prakt. Geol.*, **27**. 87, 1919 ; W. Raabe, *Mitt. Kaiser Wilhelm Ist.*, **9**. 117, 1927 ; A. Buchrucker, *Stahl Eisen*, **11**. 561, 1891 ; J. Lowag, *Oesterr. Zeit. Berg. Hütt.*, **50**. 608, 623, 635, 1902 ; **51**. 146, 1903 ; A. Schmidt, *Erzbergbau*, 67, 1907.
²⁰ A. H. Curtis, *Manganese Ores*, London, 70, 1919.
²¹ Anon., *Mining Journ.*, **121**. 318, 1918 ; A. W. Stelzner and A. Bergeat, *Die Erzlagerstätten*, Leipzig, 241, 1904 ; A. H. Curtis, *Manganese Ores*, London, 80, 1919 ; A. Beck and W. H. Weed, *The Nature of Ore Deposits*, New York, 104, 1905 ; J. Harden, *Met. Chem. Engg.*, **17**. 701, 1917 ; N. H. Magnusson, *Sveriges Geol. Undersökning*, 13, 1929 ; C. H. Lundström, *Jernkontorets Ann.*, **45**. 313, 1891.
²² A. Butts, *Min. Industry*, **25**. 493, 1916 ; J. Aston, *ib.*, **24**. 490, 1915 ; F. Drake, *ib.*, **10**. 477, 1901 ; *Trans. Amer. Inst. Min. Eng.*, **28**. 191, 841, 1898 ; H. K. Scott, *Journ. Iron Steel Inst.*, **94**. ii, 289, 1916 ; *Trans. Amer. Inst. Min. Eng.*, **56**. 68, 1916 ; E. C. Harder, *ib.*, **56**. 31, 1916 ; L. Dominian, *Eng. Min. Journ.*, **104**. 647, 1917 ; S. H. Ball and B. Low, *ib.*, **103**. 410, 1917 ; L. C. David, *ib.*, **99**. 47, 681, 1915 ; V. C. Svimonoff, *ib.*, **120**. 690, 1925 ; D. Guimaraes, *Ann. Acad. Bras.*, **1**. 171, 179, 1929 ; E. de Oliveira, *ib.*, **1**. 173, 1929 ; N. Kozoffsky, *Gorny*

Journ., **4.** 1, 1891 ; *Gornozavodsky Zistok*, **1.** 269, 1891 ; A. Ernst, *Geognostische und bergbauliche Skizzen über die Kaukauausländer*, Warstein, 1891 ; P. W. J. Stevens, *Foreign Office Rept. London*, 307, 1893 ; *Diplomatic and Consular Reports*, 2623, 1901 ; H. Seger, *Sprechs.*, **24.** 326, 1891 ; L. J. Igelström, *Geol. För. Förh. Stockholm*, **12.** 137, 1892 ; R. Helmhacker, *Neues Jahrb. Min.*, i, 33, 1895 ; F. Drake, *Trans. Amer. Inst. Min. Eng.*, **28.** 191, 841, 1899 ; A. Pourcel, *Ann. Mines*, (9), **13.** 664, 1899 ; E. Zeidler, *Rev. Univ. Mines*, **17.** 69, 1899 ; N. Grinew, *Geol. Centr.*, **3.** 7, 1903 ; P. Goluboff, *ib.*, **3.** 7, 1903 ; J. Demaret-Freson, *Echo Ind.*, 1, 1902 ; A. Kandélaky, *Glückauf*, **41.** 764, 1905 ; C. Rabut, *Board Trade Journ.*, **56.** 80, 1907 ; R. Grimshaw, *Eng. Min. Journ.*, **84.** 1158, 1907 ; A. Schmidt, *Die nordbayrischen Eisen und Manganvorkommen*, Kattowitz, 1913 ; S. Dick, *Die bergwirtschaftlichen Grundlagen des Manganerzbergbaues von Tschiaturi*, Düsseldorf, 1927 ; J. V. W. Reynders, *Iron Age*, **118.** 924, 1926 ; *Min. Met.*, **7.** 515, 1926; V. A. Selsky, *Mining Journ.*, **151.** 958, 1925 ; Anon., *ib.*, **141.** 477, 1923 ; N. Sokoloff, *Mém. Comit. Géol. St. Petersburg*, **18.** 61, 1901 ; *Die Manganerzlager des Gouvernements Yekaterinoslaw*, St. Petersburg, 1902 ; J. Demaret-Freson, *Les champs des manganèse de la Tomakovka*, Bruxelles, 1903 ; S. Prauss, *Stahl Eisen*, **26.** 350, 1906 ; A. Kaysser, *ib.*, **27.** 296, 1907 ; E. Schnass, *ib.*, **50.** 918, 959, 1914 ; G. Lebedeff, *Proc. Russ. Min. Soc.*, **13.** 1, 1878 ; C. R. King, *Eng. Mag.*, **48.** 481, 1915 ; Anon., *Génie Civil*, **67.** 139, 1915 ; L. Persoz, *Tech. Moderne*, **19.** 792, 1927 ; W. de la Sauce, *Beitrag zur Kenntnis der Manganerzlagerstätte von Tschiaturi im Kaukasus*, Halle, 1926 ; *Abh. prakt. Geol. Berg.*, **8.** 90, 1926 ; D. Zeretelli, *Manganese Ore, with Special Reference to Georgian Ore*, London, 1925 ; K. C. Chlebnikoff, *Zeit. prakt. Geol.*, **26.** 89, 1918 ; M. Stromberg, *Eng. Min. Journ.*, **101.** 894, 1916 ; F. W. Cauldwell, *Min. Eng. World*, **37.** 65, 1912 ; L. J. Burk, *Eng. Min. Journ.*, **125.** 1016, 1928 ; A. Marcus, *Mining Journ.*, **167.** 915, 1929 ; J. Roberts, *ib.*, **62.** 990, 1892 ; E. de Hautpick, *ib.*, **98.** 749, 1912.

²³ A. Gaudry, *Mém. Soc. Géol. France*, (2), **7.** 191, 1860.

²⁴ E. Halse, *Trans. Inst. Min. Met.*, **23.** 209, 1914 ; L. Dominian, *Eng. Min. Journ.*, **78.** 185, 1904 ; F. Kossmat, *Mitt. Geol. Ges. Wien*, **3.** 277, 1909.

²⁵ L. L. Fermor, *Trans. Min. Geol. Inst. India*, **1.** 69, 71, 221, 1907 ; *Mem. Geol. Sur. India*, **37.** 1, 1909 ; *Records Geol. Sur. India*, **31.** 47, 1904 ; **33.** 159, 167. 172, 200, 207, 229, 1906 ; **34.** 167, 171, 1906 ; **36.** 295, 301, 1908 ; **37.** 1, 1909 ; **46.** 140, 168, 1915 ; **47.** 135, 1915 ; **50.** iv, 268, 1919 ; **64.** 172, 1930 ; *The Manganese Deposits of India*, Calcutta, 1909 ; R. B. Foote, *Mem. Geol. Sur. India*, **25.** 194, 1897 ; A. Ghose, *Trans. Manchester Geol. Min. Soc.*, **30.** 307, 1908 ; *Journ. Soc. Arts*, **55.** 908, 1907 ; *Iron Coal Trades Rev.*, **81.** 239, 1909 ; R. A. Becker, *Board Trade Journ.*, **59.** 246, 1907 ; **60.** 292, 1908 ; B. Jayaram, *Rec. Dept. Mines Geol. Mysore State*, **16.** ii, 71, 1919 ; R. O. Ahlers, *Trans. Inst. Min. Met.*, **18.** 133, 143, 150, 1908 ; H. K. Scott, *Trans. Amer. Inst. Min. Eng.*, **56.** 68, 1916 ; E. C. Harder, *ib.*, **56.** 31, 1916 ; E. W. Wetherell, *Eng. Min. Journ.*, **82.** 821, 964, 1906 ; **83.** 1190, 1907 ; *Mining Journ.*, **81.** 780, 1907 ; **82.** 228, 1907 ; D. Guimaraes, *Ann. Acad. Bras.*, **1.** 171, 179, 1929 ; E. de Oliveira, *ib.*, **1.** 173, 1929 ; C. R. von Schwarz, *Stahl Eisen*, **21.** 337, 1901 ; Anon., *Mech. Eng.*, **21.** 561, 1908 ; W. Venator, *Stahl Eisen*, **26.** 142, 213, 1906 ; H. Hänig, *Oesterr. Zeit. Berg. Hütt.*, **61.** 600, 1913 ; R. Stokes, *Mining World*, **24.** 719, 1906 ; P. N. Bose, *Records Geol. Sur. India*, **21.** 71, 1888 ; **22.** 216, 1889 ; F. R. Mallet, *ib.*, **12.** 73, 99, 1879 ; **16.** 96, 1883 ; T. W. H. Hughes, *ib.*, **7.** 125, 1874 ; T. H. Holland, *ib.*, **32.** 55, 144, 1904 ; **33.** 94, 1906 ; T. H. Holland and H. H. Hayden, *ib.*, **47.** 160, 1916 ; **48.** 50, 1917 ; A. J. Scott, *Edin. Phil. Journ.*, (1), **53.** 277, 1852 ; G. B. Tremenheere, *Journ. Asiatic Soc. Bengal*, **10.** 852, 1841 ; T. J. Newbold, *Madras Journ. Lit. Science*, **11.** 44, 1840 ; E. Krenkel, *Zeit. prakt. Geol.*, **38.** 81, 1930 ; W. F. Smeeth and P. S. Iyengar, *Bull. Dept. Mines Geol. Mysore State*, 7, 1906 ; Anon., *Mining Journ.*, **114.** 581, 1916 ; S. B. Banerjea, *Eng. Min. Journ.*, **122.** 254, 1926 ; E. N. T. Slater, *ib.*, **109.** 1155, 1920 ; B. V. Mellon, *Trans. Min. Geol. Inst. India*, **23.** 80, 1928 ; E. H. Dennison, *Ind. World*, **41.** 575, 1907 ; P. Martell, *Glückauf*, **43.** 816, 1907 ; M. Nicault, *Echo Mines*, **34.** 631, 1907 ; R. A. Becher, *Board Trade Journ.*, **60.** 292, 1908.

²⁶ W. R. Dunstan, *Rep. Min. Sur. Ceylon*, 8, 14, 1904.

²⁷ A. A. Sankoff, *Compt. Rend. Russ. Acad.*, 77, 1926.

²⁸ T. Posewitz, *Borneo : its Geology and Mineral Resources*, London, 1892 ; A. Dieseldorff, *Zeit. prakt. Geol.*, **14.** 10, 1906 ; W. G. Darby, *Ann. Series Foreign Office*, 3715, 1906.

²⁹ W. D. Smith, *Philippine Journ. Science*, **2.** 170, 1907 ; *Mineral Resources of the Philippine Islands*, Manila, 1909.

³⁰ V. K. Ting, *Bull. Chinese Geol. Sur.*, 4, 1922 ; *Genie Civil*, **58.** 321, 1908.

³¹ A. M. Stelzner and A. Bergeat, *Die Erzlagerstätten*, Leipzig, 716, 1906 ; G. T. Holloway, *Trans. Inst. Min. Met.*, **21.** 567, 1912 ; J. H. Snodgrass, *Mining World*, **30.** 790, 1909 ; A. S. Brown, *Eng. Mag.*, **40.** 568, 1910.

³² J. Barthoux, *Ann. Mines*, (11), **3.** 261, 1923.

³³ Anon., *Rassegna Min.*, **28.** 233, 1908.

³⁴ A. de la Croix, *Ann. Series Foreign Office*, 3712, 1906.

³⁵ W. F. Hume and T. Barron, *Topography and Geology of the Peninsula of Sinai*, Sur. Dept. Egypt, 1907 ; J. Ball, *Geography and Geology of West Central Sinai*, Survey Dept. Egypt, 1916 ; J. Barthoux, *Ann. Mines*, (11), **3.** 261, 1923.

³⁶ R. A. Farquharson, *First Report on the Geology and Mineral Resources of British Somaliland*, London, 1924.

³⁷ G. Castelli, *Rassegna Min.*, **62.** 101, 125, 1925.

³⁸ S. H. Ball and M. K. Shaler, *Econ. Geol.*, **9.** 648, 1914 ; D. Guimaraes, *Ann. Acad. Bras.*, **1.** 171, 179, 1929 ; E. de Oliveira, *ib.*, **1.** 173, 1929.

[39] D. W. Bishopp and W. J. Hughes, *Trans. Inst. Min. Met.*, **39**. 142, 1930; A. E. Kitson, *Trans. Amer. Inst. Min. Eng.*, **75**. 372, 1927; N. R. Junner, *ib.*, **75**. 385, 1927; S. H. Ford, *Mining Mag.*, **17**. 271, 1917; A. E. Kitson, *Bull. Gold Coast Geol. Sur.*, 1, 1925; *The Mineral and Potential Water Power Resources of the Gold Coast, with Remarks on Prospecting Methods*, London, 1926; E. A. de la Rue, *Bull. Soc. Min.*, **51**. 275, 1928.

[40] A. H. Curtis, *Manganese Ores*, London, 55, 1919; R. Dent, *Canadian Min. Journ.*, **52**. 150, 1931.

[41] A. B. Welsh, *Rept. Mines Industries, Union of S. Africa*, 1917; T. G. Trevor, *Mining Mag.*, **20**. 313, 1919; *Year-book Union of S. Africa*, 448, 1917; F. H. Hatch, *Report on Mines and Mineral Resources of Natal*, London, 81, 1910; L. T. Nel, *Publ. Union South Africa Geol. Sur.*, 1, 1929; H. M. Pezzani, *Iron Coal Trades Rev.*, **118**. 540, 1929; A. L. Hall, *Trans. Geol. Soc. South Africa*, **29**. 17, 1926; Anon., *Board Trade Journ.*, **64**. 337, 586, 1908.

[42] H. P. Brumell, *Amer. Geol.*, **10**. 80, 1892; W. F. Jennison, *Journ. Mining Soc. Nova Scotia*, **8**. 106, 1905; *Journ. Fed. Canada Min. Inst.*, 167, 1898; R. P. Hoyt, *Ann. Rep. Geol. Sur. Canada*, **11**. 107, 1901; G. C. Mackenzie, *Trans. Canada Min. Inst.*, **22**. 305, 1919; W. H. Smith, *Mining Journ.*, **108**. 65, 1915; G. A. Young, *Econ. Geol. Canada Geol. Sur.*, 1, 1926; Anon., *Canadian Mining Journ.*, **39**. 320, 1918; H. E. Kramm, *ib.*, **33**. 660, 1912; E. Gilpin, *The Minerals of Nova Scotia*, Halifax, 59, 1901; E. C. Harder, *Bull. U.S. Geol. Sur.*, 427, 1910; R. A. F. Penrose, *Ann. Rept. Geol. Sur. Arkansas*, 1. 496, 1890; E. D. Ingall, *Ann. Rept. Geol. Sur. Canada*, 148, 1903; N. C. Dale, *Bull. Amer. Geol. Soc.*, **15**. 168, 1903; **25**. 73, 1914.

[43] E. C. Harder, *Mining World*, **29**. 946, 1908; **30**. 354, 1907; *Canada Min. Journ.*, **29**. 431, 1908; *Bull. U.S. Geol. Sur.*, 380, 1909; 427, 1910; *Trans. Amer. Inst. Min. Eng.*, **58**. 453, 1918; E. C. Harder and D. F. Hewett, *ib.*, **63**. 3, 1920; E. C. Harder and A. W. Johnston, *Bull. U.S. Geol. Sur.*, 660, 1917; H. K. Scott, *Trans. Amer. Inst. Min. Eng.*, **56**. 68, 1916; D. F. Hewett, *ib.*, **56**. 428, 1917; *Bull. U.S. Geol. Sur.*, 640, 1917; 725, 1921; 795, 1927; *Eng. Min. Journ.*, **104**. 931, 1917; D. F. Hewett, G. W. Stose, F. J. Katz, and H. D. Miser, *Bull. U.S. Geol. Sur.*, 680, 1918; H. D. Miser, *ib.*, 660, 1917; 715, 1920; 734, 1923; *Journ. Acad. Sciences*, **10**. 1, 1920; J. E. Wolf, *Bull. U.S. Geol. Sur.*, 213, 1902; 214, 1903; W. H. Weed, *ib.*, 213, 1902; J. T. Pardee, *Eng. Min. Journ.*, **105**. 1076, 1918; **106**. 308, 1918; *Bull. U.S. Geol. Sur.*, 690, 1918; 725, 1921; 795, 1927; J. T. Pardee and E. L. Jones, *ib.*, 710, 1919; J. T. Pardee and H. M. Parks, *Eng. Min. Journ.*, **106**. 872, 1918; S. M. Ball, *ib.*, **87**. 1056, 1909; E. L. Jones, *Bull. U.S. Geol. Sur.*, 710, 1919; 715, 1920; E. L. Jones and F. L. Ransome, *ib.*, 710, 1920; A. Butte, *Min. Ind.*, **25**. 493, 1916; J. Aston, *ib.*, **24**. 485, 1915; J. W. Nesmith, *Iron Age*, **47**. 1077, 1890; J. L. Jarman, *Amer. Chem. Journ.*, **11**. 39, 1889; T. Shiras, *Eng. Min. Journ.*, **104**. 1079, 1917; **105**. 778, 1918; J. B. Umpleby, *ib.*, **104**. 1140, 1917; Anon., *Min. Journ.*, **117**. 416, 1917; **121**. 230, 1918; Anon., *Chem. Met., Engg.*, **18**. 625, 1918; R. A. F. Penrose, *Ann. Rep. Arkansas Geol. Sur.*, **1**. 1, 1890; *Journ. Geol.*, **1**. 275, 1893; J. F. Kemp, *The Ore Deposits of the United States*, New York, 416, 1900; F. L. Nason, *Trans. Amer. Inst. Min. Eng.*, **24**. 121, 1894; C. E. Hall, *ib.*, **20**. 1, 46, 1891; T. L. Watson, *ib.*, **34**. 207, 643, 1904; *Bull. Geol. Sur. Georgia*, 14, 1908; *Mining World*, **30**. 643, 1909; T. L. Watson and C. Catlett, *Trans. Amer. Inst. Min. Eng.*, **34**. 207, 1904; T. L. Watson and E. T. Wherry, *Journ. Washington Acad.*, **8**. 550, 1918; E. Newton, *Bull. Minnesota School Mines Exp. Station*, 5, 1918; *Trans. Amer. Inst. Min. Eng.*, **61**. 297, 1919; C. Zapffe, *ib.*, **71**. 372, 1925; W. P. Blake, *ib.*, **41**. 647, 1910; H. V. Wallace, *Min. Eng. World*, **35**. 103, 1910; S. F. Emmons, *The Geology and Mining Industry of Leadville*, Washington, 1886; S. F. Emmons and J. D. Irving, *Bull. U.S. Geol. Sur.*, 320, 1907; A. Lakes, *Colliery Eng.*, **16**. 267, 1896; E. J. Chibas, *Trans. Amer. Soc. Civil Eng.*, **36**. 65, 1896; *Trans. Amer. Inst. Min. Eng.*, **27**. 63, 1895; **33**. 200, 1897; A. A. Wheeler, *Mineral Ind.*, **8**. 420, 1901; W. R. Crane and E. R. Easton, *Resources of Tennessee*, **9**. 48, 1919; F. A. Hale, *Eng. Min. Journ.*, **105**. 775, 1918; C. Hafer, *ib.*, **98**. 1135, 1914; J. H. Watkins, *ib.*, **102**. 545, 1916; L. G. Lackey, *ib.*, **89**. 867, 1909; S. M. Ball, *ib.*, **87**. 1056, 1908; M. Haney, *ib.*, **100**. 1659, 1918; **105**. 875, 1918; *Iron Age*, **100**. 984, 1917; **101**. 1659, 1918; R. W. Jones, *Eng. Min. Journ.*, **105**. 779, 1918; P. M. Ostrand, *ib.*, **105**. 269, 1918; W. S. Palmer, *ib.*, **105**. 780, 1918; R. W. Petre, *ib.*, **101**. 1019, 1916; G. W. Stose, *ib.*, **110**. 256, 1920; *Bull. Virginia Geol. Sur.*, 17, 1919; 23, 1922; G. W. Stose and F. C. Schrader, *Bull. U.S. Geol. Sur.*, 737, 1923; F. C. Schrader, R. W. Stose and S. Sanford, *ib.*, 624, 1917; G. A. Joslin, *Min. Scient. Press*, **113**. 947, 1916; G. D. Louderbach, *ib.*, **116**. 451, 1918; J. J. Runner, *ib.*, **114**. 128, 1917; W. A. Whitaker and W. H. Twenthofel, *Econ. Geol.*, **12**. 473, 1917; J. H. Cole, *Eng. Min. Journ.*, **124**. 165, 1927; T. Swann, *Chem. Met. Engg.*, **19**. 672, 1918; S. H. Dolbear, *ib.*, **12**. 721, 1914; R. L. Mann, *Min. Eng. World*, **44**. 743, 1914; Anon., *Iron Age*, **97**. 776, 1916; M. Haney, *ib.*, **101**. 1659, 1918; C. S. Ross and E. V. Shannon, *Amer. Min.*, **14**. 106, 1929; B. A. Ludgate, *Bull. Amer. Iron Steel Assoc.*, **25**. 1, 1892; *Iron*, **38**. 490, 1892; J. M. Couper, *Amer. Manf.*, **51**. 367, 1892; W. M'Govern, *ib.*, **58**. 551, 1895; W. M. Brewer, *ib.*, **60**. 440, 1897; C. Catlett, *Eng. Min. Journ.*, **64**. 156, 1897; C. W. Hayes, *Bull. U.S. Geol. Sur.*, 213, 1902; S. Paige, *ib.*, 450, 1911; R. H. Euler, *Trans. Amer. Inst. Min. Eng.*, **46**. 56, 1913; J. V. W. Reynders, *ib.*, **75**. 191, 1927; M. V. Healey and A. L. Johns, *Information Circular Dept. Commerce U.S. Bur. Mines*, 6274, 1930; J. D. Weeks, *Ann. Rep. U.S. Geol. Sur.*, **16**. iii, 423, 1894; **17**. iii, 201, 1895; E. H. Wells, *Bull. New Mexico School Mines*, 2, 1918; A. H. Means, *Econ. Geol.*, **1**. 1, 1915; E. A. Schubert, *Iron Trade Rev.*, **60**. 1032, 1917; W. H. Bradley, E. Huguein, C. A. Logan, W. B. Tucker, and C. A. Waring, *Bull. California State Mining Bur.*, 76, 1918; R. D. George,

Bull. Univ. Colorado, 110, 1927 ; J. P. D. Hull, L. la Forge and W. R. Crane, *Bull. Geol. Sur. Georgia*, 35, 1915 ; W. B. Jones, *Bull. Alabama Geol. Sur.*, 28, 32, 1926 ; W. Lindgren, L. C. Graton and C. H. Gordon, *Prof. Paper U.S. Geol. Sur.*, 68, 1910 ; A. C. Spencer, *ib.*, 96. 1917 ; E. Sloan, *Bull. Carolina Geol. Sur.*, (4), 2. 95, 1908 ; G. A. Muilenberg, *Bull. Colorado Geol. Sur.*, 15, 1919 ; H. B. Patton, *ib.*, 9, 1915 ; W. A. Nelson, *Tennessee Geol. Sur.*, 1. 220, 1911 ; A. H. Purdue, *ib.*, 6. 111, 1916 ; 8. 46, 1918 ; A. C. Reeds, *Bull. Oklahoma Geol. Sur.*, 3, 1910 ; S. Shedd, *Bull. Washington Div. Geol.*, 30, 1924 ; J. T. Singewald, *Bull. Maryland Geol. Sur.*, 9. iii, 325, 1911 ; R. V. Ageton, *Eng. Min. Journ.*, 116. 181, 1923 ; A. E. Fritzberg, *ib.*, 124. 645, 1927 ; P. C. Jenkins, *ib.*, 105. 1082, 1918 ; H. V. Maxwell, *ib.*, 107. 149, 1919 ; E. D. Wilson and G. M. Butler, *Bull. Univ. Arizona*, 127, 1930 ; E. K. Judd, *Eng. Min. Journ.*, 83. 478, 1907 ; *Min. Ind.*, 15. 562, 1907 ; A. F. Rogers, *Amer. Journ. Science*, (5), 8. 145, 1924 ; T. L. Watson and E. T. Wherry, *Journ. Washington Acad.*, 8. 550, 1918 ; C. S. Ross and P. F. Kerr, *Amer. Min.*, 17. 1, 1932 ; J. E. Mills, *Amer. Chemist*, 28. 13, 1873.

   [44] J. G. Aguilera, *Trans. Amer. Inst. Min. Eng.*, 32. 505, 1902 ; C. Biddle, *Eng. Min. Journ.*, 82. 361, 1907 ; E. Halse, *Trans. North England Inst. Min. Mech. Eng.*, 41. 302, 1892 ; *Trans. Fed. Inst. Min. Eng.*, 3. 934, 1892.

   [45] J. S. Cox, *Eng. Mag.*, 16. 765, 1899 ; *Mines Minerals*, 19. 109, 1899 ; P. M. Tyler, *Iron Age*, 111. 275, 1923 ; A. C. Spencer, *Bull. U.S. Geol. Sur.*, 213, 1903 ; *Eng. Min. Journ.*, 74. 247, 1902 ; H. Souder, *Trans. Amer. Inst. Min. Eng.*, 35. 308, 1904 ; E. F. Burchard, *ib.*, 63. 51, 1920 ; Anon., *Iron Trade Rev.*, 63. 1238, 1918 ; B. Orton, *Stahl Eisen*, 34. 1731, 1914 ; C. W. Hayes, T. W. Vaughan and A. C. Spencer, *A Geological Reconnaissance of Cuba*, Washington, 62, 1901 ; J. G. Sawkins and L. Barrett, *Reports on the Geology of Jamaica*, London, 1869 ; E. S. Murias, *Eng. Min. Journ.*, 114. 197, 1922 ; E. J. Chibas, *Iron Age*, 49. 200, 1892.

   [46] J. D. Sears, *Bull. U.S. Geol. Sur.*, 710, 1919 ; A. H. Curtis, *Manganese Ores*, London, 100, 1919 ; E. J. Chibas, *Trans. Amer. Inst. Min. Eng.*, 27. 63, 1897 ; E. G. Williams, *ib.*, 33. 197, 1902 ; Anon., *Iron Trade Rev.*, 60. 424, 1917 ; A. M. Yonge, *Eng. Min. Journ.*, 104. 738, 1927 ; J. F. Sheridan, *Iron Age*, 114. 444, 1924.

   [47] E. C. Harder, *Trans. Amer. Inst. Min. Eng.*, 56. 31, 1916 ; K. Thomas, *ib.*, 59. 485, 1917 ; J. T. Singewald and B. L. Miller, *ib.*, 56. 7, 1916 ; J. C. Branner, *ib.*, 29. 756, 1900 ; J. Lustosa and J. C. Branner, *Eng. Min. Journ.*, 86. 1196, 1908 ; *Brazilian Eng. Min. Rev.*, 3. 45, 78, 94, 124, 141, 157, 191, 1907 ; A. Butts, *Min. Ind.*, 25. 493, 1916 ; D. Guimaraes, *Ann. Acad. Bras.*, 1. 171, 179, 1929 ; E. de Oliveira, *ib.*, 1. 173, 1929 ; *Echo Mines*, 57. 686, 1929 ; M. R. Lisboa, *Rev. Univ. Mines*, 44. 1, 1899 ; *Brazilian Eng. Min. Rev.*, 3. 6, 83, 97, 1907 ; F. L. Garrison, *Min. Scient. Press*, 114. 330, 1917 ; H. K. Scott, *O Manganez no Brazil*, Rio de Janeiro, 1902 ; *Trans. Amer. Inst. Min. Eng.*, 56. 68, 1916 ; *Journ. Iron Steel Inst.*, 57. i, 188, 1900 ; Anon., *Min. Journ.*, 119. 624, 1917 ; *Zeit. angew. Chem.*, 22. 321, 1909 ; O. A. Derby, *Amer. Journ. Science*, (4), 12. 19, 1901 ; (4), 25. 213, 1908 ; J. Birkinbine, *Min. Resources U.S. Geol. Sur.*, 140, 1899 ; 140, 1901 ; W. Venator, *Stahl Eisen*, 28. 876, 1908 ; J. G. Michaeli, *Eng. Min. Journ.*, 72. 818, 1902 ; V. C. Böhm, *Oester. Zeit. Berg. Hütt.*, 58. 565, 1910 ; F. Katzer, *ib.*, 46. 41, 1898 ; A. Stange, *Mining World*, 34. 445, 1910 ; A. de Belmont, *ib.*, 24. 522, 1906 ; M. Schwerber, *Metall Erz*, 24. 329, 1927 ; F. Greven, *Stahl Eisen*, 19. 439, 1899 ; D. Bellet, *Rev. Technique*, 1, 1899 ; J. W. Furniss, *Amer. Manf.*, 65. 167, 1899 ; J. P. Calogeras, *Iron Coal Trades Rev.*, 72. 205, 1906 ; A. Camara, *Brazilian Eng. Min. Rev.*, 3. 37, 1907 ; E. Hussak, *Ann. Escola Minas Ouro Preto*, 9, 1907 ; *Mining Journ.*, 83. 653, 1908 ; R. Stappenbeck, *Mining Journ.*, 154. 186, 1926 ; E. Teixeira, *Eng. Min. Journ.*, 131. 370, 1931.

   [48] C. Vattier, *Bull. Soc. Scient. Ind. Marseille*, 31. 13, 1903 ; *Bull. Soc. Ing. Civ.*, 64. 159, 1910 ; R. Stappenbeck, *Mining Journ.*, 154. 816, 1926 ; E. C. Harder, *Trans. Amer. Inst. Min. Eng.*, 56. 31, 1916 ; H. K. Scott, *ib.*, 56. 68, 1916.

   [49] E. Marstrander, *Mining Mag.*, 14. 315, 1916.

   [50] H. D. Hoskold, *Mémoire général sur les mines de la république Argentine*, Buenos Aires, 275, 1889.

   [51] B. Dunstan, *Queensland Govt. Mining Journ.*, 18. 286, 1917 ; H. E. Garraway, *Board Trade Journ.*, 60. 427, 1908 ; L. C. Ball, *Publication Geol. Sur. Queensland*, 189, 1904 ; H. I. Jensen, *Queensland Govt. Mining Journ.*, 20. 55, 1919 ; C. C. Morton, *ib.*, 30. 96, 1929 ; Anon., *Iron Coal Trades Rev.*, 87. 52, 1913 ; H. P. Woodward, *Ann. Rept. Govt. Geol.*, 1888–89, 25, 1890.

   [52] F. W. Hutton and G. H. F. Ulrich, *Geology of Otago*, Wellington, 149, 1875 ; F. W. Hutton, *Trans. N.Z. Inst.*, 1. 167, 1869 ; J. A. Pond, *ib.*, 21. 355, 1889 ; S. H. Cox, *ib.*, 14. 426, 1882 ; F. C. Morgan, *N.Z. Journ. Science*, 2. 112, 1919 ; J. Plummer, *Eng. Min. Journ.*, 59. 508, 1895.

   [53] L. L. Fermor, *The Manganese Deposits of India*, Calcutta, 21, 1909 ; *Records Geol. Sur. India*, 33. 176, 1906 ; M. Berthelot, *Compt. Rend.*, 143. 477, 1906 ; W. N. Hartley and H. Ramage, *Journ. Chem. Soc.*, 71. 533, 1897.

   [54] C. Benedicks, *Bull. Geol. Inst. Upsala*, 7. 271, 1906 ; J. Krenner, *Zeit. Kryst.*, 43. 473, 1907 ; K. Schlossmacher, *ib.*, 75. 399, 1930.

   [55] G. Forchhammer, *Overs. Danske Vid. Selsk. Förh.*, 91, 1854 ; *Pogg. Ann.*, 95. 60, 1855 ; E. C. Harder, *Manganese Deposits of the United States*, Washington, 24, 1910 ; L. L. Fermor, *The Manganese Deposits of India*, Calcutta, 1909.

   [56] F. W. Clarke, *The Data of Geochemistry*, Washington, 34, 1924 ; D. A. Wells, *Proc. Amer. Assoc.*, 275, 1851 ; *Amer. Journ. Science*, (2), 13. 9, 1852 ; E. J. Chapman, *Phil. Mag.*, (4), 3. 144, 1852 ; G. Bertrand, *Bull. Soc. Chim.*, (4), 35. 1522, 1924 ; L. Picciardi, *Compt. Rend.*, 94.

M

586, 1657, 1882 ; L. Dieulafait, *ib.*, **96**. 125, 718, 1883 ; **98**. 589, 643, 1884 ; H. Moissan, *ib.*, **136**. 144, 1903 ; R. Böttger, *Jahrb. phys. Ver. Frankfurt a. M.*, 27, 1856 ; L. Raab, *Neues Jahrb. Min.*, 517, 1871 ; A. Vogel, *Repert. Pharm.*, (2), **19**. 423, 1870 ; W. Crum, *Liebig's Ann.*, **55**. 219, 1845 ; J. Volhard, *ib.*, **198**. 318, 1879 ; L. Azéma, *Bull. Soc. Min.*, **36**. 133, 1913 ; C. W. Scheele, *Svenska Akad. Handl.*, **35**. 89, 177, 1774 ; *Abhand. Akad. Stockholm*, **36**. 95, 183, 1774 ; *Opuscula chemica et physica*, Lipsiæ, **1**. 227, 1788 ; London, 53, 1901 ; *Crell's Die neuesten Entdeckungen in der Chemie*, **1**. 112, 140, 1781 ; *Nachgelassene Briede und Aufzeichnungen*, Stockholm, 120, 1892 ; R. Wegscheider, *Zeit. anal. Chem.*, **29**. 20, 1890 ; B. Platz, *Dingler's Journ.*, **253**. 204, 1884 ; F. B. Guthrie and L. Cohen, *Agric. Gaz. New South Wales*, **21**. 219, 1910 ; A. Contino, *Staz. Sper. Agrar. Ital.*, **44**. 51, 1911 ; A. Leclerc, *Compt. Rend.*, **75**. 1209, 1871 ; P. de Sornay, *Bull. Assoc. Chim. Sucr. Dist.*, **30**. 96, 1912 ; O. M. Shedd, *Journ. Ind. Eng. Chem.*, **6**. 660, 1914 ; J. J. Skinner and M. X. Sullivan, *Bull. U.S. Dept. Agric.*, 42, 1914 ; J. S. McHargue, *Journ. Agric. Research*, **30**. 193, 1925 ; E. Dittler, *Tschermak's Mitt.*, (2), **36**. 164, 1924.

   [57] G. Forchhammer, *Om Sövandets bestanddele*, Kiöbenhaon, 13, 1859 ; *Overs. Danske Vid. Selsk. Forh.*, 91, 1854 ; *Pogg. Ann.*, **95**. 60, 1855 ; *Proc. Roy. Soc. Edin.*, **2**. 308, 1850 ; L. Dieulafait, *Compt. Rend.*, **96**. 125, 718, 1883 ; **98**. 589, 643, 1884 ; A. Carnot, *ib.*, **111**. 192, 1890 ; S. de Luca, *ib.*, **70**. 408, 1870 ; F. Jadin and A. Astruc, *ib.*, **157**. 338, 1913 ; **158**. 903, 1914 ; **159**. 332, 1914 ; **162**. 196, 643, 1916 ; B. M. Lersch, *Hydrochemie*, Berlin, 405, 1864 ; J. Murray, *Scottish Geog. Mag.*, **3**. 77, 1887 ; **4**. 41, 1888 ; *Challenger Reports—Deep-sea Deposits*, London, 341, 1891 ; *Proc. Roy. Soc. Edin.*, **9**. 255, 1876 ; J. Murray and R. Irvine, *Trans. Roy. Soc. Edin.*, **37**. 721, 1895 ; R. Irvine and J. Gibson, *Proc. Roy. Soc. Edin.*, **18**. 54, 1890 ; J. Y. Buchanan, *ib.*, **18**. 17, 1890 ; *Trans. Roy. Soc. Edin.*, **36**. 482, 1891 ; *Chem. News*, **44**. 253, 1881 ; C. W. von Gümbel, *Sitzber. Akad. München*, **8**. 197, 1878 ; *Forschungreise der S.M.S. Gazelle*, Berlin, **2**. 33, 1890 ; D. A. Wells, *Proc. Amer. Assoc.*, 275, 1851 ; *Amer. Journ. Science*, (2), **13**. 9, 1852 ; F. G. Novy, *Journ. Anal. Chem.*, **1**. 385, 1887 ; W. P. Mason, *Chem. News*, **61**. 123, 1890 ; O. Materne, *Bull. Soc. Chim. Belg.*, **18**. 363, 1905 ; B. A. Burrell, *Journ. Chem. Soc.*, **69**. 536, 1896 ; E. von Raumer, *Zeit. anal. Chem.*, **42**. 590, 602, 1903 ; G. Lunge and R. E. Schmidt, *ib.*, **25**. 309, 1886 ; R. Woy, *Zeit. öffentl. Chem.*, **12**. 121, 1906 ; E. Bechi, *Ber.*, **5**. 292, 1872 ; M. Gläser and W. Kalmann, *ib.*, **21**. 2879, 1888 ; M. Weibull, *Zeit. Nahr. Genussm.*, **14**. 403, 1907 ; C. A. H. Wolzogen-Kühr, *Water en Gas*, 31, 39, 1926 ; *Water and Water Eng.*, **28**. 216, 1926 ; E. Ludwig, *Tschermak's Mitt.*, (2), **4**. 182, 1882 ; (2), **11**. 303, 1890 ; C. du Ponteil, *Liebig's Ann.*, **96**. 193, 1855 ; E. H. S. Bailey, *Journ. Amer. Chem. Soc.*, **26**. 714, 1904 ; A. H. Wiebe, *Science*, (2), **71**. 248, 1930 ; E. H. S. Bailey and F. B. Porter, *Univ. Kansas Geol. Sur.*, **7**. 130, 1902 ; R. W. Townsend, *L'Instit.*, **12**. 57, 1844 ; *B.A. Rep.*, 38, 1843 ; C. M. Kersten, *Kersten's Arch. Min.*, **16**. 372, 1842 ; C. H. Bothamley, *Journ. Chem. Soc.*, **39**. 502, 1881 ; **63**. 685, 1893 ; T. E. Thorpe, *ib.*, **65**. 772, 1894 ; R. Nasini, M. G. Levi and F. Ageno, *Gazz. Chim. Ital.*, **39**. ii, 481, 1909 ; C. F. Eichleiter, *Jahrb. geol. Reichsanst. Wien*, **57**. 529, 1907 ; W. F. Hillebrand, *Bull. U.S. Geol. Sur.*, 113, 1893 ; J. K. Haywood, F. A. Gooch and J. E. Whitfield, *ib.*, 47, 1888 ; *Rept. U.S. Geol. Sur.*, 1902 ; A. Goldberg, *Ber. Naturw. Ges. Chemnitz*, 74, 108, 1904 ; F. Ragsky, Carlsbad, Marienbad, Franzenobad und ihre Umgebung, Prag, 76, 1863 ; M. B. Harden, *Amer. Chemist*, **4**. 247, 1874 ; J. Bouquet, *Ann. Chim. Phys.*, (3), **42**. 304, 1854 ; H. Braconnot, *ib.*, (2), **18**. 221, 1821 ; C. R. Fresenius, *Jahrb. Naturk. Nassau*, **6**. 174, 1850 ; *Journ. prakt. Chem.*, (1), **64**. 347, 1855 ; (1), **95**. 151, 1865 ; (1), **103**. 335, 1867 ; (2), **6**. 66, 1872 ; E. F. Leuchs, *ib.*, (2), **21**. 399, 1880 ; *Pogg. Ann.*, **14**. 499, 1828 ; J. J. Berzelius, *Gilbert's Ann.*, **74**. 149, 1823 ; P. Berthier, *Ann. Chim. Phys.*, (2), **20**. 187, 1822 ; J. Löwe, *Jahresb. Phys. Ver. Frankfurt*, 58, 1855 ; C. Bromeis, *Jahresb. Wetterauischen Ges. Nat.*, 47, 1847 ; G. Wolf, *Med. Jahrb. öesterr. States*, 3, 1, 137, 277, 1848 ; **64**. 21, 163, 1848 ; H. Göttl, *Viertelj. prakt. Chem.*, **5**. 161, 1856 ; A. von Planta, *Jahrb. Naturf. Ges. Graubündens*, 138, 1870 ; *Liebig's Ann.*, **155**. 161, 1870 ; S. Yoshimura, *Japan. Journ. Geol.*, **8**. 269, 1931.

   [58] G. Forchhammer, *Om Sovandets bestanddele*, Kiöbenhaon, 13, 1859 ; *Overs. Danske Vid. Selsk. Forh.*, 91, 1854 ; *Pogg. Ann.*, **95**. 60, 1855 ; *Proc. Roy. Soc. Edin.*, **2**. 308, 1850 ; F. P. Dunnington, *Journ. Amer. Chem. Soc.*, **2**. 141, 1880 ; E. J. Maumené, *Compt. Rend.*, **98**. 845, 1056, 1416, 1884 ; *Bull. Soc. Chim.*, (2), **41**. 451, 1884 ; (2), **42**. 305, 1884 ; G. Bertrand, *ib.*, (3), **17**. 619, 753, 1897 ; *Rev. Gén. Chim.*, **8**. 205, 1905 ; *Compt. Rend.*, **124**. 1032, 1355, 1897 ; G. Bertrand and A. Villiers, *ib.*, **122**. 1134, 1896 ; **124**. 1032, 1355, 1897 ; A. Villiers, *ib.*, **124**. 1349, 1897 ; G. Bertrand and M. Rosenblatt, *ib.*, **173**. 333, 118, 1921 ; **174**. 491, 1922 ; J. A. Trillat, *ib.*, **136**. 1305, 1903 ; M. Balland, *ib.*, **125**. 429, 1897 ; G. Guérin, *ib.*, **125**. 311, 1897 ; A. Livach, *ib.* **124**. 1520, 1897 ; G. Campani, *Gazz. Chim. Ital.*, **6**. 464, 1876 ; E. F. von Gorup-Besanez, *Liebig's Ann.*, **100**. 106, 1856 ; **118**. 220, 1861 ; C. W. Scheele, *Svenska Akad. Handl.*, **35**. 89, 177, 1774 ; *Abhand. Akad. Stockholm*, **36**. 95, 183, 1774 ; *Opuscula chemica et physica*, Lipsiæ, **1**. 227, 1788 ; London, 53, 1901 ; *Crell's Die neuesten Entdeckungen in der Chemie*, **1**. 112, 140, 1781 ; *Nachgelassene Briefe und Aufzeichnungen*, Stockholm, 120, 1892 ; R. Böttger, *Jahrb. Phys. Ver. Frankfurt a. M.*, 27, 1856 ; F. A. Flückiger, *Pharm. Journ.*, (3), **16**. 621, 1886 ; J. Kachler, *Monatsh.*, **7**. 410, 1886 ; J. E. de Vrij, *Pharm. Journ.*, (3), **1**. 583, 1871 ; *Chem. News*, **23**. 155, 1871 ; *Amer. Journ. Pharm.*, (4), **1**. 125, 1871 ; A. Domergue and C. Nicolas, *Journ. Pharm. Chim.*, (5), **25**. 302, 1892 ; G. Stein, *Chem. Ztg.*, **12**. 446, 1888 ; L. Medicus, *Repert. anal. Chem.*, 60, 1885 ; L. Rössler, *Mitt. Chem. Physiol. Versuch. Stat.*, 1, 1885 ; A. Alessi, *Chem. Centr.*, ii, 1517, 1902 ; A. Hilger, *Zeit. Oesterr. Apoth.*, **43**. 268, 1881 ; E. O. von Lippmann, *Ber.*, **21**. 3482, 1888 ; **30**. 3037, 1897 ; T. J. Herapath, *Journ. Chem. Soc.*, **2**. 4, 1850 ; T. Richardson, *Phil. Mag.*, (3), **31**. 336, 1847 ; W. F. Salm-Hortsdar, *Journ. prakt. Chem.*, (1), **52**. 1, 1851 ;

(1), **54**. 129, 1851 ; J. von Liebig, *Familiar Letters on Chemistry*, London, 459, 1851 ; *Nouvelles lettres sur la chimie*, Paris, 251, 1852 ; L. L. Fermor, *The Manganese Deposits of India*, Calcutta, 19, 1909 ; J. S. McHargue, *Journ. Agric. Research*, **23**. 395, 1923 ; **27**. 417, 1924 ; **30**. 193, 1925 ; *Journ. Amer. Chem. Soc.*, **36**. 2532, 1914 ; **44**. 1592, 1922 ; *Journ. Ind. Eng. Chem.*, **19**. 274, 1927 ; L. E. Westman and R. M. Rowat, *Journ. Amer. Chem. Soc.*, **40**. 558, 1918 ; N. Passerini, *Bol. Ist. Agrar. Scandicci*, (2), **6**. 3, 1905 ; O. Prandi and A. Civetta, *Staz. Sper. Agrar. Ital.*, **44**. 66, 1911 ; G. Massol, *Bull. Soc. Chim.*, (4), **1**. 953, 1907 ; P. Pichard, *Compt. Rend.*, **126**. 1882, 1898 ; F. Jadin and A. Astruc, *ib.*, **155**. 406, 1912 ; **156**. 2023, 1913 ; **159**. 268, 1914 ; *Bull. Soc. Chim.*, (4), **31**. 917, 1922 ; H. Marcelet, *Bull. Sci. Pharmacol.*, **20**. 480, 1913 ; C. C. McDonnell and R. C. Roark, *Journ. Agric. Research*, **11**. 77, 1917 ; W. P. Headden, *ib.*, **5**. 349, 1915 ; A. Hafner and H. Krist, *Zeit. oesterr. Apoth. Ver.*, **45**. 387, 1907 ; D. H. Wester, *Pharm. Weekbl.*, **59**. 51, 1922 ; **60**. 446, 1923 ; *Biochem. Zeit.*, **118**. 158, 1921 ; J. S. Jones and D. E. Bulles, *Journ. Ind. Eng. Chem.*, **13**. 524, 1921 ; G. Bruni and C. Pelizzola, *Atti Accad. Lincei*, (5), **30**. ii, 37, 1921.

[59] J. McCrae, *Journ. South African Chem. Inst.*, **6**. 18, 1923 ; E. N. Horsford, *Amer. Journ. Science*, (2), **11**. 259, 1851 ; G. Campani, *Gazz. Chim. Ital.*, **2**. 269, 1872 ; E. J. Maumené, *Compt. Rend.*, **98**. 845, 1056, 1416, 1884 ; *Bull. Soc. Chim.*, (2), **41**. 451, 1884 ; (2), **42**. 305, 1884 ; G. Forchhammer, *Om Sovandets bestanddele*, Kiöbenhaon, 13, 1859 ; *Overs. Danske Vid. Selsk. Forh.*, 91, 1854 ; *Pogg. Ann.*, **95**. 60, 1855 ; *Proc. Roy. Soc. Edin.*, **2**. 308, 1850 ; H. C. Bradley, *Journ. Biol. Chem.*, **3**. 151, 1907 ; **7**. 36, 1910 ; **8**. 237, 1910 ; J. Cotte, *Compt. Rend. Soc. Biol.*, **53**. 139, 1903 ; E. Cottereau, *Journ. Chim. Méd.*, (3), **5**. 179, 1849 ; A. Béchamp, *Compt. Rend.*, **49**. 895, 1859 ; P. Pichard, *ib.*, **126**. 1882, 1898 ; E. Pollacci, *Nuovo Cimento*, (2), **4**. 41, 1870 ; F. von Oefele, *Pharm. Centrh.*, **46**. 683, 1905 ; H. M. Fox and H. Ramage, *Nature*, **126**. 682, 1930 ; B. du Buisson, *Sur l'existence du manganèse dans le sang humain*, Lyon, 1852 ; *Journ. Pharm. Chim.*, (3), **26**. 420, 1804 ; *Rev. Méd. France*, **1**. 201, 275, 1852 ; **2**. 144, 1852 ; P. Carles, *Ann. Chim. Anal.*, **6**. 355, 1912 ; L. N. Vauquelin, *Encyclopédie méthodique*, Paris, **5**. 670, 1808 ; J. J. Berzelius, *Schweigger's Journ.*, **7**. 76, 1813 ; *Ann. Chim. Phys.*, (2), **5**. 149, 1817 ; M. E. Chevreul, *ib.*, (2), **4**. 42, 1817 ; N. A. E. Millon, *ib.*, (3), **23**. 372, 508, 1848 ; *Compt. Rend.*, **26**. 41, 1848 ; *Edin. Phil. Journ.*, **44**. 309, 1848 ; A. Riche, *Journ. Pharm. Chim.*, (4), **27**. 538, 1878 ; G. Bertrand, *Rev. Gén. Chim.*, **8**. 205, 1905 ; G. Bertrand and F. Medigreceànu, *Compt. Rend.*, **194**. 941, 1450, 1912 ; **155**. 82, 1912 ; *Ann. Inst. Pasteur*, **27**. 1, 1913 ; H. Oidtmann, *Die anorganische Bestandtheile der Leber und Milz und der meisten anderen thierischen Drüsen*, Linnich, 153, 1858 ; J. S. McHargue, *Journ. Agric. Research*, **27**. 417, 1924 ; **30**. 193, 1925 ; E. F. Hopkins, *Science*, (2), **72**. 609, 1930.

§ 3. The Preparation of Manganese

The manganese ores as mined may require a preliminary concentration or cleaning. Ores containing rock fragments and clay impurities can be dried and the clay pulverized by passage through a revolving drum, and the clay removed by a revolving screen. The coarse manganese and waste can then be passed to a picking belt, when a separation is made. Free silica can be removed by washing. The method of concentrating low-grade ore, however, depends on the nature of the ore. High-grade ores may require no preliminary treatment. The commonest ores are manganese oxides, carbonates, or silicates.[1]

F. Staaden and C. Heinzerling proposed to treat ores with a small proportion of manganese with water containing magnesium chloride or oxychloride, with hydrochloric acid, or with gaseous hydrogen chloride, so that soluble manganous chloride is formed. W. Diehl said that hydrochloric acid is the best solvent. F. Staaden and C. Heinzerling said that ferruginous ores are best treated with sulphur dioxide so as to convert the manganese into sulphate, and subsequently into chloride, by treatment with calcium or magnesium chloride. The Deutsche Solvay-Werke roasted the ore with ferric oxide and alkali carbonate, and leached out the manganate—*vide infra*, the manganates. F. Staaden heated a powdered mixture of the ore with pyrites, and A. G. Friedrichssegen, a mixture with spathic iron ore and zinc blende. In both cases the manganese compounds were removed by extraction with water. In J. T. Jones's process, examined by P. Christensen and W. H. Hunter, the ore is subjected to a low temp. reduction to form metallic iron and a slag. The manganiferous slag is then smelted for a manganese alloy. These methods cannot compete with the simpler process required when high grade ores are employed. Until comparatively recently, manganese was *une curiosité de laboratoire*, but when the valuable properties which it imparts to some alloys were recognized, it became one of the world's important metals. Indeed, ordinary commercial steel cannot be satisfactorily manufactured without its quota of manganese—say 0·4 to 1·0 per cent. Mn. A. G. Betts heated the silicate ore with iron sulphide, to form metallic iron, manganese sulphide, and a ferrous silicate slag. The manganese sulphide layer is then treated for manganese. Manganese has been prepared by the following processes :

The reduction of oxides, etc., by carbon.—The early workers—*vide supra*, the history of manganese, J. F. John,[2] P. Berthier, M. Faraday, etc.—prepared manganese, contaminated by more or less carbide, by mixing manganese oxide and powdered carbon with oil, and pressing the pasty mass into a charcoal crucible ; the mixture was then covered with charcoal and a lid luted on the crucible. The whole was then heated in a blast furnace for an hour. The metal was purified by melting it under borax. According to H. C. Greenwood, reduction of the oxide by carbon begins at 1105°. H. St. C. Deville reduced the oxide with sugar charcoal, using, as recommended by J. F. John, rather less carbon than is needed for the reduction, so as to avoid, as much as possible, the production of carbide. H. Tamm recommended the carbon reduction using a flux of soda-lime, glass, and fluorspar, and purifying the product by fusing it with half its own weight of manganese carbonate. The product contained 99·91 per cent. Mn. H. V. Regnault, J. Mason and A. Parkes, and L. Troost and P. Hautefeuille used a similar process. A. Valenciennes employed a crucible lined with magnesia for the reduction. J. E. Loughlin used potassium cyanide, and animal charcoal as the reducing agent. H. Moissan heated a mixture of manganese oxide and carbon in an electric arc furnace for a few minutes. The metal contained 6·35 to 14·59 per cent. of carbon ; but if the reduction is effected in the presence of an excess of oxide, as little as 3·6 per cent. of carbon may be present as carbide. If the heating be too intense, or too long, the yield may be small, owing to the volatilization of the metal. To guard against too intense a heating the mixture was reduced in a carbon crucible closed by a lid. E. W. Hopkins proposed to make the metal free from carbon by forcing the vapour of the metal—obtained by heating a mixture of the metal oxide and charcoal—through a layer of oxide. If alloys are desired, say a manganese-copper alloy, the vapour of the manganese can be passed through a layer of copper oxide. J. W. Cabot and S. W. Vaughan heated high grade ferromanganese in a blast furnace with a mixture of 100 parts of bessemer slag, 60 parts of coke, and 60 parts of limestone. A. Sternberg and A. Deutsch reduced oxy-compounds of manganese and the alkaline earths by carbon at 1000° to 1400°. C. M. J. Limb reduced psilomelane—native barium manganite—by carbon at a high temp., and employed the by-product for making barium carbide. R. Saxon reduced manganese oxides by calcium carbide. E. G. L. Roberts and E. A. Wraight discussed the elimination of carbon by heating the carburetted metal and manganese oxide above 1670°, at which temp. the reaction $Mn_3C+MnO=4Mn+CO$ occurs. G. E. R. Nilson discussed this subject. H. H. Meyer reduced manganous oxide, silicate, and phosphate in the blast furnace.

The reduction of the oxides by metals, etc.—C. and A. Tissier showed that although powdered aluminium reduces many metal oxides, sometimes with explosive violence, it does not reduce the oxides of zinc and manganese. On the other hand, W. H. Greene and W. H. Wahl obtained the metal by heating a mixture of manganese oxide with metallic aluminium or magnesium and a flux of cryolite or fluorspar in a crucible lined with lime or magnesia. J. Debuigne, and F. L. Garrison used a similar process. In H. Goldschmidt's thermite process, a mixture of manganese oxide and coarsely powdered aluminium, in a crucible, is ignited by a piece of magnesium ribbon surrounded by a little barium dioxide. The resulting metal is free from carbon, but it contains silicon, iron, etc. To avoid undue contamination with aluminium, the oxide is kept in slight excess. This process is employed industrially. F. Fujibayashi recommended a mixture of manganese tritatetroxide 100, and manganese dioxide 15 to 20, along with 90 per cent. of the calculated amount of powdered aluminium—the yield was 85 to 90 per cent. of the theoretical.

M. L. V. Gayler obtained manganese of 99·3 per cent. purity by reducing the purified oxide with purified aluminium—the thermite process—and then distilling it in a quartz vessel under reduced press. Commercial manganese prepared by the thermite process may have 0·09 per cent. S ; 0·65 to 1·61, Si ; 0·02 to 0·12, C ; 0·94 to 1·82, Fe ; 0·29 to 0·79, Al ; 0·08, P ; 0·15, Cu ; and 96·45 to 98·0, Mn. P. Lebeau found as much as 5·25 per cent. of silicon in manganese prepared by the thermite process. J. H. Brennan used the silico-thermic process. L. Weiss and O. Aichel reduced the oxide by heating it with mischmetall. S. Heuland melted the manganese ore in an electric furnace with a reducing agent sufficient to furnish only a small proportion of metal. This metal will contain all the deleterious impurities in the ores, *e.g.* phosphorus, carbon, or iron. The remainder of the metal is then reduced from the fused slag by heating it with calcium silicide.

The reduction of halogen salts by metals.—E. Frémy prepared manganese by passing the vapour of sodium over red-hot manganese chloride. C. Brunner heated in a crucible a mixture of two parts of manganese fluoride or chloride and one part of sodium covered with a layer of sodium chloride and fluorspar. The product was purified by fusing it under sodium chloride to which a little potassium nitrate or chlorate had been added. C. Bullock, and J. E. Loughlin also used the sodium reduction process. W. Diehl also reduced the double sodium or potassium manganese chloride, R_2MnCl_4, with sodium. E. Glatzel prepared manganese by heating a mixture of finely-divided, anhydrous manganese chloride (100 grms.) and dry, powdered potassium chloride (200 grms.) in a covered Hessian crucible until it just melts, and then adding magnesium (15 grms.) in portions of 3 to 4 grms. at intervals of 2 to 3 minutes ; if the fused mass is too hot a very violent reaction occurs, and the contents of the crucible are thrown out. The crucible is covered again, heated more strongly, and then allowed to cool slowly in the furnace. The yield of manganese is 20 to 25 grms., the metal containing traces only of silica and being quite free from magnesium.

The reduction of solutions of manganese salts by metals.—W. B. Giles obtained the metal by treating a soln. of manganous chloride with sodium amalgam. Hydrogen is evolved, and an amalgam of manganese is formed. This is quickly washed, and dried. When the amalgam is heated in a tube, closed at one end, the mercury is driven off, and powdered manganese remains. H. D. Royce and L. Kahlenberg recommended heating the amalgam to dull redness in a current of hydrogen, so as to prevent the oxidation of the manganese as the mercury is driven off. The powder can then be melted in an atm. of hydrogen. According to G. A. Maack, and T. L. Phipson, manganese can be precipitated from a neutral soln. of manganese chloride or nitrate by means of magnesium. On the other hand, Z. Roussin, and A. Commaille obtained only manganese hydroxide by this method ; and S. Kern showed that manganosic oxide is formed in two stages : $3MnCl_2+3Mg+3H_2O=3MnO+3MgCl_2+3H_2$; and the manganous oxide is oxidized by water : $3MnO+H_2O=H_2+Mn_3O_4$. Similar results were obtained by D. Tommasi, and K. Seubert and A. Schmidt with soln. of manganese sulphate and chloride ; while H. N. Warren said that the metal is precipitated by magnesium, wrapped round with a few coils of asbestos paper, from soln. of manganese acetate. J. G. Hibbs and E. F. Smith tried the action of magnesium on aq. soln. of manganese chloride in the presence of alcohol and of a mixture of alcohol and ether, so as to hinder the oxidation of the manganese. The deposit contained a kind of hydrated oxide ; the presence of free manganese was not proved. The presence of mercury in W. B. Giles's experiment hinders the oxidation of the precipitated manganese by water by forming an amalgam. J. A. Poumarède reported that zinc will precipitate manganese from soln. of its salts, but probably the same remarks apply here as in the case of magnesium. According to G. A. Maack, aluminium has very little action on cold soln. of manganese salts, but with warm soln. of the sulphate or chloride manganese is precipitated ; there is very little action with soln. of the nitrate.

Electrolytic processes.—R. Böttger, C. Luckow, and W. Wernicke observed that manganese is deposited as a hydrated peroxide or a permanganate is formed when the neutral or acidic soln. is electrolyzed. G. Gore electrolyzed fused manganous fluoride and also a dil. soln.; in the former case the black deposit on the cathode was not manganese. R. Bunsen obtained manganese by the electrolysis of an aq. soln. of manganous chloride, using platinum electrodes. If the current be too low, manganosic oxide is deposited. T. Moore obtained manganese by the electrolysis of a neutral soln. containing a large excess of ammonium thiocyanate, and a current of high density; and E. F. Smith and L. K. Frankel found that the metal is deposited greyish-white and compact from soln. containing an excess of potassium thiocyanate. P. P. Fedotéeff found that under the most favourable conditions, with a neutral or weakly acid $6 \cdot 5N$-soln. of manganous chloride, at 5°, and a current density of 20 amps. per sq. dm., the deposit on the copper cathode contained about 65 per cent. of manganese and 35 per cent. of hydrated oxide. According to G. D. van Arsdale and C. G. Meier, manganese can be obtained by the electrolysis of a neutral molar soln. of manganous sulphate at 23°, with electrode densities of 1 to $4 \cdot 6$ amps. per sq. dm., and they obtained current efficiencies of 73 to 89 per cent. (Fig. 3). The maximum occurred with about 2 amps. per sq. dm. Using a current density of $0 \cdot 9$ amps. per sq. dm., and with increasing acidity, the current efficiency fell rapidly, almost linearly, becoming zero with $0 \cdot 36$ per cent. H_2SO_4 (Fig. 4). A. J. Allmand and A. N. Campbell showed that the deposits of manganese obtained under these conditions are very impure; they also observed that the deposition of manganese ceases with soln. containing $0 \cdot 36$ per cent. H_2SO_4; and that manganese of a high degree of purity and in a coherent form can be prepared in small amounts by using

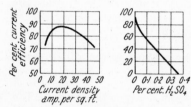

FIGS. 3 and 4.—The Effect of Current Density and of Acidity of Solution on the Deposit of Manganese.

a catholyte containing 300 grms. of manganous sulphate tetrahydrate, 100 grms. of ammonium sulphate, and $2 \cdot 5$ grms. of sulphuric acid per litre, the acidity being maintained by suitable additions of acid. Using a rotating cathode, current efficiencies of 50 to 60 per cent. were obtained. Using a standard electrolyte of ammonium and manganous sulphates, no marked improvement was obtained with additions of gum arabic, dextrin, and gelatin, and the deposit was less pure. Using a burnisher on a rotating electrode, the current efficiency was reduced to $8 \cdot 6$ per cent. The use of thiocyanate as electrolyte gave a more coherent but more impure deposit; and the use of manganese and ammonium perchlorates gave a catholyte which rapidly hydrolyzed. Hydrogen dioxide, potassium chlorate, nitrobenzene, and cinnamic acid were tried as depolarizers, but their effect on the cathode deposit was nugatory. They found that the best conditions for the electrodeposition of pure manganese consist in the electrolysis of a soln. containing manganous and ammonium sulphates (the catholyte) separated by a diaphragm from the anolyte (ammonium sulphate soln.), the $H^{\cdot}$-conc. being kept at 10^{-6} to 10^{-8} by the regulated addition, as required, of sulphuric acid or of ammonia. The temp. is 30° and the current density at the cathode 10 to 15 amps. per sq. dm. The rotating aluminium cathode has a burnisher lightly pressing against it. The subject was discussed by C. N. Otin, H. Bardt, and J. Brezina.

A. Guntz prepared the amalgam by the electrolysis of a conc. soln. of manganous chloride, using a mercury cathode. The amalgam was rapidly washed, passed through leather, dried, and distilled in vacuo at 200° to 250° to remove the mercury. A similar process was used by W. Diehl, and H. Moissan. O. Prelinger obtained the amalgam by passing an electric current—11 volts and 22 to 23 c.c. of electrolytic gas per min.—from a mercury cathode (20 c.c.) through a sat. aq. soln. of 75 c.c.

of manganous chloride to an anode of carbon or platinum-iridium contained in a porous vessel. The temp. rises to 70°, and after 5 to 6 hrs. the mercury assumes a pasty consistency. The paste is quickly washed by running water without undergoing appreciable decomposition, the excess of mercury squeezed out through linen, and the residue dried over calcium chloride in an atm. of hydrogen. The mercury was distilled off. E. Kuh employed a similar process, and melted the powder in a magnesia boat in vacuo, and also distilled the metal, obtaining it as a *wunderschöne metallische Kruste*. M. L. V. Gayler obtained 99·99 per cent. manganese by distilling the metal above its m.p. at 1 to 2 mm. press.; and J. B. Friauf said that the process is impracticable because of the great losses. H. S. Booth and M. Merlub-Sobel prepared the metal by the electrolysis of a soln. of manganous thiocyanate in liquid ammonia.

A. Simon obtained manganese by dissolving a lower oxide of manganese or ferromanganese in fused calcium fluoride, alone or mixed with other fluorides to make it more fusible. The metal is freed from phosphorus and silicon by the action of fluorine on the carbon anode, whereby carbon tetrafluoride is formed, which reacts with silica : $SiO_2 + CF_4 = CO_2 + SiF_4$; and manganese phosphide reacts : $2P_2Mn_3 + 3Mn + 3CF_4 = 4PF_3 + 3Mn_3C$; and the phosphorous fluoride also reacts with silica : $3SiO_2 + 4PF_3 = 3SiF_4 + P_4O_6$. G. Neuendorff and F. Sauerwald obtained the metal by the electrolysis of the fused silicate.

Ferromanganese was formerly made in crucibles ; H. H. Meyer [3] discussed the manufacture of manganese in blast-furnaces similar to those used for making pig-iron. The manufacture was discussed by W. Henderson, T. L. Joseph and co-workers, P. M. Tyler, H. Thaler, R. M. Keeney, J. E. Stead, F. Kohn, A. Pourcel, H. Bessemer, W. Armstrong, etc. The manufacture of ferromanganese in electric furnaces was described by E. S. Bardwell, C. D. Grier, J. W. Richards, F. Sauerwald and G. Neuendorff, G. Neuendorff, G. Gin, etc.—*vide* iron and manganese alloys.

J. Strong and C. H. Cartwright [4] prepared **mirrors** or thin films of manganese by condensation from the vapour. V. Kohlschütter and J. Tüscher prepared aerosols or **colloidal manganese** by vaporizing the metal in the arc, and suddenly condensing the vapour in air; T. Svedberg, by spluttering in *iso*butyl alcohol, ether, etc.; and H. Kuzel, by the trituration of the mechanically or electrically subdivided metal alternately with acidic and alkaline soln.

REFERENCES.

[1] O. M. Weld, *Manganese—Uses, Preparation, Mining Costs, and the Production of Ferro-Alloys*, Washington, 1920 ; T. J. Martin, *Trans. Amer. Electrochem. Soc.*, **57**. 467, 1930 ; E. Newton, *Bull. Bur. Mines*, **173**. 27, 1920 ; W. R. Crane, *ib.*, **173**. 45, 1920 ; C. E. van Barneveld, *ib.*, **173**. 57, 1920 ; P. Christensen and W. H. Hunter, *ib.*, **173**. 71, 1920 ; F. Staaden and C. Heinzerling, *German Pat.*, *D.R.P.* 50145, 1889 ; Deutsche Solvay-Werke, *ib.*, 82980, 1895 ; 56397, 1891 ; A. G. Friedrichssegen, *ib.*, 35836, 1886 ; F. Staaden, *ib.*, 39106, 1886 ; *Dingler's Journ.*, **264**. 614, 1887 ; W. Diehl, *Chem. Ztg.*, **14**. 668, 1890 ; *Chem. Ind.*, **8**. 206, 318, 1885 ; J. T. Jones, *U.S. Pat. No.* 1288422, 1919 ; H. and A. J. Trumbo, *ib.*, 1710522, 1929 ; S. G. S. Dicker, *Brit. Pat. No.* 284098, 1927 ; T. Shiras, *Eng. Min. Journ.*, **105**. 778, 1918 ; K. R. Krishnaswami, *Journ. Indian Inst. Science*, **10**. A, 65, 1927 ; E. Newton, *Trans. Amer. Inst. Min. Eng.*, **61**. 297, 1919 ; F. D. de Vaney and W. H. Coghill, *Rept. U.S. Bur. Mines Investigations*, 2902, 1928 ; A. G. Betts, *U.S. Pat. No.* 1703657, 1929.

[2] M. Faraday, *Journ. Science Arts*, **6**. 358, 1819 ; W. B. Giles, *Phil. Mag.*, (4), **24**. 328, 1862 ; C. Brunner, *Pogg. Ann.*, **101**. 264, 1857 ; **103**. 139, 1857 ; *Dingler's Journ.*, **144**. 184, 1857 ; **147**. 122, 1858 ; *Mitt. Naturf. Ges. Bern*, 72, 135, 1857 ; G. Gore, *Electrochemistry*, London, 95, 1906 ; W. Wernicke, *Zeit. Chem.*, (2), **7**. 85, 1870 ; *Pogg. Ann.*, **141**. 109, 1870 ; R. Böttger, *ib.*, **50**. 45, 1840 ; K. Seubert and A. Schmidt, *Liebig's Ann.*, **267**. 218, 1892 ; R. Saxon, *Chem. News*, **137**. 216, 1928 ; H. H. Meyer, *Mitt. Kaiser Wilhelm Inst. Düsseldorf*, **9**. 273, 1927 ; Z. Roussin, *Journ. Pharm. Chim.*, (4), **3**. 413, 1866 ; L. Troost and P. Hautefeuille, *Met. Rev.*, **1**. 177, 1877 ; *Ann. Chim. Phys.*, (5), **7**. 155, 1876 ; *Compt. Rend.*, **80**. 964, 1875 ; E. Frémy, *ib.*, **44**. 632, 1857 ; C. and A. Tissier, *ib.*, **43**. 1187, 1856 ; J. A. Poumarède, *ib.*, **22**. 948, 1846 ; A. Commaille, *ib.*, **63**. 556, 1866 ; M. Berthelot, *ib.*, **93**. 757, 1881 ; A. Valenciennes, *ib.*, **70**. 607, 1870 ; H. Moissan, *ib.*, **88**. 180, 1879 ; **116**. 349, 1893 ; *Bull. Soc. Chim.*, (3), **11**. 13, 1894 ; *Le four électrique*, Paris, 217, 1897 ; London, 150, 1904 ; *Ann. Chim. Phys.*, (5), **21**. 231, 1880 ; (7), **3**. 286, 1896 ; H. St.

C. Deville, *ib.*, (3), **46**. 182, 1856 ; H. V. Regnault, *ib.*, (2), **62**. 350, 1836 : A. Guntz, *Bull. Soc. Chim.*, (3), **7**. 275, 1892 ; D. Tommasi, *ib.*, (3), **21**. 885, 1899 ; J. F. John, *Gehlen's Journ.*, **3**. 452, 1807 ; **4**. 436, 1807 ; *Ann. Phil.*, **2**. 172, 263, 1813 ; **3**. 413, 1813 ; E. Glatzel, *Ber.*, **22**. 2857, 1889 ; *Eng. Min. Journ.*, **49**. 452, 1890 ; W. Diehl, *Chem. Ind.*, **8**. 206, 318, 1885 ; *Chem. Ztg.*, **14**. 668, 1890 ; O. Prelinger, *Monatsh.*, **14**. 353, 1893 ; *Sitzber. Akad. Wien*, **102**. 346, 1893 ; H. Gold-schmidt and C. Vautin, *Journ. Soc. Chem. Ind.*, **17**. 543, 1898 ; H. Goldschmidt, *Zeit. Elektrochem.*, **4**. 494, 1898 ; *Liebig's Ann.*, **301**. 19, 1898 ; *German Pat.*, *D.R.P.* 175885, 1905 ; T. Goldschmidt, *Aluminogenetische Metalle und Legierungen*, Essen, 1905 ; C. M. J. Limb, *German Pat.*, *D.R.P.* 130664, 1900 ; 176615, 1905 ; L. Voltmer, *ib.*, 74949, 1894 ; F. Kruppe, *ib.*, **8**. 81225, 1895 ; E. W. Hopkins, *ib.*, 138808, 1900 ; 161559, 1904 ; A. Sternberg and A. Deutsch, *ib.*, 69704, 1898 ; J. W. Cabot and S. W. Vaughan, *U.S. Pat. No.* 556457, 1896 ; A. G. Betts, *ib.*, 1703657, 1929 ; H. Tamm, *Chem. News*, **26**. 37, 111, 1872 ; T. S. Hunt, *Trans. Amer. Inst. Min. Eng.*, **14**. 492, 1885 ; *Chem. News*, **53**. 64, 1886 ; S. Kern, *ib.*, **33**. 112, 236, 1876 ; C. Bullock, *Journ. Franklin Inst.*, **128**. 62, 1889 ; *Chem. News*, **60**. 20, 1889 ; H. N. Warren, *ib.*, **60**. 187, 1889 ; **61**. 183, 1890 ; T. Moore, *ib.*, **53**. 209, 1886 ; F. L. Garrison, *ib.*, **67**. 114, 1893 ; J. E. Loughlin, *ib.*, **25**. 139, 1872 ; *Amer. Chemist*, **1**. 454, 1871 ; *Bull. Soc. Chim.*, (2), **17**. 557, 1872 ; A. Simon, *Brit. Pat. No.* 17190, 1900 ; J. Debuigne, *ib.*, 221233, 1924 ; H. Bardt, *ib.*, 194340, 1921 ; G. E. R. Nilson, *ib.*, 260232, 1926 ; W. H. Greene and W. H. Wahl, *ib.*, **82**. 1893 ; *Trans. Amer. Inst. Min. Eng.*, **21**. 887, 1893 ; J. Mason and A. Parkes, *Brit. Pat. No.* 2677, 1870 ; *Ber.*, **4**. 534, 1871 ; S. Heuland, *French Pat. No.* 602448, 1925 ; R. Bunsen, *Pogg. Ann.*, **91**. 619, 1854 ; *Ann. Chim. Phys.*, (3), **41**. 355, 1854 ; T. Fujibayashi, *Journ. Japan. Chem. Ind.*, **25**. 499, 1922 ; J. G. Hibbs and E. F. Smith, *Journ. Amer. Chem. Soc.*, **16**. 822, 1894 ; T. L. Phipson, *Proc. Roy. Soc.*, **13**. 217, 1864 ; *Chem. News*, **93**. 119, 1906 ; G. A. Maack, *Untersuchungen über das Verhalten des Magne-siums und Aluminiums zu den Salzlösungen verschiedener Metalle*, Göttingen, 1862 ; H. D. Royce and L. Kahlenberg, *Trans. Amer. Elektrochem. Soc.*, **50**. 137, 1926 ; G. D. van Arsdale and C. G. Meier, *ib.*, **33**. 109, 1918 ; H. C. Greenwood, *Journ. Chem. Soc.*, **93**. 1491, 1908 ; P. Berthier, *Traité des essais par la voie sèche*, Paris, **2**. 175, 1834 ; *Ann. Chim. Phys.*, (2), **20**. 187, 1822 ; P. Lebeau, *ib.*, (8), **1**. 553, 1904 ; M. L. V. Gayler, *Metallwirt.*, **9**. 677, 1930 ; *Journ. Iron Steel Inst.*, **115**. i, 393, 1927 ; R. Hadfield, *ib.*, **115**. i, 211, 1927 ; E. G. L. Roberts and E. A. Wraight, *ib.*, **70**. ii, 229, 1906 ; J. Brezina, *Rec. Trav. Chim. Pays-Bas*, **44**. 520, 1925 ; J. H. Brennan, *U.S. Pat. No.* 1768112, 1930 ; A. J. Allmand and A. N. Campbell, *Trans. Faraday Soc.*, **19**. 559, 1924 ; **20**. 379, 1924 ; E. F. Smith and L. K. Frankel, *Journ. Anal. Chem.*, **3**. 386, 1889 ; L. Weiss and O. Aichel, *Liebig's Ann.*, **337**. 370, 1904 ; G. Grube and H. Metzger, *Zeit. Elektrochem.*, **29**. 17, 100, 1923 ; C. N. Otin, *ib.*, **15**. 385, 386, 1909 ; G. Neuendorff and F. Sauerwald, *ib.*, **34**. 199, 1928 ; F. Förster, *Elektrochemie wässeriger Lösungen*, Leipzig, 560, 1922 ; E. Kuh, *Die Darstellung des chemische reinen Mangans und die Bestimmung der wichtigsten physikalischen Konstanten desselben*, Zürich, 1911 ; P. P. Fedotéeff, *Zeit. anorg. Chem.*, **130**. 18, 1923 ; J. B. Friauf, *Trans. Amer. Soc. Steel Treating*, **18**. 213, 1930 ; C. Luckow, *Zeit. anal. Chem.*, **19**. 1, 1880 ; H. S. Booth and M. Merlub Sobel, *Journ. Phys. Chem.*, **35**. 3303, 1931.

³ W. Henderson, *Brit. Pat. No.* 689, 1865 ; H. Meyer, *Ueber die Reduktion von Manganoxydul, Kieselsäure, und Phosphorsäure im Hochofen*, Dusseldorf, 1927 ; P. M. Tyler, *Iron Age*, **106**. 711, 1920 ; E. S. Bardwell, *Trans. Amer. Electrochem. Soc.*, **38**. 333, 1920 ; J. W. Richards, *ib.*, **37**. 169, 1920 ; C. D. Grier, *Bull. Washington Univ. Eng. Exp. Station*, 5, 1920 ; *Min. Scient. Press.*, **121**. 132, 1920 ; H. Thaler, *Stahl Eisen*, **34**. 1481, 1914 ; R. M. Keeney, *Bull. U.S. Bur. Mines*, 77, 1915 ; Anon., *Iron Coal Trades Rev.*, **94**. 39, 1917 ; F. Kohn, *Iron and Steel Manufacture*, London, 1868 ; *Journ. Iron Steel Inst.*, **2**. i, 70, 1871 ; R. A. Hadfield, *ib.*, **115**. i, 211, 1927 ; J. E. Stead, **101**. i, 33, 1920 ; E. G. L. Roberts and E. A. Wraight, *ib.*, **70**. ii, 229, 1906 ; G. Gin, *La fabrication électrique du ferromanganèse en France*, Paris, 1901 ; W. Armstrong, *B.A. Rep.*, 164, 1865 ; H. Bessemer, *ib.*, 165, 1865 ; A. Pourcel, *Le Génie Civil*, **7**. 3, 21, 50, 1885 ; F. Sauer-wald and G. Neuendorff, *Zeit. Elektrochem.*, **31**. 643, 1925 ; G. Neuendorff, *Ueber die Schmelzfluss-electrolyse von Eisen, Chrom, und Mangan*, Breslau, 1927 ; T. L. Joseph, E. P. Barrett and C. E. Wood, *Tech. Publ. Amer. Inst. Min. Eng.*, 310, 1930.

⁴ V. Kohlschütter and J. Tüscher, *Zeit. Elektrochem.*, **27**. 225, 1921 ; H. Kuzel, *Austrian Pat. No.* 2572, 2573, 1906 ; *German Pat.*, *D.R.P.* 186980, 194348, 197379, 1905 ; 199962, 1907 ; T. Svedberg, *Ber.*, **38**. 3616, 1905 ; **39**. 1705, 1906 ; *Die Methoden zur Herstellung kolloiden Lösungen anorganischer Stoffe*, Dresden, 488, 1920 ; J. Strong and C. H. Cartwright, *Phys. Rev.*, (2), **37**. 228, 1931.

§ 4. The Physical Properties of Manganese

The properties of manganese described in the literature differ, showing that the impurities which characterize the metal obtained by different processes modify many of the properties. The metal prepared by reducing the halide with sodium in C. Brunner's ¹ process was reported by C. Bullock to be steel-grey, brittle, and so hard that a file will not scratch it, and it will scratch glass ; whereas the metal prepared by H. Goldschmidt's process is said to resemble iron but to have a reddish tinge ; it is also said to be hard and brittle, but not to scratch glass. The metal obtained by distilling mercury from the amalgam at a dull red-heat was described by O. Prelinger as a grey, porous, non-pyrophoric mass which is readily reduced to powder. E. Frémy regarded his specimen as crystalline, and R. Bunsen also said that the electrodeposited metal is crystalline. M. L. V. Gayler described the metal electrodeposited at 27° as a bright, silver-grey mass, and that desposited at 34° is also bright and silver-grey. It shows treeing at the edges of the cathode and in isolated patches. The distilled 99·99 per cent. manganese is silver-grey in colour, and is very brittle. When the distillate is melted down into ingots, numerous cracks appear in the cooling ingot. These cracks cause the ingot to fall to pieces with the slightest press., and they are associated with a transformation in the metal, and not with the normal shrinkage. The specimens when polished and etched with 6 per cent. alcoholic nitric acid, or 0·5 per cent. alcoholic hydrochloric acid, show numerous cracks ; and if tempered by heat, the sample is liable to crumble to pieces when quenched, or when treated with the etching fluid. Some changes in the crystalline structure have been observed to occur about 742°, but no perceptible change occurs at 682°. A marked change in vol. occurs about one or both these temp.

P. Groth placed manganese in the list of elements which form cubic crystals, apparently because M. Levin and G. Tammann found that it yields a continuous series of isomorphous mixtures with iron. Attempts by A. W. Hull and W. P. Davey, and J. F. T. Young to determine the crystal form from the **X-radiograms** were not successful, for the pattern obtained appeared to be too complex for the cubic system. A. Westgren and G. Phragmén, however, inferred that manganese exists in at least three **allotropic forms**—*vide infra*, magnetic susceptibility. There is α-manganese which is stable at ordinary temp. and gives an X-radiogram corresponding with the cubic system, and at higher temp. this changes into β-manganese, which is also cubical, but slightly denser ; whereas electrolytic manganese is tetragonal, with the same sp. gr. as α-manganese. It is designated γ-manganese ; whereas A. J. Bradley called it α-manganese, and A. Westgren and G. Phragmén's α- and β-form were called respectively the β- and γ-forms. A. J. Bradley and J. Thewlis found that for ordinary manganese the cubic lattice has $a=8·894$ A. There are 58 atoms per cell. Each lattice point has a cluster of 29 atoms, and the clusters have tetrahedral symmetry. The interatomic distances range from 2·25 A. to 2·95 A. and indicate an unequal distribution of electrons. A. J. Bradley showed that the α- and β-forms are normally present in commercial manganese, and that the α-form is stable in the range 150° to 180°, and the β-form is stable above 650°. Both forms are stable within the range 650° to 850°, and the phenomenon corresponds with isodynamic allotropy, because there is a definite equilibrium mixture of the two allotropes corresponding with each temp. J. D. Bernal favoured this interpretation, but not so E. Persson and E. Oehman, and A. J. Bradley said that the pure β-form of manganese is obtained by raising the temp. above 850° in vacuo, and suddenly quenching ; whereas the pure α-form is difficult to obtain by heat treatment alone, although it is produced when the β-form is sublimed in vacuo. It has not been possible to interpret the X-radiograms of the α- and β-forms of manganese, but the low order of symmetry suggests the monoclinic or rhombic systems. The third allotropic form, γ-manganese,

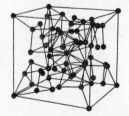

FIG. 5.—Model of Space Lattice of α-Manganese with $a=8·89$ A.

FIG. 6.—Model of Space Lattice of β-Manganese with $a=6·29$ A.

has been obtained only by electrodeposition. The X-radiograms correspond with a body-centred, tetragonal lattice with the axial ratio $a:c=1:1·34$, or a face-centred tetragonal lattice with the axial ratio $a:c=1:0·9445$. Assuming the face-centred lattice, the edges of unit cell are $a=3\cdot764$ A., and $c=3\cdot556$ A. The volume of unit cell, containing 4 atoms, is $50\cdot3\times10^{-24}$ c.c., so that each atom occupies $12\cdot58\times10^{-24}$ c.c. The weight of one atom is $90\cdot6\times10^{-24}$ grm., and the corresponding density of manganese is $7\cdot21$. The distances of closest approach of atoms for manganese, iron, cobalt, and nickel are respectively $2\cdot59$, $2\cdot54$, $2\cdot51$, and $2\cdot50$ A. On heat treatment, γ-manganese passes into the a- and β-forms, but the change does not appear to be reversible. G. D. Preston found single crystals of a-manganese had a body-centred, cubic lattice with $a=8\cdot894$ A., and a density of $7\cdot44$; while β-manganese, stable above $742°$, also formed cubic crystals with a lattice of side $a=6\cdot29$ A., containing 20 atoms. The results of G. D. Preston are summarized in Figs. 5 and 6. Observations were made by S. von Oldhausen, A. Karlsson, T. Ishiwara, and A. Osawa.

Working with distilled, $99\cdot99$ per cent. manganese, M. L. V. Gayler observed arrests on the cooling curve $1195°$, $1005°$, $740°$, and $681°$; and on the heating curve there is a change of direction at $684°$, and arrests at $740°$, $744°$, $1043°$, and $1188°$. S. Umino found arrests at $835°$ and $1044°$. She concluded that only one of the two lower critical temp., $742°$, is accompanied by a change in physical structure; no such change is apparent at $682°$. It is generally taken that $742°$ is the transition point of the $a \rightleftharpoons \beta$ change. C. H. M. Jenkins and M. L. V. Gayler studied this subject. According to E. Persson and E. Oehman, pure manganese when quenched gives nothing but β-manganese, but if manganese be alloyed with some copper, iron, nickel, or cobalt, the m.p. curves are unbroken, and the alloys have a face-centred, cubic lattice. Alloys of manganese with even less than 5 per cent. of copper have a face-centred, tetragonal lattice. The higher the copper content the more does the structure approximate to the face-centred, cubic lattice, thus :

Copper			$3\cdot8$	$8\cdot2$	$10\cdot5$	$15\cdot0$ per cent.
a	.	.	$3\cdot771$	$3\cdot765$	$3\cdot763$	$3\cdot755$
c	.	.	$3\cdot556$	$3\cdot601$	$3\cdot617$	$3\cdot660$
$a:c$	.	.	$1:0\cdot943$	$1:0\cdot956$	$1:0\cdot961$	$1:0\cdot975$

By extrapolation the values for manganese alone become $a=3\cdot776$, $c=3\cdot525$, and $a:c=1:0\cdot934$. These values agree closely with those obtained by A. Westgren and G. Phragmén. The high temp. phase obtained by quenching these alloys and the γ-manganese obtained by electrolysis are the same. By plotting the maximum manganese content in the γ-phase at different temp., the transition point of $\gamma \rightleftharpoons \beta$-manganese approximates $1191°$. With iron and nickel alloys the γ-phase can be obtained only by quenching from temp. exceeding $1024°$; and for an alloy with $21\cdot8$ per cent. of iron, $a=3\cdot705$, $c=3\cdot619$, and $a:c=1:0\cdot976$; whilst with an alloy having $15\cdot7$ per cent. of nickel, $a=3\cdot736$, $c=3\cdot606$, and $a:c=1:0\cdot965$. The cobalt-manganese alloys do not show the γ-phase, but an alloy with $11\cdot5$ per cent. of cobalt quenched from $1100°$ gave evidence of the presence of γ- and β-manganese lines. E. Oehman's observations on the alloy with iron are discussed in connection with the iron-manganese alloys. G. Hägg also found a high temp., face-centred, tetragonal phase in his study of the manganese-nitrogen alloys. E. Persson and E. Oehman added that since β-manganese is brittle at room temp., γ-manganese is malleable, hence the transition should be accompanied by a sudden change in physical properties. In agreement with this inference, they found that both a- and β-manganese are much less brittle at $600°$ than at room temp., and at $900°$ C. the β-manganese is in fact malleable, although very hard. At $1160°$ the hardness is still considerable, while at $1200°$ the metal has become extremely soft. An alloy with $21\cdot8$ per cent. of iron is hard at $1100°$, but very soft at $1150°$ C., while an alloy with 8 per cent. of copper is quite soft at $980°$. There seems to be no doubt, therefore, that the transition point $\gamma \rightleftharpoons \beta$ is $1191°$. The point $1024°$, on the other hand, does not seem to be accompanied by any change in crystal structure. It may be mentioned that the higher point in M. L. V. Gayler's curves is more pronounced than the lower. In no case has the γ-manganese phase been found in equilibrium with the face-centred cubic one (copper, γ-iron, etc.). This does not prove that the cubic lattice continuously changes into the tetragonal, but if a two-phase range exists, it must certainly be very narrow. S. Sekito found for α-manganese that the cubic crystals have a lattice with $a=8\cdot904$ A., 58 atoms per unit cell and a range of stability up to $800°$; for β-manganese, a cubic lattice with $a=6\cdot288$ A., 20 atoms per unit cell, and a range of stability from about $800°$ to about $1100°$; and for γ-manganese a tetragonal cell with $a=3\cdot776$ A., and $a:c=1:0\cdot940$, and a range of stability over $1100°$. When copper forms a solid soln. with manganese, the axial ratio $c:a$ increases with the copper content until it becomes unity. W. Schmidt obtained evidence of another form, ϵ-manganese, with a close-packed, hexagonal lattice in iron alloys with 16 to 20 per cent. manganese. E. Oehman's observations on the range of stability of this phase are discussed in connection with the iron-manganese alloys, and he found for the lattice $a=2\cdot541$ A., $c=4\cdot106$ A., and $a:c=1:1\cdot616$. It is not stable below $500°$.

The **specific gravity** of manganese naturally depends on its degree of purity, so that of the early workers, J. G. Gahn gave $7\cdot05$; T. Bergman, and P. J. Hjelm, $7\cdot0$; J. F. John, $8\cdot013$; R. Böttger, $8\cdot03$; H. Davy, $6\cdot85$; C. Brunner, $7\cdot138$ to $7\cdot207$; C. Bullock, $7\cdot231$ (fused); J. E. Loughlin, $7\cdot84$ to $7\cdot99$; D. Zereteli, $7\cdot7$; O. Prelinger, $7\cdot4212$ at $4°$ (powder); E. Glatzel, $7\cdot376$ at $22°/4°$ (fused); E. Kuh, $7\cdot241$ at $0°$, and $7\cdot232$ at $20°$ (fused); and R. Frilley, $7\cdot40$ at $15°/4°$ (fused). A. N. Campbell gave $7\cdot034$ to $7\cdot080$ for the sp. gr. of nodules of the electrolytic metal, and added that these are minimum values, because pores filled with hydrogen or vacuous may be present. He also discussed the at. vol. A. Westgren and G. Phragmén calculated from the X-radiograms, $7\cdot21$ for sp. gr. of the fused α-metal; $7\cdot29$ for the β-metal; and $7\cdot21$ for the γ-metal; while A. J. Bradley gave $7\cdot21$ for the electrolytic or γ-metal. According to Y. Matsuyama, manganese contracts $1\cdot69$ per cent. of its vol. on solidification. K. Honda and co-workers gave $-4\cdot50$ per cent. for the change in vol., $\delta v/v$, on melting manganese, and for manganese with 1 per cent. of carbon, $-1\cdot60$ per cent. M. N. Saha calculated the **atomic radius** to be $0\cdot98\times10^{-8}$ cm.; G. Natta, $0\cdot90$ A.; M. L. Huggins, $1\cdot39$ A. (bivalent); and W. L. Bragg, $1\cdot47$ A., and for electronegative manganese $1\cdot17$ A. A. Ferrari gave $2\cdot50$ A. for the diameter of quadrivalent $Mn^{\cdots\cdot}$-ions, and $2\cdot95$ A. for bivalent $Mn^{\cdot\cdot}$-ions. G. Natta and L. Passerini found that if the at. radius of oxygen is $1\cdot32$ A., that of manganese is $0\cdot89$ A. H. G. Grimm, A. Kapustinsky, V. M. Goldschmidt, L. Pauling, E. T. Wherry, A. M. Berkenheim, J. C. Slater, W. F. de Jong and H. W. V. Willems, E. Rabinowitsch and E. Thilo, and E. Herlinger studied this subject. It follows from this work that for septivalent manganese atoms, the effective at. radius is $0\cdot46$ A.; for quadrivalent atoms, $0\cdot50$ to $0\cdot52$ A.; for bivalent atoms, $0\cdot80$ to $0\cdot91$ A.; and for neutral manganese atoms, $1\cdot17$ to $1\cdot54$ A. A. Kapustinsky studied the effect of hydration or solvation. E. Persson obtained for the at. vol. of α-Mn, $12\cdot13$ A.^{3}; of β-Mn, $12\cdot50$ A.^{3}; and of γ-Mn, $12\cdot58$ A.^{3}. A. N. Campbell, W. Biltz and K. Meisel, and J. J. Saslawsky discussed the at. vol.; and P. Vinassa, the mol. number. W. Biltz and K. Meisel gave $7\cdot26$ for the at. vol. at absolute zero.

As indicated above, M. L. V. Gayler, and others have noted the brittleness and **hardness** of the metal; J. B. Dumas noted that the manganese he tried scratched steel. J. R. Rydberg gave 6 for the scratching hardness on Mohs' scale. T. Turner said that the hardness of manganese is 1456 when that of iron is 1375, that of copper is 1360, and that of the diamond, 3010. W. C. Roberts-Austen found the **tensile strength** to be $7\cdot99$ tons per sq. in., and the elongation $29\cdot7$ per cent. on a 3-in. test-piece. W. Widder found that the elastic modulus is approximately a linear function of the temp. $E=E_{20}\{1-0\cdot001587(\theta-20)\}$. T. W. Richards gave $0\cdot82\times10^{-6}$ for the **compressibility** of the metal in sq. cm. per kilogram between 100 and 510 kgrms. per sq. cm. P. W. Bridgman measured this constant and found at $30°$ $-\delta v/v_0=7\cdot91\times10^{-7}p-5\cdot3\times10^{-12}p^2$; and at $75°$, $-\delta v/v_0=8\cdot08\times10^{-7}p-4\cdot8\times10^{-12}p^2$. These and T. W. Richards' value are said to be out of line with the neighbours of manganese in the periodic table, whereas a value $5\cdot6\times10^{-7}$ would make a better fit. G. A. Tomlinson discussed the **cohesive forces.** F. C. Kelley discussed the **diffusion** of manganese in iron; and J. H. Hildebrand and co-workers, the **internal pressure.**

According to J. Disch,[2] the coeff. of **thermal expansion** of manganese is 0.0_4228 between $0°$ and $100°$; and 0.0_4159 between $-190°$ and $0°$; while E. Kuh gave 0.0_420697 between $20°$ and $85°$. W. Widder gave $\beta=0.0000261$ at $20°$ and 0.0000213 at $-190°$. H. V. Regnault gave 0.1332 for the **specific heat** between $13°$ and $97°$; and H. Kopp, 0.127. J. Dewar gave 0.0229 between $-253°$ and $-196°$; T. W. Richards and F. G. Jackson, 0.0931 between $-188°$ and $20°$; T. Estreicher and M. Staniewsky, 0.0945 between $-188°$ and $13°$, and 0.0945 between $-79.2°$ and $15°$; and N. Stücker gave 0.1211 between $20°$ and $100°$, and 0.1673 between $20°$ and $550°$. N. Stücker gave for the true sp. ht., c:

	60°	125°	225°	325°	425°	525°
c	0.12109	0.12790	0.16644	0.17830	0.17257	0.24774

$c=0.1279+0.000181(\theta-125)+0.0_520(\theta-125)^2$, between $125°$ and $225°$; $c=0.1279+0.000519(\theta-125)-0.0_513(\theta-125)^2$, between $125°$ and $325°$; $c=0.1783-0.000121(\theta-325)+0.0_66(\theta-325)^2$, between $325°$ and $425°$; $c=0.1783-0.000462-(\theta-325)+0.0_540(\theta-325)^2$, between $325°$ and $525°$; $c=0.1279+0.000204-(\theta-125)+0.0_62(\theta-125)^2$, between $125°$ and $525°$; and $c=0.1211+0.000105(\theta-60)$, between $60°$ and $125°$. R. Lämmel gave 0.0979 at $-100°$; 0.1072 at $0°$; 0.1309 at $300°$; and 0.1652 at $500°$; or $c=0.10722+0.0_478012\theta-0.0_611085\theta^2+0.0_9381780\theta^3$. The corresponding **atomic heats** are 1.26 at $-253°$ to $-196°$; 5.89 at $0°$; 7.19 at $300°$; and 9.07 at $500°$. E. Kuh gave 0.12130 for the sp. ht. at $98.5°$ and 6.68 for the at. ht. of fused manganese. J. Maydel discussed some relations of the sp. ht. and gave 0.11542 and 6.36, respectively, for the sp. and at. ht. of the powdered metal. He also represented the at. ht. by $A=8.734-938.9(\theta+352)^{-1}$.

H. St. C. Deville observed that the **melting point** of manganese is above that of iron. P. A. van der Weyde, and T. Carnelley gave $1900°$ for the m.p.; K. Hiege, $1260°$; F. Heinrich, $1250°$; W. C. Heraeus, $1245°$; M. Levin, and G. Tammann, $1247°$; W. R. Mott, $1207°$; F. Wüst and co-workers, $1210°$; E. Tiede and E. Birnbräuer, $1290°$; R. S. Williams, $1228°$ for 98.7 per cent. Mn; R. Sahmen, $1214°$ for 99.3 per cent. Mn; A. D. Dourdine, $1235°$; G. Hindrichs, $1207°$ for 98 per cent. Mn; S. F. Schemtschuschny and N. N. Effimoff, $1245°$ for 99.4 per cent. Mn; N. Baar, $1209°$ for 98.78 per cent. Mn; G. Arrivant, $1235°$ for manganese with less than 0.5 per cent. Fe; E. Newbery and J. N. Pring, $1230°\pm5°$; J. Johnston, $1225°$; S. Umino, $1221°$; G. K. Burgess and R. G. Waltenberg, $1255°$ for 97 to 98 per cent. Mn; F. Doerinckel, $1244°$ for 99.4 per cent. Mn; R. Hadfield, $1240°$ in vacuo for 97.47 and 98.40 per cent. Mn; O. Ruff and E. Gersten, $1243°$ for 98.7 per cent. Mn; and M. L. V. Gayler, $1245°$ on the heating curve, and $1242°$ on the cooling curve of 99.99 per cent. Mn. W. Widder discussed the relation between the m.p. and the elastic constants; W. Crossley, between the at. vol. and the m.p.; and T. Carnelley, between the m.p. and the coeff. of thermal expansion. Z. Herrmann estimated the energy of manganese at the m.p. The ready **volatilization** of manganese was noted by S. Jordan, E. Kuh, W. N. Hartley, R. Lorenz and F. Heusler, and H. Moissan, and this even at temp. just above its m.p. H. C. Greenwood gave $1900°$ for the **boiling point** of manganese at 760 mm.; O. Ruff and W. Bormann, $1510°$ at 30 mm. press.; W. R. Mott, $2400°$ (calculated); while R. W. Millar gave $1900°$ at 760 mm.; $1820°$ at 500 mm.; $1555°$ at 100 mm.; $1465°$ at 50 mm.; $1285°$ at 10 mm.; $1080°$ at 1 mm.; and $925°$ at 0.1 mm. press. O. Ruff and co-workers gave $1526°$ for the beginning of the boiling of manganese saturated with carbon. R. W. Millar represented the **vapour pressure,** p mm., by $\log p=2.963$ $\log T-12700T^{-1}+18.621$; and J. Johnston, $\log p=-12300T^{-1}+8.55$, and

p mm.	10^{-3}	10^{-2}	10^{-1}	1	10	50	100	760
B.p.	790°	890°	1020°	1170°	1360°	1530°	1610°	1900°

F. Wüst and co-workers, and W. Herz gave for the **heat of fusion** at 1210°, 36·7 cals. per gram, or 2·01 Cals. per gram atom ; E. Kordes gave 1·36 units for the entropy change on melting. S. Umino gave 64·8 cals. per gram ; and for the **heat of transformation** at 835°, 2·88 cals. per gram ; and at 1044°, 4·53 cals. per gram. A. Guntz found that the **heat of oxidation** of the pyrophoric metal $(Mn,O)=90·6$ Cals. ; and that of the fused metal, $(Mn,O)=94·8$ Cals. ; hence the **heat of formation** of the more chemically active pyrophoric metal from the metal which has been fused is 3·8 Cals. H. von Jüptner gave $2Mn+O_2=2MnO+181·9$ Cals. ; and $Mn+O_2=MnO_2+125·3$ Cals. J. Thomsen found that the **heat of solution** of the fused metal in hydrochloric acid is 49·7 Cals. F. Wüst and co-workers gave 24·14 cals. for the heat of transformation of manganese into an allotropic form between 1070° and 1130°. G. N. Lewis and co-workers found the **entropy** of manganese to be 7·3 Cals. per degree at 25° and one atm. press. ; W. Herz, 11·00 ; and E. D. Eastman calculated 6·9 to 8·2 Cals. per degree by two different methods. B. Bruzs gave 20·2 for the entropy at the m.p., and 7·3 at 25°. R. D. Kleeman discussed the internal and free energy of manganese ; and W. Herz, the entropy.

H. von Wartenberg [3] gave $\mu=2·49$ for the **index of refraction** of manganese for the wave-length $\lambda=5790$; $k=3·89$ for the **index of absorption** ; and $R=64$ per cent. for the **reflecting power** ; J. T. Littleton gave for $\lambda=5893$, $\mu=2·41$, $k=3·88$, and $R=64·0$; while V. Fréedericksz gave :

λ	2570	3250	3600	4140	4680	5320	5880	6680
μ	0·661	1·005	1·159	1·390	1·653	1·846	2·246	2·619
k	1·186	1·758	2·078	2·495	2·833	3·267	3·753	4·050
R	36·5	42·9	48·3	53·4	56·1	60·4	63·5	64·5

G. Pfestorf gave :

λ	578	546	436	406	366	313	281	254
μ	1·88	1·83	1·38	1·30	1·12	1·05	0·90	0·83
k	1·85	1·73	1·92	1·90	2·00	2·03	2·04	2·02
R	55·3	59·5	56·5	54·3	52·8	52·1	48·3	46·0 per cent.

J. H. Gladstone found the **molecular refraction** of manganese in its salts to be 0·222 ; and in the permanganates, 0·476 ; W. J. Pope gave 14·04 for the atomic refraction of manganese in manganous salts ; and J. H. Gladstone, 11·5. A. E. H. Tutton discussed this subject.

According to J. B. Nathanson, the reflecting power of manganese, distilled in vacuo, is from 61·6 to 63·5 per cent. for wave-lengths 4600 A. to 6800 A. The values at the blue end of the spectrum are greater and those at the red end are less than those obtained for manganese prepared in other ways.

W. Biltz [4] discussed the colour of manganese compounds. A colourless gas flame is coloured green by manganous chloride. W. A. Miller found green bands in the spectrum of manganous chloride in the alcohol flame, but he thought that the result was due to the chlorine, because other chlorides gave a green flame.

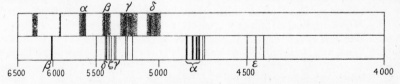

Figs. 7 and 8.—The Flame and Spark Spectra of Manganese.

L. de Boisbaudran compared the result with the green flame of boric acid. According to J. Formanek, manganous chloride gives a **flame spectrum** which quickly vanishes as the manganese is oxidized. The flame spectrum, Fig. 7, consists of orange-yellow bands 6205 and 6179 ; a narrow yellow band 5848 ; a yellowish-green band $\alpha=5592$; and green bands $\beta=5424$, 5392, and 5360 ; $\gamma=5320$, 5193, and 5158 ; and δ=5052, 5014, and 4984.   These bands are produced when a large proportion of manganous chloride is present in the flame ; with a small quantity of the salt only the α, β, and γ bands are produced.   Other manganese salts do not give this spectrum.   H. Casaretto examined the band spectrum of manganous chloride in the oxy-coal-gas blowpipe flame ; and R. Mecke, the band spectrum of manganous oxide.   The flame spectrum of manganese was examined by W. A. Miller, R. T. Simmler, R. Böttger, M. A. Catalan, A. Mitscherlich, J. Müller, A. R. Leeds, L. de Boisbaudran, A. Gouy, J. N. Lockyer, W. N. Hartley, O. Vogel, C. de Watteville, A. Hagenbach and H. Konen, H. Auerbach, J. Plücker and J. W. Hittorf, and E. Diacon.   The spectrum in the oxyhydrogen or coal-gas flame was examined by W. N. Hartley, W. N. Hartley and H. W. Moss, and H. Casaretto. One way of controlling the bessemer steel process is to watch for the vanishing of the manganese bands from the flame spectrum ; it is then assumed that the decarbonization of the iron is complete.   The spectrum of the bessemer flame has been examined by W. M. Watts, W. N. Hartley, and C. J. Lundström.   The more important lines of the **spark spectrum** of a manganous chloride soln. are : an orange-yellow line 6017, β, Fig. 8 ; the green lines 5420, 5413-δ, 5377-ζ, and 5341-γ ; the four blue lines α, 4824, 4784, 4766, and 4754 ; and the indigo-blue line 4462-ϵ. There are numerous other lines of minor importance in the recognition of the manganese spark spectrum.   Observations were made by W. A. Miller, W. Huggins, W. F. Meggers and co-workers, F. Exner and E. Haschek W. Beckmann, R. Thalén, W. N. Hartley, W. N. Hartley and H. W. Moss, E. O. Hulburt, W. Kraemer, A. W. Smith and M. Muskat, J. N. Lockyer, K. Burns, M. A. Catalan, S. P. de Rubies, E. Back, G. Ciamician, J. Parry and A. E. Tucker, F. McClean, A. de Gramont, E. Demarçay, W. E. Adeney, O. Lohse, C. Fritsch, A. Hagenbach and H. Konen, J. H. Pollok and A. G. G. Leonard, L. Janicki, J. M. Eder and E. Valenta, and C. M. Kilby.   According to W. N. Hartley, 0·0001 per cent. of manganese can be detected in a soln. by the spectral lines.   The **arc spectrum** was examined by J. R. Capron, A. Sellerio, R. Thalén, F. Exner and E. Haschek, R. Frerichs, S. P. de Rubies and J. Dorronsoro, S. P. de Rubies, C. C. Kiess and W. F. Meggers, W. F. Meggers and co-workers, S. Wirminghaus, A. S. King, G. S. Monk, K. Burns, J. C. McLennan and A. B. McLay, E. Back, B. Hasselberg, R. E. Loving, A. Hagenbach and H. Konen, M. A. Catalan, A. Hornli, W. J. Humphreys, H. Fuchs, and C. M. Kilby.   The spectrum of the dust in explosions of gases was examined by G. D. Liveing and J. Dewar ; the **absorption spectrum** of the vapour, by J. N. Lockyer and W. C. Roberts-Austen, R. V. Zumstein, G. A. Hemsalech, A. S. King, R. G. Loyarte and A. T. Williams, J. Fridrichson, J. C. McLennan and E. Cohen. A. W. Smith and M. Muskat, J. Parry, W. Grotrian, and H. Geisler ; the **ultra-violet spectrum,** by W. A. Miller, R. J. Lang, L. and E. Bloch, S. Wirminghaus, J. Schönn, A. Cornu, and F. Exner and E. Haschek ; and the **ultra-red spectrum,** by C. C. Kiess and W. F. Meggers, and H. M. Randall and E. F. Barker.   The *anomalous dispersion* was examined by L. Puccianti, and H. Geisler ; the *self-induction,* by G. A. Hemsalech, and C. M. Kilby ; the *enhanced lines,* by M. Kimura and G. Nakamura ; the *ultimate rays,* by A. T. Williams ; the effect of *pressure,* by W. J. Humphreys, and G. S. Monk ; and the effect of a *magnetic field*—the **Zeeman effect**—by A. A. Michelson, E. Back, J. E. Purvis, O. Lüttwig, J. H. van Vleck and A. Frank, W. C. van Geel ; J. Parry discussed the periodic law and spectra ;   and H. Kayser and C. Runge, K. Bechert and M. A. Catalan, H. N. Russell, A. Sommerfeld, S. Goudsmit, D. R. Hartree, R. A. Sawyer, J. C. McLennan and A. B. McLay, G. Wentzel, F. Croze, S. Kawata, C. C. Kiess and O. Laporte, W. F. Meggers and co-workers, O. S. Duffendack and J. G. Black, R. Frerichs, H. E. White, R. C. Gibbs and H. E. White, H. E. White and R. Ritschl, E. Paulson, A. E. Ruark and R. L. Chenault, and P. G. Nutting, the structure of the lines, and the **series spectra.**   M. A. Catalan said that the flame, arc, and spark spectra of manganese, like those of other elements, are formed by two classes of lines, some belonging to the neutral atom, and some to the ionized atom, Mn+. There are triplet series and combination lines in the spectrum of the neutral atom. The lines of ionized manganese, enhanced lines, also form triplets ; there is a system of sharp, diffuse, and principal triplets, and another system of narrower triplets corresponding with the single line systems

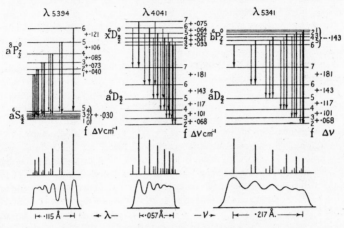

FIG. 9.—Hyperfine Structure of the Spectrum of Manganese.

in the alkaline earths, as in the case of the neutral atom. Each spectral line in manganese is really a tiny multiplet. H. E. White and R. Ritschl represented the fine structure of the manganese lines 5394, and 4041 at liquid air temp., and 5341 from a vacuum furnace in Fig. 9, and the 4823, 4783, and 4754 lines at liquid air temp. in Fig. 10. The subject was discussed by R. S. Seward.

I. Lifschitz and E. Rosenbohm [5] examined the **absorption spectrum** of manganese salts. According to P. Lambert, the absorption spectrum of manganous chloride has an intense broad band between 5130 and 5575 ; a broad, less intense band between 4200 and 4425 ; and a group of six narrow bands 4102·5 to 4122·5, 4052·5 to 4080, 4020 to 4032·5, 4000 to 4010, 3962·5 to 3977·5, and 3945 to 3957·5. According to J. Formanek, a neutral soln. of manganous chloride reacts with tincture of alkanna without changing the colour of the liquid, but the absorption spectrum is displaced to the left, and a band appears at 6145. If aq. ammonia is added—not enough to produce a turbidity—the liquid becomes blue,

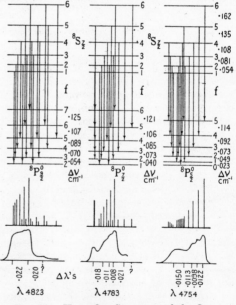

FIG. 10.—Hyperfine Structure of the Octet System of the Manganese Spectrum.

and the absorption spectrum shows bands at 6171, 5707 and 5303. The presence of iron or chromium interferes with the results. W. A. Miller, and E. Luck observed the absorption spectrum of manganic chloride. W. Friederichs gave 5274, 5212, 5070, 5002, 4882, 4829, 4708, 4663, 4543, and 4390. J. M. Hiebendaal found a feeble band at 5890 to 5440 with a soln. of manganous phosphate in water. Observations on the manganous salts were also made by H. W. Vogel, F. Hoppe-Seyler, J. Moir, C. J. W. Grieveson, N. von Klobukoff, C. Kubierschky, and J. M. Hiebendaal. W. Jäschke and J. Meyer examined the absorption spectra of potassium manganate and permanganate, of manganese tetrachloride, of manganic chloride, sulphate, and phosphate, and of manganous chloride and sulphate. The absorption spectra of all the compounds show great similarity, particularly in respect of the band in the red ; this band is very persistent, and only disappears with the very dilute soln. of permanganate and manganous chloride. The central band appears, however, to be influenced by the valency, in the sense that it moves towards the red end of the spectrum with increasing valency. The violet end of the spectrum is most sensitive to changes in valency, but they were unable to make any measurements in that region or in the ultra-violet portion of the spectrum. The absorption spectrum of the permanganates can be recognized in soln. diluted 1 : 250,000. J. Formanek observed eight bands at 5710, 5473, 5256, 5054, 4870, 4707, 4544, and 4395—Fig. 11. L. de Boisbaudran observed bands at 5703, 5465, 5246, 5045, 4861, 4694, and 4543. A. Hagenbach and R. Percy's measurements gave 4388, 4537, 4695, 4866, 5050, 5249, 5461, and 5695. The bands are so related that there is a constant difference between the oscillation frequencies of successive members of the group. J. Formanek's broad band at 6370 can be resolved into the four bands at 5949, 6264, 6528, and 6862, so that these form a continuous series with the other eight bands. E. Adinolfi observed that the absorption spectrum is not influenced by the extent to which the salt is ionized in soln. Observations were also made by H. Kayser, T. R. Simmler, J. Müller, J. H. Gladstone, F. Hoppe-Seyler, J. Moir, A. Hantzsch and R. H. Clark, J. E. Purvis, T. R. Merton, W. Ostwald, V. R. von Kurelec, C. J. W. Grieveson, E. Adinolfi, H. Gombos, G. G. Stokes, H. Bremer, C. Pulfrich, H. Morton and H. C. Bolton, C. Christensen,

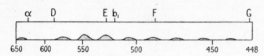

FIG. 11.—Absorption Spectrum of Potassium Permanganate Solutions.

K. Stöckl, W. N. Hartley, J. M. Hiebendaal, and K. Vierordt. J. L. Soret observed a band in the ultra-violet between 3900 and 2750. H. Bremer found that the bands are displaced about 50 A. towards the red as the temp. rises from 20° to 80°, and H. Morton and H. C. Bolton, and W. N. Hartley also observed a displacement of the bands with a rise of temp., but J. M. Hiebendaal observed that temp. has no influence on the position of the bands. K. Stöckl gave for conc. soln. 5645, 5410, 5225, 5065, and 4875 ; and for dil. soln. 5655, 5465, 5265, 5050, and 4890. H. W. Vogel found that the spectrum of the solid differs from that of the soln. by a stronger absorption between the bands. J. Holluta examined the absorption spectrum of the manganates, and the manganito manganates. G. B. Rizzo found the spectrum of manganese-tinted glass showed bands at 6740, 6560, 6380, 6030, 5900, 5830, and 5540 at 15° ; at 6860, 6620, 6460, 6040, 5920, 5840, and 5540 at 300° ; and 6660, 6500, 6050, 5930, 5850, and 5540. V. R. von Kurelec measured the absorption bands of potassium permanganate dissolved in various solvents. E. Viterbi studied the ultra-violet absorption spectrum of potassium permanganate soln. ; C. L. Cross, the spectrum of manganese in glass ; and K. Schlossmacher, the spectrum of manganese in spinels.

J. Fridrichson [6] examined the **resonance spectrum** of manganese vapour; and L. de Boisbaudran, the **fluorescence spectrum** of manganese compounds in vacuo, under the influence of the electrical discharge. Many manganese compounds do not fluoresce after calcination, but they impart fluorescing properties to non-fluorescing substances. Thus, A. E. Becquerel, L. Bruninghaus, and V. Klatt and P. Lenard observed this with calcium sulphide (q.v.) ; J. R. Mourelo, with strontium sulphide ; and H. Grüne, and the Chininfabrik Braunschweig, with zinc sulphide. A. Dauvillier discussed the green fluorescence with manganese glass exposed to cathode rays ; and A. Karl, the **triboluminescence** of the oxides and sulphides of manganese. According to T. Tanaka, manganese is the principal agent in the cathodoluminescence of artificial rubies, and spinel. W. G. Guy observed no **radioactivity** with the salts of manganese.

The absorption of the X-rays was studied by U. Andrewes and co-workers,[7] T. E. Aurén, and K. Chamberlain. The **X-ray spectrum** of manganese has lines in the K-series at a_1a, 2·09777 ; a_3a_4, 2·0879 ; $\beta_1\beta$, 1·902 ; and $\beta_2\gamma$, 1·892. The K-series was observed by V. Dolejsek, V. Dolejsek and K. Pestrecoff, V. Dolejsek and H. Filcakova, G. Kettmann, S. Björek, S. Eriksson, R. Thoroeus, S. Idei, S. Pastorello, G. B. Deodhar, K. Chamberlain, B. Kievit and G. A. Lindsay, H. Beuthe, T. Wetterblad, O. Stelling, G. Ortner, A. E. Lindh, H. R. Robinson, H. Walter, D. M. Bose, W. Duane and K. F. Hu, B. C. Mukherjee and B. B. Ray, W. Duane and. H. Fricke, J. Schrör, E. Hjalmar, N. Seljakoff and co-workers, R. C. Gibbs and H. E. White, H. R. Robinson, D. Coster, M. Siegbahn, and N. Stensson ; the L-series, by S. Björek, C. E. Howe, J. Schrör, H. Hirata, R. Thoroeus, R. Thoroeus and M. Siegbahn, B. C. Mukherjee and B. B. Ray, and M. J. Druyvesteyn ; and the M-series, by U. Andrewes and co-workers, S. Björek, B. C. Mukherjee and B. B. Ray, and M. Levi. W. Duane and H. Fricke found the critical absorption wave-length is $1·8893 \times 10^{-8}$ cm. O. W. Richardson and F. S. Robertson, and F. C. Chalklin examined the emission of soft X-rays from manganese ; L. P. Davis, the effect of oxidation on the emission of soft X-rays ; and J. Fridrichson, the resonance radiation of manganese vapour.

D. R. Hartree [8] calculated 14·5 volts for the **ionizing potential** ; M. A. Catalan, and J. G. Black and O. S. Duffendack gave 7·4 volts, and S. C. Biswas, 7·36 volts for the Mn-II spectrum ; H. N. Russell also gave 7·40 volts for the first ionization potential, and 15·70 volts for the second one. A. C. Davies and F. Horton, F. C. Chalklin, and B. B. Ray and R. C. Mazumdar discussed the critical potentials for soft X-rays ; A. Hantzsch and H. Carlsohn, the work of ionization ; C. E. Eddy and co-workers, the analysis of manganese by means of the X-rays ; D. M. Yost, the absorption of X-rays by manganous salts ; R. W. James and G. W. Brindley, the scattering of X-rays ; H. B. Wahlin, the emission of positive ions by the heated metal ; R. H. Ghosh, the relation between the electronic structure and the ionizing potential ; and H. N. Russell, the ionization in the solar atmosphere, and the ionizing potential. W. Herz gave $7·52 \times 10^{-12}$ for the **vibration frequency ;** and J. E. P. Wagstaff, $7·5 \times 10^{-12}$. M. von Laue,[9] A. Goetz, and W. Espe studied the emission of electrons from the metal at a high temp. N. Piltschikoff observed that manganese emits positive Moser's rays. T. Pavolini, and O. W. Richardson and F. S. Robertson studied the photoelectric effect ; U. Nakaya, the influence of adsorbed gas on the phenomenon ; J. Fridrichson, the fluorescence of the vapour ; and R. E. Nyswander and B. E. Cohn, the effect of manganese on the thermoluminescence of glass. R. Robl observed no luminescence in ultra-violet light.

According to E. Kuh,[10] the **electrical resistance** of manganese is 0·00015298 ohm, and the **electrical conductivity,** 1225×10^4 mhos. A. Schulze gave 0·0000044 for the sp. resistance. W. Meissner and B. Voigt measured the resistance of two different samples of manganese down to $-271·8°$, and found for the ratio, r, of the resistance, R, at the given temp. to the resistance, R_0, at 0°, when for I, $R_0=5·161 \times 10^{-3}$ ohm at 0·16°, and for II, $6·486 \times 10^{-3}$ ohm :

		0·16	$-184·10°$	$-252·54°$	$-268·80°$	$-271·49°$	$-271·78°$
r for I .	. 1		0·9776	1·0020	0·9765	0·9581	—
r for II .	. 1		0·9695	1·0082	0·9900	—	0·9860

P. W. Bridgman studied the press. coeff. of the resistance of manganese, at 30°, up to 12,000 kgrms. per sq. cm., and obtained $\delta R/R_0=-7·012 \times 10^{-6}p+5·63 \times 10^{-11}p^2$. K. F. Herzfeld, and K. Höjendahl studied this subject from the point of view of the electron theory. P. Kapitza examined the effect of a magnetic field on the electrical conductivity of manganese.

J. B. Seth and co-workers studied the e.m.f. developed by manganese in contact with a rotating steel disc. H. D. Royce and L. Kahlenberg [11] obtained values for the **electrode potential** of manganese against aq. soln. of manganous salts, in the absence of oxygen, by using a liquid or pasty manganese amalgam electrode which is continuously stirred. The potential is independent of the concentration of the amalgam above 1·2 per cent. manganese. Neglecting the liquid junction potential, and taking the potential of the normal calomel electrode as 0·560 volt, the potential of manganese against $0·5N$-$MnSO_4$ is $-1·452$ volt; N-$MnSO_4$, $-1·449$ volt; N-$MnCl_2$, $-1·436$ volt; and N-$Mn(NO_3)_2$, $-1·232$ volt. B. Neumann gave 0·815 volt for normal soln. of the sulphate; 0·824 volt, chloride; and 0·560 volt, nitrate; V. Nejedly gave the e.m.f. $E=1·510$ volt, and $dE/d\theta=0·0001510$ volt for the temp. coeff. of the e.m.f. of manganese in a soln. of $0·001N$-$MnCl_2$ and $0·1N$-KCl. H. Gerding gave for the normal electrode potential of manganese in aluminium sulphate $E_H=-1·0$ volt. Observations on the potential of manganese were also made by T. J. Martin and A. J. Helfrecht, R. Lorenz and G. Hostelet, A. Thiel and W. Hammerschmidt, E. Newbery, and W. Muthmann and F. Fraunberger. S. Kyropoulos detected a different potential in different parts of the same metal in soln. of potassium ferrocyanide. O. Bauer observed that in a 1 per cent. soln. of sodium chloride, and with a normal calomel electrode, the potential was $-1·305$ volt at the start; $-1·200$ volt after an hour; and $-1·120$ volt after 120 hrs. G. Grube and K. Huberich measured the oxidation potential of soln. of manganese sulphates in sulphuric acid—*vide* manganous sulphate. A. N. Campbell found that the e.m.f. of the cell $Mn \mid M$-$MnSO_4 \mid 3N$-KCl $\mid Hg_2Cl_2$ (with $3N$-KCl) $\mid Hg$ is $-0·797$ volt at 12°; and the potential of the half element $Mn \mid 0·1M$-$MnSO_4$ is $-0·821$ volt. The **hydrogen over-voltage** with respect to N-Na_2SO_4 and 0·02-NaOH at 16° is:

Over-voltage	.	0·615	0·644	0·705	0·755	0·823	0·850	1·044 volt
Current density	.	0·47	0·63	1·33	2·33	4·00	5·00	10·00 amp. per sq. dm.

and with a current density of 3·33 amp. per sq. dm. :

	15·5°	53·5°	71°	84°
Over-voltage	0·801	0·622	0·507	0·393 volt

For the normal potential of quadrivalent manganese ions in the presence of bivalent manganese ions, A. N. Campbell gave, on the hydrogen scale, 1·465 volts at 16°. According to W. Muthmann and F. Fraunberger, manganese is in many respects analogous to zinc, and does not show **passivity ;** on the other hand, E. Müller supposed that it does possess a very labile passivity, best shown when it is used as anode in a soln. of acidic sodium phosphate. With a high enough current density —say 0·075 to 0·15 amp. per sq. cm.—it passes into a soln. as tervalent manganic phosphate and liberates oxygen. The ammeter or the electrometer shows that pulsations occur ; with the minimum values for the e.m.f., hydrogen is evolved vigorously at the electrode, so that both hydrogen and oxygen appear. This subject has been discussed by H. Kuessner, G. Grube and co-workers, and A. Günther-Schulze. The **electrodeposition** of manganese has been discussed in connection with the preparation of manganese. According to H. Kuessner, with a manganese anode in neutral solutions (of potassium chloride or sulphate), the metal dissolves, and both hydrogen and oxygen are evolved, the whole of the metal finally present in the soln. being bivalent. Manganese itself dissolves, with evolution of hydrogen, but the rate is too slow to account for the quantities of hydrogen observed ; it is, therefore, thought probable that univalent manganese ions are formed, which react with the hydrogen ions in the soln. thus : $2Mn +2H^{\cdot}=2Mn^{\cdot\cdot}+H_2$. From 8 to 10 per cent. of the manganese dissolves in this way. The oxygen is evolved when the potential of the manganese anode is more than 0·3 volt more negative than the normal hydrogen electrode, whilst hydroxyl ions could only be discharged directly if it were 1·62 volts more positive ; the oxygen is, therefore, a secondary product. The potential measurements show further that the dissolution of manganese accompanied by evolution of oxygen at the anode and of hydrogen at the cathode is a process which takes place of its own accord ; hence the gain of free energy due to the conversion of metallic manganese into ions cannot be less than the loss due to the decomposition of water. Following this out quantitatively, it appears that the manganese must dissolve primarily in the form of tervalent ions, which then react with hydroxyl ions thus : $2Mn^{...}+2OH'$ $=2Mn^{..}+H_2O+\frac{1}{2}O_2$. Increasing the alkalinity of the electrolyte leads to the formation of manganese ions of higher valency in increasing quantity. E. Müller found that when manganese is used as an anode in electrolysis, the manganese becomes passive in alkaline soln. of sodium sulphate or phosphate, but behaves normally in acidic and neutral soln. E. Müller also found that manganese dissolves in weakly acidic soln. of sodium phosphate as manganic phosphate at a high current density (7·5 to 15 amp. per sq. dm.), and oxygen is simultaneously evolved. The ammeter shows that pulsations are set up, and with the lowest value of the e.m.f., hydrogen is violently evolved at the electrode. This evolution again ceases, and the issuing gas contains oxygen and hydrogen, the presence of which may be shown by exploding the mixture. The passivity of manganese is so labile that, as anode, it falls back into the active condition. G. Grube and H. Metzger observed that with hot, conc. soda-lye, manganese passes into soln.—at low current densities as bivalent atoms ; at medium current densities as tervalent atoms ; and at still higher current densities as sexavalent atoms, which formed manganate. At room temp., however, or in dil. soda-lye, the manganese dissolves immediately in the septavalent condition. A. N. Campbell observed that the potential of manganese with no current flowing is —0·795 volt ; and with a current density of 0·7 to 7·0 amp. per sq. dm. it is —0·725. This gives 0·070 volt as the measure of the passivity. Hydrogen was freely evolved at the cathode, but no visible gas at the manganese anode. The soln. became somewhat cloudy, through precipitation of basic manganese sulphate in the neighbourhood of the cathode. Metallic manganese also was deposited on the cathode. There was no formation of permanganate. R. Saxon, and I. Slendyk made some observations on the subject. J. Chloupek found the normal potential of platinum for mixtures of equal proportions of tervalent and bivalent manganese phosphates in phosphoric acid soln. is 0·98 to 1·18 volts on the hydrogen scale. The instability of the soln. makes the results variable. B. N. Chuckubutti obtained Nobili's rings by the electrodeposition of manganese from a soln. of manganese sulphate on a brass plate.

A. Heydweiller gave 44 for the **ionic mobility** of manganese, $\frac{1}{2}Mn^{..}$, at 18°. E. Gapon and I. Z. Khaskes studied the hydration of bivalent manganese ions. Observations were also made by W. Althammer. W. Ostwald gave 240 cals. for the **heat of ionization** per valence. J. Thiele discussed the thermoelectric properties. H. Zahn and H. Schmidt found that the coeff. R of the Hall effect is —93×10^{-5}, and the coeff. Q of the thermo-magnetic effect is —15×10^{-6}. According to J. Brezina, with neutral or acidic soln. of manganous chloride, the electro-deposition of manganese at the dropping cathode proceeds reversibly, the deposition potential from a molar soln. being —1·326 volts, relative to the normal calomel electrode. The polarization curves permit the detection of manganous salts in soln. down to 10^{-6} mols per litre. The deposition potential becomes negative in the presence of ammonia owing to the formation of complex cations. W. Ogawa studied the activation of galena as a radio-detector by manganese salts. The simultaneous precipitation of manganese and zinc was discussed by O. C. Ralston. H. Nagaoka and T. Futagami discussed the spluttering of manganese by the disruptive discharge in a magnetic field ; M. Haitinger, the intensity of the ultra-violet light from a manganese arc-light ; and C. E. Mendenhall and L. R. Ingersoll found that small globules of metal on Nernst's glower move against the current. K. Meyer and A. Günther-Schulze studied the cathodic spluttering of manganese.

There has been some discussion as to whether manganese is **paramagnetic or** not. The paramagnetism has been attributed to the presence of its oxides or of metallic iron as impurities. M. Faraday, and E. Seckelson found specimens of electrolytic manganese to be ferromagnetic ; and P. Weiss and H. K. Onnes obtained a sample of manganese, as a grey powder, by electrolyzing a soln. of the purified chloride, with a mercury cathode, and subsequently distilling off the mercury ; when the powder was compressed in the form of a rod, it was paramagnetic. The powder was fused in a magnesia boat, and the external film of oxide was turned off with a diamond-pointed tool. The rod was ferromagnetic. Fig. 12 represents the hysteresis curve—*vide* iron. P. Kapitza studied the magnetic properties of manganese. The maximum value of the sp. magnetization is a hundred times weaker

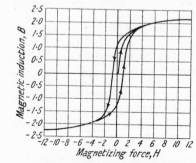

FIG. 12.—Cyclic Magnetization of Manganese—Hysteresis Loop.

than that of iron, and the coercive force is 670 gauss—that is, ten times as strong as that of steel used for making good permanent magnets. The rod was strongly attracted between the poles of a magnet, and placed itself perpendicular to the field. Hence, manganese of the same degree of purity can occur in two states—paramagnetic and ferromagnetic. E. Wiedemann [12] found that the **atomic magnetism** of manganese in potassium manganic oxalate is 70·58 and in the fluoride 43·25 when that of iron in $FeCl_3$ is 100. P. Collet gave $56·5 \times 10^{-6}$ unit for the manganese in potassium permanganate (*q.v.*). O. Liebknecht and A. P. Wills made some observations on the paramagnetism of manganese salts. K. Honda and T. Sone gave $10·1 \times 10^{-6}$ unit for the **magnetic susceptibility** of manganese at 18°, and 20×10^{-6} unit at 1000°. M. Owen gave $8·39 \times 10^{-6}$ mass unit ; E. Kuh, 2130×10^{-6} and 1080×10^{-6} ; and T. Ishiwara, $9·66 \times 10^{-6}$ mass unit ; while K. Ihde gave 80×10^{-6} vol. unit. K. Honda and T. Sone observed a discontinuity in the curve for the magnetic susceptibility of manganese at 1040° ; and Y. Shimizu found that the magnetic susceptibility of 99·9 per cent. manganese at room temp. is $7·55 \times 10^{-6}$ mass unit, and at higher temp. the value changes as indicated in Fig. 13. There is an abrupt increase at 810° corresponding with the allotropic $\alpha \rightarrow \beta$ transformation ; and one at 1100° corresponding with the $\beta \rightarrow \gamma$ transformation. According to R. Hadfield and co-workers, powdered manganese has a paramagnetic susceptibility of $11·0 \times 10^{-6}$ mass unit ; cast manganese is ferromagnetic, but after repeated

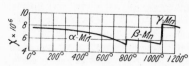

FIG. 13.—The Magnetic Susceptibility of Manganese at Different Temperatures.

heating to redness and washing with hydrochloric acid, the mass susceptibility gradually fell from 2000×10^{-6}, approaching the value for powdered manganese. The ferromagnetic properties were inferred to be due to occluded hydrogen. Manganese steels gave variable and large values, which were greatly reduced, after washing with hydrochloric acid to remove surface ferriferous impurities, to the order of 75 to 100×10^{-6}. W. Lepke found that for a field strength of H kilogauss, the mass susceptibilities $\times 10^6$ of massive and powdered manganese are :

H	.	.	0·8	1·0	2·1	7·0	10·0	16·0	18·9
Mass	.	.	9·4	10·3	10·5	9·9	9·8	9·5	9·4
Powd.	.	.	—	10·7	11·6	10·3	10·2	9·7	9·6

R. H. Weber, A. Duperier, J. H. van Vleck and A. Frank, B. Cabrera, and K. Ihde made observations on this subject—*vide infra*, cupromanganese. M. Faraday suggested that possibly manganese at ordinary temp. is above its critical point, but P. Weiss and H. K. Onnes observed no indication of a ferromagnetic state at —259°.

C. E. Guillaume's suggestion that Heusler's alloys owe this magnetic state to the effect of aluminium in raising the temp. of magnetic transformation has no experimental support. P. Weiss and H. K. Onnes found that the magnetic induction, B, and intensity, H, curve showed the large coercive force of 670 C.G.S. units. Even at $H=12,000$ the specimen was not saturated. This agrees with the assumption that this element possesses a ferromagnetic property. The saturation intensity, l, deduced from the manganese alloys is $l_s=2300$, whereas that for iron is 1700. H. Freese, and I. Tamm studied the magnetizability of thin films of manganese ; E. H. Williams, the relation of magnetism and valency ; and J. C. Thomson, the relation between magnetism and thermoelectric force. S. S. Bhatnagar and co-workers found that manganese salts lose their paramagnetism and become diamagnetic when adsorbed on charcoal. The subject was studied by D. M. Bose, and L. Sambi and L. Szegö ; P. Weiss, C. Sadron, and E. C. Stoner discussed the magnetic moment of manganese ; and P. Weiss, A. Chatillon, and B. Cabrera, the structure of the magnetic molecules ; and J. C. Slater, the place of manganese in the theory of magnetism—*vide* iron.

REFERENCES.

[1] C. Brunner, *Pogg. Ann.*, **101**. 264, 1857 ; **103**. 139, 1857 ; *Dingler's Journ.*, **144**. 184, 1857 ; **146**. 44, 1857 ; **147**. 122, 1858 ; *Mitt. Naturf. Ges. Bern*, 72, 135, 1857 ; J. ·B. Dumas, *Traité de chimie appliquée aux arts*, Paris, **2**. 19, 1830 ; E. Persson and E. Oehman, *Nature*, **124**. 333, 1929 ; E. Oehman, *Metallwirtschaft*, **9**. 825, 1930 ; *Svenska Kem. Tids.*, **42**. 210, 1930 ; *Zeit. phys. Chem.*, **8**. B, 81, 1930 ; E. Persson, *ib.*, **9**. B, 25, 1930 ; S. Sekito, *Zeit. Kryst.*, **72**. 406, 1929 ; A. Kapustinsky, *Zeit. phys. Chem.*, **144**. 187, 1929 ; P. W. Bridgman, *Proc. Amer. Acad.*, **64**. 51, 1929 ; W. Schmidt, *Arch. Eisenhüttenwesen*, **3**. 293, 1929 ; J. C. Slater, *Phys. Rev.*, (2), **36**. 57, 1930 ; A. Osawa, *Science Rep. Tohoku Univ.*, **19**. 247, 1930 ; C. H. M. Jenkins and M. L. V. Gayler, *Proc. Roy. Soc.*, **129**. A, 91, 1930 ; T. Ishiwara, *Kinzokuno Kenkyu*, **3**. 13, 1926 ; A. Karlsson, *Arkiv. Mat. Astron. Fys.*, **22**. A, 9, 1930 ; G. Natta and L. Passerini, *Atti Congresso Chim. Pura Applicata*, **3**. 365, 1930 ; K. Honda, Y. Matsuyama and Y. Isobe, *Bull. Inst. Phys. Chem. Research Tokyo*, **9**. 906, 1930 ; *Scient. Papers Inst. Phys. Chem. Research*, **14**. 275, 1930 ; G. A. Tomlinson, *Phil. Mag.*, (7), **11**. 1009, 1931 ; W. Biltz and K. Meisel, *Zeit. anorg. Chem.*, **198**. 191, 1931 ; C. Bullock, *Chem. News*, **60**. 20, 1889 ; *Journ. Franklin. Inst.*, **128**. 62, 1889 ; A. M. Berkenheim, *Zeit. phys. Chem.*, **141**. 35, 1929 ; H. Goldschmidt, *Zeit. Elektrochem.*, **4**. 494, 1898 ; *Liebig's Ann.*, **301**. 19, 1898 ; *German Pat.*, *D.R.P.* 175885, 1905 ; O. Prelinger, *Monatsh.*, **14**. 353, 1893 ; *Sitzber. Akad. Wien*, **102**. 346, 1893 ; R. Bunsen, *Pogg. Ann.*, **91**. 619, 1854 ; M. L. V. Gayler, *Journ. Iron Steel Inst.*, **115**. i, 393, 1927 ; *Nature*, **124**. 840, 1929 ; ·E. Frémy, *Compt. Rend.*, **44**. 632, 1857 ; A. Westgren and G. Phragmén, *Zeit. Physik*, **33**. 777, 1925 ; A. J. Bradley and J. Thewlis, *Proc. Roy. Soc.*, **115**. A, 456, 1927 ; A. J. Bradley, *Phil. Mag.*, (6), **50**. 1018, 1925 ; J. F. T. Young, *ib.*, (6), **46**. 291, 1923 ; W. L. Bragg, *ib.*, (6), **40**. 169, 1920 ; A. W. Hull and W. P. Davey, *Journ. Amer. Opt. Soc.*, **5**. 479, 1921 ; *Phys. Rev.*, (2), **17**. 549, 1921 ; M. L. Huggins, *ib.*, (2), **28**. 1086, 1926 ; D. Zereteli, *Manganese Ore, with special reference to the Georgian Ore*, London, 1, 1925 ; P. Groth, *Elemente der physikalischen und chemischen Krystallographie*, München, 274, 1921 ; *Chemische Krystallographie*, Leipzig, **1**. 36. 1906 ; M. Levin and G. Tammann, *Zeit. anorg. Chem.*, **47**. 136, 1905 ; S. Umino, *Science Rep. Tohoku Univ.*, **16**. 775, 1927 ; H. Davy, *Elements of Chemical Philosophy*, London, 1812 ; J. F. John, *Gehlen's Journ.*, **3**. 452, 1807 ; **4**. 436, 1807 ; *Ann. Phil.*, **2**. 172, 263, 1813 ; **3**. 413, 1813 ; P. J. Hjelm, *Vet. Akad. Handl. Stockholm*, **39**. 82, 1778 ; *Crell's Die neuesten Entdeckungen in der Chemie*, **5**. 164, 1782 ; T. Bergman, *De mineris ferri albis*, Upsala, 1774 ; *Opuscula physica et chemica*, Lipsiæ, **2**. 184, 1792 ; London, **2**. 203, 1798 ; J. G. Gahn, in T. Bergman, *De mineris ferri albis*, Upsala, 1774 (*vide supra*) ; E. Glatzel, *Ber.*, **22**. 2857, 1889 ; *Eng. Min. Journ.*, **49**. 452, 1890 ; J. E. Loughlin, *Chem. News*, **25**. 139, 1872 ; *Amer. Chemist*, **1**. 454, 1871 ; *Bull. Soc. Chim.*, (2), **17**. 557, 1872 ; E. Kuh, *Die Darstellung des chemische reinen Mangans und die Bestimmung der wichtigsten physikalischen Konstanten desselben*, Zürich, 1911 ; R. Frilley, *Recherches sur les alliages métalliques siliciés et contributions à l'étude des densités des alliages*, Angers, 1911 ; R. Böttger, *Tabellarische Uebersicht der specifischen Gewichte der Körper*, Frankfort, 1837 ; A. N. Campbell, *Journ. Chem. Soc.*, **123**. 892, 2323, 1923 ; **127**. 1487, 1925 ; *Trans. Faraday Soc.*, **22**. 46, 1926 ; W. C. Roberts-Austen, *Proc. Roy. Soc.*, **43**. 425, 1888 ; *Chem. News*, **57**. 133, 1888 ; G. Vinassa, *Gazz. Chim. Ital.*, **58**. 179, 1928 ; J. R. Rydberg, *Zeit. phys. Chem.*, **33**. 353, 1900 ; G. Hägg, *Nature*, **121**. 826, 1928 ; **122**. 314, 1928 ; H. G. Grimm, *ib.*, **122**. 177, 1926 ; T. W. Richards, *Journ. Amer. Chem. Soc.*, **37**. 1643, 1915 ; J. H. Hildebrand, T. R. Hogness and·N. W. Taylor, *ib.*, **45**. 2828, 1923 ; M. N. Saha, *Nature*, **107**. 682, 1921 ; F. C. Kelley, *Trans. Amer. Inst. Min. Eng.*, **76**. 390, 1928 ; G. D. Preston, *Phil. Mag.*, (7), **5**. 1198, 1207, 1928 ; W. Widder, *Phys. Zeit.*, **26**. 618, 1925 ; A. Ferrari, *Atti Accad. Lincei*, (6), **3**. 275, 1926 ; G. Natta, *Gazz. Chim. Ital.*, **58**. 344, 1928 ; Y. Matsuyama, *Bull. Japan. Inst. Phys. Chem. Research*, **7**. 731, 1928 ; *Science Rep. Tohoku Univ.*, **18**. 733. 1929 ;

S. von Oldhausen, *Zeit. Kryst.*, **61**. 463, 1925 ; J. D. Bernal, *Trans. Faraday Soc.*, **25**. 367, 1929 ; W. F. de Jong and H. W. V. Willems, *Physica*, **7**. 74, 1927 ; T. Turner, *Chem. News*, **55**. 179, 1887 ; *Proc. Birmingham Phil. Soc.*, **5**. 291, 1887 ; E. Herlinger, *Zeit. Kryst.*, **80**. 465, 1931 ; V. M. Goldschmidt, *Skr. Norske Vid. Akad.*, **2**, 1926 ; E. T. Wherry, *Amer. Min.*, **14**. 54, 1929 ; L. Pauling, *Journ. Amer. Chem. Soc.*, **49**. 765, 1927 ; K. Honda, Y. Matuyama and T. Isobé, *Science Rep. Tohoku Univ.*, **20**. 594, 1931 ; W. Biltz and K. Meisel, *Zeit. anorg. Chem.*, **198**. 191, 1931 ; J. J. Saslawsky, *ib.*, **146**. 315, 1925 ; **204**. 222, 1932 ; *Zeit. phys. Chem.*, **109**. 111, 1924 ; **113**. 111, 1924 ; E. Rabinowitsch and E. Thilo, *ib.*, **6**. B, 284, 1929.
  ² P. H. van der Weyde, *Ber.*, **12**. 441, 1879 ; T. W. Richards and F. G. Jackson, *Zeit. phys. Chem.*, **70**. 414, 1910 ; H. V. Regnault, *Ann. Chim. Phys.*, (3), **63**. 18, 1861 ; H. St. C. Deville, *ib.*, (3), **46**. 182, 1856 ; H. Kopp, *Liebig's Ann. Suppl.*, **3**. 290, 1865 ; S. Jordan, *Compt. Rend.*, **86**. 1374, 1878 ; *Journ. Iron Steel Inst.*, **48**. ii, 126, 1895 ; W. N. Hartley, *ib.*, **48**. ii, 95, 1895 ; *Proc. Roy. Soc.*, **54**. 5, 1893 ; *Chem. News*, **67**. 279, 1893 ; T. Turner, *Chem. News*, **55**. 179, 1887 ; *Proc. Birmingham Phil. Soc.*, **5**. 291, 1887 ; W. L. Bragg, *Phil. Mag.*, (6), **40**. 169, 1920 ; T. Estreicher and M. Staniewsky, *Anz. Akad. Krakau*, 834, 1912 ; H. Moissan, *Compt. Rend.*, **88**. 180, 1879 ; **116**. 349, 1893 ; *Bull. Soc. Chim.*, (3), **11**. 13, 1894 ; *Le four électrique*, Paris, 217, 1897 ; London, 150, 1904 ; *Ann. Chim. Phys.*, (5), **21**. 231, 1880 ; (7), **3**. 286, 1896 ; E. Kuh, *Die Darstellung des chemische reinen Mangans und die Bestimmung der wichtigsten physikalischen Konstanten desselben*, Zürich, 1911 ; M. L. Huggins, *Phys. Rev.*, (2), **21**. 205, 1923 ; T. Carnelley, *Proc. Roy. Soc.*, **29**. 190, 1879 ; *Chem. News*, **39**. 281, 1879 ; *Ber.*, **12**. 439, 1879 ; O. Ruff and E. Gersten, *ib.*, **46**. 4003, 1913 ; O. Ruff and W. Bormann, *Zeit. anorg. Chem.*, **88**. 365, 1914 ; O. Ruff, W. Bormann and F. Keilig, *Ueber des Verhalten von Kohlenstoff gegen Mangan, Nickel, Eisen, und Kobalt*, Berlin, 1918 ; N. Stücker, *Sitzber. Akad. Wien*, **114**. 657, 1905 ; A. Guntz and J. Férée, *Bull. Soc. Chim.*, (3), **15**. 132, 1896 ; A. Guntz, *Compt. Rend.*, **122**. 465, 1896 ; R. Lämmel, *Ann. Physik*, (4), **16**. 551, 1905 ; W. F. de Jong and H. W. V. Willems, *Physica*, **7**. 74, 1927 ; H. C. Greenwood, *Proc. Roy. Soc.*, **82**. A, 396, 1909 ; **83**. A, 483, 1910 ; J. Dewar, *ib.*, **89**. A, 158, 1913 ; E. Newbery and J. N. Pring, *ib.*, **92**. A, 276, 1916 ; W. C. Heraeus, *Zeit. Elektrochem.*, **8**. 185, 328, 1902 ; R. S. Williams, *Zeit. anorg. Chem.*, **55**. 1, 1907 ; R. Sahmen, *ib.*, **57**. 1, 1908 ; W. Herz, *ib.*, **170**. 237, 1928 ; **177**. 116, 1928 ; **180**. 284, 1929 ; E. Tiede and E. Birnbräuer, *ib.*, **87**. 129, 1914 ; E. Kordes, *ib.*, **160**. 67, 1927 ; J. Maydel, *ib.*, **178**. 113, 1929 ; **186**. 289, 1930 ; Z. Herrmann, *ib.*, **198**. 204, 1931 ; G. Hindrichs, *ib.*, **59**. 414, 1908 ; S. F. Schemtschuschny and N. N. Effimoff, *ib.*, **58**. 243, 1908 ; N. Baar, *ib.*, **70**. 259, 1911 ; K. Hiege, *ib.*, **83**. 253, 1914 ; R. Lorenz and F. Heusler, *ib.*, **3**. 225, 1893 ; M. Levin and G. Tammann, *ib.*, **47**. 136, 1905 ; F. Doerinckel, *ib.*, **50**. 117, 1906 ; F. Heinrich, *Ferrum*, **12**. 42, 1914 ; G. K. Burgess, *Chem. News*, **97**. 28, 1908 ; *Bull. Bur. Standards*, **3**. 345, 1907 ; G. K. Burgess and R. G. Waltenberg, *ib.*, **10**. 79, 1914 ; *Journ. Washington Acad.*, **3**. 371, 1913 ; *Brass World*, **9**. 349, 1913 ; J. Disch, *Zeit. Physik*, **5**. 173, 1921 ; R. W. Millar, *Journ. Ind. Eng. Chem.*, **17**. 34, 1925 ; R. Hadfield, *Journ. Iron Steel Inst.*, **115**. i, 211, 1927 ; M. L. V. Gayler, *ib.*, **115**. i. 393, 1927 ; W. R. Mott, *Trans. Amer. Electrochem. Soc.*, **34**. 255, 1918 ; O. P. Watts, *ib.*, **12**. 141, 1908 ; F. Wüst, A. Meuthen and R. Dürrer, *Forsch. Arb. Ver. deut. Ing.*, 204, 1918 ; J. Thomsen, *Thermochemische Untersuchungen*, Leipzig, **3**. 271, 1883 ; G. N. Lewis, G. E. Gibson and W. M. Latimer, *Journ. Amer. Chem. Soc.*, **44**. 1008, 1922 ; E. D. Eastman, *ib.*, **45**. 80, 1923 ; G. Arrivant, *Zeit. anorg. Chem.*, **83**. 194, 1913 ; *Rev. Mét.*, **10**. 1256, 1913 ; *Compt. Rend.*, **156**. 1539, 1913 ; *Procès-verbal Soc. Bordeaux*, 9, 1904 ; R. D. Kleeman, *Journ. Phys. Chem.*, **31**. 1669, 1927 ; B. Bruzs, *ib.*, **31**. 681, 1927 ; A. D. Dourdine, *Rev. Soc. Russe Mét.*, **1**. 11, 341, 1912 ; *Rev. Mét.*, **12**. 125, 1915 ; H. von Jüptner, *Beiträge zur Theorie der Eisenhüttenprozesse*, Stuttgart, 8, 1907 ; J. Johnston, *Journ. Ind. Eng. Chem.*, **9**. 873, 1917 ; S. Umino, *Science Rep. Tohoku Univ.*, **16**. 775, 1927 ; Kinzoku Kenku, **3**. 385, 1926 ; *Trans. Amer. Soc. Steel Treating*, **10**. 830, 1926 ; W. Widder, *Phys. Zeit.*, **26**. 618, 1925 ; J. H. Hildebrand, T. R. Hogness and N. W. Taylor, *Journ. Amer. Chem. Soc.*, **45**. 2828, 1923 ; W. Crossley, *Chem. News*, **2**. 88, 1860.
  ³ H. von Wartenberg, *Verh. deut. phys. Ges.*, **12**. 105, 1910 ; J. T. Littleton, *Phys. Rev.*, (1), **33**. 453, 1911 ; V. Fréedericksz, *Ann. Physik*, (4), **34**. 784, 792, 1911 ; G. Pfestorf, *ib.*, (4), **81**. 906, 1926 ; J. H. Gladstone, *Phil. Mag.*, (4), **36**. 311, 1868 ; *Proc. Roy. Soc.*, **18**. 49, 1870 ; **60**. 140, 1896 ; W. J. Pope, *Journ. Chem. Soc.*, **69**. 1530, 1896 ; A. E. H. Tutton, *ib.*, **71**. 735, 1897 ; J. B. Nathanson, *Journ. Amer. Opt. Soc.*, **20**. 593, 1930.
  ⁴ J. Formanek, *Die qualitative Spektralanalyse anorganischer und organischer Körper*, Berlin, 132, 1905 ; R. T. Simmler, *Beiträge zur chemischen Analyse durch Spectral beobachtungen*, Bern, 1861 ; *Pogg. Ann.*, **115**. 242, 425, 1862 ; A. Mitscherlich, *ib.*, **121**. 459, 1874 ; J. Müller, *ib.*, **128**. 335, 1866 ; W. Biltz, *Zeit. anorg. Chem.*, **127**. 169, 1923 ; W. A. Miller, *Phil. Mag.*, (3), **27**. 81, 1845 ; *Phil. Trans.*, **152**. 861, 1862 ; R. J. Lang, *ib.*, **224**. A, 371, 1924 ; W. Huggins, *ib.*, **154**. 139, 1864 ; J. Plücker and J. W. Hittorf, *ib.*, **155**. 1, 1865 ; J. N. Lockyer, *ib.*, **163**. 253, 1873 ; *Proc. Roy. Soc.*, *Tables of Wave-lengths of Enhanced Lines*, London, 1906 ; **43**. 117, 1887 ; **65**. 452, 1900 ; J. N. Lockyer and W. C. Roberts-Austen, *ib.*, **23**. 344, 1875 ; C. J. Lundström, *ib.*, **59**. 76, 1895 ; G. D. Liveing and J. Dewar, *ib.*, **36**. 471, 1884 ; W. N. Hartley and H. W. Moss, *ib.*, **87**. A, 38, 1912 ; W. N. Hartley, *ib.*, **34**. 81, 1881 ; **54**. 5, 1893 ; **56**. 192, 193, 1894 ; **79**. A, 242, 1907 ; *Phil. Trans.*, **185**. 161, 1629, 1894 ; R. Böttger, *Journ. prakt. Chem.*, (1), **65**. 392, 1862 ; E. Diacon, *Ann. Chim. Phys.*, (4), **6**. 5, 1865 ; R. Thalén, *ib.*, (4), **18**. 202, 1869 ; *Om spectralanalys*, Upsala, 1866 ; *Nova Acta Upsala*, (3), **6**. 9, 1868 ; (5), **12**. 1, 1884 ; A. J. Angström, *Recherches sur le spectre solaire*, Upsala, 1868 ; A. R. Leeds, *Quart. Journ. Science*, **8**. i, 59, 1871 ; W. M. Watts, *Phil. Mag.*, (4), **45**. 81, 1873 ; A. E. Ruark and R. L. Chenault, *ib.*,

(7), **50**. 937, 1925 ; A. Hornli, *Jahrb. Rad. Elektron.*, **18**. 297, 1921 ; L. de Boisbaudran, *Spectres lumineux*, Paris, 1874 ; *Compt. Rend.*, **76**. 833, 1873 ; A. Gouy, *ib.*, **84**. 231, 1877 ; A. de Gramont, *ib.*, **118**. 591, 1894 ; **126**. 1513, 1898 ; *Bull. Soc. Min.*, **21**. 109, 1898 ; *Analyse spectrale direct des minéraux*, Paris, 1895 ; G. Ciamician, *Sitzber. Akad. Wien*, **76**. 499, 1877 ; J. M. Eder and E. Valenta, *ib.*, **118**. 519, 1909 ; F. Exner and E. Haschek, *ib.*, **104**. 909, 1895 ; **105**. 389, 1896 ; **106**. 36, 1897 ; *Wellenlängen-Tabellen für spectralanalytische untersuchungen auf Grund der ultravioletten Funkenspectren der Elemente*, Leipzig, 1902 ; *Wellenlängen-Tabellen für spectral-analytische untersuchungen auf Grund der ultravioletten Bogenspectren der Elemente*, Leipzig, 1904 ; J. R. Capron, *Photographed Spectra*, London, 1877 ; J. Parry and A. E. Tucker, *Engg.*, **27**. 127, 429, 1879 ; **28**. 141, 1879 ; J. Schönn, *Wied. Ann.*, **9**. 483, 1880 ; **10**. 143, 1880 ; J. C. McLennan and A. B. McLay, *Trans. Roy. Soc. Canada*, (3), **20**. 89, 1926 ; J. C. McLennan and E. Cohen, *ib.*, (3), **20**. 365, 1926 ; A. Cornu, *Ann. École Norm.*, (2), **9**. 21, 1880 ; *Journ. École Polyt.*, **53**. 175, 1883 ; F. McClean, *Monthly Notices Astron. Soc.*, **52**. 22, 1891 ; J. Parry, *Nature*, **45**. 253, 1892 ; A. A. Michelson, *ib.*, **59**. 440, 1899 ; S. Goudsmit, *Phys. Rev.*, (2), **31**. 946, 1928 ; (2), **35**. 440, 1929 ; *Nature*, **113**. 238, 1924 ; D. R. Hartree, *ib.*, **116**. 356, 1925 ; R. A. Sawyer, *ib.*, **117**. 155, 1926 ; *Phys. Rev.*, (2), **35**. 440, 1930 ; H. Kayser, *Handbuch der Spectroscopie*, Leipzig, **5**. 727, 1910 ; H. Kayser and C. Runge, *Wied. Ann.*, **52**. 93, 1894 ; *Sitzber. Akad. Berlin*, 153, 1893 ; R. G. Loyarte and A. T. Williams, *Phys. Zeit.*, **30**. 68, 1929 ; K. Burns, *Publ. Allegheny Obs. Pittsburg*, **8**. 1, 1930 ; E. Paulson, *Arksskrift Univ. Lund.*, **10**. 12, 1914 ; *Beiträge zur Kenntnis der Linienspektren*, Lund, 1914 ; *Ann. Physik*, (4), **45**. 419, 1914 ; H. N. Russell, *Astrophys. Journ.*, **66**. 233, 1927 ; J. Fridrichson, *Zeit. Physik*, **64**. 43, 1930 ; **68**. 550, 1931 ; O. Vogel, *Zeit. anorg. Chem.*, **5**. 42, 1894 ; E. Demarçay, *Spectres électriques*, Paris, 1895 ; H. A. Rowland, *A Preliminary Table of Solar Spectrum Wave-lengths*, Chicago, 1898 ; *Astrophys. Journ.*, **1**. 29, 131, 222, 295, 337, 1895 ; **2**. 45, 109, 188, 306, 360, 1895 ; **3**. 141, 201, 356, 1896 ; **4**. 106, 278, 1896 ; **5**. 11, 109, 181, 1897 ; **6**. 384, 1897 ; W. J. Humphreys, *ib.*, **6**. 169, 1897 ; **26**. 18, 1907 ; R. E. Loving, *ib.*, **22**. 285, 1905 ; P. G. Nutting, *ib.*, **23**. 64, 1906 ; Lord Blythwood and W. A. Scoble, *ib.*, **24**. 125, 1906 ; C. M. Kilby, *ib.*, **30**. 243, 1909 ; A. S. King, *ib.*, **21**. 236, 1905 ; **53**. 133, 1921 ; *Ann. Physik*, (4), **16**. 360, 1905 ; H. M. Randall and E. F. Barker, *Astrophys. Journ.*, **49**. 54, 1919 ; G. S. Monk, *ib.*, **57**. 222, 1923 ; B. Hasselberg, *Svenska Akad. Handl.*, **30**. 2, 1897 ; W. E. Adeney, *Proc. Roy. Soc. Dublin*, (2), **7**. 331, 1901 ; J. H. Pollok and A. G. G. Leonard, *ib.*, (2), **11**. 217, 1907 ; G. A. Hemsalech, *Recherches expérimentales sur les spectres d'étincelles*, Paris, 1901 ; *Phil. Mag.*, (6), **40**. 296, 1920 ; O. Lohse, *Publ. Astrophys. Obs. Potsdam*, **12**. 109, 1902 ; C. de Watteville, *Compt. Rend.*, **135**. 1329, 1902 ; F. Croze, *ib.*, **177**. 1285, 1923 ; **178**. 200, 1924 ; H. Nagaoda, D. Nukiyama and T. Futagami, *Proc. Acad. Japan*, **3**. 392, 398, 403, 409, 415, 1927 ; C. Fritsch, *Ann. Physik*, (4), **16**. 793, 1905 ; R. Frerichs, *ib.*, (4), **81**. 807, 1926 ; H. N. Russell, *ib.*, **66**. 184, 1927 ; W. Miller, *Phys. Zeit.*, **7**. 896, 1906 ; *Zeeman-effekt an Magnesium, Calcium, Strontium, Zink, Kadmium, Mangan, und Chrom*, Leipzig, 1907 ; *Ann. Physik*, (4), **24**. 105, 1907 ; L. Janicki, *ib.*, (4), **29**. 833, 1909 ; A. Sommerfeld, *ib.*, (4), **70**. 32, 1923 ; *Phys. Zeit.*, **24**. 360, 1923 ; L. and E. Bloch, *Journ. Phys. Rad.*, (6), **6**. 154, 1925 ; L. Puccianti, *Nuovo Cimento*, (5), **9**. 393, 1905 ; A. Hagenbach and H. Konen, *Atlas of Emissionsspectra*, Jena, 1905 ; J. E. Purvis, *Proc. Cambridge Phil. Soc.*, **14**. 41, 1906 ; H. Geisler, *Zur anomalen Dispersion des Lichtes in metalldämpfen*, Bonn, 1909 ; *Zeit. wiss. Photochem.*, **7**. 80, 1909 ; H. Auerbach, *ib.*, **7**. 30, 1909 ; W. Beckmann, *ib.*, **4**. 335, 1907 ; H. Fuchs, *ib.*, **14**. 239, 263, 1915 ; S. Wirminghaus, *ib.*, **20**. 229, 1921 ; *Der Poleffekt im Bogenspektrum des Mangans*, Leipzig, 1921 ; O. Lüttig, *Das Zeeman-Phänomen im sichtbaren von Mangan und Argon*, Halle a. S., 1911 ; H. Casaretto, *Zeit. wiss. Photochem.*, **8**. 381, 1910 ; *Ueber das Bandenspectrum das bei Einführung von Manganchlorür in die Sauerstoff-Leuchtgasflamme entsteht*, Bonn, 1910 ; W. Jäschke and J. Meyer, *Zeit. phys. Chem.*, **83**. 281, 1913 ; M. A. Catalan, *Phil. Trans.*, **223**. A, 127, 1922 ; *Compt. Rend.*, **176**. 84, 1923 ; *Anal. Fis. Quim*, **21**. 321, 1923 ; **26**. 67, 1928 ; K. Bechert and M. A. Catalan, *Zeit. Physik*, **37**. 658, 1926 ; E. Back, *ib.*, **15**. 206, 1923 ; G. Wentzel, *ib.*, **24**. 104, 1923 ; W. Grotrian, *ib.*, **18**. 169, 1923 ; W. C. van Geel, *ib.*, **33**. 836, 1925 ; R. Mecke, *ib.*, **42**. 392, 1927 ; R. V. Zumstein, *Phys. Rev.*, (2), **26**. 765, 1925 ; (2), **27**. 106, 1926 ; J. H. van Vleck and A. Frank, *ib.*, (2), **34**. 1494, 1929 ; A. Smitt and M. Muskat, *ib.*, (2), **29**. 663, 1927 ; S. P. de Rubies and J. Dorronsoro, *Anal. Fis. Quim*, **25**. 211, 374, 1927 ; S. P. de Rubies, *ib.*, **25**. 494, 1927 ; M. Kimura and G. Nakamura, *Science Papers Inst. Phys. Chem. Japan*, **3**. 51, 1925 ; J. Moir, *Trans. Roy. Soc. South Africa*, **10**. 33, 1921 ; J. W. Grieveson, *Phil. Mag.*, (6), **49**. 1006, 1925 ; A. T. Williams, *Anal. Soc. Cient. Argentina*, **97**. 15, 1924 ; C. C. Kiess, *Bur. Standards Journ. Research*, **1**. 75, 1928 ; C. C. Kiess and O. Laporte, *Science*, (2), **63**. 234, 1926 ; W. F. Meggers, C. C. Kiess and F. M. Walters, *Journ. Amer. Opt. Soc.*, **9**. 355, 1924 ; C. C. Kiess and W. F. Meggers, *Bull. Bur. Standards*, **16**. 51, 1920 ; A. W. Smith and M. Muskat, *Phys. Rev.*, (2), **29**. 663, 1927 ; H. E. White and R. Ritschl, *ib.*, (2), **35**. 208, 1146, 1930 ; R. C. Gibbs and H. E. White, *ib.*, (2), **29**. 359, 917, 1927 ; (2), **33**. 157, 1929 ; H. E. White, *ib.*, (2), **33**. 672, 914, 1098, 1929 ; (2), **35**. 208, 1930 ; (2), **36**. 1800, 1930 ; E. O. Hulburt, *ib.*, (2), **25**. 888, 1925 ; O. S. Duffendack and J. G. Black, *ib.*, (2), **34**. 35, 1929 ; R. S. Seward, *ib.*, (2), **37**. 344, 1931 ; A. Sellerio, *Nuovo Cimento*, (6), **25**. 69, 1923 ; S. Kawata, *Mem. Coll. Kyoto*, **14**. A, 227, 1931 ; W. Kraemer, *Zeit. Elektrochem.*, **38**. 51, 1932.

⁵ H. Kayser, *Handbuch der Spectroscopie*, Leipzig, **3**. 414, 1905 ; H. Bremer, *Einfluss der Temperatur gefärbter Lösungen auf die Absorption spectren derselben*, Erlangen, 1890 ; C. Christensen, *Overs. Danske Selsk. Förh.*, 217, 1882 ; *Wied. Ann.*, **19**. 256, 1883 ; C. Pulfrich, *ib.*, **14**. 177, 1881 ; R. J. Lang, *Phil. Trans.*, **224**. A, 371, 1924 ; J. Formanek, *Die qualitative Spektral-*

analyse anorganischer und organischer Körper, Berlin, 132, 1905 ; H. W. Vogel, *Praktische Spectralanalyse irdischer Stoffe*, Berlin, 1889 ; *Sitzber. Akad. Berlin*, 409, 1878 ; *Ber.*, **8**. 1533, 1875 ; **11**. 913, 1363, 1878 ; G. Krüss, *ib.*, **18**. 1580, 1885 ; J. M. Hiebendaal, *Onderzoek over eenige Absorptiespectra*, Utrecht, 1873 ; K. Stöckl, *Messungen über die Dispersion und Absorption von Lösungen anomalbrechender Substanzen bis zu grossen Verdünnusegen*, München, 1900 ; K. Vierordt, *Die Anwendungen des Spectralapparates zur Photochemie der Absorptionspectren und zur quantitativen chemischen Analyse*, Tübingen, 1873 ; J. H. Gladstone, *Journ. Chem. Soc.*, **10**. 79, 1858 ; *Phil. Mag.*, (4), **14**. 418, 1857 ; W. A. Miller, *ib.*, (3), **27**. 81, 1845 ; L. de Boisbaudran, *Spectres lumineux*, Paris, 1874 ; W. N. Hartley, *Trans. Roy. Soc. Dublin*, (2), **7**. 253, 1900 ; *Journ. Chem. Soc.*, **101**. 826, 1912 ; T. R. Merton, *ib.*, **99**. 637, 1911 ; F. Hoppe-Seyler, *Journ. prakt. Chem.*, (1), **90**. 303, 1863 ; N. von Klobukoff, *ib.*, (2), **32**. 122, 1885 ; C. Kubierschky, *ib.*, (2), **31**. 93, 1885 ; H. Morton and H. C. Bolton, *Chem. News*, **28**. 115, 1873 ; J. Müller, *Pogg. Ann.*, **128**. 335, 1866 ; R. T. Simmler, *ib.*, **115**. 242, 425, 1862 ; C. P. Smyth, *Trans. Roy. Soc. Edin.*, **28**. 779, 1879 ; J. L. Soret, *Arch. Sciences Genève*, (2), **61**. 322, 1878 ; G. G. Stokes, *Phil. Trans.*, **142**. 463, 1852 ; **143**. 385, 1853 ; *Phil. Mag.*, (4), **6**. 393, 1853 ; W. Friederichs, *Ueber Absorptionsspektra von Dämpfen*, Bonn, 1905 ; *Zeit. wiss. Photochem.*, **3**. 154, 1905 ; E. Luck, *Zeit. anal. Chem.*, **8**. 405, 1869 ; G. B. Rizzo, *Atti Accad. Torino*, **26**. 632, 1891 ; P. Lambert, *Compt. Rend.*, **141**. 357, 1905 ; J. Moir, *Trans. Roy. Soc. South Africa*, **8**. 45, 1919 ; A. Hagenbach and R. Percy, *Helvetica Chim. Acta*, **5**. 454, 1922 ; E. Adinolfi, *Atti Accad. Lincei*, (5), **29**. ii, 87, 1920 ; (6), **3**. 196, 1926 ; J. Holluta, *Zeit. phys. Chem.*, **106**. 324, 1923 ; A. Hantzsch and R. H. Clark, *ib.*, **63**. 367, 1908 ; W. Ostwald, *ib.*, **9**. 579, 1892 ; R. V. Zumstein, *Phys. Rev.*, (2), **26**. 765, 1925 ; C. L. Cross, *ib.*, (2), **27**. 108, 1926 ; J. E. Purvis, *Proc. Cambridge Phil. Soc.*, **15**. 247, 1909 ; E. Viterbi, *Gazz. Chim. Ital.*, **55**. 127, 1925 ; H. Gombos, *ib.*, **151**. 7, 1924 ; V. R. von Kurelec, *Biochem. Zeit.*, **180**. 65, 1927 ; S. P. de Rubies, *Anal. Fis. Quim*, **25**. 494, 1927 ; I. Lifschitz and E. Rosenbohm, *Zeit. phys. Chem.*, **97**. 1, 1921 ; K. Schlossmacher, *Zeit. Kryst.*, **75**. 399, 1930 ; C. J. W. Grieveson, *Phil. Mag.*, (6), **49**. 1006, 1925 ; W. Jäschke and J. Meyer, *Zeit. phys. Chem.*, **83**. 281, 1913.

    ⁶ L. de Boisbaudran, *Compt. Rend.*, **103**. 468, 629, 1064, 1886 ; A. E. Becquerel, *ib.*, **103**. 1098, 1886 ; **104**. 551, 1887 ; **107**. 892, 1889 ; J. R. Mourelo, *ib.*, **129**. 1236, 1899 ; A. Karl, *ib.*, **146**. 1104, 1908 ; V. Bruninghaus, *ib.*, **144**. 839, 1040, 1907 ; A. Dauvillier, *ib.*, **181**. 601, 1925 ; V. Klatt and P. Lenard, *Wied. Ann.*, **38**. 90, 1889 ; H. Grüne, *Ber.*, **37**. 3076, 1904 ; Chininfabrik Braunschweig, *German Pat.*, *D.R.P.* 163648, 1905 ; W. G. Guy, *Theses Univ. Chicago*, **4**. 87, 1926 ; T. Tanaka, *Journ. Amer. Opt. Soc.*, **8**. 501, 1924 ; J. Fridrichson, *Zeit. Physik*, **64**. 43, 1930 ; **68**. 550, 1931.

    ⁷ O. Stelling, *Ber.*, **60**. B, 650, 1927 ; *Zeit. phys. Chem.*, **117**. 161, 1925 ; V. Dolejsek, *Compt. Rend.*, **174**. 441, 1922 ; V. Dolejsek and K. Pestrecoff, *Nature*, **123**. 412, 1929 ; *Zeit. Physik*, **53**. 566, 1929 ; V. Dolejsek and H. Filcakova, *Nature*, **123**. 412, 1929 ; H. Hirata, *Proc. Roy. Soc.*, **105**. A, 40, 1924 ; U. Andrewes, A. C. Davies and F. Horton, *ib.*, **117**. A, 649, 1928 ; O. W. Richardson and F. S. Robertson, *ib.*, **115**. A, 280, 1927 ; **124**. A, 188, 1929 ; L. P. Davis, *ib.*, **124**. A, 268, 1929 ; C. E. Eddy, T. H. Laby and A. H. Turner, *ib.*, **124**. A, 249, 1929; G. B. Deodhar, *ib.*, **131**. A, 476, 633, 1931 ; R. C. Gibbs and H. E. White, *Proc. Nat. Acad.*, **12**. 675, 1926 ; **13**. 525, 1927 ; W. Duane and K. F. Hu, *Phys. Rev.*, (2), **14**. 516, 1919 ; W. Duane and H. Fricke, *ib.*, (2), **17**. 529, 1921 ; C. E. Howe, *ib.*, (2), **33**. 1088, 1929 ; (2), **35**. 717, 1930 ; B. Kievit and G. A. Lindsay, *ib.*, (2), **35**. 292, 1930 ; (2), **36**. 648, 1930 ; K. Chamberlain, *Nature*, **114**. 500, 1924 ; *Phys. Rev.*, (2), **26**. 525, 1925 ; D. M. Bose, *ib.*, (2), **27**. 527, 1926 ; J. Schrör, *Ann. Physik*, (4), **80**. 297, 1925 ; S. Pastorello, *Nuovo Cimento*, (7), **6**. 50, 1929 ; D. M. Yost, *Phil. Mag.*, (7), **8**. 845, 1929 ; E. Hjalmar, *Zeit. Physik*, **1**. 439, 1920 ; *Phil. Mag.*, (6), **41**. 675, 1921 ; R. Thoroeus and M. Siegbahn, *Arkiv Mat. Astron. Fys.*, **19**. 12, 1925 ; R. Thoroeus, *Phil. Mag.*, (7), **1**. 312, 1926 ; (7), **2**. 1007, 1926 ; T. E. Aurén, *ib.*, (6), **33**. 471, 1917 ; H. R. Robinson, *ib.*, (6), **50**. 241, 1925 ; F. C. Chalklin, *ib.*, (7), **9**. 847, 1930 ; W. Herz, *Zeit. anorg. Chem.*, **177**. 116, 1928 ; M. Siegbahn, *Jahrb. Rad. Elektron.*, **13**. 296, 1916 ; M. Levi, *Trans. Roy. Soc. Canada*, (3), **18**. 159, 1924 ; S. Idei, *Science Rep. Tohoku Univ.*, **19**. 551, 641, 1930 ; N. Stensson, *Zeit. Physik*, **3**. 60, 1920 ; T. Wetterblad, *ib.*, **49**. 670, 1928 ; N. Seljakoff, A. Krasnikoff and T. Stellezky, *ib.*, **45**. 548, 1927 ; S. Eriksson, *ib.*, **48**. 360, 1928 ; N. Seljakoff and A. Krasnikoff, *ib.*, **33**. 601, 1925 ; *Nature*, **117**. 554, 1926 ; G. Ortner, *ib.*, **117**. 823, 1926 ; D. Coster, *Zeit. Physik*, **25**. 83, 1924 ; A. E. Lindh, *ib.*, **31**. 210, 1925 ; H. Beuthe, *ib.*, **60**. 603, 1930 ; H. Walter, *ib.*, **30**. 357, 1924 ; M. J. Druyvesteyn, *ib.*, **43**. 707, 1927 ; G. Kettmann, *ib.*, **53**. 198, 1929 ; S. Björek, *ib.*, **53**. 228, 1929 ; B. C. Mukherjee and B. B. Ray, *ib.*, **57**. 45, 1929 ; J. Fridrichson, *ib.*, **68**. 550, 1931.

    ⁸ W. Espe, *Ann. Physik*, (5), **2**. 381, 1929 ; H. B. Wahlin, *Phys. Rev.*, (2), **37**. 467, 1931; D. R. Hartree, *Nature*, **116**. 356, 1925 ; H. N. Russell, *Astrophys. Journ.*, **55**. 354, 1922 ; **66**. 233, 1927 ; W. Herz, *Zeit. anorg. Chem.*, **163**. 221, 1927 ; **170**. 237, 1928 ; M. A. Catalan, *Anal. Fis. Quim*, **21**. 42, 1926 ; R. H. Ghosh, *Journ. Indian Chem. Soc.*, **4**. 423, 1927 ; S. C. Biswas, *ib.*, **5**. 561, 1928 ; J. C. Black and O. S. Duffendack, *Science*, (2), **66**. 401, 1927 ; A. Hantzsch and H. Carlsohn, *Zeit. anorg. Chem.*, **160**. 5, 1926 ; A. C. Davies and F. Horton, *Phil. Mag.*, (7), **2**. 1253, 1926 ; F. C. Chalklin, *ib.*, (7), **9**. 847, 1930 ; B. B. Ray and R. C. Mazumdar, *Zeit. Physik*, **53**. 646, 1929 ; C. E. Eddy, T. H. Laby and A. H. Turner, *Proc. Roy. Soc.*, **124**. A, 249, 1929 ; D. M. Yost, *Phil. Mag.*, (7), **8**. 845, 1929 ; J. E. P. Wagstaff, *ib.*, (6), **47**. 66, 1924 ; R. W. James and G. W. Brindley, *Zeit. Kryst.*, **78**. 470, 1931.

    ⁹ M. von Laue, *Sitzber. Akad. Berlin*, 334, 1923 ; A. Goetz, *Phys. Zeit.*, **24**. 377, 1923 ;

N. Piltschikoff, *ib.*, **7**. 69, 1906 ; J. E. P. Wagstaff, *Phil. Mag.*, (6), **47**. 66, 1924 ; O. W. Richardson and F. S. Robertson, *Proc. Roy. Soc.*, **124**. A, 188, 1929 ; U. Nakaya, *ib.*, **124**. A, 616, 1929 ; R. E. Nyswander and B. E. Cohn, *Journ. Amer. Optical Soc.*, **20**. 131, 1930 ; T. Pavolini, *Ind. Chimica*, **5**. 1107, 1930 ; W. Espe, *Ann. Physik*, (5), **2**. 381, 1929 ; J. Fridrichson, *Bull. Acad. Polonaise*, **2**. 69, 1931 ; R. Robl, *Zeit. angew. Chem.*, **39**. 608, 1926.

[10] V. Nejedly, *Coll. Czechosl. Chem. Comm.*, **1**. 319, 1929 ; P. Kapitza, *Proc. Roy. Soc.*, **105**. A. 691, 1924 ; **106**. A, 602, 1924 ; **115**. A, 658, 1927 ; **119**. A, 358, 1928 ; **123**. A, 292, 342, 1929 ; O. Bauer, *Internat. Zeit. Metallog.*, **10**. 129, 1919 ; P. W. Bridgman, *Proc. Amer. Acad.*, **64**. 51, 1929 ; W. Meissner and B. Voigt, *Ann. Physik*, (5), **7**. 892, 1930 ; E. Kuh, *Die Darstellung des chemische reinen Mangans und die Bestimmung der wichtigsten physikalischen Konstanten desselben*, Zürich, 1911 ; K. Höjendahl, *Phil. Mag.*, (6), **48**. 349, 1924 ; K. F. Herzfeld, *Phys. Rev.*, (2), **29**. 701, 1924 ; A. Schulze, *Zeit. Metallkunde*, **15**. 155, 1923 ; J. B. Seth, B. Gulati and S. Singh, *Phil. Mag.*, (7), **12**. 409, 1931.

[11] E. Gapon and I. Z. Khaskes, *Journ. Russ. Phys. Chem. Soc.*, **58**. 1384, 1926 ; H. D. Royce and L. Kahlenberg, *Trans. Amer. Electrochem. Soc.*, **50**. 137, 1927 ; T. J. Martin and A. J. Helfrecht, *ib.*, **53**. 83, 1928 ; H. Nagaoka and T. Futagami, *Proc. Acad. Tokyo*, **3**. 643, 1927 ; C. N. Otin, *Zeit. Elektrochem.*, **15**. 385, 386, 1909 ; H. Kuessner, *ib.*, **16**. 754, 1910 ; E. Müller, *ib.*, **10**. 519, 1904 ; **11**. 755, 1905 ; G. Grube and H. Metzger, *ib.*, **28**. 568, 1922 ; **29**. 17, 100, 1923 ; G. Grube, *ib.*, **33**. 389, 1927 ; G. Grube and K. Huberich, *ib.*, **29**. 8, 1923 ; O. C. Ralston, *Eng. Min. Journ.*, **130**. 606, 1930 ; J. Chloupek, *Coll. Czechoslov. Chem. Comm.*, **2**. 129, 1930 ; R. Saxon, *Chem. News*, **142**. 197, 1931 ; W. Ostwald, *Zeit. phys. Chem.*, **11**. 501, 1893 ; A. Heydweiller, *ib.*, **89**. 281, 1915 ; W. Althammer, *Ueber die Beweglichkeiten der Ionen ternärer Elektrolyte*, Halle, 1913 ; A. N. Campbell, *Journ. Chem. Soc.*, **123**. 892, 2323, 1923 ; *Trans. Faraday Soc.*, **22**. 46, 1926 ; A. J. Allmand and A. N. Campbell, *ib.*, **19**. 559, 1923 ; **20**. 379, 1924 ; J. Brezina, *Rec. Trav. Chim. Pays-Bas*, **44**. 520, 1925 ; H. Zahn and H. Schmidt, *Verh. deut. phys. Ges.*, **9**. 98, 1907 ; R. Lorenz and G. Hostelet, *Traité pratique d'électrochimie*, Paris, 308, 1905 ; W. Muthmann and F. Fraunberger, *Sitzber. Bayr. Akad. Wiss.*, **34**. 201, 1904 ; B. Neumann, *Zeit. phys. Chem.*, **14**. 217, 1894 ; H. Gerding, *ib.*, **151**. 190, 1930 ; W. J. Müller, *ib.*, **48**. 577, 1904 ; *Zeit. Elektrochem.*, **10**. 518, 1904 ; **11**. 755, 1905 ; S. Kyropoulos, *Zeit. anorg. Chem.*, **114**. 157, 1920 ; A. Thiel and W. Hammerschmidt, *ib.*, **132**. 15, 1924 ; B. N. Chuckubutti, *Proc. Indian Assoc. Science*, **9**. 83, 1924 ; J. Thiele, *Ann. Physik*, (4), **72**. 549. 1923 ; A. Günther-Schulze, *Zeit. Physik*, **3**. 349, 1920 ; W. Ogawa, *Journ. Japan. Soc. Chem. Ind.*, **31**. 486, 1928 ; V. Nejedly, *Coll. Czechosl. Chem.*, **1**. 319, 1929 ; O. Bauer, *Internat. Zeit. Metallog.*, **10**. 129, 1919 ; E. Newbery, *Journ. Chem. Soc.*, **109**. 1066, 1916 ; E. Seckelson, *Wied. Ann.*, **67**. 37, 1899 ; P. Weiss and H. K. Onnes, *Trans. Faraday Soc.*, **8**. 157, 1912 ; *Arch. Sciences Genève*, (4), **30**. 341, 449, 1910 ; *Compt. Rend.*, **150**. 687, 1910 ; P. Kapitza, *Proc. Roy. Soc.*, **131**. A, 223, 243, 1931 ; M. Haitinger, *Mikrochemie*, (2), **3**. 430, 1931 ; K. Meyer and A. Günther-Schulze, *Zeit. Physik*, **71**. 279, 1931 ; I. Slendyk, *Coll. Czech. Chem. Comm.*, **3**. 385, 1931 ; C. E. Mendenhall and L. R. Ingersoll, *Phil. Mag.*, (6), **15**. 205, 1908.

[12] E. Wiedemann, *Wied. Ann.*, **32**. 452, 1887 ; O. Liebknecht and A. P. Wills, *Ber.*, **33**. 443, 1900 ; P. Weiss, *Trans. Amer. Electrochem. Soc.*, **55**. 75, 1929 ; *Nature*, **129**. 95, 1932 ; P. Weiss and H. K. Onnes, *Trans. Faraday Soc.*, **8**. 157, 1912 ; *Arch. Sciences Genève*, (4), **30**. 341, 449, 1910 ; *Compt. Rend.*, **150**. 687, 1910 ; P. Weiss and P. Collet, *ib.*, **178**. 2146, 1924 ; P. Collet, *ib.*, **183**. 1031, 1926 ; E. Kuh, *Die Darstellung des chemische reinen Mangans und die Bestimmung der wichtigsten physikalischen Konstanten desselben*, Zürich, 1911 ; B. Cabrera, *Journ. Phys. Rad.*, (6), **3**. 443, 1922 ; A. Duperier, *Anal. Fis. Quim.*, **22**. 383, 1924 ; J. C. Slater, *Phys. Rev.*, (2), **36**. 57, 1930 ; I. Tamm, *Zeit. Physik*, **32**. 582, 1925 ; K. Honda, *Ann. Physik*, (4), **32**. 1027, 1910 ; *Science Rep. Tohoku Univ.*, **1**. 1, 1912 ; **3**. 139, 1914 ; **4**. 215, 1915 ; Y. Shimizu, *ib.*, **19**. 411, 1930 ; T. Ishiwara, *ib.*, **3**. 303, 1914 ; **4**. 215, 1915 ; **5**. 53, 1916 ; K. Honda and T. Sone, *ib.*, **2**. 25, 1913 ; T. Sone, *ib.*, **3**. 223, 1914 ; **8**. 115, 1919 ; *Phil. Mag.*, (6), **39**. 150, 1920 ; E. C. Stoner, *ib.*, (7), **8**. 250, 1929 ; A. Chatillon, *Ann. Physique*, (10), **9**. 187, 1928 ; S. S. Bhatnagar, K. N. Mathur and P. L. Kapar, *Indian Journ. Physics*, **3**. 53, 1928 ; M. Owen, *Ann. Physik*, (4), **37**. 657, 1912 ; R. H. Weber, *ib.*, (4), **36**. 624, 1911 ; E. Seckelson, *Wied. Ann.*, **67**. 37, 1899 ; E. Newbery, *Journ. Chem. Soc.*, **109**. 1066, 1916 ; W. Lepke, *Untersuchungen über die Magnetisierbarkeit von Mangan und Chrom in massivem und pulverförmigen Zustande*, Marburg, 1913 ; M. Faraday, *Journ. Science Arts*, **6**. 358, 1819 ; C. E. Guillaume, *Proc. Akad. Amsterdam*, **16**. 987, 1914 ; *Arch. Sciences Genève*, (4), **24**. 381, 1907 ; E. H. Williams, *Phys. Rev.*, (2), **28**. 167, 1926 ; J. C. Thomson, *Chem. News*, **129**. 156, 1924 ; K. Ihde, *Untersuchungen über die Magnetisierbarkeit von Mangan, Mangankupfer und Chrom*, Marburg, 1912 ; R. Hadfield, C. Chéneveau and C. Géneau, *Proc. Roy. Soc.*, **94**. A, 65, 1917 ; P. Kapitza, *ib.*, **131**. A, 223, 243, 1931 ; H. Freese, *Phys. Zeit.*, **29**. 191, 1928 ; M. Faraday, *Phil. Trans.*, **136**. 21, 41, 1846 ; J. H. van Vleck and A. Frank, *Phys. Rev.*, (2), **34**. 1494, 1929 ; D. M. Bose, *Zeit. Physik*, **65**. 677, 1930 ; L. Cambi and L. Szegö, *Ber.*, **64**. B, 2591, 1931 ; C. Sadron, *Compt. Rend.*, **193**. 1070, 1931.

§ 5. The Chemical Properties of Manganese

W. Guertler [1] discussed the chemical affinity of manganese. F. Fischer and F. Schröter observed no reaction when manganese is sparked beneath liquid **argon**. L. Troost and P. Hautefeuille made observations on the absorption of gases by molten manganese ; they found that the solubility of **hydrogen** in molten cast-iron is increased in the presence of manganese, and that manganiferous iron retains more hydrogen than ordinary cast-iron.   A. J. Allmand and A. N. Campbell found that electrodeposited mangan ese contained 12·6 c.c. of hydrogen, at n.p. θ, per gram, or 89 c.c. of hydrogen per c.c. of metal.   The manganese suffers no perceptible change when the occluded gas is withdrawn ; the metal is as brittle as before. R. Lorenz and F. Heusler observed no evidence of the formation of a *manganese hydride* when the metal is heated in hydrogen.   G. F. Hüttig discussed this subject. G. Hägg studied the mol, vol.

According to H. Davy,[2] when manganese is heated strongly in **oxygen,** it burns with great brilliancy, throwing off brilliant sparks ; and A. N. Campbell added that owing to the volatility of the manganese, the oxide which is formed cannot be weighed.   According to G. Tammann and N. I. Nikitin, the powder is not pyrophoric if over 50 per cent. manganous oxide is present, even if the metal is reduced at a low temp.   The observation of G. C. Stone that permanganic anhydride can be formed by the combustion of manganese in air has not been confirmed. J. Bachmann found that when manganese is heated in **air,** it rapidly forms the tritetroxide, without incandescence.   H. Davy said that manganese is immediately tarnished in air, becoming grey, brown, and at last black.   Ordinary, impure manganese obtained by the carbon reduction process was found by J. J. Berzelius to be readily oxidized at room temp.   N. G. Sefström observed that if 6 to 7 per cent. of silicon is present, the regulus can be heated to redness without oxidation, and it also resists attack by aqua regia.   J. J. Berzelius imagined that the presence of silicon is not a sufficient explanation of the phenomenon, because platinum alloyed with silicon is attacked by aqua regia ; he said that the difference is due to the existence of the metal in two *allotropic forms* : a-manganese which is active chemically, and β-manganese, inactive.   This hypothesis has not been confirmed. H. Moissan found that the manganese formed by distilling mercury from the amalgam below 360° is pyrophoric ; but A. Guntz and J. Férée showed that the metal obtained by heating the amalgam at a red-heat is non-pyrophoric.   H. Moissan found that the metal obtained by the electric arc furnace process behaves very much like iron in air.   H. Goldschmidt observed that the metal obtained by the aluminothermite process can be kept indefinitely in air without oxidation.   M. L. V. Gayler also found that the 99·99 per cent. manganese, obtained by distillation in vacuo, does not tarnish in air.   On the other hand, R. Bunsen found that the metal he obtained by electrodeposition oxidizes in moist air as rapidly as potassium.   The impure forms of manganese also decompose **water** at ordinary temp. with the evolution of hydrogen ; this was noticed by J. F. John, J. Bachmann, R. Bunsen, J. E. Loughlin, and H. St. C. Deville.   J. Bachmann said that the hydrogen evolved has a fœtid odour—indicating impurities in the metal.   H. V. Regnault said that finely-divided manganese kept under water at ordinary temp. slowly liberates hydrogen, but if heat be applied, even below 100°, the evolution of gas is rapid, and a yellowish-brown powder is formed which becomes dark brown on exposure to air.   H. Moissan also observed that pyrophoric manganese decomposes water slowly in the cold, and rapidly at 100° ; and similar results were obtained by O. Prelinger.   C. Brunner found that the metal contaminated with silicon is only attacked by water very slowly, a film of oxide being formed after some days' contact.   A. N. Campbell observed that with powdered, electrolytic manganese in contact with water no gas was evolved over-night and the metal remained dead-black, but a freshly cut surface exposed to moist air soon tarnished by a phenomenon analogous to rusting ; the same manganese is slowly attacked by boiling water, forming bubbles of gas and a brown hydrated oxide.   If the metal be heated in a current of steam, at the temp. of a bunsen flame, tiny bubbles of gas are formed, but the action is very slow.   L. J. Thénard found that **hydrogen dioxide** is vigorously decomposed by manganese.

According to H. Moissan, massive manganese is attacked by **fluorine** only superficially at ordinary temp., but the powdered metal furnishes a mixture of di- and trifluorides and the rise of temp. is so great that the platinum boat containing the metal was melted. H. Davy found that heated manganese takes fire in **chlorine** and burns brilliantly. A. N. Campbell observed that the metal ignites in chlorine at a red-heat, forming a light brown, highly crystalline powder, probably manganous chloride, but combustion appears to be incomplete. Observations were also made by H. Moissan, and J. B. Berthemot. C. J. Löwig found that when powdered manganese is heated in **bromine,** manganous bromide is formed ; while A. N. Camp- bell observed that boiling bromine does not attack the metal, but bromine-water was found by J. B. Berthemot to form manganous bromide. W. Engelhardt said that colloidal manganese does not react with **iodine,** and R. Hanslian found that boiling or freezing iodine has no perceptible action on manganese. J. F. John, and C. Brunner observed that manganese readily dissolves in dil. **hydrochloric acid,** with the evolution of hydrogen ; A. N. Campbell obtained a similar result with the electro-deposited metal.

K. Jellinek and J. Zakowsky, and W. Guertler discussed the affinity of manganese for **sulphur.** According to O. Prelinger, sulphur unites directly with manganese at a high enough temp., but at the temp. employed by A. N. Campbell no action occurs when manganese is heated with an excess of sulphur ; and, according to E. Beutel and A. Kutzelnigg, surface films are produced by heating the metal in contact with the sulphides of copper, silver, mercury, and lead. O. Bauer and H. Arndt found that manganese is not attacked by sulphur or plastilin. E. H. Harvey found that man- ganese is attacked by **sulphur monochloride** at room temp. ; H. E. Patten observed no attack, and similarly also with **thionyl chloride**. A. Guntz observed that pyro- phoric manganese burns with a brilliant flame when heated in **sulphur dioxide :** $3Mn+SO_2=MnS+2MnO+82\cdot4$ Cals.—no sulphite or sulphate is produced. P. Schützenberger found that manganese reduces acid **sodium sulphite** to hypo- sulphite. C. Brunner, and J. F. John observed that conc. **sulphuric acid** acts on manganese very slowly ; and O. Prelinger found that with non-pyrophoric man- ganese, the action of the conc. acid is very slow, but with warm conc. acid, sulphur dioxide is evolved ; A. N. Campbell found that the reaction corresponds with the equation : $Mn+2H_2SO_4=MnSO_4+2H_2O+SO_2$. R. H. Adie observed that gas is evolved with conc. sulphuric acid and manganese at 120° to 155°, and no hydrogen sulphide is formed. Dil. sulphuric acid was observed by J. F. John to dissolve manganese rapidly ; and, added A. N. Campbell, the reaction virtually ceases with a dilution of $0\cdot005N$-H_2SO_4. J. Bachmann found that when the hydrogen produced by the action of dil. sulphuric acid on manganese is exploded with an excess of oxygen, a white, greasy substance is formed with the disagreeable odour of the gas— possibly silica derived from impurities in the metal. E. Beutel and A. Kutzelnigg found that manganese in a boiling soln. of **sodium thiosulphate** and lead acetate acquires a sequence of colours from yellow to steel-blue, presumably owing to a film of sulphide. M. G. Levi and co-workers found that manganese dissolves in soln. of **ammonium and potassium persulphates**, forming violet soln.

W. C. Heraeus observed that when manganese prepared by the alumino-thermite process is heated at 1210° to 1220° in a current of **nitrogen,** it burns, forming white fumes of nitride; and S. Hilpert and co-workers, A. P. Lidoff, I. Zschukoff, G. Valensi, L. Duparc and co-workers, R. Ochsenfield, and A. N. Campbell obtained a nitride in a similar manner. O. Meyer observed that manganese is but slightly attacked by **titanium nitride** at 1400°. G. Gore found that manganese is insoluble in liquid **ammonia.** O. Prelinger, and L. Santi found that manganese is attacked by a soln. of **ammonium chloride :** $Mn+4NH_4Cl=MnCl_2.2NH_4Cl+2NH_3+H_2$. N. Pfanner studied the action of manganese on soln. of **hydroxylamine salts**—*vide infra,* complex salts of manganous chloride and sulphate. J. J. Sudborough observed that manganese is only slightly attacked when heated for some days in **nitrosyl chloride.** When manganese is heated in **nitric oxide,** at a temp. below the decomposition point of the gas, E. Müller and H. Barck found that the metal acts on nitric oxide at 300°, and that there is a 68 per cent. decomposition at 400°, and complete decomposition at 500° ; some nitride is formed at 400°. F. Emich found that it yields a product similar to that obtained by heating it in oxygen. According to A. Guntz, pyrophoric manganese at a gentle heat burns in a current of **nitrogen peroxide**, forming manganese monoxide, dioxide, and nitride. C. Brunner showed that conc. **nitric acid** reacts with powdered manganese with incandescence and a feeble explosion ; while dil. nitric acid dissolves the metal, as was also observed by O. Prelinger, and E. Glatzel. H. Moissan said that pyrophoric manganese is made incandescent by drops of conc. nitric acid. According to C. Montemartini, when manganese dissolves in nitric acid, ammonia is formed, as well as nitrogen and nitrous oxide, and so much hydrogen that the evolved gas will not explode until oxygen has been added. A. N. Campbell found that with nitric acid of different concentrations the percentage composition of the gas was as follows :

		Gas			
Nitric acid		NO_2	NO	N_2O	H_2
100 per cent.	.	100	—	—	—
50 ,,	.	68	16	16	—
25 ,,	.	0·1	39	20	40
12·5 ,,	.	—	13	1	86

C. C. Palit and N. R. Dhar found that the reaction of manganese with 13 and 26 per cent. nitric acid is rapid with or without nitrous acid. B. Pelletier, and H. Moissan observed that manganese reacts directly with **phosphorus** when a mixture of the two is heated, forming manganese phosphide (*q.v.*). H. Moissan observed that pyrophoric manganese burns when heated in a current of the vapour of **phosphorus pentachloride.** E. Wedekind obtained an arsenide by heating manganese with **arsenic ;** and with **antimony** an antimonide is formed. O. Prelinger, and A. N. Campbell found that manganese reduces arsenic from a warm soln. of an **arsenic salt ;** antimony is likewise separated from a warm soln. of an **antimony salt ;** and bismuth from a warm soln. of a **bismuth salt.** H. E. Patten observed that manganese is blackened by **arsenic trichloride ;** but is not acted upon by **antimony pentachloride.**

As noted by J. F. John, manganese readily unites with **carbon,** forming a carbide (*q.v.*) ; and O. Ruff and co-workers found that the solubility of carbon in manganese increases slowly up to 7·12 per cent. as the temp. rises from 1360° to 1525°, the b.p. of the soln. at 30 mm. press. K. Kido studied this subject—*vide* the carbide. O. Meyer observed that manganese is attacked by **carbides**—silicon, chromium, and molybdenum—at 1600°. A. Westgren and G. Phragmén said that carbon dissolves in manganese the same way as in iron, not by replacing atoms of the metal in the space-lattice, but by lying between them. J. Paunescu observed that when manganese is heated in **methane,** manganese carbide is formed. E. W. Kanning and O. W. Brown studied the catalytic decomposition of heated **kerosene** by manganese. A. P. Lidoff observed that **cyanogen** is readily occluded by manganese. R. Lorenz and F. Heusler, and A. Guntz observed no formation of manganese carbonyl when the metal or carbide is heated in **carbon monoxide.** W. Heller found that manganese begins to react with carbon monoxide at 330°, and at 350° the reaction is fast, and very fast at 410°. He also made some preliminary observations on the equilibrium conditions. J. Backmann found that non-pyrophoric manganese burns readily in carbon monoxide at a red-heat ; and A. Guntz represented the reaction with pyrophoric manganese : $Mn+CO=MnO+C+33\cdot3$ Cals. L. Troost and P. Hautefeuille found that carbon monoxide is less soluble than hydrogen in the different varieties of cast-iron, and that its solubility is diminished or even annulled by the presence of manganese. According to R. Lorenz and F. Heusler, **carbon dioxide** reacts with strongly heated manganese, forming manganese monoxide and carbon monoxide ; A. Guntz represented the reaction : $2Mn+CO_2=2MnO+C+46\cdot3$ Cals. E. Müller and H. Barck found that a mixture of carbon dioxide and hydrogen passed over manganese at 800° furnished some manganese carbide and manganous oxide. According to T. Bergman, water holding carbon dioxide in soln. dissolves manganese. H. E. Patten found that manganese is attacked by **ethyl chloride,** and by **chloroform,** but not by **carbon tetrachloride.** O. Warburg examined the effect of **hydrocyanic acid** on the catalytic activity of manganese in the oxidation of cysteine. According to A. Gautier and L. Hallopeau, when manganese is heated to 1400° in a current of **carbon disulphide,** a black layer of manganese sulphide and carbide is formed. C. Brunner, and O. Prelinger observed that the metal is dissolved by **acetic acid** with the evolution of hydrogen. L. Gay and co-workers found that when dry bromine is added to finely-divided manganese suspended in **ether,** and the mixture warmed on a water-bath, a complex bromide, $MnBr_2.(C_2H_5)_2O$, is formed ; and bromine attacks **benzene** at 90°, but if manganese is present the attack begins at 75°. L. L. Steele studied the action of manganese compounds on the drying of linseed oil. O. Schmidt, and A. Korczynsky discussed its use as a catalyst in the hydrogenation of organic substances. C. Fromageot discussed manganese salts as catalysts for organic oxidations. H. Moissan found that manganese forms a boride when it is heated with **boron ;** and A. Guntz showed that when heated with **boron trichloride,** manganese chloride and boride are formed. H. Moissan observed that manganese unites directly with **silicon** at a high temp. to form a silicide (*q.v.*). R. E. Nyswander and B. E. Cohn studied the thermoluminescence of zinc borate glass activated with manganese. M. Levin and G. Tammann said that manganese destroys **porcelain** at a high temp. H. E. Patten observed no action with **stannic chloride.**

The action of manganese on the **metals** is discussed below. O. Prelinger found that soln. of many **metal salts** are reduced to the metal when warmed with manganese—*e.g.* copper, zinc, cadmium, tin, lead, chromium, iron, cobalt, and nickel salts ; A. N. Campbell found that manganese readily displaced tin, lead, copper, iron, nickel, cobalt, cadmium, and zinc from soln. of their salts. H. Schild observed the reduction of iron salts ; and N. W. Fischer observed that salts of only silver and gold were reduced to the metal by manganese. H. D. Royce and L. Kahlenberg found that manganese will replace from their salt soln. zinc and other metals which have more positive electrode potentials. With soln. containing 50 grms. of salt per litre, at 25°, manganese rapidly replaces the metal in soln. of zinc sulphate and chloride, cadmium sulphate, ferric chloride, cobalt chloride, nickel chloride, lead acetate, silver acetate, and copper sulphate ; and at 50° it slowly replaces the metal in lead nitrate, copper nitrate, and silver nitrate. O. Prelinger found that manganese gives hydrogen when it is heated with a soln. of **sodium hydroxide ;** but A. N. Campbell observed no perceptible action when manganese is boiled with a conc. soln. of soda-lye or potash-lye. H. Moissan found that manganese reacts with molten **calcium oxide,** forming manganous oxide, but much manganese is at the same time volatilized. For the action of manganese on **ferrous oxide,** *vide* ferrous oxide. C. H. Herty and O. S. True, and G. Röhl studied the reversible reaction with **ferrous sulphide :** $FeS+Mn \rightleftharpoons MnS+Fe$.

Some reactions of analytical interest.—There are compounds of manganese in which that element is bi-, ter-, quadri-, sexi-, or septi-valent. The compounds of bivalent manganese are considered here. The others are discussed later. The manganous salt soln. give no precipitate with **hydrochloric acid ;** and soln. acidified even with weak acids like formic, acetic, or succinic acid give no precipitate with **hydrogen sulphide,** and neutral soln. are incompletely precipitated, if at all, by that reagent. According to H. W. F. Wackenroder,[3] if ammonia be present, flesh-coloured hydrated manganese sulphide is precipitated ; and a similar precipitate is obtained with **ammonium or alkali sulphide.** The precipitate is insoluble in an excess of the alkali sulphide, but is soluble in conc. acetic acid. The soln. turns brown on exposure to air. The precipitate is black if a trace of iron be present. A soln. of **alkali hydroxide** gives a white precipitate of manganous hydroxide, which gradually becomes brown in air owing to the formation of manganese manganite, or hydrated manganese dioxide, $MnO(OH)_2$. The oxidation is also effected by chlorine, bromine, hypochlorites, hydrogen dioxide, etc. F. Jackson estimated that 1 part in 128,000 can be detected by soda-lye. With aq. **ammonia** half the manganese is precipitated as white hydroxide and half forms a complex salt: $2MnCl_2 + 2NH_4OH = Mn(OH)_2 + (NH_4)_2MnCl_4$, and if sufficient ammonium chloride is present, hydroxide is precipitated, since all the manganese remains in soln. as complex chloride. The ammoniacal soln. absorbs oxygen from the air, forming a precipitate of the hydrated dioxide, $MnO(OH)_2$. F. Jackson estimated that 1 part in 64,000 can be recognized by the aq. ammonia test. White manganous carbonate is precipitated by **alkali carbonates,** and when boiled for a long time with water, the precipitate passes into hydrated manganese dioxide ; **ammonium carbonate,** even in the presence of ammonium salts, precipitates the white carbonate ; but **calcium carbonate,** according to J. N. von Fuchs, gives no precipitate in hot or cold soln. ; H. Demarçay said that the three **alkaline earth carbonates,** and **magnesium carbonate** give no precipitate in cold soln., but precipitation is complete with boiling soln. ; and J. W. Döbereiner added that magnesium carbonate precipitates the manganese completely in boiling soln.—magnesia acts similarly but more quickly. E. Bauch made some observations on this subject. Normal manganous phosphate is precipitated by **sodium phosphate,** and it is soluble in mineral and acetic acids. If ammonia be added to the boiling acid soln. of the precipitate, pink scales of ammonium manganous phosphate are precipitated. With **sodium arsenate** a white precipitate of manganous arsenate is deposited. With **potassium cyanide** a brownish precipitate is first formed ; it then dissolves to produce a brown soln. When the soln. is warmed, or allowed to stand for some time, a green precipitate of $KMnCy_3$ is formed, and this dissolves in more potassium cyanide to form a yellow soln. of K_4MnCy_6. If the dil. soln. be boiled it is decomposed, and manganous hydroxide is precipitated, but ammonium sulphide gives no precipitate if a large proportion of potassium cyanide is present. The dil. soln., however, deposits manganese sulphide when boiled. With **potassium ferrocyanide,** C. H. Pfaff said that a white precipitate, soluble in hydrochloric acid, is formed even with 1 part of salt in 6000 parts of water. F. J. Otto found that the precipitate is not soluble in an excess of ferrocyanide, ammonium chloride, or other salts ; with **potassium ferricyanide** a brownish-yellow precipitate, insoluble in hydrochloric acid, is produced. According to P. Berthier, **potassium sulphite**—not ammonium sulphide —gives a precipitate of manganous sulphite when boiled. No precipitation occurs with **potassium chromate.** D. Vitali found that dil. sulphuric acid and **potassium bromate** give a gradually increasing reddish-violet colour, due to the formation of permanganate—chlorates and iodates do not give the reaction. When boiled with **potassium chlorate** in nitric acid, hydrated manganese dioxide is formed. A deep red precipitate is produced with **potassium periodate.** Conc., not dil., soln. of manganous chloride give a precipitate with **oxalic acid ;** the precipitate is not soluble in an excess of the acid, but it is soluble in hydrochloric or sulphuric acid ; **alkali oxalates** give a precipitate in conc. or dil. soln., but not in the presence of ammonium chloride or a large excess of the alkali oxalate. According to G. Denigès, 5 c.c. of the manganese sat. soln. is treated with a few drops of sodium hydroxide soln., and shaken until a brown coloration is obtained ; sat. oxalic acid soln. is then added drop by drop. The brown coloration disappears and is replaced by the red coloration characteristic of manganese salts. The reaction was also studied by H. Caron and D. Raquet. No precipitate is formed with **alkali succinate or benzoate,** or with **tincture of galls.** According to J. Volhard, if a soln. containing traces of manganese be boiled with **lead dioxide** and conc. nitric acid, diluted with water, and allowed to settle, the supernatant liquid has a violet-red colour, due to the formation of permanganate. The presence of chlorides hinders the formation of the permanganate. The reaction was studied by H. Baubigny ; H. Marshall used **ammonium persulphate** in the presence of silver nitrate as oxidizing agent ; and by its means 0·001 mgrm. of manganese per c.c. can be detected. According to A. Trillat, a soln. of **tetra-**

methyldiaminodiphenylmethane in acetic acid gives a deep blue colour with lead and manganese dioxides. This reaction is extremely delicate and may be used for the detection of these metals. The reagent is prepared by boiling 30 grms. of dimethylaniline with 10 grms. of formaldehyde and 200 c.c. of water. After cooling, the liquid is made alkaline with sodium hydroxide and a current of steam is blown through until the excess of dimethylaniline is expelled. On cooling, crystals separate, which should be recrystallized from alcohol. Five grams of the base are dissolved in 100 c.c. of water and 10 c.c. of acetic acid ; the soln. must be placed in a well-stoppered bottle and preserved in the dark.

The physiological action of manganese.—Manganese compounds appear to play an important part in many biochemical changes. The subject was discussed by G. C. Gmelin.[4] G. B. Davis and W. B. Huey reported two cases of chronic manganese poisoning with men working an electric furnace melting ferromanganese. F. Wohlwill observed that the salts cause capillary hyperæmia of the alimentary canal. H. Micheels and P. de Heen found that colloidal soln. of manganese have a more stimulating action on germinating seeds than similar soln. of tin. G. Salomone found that while a certain quantity of manganese has a beneficial influence on the development of the plant as a whole, large quantities are toxic. The toxic effect of manganic salts is greater than that of manganous salts, and is dependent on the amount of dissociation, so that it is naturally greater for the salts of the more highly ionized mineral acids than for those of the organic acids ; in other respects the poisonous effect is but slightly influenced by the nature of the anion. The very marked poisonous properties of barium manganate and permanganate are attributed to the combined influence of the barium and the manganese. Manganic acid is more poisonous in the free state than in combination. Small quantities of manganous iodide exert a favourable influence on the germination of cabbage or carrot seeds. Of the manganese salts tried, manganous sulphate and nitrate and manganese dioxide were found to exert the most beneficial action on the growth of corn. As indicated in connection with the occurrence of manganese, G. Bertrand and co-workers assumed that manganese is an essential, not an accidental constituent of plants ; it is of vital importance in the extraction of oxygen from the air whenever this is necessary for producing the various chemical changes required for the vital activity of the plant. G. Bertrand found that the latex of the *Rhus succedanea* is first white, and on exposure to air it becomes brown, and then black. The latex contains laccase, laccol, and water. The laccol forms an emulsion with the soln. of laccase in water. The laccase contains the manganese and acts as a carrier of oxygen to the laccol. Laccol is not present in all plants, but its place is taken by analogous substances—*e.g.* tannin, boletol, etc.

Experiments showing that the presence of small proportions of manganese salts in soils favoured the growth of plants, whereas larger proportions may be injurious, were cited by T. Pfeiffer and co-workers, J. J. Skinner and M. X. Sullivan, J. Stoklasa, P. Leidreiter (sugar beets, mangolds, potatoes, oats, and beans), K. Aso (radishes, barley, wheat, and peas), O. Loew and S. Honda (*Cryptomeria japonica*), O. Loew and S. Sawa (barley, rice, peas, and cabbage), P. Pichard, J. Schroeder, E. Ramann, H. Birner and B. Lucanus, P. Wagner, I. Giglioli, N. Ono, H. Molisch, A. Grégoire and co-workers (potatoes and sugar-beet), Y. Fukutome (flax), J. A. Voelcker (wheat and barley), T. Katayama (barley), M. Nagaoka (rice), W. van Dam, W. F. Sutherst (maize), J. S. McHargue, and E. P. Deatrick (wheat), C. Montemartini, R. Ricci and G. Barbera, A. Bartmann, and G. Masoni, G. d'Ippolito (wheat, maize, and lucerne), F. A. Sannino and A. Tosatti (vines), L. Hiltner and G. Korff (oats), I. Namba (onions), M. de Molinari and O. Ligot (oats and barley), A. Carlier (grass, potatoes, and mangolds), O. Schreiner and P. R. Dawson (wheat, rye, corn, and potatoes). G. Leoncini observed the favourable effects of manganese dioxide in soils on nitrification. G. Spampani, and L. Bernardini attributed the beneficial effect of manganese to the production of soluble calcium and magnesium compounds from insoluble forms, so that it is **an** indirect calcium-magnesium manure.   H. von Feilitzen found that with oats 10 kgrms. of manganese sulphate per hectare had no effect ; and S. Rhodin found that with oats one kgrm. of manganese peroxide per acre reduced the yield, and 6 kgrms. per hectare also reduced the yield with potatoes.   J. A. Voelcker obtained nugatory results with wheat ; F. Weis, and P. Ehrenberg and O. Nolte observed no change in the ash of plants ; and H. Vageler observed no stimulation with oats, lupins, and beans.   P. Nottin discussed the absorptive power of soils for manganese salts.   P. E. Brown and G. A. Minges found that manganese chloride applied at the rate of more than 2000 lbs. per acre retarded both ammonification and nitrification.   The applications of 100 and 200 lbs. increased ammonification slightly and nitrification distinctly.   Manganese sulphate increased both ammonification and nitrification when applied at the rate of 100 lbs. per acre, whilst a larger amount (2000 lbs.) has a depressing effect.   Manganese oxide applied at the rate of 2000 lbs., or more, per acre retards both ammonification and nitrification.   W. T. McGeorge observed no effect with manganese on the growth of sugar-cane.   According tc N. L. Söhngen, the formation in the soils of higher oxides of manganese from manganous salts is promoted by a high concentration of hydroxyl ions, and the reduction of these oxides by the presence of peroxides, peroxydases, and oxydases. The presence of dextrose in the soil leads to the formation of hydroxy-acids capable of decomposing the higher oxides of manganese.   C. Montemartini found that 0·001 per cent. of manganese sulphate stimulated the respiration of vine plants, garden beans, and potato plants.   J. S. McHargue also considers manganese is a necessary constituent performing an important function in the synthesis of chlorophyll.   Similar ideas were held by A. Villiers, A. Livache, etc.   E. Houtermans could not confirm C. Acqua's statement that the roots of plants in contact with manganese nitrate secrete manganese in certain places in which the nitrogen is assimilated.   F. Plate showed that with *Triticum sativum* and *Hyacinthus orientalis* grown in soln. containing one of the following salts, manganese chloride, manganese bromide, manganese nitrate, and manganese sulphate, anion and cation, are absorbed in the same proportion as that in which they exist in the soln. ; the anion chiefly reaches the shoot, whilst the cation is found especially in the root.   According to A. Rippel, the addition of soluble manganese salts to the cultures in which oats seedlings were growing produced a chlorosis which was remedied by the addition of iron.   Since the iron content of the chlorotic and normal seedlings was the same, it is concluded that manganese does not prevent the uptake of iron by the plant, but inhibits its action after absorption.   H. Coupin found a 1 : 1000 soln. of manganous chloride is toxic to wheat.   M. O. Johnson observed that manganese sulphate and dioxide caused the chlorosis of pine-apples.

O. Loew and S. Sawa observed no decided stimulating action of manganese on yeast and aspergillus.   E. Kayser and H. Marchand found that when manganese sulphate is added to fruit musts which are to be fermented with yeast, there is an increase in the amount of alcohol, glycerol, and acids formed, but the initiation of fermentation occurs later the greater the amount of manganese sulphate added.   Manganese lactate and acetate produce practically the same effect as the sulphate when added in equivalent quantity, but the phosphate and succinate lead to the production of less alcohol and more glycerol.   With manganese nitrate fermentation sets in rapidly, and the amount of sugar consumed is about the same as when manganese sulphate is added.   The addition of potassium nitrate to the must leads to a smaller consumption of sugar than when yeast is used alone.   G. Bertrand and M. Javillier, and H. I. Waterman found that manganese sulphate favoured the development of *Aspergillus niger*; indeed, G. Bertrand found that one part of manganese in 10,000,000,000 parts of an artificial culture medium had an appreciable effect in increasing the yield.   M. Rosenblatt and A. J. March found that manganese salts sometimes stimulate alcoholic fermentation and sometimes inhibit the reaction— dependent on the origin of the yeast.   The inhibitory action is independent of the medium or the form in which the manganese is added (sulphate or nitrate), but the different results with different types of yeast indicate that the sensitivity of the enzymes produced by the yeast changes with the origin of the yeast and with the composition of the medium. Increasing the concentration of sugar protects the enzymes against the manganese, and thus exerts a weakening effect on both the manganese activation and inhibition of the fermentation reaction. D. Olaru observed that one part of manganese in 200,000 parts of medium is favourable to the fixation of nitrogen by the bacteria of *leguminosæ*. The addition of a minute amount of manganese was found by G. Bertrand, and A. Bach to increase the activity of the enzyme laccase, and colloidal manganese dioxide was found by B. Sjollema to act like an oxydase towards guaiacum tincture, and hydroquinone. The processes appear to be regulated by colloidal enzymes. E. J. Witzemann has suggested that the effect of manganese on enzymic activity is due to the effect of the colloidal hydrated dioxide on the physical character of the enzyme, so that if the colloidal dioxide keeps the colloidal enzyme under conditions normally unfavourable to this effect, a positive influence on enzymic activity would be produced. J. B. Garner and W. E. King observed that $\frac{1}{458}N$-permanganate soln. is antiseptic, and $\frac{1}{511}N$-soln. is germicidal towards *Bacillus typhosus*.

The occurrence of manganese in animals has been previously discussed. G. M. Piccinini [5] found that the addition of manganese to the ordinary diet causes an increase in the iron-content of the liver and spleen, and the absorption of iron appears to be regulated by the manganese available in the body. Colloidal manganese augments *in vitro* the available oxygen of blood, and maintains this increase for some time. It seems also to have the same action *in vivo*. Colloidal manganese retards the death of guinea pigs injected with the minimum lethal dose of diphtheritic toxin. A. Trillat found that the action of a manganous salt in alkaline soln. as a carrier of oxygen is largely increased by the addition of a small proportion of proteid matter—*e.g.* white of egg. The stimulating action is attributed to its tendency to prevent the precipitation of the manganese dioxide, which is thus maintained in a colloidal state, and is consequently more chemically active. Beyond a certain limit, an increase in the amount of albumin does not accelerate the oxidation; the maximum effect is produced when one part of albumin is added to 1000 parts of the mixture, and the addition of mercuric chloride, arsenic acid, prussic acid, formaldehyde, etc., has a paralysing effect similar to that observed in the case of a soln. not containing albumin. Other proteids, such as horse-serum, and colloids, such as gelatin, dextrin, and gum arabic, have given very variable results. G. Cohn showed that the presence of manganese interferes with artificial digestion by means of pepsin. C. Richet and co-workers found that the same daily dose of manganese citrate has a slightly harmful effect and the same dose every fourth day a slightly beneficial effect on dogs. J. S. McHargue found that a diet containing manganese improved the growth of rats. He found that manganese occurs in largest proportions in plant and animal tissues showing the greatest vitamin potency, and he suggested that there is a relationship between manganese and these vital factors. G. Bertrand and F. Medigreceau found that with repeated subcutaneous injections of minute doses of manganese sulphate in four rabbits there was a marked loss in weight, and three injections of 5 mg. of manganese per kilo. of body-weight, at intervals of twenty-four hours, caused the death of the rabbit. When the manganese is subcutaneously injected, it is rapidly diffused throughout the body, and all the tissues, including the nervous tissue, become temporarily impregnated. It is readily eliminated through the liver, bile, and mucus of the alimentary canal, and a small quantity is excreted in the urine. F. Medigreceau found that the amount of manganese in transplanted mouse and rat tumours is small (0·004 to 0·012 mgrm. per 100 grms. of fresh material), which is about the same as in the normal mammary gland of the mouse. No difference in the manganese of sarcoma and carcinoma was discoverable. According to C. K. Reiman and A. S. Minot, the prolonged administration of manganese to dogs failed to produce any significant changes in manganese content of blood or tissues, or to cause any pathological symptoms. According to H. Handovsky and co-workers, acute manganese poisoning occurs only when the conc. of manganese in the blood suddenly becomes very high, and is accompanied with nervous disturbances. In chronic poisoning this high conc. is not reached, nervous symptoms are not observed, the liver is chiefly attacked, and death occurs usually with smaller amounts than in acute poisoning, the lethal doses being 40 mgrms. per kgrm. In the chronic condition manganese citrate is more rapidly absorbed and more poisonous than the chloride. About 50 per cent. of the manganese injected is excreted in the fæces, but only traces appear in the urine. Considerable amounts of manganese are found in bone, bile, pus, and ascitic fluid. In the organs most manganese is deposited in the spleen and brain, a variable quantity in the liver, and only a little in the lungs. Manganese is found in muscle only after injection of the chloride, and not of complex organic salts of manganese. Fatty degeneration of the liver, heart, and kidney sometimes occurs. The subject was discussed by J. Cahn, F. Bergamo, E. Harnack and F. Schreiber, R. F. Gayle, D. Vitali, J. R. Charles, W. F. von Oettingen and T. Sollmann, etc. J. S. McHargue, and G. Bertrand and H. Nakamura found that manganese stimulates the growth of rodents. E. F. Hopkins found that manganese is essential for the growth of *Corella*. The optimum concentration is approximately 1 in 5×10^6 ; at higher concentrations, say 1 in 5×10^4, there is a toxic effect.

J. W. H. Harrison and F. C. Garrett found that melanism is induced in the *Lepidoptera* by manganese feeding, but H. M. Fox and H. Ramage did not find manganese to be particularly associated with melanin. The spectrum of the ink sac of *Sepia* showed no manganese ; whilst that element is present to the extent of 0·008 per cent. of the dry weight of the black body wall of the Arion, but there is even more in the colourless, common genital duct.

Some uses of manganese.—It has been estimated that 90 to 95 per cent. of the world's consumption of manganese is used in the manufacture of steel—*manganese steels*—not only to deoxidize and recarburize the molten metal so as to make cleaner and sounder ingots, but also to impart strength, hardness, and other qualities to the finished product. The manganese is introduced in the form of special alloys with a percentage ratio of Mn, Fe, Si, and C respectively as follows : *ferromanganese*, 50 to 80, 40 to 8, 0·5 to 1·5, and 5 to 7 ; *spiegeleisen*, 10 to 35, 85 to 60, about 1·0, and 4 to 5 ; *silicomanganese*, 55 to 70, 20 to 5, about 25, and 0·35 ; and *silicospiegel*, 20 to 50, 67 to 43, 4 to 10, and 1·5 to 3·5.[6] There is an alloy called *manganese bronze*, which is a kind of brass to which has been added a small proportion, say 0·05 per cent., of manganese, along with small proportions of iron, aluminium, tin, and lead for strengthening the alloy, and making it denser and closer grained than the average yellow-brass casting. The composition approximates 57·0 to 59·0 per cent. Cu ; 38·0 to 40·0 Zn ; 0·25 to 1·0 Fe, Mn, Al, and Sn ; and 0·10 to 0·50 Pb.[7] The object is to produce a metal suitable for marine construction and mining machinery and wherever corrosion is a serious difficulty. There is also a series of *magnetic alloys* obtained by alloying manganese with aluminium, tin, arsenic, antimony, bismuth, and boron. They are sometimes called *Heusler's alloys*.[8]

Some of the manganiferous earths—*e.g.* wad—are used as pigments. Manganese dioxide was formerly used in the manufacture of chlorine, but the process was largely displaced by electrolytic methods. Manganese dioxide is employed in making up the dry cell, when the dioxide serves to depolarize the hydrogen. Manganese oxide is used in bleaching glass—*vide supra*, the history of manganese—or in colouring glass.[9] It is also used to impart purple tints to glasses and pottery glazes ; to produce brown glazes, and " rockingham " glazes on red bodies ; and for tinting brick clays. Manganese dioxide and various manganese salts—sulphate, borate, resinate, linoleate, and oxalate—are added as driers to linseed and other oils to make them capable of absorbing oxygen from the air during the so-called drying of the oil. Manganese chloride is used in dyeing ; manganese sulphate, in calico printing, etc. ; manganese persulphate is used as an oxidation agent in making organic products ; and manganates or permanganates are used for preserving wood, for bleaching textile fibres, and for disinfecting [10] and oxidizing purposes.[11]

REFERENCES.

[1] W. Guertler, *Metall Erz*, **22**. 199, 1925 ; L. Troost and P. Hautefeuille, *Ann. Chim. Phys.*, (5), **7**. 155, 1876 ; R. Lorenz and F. Heusler, *Zeit. anorg. Chem.*, **3**. 225, 1893 ; A. J. Allmand and A. N. Campbell, *Trans. Faraday Soc.*, **20**. 379, 1924 ; F. Fischer and F. Schröter, *Ber.*, **43**. 1442, 1454, 1910 ; G. Hägg, *Zeit. phys. Chem.*, **12**. B, 33, 1931 ; G. F. Hüttig, *Zeit. angew. Chem.*, **39**. 67, 1926.

[2] G. Röhl, *Carnegie Mem. Iron Steel Ind.*, **4**. 62, 1912 ; J. Bachmann, *Chemische Abhandlungen über das Mangan*, Wien, 1829 ; *Zeit. Phys. Math.*, (1), **6**. 172, 1829 ; (2), **1**. 262, 1832 ; *Schweigger's Journ.*, **56**. 74, 1829 ; H. V. Regnault, *Ann. Chim. Phys.*, (2), **62**. 350, 1836 ; W. Guertler, *Metall Erz*, **22**. 199, 1925 ; O. Prelinger, *Monatsh.*, **14**. 353, 1893 ; F. Emich, *ib.*, **15**. 375, 1894 ; C. Brunner, *Pogg. Ann.*, **101**. 264, 1857 ; **103**. 139, 1857 ; *Dingler's Journ.*, **144**. 184, 1857 ; **146**. 44, 1857 ; **147**. 122, 1858 ; *Mitt. Naturf. Ges. Bern*, 72, 135, 1857 ; J. F. John, *Gehlen's Journ.*, **3**. 452, 1807 ; **4**. 436, 1807 ; *Ann. Phil.*, **2**. 172, 263, 1813 ; **3**. 413, 1813 ; H. Davy, *Elements of Chemical Philosophy*, London, 1812 ; A. N. Campbell, *Journ. Chem. Soc.*, **123**. 2323, 1923 ; J. J. Sudborough, *ib.*, **59**. 73, 1891 ; N. G. Sefström, *Jernkontorets Ann.*, **13**. 324, 1829 ; *Journ. tech. ökon. Chem.*, **10**. 184, 1831 ; J. J. Berzelius, *Schweigger's Journ.*, **7**. 76, 1813 ; *Ann. Chim. Phys.*, (2), **5**. 149, 1817 ; B. Pelletier, *ib.*, (1), **1**. 105, 1789 ; (1), **13**. 120, 1792 ; (1), **14**. 113, 1792 ; H. St. C. Deville, *ib.*, (3), **46**. 182, 1856 ; J. B. Berthemot, *ib.*, (2), **44**. 392, 1830 ; L. Troost and P. Hautefeuille, *ib.*, (5), **7**. 155, 1876 ; R. Bunsen, *ib.*, (3), **41**. 355, 1854 ; *Pogg. Ann.*, **91**. 619, 1854 ; N. W. Fischer, *ib.*, **16**. 128, 1829 ; H. Moissan, *Ann. Chim. Phys.*, (5), **21**. 231, 1880 ; *Compt. Rend.*, **130**. 622, 1900 ; **134**. 136, 1902 ; *Bull. Soc. Chim.*, (3), **27**. 664, 1902 ; N. B. Pilling and R. E. Bedworth, *Journ. Inst. Metals*, **29**. 529, 1923 ; *Metal Ind.*, **22**. 360, 1923 ; *Chem. Trade Journ.*, **72**. 317, 1923 ; A. Guntz and J. Férée, *Bull. Soc. Chim.*, (3), **15**. 132, 1896 ; A. Guntz, *ib.*, (3), **7**. 275, 1892 ; *Compt. Rend.*, **114**. 115, 1892 ; G. Valensi, *ib.*, **187**. 376, 1928 ; *Journ. Chim. Phys.*, **26**. 152, 1929 ; L. Duparc, P. Wenger and C. Cimerman, *Helvetica Chim. Acta*, **12**. 806, 1929 ; H. Goldschmidt, *Zeit. Elektrochem.*, **4**. 494, 1898 ; E. Beutel and A. Kutzelnigg, *ib.*, **36**. 523, 1930 ; W. C. Heraeus, *ib.*, **8**. 185, 1902 ; E. Wedekind, *ib.*, **11**. 850, 1906 ; E. Wedekind and T. Veit, *Ber.*, **41**. 3769, 1908 ; M. L. V. Gayler, *Journ. Iron Steel Inst.*, **115**. i, 393, 1927 ; R. E. Nyswander and B. E. Cohn, *Journ. Amer. Opt. Soc.*, **20**. 131, 1930 ; J. E. Loughlin, *Amer. Chemist*, **1**. 454, 1871 ; *Chem. News*, **25**. 139, 1872 ; C. J. Löwig, *Das Brom und seine chemischen Verhältnisse*, Heidelberg, 1829 ; *Mag. Pharm.*, **23**. 11, 1828 ; **33**. 6, 1831 ; *Pogg. Ann.*, **14**. 485, 1828 ; G. C. Stone, *Journ. Amer. Chem. Soc.*, **18**. 230, 1896 ; P. Schützenberger, *Compt. Rend.*, **69**. 196, 1869 ; A. Gautier and L. Hallopeau, *ib.*, **108**. 806, 1889 ; A. P. Lidoff, *Journ. Russ. Phys. Chem. Soc.*, **35**. 1238, 1903 ; C. Fromageot, *Journ. Chim. Phys.*, **24**. 623, 1927 ; G. Tammann and N. I. Nikitin, *Journ. Russ. Phys. Chem. Soc.*, **56**. 115, 1925 ; R. Lorenz and F. Heusler, *Zeit. anorg. Chem.*, **3**. 225, 1893 ; M. Levin and G. Tammann, *ib.*, **47**. 136, 1905 ; O. Ruff and W. Bormann, *ib.*, **88**. 365, 1914 ; O. Ruff, Bormann and F. Keilig, *Ueber das Verhalten von Kohlenstoff gegen Mangan, Nickel, Eisen, und Kobalt*, Berlin, 1918 ; O. Ruff, *Ber.*, **45**. 3139, 1912 ; O. Meyer, *Ueber die Darstellung und die Eigenschaften von Karbid- und Nitridtiegeln einem Beitrag über die Reaktionen von Karbiden und Graphit mit Metalloxyden*, Aachen, 1929 ; E. Müller and H. Barck, *Zeit. anorg. Chem.*, **129**. 321, 1923 ; K. Jellinek and J. Zakowsky, *ib.*, **142**. 1, 1924 ; J. Zakowsky, *Ueber die Affinität der Metalle zum Schwefel*, Danzig, 1925 ; C. Montemartini, *Gazz. Chim. Ital.*, **22**. i, 426, 1892 ; M. G. Levi, E. Migliorini and G. Ercolini, *ib.*, **38**. i, 598, 1908 ; H. Schild, *Berg. Hütt. Ztg.*, **47**. 251, 1888 ; E. Glatzel, *Ber.*, **22**. 2857, 1889 ; *Eng. Min. Journ.*, **49**. 452, 1890 ; G. Gore, *Proc. Roy. Soc.*, **21**. 140, 1873 ; L. Santi, *Boll. Chim. Farm.*, **43**. 673, 1904 ; A. Westgren and G. Phragmén, *Zeit. Physik*, **33**. 777, 1925 ; S. Hilpert and J. Paunescu, *Ber.*, **46**. 3479, 1913 ; S. Hilpert and T. Dieckmann, *ib.*, **47**. 780, 1914 ; O. Bauer and H. Arndt, *Zeit. Metallkunde*, **18**. 85, 1926 ; R. H. Adie, *Proc. Chem. Soc.*, **15**. 133, 1899 ; *Chem. News*, **79**. 261, 1899 ; T. Bergman, *De acido aëreo*, Upsala, 1774 ; H. D. Royce and L. Kahlenberg, *Trans. Amer. Electrochem. Soc.*, **50**. 137, 1926 ; I. Zschukoff, *Ann. Inst. Anal. Phys. Chim.*, **3**. 14, 1926 ; L. Gay, F. Ducelliez and A. Raynaud, *Compt. Rend.*, **158**. 576, 1804, 1914 ; *Bull. Soc. Chim.*, (4), **15**. 273, 1914 ; A. Korczynsky, *ib.*, (4), **29**. 283, 1921 ; C. H. Herty and O. S. True, *Blast Furnace and Steel Plant*, **13**. 492, 1925 ; R. Hanslian, *Molekulargewichtsbestimmungen in gefrierendem und siedendem Iod*, Weida i. Th., 1910 ; J. Paunescu, *Ueber die Kohlenstoffaufnahme des Mangans in Methan*, Berlin, 1913 ; N. Pfanner, *Ueber die Einwirkung von metallischem Mangan auf Hydroxylaminsalze*, Erlangen, 1912 ; O. Schmidt, *Zeit. phys. Chem.*, **118**. 193, 1925 ; W. Heller, *Beiträge zur Theorie des Eisenhochofenprozesses*, Marburg, 33, 1905 ; L. J. Thénard, *Traité de chimie*, Paris, **2**. 69, 1824 ; K. Kido, *Science Rep. Tohoku Univ.*, **9**. 305, 1920 ; W. Engelhardt, *Koll. Zeit.*, **45**. 42, 1928 ; C. C. Palit and N. R. Dhar, *Journ. Phys. Chem.*, **30**. 1125, 1926 ; H. E. Patten, *ib.*, **7**. 153, 1903 ; E. H. Harvey, *Chem. Met. Engg.*, **35**. 684, 1928 ; E. W. Kanning and O. W. Brown, *Journ. Phys. Chem.*, **35**. 2689, 1931 ; O. Warburg, *Biochem. Zeit.*, **233**. 245, 1931 ; L. L. Steele, *Journ. Ind. Eng. Chem.*, **16**. 957, 1924 ; R. Ochsenfield, *Ann. Physik*, (5), **12**. 353, 1932.

[3] H. W. F. Wackenroder, *Brandes' Arch.*, **16**. 114, 1825 ; J. W. Döbereiner, *Schweigger's*

Journ., **63**. 482, 1831 ; J. N. von Fuchs, *ib.*, **62**. 192, 1831 ; H. Demarçay, *Liebig's Ann.*, **11**. 240, 1834 ; F. J. Otto, *ib.*, **42**. 348, 1842 ; J. Volhard, *ib.*, **198**. 318, 1879 ; C. H. Pfaff, *Handbuch der analytischen Chemie*, Altona, **2**. 400, 1821 ; G. Denigès, *Ann. Chim. Anal.*, **2**. 215, 1920 ; H. Caron and D. Raquet, *ib.*, **1**. 174, 205, 1919 ; P. Berthier, *Ann. Chim. Phys.*, (3), **7**. 74, 1843 ; H. Baubigny, *Compt. Rend.*, **135**. 995, 110, 1902 ; **136**. 449, 1662, 1903 ; A. Trillat, *ib.*, **136**. 1205, 1903 ; H. Marshall, *Chem. News*, **83**. 76, 1901 ; D. Vitali, *Boll. Chim. Farm.*, **37**. 545, 1898 ; F. Jackson, *Journ. Amer. Chem. Soc.*, **25**. 992, 1903 ; E. Bauch, *Analyse der Salzsoolen von Coburg nebst Beiträgen zur analytischen Chemie*, Göttingen, 1860.

⁴ G. B. Davis and W. B. Huey, *Journ. Ind. Hyg.*, **3**. 231, 1921 ; P. Ehrenberg and O. Nolte, *Landw. Vers. Stat.*, **90**. 139, 1917 ; H. Birner and B. Lucanus, *ib.*, **8**. 128, 1866 ; P. Wagner, *ib.*, **13**. 69, 218, 1871 ; T. Pfeiffer, W. Simmermacher and A. Rippel, *Fuhling's Landw. Zeit.*, **17**. 313, 1918 ; T. Pfeiffer and E. Blanck, *Landw. Vers. Stat.*, **77**. 33, 1912 ; **83**. 257, 1913 ; H. Vageler, *ib.*, **88**. 159, 1916 ; H. Micheels and P. de Heen, *Bull. Acad. Belg.*, 288, 1906 ; J. J. Skinner and M. X. Sullivan, *Bull. U.S. Dep. Agric.*, 42, 1913 ; G. Leoncini, *ib.*, **47**. 77, 1915 ; G. Salomone, *Staz. Sperim. Agrar. Ital.*, **38**. 1015, 1906 ; **40**. 97, 1907 ; L. Bernardini, *ib.*, **43**. 217, 1910 ; C. Montemartini, *ib.*, **41**. 564, 1911 ; G. Masoni, *ib.*, **44**. 85, 1911 ; **48**. 822, 1915 ; G. d'Ippolito, *ib.*, **67**. 621, 1914 ; G. Spampani, *ib.*, **19**. 5, 1890 ; R. Ricci and G. Barbero, *ib.*, **48**. 677, 1915 ; J. Stoklasa, *Biochem. Zeit.*, **91**. 137, 1918 ; *Compt. Rend.*, **152**. 1340, 1911 ; A. Livache, *ib.*, **124**. 1520, 1897 ; P. Pichard, *ib.*, **126**. 550, 1898 ; E. Kayser and H. Marchand, *ib.*, **144**. 574, 714, 1907 ; **145**. 343, 1907 ; P. Nottin, *ib.*, **155**. 1167, 1912 ; **171**. 44, 1920 ; G. Bertrand and A. Villiers, *ib.*, **122**. 1134, 1896 ; **124**. 1032, 1355, 1897 ; A. Villiers, *ib.*, **124**. 1349, 1897 ; G. Bertrand and M. Rosenblatt, *ib.*, **173**. 333, 1118, 1921 ; **174**. 491, 1922 ; G. Bertrand, *ib.*, **124**. 1032, 1355, 1897 ; **141**. 1255, 1905 ; **154**. 616, 1912 ; *Ann. Chim. Phys.*, (7), **12**. 115, 1897 ; *Rev. Gén. Chim.*, **8**. 205, 1905 ; *Bull. Soc. Chim.*, (3), **17**. 619, 753, 1897 ; (4), **11**. 494, 1912 ; G. Bertrand and M. Javillier, *ib.*, (4), **11**. 212, 1912 ; *Compt. Rend.*, **152**. 225, 900, 1911 ; H. I. Watermann, *Journ. Chem. Soc.*, **104**. 229, 1913 ; J. S. McHargue, *Journ. Agric. Research*, **23**. 395, 1923 ; **24**. 781, 1923 ; **27**. 417, 1924 ; **30**. 193, 1925 ; *Journ. Amer. Chem. Soc.*, **36**. 2532, 1914 ; **44**. 1592, 1922 ; *Journ. Ind. Eng. Chem.*, **11**. 332, 1919 ; **18**. 172, 1926 ; P. Leidreiter, *Studien über das Verhalten des Mangans in Boden zu einiger landwirtschaftlichen Kulturpflanzen*, *Bied. Zentr.*, **40**. 531. 1911 ; A. Bartmann, *Journ. Agric. Prat.*, (2), **20**. 666, 1911 ; K. Aso, *Bull. Agric. Coll. Univ. Tokyo*, **4**. 254, 1901 ; **5**. 177, 1902 ; M. Nagaoka, *ib.*, **7**. 77, 1908 ; I. Namba, *ib.*, **7**. 635, 1908 ; Y. Fukutome, *ib.*, **6**. 136, 1904 ; T. Katayama, *ib.*, **7**. 91, 1908 ; O. Loew and S. Honda, *ib.*, **6**. 126, 1904 ; O. Loew and S. Sawa, *ib.*, **5**. 161, 1902 ; N. Ono, *Journ. Coll. Science Univ. Tokyo*, **13**. 141, 1900 ; J. Schroeder, *Forstchemische und pflanzenphysiologische Untersuchungen*, Dresden, 1878 ; E. Ramann, *Bot. Centr. Beihefte*, **8**. 23, 1898 ; *Zeit. Forst. Jagdivesen*, **30**. 105, 1898 ; I. Giglioli, *Cultura del Frumento Portici*, 159, 1901 ; F. Plate, *Atti Accad. Lincei*, (5), **23**. i, 839, 1914 ; F. A. Sannino and A. Tosatti, *ib.*, (5), **22**. ii, 237, 1913 ; H. Molisch, *Verh. Ges. deut. Naturf. Aerzte*, **66**. ii, 171, 1894 ; *Bot. Centr.*, **60**. iv, 167, 1894 ; *Sitzber. Akad. Wien*, **103**. 554, 1894 ; A. Grégoire, J. Hendrick and E. Carpiaux, *Bull. Inst. Chem. Bact. Gembloux*, 75, 1908 ; J. A. Voelcker, *Journ. Roy. Agric. Soc.*, **66**. 206, 1905 ; **74**. 411, 1913 ; W. van Dam, *Chem. Weekbl.*, **4**. 391, 1907 ; W. F. Sutherst, *Transvaal Agric. Journ.*, **6**. 437, 1908 ; M. de Molinari and O. Ligot, *Ann. Gembloux*, 609, 1908 ; A. Carlier, *ib.*, 423, 1910 ; H. von Feilitzen, *Journ. Landw.*, **55**. 289, 1907 ; F. Weis, *Landbohöjskole Aarsskrift*, 239, 1919 ; E. P. Deatrick, *Mem. Cornell Univ. Agric. Exp. Stat.*, **19**. 371, 1919 ; P. E. Brown and G. A. Minges, *Soil Science*, **2**. 67, 1916 ; A. Rippel, *Biochem. Zeit.*, **140**. 315, 1923 ; M. Rosenblatt and A. J. March, *ib.*, **170**. 344, 1926 ; M. O. Johnson, *Bull. Hawaii Agric. Exp. Stat.*, 52, 1924 ; W. T. McGeorge, *ib.*, 49, 1925 ; D. Olaru, *Compt. Rend.*, **160**. 280, 1915 ; E. Houtermans, *Anz. Akad. Wien*, **49**. 246, 1912 ; L. Hiltner and G. Korff, *Pratbl. Pflanzenbau Pflanzenschulz*, **15**. 549, 1917 ; C. Acqua, *Atti Accad. Lincei*, (5), **19**. i, 339, 1910 ; N. L. Söhngen, *Chem. Weekbl.*, **11**. 240, 1914 ; B. Sjollema, *ib.*, **6**. 287, 1909 ; A. Bach, *Ber.*, **43**. 364, 1910 ; G. M. Piccinini, *Proc. Internat. Congr. Appl. Chem.*, **19**. 263, 1912 ; *Biochem. Terap. Sper.*, **2**. 385, 1911 ; E. J. Witzemann, *Journ. Amer. Chem. Soc.*, **37**. 1089, 1915 ; J. B. Garner and W. E. King, *Amer. Chem. Journ.*, **35**. 144, 1906 ; G. C. Gmelin, *Schweigger's Journ.*, **43**. 110, 1825 ; *Edin. Journ. Med.*, **3**. 324, 1827 ; O. Schreiner and P. R. Dawson, *Journ. Ind. Eng. Chem.*, **19**. 400, 1927 ; S. Rhodin, *Landtbr. Akad. Handl. Tids. Stockholm*, 30, 1908 ; H. Coupin, *Compt. Rend.*, **132**. 645, 1901 ; F. Wohlwill, *Arch. Exp. Path. Pharm.*, **56**. 403, 1907.

⁵ D. Vitali, *Boll. Chim. Farm.*, **43**. 493, 1904 ; G. M. Piccinini, *Arch. Farm. Sperim.*, 9, 1910 ; *Biochem. Terap. Sperim.*, 2, 1910 ; A. Trillat, *Compt. Rend.*, **137**. 922, 1903 ; **138**. 94, 274, 1904 ; C. Richet, M. Gardner and M. Goodbody, *ib.*, **181**. 1105, 1925 ; R. F. Gayle, *Journ. Amer. Med. Assoc.*, **85**. 2008, 1925 ; G. Cohn, *Ueber das Mangan in physiologischer Hinsicht nebst Versuchen über den Einfluss von Mangan und Eisen auf die Pepsinverdauung*, Berlin, 1902 ; J. S. McHargue, *Amer. Journ. Physiol.*, **72**. 583, 1925 ; **77**. 245, 1926 ; *Journ. Agric. Research*, **27**. 417, 1924 ; **30**. 193, 1925 ; J. R. Charles, *Brain*, **50**. 30, 1927 ; H. Handovsky, H. Schulz, and M. Stämmler, *Arch. Exp. Path. Pharm.*, **110**. 265, 1926 ; J. Cahn, *ib.*, **18**. 129, 1884 ; F. Bergamo, *Il Farmacista Italiana*, **12**. 345, 1888 ; E. Harnack and F. Schreiber, *Arch. Exp. Path. Pharm.*, **46**. 372, 1901 ; G. Bertrand and F. Medigreceau, *Compt. Rend.*, **155**. 1556, 1912 ; G. Bertrand and H. Nakamura, *ib.*, **186**. 1480, 1928 ; F. Medigreceau, *Proc. Roy. Soc.*, **86**. B, 174, 1913 ; J. W. H. Harrison and F. C. Garrett, *ib.*, **99**. B, 241, 1926 ; H. M. Fox and H. Ramage, *Nature*, **126**. 682, 1930 ; C. K. Reiman and A. S. Minot, *Journ. Biol. Chem.*, **45**. 133, 1920 ; W. F. von Oettingen and T. Sollmann, *Journ. Ind. Hyg.*, **9**. 48, 1927 ; E. F. Hopkins, *Science*, (2), **72**. 609, 1930.

[6] E. Newton, *Bull. Univ. Minnesota*, 5, 1918 ; R. Cazaud, *Aciers Spéciaux*, **5**. 271, 1930 ; *Metals Alloys*, **1**. 678, 1930 ; E. Priwoznik, *Oesterr. Zeit. Berg. Hütt.*, **59**. 582, 1911 ; C. M. Weld, *Manganese*, Washington, 6, 1920 ; G. M. Dyson, *Chem. Age*, **14**. 10, 1926 ; P. Bonds, *South African Min. Eng. Journ.*, **40**. 339, 505, 1930.

[7] E. F. Sperry, *Brass World*, **1**. 399, 1905 ; P. E. McKinney, *Trans. Amer. Inst. Min. Eng.*, **60**. 374, 1919 ; A. R. von Schrötter, *Sitzber. Akad. Wien*, **63**. 453, 1870.

[8] F. Heusler, *Zeit. angew. Chem.*, **17**. 260, 1904 ; E. Haupt, *Naturw. Rund.*, **21**. 69, 1906 ; J. G. Gray, *Proc. Roy. Soc.*, **77**. 256, 1906 ; Isabellenhütte, *German Pat.*, *D.R.P.* 144584, 1903.

[9] K. Fuwa, *Journ. Japan. Cer. Soc.*, 366, 1923 ; W. D. Bancroft and R. L. Nugent, *Journ. Phys. Chem.*, 33, 481, 1929.

[10] H. B. Condy, *Brit. Pat. No.* 10015, 1884.

[11] L. L. Steele, *Journ. Ind. Eng. Chem.*, **16**. 957, 1924.

§ 6. The Atomic Weight and Valency of Manganese

W. Manchot [1] and co-workers, and G. Grube and W. Brause discussed complex salts of *univalent* manganese. In manganous salts the manganese behaves as a *bivalent* element ; thus, when dissolved in bismuth trichloride or in urethane, manganous chloride has a mol. wt. corresponding with the formula $MnCl_2$. Manganous sulphate is isomorphous with the analogous sulphates of zinc and magnesium ; and manganous carbonate is isomorphous with calcium and magnesium carbonates. Manganese is *tervalent* in the manganic salts ; thus in manganic acetylacetonate the vapour density and the mol. wt. in benzene correspond with the formula $Mn(C_5H_7O_2)_3$; and in the manganic alums the salts are isomorphous with those containing tervalent aluminium. J. Meyer and W. Schramm, and G. A. Barbieri discussed the tervalent manganese compounds. Manganese is probably *quadrivalent* in the salts $2KF.MnF_4$, $2KCl.MnCl_4$, etc., of E. Weinland and O. Lauenstein, A. Yakimach, R. J. Meyer and H. Best, G. Neumann, and W. B. Holmes and E. V. Manuel. In the dioxide also the manganese may be quadrivalent, as advocated by L. Marino, $O=Mn=O$, or it may be bivalent :

$$Mn\!\!<\!\!\begin{array}{c} O \\ \cdot \\ O \end{array}$$

In the manganates, manganese is probably *sexivalent*, since potassium manganate, K_2MnO_4, is isomorphous with the sulphate, K_2SO_4 ; and the manganese is probably *septivalent* in the permanganates. This is in agreement with the isomorphism of the permanganate, $KMnO_4$, and the perchlorate, $KClO_4$.

In seeking resemblances between the elements, the isomorphism rule can easily be pushed too far—*qui nimium probat, nihil probat*. It has been said that although a great many facts can be cited in establishing a relation between isomorphism and the position of an element in the periodic table, yet facts show that there may be isomorphous compounds amongst quite different groups of elements in the periodic table. Thus, it could be argued that iron belongs to the sulphur family because of the isomorphism between potassium ferrate and the corresponding sulphate. Lead is placed with carbon in spite of the absence of isomorphous compounds and of its isomorphism with the alkali family. The isomorphism of the sulphates and tellurates and of the sulphides and tellurides indicates that tellurium belongs to the sulphur family, although the isomorphism between K_2TeCl_6, K_2OsCl_6, and K_2IrCl_6 would make tellurium a member of the eighth group, and a similar agreement applied to Cs_2SnCl_6 and Cs_2TeCl_6 and to potassium tellurium and potassium zirconium oxalates would make tellurium a member of the tin family. The isomorphism between $KMnO_4$ and $KClO_4$ favours placing manganese in the seventh group, but the isomorphism of K_2MnO_4 and of K_2SO_4 would agree with manganese in the sulphur group, and the analogies between manganese and tin tetrachlorides would put manganese and tin in the same family. Platinum would be grouped with tin and lead if we were guided by the isomorphism of the plumbates, stannates, and platinates. The establishing of a family likeness between elements because of the isomorphism of some of their compounds is unscientific and arbitrary. Isomorphism seems to depend more on a similarity of chemical constitution than on family resemblances of the elements concerned.

D. I. Mendeléeff's arguments [2] for placing manganese in the seventh group of the periodic table were based mainly on the maximum heptavalency of the element, e.g. the apparent similarity of the chlorine and manganese dioxides and of the perchlorates and permanganates, although by the same argument it could be argued that vanadium has a place in that group because of the apparent similarity between the chlorates and vanadates. The arguments based on isomorphism are similarly open to question. F. R. von Bichowsky argued that it would be better to place manganese with the iron family in the eighth group, because (1) manganese is at the end of the Ti, V, Cr row, the titanyl, vanadyl, and chromyl salts, and these salts become more stable in that order ; consequently, stable manganyl salts might be anticipated, but this is not the case ; (2) while the barium salts of titanic, vanadic, and chromic acid are all slightly soluble, barium permanganate is very soluble ; (3) titanium, vanadium, and chromium form per salts, but manganese does not form a higher per salt than the permanganates ; (4) the titanates, vanadates, and chromates are stable in alkaline soln. and unstable in acid soln. ; permanganates are more stable in acid soln. ; (5) the titanous, vanadous, and chromous salts are powerful reducing agents ; (6) the manganous halides are isomorphous with the ferrous halides, but not with the chromous halides ; (7) the hydrates of manganous chloride are isomorphous with those of cobalt ; and the manganous salts and the corresponding salts of the iron family closely resemble one another, but not so with the manganous salts of the titanium, vanadium, and chromium group ; (8) there is a marked contrast with the sulphides : manganese sulphide belongs to the iron group rather than to the other group ; (9) similar remarks apply to the carbonates ; likewise (10) the ferric, manganic, cobaltic, and nickelic salts are all oxidizing agents, but the corresponding salts of titanium, vanadium, and chromium are reducing agents ; (11) the metal alloys also favour placing manganese with iron ; likewise also (12) the carbides and silicides ; and (13) the colours of salts with the different valencies of manganese favour the view that the normal valency of manganese is even, not odd. All this, of course, is purely circumstantial evidence, and it can be matched with arguments of a similar type for the opposition. The subject was discussed by M. M. Gerber.

J. Dalton [3] estimated the atomic weight of manganese to be 40 when that of oxygen is 7. In 1813, from the observations of previous workers, J. J. Berzelius said that it appeared as if manganese forms a series of oxides with manganese and 1, 2, 4, 6, and 8 at. proportions of oxygen ; and later he gave 711·57 for the at. wt. when that of oxygen is 100. This reduces to 113·85 if the at. wt. of oxygen be 16. In 1818, he represented the oxides $Mn : O = 1 : 2, 1 : 4$, and $3 : 8$. The at. wt. was halved, and then the at. wt. was represented by 56·93 ; and later by 55. J. J. G. Meinecke, in 1817, and T. Thomson, in 1822, represented the at. wt. by 56 ; C. G. Bischof, in 1819, gave $2 \times 56·93$; L. Gmelin, and C. M. Despretz, in 1826, gave 28, or $\frac{1}{2}$ of 56, for the eq. wt. ; L. J. Thénard, in 1826, gave 57·02 ; P. T. Meissner, in 1834, 55·43 ; and O. B. Kühn, in 1837, gave 27·7 for the eq. wt. Observations were also made by J. F. John, G. Forchhammer, and H. Davy. A number approximating 55 fits in with Avogadro's theory extended to soln. ; with the sp. ht. rule ; with the isomorphism rule for compounds of bivalent Mn, Mg, Zn, Fe, Co, and Ni ; for compounds of tervalent Mn, Al, Ga, In, Tl, Ti, V, Cr, Fe, Co, and Rh ; for sexivalent Mn, S, Se, Cr, Fe, and probably Mo and W ; and septavalent Mn and Cl. The position assigned to manganese in the seventh group of the periodic table along with the halogens is not so good. The septavalency of manganese in Mn_2O_7 and of chlorine in Cl_2O_7 is usually over-emphasized in attempting to justify the association of manganese with the halogens in the periodic table. It is much more closely related with the iron family of elements in the eighth group elements. The subject was discussed by E. H. Büchner, J. Parry, H. Reynolds, F. R. von Bichowsky, R. G. W. Norrish, G. Oddo, and H. Teudt.

The relation between the affinity and density of the elements was discussed by E. Donath and J. Mayrhofer ; between the affinity and decomposition temp. of the amines, by F. Ephraim, W. Biltz, and A. Werner, and they obtained the order $Ni > Co > Fe > Mn > Cu > Cd > Zn > Mg$; between the affinity and the heats of formation of various compounds, by H. Moissan, and M. Berthelot, and they obtained the order Cr, Mn, Fe, Co, and Ni.

In 1810, J. J. Berzelius oxidized manganese with nitric acid, and after converting the nitrate to oxide, obtained the at. wt. 56·7 from the assumed ratio $2Mn : Mn_2O_3$. The number is a little too high ; presumably some Mn_3O_4 was also present. If the data be calculated for the ratio $Mn_3 : Mn_3O_4$, it gives 50·4. R. Brandes, from the analysis of the chloride, $MnCl_2.nH_2O$, obtained the at. wt. 57. J. A. Arfvedson's data gave 55·9 for the ratio $MnCl_2 : 2AgCl$; and from the same ratio J. J. Berzelius obtained 54·88 ; E. Turner, 54·9 ; and G. P. Baxter and M. A. Hines, 54·932. J. B. A. Dumas obtained 54·92 from the ratio $MnCl_2 : 2Ag$; J. Dewar and A. Scott, 54·85 ; and G. P. Baxter and M. A. Hines, 54·934. G. P. Baxter and M. A. Hines also calculated 54·930 from the ratio $MnBr_2 : 2AgBr$. E. Turner calculated 56·0 from the ratio $MnCO_3 : CO_2$; E. R. Schneider, 54·03 from the ratio $MnC_2O_4 : 2CO_2$; and 54·08 from the ratio $Mn_3O_4 : H_2O$. E. Turner obtained 56·0 from the ratio $MnO : MnSO_4$; J. J. Berzelius, 55·28, J. C. G. de Marignac, 55·07, and J. M. Weeren, 55·01. C. von Hauer obtained 54·90 from the ratio $MnSO_4 : MnS$, and J. M. Weeren, 55·02. C. von Hauer calculated 55·02 from the ratio $3MnO : Mn_3O_4$; J. Dewar and A. Scott, 54·91 from the ratio $AgMnO_4 : (Ag+MnO)$, and 54·938 from the ratio $AgMnO_4 : KBr$. Assuming that the at. wts. of silver are 107·880, 107·876, and 107·871, B. Brauner (1913) computed 54·932, 54·930, and 54·927 respectively for the best representative values of the at. wt. of manganese. L. Meyer and K. Seubert (1883) computed 54·8 for H unity ; and F. W. Clarke (1910) gave 54·947 for the best representative value. The International Table for 1927 gave 54·93.

The **atomic number** of manganese is 25. P. Vinassa discussed the molecular numbers of compounds of manganese. No **isotopes** of manganese have been observed.[4] The **atomic disruption** of the atom has not yet been observed by E. Rutherford and J. Chadwick, or by H. Pettersson and G. Kirsch. A. L. Foley made experiments on this subject. The **electronic structure,** according to N. Bohr, is (2) for the K-shell ; (4, 4) for the L-shell ; (4, 4, 5) for the M-shell ; and (2) for the N-shell. The subject was discussed by H. Collins, J. D. M. Smith, S. Meyer, R. N. Ghosh, D. M. Bose, B. Cabrera, C. G. Bedreag, A. Sommerfeld, P. D. Foote, R. Ladenburg, C. D. Niven, R. Samuel and E. Markowicz, D. Avdalian, and by W. H. Rothery.

REFERENCES.

[1] E. Weinland and O. Lauenstein, *Zeit. anorg. Chem.*, **20**. 40, 1899 ; J. Meyer and W. Schramm, *ib.*, **157**. 190, 1926 ; R. J. Meyer and H. Best, *ib.*, **22**. 169, 1899 ; L. Marino, *ib.*, **56**. 233, 1907 ; G. Neumann, *Monatsh.*, **15**. 489, 1894 ; W. B. Holmes and E. V. Manuel, *Journ. Amer. Chem. Soc.*, **30**. 1192, 1908 ; G. A. Barbieri, *Ber.*, **60**. B, 2421, 1927 ; W. Manchot and H. Gall, *Ber.*, **60**. B, 191, 1927 ; **61**. B, 1135, 1928 ; G. Grube and H. Brause, *ib.*, **60**. B, 2273, 1927 ; A. Yakimach, *Compt. Rend.*, **190**. 681, 1930.

[2] D. I. Mendeléeff, *The Principles of Chemistry*, London, 2. 329, 1905 ; F. R. von Bichowsky, *Journ. Amer. Chem. Soc.*, **40**. 500, 1040, 1918 ; M. M. Gerber, *Chem. News*, **42**. 242, 1881.

[3] J. Dalton, *A New System of Chemical Philosophy*, Manchester, 2. 265, 1810 ; H. E. Roscoe and A. Harden, *A New View of the Origin of Dalton's Atomic Theory*, London, 1896 ; J. J. G. Meinecke, *Die chemische Messkunst*, Halle, 1817 ; L. Gmelin, *Handbuch der theoretischen Chemie*, Frankfurt a. M., 1826 ; T. Thomson, *A System of Chemistry*, Edinburgh, 1822 ; *Ann. Phil.*, (2), **1**. 241, 1821 ; C. G. Bischof, *Lehrbuch der Stöchiometrie*, Erlangen, 1819 ; C. M. Despretz, *Élémens de chimie théorique et pratique*, Paris, 1830 ; L. J. Thénard, *Traité de chimie élémentaire*, Paris, 1826 ; P. T. Meissner, *Chemische Aequivalen-oder Atomenlehre*, Wien, 1834 ; O. B. Kühn, *Lehrbuch der Stöchiometrie*, Leipzig, 1837 ; E. Turner, *Trans. Roy. Soc. Edin.*, **11**. 143, 1831 ; *Phil. Mag.*, (2), **4**. 22, 1828 ; H. Teudt, *Zeit. anorg. Chem.*, **106**, 192, 1919 ; W. Biltz, *ib.*, **81**. 522, 1913 ; F. Ephraim, *Zeit. phys. Chem.*, **81**. 522, 1913 ; G. Oddo, *Gazz. Chim. Ital.*, **50**. ii, 217, 1920 ; M. Berthelot, *Compt. Rend.*, **90**. 1511, 1880 ; *Ann. Chim. Phys.*, (5), **21**. 396, 1880 ; H. Moissan, *ib.*, (5), **21**. 253, 1880 ; A. Werner, *Neuere Anschauungen auf dem Gebiete der*

anorganischen Chemie, Braunschweig, 1923 ; E. Donath and J. Mayrhofer, *Ber.*, **16**. 1588, 1883 ;
J. J. Berzelius, *Afhand. Fys. Kemi*, **3**. 149, 1810 ; *Akad. Handl. Stockholm*, **35**. 212, 1813 ; *Pogg.
Ann.*, **18**. 74, 1830 ; E. R. Schneider, *Liebig's Ann.*, **113**. 77, 1860 ; *Phil. Mag.*, (4), **18**. 268, 1859 ;
Pogg. Ann., **107**. 605, 1859 ; R. Brandes, *ib.*, **22**. 225, 1818 ; C. von Hauer, *Journ. prakt. Chem.*,
(1), **72**. 360, 1857 ; *Sitzber. Akad. Wien*, **25**. 124, 1857 ; J. B. A. Dumas, *Ann. Chim. Phys.*, (3),
55. 151, 1859 ; J. C. G. de Marignac, *ib.*, (6), **1**. 289, 1884 ; P. Berthier, *ib.*, (2), **20**. 186, 1822 ;
J. Dewar and A. Scott, *Proc. Roy. Soc.*, **35**. 44, 1883 ; R. G. W. Norrish, *Chem. News*, **124**. 16,
1922 ; H. Davy, *Phil. Trans.*, **102**. 181, 1812 ; G. Forchhammer, *Ann. Phil.*, **16**. 130, 1820 ; **17**.
50, 1821 ; *De mangano*, Hafnia, 1820 ; J. A. Arfvedson, *Afhand. Fys. Kemi*, **6**. 222, 1818 ; *Ann.
Phil.*, **7**. 267, 1824 ; *Schweigger's Journ.*, **42**. 202, 1818 ; J. F. John, *ib.*, **7**. 76, 1813 ; *Ann. Phil.*,
2. 172, 263, 1813 ; **3**. 413, 1813 ; *Gehlen's Journ.*, **3**. 452, 1807 ; **4**. 436, 1807 ; F. W. Clarke,
A Recalculation of the Atomic Weights, Washington, 415, 1910 ; *Phil. Mag.*, (5), **12**. 101, 1881 ;
Amer. Chem. Journ., **3**. 263, 1881 ; J. M. Weeren, *Stahl Eisen*, **13**. 559, 1893 ; *Atomgewichtsbestimmung des Mangans*, Halle, 1890 ; L. Meyer and K. Seubert, *Die Atomgewichte der Elemente*,
Leipzig, 242, 1883 ; B. Brauner in R. Abegg, *Handbuch der anorganischen Chemie*, Leipzig, **4**.
ii, 599, 1913 ; G. P. Baxter and M. A. Hines, *Journ. Amer. Chem. Soc.*, **28**. 1560, 1906 ; F. R. von
Bichowsky, *ib.*, **40**. 1040, 1918 ; J. Parry, *Nature*, **45**. 253, 1892 ; H. Reynolds, *Chem. News*,
6. 260, 1907 ; E. H. Büchner, *Chem. Weekbl.*, **12**. 336, 1915.
  [4] F. W. Aston, *Isotopes*, London, 142, 1922 ; *Nature*, **112**. 449, 1923 ; *Journ. Soc. Chem. Ind.*—
Chem. Ind., **42**. 935, 1923 ; *Phil. Mag.*, (6), **47**. 385, 1924 ; (6), **49**. 1191, 1925 ; W. H. Rothery,
ib., (7), **11**. 649, 1931 ; D. M. Bose, *ib.*, (7), **5**. 1048, 1928 ; *Zeit. Physik*, **33**. 213, 1926 ; **43**. 864,
1927 ; H. Pettersson and G. Kirsch, *Atomzertrummerung*, Leipzig, 1926 ; B. Cabrera, *Anal. Fis.
Quim.*, **20**. 92, 1922 ; *Journ. Phys. Rad.*, (6), **3**. 443, 1922 ; N. Bohr, *Nature*, **112**. Suppl., 1923 ;
E. Rutherford and J. Chadwick, *ib.*, **107**. 41, 1921 ; A. Sommerfeld, *Ann. Physik*, (4), **70**. 32, 1923 ;
R. Ladenburg, *Zeit. phys. Chem.*, **126**. 133, 1927 ; P. D. Foote, *Trans. Amer. Inst. Min. Eng.*, **73**.
628, 1926 ; J. D. M. Smith, *Journ. Chem. Soc.*, 2029, 1927 ; H. Collins, *Chem. News*, **131**. 355,
1925 ; S. Meyer, *Naturwiss.*, **15**. 623, 1927 ; R. N. Ghosh, *Journ. Indian Chem. Soc.*, **4**. 423, 1927 ;
C. G. Bedreag, *Compt. Rend.*, **179**. 768, 1924 ; **180**. 653, 1925 ; A. L. Foley, *Proc. Indian Acad.*,
34. 185, 1925 ; C. D. Niven, *Phil. Mag.*, (7), **3**. 1314. 1927 ; R. Samuel and E. Markowicz, *Zeit.
Physik*, **38**. 22, 1926 ; D. Avdalian, *Ukrainsky Khem. Zhurn.*, **4**. 95, 1929 ; P. Vinassa, *Gazz.
Chim. Ital.*, **58**. 178, 1928.

§ 7. The Alloys and Intermetallic Compounds of Manganese

R. von Gersdorff [1] made **copper-manganese alloys** about 1840. According to
E. A. Lewis, the two metals can be readily alloyed in all proportions ; and he made
the alloys by melting the mixed metals under a layer of borax ; S. F. Schemtschuschny and co-workers melted the mixed metals under a layer of barium chloride ;
and R. Sahmen melted the mixture in an atm. of hydrogen. S. Wologdine melted
the mixed metals under a layer of charcoal in a crucible lined with magnesia.
F. Gloger melted copper oxide with an excess of manganese silicide and found that
the silicon reduced the cuprous oxide, forming cupromanganese free from silicon.
G. A. Dick melted a mixture of ferromanganese, copper, and silicon ; A. R. von
Schrötter heated a mixture of copper hammer-slag, manganese dioxide, and carbon ;
J. F. Allen heated a mixture of copper oxide, manganese oxide, and carbon ;
C. Schwarz and A. Weishut used an analogous process ; while F. von Kügelgen
reduced a mixture of copper oxide and chloride and manganese oxide by calcium
carbide under a layer of calcium chloride. Analyses of commercial alloys were
made by H. Winter, E. W. L. Biermann, and E. Priwoznik. The uses of the alloys
were discussed by M. Levitzky, A. Carnot, L. Archbutt, N. Parravano, E. A. Lewis,
and C. Heusler. G. Sirovich and A. Cartoceti showed that copper can be cemented
by ferromanganese or chromomanganese. G. Sirovich and A. Cartoceti discussed the cementation of copper by chromomanganese with 30·4 per cent. of
chromium and 63·8 per cent. of manganese. The chromium does not penetrate
the copper, but it favours the penetration of manganese more than does the iron
of ferromanganese. The segregation of alloys was discussed by G. Masing,
O. Bauer and H. Arndt, and W. Dinkler.

S. Wologdine thought that there exists a compound *copper tetramanganeside*,
$CuMn_4$, but S. F. Schemtschuschny and co-workers, and R. Sahmen showed that
the two elements form a continuous series of solid soln. E. A. Lewis thought that
the series was broken between 20 and 95 per cent. of copper. S. F. Schemtschuschny
and co-workers represented the f.p. curve by Fig. 14, which has been modified by

E. Persson to suit his observations on the X-radiograms of the alloys. The curve is continuous, with a minimum at 868° and 35·5 per cent. manganese. At compositions 10 and 15 per cent. of manganese, the interval between the liquidus and solidus curves is a maximum, and the two curves coincide at the minimum. R. Sahmen confirmed these results, obtaining a minimum at 866° with 35 per cent. of manganese. E. C. Bain, and M. R. Andrews showed that the X-radiograms of the alloys indicate that there is a wide difference in the lattices of the limiting metals, and that there is a region from 60 to 90 per cent. manganese where the lattices overlap.

T. Ishiwara's results are summarized in Fig. 15. The liquidus curve $C'EM'$ agrees with the observations of S. F. Schemtschuschny and co-workers, and R. Sahmen, and the solidus agrees with the corresponding curve on R. Sahmen's diagram. T. Ishiwara found that alloys annealed at 830° containing less than 20 per cent. of manganese were homogeneous, but those with more manganese were heterogeneous. This is in agreement with the horizontal line ED, and the solidus DM', and the region for the solid soln. γ, which is bounded also by the curve M_2I, and the curve DJ. The eutectoid line is represented by FJK. The

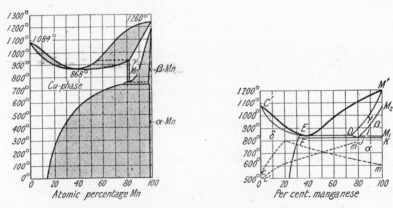

FIGS. 14 and 15.—Freezing-Point Curves of the System : Cu–Mn.

dotted curve cm represents the magnetic susceptibility of the alloys ; and $c'm'$, Rockwell's hardness. O. Bauer and H. Arndt discussed the segregation of the alloys.

R. Sahmen said that the alloy with 5 per cent. manganese is brass-yellow ; with 10 per cent. manganese, pale yellow ; and with 20 per cent. manganese, grey. H. Behrens added that the alloy with 10 per cent. manganese is reddish, and that with 30 per cent. manganese polishes tin-white. S. Wologdine also said that alloys with 0 to 40 per cent. manganese have a more or less reddish tinge, gradually becoming greyish-white. A. Valenciennes, and E. F. Dürre also made some observations on the colour of these alloys. H. Behrens said that the microstructure, after etching with aq. ammonia, shows a fine, irregular net-work ; and S. Wologdine added that heterogeneous dendrites of copper occur in alloys with up to 40 per cent. manganese, whilst alloys with 40 to 78 per cent. manganese have white, hard crystals in a dark matrix. R. A. Patterson found that in the formation of solid soln. by adding up to 30 per cent. to copper, the atoms of copper in the face-centred lattice are replaced by manganese atoms, with an increase in the side of the cube from 3·60 A. to 3·70 A. E. C. Bain discussed the X-radiograms. For S. Sekito's, E. Persson and E. Oehlman's observations, *vide supra*, manganese. Z. Nishiyama also studied the subject. E. Persson's observations on the parameter constants of the alloys are :

Manganese .	0	16·9	41·5	77	84·0	90·2	92·7	96·4 at. per cent.
a in Cu-phase	3·607	3·670	3·730	3·742	—	—	—	— A.
γ-Mn { a .	—	—	—	—	3·738	3·763	3·763	3·771 A.
c .	—	—	—	—	3·713	3·629	3·617	3·556 A.
c/a .	—	—	—	—	0·993	0·965	0·961	0·943 A.
β-Mn, a .	—	—	—	—	—	6·304	6·302	6·212 A.
a-Mn, a .	—	—	—	8·906	8·903	8·917	8·904	— A.

The results for the copper and γ-manganese phases are summarized in Fig. 16.

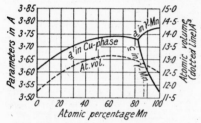

FIG. 16.—Lattice Parameters of the Copper and Manganese Phases.

A. L. Norbury gave for alloys with 2·40, 7·20, 15·37, and 31·08 per cent. of Mn, the sp. gr. 8·796, 8·564, 8·126, and 7·810 for the annealed metal, and for the first two samples after hammering, respectively 8·819 and 8·574. E. Münker observed that alloys with 0, 0·04, 0·19, 0·98, and 1·49 per cent. manganese had the respective sp. gr. 9·008, 8·905, 8·903, 8·860, and 8·820 at 4°. E. A. Lewis found the sp. gr. of the alloys at 15·5° to be :

Mn .	1	5	10	15	20	25	30	40	50 per cent.
Sp. gr. .	8·935	8·757	8·425	8·102	8·284	7·782	7·746	7·324	7·332

The alloys with higher proportions of manganese contained too many air-blebs to justify a determination of the sp. gr. E. Persson's curve for the at. vol. of the alloys is shown in Fig. 16. Z. Nishiyama obtained the following results between 16° and 18·3° for the sp. gr., and the elastic modulus, E kgrms. per sq. c m. :

Mn. .	0	0·5	1	2	5	10	15	25 per cent.
Sp. gr. .	8·9487	8·9084	8·8949	8·8792	8·8375	8·5127	8·3183	8·0072
$E \times 10^{-6}$.	1·204	1·276	1·289	1·281	1·265	1·233	1·214	1·199

The hardness, in kgrms. per sq. mm., was found by S. Wologdine to be :

Mn .	0	1·6	20	40	60	74·75	79·0	80·7	93·0 per cent.
Hardness	50	68·4	121	146	180	193	374	247	241

The curve rises irregularly but gradually with increasing manganese up to about 70 per cent., and it then rises rapidly up to 78 per cent. ; it subsequently falls up to 86·0 per cent. and thereafter rises again. S. F. Schemtschuschny and W. Petraschewitsch found that the hardness reaches a maximum with between 25 and 35 at. per cent. of copper. Observations were also made by R. Sahmen, L. Guillet, N. S. Kurnakoff and S. F. Schemtschuschny, H. Behrens, and A. Valenciennes. According to S. Wologdine, alloys with up to 40 per cent. manganese may be worked cold or hot ; E. F. Sperry said alloys with up to 30 per cent. manganese can be worked cold or hot ; but E. A. Lewis stated that they can be worked only when hot. L. Guillet found that alloys with up to 40 per cent. of manganese can be rolled. L. Weiller added that alloys with 8 per cent. of manganese can be rolled, but with 12 to 15 per cent. the alloys are brittle. C. Heusler, A. Valenciennes, and J. F. Allen made observations on this subject. Z. Nishiyama's results for the elastic constants are indicated above. According to C. Heusler the tensile strength of the alloys varies from 26 to 41 kgrms. per sq. mm. ; the elastic limit is 15 to 20 kgrms. per sq. mm. ; and the elongation 19 to 29 per cent. E. A. Lewis added that the tensile strength of copper can be increased 26 per cent. by the addition of manganese, whilst the elongation gradually approaches zero as the proportion of manganese is increased to 32 per cent. Observations were also made by E. F. Sperry, A. K. Huntington, E. F. Law, F. W. Webb, A. Schulz, W. B. Parker, and E. le Blant. According to M. Rudeloff, the effect of temp. on an alloy with 5 to 6 per cent. of manganese is not very marked, being :

	15°	100°	200°	300°	400°	
Tensile strength .	35·9	35·6	35·7	33·5	25·9	kgrms. per sq. mm.
Elongation . .	40·0	32·4	36·5	37·1	23·7	per cent.
Contraction .	72·7	60·2	52·4	51·9	—	per cent.

A. Valenciennes found that alloys with 3 to 20 per cent. of manganese are as sonorous as bronze. A. Eucken and K. Dittrich discussed the thermal conductivity. A. W. Smith gave for the thermal conductivity k cals. per second per cm. cube at 59°, and the electrical conductivity in mhos $\times 10^{-4}$ at 23° :

Cu .	100	90	80	70	60	40	20 per cent.
Thermal .	0·918	0·065	0·041	0·032	0·031	0·027	0·025
Electrical .	50·8	2·76	1·59	1·11	0·916	0·820	0·687

K. Dittrich studied the Wiedemann and Franz's conductivity law—**3.** 21, 5—for copper-manganese alloys. K. Feussner and S. Lindeck found that the electrical conductivity curve has a flat minimum with about 33 at. per cent. of manganese. The electrical resistance, R microhms per cm. cube, and the temp. coeff. of the alloys are :

Mn	3·5	4·4	6·25	7·8	12·3	24·95	30·0 per cent.
R	14·99	17·56	23·61	28·43	43·0	81·2	107·3
a	$0·0_3222$	$0·0_3185$	$0·0_475$	$0·0_426$	—	$0·0_55$	$0·0_518$

The resistance of alloys with 3·5 to 6·25 per cent. Mn increases linearly with temp. and with a higher proportion of manganese attains a maximum at 40° to 60°. The conductivity of an alloy with 22 per cent. of manganese was found by E. F. Sperry to be 3·89 per cent. of that of hard-drawn copper. S. Kimuri and K. Sakamaki, and S. F. Schemtschuschny and co-workers discussed the electrical resistance of the alloys. S. F. Schemtschuschny and W. Petraschewitsch represented the sp. resistance, R ohms, of alloys with :

Copper .	100	95·5	79·5	57·5	33·5	10·1	3 at. per cent.
$R \times 10^6$ { 25° .	1·81	15·56	59·15	118·0	135·8	104·1	92
100° .	2·32	15·80	59·15	118·2	139·1	118·1	114·5

W. Guertler gave for the ratio of the resistance at $\theta°$ to that at 0° the results indicated in Fig. 17. For a 12·3 per cent. alloy, the temp. coeff. is positive above and negative below 40°. G. Tammann and E. Vaders observed no sharp limiting concentration for the action of reagents on the copper-manganese alloys, but the potential showed a sudden change at the concentration 0·5 mol Cu, and the decomposition potential of the element $Cu \mid MnCl_2 \mid Mn_nCu_{1-n}$ is independent of the composition of the alloy when $n < 5$; with $n > 5$ it decreases with decreasing amount of copper to zero. M. G. Corson made alloys resistant to inorganic acids by alloying copper with 35 to 55 per cent. manganese. O. Bauer and H. Arndt found an alloy of 66·7 per cent. of copper is not attacked by sulphur at 400° even after 5 hrs., whereas copper alone loses 2 grms. per sq. dm. in the same time. The thermoelectric force was found by K. Feussner and S. Lindeck to have a small negative value against copper, and with alloys

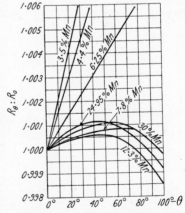

FIG. 17.—The Electrical Resistance at Different Temperatures.

with 12·3, 24·95, and 30·0 per cent. manganese to be respectively −1·4, −2·4, and −3·2 microvolts per degree. R. Sahmen observed that none of the alloys is magnetizable at ordinary temp. S. Kimura and Z. Isawa, and A. L. Norbury discussed the thermoelectric properties of solid soln. of copper and manganese.

K. Ihde found that the magnetic susceptibilities, χ, of a copper alloy with 30 per cent. manganese, and of powdered manganese with a field strength of H gauss, are :

H . . .	1000	2000	3000	4000	5000	5500
$\chi \times 10^{-6}$ { Mn .	101·5	90·6	84·0	79·1	74·6	73·6
{ Mn–Cu .	325	370	359	349	339	336

G. Eger studied the magnetic properties of the alloys, and H. Endo found the susceptibility of the alloys gave a maximum with 70 to 80 per cent. of copper corresponding with the minimum on the f.p. curve.

Copper .	0	20	50	60	70	80	90	100 per cent.
$\chi \times 10^{-6}$.	10·60	13·45	18·96	24·96	34·38	38·18	21·34	0·084

According to A. Valenciennes, an alloy with 15 per cent. of manganese remains unchanged when exposed to air, while E. A. Lewis found that alloys with 70 to 80 per cent. of manganese disintegrate to powder in a few weeks, but not so with the 90 per cent. alloys. According to S. F. Schemtschuschny and co-workers, the peculiar smell emitted by 78 to 100 per cent. manganese, observed by S. Wologdine, occurs only when traces of carbide are present in the metal. G. Tammann and H. Bredemeier discussed the oxide colour films. A. Carnot found that sea-water does not attack alloys with small proportions of manganese. S. Wologdine found that iodine scarcely affects the $CuMn_4$-alloy, but it blackens all the other alloys. A. R. von Schrötter observed that an 18 per cent. alloy is easily dissolved by nitric acid, while it is but little attacked by boiling sulphuric acid, diluted with twice its vol. of water, by hydrochloric acid, or by mercury. R. Sahmen said that alloys with 0 to 35 per cent. manganese are attacked by nitric acid, but not by dil. sulphuric acid. E. Griffiths and F. H. Schofield studied the thermal and electrical conductivities of some alloys; and A. W. Smith, the electrical conductivity. S. F. Schemtschuschny and co-workers found that the alloys are attacked by a mixture of ferric chloride and hydrochloric acid more easily the higher the proportion of contained manganese. C. S. Smith studied the **copper-manganese-silicon alloys.**

E. Pannain[2] found that **silver-manganese alloys** are formed with difficulty, but if a third metal—*e.g.* copper—is present, alloys are more easily formed. The alloys were also prepared by P. Siebe. According to G. Hindrichs, silver and manganese form immiscible liquids with between 30 and 88 per cent. manganese. No solid

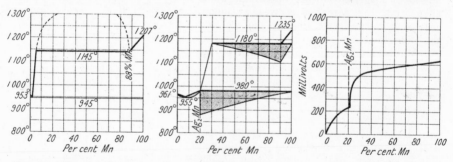

FIG. 18.—Freezing-Point Curves of the System : Mn–Ag.

FIG. 19.—Freezing-Point Curve of the System : Mn–Ag.

FIG. 20.—Electromotive Force of Mn–Ag-Alloys.

soln. are formed. On the other hand, G. Arrivant found evidence of the existence of **silver hemimanganeside,** $MnAg_2$, and said that this compound forms a continuous series of mixed crystals with silver (Fig. 18), and its limit of miscibility, in the liquid state, with manganese is about 30 per cent. Mn. This is borne out by the microstructure, and by the e.m.f. of such mixtures against a silver electrode.

If the alloys rich in manganese be treated with dil. acids, and the residue be rubbed up with 10 per cent. hydrochloric acid, the hemimanganeside is formed of sp. gr. 8·81 at 0°. When pounded in an agate mortar, it splits into plates. It is stable in air, and reacts with acids like silver. Alloys with up to 20 per cent. of manganese appear homogeneous under the microscope ; and after etching with nitric acid appear corroded like silver ; alloys with a higher proportion of manganese when treated similarly show dendritic crystallization. Alloys with more than 35 per cent. of silver separate into two layers. Alloys with over 90 per cent. of manganese are very brittle. W. Schmidt, and M. Hansen and G. Sachs measured the electrical conductivity of alloys of silver and manganese. The e.m.f. of a silver electrode, depolarized by manganese dioxide, in contact with 10 per cent. of a soln. of manganese sulphate is :

Mn	.	0	2·5	6·0	20·15	29	40	60	80	100 per cent.
Millivolts		16	90	150	250	540	490	610	635	630

There is a drop in the conductivity of alloys with between 23 and 20 per cent. of manganese corresponding with the formation of the hemimanganeside (Fig. 20), and again from 20 to 0 per cent. of manganese as a solid soln. is formed. P. Siebe studied the action of chemical reagents on these alloys. F. Saeftel and G. Sachs studied some alloys rich in silver. G. Tammann and E. Vaders observed a limit for the action of chemical reagents on silver-manganese alloys when the mol. proportion of silver is 0·75. L. Jordan and co-workers studied the tarnish resistance of these alloys. M. Keinert studied the **copper-silver-manganese alloys.**

The **gold-manganese alloys** were first investigated by W. C. Roberts-Austen,[3] and F. Osmond. N. Parravano examined the thermal diagram and reported that manganese dissolves in the solid state in gold in proportions up to 10·5 per cent., and gold in manganese up to 25 per cent. A sharp maximum occurs at **gold manganeside,** AuMn, this compound being capable of dissolving either gold or manganese in the solid state. A liquid miscibility gap occurs between 50 per cent. and 57·5 per cent. of manganese, and certain complex transformations, the nature of which has not been determined, take place in the solid state. Manganese thus differs markedly in behaviour from iron, cobalt, and nickel, and gold from its homologue, copper. The hardness curve exhibits a minimum in exact correspondence with the maximum of the fusion curve. L. Hahn and S. Kyropoulos obtained rather different results. They observed a temp. interval during the

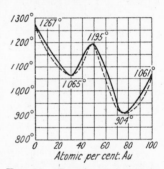

FIG. 21.—Freezing-Point Curve of the System : Au–Mn.

freezing of even the pure metals amounting to 5° for gold and 17° for manganese. The f.p. curve of the series has a maximum at 50 at. per cent., with minima at 33 and 75 at. per cent. of gold respectively (Fig. 21). The crystals exhibit cores, but form only a single solid soln. They do not become homogeneous on alloying for five hours at 700° or one hour at 1000°. The hardness falls with the addition of gold, reaching a minimum at the first minimum f.p. It then increases slightly up to the maximum on the f.p. curve and then falls regularly. Boiling the alloys with water leads to the formation of manganese dioxide. The same result occurs with 20 per cent. hydrochloric acid, so that chlorine is liberated and gold passes into soln., but is reprecipitated as long as manganese remains. G. Tammann and E. Vaders observed that in the action of chemical reagents there is a sharp limit with 0·50 mol of Au. J. O. Linde studied the electrical resistance of the alloys.

H. N. Warren [4] reported a **calcium-manganese alloy** to be formed by heating manganese oxide with calcium carbide, but H. Moissan obtained manganese tritacarbide in the electric furnace from manganese oxide and calcium carbide. According to A. Terreil,[5] a **magnesium-manganese alloy** is formed when magnesium is heated with anhydrous manganese chloride. It is not so hard as the manganese-aluminium alloy. W. Schmidt found that manganese alloys with magnesium, up to about 4 per cent. of manganese forming intermetallic compounds. H. E. Bakken and V. Wood reported that the alloys are solid soln. when at least 3·20 per cent. of manganese is present; J. A. Gaun found that while some manganese is present as solid soln., most of it is in the elementary state as small bluish-grey particles scattered through the crystals of magnesium; and G. W. Pearson showed that the solid soln. extend beyond 2·7 per cent. of manganese, and, in the higher ranges, that metal may show up as angular masses, and in the still higher ranges (35 to 100 per cent. manganese) it appears as irregular masses in a background of magnesium. E. Schmid and G. Siebel found that the solubility curve drops from 3·4 per cent. with the eutectic at 645° to zero at 200°. The lattice constants of alloys with 2·5 per cent. of manganese were measured.

E. A. Lewis prepared some **zinc-manganese alloys**. According to P. Siebe, alloys of zinc and manganese can be prepared containing only up to 50 per cent. of zinc (Fig. 22). Those containing 0 to 11 per cent. of manganese show an arrest at 416°, the eutectic point. The eutectic compound contains a very small, undetermined quantity of manganese, which lowers the m.p. of zinc 3°. The mixed

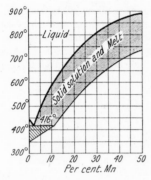

FIG. 22.—Freezing-Point Curve in the System : Mn–Zn.

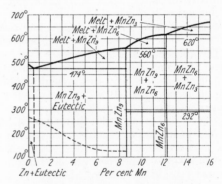

FIG. 23.—Portion of Equilibrium Diagram of the System : Mn–Zn.

crystal constituent of the eutectic contains 11 per cent. of manganese, and a series of mixed crystals is formed containing up to 50 per cent. of manganese. The alloys are brittle and increase in hardness as the manganese content increases. C. L. Ackermann gave 414° with 0·4 to 0·5 per cent. manganese for the eutectic. N. Parravano and U. Perret reported that the thermal diagram shows two compounds, **manganese trizincide**, $MnZn_3$, and *manganese heptazincide*, $MnZn_7$. He added that the alloys with 1 to 30 per cent. Mn are hard and brittle; and those with 5 to 20 per cent. manganese are porous. The work of C. L. Ackermann on this subject is summarized in Fig. 22; and observations were also made by P. Gieren. W. N. Pierce said that the eutectic $MnZn_7 + Zn$ occurs with 0·9 per cent. manganese. The heptazincide of N. Parravano and U. Perret is considered to be **manganese hexazincide**, $MnZn_6$, and the temp. zone of its existence is shown in Fig. 23; it melts at 620°. There is also formed **manganese enneazincide**, $MnZn_9$, melting at 560°. These two compounds are totally immiscible with each other in the solid state, but below about 290° alloys containing both compounds undergo some sort of transformation, possibly associated with a reaction between the two compounds or with their decomposition into $MnZn_3$ and zinc. Manganese increases the hardness of zinc considerably, the alloy with 5 per cent. Mn having a Brinell number of 122; at the same time the tensile strength is appreciably increased, whereas the compression strength is much reduced. N. Parravano and co-workers observed that with alloys with up to 23·3 per cent. Mn there are three phases : (i) a solid soln. of manganese in zinc, the η-phase, with a hexagonal lattice similar to that of zinc and having up to 0·98 per cent. Mn ; (ii) an ε-phase with a hexagonal lattice different from that of zinc, and corresponding with MnZn₇— 16 atoms per unit lattice ; and (iii) a γ-phase having a body-centred lattice corresponding with MnZn₃—48 atoms per unit lattice. C. L. Ackermann found Brinell's hardness of alloys with 0, 0·50, 1·0, 2·2, and 5·0 per cent. of manganese to be, respectively, 53·5, 74·5, 88, 90·5, and 121. The results for the impact, with a load of 4900 kgrms., falling from a height of 40 cms., such that the specific impact energy is 111 cms. per kgrm. per c.c., are shown in Fig. 24 ; the compression results are shown by the dotted lines in Fig. 24. Small quantities of manganese improve the resistance of zinc to repeated impacts, but more than 3 per cent. Mn has the reverse

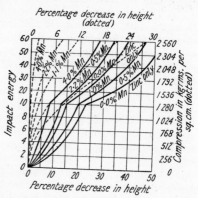

FIG. 24.—Compression and Impact Tests of the Zinc-Manganese Alloys.

effect. Alloys with up to 8·5 per cent. Mn have a negative potential against zinc in *N*-zinc sulphate soln. ; those containing the compound MnZn₉ have a small positive potential and those containing MnZn₆ a much smaller positive potential under the same conditions, whereas the potential of MnZn₉ itself is equal to that of pure zinc. The electrode potentials, E volts at 20°, were :

Mn	.	0·4	1·0	6·35	8·50	8·60	10·70	12·50	13·70	16·70
E	.	−5	−6	−6	0	+6	+6	+6	+2	+2

O. Heusler studied the ternary system, the **copper-zinc-manganese alloys,** with less than 50 per cent. manganese. On reference to the copper-zinc binary equilibrium diagram, there are phases with the α-, β-, γ-, δ-, ε-, and η-solid soln. The ranges of composition of the phases are indicated in Fig. 25. O. Heusler also studied the effect of annealing at 340° ; and some isothermal melting-points are

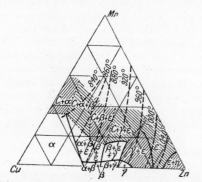

FIG. 25.—Phases in the Ternary System : Cu–Zn–Mn.

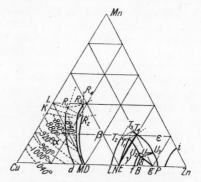

FIG. 26.—The Ternary System : Cu–Zn–Mn.

represented by the broken lines. O. Heusler observed that feebly diamagnetic brass becomes ferromagnetic when it is alloyed with manganese. The strongest ferromagnetism was exhibited by the alloy with 22 per cent. Cu, 22 per cent. Mn, and 56 per cent. Zn. The zone $CudR_1LCu$, Fig. 26, includes ternary α-solid soln. rich in copper ; dMR_3R_1d, α- and β-solid soln. ; R_3MeT_2, ternary β-solid soln. ;

$efU_2T_1T_2e$, ternary γ-solid soln., and mixtures with β-solid soln.; fPU_3U_2F, ternary δ-solid soln. and mixtures with γ- and ϵ-solid soln.; and T_3U_3PZni, ternary ϵ- and η-solid soln. with their mixtures. The α- and β-solid soln. were studied by W. Rosenhain and F. C. A. H. Lantsberry, and O. Heusler.

G. Tammann and J. Hinnüber [6] found the solubility of manganese in mercury to be 2.5×10^{-4} per cent. N. M. Irvin and A. S. Russell gave 0·001 per 100 grms. of mercury. According to R. Böttger, when sodium amalgam is placed in a conc. soln. of manganese sulphate, hydrogen is evolved, and manganous oxide is formed, but under a conc. soln. of manganous chloride some **manganese amalgam** is formed. C. F. Schönbein, W. B. Giles, J. Schumann, and H. Moissan also obtained the amalgam in an analogous manner. W. Ramsay, J. Schumann, H. Moissan, E. Kuh, A. N. Campbell, and O. Prelinger also prepared the amalgam by the electrolysis of soln. of manganous chloride with a mercury cathode. A. Guntz squeezed the product between leather and then between paper to get rid of the excess of mercury. The amalgam is silvery-white and more or less viscid. It can be obtained in needle-like crystals. O. Prelinger said that the excess of mercury is squeezed from the amalgam in Swedish leather, between two pieces of hard wood, under a press. of 2000 kgrms. per sq. cm.; the peripheral portion of the pressed cake is broken off and the central portion broken up and again compressed. The operation is repeated until pieces punched from the centres of successive discs have the same composition. The residue has the composition of *manganese hemipentamercuride*, Mn_2Hg_5, and a sp. gr. 12·823. This product has a slate-grey colour, and assumes a metallic lustre when rubbed or cut. At ordinary temp. it oxidizes very slowly in the air, metallic mercury being eliminated. At 100° to 110° it decomposes slowly into its elements. It decomposes water and acids at the ordinary temp. Manganese amalgam is electro-positive to manganese, so that heat is probably absorbed in its formation. A solution of the compound in mercury is not attacked by dry air, but is quickly oxidized by moist air to manganic oxide, Mn_2O_3, which forms a fine dust on the surface of the liquid. E. Kuh found that the ordinary amalgam is stable when confined in a vacuum desiccator over calcium chloride; but in air it is the more stable the smaller the excess of mercury it contains. W. B. Giles added that the amalgam acquires a brown skin when exposed to air, forming, said J. Schumann, powdered manganese oxide and mercury. W. Ramsay found the mol. wt. of manganese to be 112·4 when calculated from the lowering of the vap. press. of mercury by manganese. C. F. Schönbein found that when the amalgam is shaken with air and acidulated water, some hydrogen dioxide is formed. The amalgam is slowly decomposed by water, and, according to W. Ramsay, it is decomposed by alcohol. According to R. Böttger, water or dil. acids may form some hydrogen. O. Prelinger found that when heated in hydrogen, mercury is vaporized, and manganese powder remains; with nitrogen, manganese nitride is formed with incandescence. According to A. S. Russell and co-workers, the order zinc, cadmium, manganese, thallium, tin, lead, copper, chromium, iron, bismuth, cobalt, and nickel is the order of removal of these metals from their amalgams by an oxidizing agent; and their positions in the potential series are Cr, Mn, Fe, Co, Ni.

C. and A. Tissier [7] reported that manganese oxide is not reduced in a dry way by aluminium, but something must have gone wrong, for reduction readily occurs in the alumino-thermite process. L. Guillet prepared the **aluminium-manganese alloys** by this process, and C. Combes, by heating aluminium with manganese sulphide or chloride. A. J. Bradley and P. Jones observed, by means of the X-radiograms, seven different phases in the Mn-Al alloys: (i) $Al+Al_7Mn$; (ii) Al_7Mn and Al_3Mn; (iii) Al_3Mn and a solid soln. extending over 50 to over 59 per cent. Mn; (iv) a phase with this solid soln. and a phase with the β-form of manganese; (v) a phase with the β-form of manganese, alone, and (vi) with the β- and α-forms; and (vii) a phase with α-manganese. S. Daniels studied alloys with up to 9·6 per cent. of manganese. He observed that the tensile strength was raised from 5·25 tons per sq.

in. for the alloy containing no manganese to 7·6 tons per sq. in. with 1·02 per cent·
Mn, but the elongation (on 2 ins.) fell rapidly from 38·5 per cent. to 22·6 per cent·
and then to 2·6 per cent. with no manganese, 1·02 per cent., and 2·88 per cent. Mn
respectively. The Brinell hardness numbers gradually increased from 20 to 48
with increasing manganese content. E. Ludwik found that Brinell's hardness of
some binary aluminium alloys could be represented by $H=a+b \log P_v$, where a
is a constant dependent on the nature of the other component ; b is a constant ;
P_v the vol. per cent. of the compound of the added metal ; and H is the depth the
ball sinks expressed in μ. K. Röth found that for aluminium-manganese alloys,
when the compound Al_3Mn is present, $H=568-200 \log P_v$, and

Mn	.	0·5	0·8	1·6	2·4	4·4	7·6	7·9	10·0 per cent.
P_v	.	0·4	0·7	1·5	2·2	4·1	7·2	7·8	10·0
H .	.	648	605	528	500	460	396	400	384μ

S. Daniels found that the presence of manganese increased the shrinkage and
promoted porosity when present in appreciable quantity. The alloy containing
4·6 per cent. of manganese machined like cast-iron, probably owing to the presence of
the hard and brittle compound $MnAl_2$. The alloys were readily attacked by
distilled water during 30 days' immersion, but showed only a slight corrosion after
100 hrs. in salt spray. Heat treatment at 580° for 96 hrs., followed by quenching
in water and ageing at 149° for 2 hrs., did not materially alter either the physical
or mechanical properties or the corrodibility.

D. J. McAdam observed that the simultaneous action of corrosion and fatigue—
corrosion-fatigue—may cause failure at stresses far below the ordinary endurance
limit—*vide* the corrosion of iron. With an aluminium-manganese alloy containing
97·98 per cent. of aluminium and 1·22 per cent. of manganese, the static mechanical
tests were :

	Tensile strength (lbs. per sq. in.)	Elastic limit (lbs. per sq. in.)	Proportional limit (lbs. per sq. in.)	Elongated (per cent. in 2 ins.)	Reduction of area (per cent.)
Hard . .	29,600	13,300	11,500	12·3	46·3
Half-annealed	23,800	13,000	9,300	19·7	57·3
Annealed .	16,700	2,200	1,900	64·2	70·3

The corrosion-fatigue graphs represent the stresses and the logarithms of the
number of cycles for specimens tested in air (fatigue curve), in a corroding fresh
carbonate water, and in a corroding river salt-water having about one-third the

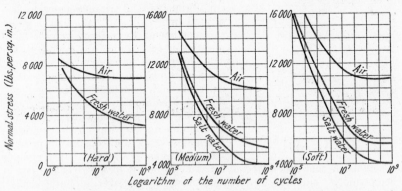

Figs. 27, 28, and 29.—The Fatigue and Corrosion-Fatigue of Manganese-Aluminium
Alloys.

saline contents of sea-water, and with cycles of 1450 revs. per minute. The results
shown in Figs. 27, 28, and 29 refer to the 1·22 per cent. manganese alloy in the
three states just indicated—namely, hard, medium, and soft. C. S. Taylor and
J. D. Edwards studied the thermoelectric force of the alloys.

S. Daniels also studied the metallography or microstructure ; and Z. Nishiyama, and A. Westgren and W. Ekman, the X-radiograms of these alloys. G. Hindrichs studied the f.p. of the Al–Mn-system, Fig. 30, and found that alloys containing between 57 and 86 per cent. of aluminium separate into two liquid layers ; and that there are indications of the formation of the two compounds $MnAl_3$, and Mn_3Al. T. Ishiwara's results are summarized in Fig. 31, and the curve corresponds in the main with that of G. Hindrichs, but the results are interpreted differently in some respects. There is a maximum B in the f.p. curve $A'JCBM'$ corresponding with the formation of the aluminium tritamanganeside, Al_3Mn. At the horizontal line

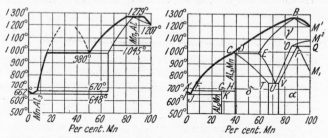

FIGS. 30 and 31.—Freezing-Point Curve of the System : Mn–Al.

FGH there is a reaction between the liquid F and the compound Al_3Mn resulting in the formation of **aluminium pentitamanganeside,** Al_5Mn. At the temp. corresponding with OPQ there is a peritectoid reaction in the solid alloy resulting in the formation of a solid soln., Pa, from the solid soln. $O\gamma$ and the solid Q or β-Mn ; and at the temp. TV there is an eutectoid reaction between solid soln. $U\gamma$ and $T\delta$ resulting in the formation of the solid soln. Va. Manganese exists in three allotropic forms a, β, and γ. E. H. Dix and W. D. Keith studied the aluminium end of the system. Observations were also made by H. Schirmeister, and E. Rassow. L. Guillet said that the alloys with a high proportion of manganese are very stable in air, but those with $Al : Mn = 1 : 2$ and $1 : 5$ easily disintegrate, and contain *aluminium tritadimanganeside,* Mn_2Al_3. He also said that there are probably **aluminium tetritamanganeside,** Al_4Mn, and **aluminium tritamanganeside,** Al_3Mn. The conditions of equilibrium of the tritamanganeside are indicated in Fig. 31. F. R. Michel prepared this compound by melting ten parts of a mixture of manganous chloride and sodium chloride with 5 parts of aluminium and 20 parts of a mixture of sodium and potassium chlorides, and then melting the regulus with 8 parts of aluminium under a flux of the alkali chloride, and removing the excess of aluminium by very dil. hydrochloric acid.

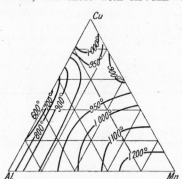

FIG. 32.—Melting-Points of Ternary Mixtures : Mn–Al–Cu.

Acicular crystals and quadratic prisms remain. The sp. gr. is 3·402. The compound is not soluble in cold, dil. or conc. nitric acid, but it dissolves in the hot acid. The compound is soluble in hydrochloric acid, and in dil. sulphuric acid ; but with hot, conc. sulphuric acid some sulphur separates out. The compound decomposes water at 100° ; with boiling, conc., aq. ammonia, hydrogen is evolved ; and with dil. soda-lye the aluminium is dissolved, and oxidized manganese remains. W. Haas said that alloys of aluminium with manganese—say 2 per cent.—resist corrosion by sea-water better than the common aluminium alloys. D. J. McAdam studied this subject. O. Brunck reported Mn_2Al_7—possibly $MnAl_3$—to be formed by melting a mixture of manganese with six times its weight of aluminium under a layer of sodium chloride, and treating the crystalline regulus with 2 per cent. hydrochloric acid. The tin-white crystals are soluble in conc. hydrochloric acid. The conditions of equilibrium of **aluminium trimanganeside,** $AlMn_3$, are indicated in Fig. 31. A. Terreil obtained it by reducing manganous chloride with aluminium. It scratches glass, and the fracture recalls that of amalgamated zinc. W. Krings and W. Ostmann could not confirm the existence of aluminium tritamanganeside, but they obtained the tetritamanganeside. In the ternary system, Al–Mn–Cu, Fig. 32, there is a ternary eutectic with 29·6 per cent. of copper, 3 per cent. of manganese, and 67·4 per cent. of aluminium, at 536°. There is an area of ternary mixed crystals and a polyphase area, but no evidence of a ternary compound. If less than 45 per cent. of copper is present, two liquid layers are formed. S. F. Herman and F. T. Sisco, R. L. Templin and D. A. Paul, and E. T. Richards studied the elastic properties of the alloys.

About 1901, F. Heusler accidentally discovered that the turnings of a manganese alloy were magnetic ; and F. Heusler and co-workers observed that a copper-manganese alloy itself is non-magnetic, but when associated with a third element—zinc, tin, arsenic, antimony, bismuth, or boron—the alloy becomes more or less magnetic, and in the case of aluminium a good ferromagnetic alloy is produced, for it is strongly attracted by the poles of a magnet and it is capable of retaining permanent magnetism. Some binary compounds—e.g. manganese boride, arsenide, antimonide, and bismuthide (q.v.)—were also found to be magnetic to a less degree. The more important ternary alloys are those in which aluminium is the third component, and these are usually understood by the term **Heusler's alloys.** The best results are obtained with alloys containing approximately atomic proportions of these elements, namely, 62·5 per cent. Cu, 25 per cent. Mn, and 12·5 per cent. Al—Fig. 33. As the proportion of copper is reduced, the magnetic quality improves, but if less than 60 per cent. of copper be present, the alloy is too hard and brittle to be worked on a lathe. H. H. Potter studied the effect of magnetization on the electrical resistance, and also the magneto-caloric effect of these alloys.

L. Harang found that the ternary alloys of aluminium, manganese, and copper show three cubic lattices : (i) a face-centred one of varying size ; (ii) a body-centred one, with $a=2·975$ A.·, of man-ganese and aluminium ; and (iii) a simple cubic lattice, with $a=8·71$ A., of alu-minium and copper. E. Persson also discussed this subject. J. F. T. Young observed a face-centred cubic lattice with $a=3·70$ A., and a body-centred lattice with $a=2·98$ A. This agrees with the assumption that the alloys are solid soln. of a manganese-aluminium alloy in copper. The subject was studied by H. O. Dorum. H. H. Potter found that the alloy crystallizes as a body-centred lattice with $a=2·95$ A. ; that the alu-minium atoms are distributed on a face-centred cube with $a=5·9$ A. The direc-tional magnetic properties are the same

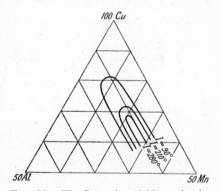

FIG. 33.—The Intensity of Magnetization of some Cu–Mn–Al Alloys.

as those of nickel, which has a face-centred cubic lattice. It is probable that the manganese atoms lie on a face-centred cubic lattice. E. Persson's X-radio-grams of the Cu–Mn–Al alloys show that the magnetism is definitely associated with the crystalline structure denoted by the β-phase. This consists of a body-centred cubic lattice, with the Al atoms so distributed as to form a face-centred cubic superstructure. This crystalline form is magnetizable only when the Mn content exceeds a certain minimum value corresponding with $(Cu,Mn)_3Al$. The lattice parameter of the β-phase in quenched alloys increases with increasing manganese content. The highest manganese content in the β-phase corresponds with maximum magnetizability. In tempered alloys the β-phase is resolved into two crystalline forms of similar structure—one is a β-Cu-Al phase free from manganese, and the other a β-phase with the maximum manganese concentration corresponding with CuMnAl, and called the β'-phase. The simultaneous occurrence of the two phases is taken to mean that their crystalline forms are different. The β'-phase is considered to be characterized by a twofold superstructure, in which one of its four face-centred lattices is probably composed chiefly of Al-atoms, another chiefly Mn-atoms, and the two remaining ones almost exclusively Cu-atoms. All the alloys with the β'-phase are ferromagnetic, and this agrees with an observation of H. H. Potter to the effect that the ferromagnetism of the Heusler alloys is intimately connected with the orientation of the Mn-atoms in the face-centred structure. When a (Cu,Mn)Al-phase appears with the higher concentrations of aluminium, the alloy is non-magnetic. Unlike A. Kussmann and B. Scharnoff, S. Valentiner and G. Becker infer that the magnetic properties cannot be referred to any definite lattice or phase ingredient.

According to A. A. Knowlton, there is no simple relation between composition and magnetic properties. The alloys showed no sign of recalescence; the critical temp. for one specimen was 0° and for another 200°. The microstructure shows three types of crystals : (1) bright ones, unaffected by the etching fluid (HCl and FeCl$_3$) ; (2) dark ones, deeply etched ; and (3) yellowish ones of the nature of a matrix. Crystals of the first type were evidently the magnetic ones, as no specimen from which these were absent was magnetic, and the value of the intensity of magnetization, I, could be estimated with a fair degree of approximation from the area of these crystals. E. B. Stephenson also examined the microstructure of these alloys. The microstructure varies greatly with the heat treatment. The variations in the electrical conductivity and hardness with the age of the alloys were studied by F. Heusler and E. Dönnges. G. A. Shakespear examined the expansion effect between 250° and 300°. A. Rosenheim and co-workers, and E. Morlet studied the mechanical properties of the alloys. E. Morlet studied the effect of manganese on the hardness of the copper-aluminium alloys ; and G. Masing, the age-hardening of the alloys. P. W. Bridgman found for the alloy *therlo*—Cu, 85 ; Mn, 13 ; Al, 2—

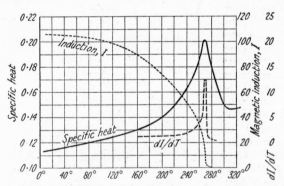

the cubic compressibility 0.7×10^{-6}; the reciprocal of Young's modulus, 0.69×10^{-6}; and Poisson's ratio, 0.33.

E. Dippel found the sp. ht. of an alloy slowly cooled was 0.10589, and that of an alloy heated to 600° and rapidly chilled, 0.10709. W. Sucksmith and H. H. Potter found that the sp. ht. curve, Fig. 34, changes rapidly near the critical temp., about 280°, showing that heat is rapidly absorbed as the substance

Fig. 34.—The Effect of Temperature on the Specific Heat, Magnetic Induction, and the Rate of Change of the Magnetic Induction with Temperature.

changes from a ferro-magnetic to a paramagnetic state. J. R. Ashworth studied the relations between the thermal and magnetic constants.

S. Fabiani found for the alloy Cu : Mn : Al=$58.9 : 26.5 : 14.6$, the absorption coeff. k, and the index of refraction μ, for light of wave-length λ :

λ	.	.	4970	5440	5893	6380	7070
k	.	.	2.92	3.18	3.42	3.65	3.93
μ	.	.	1.90	2.08	2.24	2.39	2.28

J. C. McLennan and co-workers gave 725 for the resistance, R microhms, of Heusler's alloy at 27°; 696 at 0°; 311 at −88°; 208 at −268·8°; and 203 at −271°. P. W. Bridgman observed that the resistance of the alloy *therlo*—Cu, 85; Mn, 13; Al, 2—taking unity at 0°, is 1·00120 at 50°, and 1·00104 at 100°. The press. coeff. at 0 and 12,000 kgrms. press. per sq. cm. are respectively $0·0_52361$ and $0·0_52273$ at 0°; $0·0_52386$ and $0·0_52318$ at 50°; and $0·0_52367$ and $0·0_52320$ at 100°. The resistance passes through a maximum between 0° and 75°. When under tension, the resistance changes in accord with the tension coeff., $−0·0_673$. The magnetic induction curve, I, and the curve showing the rate of change of the magnetic induction with temp., $dI|dT$, are also shown in Fig. 34. The results show that the magnetic and thermal phenomena are intimately connected, and that the magnetic change is associated with a heat of transformation. W. Preusser's observations on the intensity of magnetization, I, of the ternary alloys of different composition are shown in Fig. 35. F. Heusler and F. Richarz showed that forged copper alloys with 20 per cent. or less manganese and 6 per cent. aluminium are entirely non-magnetic when quenched from a red-heat in water or mercury, but after heating for several hours in boiling xylene, a maximum degree of magnetizability is reached, and the alloy is found to be free from hysteresis. The same alloys, slowly cooled, show hysteresis, which is the greater the slower the cooling through the critical range. The magnetic susceptibility decreases rapidly with an increase in the proportion of aluminium. The maximum susceptibility is obtained when the alloys have the composition AlM_3, where M represents manganese and copper, which replace one another isomorphously in the compound. In this isomorphous series the magnetic susceptibility increases with increasing manganese, and a maximum should be reached by the compound $AlMn_3$, which is to be examined for its magnetic properties. A. Kussmann and B. Scharnoff traced the anomalies to a change of phase in the neighbourhood of 130°. J. A. Fleming and R. Hadfield found that the curves representing the remanence, B, and the intensity, H, of the magnetic field are similar to those for cast-iron. An alloy with 61·68 Cu, 22·57 Mn, 13·63 Al, and 1·51 Pb gave E. B. Stephenson the results shown in Fig. 35. The saturation intensity is about one-fourth that of iron. According to A. A. Knowlton, the critical range of temp. of magnetic transformation is from 250° to 450° according to the composition. The change from the magnetic state occurs over this range of temp. If the alloy be quenched 50° to 100° above the upper limit, it is almost non-magnetic, but if the temp. be now raised to 120°, maintained there for some hours, and then cooled slowly, the magnetic property reappears. This tempering brings about favourable changes which at ordinary temp. would require a year or more of ageing. A. D. Ross found that quenching from still higher temp. greatly reduces the magnetic hysteresis and the coercive force is about one-sixth that of soft iron. The loss of magnetic susceptibility which results from quenching may be restored by ageing at 120°, but the low coercive force persists, so that the alloys may be used for replacing iron in iron-cored electromagnetic instruments. At the temp. of liquid air the permeability in fields up to 200 C.G.S. units may be 25 per cent. greater than at ordinary temp. An alloy made feebly magnetic by quenching from a high temp. has its magnetism largely restored on cooling to 190°, although the improvement is not maintained on returning to the ordinary temp. According to W. Krings and W. Ostmann, the maximum susceptibility of Heusler's alloys lies at the point of intersection of Cu_3Al and $AlMn_3$. Alloys containing more than 30 per cent. of manganese, which have not been previously investigated, are also magnetic. The increase and decrease of magnetic properties are accompanied by changes of structure. In contradistinction to Heusler's alloys, which attain their maximum magnetic susceptibility after being

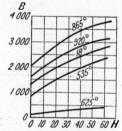

Fig. ·35.—The Magnetic Induction and Intensity of the Magnetic Field.

heated at 144° for a long period, alloys of high manganese content exhibit their maximum magnetic properties after ageing at a high temp., whereas ageing at 144° causes all magnetic effects to vanish. The magnetostriction was studied by L. W. Austin, K. E. Guthe and L. W. Austin, and J. C. McLennan ; K. E. Guthe and L. W. Austin tested samples for the modulus of elasticity ; H. Zahn and H. Schmidt found the coeff. R for the Hall effect is 1300×10^{-5}, and that the coeff. Q for the thermomagnetic effect is -500×10^{-6}.

The magnetic properties of the alloys were also studied by B. V. Hill, A. Gray, H. O. Dorum, etc. B. V. Hill said that the magnetic effect is reversible up to about 375°, but at 500°, irreversible. Many attempts have been made to locate the magnetic unit. J. A. Fleming and R. Hadfield assumed that the magnetic properties of these alloys are due to molecular grouping, and are not characteristic of the elements themselves. F. Heusler, as indicated above, regards the magnetic unit as a complex, $\{Al(Cu,Mn)_3\}_n$. The aluminium and copper in the complex can be replaced isomorphously, or, as A. D. Ross expressed it, solid soln. of Cu_3Al and Mn_3Al may be formed. This leaves it an open question whether the magnetism

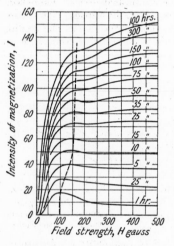

FIG. 36.—The Intensity of Magnetization for Different Field Strengths with Different Times of Ageing.

is to be attributed to the simple molecules, $Al(Cu,Mn)_3$, to complexes, $\{Al(Cu,Mn)_3\}_n$, or to a particular crystal lattice. O. von Auwers and co-workers studied the ageing of the alloys between 100° and 300° required to develop full magnetic power. One effect of this treatment is to raise the magnetic transition temp. along a curve similar to a magnetization curve. When magnetization is plotted against time of ageing for different field strengths, a series of curves is obtained, of which those for lower field strengths show a sharp maximum, with a subsequent fall to a constant magnetization (Fig. 36). In the curves for high field strengths the maximum is flattened out and the corresponding point is followed by a gradual rise in magnetization as the time of ageing increases. The ageing process appears to involve two superimposed molecular changes. At the magnetic transition point, the magnetic particles become dissociated. On quenching from about 600° the alloy contains very few magnetic molecules. By slow cooling or by the ageing process the particles again become associated and the magnetization and coercive force both increase. With low field strengths the coercive force—that is, the intermolecular force— predominates over the magnetizing force, and this explains the maximum in the above-mentioned curves. The highest point of the magnetization curve is reached when the coercive force is a maximum, that is, when the maximum number of magnetic particles are present. The coercive force depends on the temp. of ageing, and reaches a maximum with temp. from 190° to 260°. Above this temp. it falls off rapidly, presumably because the dissociation of the particles has then commenced. L. Harang's X-radiograms did not agree with the assumption that the magnetism is tied up with a complex $(AlM_3)_n$, where M denotes an isomorphous mixture of copper and manganese, for the magnetic character cannot be associated with any single lattice. J. R. Ashworth discussed the temp. coeff. of the resistance and the thermoelectric power ; and also the application of an equation of state— vide iron—to these alloys. W. Sucksmith and H. H. Potter compared P. Weiss's theory of the relation between the sp. ht. and the magnetization of these alloys. E. Persson attributed the magnetism of the Cu–Mn–Al alloys to a β-phase, consisting of $(Cu,Mn)_3Al$, which is formed in the quenched alloys, with aluminium in solid soln. This phase on annealing breaks up into a β-copper-aluminium phase and the Cu_2MnAl phase with a maximum manganese content. The higher the proportion of manganese : $(Cu,Mn)_3Al$, the stronger the magnetization. J. R. Ashworth discussed the relations of the magnetic and thermal constants. H. H. Potter studied the magnetic properties of the **silver-manganese-aluminium alloys.** P. Hidnert and W. T. Sweeney measured the coeff. of expansion of **magnesium-manganese-aluminium alloys ;** and E. Griffiths and F. H. Schofield, the thermal and electrical conductivities of some aluminium bronzes alloyed with manganese. W. Sucksmith and L. F. Bates found the ratio of the gyromagnetic effect to be $K=0·501$—*vide* the magnetism of iron.

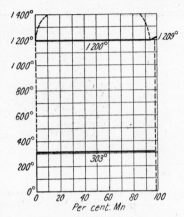

N. Baar [8] found that molten manganese and thallium are almost immiscible at 1200°, but the f.p. of manganese is slightly lowered by the addition of thallium, showing that a **thallium-manganese alloy** is formed—Fig. 37.

C. S. Smith,[9] and E. Voce studied some **copper-silicon-manganese alloys ;** and H. A. Bedworth, the resistance of the alloys to acids. E. Voce represented an approximation to the solid phases in the ternary manganese-silicon-copper alloys by Fig. 38. He measured the mechanical properties of the alloys and the

Fig. 37.—Freezing-Point Curve of the System : Mn–Tl.

results for the annealed alloys are summarized in Figs. 39 to 41, where the curves represent the data in tons per sq. in. He found that copper and silicon-copper resisted conc. sulphuric acid fairly well, but silicon-manganese-copper alloy was moderately attacked. All the metals resisted normal and decinormal sulphuric acid quite well, the rate of attack being from 8 to 13 mgrms. per sq. cm. per month. " Mine water " —*i.e.* normal sulphuric acid containing dissolved sulphates—is three or four times as corrosive as the same acid free from sulphates. Normal and decinormal hydrochloric acid attacked all the alloys to a greater extent than sulphuric acid of the

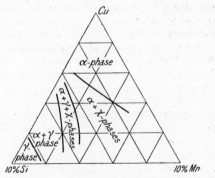

Fig. 38.—Phases in Chill-Cast Si–Mn–Cu Alloys.

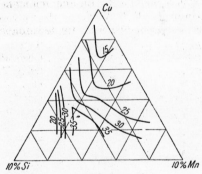

Fig. 39.—Tensile Strength of Annealed Si–Mn–Cu Alloys.

same concentrations, the loss in weight varying from about 30 to 90 mgrms. per sq. cm. per month. As might be expected, normal nitric acid rapidly attacks copper and the silicon alloys. On the other hand, decinormal nitric acid has scarcely more action than sulphuric acid of the same concentration. All the metals showed a fair degree of resistance to normal formic and acetic acids (8–15 mgrms. per sq. cm. per month), and mixing the two acids did not increase the rate of attack. **In** synthetic sea-water there was little to choose between the alloys. When the alloys were exposed to air at 725° to 825°, the scale formed on silicon-copper alloys resembled that ordinarily formed on copper, in so far as it consisted of a black cupric oxide layer superimposed upon a firmly adherent cuprous oxide film. In the case of alloys containing appreciable quantities of silicon the cuprous oxide film is buff in colour and contrasts strongly with the red oxide produced on copper. The

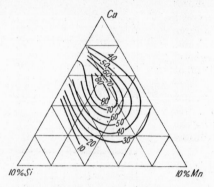

FIG. 40.—Percentage Elongation of Annealed Si–Mn–Cu Alloys.

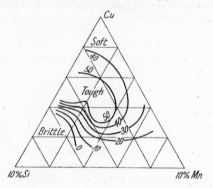

FIG. 41.—Izod Impact Values of Annealed Si–Mn–Cu Alloys.

modification of the colour is probably due to the admixture of silica. The resistance of silicon-copper alloys to high-temperature oxidation in the neighbourhood of 700° increases with the silicon content. At 725° the rate of oxidation of an alloy containing 4·58 per cent. silicon was from one-fourth to one-seventh that of copper. The adherence of the outer layer of black oxide was likewise a function of the silicon content. For the 4·58 per cent. silicon alloy it was very firmly adherent. At temp. above 800° the oxidation rate increases and approximates to that of pure copper. The addition of 1 per cent. manganese to a 4 per cent. silicon alloy did not appreciably alter the rate of oxidation, but rendered the black oxide much less adherent. In 1773, R. Dovey patented the use of "mangonize oar" with alloys of copper, zinc, and tin to produce an alloy "in all respects resembling gold." T. Goldschmidt made **tin and manganese alloys** by the aluminothermite process. According to R. S. Williams, the f.p. curve of these alloys, Fig. 42, has a break at 989°, corresponding with **tin tetramanganeside**, $SnMn_4$, which decomposes below

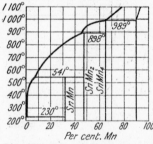

FIG. 42.—Freezing-Point Curve of the System: Mn–Sn.

its m.p., and not only shows considerable magnetic permeability, but is permanently magnetic. It is fairly hard—hardness on Mohs' scale 4 to 5—it is not so brittle as manganese, and takes a good polish. A second break occurs at 898°, corresponding with **tin dimanganeside**, $SnMn_2$, which decomposes below its m.p. It shows a slight magnetic permeability, and it is softer than the tetramanganeside—hardness 3 to 4—and is less readily attacked by dil. acids. A third break occurs at 541°, and probably corresponds with **tin manganeside**, $SnMn$. This compound has but a slight magnetic permeability. It decomposes below its m.p. and is silvery-white. A series of mixed crystals extends from about 95 to 100 at. per cent. of manganese. H. H. Potter studied the magnetic properties of $SnMn_4$ and $SnMn_2$; and P. Martin, Kerr's effect. N. A. Puschin measured the potential curve, E millivolt, of $SnMn_n$ against tin in N-KOH, and found :

n	20	50	55	65	73	75·5	75·6	77	84	86	100
E	−10	−4	16	33	44	755	720	890	865	885	930

With 50 at. per cent. of manganese the alloy makes a jump, probably corresponding with the SnMn-compound, and with 75 at. per cent. manganese there is a sharp break, corresponding with $SnMn_3$. H. Fassbender examined the magnetic properties of the Mn–Sn alloys, and he obtained a maxima on the susceptibility curve corresponding with $SnMn_4$. F. Heusler studied the magnetic properties of the ternary alloys—tin, manganese, and copper. L. Harang found from the X-radiograms of the ternary alloys of tin, manganese, and copper that a high tin content corresponds with a hexagonal lattice, possibly due to a compound of copper and tin. A. D. Ross and R. C. Gray found that the ternary alloys of copper, manganese, and tin with the 14 to 18 per cent. of tin are more magnetic at −190° than at ordinary temp. The quenching of the ternary alloys from 350° to 580° produces complex changes, the coercive force being always diminished, and the effect cannot be reversed by again annealing. The quenched alloys are more improved in magnetic properties by cooling to −190° than those in the normal condition. Baking at 180° to 200° diminishes the susceptibility and increases the coercive force. F. Heusler found that in these alloys the maximum of magnetic properties is found, in accordance with the general rule, in the alloy in which the sum of the manganese and copper atoms is three times the number of tin atoms. In the aluminium series the maximum is reached at $(AlMnCu_2)_n$. The ferromagnetic quality falls off much more rapidly from the maximum in the tin series than in the aluminium series.

R. S. Williams prepared **lead and manganese alloys** by melting the two elements at about 1500°; and A. Stavenhagen and E. Schuchard, by reducing a mixture of the oxides with aluminium. J. F. Allen also prepared these alloys. R. S. Williams said that fused manganese dissolves 10 per cent. of lead and its m.p. is at the same time lowered from 1228° to 1198°. At the same temp. lead dissolves about 12 per cent. of manganese, but the manganese separates out completely as the temp. falls to the m.p. of lead. The equilibrium diagram is shown in Fig. 43. This subject was also studied by K. Bornemann. The alloys are not magnetizable.

G. Arrivant [10] prepared **molybdenum-manganese alloys** containing 12·25 to 29·64 per cent. Mn by fusing a mixture of the metallic powders at 1500° in a current of hydrogen, and also by reducing a mixture of the oxides by means of aluminium. The alloys are hard and brittle, and are readily soluble in dil. or conc. mineral acids.

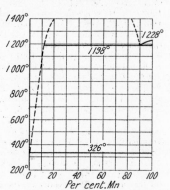

FIG. 43.—Freezing-Point Curve of the System : Mn–Pb.

These alloys are said to consist of free manganese associated with **molybdenum hexamanganeside**, Mn_6Mo, which can be separated by means of dil. acetic acid, or ammonium acetate, in dil. alcoholic soln., in which the compound is insoluble. It forms plates of sp. gr. 7·28 at 0°. In a similar manner **molybdenum tetramanganeside**, Mn_4Mo, is produced as a granular powder of sp. gr. 7·62. The compounds are attacked by chlorine, or strong mineral acids at ordinary temp.; by water at 250°; and by alkali carbonates, nitrates, or hydrosulphates at a red-heat. Alloys richer in manganese are obtained by the alumino-thermite process. They are hard, brittle, silver-white, non-magnetic, and readily soluble in hot, conc. nitric or sulphuric acid, or fused alkali hydrosulphate. The alloys consist of manganese associated with one of the three compounds Mn_2Mo, $MnMo_2$, or $MnMo$. When the alloy with 35·11 to 43·94 per cent. Mo is treated with a 10 per cent. alcoholic soln. of acetic acid, **molybdenum dimanganeside**, Mn_2Mo, is left as a steel-grey powder of sp. gr. 8·37 at 0°. By treating alloys with 43·57 to 59·25 per cent. Mo with dil. hydrochloric acid, there remains **molybdenum manganeside**, $MoMn$, as a steel-grey powder of sp. gr. 8·60 at 0°; and by treating alloys with 64·70 to 72·27 per cent. of Mo with conc. hydrochloric acid, there remains a steel-grey powder of **molybdenum hemimanganeside,** $MnMo_2$, of sp. gr. 8·70 at 0°. These three compounds are attacked by chlorine at ordinary temp., or with incandescence at 300°, by oxygen or sulphur at a red-heat, and by water-vapour at 250°. Hydrochloric and hydrofluoric acids dissolve only the dimanganeside. W. Guertler and T. Liepus studied the corrodibility of the copper-manganese-molybdenum alloys. J. J. and F. de Elhuyar [11] prepared **manganese and tungsten alloys ;** and G. Arrivant prepared alloys containing 12·21 to 60·05 per cent. of tungsten, by reducing with aluminium a mixture of the oxides of the two metals with their respective peroxides ; they form hard, brittle ingots, steel-grey in colour, and non-magnetic. These alloys, which do not contain any definite compounds of the two metals, are slowly oxidized in the air, and completely dissolved by boiling conc. sulphuric acid or by fused alkali hydrogen sulphates ; dil. acids attack them in the cold, dissolving the manganese and leaving the tungsten in the form of a heavy, metallic, steel-grey powder having a sp. gr. 15·28 at 0°. Alloys of tungsten and manganese containing not more than 25 per cent. of the former metal can also be prepared by fusing a mixture of the metallic powders in a current of hydrogen. H. List said that the two elements do not form alloys. A. Stavenhagen and E. Schuchard obtained **uranium-manganese alloys** by the thermite process.

REFERENCES.

[1] R. von Gersdorff, in A. R. von Schrötter, *Sitzber. Akad. Wien,* **63.** 453, 1871 ; E. A. Lewis, *Chem. News,* **86.** 211, 1902 ; *Journ. Soc. Chem. Ind.,* **21.** 842, 1902 ; L. Archbutt, *ib.,* **21.** 844, 1902 ; A. R. von Schrötter, *Sitzber. Akad. Wien,* **63.** 453, 1871 ; S. Wologdine, *Rev. Mét.,* **4.** 27, 1907 ; J. F. Allen, *Chem. News,* **22.** 194, 1870 ; *B.A. Rep.,* 50, 1870 ; F. von Kügelgen, *Zeit. Elektrochem.,* **7.** 563, 1901 ; G. A. Dick, *Brit. Pat. No.* 6172, 1884 ; C. Schwarz and A. Weishut, *German Pat., D.R.P.* 95443, 1896 ; F. Gloger, *Met.,* **3.** 253, 1906 ; G. Sirovich and A. Cartoceti, *Gazz. Chim. Ital.,* **51.** ii, 245, 1921 ; **52.** i, 436, 1922 ; N. Parravano, *ib.,* **42.** ii, 385, 513, 589, 1912 ; S. F. Schemtschuschny, G. G. Urasoff and A. Rykovkoff, *Ann. Polyt. Inst. St. Petersburg,* **8.** 29, 1907 ; *Journ. Russ. Phys. Chem. Soc.,* **38.** 1050, 1906 ; **39.** 787, 1907 ; *Zeit. anorg. Chem.,* **57.** 253, 1908 ; R. Sahmen, *Ueber die Legierungen des Kupfers mit Kobalt, Eisen, Mangan und Magnesium,* Leipzig, 1908 ; *Zeit. anorg. Chem.,* **57.** 22, 1908 ; N. S. Kurnakoff and S. F. Schemt-schuschny, *ib.,* **60.** 10, 1908 ; S. F. Schemtschuschny and W. Petraschewitsch, *Bull. Acad. St. Petersburg,* (11), **6.** 863, 1917 ; S. F. Schemtschuschny, S. A. Pogoden and V. A. Finkeizen, *Russ. Acad. Science,* 3, 1923 ; H. Behrens, *Das mikroskopische Gefüge der Metalle und Legierungen,* Hamburg, 125, 1894 ; E. F. Dürre, *Handbuch der Eisengiessereibetrieb,* Leipzig, **I.** 285, 1890 ; E. F. Law, *Alloys and their Industrial Applications,* London, 158, 1914 ; F. W. Webb, *Proc. Inst. Civil Eng.,* **150.** 106, 1902 ; A. Schulz, *Die Turbine,* **9.** 227, 1913 ; W. B. Parker, *Journ. Inst. Metals,* **14.** 25, 1915 ; E. C. Bain, *Chem. Met. Engg.,* **28.** 21, 1923 ; *Trans. Amer. Inst. Min. Eng.,* **68.** 625, 1922 ; M. R. Andrews, *Phys. Rev.,* (2), **18.** 245, 1921 ; Z. Nishiyama, *Journ. Study Metals,* **6.** 17, 1929 ; *Science Rep. Tohoku Univ.,* **18.** 359, 1929 ; T. Ishiwara, *ib.,* **19.** 499, 1930 ; *Kinzoku no Kenkyu,* **6.** 383, 1929 ; *Proc. World's Eng. Congr. Tokyo,* **36.** 143, 1931 ; C. S. Smith, *Tech. Publ. Amer. Inst. Min. Eng.,* 292, 1930 ; K. Dittrich, *Beiträge zur Kenntnis des Wiedemann-Franz's Gesetzes,* Hirschberg i. Schl., 1926 ; A. Eucken and K. Dittrich, *Zeit. phys. Chem.,* **125.** 211, 1927 ; W. Dinkler, *Giesserei Ztg.,* **23.** 531, 1926 ; O. Bauer and H. Arndt, *Zeit. Metallkunde,* **13.** 407, 559, 1921 ; G. Masing, *ib.,* **17.** 251, 1925 ; A. Valenciennes, *Compt. Rend.,* **70.** 607, 1870 ; L. Guillet, *Étude industrielle des alliages métalliques,* Paris, 757, 1906 ; *Compt. Rend.,* **144.** 847, 1008, 1907 ; *Rev. Mét.,* **4.** 627, 1907 ; E. le Blant, *Proc. Inst. Mech. Eng.,* 338, 1907 ; *Congrès Internat. Méthodes Essai Mat. Construction,* **2.** 267, 1900 ; *Rev. Mét.,* **5.** 446, 1908 ; A. K. Huntington, *ib.,* **5.** 443, 1908 ; *Proc. Inst. Mech. Eng.,* 37, 1907 ; E. F. Sperry, *Brass World,* **1.** 255, 1905 ; *Met.,* **3.** 250, 1906 ; C. Heusler, *Dingler's Journ.,* **285.** 113, 1892 ; *Sitzber. Ver. Beförd. Gewerbfl.,* 75, 1881 ; *Sitzber. Niederrh. Ges. Bonn,* 99, 1883 ; L. Weiller, *Stahl Eisen,* **10.** 391, 1890 ; *Bull. Soc. Ind. Min.,* **3.** 985, 1889 ; K. Feussner and S. Lindeck, *Abhand. Phys. Tech. Reichsanst.,* **2.** 511, 1895 ; A. Carnot, *Bull. Soc. Enc. Nat. Ind.,* (3), **11.** 467, 1884 ; *Berg. Hütt. Ztg.,* **44.** 489, 1885 ; E. W. L. Biermann, *ib.,* **37.** 184, 1878 ; M. Levitzky, *ib.,* **39.** 64, 1880 ; *Rev. Univ.,* **6.** 469, 1882 ; E. Münker, *Met.,* **9.** 197, 1912 ; E. Persson and E. Oehlman, *Nature,* **124.** 333, 1925 ; E. Persson, *Zeit. phys. Chem.,* **9.** B, 25, 1930 ; H. Winter, *Gluckauf,* **44.** 50, 1908 ; E. Priwoznik, *Berg. Hütt. Jahrb.,* **40.** 479, 1892 ; *Zeit. angew. Chem.,* **6.** 181, 1893 ; M. Rudeloff, *Mitt. Tech. Versuchsanst.,* **11.** 292, 1893 ; **13.** 29, 1895 ; W. Guertler, *Jahrb. Rad. Elektron.,* **5.** 17, 1908 ; G. Tammann and E. Vaders, *Zeit. anorg. Chem.,* **121.** 193, 1922 ; G. Tammann and H. Bredemeier, *ib.,* **136.** 337, 1924 ; R. A. Patterson, *Phys. Rev.,* (2), **23.** 552, 1924 ; *Journ. Ind. Eng. Chem.,* **16.** 689, 1924 ; K. Ihde, *Untersuchungen über die Magnetisierbarkeit von Mangan, Mankankupfer und Chrom,* Marburg i. H., 1912 ; M. G. Corson, *U.S. Pat. No.* 1657957, 1928 ; *Trans. Amer. Inst. Min. Eng.,* **75.** 191, 1927 ; A. L. Norbury, *Phil. Mag.,* (7), **2.** 1188, 1926 ; *Trans. Faraday Soc.,* **19.** 586, 1924; A. Eucken and K. Dittrich, *Zeit. phys. Chem.,* **125.** 211, 1927 ; H. Endo, *Science Rep.*

Tohoku Univ., **14.** 479, 1925 ; O. Bauer and H. Arndt, *Zeit. Metallkunde*, **13.** 499, 1921 ; **18.** 85, 1926 ; S. Kimuri and Z. Isawa, *Phys. Rev.*, (2), **20.** 441, 1922 ; S. Kimuri and K. Sakamaki, *Researches Electrotech. Lab. Japan*, 114, 1922 ; Anon., *Metal Ind.*, **14.** 221, 1919 ; G. Eger, *Zeit. Metallkunde*, **10.** 82, 1919 ; E. Griffiths and F. H. Schofield, *Journ. Inst. Metal*, **39.** 337, 1928 ; A. W. Smith, *Phys. Rev.*, (2), **23.** 307, 1924 ; *Bull. Eng. Exp. Station Univ. Ohio*, 31, 1928 ; S. Sekito, *Zeit. Kryst.*, **72.** 406, 1929 ; O. Bauer and H. Arndt, *Zeit. Metallkunde*, **13.** 497, 559, 1921.

² E. Pannain, *Gazz. Chim. Ital.*, **38.** i, 349, 1908 ; G. Hindrichs, *Ueber einige Chrom- und Manganlegierungen*, Leipzig, 1908 ; *Zeit. anorg. Chem.*, **59.** 437, 1908 ; P. Siebe, *ib.*, **108.** 161, 1919 ; G. Arrivant, *ib.*, **83.** 194, 1913 ; *Rev. Mét.*, **10.** 1256, 1913 ; *Compt. Rend.*, **156.** 1539, 1913 ; *Procès-verbal Soc. Bordeaux*, 9, 1904 ; G. Tammann and E. Vaders, *Zeit. anorg. Chem.*, **121.** 193, 1922 ; M. Hansen and G. Sachs, *Zeit. Metallkunde*, **20.** 151, 1928 ; W. Schmidt, *ib.*, **20.** 400, 1928 ; F. Saeftel and G. Sachs, *ib.*, **17.** 155, 258, 294, 1925 ; *Naturwiss.*, **13.** 744, 1925 ; L. Jordan, L. H. Grenall and H. K. Herschman, *Trans. Amer. Inst. Min. Eng.*, **75.** 151, 1927 ; H. Endo, *Science Rep. Tohoku Univ.*, **14.** 479, 1925 ; M. Keinert, *Zeit. phys. Chem.*, **156.** 291, 1931 ; *Das System Silber-Kupfer-Mangan*, Leipzig, 1931.

³ W. C. Roberts-Austen, *Proc. Inst. Mech. Eng.*, 543, 1891 ; *Engg.*, **52.** 548, 1891 ; *Phil. Trans.*, **179.** 339, 1888 ; F. Osmond, *ib.*, **187.** 417, 1896 ; *Bull. Soc. Enc. Nat. Ind.*, (5), **1.** 1136, 1896 ; N. Parravano, *Gazz. Chim. Ital.*, **45.** i, 293, 1915 ; G. Tammann and E. Vaders, *Zeit. anorg. Chem.*, **121.** 193, 1922 ; L. Hahn and S. Kyropoulos, *ib.*, **95.** 105, 1916 ; J. O. Linde, *Ann. Physik*, (5), **10.** 52, 1931.

⁴ H. N. Warren, *Chem. News*, **75.** 2, 1897 ; H. Moissan, *Compt. Rend.*, **127.** 840, 1897.

⁵ A. Terreil, *Bull. Soc. Chim.*, (2), **21.** 289, 1874 ; E. A. Lewis, *Chem. News*, **86.** 211, 1902 ; *Journ. Soc. Chem. Ind.*, **21.** 842, 1902 ; P. Siebe, *Zeit. anorg. Chem.*, **108.** 161, 1919 ; O. Heusler, *ib.*, **159.** 37, 1926 ; P. Gieren, *Beiträge zur Kenntnis der gegossenen Zinklegierungen unter besonderer Berücksichtigung ihrer Verwertbarkeit als Lagermetall*, Berlin, 11, 1919 ; W. N. Pierce, *Trans. Amer. Inst. Min. Eng.*, **68.** 767, 1923 ; G. Eger, *Zeit. Metallkunde*, **10.** 82, 1919 ; N. Parravano and U. Perret, *Gazz. Chim. Ital.*, **45.** i, 1, 1915 ; N. Parravano and V. Montoro, *Mem. Accad. Italia*, **1.** 4, 1930 ; N. Parravano and V. Caglioti, *Atti Accad. Lincei*, (6), **14.** 166, 1931 ; W. Schmidt, *Zeit. Metallkunde*, **19.** 452, 1927 ; C. L. Ackermann, *ib.*, **19.** 200, 1927 ; J. A. Gaun, *Mining Met.*, **9.** 449, 1928 ; *Trans. Amer. Inst. Min. Met. Eng.*, 309, 1929 ; H. E. Bakken and V. Wood, *Handbook Amer. Soc. Steel Treating*, 560, 1929 ; G. W. Pearson, *Journ. Ind. Eng. Chem.*, **22.** 367, 1930 ; O. Heusler, *Zeit. anorg. Chem.*, **159.** 37, 1926 ; E. Schmid and G. Siebel, *Metallwirtschaft*, **10.** 923, 1931 ; W. Rosenhain and F. C. A. H. Lantsberry, *Proc. Inst. Mech. Eng.*, 119, 1910.

⁶ W. Ramsay, *Journ. Chem. Soc.*, **55.** 532, 1889 ; A. S. Russell and D. C. Evans, *ib.*, **127.** 2221, 1925 ; A. S. Russell, *ib.*, 2398, 1929 ; A. S. Russell, D. C. Evans and S. W. Rowell, *ib.*, 1872, 1926 ; N. M. Irvin and A. S. Russell, *ib.*, 891, 1932 ; A. N. Campbell, *ib.*, **125.** 1713, 1924 ; W. B. Giles, *Phil. Mag.*, (4), **24.** 328, 1862 ; C. F. Schönbein, *Pogg. Ann.*, **112.** 445, 1861 ; E. Kuh, *Die Darstellung des chemische reinen Mangans und die Bestimmung der wichtigsten physikalischen Konstanten desselben*, Zürich, 22, 1911 ; J. Schumann, *Untersuchungen von Amalgamen*, Leipzig, 1891 ; *Wied. Ann.*, **43.** 110, 1891 ; H. Moissan, *Ann. Chim. Phys.*, (5), **21.** 199, 1880 ; *Compt. Rend.*, **88.** 180, 1879 ; *Bull. Soc. Chim.*, (2), **31.** 150, 1879 ; A. Guntz, *ib.*, (3), **7.** 275, 1892 ; O. Prelinger, *Sitzber. Akad. Wien*, **102.** 346, 1893 ; *Monatsh.*, **14.** 353, 1893 ; R. Böttger, *Journ. prakt. Chem.*, (1), **3.** 283, 1834 ; (1), **12.** 350, 1837 ; G. Tammann and J. Hinnüber, *Zeit. anorg. Chem.*, **160.** 249, 1927.

⁷ C. and A. Tissier, *Compt. Rend.*, **43.** 1187, 1856 ; C. Combes, *ib.*, **122.** 1482, 1896 ; L. Guillet, *ib.*, **134.** 236, 1902 ; *Rev. Mét.*, **18.** 681, 1921 ; S. Daniels, *Journ. Ind. Eng. Chem.*, **18.** 125, 1926 ; H. Schirmeister, *Stahl Eisen*, **35.** 649, 996, 1915 ; *Beiträge zur Kenntnis der binären Aluminiumlegierungen hinsichtlich ihrer technischen Eigenschaften*, Düsseldorf, 1914 ; S. Fabiani, *Krak. Akad. Anz.*, 194, 1917 ; Z. Nishiyama, *Journ. Study Metals*, **6.** 17, 1929 ; E. Morlet, *Compt. Rend.*, **189.** 102, 1929 ; *Rev. Mét.*, **26.** 464, 554, 593, 1929 ; H. O. Dorum, *Arhand. Norske Vid. Akad.*, 10, 1929 ; *Ueber die magnetischen Eigenschaften der Heuslerschen Legierungen und ihre Kristallstruktur*, Oslo, 1929 ; E. Ludwik, *Zeit. Oesterr. Ing. Arch. Ver.*, 11, 1907 ; E. Rassow, *Hanszeit. V.A.W.*, **1.** 187, 1929 ; J. C. McLennan, J. F. Allen and J. O. Wilhelm, *Trans. Roy. Soc. Canada*, (3), **24.** 1, 1930 ; *Phil. Mag.*, (7), **10.** 500, 1930 ; R. L. Templin and D. A. Paul, *Tech. Publ. Amer. Soc. Min. Eng.*, 366, 1930 ; S. F. Herman and F. T. Sisco, *ib.*, 365, 1930 ; G. Masing, *Zeit. Metallkunde*, **22.** 90, 1930 ; J. R. Ashworth, *Phil. Mag.*, (7), **10.** 681, 1930 ; *Proc. Phys. Soc.*, **42.** 449, 1930 ; *Nature*, **121.** 323, 1928 ; T. Ishiwara, *Science Rep. Tohoku Univ.*, **19.** 499, 1930 ; *Kinzoku no Kenkyu*, **3.** 13, 1926 ; *Proc. World's Eng. Congr. Tokyo*, **36.** 143, 1931 ; W. Sucksmith and H. H. Potter, *Proc. Roy. Soc.*, **112.** A, 157, 1926 ; W. Sucksmith and L. F. Bates, *ib.*, **104.** A, 499, 1923 ; P. Weiss, *Journ. Phys.*, (5), **7.** 249, 1908 ; E. Griffiths and F. H. Schofield, *Journ. Inst. Metals*, **39.** 337, 1928 ; A. Westgren and W. Ekman, *Arkiv Kemi Min. Geol.*, **10.** 11, 1931 ; A. Terreil, *Bull. Soc. Chim.*, (2), **21.** 289, 1874 ; F. R. Michel, *Ueber krystallisirte Verbindungen des Aluminiums mit Metallen*, Göttingen, 26, 1860 ; *Liebig's Ann.*, **115.** 102, 1860 ; O. Brunck, *Ber.*, **34.** 2735, 1901 ; G. Hindrichs, *Ueber einige Chrom- und Manganlegierungen*, Leipzig, 1908 ; *Zeit. anorg. Chem.*, **59.** 444, 1908 ; O. Heusler, *ib.*, **159.** 37, 1927 ; **171.** 126, 1928 ; F. Heusler, *ib.*, **88.** 185, 1914 ; *ib.*, **161.** 159, 1927 ; *Verh. Gewerbefleiss*, 277, 1903 ; *Zeit. angew. Chem.*, **17.** 260, 1904 ; **25.** 2253, 2651, 1912 ; *Schrift. Naturf. Ges. Marburg*, 1, 1908 ; *Wallach's Festschrift*, 467, 1909 ; *Zeit. Physik*, **10.** 403, 1922 ; *Verh.*

deut. phys. Ges., **5**. 219, 1903; F. Heusler, W. Starck and E. Haupt, *ib.*, **5**. 220, 1903; F. Heusler and F. Richarz, *Zeit. anorg. Chem.*, **61**. 265, 1909; F. Heusler and E. Dönnges, *ib.*, **171**. 146, 1928; F. Heusler, F. Richarz, W. Starck and E. Haupt, *Schrift. Naturf. Ges. Marburg*, **13**. 237, 1904; E. Haupt, *Natur. Rund.*, **21**. 69, 1906; **22**. 209, 221, 1907; *Schrift. Naturf. Ges. Marburg*, 203, 1908; F. Richarz, *ib.*, 204, 1908; E. Take, *ib.*, 35, 1905; 203, 1908; *Alterungs- und Umwandlungs-Studien an Heuslerschen Ferromagnetisier baren Aluminium-Manganbronzen insbesondere an Schmiedeproben*, Berlin, 1911; *Ann. Physik*, (4), **20**. 849, 1906; *Trans. Faraday Soc.*, **8**. 169, 1912; *Verh. phys. ges. Physik*, **7**. 133, 1905; L. W. Austin, *ib.*, **6**. 211, 1904; H. Fassbender, *ib.*, **10**. 256, 1908; P. Asteroth, *ib.*, **10**. 21, 1908; *Natur. Rund.*, **23**. 249, 1908; *Der Einfluss der thermischen und mechanischen Vorgeschichte auf die magnetischen Eigenschaften insbesonders die Hysterese, Heuslerscher Legierungen*, Marburg i. H., 1907; A. Kussmann and B. Scharnoff, *Zeit. Physik*, **47**. 770, 1928; **51**. 757, 1928; L. Gümlich, *Ann. Physik*, (4), **16**. 535, 1905; B. V. Hill, *Phys. Rev.*, (1), **21**. 335, 1905; J. C. McLennan, *ib.*, (1), **24**. 449, 1907; A. A. Knowlton, *ib.*, (1), **30**. 123, 1910; A. A. Knowlton and O. C. Clifford, *ib.*, (1), **30**. 125, 1910; *Trans. Faraday Soc.*, **8**. 195, 1912; S. Hilpert, T. Dieckmann and E. Colver-Glauert, *ib.*, **8**. 207, 1912; R. Hadfield, *Chem. News*, **90**. 180, 1904; J. A. Fleming and R. Hadfield, *Proc. Roy. Soc.*, **76**. A, 271, 1905; A. Gray, *ib.*, **77**. A, 256, 1906; J. F. T. Young, *Phil. Mag.*, (6), **46**. 291, 1923; E. Wedekind, *Zeit. angew. Chem.*, **25**. 2524, 1912; **26**. 72, 1913; W. Preusser, *Ueber die Abhangigkeit der magnetischen Eigenschaften Heuslerscher Aluminium-Manganbronzen von ihrer chemischen Zusammensetzung*, Marburg i. H., 1908; A. D. Ross, *Trans. Faraday Soc.*, **8**. 185, 1912; *Proc. Roy. Soc. Edin.*, **27**. 88, 1907; A. D. Ross and R. C. Gray, *ib.*, **31**. 85, 1910; *Zeit. anorg. Chem.*, **63**. 349, 1909; K. Röth, *ib.*, **191**. 181, 1930; K. E. Guthe and L. W. Austin, *Bull. Bur. Standards*, **2**. 297, 1906; H. Zahn and H. Schmidt, *Verh. deut. phys. Ges.*, **9**. 98, 1907; W. Haas, *Giesserei Ztg.*, **23**. 328, 1926; P. Hidnert and W. T. Sweeney, *Journ. Research Bur. Standards*, **1**. 771, 1928; D. J. McAdam, *Proc. Amer. Soc. Testing Materials*, **27**. ii, 102, 1927; C. S. Taylor and J. D. Edwards, *Trans. Amer. Electrochem. Soc.*, **56**. 53, 1929; E. B. Stephenson, *Magnetic Properties of Heusler Alloys*, Urbana, 1910; *Phys. Rev.*, (1), **30**. 127, 1910; P. W. Bridgman, *Proc. Amer. Acad.*, **56**. 61, 1921; **57**. 41, 1922; E. H. Dix and W. D. Keith, *Trans. Amer. Inst. Min. Eng.*, **75**. 87, 1927; O. von Auwers, *Zeit. anorg. Chem.*, **108**. 49, 1919; *Ann. Physik*, (4), **63**. 847, 1920; O. von Auwers and H. Weinnoldt, *Zeit. Physik*, **51**. 574, 1928; S. Valentiner and G. Becker, *ib.*, **57**. 283, 1929; E. Persson, *ib.*, **57**. 115, 1929; *Naturwiss.*, **16**. 613, 1928; W. Krings and W. Ostmann, *Zeit. anorg. Chem.*, **163**. 145, 1927; L. Harang, *Zeit. Kryst.*, **65**. 261, 1927; *Phys. Zeit.*, **27**. 204, 1926; W. Rosenhain and F. C. A. H. Lantsberry, *Proc. Inst. Mech. Eng.*, 119, 1910; W. Rosenhain, S. L. Archbutt and D. Hanson, *Reports of Light Alloys Sub-committee (Aeronautics)*, London, 51, 1921; G. A. Shakespear, *ib.*, **48**. 1921; H. H. Potter, *Proc. Phys. Soc.*, **41**. 135, 1929; *Phil. Mag.*, (7), **12**. 255, 1931; A. J. Bradley and P. Jones, *ib.*, (7), **12**. 1137, 1931; E. Dippel, *Ann. Physik*, (4), **42**. 889, 1913; H. H. Potter, *Phil. Mag.*, (7), **13**. 233, 1932; E. T. Richards, *Das Metal*, **51**. 65, 1930.

    [8] N. Baar, *Zeit. anorg. Chem.*, **70**. 352, 1911.

    [9] R. S. Williams, *Ueber die Legierungen des Antimons mit Mangan, Chrom, Silicium und Zinn ; des Wismuts mit Chrom und Silicium und des Mangans mit Zinn und Blei*, Leipzig, 1907; *Zeit. anorg. Chem.*, **55**. 1, 1907; A. Stavenhagen and E. Schuchard, *Ber.*, **35**. 910, 1902; J. F. Allen, *Chem. News*, **22**. 194, 1870; *B.A. Rep.*, 50, 1870; K. Bornemann, *Met.*, **8**. 361, 1911; F. Heusler, *Schriften Naturf. Ges. Marburg*, **13**. 5, 1904; *Zeit. anorg. Chem.*, **88**. 185, 1914; T. Goldschmidt, *Aluminogenetische Metalle und Legierungen*, Essen, 1905; W. Guertler and T. Liepus, *Zeit. Metallkunde*, **17**. 310, 1925; H. Fassbender, *Verh. deut. phys. Ges.*, **10**. 256, 1908; N. A. Puschin, *Journ. Russ. Phys. Chem. Soc.*, **39**. 869, 1907; A. D. Ross and R. C. Gray, *Proc. Roy. Soc. Edin.*, **31**. 85, 1910; L. Harang, *Zeit. Kryst.*, **65**. 261, 1927; R. Dovey, *Brit. Pat. No.* 1055, 1773; C. S. Smith, *Tech. Publ. Amer. Inst. Min. Eng.*, 292, 1930; H. A. Bedworth, *ib.*, 189, 1929; P. Martin, *Ann. Physik*, (4), **39**. 625, 1912; E. Voce, *Journ. Inst. Metals*, **44**. 331, 1930; *Engg.*, **130**. 441, 1930; H. H. Potter, *Phil. Mag.*, (7), **12**. 255, 1931; W. Guertler and T. Liepus, *Zeit. Metallkunde*, **17**. 310, 1925.

    [10] G. Arrivant, *Compt. Rend.*, **143**. 285, 464, 1906.

    [11] G. Arrivant, *Compt. Rend.*, **143**. 594, 1906; J. J. and F. de Elhuyar, *Análisis quimico del volfram y examen de un nuevo metal que entra en su composicion*, Bascongada, 1783; *A Chemical Analysis of Wolfram and Examination of a New Metal which enters into its Composition*, London, 1785; *Chemische Zerkliederung des Wolframs*, Halle, 1786; *Mém. Acad. Toulouse*, **2**. 141, 1784; H. List, *Edel-Erden Erz*, **4**. 66, 1923; A. Stavenhagen and E. Schuchard, *Ber.*, **35**. 909, 1902.

§ 8. Manganous Oxide and Hydroxide

C. W. Blomstrand [1] observed that the emerald-green, cubic crystals occurring in the manganiferous dolomite of Längban, Wermland, Sweden, consist of **manganous oxide**, or **manganese monoxide**, MnO, contaminated with about a half per cent. of iron. He called the mineral **manganosite**. A. Sjögren also found this oxide occurred in the Moss Mine, Nordmask, Wermland, Sweden. The manganese oxides were studied by R. Phillips in 1829. A. Geuther said that pyrolusite heated to bright redness furnishes the monoxide, but W. Biltz's observations—*vide infra*—show that more probably the manganosic oxide, Mn_3O_4, is formed. C. W. Scheele obtained the monoxide by heating manganous carbonate to redness out of contact with air ; H. Davy, by heating manganous hydroxide ; and J. von Liebig, F. Kessler, J. Bachmann, J. L. Lassaigne, and A. Gorgeu, by heating manganous oxalate. E. G. L. Roberts and E. A. Wraight obtained the monoxide by fusing manganese dioxide in a magnesia-lined crucible ; and E. Tiede and E. Birnbräuer said that the dioxide is reduced to the monoxide when it is heated to 1650° in vacuo. J. A. Arfvedson prepared the monoxide by heating manganous carbonate to redness in a current of hydrogen ; G. Forchhammer, E. Turner, J. N. von Fuchs, E. R. Schneider, and F. Kessler, manganosic oxide ; and C. R. A. Wright and A. P. Luff, and H. Moissan, manganese dioxide. H. Moissan added that the reduction of manganese dioxide by hydrogen occurs at 280°, and of manganosic oxide, prepared at a low temp., at 260°. L. Wöhler found that the equilibrium constant $C_{H_2O}/C_H = K$ in the reaction $Mn_3O_4 + H_2 \rightleftharpoons H_2O + 3MnO$, is 34·6 at 450°. K. Stammer reduced manganosic oxide to manganous oxide by heating it in carbon monoxide. A. Guntz found that manganese and carbon dioxide begin to react : $Mn + CO = MnO + C + 33·3$ Cals. at 350° ; and the reaction with carbon dioxide : $2Mn + CO_2 = 2MnO + C + 46·3$ Cals. also occurs at a high temp., as shown by A. Guntz, and R. Lorenz and F. Heusler. According to P. Berthier, manganese dioxide is formed when one of the higher manganese oxides is heated in a carbon crucible to the beginning of a white-heat. J. Mactear mixed a soln. of manganous sulphate with sufficient magnesium chloride to be eq. to the sulphate and any free sulphuric acid in the soln. When the liquid is evaporated out of contact with air, hydrogen chloride is copiously evolved and there is formed a mixture of manganous oxide and magnesium sulphate from which the latter can be removed by washing. J. von Liebig and F. Wöhler heated to redness a mixture of equal parts of manganous chloride, sodium carbonate, and ammonium chloride. The manganous carbonate first formed decomposes into the oxide, and the ammonium chloride prevents the formation of higher oxides. The fused mass is lixiviated, washed, and dried. D. C. Knab obtained the monoxide by heating one of the higher oxides with sulphur—some oxysulphide is also produced. J. J. Ebelmen prepared crystals of manganese oxide by heating manganese borate with lime ; crystals are also produced in J. von Liebig and F. Wöhler's process ; and H. St. C. Deville obtained crystals by reducing a higher oxide with hydrogen containing a trace of hydrogen chloride. A. Gorgeu heated to redness manganous chloride in water-vapour, with the exclusion of oxidizing gases, for a long time, and obtained crystals of manganous oxide. F. Doerinckel melted manganous oxide with silica and found that crystals of manganosite separated from the molten mass. V. Kohlschütter and J. L. Tüscher obtained an aerosol of manganese oxide by vaporizing the metal in an electric arc in a current of air.

According to P. Oberhoffer and K. d'Huart, when oxygen gas is passed over molten manganese, a molten green layer is formed on the surface of the metal. This layer contains a light-coloured constituent, which crystallizes first, and a dark-coloured, non-metallic constituent, which solidifies last. C. Benedicks

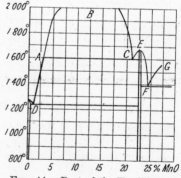

FIG. 44.—Part of the Equilibrium Curves of the System : Mn–O.

and H. Löfquist constructed a provisional equilibrium diagram, Fig. 44, based on the analogy between manganous oxide and ferrous oxide (*q.v.*). There is presumably a region of immiscibility, *ABC*, with manganous oxide and manganese ;

and a eutectic at D. The maximum at E refers to manganous oxide; and since the next higher oxide is manganosic oxide, Mn_3O_4, there is supposed to be a V-eutectic, at F.

The oxide was analyzed by J. A. Arfvedson, J. J. Berzelius, H. Davy, T. Bergman, H. Moissan, G. Forchhammer, and C. von Hauer, and the results are in agreement with the formula MnO. Manganosite was analyzed by C. W. Blomstrand, and C. Palache. G. Forchhammer, J. A. Arfvedson, E. Turner, J. J. Berzelius, J. von Liebig and F. Wöhler, and J. M. Weeren describe the monoxide as an amorphous or crystalline, green or greenish-yellow powder. W. Biltz discussed the **colour** of the derivatives of manganous oxide. H. St. C. Deville said that the emerald-green crystals are regular octahedra; while C. W. Blomstrand described the cubic **crystals** of manganosite as minute octahedra, which are emerald-green when fresh, and become black on exposure to air. According to A. Sjögren, the crystals resemble those of periclase. E. S. Larsen, and P. Klein found that manganosite is green in transmitted light. P. Klein studied the **corrosion figures** with hydrochloric and sulphuric acids. G. R. Levi found that the **X-radiogram** agrees with a cubical lattice of the sodium chloride type with $a=4\cdot40$ A. and the calculated sp. gr. 5·46. A. J. Bradley obtained similar results with $a=4\cdot45$ A. E. Broch gave $a=4\cdot435$ A.; H. Ott, $a=4\cdot47$ A. and a calculated density 5·22; and C. Fontana, $a=4\cdot409$ A. and a density of 5·429. Observations were also made by V. M. Goldschmidt, G. Natta, and H. Ott. According to G. Aminoff, the radius of the hydrogen atom in the hydroxide is 1·05 A. The structure of the hydroxide is expressed by the substitution in $H_2O.O.H_2$ of the continuous hydrogen atoms of adjacent trigonal axes by manganese in the direction of these axes. E. J. Cuy gave 2·20 A. for the interatomic distance. According to W. Herapath, the **specific gravity** is 4·726 at 17°; while C. F. Rammelsberg gave 5·091; D. Müller, 5·4; L. Playfair and J. P. Joule gave 5·30; and V. H. Veley, 5·010 at 4°. G. R. Levi gave 5·432 for the sp. gr. of the fused oxide. C. W. Blomstrand gave 5·18 for the sp. gr. of manganosite, and 5 to 6 for the hardness. C. Palache gave 5·346 for the sp. gr. of manganosite. M. Meyer and B. Havas found the coeff. of cubical **thermal expansion** to be $0\cdot0_622$. H. V. Regnault gave 0·15703 for the **specific heat** between 13° and 98°. R. W. Millar found the **molecular heat** of manganous oxide to be:

	$-202\cdot6°$	$-184\cdot5°$	$-164\cdot9°$	$-146\cdot2°$	$-117\cdot4°$	$-69\cdot7°$	$-25\cdot9°$	$-0\cdot1°$	$37\cdot2°$
C_p .	4·426	6·348	9·829	7·470	8·124	9·173	9·729	9·992	10·3

The results are plotted in Fig. 45. There is a marked discontinuity between 110° K. and 118° K. I. Meydell studied the subject. C. M. Despretz found that the oxide melts at a high temp. E. Tiede and E. Birnbräuer gave 1650° for the **melting-point**. J. H. Andrew and co-workers gave 1585°. C. Benedicks and H. Löfquist estimate the m.p. to be near 1700°. H. le Chatelier obtained for the **heat of formation** 90·8 Cals.; M. Berthelot, 90·9 Cals.; D. Müller, and W. A. Roth, 93·5 Cals.; and H. von Jüptner gave $2Mn+O_2=2MnO +181\cdot8$ Cals. G. Beck discussed the energy of formation. R. W. Millar calculated 14·92 for the **entropy** at 25°; and for $Mn+\frac{1}{2}O_2$ $=MnO$, the change of entropy is $-17\cdot0$, and the change of **free energy**, $-85,830$ cals. G. Beck studied the energy of the oxide.

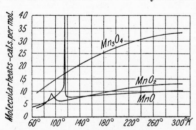

FIG. 45.—The Molecular Heats of the Manganese Oxides.

W. Biltz calculated for the temp. of **dissociation**, 4050° when $p=1$ atm. The temp. of dissociation and the e.m.f. series are in accord for the following metals and their oxides:

	Ag	Hg	Cu	Pb	Co	Fe	Mn
θ .	488°	723°	2073°	2513°	3133°	3298°	4050°
Potential .	$+0\cdot771$	$+0\cdot753$	$-0\cdot329$	$-0\cdot151$	$-0\cdot232$	$-0\cdot344$	$-1\cdot075$ volts

H. Styri calculated for the **dissociation pressure** of manganous oxide, p, $2MnO=2Mn+O_2-181,600$ cals., log $p=-14.7$ at $1500°$; -13.5 at $1600°$; -12.4 at $1700°$. N. Parravano and G. Malquori gave for the dissociation pressure at $600°$ log $p_{O_2}=-37.573$. H. von Jüptner calculated for the dissociation $2MnO=2Mn+O_2$, the press. p atm., from log $p=-39562T^{-1}+1.75$ log $T=2.9$ (*vide infra*, MnO_2), so that:

	600°	1000°	1400°	1800°	2200°	2400°
p	$0.0_{58}5311$	$0.0_{31}3076$	$0.0_{19}1115$	$0.0_{13}3295$	0.0_94640	0.0_71703

W. E. Ford found the **index of refraction** for Na-light to be 2.18; and E. S. Larsen, 2.16. E. L. Nichols and D. T. Wilbur found manganese oxide showed no flame luminescence. T. W. Case observed no change in the electrical conductivity on exposure to light. O. F. Tower studied the potential of manganese dioxide electrodes in an alkaline soln. of manganous hydroxide. R. Whytlaw-Gray and co-workers, and E. Thomson found that the particles exhibiting Brownian movement form chains under the influence of an electrostatic field.

M. le Blanc and H. Sachse found the **electrical conductivity** to be 10^{-3} mho. E. Wedekind and C. Horst gave 56.16×10^{-6} mass unit for the **magnetic susceptibility** at $14.8°$; and P. Théodoridès, 67.46×10^{-6} mass unit. Comparative measurements were made by P. Hausknecht. E. H. Williams discussed the structure of the paramagnetic oxide. K. Honda and T. Sone's observations showed that the magnetic susceptibilities $\chi \times 10^6$, at different temp., are:

	−189°	−76°	2°	275°	558°	738°	1013°	1149°	1296°
$\chi \times 10^6$	89.9	87.0	77.7	59.7	43.2	35.4	30.5	30.3	28.7

J. A. Arfvedson, and C. and A. Tissier found that manganous oxide is not decomposed by **hydrogen** at a bright red-heat; and F. Glasèr observed that the decomposition by hydrogen begins at $1300°$; H. H. Meyer gave $1200°$. E. Newbery and J. N. Pring said that reduction occurs at $2000°$ with hydrogen at 150 atm. press. H. S. Taylor and A. T. Williamson found that the absorption of hydrogen is very small, and they studied its catalytic effect in the oxidation of hydrogen. J. V. Vaughan and W. A. Lazier studied manganese oxide as a catalyst in hydrogenation reactions. E. R. Schneider found that when strongly heated in **oxygen**, manganous oxide forms manganic oxide, Mn_2O_3. The monoxide obtained by reducing a higher oxide at a low temp. in hydrogen was found by C. R. A. Wright and A. E. Menke not to be spontaneously oxidized in **air** unless free alkali is present; but if a trace of alkali be present, the monoxide takes up oxygen from the air, and acquires a brown or black film. C. W. Scheele, and J. von Liebig observed that when the oxide is exposed to the air, it becomes brown in a few days; and if it be heated below redness, by red-hot charcoal, it glows rapidly to form manganosic oxide. N. N. Mittra and N. R. Dhar studied the oxidation of manganous hydroxide in air. H. Moissan found that the monoxide obtained by reducing higher oxides in hydrogen at $260°$ oxidizes with sparking at $140°$; and A. Gorgeu found that the oxide obtained by heating the oxalate at $200°$ to $420°$ is pyrophoric, forming manganosic oxide in air. The denser varieties of manganous oxide were found by J. A. Arfvedson to form manganosic oxide, without incandescence, at a dull red-heat. H. St. C. Deville found that the crystalline monoxide behaves similarly. H. V. Regnault observed that manganous oxide is not decomposed by boiling **water,** but when heated to redness in water-vapour, hydrogen and manganosic oxide are formed. A. von Kiss and F. E. Lederer studied the effect of manganese salts on the decomposition of **hydrogen dioxide.** R. Wasmuth studied the attack of the heated oxide by **chlorine.** L. E. Rivot and co-workers observed that in the presence of alkali-lye at $40°$ to $50°$ chlorine oxidizes it to alkali permanganate; at $0°$ manganic oxide is formed, which if the temp. be allowed to rise, passes into soln. as green alkali manganate. H. Rose found that **hydrochloric acid** dissolves manganese oxide to form manganous chloride, and if the monoxide be quite free from higher oxides, no chlorine is developed, and, according to L. Santi, the formation of manganous chloride.

C. Langlois observed that **periodic acid** is reduced to iodic acid, and manganic iodate is formed.

J. A. Arfvedson found that when the monoxide is heated with **sulphur,** sulphur dioxide and manganese oxysulphide are formed ; while with **hydrogen sulphide,** water and manganese sulphide are produced. The reaction with sulphur vapour, and hydrogen sulphide was studied by K. Hilgenstock. R. Wagner obtained similar results. E. Priwoznik observed that **ammonium sulphide** at 100° converts it into flesh-coloured manganous sulphide. D. L. Hammick found that when manganous oxide is heated in **sulphur dioxide,** the reaction is accompanied by a dull red glow ; sulphur and sulphur trioxide are produced, as well as a green powder containing manganese sulphide and sulphate, as well as traces of the higher oxides. With a more prolonged heating to dull redness, there is a slow production of sulphur trioxide, but no free sulphur, and the brown solid becomes white manganous sulphate. The primary reaction is supposed to be $7MnO+10SO_2=MnS+6MnSO_4+SO_3+2S$; among other secondary reactions there is $MnS+5MnSO_4=2Mn_3O_4+6SO_2$. The reaction was studied by K. Hilgenstock. The oxide readily dissolves in **sulphuric acid** to form manganous sulphate.

O. Meyer found that manganous oxide is vigorously attacked by **titanium nitride** at a high temp. L. Santi observed that a hot conc. soln. of **ammonium chloride** converts manganous oxide into chloride, with the evolution of ammonia. P. Sabatier and J. B. Senderens found that **nitrous oxide** or **nitric oxide,** at 350°, converts manganous oxide into manganosic oxide without glowing ; while **nitrogen peroxide,** at 500°, forms manganic oxide. The oxide readily dissolves in **nitric acid** to form manganous nitrate, and in **phosphoric acid** to form the phosphate.

According to J. A. Arfvedson, and C. and A. Tissier, manganese monoxide is decomposed by **carbon** at a bright red-heat ; but not by **carbon monoxide.** H. C. Greenwood said that no reduction with carbon occurs at 500° to 600°, but at 1100° to 1200° it is reduced to manganese. N. Parravano and G. Malquori gave $\log p_{CO_2}-1\cdot38$ for the dissociation press. $2MnO+C=CO_2+2Mn$, at 1500°. H. H. Meyer said that the reaction with carbon starts at 900° to 950° ; and with carbon monoxide at 1200°. E. Nishibori studied the reaction with carbon monoxide. O. Meyer found that manganese oxide is attacked by **carbides**—silicon, chromium, and molybdenum—at a high temp. O. Houghton said that the reaction with silicon carbide begins at 1350°. The reaction was also studied by E. H. Schulz and A. Kanz. The reaction with **carbon disulphide** was studied by K. Hilgenstock ; and with ethyl and isopropyl alcohols, by A. T. Williamson and H. S. Taylor. E. Donath observed that **glycerol,** in alkaline liquids, dissolves manganous oxide, forming a red liquid in the presence of oxygen. J. Milbauer found manganous oxide is converted into potassium manganous sulphide when heated with **potassium thiocyanate.** P. Sabatier and A. Mailhe found that manganous oxide facilitates the catalytic reduction of **organic acids** to aldehydes and ketones. J. Aloy and C. Rabaut said that the presence of manganese oxide favours the saponification of benzoylated **cyanohydrins** by acetic acid. J. Fiedler found acid manganous oxalate is decomposed in light. G. Rauter found that when the monoxide is heated with **silicon tetrachloride,** manganous chloride, silica, and chlorine are formed. A. B. du Jassonnaix found that **boron** reduces the manganese oxides in an electric furnace. C. H. Burgess and A. Holt showed that the monoxide can dissolve in molten **boric oxide**—*vide infra,* manganous chloride and sulphate. L. Kahlenberg and W. J. Trautmann observed no reaction when a mixture of powdered **silicon** and manganous oxide is heated. For the reaction $MnO+Fe=FeO+Mn$, *vide* ferrous oxide. V. Macri studied the reducing action of salts of manganous oxide. He found that manganous sulphate completely precipitates the silver from a hot ammoniacal silver nitrate soln. The white precipitate formed by addition of the manganous salt to ammoniacal mercuric nitrate soln. turns grey and then brown on boiling, and, after treatment with sulphur dioxide soln. or an acidified soln. of a sulphite, leaves a heavy, brownish-grey, pulverulent deposit, which is not dissolved by dil. nitric acid, but is readily attacked by the concentrated acid, with formation of nitrous fumes. When an ammoniacal soln. of copper and manganous sulphates is boiled, cuprous oxide is precipitated ; the supernatant colourless liquid gradually becomes blue in the air. The addition of ammonia to a soln. containing a cobalt and a manganous salt yields a precipitate of manganous hydroxide, which gradually becomes brown, not, however, by direct redüetion of the cobalt oxide, since the latter first undergoes peroxidation in the air, and then gives up its oxygen to the manganese, especially on shaking. No tests were made with gold or platinum, but the hydroxides of other metals are not oxidized by manganous salts. R. Schenck and H. Wesselkock studied the action of manganese oxide on the oxidation of **nickel** and **cobalt** at 900° in an atm. of carbon dioxide. G. Natta and L. Passerini observed that **calcium oxide** forms an incomplete series of solid soln. with manganous oxide. When 75 to 100 per cent. of calcium oxide is present, the space-lattice has $a=4.76$ to 4.72 A., when the space-lattice of manganous oxide has $a=4.79$, and of calcium oxide, $a=4.415$. When 35 to 50 per cent. of manganous oxide is present, the value of a falls, and two series of solid soln. are formed ; and when 75 to 90 per cent. of manganous oxide is present, the solid soln. has a lattice with $a=4.42$ to 4.48. Incomplete miscibility occurs with calcium and manganous oxides. L. Passerini made analogous observations with **magnesium oxide,** which forms two series of solid soln. The mineral *manganbrucite*, $(Mg,Mn)O$, was found by L. H. Bauer and H. Berman to have the indices of refraction $\omega=1.59$, and $\epsilon=1.60$. F. de Carli found that **lead dioxide** at 250° to 300° oxidizes manganese oxide to a higher oxide. According to G. Natta and L. Passerini, and L. Passerini, **cadmium oxide** forms solid soln. with manganous oxide. Similarly, partial miscibility occurs with manganous oxide and **cobaltous oxide,** but incomplete miscibility with manganous oxide and **nickelous oxide.** J. H. Andrew and co-workers studied the solid soln. formed by mixtures with ferrous oxide. W. Biltz and co-workers obtained spinels, $MnO.R_2O_3$, with R_2O_3 represented by **alumina, ferric oxide,** and **chromic oxide.** W. Biltz discussed the mol. vol. of $MnO.Al_2O_3$. G. L. Clark and co-workers found the lattice constant, a, of the spinels, **manganese aluminate, chromite,** and **ferrite** to be respectively 8·271, 8·436, and 8·457 A. respectively. E. Diepschlag and E. Horn investigated the action of the oxide on ferric oxide, and the formation of manganous ferrite. H. Pélabon and M. Delwaulle observed that when manganous oxide is added to a conc. soln. of **mercuric chloride,** manganese oxides—Mn_3O_4, Mn_2O_3, and MnO_2—and mercurous chloride are formed. C. Montemartini and A. Vernazza studied the reaction with soln. of chromic sulphate.

L. J. Igelström found a **hydrated manganous oxide,** $MnO.H_2O$, or **manganous hydroxide,** $Mn(OH)_2$, in white crystals occurring at Pajsberg, Filipstadt, Sweden ; and A. Sjögren obtained it at Längbanshytta, and Nordmark, Sweden. The mineral was called **pyrochroite**—from $\pi\tilde{v}\rho$, fire, and $\chi\rho\acute{o}a$, colour—in allusion to its change of colour on ignition. The mineral has also been reported by L. J. Igelström, from Grythyttan, Oerebro, Sweden ; by G. A. Kenngott, from St. Gallen, Switzerland ; and by J. D. Dana, from Franklin Furnace, New Jersey. The so-called *wiserite* of W. Haidinger was reported by D. F. Wiser to be a manganous carbonate, but G. A. Kenngott showed that it is the hydrated oxide. Analyses of pyrochroite were reported by L. J. Igelström, H. Sjögren, A. E. Nordenskjöld, and L. Stahre. P. Groth represented it by the formula $Mn(OH)_2$, and H. Laspeyres regarded H_2MnO_2 as *manganous acid* or as *hypomanganous acid*. G. Aminoff described a rhombic modification of the $Mn(OH)_2$ which he found more or less altered in the limestone at Langban, Sweden; and he called it **bäckströmite**—after H. Bäckström.. X-radiograms of the altered mineral show that it has more or less changed to pyrochroite. The rhombic crystals have the axial ratios $a:b:c=0.7393:1:0.6918$. Some crystals have a good cleavage parallel to (010). Hydrated manganous oxide is formed as a white precipitate when alkali hydroxide is added to a soln. of a manganous salt. It is not soluble in an excess of alkali-lye, but is dissolved by ammonium chloride soln., and it gradually becomes brown on exposure to air. H. E. Patten observed that if precipitated from a soln. of manganous chloride and potassium sulphate, the precipitate is contaminated with adsorbed sulphate. E. Donath showed that the presence of glycerol, J. Lefort and P. Thibault the presence of gum arabic, and O. Tamm the presence of sodium tartrate or citrate, or cane-sugar, hinder the precipitation.

C. A. L. de Bruyn observed that a soln. of **colloidal manganous hydroxide** is formed by treating a soln. of a manganous salt with alkali in the presence of gelatin, or albumen (A. Trillat), nucleic acid (L. Sarason), or glycogen (L. Hugounenq and J. Loiseleur). W. Spring and G. de Boeck, and W. Knaust obtained it by treating a soln. of potassium permanganate with sodium hyposulphite. O. Fisseler prepared colloidal manganous hydroxide by adding the calculated quantity of manganese sulphate to a soln. of 3 grms. of sodium protalbinate or lysalbinate in water. By adding soda-lye, a milk-white turbidity is produced by the colloidal manganous hydroxide. This can be dialyzed, and evaporated over a water-bath at 70°, and finally over sulphuric acid in vacuo. The scaly product forms a brown sol with water. Kalle and Co. also prepared the colloid in an analogous way—*vide infra* for K. C. Sen and N. R. Dhar's observations. H. E. Patten observed that when alkali hydroxide is added to a soln. of a manganous salt, white, gelatinous manganous oxide is precipitated. The hydrated oxide adsorbs chlorides slightly and sulphates strongly, so that chlorides are not adsorbed in the presence of sulphates. The fine state of subdivision of the colloid favours its oxidation to the hydrated dioxide, and, according to G. Bertrand, and A. Villiers, the hydrated dioxide again forms colloidal manganous oxide in the presence of reducing agents like hydroquinone or gallic acid. The manganous hydroxide thus acts as an oxydase or oxygen-carrier in catalyzed reactions—*e.g.* the rapid drying of manganese oxide paints, varnishes, and siccatives—and A. Livache considers that the drying oil—*e.g.* linseed oil—plays the double rôle of protective colloid and oxygen-consuming reducing agent.

The hydrated oxide is partially precipitated by ammonia from soln. of manganous salts, and, according to C. Vincent, by dimethylaniline. H. Rose observed that tartaric acid hinders the precipitation by ammonia. According to W. Herz, a mixture of equal vols. of normal soln. of manganous sulphate and ammonium chloride in an atm. of hydrogen gives a cloudiness on the addition of about one and a half times the quantity of $0\cdot1N$-soln. of ammonia; the further addition of ammonia does not appreciably increase the precipitate, which is deposited after the mixture has remained for some hours. The reaction which takes place when manganous hydroxide is treated with soln. of ammonium chloride, nitrate, and sulphate in an atm. of hydrogen is expressed by the equation $Mn(OH)_2+2NH_4Cl \rightleftharpoons MnCl_2+2NH_4OH$. The reaction does not follow the laws of mass reaction, and the results do not agree with those obtained by J. M. Lovén for magnesium salts. The abnormal results are probably due to the combination of the manganese and ammonia to form complex cations. T. Curtius and F. Schrader found that hydrazine hydrate also precipitates the hydrated monoxide. H. W. Morse showed that there is evidence of a periodicity in the precipitation of the hydroxide. M. Pariselle and M. Laude discussed the joint precipitation of manganous hydroxide and alumina. W. Knaust studied the coagulation of the sol peptized by phosphoric acid.

R. Lorenz obtained the hydroxide electrolytically using a platinum cathode, a plate of manganese as anode, and aq. soln. of alkali chloride, sulphate, or nitrate. A. C. Becquerel obtained tabular crystals of the hydrated monoxide by electrocapillary action between soln. of potassium hydroxide and manganous nitrate. E. Weinschenk, and A. Commaille prepared crystals of the hydrate by allowing manganous oxide to stand in contact with ammoniacal soln. According to A. de Schulten, artificial pyrochroite is produced by the following process :

300 grms. of potassium hydroxide are dissolved in 500 c.c. of water, boiled for some

time in a flask through which a current of hydrogen or coal gas is passing, and a recently boiled soln. of 15 to 17 grms. of crystallized manganous chloride in 15 c.c. of water is introduced by means of a funnel with a stopcock. The flask is then heated to about 160°, when the whole of the manganous hydroxide dissolves. As the liquid cools, it deposits crystallized manganous hydroxide, and becomes almost solid. The crystals are washed with recently-boiled water, alcohol, and ether, and dried at a gentle heat in a current of hydrogen. If sodium hydroxide is used, the precipitate does not dissolve even in conc. soln. at 200°, but it becomes crystalline.

Pyrochroite is white, but becomes bronze-coloured and then black on exposure to air ; thin pieces appear flesh-coloured in transmitted light. The mineral usually occurs foliated like brucite, and, according to G. Flink, it furnishes trigonal, tabular, or columnar crystals with the axial ratio $a : c = 1 : 1.3999$; G. Aminoff gave 1 : 4004, and added that it is isomorphous with brucite. The basal cleavage is complete. The crystals were studied by J. Beckenkamp. W. Knaust observed that the precipitated hydrogel is at first amorphous, but becomes crystalline with increasing age. The hydrosol coagulates in 30 minutes at 100°, in 90 minutes at 80°, and in 255 minutes at 60°. G. Aminoff found that the X-radiograms agreed with a space-lattice having the dimensions $a = 3.34$ A., $c = 4.68$ A., and $a : c = 1 : 1.40$, and one mol. per unit cell. G. Natta discussed the isomorphism of the rhombohedral bivalent hydroxides from the point of view of the space-lattice, and the radius of the metal ions. G. Natta and L. Passerini studied the isomorphism of the cadmium and manganous hydroxides. H. Sjögren studied the percussion figures and observed that the birefringence is strong and negative ; and the indices of refraction for red-light are $\omega = 1.723$, and $\epsilon = 1.681$. The pleochroism is strong. A. de Schulten described the artificial crystals as flattened, transparent, hexagonal prisms as with polychroite. The crystals have a reddish tinge. The precipitated hydroxide is white and flocculent. G. Natta and L. Passerini observed the formation of solid soln. of manganous and cadmium hydroxides by precipitation. A. de Schulten gave 3.258 for the sp. gr. of the artificial crystals at 13° ; and H. Sjögren, 3.2435 for the mineral crystals. P. Hausknecht found the magnetic susceptibility to be nearly $2\frac{1}{2}$ times that of manganous oxide, and P. Koechlin gave 3.3. The hardness is 2 to 3. H. le Chatelier gave for the heat of formation $(Mn,O) = 90.8$ Cals. ; and $(Mn,O,H_2O) = 94.7$ Cals. J. Thomsen, 94.8 Cals., and M. Berthelot, 95.1 Cals. J. Thomsen gave for the heat of neutralization with sulphuric acid 26.48 Cals. ; hydrochloric acid, 22.95 Cals. ; nitric acid, 22.95 Cals. ; and dithionic acid, 22.78 Cals. J. Thomsen also gave for the heat of oxidation of the hydrated monoxide to the hydrated dioxide, 21.511 Cals. F. Allison and E. J. Murphy studied the magneto-optic properties.

J. Meyer and W. Gulbins found that when alkaline soln. of colloidal manganous hydroxide in gelatin are exposed to air, oxidation to manganic oxide occurs in a few days; if a few drops of perhydrol be present, the oxidation does not go entirely to manganic oxide ; with ammoniacal soln. manganic oxide is formed ; and with potassium manganicyanide, manganic hydroxide is formed. Alkaline soln. of colloidal manganous hydroxide were completely oxidized to manganic oxide in five days. O. Sackur and E. Fritzmann gave for the **solubility product** $[Mn^{..}][OH]^2 = 4 \times 10^{-14}$, and H. T. S. Britton, 1.3×10^{-14}. W. R. G. Atkins found that the precipitation of the hydroxide from a soln. of manganous chloride occurred when the H·-ion conc. is between $p_H = 8.6$ and 9.2 ; and H. T. S. Britton, when $p_H = 8.85$. The results for the **electrometric titration** of manganous chloride soln obtained by H. T. S. Britton with 0.9N-NaOH, and 100 c.c. of 0.24M-MnCl₂, at 18°, are summarized in Fig. 46. According to B. Schrager, manganous hydroxide shows acidic properties.

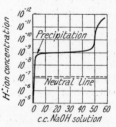

Fig. 46.—Electrometric Titration of a Solution of Manganous Chloride.

G. Aminoff observed that analyses of the mineral bäckströmite—*vide supra*—

show that the composition is nearer that of manganite. There is an excess of oxygen beyond that required for manganous oxide. The crystals represent double pseudomorphs, bäckströmite→pyrochroite→manganite. The compounds $Mg(OH)_2$, $Ca(OH)_2$, and $Cd(OH)_2$ form a trigonal series, and $Ca(OH)_2$ and $Zn(OH)_2$ a rhombic series.

A. de Schulten said that the crystalline hydroxide furnishes grey manganous oxide when it is heated in hydrogen. The white, precipitated hydroxide turns brown in air, forming, according to R. Phillips, brown, hydrated dioxide; and, according to W. Weldon, brown manganic hydroxide, or, in the presence of calcium hydroxide and chloride, calcium manganite. A. Gorgeu added that in the presence of water and an excess of manganous salt, it is rapidly oxidized to hydrated manganosic oxide, and then to hydrated manganic oxide. C. Engler and J. Weissberg found that some manganese dioxide and hydrogen dioxide are formed during the oxidation of manganous hydroxide. According to J. Meyer and R. Nerlich, manganous hydroxide in suspension or in colloidal soln. is oxidized by atm. air directly to manganese dioxide, whilst complex manganous salts in ammoniacal or alkaline soln. are oxidized to manganic hydroxide. Manganous ions are not oxidized at all by atm. oxygen. Acceptors such as sodium sulphite or arsenite had no influence on the velocity or course of the reaction. Manganous hydroxide precipitated by sodium, potassium, calcium, or barium hydroxide gave in each case manganese dioxide, but a soln. of manganous hydroxide in excess of ammonia in presence of ammonium chloride gave a precipitate of manganic hydroxide of a characteristic yellowish-brown colour—*vide infra*, manganous chloride. The subject was studied by D. Köszegi.

A. de Schulten observed that when the crystalline hydroxide is heated to redness in air, the manganosic oxide which is produced retains the form of the original hydroxide; and while crystalline manganous hydroxide alters very slowly in air, the oxidation proceeds rapidly in the presence of traces of alkali. The oxidation products were discussed by D. Köszegi. W. Herz gave 0.6×10^{-4} mol $Mn(OH)_2$ per litre for the solubility of the hydrated oxide; O. Sackur and E. Fritzmann gave 2.15×10^{-5} at $18°$; and O. Tamm gave 2×10^{-4}. A. Quartaroli observed that the hydroxide has no influence on the decomposition of hydrogen dioxide by silver oxide. F. Muck observed that the hydrated monoxide is rapidly oxidized to the hydrated dioxide by chlorine, and bromine, while the oxidation is slow with iodine. Crystalline manganous hydroxide was found by A. de Schulten to dissolve readily in hydrochloric acid, and in a soln. of ammonium chloride. R. H. Brett found that the soln. of manganous hydroxide, carbonate, or phosphate gives no precipitate with hydrogen sulphide. C. Langlois found that periodic acid is reduced to iodic acid. J. B. Senderens observed that when the hydroxide is boiled with sulphur and water, manganous thiosulphate is formed; and F. Muck noted that the fresh precipitate is easily transformed into manganous sulphide by ammonium sulphide, and with difficulty by sodium sulphide. J. Meyer and W. Schramm studied the action of sulphur dioxide (*q.v.*). F. Kuhlmann observed no reducing action on nitric oxide. O. Tamm found that the solubility of manganous hydroxide in a $0.5N$-soln. of sodium tartrate is 0.0068 mol per litre; $0.5N$-soln. of sodium malate, 0.0042 mol per litre; and $0.5N$-soln. of sodium citrate, 0.0126 mol per litre. E. Donath said that the hydroxide is soluble in glycerol soln.; and K. C. Sen and N. R. Dhar observed that manganous hydroxide is not precipitated by alkali hydroxide from soln. containing sucrose, dextrose, lævulose, galactose, lactose, mannose, dextrin, starch, or glycerol, probably owing to the peptization of the hydroxide to form a colloidal soln. C. and A. Tissier found that boric acid soln. dissolve it, forming a liquid stable in air. J. Post found that the hydrated monoxide is soluble in soln. of manganous chloride, and of calcium chloride. According to K. Milberg, freshly-precipitated manganous hydroxide reacts quantitatively with copper sulphate, forming manganous sulphate and copper hydroxide. H. Pélabon and M. Delwaulle investigated the action of mercuric chloride on manganous oxide, and obtained products analogous to those obtained by the action of mercuric oxide on manganous chloride (*q.v.*). R. Schenck and H. Wesselkock examined the accelerating influence of manganese oxide on the equilibrium between cobalt oxide and hydrogen.

REFERENCES.

[1] C. W. Blomstrand, *Ber.*, **8**. 130, 1875 ; *Geol. För. Förh. Stockholm*, **2**. 179, 1874 ; **3**. 123, 1876 ; G. Aminoff, *ib.*, **40**. 535, 1918 ; **41**. 407, 473, 1919 ; **43**. 389, 1921 ; L. Stahre, *ib.*, **4**. 163, 1878 ; A. E. Nordenskjöld, *ib.*, **4**. 163, 1878 ; R. Phillips, *Phil. Mag.*, (2), **5**. 209, 1829 ; (2), **6**. 281, 1829 ; A. Sjögren, *Geol. För. Förh. Stockholm*, **2**. 131, 531, 1874 ; **3**. 181, 1876 ; **4**. 158, 1878 ; *Neues Jahrb. Min.*, 538, 1877 ; 613, 1879 ; *Ber.*, **12**. 1723, 1879 ; H. Sjögren, *Geol. För. Förh. Stockholm*, **27**. 37, 1905 ; *Zeit. Kryst.*, **10**. 149, 1885 ; **32**. 611, 1900 ; **43**. 634, 1907 ; T. Curtius and F. Schrader, *Journ. prakt. Chem.*, (2), **50**. 321, 1894 ; H. St. C. Deville, *Compt. Rend.*, **53**. 199, 1861 ; M. Pariselle and M. Laude, *ib.*, **184**. 1176, 1927 ; J. J. Ebelmen, *ib.*, **33**. 535, 1851 ; *Ann. Chim. Phys.*, (3), **33**. 34, 1851 ; J. Nicklès, *ib.*, (3), **22**. 31, 1848 ; A. Gorgeu, *ib.*, (6), **4**. 523, 1885 ; *Bull. Soc. Chim.*, (2), **49**. 664, 1888 ; (3), **1**. 405, 1889 ; *Compt. Rend.*, **84**. 177, 1877 ; **106**. 703, 1888 ; **108**. 948, 1889 ; C. and A. Tissier, *ib.*, **39**. 102, 1854 ; **43**. 1187, 1856 ; A. de Schulten, *Oefvers. Finska Soc. Förh.*, **30**. 73, 1887 ; *Geol. För. Förh. Stockholm*, **10**. 129, 1888 ; *Bull. Soc. Min.*, **10**. 326, 1887 ; *Compt. Rend.*, **105**. 1265, 1887 ; H. le Chatelier, *ib.*, **122**. 80, 1896 ; A. Commaille, *ib.*, **63**. 556, 1866 ; G. Charpy, *ib.*, **148**. 560, 1909 ; A. B. du Jassonnaix, *ib.*, **139**. 1269, 1904 ; P. Sabatier and J. B. Senderens, *ib.*, **114**. 1429, 1892 ; **115**. 236, 1892 ; **120**. 618, 1895 ; *Ann. Chim. Phys.*, (7), **7**. 348, 1896 ; J. B. Senderens, *Bull. Soc. Chim.*, (3), **6**. 800, 1891 ; C. Vincent, *ib.*, (2), **33**. 156, 1880 ; A. Cornu, *ib.*, (2), **5**. 64, 1863 ; H. Pélabon and M. Delwaulle, *ib.*, (4), **47**. 156, 1930 ; J. Aloy and C. Rabaut, *ib.*, (4), **19**. 44, 1916 ; A. Guntz, *ib.*, (3), **7**. 275, 1892 ; *Compt. Rend.*, **114**. 115, 1892 ; A. Guntz and C. G. Särnstrom, *Tek. Tids.*, **23**. 61, 1893 ; *Zeit. angew. Chem.*, **6**. 729, 1893 ; A. Geuther, *Jena Zeit.*, **2**. 127, 1865 ; H. Laspeyres, *Journ. prakt. Chem.*, (2), **13**. 187, 1876 ; C. W. Scheele, *Svenska Akad. Handl.*, **35**. 89, 177, 1774 ; *Abhand. Akad. Stockholm*, **36**. 95, 183, 1774 ; *Opuscula chemica et physica*, Lipsiæ, **1**. 227, 1788 ; London, 53, 1901 ; *Crell's Die neuesten Entdeckungen in der Chemie*, **1**. 112, 140, 1781 ; *Nachgelassene Briefe und Aufzeichnungen*, Stockholm, 120, 1892 ; T. Bergman, *De mineris ferri albis*, Upsala, 1774 ; *Opuscula physica et chemica*, Lipsiæ, **2**. 184, 1792 ; London, **2**. 203, 1798 ; J. Bachmann, *Chemische Abhandlungen über des Mangan*, Wien, 1829 ; *Zeit. Phys. Math.*, (1), **6**. 172, 1829 ; (2), **1**. 262, 1832 ; *Schweigger's Journ.*, **56**. 74, 1829 ; R. Koechlin, *Tschermak's Mitt.*, (2), **35**. 9, 1921 ; P. Groth, *Chemische Krystallographie*, Leipzig, **1**. 118, 1906 ; J. M. Weeren, *Stahl Eisen*, **13**. 559, 1893 ; *Atomgewichtsbestimmung des Mangans*, Halle, 1890 ; J. J. Berzelius, *Afhand. Fys. Kemi*, **3**. 149, 1810 ; *Akad. Handl. Stockholm*, **35**. 212, 1813 ; *Pogg. Ann.*, **18**. 74, 1830 ; J. A. Arfvedson, *Afhand. Fys. Kemi*, **6**. 222, 1818 ; *Ann. Phil.*, **7**. 267, 1824 ; *Schweigger's Journ.*, **42**. 202, 1818 ; H. Rose, *Ausführliches Handbuch der analytischen Chemie*, Braunschweig, **1**. 77, 1851 ; H. Davy, *Phil. Trans.*, **102**. 181, 1812 ; P. Klein, *Jahresb. Schles. Ges.*, **56**. 63, 1879 ; F. Doerinckel, *Met.*, **8**. 201, 1911 ; E. Bertrand, *Bull. Soc. Min.*, **4**. 11, 1881 ; J. Morel, *ib.*, **15**. 9, 1892 ; S. Glinka, *ib.*, **10**. 63, 1887 ; C. Fontana, *Gazz. Chim. Ital.*, **56**. 396, 1926 ; G. R. Levi, *ib.*, **54**. 704, 1924 ; *Rend. Ist. Lombardo*, **57**. 619, 1924 ; V. Macri, *Boll. Chim. Farm.*, **58**. 201, 1919 ; G. Forchhammer, *Ann. Phil.*, **16**. 130, 1820 ; **17**. 50, 1821 ; *De mangano*, Hafnia, 1820 ; E. Turner, *Trans. Roy. Soc. Edin.*, **11**. 143, 1831 ; *Phil. Mag.*, (2), **4**. 22, 1828 ; C. M. Despretz, *Ann. Chim. Phys.*, (3), **43**. 322, 1855 ; H. Moissan, *ib.*, (5), **21**. 232, 1880 ; H. V. Regnault, *ib.*, (2), **62**. 349, 1836 ; (3), **1**. 129, 1841 ; J. L. Lassaigne, *ib.*, (2), **40**. 329, 1829 ; C. Langlois, *ib.*, (3), **34**. 257, 1852 ; P. Berthier, *ib.*, (2), **20**. 187, 1822 ; A. C. Becquerel, *Compt. Rend.*, **79**. 85, 1874 ; M. Meyer and B. Havas, *Sprech.*, **44**. 180, 1909 ; E. Priwoznik, *Liebig's Ann.*, **171**. 115, 1873 ; G. Rauter, *ib.*, **270**. 236, 1892 ; E. Newbery and J. N. Pring, *Proc. Roy. Soc.*, **92**. A, 276, 1916 ; J. von Liebig, *ib.*, **95**. 116, 1855 ; J. von Liebig and F. Wöhler, *Pogg. Ann.*, **21**. 584, 1831 ; C. F. Rammelsberg, *Sitzber. Akad. Berlin*, 97, 1885 ; *Pogg. Ann.*, **124**. 513, 1865 ; K. Stammer, *ib.*, **82**. 135, 1851 ; L. J. Igelström, *ib.*, **122**. 181, 1864 ; *Oefvers. Akad. Stockholm*, **21**. 205, 1886 ; G. Flink, *Biheng. Akad. Stockholm*, **12**. 2, 1886 ; *Bull. Geol. Inst. Upsala*, 9, 1900 ; *Neues Jahrb. Min.*, ii, 84, 1888 ; L. E. Rivot, F. S. Beudant and P. A. Daguin, *Ann. Mines*, (5), **4**. 221, 1853 ; C. Palache, *Amer. Journ. Science*, (4), **29**. 177, 1910 ; W. E. Ford, *ib.*, (4), **38**. 502, 1914 ; L. Santi, *Boll. Chim. Farm.*, **43**. 673, 1904 ; E. S. Larsen, *Bull. U.S. Geol. Sur.*, 679, 1921 ; A. Trillat, *Bull. Soc. Chim.*, (3), **31**. 811, 1904 ; *Compt. Rend.*, **138**. 274, 1904 ; G. Bertrand, *ib.*, **124**. 1032, 1355, 1897 ; A. Villiers, *ib.*, **124**. 1349, 1897 ; A. Livache, *ib.*, **97**. 1311, 1883 ; **124**. 1520, 1897 ; H. H. Meyer, *Mitt. Kaiser-Wilhelm Inst.*, Düsseldorf, **9**. 273, 1927 ; K. Honda and T. Sone, *Science Rep. Tohoku Univ.*, **3**. 139, 1914 ; T. W. Case, *Phys. Rev.*, (2), **9**. 305, 1917 ; E. L. Nichols and D. T. Wilbur, *ib.*, (2), **17**. 707, 1921 ; V. M. Goldschmidt, *Skrift. Norske Akad.*, 1, 1926 ; 1, 1927 ; D. Müller, *Beiträge zur anorganischen Thermochemie mit der kalorimetrischen Bombe*, Braunschweig, 1929 ; H. Ott, *Zeit. Kryst.*, **63**. 222, 1926 ; J. Beckenkamp, *ib.*, **58**. 32, 1923 ; G. Natta, *Gazz. Chim. Ital.*, **58**. 344, 1928 ; G. Natta and L. Passerini, *ib.*, **58**. 597, 1928 ; **59**. 129, 144, 1929 ; *Atti Cong. Naz. Chim.*, **3**. 365, 1929 ; L. Passerini, *Gazz. Chim. Ital.*, **59**. 144, 1929 ; **60**. 535, 1930 ; A. Quartaroli, *ib.*, **57**. 234, 1927 ; P. Hausknecht, *Magnetochemische Untersuchungen*, Strassburg, 1913 ; J. Fiedler, *De lucis effectibus chemicis in corpora anorganica*, Uratislaviæ, 1835 ; R. H. Brett, *Phil. Mag.*, (3), **10**. 95, 1837 ;

H. von Jüptner, *Beiträge zur Theorie der Eisenhüttenprozesse*, Stuttgart, 8, 1907 ; O. F. Tower, *Zeit. phys. Chem.*, **18**. 17, 1895 ; R. W. Millar, *Journ. Amer. Chem. Soc.*, **50**. 1875, 1928 ; R. Schenck and H. Wesselkock, *Zeit. anorg. Chem.*, **184**. 39, 1929 ; I. Meydell, *ib.*, **186**. 289, 1930 ; W. Biltz, A. Lemke and K. Meisel, *ib.*, **186**. 373, 1930 ; F. de Carli, *Gazz. Chim. Ital.*, **56**. 55, 1926 ; W. A. Roth, *Arch. Eisenhüttenwesen*, **3**. 339, 1929 ; *Stahl Eisen*, **49**. 1763, 1929 ; *Zeit. angew. Chem.*, **42**. 981, 1929 ; R. Wasmuth, *ib.*, **43**. 98, 125, 1930 ; H. W. Morse, *Journ. Phys. Chem.*, **34**. 1555, 1930 ; K. Hilgenstock, *Der Schwefel im Eisen*, Erlangen, 1893 ; L. H. Bauer and H. Berman, *Amer. Min.*, **15**. 340, 1930 ; B. Schrager, *Coll. Czech. Chem. Comm.*, **1**. 275, 1929 ; W. Spring and G. de Boeck, *Bull. Soc. Chim.*, (2), **48**. 170, 1887 ; W. Knaust, *Ueber Sole von Eisenhydroxyd und Manganhydroxyd in ihrer Beziehung zur Bildung der sogenannten Schutzminden und des Laterits*, Jena, 1930 ; *Chemie Erde*, **4**. 529, 1930 ; H. Styri, *Journ. Iron Steel Inst.*, **108**. ii, 189, 1923 ; O. Meyer, *Ueber die Darstellung und die Eigenschaften von Karbid- und Nitridtiegeln nebst einem Beitrag über die Reaktionen von Karbiden und Graphit mit Metalloxyden*, Aachen, 1929 ; *Arch. Eisenhüttenwesen*, **4**. 193, 1930 ; O. Houghton, *Chem. Met. Engg.*, **30**. 739, 1924 ; E. H. Schulz and A. Kanz, *Mitt. Forschungsinst. Stahlw.*, **1**. 2, 1928 ; H. S. Taylor and A. T. Williamson, *Journ. Amer. Chem. Soc.*, **53**. 813, 1931 ; P. Oberhoffer and K. d'Huart, *Stahl Eisen*, **39**. 165, 196, 1919 ; C. Benedicks and H. Löfquist, *Non-Metallic Inclusions in Iron and Steel*, London, 72, 1930 ; E. Nishibori, *Chikashige's Aniv. Vol.*, 295, 1930 ; L. Kahlenberg and W. J. Trautmann, *Zeit. Amer. Electrochem. Soc.*, **39**. 377, 1921 ; L. Wöhler and O. Balz, *Zeit. Elektrochem.*, **27**. 406, 1921 ; V. Kohlschütter and J. L. Tüscher, *ib.*, **27**. 225, 1921 ; K. C. Sen and N. R. Dhar, *Koll. Zeit.*, **33**. 193, 1923 ; J. Meyer and R. Nerlich, *Zeit. anorg. Chem.*, **116**. 117, 1921 ; J. Meyer and W. Gulbins, *ib.*, **155**. 66, 1926 ; J. Meyer and W. Schramm, *ib.*, **132**. 226, 1923 ; R. Lorenz, *ib.*, **12**. 436, 1896 ; J. Milbauer, *ib.*, **42**. 433, 1904 ; W. Biltz, *ib.*, **127**. 169, 572, 1923 ; **193**. 321, 1930 ; *Zeit. phys. Chem.*, **67**. 572, 1909 ; W. Biltz and H. Müller, *Zeit. anorg. Chem.*, **163**. 257, 1927 ; P. Sabatier and A. Mailhe, *Compt. Rend.*, **158**. 830, 985, 1914 ; L. Hugounenq and J. Loiseleur, *ib.*, **182**. 851, 1926 ; G. Beck, *ib.*, **156**. 288, 1926 ; **182**. 334, 1929 ; H. N. Mittra and N. R. Dhar, *ib.*, **122**. 146, 1922 ; E. Tiede and E. Birnbräuer, *ib.*, **87**. 129, 162, 1914 ; R. Whytlaw Gray, J. B. Speakman and E. Thomson, *Nature*, **107**. 619, 1921 ; E. Thomson, *ib.*, **107**. 520, 553, 1921 ; H. T. S. Britton, *Journ. Chem. Soc.*, **127**. 2110, 1925 ; W. R. G. Atkins, *Trans. Faraday Soc.*, **18**. 310, 1923 ; M. Berthelot, *Thermochimie*, Paris, **2**. 265, 1897 ; C. R. A. Wright and A. E. Menke, *Journ. Chem. Soc.*, **37**. 28, 1880 ; C. R. A. Wright and A. P. Luff, *ib.*, **33**. 522, 1878 ; H. C. Greenwood, *ib.*, **93**. 1491, 1908 ; D. L. Hammick, *ib.*, **111**. 379, 1917 ; V. H. Veley, *ib.*, **37**. 581, 1880 ; **41**. 56, 1882 ; S. P. O. Pickering, *ib.*, **37**. 128, 1890 ; *Chem. News*, **44**. 189, 201, 213, 225, 1881 ; C. H. Burgess and A. Holt, *ib.*, **88**. 269, 1903 ; *Proc. Chem. Soc.*, **19**. 221, 1903 ; *Trans. Cer. Soc.*, **5**. 163, 1906 ; L. Playfair and J. P. Joule, *Mem. Chem. Soc.*, **3**. 37, 1846 ; Kalle and Co., *German Pat.*, *D.R.P.* 180729, 1901 ; L. Sarason, *ib.*, 272386, 1913 ; F. Glaser, *Zeit. anorg. Chem.*, **36**. 1, 1903 ; W. Herz, *ib.*, **21**. 243, 1899 ; **22**. 279, 1899 ; J. M. Lovén, *ib.*, **11**. 404, 1896 ; R. Lorenz and F. Heusler, *ib.*, **3**. 225, 1893 ; K. Milberg, *Chem. Ztg.*, **30**. 511, 1906 ; H. E. Patten, *Journ. Amer. Chem. Soc.*, **25**. 186, 1903 ; F. Allison and E. J. Murphy, *ib.*, **52**. 3796, 1930 ; E. J. Cuy, *ib.*, **49**. 201, 1927 ; C. A. L. de Bruyn, *Zeit. phys. Chem.*, **29**. 562, 1898 ; *Rec. Trav. Chim. Pays-Bas*, **19**. 236, 1900 ; E. R. Schneider, *Liebig's Ann.*, **113**. 37, 1860 ; *Phil. Mag.*, (4), **18**. 268, 1859 ; *Pogg. Ann.*, **107**. 605, 1859 ; C. von Hauer, *Journ. prakt. Chem.*, (1), **72**. 360, 1857 ; *Sitzber. Akad. Wien*, **25**. 124, 1857 ; F. Muck, *Zeit. Chem.*, (2), **6**. 6, 1870 ; *Sitzber. Niederrh. Ges. Bonn*, 204, 1869 ; O. Fisseler, *Ueber colloidale Verbindungen des Eisens, Mangans, und Kupfer*, Erlangen, 1904 ; N. Parravano and G. Malquori, *Gazz. Chim. Ital.*, **58**. 279, 1928 ; C. Engler and J. Weissberg, *Kritische Studien über Autoxydation*, Braunschweig, 111, 1904 ; J. Thomsen, *Thermochemische Untersuchungen*, Leipzig, **3**. 270, 1883 ; *Ber.*, **6**. 1434, 1873 ; T. Rowan, *ib.*, **4**. 858, 1871 ; *Chem. News*, **23**. 79, 1871 ; E. Wedekind, *Zeit. angew. Chem.*, **33**. 87, 1924 ; E. Wedekind and C. Horst, *Ber.*, **45**. 262, 1912 ; **48**. 105, 1915 ; C. Horst, *Ueber die Abhängigkeit der Magnetisierbarkeit anorganischer Verbindungen von der Wertigkeit des Hauptelementes, untersucht an den Oxyden und Sulfiden einiger Schwermetalle*, Freiburg, 1912 ; F. Kessler, *Zeit. anal. Chem.*, **11**. 270, 1872 ; P. Théodoridès, *Ann. Sciences Genève*, (5), **3**. 161, 1912 ; *Compt. Rend.*, **171**. 948, 1920 ; *Journ. phys. Rad.*, (6), **3**. 1, 1922 ; D. C. Knab, *Brit. Pat. No.* 3082, 1877 ; *Chem. Ind.*, **2**. 221, 1878 ; J. Mactear, *ib.*, **9**. 77, 1886 ; *Brit. Pat. No.* 10813, 1884 ; F. Kuhlmann, *Dingler's Journ.*, **211**. 25, 1874 ; R. Wagner, *ib.*, **195**. 532, 1870 ; E. Donath, *ib.*, **229**. 542, 1878 ; J. N. von Fuchs, *Schweigger's Journ.*, **60**. 345, 1830 ; E. Broch, *Zeit. phys. Chem.*, **127**. 446, 1927 ; W. Weldon, *Brit. Pat. No.* 4079, 1883 ; E H. Williams, *Phys. Rev.*, (2), **28**. 167, 1926 ; J. Lefort and P. Thibault, *Pharm. Journ.*, (3), **13**. 301, 1882 ; E. Weinschenk, *Centr. Min.*, 487, 1905 ; *Zeit. Kryst.*, **17**. 486, 1890 ; O. Lüdecke, **11**. 255, 1886 ; J. Post, *Verh. Beford. Gewerbefl. Preussen*, **158**. 468, 1879 ; E. G. L. Roberts and E. A. Wraight, *Journ. Iron Steel Inst.*, **70**. ii, 229, 1906 ; O. Sackur and E. Fritzmann, *Zeit. Elektrochem.*, **15**. 842, 1909 ; J. D. Dana, *A System of Mineralogy*, New York, 253, 1892 ; O. Tamm, *Zeit. phys. Chem.*, **74**. 496, 1910 ; G. A. Kenngott, *Die Minerale der Schweiz nach ihren Eigenschaften und Fundorten*, Leipzig, 294, 1866 ; *Uebersicht der Resultate mineralogischer Forschungen*, Leipzig, 1868 ; *Neues Jahrb. Min.*, 440, 1866 ; D. F. Wiser, *ib.*, 510, 1842 ; W. Haidinger, *Handbuch der bestimmenden Mineralogie*, Wien, 493, 1845 ; W. Herapath, *Phil. Mag.*, (1), **64**. 321, 1824 ; A. J. Bradley, *ib.*, (6), **50**. 1018, 1925 ; A. von Kiss and F. E. Lederer, *Rec. Trav. Chim. Pays-Bas*, **46**. 453, 1927 ; J. V. Vaughan and W. A. Lazier, *Journ. Amer. Chem. Soc.*, **53**. 3719, 1931 ; A. T. Williamson and H. S. Taylor, *ib.*, **53**. 3270, 1931 ; C. Montemartini and A. Vernazza, *Boll. Staz. Sperim. Ind. Pelli*, **9**. 276, 1931 ; J. H. Andrew, W. R. Mad-

docks and D. Howat, *Journ. Iron Steel Inst.*, **125**. ii, 283, 1931; J. H. Andrew, W. R. Maddocks
and E. A. Fowler, *ib.*, **125**. ii, 295, 1931; D. Köszegi, *Zeit. anal. Chem.*, **86**. 346, 1931; E. Diepschlag and E. Horn, *Stahl Eisen*, **51**. 329, 1931; *Arch. Eisenhüttenwesen*, **4**. 375, 1931; *Ueber
die Umsetzungen von Eisensulfid, Mangansulfid und Kalziumsulfid mit den Oxyden des Eisens
und dabei auftretende Nebenreaktionen*, Düsseldorf, 1931; G. L. Clark, A. Ally and A. E. Badger,
Amer. Journ. Science, (5), **22**. 539, 1931; M. le Blanc and H. Sachse, *Phys. Zeit.*, **32**. 887,
1931.

§ 9. Manganosic Oxide, or Manganese Tritatetroxide

The *schwarz Braunsteinerz* of A. G. Werner,[1] the *schwarz Manganerz* of
D. L. G. Karsten, and the *blättricher schwarz Braunstein* of J. F. L. Hausmann
were called by W. Haidinger **hausmannite**—after J. F. L. Hausmann. It occurs
near Ilmenau, Thuringia; Ilefeld, Harz; Filipstad, Wermland; Längban, Jakobsberg, Nordmark, and Grythyttan, Sweden; Framont, Alsace, etc. Analyses
reported by E. Turner, W. V. Smitheringale, C. F. Rammelsberg, H. D. Miser and
J. G. Fairchild, L. J. Igelström, and A. Gorgeu are in agreement with the formula
for **manganosic oxide**, $MnO.Mn_2O_3$—that is, **manganese tritatetroxide**, Mn_3O_4.
Similarly with analyses of the artificial product reported by J. A. Arfvedson,
J. J. Berzelius, T. Bergman, G. Forchhammer, E. R. Schneider, and M. Schaffner.
P. Berthier regarded this oxide as a compound, $2MnO.MnO_2$, on account of its
behaviour towards conc. nitric acid; and R. Hermann adopted a similar hypothesis
because Mn_3O_4 and Fe_3O_4 are not isomorphous; and the hypothesis was favoured
by C. F. Rammelsberg, and B. Franke. H. Laspeyres regarded it as a salt of the
acid $H_{10}MnO_8$, namely, Mn_5MnO_8. A. Gorgeu at first adopted P. Berthier's hypothesis, but later, in view of O. T. Christensen's observation that dil. acetic acid
splits the oxide into manganous and manganic acetates, and H. Rose's observations
on the action of a soln. of ammonium chloride, he regarded it as *manganous hypomanganite*, $MnO.Mn_2O_3$, or $Mn(MnO_2)_2$. H. D. Miser and J. G. Fairchild represented
it by the formula Mn_2MnO_5. P. Groth, and several other writers also regard it as
a salt of *orthomanganous acid*, H_4MnO_4, namely, $Mn_2(MnO_4)$, or *manganous ortho-
manganite*. J. Meyer and R. Kanters—*vide supra*—showed that Mn_3O_4 is better
regarded as $MnO.Mn_2O_3$, than as $2MnO.MnO_2$.

Manganese tritatetroxide is formed when manganese oxidizes in air at ordinary
temp., and more rapidly when heated in oxygen; the powdered metal oxidizes with
a glow. Manganous oxide glows when heated in air, forming this oxide, and it is
also formed, according to H. V. Regnault, when manganous oxide is heated in
steam. The higher oxides of manganese form the tritatetroxide when strongly
heated. T. Sidot obtained crystals of the oxide in this way. W. Biltz represented
the reaction by the equation: $6Mn_2O_3 = 4Mn_3O_4 + O_2 - 50.4$ Cals., and found for
the press. of the oxygen, p atm., at different temp. :

	887°	940°	1007°	1090°	1127°
p . . .	0.045	0.21	0.42	1.00	2.69

This subject was examined by P. Askenasy and S. Klonowsky, C. R. Fresenius,
L. Wöhler and O. Balz, C. Friedheim, and F. A. Gooch and M. Austin—*vide infra*,
manganese hemitrioxide. C. R. A. Wright and A. P. Luff, I. L. Bell, and
C. R. Fresenius also observed that the tritatetroxide is formed when manganous
carbonate or hydroxide is vigorously heated in air; and J. L. Lassaigne obtained
a similar result with manganous oxalate. J. Volhard obtained it by heating a
mixture of mercuric oxide and manganous chloride. Crystals of the tritatetroxide
are formed, according to H. St. C. Deville, when the amorphous oxide is heated
to redness in a slow current of hydrogen chloride. C. von Hauer obtained the
crystals by heating ammonium manganous chloride or a mixture of ammonium
chloride and manganous oxide in air; H. Debray, by strongly heating a mixture
of manganous and potassium sulphate; A. Daubrée, and H. Debray, by heating

manganous chloride in steam ; A. E. Nordenskjöld, by heating the amorphous oxide with borax ; F. Kuhlmann, by roasting a mixture of calcium chloride and manganous oxide ; P. Ebell, by heating the oxide with glass—on cooling the manganese tritatetroxide separates out in crystals ; and L. Bourgeois, by heating a mixture of manganese dioxide and silica. F. Kuhlmann also observed crystals of this oxide as a furnace product.

Hausmannite occurs granular and massive, as well as crystalline, and its colour is brownish-black with a chestnut-brown, or, according to J. L. C. Schröder van der Kolk, a reddish-brown streak. Hence it is also called *red oxide of manganese*. O. Mügge said that in very thin layers the **colour** is deep brownish-red. W. Biltz discussed the colour of the derivatives of this oxide. The tetragonal **crystals** were found by W. Haidinger to have the axial ratio $a : c = 1 : 1.1743$; G. Flink gave $1 : 1.1573$, and V. Goldschmidt, $1 : 1.1554$. The habit is usually octahedral ; the (113)-faces are usually bright and smooth, the (111)-face striated, and the (111) : (113)-edge, dull. **Twinning** occurs about the (101)-plane, and the twinning may be repeated to fivelings. The (001)-**cleavage** is nearly perfect, but the (101)- and (111)-cleavages are indistinct. The crystals were also examined by H. Dauber, J. Orcel and S. Pavlovitch, and R. Koechlin. M. L. Huggins examined the structure by the **X-radiogram** method. G. Aminoff found that the X-radiograms of the crystals agree with the assumption that the space-lattice is body-centred and tetragonal, with $a = 5.75$, and $c = 9.42$ A., or face-centred, with $a = 8.14$, and $c = 9.42$ A. There are eight mols. of $Mn(Mn_2O_4)$ per unit cell. The general structure resembles that of magnetite, except that the axial ratio is $a : c \rightleftharpoons 1 : 1.16$ instead of $1 : 1$. W. V. Smitheringale discussed the X-radiogram, and the etching of the mineral with different etching liquids ; G. A. Thiel also discussed the action of various reagents—hydrochloric and sulphuric acids, hydrogen dioxide, and soln. of ferrous and stannous chlorides. S. Holgersson observed no evidence of a cubic form.

C. F. Rammelsberg gave 4.856 for the **specific gravity** of hausmannite ; W. Haidinger, 4.722 ; and A. Gorgeu, 4.91. For the artificial oxide A. Gorgeu gave 4.80 ; L. Playfair and J. P. Joule, 4.325 to 4.746 ; and C. F. Rammelsberg, 4.718 ; and for the dispersed oxide H. P. Walmsley gave 4.709. The **hardness** of hausmannite is 5.0 to 5.5. The coeff. of cubical **thermal expansion** was found by L. Playfair and J. P. Joule to be 0.00522 between 0° and 100°. E. Jannettaz made observations on the relative **heat conductivity** of the crystals in different directions. P. E. W. Oeberg gave 0.1520 for the **specific heat**. R. W. Millar found the **molecular heat** of manganosic oxide, Mn_3O_4, to be :

	$-200.8°$	$-169.4°$	$-121.1°$	$-72.6°$	$-20.5°$	$-1.5°$	$32.2°$
C_p .	9.725	15.02	22.14	27.37	31.28	32.45	33.46

The results are plotted in Fig. 36. J. Maydell studied the mol. ht. G. Spezia observed that hausmannite melts to a black enamel in the gas-flame fed with warm air ; and O. Mügge observed that no oxygen is given off or absorbed between 940° and 1300°. H. von Wartenberg and W. Gurr gave 1705° for the **melting-point**. M. Berthelot, and H. le Chatelier both found the **heat of formation** to be $(3Mn,2O_2)$ $= 328$ Cals. ; D. Müller, and W. A. Roth, 345 Cals. ; and O. Ruff and E. Gersten, 329 Cals. A. Simon and F. Feher gave $(6MnO,O_2) = 72$ Cals. ; R. W. Millar gave 35.73 for the **entropy** of Mn_3O_4 ; and for the reaction $3Mn + 2O_2 = Mn_3O_4$ he gave the change of entropy -84.6 at 25°, and for the change of **free energy**, $-302,800$ cals. E. S. Larsen gave for the **indices of refraction** $\omega = 2.46$, and $\epsilon = 2.15$. The crystals are not pleochroic and the optical character is negative. R. D. Harvey examined the **electrical conductivity.** T. W. Case observed no change in the electrical conductivity on exposure to light. W. Flight observed no **thermoelectric current** with hausmannite. E. Wedekind and C. Horst found the **magnetic susceptibility** to be 65.5×10^{-6} mass unit at 15.5°. E. Feytis found 74.3×10^{-6}. K. Honda and T. Sone found that the magnetic susceptibility, $\chi \times 10^6$, changes abruptly with temp. at 1080°, corresponding with the passage of manganosic oxide to manganous oxide :

	$-175°$	$-99°$	$20°$	$304°$	$559°$	$794°$	$1080°$	$1198°$
$\chi \times 10^6$.	126·0	76·0	55·8	40·7	33·3	28·2	25·6	24·7

J. Meyer and R. Kanters observed that the chemical behaviour of manganosic oxide favours the view that the manganese in it is tervalent, and that the oxide is to be regarded as $MnO.Mn_2O_3$, rather than as $2MnO.MnO_2$. When manganosic oxide is heated to redness in **hydrogen,** it is reduced to manganous oxide (q.v.). According to W. Müller, when manganese dioxide is heated in hydrogen at 202°, it forms Mn_3O_4; and, according to H. Moissan, the artificial dioxide in dry hydrogen at 230° passes into Mn_2O_3, and at a higher temp. into MnO. W. Müller said that the action with Mn_3O_4 begins near 330°, and progresses slowly at 360°, while C. R. A. Wright and A. P. Luff found that the reduction of the amorphous oxide begins at 255°; and F. Glaser found that manganese dioxide passes into manganosic oxide in hydrogen, and at 296° it passes into manganous oxide. E. R. Schneider found that when heated in **oxygen,** manganosic oxide passes into manganic oxide, and, added A. Gorgeu, this occurs the more easily the finer the state of subdivision ; the oxidation begins at 170° and involves the intermediate formation of $2MnO.3MnO_2$. A. Gorgeu, and M. Martinon also studied the action of **hydrogen dioxide**—*vide infra,* manganese dioxide. F. J. Otto observed that when heated with **hydrochloric acid,** manganous chloride and chlorine are formed. H. Rose observed that a hot soln. of **ammonium chloride** dissolves manganous oxide, leaving a residue of manganic oxide, while when manganosic oxide is heated with ammonium chloride, manganous chloride is formed. H. Rose also observed that when heated with **sulphur** in hydrogen, manganese sulphide is formed. C. W. Davis studied the action of sulphurous acid. E. Turner found that when treated with boiling **sulphuric acid** (1 : 11), a soln. of manganous sulphate and nearly the theoretical proportion of manganese dioxide—$Mn_3O_4=2MnO+MnO_2$— are formed—*vide infra,* manganosic sulphate. G. Forchhammer found that with hot, conc. sulphuric acid, oxygen and manganous sulphate are formed ; and when heated with potassium hydrosulphate, 100 parts of manganosic oxide give 7·566 parts of oxygen—theory for $Mn_3O_4=3MnO+O$ corresponds with 7 parts of oxygen. According to P. Berthier, and G. Forchhammer, boiling conc. or dil. **nitric acid** extracts manganous oxide, and leaves manganese dioxide, in accord with $Mn_3O_4=2MnO+MnO_2$. The influence of mercury on the action was studied by J. Meyer and R. Kanters : $Mn_3O_4 +2Hg+8HNO_3=2HgNO_3+3Mn(NO_3)_2+4H_2O$. H. Rose found that when treated with syrupy **phosphoric acid,** manganic phosphate is formed. P. Berthier found that manganosic oxide is reduced to the metal when it is heated to a high temp. with **carbon.** F. Fischer and F. Bangert observed that **methane** reacts with the oxide at 800° to 1000° to form a carbide. A. Kutzelnigg observed that a soln. of **potassium ferrocyanide** is oxidized by manganosic oxide. The trita-tetroxide is reduced when heated with **carbon monoxide,** forming manganous oxide (q.v.)— I. L. Bell said that the reaction occurs at the m.p. of zinc ; C. R. A. Wright and A. P. Luff found that the action begins at 240°. O. T. Chris-

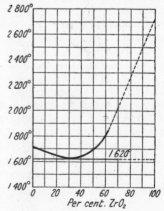

FIG. 47.—The Melting-Point Curve of the System : ZrO_2–Mn_3O_4.

tensen found that **acetic acid** attacks the calcined oxide the less the stronger the acid, and at 100° the acetic acid forms a mixture of manganous and manganic acetates. H. C. Bolton found that **citric acid** attacks hausmannite, and if potassium iodide is present, a brownish-red soln. is formed. W. Thomson and F. Lewis studied the action on **indiarubber.** H. von Wartenberg and W. Gurr found that **zirconia** reacts with manganosic oxide, Mn_3O_4, as summarized by the m.p. curve, Fig. 47. According to R. Wagner, when manganosic oxide is heated with **alkali carbonate and nitrate** out of contact with air, nitric oxide is given off : $6Mn_3O_4 + 2KNO_3 = 9Mn_2O_3 + K_2O + 2NO$; the product does not form a green colour when dissolved in dil. soda-lye.

Manganosic oxide dissolves in hot, conc. phosphoric acid, hot acetic acid, and cold, conc. sulphuric, hydrochloric, oxalic, or tartaric acids without neutralizing the acid. The soln. in phosphoric and sulphuric acids are columbine-red, and those in the other acids are daik brown. The liquids probably contain a mixture of manganic and manganous salts. Heating, diluting with water, or treating with reducing agents transforms the soln. into that of a manganous salt. If the soln. in acid be treated with potash-lye, what has been regarded as **hydrated manganosic oxide** is precipitated. According to F. J. Otto, when an ammoniacal soln. of manganous chloride containing ammonium chloride is treated with an excess of freshly-precipitated hydrated manganese dioxide, and the soln. gradually heated, a yellowish-brown hydrated manganosic oxide is precipitated. O. T. Christensen prepared it by a similar process. According to F. J. Otto, a similar product is obtained when ammonia is added to an ammoniacal soln. of manganous chloride, containing ammonium chloride, which has been exposed to the air for a long time. It is also formed by the action of an ammoniacal soln. of ammonium sulphite on hydrated manganese dioxide—the reaction is slow in the cold, but rapid if heated. A. Gorgeu obtained it by shaking a soln. of a manganous salt with alkali in air ; C. F. Rammelsberg, by allowing a soln. of a manganous salt to stand exposed to air for a long time ; and H. Schjerning, by the action of a mixture of sodium sulphide and thiosulphate on potassium permanganate. R. Lorenz made the hydrated oxide by electrolyzing an aq. agitated soln. of sodium chloride, sulphate, or nitrate with a platinum cathode and a manganese anode.

The yellowish-brown product has a slight tinge of red. F. J. Otto added that it is not altered by a boiling soln. of ammonium chloride, but it is decomposed by dil. acids into a manganous salt and brownish-black hydrated dioxide. According to O. T. Christensen, the colour of the precipitated hydrated oxide may be yellow, brown, reddish-brown, or chocolate-brown, according to conditions of formation. A. Gorgeu obtained it as a chocolate-brown crystalline mass, and found that dil. nitric oxide yields two-thirds of the manganese as manganous nitrate and one-third as hydrated dioxide. The air-dried hydrate contains 3·5 to 27 per cent. of water, and that dried in vacuo has 2·5 to 7 per cent. of water. J. Post found that if hydrated manganosic oxide be heated 15·5 his. to 250° to 300°, it takes up oxygen to form manganic oxide.

L. L. Fermor described a mineral from Beldongu, Central Provinces, India, and called it **vredenburgite.** Its composition approximates $3Mn_3O_4.2Fe_2O_3$. It forms brownish-black or chocolate-brown octahedral or tetragonal pyramids of sp. gr. 4·74 to 4·84 and hardness 6·5. The mineral **rancieite,** or *rancierite,* a hydrated manganese oxide from Rancié, Ariège, France, was described by A. Leymerie, and A. Lacroix, and was probably the *manganèse argentin* of R. J. Haüy. According to J. O. Haas, that from Lacampe, Aude, France, has the formula $MnO_2.2MnO.2H_2O$, with some bivalent manganese replaced by lime, ferrous iron, or alkalies. The sp. gr. is 3·25 to 3·30.

REFERENCES.

[1] R. Lorenz, *Zeit. anorg. Chem.,* **12.** 436, 1896 ; H. Rose, *Pogg. Ann.,* **121.** 318, 1864 ; *Sitzber. Akad. Berlin,* 200, 1848 ; *Ausführliches Handbuch der analytischen Chemie,* Braunschweig, **1.** 78, 1851 ; F. J. Otto, *Liebig's Ann.,* **93.** 372, 1855 ; J. Volhard, *ib.,* **198.** 330, 1879 ; M. Schaffner, *ib.,* **51.** 168, 1863 ; H. D. Miser and J. G. Fairchild, *Journ. Washington Acad.,* **10.** 1, 1920 ; O. T. Christensen, *Journ. prakt. Chem.,* (2), **28.** 1, 1883 ; *Zeit. anorg. Chem.,* **27.** 322, 1901 ; F. A. Gooch and M. Austin, *ib.,* **17.** 264, 1898 ; *Amer. Journ. Science,* (4), **5.** 260, 1898 ;

R. W. Millar, *Journ. Amer. Chem. Soc.*, **50**. 1875, 1928 ; C. R. Fresenius, *Zeit. anal. Chem.*, **11**. 290, 1872 ; R. Wagner, *ib.*, **18**. 553, 1879 ; C. Friedheim, *ib.*, **38**. 690, 1899 ; B. Franke, *Journ. prakt. Chem.*, (2), **36**. 31, 166, 451, 1889 ; H. Laspeyres, *ib.*, (2), **13**. 186, 1876 ; H. Schjerning, *ib.*, (2), **45**. 528, 1892 ; R. Hermann, *ib.*, (1), **43**. 50, 1848 ; *Pogg. Ann.*, **74**. 303, 1848 ; M. Martinon, *Bull. Soc. Chim.*, (2), **43**. 355, 1885 ; E. Turner, *Trans. Roy. Soc. Edin.*, **11**. 143, 1831 ; *Phil. Mag.*, (2), **4**. 22, 1828 ; L. L. Fermor, *Mem. Geol. Sur. India*, **37**. 44, 1909 ; H. C. Bolton, *Ann. New York Acad.*, **1**. 158, 1879 ; *Chem. News*, **38**. 168, 1878 ; I. L. Bell, *ib.*, **23**. 258, 1871 ; C. F. Rammelsberg, *Pogg. Ann.*, **14**. 222, 1828 ; **124**. 523, 1865 ; *Handbuch der Mineralchemie*, Leipzig, 178, 1860 ; 144, 1875 ; *Sitzber. Akad. Berlin*, 97, 1885 ; C. von Hauer, *Sitzber. Akad. Wien*, **13**. 453, 1854 ; H. Moissan, *Ann. Chim. Phys.*, (5), **21**. 233, 1880 ; J. L. Lassaigne, *ib.*, (2), **40**. 329, 1929 ; P. Berthier, *ib.*, (2), **20**. 187, 1822 ; H. V. Regnault, *ib.*, (2), **62**. 349, 1836 ; J. A. Arfvedson, *Afhand. Fys. Kemi*, **6**. 222, 1818 ; *Ann. Phil.*, **7**. 267, 1824 ; *Schweigger's Journ.*, **42**. 202, 1818 ; J. J. Berzelius, *Afhand. Fys. Kemi*, **3**. 149, 1810 ; *Akad. Handl. Stockholm*, **35**. 212, 1813 ; *Pogg. Ann.*, **18**. 74, 1830 ; G. Forchhammer, *Ann. Phil.*, **16**. 130, 1820 ; **17**. 50, 1821 ; *De mangano*, Hafnia, 1820 ; T. Bergman, *De mineris ferri albis*, Upsala, 1774 ; *Opuscula physica et chemica*, Lipsiæ, **2**. 184, 1792 ; London, **2**. 203, 1798 ; R. D. Harvey, *Econ. Geol.*, **23**. 778, 1928 ; W. Müller, *Pogg. Ann.*, **136**. 51, 1869 ; A. E. Nordenskjöld, *ib.*, **114**. 612, 1861 ; E. R. Schneider, *ib.*, **107**. 605, 1859 ; H. Dauber, *ib.*, **94**. 406, 1855 ; C. R. A. Wright and A. P. Luff, *Journ. Chem. Soc.*, **33**. 522, 1878 ; A. Gorgeu, *Bull. Soc. Chim.*, (2), **49**. 665, 1888 ; (3), **3**. 606, 1890 ; (3), **9**. 653, 1893 ; (3), **29**. 1109, 1903 ; *Bull. Soc. Min.*, **16**. 139, 1893 ; *Compt. Rend.*, **84**. 177, 1877 ; **96**. 1144, 1883 ; **106**. 743, 1888 ; **110**. 857, 1890 ; H. le Chatelier, *ib.*, **122**. 80, 1896 ; F. Kuhlmann, *ib.*, **52**. 1283, 1861 ; H. St. C. Deville, *ib.*, **53**. 199, 1861 ; H. Debray, *ib.*, **52**. 985, 1861 ; A. Daubrée, *Ann. Mines*, (5), **1**. 124, 1852 ; T. Sidot, *Compt. Rend.*, **69**. 201, 1869 ; E. Feytis, *ib.*, **152**. 710, 1911 ; L. Wöhler and O. Balz, *Zeit. Elektrochem.*, **27**. 406, 1921 ; W. Biltz, *Zeit. phys. Chem.*, **67**. 572, 1909 ; *Zeit. anorg. Chem.*, **127**. 169, 372, 1923 ; A. Lacroix, *Minéralogie de la France et de ses colonies*, Paris, **4**. 25, 1910 ; P. Ebeil, *Dingler's Journ.*, **220**. 64, 155, 1876 ; R. J. Haüy, *Traité de minéralogie*, Paris, **4**. 245, 1801 ; J. Post, *Verh. Beford. Gewerbefl. Preussen*, **58**. 468, 1879 ; L. Playfair and J. P. Joule, *Journ. Chem. Soc.*, **1**. 121, 1849 ; *Mem. Chem. Soc.*, **3**. 80, 1846 ; A. G. Werner, *Berg. Journ.*, 386, 1789 ; J. F. L. Hausmann, *Handbuch der Mineralogie*, Göttingen, 293, 1813 ; 405, 1847 ; D. L. G. Karsten, *Mineralogische Tabellen*, Berlin, 72, 100, 1808 ; W. Haidinger, *Edin. Journ. Science*, **4**. 41, 1826 ; *Pogg. Ann.*, **7**. 232, 1926 ; *Trans. Roy. Soc. Edin.*, **11**. 127, 1827 ; L. J. Igelström, *Oefvers. Akad. Stockholm*, 606, 1865 ; G. Flink, *Bihang. Svenska Akad. Handl.*, **16**. 4, 1890 ; *Arkiv Kemi Min. Geol.*, **3**. 35, 1910 ; *Geol. För. Förh. Stockholm*, **41**. 329, 1919 ; V. Goldschmidt, *Krystallographische Winkeltabellen*, Berlin, 172, 1897 ; P. Groth, *Chemische Krystallographie*, Leipzig, **2**. 307, 1908 ; J. L. C. Schröder van der Kolk, *Centr. Min.*, 80, 1901 ; O. Mügge, *ib.*, 73, 1916 ; J. R. Blum, *Die Pseudomorphosen des Mineralreichs*, Stuttgart, 169, 260, 1843 ; E. S. Larsen, *Bull. U.S. Geol. Sur.*, 679, 1921 ; M. Berthelot, *Thermo-chimie*, Paris, **2**. 265, 1897 ; W. V. Smitheringale, *Econ. Geol.*, **24**. 481, 1929 ; G. A. Thiel, *ib.*, **19**. 107, 1924 ; J. Meyer and R. Kanters, *Zeit. anorg. Chem.*, **185**. 172, 178, 1929 ; J. Maydell, *ib.*, **186**. 289, 1930 ; H. von Wartenberg and W. Gurr, *ib.*, **196**. 374, 1931 ; W. A. Roth, *Zeit. angew. Chem.*, **42**. 981, 1929 ; *Arch. Eisenhuttenwesen*, **3**. 339, 1929 ; *Stahl Eisen*, **49**. 1763, 1929 ; S. Holgersson, *Fysiogr. Sellk. Handl.*, **38**. 1, 1929 ; *Arsskr. Lunds Univ.*, (2), **23**. 9. 1929 ; *Rönt-genographische Untersuchungen der Mineralien der Spinellgruppe und von synthetisch dargestellten Substanzen von Spinelltypus*, Lund, 1927 ; E. Diepschlag and F. Wulfestieg, *Journ. Iron Steel Inst.*, **120**. ii, 297, 1929 ; F. Fischer and F. Bangert, *Brennstoff Chem.*, **10**. 261, 1929 ; C. W. Davis, *Rept. Investigations U.S. Bur. Mines*, 3024, 1930 ; A. Kutzelnigg, *Ber.*, **63**. B, 1753, 1930 ; P. E. W. Oeberg, *Oefvers. Akad. Förh.*, 8, 1885 ; O. Ruff and E. Gersten, *Ber.*, **46**. 405, 1913 ; E. Wedekind, *Zeit. angew. Chem.*, **33**. 87, 1924 ; E. Wedekind and C. Horst, *Ber.*, **45**. 262, 1912 ; **48**. 105, 1915 ; C. Horst, *Ueber die Abhängigkeit der Magnetisierbarkeit anorganischer Verbin-dungen von der Wertigkeit des Hauptelementes, untersucht an den Oxyden und Sulfiden einiger Schwermetalle*, Freiburg, 1912 ; D. Müller, *Beiträge zur anorganischen Thermochemie mit der kalorimetrischen Bombe*, Braunschweig, 1929 ; E. Jannettaz, *Bull. Soc. Min.*, **15**. 137, 1892 ; L. Bourgeois, *ib.*, **6**. 66, 1883 ; J. O. Haas, *ib.*, **44**. 95, 1921 ; A. Leymerie, *Bull. Soc. Geol.*, **20**. 245, 1862 ; J. Orcel and S. Pavlovitch, *Compt. Rend.*, **187**. 1295, 1928 ; H. P. Walmsley, *Phil. Mag.*, (7), **7**. 1097, 1929 ; C. Doelter and E. Hussak, *Neues Jahrb. Min.*, i, 175, 1884 ; M. L. Hug-gins, *Phys. Rev.*, (2), **21**. 719, 1923 ; K. Thaddéeff, *Zeit. Kryst.*, **20**. 350, 1892 ; G. Aminoff, *ib.*, **64**. 475, 1927 ; G. Spezia, *Atti Accad. Torino*, **22**. 419, 1887 ; W. Flight, *Phil. Mag.*, (4), **30**. 339, 1865 ; T. W. Case, *Phys. Rev.*, (2), **9**. 305, 1917 ; R. Koechlin, *Tschermak's Mitt.*, (2), **27**. 260, 1908 ; F. Glaser, *Zeit. anorg. Chem.*, **36**. 1, 1903 ; R. J. Meyer and K. Rötgers, *ib.*, **57**. 104, 1908 ; K. Rötgers, *Die Dissoziationtemperaturen der Manganoxyde MnO₂ und Mn₂O₃ in Luft- und Sauer-stoff-atmosphäre*, Berlin, 1907 ; P. Askenasy and S. Klonowsky, *Zeit. Elektrochem.*, **16**. 107, 1910 ; S. Klonowsky, *Ueber die Manganatschmelze und die Ueberführung von Kaliunmanganat in Kaliumpermanganat auf elektrolytischen Wege*, Karlsruhe, 1910 ; K. Honda and T. Sone, *Science Rep. Tohoku Univ.*, **3**. 139, 1914 ; A. Simon and F. Feher, *Zeit. Elektrochem.*, **38**. 137, 1932 ; W. Thomson and F. Lewis, *Proc. Manchester Lit. Phil. Soc.*, **4**. 266, 1891 ; *Chem. News*, **64**. 169, 1891.

§ 10. Manganic Oxide, or Manganese Hemitrioxide

The mineral **braunite**—named after M. Braun—was described by W. Hai dinger [1]; it was called *Hartbraunstein* by J. F. L. Hausmann; *marceline*, by F. S. Beudant; *Heterokline*, by A. Breithaupt; and *leptonematite* and *pesillite*, by M. Adam. It occurs near Ilmenau, and Elgersburg, Thuringia : Ilefeld, Harz ; St. Marcel, Piedmont ; at Elba ; at Botnedal, Norway ; at Jakobsberg, Längban, Grythyttan, and Glakärn, Sweden ; Vizianagram, Bimlipatam, etc., in India ; and in the Wellington district, etc., in New South Wales. Analyses were reported by C. F. Rammelsberg, F. Buckeisen, H. Rose, J. J. Berzelius, P. Berthier, A. J. Scott, F. R. Mallet, G. Flink, C. von Evreinoff, W. Elderhorst, A. A. Damour, T. Scheerer, E. Turner, E. Schweizer, G. Meneghini, B. Jezek, A. Gorgeu, A. Liversidge, and L. L. Fermor. Braunite is usually associated with silica, and C. F. Rammelsberg represented it by the formula $3Mn_2O_3.MnSiO_3$, and later gave $MnO.(Mn,Si)O_2$. A. Gorgeu regarded it as a salt with the general formula $RO(Mn,Si)O_2$; whilst G. Flink, and L. L. Fermor represented it by the formula $mRMnO_3.nRSiO_3$ where $m : n$ is usually between $4 : 1$ and $3 : 1$; R is mainly Mn. E. Turner probably overlooked the presence of silica, and represented braunite by the formula Mn_2O_3, but R. F. Penrose, and G. Meneghini reported samples respectively from Arkansas and Elba to be virtually free from silica. F. von Kobell regarded the silica as a non-essential constituent of braunite. R. Hermann regarded the mineral as a compound $MnO.MnO_2$, and this is in agreement with E. Turner's observations that dil. acids decompose the mineral into a mixture of MnO and MnO_2. G. Rose pointed out that braunite appears to have a constitution different from that of artificial manganese hemitrioxide, which can replace alumina and ferric oxide in epidote and manganic alum, while braunite seems to behave like a salt. O. T. Christensen regarded braunite as a sesquioxide, but H. Laspeyres supposed it to be a manganese salt of orthomanganous acid, H_6MnO_6, namely, Mn_3MnO_6, and P. Groth considered braunite to be a salt of metamanganous acid, H_2MnO_3, namely, $MnMnO_3$, mixed with more or less metasilicate, $MnSiO_3$. The artificial oxide was analyzed by G. Forchhammer, J. A. Arfvedson, H. Davy, J. F. John, H. Moissan, and E. R. Schneider ; and J. Meyer and R. Kanters showed that it contains tervalent manganese.

According to J. R. Blum, braunite occurs in nature in pseudomorphs after manganite. S. Meunier prepared black, octahedral crystals with a brown streak by melting manganese dioxide with cryolite—some corundum, and manganese aluminate are formed at the same time. According to J. J. Berzelius, and R. Hermann, manganese hemitrioxide is formed when manganese dioxide or manganous nitrate is heated to dull redness in air. E. R. Schneider obtained the hemitrioxide by heating the dioxide, the tritatetroxide, or the monoxide in oxygen. W. Dittmar found that at the temp. of a bunsen flame manganese tritatetroxide is the main product. C. F. Rammelsberg obtained the hemitrioxide by heating manganite at dull redness, and L. Carius by heating artificial manganic hydroxide. W. Biltz represented the reaction with manganese dioxide by the equation : $4MnO_2 = 2Mn_2O_3 + O_2 - 30.9$ Cals., and he found for the press. of oxygen, p atm., at different temp. :

	477°	530°	565°	587°
p	0.065	0.21	1.00	1.20

R. J. Meyer and K. Rötgers found that the reactions $MnO_2 \rightleftharpoons Mn_2O_3 \rightleftharpoons Mn_3O_4$ are reversible, and that manganese dioxide passes into the hemitrioxide at 530° in air and at 565° in oxygen ; while manganese hemitrioxide passes into the tritatetroxide at 940° in air and 1090° in oxygen—*vide supra*, manganese tritatetroxide. These observations are not fully in agreement with those of P. Askenasy and S. Klonowsky, discussed in connection with manganese dioxide. H. Moissan observed that the artificial dioxide in dry hydrogen passes into the hemitrioxide at 230°. R. Bunsen and G. Krieger observed that when precipitated by means of sodium carbonate from a mixed soln. of a manganous salt and a copper, calcium, strontium, barium, magnesium, zinc, cadmium, lead, or bismuth salt, and the washed precipitate is calcined in air, the manganous hydrate is converted into manganese hemitrioxide ; and A. Classen obtained a similar result when a mixed precipitate of zinc and manganese oxalates is similarly treated.

J. Meyer and R. Kanters observed that precipitated manganic oxide is more reactive chemically before it has been calcined ; this is shown by its solubility in a soln. of ammonium chloride. M. Berthelot observed that dry manganous iodide burns like tinder when heated in oxygen, forming iodine and manganese hemitrioxide ; and manganous bromide behaves in an analogous manner at a dull red-heat. M. Berthelot found that dry manganous chloride forms the hemitrioxide when heated in dry oxygen ; and D. C. Knab obtained a similar result by heating the chloride in air. According to C. M. Tessié du Motay, when steam is passed over an alkali manganate at 450°, oxygen is given off and a mixture of alkali hydroxide and manganese hemitrioxide remains. O. Michel and E. Grandmougin found that when manganese dioxide is heated in ammonia gas, nitrogen, water, and the hemitrioxide are formed. C. Lepierre observed the formation of the hemitrioxide when manganous carbonate is heated with molten potassium nitrate ; and W. Spring and M. Lucion, when a mixture of barium dioxide and manganous chloride is triturated in a mortar. H. B. Weiser and G. L. Mack prepared an **organosol** of manganic oxide in propyl alcohol.

Braunite occurs massive and also crystalline. The colour is dark brownish-black to steel-grey. W. Biltz discussed the colour of the derivatives of this oxide. W. Haidinger found the crystals to be tetragonal, with the axial ratio $a : c = 1 : 0.9850$, and the habit is octahedral, with the angles nearly isometric ; G. Flink gave $a : c = 1 : 0.99218$. M. J. Schuster regarded the crystals as rhombohedral with a tetartohedral development, but this is doubtful. The (001)-faces of the crystals are faintly striated ; the (221)-faces are uneven and striated ; and the (421)-faces are smooth and even. Twinning occurs about the (101)-plane ; the (111)-cleavage is perfect. M. L. Huggins examined the structure by the X-radiogram method. P. E. Wretblad found that the cubic crystals have $a = 9.391$ A. G. Aminoff, and W. V. Smitheringale discussed the X-radiograms, and the action of various etching reagents. G. A. Thiel also studied the action of various reagents—hydrochloric and sulphuric acids, hydrogen dioxide, and soln. of ferrous and stannous chlorides. The crystals were examined by G. vom Rath, J. Orcel and S. Pavlovitch, A. Schmidt, and G. Flink. C. Drucker and R. Hüttner made some observations on the X-radiograms. W. Zachariasen found the X-radiogram corresponds with the rhombohedron with hexagonal axes of the corundum type of space-lattice with $a = 9.41$; and in bixbyite, $(Fe,Mn)_2O_3$, $a = 9.35$ A. The oxygen atoms are distant 2.10 A., and in bixbyite, 2.08 A. P. E. Wretblad gave for the cubic oxide $a = 9.391$ A. The sp. gr. of braunite is 4.75 to 4.82 ; S. Pavlovitch gave 4.81 ; and for the black hemitrioxide C. F. Rammelsberg gave 4.325 ; and K. S. Rao, 4.22 to 4.8. The hardness of braunite is 6.0 to 6.5. S. Pavlovitch found that braunite, in nitrogen at 1190°, formed minute crystals, and at 1400°, in 4 hrs., 2.78 to 3.80 per cent. of oxygen was evolved. E. Jannettaz compared the thermal conductivity in different directions of the crystals, and obtained an isothermal ellipse with an eccentricity of 0.85. P. E. W. Oeberg found the sp. ht. to be 0.1620 between 15° and 99°. If the hemitrioxide be strongly heated, G. Forchhammer, and R. Hermann found that it loses 3.05 to 3.50 per cent. of oxygen and passes into the tritatetroxide. A. Gorgeu, W. Dittmar, W. Biltz, and R. J. Meyer and K. Rötgers made observations on this subject—*vide supra*. A. Simon and F. Feher gave for the heat of formation $4Mn_3O_4 + O_2 \rightarrow 6Mn_2O_3 + 54$ Cals. C. Doelter said that braunite is opaque to the X-rays. W. Flight observed a thermoelectric current. L. L. Fermor found that Indian braunite is magnetic, and if a high proportion of iron is present, the magnetism is strong. K. S. Rao found that braunite is paramagnetic ; and it has an axis of minimum magnetizability. R. D. Harvey examined the electrical conductivity ;

and E. Diepschlag and F. Wulfestieg, the high temp. conductivity of mixtures with magnesia, alumina, and silica. E. Wedekind and C. Horst found the magnetic susceptibility to be $41 \cdot 99 \times 10^{-6}$ mass unit. K. S. Rao gave $0 \cdot 4 \times 10^{-3}$ for the maximum susceptibility. There is an axis of maximum symmetry with a perpendicular plane in which the susceptibility is independent of orientation. Along the axis of symmetry the susceptibility is a minimum, and in the plane a maximum ; the difference is about 2 per cent. K. Honda and T. Sone found that the change of magnetic susceptibility, $\chi \times 10^6$, with temp. undergoes a transition about 933° as manganic oxide passes to manganosic oxide :

	$-184°$	$-90°$	$-4°$	$21°$	$116°$	$388°$	$669°$	$928°$	$990°$
$\chi \times 10^6$.	150·0	99·2	73·0	69·0	58·4	42·9	33·8	27·9	27·7

The hemitrioxide was found by W. Müller to be reduced to manganous oxide by hydrogen at a red-heat ; S. Hauser found the reduction occurs between 243° and 262° ; and F. Glaser said that at 230° it is reduced by hydrogen to the tritatetroxide. O. T. Christensen obtained similar results with other reducing agents. For M. Martinon's observations on the action of hydrogen dioxide, *vide infra*, manganese dioxide. O. T. Christensen found that when the oxide is heated with hydrochloric acid, it forms manganous chloride, with the evolution of oxygen ; it dissolves in hot, conc. sulphuric acid with the evolution of oxygen, and, according to E. Turner, it also dissolves in boiling, dil. sulphuric acid. K. Thaddéeff found that the native manganese oxides give a violet colour when heated with conc. sulphuric acid diluted with its own vol. of water. P. Berthier observed that with boiling nitric acid part of the manganese passes into soln. as manganous nitrate, and part remains undissolved as manganese dioxide. O. T. Christensen found that when the hemitrioxide is treated with dil. sulphuric or nitric acid, half the manganese passes into soln. ; but, according to J. Meyer and R. Kanters, if mercury be present : $Mn_2O_3 + 2Hg + 6HNO_3 = 2HgNO_3 + 2Mn(NO_3)_2 + 3H_2O$. Calcined manganese hemitrioxide is only slightly attacked by acetic acid. W. Heintz found that with phosphoric acid manganous phosphate is formed. W. H. Coghill and J. B. Clemmer studied the soap flotation of the manganese oxides.

In 1772, J. B. L. Romé de l'Isle [2] described the crystals of a mineral which he called *manganaire cristallisée* ; and in 1804, R. J. Haüy described it as *manganèse oxyde métalloïde* ; while A. G. Werner, L. A. Emmerling, and M. H. Klaproth called it *Graubraunsteinerz* ; J. F. L. Hausmann, *Graubraunstein* ; D. L. G. Karsten, and C. C. von Leonhard, *Graumanganerz* ; A. Breithaupt, *Glanzmanganerz* ; C. Hartmann, *Braunmanganerz* ; F. A. Quenstedt, *Braunmangan* ; F. Mohs, and R. Jameson, *prismatoidal or prismatic manganese ore* ; W. Haidinger, **manganite ;** F. S. Beudant, *acerdèse*—from ἀκερδής, unprofitable—in allusion to its being of little value as a bleaching agent for glass ; and T. Thomson, *newkirkite* from Neukirchen, Alsace. Manganite occurs in Cornwall, Cumberland, Devonshire, and Somerset, England ; Aberdeenshire, Scotland ; Ross and Dublin, in Ireland ; Piedmont, Emilia, Bologna, Ravenna, Scandiano, Tuscany, and Sardinia, Italy ; Alemtejo, Portugal ; Estremadura, Jaén, Huelva, Aragonia, Ternel, Zamora, and Asturia, Spain ; Hautes-Pyrénées, Ariège, Pyrénées-Orientales, Aude, Isère, Vosges, Mayenne, and Basses-Pyrénées, France ; Ilefeld, Harz ; Ilmenau and Oehrenstock, Thuringia ; Undenaes and Längban, Sweden ; Christiansand, Norway ; Bogoslowsk and Jekaterinburg, Urals ; Transcaucasus ; Owani, Japan ; Cape Colony and French Congo, Africa ; Santiago, Cuba ; Tarapaca, Chili ; Tarma, and Bongara, Peru ; Negaunee, Michigan ; Douglas Co., Colorado ; Nova Scotia, New Brunswick, Gloucester Co., King's Co., and Restigouche Co., Canada ; Victoria. Analyses of the mineral by L. Gmelin, E. Turner, C. F. Rammelsberg, A. Gorgeu, C. M. Kersten, V. Sevoz and J. Breuilhs, J. A. Arfvedson, W. H. Hobbs, H. How, C. W. Blomstrand, C. C. von Leonhard, L. C. Beck, G. Dupouy, and F. Kovar correspond approximately with **hydrated manganese hemitrioxide,** $Mn_2O_3.H_2O$, or $H_2Mn_2O_6$. The so-called *manganese ochre* found by G. de Geer in the neighbourhood of Upsala is an impure hydrated hemitrioxide or tritatetroxide ; and likewise also a deposit found by G. di Boccard in the neighbourhood of Eugania. When the artificial product is dried at 100° B. Franke, and J. Meyer found that it approximates in composition to $Mn_2O_3.H_2O$. H. Laspeyres regarded manganite as a derivative of a hypothetical acid, $H_{10}MnO_8$—namely, $H_4Mn_3MnO_8$ or $2H_2Mn_2O_4$ with bivalent manganese; P. Groth represented it as a derivative of $Mn(OH)_3$ by the loss of water to form $MnO(OH)$, and W. W. Coblentz's observations on the ultra-red spectrum showed that the absorption band of hydroxyl is present but no water bands. C. F. Rammelsberg found that, unlike braunite and hausmannite, manganite is not decomposed by conc. nitric acid, and concluded that it is a true sesquioxide like geothite and diaspore. On the contrary, A. Gorgeu found that boiling nitric acid acts on the finely-powdered mineral, converting half the manganese into manganous nitrate and half into hydrated manganese dioxide ; hence he wrote the formula $MnO.MnO_2.H_2O$. B. Franke also found that the artificial oxide with dil. sulphuric acid forms a manganous salt and hydrated manganese dioxide : $Mn : O_2 : Mn : (OH)_2+H_2SO_4=MnSO_4+H_2O+(HO)_2MnO$, and he therefore regarded it as being constituted with bi- and quadrivalent manganese :

$$Mn{\diagup O \atop \diagdown O}Mn{\diagup OH \atop \diagdown OH}$$

M. Sem discussed this subject ; and he supposed that there are two classes of manganic salts, distinguished by their colour—violet and brown—but J. Meyer said that this is not right, because manganic salts exist in soln. in various colours—violet, brown, red, dark green, and olive-green ; and the whole of these differently coloured soln. have practically identical absorption spectra. F. Hebler regarded the artificial hydrate—variously written $Mn_2O_3.H_2O$, $MnO_2(HO)_2$, and $HMnO_2$—to be hydrogels ; but F. Wilborn considered natural manganite to be a definite compound.

L. Carius obtained hydrated manganese hemitrioxide by heating to 138° finely-divided, artificial manganese dioxide with conc. sulphuric acid, mixing the soln. of manganic sulphate in sulphuric acid with an excess of water, and washing the resulting precipitate with water. B. Franke obtained it by the action of dil. soda-lye on a soln. of potassium manganic sulphate. It is not certain what are the products obtained by P. Berthier by the action of chlorine, not in excess, on manganous carbonate suspended in water, and by R. Hermann by passing air through a soln. of a manganous salt in ammoniacal ammonium chloride. According to F. Kuhlmann, in a furnace for calcining the residue in the manufacture of chlorine from manganese dioxide and hydrochloric acid, when mixed with limestone, black crystals of manganese tritatetroxide were obtained, which, according to A. des Cloizeaux, are pseudomorphs after manganite. According to C. M. Kersten, crystals of manganite are formed in the thermal springs of Carlsbad ; and, according to R. W. Townsend, and J. Noggerath, they are likewise formed in the thermal springs of Cape Colony. According to A. Anargyros, what was probably **colloidal manganic oxide** was obtained by reducing potassium permanganate by sodium arsenite at 65° to 70°. The brown colloidal soln. can be kept for over a month ; it liberates oxygen from hydrogen dioxide—more rapidly in alkaline than in neutral soln. H. B. Weiser and G. L. Mack prepared an organosol with propyl alcohol.

Manganite occurs in columnar and, more rarely, in granular masses ; it also occurs in stalactic masses, and in crystals which are frequently grouped in bundles. The colour is dark steel-grey or iron-black, and J. L. C. Schröder van der Kolk said that the streak is reddish-brown or black. T. Thomson, and J. F. L. Hausmann found that the colour of thin splinters in transmitted light is sometimes brown. J. Meyer said that when formed by the hydrolysis of manganic cyanide, it is a black, gelatinous mass, which becomes less hydrated when heated with the mother-liquor, and it then changes in colour from black to brown, resembling ferric hydroxide. The colour change is due either to the decomposition of the hydrate or to a change in the size and physical character of the particles. J. Meyer and R. Nerlich found that the oxidation of a soln. of manganous chloride made alkaline by ammonia, and mixed with ammonium chloride, is the most convenient way of making manganic oxide—*vide infra*, manganous chloride. According to W. Haidinger, the rhombic crystals of manganite have the axial ratios $a : b : c = 0.84407 : 1 : 0.54484$. Contact twinning occurs about the (011)-plane. There are also cruciform twinning and often repeated twinning with the composition face parallel or inclined, analogous to rutile. The prismatic crystals may be long and terminated by the (001)-face or by a zone of macropyramids with the planes striated parallel to their mutual intersections. The prismatic crystals may be short and terminated by the (001)-face with numerous macrodomes or by highly complex macropyramids. The prismatic faces are deeply striated vertically. The crystals were described by J. B. L. Romé de l'Isle, R. J. Haüy, W. Phillips, F. Mohs, C. F. Naumann, J. D. Dana, A. Sadebeck, V. Goldschmidt, F. Zambonini, F. Rutley, T. Haege, A. Lévy, K. Busz, R. Brauns, A. Lacroix, G. P. Traverso, P. Groth, A. d'Achiardi, E. Manasse, W. P. Jervis, R. P. Greg and W. G. Lettsom, J. H. Collins, M. F. Heddle, L. H. Borgström, J. Samojloff, A. Raimondi, W. H. Hobbs, G. Rose, S. R. B. Cook and co-workers, etc. The hemihedral crystals were discussed by P. Groth, W. Haidinger, and A. Sadebeck ; the corrosion figures, by R. Koechlin ; and the isomorphism with diaspore and goethite, by G. Rose, A. Breithaupt, and J. F. L. Hausmann, and with chrysoberyl, by E. Kayser. G. Flink described rhombic crystals of what he called *sphenomanganite* from Längban, Sweden ; the mineral closely resembles manganite. The (010)-cleavage of manganite is perfect ; and the (110)- and (001)-cleavages are distinct. W. H. Zachariasen found that the X-radiogram corresponds with a body-centred space-lattice of the corundum type with $a = 9.41$ A. and the calculated density of 5.00. W. V. Smitheringale studied the X-radiograms, and also the action of various etching liquids on manganite. G. A. Thiel also discussed the action of various reagents—sulphuric and hydrochloric acids, hydrogen dioxide, and soln. of ferrous and stannous chlorides. W. F. de Jong obtained for the space-lattice of manganite $a = 4.46$ A., $b = 5.28$ A., and $c = 2.88$ A. A. Ferrari and A. Scherillo gave $a = 4.41$ A., $b = 5.19$ A., and $c = 2.83$ A., with 2 mols. of $MnO(OH)$ per unit cell.

The sp. gr. given by C. F. Rammelsberg is 4.335 ; W. Haidinger, 4.312 to 4.338 ; A. Gorgeu, 4.34 to 4.39 ; and E. Manasse, 4.27. The hardness ranges from 3 to 4. O. Mügge found that the crystals embedded in sodium nitrate, and at a press. of 4300 kgrms. per sq. cm., suffer a displacement along the (010)- and parallel to the (001)-faces. The sp. ht., according to H. Kopp, is 0.176 between 20° and 52°. J. Königsberger found that the extinction coeff. for $\lambda = 0.5$ to 4.0μ is 15 ; for $\lambda = 1.6$ to 4.0μ, 14 ; for $\lambda = 4.0$ to 40μ, 56 ; and for $\lambda = 15$ to 40μ, 78 ; the reflecting power is 0.25 ; and the observed absorption is 200 times greater than the value calculated from the electrical conductivity. E. S. Larsen gave for the index of refraction $a = 2.24$, $\beta = 2.24$, and $\gamma = 2.53$; J. Orcel and S. Pavlovitch discussed the optical properties of the mineral. J. Königsberger observed that the birefringence is very strong ; and, added E. S. Larsen, the optical character is negative. W. W. Coblentz found that no sharp bands occur in the ultra-red transmission spectrum over the region extending to 9μ, but there are faint bands at 3μ (hydroxides) and at 6.2μ. R. D. Harvey examined the electrical conductivity. F. Beijerinck found that if manganite is free from pyrolusite, it is a non-conductor of electricity. K. Honda and T. Sone gave for the magnetic susceptibility of manganic oxide, Mn_2O_3 :

	−184°	−90°	−4°	21°	194°	510°	876°	1100°	1318°
$\chi \times 10^6$.	150.0	99.2	73.0	69.0	53.0	38.4	30.4	27.7	25.4

E. H. Williams discussed the structure of the paramagnetic oxide. J. R. Blum found that in nature manganite is readily transformed into pyrolusite, hausmannite, and braunite. J. Meyer and R. Nerlich observed that the acid hydrolysis of man-

ganic salts leads to the formation of manganese dioxide and manganous salt, whilst
alkaline hydrolysis merely precipitates manganic hydroxide. By acid hydrolysis,
however, probably manganic hydroxide is first formed and at once decomposed,
since it is shown that manganic hydroxide is decomposed by dil. mineral acids into
manganese dioxide and manganous salt. That manganic hydroxide is a true
tervalent manganese compound is probable from the fact that dil. hydrofluoric
acid, hydrocyanic acid, and oxalic acid dissolve it completely, to form complex
manganic compounds. Conc. sulphuric, selenic, phosphoric, and hydrochloric
acids also dissolve it completely, but conc. nitric acid oxidizes it completely to
manganese dioxide. K. Fredenhagen and G. Cadenbach studied the action of
hydrofluoric acid on the oxide.

L. Carius observed that when manganite is heated in air, it forms manganese
tritatetroxide ; and A. Gorgeu added that at 300° it forms pseudomorphous
manganese dioxide, while braunite remains unchanged. B. Franke found that the
artificial crystals lose no water at 120°, but at higher temp. water is given off.
N. Kurnakoff and V. Cernych said that a loss of water without the loss of oxygen
occurs when manganite is heated to 365°–400°. M. Martinon found that with an
acidic soln. of hydrogen dioxide, oxygen is given off and manganous oxide is formed ;
and in an alkaline soln. manganese dioxide is first formed, which then decomposes
the hydrogen dioxide. J. Meyer found that the precipitated manganic hydroxide
forms an unstable soln. with conc. hydrochloric acid and a stable soln. with
hydrofluoric acid. A. Wagner found that hydrogen sulphide slowly forms
manganous sulphide and sulphate, sulphur, and water. J. Meyer and W. Schramm
observed that the reaction of sulphur dioxide with manganic hydroxide suspended
in water proceeds in two ways, the manganic sulphite first formed decomposing
according to the equations $Mn_2(SO_3)_3 = MnSO_3 + MnS_2O_6$, and $Mn_2(SO_3)_3 = MnSO_4$
$+MnSO_3 + SO_2$; there is no reduction to manganous salts, nor any decomposition
of the manganic salt into manganous salts and the dioxide. The solvent action of
sulphurous acid was studied by C. W. Davis. According to L. Carius, with conc.
sulphuric acid at 100° green manganic sulphate is formed without the evolution
of oxygen. H. C. H. Carpenter observed the formation of manganous sulphate and
dithionate by the action of sulphurous acid on the hydrated oxide, $Mn_2O_2(OH)_2$.
B. Franke observed that the hydrated oxide may be decomposed by hot, conc.
sulphuric acid to form manganous sulphate and $MnO_2.H_2O$, as indicated above.
L. Carius found that dil. sulphuric acid, cold or gently warmed, does not decompose
manganite free from manganous oxide, but if that oxide be present, some manganite
may be dissolved. J. Meyer said that precipitated manganic hydroxide forms
stable soln. with sulphuric and phosphoric acids. P. Berthier found that manganese
hemitrioxide is decomposed by conc. nitric acid, forming manganous nitrate and
hydrated manganese dioxide. H. C. Bolton found that manganite is attacked by
citric acid less readily than pyrolusite. R. Hermann observed that the hemitrioxide forms a reddish-brown soln. with tartaric acid, and in 24 hrs. the soln.
deposits manganous tartrate and forms formic acid and carbon dioxide ; oxalic
and malic acids are reduced, with the evolution of carbon dioxide, and a manganous
salt is formed. Formic, acetic, benzoic, and hippuric acids are without action.
E. Reichardt found that when moist manganite mixed with magnesia alba, or
alkali carbonate, with or without water, is shaken up with air, a nitrate is formed.
J. Meyer and W. Schramm observed that a complex acid is formed with malonic
acid. H. von Wartenberg and W. Gurr observed that a eutectic is formed with
zirconia.

The hydrated manganese hemitrioxide is supposed to exhibit slight acidic
properties in certain minerals. If the compounds of manganese dioxide with the
bases be called **permanganites,** the compounds of manganese hemitrioxide with
the bases will be called by the unfortunate term **manganites.** H. Credner [3]
described a black or brown crystalline mineral, *Kupferhaltiger Manganerz*, from
Friedrichsroda, Thuringia. Analyses by H. Credner, and C. F. Rammelsberg agree

with $4(CuO,MnO).Mn_2O_3$.   C. F. Rammelsberg called the mineral **crednerite**. H. Laspeyres regarded it as a salt, $Cu_3Mn_3MnO_9$, of the acid $H_{12}MnO_9$. The analyses of a sample from Mendip Hills, Somersetshire, by L. J. Spencer and E. D. Mountain agree with **copper manganite,** $CuO.Mn_2O_3$, or $Cu(MnO_2)_2$. The mineral occurs in Somersetshire in radiating fan-like groups or hemispherical masses of thin, iron-black plates with a bright, metallic lustre. The mineral is perhaps monoclinic, pseudohexagonal by twinning. The cleavages are perfect. The hardness is 4, and the sp. gr. 5·03. H. Credner gave 4·5 to 5·0 for the hardness, and 4·89 to 5·07 for the sp. gr. C. F. Rammelsberg found the sp. gr. to be 4·95 to 4·97. L. J. Spencer and E. D. Mountain found that the mineral dissolves in conc. hydrochloric acid with the evolution of chlorine, but resists attack by nitric acid. A. Gorgeu obtained copper manganite, $CuO.Mn_2O_3$, by heating the tetritamanganite to redness. According to E. A. Schneider, when an ammoniacal cupric oxide soln. is mixed with soda-lye and to the deep blue soln. manganous chloride is added drop by drop, with constant stirring, and the copper oxide and manganic oxides are used in the molecular ratio 1 : 1 or 2 : 1, the whole of the copper is at once removed, but with the ratios 3 : 1 or 4 : 1 or 5 : 1 a portion of the copper remains in soln. The black precipitate thrown down in each case seems to have the composition of **copper tritamanganite,** $3CuO.Mn_2O_3$, although, if an excess of copper soln. is not used, the precipitate approximates **copper hemimanganite,** $2CuO.Mn_2O_3$. The compounds are oxidized by exposure to air. H. Rose appears to have prepared a **silver manganite,** $Ag_4O.Mn_2O_3$, by the action of a warm soln. of manganous sulphate on an excess of moist silver oxide, or adding manganous sulphite to an ammoniacal soln. of silver oxide ; and F. Wöhler, by adding alkali-lye to a mixed soln. of a silver and a manganous salt. H. Rose also reported $Ag_4O.Ag_2O.Mn_2O_3$ to be formed by the action of a cold soln. of manganous sulphate on moist silver oxide. G. Barbieri said that $Ag_4O.Mn_2O_3$ is not formed, but rather a mixture of silver and manganese dioxide.

A. Gorgeu[4] prepared **magnesium manganite,** $MgO.Mn_2O_3$, or $Mg(MnO_2)_2$, by melting a mixture of dried manganese, sodium, and magnesium sulphates in the proportions 3 : 1 : 3. The cold product containing some zincite is washed with hot water, and then allowed to stand for 15 minutes in 5 per cent. acetic acid. The brown, octahedral crystals are probably analogous to hausmannite—*magnesium-hausmannite.* It was also prepared by igniting magnesium tetrapermanganite. G. E. Moore described a mineral from Sterling Hill, New Jersey, and he called it **hetaerolite**—from $\dot{\epsilon}\tau\alpha\hat{\imath}\rho o\varsigma$, companion—in allusion to its occurring intimately associated with chalcophanite. It forms botryoidal coatings with a columnar structure. C. F. Naumann called it *hetairite.* J. Orcel and S. Pavlovitch studied the optical properties of the mineral. G. M. Butler called the sample from the Wolftone mine, Leadville, Colorado, *wolftonite.* It contains zinc and manganese and was hence called *zinc-hausmannite.* The formula corresponding with the analysis of W. E. Ford and W. M. Bradley is **zinc manganite,** $ZnO.Mn_2O_3.\frac{1}{2}H_2O$, and from the analysis reported by C. Palache, $ZnO.Mn_2O_3$, or $Zn(MnO_2)_2$. The hardness is 5·5 to 6·0 ; and the sp. gr. given by G. E. Moore is 4·933, that by C. Palache is 4·85, and that by W. E. Ford and W. M. Bradley is 4·6. The index of refraction is over 1·78. E. S. Larsen gave for the tetragonal crystals the indices of refraction $\omega=2\cdot26$ to 2·34, and $\epsilon=2\cdot10$ to 2·14 ; C. Palache gave $\omega=2\cdot35$ and $\epsilon=2\cdot10$. The optical character is negative ; the pleochroism is feeble. E. Divers assumed that $ZnO.Mn_2O_3.nH_2O$ is formed in the working of the Leclanché cell by the action of ammonium zinc chloride on manganese dioxide. A. Gorgeu fused a mixture of manganous, sodium, and zinc sulphates, washed the product with water and dil. acetic acid, and obtained zinc manganite in crystals resembling those of hausmannite ; **cadmium manganite,** $CdO.Mn_2O_3$, was produced by igniting cadmium pentapermanganite. G. Flink reported a **hydrated lead manganite,** $2PbO.Mn_2O_3.H_2O$, at Langban, Sweden. The pitch-black, lustrous mineral was named **quenselite**—after P. Quensel. The monoclinic crystals have the axial ratios

$a : b : c = 0.9767 : 1 : 1.667$, and $\beta = 93.6°$. The basal cleavage is somewhat micaceous and perfect ; the streak of the opaque mineral is dark brownish-grey. The sp. gr. is 6·842, and the hardness 2·5. Hausmannite, *manganese tritatetroxide—vide supra*—may be regarded as **manganous manganite,** $MnO.Mn_2O_3$, or $Mn(MnO_2)_2$. According to A. Gorgeu, **cobalt manganite,** $CoO.Mn_2O_3$, is obtained by igniting cobalt hexapermanganate ; and **nickel manganite,** $NiO.Mn_2O_3$, from nickel penta-permanganite. M. Rüger also obtained the cobalt salt. The black mineral **lubeckite,** described by J. Morozewiçz, occurs at Miedzianka, Poland. The analysis corresponds with the formula for **copper cobaltic manganite,** $4CuO.\frac{1}{2}Co_2O_3, Mn_2O_3.4H_2O$. Its sp. gr. is 4·8, and its hardness 2 to 3. A. Gorgeu observed that when freshly precipitated hydrated manganese dioxide is digested in a hot aq. soln. of cobalt sulphate, part of the manganese is dissolved, and the insoluble product obtained consists of cobalt mangano-cobaltite, which on ignition at a red-heat furnishes a product which is not a mixture of the oxides Mn_3O_4 and Co_3O_4, since the latter is unstable at a red-heat ; and it is considered to be **manganous cobaltous cobalti-manganite,** $MnO.CoO.Mn_2O_3.Co_2O_3$.

REFERENCES.

[1] W. Haidinger, *Edin. Journ. Science*, **4**. 48, 1826 ; *Trans. Roy. Soc. Edin.*, **11**. 137, 1827 ; J. F. L. Hausmann, *Handbuch der Mineralogie*, Göttingen, 222, 1847 ; F. S. Beudant, *Traité élémentaire de minéralogie*, Paris, **2**. 188, 1832 ; A. Breithaupt, *Vollständiges Handbuch der Mineralogie*, Dresden, **3**. 801, 1847 ; *Pogg. Ann.*, **49**. 204, 1840 ; M. Adam, *Tableau minéralogique*, Paris, 75, 1869 ; C. F. Rammelsberg, *Handbuch der Mineralchemie*, Leipzig, 160, 1875 ; *Pogg. Ann.*, **124**. 515, 1865 ; *Sitzber. Akad. Berlin*, 97, 1885 ; A. A. Damour, *Ann. Mines*, (4), **1**. 400, 1842 ; F. R. Mallet, *A Manual of the Geology of India*, Calcutta, **4**. 55, 1887 ; A. Liversidge, *The Minerals of New South Wales*, London, 110, 1888 ; M. J. Schuster, *Tschermak's Mitt.*, (2), **7**. 443, 1884 ; G. vom Rath, *Sitzber. Niederrh. Ges. Bonn*, 225, 1882 ; A. Schmidt, *Zeit. Kryst.*, **11**. 603, 1886 ; K. Busz, *ib.*, **15**. 624, 1889 ; L. J. Igelström, *Bull. Soc. Min.*, **8**. 412, 1885 ; G. Flink, *Bihang. Akad. Handl. Stockholm*, **12**. 7, 1888 ; **16**. 4, 1891 ; *Arkiv Kemi Min. Geol.*, **3**. 35, 1910 ; *Geol. För. Förh. Stockholm*, **41**. 329, 1919 ; C. W. Blomstrand, *ib.*, **2**. 183, 1874 ; O. Michel and E. Grandmougin, *Ber.*, **26**. 2567, 1893 ; J. Orcel and S. Pavlovitch, *Compt. Rend.*, **187**. 1295, 1928 ; J. J. Berzelius, *Schweigger's Journ.*, **26**. 263, 1819 ; K. S. Rao, *Proc. Indian Assoc. Science*, **6**. 87, 1920 ; P. Berthier, *Ann. Mines*, (1), **6**. 303, 1821 ; *Ann. Chim. Phys.*, (2), **20**. 187, 1822 ; (2), **51**. 100, 1832 ; H. Moissan, *ib.*, (5), **21**. 232, 1880 ; M. Berthelot, *ib.*, (5), **15**. 185, 1878 ; A. J. Scott, *Edin. Phil. Journ.*, **53**. 277, 1852 ; E. Turner, *Phil. Mag.*, (2), **4**. 22, 96, 1828 ; (2), **5**. 255, 1829 ; *Trans. Roy. Soc. Edin.*, **11**. 143, 1831 ; E. Schweizer, *Journ. prakt. Chem.*, (1), **23**. 280, 1841 ; R. Hermann, *Pogg. Ann.*, **74**. 303, 1848 ; *Journ. prakt. Chem.*, (1), **43**. 51, 1848 ; H. Laspeyres, *ib.*, (2), **13**. 185, 1876 ; O. T. Christensen, *Oefvers. Vid. Selks. Förh.*, 94, 1896 ; *Journ. prakt. Chem.*, (2), **28**. 1, 1883 ; B. Franke, *ib.*, (2), **36**. 31, 451, 1887 ; T. Scheerer, *Pogg. Ann.*, **65**. 281, 1845 ; W. Müller, *ib.*, **136**. 51, 1869 ; C. von Evreinoff, *ib.*, **49**. 208, 1840 ; G. Rose, *ib.*, **121**. 318, 1864 ; H. Rose, *ib.*, **121**. 318, 1869 ; W. Heintz, *ib.*, **74**. 449, 1847 ; E. R. Schneider, *ib.*, **107**. 605, 1859 ; G. Meneghini, *Amer. Journ. Science*, (2), **14**. 62, 1852 ; W. H. Hobbs, *ib.*, (3), **50**. 125, 1895 ; F. Bukeisen, *Sitzber. Akad. Wien*, **24**. 287, 1857 ; B. Jezek, *Roz. Böhm. Akad. Prag.*, **13**. 7, 1908 ; A. Gorgeu, *Compt. Rend.*, **106**. 703, 1101, 1888 ; *Bull. Soc. Chim.*, (2), **49**. 668, 753, 1888 ; *Bull. Soc. Min.*, **11**. 196, 1888 ; **16**. 143, 1893 ; E. Jannettaz, *ib.*, **15**. 138, 1892 ; S. Meunier, *ib.*, **10**. 197, 1887 ; L. L. Fermor, *Mem. Geol. Sur. India*, **37**. 68, 1909 ; R. F. Penrose, *Ann. Rep. Geol. Sur. Arkansas*, **1**. 149, 1850 ; W. Elderhorst, *First Report of the Geological Reconnaissance of the Northern Counties of Arkansas*, Little Rock, 164, 1858 ; E. Diepschlag and F. Wulfestieg, *Journ. Iron Steel Inst.*, **120**. ii, 297, 1929 ; C. W. Davis, *Rept. Investigations U.S. Bur. Mines*, 3024, 1930 ; F. von Kobell, *Sitzber. München Akad.*, **1**. 164, 1871 ; P. Groth, *Chemische Krystallographie*, Leipzig, **1**. 115, 1906 ; **2**. 307, 1908 ; *Die Mineralien-sammlung der Universität Strassburg*, Strassburg, 79, 1878 ; J. R. Blum, *Die Pseudomorphosen des Mineralreichs*, Stuttgart, 88, 1879 ; K. Thaddéeff, *Zeit. Kryst.*, **20**. 350, 1892 ; P. E. W. Oeberg, *Oefvers Akad. Förh. Stockholm*, **42**. 8, 1885 ; C. Doelter, *Neues Jahrb. Min.*, ii, 96, 1896 ; D. C. Knab, *Brit. Pat. No.* 3082, 1877 ; *Chem. Ind.*, **2**. 221, 1878 ; E. Wedekind, *Zeit. angew. Chem.*, **33**. 87, 1924 ; E. Wedekind and C. Horst, *Ber.*, **45**. 262, 1912 ; **48**. 105, 1915 ; C. Horst, *Ueber die Abhängigkeit der Magnetisierbarkeit anorganischer Verbindungen von der Wertigkeit des Hauptelementes, untersucht an den Oxygen und Sulfiden einiger Schwermetalle*, Freiburg, 1912 ; G. Forchhammer, *Ann. Phil.*, **16**. 130, 1820 ; **17**. 50, 1821 ; *De manguno*, Hafnia, 1820 ; J. A. Arfvedson, *Afhand. Fys. Kemi*, **6**. 222, 1818 ; *Ann. Phil.*, **7**. 267, 1824 ; *Schweigger's Journ.*, **42**. 202, 1818 ; H. Davy, *Phil. Trans.*, **102**. 181, 1812 ; J. F. John, *Gehlen's Journ.*, **3**. 452, 1807 ; **4**. 436, 1807 ; *Ann. Phil.*, **2**. 172, 263, 1813 ; **3**. 413, 1813 ; R. D. Harvey, *Econ. Geol.*, **23**. 778, 1928 ; C. Lepierre, *Compt. Rend.*, **120**. 924, 1895 ; H. B. Weiser and G. L. Mack, *Journ. Phys. Chem.*, **34**. 86, 101, 1930 ; W. Zachariasen, *Zeit. Kryst.*, **67**. 455, 1928 ;

W. Spring and M. Lucion, *Bull. Soc. Chim.*, (3), **3**. 4, 1890 ; M. Martinon, *ib.*, (2), **43**. 355, 1885 ;
S. Hauser, *Ueber Reduktion einiger Metalloxyde durch Gase*, Strassburg, 1907 ; A. Classen, *Zeit. anal. Chem.*, **16**. 315, 471, 1877 ; **18**. 175, 1879 ; W. Flight, *Phil. Mag.*, (4), **30**. 339, 1865 ;
M. L. Huggins, *Phys. Rev.*, (2), **21**. 719, 1923 ; W. Dittmar, *Journ. Chem. Soc.*, **17**. 294, 1864 ;
W. Biltz, *Zeit. phys. Chem.*, **67**. 561, 1909 ; *Zeit. anorg. Chem.*, **127**. 169, 372, 1923 ; C. Drucker
and R. Hüttner, *Zeit. phys. Chem.*, **131**. 237, 1928 ; *Die thermische Dissoziation des Mangan-dioxydes*, Leipzig, 1928 ; P. Askenasy and S. Klonowsky, *Zeit. Elektrochem.*, **16**. 107, 1910 ;
S. Klonowsky, *Ueber die Manganatschmelze und die Ueberführung von Kaliummanganat in Kaliumpermanganat auf elektrolytischen Wege*, Karlsruhe, 1910 ; F. Glaser, *Zeit. anorg. Chem.*, **36**. 1, 1903 ; J. Meyer, *ib.*, **81**. 385, 1913 ; J. Meyer and R. Nerlich, *ib.*, **116**. 117, 1921 ; J. Meyer
and R. Kanters, *ib.*, **185**. 172, 178, 1929 ; P. E. Wretblad, *ib.*, **189**. 329, 1930 ; R. J. Meyer
and K. Rötgers, *ib.*, **57**. 104, 1908 ; K. Rötgers, *Die Dissoziationtemperaturen der Manganoxyde
MnO_2 und Mn_2O_3 in Luft- und Sauerstoff-atmosphäre*, Berlin, 1907 ; C. M. Tessié du Motay,
L'Instit., **36**. 48, 1868 ; *Dingler's Journ.*, **186**. 231, 1867 ; *Bull. Soc. Enc. Nat. Ind.*, (2), **14**. 472,
1867 ; W. V. Smitheringale, *Econ. Geol.*, **24**. 481, 1929 ; G. A. Thiel, *ib.*, **19**. 107, 1924 ; L. Carius,
Liebig's Ann., **98**. 63, 1856 ; K. Honda and T. Sone, *Science Rep. Tohoku Univ.*, **3**. 139, 1914 ;
R. Bunsen and G. Krieger, *Liebig's Ann.*, **87**. 257, 1853 ; S. Pavlovitch, *Compt. Rend.*, **192**. 1400,
1931 ; G. Aminoff, *Svenska Vet. Handl.*, (3), **9**. 5, 1931 ; A. Simon and F. Feher, *Zeit. Elektrochem.*,
38. 137, 1932 ; W. H. Coghill and J. B. Clemmer, *Tech. Publ. Amer. Inst. Min. Eng.*, 445, 1932.
    ² C. C. von Leonhard, *Handbuch der Oryktognosie*, Heidelberg, 371, 1821 ; J. B. L. Romé de
l'Isle, *Cristallographie*, Paris, **3**. 101, 1783 ; *Essai de cristallographie*, Paris, 331, 1772 ; R. J. Haüy,
Traité de minéralogie, Paris, **4**. 246, 1801 ; A. G. Werner, *Berg. Journ.*, **1**. 369, 1789 ; *Letztes
Mineralsystem*, Freiberg, 24, 1817 ; L. A. Emmerling, *Lehrbuch der Mineralogie*, Giessen, **2**.
522, 1796 ; J. F. L. Hausmann, *Handbuch der Mineralogie*, Göttingen, 289, 1813 ; **2**. 390, 1847 ;
M. H. Klaproth, *Beiträge zur chemischen Kenntnis der Mineralkörper*, Berlin, **3**. 308, 1802 ;
F. Mohs, *Grundriss der Mineralogie*, Dresden, **2**. 488, 1824 ; R. Jameson, *A System of Mineralogy*,
Edinburgh, **3**. 251, 1820 ; *Manual of Mineralogy*, Edinburgh, 256, 1821 ; A. Breithaupt, *Voll-
ständige Charakteristik des Mineralsystems*, Dresden, 240, 1823 ; *Journ. prakt. Chem.*, (1), **19**.
103, 1840 ; F. S. Beudant, *Traité élémentaire de minéralogie*, Paris, **2**. 678, 1832 ; F. A. Quenstedt,
Handbuch der Mineralogie, Tübingen, 531, 1855 ; C. Hartmann, *Handwörterbuch der Mineralogie
und Geologie*, Weimar, **2**. 469, 1843 ; W. Haidinger, *Edin. Journ. Science*, **4**. 41, 1826 ; *Trans.
Roy. Soc. Edin.*, **11**. 122, 1827 ; *Pogg. Ann.*, **7**. 225, 1826 ; **14**. 199, 1828 ; W. Phillips, *Introduction to Mineralogy*, London, 243, 1823 ; T. Thomson, *Outlines of Mineralogy, Geology, and
Mineral Analysis*, London, **1**. 509, 1836 ; D. L. G. Karsten, *Mineralogische Tabellen*, Berlin,
1800 ; L. Gmelin, *Schweigger's Journ.*, **42**. 208, 1824 ; J. A. Arfvedson, *ib.*, **42**. 209, 1824 ; **26**.
263, 1819 ; J. J. Berzelius, *ib.*, **26**. 262, 1819 ; E. Turner, *Trans. Roy. Soc. Edin.*, **11**. 142, 1827 ;
Phil. Mag., (2), **5**. 255, 1829 ; *Pogg. Ann.*, **14**. 220, 1828 ; R. Hermann, *ib.*, **74**. 303, 1848 ;
C. F. Rammelsberg, *ib.*, **124**. 513, 1865 ; *Sitzber. Akad. Berlin*, 97, 1885 ; *Handbuch der Mineralchemie*, Leipzig, 183, 1875 ; C. M. Kersten, *Kersten's Arch.*, **19**. 754, 1846 ; J. Noggerath, *ib.*,
16. 537, 1845 ; R. W. Townsend, *B.A. Rep.*, 38, 1843 ; V. Sevoz and J. Breuilhs, *Bull. Soc.
Ind. Min.*, **6**. 29, 1860 ; *Rev. Géol.*, **1**. 57, 1860 ; W. H. Hobbs, *Amer. Journ. Science*, (3), **50**.
125, 1895 ; H. How, *Phil. Mag.*, (4), **31**. 166, 1866 ; A. des Cloizeaux, *Compt. Rend.*, **52**. 1323,
1861 ; F. Kuhlmann, *ib.*, **52**. 1283, 1861 ; R. D. Harvey, *Econ. Geol.*, **23**. 778, 1928 ; G. de Geer,
Geol. För. Förh. Stockholm, **6**. 42, 1882 ; L. H. Borgström, *ib.*, **23**. 559, 1901 ; C. W. Blomstrand,
ib., **2**. 183, 1874 ; G. Flink, *ib.*, **41**. 329, 1919 ; **47**. 377, 1925 ; G. di Boccard, *Riv. Min. Crist.
Ital.*, **4**. 55, 1889 ; F. Kovar, *Zeit. Chem. Ind. Prag.*, 1, 1898 ; 155, 1901 ; *Neues Jahrb. Min.*,
i, 25, 1900 ; K. Fredenhagen and G. Cadenbach, *Zeit. phys. Chem.*, **146**. 245, 1930 ; C. W. Davis,
Rept. Investigations U.S. Bur. Mines, 3024, 1930 ; G. Dupouy, *Études minéralogiques sur
l'Indochine française*, Paris, 122, 1913 ; L. C. Beck, *Report on the Mineralogy of the State of New
York*, Albany, 406, 1842 ; G. Rose, *Das Krystallochemische Mineralsystem*, Leipzig, 165, 1838 ;
Reise nach dem Ural, dem Altai, und dem kaspischen Meere, Berlin, **2**. 451, 1842 ; A. Sadebeck,
Angewandte Krystallographie, Berlin, 115, 1876 ; *Zeit. deut. geol. Ges.*, **31**. 206, 1879 ; J. D. Dana,
A System of Mineralogy, New York, 248, 1892 ; C. F. Naumann, *Lehrbuch der reinen und
angewandten Krystallographie*, Leipzig, **2**. 260, 1830 ; V. Goldschmidt, *Index der Krystallformen
der Mineralien*, Berlin, **2**. 350, 1890 ; F. Zambonini, *Zeit. Kryst.*, **34**. 229, 1901 ; J. Samojloff,
ib., **37**. 493, 1903 ; *Proc. Russ. Min. Soc.*, (2), **39**. 329, 1902 ; F. Rutley, *Min. Mag.*, **10**.
21, 1891 ; R. Brauns, *Neues Jahrb. Min.*, i, 252, 1886 ; G. P. Traverso, *ib.*, ii, 220, 1899 ;
T. Haege, *Die Mineralien des Siegerlandes und der abgrenzenden Bezirke*, Siegen, 24, 1887 ;
A. Lévy, *Description d'une collection de minéraux, formée par M. Henri Heuland*, Londres,
3. 285, 1837 ; E. Halle, *Die minerale Steiermarks*, Graz, 46, 1885 ; V. R. von Zepharovich,
Mineralogisches Lexicon für das Kaiserthum Oesterreich, Wien, 264, 1859 ; 199, 1873 ; W. P. Jervis,
I Tesori sotterranei dell'Italia, Turin, **2**. 119, 1874 ; A. d'Achiardi, *Mineralogia dell Toscana*,
Pisa, **1**. 109, 1872 ; E. Manasse, *Proc. Toscana Soc.*, **15**. 21, 1906 ; R. P. Greg and W. G. Lettsom,
Manual of the Mineralogy of Great Britain and Ireland, London, 289, 1858 ; J. H. Collins, *A
Handbook to the Mineralogy of Cornwall and Devon*, London, 67, 1876 ; M. F. Heddle, *The
Mineralogy of Scotland*, Edinburgh, **1**. 108, 1901 ; A. Raimondi, *Minéraux du Perou*, Paris, 235,
1878 ; H. C. H. Carpenter, *Journ. Chem. Soc.*, **81**. 1, 1902 ; W. H. Zachariasen, *Zeit. Kryst.*, **67**.
455, 1928 ; *Skrift. Norske Akad.*, 4, 1928 ; F. Hebler, *Farben Ztg.*, **31**. 155, 1925 ; F. Wilborn,
ib., **31**. 328, 1925 ; M. Rüger, *Ker. Rund.*, **31**. 79, 87, 99, 110, 1923 ; B. Franke, *Journ. prakt.
Chem.*, (2), **36**. 31, 451, 1887 ; H. Laspeyres, *ib.*, (2), **13**. 186, 1876 ; R. Bunsen and G. Krieger, *ib.*,

(1), **61**. 472, 1854 ; *Liebig's Ann.*, **87**. 257, 1853 ; L. Carius, *ib.*, **98**. 63, 1856 ; E. Kayser, *Zeit. deut. geol. Ges.*, **22**. 182, 1870 ; W. W. Coblentz, *Investigations of Infra-red Spectra*, Washington, 41, 1906 ; *Jahrb. Rad. Elektron.*, **3**. 397, 1907 ; O. Mügge, *Centr. Min.*, 1, 1922 ; J. L. C. Schröder van der Kolk, *ib.*, 80, 1901 ; N. Kurnakoff and V. Cernych, *ib.*, 359, 1928 ; J. Königsberger, *ib.*, 601, 1908 ; *Phys. Zeit.*, **4**. 495, 1903 ; A. Wagner, *Dingler's Journ.*, **195**. 532, 1870 ; E. Reichardt, *Journ. Landwirtsch.*, **26**. 167, 1878 ; H. Haga and F. M. Jäger, *Versl. Akad. Amsterdam*, **24**. 1612, 1916 ; R. Koechlin, *Tschermak's Mitt.*, (2), **9**. 24, 1887 ; M. Martinon. *Bull. Soc. Chim.*, (2), **43**. 355, 1885 ; A. Gorgeu, *ib.*, (3), **9**. 650, 1893 ; *Bull. Soc. Min.*, **11**. 196, 1888 ; **16**. 134, 1893 ; *Compt. Rend.*, **106**. 948, 1101, 1888 ; A. Anargypos, *ib.*, **181**. 419, 1925 ; J. Orcel and S. Pavlovitch, *ib.*, **187**. 1295, 1928 ; W. V. Smitheringale, *Econ. Geol.*, **24**. 481, 1929 ; G. A. Thiel, *ib.*, **19**. 107, 1924 ; P. Groth, *Chemische Krystallographie*, Leipzig, **1**. 115, 1906 ; *Die Mineraliensammlung der Universität Strassburg*, Strassburg, 79, 1878 ; K. Honda and T. Sone, *Science Rep. Tohoku Univ.*, **3**. 139, 1914 ; E. S. Larsen, *Bull. U.S. Geol. Sur.*, 679, 1921 ; H. Kopp, *Liebig's Ann. Suppl.*, **3**. 290, 1865 ; F. Beijerinck, *Neues Jahrb. Min. B.B.*, **11**. 455, 1897 ; H. C. Bolton, *Ann. New York Acad.*, **1**. 158, 1879 ; *Chem. News*, **36**. 249, 260, 1877 ; **37**. 14, 24, 65, 86, 98, 148, 1878 ; *Min. Mag.*, **1**. 136, 1877 ; H. B. Weiser and G. L. Mack, *Journ. Phys. Chem.*, **34**. 86, 1930 ; W. F. de Jong, *Naturwet. Tijds.*, **12**. 69, 1930 ; J. R. Blum, *Die Pseudomorphosen des Mineralreichs*, Stuttgart, 169, 1843 ; 88, 1879 ; A. Lacroix, *Minéralogie de la France et de ses colonies*, Paris, **3**. 353, 1901 ; *Bull. Soc. Min.*, **23**. 255, 1900 ; K. Busz, *Zeit. Kryst.*, **15**. 624, 1889 ; P. Berthier, *Ann. Mines*, (1), **6**. 595, 1821 ; *Ann. Chim. Phys.*, (2), **20**. 187, 344, 1822 ; J. Meyer, *Zeit. Elektrochem.*, **22**. 201, 1916 ; *Zeit. anorg. Chem.*, **81**. 385, 1913 ; J. Meyer and R. Nerlich, *ib.*, **116**. 117, 1921 ; J. Meyer and W. Schramm, *ib.*, **123**. 56, 1922 ; **132**. 226, 1923 ; E. Divers, *Chem. News*, **46**. 259, 1882 ; M. Sem, *Zeit. Elektrochem.*, **21**. 426, 1915 ; **23**. 98, 1917 ; *Ueber die Elektrooxydation von Manganosalzen in sauren Lösungen und einige dabei erhaltene Verbindungen*, Darmstadt, 1914 ; E. H. Williams, *Phys. Rev.*, (2), **28**. 167, 1926 ; S. R. B. Cook, W. Howes and A. H. Emery, *Amer. Min.*, **16**. 209, 1931 ; A. Ferrari and A. Scherillo, *Zeit. Kryst.*, **78**. 496, 1931 ; H. von Wartenberg and W. Gurr, *Zeit. anorg. Chem.*, **196**. 374, 1931.

³ H. Credner, *Neues Jahrb. Min.*, 6, 1847 ; *Pogg. Ann.*, **74**. 558, 1848 ; C. F. Rammelsberg, *ib.*, **74**. 560, 1848 ; G. Barbieri, *Gazz. Chim. Ital.*, **53**. 645, 1923 ; H. Rose, *Pogg. Ann.*, **101**. 229, 1857 ; F. Wöhler, *ib.*, **41**. 344, 1837 ; H. Laspeyres, *Journ. prakt. Chem.*, (2), **13**. 187, 1876 ; L. J. Spencer and E. D. Mountain, *Min. Mag.*, **20**. 86, 1923 ; E. A. Schneider, *Amer. Chem. Journ.*, **9**. 271, 1887 ; A. Gorgeu, *Bull. Soc. Chim.*, (3), **29**. 1111, 1167, 1903.

⁴ J. Orcel and S. Pavlovitch, *Compt. Rend.*, **187**. 1295, 1928 ; C. Palache, *Amer. Min.*, **13**. 308, 1928 ; *Amer. Journ. Science*, (4), **29**. 180, 1910 ; W. E. Ford and W. M. Bradley, *ib.*, (4), **35**. 602, 1913 ; G. E. Moore, *ib.*, (3), **14**. 423, 1877 ; E. S. Larsen, *Bull. U.S. Geol. Sur.*, 679, 1921 ; C. F. Naumann, *Elemente der Mineralogie*, Leipzig, 371, 1881 ; G. M. Butler, *Econ. Geol.*, **8**. 8, 1913 ; A. Gorgeu, *Bull. Soc. Chim.*, (3), **29**. 1111, 1903 ; J. Morozewicz, *Bull. Acad. Cracovie*, 185, 1918 ; E. Divers, *Chem. News*, **46**. 259, 1882 ; G. Flink, *Geol. För. Förh. Stockholm*, **41**. 329, 1919 ; **47**. 377, 1925 ; M. Rüger, *Ker. Rund.*, **31**. 79, 87, 99, 110, 1923.

§ 11. Manganese Dioxide

A. Breithaupt [1] described a light grey manganese oxide—*Graumanganerz*—which he called **polianite**—from πολιός, grey, or πολιαίνεσθαι, to become grey. It is distinguished from pyrolusite by its hardness and its anhydrous character. It occurs at Platten, and Joachimsthal, Bohemia, and in a few other localities. It is comparatively rare. Analyses were reported by C. F. Plattner, C. F. Rammelsberg, S. L. Penfield, A. Gorgeu, and L. L. Fermor. The results agree with the formula for **manganese dioxide**, MnO_2. The colour of polianite is light steel-grey, or iron-grey. J. L. C. Schröder van der Kolk said that the streak is black or grey with a reddish-brown tinge. The mineral occurs in composite parallel groupings of minute crystals having a rough summit and a rhombic form. A. Breithaupt, and R. Köchlin considered that the crystals belong to the rhombic system, but E. S. Dana, and A. Rosati and H. Steinmetz showed that the crystals are tetragonal, and are isomorphous with cassiterite, plattnerite, zircon, and rutile. E. S. Dana gave for the axial ratio $a : c = 1 : 0.66467$, and A. Rosati and H. Steinmetz, $1 : 0.6621$. The crystals are often pseudomorphs after manganite. The (110)-cleavage is perfect. A. Breithaupt gave 4.838 to 4.880 for the sp. gr. ; C. F. Rammelsberg, 5.026 ; and S. L. Penfield, 4.992. The mineral is brittle, and its hardness is 6.0 to 7.0.

The history of the mineral **pyrolusite** has been discussed in connection with that of manganese. The mineral *varvicite*, or *varvacite*, obtained by R. Phillips in Warwickshire, was considered by A. Breithaupt to be intermediate between pyrolusite and manganite. Related minerals were obtained by A. Duflos, and

E. Turner from Ilefeld, Harz ; and by P. H. Walker, from Austinville, Virginia. Numerous analyses of pyrolusite have been reported by P. Berthier, J. A. Arfvedson, L. Gmelin, E. Riegel, E. Turner, V. Sevoz and J. Breuilhs, H. Ludwig, T. L. Phipson, I. Domeyko, L. Brackebusch, A. Liversidge, E. F. Smith, D. T. Day, J. L. Jarman, J. and H. S. Pattinson, A. Gorgeu, N. Kozowsky, F. Kovar, C. Rimatori, F. Drake, L. L. Fermor, H. Jimeno, C. A. Tenne and D. S. Calderon, A. Serra, F. Kossmàt, G. Dupouy, H. How, C. R. A. Wright and A. E. Menke, M. M. P. Muir, F. T. Teschemacher and J. D. Smith, M. Scheffler, A. Schwarzenberg and A. Engelhardt, J. B. J. D. Boussingault, etc. The results range from 77·60 to 83·56 per cent. MnO ; 3·13 to 17·90 per cent. O_2 ; 0 to 0·50 per cent. CaO ; 0 to 2·31 per cent. BaO ; 0 to 0·1 per cent. MgO ; 0 to 3·0 per cent. $(K,Na)_2O$; 0 to 0·50 per cent. PbO and CuO ; 0 to 0·22 per cent. NiO ; 0 to 0·27 per cent. CoO ; 0 to 0·91 per cent. Al_2O_3 ; 0 to 4·31 per cent. Fe_2O_3 ; 0 to 2·21 per cent. SiO_2 ; 0 to 0·1 per cent. SO_3 ; 0 to 0·5 per cent. P_2O_5 ; and 0·50 to 5·0 per cent. H_2O. Traces of lithium, zinc, silver, bismuth, thallium, indium, rare earths, arsenates, and fluorine have also been reported. P. Askenasy and C. L. Rényi, H. Bischoff, and H. St. C. Deville and H. Debray found nitrates present ; R. J. Kane, chlorides ; A. Kundert, silver ; F. Wöhler, thallium ; and C. Huber, vanadium. The results agree with those required for a more or less impure manganese dioxide, MnO_2 or $MnO_2.nH_2O$. E. Donath and H. Leopold discussed pyrolusite and its applications.

H. Heymann found that in nature pyrolusite occurs in pseudomorphs after manganite, calcite, and rhodochrosite ; while J. R. Blum observed pseudomorphs after dolomite and smithsonite. E. Döll, S. von Szentpetery, W. Haidinger, and V. Lenher discussed this subject. T. Schlösing obtained manganese dioxide by heating manganese nitrate between 150° to 195° ; F. Kuhlmann recommended 200° ; and A. Gorgeu added that if the nitrate be slowly decomposed at 155° to 162°, the product is crystalline and resembles polianite. The same product is obtained in the presence of manganese chloride or sulphate, or of the nitrates of calcium, strontium, barium, magnesium, potassium, and sodium, for these products can afterwards be washed away from the crystalline dioxide. If ferric nitrate be present, the manganese dioxide will be contaminated by ferric oxide. C. R. A. Wright and A. E. Menke obtained the crystalline dioxide by heating a mixture of manganese and potassium nitrates, and washing the alkali salt away from the cold product. P. Berthier, G. J. Young, and G. Wischin also obtained the dioxide by calcining the nitrate. F. Göbel, and H. Moissan prepared the dioxide by heating to 300° a mixture of manganous carbonate with twice its weight of potassium chlorate. According to J. B. Hannay, when a conc. nitric acid soln. of a manganous salt is warmed in the presence of crystals of potassium chlorate, the whole of the manganese is precipitated as manganese dioxide ; and if a salt of iron is present, the precipitate is a complex manganate of iron and manganese, $2Fe_2(MnO_4)_3.Mn(MnO_4)$. $12H_2O$, or $Fe_2(MnO_4)_3.MnO_2.6H_2O$. The manganese dioxide precipitated in the absence of iron appears as a black mass of crystalline plates which under the microscope are steel-grey. The thinner plates are transparent and purplish-red. They are free from water. F. Beilstein and L. Jawein used a similar process. C. R. A. Wright and A. E. Menke were unable to prepare the anhydrous dioxide from the hydrated dioxide either by standing it over conc. sulphuric acid or by heating it to 200°. Oxygen is slowly evolved at 210°. A. Gorgeu, however, found that nearly all the water can be slowly driven off at 200°. W. A. Whitesell and J. C. W. Frazer said that specially active manganese dioxide for catalytic reaction can be prepared (a) by the decomposition of potassium permanganate with conc. nitric acid ; (b) by treating E. Frémy's oxide with conc. nitric acid, diluting, and washing ; (c) by the oxidation of manganous sulphate with potassium permanganate in nitric acid soln. ; and (d) by the oxidation of precipitated manganous hydroxide. J. Meyer and R. Kanters prepared hydrated manganese dioxide by passing sulphur dioxide into a soln. of potassium permanganate at 75°, and washing the precipitate with dil. sulphuric acid and water. When dried at 100° to 105°, the composition is $MnO_2.H_2O$, and when heated to 200° to 225°, some oxygen is lost, but the water content is not reduced below 3·74 per cent. Methods were also described by S. Kaneko and co-workers, D. J. Brown and R. F. Tefft, and Y. Kato and T. Matsuhashi. Y. Kato and K. Yamamoto heated the lower oxides with 3 to 5 per cent. of an alkali hydroxide or carbonate in air or oxygen at 500°, and washed the ground product with water and then with dil. acid. For the electrolytic process, *vide infra*, the hydrated dioxide.

Pyrolusite is iron-black or dark steel-grey, occasionally with a bluish tinge. The mineral usually occurs massive and granular. with reniform coats. It is commonly columnar. The crystals are usually pseudomorphs after manganite. According to E. C. Harder, pyrolusite occurs associated " with psilomelane, either lining or filling cavities in it, or occurring in alternating layers with it in botryoidal masses. In such masses, it consists of numerous parallel needles arranged perpendicularly to the faces of the layers." The association of pyrolusite with psilomelane indicates that this pyrolusite is an alteration product of that mineral. In 1892, J. D. Dana said that it was not definitely known whether pyrolusite was an independent mineral species with a crystalline form of its own, or only a secondary mineral derived chiefly from the dehydration of manganite or the hydration of polianite. A. St. John, however, found that the X-radiogram of polianite agrees with a space-lattice having a body-centred tetragonal array of MnO_2-groups with an axial ratio $a : c = 1 : 0.651$; edge, 4·44 A. ; and density, 5·043. The oxygen atoms lie on a face-centred tetrahedral lattice and the manganese on a body-centred lattice, a manganese atom being at the centre of alternate tetrahedra of oxygen atoms. Since the pattern of pyrolusite is similar, any external form leading to its classification as rhombic is due to pseudomorphism. A. Ferrari also obtained a tetragonal lattice with $a : c = 1 : 0.625$, $a = 4.865$ A., and $c = 3.284$ A. ; sp. gr. 5·27 ; and said that the supposed rhombic form of pyrolusite is pseudomorphous. Polianite, pyrolusite, and the artificial dioxide have the same tetragonal space-lattice. V. M. Goldschmidt gave for the space-lattice of the rutile type $a = 4.41$ A., $c = 2.88$ A., and $a : c = 1 : 0.6525$. Some observations were made by C. Drucker and R. Hüttner, M. L. Huggins, and J. E. L. Jones and B. M. Dent. W. V. Smitheringale discussed the X-radiograms, and also the action of various etching liquids ; G. A. Thiel also studied the action of various reagents on the mineral—sulphuric and hydrochloric acids, hydrogen dioxide, and soln. of ferrous and stannous chlorides. The crystals were discussed by W. Haidinger, W. H. Miller, A. Gorgeu, A. Breithaupt, R. Köchlin, J. D. Dana, etc. A. F. Rogers attributed the fibrous character of pyrolusite to its occurrence as a pseudomorph, but E. T. Wherry and T. L. Watson said that the fibres are sometimes the result of primary crystallization and not pseudomorphous after manganite. E. Turner gave 4·819 for the sp. gr. of pyrolusite ; V. Sevoz and J. Breuilhs, 4·81 ; S. L. Penfield, 4·732 to 4·858 ; A. Gorgeu, 4·75 to 5·10 ; L. Playfair and J. P. Joule, 4·81 ; L. L. Fermor, 4·47 to 4·94 ; A. Breithaupt, 4·838 to 4·880 ; C. F. Rammelsberg, 5·026 ; J. D. Dana, 4·732 to 4·858 ; and J. L. Jarman, 4·69. J. B. Hannay gave 4·935 for the artificial crystals. Pyrolusite is much softer than polianite, having a hardness between 2 and 3 ; R. Köchlin found that it has soft and hard parts, so that when the powder is rubbed on glass, some granules may scratch the glass.

F. Richarz represented manganese dioxide by the formula $O=Mn=O$. H. Laspeyres regarded manganese dioxide as a manganous manganate, $Mn(MnO_4)$, but F. Beijerinck considered that in such a case the electrical conductivity should be smaller than what it is. A. Guyard regarded the dioxide as a permanganate, $3MnO.Mn_2O_7$, that is, $(MnO_2)_5$. W. Spring and M. Lucion do not recommend the simple formula $MnO.MnO_3$, but favour that based on A. Guyard's hypothesis. C. W. Eliot and F. H. Storer represented the dioxide as a basic manganic manganate, $Mn_2O_3.MnO_3$, that is, $(MnO_2)_3$; and B. Franke supposed the hydrate $3MnO_2.2H_2O$ to be a polymanganic acid : $(HO)_2Mn=O_2=Mn=O_2=Mn(OH)_2$. R. T. Colgate said it is more than probable that manganese dioxide is not simple, but consists of complexes of the type $(MnO_2)_n$, in which the value of n is at least 4 and may well be some multiple of this. The eight oxygen atoms in the complex may be pictured as so packed that they form a cube, each of four faces of which contains in addition a single manganese atom, the four atoms being in one plane. Such an arrangement is formulated in the following figure, with circles for oxygen atoms and black discs for manganese atoms. Freshly precipitated manganese dioxide is slightly soluble in a conc. soln. of hydrogen dioxide, cooled to $-20°$, and the resulting soln. gives off oxygen at ordinary temp. Hence, G. Bredig and A. Marck suggest that the soln. contains a true manganese superoxide,

$$\mathrm{Mn}\!\!\begin{array}{c} \mathrm{O} \\ \vdots \\ \mathrm{O} \end{array} \qquad \text{or} \qquad \mathrm{Mn}\!\!\begin{array}{c} \mathrm{O} \\ \vdots \\ \mathrm{O} \end{array}$$

isomeric with ordinary manganese dioxide, $O{=}Mn{=}O$. J. Orcel and S. Pavlovitch discussed the optical properties of polianite ; and W. Biltz, the colour of the derivatives of the oxide. According to W. Biltz, the fact that natural manganese dioxide always contains basic oxide points to its acidic nature—**manganous acid.** Treatment of manganese dioxide containing water with liquid ammonia removes all the water except 1 mol. Moreover, the existence of the compounds $(NH_4)_2MnO_3$ and NH_4HMnO_3 is indicated by the isothermal decomposition of the ammoniate.

W. Spring said that when the dioxide is subjected to a high press. it takes on a metallic lustre. As indicated below, O. Sackur and E. Fritzmann calculated from the electrochemical data the **dissociation pressure** $6·3 \times 10^{-23}$ atm. at $18°$. The low value here obtained agrees with the ready oxidation of manganous hydroxide in air. Observations were also made by E. Moles and M. Crespi. C. Zengelis observed a discoloration on silver suspended over manganese dioxide in a closed vessel ; this is taken to indicate a slight vaporization at ordinary temp. P. Berthier found that at dull redness manganese dioxide loses oxygen to form manganese hemitrioxide, and at a higher temp. it forms the tritatetroxide. When heated in oxygen, E. R. Schneider said that the hemitrioxide is formed ; and W. Dittmar found that when heated by a bunsen burner in dry oxygen, air, or nitrogen, the hemitrioxide is formed ; but at about $660°$, in air, nitrogen, or in vacuo, the tritatetroxide is produced. J. B. Hannay observed that at a red-heat, in oxygen, the dioxide passes into the tritatetroxide. C. R. A. Wright and A. P. Luff added that the evolution of oxygen from finely crystalline pyrolusite begins at $390°$; and A. Geuther stated that when heated to bright redness, manganese monoxide is formed. H. Moissan found that in the electric arc furnace the dioxide rapidly melts, bubbles with the evolution of oxygen, and passes into the monoxide. C. Schubert, and W. Hempel and C. Schubert said that decomposition begins between $470°$ and $500°$, and is ended at $1280°$. These observations are not all concordant. The work of R. J. Meyer and K. Rötgers, and W. Biltz on the thermal decomposition of the dioxide has been discussed in connection with manganese hemitrioxide and tritatetroxide—*vide supra* ; the decomposition begins at $530°$ in air, and at $565°$ in oxygen. J. Meyer and R. Kanters observed that some oxygen is lost at $200°$ to $230°$. P. Askenasy and S. Klonowsky found that when the dioxide is heated in vacuo for 24 hrs. at $230°$ and another 2 hrs. in dry oxygen at $400°$, it exhibits the following press., p mm., of oxygen at different temp. :

	382°	406°	448°	478°	536°
p . .	23	(77)	125	200	>1040

The observed press., 77 mm., at $406°$ is too high, and was obtained by absorption, which is very slow at that temp. The observations of R. J. Meyer and K. Rötgers were made upon a form of dioxide first heated to $500°$, which attains equilibrium very slowly, and the results, in consequence, are not reliable. P. Askenasy and

S. Klonowsky represented these results for the reaction $2Mn_2O_3+O_2\rightarrow4MnO_2$ by $\log p=-24944/4\cdot571T+1\cdot75 \log T+0\cdot001446T+2\cdot8$. S. Klonowsky's curve is shown in Fig. 48. F. Bahr and O. Sackur found a dissociation press. of 816 mm. at 572°. R. J. Meyer and K. Rötgers found that the reaction $4MnO_2$ $=2Mn_2O_3+O_2$ begins in air at 530°, and in oxygen at 568°. H. Saito studied the effect of heating manganese dioxide in air. C. Drucker and R. Hüttner found that the dissociation press. depends on the physical state of the dioxide; with compact masses the press. was 125 mm. at 530°, and with fine powder, 125 mm. at 450°. It is supposed that the MnO_2 and Mn_2O_3 form a solid soln., but since the isotherms are not constant it is assumed that the solid soln. is formed in definite layers, which to some extent protect the interior from decomposition. The X-radiograms of the products agree that Mn_2O_3 is formed in the thermal decomposition of manganese dioxide. The dissociation press., p mm., of the artificial dioxide is :

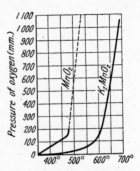

FIG. 48.—Dissociation Pressures of Manganese Dioxide.

	410°	450°	548°	586°	616°	652°	668°
p .	2	5	40	109	235·5	268	763

A. Simon and F. Feher measured the dissociation press. of the dioxide, and observed breaks just over 600° corresponding with the formation of Mn_2O_3, and near 1000° corresponding with the formation of Mn_3O_4. M. Blumenthal observed the formation of no compound between MnO_2 and Mn_2O_3 below 850° in the thermal dissociation of manganese dioxide. H. von Jüptner calculated for the dissociation press., p atm., in the reaction $MnO_2=Mn+O_2$, $\log p=-27418T^{-1}+1\cdot75 \log T+2\cdot8$; and for $2MnO_2=2MnO+O_2$, $\log p=-11667T^{-1}+1\cdot75 \log T+2\cdot8$ (vide infra, MnO), and

Products	600°	1000°	1400°	1800°	2200°	2400°
p { Mn .	0·0$_{38}$9230	0·0$_{19}$4285	0·0$_{11}$5265	0·0$_6$1839	0·0$_3$1536	0·0$_2$1955
{ MnO .	0·0$_{11}$1648	0·0$_3$2415	0·9378	103·5	2218	7130

G. Spezia said that pyrolusite melts in the oxidizing blowpipe flame to form a black enamel. H. Kopp gave 0·159 for the **specific heat** between 17° and 48° ; and A. S. Russell found the mean sp. ht., c, and the mol. ht., C, to be :

	−78° to −188°	0° to −78·2°	48·3° to 2·4°
c .	0·0978	0·1407	0·1642
C .	8·50	12·23	14·27

The results fit W. Nernst and F. Lindemann's equation fairly well. R. W. Millar found the **molecular heat** of manganese dioxide to be :

	−200·2°	−189·6°	−180·1°	−177·4°	−124·2°	−73·5°	−23·2°	20·8°
C_p .	3·901	5·370	8·858	6·406	7·996	10·35	12·19	13·53

The results are plotted in Fig. 30. There is a marked discontinuity between 87·743° K. and 98·437° K. J. Maydell studied the mol. ht. M. Berthelot calculated from H. le Chatelier's observations on the **heat of formation** $(Mn,O_2)=125\cdot3$ Cals. ; $(MnO,O)=30\cdot4$ Cals. O. Sackur and E. Fritzmann gave $(MnO,O)=19\cdot6$ Cals. ; H. von Jüptner, $Mn+O_2=MnO_2+125\cdot3$ Cals. ; and $2MnO+O_2=2MnO_2+53\cdot32$ Cals. ; C. Drucker and R. Hüttner gave 26 Cals. for the decomposition of manganese dioxide into Mn_3O_4, and R. J. Meyer and K. Rötgers, $4MnO_2=2Mn_2O_3+O_2-50\cdot8$ Cals. ; A. Simon and F. Feher obtained for the change $4MnO_2\rightarrow2Mn_2O_3+O_2$, 26 Cals. ; M. Blumenthal gave $\log p=Q/4\cdot6T+1\cdot75 \log T+2\cdot8$ for the heats of dissociation, Q, and obtained 37·1 Cals. for pyrolusite ; 27·9 Cals. for amorphous and 28·5 Cals. for crystalline manganese dioxide ; and W. G. Mixter gave (Mn,O_2) $=119\cdot6$ Cals. J. C. W. Frazer and C. E. Greider made observations on this subject.

They gave $MnO_2 \rightarrow MnO(+O) = -7.0$ cals. ; $1.5MnO_2 \rightarrow 0.5Mn_3O_4(+O) = -23.2$ cals.
R. W. Millar gave 13.93 for the **entropy** ; -42.6 for the change of entropy in the
reaction $Mn+O_2=MnO_2$, and $-122,600$ cals. for the change of **free energy.**
J. Thomsen gave $(Mn,O_2,H_2O)=166.33$ Cals. ; and $Mn(OH)_2+O=MnO(OH)_2$ (or
$MnO_2.H_2O)+21.56$ Cals. P. Askenasy and S. Klonowsky calculated for the heat of
the reaction $2Mn_2O_3+O_2 \rightarrow 4MnO_2$, 24,944 cals. J. Ewles found that the dioxide
exhibits a faint cathodoluminescence. G. Fournier studied the absorption of β-rays ;
and O. Stelling, the K-series of X-rays. C. Doelter observed no coagulation of the
colloid in radium rays. F. Beijerinck found that pyrolusite is a better electrical
conductor than polianite, and in contact with metals acquires an electric charge.
The subject was discussed by R. D. Harvey. F. Streintz observed that the
electrical conductivity of a cm. cube of the compressed powder is 0.16 mho at $0°$;
and M. le Blanc and H. Sachse, 10^{-2} mho, at $20°$. P. Fischer examined the electrical
conductivity of mixtures of manganese dioxide with copper oxide, lead dioxide, and
potassium bromide. E. W. von Siemens and J. G. Halske found that electrodes—
anodes—can be made from compressed manganese dioxide. A. A. Somerville
found that the electrical resistance is 10,000,000 ohms at $120°$ and 70 ohms at $1100°$.
T. W. Case observed no change in the electrical conductivity on exposure to light.
Measurements of the **electrode potential** of manganese dioxide were made by
C. Wheatstone, W. Beetz, H. Buff, F. M. Raoult, R. B. Clifton, W. H. Preece,
K. Schreber, L. Kahlenberg, and W. A. Smith. According to J. K. H. Inglis, a
platinum electrode coated with manganese dioxide and immersed in an acidic soln.
of a manganous salt changes in accord with $MnO_2+4H \rightleftharpoons Mn^{..}+2H_2O+2F$, in
which these are the intermediate stages: $MnO_2+2H \rightleftharpoons Mn^{..}+H_2O+\frac{1}{2}O_2$ and
$\frac{1}{2}O_2+2H \rightleftharpoons H_2O+2F$; or else $MnO_2+4H \rightleftharpoons Mn^{....}+2H_2O$ and $Mn^{....} \rightleftharpoons Mn^{..}+2F$.
Both hypotheses give the same results for the oxidation potential, namely, $\epsilon=\epsilon_0$
$+(RT/2F)$ log $([H^.]^4/['Mn^{..}])$ volt, where ϵ_0 represents the potential when the $H^.$
and $Mn^{..}$ concentrations of the soln. are unity. With cells of the type
$MnO_2 : MnSO_4,H_2O : KCl_{sat. soln.} : 0.1N-KCl,Hg_2Cl_2 : Hg$, at room temp., ϵ_0 can be
calculated from the degree of ionization of the electrolyte, when $\epsilon_0=E-$
$(0.058/2)$ log $(C^4{}_H./C_{Mn^{..}})$, when C denotes the concentrations of acid and manganous
salt in mols per litre, E volt is the observed potential, and ϵ_0 volt the normal potential
referred to the $0.1N$-calomel electrode, at room temp. :

$C_{Mn^{..}}$	.	0.01	0.001	0.0001	0.01	0.001	0.0001
$C_H.$	.	0.05	0.05	0.05	0.005	0.005	0.005
E	.	0.935	0.958	0.986	0.821	0.851	0.874
ϵ_0	.	0.993	0.987	0.986	0.995	0.996	0.990

Hence, the oxidation potential against the decinormal calomel electrode is nearly
1.00 volt, or 1.35 volt against the normal hydrogen electrode. O. F. Tower found
similar values of ϵ_0 for dil. nitric acid soln. of manganous nitrate and dil. sulphuric
acid soln. of manganous sulphate. J. Scobai obtained for manganese dioxide in
$N-H_2SO_4$, 0.628 volt against a normal mercurous sulphate electrode ; with the
dioxide in $12N-H_2SO_4$, 0.752 volt ; in $22N-H_2SO_4$, 0.93 volt ; and in conc. H_2SO_4,
1.1 volt. R. C. Wells found the potential of pyrolusite against $N-KCl$ to be 0.93
volt ; D. J. Brown and H. A. Liebhafsky gave 1.236 volts for the oxidation potential
of the reaction $MnO_2+4H^.+2e \rightleftharpoons Mn^{..}+2H_2O$ in soln. of perchloric acid. S. Popoff
and co-workers were unable to measure the potential of the permanganate-hydrogen-
manganese dioxide electrode ; and the manganese dioxide-hydrogen-manganous
electrode was irreversible, nor could a value be calculated from the potentials of
manganese dioxide electrodes. C. E. Ruby found the electrode potentials :
$MnO_2+4OH'+2 \oplus = MnO_4''+2H_2O-0.664$ volt ; $MnO_2+4OH'+3 \oplus = MnO_4'$
$+2H_2O-0.647$ volt ; and $MnO_2+2H_2O+3 \oplus = MnO_4'+4H^{..}--1.757$ volts, at $25°$.
D. J. Brown and R. F. Tefft found that from e.m.f. measurements of the cell
$H_2|HClO_4(m_1)|HClO_4(m_2),KMnO_4(m_3)|MnO_2$, at $25°$, the oxidation potential of
the reaction $MnO_4'+4H^.+3e=MnO_2+2H_2O$ was found to be 1.586 volts. This
value decreases with decreasing acid concentration exactly as required by theory.

Pure manganese dioxide could not be obtained electrolytically. C. Drucker and R. Hüttner studied the e.m.f. of the cells Pt|Mn dioxide, electrolyte | sat. soln. KCl|N-KCl, HgCl|Hg, where the electrolyte was sulphuric acid and manganous sulphate or monochloracetic acid, manganous sulphate, and 0·1N-NaOH. They calculated -0.79 volt for the change $Mn_2O_3+6H^{\cdot}+2\oplus \rightarrow 2Mn^{\cdot\cdot}+3H_2O$. It is inferred that the manganese dioxide passes into manganic oxide and not into manganosic oxide, as supposed by K. Arndt and co-workers. Observations were also made by J. K. H. Inglis, W. A. Smith, C. E. Ruby, Y. Kato and T. Matsuhashi, S. Popoff and co-workers, and O. Sackur and W. Taegener.

O. F. Tower found that the conc. of the H -ions in a soln. at a manganese dioxide electrode has about four times as much influence on the e.m.f. as the conc. of the Mn··-ions. T. J. Martin and A. J. Helfrecht's results for the electrode potentials of manganese dioxide—artificial with 82·5 per cent. MnO_2; and natural ore with 67·5, 74·8, and 88·9 per cent. MnO_2—are summarized in Fig. 49. L. Kahlenberg and A. S. McDaniel found the oxidation potential depends on the nature of the solvents, being less in basic solvents than in water or in neutral solvents. The electrode potential of manganese dioxide in water is -0.978 volt; in acetone, -1.137 volts; in pyridine, -0.698 volt; and in amylamine, -0.476 volt. The presence of a little water has a great effect in the case of acetone, but for pyridine and amylamine the effects increase slowly as the quantity of water increases, so that the constant for water is attained when from 90 to nearly 100 per cent.

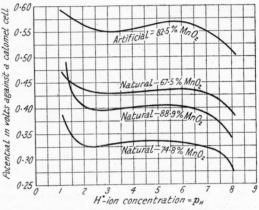

FIG. 49.—The Effect of the H·-ion Concentration on the Electrode Potential of Manganese Dioxide.

of water has been added. When sulphuric acid is used instead of a soln. of lithium chloride, the e.m.f. rises from -0.978 to -1.566 volts.

W. Hähnel measured the concentration of the iodine formed in the reaction $MnO_2+4H^{\cdot}+2I'{\rightleftharpoons}Mn^{\cdot\cdot}+2H_2O+I_2$. The results were erratic, owing (i) to the solubility of iodine in a 1·1 mol. soln. of manganous chloride, being 6.23×10^{-3} when its solubility in water is 3.7×10^{-3} mol per litre, showing that some combination occurs ; and (ii) to the oxidation of iodide to iodate by the manganese dioxide when the conc. of the iodine ions is small enough to permit of the existence of measurable quantities of iodate ions. Equilibrium is attained very slowly. From these imperfect results, the normal oxidation potential of manganese dioxide works out to be greater than 1·2 volts when referred to the normal hydrogen electrode. The potential which just deposits manganese dioxide from a soln. of manganese sulphate depends on the acidity of the soln. The results show that $\epsilon_0=E-0.0295 \log ([H^{\cdot}]^4/[Mn^{\cdot\cdot}])$ gives $\epsilon_0=1.35$ volts nearly. Analogous results were obtained with a bromide in place of iodide. When chlorine is passed into a neutral or faintly acid soln. of manganese chloride, the dioxide is precipitated. It is found that in a 0·22N-soln. of manganous chloride, precipitation occurs when the conc. of the hydrogen ions is 0·0101, and does not occur when it is 0·013 mol per litre. This result leads to a value of about 1·57 volts for the normal potential of manganese dioxide, but in calculating this the formation of manganic chloride in the soln. is neglected, the effect of which is to make the calculated value too large. O. Sackur and E. Fritzmann found the e.m.f. of the combination : oxygen at one atm. press. | sat. soln. MnO | MnO_2 | Pt, in which the reaction is $2MnO+O_2=2MnO_2$, to be 0·32 volt.   This gives $6·3 \times 10^{-23}$ atm. for the dissociation press. of manganese dioxide at 18°.   H. A. J. Wilkens and H. B. C. Nitze discussed the magnetic separation of pyrolusite ; F. Daniels, H. D. Holler and L. M. Ritchie, B. M. Thompson, K. Fischbeck and E. Einecke, W. C. Phalen, R. Hüttner, C. Drotschmann, K. Arndt and co-workers, C. Drucker, A. Keller, J. Meyer and R. Kanters, V. P. Ilinsky and N. P. Lapin, S. Kaneko, N. S. Krivolutskaya and G. G. Morozoff, V. A. Kostjejeff, and E. Divers discussed the action of manganese dioxide in Leclanché cells ; and P. Fischer, the conductivity of mixtures of cupric oxide and manganese dioxide.

E. T. Wherry found pyrolusite to be a fair **radio-detector ;** and C. Tissot constructed a sensitive detector from pyrolusite and a metal.   The combination acts without an auxiliary current, so that its activity does not depend on a change of resistance, and it is supposed to be a thermoelectric effect produced by the electric waves.   R. Bunsen placed pyrolusite beyond bismuth in the **thermoelectric series.**   E. Wedekind and C. Horst gave $14·58 \times 10^{-6}$ mass unit for the **magnetic susceptibility** of the dioxide at 14°. and S. Meyer gave 27×10^{-6} mass unit at 17°.   Observations were also made by P. Hausknecht, and G. Grenet. F. Stutzer and co-workers gave 128×10^{-6} for the coeff. of magnetization.   G. Wistrand gave $37·3 \times 10^{-6}$ mass unit for the magnetic susceptibility.   K. Honda and T. Sone plotted the magnetic susceptibility, $\chi \times 10^6$, with temp. and observed irregularities on the curve corresponding with the transformations : $MnO_2 \rightleftharpoons Mn_2O_3$ at 525° ; $Mn_2O_3 \rightleftharpoons Mn_3O_4$ at 933° ; and $Mn_3O_4 \rightleftharpoons MnO$ at 1160°.   The results up to 535° are :

	$-186°$	$-106°$	$-3°$	$21°$	$111°$	$396°$	$527°$	$535°$
$\chi \times 10^6$.	74·9	49·9	39·9	38·4	33·7	24·0	22·8	25·9

A. F. Benton found that no **helium** is adsorbed by manganese dioxide between −79° and 184°.   According to W. Müller, G. Forchhammer, E. Turner, and **M.** Ravack, **hydrogen** reduces manganese dioxide to the tritatetroxide at 202° ; C. R. A. Wright and A. P. Luff found that pyrolusite begins to be reduced at 190° ; F. Glaser, that the dioxide is reduced to the hemitrioxide at 183° ; and **L.** Benedek, that pyrolusite passes first into the hemitrioxide, then into the tritatetroxide at 280°, and finally into the monoxide.   S. Hauser said that reduction occurs between 230° and 245°.   According to H. Moissan, hydrogen at 230° reduces the dioxide to the hemitrioxide, if more strongly heated, to the tritatetroxide, and at 280°, to the monoxide ; while E. Newbery and J. N. Pring found that the dioxide is reduced to metal by hydrogen at 2000° and 150 atm. press.   H. Saito, and J. C. W. Frazer and C. E. Greider studied the heat of reduction by hydrogen of manganese dioxide.   A. de Hemptinne found that there is a slow reduction of manganese dioxide by hydrogen at ordinary temp. and press., and the product quickly re-oxidizes in air.   A. F. Benton studied the adsorption of hydrogen and of **oxygen** by manganese dioxide and found that at −79°, 0°, and 25° respectively 0·070, 0·11, and 0·039 c.c. of hydrogen at n.p. θ are adsorbed per gram, and that at 25° and 110° respectively 0·234 and 0·085 c.c. of oxygen at n.p. θ are adsorbed per gram.   The actions of **air,** and oxygen are indicated above.   J. L. Odier said that when manganese dioxide is heated in air, nitrogen oxides are produced. P. Askenasy and E. L. Rényi obtained also these oxides at 280°, and more at a higher temp., not exceeding 700°.   The oxides are also produced in an atm. of carbon dioxide, and the nitrogen oxide is derived from the manganese dioxide itself, which contains 0·002 per cent.—*vide supra,* nitrates in manganese dioxide. O. Brunck found that the dioxide can be heated above 320° in an atm. of **ozone** and oxygen, but not in air or carbon dioxide.   The dioxide does not act on **water.** W. C. Bray and H. D. Draper, C. E. Lanning, and H. W. Foote and J. K. Dixon studied the adsorption of water by the dioxide.   A. Gorgeu found that pyrolusite has no action on litmus paper, but F. von Kobell added that some varieties, after calcination, have an alkaline reaction.   According to L. J. Thénard, a soln. of

hydrogen dioxide loses all its active oxygen when in contact with manganese dioxide without the latter losing any oxygen. G. Bredig and R. M. von Berneck found that the action of one part of manganese dioxide in 10,000,000 parts of soln. is appreciable. A. Geuther, and B. C. Brodie said that some manganese dioxide is reduced in the presence of acids, and A. Baumann represented the reaction: $MnO_2+H_2O_2=MnO+H_2O+O_2$. A. Gorgeu found that the manganese dioxide remains intact if the hydrogen dioxide is slightly alkaline, but if slightly acidic, a little manganese dioxide is reduced. Hydrated manganese dioxide prepared in the cold decomposes hydrogen dioxide and at the same time is reduced to an extent depending on the proportion of hydrogen dioxide employed. The limit at which hydrogen dioxide has no action on manganese dioxide is represented by the basic manganite $MnO_2.2MnO.\frac{1}{4}H_2O$, which can be obtained by the prolonged action of a current of air on manganous hydroxide suspended in its own mother-liquor. Since hydrogen dioxide reduces only the oxides above this limit, it would seem that the oxidizing action of the dioxide on manganous hydroxide ought to cease at the same point. This, however, is not the case ; the manganous hydroxide can be oxidized even to a higher degree than the acid manganite $MnO_2.MnO$. The decomposition of hydrogen dioxide is more rapid in presence of a strong base, and the oxidation of the manganese is at first partly determined by the influence of the basic function of the manganous hydroxide, assisted afterwards by the acid function of the dioxide which is formed. The higher oxidation may be regarded as due to the action of nascent oxygen. M. Martinon found that in a strongly acidified soln. a mol of hydrogen dioxide gives a mol of oxygen and at the same time the manganese dioxide is reduced to the monoxide ; but in alkaline soln. a mol of hydrogen dioxide gives a gram-atom of oxygen and the manganese dioxide remains unchanged. The results with manganese tritatetroxide and hemitrioxide are similar. G. Tammann found that a trace of silver sulphate accelerates the rate of decomposition. The reaction was studied by A. Lottermoser and R. Lehmann, A. von Kiss and F. E. Lederer, F. Wöhler and A. Geuther, L. Swiontkowsky, G. Bredig and A. Marck, A. Marck, E. Schöne, M. Martinon, R. Engel, T. Gigli, B. C. Brodie, A. Carnot, and S. M. Tanatar. G. Bredig and A. Marck found that in the decomposition of hydrogen dioxide by colloidal manganese dioxide, in conc. alkaline soln., the rate of decomposition diminishes rapidly with the conc. of the alkali. Substances such as hydrogen sulphide, hydroxylamine, mercuric cyanide, potassium cyanide, iodine, carbon monoxide, and mercuric chloride, which act as " poisons " in the decomposition of hydrogen dioxide by colloidal metals, exert no depressing influence on the activity of manganese dioxide. On the other hand, sodium hydrophosphate reduces appreciably the rate of the reaction, and this is attributed to the formation of manganese phosphates. In the presence of mercuric chloride the hydrogen dioxide is more rapidly decomposed, and this is probably due to the simultaneous action of the colloidal mercury which is formed by reduction of the mercuric chloride by the hydrogen dioxide, in which reaction, also, the colloidal manganese dioxide acts as a catalyst. In the absence of free alkali no catalytic decomposition is observed, and the soln. obtained in these circumstances is quite colourless. In the further investigation of the cause of the disappearance of the brown colour, it has been found that freshly-precipitated manganese dioxide dissolves to an appreciable extent in conc. hydrogen dioxide soln. cooled to $-20°$. At the ordinary temp. the resulting soln. evolves oxygen very readily. It is supposed that a manganous salt of hydrogen dioxide is present in the colourless

soln. ; this salt—*vide supra*—$Mn\!\!\begin{smallmatrix}O\\ \text{iii}\\ O\end{smallmatrix}$, is isomeric with manganese dioxide, $Mn\!\!\begin{smallmatrix}O\\ O\end{smallmatrix}$.

In the so-called *oxygen bath* produced by adding a mixture of perborate and permanganate to the bath water, hydrogen dioxide and colloidal manganese dioxide are produced, and the latter catalyzes the decomposition of the former, producing a supersaturated soln. of oxygen, which is liberated in small bubbles on the skin of the bather. The effect of electrolytes in the bath water on the evolution of oxygen is so marked that it led A. Lottermosei and R. Lehmann to investigate the influence of various salts on the decomposition of hydrogen dioxide by manganese dioxide at 30°. The reaction is very sensitive to accidental impurities, and also the velocity depends on the order in which the reagents are added to the water in which the reaction takes place. The assumption that the increase in the velocity constants is to be explained by the formation and subsequent decomposition of a hydrogen dioxide salt could not be confirmed. The influence of the cations of the added salts, which all have the same anion, follows the lyotropic series Ba··>Sr··>Ca··>Na·>K·>Li·, in which Ba·· accelerates the reaction to the greatest extent and Li· retards it the most. At higher concentrations, barium falls after calcium. Mg·· and NH₄·, on account of the reduction of the conc. of the hydroxyl ion which they produce, strongly retard the reaction.

When manganese dioxide suspended in hot alkali-lye is treated with **chlorine,** alkali permanganate is formed. The reaction proceeds more quickly with the hydrated dioxide. L. E. Rivot and co-workers found that the reaction does not occur at a low temp. ; at 0° a dark brown substance is formed ; and at 15° to 20° the product is dark green. F. P. Venable and D. H. Jackson found that the dioxide is chlorinated at 460° by a mixture of chlorine and carbon monoxide. According to M. Berthelot, the hydrohalide acids undergo complex reactions, liberating respectively chlorine, bromine, and iodine. O. Ruff and H. Krug found that **chlorine trifluoride** reacts with manganese dioxide with incandescence. G. Gore, and O. T. Christensen observed that manganese dioxide is very sparingly soluble in **hydrofluoric acid,** and that it does not dissolve in the water-free acid. K. Fredenhagen and G. Cadenbach studied the action of this acid. According to G. Gore, dry liquid **hydrogen chloride** whitens manganese dioxide without the evolution of gas or dissolution ; and R. E. Hughes found that the dry gas attacks the dry dioxide. M. Berthelot observed that cold **hydrochloric acid** dissolves manganese dioxide, with the evolution of some chlorine and the formation of a dark brown soln. containing manganese trichloride or tetrachloride or a complex of the tetrachloride and hydrogen chloride —*vide infra* ; when heated, the reaction is symbolized : $MnO_2 + 4HCl = MnCl_2 + 2H_2O + Cl_2$; while a mixture of alkali chloride and sulphuric acid forms manganese sulphate and chlorine. V. Dolejsek and J. Heyrovsky observed that the higher chloride of rhenium or dwimanganese passes over with the chlorine. According to T. Schlösing, a mixture of hydrochloric and nitric acids forms chlorine and manganous nitrate. C. W. Hempel, M. M. P. Muir, and W. Hähnel found that dil. sulphuric acid and **potassium iodide** react with the dioxide, liberating iodine. According to G. Vortmann, C. L. Müller and G. Kircher, C. W. Hempel, and E. Pollacci, the **chlorides** furnish chlorine only in the presence of strong acids— *e.g.* sulphuric acid ; the **bromides** give bromine in the presence of weak acids— *e.g.* acetic acid ; and the **iodides** yield iodine in the presence of the weakest of acids—*e.g.* carbonic acid. M. M. P. Muir found that the velocity of the reaction between manganese dioxide and hydrochloric acid is much accelerated in the presence of potassium iodide. A. Baudrimont observed that the m.p. of **potassium chlorate** is lowered by the presence of manganese dioxide, and the decomposition of the salt is accelerated without forming intermediate perchlorate. The reaction was studied by H. M. McLaughlin and F. E. Brown, F. E. Brown and co-workers, O. Brunck, W. Spring and E. Prost, E. Jungfleisch, G. J. Fowler and J. Grant, A. Wagner, E. Wiederhold, A. Vogel, F. Bellamy, H. N. Warren, G. Krebs, C. F. Schönbein, J. C. Poggendorff, M. E. Chevreul, J. C. G. de Marignac, C. H. L. von Babo, W. R. E. Hodgkinson and F. K. S. Lowndes, H. MacLeod, E. J. Mills and G. Donald, W. H. Sodeau, Y. Kato and T. Matsuhashi, and V. H. Veley—*vide* **1.** 8. 7.

J. A. Arfvedson found that when manganese dioxide is heated with **sulphur,** sulphur dioxide and manganous sulphide are formed. A. Wagner, and E. Donath observed that iron-free pyrolusite decomposes **hydrogen sulphide,** forming a sulphide which, in a current of carbon dioxide, gives off hydrogen sulphide, but retains a little sulphur. According to A. de Hemptinne, manganese dioxide rapidly absorbs hydrogen sulphide from a mixture of this gas with hydrogen, manganese sulphides being formed. The absorption is much more rapid than with dry hydrogen sulphide alone, although in presence of moisture this gas is readily absorbed by manganese dioxide. E. Priwoznik found that yellow **ammonium polysulphide** at 100° forms green manganous sulphide ; while E. Donath and F. Müllner found that when the dioxide is boiled with **metal sulphides** a thiosulphate is formed. R. E. Hughes observed no reaction between dry **sulphur dioxide** and dry manganese dioxide ; but J. Meyer and W. Schramm observed that when the dioxide is suspended in water, two reactions occur, according to the equations $2MnO_2+4SO_2$ $=Mn_2(SO_3)_3+SO_3=MnSO_4+SO_2+MnS_2O_6$ and $MnO_2+SO_2=MnSO_4$; the latter is favoured and the former repressed by increase of temp. E. J. Russell and N. Smith said that manganese dioxide does not react with sulphur dioxide, but, according to D. L. Hammick, if the manganese dioxide be finely divided, inter-action occurs at dull redness, with the evolution of light and heat. The reddish-brown powder which is formed contains manganese sulphate and one or both of Mn_2O_3 and Mn_3O_4. With a prolonged heating, manganous sulphate is formed—*vide* sulphur dioxide. The reaction was also studied by J. Meyer, J. Meyer and W. Schramm, and T. S. Dymond and F. Hughes—*vide* sulphur dioxide. A. Over-beck, J. Meyer, and J. J. Welter and J. L. Gay-Lussac found that manganese dioxide dissolves in an aq. soln. of sulphur dioxide, forming manganous sulphate and dithionate ($q.v.$). C. W. Davis studied the solvent action of sulphurous acid. F. J. Otto observed that **ammonium sulphite** in ammoniacal soln. reduces the dioxide to the monoxide. According to G. Scurati-Manzoni, **zinc, aluminium, and chromic sulphites** react with hydrated manganese dioxide to form manganous sulphate and the corresponding hydroxide. According to H. Hess, and L. Carius, when manganese dioxide is heated with conc. sulphuric acid to 110°, one-fourth of the oxygen is evolved and manganic sulphate is formed : $2MnO_2+3H_2SO_4=Mn_2(SO_4)_3+3H_2O+O$; and if heated more vigorously, another fourth of oxygen is given off and manganous sulphate is formed : $Mn_2(SO_4)_3=2MnSO_4+SO_3+O$. According to P. Berthier, F. Jones, F. Göbel, E. Donath, and C. R. Fresenius and H. Will, the dioxide does not dissolve in dil. sulphuric acid, except in the presence of organic substances—*e.g.* oxalic acid or sugar—which take up the peroxidic oxygen. K. Thaddéeff found that boiling **sulphuric acid** does not acquire a colour such as is obtained with braunite. C. R. A. Wright and A. E. Menke found that the artificial dioxide produces no coloration when in contact with cold sulphuric acid for 24 hrs. ; and H. A. von Vogel, and C. F. Schönbein observed the formation of manganic sulphate when the dioxide is in contact with cold sulphuric acid—*vide infra* for the action of mercury on the reaction. For the adsorption of acids by manganese dioxide, and the weak basic properties of the dioxide, *vide infra*, the action of hydrogen on potassium permanganate. E. Bamberger found that at ordinary temp. **mono-persulphuric acid** decomposes manganese dioxide with the evolution of ozonized oxygen ; and M. Traube said that the hydrated dioxide forms manganese sulphate and free oxygen when it dissolves in **persulphuric acid ;** under these conditions the anhydrous dioxide is not reduced. A. Seyewetz and P. Trawitz observed that when the dioxide is boiled with a soln. of **ammonium persulphate,** violet per-manganate is produced—the coloration is so sensitive that 1 : 100,000 parts of manganese can be detected. According to W. Schmid, and A. Laugier, **selenious acid** forms selenic acid as it reduces manganese dioxide, and L. Marino and V. Squin-tana found that some manganous selenite, $Mn(SeO_3)_2$, is formed.

A. F. Benton found that at 25°, 110°, and 184° respectively 0·301, 0·081, and. 0·038 c.c. of **nitrogen** at n.p. θ are adsorbed per gram of manganese dioxide. F. Kuhl-mann, and O. Michel and E. Grandmougin found that when manganese dioxide is heated in a current of **ammonia,** the reaction can be symbolized : $6MnO_2+2NH_3$ $=N_2+3Mn_2O_3+3H_2O$, and if the temp. be higher, some nitrous fumes are pro-duced. N. Smith added that in the presence of manganese dioxide, aq. ammonia forms nitrites and nitrates when exposed to air. G. Leoncini and C. Pieri found that **ammonium salts** are not oxidized by manganese dioxide at ordinary temp. According to E. Divers, soln. of **ammonium chloride** in the presence of certain metals—*e.g.* zinc—are decomposed by manganese dioxide ; hydrogen is given off and some metal passes into soln. C. Drotschmann found that in the Leclanché cell, abnormal amounts of manganese were found in the electrolytes in which artificial pyrolusite was used, although the dissolution of manganese did not appear to be a direct consequence of the depolarizing action of the manganese dioxide. The enhanced chemical action of the artificial variety caused a greater attack on the zinc. The development of free ammonia in the electrolyte of a cell when kept for 14 days was greater when the zinc electrode was completely immersed than when it was partly exposed to the air. Less hydrogen was developed by a cell containing artificial manganese dioxide than by one containing the natural product when kept on open circuit. F. Fischer and F. Bangert observed that at 800° to 1000° **methane** reacts with the oxide, forming a carbide. A. Purgotti found that the dioxide reacts with an acid soln. of **hydrazine sulphate** in accord with $2MnO_2+N_2H_4.H_2SO_4+H_2SO_4=2MnSO_4+4H_2O+N_2$; and with a neutral soln. in accord with $2MnO_2+2(N_2H_4.H_2SO_4)+H_2O=2MnSO_4+4H_2O+N_2$ $+N_2H_4.H_2O$. E. J. Cuy and co-workers studied the reaction. H. Goldberg found that when the dioxide is heated with **potassium azide,** potassium manganate is formed. P. Sabatier and J. B. Senderens found that at 400° **nitric oxide** reduces manganese dioxide to the hemitrioxide. H. A. Auden and G. J. Fowler observed that at ordinary temp. a basic nitrate is slowly produced by nitric oxide ; the action is faster at a higher temp. According to G. Kastner, and C. F. Schönbein, nitric oxide in the presence of water acts on the dioxide, forming manganous nitrite, and if a large excess of dioxide be present, manganous nitrate. P. Sabatier and J. B. Senderens observed that **nitrogen peroxide** forms a nitrate. With **nitrous acid,** manganous nitrate is formed. According to P. Berthier, F. Jones, F. Göbel, E. Donath, and C. R. Fresenius and H. Will, the dioxide does not dissolve in **nitric acid** unless an organic substance is present—*e.g.* oxalic acid or sugar— which takes up the peroxidic oxygen—*vide infra* for the action of mercury on the reaction. H. Bornträger found that manganese dioxide readily dissolves in **nitrosylsulphonic acid.** F. Wöhler found that when manganese dioxide is heated with **sodium nitrate,** in the absence of air, the nitrate is completely decomposed, but no manganate is formed ; but in air, J. G. Gentele found that sodium manganate is produced. F. Kuhlmann added that impure pyrolusite is more active than the pure dioxide. According to J. W. Gatehouse, in the presence of manganese dioxide **ammonium nitrate** decomposes between 165° and 200°, in accord with : $MnO_2+4NH_4NO_3=Mn(NO_3)_2+8H_2O+3N_2$—alone, the ammonium nitrate decomposes at 215°. L. C. A. Barreswil showed that when the dioxide is heated with syrupy **phosphoric acid,** or with an **alkali phosphate,** violet manganic phosphate is produced. A. Michaelis observed no reaction occurs between **phosphorus trichloride** and manganese dioxide at 200°. L. C. A. Barreswil found that **arsenic acid** forms manganic arsenate when it is heated with manganese dioxide, and at a higher temp. oxygen is evolved. C. Reichard found that **arsenious acid** is oxidized by manganese dioxide in alkaline soln. at 50°.

The dioxide is reduced to the metal (*q.v.*) by **carbon** at a high temp. G. Tammann and A. Sworykin said that the reaction with sugar charcoal starts at 460°, and with graphite at 550° ; and that $2MnO_2+C_{amorphous}=2MnO+CO_2+26.6$ Cals. H. Bähr and F. Fallböhmer observed that the addition of manganese dioxide to coal favours the reactivity of the resulting coke as a catalyst in the reaction $C+CO_2=2CO$. Confirmatory results were obtained by J. H. Jones and co-workers. H. S. Taylor and co-workers discussed the activation of manganese dioxide as a catalyst by chromic oxide. I. L. Bell observed that at about 420° manganese dioxide is reduced to the monoxide by **carbon monoxide ;** with pyrolusite, C. R. A. Wright and A. P. Luff found that the reaction begins at about 87°, and no carbonate is formed. H. Saito studied this reaction; and W. A. Whitesell and J. C. W. Frazer, H. S. Taylor, and A. F. Benton found that at $-79°$, $0°$, and $25°$ respectively 6·92, 1·90, and 1·26 c.c. at n.p. θ of carbon monoxide are adsorbed per gram. H. Tropsch and A. von Philippovich, J. A. Almquist and W. C. Bray, W. M. Hoskins and W. C. Bray, W. C. Bray and G. J. Doss, H. D. Draper, B. Neumann and co-workers, H. A. J. Pieters, E. J. Witzemann, and W. E. Kuentzel studied the catalytic effect of manganese dioxide on the oxidation and decomposition of carbon monoxide, etc., and W. P. Yant and C. O. Hawk, on the oxidation of methane. F. Merck and E. Wedekind, and E. Baur studied the action of the catalyst *hopcalite*—$MnO_2 : CuO = 60 : 40$ per cent.—on the oxidation of carbon monoxide. C. E. Lanning, and A. F. Benton studied the adsorption of carbon monoxide and of **carbon dioxide** by manganese dioxide and found that at $0°$, $25°$, $100°$, and $184°$ respectively 8·66, 6·17, 1·20, and 0·12 c.c. of the carbon dioxide at n.p. θ are adsorbed per gram; and H. W. Foote and J. K. Dixon showed that water retards the adsorption of carbon dioxide by manganese dioxide. P. Sabatier and A. Mailhe discussed the catalytic effect of manganese dioxide in the dehydration of ethyl alcohol; and H. D. Draper, the pore vol. of the dioxide as a catalyst. J. C. W. Frazer and C. E. Greider studied the heats of reduction of manganese dioxide by carbon monoxide. T. Bergman found that pyrolusite is attacked by water with carbon dioxide in soln. L. Hackspill and R. Grandadam observed that manganese dioxide is partially reduced by **sodium cyanide** to the metal when heated at $570°$ to $700°$ in vacuo; and A. Kutzelnigg, that the powder oxidized a soln. of **potassium ferrocyanide**, possibly—in part—by adsorbed oxygen. H. W. Foote and J. K. Dixon studied the adsorption of **benzene** vapour by manganese dioxide. J. W. Döbereiner found that when manganese dioxide is warmed with **alcohol** and sulphuric acid, aldehyde and other products are formed; and A. Baudrimont found that with **ethylsulphuric acid,** aldehyde is formed. J. C. W. Frazer and C. E. Greider studied the heat of oxidation of carbon monoxide by manganese dioxide. A. Brighenti observed that manganese dioxide acts catalytically in oxidizing methyl, ethyl, and propyl alcoholic soln. of the corresponding alcoholates, and also the vapours of these **alcohols.** C. Matignon and R. Trannoy found that manganese dioxide acts like platinum in accelerating the oxidation of **ether.** H. C. Bolton found that the dioxide is decomposed by citric acid in the cold, readily so when heated—$9MnO_2 + 10H_8C_6O_7 = 9MnH_6C_6O_7 + 13H_2O + 6CO_2$; **oxalic acid** acts more quickly. K. Schröder observed that some of the reduced oxide may be re-oxidized by atm. oxygen. According to A. Skrabal, the reaction between oxalic acid and manganese dioxide is similar to that with potassium permanganate. The reaction between permanganate and oxalic acid takes place in the following stages: (*incubation period*) (1) $C_2H_2O_4 + KMnO_4 \rightarrow Mn^{\cdots} + CO_2$ (measurable); (2) $C_2H_2O_4 + Mn^{\cdots} \rightarrow Mn(OH)_2 + CO_2$ (practically instantaneously); (*induction period*) (3) $Mn(OH)_2 + KMnO_4 \rightarrow Mn^{\cdots}$ (less quickly than the former stage); (4) $Mn^{\cdots} + C_2H_2O_4 \rightarrow Mn(OH)_2 + CO_2$ (practically instantaneously); (5) $Mn^{\cdots} + C_2H_2O_4 \rightarrow [Mn(OH)_3.C_2H_2O_4]$ (practically instantaneously); (6) $2Mn^{\cdots} \rightarrow Mn(OH)_2 + Mn(OH)_4$ (practically instantaneously); (*end period* I); (7) $[Mn(OH)_3.C_2H_2O_4] \rightarrow Mn^{\cdots}$ (measurable); (8) $C_2H_2O_4 + Mn^{\cdots} \rightarrow Mn(OH)_2 + CO_2$ (practically instantaneously); (*end period* II); (9) $Mn(OH)_2 + Mn(OH)_4 \rightarrow 2Mn^{\cdots}$ (less quickly than the former stage); (10) $C_2H_2O_4 + Mn^{\cdots} \rightarrow Mn(OH)_2 + CO_2$ (practically instantaneously). The rate of stage (1) increases with increase of amount of acid present. Stage (4) is conditioned by the rate at which the ions $Mn^{\cdots}$ are formed in stage (3). In the presence of manganese sulphate the incubation period is not observed, whilst the measurable reaction in the induction period proceeds very quickly. If the conditions for the formation of complex manganic salts are favourable, that is, if the concentration of oxalic acid is great and that of hydrogen ions small, stage (5) proceeds more quickly than any other stage in the induction period, and the end period is expressed by (7) and (8). Otherwise, stage (6) is the most rapid in the induction period and the end period is expressed by (9) and (10). A. Skrabal and J. Preiss obtained analogous results with **formic acid.** D. Talmud and N. M. Lubman found that the flotability of manganese dioxide in **oleic acid** or mixtures of oleic acid and ammonia is a maximum when $p_H = 7$. G. Bruni and C. Pelizzola found that colloidal manganese dioxide causes raw **caoutchouc** to become tacky by catalytic oxidation. W. Thomson and F. Lewis studied its action on **indiarubber.** W. E. Adeney noted the reduction of the dioxide to manganous carbonate by bacterial fermentation. The decomposition of the dioxide by dil. sulphuric or nitric acid in the presence of oxalic acid or **sugar** was studied by P. Berthier, F. Jones, and C. R. Fresenius and H. Will. G. Leoncini and C. Pieri found that manganese dioxide is incapable of oxidizing **organic nitrogen** at ordinary temp.; ammonium compounds are not oxidized; fatty amides are oxidized to nitric acid in boiling aq. soln., with or without acid or alkali, but not below 30°; but amino-acids and purine-derivatives are not oxidized.

L. Kahlenberg and W. J. Trautmann observed that when a mixture of powdered **silicon** and manganese dioxide is heated over the bunsen burner, a sudden glowing occurs, and at a higher temp. reduction occurs. According to G. Rauter, when **silicon tetrachloride** is heated with the dioxide, chlorine, silica, and manganous chloride are formed. F. Knapp found that pyrolusite dissolves in molten **glass** as manganese oxide and oxygen is evolved; on cooling the oxide crystallizes out; if an excess of soda be added, and the mass extracted with sulphuric acid, manganosic oxide remains. Manganese dioxide is used as a bleaching agent for glass— *vide supra.*

L. Franck found that the dioxide is readily reduced by **aluminium** at a high temp. V. Shuleikin and X. Solovova studied the liberation of heat in the thermite reaction with aluminium. J. Meyer and R. Kanters found that neither manganese dioxide nor **mercury** dissolves in cold, dil. sulphuric or nitric acid, yet together they dissolve readily: $MnO_2 + 2Hg + 4HNO_3 = Mn(NO_3)_2 + 2HgNO_3 + 2H_2O$ by a kind of coupled reaction. With sulphuric acid: $2MnO_2 + 3Hg + 3H_2SO_4 = 2MnSO_4 + HgSO_4.Hg_2O + 3H_2O$. If a 25 per cent. soln. of ammonium, calcium, or magnesium chloride is used in place of acid, the mercury is dissolved, although to a much smaller extent, in the form of mercuric chloride.

F. de Carli found that mixtures of **cuprous oxide** and manganese dioxide begin to react at 350°; no reaction was observed with **cupric oxide.** G. N. Lewis found that the decomposition of **silver oxide** is accelerated by manganese dioxide. D. Balareff said that **barium oxide** reacts vigorously with manganese dioxide below 300°, with the evolution of much heat. Barium oxide containing a trace of water reacts with manganese dioxide at 240°, but **calcium oxide** does not do so below 930°. F. de Carli found a mol of barium, **strontium oxide,** or calcium oxide mixed with 1, 2, or 3 mols of manganese dioxide begins to react at 150° to 250°. No reaction was observed with **magnesium, zinc, or cadmium oxide ; stannous oxide** begins to react at 180°; but no reaction was observed with **lead oxide** or **chromic oxide.** In general, R. Böttger showed that manganese dioxide or its hydrate behaves as an oxidizing agent. Thus, H. A. von Vogel, J. W. C. Harvey, and C. Schorlemmer and T. E. Thorpe showed that it oxidizes **stannous chloride** to stannic chloride. A. Gorgeu found that unlike the hydrated dioxide, the neutral and dry dioxide is not hydrated by contact with soln. of **alkali hydroxide.** O. Dieffenbach found that pyrolusite is difficult to hydrate in this way, but if heated with alkali-lye under press., hydration occurs. G. Forchhammer, E. Mitscherlich, W. Spring and M. Lucion, T. Monticelli and N. Covelli, P. F. Chevillot and W. F. Edwards, C. W. Eliot and F. H. Storer, and N. Beketoff found that when manganese dioxide is heated with potassium hydroxide in the absence of air, potassium manganate and manganese hemitrioxide are formed : $3MnO_2 = MnO_3 + Mn_2O_3$—*vide infra.* C. Binks and J. Macqueen, C. Taquet, and J. Townsend observed that when the dioxide is heated with **magnesium chloride,** chlorine, magnesia, and manganous chloride are produced : $MnO_2 + 2MgCl_2 = MnCl_2 + Cl_2 + 2MgO$. Hydrated manganese dioxide exhibits acidic properties; A. Gorgeu, and J. M. van Bemmelen found that it reddens litmus, it takes up alkalies, and alkaline earths from soln., it liberates carbon dioxide from carbonates, and it imparts an acidic reaction to neutral soln. of salts of the alkalies, alkaline earths, and silver. Hydrated manganese dioxide exhibits basic properties, which are rather feeble. It forms salts—**permanganites.** For compounds with various bases, *vide infra*, the permanganites. H. N. Morse found that a neutral soln. of **potassium permanganate** is reduced by manganese dioxide ; the soln. remains neutral, and all the alkali goes into the precipitate—*vide infra*, potassium permanganate. The reaction was studied by F. W. Skirrow. A. Gorgeu observed that the hydrated dioxide, if of a high degree of purity, does not decolorize a soln. of potassium permanganate.

P. Berthier,[2] A. Gorgeu, and J. Volhard prepared **hydrated manganese dioxide,** approximating $MnO_2.H_2O$, or **manganese oxydihydroxide,** $MnO(OH)_2$, by repeatedly boiling manganous oxide or hydroxide or one of the oxides between manganese monoxide and dioxide with conc. nitric acid. When the wash-water is no longer acidic, the hydrated oxide is peptized to form a brown fluid which is not flocculated by filtration, by shaking, or by standing for a long time ; but the addition of an acid, ammonia, or electrolyte coagulates the dispersed solid. G. Forchhammer heated manganous carbonate in air to 260°, and extracted the remaining manganous oxide or carbonate with hot nitric acid or cold, dil. hydrochloric acid. The nearest approach to MnO_2 obtained by W. Reissig was by heating the carbonate for 3 hrs. at 300°. The hydrated dioxide is also produced when a manganous salt is treated with an oxidizing agent. For example, B. C. Brodie, and C. Friedheim treated manganous hydroxide with an alkaline soln. of hydrogen dioxide. The reaction is the basis of a process by P. Jannasch and co-workers for the separation of manganese and zinc in ammoniacal soln. by the addition of hydrogen dioxide, when the manganese is precipitated as $MnO(OH)_2$. The process was examined by A. J. Walker and W. Farmer. A. Mailfert, and L. Maquenne precipitated hydrated manganese dioxide with ozone ; and M. Geloso, and G. von Knorre, with ammonium persulphate. The subject was discussed by H. Baubigny, A. Carnot, E. Donath and R. Jeller, M. Dittrich, M. Dittrich and C. Hassel, and F. M. Raoult. According to O. Dieffenbach, native oxides which are attacked with difficulty by alkali-lye are readily hydrated if heated under press. P. Berthier passed an excess of chlorine through water holding in suspension finely-divided manganous carbonate, and extracted the unconverted carbonate from the product by cold, dil. nitric acid, or, according to A. Gorgeu, by boiling with at least 10 per cent. nitric acid. F. J. Otto found that the product of the action of chlorine is the hydrated dioxide, but that the subsequent treatment with nitric acid reduces some of the dioxide. R. Phillips, V. Eggertz, C. R. Fresenius, E. and B. Klimenko, J. Post, A. Gorgeu, R. Böttger, J. Pattinson, J. Volhard, C. Meineke, and E. M. Dingler used sodium or calcium hypochlorite as oxidizing agent ; and C. R. A. Wright and A. W. Menke, S. G. Simpson, and G. C. Winkelblech, bromine. C. F. Rammelsberg obtained the hydrated dioxide as a black precipitate by allowing a soln. of manganous bromate to stand for a short time. Mixtures of a chlorate and nitric acid were used for the oxidation by F. Beilstein and L. Jawein, J. B. Hannay, A. Carnot, W. Hampe, A. P. Ford, F. A. Gooch and M. Austin, R. Mackintosh, and G. C. Stone. According to W. W. Fisher, when the dark brown liquid obtained by dissolving manganese dioxide, hemitrioxide, or tritatetroxide in cold, conc. hydrochloric acid is diluted with a large proportion of water, it soon deposits a brown precipitate of the hydrated dioxide. S. U. Pickering, however, found that the composition of the precipitate from manganese trichloride soln. and from the brown soln. prepared by W. W. Fisher ranged from $16MnO_2.5MnO$ to $36MnO_2.5MnO$, or from $11MnO_2.5Mn_2O_2$ to $31MnO_2.5Mn_2O_3$. C. R. A. Wright and A. E. Menke also observed that if the original dioxide contains alkali the precipitate also contains alkali. C. F. Schönbein, and J. M. van Bemmelen found that soln. of manganese tetracetate or disulphate quickly decompose, depositing the hydrated dioxide.

B. Franke found that a soln. of potassium manganic sulphate in dil. sulphuric acid, quickly formed a precipitate of hydrated dioxide, which was quickly filtered, washed successively with water, alcohol, and ether, and dried.

The hydrated dioxide was prepared by E. Mitscherlich by boiling a soln. of potassium manganate or permanganate with an excess of sulphuric, nitric, or oxalic acid , he represented the composition of the precipitate by $MnO_2.H_2O$; and when dried over conc. sulphuric acid, C. F. Rammelsberg, and T. Morawsky and J. Stingl represented the composition by the formula $3MnO_2.2H_2O$; E. Frémy represented the air-dried precipitate by $10MnO_2.MnO.22\frac{1}{2}H_2O$; and A. Lumière and A. Seyewetz, by $2MnO_2.H_2O$; C. R. A. Wright and A. E. Menke gave for the composition of products dried for some months over conc. sulphuric acid : $K_2O.27MnO_2.2MnO.8H_2O$, and $K_2O.32MnO_2.2MnO.22H_2O$, and J. M. van Bemmelen studied the adsorption of alkalies by the colloidal product. Hydrated manganese dioxide is also a product of the action of many reducing agents on soln. of potassium permanganate, but T. Morawsky and J. Stingl, and C. R. A. Wright and A. E. Menke found that the product always contained some alkali—say $K_2O.8MnO_2.3H_2O$. N. C. H. Schjerning boiled a soln. of potassium permanganate with a mixture of sodium trisulphide and thiosulphate ; T. Macalpine reduced an alkaline soln. of potassium permanganate with acetylene ; A. Steopoe, with

TABLE I.—ACTIVE OXYGEN IN THE PRODUCTS OF THE REDUCTION OF POTASSIUM PERMANGANATE (O : MnO)

Reducing agent	1 per cent. $KMnO_4$ soln.		0·1 per cent. $KMnO_4$ soln.	
	Neutral	Acidic	Neutral	Acidic
Sulphite . . .	0·990	0·915	0·910	0·995
Thiosulphate . .	0·795	1·000	0·825	0·930
Potassium iodide .	0·990	1·000	0·975	0·990
Potassium arsenite .	—	0·500	—	0·720
Methyl alcohol . .	0·885	0·930	0·980	1·000
Ethyl alcohol . .	0·905	0·985	1·000	0·985
Propyl alcohol . .	0·965	0·995	1·000	0·985
Glycerol . . .	0·675	0·830	0·785	0·845
Acetone . . .	—	0·795	—	0·890
Oxalic acid . .	0·665	—	0·600	—

ethylene ; and W. Spring and G. de Boeck treated a soln. of the permanganate with sodium thiosulphate. M. Gröger examined the action of different reducing agents on acidic and neutral soln. of potassium permanganate, and represented the number of atoms of active oxygen per mol. of MnO in the product—Table I. According to M. Geloso, in the titration of soln. of potassium permanganate with 0·1N-sodium arsenite, within a certain range of concentration of sulphuric acid, the manganese oxide is reduced to Mn_3O_5 ; in neutral soln., or with insufficient acid, a brown turbidity or a yellow coloration is obtained, whilst an excess of acid gives a pink soln., the corresponding states of oxidation of the manganese ranging continuously from MnO_2 through Mn_6O_{11} and Mn_3O_5 to Mn_2O_3. The end-point is similar with certain concentrations of nitric acid, but never in presence of tartaric or phosphoric acids. The degree of oxidation of the manganese at the end-point is affected considerably by $Ag^{.}$-ions, less by $AsO_4{}'$-ions, whilst in presence of $Mn^{..}$-ions the reduction proceeds quantitatively to MnO_2. The variation in composition of the reduction product with various conditions proves that the formulæ Mn_3O_5 and Mn_6O_{11} do not represent definite compounds, the green liquid being a colloidal soln. of MnO_2 with other substances adsorbed. This sol has a wide absorption band extending to 4900 A., and it polarizes the light it scatters. A similar colloidal soln. is obtainable by adding sulphuric acid to a soln. containing permanganate and arsenite and diluting the product. The hydrated dioxide is also formed when a soln. of potassium permanganate is treated with a manganous salt. G. Forchhammer used a mixture of 2 mols of the permanganate and 3 mols of the manganous salt in dil. soln. : $3MnCl_2+2KMnO_4+2H_2O=2KCl+4HCl+5MnO_2$. This reaction was found by A. Gorgeu to occur when a manganous salt is gradually added to a soln. of the permanganate and the liquid neutralized by calcium carbonate ; when the permanganate is added to the soln. of manganous salt, precipitation is complete when 2 mols of the permanganate have been added to 4 mols of the manganous salt : $4MnCl_2+2KMnO_4+3H_2O=2KCl+6HCl+5MnO_2.MnO$, and if more permanganate be added the reaction progresses : $3(5MnO_2.MnO)+2KMnO_4+2HCl=2KCl+20MnO_2+H_2O$ without the evolution of chlorine or of oxygen. When conc. soln. are used, F. Jones represented the reaction : $2MnCl_2+2KMnO_4=2Mn_2O_3+2KCl+Cl_2+O_2$. Observations were also made by A. Guyard, J. Volhard, J. Meyer and R. Kanters, C. Meineke, C. Winkler, C. G. Särnström, R. Schöffel and E. Donath, N. Wolff, W. Hampe, W. Spring and M. Lucion, R. Habich, T. Morawsky and J. Stingl, and C. R. A. Wright and A. E. Menke. These observers noted the adsorption of alkali by the precipitate, and A. Gorgeu observed that some of the precipitated hydrated dioxide seems to be reduced by the nitric or permanganic acid. O. T. Christensen recommended gradually adding 180 grms. of manganous acetate in two litres of warm water, acidified with acetic acid, to a warm soln. of 79 grms. of potassium permanganate in 1500 c.c. of water. The precipitate was washed by decantation with warm water. E. Krause hydrated pyrolusite by heating it for 8 hrs. with soda-lye at 235° under 8 atm. press. ; and Y. Kato and T. Matsuhashi obtained $MnO_2.H_2O$ by oxidizing the lower oxides with oxygen, using sodium hydroxide as catalyst. D. N. Ghosh obtained the hydroxide as a rhythmic precipitate.

C. Luckow obtained hydrated manganese dioxide by the electrolysis of a dil., feebly-acid soln. of a manganous salt—say the acetate or nitrate—free from chlorides. With a feeble current the anodic deposit has the composition $MnO_2.H_2O$. C. F. Boehringer, A. C. Becquerel, M. Berthelot, N. W. Fischer, A. Classen, A. Classen and M. A. von Reis, A. Riche, A. Brand, C. Engels, J. Köster, A. Piccini, K. Elbs, F. W. Skirrow, E. Frei, L. Schucht, F. Rüdorff, A. P. Rollet, C. N. Otin and E. Grave, the Badische Anilin- und Sodafabrik, M. G. Levi and F. Ageno, and J. Oesch, also obtained it by the electrolysis of soln. of manganous chloride, etc. G. D. van Arsdale and C. G. Maier found that the hydrated dioxide can be deposited from warm acidic soln. containing more than 5 per cent. of manganous sulphate as a dense, black, lustrous film when the current density is 275 amp. per sq. m. The anodic deposit may be obtained with a 100 per cent. efficiency. The efficiency is decreased by acids in cold soln., but with soln. at 65° to 75° the effect is less. Impurities which are reducing agents decrease the current efficiency proportionally with the amount present. The reactions which occur are assumed to be $Mn^{..}+2\oplus=Mn^{....}$; followed by hydrolysis, $Mn^{....}+3H_2O=H_2MnO_3+4H^{.}$; and in acidic soln. this product is deposited as the hydrated dioxide, but in neutral soln. there is also a deposit of the hemitrioxide : $Mn^{..}+H_2MnO_3 \rightleftharpoons Mn(MnO_3)+2H^{.}$. F. Hebler found that the composition of the precipitated manganese hydroxides varies considerably.

The peptization of **colloidal hydrated manganese dioxide,** by dil. alkali-lye, or by washing out the excess of adsorbed salts, was observed by A. Gorgeu, K. C. Sen and N. R. Dhar, and by J. M. van Bemmelen—*vide supra.* L. Swiontkowsky, and G. Bredig and A. Marck obtained a coffee-coloured colloidal soln. by reducing a soln. of potassium permanganate with neutral hydrogen dioxide ; and W. Spring and G. de Boeck obtained similar results during the washing of the precipitate obtained by the action of a hypochlorite on manganous hydroxide, or of sodium thiosulphate on potassium permanganate. During the later stages of the washing, a deep brown colloidal soln. is formed. E. Deiss obtained a fairly stable colloidal soln. by reducing a soln. of potassium permanganate by arsenious acid. If the liquid be evaporated to dryness over sulphuric acid, the colloidal soln. is re-formed by shaking the dry mass with water. When the soln. is allowed to drop into still water, vortex rings are formed resembling those obtained by J. J. Thomson and H. F. Newall with other liquids. The first vortex ring which is formed breaks up into several small rings, and these in turn break into others. All these rings are connected with each other by thin lines of hydrated dioxide, giving the whole system the appearance of a cluster or festoon of rings. If the colloidal soln. be dropped into a salt soln., the hydrated dioxide is precipitated in the form of miniature rings, and by using a very dil. soln. the system of rings will form before coagulation occurs. E. J. Witzemann prepared the colloidal dioxide by the incomplete reduction of a soln. of potassium permanganate by a soln. of glucose in the presence of a little alkali. The colloid can thus be obtained as a viscous liquid, which soon sets to a stiff jelly. E. J. Cuy prepared the colloidal soln. by adding a drop of conc. aq. ammonia every three minutes to $0 \cdot 05N$-$KMnO_4$, at 90°, until all the permanganate is reduced. The only impurity is alkali hydroxide, which has a marked stabilizing influence. B. Sjollema obtained the colloid by treating manganese sulphate or acetate with potassium sodium tartrate, and then with hydrogen dioxide and dil. soda-lye. G. Bredig and A. Marck prepared the colloid by the action of hydrogen dioxide on a neutral soln. of potassium permanganate. The hydrogen dioxide soln. should not contain more than 3 per cent. and the permanganate soln. not more than 16 grms. per litre. The resulting brown soln. is then subjected to dialysis until the electric conductivity reaches a constant value. A. Trillat said that a stable colloidal soln. can be readily obtained by oxidizing a manganous salt in the presence of a protective colloid—e.g. albumin, dextrin, gum arabic, sodium albuminates, or starch. E. Deiss observed that colloidal ferric and aluminium hydroxides act as protective colloids if the amount of manganese in soln. is relatively small. If larger quantities of manganese are present, ferric hydroxide behaves quite differently, in that it favours the precipitation of the dioxide. The hydrosol free from alkali was prepared by S. S. Joshi and T. S. Narayan, and S. Sarvottam and T. S. Narayan. O. Fisseler added a soln. of manganous sulphate to one of sodium lysalbinate or protalbinate, and then treated the liquid with sodium hypochlorite. The dialyzed liquid can be evaporated on a water-bath at 70°, and finally in vacuo over sulphuric acid. The black, glistening plates form a dark brown colloidal soln. when digested with water. G. Bredig and A. Marck found that colloidal soln. of manganese dioxide exhibit large numbers of ultramicroscopic particles. Coagulation takes place on addition of salts, although potassium permanganate is without effect. Acids also bring about coagulation, but small quantities of alkali hydroxides have apparently no influence on the stability of the soln. The stability is dependent on the conditions of preparation, and increases with the dilution of the hydrosol. In presence of gelatin, flocculation by neutral salts is not brought about so readily. The colloidal particles move toward the anode in an electric field. For its action on hydrogen dioxide, vide supra, manganese dioxide. According to A. Steopoe, colloidal soln. of manganese dioxide have been prepared by passing ethylene through potassium permanganate soln., the particular advantage of this method being that the removal of electrolytes is unnecessary, since the oxidation product of the ethylene, viz., glycol, is electrochemically indifferent, and the potassium hydroxide formed is without influence on the stability of the sol. The sol is more stable in stoppered than in unstoppered vessels owing in the latter case to the action of atm. carbon dioxide. In a series of sols containing from 2·2125 to 0·0470 per cent. of manganese dioxide, those of intermediate conc. showed the maximum stability, the dil. sols being almost as unstable as the conc. ones. After preparation the sols separate into two or three transparent, yellow to brown layers, which on stirring do not re-separate. On long keeping, the layers disappear of their own accord, and they are not formed at all in the presence of protective colloids. The phenomenon is explained by assuming that the separation into layers indicates a separation of particles according to their size, and that the final homogenization represents the disappearance of the smaller particles to the advantage of the larger. N. R. Dhar discussed the colour of the hydrosols. The coagulation was studied by S. Prakash and N. R. Dhar, and J. Mukherjee and co-workers; and the rhythmic precipitation, by D. N. Ghosh. S. Roy and N. R. Dhar observed that insolation favours the coagulation of the hydrosol.

E. Deiss showed that it is probable that the precipitation of manganese dioxide is always preceded by the temporary formation of a colloidal soln. of the substance, coagulation resulting as a consequence of the presence of electrolytes. The formation of the iridescent flakes of manganese dioxide, which can be frequently observed in the oxidation or reduction of manganese compounds, is also attributable to the transient formation of a colloidal soln. N. R. Dhar and co-workers, S. C. Chatterji, and P. B. Ganguly and N. R. Dhar studied the precipitation of colloidal manganese dioxide by electrolytes in the presence of a protective gelatin; and also the adsorption of ions by the colloid. It was found that an ion with the highest precipitation value for the colloid is most strongly adsorbed by the colloid, and conversely. According to B. Ghosh, the adsorption of cations from salt soln. proceeds in the decreasing order: Ba, Sr, Mg, K, Na, and Li; and of the acids H_3PO_4, H_2SO_4, and HNO_3. The subject was studied by S. Ghosh and N. R. Dhar, M. N. Chakravarti and co-workers, and W. Engelhardt. W. Hümmelchen and H. Kappen found that the decomposition of potassium sulphate in aq. soln. by hydrated manganese dioxide is very rapid, for the amount of sulphuric acid formed in 5 mins. is the same as that formed in 3 hrs.—65 per cent. of the potassium in $0.0025N$-K_2SO_4 was adsorbed, but only 6 per cent. of that from a $0.1N$-soln. S. Liepatoff regarded the adsorption of a base from a salt as a chemical process of distribution of base between the acid of the adsorbent and that remaining in soln. W. Chlopin and A. Balandin studied the adsorption of barium chloride and found the effect to be due partly to the reaction $MnO(OH)_2 + BaCl_2 = BaMnO_3 + 2HCl$ and to the adsorption of one of the resultants of the reaction by the colloid. The adsorption of salt soln. was studied by M. Mehrotra and K. C. Sen; and of arsenic trioxide, by K. C. Sen. P. N. Pavloff showed that in the adsorption of silver from a neutral soln. of silver nitrate by freshly prepared hydrated manganese dioxide, the soln. becomes strongly acid. The adsorption of silver ions is regarded as a chemical process which can be explained by the amphoteric character of manganese dioxide, for in this case it acts as an acid. This subject was studied by H. B. Weiser, F. Häffner, L. S. Levy, and N. Schiloff. According to M. Geloso, in the precipitation of hydrated manganese dioxide from a soln. of manganous sulphate by ammonium persulphate, in the presence of iron, nickel, and copper salts, the metals are adsorbed in accord with $u = kC^{1/n}$—confer 5. 39, 9. With ferric ammonium sulphate soln., the adsorption of iron is a function of the concentration of the ferric soln. For each concentration there is an adsorption pressure corresponding with each temp.; the system is thus univariant and no compounds are formed. As the amount of adsorption increases with rise of temp., the phenomenon is endothermic; moreover, adsorption is correlated with the state of aggregation of the precipitate, as its extent is much decreased by prolonged digestion of the precipitate before adding the ferric soln. The relative amount of precipitant (ammonium persulphate) which conditions the size of the solid particles formed thus has some influence on the adsorption. G. Kreimer observed the preferential adsorption of iron from soln. containing aluminium sulphate; and A. W. Pilkoff, the adsorption of radioactive ionium, and uranium-X. H. Udluft found that dolomite adsorbs ferric hydroxide sol but not manganese dioxide sol, whereas clay adsorbs both. Manganese dioxide and ferric hydroxide sols exert a protective action on one another. Humus, however, precipitates ferric hydroxide but not manganese dioxide. The hydrogen carbonate ion precipitates ferric hydroxide when unprotected, but not manganese dioxide and humus sols. According to B. Sjollema, colloidal manganese dioxide gives characteristic reactions with oxydase reagents, irrespective of whether it has been dialyzed or not. It at

once imparts a blue colour to an alcoholic soln. of guaiacum resin, and to a soln. of
p-phenylenediamine hydrochloride. In the presence of light it oxidizes quinol
rapidly, yielding crystals of quinhydrone. Aniline sulphate is at once coloured
violet or blue. Pyrogallol is oxidized, yielding a dark-coloured precipitate. It acts
as a catalyst, decomposing hydrogen dioxide. It does not oxidize hydriodic acid in
neutral, alkaline, or acidic soln. It does not oxidize tyrosine in acidic or alkaline
soln., in this respect resembling the ordinary oxydases. By agitating samples of
quinol soln. with colloidal manganese dioxide, some in presence of peroxydase from
horse-radish, that is, *Cochlearia armoracia*, and some without it, it can be shown that
the oxidation of the quinol and its transformation into quinhydrone by the manganese dioxide is facilitated by the presence of the peroxydase. In the oxidation of
quinol, a mixture of colloidal manganese dioxide and a peroxydase behaves like the
system peroxydase+oxygenase, so that the manganese plays the part of oxygenase.
The coagulation of the colloidal soln. was discussed by S. Ghosh and N. R. Dhar,
N. G. Chatterji and N. R. Dhar, A. Ivanitzkaja and L. Orlova ; and the mutual
precipitation of manganese dioxide, ferric oxide, alumina, and silica by
W. N. Simakoff. M. A. Iljinsky and co-workers studied the adsorption of manganese
dioxide from solid suspensions in water by wool, cotton, and silk fibres.

The general properties of the hydrated dioxide have been discussed in connection
with the ordinary dioxide. A. Simon and F. Feher doubted if a stable stoichiometric

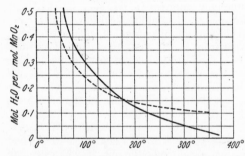

hydrate of manganese dioxide
exists. This is in agreement with
the fact that water begins to be
evolved at 70°, and there is no evidence of a definite compound on
the vap. press. curves. The results
with two samples are summarized
in Fig. 50. Acetone and alcohol
remove a large proportion of the
water of hydration, leaving MnO_2.
0·45 to $0.50H_2O$. The hydrated
dioxide is a black or brownish-black
flocculent powder which, in the
presence of other metal oxides, may

FIG. 50.—Vapour Pressure Curves of Hydrated
Manganese Dioxides.

have its tint modified. J. M. van Bemmelen obtained a red variety by the hydrolysis
of a soln. of the disulphate. W. Wernicke gave 2·58 for the sp. gr. of the hydrate ;
and for the indices of refraction for the E-, D-; and C-lines, respectively 1·944,
1·862, and 1·801. A. Soos studied the optical properties. P. Hausknecht found
that the magnetic susceptibility is about twice that of anhydrous manganese dioxide.
C. R. A. Wright and A. E. Menke said that when confined over conc. sulphuric
acid, the hydrated dioxide slowly loses water for many months ; and at 100°
water is lost until the composition of the hydrated dioxide is $3MnO_2.H_2O$ or
$4MnO_2.H_2O$, but it cannot be freed from water by heating it to 100°, or even to
210°, at which temp. it begins to give off oxygen. A. Gorgeu gave 400° for its
temp. of decomposition. According to C. Drucker and R. Hüttner, the monohydrate dried at the following temp. contains the proportions of water indicated :

	100°	163°	275°	315°	400°	547°	(700°)
H_2O . .	6·7	4·6	3·3	2·4	1·8	0·9	0·3 per cent.

W. C. Bray and H. D. Draper studied the adsorption isotherms. For the decomposition of the dioxide with the evolution of oxygen, *vide supra*. H. N. Morse said
that the precipitated hydrated dioxide is stable only in the presence of potassium
permanganate or of manganese hemiheptoxide—otherwise it loses oxygen, forming
a lower oxide. W. Hümmelchen and H. Kappen studied the decomposition of
soln. of neutral salts, whereby an acid is liberated when in the presence of hydrated
manganese dioxide. G. Almkvist found that a litre of water at 20° dissolves

0·43 mgrm. of the hydroxide, $MnO(OH)_2$. E. Ebler and W. Bender found colloidal hydrated manganese dioxide is better than colloidal silica for the adsorption of radium salts from soln. The de-sorption is effected by dissolving the product in hydrochloric acid, and passing in hydrogen chloride to precipitate the radium. For the action on hydrogen dioxide, *vide supra*, manganese dioxide. Hydrated manganese dioxide develops an acidic reaction in contact with neutral salts. The acidic reaction may be conditioned by the relative solubilities of the complex acidic solid and its corresponding salts—as advocated by A. F. Joseph in connection with clays ; or the liberation of an acid may be due to an interchange between the cations in soln. and the hydrogen ions of the hydrate, as advocated by J. N. Mukherjee. According to B. Ghosh, there is a parallelism between the effect of neutral salts on the electric charge of hydrated manganese oxides and the conc. of the liberated H·-ions. The capacity of the different cations to liberate H·-ions is in the order $Ba > Sr > Mg > K > Na > Li$, and this order also represents the capacity of these ions to neutralize the negative charge of the surface. The bivalent cations reverse the sign of the charge of the surface, showing that the primarily adsorbed ions are univalent. The electrical adsorption of one bivalent cation will therefore liberate one hydrogen ion. In addition, hydrogen ions are probably replaced by cations penetrating into the mobile sheet of the double layer on account of their osmotic press.

Manganese dioxide is amphoteric, in that it unites with acids to form salts, and with bases to form the so-called permanganites—*vide infra*. There is a group of colloidal hydrated manganese oxide minerals to which F. Klockmann [3] applied the term *manganomelanes*. They were originally amorphous, but some of them afterwards crystallized. The analyses of the various members of the group show great variations, so that specific chemical formulæ have not much support. F. Cornu emphasized the need for separating the colloidal gel forms from the crystalline varieties. This distinction, however, as just indicated, may depend only on whether or not the conditions had been favourable for crystallization after the mineral was formed. The great tendency of the hydrated manganese oxides to adsorb various oxides was emphasized by F. Cornu and co-workers. This explains many of the variations in the analytical data, and how the members of virtually the same mineral species have received different names. F. Cornu and H. Leitmeier traced the hydration sequence in the group : Wad→psilomelane→heptonematite→ pyrolusite.

The *derb Brunsten* of J. G. Wallerius was called *magnesia indurata* by A. Cronstedt, and *schwarz Braunsteinerz* by A. G. Werner, and others. It occurs in bluish-, brownish-, or greyish-black masses which may be botryoidal, reniform, or stalactitic. W. Haidinger called the mineral **psilomelane**—from ψιλός, smooth or naked, and μέλας, black, Analyses were reported by J. F. Bahr, P. Berthier, A. P. Bolley, V. C. Butureanu, H. Copaux, J. W. Döbereiner, G. Dupouy, J. J. Ebelmen, S. F. Emmons, L. L. Fermor, F. Field, W. E. Ford and W. M. Bradley, A. Frenzel, J. N. von Fuchs, L. Gmelin, A. Gorgeu, M. F. Heddle, F. Katzer, H. F. Keller, C. M. Kersten, M. H. Klaproth, F. von Kobell, F. Kossmat and C. von John, N. Kurnakoff and N. Podkopajeff, W. A. Lampadius, A. Lacroix, G. Langhans, C. von Leonhard, K. List, T. Morawsky and J. Stingl, P. Poni, C. F. Rammelsberg, C. Rimatori, L. E. Rivot, M. Savul, E. E. Schmid, A. Schwager and C. W. von Gümbel, H. K. Scott, V. Sevoz and J. Breuilhs, E. Turner, B. Walter, A. Weisbach, and E. T. Wherry, etc. The results show the presence of up to 17 per cent. of BaO, up to 4 per cent. of K_2O, up to 7 per cent. of Fe_2O_3, up to 12 per cent. of water, together with smaller proportions of calcium, strontium, magnesium, aluminium, copper, nickel, lead, zinc, thallium, vanadium, and lithium, as well as antimonates, arsenates, phosphates, chlorides, carbonates, sulphates, silicates, titanates, and sulphides. E. Turner regarded these psilomelanes as mixtures of pyrolusite with $n\mathrm{BaO}.Mn_2O_3$, and C. F. Rammelsberg (1841), with $RO.2MnO_2.2H_2O$. K. List gave $2(Mn,R)O.3MnO_2.H_2O$; E. E. Schmid, $8(Mn,R)O.12MnO_2.4H_2O$;

C. F. Rammelsberg (1875), $RO.4MnO_2.1$ to $1\frac{1}{2}H_2O$; and C. F. Rammelsberg (1895), $RO.24MnO_2.4$ to $5H_2O$. H. Laspeyres represented the psilomelanes as derivatives of the acid H_4MnO_5, e.g. $H_2Mn(MnO_5)$. L. L. Fermor regarded them as mixtures of $mR''_2MnO_5.nR'''_4(MnO_5)_3$, where R is mainly manganese. P. Groth regarded the psilomelanes as mixtures of manganous permanganite with a part of the bivalent manganese replaced by Ba, Ca, Mg, Co, Cu, and alkalies. Hence, these are the so-called *baryta-psilomelanes*, *lime-psilomelanes*, *alkali-psilomelanes*, *iron-psilo-melanes*, *lithia-psilomelanes*, *copper-psilomelanes*, and *cobalt-psilomelanes*. F. Cornu regarded them as colloidal manganese dioxide with variable quantities of adsorbed manganous and other oxides, etc., of other elements. S. R. B. Cooke and co-workers discussed the identification of psilomelane and manganite. A. E. Reuss, and J. R. Blum found pseudomorphs after calcite, rhodochrosite, fluorite, barytes, and pharmacosiderite. Crystalline varieties of psilomelane were described by J. J. Ebelmen, C. F. Rammelsberg, E. E. Schmid, A. Gorgeu, H. Laspeyres, and A. Lacroix, and they include the varieties romanechite, calvonigrite, leptonematite, and rancieite. J. Orcel and S. Pavlovitch discussed the optical properties of psilomelane. The sp. gr. ranges from 3·3 to 4·7, and the hardness from 5 to 7. F. Beijerinck said that the mineral is a conductor of electricity, and F. Braun, and H. Meyer, that it is a unipolar conductor; but O. Weigel found that if adsorbed water be removed from the pores, the dried mineral shows no unipolar conductivity. E. T. Wherry said that it is a poor radiodetector; W. Ogawa also studied the mineral from this point of view, and he found that there is a thermoelectric current of 79000μ volt with psilomelane and copper, and that the current flows from the mineral to the copper at the hot junction. R. Ambronn gave 268×10^{-6} for the coeff. of magnetization; and the subject was studied by G. Grenet. R. D. Harvey discussed the electrical conductivity of psilomelane; and H. A. J. Wilkens and H. B. C. Nitze, the magnetic separation of the mineral. C. W. Davis studied the solvent action of sulphurous acid. K. Thaddéeff found that boiling sulphuric acid colours the mineral violet; and H. C. Bolton, that with boiling citric acid, carbon dioxide is given off. The mineral also gives other reactions characteristic of hydrated manganese dioxide.

Varieties of psilomelane which have received special names are the barytiferous alkali psilomelane named by A. Lacroix *ebelmenite*—named after J. J. Ebelmen; *lithion-psilomelane*, or the *lithiophorite* of A. Frenzel, from Salm Chateau, Belgium, described by H. Laspeyres; the *skemmatite*—after σκέμμα, a question—from Iva, S. Carolina, described by W. E. Ford and W. M. Bradley; *calvonigrite*, from Kalteborn, near Eiserfeld, with a composition between H_4MnO_5 and H_6MnO_6, and sp. gr. 4·361, described by H. Laspeyres; *rancieite*—not *rancierite*—from Rancié in Ariège, France, so named by A. Lacroix. It is a lime-psilomelane with a sp. gr. between 3·0 and 3·2. It was the *chaux de manganèse argentin* of J. B. L. Romé de l'Isle, and the *manganèse oxyde argentin* of R. J. Haüy. A. Lacroix named the psilomelane from Romanèche, *romanechite*. Its sp. gr. is 4·55, and its composition approximates $H_2(Mn,Ba)Mn_3O_8$. The *leptonematite* or *pesillite* of A. Breithaupt, and M. Adam, regarded as varieties of braunite, may be psilomelanes. The *beldongrite* is a variety found by L. L. Fermor at Beldongri, Central Provinces, India. Its sp. gr. is 3·22. The *lithiophorite* of C. Winkler, F. von Kobell, A. Frenzel, and A. Weis-bach is a psilomelane with lithia and alumina. The sp. gr. is 3·1 to 3·6. A. Breithaupt called the lithiophorite from Rengersdorf, *kakochlor*. It has a composition approximating $AlMn_3O_7.4H_2O$. The copper-psilomelane *lampadite* was described by W. A. Lampadius, and A. Frenzel, and represented by C. F. Rammelsberg by $2(MnO.CuO).2MnO_2.3H_2O$, or $mCuO.nMnO_2.aq.$, and by H. Laspeyres by $H_4RMn(Mn_4O_7)$. Its sp. gr. is 3·0 to 3·2. The *pelokonite* of C. F. Richter, and C. M. Kersten, having a sp. gr. 2·5 to 2·7, and *lepi-dophœite* of A. Weisbach, having a sp. gr. 2·89 to 3·04, are related to lampadite. A cobalt-psilomelane was named *asbolite*—from ἀσβόλη, soot—by A. Breithaupt. C. F. Rammels-berg represented it by the formula $(CoO)(CuO).2MnO_2.4H_2O$, and H. Laspeyres by $H_8RMn(MnO_9)$. It was analyzed by M. H. Klaproth, J. W. Döbereiner, C. F. Rammels-berg, N. Kurnakoff and N. Podkopajeff, H. Copaux, and A. Lacroix. Its sp. gr. is 2·1 to 2·2. Asbolite appears to be the *cobaltum nigrum* of G. Agricola, the *cobalt terrea fuliginea* of J. G. Wallerius, the *ochra cobalt nigra* of A. Cronstedt, and the *aithalite* of M. Adam. The iron-psilomelane obtained by P. Poni from Brosteni, Roumania, was called *brostenite*. Analyses were reported by V. C. Butureanu, M. Savul, B. Walter, and F. Kossmat and C. von John; they vary from $RO.2$ to $5MnO_2.1$ to $3H_2O$. The sp. gr. is 3·104 to 3·61.

W. V. Smitheringale discussed the X-radiogram, and the action of various etching liquids; and G. A. Thiel, and S. R. B. Cooke and co-workers observed the action of various reagents on psilomelane, and wad—sulphuric and hydrochloric acids, hydrogen dioxide, and soln. of ferrous and stannous chlorides.

The mineral called **wad** is a soft, black, earthy or compact mineral which may also occur in amorphous, reniform masses, and also as an incrustation and as stains. A branching form is called *dendrite*. It consists of various manganese oxides with cobalt, copper, iron, baryta, alumina, silica, and up to over 20 per cent. of water. A variety of wad is called *bog manganese*. Wad is the *magnesia friabilis terriformis* of A. Cronstedt [4]; the *earthy ochre of manganese* of R. Kirwan; the *manganschaum* of D. L. G. Karsten; and the *groroilite* of P. Berthier. The Derbyshire wad is sometimes pseudomorphous with barytes, and that of Leadhills, with *calcite*. The "wad" of the Cumberland miners is graphite. J. J. N. Huot's *oustite* is the French spelling of wad. Analyses were reported by M. H. Klaproth, E. Turner, L. C. Beck, C. F. Rammelsberg, M. Scheffler, L. J. Igelström, A. S. Woodward, A. Liversidge, M. Weibull, C. Rimatori, B. Bertolio, H. Ludwig, J. Redtenbacher, J. H. L. Vogt, E. Dittler, A. Gorgeu, V. C. Butureanu, C. P. Williams, E. H. S. Bailey, L. L. Fermor, and S. Popoff. A. Lacroix said that wad cannot be regarded as a definite chemical compound; C. F. Rammelsberg also added: *Alle sonstigen Untersuchungen von Wad lehren dass es Gemenge sind*. That from Upton Pine, Devonshire, can be represented by $MnO.9MnO_2.6H_2O$. The sp. gr. of wad is 2·3 to 3·7. K. Thaddéeff said that some samples are strongly coloured by sulphuric acid, others are feebly coloured, and yet others not at all coloured.

There are some varieties which have received special names: The *wackenrodite* of M. Adam was analyzed by H. W. F. Wackenroder; it came from Schapbach, Baden, and C. Rimatori described a similar mineral from Bosa and Montresta, Sardinia. The *césarolite* from Tunis, analyzed by H. Buttgenbach and C. Gillet, approximates $H_2PbMn_3O_8$. Its sp. gr. is 5·29. K. Reissacher described a mineral from Wildbad, Gastein, Austria; it was called *reissacherite*, and contained 27·27 per cent. of water. According to H. Mache, a radioactive substance producing an emanation obtained from the gases and water is found in the reissacherite of the deposits from the thermal springs of Gastein. This mineral, which has a radioactivity approximately equal to that of uranyl nitrate, contains manganese dioxide, ferric oxide, calcium carbonate, barium, and strontium, but neither sulphuric acid nor uranium; on separation, the radioactive substance is obtained along with the barium and is presumably radium. F. von Kobell described *rabdionite* obtained from the Urals; its composition approximates $(Cu,Mn,Co)O.(Fe,Mn)_2O_3.2H_2O$, and its sp. gr. is 2·80. G. de Geer, and T. Fegraeus described the *manganese ochre* from Aas, Upsala. It approximates $Mn_3O_4.4H_2O$. K. Nenadkewitsch obtained *zinkdibraunite* from the zinc mines of Olkusz. Its composition approximates $ZnO.2MnO_2.2H_2O$. A. Brunlechner described *zinkmanganerz* from Bleiberg, Carinthia.

A group of oxides intermediate between the monoxide and dioxide has been reported. The members of the group are usually regarded as *manganous manganites* of the type $MnO.nMnO_2$. In order to keep the nomenclature more or less consistent, they are here called **permanganites**. V. H. Veley [5] said that if the hydrated higher oxides are heated in dry nitrogen at 60° to 200°, they are simply dehydrated, and the product readily absorbs oxygen. He thus prepared $Mn_{24}O_{32}.3H_2O$; $Mn_{24}O_{44}.2(4, 6, or 8)H_2O$; $Mn_{24}O_{45}.8H_2O$; $Mn_{24}O_{46}.2(or 3)H_2O$; and $Mn_{24}O_{47}.2H_2O$. A. Gorgeu prepared some by the action of a manganous salt on the so-called alkali or calcium manganites; A. Guyard, by the action of manganous salts on potassium manganate or permanganate—the products ranged between $3MnO.2MnO_2$ and $MnO.5MnO_2$; and S. U. Pickering, by diluting with water a soln. of hydrated manganese dioxide in hydrochloric acid—the products ranged between $5MnO.16MnO_2$ and $5MnO.36MnO_2$, and appeared to be intermediate stages in the oxidation of manganous oxide to hydrated manganese dioxide (*q.v.*).

B. Franke reported $2MnO.3MnO_2$ to be formed by treating potassium manganic sulphate, $5K_2SO_4.2Mn_5(SO_4)_8$, with water acidulated with sulphuric acid, and washing the product successively with water, alcohol, and ether. The small, dark brown plates form manganous sulphate and hydrated manganese dioxide when they are allowed to stand in the mother-liquor. W. Reissig reported $MnO.2MnO_2$ to be formed when manganous carbonate is heated in air to 300°. A. Carnot represented the product of the action of hydrogen dioxide on a manganous salt by $MnO.5MnO_2$; A. Gorgeu obtained rather less peroxidic oxygen; while R. Haas said that hydrogen dioxide with manganous hydroxide gives products ranging from Mn_2O_3 to Mn_5O_8. A. Gorgeu obtained the 1 : 5 oxide by the action of chlorine on water with manganous carbonate in suspension; J. Post obtained a product with more dioxide, and A. Gorgeu observed that in the extreme case, with a prolonged action, hydrated manganese dioxide is formed. V. H. Veley obtained $MnO.5MnO_2.3\frac{1}{3}H_2O$, by the action of chlorine on manganous acetate soln. at 52°, when the washed product was dried at 30°–40° in air; when dried at 60°–100°, $MnO.5MnO_2.2H_2O$ was formed; when dried at 160°–170°, $MnO.11MnO_2.1\frac{1}{2}H_2O$; and at 200°–250°, $MnO.11MnO_2.H_2O$. If heated in oxygen, that gas is absorbed at 100°, while at 180°–190° $MnO.23MnO_2.2H_2O$ is formed, and at a red-heat Mn_2O_3 is produced. C. Lepierre obtained $MnO.5MnO_2$ as a brown, crystalline powder of sp. gr. 3·41, by melting manganous sulphate for some hours with potassium nitrate. W. Spring and M. Lucion, A. Carnot, and G. C. Stone obtained $MnO.10MnO_2$, by treating a manganous salt with nitric acid—with or without potassium chlorate; and O. T. Christensen obtained $MnO.22MnO_2.28H_2O$ by boiling a soln. of ammonium manganate with nitric acid.

A. Guyard suggested that the reaction between a manganous salt and potassium permanganate can be represented $3MnO.A + K_2O.Mn_2O_7 = K_2O.A + 2A + 3MnO + Mn_2O_7$, where A stands for the acid anhydride. He supposed that the $3MnO.Mn_2O_7$ then changed to manganese dioxide : $3MnO.Mn_2O_7 = 5MnO_2$, and suggested that the following *manganous manganates*, $3MnO.MnO_3$, $4MnO.MnO_3$, and $5MnO.MnO_3$ exist, as well as the *manganous permanganates*, $3MnO.Mn_2O_7$, $4MnO.Mn_2O_7$, and $5MnO.Mn_2O_7$.

REFERENCES.

[1] A. Breithaupt, *Vollständige Charakteristik des Mineralsystems*, Dresden, 103, 241, 1823 ; 231, 1832 ; *Vollständiges Handbuch der Mineralogie*, Dresden, 3. 849, 1847 ; *Jahrb. Berg. Hütt.*, 60, 1845 ; *Pogg. Ann.*, 61. 191, 1844 ; W. Haidinger, *Edin. Journ. Science*, 9. 304, 1828 ; *Pogg. Ann.*, 11. 4, 1827 ; *Handbuch der bestimmenden Mineralogie*, Wien, 306, 555, 1845 ; *Jahrb. geol. Reichsanst Wien*, 5. 1, 1854 , P. Groth, *Die Mineraliensammlung der Universität Strassburg*, Strassburg, 112, 1878 ; *Chemische Krystallographie*, Leipzig, 1. 81, 1906 ; W. H. Miller, *Introduction to Mineralogy*, London, 234, 1852 ; C. F. Plattner, *Pogg. Ann.*, 61. 192, 1844 ; C. F. Rammelsberg, *ib.*, 124. 513, 1865 ; *Handbuch der Mineralchemie*, Leipzig, 174, 1875 ; J. F. L. Hausmann, *Handbuch der Mineralogie*, Göttingen, 224, 1847 ; J. D. Dana, *A System of Mineralogy*, New York, 244, 1892 ; A. Gorgeu, *Ann. Chim. Phys.*, (3), 66. 159, 1862 ; *Bull. Soc. Min.*, 2. 122, 1879 ; 11. 196, 1888 ; 16. 100, 1893 ; *Compt. Rend.*, 88. 796, 1879 ; 110. 857, 1890 ; *Bull. Soc. Chim.*, (2), 49. 753, 1888 ; (2), 3. 606, 1890 ; A. Guyard, *Chem. News*, 9. 13, 1864 ; *Bull. Soc. Chim.*, (2), 1. 89, 1864 ; M. Martinon, *ib.*, (2), 43. 355, 1885 ; R. Engel, *ib.*, (3), 6. 17, 1891 ; E. S. Dana, *Amer. Journ. Science*, (3), 35. 247, 1888 ; S. L. Penfield, *ib.*, (3), 35. 247, 1888 ; R. Köchlin, *Tschermak's Mitt.*, (2), 9. 29, 1887 ; L. L. Fermor, *Mem. Geol. Sur. India*, 37. 78, 1900 ; H. Laspeyres, *Journ. prakt. Chem.*, (2), 13. 182, 1876 ; B. Franke, *ib.*, (2), 36. 451, 1887 ; H. A. von Vogel, *ib.*, (1), 1. 449, 1834 ; *Kastner's Arch.*, 23. 85, 1832 ; W. Schmid, *Journ. prakt. Chem.*, (1), 98. 136, 1866 ; E. Riegel, *ib.*, (1), 45. 455, 1848 ; *ib.*, (1), 16. 319, 1848 ; F. Beijerinck, *Neues Jahrb. Min. B.B.*, 11. 443, 1897 ; A. Rosati and H. Steinmetz, *Zeit. Kryst.*, 53. 394, 1914 ; K. Thaddéeff, *ib.*, 20. 350, 1892 ; H. Kunheim, *Ueber die Einwirkung des Wasserdampfes auf Chlormetalle bei hoher Temperatur*, Göttingen, 1861 ; J. L. C. Schröder van der Kolk, *Centr. Min.*, 80. 1901 ; A. Ferrari, *Atti Accad. Lincei*, (6), 3. 224, 1926 ; A. S. Russell, *Phys. Zeit.*, 13. 59, 1912 ; E. C. Harder, *Manganese Deposits of the United States*, Washington, 18, 1910 ; R. Phillips, *Phys. Mag.*, (2), 5. 213, 1829 ; (2), 6. 281, 1829 ; (2), 7. 284, 1830 ; H. How, *ib.*, (4), 31. 168, 1866 ; P. H. Walker, *Amer. Chem. Journ.*, 10. 41, 1888 ; J. L. Jarman, *ib.*, 11. 39, 1889 ; T. Gigli, *Chem. Ztg.*, 17. 186, 1893 ; F. Knapp, *Natur. Rund.*, 9. 413, 431, 1894 ; C. Binks and J. Macqueen, *Brit. Pat. No.* 1240, 1860 ; *Le Technologiste*, 23. 627, 1862 ; A. Baumann, *Zeit. angew. Chem.*, 3. 72, 1890 ; G. Forchhammer, *De mangano*, Hafnia, 1820 ; *Ann. Phil.*, 16. 130, 1820 ; 17. 50, 1821 ; W. Hempel and C. Schubert, *Zeit. Elektrochem.*, 18. 729, 1912 ; J. Scobai, *ib.*, 9. 879, 1903 ; W. Hähnel, *ib.*, 15. 834, 1909 ; *Die Oxydationskraft des Braunsteins*, Breslau, 1910 ; O. Sackur and E. Fritzmann, *Zeit. Elektrochem.*, 15. 842, 1909 ; P. Askenasy and S. Klonowsky, *ib.*, 16. 107, 1910 ; S. Klonowsky, *Ueber die Manganatschmelze und die Ueberführung von Kaliummanganat in Kaliumpermanganat auf elektrolytischen Wege*, Karlsruhe, 1910 ; G. Krebs, *Zeit. Chem.*, (2), 6. 243, 1870 ; W. Nernst and F. Lindemann, *Sitzber. Akad. Berlin*, 501, 1911 ; W. G. Mixter, *Amer. Journ. Science*, (4), 30. 193, 1911 ; J. Thomsen, *Thermochemische Untersuchungen*, Leipzig, 2. 460, 1882 ; 3. 270, 1883 ; E. W. von Siemens and J. G. Halske, *German Pat., D.R.P.* 221130, 1908 ; O. Dieffenbach, *ib.*, 195524, 1904 ; C. Taquet, *ib.*, 30839, 1884 ; *French Pat. No.* 160593, 1884 ; L. Playfair and J. P. Joule, *Mem. Chem. Soc.*, 3. 57, 1846 ; C. Wheatstone, *Phil. Trans.*, 133. 216, 1843 ; W. Beetz, *Fortsch. Phys.*, 3. 371, 1847 ; *Pogg. Ann.*, 78. 35, 1849 ; H. Buff, *Liebig's Ann., Suppl.*, 4. 264, 1866 ; *Liebig's Ann.*, 92. 117, 1854 ; 101. 1, 1857 ; 102.

265, 1857 ; L. Swiontkowsky, *ib.*, **141**. 205, 1867 ; F. M. Raoult, *Ann. Chim. Phys.*, (4), **2**. 371, 1864 ; R. B. Clifton, *Proc. Roy. Soc.*, **26**. 299, 1877 ; W. H. Preece, *ib.*, **35**. 48, 250, 1883 ; K. Schreber, *Wied. Ann.*, **36**. 622, 1889 ; S. Meyer, *ib.*, **68**. 325, 1899 ; **69**. 236, 1899 ; *Ann. Physik*, (4), \1. 664, 1900 ; J. J. Welter and J. L. Gay-Lussac, *Ann. Phil.*, **16**. 352, 1819 ; *Ann. Chim. Phys*, (2), 10. 312, 1819 ; P. F. Chevillot and W. F. Edwards, *ib.*, (3), **4**. 290, 1842 ; E. Pollacci, *L'Orosi*, **8**. 325, 1885 ; *Ann. Chim. Med. Farm.*, (4), **2**. 214, 1885 ; T. Monticelli and N. Covelli, *Storia dei fenomeni del Vesuvio avvenuti negli anni 1821, 1822, e parte del 1823*, Napoli, 1842 ; E. Wiederhold, *Pogg. Ann.*, **116**. 171, 1862 ; **118**. 186, 1863 ; J. C. Poggendorff, *ib.*, **77**. 17, 1849 ; R. T. Colgate, *Journ. Soc. Chem. Ind.*, **32**. 893, 1913 ; A. Duflos, *Schweigger's Journ.*, **64**. 81, 1832 ; F. Göbel, *ib.*, **67**. 77, 1833 ; J. W. Döbereiner, *ib.*, **14**. 208, 1815 ; **28**. 247, 1820 ; J. A. Arfvedson, *ib.*, **42**. 212, 1824 ; *Pogg. Ann.*, **1**. 50, 1824 ; *Liebig's Ann.*, **14**. 133, 1822 ; E. Turner, *Edin. Journ. Science*, **2**. 213, 1830 ; *Trans. Roy. Soc. Edin.*, **9**. 143, 1838 ; *Phil. Mag.*, (2), **4**. 22, 1828 ; (2), **5**. 254, 1829 ; P. Berthier, *Ann. Chim. Phys.*, (2), **20**. 344, 1822 ; (2), **51**. 79, 1832 ; P. Sabatier and A. Mailhe, *ib.*, (8), **20**. 289, 1910 ; H. Moissan, *ib.*, (5), **21**. 232, 1880 ; *Bull. Soc. Chim.*, (3), **9**. 955, 1893 ; *Compt. Rend.*, **115**. 1034, 1892 ; H. le Chatelier, *ib.*, **122**. 80, 1896 ; M. Berthelot, *ib.*, **96**. 88, 1883 ; *Ann. Chim. Phys.*, (5), **30**. 543, 1883 ; *Bull. Soc. Chim.*, (2), **35**. 664, 1881 ; A. Seyewetz and P. Trawitz, *ib.*, (3), **29**. 868, 1903 ; *Compt. Rend.*, **137**. 130, 1903 ; C. Matignon and R. Trannoy, *ib.*, **142**. 1210, 1906 ; A. Laugier, *ib.*, **104**. 1508, 1887 ; C. A. Tenne and D. S. Calderon, *Mineralfundstätten der Iberischen Halbinsel*, Berlin, 112, 1902 ; H. Jimeno, *Anal. Soc. Espan. Hist. Nat.*, **28**. 80, 1899 ; L. Gmelin, *Zeit. Min.*, **2**. 75, 1825 ; H. Ludwig, *Arch. Pharm.*, (2), **143**. 194, 1870 ; M. Scheffler, *ib.*, (2), **35**. 260, 1843 ; T. L. Phipson, *Bull. Soc. Chim.*, (2), **26**. 9, 1876 ; *Chem. News*, **33**. 243, 1876 ; M. M. P. Muir, *ib.*, **35**. 6, 1877 ; **44**. 237, 1881 ; I. Domeyko, *Elementos de mineralojia*, Santiago, 117, 1879 ; L. Brackebusch, *Las Especies minerales de la república Argentina*, Buenos Ayres, 25, 1879 ; *Anal. Soc. Cient. Argentina*, **8**. 5, 81, 1879 ; A. Liversidge, *The Minerals of New South Wales*, London, 109, 1888 ; V. Sevoz and J. Breuilhs, *Bull. Soc. l'Ind. Min.*, **6**. 29, 1860 ; *Rev. Géol.*, **1**. 57, 1860 ; E. F. Smith, *Journ. Amer. Chem. Soc.*, **5**. 272, 1883 ; H. Goldberg, *ib.*, **34**. 886, 1912 ; D. T. Day, *Min. Resources U.S. Geol. Sur.*, 551, 1884 ; J. and H. S. Pattinson, *Journ. Soc. Chem. Ind.*, **8**. 676, 1889 ; N. Kozowsky, *Gornozavodsky Zistok*, **1**. 269, 1888 ; F. Kovar, *Zeit. Chem. Ind. Prag*, 1, 1898 ; 155, 1901 ; *Neues Jahrb. Min.*, i, 25, 1900 ; F. Drake, *Trans. Amer. Inst. Min. Eng.*, **28**. 191, 841, 1898 ; C. Rimatori, *Atti Accad. Lincei*, (5), **10**. ii, 229, 1901 ; A. Serra, *ib.*, (5), **20**. i, 130, 1911 ; F. Kossmat, *Zeit. prakt. Geol.*, **13**. 324, 1905 ; G. Dupouy, *Études minéralogiques sur l'Indochine française*, Paris, 102, 1913 ; F. Bellamy, *Monit. Scient.*, (4), **1**. 1145, 1887 ; F. T. Teschemaker and J. D. Smith, *Chem. News*, **17**. 244, 1868 ; *Zeit. anal. Chem.*, **8**. 509, 1869 ; H. Bornträger, *ib.*, **26**. 741, 1887 ; A. Wagner, *ib.*, **21**. 507, 1882 ; *Dingler's Journ.*, **195**. 532, 1870 ; J. B. Hannay, *Min. Mag.*, **2**. 90, 1878 ; *Journ. Chem. Soc.*, **33**. 269, 1878 ; E. J. Mills and G. Donald, *ib.*, **41**. 23, 1882 ; W. H. Sodeau, *ib.*, **81**. 1066, 1902 ; H. MacLeod, *ib.*, **55**. 184, 1889 ; **65**. 202, 1894 ; **69**. 1015, 1896 ; G. J. Fowler and J. Grant, *ib.*, **57**. 272, 1890 ; D. L. Hammick, *ib.*, **111**. 279, 1917 ; E. J. Russell and N. Smith, *ib.*, **77**. 340, 1900 ; F. Jones, *ib.*, **33**. 100, 1878 ; T. S. Dymond and F. Hughes, *ib.*, **71**. 314, 1897 ; C. R. A. Wright and A. E. Menke, *ib.*, **37**. 22, 1880 ; C. R. A. Wright and A. P. Luff, *ib.*, **33**. 518, 1878 ; W. Dittmar, *ib.*, **17**. 294, 1864 ; G. Gore, *ib.*, **22**. 368, 1869 ; *Phil. Mag.*, (4), **29**. 546, 1865 ; C. Tissot, *Compt. Rend.*, **147**. 37, 1908 ; H. St. C. Deville and H. Debray, *ib.*, **50**. 868, 1860 ; P. Sabatier and J. B. Senderens, *ib.*, **114**. 1476, 1892 ; L. C. A. Barreswil, *ib.*, **44**. 657, 1857 ; A. Baudrimont, *Journ. Pharm. Chim.*, (4), **40**. 161, 1871 ; *Compt. Rend.*, **62**. 129, 1866 ; **73**. 254, 1871 ; A. Carnot, *ib.*, **116**. 1295, 1893 ; *Bull. Soc. Chim.*, (3), **1**. 277, 409, 594, 781, 1889 ; (3), **9**. 214, 613, 1893 ; N. Beketoff, *ib.*, (1), **1**. 22, 1859 ; M. E. Chevreul, *Compt. Rend.*, **29**. 296, 1849 ; G. Fournier, *ib.*, **183**. 37, 1926 ; L. Hackspill and R. Grandadam, *ib.*, **180**. 930, 1925 ; J. Durocher, *ib.*, **34**. 870, 1853 ; J. B. J. D. Boussingault, *ib.*, **50**. 890, 1860 ; T. Schlösing, *ib.*, **55**. 284, 1862 ; F. Kuhlmann, *ib.*, **55**. 246, 1862 ; *Dingler's Journ.*, **211**. 25, 1874 ; R. Bunsen, *Pogg. Ann.*, **123**. 505, 1864 ; W. Müller, *ib.*, **136**. 60, 1869 ; E. R. Schneider, *ib.*, **107**. 605, 1859 ; H. Hess, *ib.*, **52**. 116, 1841 ; E. Mitscherlich, *ib.*, **25**. 287, 1832 ; *Schweigger's Journ.*, **65**. 62, 1832 ; C. Schubert, *Beiträge zur Kenntnis der Dissoziation einiger Oxyde, Karbonate und Sulfide*, Weida i. Thur., 15, 1910 ; J. K. H. Inglis, *Zeit. Elektrochem.*, **9**. 226, 1903 ; O. Sackur and W. Taegener, *ib.*, **18**. 721, 1912 ; R. Böttger, *Chem. Centr.*, (3), **11**. 351, 1880 ; H. Heymann, *Sitzber. Niederrh. Ges. Bonn*, 95, 1869 ; J. R. Blum, *Die Pseudomorphosen des Mineralreichs*, Stuttgart, 140, 1847 ; 109, 1852 ; A. Vogel, *Repert. Pharm.*, (3), **3**. 145, 1849 ; F. von Kobell, *Neues Jahrb. Min.*, 403, 1834 ; G. Spezia, *Atti Accad. Torino*, **22**. 419, 1887 ; F. Wöhler, *Berg. Hütt. Ztg.*, **23**. 119, 1864 ; *Liebig's Ann.*, **119**. 375, 1861 ; F. Wöhler and A. Geuther, *ib.*, **91**. 127, 1854 ; H. Bischoff, **129**. 375, 1864 ; C. Huber, *ib.*, **130**. 369, 1864 ; A. Schwarzenberg and A. Engelhardt, *ib.*, **41**. 262, 1842 ; F. J. Otto, *ib.*, **93**. 377, 1855 ; J. Volhard, *ib.*, **198**. 354, 1879 ; C. W. Hempel, *ib.*, **107**. 100, 1858 ; E. Priwoznik, *ib.*, **171**. 115, 1874 ; E. Schöne, *ib.*, **196**. 71, 1879 ; G. Rauter, *ib.*, **270**. 236, 1892 ; L. Carius, *ib.*, **98**. 63, 1856 ; W. Spring, *Bull. Acad. Belg.*, (3), **16**. 53, 1888 ; *Bull. Soc. Chim.*, (2), **50**. 218, 1888 ; W. Spring and M. Lucion, *ib.*, (3), **3**. 4, 1890 ; W. Spring and E. Prost, *ib.*, (3), **1**. 340, 1889 ; H. Kopp, *Liebig's Ann. Suppl.*, **3**. 290, 1865 ; C. W. Eliot and F. H. Storer, *Proc. Amer. Acad.*, **5**. 192, 1862 ; *Chem. News*, **6**. 121, 136, 145, 157, 169, 182, 207, 217, 1862 ; F. Richarz, *Ber.*, **21**. 1675, 1888 ; O. Michel and E. Grandmougin, *ib.*, **26**. 2567, 1893 ; F. Beilstein and L. Jawein, *ib.*, **12**. 1530, 1879 ; H. N. Morse, *ib.*, **30**. 48, 1897 ; E. Bamberger, *ib.*, **33**. 1950, 1900 ; C. Reichard, *ib.*, **30**. 1913, 1897 ; M. Traube, *ib.*, **22**. 1524, 1889 ; J. Meyer, *ib.*, **34**. 3606, 1901 ; S. M. Tanatar, *ib.*, **33**. 205, 1900 ; O. Brunck, *Zeit. anorg. Chem.*, **10**. 236, 1895 ; *Ber.*,

26. 1790, 1893 ; J. Townsend, *Brit. Pat. No.* 3483, 1874 ; *Ber.*, **9**. 648, 1876 ; E. Wedekind, *Zeit. angew. Chem.*, **33**. 87, 1924 ; E. Wedekind and C. Horst, *Ber.*, **45**. 262, 1912 ; **48**. 105, 1915 ; C. Horst, *Ueber die Abhängigkeit der Magnetisierbarkeit anorganischer Verbindungen von der Wertigkeit des Hauptelementes, untersucht an den Oxyden und Sulfiden einiger Schwermetalle*, Freiburg, 1912 ; C. L. Müller and G. Kircher, *Ber.*, **15**. 812, 1882 ; G. Vortmann, *ib.*, **13**. 325, 1880 ; A. Kutzelnigg, *ib.*, **63**. 1753, 1930 ; J. Meyer and W. Schramm, *Zeit. anorg. Chem.*, **132**. 226, 1923 ; S. von Szentpetery, *Mitt. Min. Geol. Sammlung Siebenburg. Nat. Museum*, **4**. 214, 1918 ; S. Hauser, *Ueber Reduktion einiger Metalloxyde durch Gase*, Strassburg, 1907 ; G. Bredig and A. Marck, *Bemmelen's Gedenkboek*, 342, 1910 ; A. Marck, *Die Katalyse des Wasserstoffsperoxides durch Kolloides Mangandioxyd*, Heidelberg, 1907 ; A. Lottermoser and R. Lehmann, *Koll. Zeit.*, **29**. 250, 1921 ; A. F. Rogers, *Journ. Geol.*, **25**. 530, 1917 ; E. T. Wherry and T. L. Watson, *Journ. Washington Acad.*, **8**. 550, 1918 ; E. T. Wherry, *Proc. U.S. Nat. Museum*, **51**. 81, 1916 ; *Amer. Min.*, **10**. 28, 1925 ; V. M. Goldschmidt, *Skrift. Norske Akad.*, 1, 1926 ; E. Jungfleisch, *Bull. Soc. Chim.*, (2), **15**. 6, 1871 ; C. H. L. von Babo, *Ber. Ver. Ges. Freiburg*, **1**. 365, 1858 ; **2**. 331, 1862 ; J. C. G. de Marignac, *Bibl. Univ.*, **40**. 145, 1842 ; *Compt. Rend.*, **14**. 570, 1842 ; *Liebig's Ann.*, **44**. 13, 1842 ; K. Fischbeck and E. Einecke, *Zeit. anorg. Chem.*, **167**. 28, 1927 ; J. A. Almquist and W. C. Bray, *Journ. Amer. Chem. Soc.*, **45**. 2305, 1923 ; W. A. Whitesell and J. C. W. Frazer, *ib.*, **45**. 2841, 1923 ; W. M. Hoskins and W. C. Bray, *ib.*, **48**. 1454, 1926 ; W. C. Bray and G. J. Doss, *ib.*, **48**. 2060, 1926 ; W. P. Yant and C. O. Hawk, *ib.*, **49**. 1454, 1927 ; L. Pauling, *ib.*, **49**. 765, 1927 ; E. J. Cuy, M. E. Rosenberg and W. C. Bray, *ib.*, **46**. 1796, 1924 ; D. J. Brown and R. F. Tefft, *ib.*, **48**. 1128, 1926 ; D. J. Brown and H. A. Liebhafsky, *ib.*, **52**. 2595, 1930 ; S. Popoff, J. A. Riddick and W. W. Becker, *ib.*, **52**. 2624, 1930 ; S. Popoff, A. H. Kunz, J. A. Riddick and W. W. Becker, *Proc. Iowa Acad.*, **36**. 263, 1929 ; C. E. Ruby, *Journ. Amer. Chem. Soc.*, **43**. 300, 1921 ; J. C. W. Frazer and C. E. Greider, *Journ. Phys. Chem.*, **29**. 1099, 1925 ; H. S. Taylor, *ib.*, **30**. 145, 1926 ; *Journ. Amer. Chem. Soc.*, **52**. 5298, 1930 ; **53**. 578, 1931 ; H. A. J. Wilkens and H. B. C. Nitze, *Trans. Amer. Inst. Min. Eng.*, **26**. 351, 1896 ; F. Daniels, *Trans. Amer. Electrochem. Soc.*, **53**. 45, 1928 ; R. Hüttner, *Der augenblickliche Stand unserer Kenntnise vom Leclancheelement*, Leipzig, 1928 ; *Die thermische Dissoziation des Mangandioxydes*, Leipzig, 1927 ; C. Drotschmann, *Zeit. Elektrochem.*, **35**. 194, 1929 ; J. Orcel and S. Pavlovitch, *Compt. Rend.*, **187**. 1295, 1928 ; A. Overbeck, *Arch. Pharm.*, (2), **77**. 2, 1854 ; F. Streintz, *Ann. Physik*, (4), **9**. 864, 1902 ; L. Benedek, *Magyar Chem. Folyoirat*, **14**. 85, 1908 ; A. St. John, *Phys. Rev.*, (2), **21**. 389, 1923 ; L. E. vot, F. S. Beudant, and P. A. Daguin, *Ann. Mines*, (5), **4**. 221, 1853 ; C. R. Fresenius and h. Will, *Neue Verfahrungsweisen zur Prüfung Potassche und Soda, der Aschen, der Säuren, insbesondere des Essigs, sowie des Braunsteins, auf ihren wahren Gehalt und Handelswerth*, Heidelberg, 1843 ; London, 1843 ; G. Wischin, *Brit. Pat. No.* 1524, 1890 ; *German Pat.*, *D.R.P.* 54822, 1890 ; E. Boettcher, *Centr. Elektrotechnik*, **12**. 87, 1889 ; A. Geuther, *Jena Zeit.*, **2**. 127, 1865 ; A. Michaelis, *ib.*, **7**. 110, 1871 ; F. Glaser, *Zeit. anorg. Chem.*, **36**. 1, 1903 ; F. Bahr and O. Sackur, *ib.*, **73**. 101, 1911 ; D. Balareff, *ib.*, **136**. 216, 1924 ; R. J. Meyer and K. Rötgers, *ib.*, **57**. 104, 1908 ; K. Rötgers, *Die Dissoziationtemperaturen der Manganoxyde MnO₂ und Mn₂O₃ in Luft- und Sauerstoff-atmosphäre*, Berlin, 1907 ; F. W. Skirrow, *Zeit. anorg. Chem.*, **33**. 25, 1902 ; A. Skrabal, *ib.*, **42**. 1, 1904 ; A. Skrabal and J. Preiss, *Monatsh.*, **27**. 509, 1906 ; I. L. Bell, *Chem. News*, **23**. 258, 1871 ; E. Divers, *ib.*, **46**. 259, 1882 ; C. Schorlemmer and T. E. Thorpe, *ib.*, **47**. 2, 1883 ; J. W. C. Harvey, *Chem. News*, **47**. 2, 1883 ; A. von Kiss and F. E. Lederer, *Rec. Trav. Chim. Pays-Bas*, **46**. 453, 1927 ; W. C. Bray and H. D. Draper, *Proc. Nat. Acad.*, **12**. 295, 1926 ; G. Leoncini and C. Pieri, *Staz. Sperim. Agrar. Ital.*, **45**. 224, 1912 ; K. Schröder, *Zeit. öffentl. Chem.*, **16**. 270, 290, 1910 ; F. P. Venable and D. H. Jackson, *Journ. Elisha Mitchell Scient. Soc.*, **35**. 87, 1920 ; H. Tropsch and A. von Philippovich, *Abhand. Kenntnis Kohle*, **7**. 44, 1925 ; R. J. Kane, *Quart. Journ. Science*, **2**. 286, 1828 ; J. E. L. Jones and B. M. Dent, *Phil. Mag.*, (7), **3**. 1204, 1927 ; E. Newbery and J. N. Pring, *Proc. Roy. Soc.*, **92**. A, 276, 1916 ; L. Franck, *Chem. Ztg.*, **22**. 236, 1898 ; T. Bergman, *De acido aëreo*, Upsala, 1774 ; C. Zengelis, *Zeit. phys. Chem.*, **50**. 219, 1904 ; E. Moles and M. Crespi, *ib.*, **100**. 337, 1922 ; C. Drucker and R. Hüttner, *ib.*, **131**. 237, 1928 ; W. A. Smith, *Zeit. phys. Chem.*, **21**. 93, 1896 ; O. Stelling, *ib.*, **117**. 161, 1925 ; G. Bruni and C. Pelizzola, *Atti Accad. Lincei*, (5), **30**. ii, 37, 1921 ; L. Marino and V. Squintani, *ib.*, (5), **20**. i, 447, 1911 ; F. de Carli, *ib.*, (6), **4**. 577, 1926 ; V. Lenher, *Econ. Geol.*, **11**. 115, 1916 ; *Journ. Amer. Chem. Soc.*, **38**. 638, 1916 ; F. E. Brown and J. A. Burrows, *ib.*, **48**. 1790, 1926 ; F. E. Brown, J. A. Burrows and H. H. McLaughlin, *ib.*, **45**. 1343, 1923 ; H. M. McLaughlin and F. E. Brown, *ib.*, **50**. 782, 1928 ; W. E. Kuentzel, *ib.*, **52**. 437, 445, 1930 ; E. J. Witzemann, *ib.*, **52**. 640, 1930 ; C. E. Lanning, *ib.*, **52**. 2411, 1930 ; A. F. Benton, *ib.*, **45**. 887, 900, 1923 ; R. W. Millar, *ib.*, **50**. 1875, 1928 ; H. D. Draper, *ib.*, **50**. 2637, 1928 ; **51**. 2637, 1929 ; S. G. Simpson, *ib.*, **45**. 1883, 1923 ; P. Askenasy and E. L. Rényi, *Zeit. Elektrochem.*, **19**. 23, 1913 ; P. Fischer, *ib.*, **32**. 538, 1926 ; T. W. Case, *Phys. Rev.*, (2), **9**. 305, 1917 ; J. L. Odier, *Journ. Phys.*, **46**. 464, 1798 ; J. Ewles, *Phil. Mag.*, (6), **45**. 957, 1923 ; K. Honda and T. Sone, *Science Rep. Tohoku Univ.*, **3**. 139, 1914 ; H. Saito, *ib.*, **16**. 37, 1927 ; H. von Jüptner, *Beiträge zur Theorie der Eisenhüttenprozesse*, Stuttgart, 8, 1907 ; A. de Hemptinne, *Bull. Acad. Belg.*, (5), **8**. 71, 1922 ; T. J. Martin and A. J. Helfrecht, *Trans. Amer. Electrochem. Soc.*, **53**. 83, 1928 ; L. Kahlenberg and W. J. Trautmann, *ib.*, **39**. 377, 1921 ; R. C. Wells, *ib.*, **22**. 311, 1912 ; G. Tammann and A. Sworykin, *Zeit. anorg. Chem.*, **170**. 62, 1928 ; G. J. Young, *Eng. Min. Journ.*, **114**. 980, 1922 ; J. Meyer and R. Kanters, *Zeit. anorg. Chem.*, **185**. 172, 178, 1929 ; J. Maydell, *ib.*, **186**. 289, 1930 ; O. Ruff and H. Krug, *ib.*, **190**. 270, 1930 ; F. Merck and E. Wedekind, *ib.*, **192**.

113, 1930 ; E. Donath and H. Leopold. *Der Braunstein und seine Anwendungen*, Stuttgart, 1929; S. Kaneko, C. Nemoto and S. Makino, *Journ. Soc. Chem. Ind. Japan*, **32**. 205, 1929; S. Kaneko, *ib.*, **32**, 120, 1929 ; Y. Kato and T. Matsuhashi, *ib.*, **32**. 313, 315, 1929 ; **34**. 312, 1931 ; *Proc. World Eng. Congress. Tokyo*, **31**. 305, 1929 ; H. W. Foote and J. K. Dixon, *Journ. Amer. Chem. Soc.* **52**. 2170, 1930 ; **53**. 55, 1931 ; H. S. Taylor and A. T. Williamson, *ib.*, **53**. 813, 1931 ; D. Talmud and N. M. Lubman, *Koll. Zeit.*, **50**. 159, 1930 ; E. Baur, *Zeit. Elektrochem.*, **36**. 410, 1930 ; B. Neumann, C. Kröger and R. Iwanowsky, *ib.*, **37**. 121, 1931 ; N. S. Krivolutskaya and G. G. Morozoff, *Zuhr. Prąkladnoi Khim.*, **2**. 703, 1929 ; S. Prakash and N. R. Dhar, *Journ. Indian Chem. Soc.*, **7**. 417, 1930 ; H. Bähr and F. Fallböhmer, *Gas Wasserfach*, **69**. 909, 929, 943, 1926 ; J. H. Jones, J. G. King and F. S. Sinnatt, *The Reactivity of Coke*, London, 1930 ; F. Stutzer, W. Gross and K. Bornemann, *Metall Erz*, **6**. 1, 1918 ; G. Grenet, *Ann. Physique*, (10), **13**. 263, 1930 ; F. Fischer and F. Bangert, *Brennstoff Chem.*, **10**. 261, 1929 ; Y. Kato and K. Yamamoto, *Brit. Pat. No.* 330257, 1929 ; C. W. Davis, *Rept. Investigations U.S. Bur. Mines*, 3024, 1930 ; E. Döll, *Verh. geol. Reichsanst.*, 456, 1895 ; V. A. Kostjejeff, *Trans. Amer. Electrochem. Soc.*, **58**. 155, 1930 ; V. Shuleikin and X. Solovova, *Zeit. phys. Chem.*, **149**. 434, 1930 ; A. Kundert, *Chem. Analyst*, **19**. 11, 1930 ; V. P. Ilinsky and N. P. Lapin, *Zhur. Prakladnoi Khim.*, **1**. 176, 1928 ; W. V. Smitheringale, *Econ. Geol.*, **24**. 481, 1929 ; G. A. Thiel, *ib.*, **19**. 107, 1924 ; C. Doelter, *Das Radium und die Farben*, Dresden, 1910 ; M. L. Huggins, *Phys. Rev.*, (2), **21**. 716, 719, 1923 ; K. Arndt, H. Walter and E. Zender, *Zeit. angew. Chem.*, **39**. 1426, 1926 ; V. Dolejsek and J. Heyrovsky, *Chem. Listy*, **20**. 4, 1926 ; A. A. Somerville, *Met. Chem. Engg.*, **10**. 422, 1912 ; W. C. Phalen, *ib.*, **21**. 196, 1919 ; W. E. Adeney, *Trans. Roy. Dublin Soc.*, (2), **6**. 269, 1897 ; P. Hausknecht, *Magnetochemische Untersuchungen*, Strassburg, 1927 ; G. Wistrand, *Magnetiska Susceptibiliteten hos Kvarts, Tellur och Några, Holmiumföreningar*, Upsala, 1916 ; R. D. Harvey, *Econ. Geol.*, **23**. 778, 1928 ; H. A. Auden and G. J. Fowler, *Chem. News*, **72**. 163, 1895 ; J. W. Gatehouse, *ib.*, **35**. 118, 1877 ; W. R. E. Hodgkinson and F. K. S. Lowndes, *ib.*, **58**. 260, 1888 ; **59**. 63, 1889 ; H. N. Warren, *ib.*, **58**. 247, 1889 ; V. H. Veley, *ib.*, **58**. 260, 1888 ; *Journ. Chem. Soc.*, **37**. 581, 1880 ; **41**. 56, 1882 ; N. Smith, *ib.*, **89**. 473, 1906 ; O. F. Tower, *ib.*, **18**. 35, 1895 ; **21**. 90, 1896 ; **32**. 566, 1900 ; G. N. Lewis, *ib.*, **52**. 235, 1905 ; G. Tammann, *ib.*, **3**. 25, 1889 ; G. Bredig and R. M. von Berneck, *ib.*, **31**. 258, 1900 ; K. Fredenhagen and G. Cadenbach, *ib.*, **146**. 245, 1930 ; W. Biltz, *Gött. Nachr.*, 189, 1930 ; *Zeit. anorg. Chem.*, **127**. 169, 372, 1923 ; *Zeit. phys. Chem.*, **67**. 572, 1909 ; L. Kahlenberg, *ib.*, **17**. 577, 1895 ; L. Kahlenberg and A. S. McDaniel, *Trans. Amer. Electrochem. Soc.*, **9**. 365, 1906 ; E. Donath and F. Müllner, *Ber. Oesterr. Ges. Förd. Chem. Ind.*, **9**. 129, 1887 ; *Dingler's Journ.*, **267**. 143, 1888 ; E. Donath, *ib.*, **263**. 248, 1887 ; *Chem. Ztg.*, **12**. 1191, 1888 ; R. E. Hughes, *Phil. Mag.*, (5), **35**. 531, 1893 ; O. T. Christensen, *Journ. prakt. Chem.*, (2), **34**. 41, 1886 ; (2), **35**. 69, 82, 1887 ; J. G. Gentele, *ib.*, (1), **82**. 58, 1861 ; C. F. Schönbein, *ib.*, (1), **41**. 225, 1847 ; (1), **65**. 96, 1855 ; (1), **74**. 325, 1858 ; *Verh. Naturf. Ges. Basel*, 2. 113, 1858 ; *Pogg. Ann.*, **72**. 459, 1847 ; J. M. van Bemmelen, *ib.*, (2), **23**. 324, 1881 ; *Ber.*, **13**. 1466, 1880 ; G. Kastner, *Kastner's Arch.*, **26**. 295, 1854 ; L. J. Thénard, *Traité de chimie*, Paris, 7. 478, 1836 ; P. Thénard, *Compt. Rend.*, **75**. 177, 1872 ; H. C. Bolton, *Ann. New York Acad.*, **1**. 158, 1879 ; *Chem. News*, **36**. 249, 260, 1877 ; **37**. 14, 24, 65, 86, 98, 148, 1878 ; *Min. Mag.*, **1**. 136, 1877 ; A. Purgotti, *Gazz. Chim. Ital.*, **26**. ii, 559, 1896 ; A. Brighenti, *ib.*, **36**. i, 187, 1906 ; G. Scurati-Manzoni, *ib.*, **13**. 547, 1883 ; **14**. 359, 1884 ; B. C. Brodie, *Proc. Roy. Soc.*, **12**. 209, 1862 ; H. D. Holler and L. M. Ritchie, *Scient. Paper Bur. Standards*, 364, 1920 ; B. M. Thompson, *Journ. Ind. Eng. Chem.*, **20**. 1176, 1928 ; E. Frémy, *Compt. Rend.*, **82**. 475, 1231, 1876 ; A. Simon and F. Feher, *Zeit. Elektrochem.*, **38**. 137, 1932 ; M. Ravack, *Pogg. Ann.*, **107**. 605, 1859 ; W. Thomson and F. Lewis, *Proc. Manchester Lit. Phil. Soc.*, **4**. 266, 1891 ; *Chem. News*, **64**. 169, 1891 ; C. Drucker, *Bodenstein's Festband*, 912, 1931 ; Y. Kato and T. Matsuhashi, *Journ. Soc. Chem. Ind. Japan*, **34**. 312, 1931 ; H. A. J. Pieters, *Chem. Weekbl.*, **28**. 250, 1931 ; A. Keller, *Zeit. Elektrochem.*, **37**. 342, 1931 ; S. Popoff, A. H. Kunz, J. A. Riddick and W. W. Becker, *Proc. Iowa Acad.*, **36**. 263, 1929 ; M. Blumenthal, *Rocz. Chem.*, **11**. 855, 1931 ; M. le Blanc and H. Sachse, *Phys. Zeit.*, **32**. 887, 1931.

² C. F. Rammelsberg, *Ber.*, **8**. 233, 1875 ; *Pogg. Ann.*, **55**. 57, 1842 ; W. Wernicke, *ib.*, **139**. 132, 1870 ; **141**. 116, 1870 ; E. Mitscherlich, *ib.*, **25**. 287, 1832 ; R. Böttger, *Jahrb. phys. Ver. Frankfurt*, 47, 1858 ; P. Berthier, *Ann. Chim. Phys.*, (2), **51**. 19, 1832 ; A. C. Becquerel, *ib.*, (2), **43**. 380, 1830 ; A. Gorgeu, *ib.*, (3), **66**. 153, 1862 ; *Bull. Soc. Chim.*, (3), **4**. 16, 1890 ; *Compt. Rend.*, **110**. 1134, 1890 ; E. Frémy, *ib.*, **82**. 475, 1231, 1876 ; A. Mailfert, *ib.*, **94**. 860, 1186, 1882 ; L. Maquenne, *ib.*, **94**. 795, 1882 ; A. P. Rollet, *ib.*, **189**. 34, 1929 ; H. Baubigny, *ib.*, **135**. 965, 1110, 1902 ; **136**. 449, 1325, 1662, 1903 ; A. Carnot, *ib.*, **116**. 1375, 1893 ; A. Guyard, *Bull. Soc. Chim.*, (2), **1**. 81, 1863 ; A. Lumière and A. Seyewetz, *ib.*, (3), **7**. 538, 1892 ; W. Spring and G. de Boeck, *ib.*, (2), **48**. 170, 1887 ; W. Spring and M. Lucion, *ib.*, (3), **3**. 4, 1890 ; W. Spring, *Ber.*, **16**. 1142, 1883 ; H. N. Morse, *ib.*, **30**. 48, 1897 ; E. and B. Klimenko, *Journ. Russ. Phys. Chem. Soc.*, **27**. 189, 1895 ; *Ber.*, **29**. 478, 1896 ; J. M. van Bemmelen, *ib.*, **13**. 1466, 1880 ; *Die Absorption*, Dresden, 90, 1910 ; *Journ. prakt. Chem.*, (2), **23**. 324, 1881 ; F. Beilstein and L. Jawein, *ib.*, **12**. 1528, 1879 ; R. Schenck, H. Semiller and V. Falcke, *ib.*, **40**. 1724, 1907 ; E. M. Dingler, *Kastner's Arch.*, **18**. 252, 1829 ; N. W. Fischer, *ib.*, **16**. 219, 1829 ; R. Phillips, *Phil. Mag.*, (2), **5**. 209, 1829 ; B. C. Brodie, *Proc. Roy. Soc.*, **12**. 209, 1862 ; C. Luckow, *Dingler's Journ.*, **177**. 231, 1865 ; **178**. 42, 1865 ; *Zeit. anal. Chem.*, **8**. 24, 1869 ; **19**. 1, 1881 ; A. Brand, *ib.*, **23**. 581, 1884 ; L. Schucht, *ib.*, **22**. 492, 1883 ; S. U. Pickering, *Chem. News*, **43**. 189, 201, 213, 225, 1881 ; *Journ. Chem. Soc.*, **35**. 654, 1879 ; **37**. 128, 1880 ; C. R. A. Wright and A. E. Menke, *ib.*, **37**. 35, 1880 ; W. W. Fisher, *ib.*, **33**. 409, 1878 ; F. Jones, *ib.*, **33**. 100, 1878 ;

J. B. Hannay, *ib.*, **33**. 269, 1878 ; B. Ghosh, *ib.*, 2605, 1926 ; J. Pattinson, *ib.*, **35**. 365, 1879 ; *Chem. News*, *ib.*, **21**. 267, 1870 ; **41**. 179, 1880 ; *Journ. Soc. Chem. Ind.*, **5**. 422, 1886 ; J. and H. S. Pattinson, *ib.*, **10**. 333, 1891 ; O. T. Christensen, *Zeit. anorg. Chem.*, **27**. 322, 1901 ; A. Piccini, *ib.*, **20**. 12, 1899 ; F. W. Skirrow, *ib.*, **33**. 25, 1902 ; F. A. Gooch and M. Austin, *ib.*, **17**. 258, 1898 ; *Amer. Journ. Science*, (4), **5**. 260, 1898 ; E. Pollacci, *Ann. Chim. Med. Farm.*, (4), **2**. 214, 1885 ; *L'Orosi*, **8**. 325, 1885 ; O. Dieffenbach, *German Pat.*, *D.R.P.* 195524, 1904 ; C. F. Schönbein, *Verh. Naturf. Ges. Basel*, **2**. 113, 1858 ; *Journ. prakt. Chem.*, (1), **74**. 325, 1858 ; T. Morawsky and J. Stingl, *ib.*, (2), **18**. 78, 1878 ; B. Franke, *ib.*, (2), **36**. 31, 451, 1887 ; N. C. H. Schjerning, *ib.*, (2), **45**. 528, 1892 ; G. Scurati-Manzoni, *Gazz. Chim. Ital.*, **13**. 567, 1883 ; **14**. 359, 1884 ; G. C. Winkelblech, *Liebig's Ann.*, **13**. 262, 1835 ; F. J. Otto, *ib.*, **93**. 377, 1855 ; J. Volhard, *ib.*, **198**. 318, 1789 ; W. Reissig, *ib.*, **103**. 27, 1857 ; L. Swiontkowsky, *ib.*, **141**. 205, 1867 ; O. Fisseler, *Ueber colloidale Verbindungen des Eisens, Mangans, und Kupfers*, Erlangen, 1904 ; A. Marck, *Die Katalyse des Wasserstoffsuperoxyds durch kolloidales Mangandioxyd*, Heidelberg, 1907 ; G. Bredig and A. Marck, *Bemmelen's Gedenkboek*, 342, 1910 ; A. Ivanitzkaja and L. Orlova, *Koll. Beihefte*, **18**. 1, 1923 ; A. Travers, *Bull. Soc. Chim.*, (4), **37**. 456, 1925 ; A. Trillat, *ib.*, (3), **31**. 811, 1904 ; *German Pat.*, *D.R.P.* 227491, 1904 ; *Compt. Rend.*, **138**. 274, 1904 ; M. Geloso, *ib.*, **174**. 1629, 1922 ; **176**. 1884, 1923 ; **178**. 1001, 1924 ; *Ann. Chim. Phys.*, (10), **6**. 352, 1926 ; *Bull. Soc. Chim.*, (4), **37**. 641, 1925 ; J. J. Thomson and H. F. Newall, *Proc. Roy. Soc.*, **39**. 417, 1886 ; A. Soos, *Chem. Rund. Mitteleuropa*, **3**. 129, 137, 148, 1926 ; E. J. Witzemann, *Journ. Amer. Chem. Soc.*, **37**. 1079, 1915 ; **39**. 37, 1917 ; N. Schiloff, *Zeit. phys. Chem.*, **100**. 425, 1922 ; E. J. Cuy, *Journ. Phys. Chem.*, **25**. 415, 1921 ; N. R. Dhar, K. C. Sen, and S. Ghosh, *ib.*, **28**. 457, 1924 ; P. B. Ganguly and N. R. Dhar, *ib.*, **26**. 701, 836, 1922 ; *Koll. Zeit.*, **31**. 16, 1922 ; S. C. Chatterji, *Proc. Indian Science Congr.*, **17**. 130, 1921 ; S. Ghosh and N. R. Dhar, *Journ. Phys. Chem.*, **30**. 628, 1926 ; **31**. 187, 649, 1927 ; M. N. Chakravarti and N. R. Dhar, *ib.*, **31**. 997, 1927 ; M. N. Chakravarti, S. Ghosh and N. R. Dhar, *ib.*, **34**. 326, 1930 ; D. N. Ghosh, *Journ. Indian Chem. Soc.*, **7**. 509, 1930 ; J. Mukherjee, S. R. Choudhury and M. R. S. Rao, *ib.*, **7**. 803, 1930 ; P. N. Pavloff, *Koll. Zeit.*, **35**. 375, 1924 ; E. Deiss, *ib.*, **6**. 69, 1910 ; H. Udluft, *ib.*, **34**. 233, 1924 ; S. Liepatoff, *ib.*, **39**. 127, 1926 ; *Journ. Russ. Phys. Chem. Soc.*, **57**. 450, 1925 ; **58**. 983, 1926 ; *Zeit. anorg. Chem.*, **152**. 73, 1926 ; **157**. 22, 1926 ; W. Chlopin and A. Balandin, *ib.*, **149**. 157, 1925 ; A. Steopoe, *Bull. Chim. Soc. Romana*, **28**. 83, 1925 ; **29**. 11, 1926 ; *Koll. Zeit.*, **39**. 35, 1926 ; H. B. Weiser, *Journ. Phys. Chem.*, **29**. 955, 1925 ; *The Hydrous Oxides*, New York, 294, 1926 ; T. Macalpine, *Brit. Pat. No.* 3381, 1899 ; M. G. Levi and F. Ageno, *Atti Accad. Lincei*, (5), **15**. ii, 615, 1906 ; *Gazz. Chim. Ital.*, **37**. i, 368, 1907 ; E. Frei, *Ueber das Verhalten der Mangansalze an der Anode*, Giessen, 1901 ; E. Krause, *Versuche zur Oxydation von hydratischem Mangandioxyd in alkalischer Suspension*, Leipzig, 1907 ; C. F. Boehringer, *German Pat.*, *D.R.P.* 117129, 1899 ; W. C. Bray and H. D. Draper, *Proc. Nat. Acad.*, **12**. 295, 1926 ; J. Post, *Verh. Ver. Ref. Gewerbefl.*, **60**. 297, 1881 ; R. Habich, *Zeit. anal. Chem.*, **3**. 474, 1864 ; C. R. Fresenius, *ib.*, **11**. 295, 1872 ; V. Eggertz, *ib.*, **7**. 495, 1868 ; C. Friedheim, *ib.*, **38**. 681, 1899 ; L. Schucht, *ib.*, **22**. 493, 1883 ; C. Winkler, *ib.*, **3**. 423, 1864 ; G. Forchhammer, *Overs. Dansks. Selsk. Forh.*, 91, 1856 ; J. Thomsen, *Thermochemische Untersuchungen*, Leipzig, **2**. 460, 1882 ; **3**. 271, 1883 ; C. Meineke, *Repert. Anal. Chem.*, **3**. 337, 1883 ; **5**. 1, 1885 ; **7**. 54, 1887 ; E. Donath and R. Jeller, *ib.*, **7**. 36, 1887 ; R. Schöffel and E. Donath, *Oester. Zeit. Berg. Hütt.*, **31**. 229, 1883 ; *Monatsh.*, **7**. 639, 1886 ; F. Rüdorff, *Zeit. angew. Chem.*, **3**. 197, 1890 ; **15**. 6, 1902 ; G. von Knorre, *ib.*, **14**. 1149, 1901 ; *Chem. Ztg.*, **27**. 53, 1903 ; M. Dittrich and C. Hassel, *Ber.*, **35**. 3266, 4072, 1902 ; M. Dittrich, *Chem. Ztg.*, **27**. 196, 1903 ; M. Gröger, *ib.*, **18**. 743, 1893 ; W. Hampe, *ib.*, **7**. 1106, 1883 ; **9**. 1083, 1885 ; *Stahl Eisen*, **11**. 331, 1891 ; N. Wolff, *ib.*, **4**. 702, 1884 ; F. M. Raoult, *Ann. Chim. Phys.*, (4), **2**. 371, 1864 ; M. Berthelot, *ib.*, (5), **5**. 318, 1875 ; *Thermochimie*, Paris, **2**. 48, 266, 1897 ; *Compt. Rend.*, **93**. 757, 1881 ; A. Riche, *ib.*, **85**. 226, 1877 ; *Bull. Soc. Chim.*, (2), **29**. 378, 1878 ; A. P. Ford, *Trans. Amer. Inst. Min. Eng.*, **9**. 347, 1880 ; F. Williams, *ib.*, **10**. 100, 1881 ; R. Mackintosh, *Amer. Chem. Journ.*, **5**. 290, 1884 ; *Chem. News*, **48**. 176, 1883 ; G. C. Stone, *ib.*, **48**. 273, 1883 ; E. Grave, *Neue Untersuchungen über die Passivität von Metallen*, Leipzig, 1911 ; *Zeit. phys. Chem.*, **77**. 513, 1911 ; L. Kahlenberg, *ib.*, **17**. 577, 1895 ; C. G. Särnström, *Berg. Hütt. Ztg.*, **40**. 425, 1881 ; *Jern. Kontorets Ann.*, **36**. 401, 1881 ; **38**. 400, 1883 ; G. D. van Arsdale and C. G. Maier, *Trans. Amer. Electrochem. Soc.*, **33**. 109, 1918 ; Badische Anilin- und Sodafabrik, *German Pat.*, *D.R.P.* 163813, 1905 ; *Zeit. Elektrochem.*, **11**. 853, 1905 ; J. Köster, *ib.*, **10**. 553, 1904 ; C. Engels, *ib.*, **2**. 416, 1896 ; **3**. 306, 1897 ; A. Classen, *ib.*, **1**. 290, 1895 ; A. Classen and M. A. von Reis, *Ber.*, **14**. 1626, 1881 ; K. Elbs, *Zeit. angew. Chem.*, **16**. 290, 1903 ; *Zeit. Elektrochem.*, **7**. 260, 1901 ; C. N. Otin, *ib.*, **15**. 386, 1909 ; W. Hümmelchen and H. Kappen, *Zeit. Pflanzenernähr. Düng.*, **3**. A, 289, 1924 ; A. J. Walker and W. Farmer, *Proc. Chem. Soc.*, **30**. 139, 1914 ; P. Jannasch, *Praktischer Leitfaden der Gewichtsanalyze*, Leipzig, 43, 1897 ; P. Jannasch and J. F. MacGregory, *Journ. prakt. Chem.*, (2), **43**. 402, 1891 ; P. Jannasch and E. von Cloedt, *Zeit. anorg. Chem.*, **10**. 405, 1895 ; P. Jannasch and H. Lehnert, *ib.*, **12**. 134, 1896 ; P. Jannasch and R. Niederhofheim, *Ber.*, **24**. 3945, 1891 ; G. Almkvist, *Zeit. anorg. Chem.*, **103**. 240, 1918 ; E. Ebler and W. Bender, *ib.*, **84**. 77, 1913 ; F. Hebler, *Farb. Ztg.*, **31**. 155, 1925 ; F. Häffner, *Die physikalisch-chemischen Vörgange bei der Aufnahme von zweiwertigem Mangan aus dem Trinkwasser an Braunstein*, München, 1925 ; Y. Kato and T. Matsuhashi, *Journ. Soc. Chem. Ind. Japan*, **32**. 313, 315, 1929 ; A. Simon and F. Feher, *Koll. Zeit.*, **54**. 49, 1931 ; S. G. Simpson, *Journ. Amer. Chem. Soc.*, **45**. 1883, 1923 ; J. N. Mukherjee, *Phil. Mag.*, (6), **44**. 321, 1922 ; *Journ. Indian Chem. Soc.*, **2**. 191, 1925 ; S. Sarvottam and T. S. Narayan, *ib.*, **7**. 882, 1930 ; S. S. Joshi and T. S. Narayan, *ib.*, **7**. 883, 1930 ; M. Mehrotra

and K. C. Sen, *ib.*, **3**. 297, 1926 ; S. S. Bhatnagar, M. Prasad and D. C. Bahl, *ib.*, **2**. 11, 1925;
S. S. Bhatnagar, K. K. Mathur and D. L. Shrivastava, *Journ. Phys. Chem.*, **28**. 387, 1924 ;
A. F. Joseph, *Journ. Chem. Soc.*, **123**. 2022, 1923 ; **127**. 2813, 1925 ; N. R. Dhar, *Journ. Indian
Chem. Soc.*, **4**. 173, 1927 ; *Journ. Phys. Chem.*, **29**. 1394, 1925 ; S. Roy and N. R. Dhar, *ib.*, **34**.
122, 1930 ; K. C. Sen and N. R. Dhar, *Koll. Zeit.*, **33**. 193, 1923 ; K. C. Sen, P. B. Ganguly and
N. R. Dhar, *Journ. Phys. Chem.*, **28**. 313, 1924 ; K. C. Sen, *Zeit. anorg. Chem.*, **171**. 275, 1928 ;
174. 82, 1928 ; *Koll. Zeit.*, **28**. 310, 1926 ; N. G. Chatterji and N. R. Dhar, *ib.*, **33**. 18, 1923 ; **37**.
2, 1923 ; *Zeit. anorg. Chem.*, **159**. 192, 1927 ; J. Oesch, *Kritische Studien über Mangan*, Berlin,
1906 ; B. Sjollema, *Chem. Weekbl.*, **6**. 287, 1909 ; *Bemmelen's Gedenkboek*, 399, 1910 ; W. Engelhardt, *Koll. Zeit.*, **45**. 42, 1928 ; W. N. Simakoff, *ib.*, **45**. 207, 1928 ; C. Drucker and R. Hüttner,
Zeit. phys. Chem., **131**. 237, 1928 ; P. Hausknecht, *Magnetochemische Untersuchungen*, Strassburg,
1913 ; M. A. Iljinsky, A. A. Balandin, M. V. Gaverdovskaja and B. T. Poliak, *Journ. Russ.
Phys. Chem. Soc.*, **58**. 241, 1926 ; L. S. Levy, *Ann. Chim. Phys.*, (10), **15**. 85, 1931 ; *Compt. Rend.*,
192. 1376, 1931 ; G. Kreimer, *Journ. Chem. Ind. Moscow*, **7**. 165, 1930 ; J. Meyer and R. Kanters,
Zeit. anorg. Chem., **185**. 172, 178, 1929 ; A. W. Pilkoff, *Journ. Russ. Gen. Chem.*, **1**. 589, 1931.
    [3] F. Klockmann, *Lehrbuch der Mineralogie*, Stuttgart, 422, 1922 ; F. Cornu, *Koll. Zeit.*, **4**.
300, 1909 ; F. Cornu and M. Lazarevic, *ib.*, **4**. 295, 1909 ; F. Cornu and H. Leitmeier, *ib.*, **4**.
285, 1909 ; H. Leitmeier, *ib.*, **4**. 280, 1909 ; J. G. Wallerius, *Mineralogia*, Stockholm, 268, 1747;
A. G. Werner, *Berg. Journ.*, 386, 1789 ; A. Cronstedt, *Mineralogia*, Stockholm, 106, 211, 1758 ;
W. Haidinger, *Trans. Roy. Soc. Edin.*, **11**. 129, 1827 ; M. F. Heddle, *ib.*, **30**. 427, 1882 ;
C. F. Rammelsberg, *Handbuch der Mineralchemie*, Leipzig, 189, 1875 ; 78, 1895 ; *Pogg. Ann.*,
54. 554, 1841 ; **68**. 513, 1846 ; E. E. Schmid, *ib.*, **129**. 154, 1865 ; K. List, *ib.*, **110**. 325, 1860 ;
C. F. Richter, *ib.*, **21**. 590, 1831 ; A. Breithaupt, *ib.*, **49**. 204, 1840 ; *Vollständige Charakteristik
des Mineralsystems*, Dresden, 240, 1832 ; *Vollständiges Handbuch der Mineralogie*, Dresden, 332,
896, 1847 ; G. Langhans, *Beiträge zur Kenntnis der Psilomelane*, Jena, 1885 ; R. Ambronn,
Methoden der angewandten Geophysik, Dresden, 1926 ; G. Grenet, *Ann. Physique*, (10), **13**. 263,
1930 ; C. W. Davis, *Rept. Investigations U.S. Bur. Mines*, 3024, 1930 ; S. R. B. Cooke, W. Howes
and A. H. Emery, *Amer. Min.*, **16**. 209, 1931 ; H. Laspeyres, *Journ. prakt. Chem.*, (2), **13**. 1,
215, 1876 ; F. von Kobell, *ib.*, (1), **109**. 427, 1870 ; A. Frenzel, *ib.*, (2), **2**. 203, 1870 ; (2), **4**. 353,
1871 ; *Neues Jahrb. Min.*, 801, 1873 ; 55, 1879 ; C. Winkler, *Journ. prakt. Chem.*, (2), **4**. 353,
1871 ; A. P. Bolley, *ib.*, (1), **103**. 478, 1868 ; T. Morawsky and T. Stingl, *ib.*, (2), **15**. 233, 1877 ;
J. F. Bahr, *ib.*, (1), **53**. 312, 1851 ; A. Gorgeu, *Bull. Soc. Min.*, **13**. 21, 1890 ; *Ann. Chim. Phys.*,
(3), **66**. 156, 1862 ; *Compt. Rend.*, **110**. 247, 1134, 1890 ; F. Kossmat and C. von John, *Zeit.
prakt. Geol.*, **13**. 315, 1905 ; L. Gmelin, *Zeit. Min.*, 2. 76, 1825 ; P. Berthier, *Ann. Chim. Phys.*,
(2), **51**. 91, 1832 ; *Ann. Mines*, (1), **6**. 301, 1821 ; J. J. Ebelmen, *ib.*, (3), **19**. 164, 1841 ;
R. D. Harvey, *Econ. Geol.*, **23**. 778, 1928 ; E. Turner, *Trans. Roy. Soc. Edin.*, **11**. 143, 1831 ;
Phil. Mag., (2), **4**. 22, 1828 ; L. L. Fermor, *Mem. Geol. Sur. India*, **37**. 100, 1909 ; J. N. von
Fuchs, *Schweigger's Journ.*, **62**. 255, 1831 ; C. M. Kersten, *ib.*, **66**. 6, 1832 ; A. Schwager and
C. W. von Gümbel, *Geognost. Jahresh.*, **7**. 57, 1895 ; S. F. Emmons, *Ann. Rep. U.S. Geol. Sur.*,
17. ii, 451, 1896 ; A. Lacroix, *Guide du visiteur à la collection de minéralogie du museum d'histoire
naturelle*, Paris, 29, 1900 ; *Minéralogie de la France et de ses colonies*, Paris, **4**. 13, 1910 ;
J. B. L. Romé de l'Isle, *Cristallographie*, Paris, 1783 ; R. J. Haüy, *Traité de minéralogie*, Paris,
1801 ; M. Adam, *Tableau minéralogique*, Paris, 75, 1869 ; H. Copaux, *Bull. Soc. Chim.*, (3),
29. 301, 1903 ; G. Agricola, *Bermannus*, Basileæ, 459, 1529 ; H. A. J. Wilkens and H. B. C. Nitze,
Trans. Amer. Inst. Min. Eng., **26**. 351, 1896 ; L. E. Rivot, *Docimasie*, Paris, **3**. 268,
1886 ; G. Dupouy, *Études minéralogiques sur l'Indochine française*, Paris, 197, 1913 ; V. Sevoz
and J. Breuilhs, *Bull. Soc. l'Ind. Min.*, **6**. 29, 1860 ; *Rev. Géol.*, **1**. 57, 1860 ; F. Katzer, *Berg.
Hütt. Jahrb.*, **54**. 203, 1906 ; H. K. Scott, *Journ. Iron Steel Inst.*, **57**. i, 179, 1900 ; E. T. Wherry,
Proc. U.S. Nat. Museum, **51**. 82, 1917 ; *Amer. Min.*, **10**. 28, 1925 ; W. E. Ford and W. M. Bradley,
Amer. Journ. Science, (4), **34**. 173, 1913 ; J. Orcel and S. Pavlovitch, *Compt. Rend.*, **187**. 1295,
1928 ; P. Groth, *Tabellarische Uebersicht der Mineralien*, Braunschweig, 36, 1882 ; 64,
1898 ; F. Beijerinck, *Neues Jahrb. Min. B.B.*, **11**. 463, 1897 ; O. Weigel, *ib.*, **21**. 338, 396, 1906 ;
H. C. Bolton, *Min. Mag.*, **4**. 187, 1882 ; F. Braun, *Pogg. Ann.*, **153**. 556, 1874 ; *Wied. Ann.*, **1**.
95, 1877 ; **4**. 476, 1878 ; **19**. 340, 1883 ; H. Meyer, *ib.*, **19**. 70, 1883 ; K. Thaddéeff, *Zeit. Kryst.*,
20. 350, 1892 ; A. E. Reuss, *Jahrb. geol. Reichsanst. Wien*, 20. 519, 1870 ; B. Walter, *ib.*, **26**. 424,
1876 ; W. V. Smitheringale, *Econ. Geol.*, **24**. 481, 1929 ; G. A. Thiel, *ib.*, **19**. 107, 1924 ; J. R. Blum,
Die Pseudomorphosen des Mineralreichs, Stuttgart, 265, 1843 ; 235, 1863 ; H. F. Keller, *Proc.
Amer. Phil. Soc.*, **47**. 79, 1908 ; A. Weisbach, *Neues Jahrb. Min.*, 848, 1878 ; ii, 113, 1880 ;
F. Field, *Chem. Gaz.*, **16**. 104, 1858 ; W. A. Lampadius, *Neues Erfahrungen in Gebiete der Chemie*,
Weimar, **2**. 70, 1815 ; C. C. von Leonhard, *Taschenbuch fur die gesammte Mineralogie*, Frankfurt,
14. 219, 1820 ; M. H. Klaproth, *Beiträge zur chemischen Kenntniss der Mineralkörper*, Berlin, **2**.
308, 1797 ; J. W. Döbereiner, *Gilbert's Ann.*, **67**. 333, 1821 ; N. Kurnakoff and N. Podkopajeff,
Proc. Russ. Min. Soc., (2), **39**. 15, 1901 ; *Russ. Berg. Journ.*, **3**. 359, 1903 ; P. Poni, *Ann. Scient.
Univ. Jassy*, **1**. 15, 1900 ; V. C. Butureanu, *ib.*, **5**. 87, 1908 ; **6**. 7, 1909 ; **7**. 183, 1912 ; M. Savul,
ib., **12**. 136, 1924 ; W. Ogawa, *Journ. Japan. Soc. Chem. Ind.*, **31**. 486, 711, 1928.
    [4] A. Cronstedt, *Mineralogia*, Stockholm, 105, 1758 ; G. Bischof, *Lehrbuch der chemischen und
physikalischen Geologie*, Bonn, **1**. 428, 1847 ; London, **1**. 160, 1854 ; D. L. G. Karsten, *Mineralogische Tabellen*, Berlin, 1808 ; J. J. N. Huot, *Manuel de minéralogie*, Paris, 241, 1841 ; P. Berthier,
Ann. Chim. Phys., (2), **51**. 19, 1832 ; M. Adam, *Tableau minéralogique*, Paris, 76, 1869 ;
W. Haidinger, *Jahresb. geol. Reichsanst. Wien*, **7**. 609, 1856 ; K. Reissacher, *ib.*, **7**. 312, 609,

T

1856 ; R. Kirwan, *Elements of Mineralogy*, London, 1784 ; M. H. Klaproth, *Beiträge zur chemischen Kenntniss der Mineralkörper*, Berlin, **3**. 311, 1802 ; E. Turner, *Edin. Journ. Science*, (2), **2**. 213, 1830 ; J. H. L. Vogt, *Zeit. prakt. Geol.*, **14**. 219, 1906 ; M. Scheffler, *Arch. Pharm.*, (2), **35**. 260, 1843 ; H. Ludwig, *ib.*, (2), **143**. 101, 1870 ; J. Redtenbacher, *Liebig's Ann.*, **41**. 308, 1844 ; E. Dittler, *Centr. Min.*, 104, 1925 ; A. Gorgeu, *Bull. Soc. Min.*, **13**. 26, 1890 ; B. Bertolio, *Boll. Com. Geol. Italia*, **27**. 405, 1896 ; C. Rimatori, *Atti Accad. Lincei*, (5), **10**. ii, 231, 1901 ; A. Liversidge, *The Minerals of New South Wales*, London, 108, 1888 ; M. Weibull, *Geol. För. Förh. Stockholm*, **6**. 509, 1883 ; G. de Geer, *ib.*, **6**. 42, 1882 ; T. Fegraeus, *ib.*, **8**. 170, 1886 ; A. S. Woodward, *Proc. Manchester Lit. Phil. Soc.*, **21**. 115, 1882 ; *Chem. News*, **45**. 241, 1882 ; C. P. Williams, *ib.*, **21**. 237, 1870 ; *Journ. Franklin Inst.*, **61**. 123, 1871 ; L. L. Fermor, *Mem. Geol. Sur. India*, **37**. 119, 1907 ; S. Popoff, *Trav. Mus. Geol. St. Petersburg*, **4**. 99, 1910 ; K. Nenadkewitsch, *ib.*, **5**. 37, 1911 ; E. H. S. Bailey, *Journ. Amer. Chem. Soc.*, **26**. 714, 1904 ; V. C. Butureanu, *Ann. Scient. Univ. Jassy*, **5**. 87, 1908 ; C. F. Rammelsberg, *Handbuch der Mineralchemie*, Leipzig, 183, 1860 ; 192, 1875 ; *Pogg. Ann.*, **62**. 157, 1844 ; L. C. Beck, *Report on the Mineralogy of the State of New York*, Albany, 55, 1842 ; A. Lacroix, *Minéralogie de France et de ses colonies*, Paris, **4**. 5, 1910 ; K. Thaddéeff, *Zeit. Kryst.*, **20**. 350, 1892 ; J. A. Dana, *A System of Mineralogy*, New York, 182, 1868 ; H. W. F. Wackenroder, *Kastner's Arch.*, **14**. 269, 1828 ; H. Buttgenbach and C. Gillet, *Bull. Soc. Geol. Belg.*, **43**. 239, 1920 ; A. Brunlechner, *Jahrb. Nat. Land. Mus. Klagenfurt*, **22**. 194, 1893 ; H. Mache, *Monatsh.*, **26**. 349, 1905 ; F. von Kobell, *Sitzber. München. Akad.*, 48, 1870 ; *Journ. prakt. Chem.*, (2), **1**. 425, 1870 ; L. J. Igelström, *Oefvers. Akad. Förh.*, 221, 1844 ; 606, 1865.
⁵ A. Gorgeu, *Ann. Chim. Phys.*, (3), **66**. 161, 1862 ; *Compt. Rend.*, **88**. 797, 1879 ; *Bull. Soc. Chim.*, (3), **3**. 781, 1890 ; A. Guyard, *ib.*, (2), **1**. 81, 1864 ; A. Carnot, *Compt. Rend.*, **116**. 1375, 1893 ; *Bull. Soc. Chim.*, (3), **1**. 275, 1889 ; C. Lepierre, *ib.*, (3), **13**. 597, 1895 ; W. Spring and M. Lucion, *ib.*, (3), **3**. 4, 1890 ; S. U. Pickering, *Journ. Chem. Soc.*, **35**. 654, 1879 ; V. H. Veley, *ib.*, **37**. 581, 1880 ; **41**. 56, 1882 ; *Chem. News*, **44**. 241, 1881 ; G. C. Stone, *ib.*, **48**. 273, 1883 ; J. Post, *Verh. Ver. Beförd. Gewerbefl.*, **58**. 468, 1879 ; *Ber.*, **12**. 1459, 1879 ; R. Haas, *ib.*, **17**. 2254, 1884 ; W. Reissig, *Liebig's Ann.*, **103**. 27, 1857 ; B. Franke, *Journ. prakt. Chem.*, (2), **36**. 170, 1887 ; O. T. Christensen, *Zeit. anorg. Chem.*, **24**. 203, 1900.

§ 12. The Permanganites

The chromites are salts of the acid anhydride Cr_2O_3, and the ferrites of the acid anhydride Fe_2O_3, so that here the salts of the acid anhydride Mn_2O_3 are called manganites ; hence, the salts of the acid anhydride MnO_2 are called **permanganites**, those of the acid anhydride MnO_3, manganates, and those of the acid anhydride Mn_2O_7, permanganates. A. Gorgeu [1] regarded hydrated manganese dioxide as *acide manganeux*, manganous acid, H_2MnO_3, so that manganese dioxide becomes manganous anhydride, MnO_2, and the salts $RO.nMnO_2$, permanganites. The acidic properties of hydrated manganese dioxide are very feeble, and as a result show a great tendency to form polymerides—**polypermanganites**. A. S. Cocosinschy represented the formation of the polypermanganites by :

$$O=Mn\begin{matrix}OH\\OH\end{matrix}=H_2Mn_2O_5 \qquad O=Mn\begin{matrix}OH\\OH\end{matrix}\ O=Mn\begin{matrix}OH\\OH\end{matrix}=H_2Mn_3O_7 \quad \cdot \quad H_2Mn_nO_{2n+1}$$

C. R. A. Wright and A. E. Menke doubted the existence of potassium permanganites as chemical individuals, since the product obtained by reducing permanganate with glycerol—*vide infra*—does not have the composition $K_2O.8MnO_2.3H_2O$ assigned to it by T. Morawsky and J. Stingl, for, neglecting the water of hydration, it varied considerably in composition—*e.g.* $K_2O.3MnO_2.9MnO_2$; $2K_2O.13MnO.22MnO_2$; and $3K_2O.2MnO.18MnO_2$. It was also found that the product of the reduction of permanganate by sulphur dioxide in the cold approximated $K_2O.2MnO.12MnO_2$. L. Swiontkowsky, and C. Weltzien also observed that the products of the reduction of permanganate by hydrogen dioxide are very variable in composition. A. Gorgeu, and J. Post found that the oxidation of manganous hydroxide by air in the presence of a soln. of potassium hydroxide approximates $K_2O.25MnO.27MnO_2.nH_2O$, which is not far from $Mn_2O_3.H_2O$. J. M. van

Bemmelen explained the variation in composition of the different alkali manganites reported by different investigators by assuming that they are mixtures of the products of the hydrolysis of one or more permanganites, while the permanganites prepared by wet processes are adsorption products of hydrated manganese dioxide with bases. A similar view was taken by E. Deiss. On the other hand, W. Biltz showed that hydrated manganese dioxide, $MnO_2.H_2O$, has acidic qualities, and he called it *manganige Säure*—our permanganous acid, H_2MnO_3. This hydrate was obtained by treating hydrated manganese dioxide with ammonia, cooled by a freezing mixture of solid carbon dioxide, and pumping off the ammonia. The residue corresponds with $MnO_2.H_2O$. If the pressure, p mm., be measured during the extraction of ammonia, and the corresponding mol. ratio $NH_3 : MnO_2$ determined, the results, when plotted, furnish the curve, Fig. 51. There are breaks corresponding with $H_2O.NH_3.MnO_2$ and $H_2O.2NH_3$.

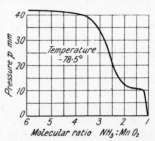

FIG. 51.—The Vapour Pressure of the Ammonium Permanganites.

MnO_2. The former, $H_2O.NH_3.MnO_2$, is taken to be the acidic salt, **ammonium hydropermanganite**, $(NH_4)HMnO_3$; and the other, $H_2O.2NH_3.MnO_2$, the normal salt, **ammonium permanganite**, $(NH_4)_2MnO_3$.

G. Rousseau melted a mixture of 3 grms. of sodium hydroxide and 1·5 grms. of manganous chloride, and then added 3 grms. of sodium nitrate, and raised the temp. to dull redness. The mixture was then kept for 4 hrs. in a covered crucible at the volatilization temp. of sodium hydroxide. At an orange-red heat **sodium pentapermanganite**, $Na_2O.5MnO_2$, is formed, and at a white-heat small, black, glistening needles of **sodium dodecapermanganite**, $Na_2O.12MnO_2$, appear. The crystals are washed with boiling water. The pentapermanganite is also formed in black, octahedral plates by adding 10 grms. of sodium chloride to the mixture used in the previous preparation, heating it until the sodium chloride is volatilized, and washing the cold product with water. If sodium permanganate be heated to 300°, and the cold mass extracted with water, there remain black microscopic crystals of **sodium octopermanganite**, $Na_2O.8MnO_2.5H_2O$. The crystals lose 4 mols. of water at 150°–180°, and all the water is lost at 250°; no other change occurs at 440°. This compound is also formed by melting a mixture of sodium manganate and chloride at 500° and washing the product with boiling water; at 800° the *tetrahydrated dodecapermanganite*, $Na_2O.12MnO_2.4H_2O$, is formed; at 1000°, **sodium hexadecapermanganite**, $Na_2O.16MnO_2.8H_2O$; at 1200°–1300°, the octopermanganite is again formed; and at a white-heat, the hydrated dodecapermanganite. P. Schottländer prepared a complex *sodium glycerylpermanganite*, $Na_2[Mn(C_3H_5O_3)_2]$, by treating manganese dioxide with glycerol and soda-lye. For A. S. Cocosinschy's observations on the action of heat on the sodium salt, *vide infra*.

According to C. F. Rammelsberg, **potassium dipermanganite**, $K_2O.2MnO_2$, is prepared by strongly heating potassium permanganate; when this is extracted with water, it is resolved into **potassium pentapermanganite**, $K_2O.5MnO_2$, thus: $5K_2Mn_2O_5=2K_2Mn_5O_{11}+3K_2O$. A. S. Cocosinschy found that the proportion of potassium in the washed product decreases with the temp. of calcination of the potassium permanganate, and similarly with the sodium salt:

	600°	700°	800°	900°	1000°	1100°
K content .	29·21	28·09	26·28	23·79	22·82	18·57 per cent.
Na content .	31·01	30·70	29·12	28·65	26·71	24·29 per cent.

A. Gorgeu found that when carbon dioxide is passed into a soln of potassium manganate, a soln. of permanganate and a yellow precipitate, $K_2O.5MnO_2.nH_2O$, are formed. The formula just indicated represents the composition of the washed product. There is probably some hydrolysis, because if washed with water containing 0·3 per cent. potassium hydroxide, the product is **potassium tetraper-manganite,** $K_2O.4MnO_2.nH_2O$; and if with water containing 1 per cent. potassium hydroxide, there remains **potassium tripermanganite,** $K_2O.3MnO_2.nH_2O$. If a soln. of potassium permanganate be decomposed by a soln. of potassium hydroxide or carbonate, a precipitate approximating $K_2O.5MnO_2.nH_2O$ is formed, and when the liquid is boiled, this product passes into soln. as potassium manganate. J. Post made some observations on this subject. If the precipitate be washed with hot water, C. R. A. Wright and A. E. Menke found that its composition corresponds with $4K_2O.21MnO_2.19H_2O$; while, according to T. Morawsky and J. Stingl, if the precipitate be washed with hot water and dried at 100°, it forms **potassium octoper-manganite,** $K_2O.8MnO_2.3H_2O$. According to P. Solstein, the permanganite $K_2O.8MnO_2.3H_2O$, or $KH_3Mn_4O_{10}$, is formed by the action of iodine on a soln. of potassium permanganate ; M. Gläser obtained a similar product by using thiosulphate in place of iodine, but M. Hönig and E. Zatzek said that the precipitate produced by thiosulphate in alkaline soln. has the composition $K_2O.6MnO_2.3H_2O$, or $KH_3Mn_3O_8$. T. Morawsky and J. Stingl obtained $K_2O.8MnO_2.3H_2O$ by reducing a neutral soln. of potassium permanganate by alcohol, glycerol, potassium thiocyanate, or potassium oxalate. G. Rousseau melted a mixture of 3 grms. of potassium carbonate and 5 grms. of potassium chloride, and added, in small quantities at a time, 3 grms. of potassium manganate. If heated for 8 hrs. at a high temp., and the cold mass extracted with water, there remains trihydrated potassium octopermanganite, in black plates which lose their water at 150° to 160°. If the operation be conducted at a lower temp., black plates of **potassium hexadecapermanganite,** $K_2O.16MnO_2.6H_2O$, are formed. They lose their water at 130°–200°, and dissolve freely in conc. hydrochloric acid. If a mixture of 10 grms. of potassium chloride and 3 grms. of potassium manganate be heated until the alkali chloride is volatilized, and the cold product washed with boiling water, black plates of **potassium dotricontapermanganite,** $K_2O.32MnO_2.10H_2O$, are formed.

J. Volhard obtained an impure copper permanganite by the action of a copper salt on a warm soln. of potassium permanganate ; and in the reaction $2KMnO_4 +3MnSO_4+7H_2O \rightleftharpoons 2KHSO_4+H_2SO_4+5H_2MnO_3$, studied by A. Guyard, and J. Volhard, if other metal salts be present, the corresponding permanganite may be formed—e.g. with zinc sulphate : $4KMnO_4+5ZnSO_4+6MnSO_4+14H_2O=4KHSO_4 +7H_2SO_4+5(HO.MnO.OZnO.MnO.OH)$. The brownish-black **copper hemiennea-permanganite** prepared by P. B. Sarkar and N. R. Dhar by adding potassium permanganate to a mixed soln. of copper and manganous sulphates and boiling has the composition $2CuO.9MnO_2.14H_2O$. A. F. Jolles also prepared copper permanganite in a similar way. According to M. Salinger, when a mixture of manganous and copper sulphates is treated with ammonium persulphate, a copper permanganite is precipitated ; and if the mixed soln. is treated with hydrogen dioxide, the precipitate has the composition of a **copper manganous permanganite,** $4CuO.MnO.7MnO_2.8H_2O$. The *lepidophœite* of A. Weisbach may be (MnO,CuO). $5MnO_2.9H_2O$—*vide supra.* A. Gorgeu obtained **copper tetrapermanganite,** $CuO.4MnO_2$, by the repeated action of a dil. soln. of a cupric salt on moist hydrated manganese dioxide ; it decomposes into the hypomanganite at a red-heat. H. Baubigny and P. Rivals obtained the impure *hydrate,* $CuO.4MnO_2.H_2O$, by evaporating a soln. of potassium bromide, copper sulphate, and potassium permanganate to dryness. The action is incomplete. A. Gorgeu found that if a cold, sat. soln. of silver permanganate is treated with hydrogen dioxide, a brown precipitate of **silver permanganite,** $Ag_2O.MnO_2$, is formed ; while if potassium octopermanganite is treated with silver nitrate, **silver octopermanganite,** $Ag_2O.8MnO_2.3H_2O$, is formed ; while M. Salinger obtained **silver decapermanganite,** $Ag_2O.10MnO_2.3H_2O$, by treating a mixture of manganous and silver nitrates with ammonium persulphate. By proceeding as in the case of the copper salt, but using soln. of silver nitrate and manganous sulphate, P. B. Sarkar and N. R. Dhar obtained deep black **silver heptapermanganite,** $Ag_2O.7MnO_2.9H_2O$; and by using a soln. of gold chloride, below 0·1 per cent. conc., they obtained a reddish-brown **gold permanganite** which contained only a small proportion of gold. The silver permanganites were also studied by M. N. Chakravarti and N. R. Dhar, and S. C. Chatterji and N. R. Dhar.

H. St. C. Deville observed the formation of a calcium permanganite in the reduction of manganese (*q.v.*) in a lime crucible. By adding a large excess of bleaching powder to a soln. of manganous chloride, so that the liquid remains alkaline, J. Pattinson, and A. Gorgeu obtained a black calcium permanganite, approximating $CaO.MnO_2$; J. Volhard also obtained permanganites of the alkaline earths by adding their salts to a hot soln. of potassium permanganate. In W. Weldon's process for chlorine (*q.v.*) the by-product of manganous chloride is treated at 55° with an excess of calcium hydroxide and a blast of air, when a black, impure calcium permanganite is precipitated : $MnCl_2+2Ca(OH)_2+O=CaO.MnO_2+CaCl_2+2H_2O$. Other products are also formed, *e.g.* $CaO.2MnO_2$ and $MnO.MnO_2$. The subject was discussed by A. Lamy, G. Lemoine, E. Mylius, J. R. Wagner and W. Schenk, W. Odling, G. Lunge, G. Lunge and B. Zahorsky, J. Wiernik, E. Kopp, C. Jezler, F. Kuhlmann, J. Post, etc. According to E. Dufau, **calcium tritapermanganite,** $3CaO.MnO_2$, is obtained by heating manganese or manganese oxide in a lime crucible in an electric arc furnace for a few minutes. The crystalline mass is not altered when heated in oxygen ; it is decomposed by cold water, and an aq. soln. of sugar dissolves both calcium and manganese oxides, to form a dark reddish-brown soln., which is decolorized by acids, and from which alcohol separates a rose-coloured precipitate. At a red-heat the compound is attacked with incandescence by chlorine and bromine to form calcium chloride or bromide respectively ; iodine acts less energetically ; hydrogen chloride attacks it below redness ; hydrochloric acid dissolves it with the evolution of chlorine ; molten potassium chlorate is without action ; cold nitric acid has very little action, but the hot acid dissolves it with the evolution of gas ; and molten potassium nitrate is without action. G. Rousseau prepared brownish-red crystals of **calcium hemipermanganite,** $2CaO.MnO_2$, by heating for an hour a mixture of calcium oxide and chloride and manganous chloride ; and black prismatic crystals of **calcium permanganite,** $CaO.MnO_2$, by heating for a couple of hours a mixture of 15 grms. of calcium chloride and 3 or 4 grms. of calcium carbonate, adding 2 grms. of manganous chloride, and extracting the cold mass with water. It is soluble in fuming hydrochloric acid and insoluble in water. If the mixture be heated for half an hour, **calcium dipermanganite,** $CaO.2MnO_2$, is formed ; and if heated for 6 hrs., black needles of **calcium tripermanganite,** $CaO.3MnO_2$, are formed. G. Rousseau represented these compounds by the graphic formulæ :

According to J. Risler, **calcium pentapermanganite,** $CaO.5MnO_2$, is formed when a mixture of potassium permanganate and calcium chloride is heated to redness and the potassium chloride extracted by boiling water from the cold product. The black crystalline mass is freely soluble in hydrochloric acid, and less soluble in nitric acid. P. B. Sarkar and N. R. Dhar added potassium permanganate to a mixed soln. of manganous and calcium chlorides and boiled the liquid. Reddish-brown **calcium heptapermanganite,** $CaO.7MnO_2.11$ to $14H_2O$, was precipitated. G. Rousseau prepared **strontium permanganite,** $SrO.MnO_2$, by heating for a few hours a molten mixture of 15 grms. of strontium chloride, 2 grms. of strontia, and a gram of manganous chloride ; if the temp. is between 1000° and 1100°, **strontium dipermanganite,** $SrO.2MnO_2$, is produced in black needles in about 8–10 hrs. J. Risler obtained a black, crystalline powder of **strontium pentapermanganite,** $SrO.5MnO_2$, by the process used for the corresponding calcium salt. P. B. Sarkar and N. R. Dhar obtained reddish-brown **strontium heptapermanganite,** $SrO.7MnO_2$.

$11H_2O$, by the process used for the calcium salt. P. Schottländer prepared *strontium diglycerylpermanganite*, $Sr[Mn(C_3H_5O_3)_2]$, by a process analogous to that used for the sodium salt. G. Rousseau prepared **barium permanganite,** $BaO.MnO_2$, in black plates or needles, by heating a mixture of 10 grms. of manganous chloride and 2 grms. of barium permanganate for about 4 hrs. at 1500°–1600°, or by similarly heating a mixture of 3 grms. of baryta and a gram of manganous chloride with an excess of barium bromide. The soluble salts are washed from the product with boiling water, and finally with acidulated water. The sp. gr. is 5·85 ; and the compound is freely soluble in hydrochloric acid with the evolution of chlorine ; it is sparingly soluble in nitric acid. T. Morawsky and J. Stingl prepared the *hydrate*, $BaO.MnO_2.H_2O$, by the action of hydrogen dioxide on barium permanganate. D. Balareff gave 240° for the reaction temp. of barium oxide and manganese dioxide. G. Rousseau obtained **barium dipermanganite,** $BaO.2MnO_2$, in black plates, by heating a mixture of 3 grms. of baryta, a gram of manganous chloride, and an excess of barium bromide to 1000° ; and also by heating barium permanganate for 15 hrs. at 320° in the absence of air. J. Risler obtained a dark olive-green, crystalline powder of **barium pentapermanganite,** $BaO.5MnO_2$, as in the case of the corresponding calcium salt. G. Rousseau reported **barium heptapermanganite,** $BaO.7MnO_2$, to be formed by heating barium permanganate, in the absence of air, for many hours at 320°. The powdered product is mixed with acidulated water, and finally washed with boiling water. P. B. Sarkar and N. R. Dhar obtained black $BaO.7MnO_2.7H_2O$, as in the case of the calcium salt. T. Morawsky and J. Stingl obtained **barium octopermanganite,** $BaO.8MnO_2.3H_2O$, by treating the corresponding potassium salt with barium chloride.

According to P. de Wilde and A. Reychler, if a mixture of magnesium sulphate and manganous chloride be heated in air at a red-heat, **magnesium manganous dipermanganite,** $3MgO.MnO.2MnO_2$, is formed. A. Gorgeu obtained **magnesium tetrapermanganite,** $MgO.4MnO_2$, by repeatedly digesting freshly-precipitated, hydrated manganese dioxide in a neutral soln. of a magnesium salt. E. Dufau obtained **magnesium permanganite** as a reddish-brown powder by heating a mixture of magnesium oxide and manganese dioxide for a few minutes in an electric arc furnace. The hard, black, crystalline mass furnishes a reddish-brown powder, which is not very stable. It is slowly decomposed by cold water, and a soln. of sugar dissolves both manganese and magnesium ; it is freely soluble in acids, evolving chlorine with hydrochloric acid, and a gas is given off with nitric acid. If a soln. of manganous chloride be treated with an excess of magnesium hydroxide, and a blast of air be passed through the mixture, magnesium permanganite is formed, as in the case of W. Weldon's process for calcium permanganite (*q.v.*). E. Bückse represented the reaction $MnCl_2+MgCl_2+2H_2O+O=MgO.MnO_2+4HCl$. W. Weldon also heated in air a mixture of manganese and magnesium chlorides and obtained chlorine and a permanganite : $2MgCl_2+MnCl_2+2O_2=3Cl_2+2(MgO.MnO_2)$. J. Volhard also obtained a magnesium permanganite by treating a warm soln. of potassium permanganate with a magnesium salt. P. B. Sarkar and N. R. Dhar obtained black **magnesium hemiheptapermanganite,** $2MgO.7MnO_2.13H_2O$, by proceeding as in the case of the copper salt. A. F. Jolles obtained barium permanganite in a similar way. J. Risler prepared **zinc pentapermanganite,** $ZnO.5MnO_2$, by the method used for the calcium salt. J. Volhard obtained a **zinc permanganite** by the action of a zinc salt on a warm soln. of potassium permanganate. M. Salinger prepared **zinc tritapermanganite,** $3ZnO.MnO_2.7\frac{1}{2}H_2O$, by treating a mixed soln. of manganous and zinc sulphates with ammonium persulphate ; if a soln. of alkali manganate and zinc sulphate be employed, the precipitate contains a higher proportion of zinc. A. Gorgeu obtained **zinc tripermanganite,** $ZnO.3MnO_2$, and **cadmium pentapermanganite,** $CdO.5MnO_2$, by digesting freshly-precipitated hydrated manganese dioxide in a neutral aq. soln. of a zinc or cadmium salt. P. B. Sarkar and N. R. Dhar obtained brownish-yellow **cadmium tridecapermanganite,** $CdO.13MnO_2$. $21H_2O$, by proceeding as in the case of the copper salt. A. F. Jolles prepared cadmium permanganite in a similar way. A. Gorgeu reported **mercury octoper-manganite,** $HgO.8MnO_2.3H_2O$, to be formed by the action of a mercuric salt on a soln. of the corresponding potassium salt. P. B. Sarkar and N. R. Dhar obtained deep black **mercuric henapermanganite,** $HgO.11MnO_2.6H_2O$, by proceeding as in the case of the copper salt.

M. Salinger did not prepare **aluminium permanganite** by adding ammonium persulphate to a soln. of ammonium aluminium sulphate and ammonium manganese sulphate ; a negative result was also obtained by the use of ammonium chromium sulphate, but J. A. Krenner, and J. Loczka described a *manganospinel,* $(Mn,Mg)(Al,Mn)_2O_4$, obtained in the slags of a blast furnace at Menyhaza, Hungary. P. B. Sarkar and N. R. Dhar obtained reddish-brown aluminium permanganite by boiling a soln. of manganous sulphate and potash-alum mixed with potassium permanganate. They also obtained a brownish-grey **thallic permanganite,** $6Tl_2O_3.5MnO_2.7H_2O$, from soln. of thallous and manganous sulphates boiled with potassium permanganate.

P. B. Sarkar and N. R. Dhar prepared grey **stannous permanganite,** 2SnO. $5MnO_2.2H_2O$, from a mixed soln. of stannous chloride and manganous sulphate, boiled with potassium permanganate. A. F. Jolles obtained insoluble **lead permanganite,** $PbO.MnO_2$, by boiling lead permanganate with a reducing liquid. It is not decomposed by neutral or alkaline soln., but if heated in air or steam, it forms lead manganate. J. Orcel and S. Pavlovitch discussed the optical properties of these minerals. P. B. Sarkar and N. R. Dhar obtained black **lead tetrapermanganite,** $PbO.4MnO_2.8H_2O$, when a mixed soln. of lead nitrate and manganous sulphate is treated with potassium permanganate. A. F. Jolles obtained lead permanganite in a similar way. J. Risler obtained **lead pentapermanganite,** $PbO.5MnO_2$, by the method used for the calcium salt. W. Lindgren and W. F. Hillebrand found a fibrous mineral of a brownish-black colour at Coronadogang, Arizona, and they called it **coronadite.** The analysis corresponds with **lead tripermanganite,** RMn_3O_7, or $R''_4H_2Mn_{12}O_{29}$. It may be regarded as a derivative of orthomanganous acid, $3H_4MnO_4=H_2Mn_3O_7+5H_2O$. E. E. Fairbanks found that it consists of hollandite and another lead mineral. L. L. Fermor found that his observations agreed with the formula $R''MnO_5$, where R denotes Pb and Mn. The sp. gr. is 5·246, and the hardness 4. H. Buttgenbach and C. Gillet described a related steel-grey mineral from Sidi-Amor-ben-Salem, Tunis ; they called it **césarolite**—after G. Césaro. In the idealized state it corresponds with PbO, 44·46 per cent. ; MnO_2, 51·95 ; H_2O, 3·59. Its sp. gr. is 5·29. Nitric acid extracts only about 3·35 per cent. of the manganese, and its formula approximates $PbO.3MnO_2.H_2O$, making it a salt of the acid $H_4Mn_3O_8$, analogous to the **romanechite** of A. Lacroix—named from its occurrence at Romanèche—and represented by $H_2(Mn,Ba)Mn_3O_8$—*vide supra,* psilomelane. F. Zambonini and V. Caglioti found that romanechite corresponds with $H_2(Mn,Ba)Mn_4O_{10}$. There is also the Indian mineral **hollandite,** described by L. L. Fermor. It occurs in tetragonal bipyramids with $a : c=1 : 0.2039$, and of a silver-grey or black colour. Its sp. gr. is 4·70 to 4·95, and its hardness 6. The analyses approximate $mR''_2MnO_5.nR'''_4(MnO_5)_3$, where R'' is mainly H_2, K_2, Mn, or Ba ; and R''', Fe, Mn. L. L. Fermor represented the relations between these minerals of what he called the hollandite group :

Hollandite group	Pb very low	H₂O high, Fe low	.	.	ROMANECHITE
	Ba low or high	H₂O low, Fe high	.	.	HOLLANDITE
	Pb high ; Ba very low	.	.	.	CORONADITE

E. E. Fairbanks found that, like coronadite, romanechite consists of hollandite and a lead mineral.

P. B. Sarkar and N. R. Dhar obtained deep black **bismuth manganite,** $Bi_2O_3.7MnO_2.10H_2O$, from a nitric acid soln. of bismuth nitrate, and manganous sulphate treated with potassium permanganate ; and brownish-red **vanadium permanganite,** $V_2O_5.5MnO_2.10H_2O$, by using ammonium metavanadate in place of the bismuth salt. M. Gröger prepared hydrated **chromium permanganite,** $Cr_2O_3.3MnO_2.nH_2O$, or $Cr_2(MnO_3)_3.nH_2O$, by allowing mixed soln. of manganous chloride and sodium chromate to stand a short time. The dark brown precipitate is formed in accord with $3MnCrO_4=CrO_3+Cr_2(MnO_3)_3$. It forms chromic acid when treated with sulphuric acid. For the work of H. Struve, E. Péchard, C. Friedheim and O. Allemann, C. Friedheim and M. Samelson, A. Rosenheim, and A. Rosenheim and H. Itzig on the complex **molybdenum permanganites,** *vide* manganese molybdates, 10. 60, 11 ; and for A. Just's, and A. Roger and E. F. Smith's observations on **tungsten permanganites,** *vide* manganese tungstates, 10. 61, 12. P. B. Sarkar and N. R. Dhar obtained reddish-brown **uranyl manganite** by the general process indicated above.

For the **manganese permanganites,** *vide supra,* manganese dioxide. S. L. Penfield and H. W. Foote obtained a black mineral, crystallizing in cubes with octahedral cleavage, from Simpson, Utah ; it was called **bixbyite**—after M. Bixby. The analysis was thought to correspond with **ferrous permanganite,** $FeO.MnO_2$, and the constitution to be $Fe(MnO_3)$. W. Zachariasen, and L. Pauling and M. D. Shappell found that the X-radiograms agreed with a space-lattice isomorphous with manganese hemitrioxide, $(Fe,Mn)_2O_3$—*vide* ferric oxide. The sp. gr. is 4·945, and the hardness, 6 to 6·5. The *brostenite,* from Brosteni, Roumania, was regarded by P. Poni as an iron manganese permanganite, $(Fe,Mn)O.2MnO_2.2H_2O$, but V. C. Butureanu, and H. Corti observed that the mineral is not uniform, or homogeneous. M. Salinger obtained **ferric permanganite,** $3Fe_2O_3.10MnO_2.3H_2O$, by adding ammonium persulphate to a soln. of ammonium ferric sulphate and ammonium manganese sulphate. A. Gorgeu obtained **ferric dodecamanganite,** $Fe_2O_3.12MnO_2$, by digesting freshly-precipitated hydrated manganese dioxide with a hot, aq. soln. of a ferric salt. The mineral **sitaparite** from Sitapar, Central Provinces, India, was described by L. L. Fermor as a dark bronze-green, crystalline mass, with a composition approximating $CaO.9Mn_2O_3.4Fe_2O_3.MnO_2$, or **calcium manganic ferric permanganite.** Its sp. gr. is 4·93 to 5·09, and its hardness is 7. M. Salinger prepared **cobalt permanganite,** $CoO.MnO_2.2H_2O$, as a brown precipitate from a soln. of cobalt sulphate and potassium permanganate ; and A. Gorgeu obtained **cobalt hexapermanganite,** $CoO.6MnO_2$, by igniting the product obtained by digesting freshly-precipitated hydrated manganese dioxide in aq. soln. of a neutral cobalt salt ; and **nickel pentapermanganite,** $NiO.5MnO_2$, was obtained in a similar way. P. B. Sarkar and N. R. Dhar treated nickel sulphate by the general process, and obtained brownish-black **nickel hexapermanganite,** $NiO.6MnO_2.11H_2O$; and they also prepared a reddish-brown **platinum permanganite,** which, like the gold salt, contained only a small proportion of basic oxide.

REFERENCES.

[1] H. St. C. Deville, *Ann. Chim. Phys.,* (3), **46**. 182, 1856 ; A. Gorgeu, *ib.,* (3), **66**. 161, 1862 ; *Compt. Rend.,* **84**. 177, 1877 ; **88**. 797, 1879 ; **110**. 1134, 1890 ; *Bull. Soc. Chim.,* (3), **3**. 781, 1890 ; (3), **4**. 16, 1890 ; (3), **29**. 1111, 1167, 1903 ; J. Risler, *ib.,* (2), **30**. 110, 1878 ; A. Guyard, *ib.,* (2), **6**. 89, 1863 ; C. R. A. Wright and A. E. Menke, *Journ. Chem. Soc.,* **37**. 34, 1880 ; J. Pattinson, *ib.,* **35**. 366, 1879 ; M. Gläser, *Monatsh.,* **6**. 329, 1885 ; **7**. 651, 1886 ; M. Hönig and E. Zatzek, *ib.,* **4**. 738, 1883 ; **6**. 492, 1885 ; **7**. 48, 1886 ; J. Post, *Verh. Ver. Beförd. Gewerbefl.,* **58**. 468, 1879 ; **60**. 297, 1881 ; *Ber.,* **12**. 1459, 1879 ; **13**. 53, 1880 ; **14**. 2061, 1881 ; T. Morawsky and J. Stingl, *Journ. prakt. Chem.,* (2), **18**. 78, 1878 ; P. Poni, *Ann. Univ. Jassy,* **1**. 15, 1900 ; V. C. Butureanu, *ib.,* **5**. 87, 1908 ; **6**. 7, 129, 1909 ; A. Fleischer, *Ber.,* **5**. 353, 1872 ; F. Kuhlmann, *ib.,* **8**. 167, 1875 ; A. Just, *ib.,* **36**. 3619, 1901 ; C. F. Rammelsberg, *ib.,* **8**. 232, 1875 ; L. Swiontkowsky, *Liebig's Ann.,* **141**. 205, 1867 ; C. Weltzien, *ib.,* **138**. 141, 1866 ; J. Volhard, *ib.,* **198**. 318, 1879 ; P. Schottländer, *ib.,* **155**. 230, 1870 ; J. M. van Bemmelen, *Arch. Néerl.,* (1), **15**. 321, 1881 ; G. Rousseau, *Compt. Rend.,* **101**. 169, 1885 ; **102**. 425, 1886 ; **103**. 261, 1886 ; **104**. 786, 1796, 1887 ; **112**. 525, 1891 ; **113**. 643, 1891 ; **114**. 72, 1892 ; **116**. 1061, 1893 ; G. Rousseau and A. Saglier, *ib.,* **99**. 139, 1884 ; E. Péchard, *ib.,* **125**. 29, 1897 ; H. Baubigny and P. Rivals, *ib.,* **124**. 955, 1897 ; F. Kessler, *Zeit. anal. Chem.,* **18**. 4, 1879 ; G. Lemoine, *Ann. Mines,* (7), **3**. 5, 1873 ; A. Lamy, *Bull. Soc. Enc. Nat. Ind.,* (3), **4**. 428, 1877 ; E. Dufau, *Ann. Chim. Phys.,* (7), **12**. 275, 1897 ; *Sur quelques oxydes doubles cristallisés obtenus à haute température,* Paris, 18, 1897 ; S. L. Penfield and H. W. Foote, *Amer. Journ. Science,* (4), **4**. 105, 1897 ; W. Zachariasen,

Zeit. Kryst., **67**. 455, 1928 ; C. Jezler, *Dingler's Journ.*, **215**. 446, 1875 ; **239**. 74, 1881 ; G. Lunge, *ib.*, **201**. 354, 1871 ; **215**. 157, 1875 ; **236**. 231, 236, 1880 ; G. Lunge and B. Zahorsky, *Zeit. angew. Chem.*, **5**. 631, 1892 ; J. Wiernik, *ib.*, **7**. 257, 1894 ; H. Buttgenbach and C. Gillet, *Ann. Soc. Géol. Belg.*, **43**. 239, 1920 ; L. L. Fermor, *Mem. Geol. Sur. India*, **37**. 96, 1909 ; **48**. 103, 1917 ; *Records Geol. Sur. India*, **61**. 146, 1928 ; W. Lindgren and W. F. Hillebrand, *Amer. Journ. Science*, (4), **18**. 449, 1904 ; E. Bückse, *Brit. Pat. No.* 16320, 1894 ; A. Lacroix, *Minéralogie de la France et de ses colonies*, Paris, **4**. 6, 1910 ; W. Odling, *Chem. News*, **23**. 210, 1871 ; W. Weldon, *ib.*, **20**. 109, 1869 ; *B.A. Rep.*, 79, 1869 ; *Brit. Pat. No.* 2389, 1871 ; 317, 2044, 1872 ; *Laboratory*, **1**. 445, 1867 ; *Dingler's Journ.*, **201**. 354, 1871 ; *Ber.*, **8**. 168, 1875 ; *Monit. Scient.*, (3), **4**. 1, 1874 ; E. Kopp, *ib.*, (2), **7**. 115, 1870 ; D. Balareff, *Zeit. anorg. Chem.*, **136**. 216, 1924 ; J. R. Wagner and W. Schenk, *Chem. Tech. Jahresb.*, **16**. 182, 1870 ; J. Orcel and S. Pavlovitch, *Compt. Rend.*, **187**. 1295, 1928 ; E. Mylius in A. W. Hofmann, *Bericht über die Entwickelung der chemischen Industrie*, Braunschweig, **1**. 113, 1875 ; A. Weisbach, *Neues Jahrb. Min.*, ii, 109, 1880 ; E. Deiss, *Zeit. Koll.*, **6**. 69, 1910 ; P. Solstein, *Pharm. Zeit.*, **32**. 659, 1877 ; A. F. Jolles, *Zeit. anal. Chem.*, **28**. 238, 1889 ; *Repert. anal. Chem.*, **7**. 485, 1889 ; *Zeit. Naturwiss.*, (5), **59**. 423, 1886 ; *Beiträge zur Kenntniss der Manganate und Manganite*, Halle, a. S., 1887 ; *German Pat., D.R.P.* 41348, 1888 ; P. de Wilde and A. Reychler, *ib.*, 53749, 1889 ; *Zeit. angew. Chem.*, **3**. 2674, 1890 ; M. Salinger, *Zur Kenntnis der Manganite*, Berlin, 14, 1902 ; *Zeit. anorg. Chem.*, **33**. 322, 1903 ; M. N. Chakravarti and N. R. Dhar, *Journ. Phys. Chem.*, **31**. 997, 1927 ; S. C. Chatterji and N. R. Dhar, *Koll. Zeit.*, **33**. 18, 1923 ; P. B. Sarkar and N. R. Dhar, *Zeit. anorg. Chem.*, **121**. 135, 1922 ; A. S. Cocosinschy, *ib.*, **186**. 176, 1930 ; **189**. 283, 1930 ; M. Gröger, *ib.*, **44**. 452, 1905 ; A. Rosenheim and H. Itzig, *ib.*, **16**. 76, 1898 ; C. Friedheim and M. Samelson, *ib.*, **24**. 65, 1900 ; A. Rosenheim, *Zeit. Elektrochem.*, **17**. 698, 1911 ; W. Biltz, *Gött. Nachr.*, 189, 1930 ; *Ueber die manganige Säure*, Berlin, 1930 ; C. Friedheim and O. Allemann, *Mitt. Naturf. Ges. Bern.*, 23, 1904 ; O. Allemann, *Ueber Permanganmolybdate*, Bern, 1904 ; H. Struve, *Bull. Acad. St. Petersburg*, (1), **2**. 142, 1854 ; *Journ. prakt. Chem.*, (1), **61**. 449, 1854 ; R. D. Hall, *Journ. Amer. Chem. Soc.*, **29**. 692, 1907 ; A. Roger and E. F. Smith, *ib.*, **26**. 1474, 1904 ; J. A. Krenner, *Zeit. Kryst.*, **43**. 473, 1907 ; J. Loczka, *ib.*, **43**. 571, 1907 ; L. Pauling and M. D. Shappell, *ib.*, **75**. 128, 1930 ; E. E. Fairbanks, *Amer. Min.*, **8**. 209, 1923 ; F. Zambonini and V. Caglioti, *Periodico Min. Roma*, **2**. 73, 1931 ; *Compt. Rend.*, **192**. 750, 1931 ; H. Corti, *Anal. Soc. Quim. Argentina*, **19**. 109, 1931.

§ 13. Manganese Trioxide and the Manganates

In 1659, J. R. Glauber [1] melted magnesia (*i.e.* pyrolusite) with fixed alkali, and obtained a mass which when dissolved in water produced a most delicate purple-coloured liquid which slowly changed its colour to blue, red, and green. The anonymous *Schlüssel zu dem Cabinet der geheimen Schatzkammer des Natur*, attributed to J. Waiz, said that when Piedmont magnesia (pyrolusite) is fused with saltpetre and the mass treated with water, a green soln. is obtained, which becomes blue, violet, and finally rose-red. Here the colours are said to appear in the reverse order to that reported by J. R. Glauber. J. H. Pott made a similar observation to that reported by J. Waiz, who was right, for C. W. Scheele observed that when manganese dioxide is fused with potassium nitrate, an intense green mass is produced, which he regarded as a salt of a manganiferous acid. It was also observed that the mass forms a green soln. with water, which when much diluted, or when allowed to stand for some time, acquires a red colour. Accordingly, C. W. Scheele named this salt *mineralisches Chamäleon*. A. F. de Fourcroy made a superficial attempt to find the composition of mineral chamaleon, and C. F. Bucholz regarded the red soln. as being formed by the oxidation of the green soln. by atmospheric oxygen. M. E. Chevreul showed that the alkali nitrate can be replaced by non-oxidizing alkali hydroxide or carbonate, as in J. R. Glauber's experiment, but P. F. Chevillot and W. F. Edwards found that the oxygen necessary for the production of the green salt is absorbed from the air. G. Forchhammer, H. Aschoff, A. Béchamp, N. Beketoff, and E. Mitscherlich then showed that the green salt, soluble in water, is the potassium salt of a dibasic acid, *manganic acid*, H_2MnO_4, where the manganese is sexavalent, and that the salt is a *manganate*, K_2MnO_4. H. Aschoff, and E. Mitscherlich also showed that the violet salt is not an acid salt of manganic acid, but represents a more highly oxidized monobasic acid, *permanganic acid*, $HMnO_4$, where the manganese is septavalent, and the salt is a *permanganate*, $KMnO_4$.

According to B. Franke,[2] when the green soln. obtained by dissolving potassium permanganate in sulphuric acid is exposed to direct sunlight in the presence of moist air, the manganese heptoxide—*vide infra*—which is formed separates and then decomposes into manganese dioxide, **manganese trioxide,** MnO_3, and a blue gas giving certain reactions of ozone, but differing from that substance in being decomposed at 150°, and in being soluble in conc. sulphuric acid. He obtained the blue gas by the action of moist air on the sulphuric acid soln. of potassium permanganate, and regarded it as **manganese tetroxide,** MnO_4, which he supposed was formed in accord with $(MnO_3)_2SO_4+H_2O=MnO_4+MnO_3+H_2SO_4$. It is said that the blue gas is best made by passing a current of carbon dioxide, sat. with moisture, on to the surface of the olive-green liquid, and leading the escaping gas through two U-tubes, one of which is empty and the other filled with calcium chloride. The manganese trioxide collects in the first tube, while the second retains the tetroxide. The tetroxide is said to be more volatile than the trioxide, to be more blue in colour, to be less readily attacked by water, and to be decomposed by the action of sulphuric acid and ether. T. E. Thorpe and F. J. Hambly were unable to obtain the slightest indication of the blue, gaseous tetroxide under these conditions.

According to B. Franke, manganese trioxide is formed as a dark red mass when the green soln. of manganese oxysulphate is distilled in the presence of water. It is best prepared by dropping 20 c.c. of the green soln. obtained by dissolving 5 to 8 grms. of potassium manganate in 100 c.c. of conc. sulphuric acid into a small bulb containing 10 grms. of dehydrated sodium carbonate : $(MnO_3)_2SO_4+Na_2CO_3$ $=Na_2SO_4+CO_2+O+2MnO_3$. The red fumes are passed into a U-tube surrounded by a freezing mixture, in which they condense to a dark red, amorphous mass. T. E. Thorpe and F. J. Hambly recommended filling the U-tube with fragments of broken glass, to prevent the pink fumes being carried along with the escaping carbon dioxide. The freezing mixture of ice and salt is necessary to retard the decomposition of the condensed product, since at ordinary temp. it gradually loses oxygen and is converted into manganese dioxide. The curious behaviour of the pink fume led them to conclude that it was really an extremely finely-divided solid. It floats in the air like a cloud of sal-ammoniac or sulphur trioxide, and like these substances may, if suspended in a sufficiently large volume of air or carbon dioxide, be passed through water practically unabsorbed. The trioxide is red in thin layers, and dull dark red, almost black, in thick layers. B. Franke said that the trioxide has a peculiar odour, and volatilizes at about 50° as a violet vapour, with partial decomposition into crystalline manganese dioxide and oxygen ; this decomposition is complete when the substance is heated. It is sparingly soluble in water ; a litre of water containing 50 mgrms. of the substance has an intense red colour. When the vapour is passed into aq. soda or potash, alkaline manganates are produced. The reaction employed for detecting small quantities of manganese by means of potassium chlorate depends on the formation of the trioxide. According to T. E. Thorpe and F. J. Hambly, when manganese trioxide is absorbed by dil. sulphuric acid, a clear pink or reddish-pink soln. is obtained, in which the manganese and oxygen are in the ratio of 1 to 3. There is no evidence to show that this soln. contains free manganic acid. If the substance were decomposed as in the aq. soln., the ratio of O to Mn would be as 1 to 3, provided that all the manganese were retained in soln. When manganese trioxide is dissolved in conc. sulphuric acid, it forms a soln. of the same colour as that obtained on dissolving potassium permanganate in oil of vitriol. This may be regarded as additional evidence for the existence of $(MnO_3)_2SO_4$. The substance is soluble in caustic potash, and gives a green soln. similar to that of potassium manganate. Manganese trioxide gives the reactions for ozone : it affects mercury and liberates iodine from potassium iodide. It blackens silver, but the stain can be shown to be due to manganese dioxide. B. Franke said that when manganese trioxide is passed into water, the manganic acid, H_2MnO_4, which is formed is very unstable and decomposes into manganese dioxide, oxygen, and a dark red soln. of permanganic acid. T. E. Thorpe and F. J. Hambly represented the reaction : $3MnO_3+H_2O=2HMnO_4+MnO_2$. Analyses by B. Franke, and by T. E. Thorpe and F. J. Hambly agree with the formula MnO_3.

F. R. Lankshear found that the dark red, amorphous solid supposed to be manganese trioxide has a m.p. —6°, and its analysis corresponds with a ratio of permanganate to manganese dioxide of 4·8 : 1. It is inferred that the alleged manganese trioxide gas is nothing more than an impure permanganic acid. According to S. R. Scholes, the violet tint of manganese glass is due to compounds of manganic oxides, because the pink soln. obtained by extracting the glass with hydrofluoric and 30 per cent. sulphuric acids gives a light brown precipitate when diluted with water.

E. Mitscherlich [3] prepared **potassium manganate,** K_2MnO_4, by heating a mixture of any oxide of manganese with potassium hydroxide, carbonate and nitrate, or a mixture of potassium hydroxide and chlorate. In the one case, with the hydroxide or carbonate, the oxygen is derived from atm. air, and in the other case, from the nitrate or chlorate. The green soln. obtained by dissolving the cold cake in water is filtered and evaporated in vacuo over sulphuric acid. Green crystals of potassium manganate are formed. A similar process was used by P. F. Chevillot and W. F. Edwards, H. McCormack, A. Béchamp, N. Beketoff, R. W. Stimson, and C. Zwenger. According to P. F. Chevillot and W. F. Edwards, a mixture of 44 parts of manganese dioxide with four times its weight of potassium hydroxide absorbs 9·4 to 10·4 parts of oxygen when it is heated in oxygen gas. A. Béchamp found that the absorption of oxygen begins at a dull red-heat, and then proceeds rapidly until completed. According to E. Mitscherlich, if manganese dioxide is heated with the alkali hydroxide or carbonate in a closed vessel, the oxygen required for the formation of the manganate is derived from the manganese dioxide : $3MnO_2$ $=Mn_2O_3+MnO_3$. N. Beketoff observed that the splitting of manganese dioxide into oxide and acid, in the presence of potassium hydroxide, begins at 130°, and the absorption of oxygen proceeds at a higher temp. The lower manganese oxides begin to take up oxygen at a dull red-heat to form the manganate. P. F. Chevillot and W. F. Edwards said that if a mixture of alkali hydroxide and manganese dioxide is heated in nitrogen, no manganate is produced, but C. W. Eliot and F. H. Storer showed that the potassium manganate is formed at about 180° in nitrogen, and at a red-heat it oxidizes some nitrogen to nitrogen oxide. According to P. F. Chevillot and W. F. Edwards, and P. Thénard, potassium permanganate at 240° is reduced to manganate. A. F. Jolles obtained potassium manganate by heating eq. amounts of potassium permanganate and potassium hydroxide at a dull red-heat; G. Kassner and H. Keller said that the manganate is not formed if eq. quantities are used : it is necessary to have 1·5 to 2·0 times more potassium hydroxide. The permanganate should be dissolved in the alkali-lye and the soln. stirred while the water is evaporated, and then the mixture heated to 200° or 300°. According to R. Luboldt, P. Thénard, and H. Aschoff, if an alkaline soln. of permanganate be treated with a feeble reducing agent, or if it is boiled with potash-lye of sp. gr. 1·33, or heated to 130°, a dark green soln. of the manganate is formed and the soln. becomes green. Oxygen is given off when the permanganate is heated with the alkali-lye.

According to P. Askenasy and S. Klonowsky, the potassium manganate of the highest degree of oxidation which can be prepared by the oxidation of an excess of the lower oxides of manganese in the presence of potassium hydroxide, in an atm. containing oxygen, contains a small excess of the alkali. The results obtained by starting with manganese dioxide or with manganese hemitrioxide are almost the same. In both cases the quantity of manganate formed increases as the temp. rises up to the point at which the press. of the oxygen is equal to the dissociation press. of the manganate ; at higher temp. the manganate is, of course, decomposed. In air the best temp. is about 600° ; in oxygen it is near 700°. Using an excess of manganese oxide, some 60 to 65 per cent. of the potassium hydroxide employed is converted into manganate under the best conditions. Prolonging the time of heating beyond one hour does not materially increase the yield. The absorption of oxygen takes place at 240°, but more slowly than at higher temp. According to H. I. Schlesinger and co-workers, when finely-powdered manganese dioxide is heated with potassium hydroxide in a current of air, complete oxidation is frequently attained only by re-moistening and re-heating the mixture. The yield of potassium manganate varies with the proportion of potassium hydroxide present; at about 300° practically all the manganese dioxide is converted into manganate when two mols. of potassium hydroxide are used for each mol. of manganese dioxide. Mangani-manganates are not formed under these conditions, but larger amounts of potassium hydroxide cause the manganate to decompose into manganimanganate. The yield of manganate is lowered when sodium hydroxide is used in place of potassium hydroxide. O. Sackur fused in a current of air manganese dioxide with an excess of alkali carbonate sufficient to hold the manganese compound in soln., and so permit of full oxidation. The absorption of oxygen by the fused mass ceases as soon as the at. proportion of available oxygen to manganese is 1·6. This value is independent of the conc. of the manganese in the fused mass, and of the press. of the oxygen above the fusion. Consequently, there is no state of equilibrium between the different stages of the oxidation of manganese in the fusion and the oxygen in the gaseous phase, but a definite compound is formed with $Mn : O = 1 : 2·6$, or Mn_5O_{13}—that is, $2MnO_2.3MnO_3$. The fused cake is dark green, and with a little water, or alkaline soln., it forms a dark green soln. of manganate and a dark brown precipitate of manganese dioxide; while with much water, or dil. acids, it forms a violet soln. of permanganate and manganese dioxide. A similar result was obtained when the potassium carbonate was replaced by potassium hydroxide, but with sodium carbonate the atomic proportion of available oxygen to manganese was 1·5 instead of 1·6. A mixture of potassium and sodium carbonates in equal proportions gave the same proportions as with sodium carbonate alone. The fusions containing sodium salts were grass-green in colour, as opposed to the dark green of the potassium compound. Calcium oxide gave similar results to sodium carbonate. When oxygen is absorbed by the fusion, carbon dioxide is simultaneously evolved, as shown by the equation : $5MnO_2 + \frac{3}{2}O_2 + nK_2CO_3 = Mn_5O_{13}, nK_2O + nCO_2$. Unless oxygen is passed for a considerable time after the evolution of carbon dioxide has ceased, the compound formed in the fusion is $5M_2O.Mn_5O_{12}$, when M is either K or Na. When oxidation is complete, the ratio of the lowering of the m.p. of alkali carbonate to the concentration of the manganese in gram-atoms per 1000 grms. of fusion is constant, and equal to 43 with potassium carbonate and 35 with sodium carbonate. Hence, the solute in each case contains one gram-atom of manganese per mol, so that their formulæ are $K_2MnO_{3·6}$ and $Na_2MnO_{3·5}$, respectively. There is no very definite relation between the oxygen absorbed and the carbon dioxide evolved, but the results agree with the assumption that $8K_2O.Mn_5O_{13}$ is formed, in accord with $5Mn_2O_3 + 10K_2CO_3 + 11O = 10CO_2 + 2(5K_2O.Mn_5O_{13})$, and $2(5K_2O.Mn_5O_{13}) + 6K_2CO_3 = 6CO_2 + 2(8K_2O.Mn_5O_{13})$. At 900° to 950° manganic oxide and potassium carbonate interact in an atm. of nitrogen in accord with $19Mn_2O_3 + 5K_2CO_3 = 5K_2O.Mn_5O_{13} + 11Mn_3O_4 + 5CO_2$. The compound $8K_2O.Mn_5O_{13}$ may be regarded as an additive compound of quadri- and sexivalent manganese, namely, potassium manganitomanganate, $2(K_2O.MnO_2).3(2K_2O.MnO_3)$. With sodium carbonate in place of potassium carbonate, sodium manganitomanganate, $4Na_2O.Mn_2O_5$, or $(2Na_2O.MnO_2)(2Na_2O.MnO_3)$, is formed, with the permanganite $2Na_2O.MnO_2$ as an intermediate product. F. Bahr and O. Sackur measured the dissociation press. of fused mixtures of manganese dioxide and potassium hydroxide, and obtained the isothermal dissociation curve, Fig. 40, at 661°, for potassium permanganate. The results show that the final product of dissociation is potassium permanganite, K_2MnO_3, which has no dissociation press., even at 1000°. In potassium manganate the atomic proportion of available oxygen to manganese is 1 : 1·6, corresponding with the composition $3K_2MnO_4.2K_2MnO_3$. The formation of products further saturated than this is attributed to supersaturation. This degree of oxygen corresponds with the compound $Mn_5O_{13}.8K_2O$. V. Auger confirmed the existence of $5K_2O.Mn_5O_{13}$ and $2Na_2O.Mn_2O_5$, and he isolated the sodium salt by heating in a silver crucible 10 grms. of potassium permanganate with 100 grms. of sodium hydroxide and 20 c.c. of water.   The crystalline mass was washed with a conc. soln. of sodium hydroxide, when the compound was obtained as a micro-crystalline, bluish-green powder, which underwent immediate decomposition on treatment with water.   For O. Dieffenbach's electrolytic process, *vide infra*, potassium permanganate.

E. Mitscherlich's analysis agreed with the formula K_2MnO_4 ; and R. T. Colgate regarded the substance as having the constitution :

$$K\ K$$
$$KO.O.Mn.O.\overset{.}{O}.\overset{.}{O}.O.Mn.O.OK$$
$$KO.O.Mn.\overset{.}{O}.\overset{.}{O}.\overset{.}{O}.\overset{.}{O}.Mn.O.OK$$
$$\overset{.}{K}\ \overset{.}{K}$$

H. Lessheim and co-workers discussed the constitution of the manganates. E. Mitscherlich said that potassium manganate furnishes green crystals ; C. Zwenger, that the crystals have a brownish-red tinge, and are not green ; while H. Aschoff added that the smallest crystals are so nearly black as to appear to be opaque. E. Mitscherlich found the axial ratios of the rhombic crystals to be $a : b : c$ $=0.5638 : 1 : 0.7570$; and added that the crystals are isomorphous with those of potassium sulphate, selenate, and chromate.   The subject was discussed by J. W. Retgers ; and the effect of manganates on the crystallization of sodium chlorate, by H. E. Buckley.   F. Bahr and O. Sackur found that when potassium manganate is heated, it dissociates into potassium permanganite and oxygen, a reaction which has the following dissociation pressures, p mm. of mercury :

	507°	516°	543°	572°	610°	629°	653°	667°
p .	. 11	15·1	27·3	52·6	138·5	221	381·5	532

P. Askenasy and S. Klonowsky obtained rather higher results, namely, 40 mm. at 548°, and 763 mm. at 661°, Fig. 52.   If the oxygen is pumped off, the dissociation press. remains constant until about two-thirds of the oxygen given by the equation $K_2MnO_4=K_2MnO_3+\frac{1}{2}O_2$ has been expelled.   Afterwards the press. of the oxygen falls.   This is taken to show that solid soln. are formed as indicated above.   E. Franke gave for the conductivity, λ, of soln. of an eq. of manganic acid in v litres of water at 25° :

	64	128	256	512	1024
v .	. 64	128	256	512	1024
λ .	. 345·2	346·6	346·1	343·9	342·8

The acid was here obviously unstable and decomposing.   According to O. Sackur and W. Taegener, and O. Sackur, the normal potential for the electrochemical change permanganate to manganate : $MnO_4'=MnO_4''$ $+F$ is $E_H=0.61$ volt, when deduced from the e.m.f. of the cell $Pt : KMnO_4,K_2MnO_4,KOH : 0.8N\text{-}KOH,HgO :$ Hg, at room temp.   This value is independent of the acidity or alkalinity of the soln. ; but it changes with the conc. of manganate and permanganate in accord with $E_H=0.61+0.058\{\log[MnO_4']-0.058\log[MnO_4'']\}$ volt.   The normal potential of the electrochemical change $MnO_4''+2H_2O=MnO_2+4OH'+2F$ is nearly $E_H=0.50$ volt for normal soln. of alkali hydroxide. This value is calculated from measurements of the e.m.f. of a cell of the type $(Pt) : K_2MnO_4,KOH :$ $0.8N\text{-}KOH,HgO : Hg.$ Since with a high concentration of alkali-lye, the separation of manganese dioxide may be attended with the evolution of oxygen, a film of man-

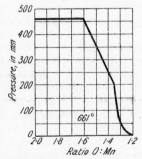

FIG. 52.—Isothermal Dissociation Curve of Potassium Manganate.

ganese dioxide is deposited on the platinum.   The variation in the potential with changes in the concentrations of potassium manganate and alkali hydroxide is represented by $E_H=0.50+0.029\{\log[MnO_4'']-0.116\log[OH']\}$ volt.   The oxidation potential also increases very much with a decrease in the alkalinity of the soln.   For a neutral molar soln. of MnO_4'', $E_H=1.31$ volts, and for a normal soln., $E_H=2.12$

volts. The soln. are not stable, and the potential for change into MnO_2 exceeds that for the change into permanganate, so that one-third of the manganate changes to manganese dioxide : $MnO_4''+4H^{\cdot}=MnO_2+2H_2O+2F$, for which $E_H=2.12$ volts, and two-thirds to permanganate : $2MnO_4''+2F=2MnO_4'$, for which $E_H=0.61$ volt. The free energy of this transformation with normal concentrations is $2F(2.12-0.61)$ volt, or $3.02F$ joules, or 69.6 Cals. The free energy changes with variations in the concentration of the acid, permanganate, and manganate in accord with $Q=69,600 +5320 \log[H^{\cdot}]+0.3990 \log[MnO_4'']-2660 \log[MnO_4']$ cals. The tendency of the manganate to change into permanganate thus increases markedly with an increase in the acidity of the soln. The change can occur even in feebly alkaline soln. O. Sackur and W. Taegener also calculated that for N-KOH soln. the dissociation press. for the change $2K_2MnO_4+2H_2O \rightleftharpoons 2MnO_2+4KOH+O_2$ is nearly 10^6 atm. C. E. Ruby gave for the molar electrode potentials at 25°, with solid manganese dioxide : $MnO_2+4OH'+2\oplus=MnO_4''+2H_2O$, -0.664 volt ; $MnO_2+4OH'+3\oplus =MnO_4'+2H_2O$, -0.647 volt ; and $MnO_2+2H_2O+3\oplus=MnO_4'+4H^{\cdot}$, -1.757 volts. C. E. Ruby also found the equilibrium constant $K=[MnO_4']^2[OH']^4/[MnO_4'']^3$ for the reaction $3K_2MnO_4+2H_2O=MnO_{2solid}+2KMnO_4+4KOH$ to be 53 at 45°. The corresponding decrease of free energy is 10,500 joules, and the e.m.f. of a cell in which it occurs is 0.054 volt. H. I. Schlesinger and H. B. Siems found the equilibrium constant for the reaction between manganate and permanganate ions $K=[MnO_4']^2[OH']^4/[MnO_4'']^3$ to be $K=16$ at 25°.

The manganates are usually supposed to contain sexivalent manganese, like the isomorphous sulphates and selenates. C. F. Schönbein regarded them as complex salts of manganese dioxide and a dioxide of an electropositive metal—*e.g.* Na_2O_2, K_2O_2, BaO_2, etc. P. F. Chevillot and W. F. Edwards observed that potassium manganate forms a green soln. with **water,** but the colour rapidly changes through blue, violet, and purple to carmine-red, in proportion as the excess of potassium hydroxide is removed from the salt by water—especially if the water is hot, or if a large proportion is present. E. Mitscherlich said that the salt is decomposed by water, yielding a red soln. of the permanganate and a deposit of hydrated manganese dioxide : $3K_2MnO_4+2H_2O=2KMnO_4+4KOH+MnO_2$. C. Fromherz added that a soln. of the salt in air-free water kept in air-tight bottles, completely filled, turns red. This shows that the affinity of water for the alkali is sufficient to decompose the salt. G. Forchhammer, and C. Fromherz noted the precipitation of hydrated manganese dioxide when the green soln. of manganate passes into a red soln. of the permanganate. The reaction was studied by H. Aschoff, and E. Mulder added that on account of the formation of potassium hydroxide, the conversion of manganate to permanganate is not complete. E. Mitscherlich observed that potassium manganate dissolves without decomposition in an aq. soln. of **potassium hydroxide,** forming a green soln., from which the salt can be separated by evaporation in vacuo. The salt so obtained is contaminated with alkali hydroxide. If the soln. in alkali-lye be exposed to air, the hydroxide is converted into carbonate, and the green manganate then changes to red permanganate and hydrated manganese dioxide. J. W. Retgers represented the reaction with a soln. of alkali hydroxide: $15K_2MnO_4+9H_2O=10KMnO_4+K_2O.5MnO_2+18KOH$—*vide supra* for the observations of P. Askenasy and S. Klonowsky, and O. Sackur. Owing to the instability of soln. of potassium manganate in water, the solubility of the salt in water cannot be satisfactorily determined ; but being stable in alkaline soln., solubility measurements for different concentrations of potassium hydroxide were made by O. Sackur and W. Taegener. The following is a selection from their results, expressed in S mols of K_2MnO_4 per litre of the alkaline soln. :

		0°	10°	20°	30°	40°	50°	60°	70°	80°
	2N-KOH	0.907	1.013	—	1.252	—	—	—	—	—
	4N-KOH	0.554	—	—	0.772	0.852	0.938	1.003	1.074	1.143
S	6N-KOH	0.155	—	0.224	0.303	0.362	—	0.469	0.528	0.587
	8N-KOH	0.063	0.070	—	0.096	0.119	0.142	0.167	0.196	0.222
	10N-KOH	0.0145	0.0152	—	0.0215	0.0305	0.0462	0.062	0.070	0.083

This shows that the solubility of the salt in dil. alkali-lye is very great ; it increases only a little with a rise of temp., and it decreases markedly with increasing concentration of the lye. According to C. M. Tessié du Motay, the salt is decomposed when heated in water vapour: $2K_2MnO_4+2H_2O=4KOH+Mn_2O_3+3O$, and the reaction has been utilized for the preparation of oxygen by H. Vogel, H. Weppen, M. Dutremblay and M. Lugan, R. D. Bowman, J. H. Parkinson, A. F. S. Bellone, G. Webb and G. H. Rayner, F. Fanta, and C. M. Tessié du Motay and C. R. M. de Maréchal. The original manganate is regenerated by heating the mixture in air. E. Mitscherlich, and P. F. Chevillot and W. F. Edwards noticed that the presence of **acids**—carbonic acid from the air, sulphuric acid, nitric acid, or other non-reducing acid—accelerates the passage of the manganate to permanganate in soln., and G. Forchhammer observed that the change is always accompanied by the deposition of hydrated manganese dioxide. H. Aschoff represented the reaction : $3K_2MnO_4 +2CO_2=2KMnO_4+MnO_2+2K_2CO_3$. This is not in agreement with T. L. Phipson's assumption that the transformation is simply an effect of the withdrawal of alkali from the permanganate. E. Mitscherlich briefly mentioned a **potassium dihydrotetramanganate,** $3K_2MnO_4.H_2MnO_4$, which he considered to be isomorphous with the salt $3K_2SO_4.H_2SO_4$.

G. Städeler found that **chlorine** transforms alkali manganate into permanganate : $2K_2MnO_4+Cl_2=2KCl+2KMnO_4$. Chlorine is evolved when a manganate is treated with conc. **hydrochloric acid,** and, according to J. W. Retgers, some manganese trichloride (q.v.) is formed. J. B. Senderens observed that when the alkali manganate soln. is boiled with **sulphur** a thiosulphate is formed, and the reaction can be represented : $2K_2MnO_4 + 5S + 2H_2O = Mn_2O_3.H_2O + 2K_2S_2O_3 + H_2S$. C. F. Schönbein found that a soln. of a manganate is reduced and decolorized by **hydrogen sulphide,** forming manganous sulphide and sulphur ; and similarly with **sulphur dioxide.** H. Aschoff found that conc. **sulphuric acid** forms anhydrous manganese heptoxide and dioxide. E. Mitscherlich added that when a soln. of potassium manganate is boiled with sulphuric acid—*vide supra*—hydrated manganese dioxide is precipitated and oxygen is evolved ; L. Kahlenberg and W. J. Trautmann observed no reaction when a mixture of powdered **silicon** and the manganate is heated over a bunsen burner, but a reaction occurs at a higher temp. The manganates detonate on red-hot **carbon.** P. F. Chevillot and W. F. Edwards noted that the presence of **ammonium carbonate** in soln. favours the transformation of manganate to permanganate ; and J. W. Retgers, L. Santi, and G. Doyer van Cleef represented the reaction with **ammonium salts** in the presence of ammonia by the equation : $3K_2MnO_4+4NH_4Cl=2KMnO_4+MnO_2+4KCl+4NH_3+2H_2O$. E. Mitscherlich observed that the manganate soln. behaves with boiling **nitric acid** as it does with sulphuric acid : $K_2MnO_4+2HNO_3=2KNO_3+MnO_2+H_2O+O$. As indicated above, **carbon dioxide** in soln. favours the transformation of manganate to permanganate. W. Müller found that when the salt is heated to redness in the vapour of **carbon disulphide,** the reaction can be represented : $K_2MnO_4+2CS_2 =K_2S_3+MnS+2CO_2$. J. Holluta studied the action of manganates on **formic acid,** and on **formaldehyde.** A. F. Jolles found that a soln. of the manganate furnishes insoluble compounds with some of the **metal oxides,** e.g. cobalt oxide. According to A. Gawalowsky, the addition of a soln. of **ferric chloride** to a soln. of a manganate furnishes oxygen and a soln. of the so-called *liquor ferri oxychlorati* ; while with **copper sulphate,** oxygen is developed and a whitish-grey precipitate, which is oxidized by nitric acid to copper sulphate, is formed. J. W. Retgers found that **thallous salts** are oxidized to thallic salts by potassium manganate. J. W. Retgers prepared mixed crystals of potassium manganate with **rubidium manganate,** Rb_2MnO_4, or with **cæsium manganate,** Cs_2MnO_4, showing that both salts are isomorphous with potassium manganate. If a neutral soln. of potassium manganate be treated with ammonium sulphate, the green soln. immediately reddens, as indicated above. An alkaline soln. of manganate decomposes the ammonium salt. Hence, **ammonium manganate,** $(NH_4)_2MnO_4$, could not be prepared.

P. F. Chevillot and W. F. Edwards prepared **sodium manganate**, Na_2MnO_4, by heating to redness a mixture of manganese dioxide and sodium hydroxide in air ; J. G. Gentele obtained the manganate by an analogous process at a dull red-heat ; and C. M. Tessié du Motay and C. R. M. de Maréchal worked the process at 400°. E. Bothe heated to redness manganese dioxide with three times its weight of sodium carbonate in a current of air and obtained a 74·6 per cent. yield of sodium manganate. F. Wöhler said that no sodium manganate is formed when a mixture of manganese dioxide and sodium nitrate is heated out of contact with air ; nor did C. M. Bradbury succeed in preparing sodium manganate by this process. V. Auger said that the salt is easily obtained by heating sodium permanganate in a silver or platinum dish with twice the calculated quantity of sodium hydroxide ; oxygen begins to form at 115°, and the reaction is complete at 125°. On cooling, sodium manganate separates in black crystals with a violet reflex. J. W. Retgers said that sodium manganate is probably not isomorphous with sodium sulphate and selenate. W. G. Mixter gave for the heat of formation $(Mn,3O,Na_2O)=169\cdot0$ Cals. ; and $(MnO_2,O,Na_2O)=49\cdot4$ Cals. E. Mitscherlich said that the salt is too soluble to allow it to be purified by crystallization from aq. soln., but J. G. Gentele said that if it be boiled with water, it forms a green soln. which can be filtered through powdered glass, and slowly cooled to 0°, when a pale green mass of radiating crystals of the *decahydrate*, $Na_2MnO_4.10H_2O$, is formed. It is dried on a porous tile. When dissolved in water, the green salt is partially decomposed. R. Funk could not prepare this green hydrate, but he always obtained crystals of sodium carbonate coloured dark green by the mother-liquor. V. Auger, however, found that when an aq. soln. of the salt is cooled by a freezing mixture, the decahydrate appears in black needles of m.p. 17°, and the crystals appear to be isomorphous with those of sodium chromate. A soln. containing an excess of sodium hydroxide deposits black prisms of the *hexahydrate*, $Na_2MnO_4.6H_2O$; and a soln. in 5 per cent. sodium hydroxide soln. deposits black prisms of the *tetrahydrate*, $Na_2MnO_4.4H_2O$, when it is concentrated by evaporation. The salt behaves towards steam as in the case of potassium manganate, and can be used for the preparation of oxygen in a similar way (*q.v.*). J. W. Retgers found that if powdered manganese dioxide be melted at a white-heat with a mixture of lithium carbonate and nitrate, the manganese dioxide does not dissolve as it does in the case of the sodium salts, and consequently he could not prepare **lithium manganate**, Li_2MnO_4—*vide infra*. A. Gawalowsky found that copper sulphate decomposes a soln. of potassium manganate—*vide supra* —and a **copper manganate**, $CuMnO_4$, has not been prepared. A. F. Jolles obtained the basic salt **copper dihydroxymanganate**, $(CuOH)_2MnO_4$, by the action of an excess of ammonia and potassium manganate on a soln. of a copper salt : $2Cu(NH_3OH)_2+K_2MnO_4=4NH_3+2KOH+(CuOH)_2MnO_4$. J. W. Retgers said that **silver manganate**, Ag_2MnO_4, appears *nicht existenzfähig zu sein*. Silver oxide seems to be too feeble a base to unite with manganic acid. A neutral soln. of silver nitrate colours red a green neutral soln. of sodium manganate, and silver permanganate is deposited. A similar reaction occurs when an ammoniacal soln. of silver nitrate and a green ammoniacal soln. of potassium manganate are mixed.

According to P. F. Chevillot and W. F. Edwards, if equal parts by weight of baryta and manganese dioxide be heated to bright redness in air, oxygen is absorbed, and a dark green insoluble mass of **barium manganate**, $BaMnO_4$, is formed. H. Abich used barium carbonate in place of baryta, and employed a higher temp. ; he thus obtained a dark green crystalline mass. G. Forchhammer, and C. Fromherz heated the manganese dioxide with barium nitrate, and washed the product with water ; they thus obtained an insoluble emerald-green powder. J. A. Hedvall and N. von Zweigbergk observed that barium dioxide begins to react at 200° with manganous oxide : $2BaO_2+MnO=BaMnO_4+BaO$; at about 140° with manganosic oxide : $5BaO_2+Mn_3O_4=3BaMnO_4+2BaO$; at 250° with manganic oxide : $3BaO_2+Mn_2O_3=2BaMnO_4+BaO$; and between 350° and 550° with manganese dioxide : $BaO_2+MnO_2=BaMnO_4$. A. Safarik added manganese dioxide to a soln. of barium hydroxide in molten potassium chlorate, and washed the product with boiling water. E. Fleischer heated a mixture of barium permanganate and barium oxide; E. Donath, a mixture of manganese dioxide or carbonate with barium dioxide; and C. Huggenberg, a mixture of manganese dioxide, barium hydroxide. and sodium nitrate. According to W. Lindner, when a soln. of potassium permanganate and barium chloride is boiled, barium manganate is precipitated, and a similar process was used by E. Fleischer, A. F. Jolles, and R. Böttger. C. Fromherz obtained the manganate by treating manganic acid with an excess of baryta-water; and E. Mitscherlich, and H. Aschoff obtained it by allowing a mixed soln. of barium permanganate and hydroxide to stand for some time. A. Gorgeu obtained barium manganate by reducing a soln. of the permanganate with hydrogen dioxide. G. Kassner and H. Keller found that barium manganate forms a permanganite when treated with hydrogen dioxide, but the manganate is re-formed when the permanganite is calcined in air. According to H. I. Schlesinger and H. B. Siems, barium manganate may be prepared by the cautious addition of a sat. soln. of potassium permanganate to a boiling sat. soln. of barium hydroxide, carbon dioxide being excluded. The bluish-black barium manganate is washed by decantation, separated, dried at 110°, and then in a vacuum desiccator over phosphorus pentoxide. It is decomposed by phosphoric acid: $3BaMnO_4 + 4H_3PO_4 = 2Ba(H_2PO_4)_2 + Ba(MnO_4)_2 + MnO_2 + 2H_2O$. The solubility product determined from the equilibrium conc. in $BaMnO_4 + K_2CO_3 \rightleftharpoons BaCO_3 + K_2MnO_4$ is $2 \cdot 6 \times 10^{-10}$, assuming that under equilibrium conditions potassium carbonate and manganate are equally ionized. E. Wedekind gave $10 \cdot 1 \times 10^{-6}$ for the magnetic susceptibility of barium manganate. A. Safarik found the green powder or acicular to tabular crystals of barium manganate to have the sp. gr. 4·85 at 23°. E. Wedekind and C. Horst examined the magnetic susceptibility. Barium manganate is insoluble in water, and decomposed by acids. G. Kassner used barium manganate for bleaching purposes, and re-calcined the resulting barium permanganite to re-form the manganate.

A. Rosenstiehl heated to redness an intimate mixture of manganese dioxide, barium nitrate, and barium hydroxide in the proportions 1 : 4 : 6 to 8, washed the product with boiling water, then with cold water, and obtained an emerald-green powder consisting of $3BaO.2MnO_3$. It is stable when dry, but is decomposed when moist and exposed to air. According to F. Rose, the product has been used as a pigment—*Cassel's green, manganese-green,* and *Rosenstiehl's green.* L. Schad, C. Vogt, and A. Buntrock used china clay or barytes as a component of the mixture used for preparing the pigment, in order to make the mass less fusible during calcination. According to G. Kassner and H. Keller, and A. F. Jolles, when the pigment is prepared in the wet way, its composition is $BaMnO_4$ with less than a mol. of water; while V. Auger and M. Billy represented it by the formula $Ba_3(MnO_4)_2.H_2O$.

P. F. Chevillot and W. F. Edwards prepared a **strontium manganate** by calcining a mixture of manganese dioxide and strontia. The pale green powder is insoluble in water. C. Fromherz obtained an analogous product by calcining a mixture of manganese dioxide with twice its weight of strontium nitrate—*vide infra.* V. Auger and M. Billy said that the **calcium manganate,** $CaMnO_4$, obtained by P. F. Chevillot and W. F. Edwards, G. Forchhammer, C. Fromherz, and E. Delaurier by calcining an intimate mixture of manganese dioxide and slaked lime or chalk is impure. It is insoluble in water, and gives off oxygen when heated—*vide infra.* A. F. Jolles obtained a basic **cadmium manganate,** $CdMnO_4.H_2O$, by the action of an excess of ammonia and potassium manganate on a soln. of a cadmium salt. According to A. Gawalowsky, **mercurous manganate** is probably formed as a black precipitate when an alkali permanganate in an alkaline soln. is treated with mercury; W. Kirchmann said that mercurous and mercuric oxides are formed; and D. Borar represented the reaction: $2KMnO_4 + 3Hg + H_2O = 3HgO + 2MnO_2 + 2KOH$. J. W. Retgers could not prepare **thallous manganate** on account of the oxidation of thallous to thallic salts by potassium manganate. A. F. Jolles obtained **lead manganate,** $PbMnO_4.2H_2O$, as a chocolate-brown powder by the action of cold soln.

of eq. proportions of lead acetate and potassium permanganate. J. B. Hannay could not prepare it by the action of nitric acid and potassium chlorate on mixed soln. of manganous and lead salts. A. F. Jolles found that lead manganate loses its water at 150°, and that it is a strong oxidizing agent.

For the **manganous manganates** of A. Guyard, *vide supra*. V. Auger and M. Billy prepared a series of *manganimanganates* or **manganitomanganates** of the type $3RO.MnO_2.MnO_3.H_2O$, or $R_3Mn_2O_8.H_2O$, by fusing at 180° to 250° mixtures of a hydroxide of an alkaline earth, sodium and potassium nitrates, and potassium permanganate. The salts are said to be constituted: $HO.R.O.MnO.O.R.O.MnO_2.O.R.OH$. J. Holluta found that manganitomanganate is probably an intermediate product in the reduction of the manganates by formic acid. The absorption spectra of manganates and manganitomanganates are different. The basic barium manganate of A. Rosenstiehl is thought by V. Auger and M. Billy to be **barium manganitomanganate**, $Ba_3Mn_2O_8.H_2O$, and it can be made by the general method as a green insoluble powder which can be heated to redness without losing its combined water. The corresponding **strontium manganitomanganate**, $Sr_3Mn_2O_8.H_2O$, is probably the same as the products reported by P. F. Chevillot and W. F. Edwards, and C. Fromherz—*vide supra*. Similarly also with the calcium manganate cited above, which V. Auger and M. Billy regarded as identical with **calcium manganitomanganate**, $Ca_3Mn_2O_8.H_2O$. By working in an analogous manner, insoluble **lithium manganitomanganate**, $Li_3Mn_2O_8.H_2O$, was obtained.

REFERENCES.

[1] J. R. Glauber, *Prosperitas Germaniæ*, Amstelodami, 1691 ; J. H. Pott, *Examen chymicum magnesiæ vitriariorum*, Berlin, 1740 ; C. F. Bucholz, *Gehlen's Journ.*, **8**. 162, 178, 1809 ; A. F. de Fourcroy, *Élémens d'histoire naturelle et de chimie*, Paris, **2**. 491, 1889 ; C. W. Scheele, *Svenska Akad. Handl.*, **35**. 89, 177, 1774 ; *Abhand. Akad. Stockholm*, **36**. 95, 183, 1774 ; *Opuscula chemica et physica*, Lipsiæ, **1**. 227, 1788 ; London, 53, 1901 ; *Crell's Die neuesten Entdeckungen in der Chemie*, **1**. 112, 140, 1781 ; *Nachgelassene Briefe und Aufzeichnungen*, Stockholm, 120, 1892 ; M. E. Chevreul, *Phil. Mag.*, **50**. 291, 1817 ; *Ann. Chim. Phys.*, (1), **4**. 42, 1817 ; P. F. Chevillot and W. F. Edwards, *ib.*, (2), **4**. 287, 1817 ; (2), **8**. 337, 1818 ; A. Béchamp, *ib.*, (3), **57**. 293, 1859 ; *Journ. Pharm. Chim.*, (3), **37**. 296, 1859 ; E. Mitscherlich, *Schweigger's Journ.*, **65**. 62, 1832 ; *Pogg. Ann.*, **25**. 287, 1832 ; *Liebig's Ann.*, **2**. 5, 1832 ; *Sitzber. Akad. Berlin*, 217, 1831 ; H. Aschoff, *ib.*, 474, 1860 ; *Ueber die Uebermangansäure und die Ueberchromsäure*, Berlin, 1861 ; *Journ. prakt. Chem.*, (1), **81**. 29, 1860 ; *Chem. News*, **4**. 103, 1861 ; *Pogg. Ann.*, **111**. 217, 1860 ; N. Beketoff, *Bull. Soc. Chim.*, (1), **1**. 43, 1859 ; G. Forchhammer, *De mangano*, Hafnia, 1820 ; *Ann. Phil.*, **16**. 130, 1820 ; **17**. [50, 1821 ; J. Waiz, *Schlüssel zu dem Cabinet der geheimen Schatzkammer der Natur*, Frankfurt, 1705.

[2] B. Franke, *Journ. prakt. Chem.*, (2), **36**. 35, 166, 1887 ; T. E. Thorpe and F. J. Hambly, *Journ. Chem. Soc.*, **53**. 175, 1887 ; F. R. Lankshear, *Zeit. anorg. Chem.*, **82**. 97, 1913 ; *Proc. Chem. Soc.*, **28**. 198, 1912 ; S. R. Scholes, *Journ. Ind. Eng. Chem.*, **7**. 1037, 1915.

[3] E. Mitscherlich, *Schweigger's Journ.*, **65**. 62, 1832 ; *Liebig's Ann.*, **2**. 5, 1832 ; *Pogg. Ann.*, **25**. 287, 1832 ; *Sitzber. Akad. Berlin*, 42, 1836 ; 217, 1831 ; H. Aschoff, *ib.*, 474, 1860 ; *Ueber die Uebermangansäure und die Ueberchromsäure*, Berlin, 1861 ; *Chem. News*, **4**. 103, 1861 ; *Pogg. Ann.*, **111**. 217, 1860 ; *Journ. prakt. Chem.*, (1), **81**. 29, 1860 ; C. F. Schönbein, *ib.*, (1), **41**. 225, 1847 ; R. Luboldt, *ib.*, (1), **77**. 315, 1859 ; G. Städeler, *ib.*, (1), **103**. 107, 1868 ; J. G. Gentele, *ib.*, (1), **82**. 58, 1861 ; A. Safarik, *ib.*, (1), **90**. 12, 1863 ; *Sitzber. Akad. Wien*, **47**. 256, 1863 ; N. Beketoff, *Bull. Soc. Chim.*, (1), **1**. 43, 1859 ; J. B. Senderens, *ib.*, (3), **7**. 511, 1892 ; E. Bothe, *ib.*, (2), **8**. 451, 1867 ; L. Schad, *ib.*, (2), **5**. 477, 1866 ; A. Guyard, *ib.*, (2), **1**. 81, 1864 ; P. F. Chevillot and W. F. Edwards, *Phil. Mag.*, **50**. 291, 1817 ; *Ann. Chim. Phys.*, (2), **4**. 287, 1817 ; (2), **8**. 337, 1818 ; A. Béchamp, *ib.*, (3), **57**. 293, 1859 ; *Journ. Pharm. Chim.*, (3), **37**. 276, 1859 ; M. Dutremblay and M. Lugan, *ib.*, (6), **6**. 392, 1897 ; H. McCormack, *Science*, (2), **53**. 49, 1921 ; P. Thénard, *Compt. Rend.*, **42**. 382, 1856 ; T. L. Phipson, *ib.*, **50**. 694, 1860 ; V. Auger, *ib.*, **150**. 470, 1910 ; **151**. 69, 1910 ; V. Auger and M. Billy, *ib.*, **138**. 500, 1904 ; A. Gorgeu, *ib.*, **110**. 958, 1890 ; *Ann. Chim. Phys.*, (3), **61**. 355, 1860 ; A. F. Jolles, *Beiträge zur Kenntniss der Manganate und Manganite*, Halle a. S., 1887 ; *Repert. anal. Chem.*, **7**. 485, 1889 ; *Zeit. anal. Chem.*, **28**. 238, 1889 ; *Zeit. Naturwiss.*, (4), **5**. 423, 1886 ; *German Pat.*, *D.R.P.* 41348, 1886 ; C. M. Tessié du Motay, *Bull. Soc. Enc. Nat. Ind.*, (2), **14**. 472, 1867 ; *L'Instit.*, **36**. 48, 1868 ; *Dingler's Journ.*, **186**. 231, 1867 ; C. M. Tessié du Motay and C. R. M. de Maréchal, *Brit. Pat. No.* 85, 1866 ; *Dingler's Journ.*, **196**. 230, 1870 ; *French Pat. No.* 68752, 1865 ; H. Vogel, *Ber.*, **3**. 901, 1870 ; R. Funk, *ib.*, **33**. 3696, 1900 ; O. Sackur, **43**. 381, 448, 1910 ; **44**. 777, 1911 ; *Zeit. Elektrochem.*, **16**. 641, 1910 ; F. Bahr and O. Sackur, in R. Abegg, *Handbuch der anorganischen Chemie*, Leipzig, **4**. ii, 858, 1913 ; F. Bahr, *Die thermische*

Bildung des Kaliummanganats aus Braunstein und Kaliumhydroxyde, Leipzig, 1911; F. Bahr and O. Sackur, *Zeit. anorg. Chem.*, **73**. 101, 1911; O. Sackur and W. Taegener, *ib.*, **18**. 718, 1912; W. Taegener, *Zur Kenntnis der wässerigen Lösungen des Kaliummanganates und des Kaliumpermanganates*, Breslau, 1913; W. Müller, *Pogg. Ann.*, **127**. 404, 1866; H. Abich, *ib.*, **23**. 338, 1831; C. Fromherz, *ib.*, **31**. 677, 1834; *Schweigger's Journ.*, **41**. 257, 1824; **44**. 327, 1825; H. Weppen, *Arch. Pharm.*, (2), **194**. 73, 1870; W. Kirchmann, *ib.*, (2), **150**. 203, 1872; E. Fleischer, *Monit. Scient.*, (3), **4**. 926, 1874; *Arch. Pharm.*, (3), **3**. 300, 1873; G. Kassner and H. Keller, *ib.*, (2), **239**. 473, 1901; G. Kassner, *German Pat.*, *D.R.P.* 31666, 1884; C. Huggenberg, *ib.*, 43690, 1887; *Ber.*, **21**. 490, 1888; *Brit. Pat. No.* 13695, 1887; C. Zwenger, *Liebig's Ann.*, **91**. 46, 1854; F. Wöhler, *ib.*, **119**. 375, 1861; *Pogg. Ann.*, **27**. 628, 1832; A. Gawalowsky, *Zeit. Oesterr. Apoth. Ver.*, **43**. 377, 1905; E. Mulder, *Scheik. Verh. Onderz.*, **1**. 62, 1857; E. Erlenmeyer and G. Lewinstein, *Zeit. Chem.*, (1), **3**. 393, 1860; W. Lindner, *ib.*, (2), **5**. 442, 1869; *Chem. Tech. Repert.*, i, 102, 1868; H. Lessheim, J. Meyer and R. Samuel, *Zeit. Physik*, **43**. 199, 1927; L. Kahlenberg and W. J. Trautmann, *Trans. Amer. Electrochem. Soc.*, **39**. 377, 1921; G. Doyer van Cleef, *Rec. Trav. Chim. Pays-Bas.*, **20**. 198, 1901; J. W. Retgers, *ib.*, **10**. 1, 1891; *Zeit. phys. Chem.*, **8**. 6, 1891; J. Holluta, *ib.*, **102**. 32, 1922; **106**. 276, 324, 1923; **107**. 249, 333, 1923; S. R. Scholes, *Journ. Ind. Eng. Chem.*, **7**. 1037, 1915; H. I. Schlesinger, R. D. Mullinix and S. Popoff, *ib.*, **11**. 317, 1919; C. W. Eliot and F. H. Storer, *Proc. Amer. Acad.*, **1**. 43, 1859; G. Forchhammer, *Die mangano*, Hafnia, 1820; *Ann. Phil.*, **16**. 130, 1820; **17**. 50, 1821; L. Santi, *Boll. Chim. Farm.*, **43**. 673, 1904; J. A. Hedvall and N. von Zweigbergk, *Zeit. anorg. Chem.*, **108**. 113, 1919; P. Askenasy and S. Klonowsky, *Zeit. Elektrochem.*, **16**. 104, 1910; S. Klonowsky, *Ueber die Manganatschmelze und die Ueberführung von Kaliummanganat in Kaliumpermanganat auf elektrolytischen Wege*, Karlsruhe, 1910; O. Dieffenbach, *German Pat.*, *D.R.P.* 195532, 1904; R. Böttger, *Polyt. Notizbl.*, **30**. 240, 1875; E. Donath, *Dingler's Journ.*, **263**. 246, 1887; A. Rosenstiehl, *ib.*, **177**. 409, 1864; *Journ. Pharm. Chim.*, (3), **46**. 344, 1864; R. D. Bowman, *Brit. Pat. No.* 7851, 1890; R. W. Stimson, *ib.*, 320845, 1928; W. G. Mixter, *Amer. Journ. Science*, (4), **30**. 193, 1910; J. H. Parkinson, *ib.*, 9457, 1891; G. Webb and G. H. Rayner, *ib.*, 13036, 1891; F. Fanta, *ib.*, 3034, 1891; C. Vogt, *Brit. Pat. No.* 131, 1864; C. E. Ruby, *Journ. Amer. Chem. Soc.*, **43**. 294, 1921; H. I. Schlesinger and H. B. Siems, *ib.*, **46**. 1965, 1924; H. I. Schlesinger, V. T. Jackson and E. E. Cordery, *Journ. Ind. Eng. Chem.*, **15**. 53, 1923; C. M. Bradbury, *Chem. News*, **59**. 151, 1889; A. Buntrock, in J. G. Gentele, *Lehrbuch der Farbenfabrikation*, Braunschweig, **2**. 414, 1909; F. Rose, *Die Mineralfarben*, Leipzig, 256, 1916; E. Delaurier, *Les Mondes*, **21**. 288, 1869; *Chem. News*, **20**. 240, 1869; D. Borar, *Journ. Chem. Soc.*, **99**. 1414, 1911; J. B. Hannay, *ib.*, **33**. 270, 1878; E. Wedekind and C. Horst, *Ber.*, **48**. 105, 1915; C. Horst, *Ueber die Abhängigkeit der Magnetisierbarkeit anorganischer Verbindungen von der Wertigkeit des Hauptelementes, untersucht an den Oxyden und Sulfiden einiger Schwermetalle*, Freiburg, 1912; E. Wedekind, *Zeit. angew. Chem.*, **37**. 87, 1924; H. E. Buckley, *Zeit. Kryst.*, **75**. 15, 1930; E. Franke, *Zeit. phys. Chem.*, **16**. 476, 1895; A. F. S. Bellone, *U.S. Pat. No.* 1826594, 1931.

§ 14. Permanganic Acid

P. F. Chevillot and W. F. Edwards [1] observed that on adding a little water to a soln. of potassium permanganate in conc. sulphuric acid, a violet vapour is given off which soon condenses and decomposes; O. Unverdorben also observed that if the permanganate be warmed with a little conc. sulphuric acid, the red vapour which is evolved attacks the lungs, and readily decomposes in the absence of water into manganese dioxide and oxygen; it forms a red soln. with water. L. Hünefeld found that it can be distilled from a conc. sulphuric acid soln. of the permanganate at 130°, and the vapour condenses to carmine-red needles, which are decomposed by water into manganic oxide and sulphuric acid. L. Gmelin said that if the permanganate is quite free from chlorine, no red vapour is produced under these conditions. F. Wöhler observed that when conc. sulphuric acid is poured over the crystals of potassium permanganate, the salt is decomposed with explosive violence and the evolution of much heat, and even flame. A cloud of finely-divided manganese oxide is also produced, and there is a copious evolution of oxygen. F. Wöhler hence concluded that permanganic acid is a gas which, at the moment of its liberation, is decomposed by the heat of the reaction into oxygen and manganese dioxide. T. E. Thorpe and F. J. Hambly, and B. Franke added that the permanganate here employed probably contained some chlorate or perchlorate, because the purified and dry salt dissolves quietly in conc. sulphuric acid without any great rise of temp. According to H. Aschoff, if conc. sulphuric acid be used, a clear, sage-green soln. is produced, and if the monohydrated acid be employed, the soln. is dark brown and it contains a number of oily drops which gradually

sink to form a very unstable, dark reddish-brown liquid which does not solidify
at −20°. H. Aschoff analyzed this reddish-brown liquid, and he obtained data
in accord with the assumption that it is a compound, **manganese heptoxide,** or
permanganic anhydride, Mn_2O_7. H. Aschoff prepared this compound by adding
to well-cooled sulphuric acid of sp. gr. 1·845, in small quantities at a time, potassium
permanganate, free from chlorine. The dark olive-green liquid forms oily drops
of manganese heptoxide, which settle to the bottom as a dark reddish-brown liquid.
Up to about 20 grms. of the permanganate can be employed without danger.
J. M. Lovén, and A. Terreil used a similar process. P. Thénard prepared what he
regarded as anhydrous permanganic acid, and A. Terreil also regarded as permanganic acid the greenish-black, oily drops of liquid which he obtained by the
action of moisture or a small proportion of water on a soln. of permanganate in
sulphuric acid. The product was probably the anhydride. Observations on the
action of sulphuric acid on permanganate were also made by M. Spiess, H. Kolbe,
R. Böttger, J. Personne and M. l'Hermite, and E. Delaurier.

B. Franke, from indirect evidence, inferred that the dark green soln. obtained
by the action of sulphuric acid on potassium permanganate contains manganic
oxysulphate, $(MnO_3)_2SO_4$, formed in accord with $2KMnO_4+H_2SO_4=K_2SO_4$
$+2HMnO_4$, and $2HMnO_4+H_2SO_4=(MnO_3)_2SO_4+2H_2O$. The argument was based
mainly on the existence of the analogous oxyfluoride, MnO_3F, and the oxychloride,
MnO_3Cl; and the difference in the colours of the soln. obtained by the use of
concentrated and monohydrated sulphuric acids—*vide supra*—corresponds with
the assumed difference in the chemical nature of the soln. T. E. Thorpe and
F. J. Hambly continue : On adding a small quantity of water to the well-cooled
green soln., manganese heptoxide is produced in accord with B. Franke's equation :
$(MnO_3)_2SO_4+H_2O=H_2SO_4+Mn_2O_7$. This accounts for the production of the
heptoxide by the use of monohydrated sulphuric acid and its non-formation
when the conc. acid is employed. According to T. E. Thorpe and F. J. Hambly,
if potassium permanganate be added in small quantities at a time to pyrosulphuric
acid, or to sulphuric acid to which sulphur trioxide has been added, as each
successive portion of the salt reaches the acid, flames are emitted, together with a
cloud of sulphur trioxide, darkened in colour by particles of manganese dioxide.
The soln. obtained is of a lavender-blue colour, and on standing deposits a pink-
coloured salt ; this on treatment with cold water forms a deep brown soln. which
ultimately deposits brown oxide of manganese. If the dark green soln. of potassium
permanganate in sulphuric acid be cautiously heated in a current of air, the violet
gaseous substance which is given off, and which condenses to a dark red, viscid
mass, was considered by A. Terreil to be permanganic acid, $HMnO_4$, but H. Aschoff
showed that it is also produced by the gradual decomposition of the heptoxide,
which contains no hydrogen. As indicated above, B. Franke, and T. E. Thorpe
and F. J. Hambly considered it to be manganese trioxide, MnO_3, while F. R. Lankshear regarded it as impure permanganic acid.

H. Aschoff described manganese heptoxide as a dark reddish-brown, oily liquid ;
A. Terreil said that its colour is greenish-black ; while J. M. Lovén said that its
colour is yellowish-green, and its sp. gr. 2·4. D. Balareff discussed the mol. vol.
He also gave for the heat of soln. $(Mn_2O_7,Aq)=(2HMnO_4,Ag)+12$ Cals. A. Simon
and F. Feher gave for the dissociation press., p mm., of the heptoxide :

	0°	2°	6°	10°	14°	21°
p	0·5	1·2	3·2	7·0	147·0	593 mm.

The heats of the reactions are $(2Mn,3\frac{1}{2}O_2)=170$ Cals. ; and $Mn_2O_7\rightarrow2MnO_2+1\frac{1}{2}O_2$
$+82$ Cals. A. Terreil thought that it formed a violet vapour with an unpleasant
metallic odour. According to H. Aschoff, the liquid does not solidify at −20°, and it
is apparently non-volatile, because it may be heated under reduced press. to 60°–65°
without the slightest evolution of vapour, but at higher temp. it is decomposed with
a sudden and violent explosion into oxygen and manganic oxide. The rapidity of

the explosion is attributed to the action of the separated manganic oxide, since P. Thénard has shown that a minute quantity of manganic oxide instantly resolves the heptoxide, even in the cold, into oxygen and manganese dioxide. P. Thénard said that the heptoxide detonates at 30° to 40°, with the formation of oxygen and manganesé dioxide. A. Terreil also noted that it decomposes when rapidly heated, and when slowly heated its temp. cannot be raised above 60° or 70°. J. M. Lovén also noted the formation of manganese dioxide when the heptoxide explodes. H. Aschoff found the heptoxide to be extremely unstable, and it slowly evolves ozonized oxygen ; as the bubbles of gas burst at the surface of the liquid, they form a violet cloud. P. Thénard, and A. Terreil noted that the heptoxide smells of ozone. J. M. Lovén added that in dry air the heptoxide can be kept many days, but in moist air it forms a violet vapour—*vide supra*. H. Aschoff observed that a drop of the heptoxide in hydrogen decomposes explosively ; and that in air it is very hygroscopic, and is gradually decomposed by the absorbed moisture ; when it is dropped into water it dissolves, forming a purple liquid, with the evolution of so much heat that it suffers partial decomposition, and the aq. soln., even when dilute, is gradually decomposed by heat into manganese dioxide and oxygen. The heptoxide decomposes by contact with sulphur, and likewise in hydrogen sulphide. It dissolves in conc. sulphuric acid without decomposition, forming an olive-green or sage-green soln.—*vide supra*. A. Terreil said that the soln. in a mol of sulphuric acid diluted with three mols of water is violet ; while there is a vigorous reaction, accompanied by light, when the heptoxide is put in contact with a few drops of a soln. of potassium sulphite. H. Aschoff found that phosphorus in contact with the heptoxide produces a violent explosion. There is also a detonation when the heptoxide is brought in contact with carbon, carbon disulphide, and with many organic substances—*e.g.* paper, ethylene, alcohol, and ether. J. F. Durand observed that the green soln. of manganese heptoxide in conc. sulphuric acid oxidizes diamond, graphite, and acetylene-black quantitatively in the cold, at different rates, to form carbon dioxide. C. A. Winkler made some observations on the reaction with ether. A. Terreil observed an explosion occurs when the heptoxide is brought in contact with fats. J. M. Lovén observed that it forms a cherry-red soln. with acetic acid. According to R. Böttger, a mixture of 2 parts of dry potassium permanganate and 3 parts of conc. sulphuric acid gives off ozonized oxygen on standing for a week, and it is a powerful oxidizing agent ; for instance, a couple of drops of the mixture in contact with a couple of drops of the following oils produce an explosion or else inflammation : nutmeg, rue, citron, cloves, marjoram, cubeb, and spikes, and with oil of thyme, and turpentine ; while methyl and ethyl alcohols, carbon disulphide, ether, ethylene chloride, benzene, coal-gas, paper, and cotton inflame without explosion ; and gun-cotton and gunpowder are not inflamed. P. Thénard, and H. Aschoff observed that silver oxide, mercuric oxide, and manganese dioxide decompose manganese heptoxide in the cold.

Soln. of manganese salts are readily oxidized to pink or violet permanganates, or **permanganic acid,** $HMnO_4$. Thus, G. Forchhammer oxidized manganous sulphate by digesting it with lead dioxide and sulphuric acid. W. Crum, and J. Volhard recommended nitric in place of sulphuric acid. The reaction was studied by T. M. Chatard, S. Peters, P. Pichard, A. Leclerc, L. L. de Koninck, T. E. Thorpe and F. J. Hambly, A. Ledebur, F. C. G. Müller, V. Deshayes, F. Osmond, O. W. Gibbs, R. Parkinson, P. A. Meerburg, J. B. J. D. Boussingault, and C. F. Schönbein. G. Forchhammer treated a green soln. of potassium manganate with lead nitrate, and the precipitate of manganese hemitrioxide and lead dioxide—after washing but not drying—was decomposed by prolonged digestion with dil. sulphuric acid (1 : 10), not in sufficient quantity to saturate the lead oxide. C. Fromherz objected that most of the permanganic acid would be decomposed after the sulphuric acid had been saturated with lead oxide. Oxidizing agents other than lead dioxide can be employed. Thus, L. Schneider, L. Dufty, J. Red drop and H. Ramage, F. Ibbotson and H. Brearley, H. Ramage, A. A. Blair,

R. S. Weston, F. J. Metzger and L. E. Marrs, F. J. Metzger and R. F. McCrackan, P. H. M. P. Brinton, W. F. Hillebrand and W. Blum, C. D. Braun, D. J. Demorest, J. R. Cain, G. Bertrand, H. Rubricus, R. A. Gortner and C. O. Rost, and H. F. U. Little recommended oxidation with sodium bismuthate or bismuthic acid ; and H. E. Walters, H. Marshall, M. R. Schmidt, H. Baubigny, H. Rubricus, A. Travers, J. Heslinga, J. Oesch, H. Kunze, P. Holland, J. J. Boyle, and M. Stanichitch recommended ammonium persulphate. A. Travers studied the oxidation of manganous salts to permanganate by ammonium persulphate in the presence of silver nitrate : $7AgNO_3 + 3(NH_4)_2S_2O_8 + 6H_2O \rightleftharpoons 3Ag_2O_2.AgNO_3 + 3(NH_4)_2SO_4 + 3H_2SO_4 + 6HNO_3$. The silver peroxynitrate acts as a catalyst. Thus if 10 per cent. of acid is previously added to the silver nitrate, the silver compound is produced in a black, colloidal form ; the manganous salt upsets the equilibrium, which is restored gradually, the liquid appearing wine-red in colour owing to the superposition of the violet of the permanganic acid on the black silver compound. A further addition of manganous salt again reverses the reaction, and the true violet of the permanganic acid is seen, followed by the above changes. O. Kühling used silver peroxide and nitric acid as oxidizing agent. According to C. F. Schönbein, soln. of manganese salts in contact with air and phosphorus become columbine-red owing to the formation of permanganic acid by oxidation by the ozone which is formed ; so also is permanganic acid formed if a manganese salt and phosphorus be shaken with ozonized air, chlorine-water, or bromine-water. H. Trommsdorff discussed the influence of manganic phosphate on the colour.

According to A. A. Maximoff, sodium and potassium permanganates decompose in alkaline soln. somewhat as typified by the equations : $2KMnO_4 + 2KOH = 2K_2MnO_4 + H_2O + \frac{1}{2}O_2$; and $K_2MnO_4 + H_2O = MnO_2 + 2KOH + \frac{1}{2}O_2$. When a permanganate is formed by the fusion of an alkali hydroxide with manganese dioxide, the presence of an alkali dioxide assists the reaction. It is supposed that even when no dioxide is added, some is formed during the reaction. In these circumstances, whereas cæsium, potassium, rubidium, and sodium should form the manganate and permanganate on fusion of their hydroxides with manganese dioxide, lithium, which does not form a dioxide, should not undergo the reaction. This has been found to be the case. Lithium permanganate could be formed only by the addition of lithium sulphate to barium permanganate. Under the conditions in which potassium permanganate gave the manganate in potassium hydroxide soln., lithium permanganate in lithium hydroxide soln. does not change, except exceedingly slowly, a change which is attributed to the presence of sodium in the glass of the containing vessel. Hydrogen dioxide so accelerates the reaction that no manganate and only manganese dioxide is formed. The reaction has been carried out quantitatively by titrating standard soln. of the permanganates with hydrogen dioxide until (i) a green colour is formed and (ii) a grey precipitate appears. This has been accomplished for lithium as well as for potassium. The results obtained are in accord with the equations : (i) $2M'MnO_4 + H_2O_2 + 2M'OH = 2M'_2MnO_4 + 2H_2O + O_2$; (ii) $2M'_2MnO_4 + 2H_2O_2 = 2M'_2O + 2H_2O + 2MnO_2 + 2O_2$. Sodium permanganate in the presence of sodium dioxide undergoes the change : $2Na_2MnO_4 + 2Na_2O_2 + 4H_2O = 2MnO_2 + 8NaOH + 2O_2$. As shown by O. Dieffenbach, the reaction is reversed in the presence of potassium ferricyanide. The reaction was brought about by adding dry sodium hydroxide to a little water, heating the mixture to boiling, and adding dry manganese dioxide. On adding sodium dioxide to the mixture, a gas is evolved and sodium manganate is formed. The reactions involving the oxidation and reduction of manganese salts are as follow : $MnO_2 + 4KOH + O_2 = MnO_2(OK)_2 + KO·OK + 2H_2O$; $2KMnO_4 + K_2O_2 = 2MnO_2(OK)_2 + O_2$; $MnO_2(OM')_2 + HO·OH = O_2 + Mn(OH)_2(OM')_2 = H_2MnO_3 + M'_2O + O_2$.

According to H. Aschoff, if manganese heptoxide be dropped into water it gradually dissolves to form a violet soln. The heat developed may decompose part of the permanganic acid—*vide supra*. J. M. Lovén added that decomposition occurs only if the soln. be too concentrated, but soln. with 20 per cent. $HMnO_4$ can be so prepared. E. Mitscherlich obtained what he regarded as permanganic acid by adding an eq. quantity of dil. sulphuric acid to a soln. of barium permanganate. M. M. P. Muir allowed the soln. to stand a few days, filtered it through glass-wool, and concentrated it in vacuo over sulphuric acid. E. Mitscherlich said the soln. decomposes at 30°–40°. H. Aschoff used a similar process. According to R. Rusconi, when 30 per cent. sulphuric acid, containing a small proportion —say 0·05 per cent.—of manganous sulphate, is electrolyzed in a U-shaped vessel using a potential difference of 5 to 6 volts, the formation of traces of permanganic acid at the anode is observable after a few minutes. If, however, the soln. contains also a few drops of sat. silver sulphate soln., the formation of permanganic acid at the anode is immediate and rapid. Similar results are obtained if the sulphuric acid is replaced by conc. sodium hydrosulphate soln. The oxidation is probably effected through the intermediate formation of a persulphate (*q.v.*).

M. M. P. Muir obtained better results by this process than by treating an eq. amount of soln. of silver permanganate and hydrochloric acid, filtering off the silver chloride, and evaporating in vacuo. L. Hünefeld recommended decomposing the barium permanganate with phosphoric acid, but the product is then impure. R. E. Wilson and co-workers obtained barium permanganate or manganate by the action of barium peroxide on manganese dioxide and fused alkali hydroxide. C. Fromherz recommended passing carbon dioxide into water with barium manganate in suspension, and kept agitated, until the green powder becomes brown. The decanted violet soln., containing permanganic acid and barium acid permanganate and acid carbonate, is boiled for 15 mins. to expel the carbon dioxide and precipitate barium carbonate. The small quantity of barium salt still in soln. is removed by adding a few drops of dil. sulphuric acid. The soln. is decanted, boiled down to three-fourths of its vol., and decanted from the precipitated hydrated manganese dioxide. If the soln. is evaporated in vacuo, over sulphuric acid, brown manganese oxide is obtained ; but if evaporated at a gentle heat, the soln. on cooling deposits carmine-red needles with 8·411 per cent. of water. E. Mitscherlich objects that the boiling would decompose permanganic acid, and the product was possibly barium hydropermanganate, because crystals of permanganic acid cannot be so obtained.

L. von Putnoky and B. von Bobest studied the anodic oxidation of soln. of manganous salts in hydrofluoric acid. In the anodic oxidation there is first formed a brown oxidation product, which is manganese trifluoride ; and this then gives place to permanganic acid. No manganese tetrafluoride could be detected in the soln. F. W. Skirrow, and E. Müller and P. Koppe obtained only the brown soln., not permanganic acid ; and M. G. Levi and F. Ageno, permanganic acid. F. Förster, indeed, said that " in the presence of hydrofluoric acid, manganous sulphate passes only into a manganic salt, because there is a strong inclination of the fluoride to form a complex with tervalent manganese, and this prevents the oxidation going further." L. von Putnoky and B. von Bobest observed that the permanganic acid can exist in the soln. only when the whole of the manganous salt has been converted into manganic salt, since, according to E. Müller and P. Koppe, any permanganic acid formed is decomposed : $HMnO_4 + 4MnF_2 + 7HF = 5MnF_3 + 4H_2O$. According to L. von Putnoky and B. von Bobest, permanganic acid is the primary product of the reaction, and so long as any manganous fluoride is present in the soln., it is converted into manganese trifluoride. The trifluoride is therefore a secondary product of all the reactions. When the manganous fluoride is all destroyed, the permanganic acid remains, and it increases in amount only at the cost of the manganese trifluoride.

H. N. Morse and J. C. Olsen electrolyzed a conc. soln. of potassium permanganate contained in a porous pot arranged so that the hydrogen formed at the cathode cannot reduce the soln., and that the alkali hydroxide also formed at the cathode can be removed. M. M. P. Muir said that the acid can be obtained in violet-blue, crystalline needles contaminated with manganese oxides. In order to obtain a fair proportion of the crystals, it is necessary to allow small quantities of a moderately conc. soln. of the acid to evaporate in the air ; if large quantities of the soln. are used, the evaporation proceeds so slowly that most of the acid has decomposed when the evaporation is finished. The evaporation should proceed under a beaker, not in a desiccator.

According to H. N. Morse and J. C. Olsen, when an aq. soln. of permanganic acid is evaporated to dryness over sulphuric acid in vacuo, a shining black solid, $MnO.20MnO_2$, is obtained. When an aq. soln. of the acid is kept in an open vessel, it gradually deposits brown, pasty solid matter, 6 to $10MnO.20MnO_2$. The aq. soln. of permanganic acid appears dark carmine-red by reflected light, and by transmitted light dark violet, or with greater dilution, reddish-blue or carmine-red. The spectrum was examined by F. Hoppe-Seyler, G. C. Stokes, R. T. Simmler, J. Müller, etc.—vide supra. C. F. Schönbein suggested that permanganic acid is really a compound of manganese dioxide and hydrogen dioxide or ozone, because with reducing agents it behaves like hydrogen dioxide or ozone itself. J. M. Lovén, and H. N. Morse and J. C. Olsen obtained concordant results for the **electrical conductivity** of aq. soln., λ mhos, at 25°, containing a mol of the acid in v litres :

v	2	4	8	16	32	64	128	256	512	1024
λ	336	354	371	377	385	392	398	403	403	400·1

The results indicate that the acid is strong and monobasic. E. Franke observed that the strength of the acid is about equal to that of nitric acid, but it is unstable and easily decomposed, so that his observations show a rapid fall in the conductivity of the soln. with dilution. J. M. Lovén calculated 0·89 for the avidity of the acid. C. M. Bradbury reviewed the evidence in support of the thesis that permanganic acid is monobasic. C. Fromherz found that the acid has just a sweet taste, which afterwards appears rough and bitter ; while G. Forchhammer said that the taste is pungent and disagreeable. C. Fromherz found that the acid stains the skin brown, but does not redden litmus ; while G. Forchhammer, and E. Mitscherlich added that the acid destroys the colouring matter of litmus and turmeric, at the same time turning them brown owing to the deposition of hydrated manganese dioxide.

O. Sackur, and O. Sackur and W. Taegener calculated the normal **potential** for the reduction of *permanganates to manganese dioxide* in alkaline soln. : $MnO_4' + 2H_2O = MnO_2 + 4OH' + 3F$ from the measurements of J. K. H. Inglis of the e.m.f. of the cell $(Pt) : MnO_2,KMnO_4.H_2SO_4 : KCl_{sat. soln.} : 0.1N\text{-}KCl : Hg_2Cl_2 : Hg$, at room temp. They found for normal alkaline soln., $[OH']=1$, $E_H=0.54$ volt, and for soln. of different concentration $E_H = 0.54 + 0.019 \log [MnO_4'] - 0.077 \log [OH']$ volt. For acid soln., $MnO_4' + 4H^{\cdot} = MnO_2 + 2H_2O + 3F$, $E_H = 1.63$ volt, for normal acidity, $[H^{\cdot}]=1$, and for other concentrations $E_H = 1.63 + 0.019 \log [MnO_4'] + 0.077 \log [H^{\cdot}]$ volt. From these values, and the results for the potential of the reduction from *permanganate to manganese monoxide*—vide supra—it follows that for the change $MnO_4' + 8H^{\cdot} = Mn^{\cdot\cdot} + 4H_2O + 5F$, for normal soln., $E_H = 1.52$ volt, and for other concentrations $E_H = 1.52 + 0.012 \log [MnO_4'] - 0.012 \log [Mn^{\cdot\cdot}] + 0.093 \log [H^{\cdot}]$ volt. O. Sackur also calculated the **free energy** of the passage from *permanganate to manganese dioxide*. Since for $4(MnO_4' + 4H^{\cdot} = MnO_2 + 2H_2O + 3F)$, $E_H = 1.63$ volt, when the potential for the liberation of oxygen is greater than is the case with water, for which $3(2H_2O + 4F = O_2 + 4H^{\cdot})$, $E_H = 1.23$ volt, then for $4MnO_4' + 4H^{\cdot} = 4MnO_2 + 2H_2O + 3O_2$, $E_H = 0.40$ volt, and the free energy of the reaction is $Q = 12F(0.4 + 0.019 \log [MnO_4'] + 0.019 \log [H^{\cdot}] - 0.0145 \log p_{O_2})$ joules. The latent pressure of the oxygen, so to speak, is unity when the reacting constituents have unit concentration, and $\log p_{O_2} = 27.6 + 1.3 \log [MnO_4'] + 1.3 \log [H^{\cdot}]$, or $p_{O_2} = 10^{27.6}$. Similarly, the free energy of the passage from *permanganate to a manganous salt* is calculated from $4(MnO_4' + 8H^{\cdot} = Mn^{\cdot\cdot} + 4H_2O + 5F)$ when $E_H = 1.52$ volt, and $5(2H_2O + 4F = O_2 + 4H^{\cdot})$ has $E_H = 1.23$ volt, so that $4MnO_4' + 12H^{\cdot} = 4Mn^{\cdot\cdot} + 6H_2O + 5O_2$, and $E_H = 0.29$ volt. Consequently, $20F(0.29 + 0.012 \log [MnO_4'] + 0.012 \log [Mn^{\cdot\cdot}] + 0.035 \log [H^{\cdot}] + 0.0145 \log p_{O_2})$ joules, and the latent pressure of the oxygen is $\log p_{O_2} = 20 + 0.8 \log [MnO_4'] - 0.8 \log [Mn^{\cdot\cdot}] + 2.4 \log [H^{\cdot}]$, so that for unit concentrations $p_{O_2} = 10^{24}$

atm. In both cases the tendency for the permanganate to give off oxygen increases with increasing acidity of the soln. The **oxidizing potentials** E_H normal acid soln., when $[H^{\cdot}]=1$, given by O. Sackur, are: $MnO_4'{\rightarrow}MnO_4''$, 0·61 volt; $O_2{\rightarrow}H_2O$, 1·23 volts; $MnO_2{\rightarrow}Mn^{\cdot\cdot}$, 1·35 volts; $MnO_4{\rightarrow}Mn^{\cdot\cdot}$, 1·52 volts; $MnO_4'{\rightarrow}MnO_2$, 1·63 volts; and $MnO_4''{\rightarrow}MnO_2$, 2·12 volts. Similarly, for normal alkaline soln., when $[OH']=1$, they are: $O_2{\rightarrow}OH'$, 0·41 volt; $MnO_4''{\rightarrow}MnO_2$, 0·50 volt; $MnO_4'{\rightarrow}MnO_2$, 0·52 volt; and $MnO_4'{\rightarrow}MnO_4''$, 0·61 volt. The results show that in acidic and alkaline soln. manganese dioxide, manganate, and permanganate have a stronger latent oxygen pressure than oxygen itself at 1 atm. press. From the e.m.f. of the cell $H_2 \mid HClO_4 \mid HClO_4, KMnO_4 \mid MnO_2$, at 25°, D. J. Brown and R. F. Tefft calculated the oxidation potential of $MnO_4'+4H^{\cdot}+3{\oplus}=MnO_2+2H_2O$ to be 1·586 volts. This value decreases with increasing acid conc. C. E. Ruby obtained $MnO_2+4OH'+2{\oplus}=MnO_4''+2H_2O$, −0·664 volt; $MnO_2+4OH'+3{\oplus}=MnO_4'+2H_2O$, −0·647 volt; and $MnO_2+2H_2O+3{\oplus}=MnO_4'+4H^{\cdot}$, −1·757 volts.

According to C. Fromherz, the aq. soln. of permanganic acid is decomposed when exposed to **light** and hydrated manganese dioxide is precipitated; the soln. is also decomposed by **heat.** Thus the decomposition is partial at 45° and complete at 100°. The evidence is not all concordant. C. Fromherz reported the decomposition to be faster the smaller the concentration of the soln., and a conc. soln. may be boiled for many hours without sensible decomposition. E. Mitscherlich observed that the soln. slowly decomposes at about 20°, and rapidly at 30° to 40°, giving off oxygen and precipitating hydrated manganese dioxide. The decomposition is completed by boiling. J. M. Lovén said that soln. with 0·5 to 1·0 per cent. $HMnO_4$ are very stable and can be boiled without loss of oxygen; and the soln. can be concentrated by boiling or by freezing. H. Aschoff observed that when the soln. is evaporated to dryness on a water-bath, oxygen and hydrated manganese dioxide are produced—*vide supra* for M. M. P. Muir's observations. C. F. Schönbein observed that the presence of finely divided platinum accelerates the decomposition of the soln. to hydrated dioxide, water, and oxygen. G. Forchhammer detected what he called an electrical odour—possibly ozone—when the soln. is evaporated or exposed to sunlight; and C. C. Frye added that when a 22 per cent. soln. is distilled with sulphuric acid some ozone is given off.

According to C. Fromherz, and F. Jones, **hydrogen** rapidly reduces a soln. of permanganic acid, forming water and hydrated manganese dioxide—*vide infra*, potassium permanganate; and F. Duran observed that it adsorbs hydrogen, and **oxygen.** H. Aschoff, and B. C. Brodie observed that **hydrogen dioxide** reduces permanganic acid completely at ordinary temp. and in the presence of an excess of acid: $2HMnO_4+5H_2O_2=2MnO+6H_2O+5O_2$; and, added P. Thénard, the decomposition occurs at a low temp. without the evolution of oxygen, and M. Berthelot suggested that at −12° the trioxide, H_2O_3, is formed and it decomposes at a higher temp. A. Gorgeu added that permanganic acid is reduced by hydrogen dioxide to a manganous salt not only in the presence of acids, but also in the presence of other substances which can dissolve manganous oxide —*e.g.* a soln. of ammonium chloride. If free acid be not present, and hydrogen dioxide be slowly added to the dil. soln., the reaction can be symbolized: $Mn_2O_7+3H_2O_2=2MnO_2+3H_2O+3O_2$, and if more hydrogen dioxide be added, the manganese dioxide is itself reduced—*vide infra*, potassium permanganate.

C. Fromherz observed that permanganic acid is not decomposed by **chlorine ;** and J. Brown found that the reaction with **hydrochloric acid** can be symbolized: $HMnO_4+7HCl=MnCl_2+4H_2O+5Cl$, but the amount of permanganic acid consumed is greater than corresponds with this equation unless the liberated chlorine be removed. The reaction was also studied with respect to titrations with permanganate in the presence of hydrochloric acid, by J. Löwenthal and E. Lenssen, C. R. Fresenius, J. Wagner, etc. The effect of manganous salts was examined by J. L. C. Zimmermann, of hydrofluoric acid, potassium fluoride, potassium sulphate, or sodium sulphate, by H. Rose, and barium chloride, by J. Wagner.

The catalytic effects of ferrous, chromium, cadmium, and manganous salts, platinum tetrachloride, and auric chloride were discussed by W. Ostwald, and J. Wagner. C. W. Hempel, and W. Lindner found that **potassium bromide** does not decompose permanganic acid in neutral soln., but in sulphuric acid soln. the **hydrobromic acid** is decomposed, slowly in the cold, rapidly when heated, and bromine is set free. C. Fromherz found that **iodine** is oxidized by permanganic acid to iodic acid ; a little **hydriodic acid** is decomposed, forming iodine and hydrated manganous oxide, but if much iodide be present, some soluble manganous iodide is formed. C. F. Schönbein also noticed that **potassium iodide** forms some iodate, with the separation of iodine and of a brown hydrated manganese oxide. R. Espenchied represented the reaction with a hydrochloric acid soln. of potassium iodide by the equation : $HMnO_4 + 5KI + 7HCl = MnCl_2 + 5KCl + 4H_2O + 5I$. C. F. Rammelsberg observed that permanganic acid has no action on **bromic acid.**

C. Fromherz said that **sulphur** is oxidized in a few days to sulphuric acid ; a little **hydrogen sulphide** colours the soln. brown, and a brown hydrated oxide is soon deposited, while an excess of hydrogen sulphide forms milk of sulphur, water, and sulphuric acid. C. F. Schönbein added that the **metal sulphides** are oxidized to sulphates. C. Fromherz found that **sulphur monochloride** separates sulphur and forms manganous sulphate ; and **sulphurous acid** is oxidized to sulphuric acid. F. Duran observed that sulphur dioxide is adsorbed by the salt. L. P. de St. Gilles added that some dithionic acid is formed when sulphurous acid acts on permanganic acid, while **thiosulphuric acid** forms sulphuric and dithionic acids. C. Fromherz observed that **sulphuric acid** does not decompose permanganic acid. F. Jones, and B. Brauner observed the evolution of oxygen from soln. of potassium permanganate and sulphuric acid during oxidation effected by their means. F. A. Gooch and E. W. Danner found that the decomposition of the permanganate by sulphuric acid increases with the amount of acid present, the time of action, and increase of temp. A 20 per cent. soln. of sulphuric acid produces no appreciable effect at ordinary temp. and under exposures of a few hours only. In five days, however, a very considerable action takes place at the ordinary temp., and heating the mixture of acid and permanganate to 80° for an hour and a half is closely comparable in its effect with that brought about by the five days' action at the ordinary temp. The change is brought about by a tendency towards reduction on the part of the acid. When the acid is not present in proportions greater than 50 per cent. of the mixture, in the early stages of the action the oxygen lost by the permanganate is liberated, but later on the decomposition of the permanganate results in the precipitation of manganese in the form of a higher oxide, or in the retention of the manganese in soln. in the form of a higher sulphate.

F. Duran found that **nitrogen** is adsorbed by the salt. According to C. F. Schönbein, an excess of **ammonia** is oxidized to ammonium nitrite when shaken with platinum sponge and permanganic acid ; the reaction proceeds slowly in the cold and rapidly when heated. The soln. of permanganic acid is slowly decolorized by **nitric oxide,** and by **hyponitrous acid,** while C. Fromherz, and L. P. de St. Gilles found that **nitrous acid** immediately forms manganous nitrate. F. Duran observed that nitrous and nitric oxides are absorbed by the salt. C. Fromherz observed no reaction with **nitric acid.** C. Fromherz found that **phosphorus** is gradually oxidized to phosphoric acid by permanganic acid ; and similarly also with **phosphine.** L. P. de St. Gilles said that **hypophosphorous acid** is not completely oxidized to phosphoric acid. T. Salzer found that **hypophosphoric acid** is oxidized to phosphoric acid. C. Fromherz observed no reaction with **phosphoric acid.** H. B. Parsons found that **arsine** is oxidized by permanganic acid to arsenious and arsenic acids ; C. Fromherz, and L. P. de St. Gilles, that **arsenic trioxide** is oxidized to the pentoxide, while **arsenic pentoxide** has no action. Permanganic acid is slowly decomposed by **antimony,** forming antimony oxide ; and **antimony trioxide** is converted into the higher oxide. H. Rose observed that **antimony trichloride** reduces permanganic acid ; and C. Fromherz found that **bismuth** is slowly oxidized by the permanganate. B. W. Gerland found that **vanadyl salts** are oxidized to vanadates.

C. Fromherz observed that **boric acid** has no action on permanganic acid, while recently ignited **carbon** rapidly decomposes the acid without developing a gas. According to J. F. Durand, amorphous carbon as acetylene black, graphite, and the diamond is quantitatively oxidized to carbon dioxide when treated in a finely divided condition with the green soln. of permanganic anhydride in conc. sulphuric acid. The reaction proceeds at ordinary temp. with different degrees of vigour in the three cases. F. Duran found that **carbon monoxide** is adsorbed by the salt and likewise also **carbon dioxide.** C. Fromherz observed that carbon dioxide has no chemical action. F. Duran observed that **methane,** as well as **ethane,** and **propane,** is adsorbed by the gas ; **carbon disulphide** forms carbon dioxide and sulphuric acid ; **potassium ferrocyanide** forms ferricyanide ; **ethylene, alcohol,** and **ether** form carbon dioxide and water ; O. Unverdorben said that **acetic acid** has no action, but L. Gmelin found that it acts very slowly, and that **oxalic acid** is oxidized to carbon dioxide and water. C. W. Hempel represented the reaction in the presence of sulphuric acid at $35°$ to $40°$ by : $2HMnO_4 + 5H_2C_2O_4 + 2H_2SO_4 = 2MnSO_4 + 10CO_2 + 8H_2O$. The influence of time, and the concentrations of the sulphuric acid, manganous sulphate, oxalic acid, and potassium permanganate were studied by A. V. Harcourt, A. V. Harcourt and W. Esson, A. Skrabal, R. Ehrenfeld, R. Luther, and N. Schiloff—*vide supra,* manganese dioxide. C. Fromherz observed that **tartaric acid** reduces permanganic acid, forming a manganous salt ; similarly with **formic acid,** a reaction studied by N. Schiloff, and J. Holluta. A. Skrabal and J. Preiss found that the oxidation of formic acid occurs in stages as in the case of oxalic acid. There is an induction period. D. Vorländer and co-workers observed that in neutral or alkaline soln. most **amines** are oxidized by permanganates, but in acidic soln. the oxidation is accelerated. **Acyl derivatives** are comparatively stable in alkaline soln., but are more easily oxidized than the amines in acidic soln. Some **organic substances**—*e.g.* sugar, gum, wood, fibre, and paper—form carbon dioxide ; other substances decompose the acid without evolving gas, but precipitating a brown manganese oxide—*e.g.* stearic and oleic acids, morphine, urea, the colouring matter of blood, gelatin, albumin, fibrin, indigo sulphate, and infusions of galls, saffron, logwood, madder, columbine, rhubarb, quassia, aloes, and Peruvian bark.

C. Fromherz observed that **tin** has no action on permanganic acid, but **zinc** and **iron** decompose the acid in a few days, while **copper, silver, mercury,** and **lead** decompose the acid in about four weeks. The metal is at the same time oxidized. C. F. Schönbein found that the action is rapid with finely-divided silver, and **platinum.** The action of permanganate on **cerous salts** is represented by the equation : $3Ce_2O_3 + 2KMnO_4 + H_2O = 6CeO_2 + 2KOH + 2MnO_2$. The reaction is complete in the presence of mercuric or zinc oxides. The reaction has been utilized in the volumetric determination of cerium, and in separating cerium from lanthanum and didymium by F. M. Stapff. O. W. Gibbs, C. A. Winkler, F. Stolba, W. Muthmann and co-workers, C. James, G. P. Drossbach, P. E. Browning, R. J. Meyer and A. Schweitzer, C. R. Böhm, E. J. Roberts, L. Stützel, M. Esposito, C. von Scheele, and C. Fromherz observed that the acid is decomposed by **cuprous, mercuric, stannous, manganous, chromic, lead, and ferrous oxides or hydroxides** and usually a higher oxide is formed. H. N. Morse represented the reaction with **lead dioxide** and an acidified soln. of permanganic acid by the equation : $2HMnO_4 + 3PbO_2 = H_2O + 2MnO_2 + 3PbO + 3O_2$. H. N. Morse and co-workers, from their study of the reduction of permanganic acid by **manganese dioxide,** inferred : (i) Permanganic acid and potassium permanganate are reduced by precipitated manganese dioxide with the liberation of three-fifths of the active oxygen of the permanganic acid ; (ii) the oxide produced by the complete reduction of a neutral soln. of potassium permanganate contains all the potassium of the original salt, and the supernatant liquid is therefore neutral ; and (iii) whether the precipitated manganese oxide is formed by the slow decomposition of a neutral soln. of potassium permanganate or by the addition of manganese sulphate to an acidified soln. of permanganate, the ratio of oxygen to manganese in it remains normal—that is, 2 : 1—only so long as unreduced permanganate or permanganic acid is present, otherwise the oxide loses oxygen, even at the ordinary temp. In the presence of permanganate, the lost oxygen is restored. Many oxidizable salts decolorize permanganic acid, forming manganous salts. F. Margueritte, for instance, observed this to occur with **ferrous salts ;** and H. Rose, with **mercurous nitrate, stannous chloride, cuprous chloride, and uranous salts.** I. Macagno observed that **molybdic salts** are oxidized to molybdates.

REFERENCES.

[1] O. Unverdorben, *Brandes' Arch,* 9. 36, 1824 ; *Quart. Journ. Science,* 2. 204, 1827 ; *Pogg. Ann.,* 7. 322, 1826 ; R. T. Simmler, *ib.,* 115. 431, 1862 ; J. Müller, *ib.,* 128. 335, 1866 ; L. Hünefeld, *Schweigger's Journ.,* 60. 133, 1830 ; C. Fromherz, *ib.,* 41. 257, 1824 ; 44. 327, 1825 ; *Pogg. Ann.,* 31. 677, 1834 ; H. Trommsdorff, *Arch. Pharm.,* (2), 80. 262, 1854 ; R. Böttger, *Ber.,* 6. 1396, 1873 ; *Pogg. Ann. Jubelbd.,* 156, 1874 ; *Journ. prakt. Chem.,* (1), 90. 161, 1863 ; F. Hoppe-Seyler, *ib.,* (1), 90. 303, 1863 ; C. F. Schönbein, *ib.,* (1), 41. 225, 1847 ; (1), 75. 99, 101, 1858 ; *Pogg. Ann.,* 72. 459, 1847 ; 78. 162, 1849 ; E. Franke, *Zeit. phys. Chem.,* 16. 476, 1895 ; B. Franke, *Journ. prakt. Chem.,* (2), 36. 31, 1887 ; M. Spiess, *ib.,* (2), 1. 241, 1870 ; H. Kolbe, *ib.,* (2), 1. 423, 1870 ; D. Balareff, *ib.,* (2), 102. 283, 1921 ; J. Volhard, *Liebig's Ann.,* 198. 354, 1879 ; R. Espenchied, *ib.,* 114. 255, 1860 ; T. Salzer, *ib.,* 187. 322, 1877 ; W. Crum, *ib.,* 55. 219, 1845 ; F. Wöhler, *ib.,* 86. 373, 1853 ; C. F. Rammelsberg, *ib.,* 52. 81, 185, 1841 ; 90. 16, 1853 ; E. Mitscherlich, *Pogg. Ann.,* 25. 287, 1832 ; 31. 677, 1834 ; 32. 8, 1834 ; J. Löwenthal and E. Lenssen, *Zeit. anal. Chem.,* 1. 329, 1862 ; C. R. Fresenius, *ib.,* 1. 361, 1862 ; C. D. Braun, *ib.,* 6. 73, 1867 ; 7. 340, 1868 ; F. Margueritte, *Compt. Rend.,* 22. 587, 1846 ; *Ann. Chim. Phys.,* (2), 18. 224, 1846 ; P. F. Chevillot and W. F. Edwards, *ib.,* (2), 8. 337, 1818 ; L. P. de St. Gilles, *ib.,* (3), 55: 374, 1858 ; *Compt. Rend.,* 46. 624, 808, 1143, 1858 ; 47. 554, 1858 ; A. Travers, *ib.,* 182. 972, 1926 ; G. Forchhammer, *De mangano,* Hafnia, 1820 ; *Ann. Phil.,* 16. 130, 1820 ; 17. 50, 1821; *Oefvers. Danske Vid. Selsk. Forh.,* 91, 1856 ; G. C. Stokes, *Phil. Mag.,* (4), 6. 393, 1853 ; J. Personne and M. l'Hermite, *Journ. Pharm. Chim.,* (3), 19. 115, 161; 1851 ; H. Aschoff, *Ueber die Uebermangansäure und die Ueberchromsäure,* Berlin, 1861 ; *Sitzber. Akad. Berlin,* 474, 1804 ; *Pogg. Ann.,* 111. 217, 1860 ; *Journ. prakt. Chem.,* (1), 81. 29, 1860 ; *Chem. News,* 4. 103, 1841 ; J. M. Lovén, *Ber.,* 25. 620, 1892 ; A. Terreil, *Bull. Soc. Chim.,* (1), 4. 40, 1862 ; *Chem. News,* 6. 57, 1862 ; V. Deshayes, *Bull. Soc. Chim.,* (2), 29. 541, 1878 ; *Chem. News,* 38. 70, 1878 ; H. Jervis, *ib.,* 81. 171, 1900 ; A. Leclerc, *ib.,* 26. 296, 1872 ; *Compt. Rend.,* 75. 1209, 1872 ; P. Pichard, *ib.,* 75. 1821, 1872 ; H. Baubigny, *ib.,* 135. 995, 1902 ; 136. 449, 1662, 1903 ; L. L. de Koninck, *Rev. Univ. Mines,* (3), 5. 308, 1889 ; A. Ledebur, *Berg. Hütt. Ztg.,* 41. 417, 1882 ; F. C. G. Müller, *Stahl Eisen,* 6. 98, 1886 ; L. Schneider, *Dingler's Journ.,* 269. 224, 1893 ; L. Dufty, *Chem. News,* 84. 248, 1901 ; J. Reddrop and H. Ramage, *Journ. Chem. Soc.,* 67. 268, 1895 ; F. Ibbotson and H. Brearley, *Chem. News,* 82. 269, 1900 ; 84. 247, 302, 1901 ; 85. 58, 1902 ; H. Ramage, *ib.,* 84. 209, 269, 1901 ; 85. 24, 95, 1902 ; A. A. Blair, *Journ. Amer. Chem. Soc.,* 26. 793, 1904 ; R. S. Weston, *ib.,* 29. 1074, 1907 ; F. J. Metzger and R. F. McCrackan, *ib.,* 32. 1250, 1910 ; W. Blum, *ib.,* 34. 1379, 1912 ; P. H. M. P. Brinton, *Journ. Ind. Eng. Chem.,* 3. 237, 376, 1911 ; W. F. Hillebrand and W. Blum, *ib.,* 3. 374, 1911 ; D. J. Demorest, *ib.,* 4. 19, 1912 ; J. R. Cain, *ib.,* 3. 360, 1911 ; G. Bertrand, *Bull. Soc. Chim.,* (4), 9. 361, 1911 ; H. Rubricus, *Stahl Eisen,* 30. 957, 1911 ; R. A. Gortner and C. O. Rost, *Journ. Ind. Eng. Chem.,* 4. 522, 1912 ; F. J. Metzger and L. E. Marrs, *ib.,* 3. 333, 1911 ; 5. 125, 1913 ; H. F. U. Little, *Analyst,* 37. 554, 1912 ; H. E. Walters, *Proc. Eng. Soc. West Pa.,* 17. 257, 1901 ; *Journ. Amer. Chem. Soc.,* 25. 392, 1903 ; 27. 1550, 1905 ; *Chem. News,* 84. 239, 1901 ; H. Marshall, *ib.,* 83. 73, 1901 ; M. R. Schmidt, *Journ. Amer. Chem. Soc.,* 32. 965, 1910 ; H. Kunze, *Stahl Eisen,* 32. 1914, 1912 ; P. Holland, *Chem. News,* 96. 2, 1907 ; J. J. Boyle, *Journ. Ind. Eng. Chem.,* 4. 202, 1912 ; M. Stanichitch, *Rev. Mét.,* 8. 891, 1911 ; J. B. J. D. Boussingault, *Ann. Chim. Phys.,* (5), 5. 190, 1854 ; P. A. Meerburg, *Chem. Weekbl.,* 2. 639, 1905 ; R. Parkinson, *Liebig's Ann.,* 86. 62, 1853 ; D. Vorländer, *ib.,* 345. 251, 1906 ; D. Vorländer, G. Blau and T. Wallis, *ib.,* 345. 261, 1906 ; O. Sackur, in R. Abegg, *Handbuch der anorganischen Chemie,* Leipzig, 4. ii, 859, 1913 ; O. Sackur and W. Taegener, *Zeit. Elektrochem.,* 18. 718, 1912 ; W. Taegener, *Zur Kenntnis der wässerigen Lösungen des Kaliumanganates und des Kaliumpermanganates,* Breslau, 1913 ; F. M. Stapff, *Journ. prakt. Chem.,* (1), 79. 258, 1860 ; C. A. Winkler, *ib.,* (1), 95. 410, 1865 ; *Zeit. anorg. Chem.,* 1. 82, 1892 ; O. W. Gibbs, *Amer. Journ. Science,* (2), 14. 204, 1852 ; (2), 37. 352, 1864 ; *Proc. Amer. Acad.,* 28. 260, 1893 ; F. Stolba, *Chem. News,* 41. 31, 1880 ; B. Brauner, *ib.,* 71. 285, 1895 ; *Journ. Chem. Soc.,* 59. 238, 1891 ; B. Brauner and F. Pavlicek, *ib.,* 81. 1264, 1902 ; *Zeit. anorg. Chem.,* 34. 209, 1903 ; B. Brauner and A. Batek, *Zeit. anorg. Chem.,* 34. 114, 1903 ; G. P. Drossbach, *German Pat.,* *D.R.P.* 143106, 1896 ; *Ber.,* 35. 2830, 1902 ; *Zeit. angew. Chem.,* 14. 657, 1901 ; C. R. Böhm, *ib.,* 16. 1129, 1903 ; *Die Zerlegbarkeit des Praseodyms und Darstellung seltener Erden mit Hilfe einer neuen Trennungsmethode,* Halle a. S., 1900 ; C. von Scheele, *Zeit. anorg. Chem.,* 17. 320,

1898 ; P. E. Browning, *ib.*, **22.** 297, 1899 ; R. J. Meyer, *ib.*, **37.** 383, 1903 ; W. Muthmann and L. Weiss, *Liebig's Ann.*, **331.** 9, 1903 ; W. Muthmann and H. Rölig, *Ber.*, **31.** 1719, 1898 ; L. Stützel, *Zur Kenntnis der seltenen Erden des Cerits*, München, 1899 ; H. Rölig, *Beiträge zur Kenntnis der seltenen Erden des Cerits*, München, 1898 ; C. James, *Journ. Amer. Chem. Soc.*, **30.** 182, 1908 ; E. J. Roberts, *Amer. Journ. Science*, (5), **31.** 350, 1911 ; *Chem. News*, **103.** 303, 1911 ; R. J. Meyer and A. Schweitzer, *Zeit. anorg. Chem.*, **54.** 104, 1907 ; M. Esposito, *Proc. Chem. Soc.*, **23.** 64, 1907 ; J. Heslinga, *Chem. Weekbl.*, **19.** 274, 1922 ; J. Holluta, *Zeit. phys. Chem.*, **106.** 276, 324, 1923 ; J. Oesch, *Kritische Studien über Mangan*, Berlin, 1906 ; R. E. Wilson, L. W. Parsons and S. L. Chrisholm, *U.S. Pat. No.* 1592480, 1926 ; O. Kühling, *Zeit. angew. Chem.*, **16.** 1145, 1903 ; A. A. Maximoff, *Journ. Russ. Phys. Chem. Soc.*, **57.** 347, 1926 ; O. Dieffenbach, *German Pat.*, *D.R.P.* 195523, 195524, 1908 ; C. E. Ruby, *Journ. Amer. Chem. Soc.*, **43.** 294, 1921 ; D. J. Brown and R. F. Tefft, *ib.*, **48.** 1128, 1926 ; H. I. Schlesinger and H. B. Siems, *ib.*, **46.** 1965, 1924 ; L. Gmelin, *Handbook of Chemistry*, London, **4.** 209, 1850 ; E. Delaurier, *Les Mondes*, **21.** 388, 1869 ; *Chem. News*, **20.** 240, 1869 ; C. C. Frye, *ib.*, **73.** 122, 1896 ; H. B. Parsons, *ib.*, **35.** 235, 1877 ; C. M. Bradbury, *ib.*, **59.** 115, 123, 136, 149, 1889 ; P. Thénard, *Compt. Rend.*, **42.** 382, 1856 ; **75.** 177, 1872 ; J. F. Durand, *ib.*, **178.** 1822, 1924 ; A. Travers, *ib.*, **182.** 927, 1926 ; M. Berthelot, *ib.*, **90.** 656, 1880 ; A. Gorgeu, *ib.*, **110.** 958, 1890 ; *Bull. Soc. Chim.*, (3), **3.** 771, 1890 ; F. Osmond, *ib.*, (2), **43.** 56, 1885 ; J. Brown, *Amer. Journ. Science*, (4), **19.** 31, 1905 ; *Zeit. anorg. Chem.*, **44.** 145, 1905 ; **47.** 314, 1905 ; A. Skrabal and J. Preiss, *Monatsh.*, **27.** 505, 1906 ; A. Skrabal, *Zeit. anorg. Chem.*, **42.** 1, 1904 ; R. Ehrenfeld, *ib.*, **33.** 117, 1903 ; F. R. Lankshear, *ib.*, **82.** 97, 1913 ; *Proc. Chem. Soc.*, **28.** 198, 1912 ; *Zeit. anorg. Chem.*, **82.** 97, 1913 ; F. A. Gooch and E. W. Danner, *Amer. Journ. Science*, (3), **44.** 301, 1892 ; T. M. Chatard, *ib.*, (3), **1.** 416, 1871 ; *Chem. News*, **24.** 196, 1871 ; S. Peters, *ib.*, **33.** 35, 1876 ; *Dingler's Journ.*, **221.** 486, 1876 ; B. C. Brodie, *Proc. Roy. Soc.*, **11.** 442, 1861 ; W. Lindner, *Zeit. Chem.*, (2), **5.** 442, 1869 ; *Chem. Tech. Repert.*, i. 102, 1868 ; H. Rose, *Handbuch der analytischen Chemie*, Braunschweig, **1.** 24, 1867 ; N. Schiloff, *Ber.*, **36.** 2735, 1903 ; J. Wagner, *Zeit. phys. Chem.*, **28.** 33, 1899 ; *Massanalytische Studien*, Leipzig, 1898 ; H. N. Morse and J. C. Olsen, *Amer. Chem. Journ.*, **23.** 431, 1900 ; H. N. Morse, A. G. Hopkins and M. S. Walker, *ib.*, **18.** 401, 1896 ; H. N. Morse, *Ber.*, **30.** 48, 1897 ; B. W. Gerland, *ib.*, **10.** 1516, 1877 ; H. Schiff, *ib.*, **8.** 258, 1875 ; J. L. C. Zimmermann, *ib.*, **14.** 779, 1881 ; *Liebig's Ann.*, **213.** 311, 1882 ; C. W. Hempel, *ib.*, **107.** 100, 1858 ; *Mémoire sur l'emploi de l'acide oxalique dans les dosages à liqueurs titrées*, Lausanne, 1853 ; A. V. Harcourt and W. Esson, *Chem. News*, 10. 171, 1864 ; *B.A. Rep.*, 29, 1865 ; *Proc. Roy. Soc.*, **14.** 470, 1865 ; *Phil. Trans.*, **156.** 193, 1866 ; **157.** 117, 1867 ; **186.** 817, 1895 ; A. V. Harcourt, *Journ. Chem. Soc.*, **20.** 460, 1867 ; T. E. Thorpe and F. J. Hambly, *ib.*, **53.** 175, 182, 1888 ; M. M. P. Muir, *ib.*, **91.** 1485, 1907 ; F. Jones, *ib.*, **33.** 95, 1878 ; W. Ostwald, *Die wissenschaftlichen Grundlagen der analytischen Chemie*, Leipzig, 140, 1897 ; I. Macagno, *Gazz. Chim. Ital.*, **4.** 567, 1874 ; J. K. H. Inglis, *Zeit. Elektrochem.*, **9.** 226, 1903 ; R. Luther, *ib.*, **12.** 596, 1906 ; A. Rusconi, *Arch. Farm. Sper.*, **27.** 94, 1919 ; R. T. Colgate, *Journ. Soc. Chem. Ind.*, **32.** 893, 1913 ; F. W. Skirrow, *Zeit. anorg. Chem.*, **33.** 25, 1902 ; E. Müller and P. Koppe, *ib.*, **68.** 160, 1910 ; M. G. Levi and F. Ageno, *Atti Accad. Lincei*, (5), **15.** ii, 549, 615, 1906 ; F. Förster, *Electrochemie wässriger Lösungen*, Leipzig, 824, 1923 ; L. von Putnoky and B. von Bobest, *Zeit. Elektrochemie*, **37.** 156, 1931 ; B. von Bobest, *Beitrag zu der Darstellung der Permangansäure und ihrer Salze*, Zalaegerszeg, 1930 ; F. Duran, *Zeit. phys. Chem.*, **156.** 195, 210, 1931 ; A. Simon and F. Feher, *Zeit. Elektrochem.*, **38.** 137, 1932.

§ 15. The Permanganates

The general preparation of the permanganates is discussed in the preceding section in connection with permanganic acid. E. Mitscherlich [1] prepared **ammonium permanganate**, NH_4MnO_4, by treating silver permanganate with an eq. quantity of a soln. of ammonium chloride, filtering the liquid, and evaporating it for crystallization. H. Aschoff employed a similar process, and R. Böttger treated eq. proportions of barium permanganate and ammonium sulphate in a similar manner. O. T. Christensen modified a process also employed by R. Böttger in which 160 grms. of potassium permanganate were dissolved in 3 litres of water at 70°–80°, and a large excess (440 grms.) of ammonium chloride added ; the soln. was evaporated to about 1600 c.c., decanted from the precipitated manganese oxide, and allowed to stand for 24 hrs. The crystals contained a little potassium salt even after two recrystallizations from water at 70°. E. Moles and M. Crespi treated soln. of 16 grms. of potassium permanganate in 300 c.c. of water at 70° with 44 grms. of ammonium chloride in 300 c.c. of water, concentrated the soln. to 200 c.c., and cooled it to 0°. G. Rapin used an electrolytic process.

The rhombic bipyramidal crystals were found by E. Mitscherlich to be isomorphous with the potassium salt, and to have the axial ratios $a:b:c$ =0·8141 : 1 : 1·31201 ; W. Muthmann gave 0·8164 : 1 : 1·3168. The (110)-cleavage is distinct. F. Rinne studied the crystals. T. V. Barker calculated the topic axial ratio to be $\chi : \psi : \omega = 3\cdot9768 : 4\cdot8711 : 6\cdot4113$. E. Moles and M. Crespi gave 2·29 for the sp. gr. ; W. Muthmann gave 2·2076 for the sp. gr. and 62·126 for the mol. vol. I. I. Saslawsky gave 2·29 for the sp. gr. and calculated the contraction which occurs in the formation of the salt from its elements. When the salt is allowed to stand in a sealed tube exposed to diffuse daylight, it slowly decomposes, forming nitrogen oxides, ammonium nitrate, and a manganese oxide with a composition $MnO.22MnO_2.nH_2O$. W. Muthmann found that the dry salt is explosive ; it sometimes detonates when rubbed in a mortar, developing a cloud of manganese dioxide and a smell of ozone. E. Moles and M. Crespi found that the salt explodes at 60°. O. T. Christensen also observed that when the salt is heated to 58° or 60° it explodes in a few hours, forming nitrogen oxides and a manganosic oxide ; if first heated slowly to between 42° and 46°, and later to 50°, the decomposition occupies some days. H. Aschoff found that 100 parts of water dissolve 7·936 parts of the salt at 15°. E. Mitscherlich found that in the absence of an excess of ammonia, the aq. soln. can be evaporated without decomposition ; but the salt easily decomposes when heated. W. Muthmann observed that the aq. soln. decomposes when boiled, giving off nitrogen, and forming hydrated manganese dioxide. O. T. Christensen observed that when the aq. soln. is boiled, it furnishes the same products as when the dry salt is heated, and in addition some nitrogen ; and when the soln. is heated with ammonia, the decomposition products are nitrogen, ammonium nitrite, a little ammonium nitrate, and a hydrated oxide, $MnO.22MnO_2.28H_2O$, with some adsorbed ammonia. For the unit tetragonal cell of tetramethylammonium permanganate, $(CH_3)_4NMnO_4$, K. Herrmann and W. Ilge gave $a = 8\cdot439$ A., $c = 6\cdot019$ A.

E. Mitscherlich prepared **lithium permanganate,** $LiMnO_4.3H_2O$, from the soln. obtained by mixing soln. of silver permanganate and lithium chloride. A. A. Maximoff obtained the lithium salt by the action of lithium sulphate on barium permanganate—*vide supra*, permanganic acid ; and E. Moles and M. Crespi, by mixing a soln. of 30·8 grms. of lithium perchlorate in 300 c.c. of water, and 30·5 grms. of potassium permanganate in 300 c.c. of water. The filtrate from the precipitated potassium perchlorate finally deposits lithium permanganate. The sp. gr. of the salt is 2·06, and it begins to decompose when heated to 190°, with the evolution of oxygen. They found $K = 5\cdot10$ for the velocity of decomposition— *vide infra*, potassium permanganate. I. I. Saslawsky discussed the contraction which occurs in the formation of the salt from its elements. Its sp. gr. is 2·6. E. Mitscherlich said that the crystals are stable in air. H. Aschoff found that 100 parts of water at 16° dissolve 71·43 parts of the salt. E. Franke found the electrical conductivity, λ, of the aq. soln. with an eq. of the salt in v litres at 25° to be :

v .	. 32	64	128	256	512	1024
λ .	. 81·79	84·63	88·22	90·49	92·81	95·19

When heated with an excess of lithium hydroxide, H. Aschoff found that the salt forms a manganate. A. A. Maximoff studied its deoxidation in alkaline soln.

P. F. Chevillot and W. F. Edwards observed that **sodium permanganate,** $NaMnO_4$. $3H_2O$, is formed when sodium manganate is dissolved in water ; and H. Aschoff, that the salt is produced when silver permanganate is decomposed by a soln. of sodium chloride, the clear soln. evaporated over sulphuric acid, and the crystals dried on porous tiles. E. Moles and M. Crespi used a similar process. C. M. Tessié du Motay prepared a soln. of the salt by treating a soln. of sodium manganate with magnesium sulphate, in accord with the equation : $3Na_2MnO_4 + 2MgSO_4 + 2H_2O = 2Mg(OH)_2 + MnO_2 + 2Na_2SO_4 + 2NaMnO_4$. E. Köstermann and co-workers studied solid soln. with potassium perchlorate. E. Moles and M. Crespi said that the crystals of the monohydrate are hygroscopic. According to E. Schering, the commercial salt is really the potassium salt associated with

some of the sodium salt. The preparation of the salt was also described by
J. Bendix, and E. Desclabissac.. For electrolytic processes, *vide infra*, potassium
permanganate. F. M. Raoult represented the composition oft he salt by $NaMnO_4$.
$3H_2O$. I. I. Saslawsky discussed the contraction which occurs in the formation
of the salt from its elements. Its sp. gr. is 2·47. P. F. Chevillot and W. F. Edwards
observed that the crystals of the trihydrate are very deliquescent ; E. Moles and
M. Crespi found that the sp. gr. is 2·46, and that the salt decomposes with the
evolution of oxygen at 170°. They found $K=0.111$ to 0.212 for the velocity of
decomposition—*vide infra*, potassium permanganate. E. Franke found the eq.
electrical conductivity, λ, of an aq. soln. with an eq. of the salt in v litres of
water at 25° to be :

v .	. 64	128	256	512	1024
λ .	. 106·3	109·4	110·9	112·0	112·7

H. Aschoff observed that when sodium permanganate is boiled with a soln. of sodium
hydroxide, some oxygen is evolved and a soln. of sodium manganate remains.
A. A. Maximoff studied its deoxidation in alkaline soln. G. Gore, and E. C. Franklin
and C. A. Kraus said-that the salt is freely soluble in liquid ammonia.

P. F. Chevillot and W. F. Edwards prepared **potassium permanganate,** $KMnO_4$,
by igniting a mixture of 1 part of manganese dioxide with 1 part of potassium
hydroxide or 1·5 parts of potassium nitrate, dissolving the cold product in water,
and evaporating the decanted red soln. for crystallization. Any manganate
formed in the roasting process is converted into permanganate by hydrolysis :
$3K_2MnO_4+2H_2O=MnO_2+4KOH+2KMnO_4$. In place of potassium nitrate,
mixtures of potassium hydroxide and chlorate were recommended by G. Forchhammer, W. Gregory, F. Wöhler, R. Böttger, N. Gräger, and J. C. Sticht. In
A. Béchamp's process 10 parts of manganese dioxide are mixed with 12 parts of
potassium hydroxide, and water to make a pasty mass, and dried. The mixture
is heated to dull redness in oxygen. The cold mass is extracted with water, and a
current of carbon dioxide is passed into the soln. to convert any manganate into
permanganate : $3K_2MnO_4+2CO_2=2K_2CO_3+MnO_2+2KMnO_4$. The soln. is then
evaporated for crystallization. The process was also used by G. Forchhammer,
J. Brock and F. Hurter, and G. Städeler. T. J. Pearsall observed that potassium
permanganate is formed when a manganese salt is treated with chlorine and potash-
lye ; and G. Städeler converted manganate into permanganate by treating the
soln. with chlorine : $2K_2MnO_4+Cl_2=2KCl+2KMnO_4$. L. E. Rivot and co-
workers found that when manganese dioxide is suspended in alkali-lye at 40° to 50°
and treated with chlorine, permanganate is formed. The process was examined
by R. Böttger, W. Reinige, J. MacMullen, R. Phillip, E. Turner, R. J. Kane,
J. B. van Mons, R. B. Stringfield, F. Krause, and W. Foster.

R. Wagner, and J. Heslinga used bromine in place of chlorine to convert the
manganate into permanganate ; F. Bayer used ozone : $2K_2MnO_4+O_3+H_2O$
$=2KMnO_4+2KOH+O_2$. When a soln. of a manganous salt is treated with
sodium hypochlorite, hydrated manganese dioxide is precipitated (*q.v.*), and on
prolonged boiling, a small proportion of sodium manganate or permanganate is
formed. M. Duyk showed that if the reaction occurs in the presence of copper
salts, the copper is precipitated and permanganate is the main product. B. E. Dixon
and J. L. White found that a small amount of sodium permanganate· is formed
even when special precautions are taken to purify both the manganese salt and the
sodium hypochlorite, so the manganese dioxide itself appears to be capable of
catalyzing the reaction. When present in quantities roughly equivalent to that of
the manganese salt, the salts of several metals, notably copper, cobalt, nickel, and
molybdenum (as molybdate), possess the property of greatly increasing the amount
of permanganate formed in this reaction. In the presence of a copper salt the
maximum amount of permanganate is formed at the end of 3 mins.' boiling, and
when one-third of the total oxygen has evolved. The alkalinity or OH'-ion conc. of

the soln. is a critical factor in the case of copper, but is comparatively unimportant in the case of cobalt, though large conc. of alkali hinder permanganate formation. Moderate amounts of manganese salts can be completely oxidized to permanganate in the presence of copper, independently of the amount of manganese present. When cobalt is used, however, the proportion of permanganate formed decreases in a regular manner with increasing amounts of manganese. The form and the mode of action of the precipitates of cobalt and copper differ in several respects. That of cobalt is flocculent, finely divided, and difficult to filter, and promotes copious evolution of oxygen from the hypochlorite throughout the reaction. The copper precipitate, at first flocculent, soon passes into a dense black residue, easily separated, and becomes considerably less active as regards hypochlorite decomposition after the formation of the permanganate has taken place. The cobalt, when used in the form of the double sodium carbonate, cannot be completely separated from the soln. by boiling, as is the case with moderate quantities of copper. B. E. Dixon and J. L. White explain the main reaction as follows : the first effect of the hypochlorite is to form copper peroxide and hydrated manganese dioxide. The oxidation of manganese dioxide to permanganate, which can proceed in the presence of manganese alone, is greatly accelerated by the copper peroxide, which gives up its active oxygen, possibly through the intermediate formation of an unstable compound of copper and manganese, and is reconverted to the cupric form. At this stage much of the hypochlorite has been decomposed, and the hydroxyl-ion concentration, due to the alkali which is necessarily present in the hypochlorite soln., becomes an important factor. The excess of hydroxyl ions has an inhibitive effect on the formation of fresh copper peroxide, and the main reaction is arrested. If, however, the carbonate–bicarbonate mixture is used, (i) its buffer action renders the influence of the alkali negligible, and (ii) owing to the delayed precipitation of the copper, much of the earlier part of the reaction takes place in the liquid phase, and the oxidation of the manganese proceeds to completion. C. M. Tessié du Motay treated the cake of manganate from the furnace—*vide supra*, the extraction of manganese—with a conc. soln. of magnesium sulphate : $3K_2MnO_4 + 2MgSO_4 = 2KMnO_4 + MnO_2 + 2K_2SO_4 + 2MgO$. C. Huggenberg recommended boiling barium manganate with a soln. of potassium carbonate while carbon dioxide is passing through the soln. The potassium permanganate passes into soln., and the precipitate of hydrated manganese dioxide and barium carbonate is treated with steam and the product used for making more barium manganate. The manufacture of permanganate on an industrial scale was discussed by E. Schütz, J. C. Sticht, M. I. Belotzerkowsky, E. Desclabissac, R. B. Stringfield, E. Geay, and J. Bendix. O. Dieffenbach observed that alkali manganates can be made by the action of permanganates on manganese dioxide or other manganese oxides suspended in a hot, conc. alkaline soln. which is kept agitated. The permanganate is produced in the soln. itself as wanted by the electrolytic or chemical oxidation of the ready-formed manganate. Other oxidizing agents can be used to start the process. The process can be symbolized : $2KMnO_4 + MnO_2 + 4KOH = 3K_2MnO_4 + 2H_2O$, and $6K_2MnO_4 + 3H_2O + 3O = 6KMnO_4 + 6KOH$; or, if the two equations are summed : $MnO_2 + KOH + 1\frac{1}{2}O = KMnO_4 + \frac{1}{2}H_2O$. The first of these three equations is reversible, but equilibrium is but slowly attained. O. Sackur and W. Taegener calculated from observations on the potential that the equilibrium constant for $[K_2MnO_4]^3 K = [KMnO_4]^2 [OH']^4$ is $K = 1.6 \times 10^{-4}$; and the equilibrium concentrations in equilibrium with a mol of $KMnO_4$ per litre—*vide supra*, manganates—are :

OH' (N)				$0.1N\text{-}K_2MnO_4$	$0.01N\text{-}K_2MnO_4$	$0.001N\text{-}K_2MnO_4$
1.0	.	.	.	0.0004	0.000013	0.0000004
0.1	.	.	.	0.04	0.0013	0.00004
0.01	.	.	.	4	0.13	0.004
0.00000001 (neutral)	.			4×10^{10}	1.3×10^9	4×10^7

The permanganate can be obtained by an electrolytic process—*vide supra*, permanganic acid. Thus, H. N. Warren electrolyzed alkali-lye, using ferromanganese as anode and a graphite plate as cathode. R. Lorenz obtained a soln. of potassium permanganate by passing a current of 1·5 volts potential between an anode of commercial manganese or ferromanganese and a cathode of porous copper oxide dipping in a soln. of potash-lye. Ferric oxide collects as anode slime. Soln. of potassium manganate can be converted into permanganate by electrolytic oxidation, with or without a diaphragm. A. N. Campbell studied the electrolytic oxidation of manganous salts to permanganates. He found that with a soln. of 0·7767 grm. of manganese as sulphate and 191 grms. of sulphuric acid per litre, the optimum conditions are at 0° and a current density of 1·7 amp. per sq. dm., and that chlorides and nitrates should be absent. Evidence of the formation of the disulphate was also obtained. Electrolytic processes were described by K. Elbs, F. W. Skirrow, O. T. Christensen, Salzbergwerk neu Stassfurt, G. Rapin, G. J. A. Griner, R. E. Wilson and co-workers, C. O. Henke and O. W. Brown, J. Roudnick, P. Askenasy and S. Klonowsky, F. Weckbach, F. Krause, A. Manasse, K. Brand and J. E. Ramsbottom, G. Grube and H. Metzger, M. de K. Thompson, A. N. Campbell, L. de Putnoky, L. de Putnoky and B. de Bobest, A. J. Hale, H. C. Jenkins and H. Woolner, R. Lorenz, W. J. Müller, G. R. White, and F. Deissler—vide supra, manganese, and manganates. P. Askenasy and S. Klonowsky found that with iron electrodes, without diaphragm, a soln. of 80–90 grms. of potassium manganate per litre at 60°, a cathodic current density of about 0·8 amp. per sq. cm., and an anodic current density 6–8 times smaller, that cathodic reduction is not important, and that potassium permanganate soon crystallizes out. About 60 per cent. of the manganate is oxidized when the theoretical quantity of electricity for complete oxidation has passed through the soln. ; the loss of efficiency is due largely to the escape of free oxygen. About 75 per cent. of the manganate can be converted, and further oxidation is balanced by cathodic reduction. Platinum electrodes and a diaphragm give rather better yields, but the voltage must be doubled or tripled. More dilute or colder soln. decrease the yield. According to K. Brand and J. E. Ramsbottom, the yield of permanganate is increased by stirring the anodic liquor, and it decreases with an increase of the anodic current density. The yield is much greater with a nickel anode than with an iron anode, indicating that the oxygen primarily formed on the nickel oxidizes faster than when formed on iron.

Analyses of potassium permanganate were made by E. Mitscherlich, H. Aschoff, A. Gorgeu, and M. V. Machuca. The results agree with the empirical formula $KMnO_4$. The hypothesis of T. L. Phipson, and A. Terreil that the salt is either K_2MnO_7 or $KHMnO_4$ was contradicted by M. V. Machuca, C. M. Bradbury, and E. J. Maumené. F. M. Raoult showed that the formula $KHMnO_4$ cannot be right, because the salt contains no combined water. The subject was discussed by J. Personne, J. Personne and M. l'Hermite, E. Erlenmeyer and G. Lewinstein, C. M. Bradbury, G. Bredig, E. Franke, and J. M. Crofts. H. E. Armstrong and R. T. Colgate regarded the acid as a per-acid of the type $MnO_2.O.OH$; and R. T. Colgate represented it by the formula :

$$KO.O.Mn.O.O : O.O.Mn.O.OK$$
$$KO.O.Mn.\ddot{O}.\dot{O} : \dot{O}.\ddot{O}.Mn.O.OK$$

P. Niggli, and A. M. Taylor discussed the **electronic structure.** According to P. F. Chevillot and W. F. Edwards, potassium permanganate crystallizes in dark purple needles having at first a sweet taste, and afterwards a rough one. The salt is stable in air, and does not redden litmus or turmeric. According to G. Foster and G. Brude, the crystals of potassium permanganate prepared in the dark and in air free from carbon dioxide and organic matter are brown and have a bronze, metallic lustre. The finely-powdered crystals, however, show a dark violet colour. When exposed to subdued daylight and ordinary air, the surfaces of the crystals develop a violet colour in a few hours, and a steel-blue lustre after two days. This change is confined to the surface layer, which acts as a protective layer to the remainder of the crystal. The change is particularly rapid in an atm. containing mineral acid. The crystals of potassium permanganate should be described as bipyramidal rhombs rather than as prisms. J. W. Retgers said that thin microscopic crystals appear red by transmitted light. E. Mitscherlich pointed out that the **crystals** are ismorphous with those of potassium perchlorate. W. Muthmann gave for the axial ratios of the rhombic bipyramids $a:b:c=0\cdot7972:1:1\cdot2982$. The (001)- and (110)-**cleavages** are perfect. T. V. Barker gave for the topic axial parameters $\chi:\psi:\omega=3\cdot856:4\cdot836:6\cdot278$. The crystals are pleochroic. The crystals were examined by C. F. Rammelsberg, H. Mark and co-workers, and P. Groth. H. E. Buckley studied the habit of the crystals grown in different media. W. Basche found that the **X-radiogram** of potassium permanganate corresponded with a rhombic lattice having $a=9\cdot10$ A., $b=5\cdot69$ A., and $c=7\cdot40$ A., and 4 mols. per unit cell. The calculated axial ratios are $1\cdot60:1:1\cdot30$. R. C. L. Mooney gave for the rhombic crystals $a=9\cdot08$ A., $b=5\cdot72$ A., and $c=7\cdot41$ A., and each unit cell has four molecules. W. Büssem and K. Herrmann studied the subject.

The possibility of forming **isomorphous mixtures** with barium sulphate was discussed by W. Geilmann and E. Wünnenberg, E. Wilke-Dörfurt and R. Pfau,

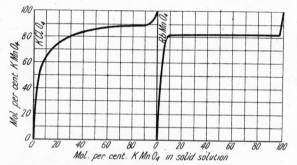

FIGS. 53 and 54.—Relations between the Composition of Solutions and Isomorphous Mixtures for the respective Systems : $KMnO_4$–$KClO_4$, and $KMnO_4$–$RbMnO_4$, at 7°.

D. Balareff and co-workers, G. Wagner, V. Chlopin and B. Nikiton, and H. Grimm and G. Wagner. G. Wagner studied the X-radiograms of the mixed crystals; and E. Köstermann and co-workers, the solid soln. with potassium borofluoride, KBF_4. F. Zambonini discussed the isomorphism of potassium permanganate and fluoborate. C. M. Bradbury observed no isomorphous mixtures are formed with sodium or silver permanganate, but the crystals are isomorphous with those of potassium perchlorate, and, added J. W. Retgers, with those of potassium periodate, KIO_4. E. Sommerfeld said that the isomorphous solid soln. of potassium permanganate and perchlorate are formed without a perceptible rise of temp. F. Rinne, and W. Muthmann and O. Kuntze found that a series of isomorphous mixtures is formed. Soln. containing C_1 and C_2 millimols respectively of potassium permanganate and perchlorate per litre at 7° furnish mixed crystals with the following mol. percentage proportion of the permanganate (Fig. 53) :

C_1	.	.	29·375	67·726	108·14	159·17	201·55	233·75	258·14
C_2	.	.	54·478	42·745	37·95	31·15	21·27	28·26	14·22
$KMnO_4$		.	2·838	9·778	19·276	40·120	84·469	94·372	96·48

Similar results were obtained with potassium and rubidium permanganates, with the same designations for the letters as before, but with C_2 standing for rubidium permanganate (Fig. 54) :

C_1	.	.	27·038	79·046	120·26	171·96	204·97	207·39	225·12
C_2	.	.	22·691	18·178	31·29	41·66	45·36	41·46	25·99
$KMnO_4$		.	3·498	13·746	34·293	74·973	99·406	99·363	99·324

A. Fock concluded that two series of isomorphous mixtures between potassium perchlorate and permanganate and potassium and rubidium permanganates are continuous, and, from an application of the partition-law, that the molecules of the salts in question have twice as great a mol. wt. in the solid state as they have in soln. The isomorphous mixtures of potassium permanganate with rubidium permanganate and with potassium perchlorate were studied by G. Tammann and A. Sworykin. T. V. Barker found that the axial ratios of the isomorphous mixtures of potassium permanganate and perchlorate, $a : b : c$—b unity—vary as follows :

$KMnO_4$	.	0·6	1·5	3·1	51·8	95·4 per cent.
a	.	0·7814	0·7817	0·7822	0·78975	0·7969
c	.	1·2807	1·2817	1·2815	1·2907	1·2985

G. Tammann and A. Sworykin discussed the protection of one salt by another in the case of a solid soln. of potassium permanganate and perchlorate in a soln. of perchlorate. H. E. Buckley studied the effect of permanganates on the crystallization of sodium chlorate.

H. Kopp found the **specific gravity** of potassium permanganate to be 2·709 to 2·710 ; and W. Muthmann, 2·7032. F. Flöttmann found that soln. sat. at 15°, 20°, and 25° had the respective sp. gr. 1·0342, 1·0391, and 1·0469. W. Muthmann gave 58·526 for the **molecular volume**. The subject was discussed by F. A. Henglein, and A. F. Hallimond. A. H. Schulze gave for the **specific volume** of aq. soln. :

	5°	10°	15°	20°	25°	30°
$0·1N$-$KMnO_4$	0·99996	1·00029	1·00095	1·00189	1·00308	1·00453
$0·01N$-$KMnO_4$	0·99991	1·00018	1·00078	1·00171	1·00248	1·00427

A. M. Patterson gave 1·035 for the sp. gr. of a sat. soln. at 15°. H. Sentis found that the **surface tension** of a 2·93 per cent. soln. at 15·4° is 73·84 dynes per cm., and the **specific cohesion,** $a^2 = 14·79$ per sq. mm. Z. Stary studied the effect of an electric field on the capillary rise. E. Ullmann, and I. D. Götz and G. P. Pamfil studied the velocity of **diffusion** of the salt ; and E. Ullmann found the diffusion coeff. to be $15·2 \times 10^{-6}$. N. P. Peskoff studied the diffusion of adsorbed permanganate from a ferric oxide hydrosol to a soln. of urea. He called the phenomenon *barophoresis*. P. Henry observed no evidence of diffusion with isomorphous crystals of potassium perchlorate and permanganate after being heated for several days. I. I. Saslawsky gave 2·71 for the sp. gr., and he calculated the contraction which occurs in forming the salt from its elements. J. N. Rakschit studied the contraction which occurs when the salt is dissolved in water. H. Kopp gave 0·179 for the **specific heat** of the solid. H. Aschoff observed that the crystals decrepitate when heated to 100° owing to included water. P. F. Chevillot and W. F. Edwards studied the **action of heat** and found that 10·8 per cent. of oxygen is given off at a temp. exceeding 200°, and a black mixture of potassium manganate and manganese dioxide remains. P. Thénard said that the reaction $2KMnO_4 = MnO_2 + K_2MnO_4 + O_2$ occurs at 240°, and when the residue is moistened with water, some oxygen is evolved. If the salt be more strongly heated, 15·3 per cent. of oxygen is given off, in accord with the equation : $2KMnO_4 = 3O + K_2O.2MnO_2$. P. Askenasy and A. Solberg found that G. Rousseau's statement that no manganate is formed at 240° is wrong even were the temp. 500°. P. Askenasy and A. Solberg showed that the evolution of oxygen from potassium permanganate begins to be appreciable at about 215°. When decomposition has commenced, oxygen continues to be evolved quite readily, even when the temp. is reduced to below 200°. The results agree with G. Rudorf's equation, but from the dissociation press. curve of manganese dioxide obtained by P. Askenasy and S. Klónowsky, Fig. 48, it is improbable that the residue contains free manganese dioxide. The dissociation press. of the residue was found to be 50 mm. at 505° ; 129 mm. at 560° ; 391 mm. at 594° ; and 400 mm. at 600°. From a comparison of the dissociation press. curves of manganese dioxide and potassium manganate, and of the residue resulting from the thermal decomposition of potassium permanganate, it is inferred that the decomposition should be represented by the equation : $10KMnO_4 = 2K_2MnO_3 + [3K_2MnO_4 + 5MnO_2] + 6O_2$, which agrees with the chlorine value of the residue. The reversibility of the reaction in which oxygen is evolved by the heated residue suggests that the entire residue or the bracketed constituents represent a chemical compound. It may be, however, that the manganate and the dioxide form a solid soln. in which the manganite is dissolved. W. Hempel and C. Schubert, and C. Schubert said that the decomposition begins at 160° ; and that the composition of the residue at 185° is $K_2Mn_2O_6$; at 570°, $K_2Mn_2O_5$; and at 1400°, $K_8Mn_8O_{14}$. E. Moles and M. Crespi found that the first sign of the decomposition of the dry salt occurs at 200°, and the pressures recorded below this temp. are due to water or to carbonates. Decomposition is complete at 240°, and the oxygen press. of the residue up to 485° correspond with those of manganese dioxide.

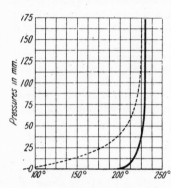

FIG. 55.—Dissociation Pressures of Potassium Permanganate.

Fig. 55 shows the dissociation curves of a sample of permanganate contaminated with carbon dioxide and water (dotted line), and of a sample of purified permanganate (continuous line). Potassium oxide is not a product of the decomposition, so that G. Rudorf's equation : $10KMnO_4 =3K_2MnO_4+7MnO_2+2K_2O+6O_2$ is not right ; rather is a permanganite formed : $10KMnO_4 =2K_2MnO_4+3K_2MnO_3+5MnO_2+13O$. E. Moles and M. Crespi concluded that the decomposition of the permanganates involves two reactions, which are autocatalytic, and they may be represented by the equation $dx/dt=(k_1+k_3x/a)(a-x)$, or $(1/t) \log \{a/(a-x)\}+(1/t) \log (1/kx)=$Constant, where $k=k_2/k_1$. For potassium permanganate, $k=0.881$. The two reactions involve a simple decomposition, and an autocatalytic decomposition which is negligible at first, but afterwards passes through a maximum value. The different velocity constants of decomposition for a number of permanganates are related with the heats of formation of the corresponding oxides. C. N. Hinshelwood and E. J. Bowen measured the rate of decomposition of potassium permanganate at 217° and 240° ; of solid soln. of potassium permanganate and perchlorate at 239° ; and of potassium permanganate and manganese dioxide at

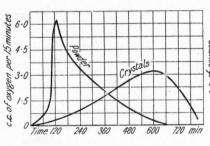

FIG. 56.—The Thermal Decomposition of Crystals and Powdered Potassium Permanganate.

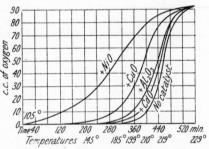

FIG. 57.—Effect of Admixed Oxides on the Thermal Decomposition of Potassium Permanganate.

220.5°. The decomposition appears to be confined to those molecules in the neighbourhood of the surface, and in the region where a progressive disintegration of the crystal structure takes place the change is strongly accelerated. Soln. in another solid causes a reduction in the rate of reaction. The results show that the molecules in the interior are under some kind of restraint ; this may be connected with the fact that in the interior the molecules are bound by valency forces on all sides, or it may be referred to the internal pressure. S. Roginsky and E. Schulz also studied the thermal decomposition of potassium permanganate powdered and crystallized, and some results are illustrated by Fig. 56. There is a period of induction and of autocatalysis for which the equation $dx/dt = kx(a-x)$ for many reactions in liquid system is not applicable. Surface again plays an important part. It was found that the decomposition is strongly accelerated by admixed NiO, Co_3O_4, MnO_2, Fe_2O_3, and CuO; less vigorously by Mn_3O_4, Ag_2O, SnO_2, and PbO; feebly by Sb_2O_5, Cr_2O_3, ZnO, Al_2O_3, CdO, and PbO_2; and very feebly or not at all by WO_3, MgO, TiO_2, HgO, CaO, U_3O_8, and SiO_2. This subject was also studied by K. Bädecker, F. Streintz, and G. Tammann and H. Bredemeier.

G. L. Voerman found the lowering of the **freezing-point** of aq. soln. containing 0·58, 1·01, 2·02, and 3·00 grms. of the salt in 100 grms. of water to be respectively —0·18°, —0·27°, —0·48°, and —0·58°. The last of the series is a eutectic mixture, so that the **eutectic temperature** is —0·58°. F. Guthrie found the eutectic temp. to be —0·57° with 2·82 per cent. of the salt. T. G. Bedford found the lowering of the f.p., $\delta\theta$, and the calculated degree of ionization, a, for soln. with n mols of the salt in 1000 grms. of soln. to be :

n	0·000615	0·00129	0·002	0·005	0·010	0·015
$\delta\theta$	—0·00225	—0·00481	—0·00732	—0·01800	—0·0357	—0·0534
a	—	—	0·970	0·935	0·920	0·915

G. Tammann found the lowering of the **vapour pressure** of water with 19·62, 56·06, and 111·13 grms. of potassium permanganate per 100 grms. of water to be 24·6 mm., 85·3 mm., and 197·1 mm. respectively. J. Thomsen calculated the **heat of formation** of the salt from its elements to be 194·825 Cals., and M. Berthelot, 200 Cals. ; A. Simon and F. Feher gave $2KMnO_4 \rightarrow 2K + 2Mn + 4O_2 + 389·63$ Cals., and $(KOHaq., HMnO_4aq.) = 13·7$ Cals. ; while for the **heat of solution,** J. Thomsen gave —10·4 Cals. ; M. Berthelot, —10·2 Cals. ; and W. A. Roth and G. Becker, —10·62 Cals. per mol. E. Moles and M. Crespi gave 60·0 Cals. for the **heat of decomposition.**

F. Flöttmann found that even 1 per cent. soln. were too deeply coloured to enable the **index of refraction** to be determined by daylight or Na-light. Observations on the **absorption spectrum** of crystals of potassium permanganate were made by G. G. Stokes, K. Schnetzler, E. Wiedemann, and J. Conroy ; of aq. soln., by G. G. Stokes, V. R. von Kurelec, A. Hagenbach and R. Percy, A. M. Taylor, C. J. W. Grieveson, H. Gombos, H. Kautsky and O. Neitzke, B. K. Mukerji and co-workers, E. Wiedemann, J. Conroy, E. Brücke, E. Pflüger, A. Hantzsch and R. H. Clark, E. Viterbi, J. E. Purvis, J. Moir, W. Ostwald, K. Schnetzler, F. Vlès and A. Simchen, H. M. Vernon, E. Adinolfi, W. N. Hartley, T. R. Merton, etc.—*vide supra*, physical properties of manganese ; and of soln. in non-aqueous solvents by A. Hantzsch and R. H. Clark. According to the ionic theory of colour, the potassium ions are colourless, whilst the MnO_4'-ions are purple, and the ions behave with respect to colour independently of one another. Further, in completely ionized soln. with one coloured ion, the coloration is independent of the colourless ion, and in partially ionized soln. the coloration is the joint effect of the colour of the salt molecule and of the coloured ion. W. Ostwald found that the absorption spectra of thirteen permanganates are the same at great dilutions ; hence it was inferred that the absorption spectrum of a salt soln. is the sum of the separate spectra due to the neutral molecules, anions, and cations ; and if the soln. is very dilute, it is completely ionized, and the colour is entirely due to the ions. W. Ostwald's proof broke down when other investigators showed that the absorption spectra of conc. soln. of permanganates are also identical. A study of the absorption spectra of soln. of cobalt, copper, nickel, and other coloured salts led R. A. Houstoun to conclude that there is no spectroscopic evidence in favour of the theory of ionization ; rather is the evidence against that theory, unless it be supported by assumptions of hydrolysis, hydration, etc. W. W. Coblentz measured the ultra-red transmission spectrum of potassium permanganate. J. E. Purvis attributed the changes which occur on diluting soln. of the permanganates to the ionizing power of water acting slowly on the dissolved permanganate so that the ionic condition $R^{\cdot}$ and $MnO_4{}'$ breaks down. The $MnO_4{}'$-ion may be broken down into $MnO_3{}''$- and O''-ions or into manganese dioxide and oxygen. In dil. soln. the tension between the molecules of water surrounding the ions must be very considerable, and it may be so great as to destroy the MnO_4 condition, so that further changes take place, which become visible in changes of colour, in changes in the width of the bands, and in the liberation of oxygen ; and these changes would be accelerated by the vibrations of light. The intermediate stages of the changes might be represented by the narrowing of the bands 1, 2, and 3, and the widening of the bands 4 and 5, and these might correspond to changes of the MnO_4-ions into MnO_3 and O-ions. According to W. N. Hartley, in dil. soln. the permanganates are hydrolyzed and then decomposed into a colloidal soln. of manganic hydroxide, $MnO(OH)_2$, and free oxygen. This action occurs even when the soln. are made in darkness and preserved in the dark. The most striking change seen in the spectra is a greatly increased general absorption, that is, a shortening of the transmitted rays. With soln. preserved in darkness it is apparently proportional to the dilution, but the effect of sunlight greatly increases the decomposition. The narrowing of the bands $\lambda\lambda 546$ and 524, and the widening of those at $\lambda\lambda 504$, 486, are easily explained by the decomposition having diminished the quantity of the permanganate or permanganic acid, and therefore weakened the bands and increased the quantity of the hydroxide, $MnO(OH)_2$, in colloidal soln. ; this has greatly extended the general absorption until it in part overlies the more refrangible of the bands. The absorption bands of permanganates are not characterized by sharpness ; they have a hazy indistinctness, with no definite boundary lines such as are commonly seen in uranium, didymium, and erbium absorption spectra. Owing to these properties, if the light is not diminished in intensity but the permanganate is reduced in quantity, the intensity of the bands will be diminished, and this will cause a reduction in their width. If, however, the intensity of the transmitted light is diminished, the reverse effect will be seen in an increased width of the bands. The intensity of the light is not diminished so far down into the green as $\lambda 524$, but the colloidal soln. of the hydroxide, $MnO(OH)_2$, not only extends the complete absorption in the direction of the bands, but also enfeebles the transmitted rays by a partial absorption extending to $\lambda 504$. Hence, two of the bands in the less refrangible rays are narrower and two in the more refrangible rays are broader than in the unaltered soln. H. Becquerel showed that the greater the conc. of the soln. the greater the shift of the bands towards the red end of the spectrum. W. N. Hartley added that this means that the conc. soln. is mainly a soln. of the salt, and that dilution causes hydrolysis ; the shift of the edge of the band to a more refrangible group of rays is precisely what might be expected by the conversion of barium permanganate into hydrogen permanganate ; furthermore, we should expect the shift to be of greater extent in the case of the barium salt than in that of the zinc permanganate, as appears to be the case. T. R. Merton measured the absorption bands in soln. of various permanganates in different solvents—water, acetone, methyl acetate, acetic anhydride, pyridine, acetonitrile, methyl, ethyl, and amyl alcohols, and ethylene glycol—and also a solid soln. of potassium permanganate and perchlorate. In the last case the general character of the spectrum is the same as in liquid soln., but the bands are shifted towards the violet. The position of the bands in water is thus intermediate between the positions in the alcohols pyridine and acetone and the positions in the solid soln. The general nature of the absorption is due to the atomic grouping MnO_4, and it is influenced very little, if at all, by the nature of the cation or the extent of ionization, the position of the points of maximum absorption being determined by the nature of the medium in which the salt is dissolved. R. W. Wood measured the absorption spectrum of soln. in liquid ammonia. The **anomalous dispersion** of potassium permanganate was studied by A. Kundt, J. J. Soret, and O. T. Christensen.

According to E. K. Rideal and R. G. W. Norrish, when a soln. of potassium permanganate is illuminated by ultra-violet light, it undergoes a marked change of electrode potential, which slowly reverts to its original value when the light is extinguished. The change in light is attributed to an alteration in the hydrogen-ion concentration of the soln. brought about by photochemical decomposition of the potassium permanganate, thus : $2KMnO_4=K_2O.2MnO_2+3O$. The compound $K_2O.2MnO_2$ is precipitated and a red sol of manganese dioxide and potassium permanganite is formed. The decomposition is unimolecular over the range of conc. studied, and it is shown how the velocity constant can be calculated either from the changes of electrode potential during illumination or from the dark-recovery curve. The value of the equilibrium constant $K=0.00149$. A photochemical stationary state is produced in the soln. owing to removal of potassium hydroxide by combination with hydrated manganese dioxide. The rate of decomposition of potassium permanganate is increased by the addition of sulphuric acid to the soln. In such soln. the reaction, throughout almost the whole of its course, is of zero order, the constant velocity indicating continuous complete absorption of the photoactive radiation. This change in the type of decomposition is connected with the non-formation of colloid in the acid soln. Ammonium nitrate, uranyl nitrate, and potassium hypochlorite soln. afford photoactive effects similar to those observed with potassium permanganate. The ultra-violet absorption spectrum has a band between 3800 and 2700 with its head at 3130. The visible radiations of the mercury lamp are not appreciably effective in decomposing the soln. of potassium permanganate ; but the line 3128 A. is taken to be mainly responsible for the photochemical action. With this assumption, and taking the coeff. of absorption for green and yellow light to be the same as for ultra-violet light, it is probable that two quanta of energy are concerned in the photochemical decomposition of the permanganate ion. Mixtures of potassium permanganate and oxalic acid are more sensitive to ultra-violet than to ordinary light. D. N. Chakravarti and N. R. Dhar studied the fluorescence of soln. A. Kailan found the salt is decomposed by radium radiations, but O. Risse observed no photolysis on exposing to X-rays. K. Chamberlain, and G. L. Clark and L. W. Pickett found that the salt is reduced by exposure to X-rays, and this interferes with the measurement of the X-rays absorption. A. E. Lindh, D. Coster, and O. Stelling studied the X-ray spectrum. E. Montignie found that after exposure to ultra-violet light, potassium permanganate affects a photographic plate. W. Schneider studied the piezoelectric effect.

G. Bredig gave for the eq. **electrical conductivity,** λ mhos, of soln. containing a mol of the salt in v litres of water at 25° :

v	32	64	128	256	512	1024
λ	121·7	125·3	128·3	130·3	131·2	132·4

and at 0°, W. C. D. Whetham found for n mols of the salt in a litre of water :

n	0·020	0·010	0·005	0·001	0·0005	0
λ	70·6	72·2	73·5	75·1	75·5	75·9

Observations on the electrical conductivity, λ, and the degree of ionization, α, at temp. between 0° and 35°, made by L. G. Winston and H. C. Jones, are as follow :

v		8	32	128	512	1024	2048	4096
	0°	59·34	63·75	66·76	66·46	64·65	63·72	62·64
λ	12·5°	80·17	87·13	91·38	91·14	89·05	86·61	87·94
	25°	104·36	113·70	119·31	117·90	113·95	110·80	111·80
	35°	124·74	136·05	142·42	141·49	137·09	133·02	133·97
	0°	0·888	0·954	1·000	0·995	0·968	0·954	0·938
α	25°	0·875	0·953	1·000	0·988	0·955	0·929	0·937
	35°	0·876	0·955	1·000	0·994	0·963	0·934	0·941

Measurements were also reported by E. Bouty, H. C. Jones and co-workers, R. Lorenz and W. Michel, P. Walden, A. Ferguson and I. Vogel, and E. Legrand. A. Berthoud said that the supposed maximum in the mol. conductivity curve is due to experimental errors. A. A. Noyes and K. G. Falk calculated for the **degree**

of ionization, a, of soln. with 0·020, 0·010, and 0·005 mols per litre the respective values a=0·913, 0·921, and 0·938 from f.p. data ; and 0·930, 0·951, and 0·968 from conductivity data—*vide supra.* The subject was discussed by H. M. Vernon. W. Bein calculated 0·559 for the **transport number** of the anion at 25°—but the result is doubtful. The subject was studied by L. Engel and W. Pauli. R. Lorenz and W. Neu measured the velocity, V, and transport number, v, of the MnO_4'-ions at 18° and 25°, and reported the following data :

	0·25N-	0·0625N-	0·015625N-	0·0078125N-	0·001953125N-	0·0004878049N-
18° $V \times 10^7$	433·1	485·2	513·3	523·6	537·6	541·0
v	41·9	46·82	49·54	50·53	51·88	52·52
25° $V \times 10^7$	503·6	564·1	596·9	608·8	625·1	628·92
v	48·60	54·33	57·60	58·75	60·32	60·92

K. F. Ochs measured the potential of platinum in soln. of permanganate and sulphuric acid. O. Sackur and W. Taegener calculated from the e.m.f. of the cell Pt : $KMnO_4,K_2MnO_4$: KOH,HgO | Hg, that the **oxidation potential** of potassium permanganate in alkaline soln. exceeds that of oxygen at one atm. press. and at room temp. The normal potential for the change MnO_4'=MnO_4''+F is E_H=0·61 volt, and the equilibrium press. of the soln., containing manganate, permanganate, and OH'-ions of normal concentration, is nearly 6×10^{13} atm.—*vide supra*, manganic and permanganic acids. D. J. Brown and A. Liebhafsky calculated for the oxidation potential of the reaction MnO_4'+8H·+5e$\rightleftharpoons$Mn·· +4H_2O+1·446 volts ; and D. J. Brown and R. F. Tefft obtained 1·586 volts for the potential of the manganese dioxide—permanganate electrode. S. Popoff and co-workers were unable to measure the potential of the permanganate—hydrogen —manganese dioxide electrode, for potassium permanganate soln. containing perchloric acid are unstable in the presence or absence of manganese dioxide. For the electrode potential of manganese dioxide in permanganate soln., *vide* manganese trioxide. F. Weigert studied the **electrolytic reduction** of soln. of potassium permanganate by a platinum cathode charged with hydrogen. At potentials smaller than that required to liberate hydrogen gas, the current passing is due to the reaction between hydrogen and the oxidizing agent in the soln. The velocity of this reaction is a function of the press. of the hydrogen and of the conc. of the oxidizing agent in the soln. in immediate contact with the cathode. If depolarization is so rapid that the depolariser at the cathode is used up, the current passing is fixed by the velocity with which the depolarizer can diffuse to the cathode. G. Baborovsky studied the electrolytic reduction of permanganate at a magnesium anode. In neutral and alkaline soln. MnO_4''-ions are primarily formed. G. Wenger and H. H. Alvarez concluded from their observations on the reduction of acidic soln. of potassium permanganate by an alternating current : (i) The reduction is strongest with rotating electrodes whatever may be their nature. (ii) Copper electrodes reduce the soln. the most rapidly, whilst aluminium in twice the time only effects a partial decomposition. (iii) In the experiment with the current the phenomenon is more pronounced at the beginning than at the end of the experiment. (iv) The reduction due to the sole action of the metal is, of course, almost negligible with platinum electrodes (non-oxidizable metal). A. W. Warrington described a two-liquid cell with potassium permanganate as the depolarizing agent ; G. P. Vincent also studied the depolarizing action of the permanganate.

E. Wedekind and C. Horst found the **magnetic susceptibility** of manganese compounds increases with the valency up to that of potassium permanganate. P. Pascal gave $25·5 \times 10^{-5}$ mass unit for the magnetic susceptibility of the salt ; E. Wedekind gave $0·18 \times 10^{-6}$. P. Collet calculated the at. magnetization of manganese, from the paramagnetism of solid potassium permanganate, to be $56·5 \times 10^{-6}$, and it is independent of the temp. between 15° and 150°. The paramagnetism is raised by impurities. The value for soln. of the salt is 62×10^{-6} and it is constant between 17° and 100°. The subject was studied by L. A. Welo and A. Baudisch,

G. Meslin, S. Freed and C. Kasper, and G. Quincke. T. Ishiwara, and K. Honda and T. Ishiwara gave for the effect of temp. on the magnetic susceptibility :

	$-170\cdot4°$	$-93\cdot5°$	$-34\cdot1°$	$9°$	$94\cdot5°$	$162\cdot0°$
$\chi \times 10^6$ ..	$0\cdot179$	$0\cdot170$	$0\cdot176$	$0\cdot175$	$0\cdot175$	$0\cdot184$

According to P. F. Chevillot and W. F. Edwards, when the crystals are heated in **hydrogen,** they become red-hot, and diminish in bulk, at first rapidly, and then slowly, with the formation of a green mixture of potassium hydroxide and manganous oxide, in accord with the equation : $2KMnO_4 + 5H_2 = 2KOH + 2MnO + 4H_2O$. F. Duran studied the absorption of hydrogen by the solid. V. Meyer and A. Saam found that the absorption of hydrogen by a 5 per cent. soln. of potassium permanganate proceeds at a uniform speed when the liquid is agitated ; and F. Hein and W. Daniel added that the solubility of hydrogen in aq. soln. is greatly favoured if silver salts, $e.g.$ the nitrate, be present. F. Jones found that a neutral aq. soln. of potassium permanganate is reduced by hydrogen : $2KMnO_4 + 4H_2 = Mn_2O_3 + 2KOH + 3H_2O$, especially when warmed ; the reduction in alkaline soln. is slow. W. Ipatieff and A. Kisseleff found that at 300° hydrogen under press. over 150 atm. reduces potassium permanganate soln. to form hausmannite, $Mn_3O_4.H_2O$. J. A. Wanklyn and W. J. Cooper found that if acidic, alkaline, or neutral soln. are allowed to stand in contact with hydrogen, the gas is absorbed and the soln. reduced. L. Delwaulle observed that in acidic soln., hydrogen precipitates manganese dioxide with the evolution of oxygen ; in neutral soln., colloidal manganese dioxide is formed, but no oxygen is evolved ; and in alkaline soln., potassium manganate is first formed, and ultimately manganese dioxide. V. Meyer and M. von Recklinghausen found that if an acidic soln. be shaken with hydrogen, some oxygen is given off as the soln. is reduced, but if the soln. is not acidified, reduction occurs without the evolution of oxygen. This evolution of oxygen soon reaches a limit, though if the soln. be allowed to stand quietly, the decomposition takes place continuously, and a far larger amount of oxygen is given off ; nevertheless, the action is not reversible. They represented the reaction :

$$\frac{H_2}{H_2} + \frac{O.O}{O.O} = 2H_2O + O_2$$

H. Hirtz and V. Meyer concluded that the production of oxygen from acidic soln. cannot be attributed to the reducing action of the precipitated hydrated manganese dioxide on the permanganate. The oxygen evolved does not contain ozone, since that gas is produced only with conc. acid. F. Hein and W. Daniel found that whilst a soln. of pure silver nitrate reacts only slowly with hydrogen at ordinary temp., a soln. of potassium permanganate in the presence of hydrofluoric acid or silver nitrate quickly absorbs hydrogen. Thus, the number of c.c. of hydrogen absorbed by a sat. soln. of potassium permanganate, mixed with various substances are as follow :

	$0\cdot02N$-HF	$0\cdot02N$-AgF	$0\cdot02N$-AgNO$_3$	$0\cdot06N$-AgNO$_3$	$0\cdot16N$-AgNO$_3$	$0\cdot02N$-AgClO$_3$
H$_2$-absorbed .	$12\cdot7$	$85\cdot2$	$100\cdot0$	$30\cdot0$	$80\cdot0$	$30\cdot0$

The nitrates of copper, mercury, and lead have very little action in favouring the absorption of hydrogen by the permanganate. With a sat. soln. of silver permanganate 30 c.c. of hydrogen were absorbed.

H. N. Morse and co-workers showed that finely-divided manganese dioxide can reduce soln. of potassium permanganate with the liberation of oxygen : $2HMnO_4 + nMnO_2 = H_2O + (n+2)MnO_2 + 1\frac{1}{2}O_2$—$vide$ $supra$, permanganic acid. The reaction was discussed by R. T. Colgate. H. Hirtz and V. Meyer thought that manganese dioxide cannot be the cause of the liberation of oxygen during the absorption of hydrogen by acidified soln., because no oxygen is evolved with neutral soln., although manganese dioxide is also present. H. N. Morse and C. L. Reese, however, thought that the liberation of oxygen by hydrogen is due to the precipitated manganese dioxide, and that the action is continuous, without the limit suggested by V. Meyer and M. von Recklinghausen. H. N. Morse and C. L. Reese said that the oxygen is evolved more rapidly during the absorption of hydrogen than is subsequently the case when the precipitated manganese dioxide reacts with the permanganic acid. The molecules of the manganese dioxide originally precipitated by a gaseous reducing agent are of greater simplicity and are capable of more rapid action than those produced by a solid like manganous sulphate. H. N. Morse and H. G. Byers concluded that with acidic soln. the liberation of oxygen is due to the reduction of the permanganic acid by the precipitated manganese dioxide, rendered active by the sulphuric acid which is present. The fact that no oxygen is liberated in neutral soln. may be due to the potassium permanganate being more stable than permanganic acid, or to the precipitated manganese dioxide being saturated with alkali, or to both causes combined. The falling off with the time of the reducing power of the manganese dioxide in acid soln. is explained by assuming the initial activity of the manganese dioxide molecules to be due to their simplicity ; as the molecules become more complex owing to polymerization, so do they lose their power of reduction. It was noticed that whilst the oxide formed in acidified soln. is, in general (especially in the more conc. soln.), more active during the first 24 hrs. than that formed in neutral soln., the converse is true after 150 hrs. In support of this, J. C. Olsen and F. S. White found that manganese dioxide precipitated from a sulphuric acid soln. of a permanganate persistently retains adsorbed sulphuric acid during the washing, whereas with nitric acid soln. the nitric acid can be easily removed by washing. The reduction of permanganic acid by manganese dioxide is attributed to the weak basic properties of manganese dioxide, and its tendency to unite with sulphuric acid rather than with nitric or permanganic acid. The amount of sulphuric acid retained by the precipitate is inversely proportional to the excess of oxygen in the precipitate, as adsorbed permanganic acid, over that required for manganese dioxide. Consequently, manganese dioxide acts as a base and combines with sulphuric or permanganic acid. The adsorbed permanganic acid readily decomposes, with the evolution of oxygen, forming a polymerized manganese dioxide, which is much less active than manganese dioxide itself. V. Meyer and co-workers rejected the hypothesis that the oxygen is derived from hydrogen dioxide, but H. E. Armstrong and R. T. Colgate assume that hydrogen dioxide is a product of the oxidation, and they represent the reaction by the equation, with manganese dioxide as catalytic agent :

$$\begin{matrix} MnO_2 \vdots O.OH \\ MnO_2 \vdots O.OH \end{matrix} + \begin{matrix} H \vdots OH \\ H \vdots OH \end{matrix} + (MnO_2) = \begin{matrix} MnO_2 \\ MnO_2 \end{matrix} + \begin{matrix} HO.OH \\ HO.OH \end{matrix} + HO.OH + (MnO_2)$$

where 3 mols. of hydrogen dioxide would be formed and, in agreement with the equation of H. N. Morse and co-workers, produce $1\frac{1}{2}$ mols. of oxygen when decomposed catalytically by manganese dioxide. G. Just and Y. Kauko observed that with neutral soln. of potassium permanganate of different concentrations, and with hydrogen mixed with varying proportions of nitrogen, the rate of reaction is proportional to the conc. of each of the reacting substances, and therefore that one mol. of hydrogen reacts primarily with one mol. of permanganate. It follows that a quinquevalent, very unstable salt of manganese is formed as an intermediate product. The manganese dioxide formed in the course of the reaction has no effect on the rate. The speed of the reaction is approximately doubled by raising the temp. from 15° to 25°. E. Wilke and H. Kuhn found the reaction not so simple as was assumed by G. Just and Y. Kauko, owing to the separation of manganese oxide. The speed of oxidation is decreased in the presence of acids or alkalies, or by exposure to X-rays. K. Volz discussed the oxidizing action of the permanganates.

A. Skrabal and J. Preiss found that in the spontaneous decomposition of soln. of potassium permanganate there is a period of induction, just as in the case of permanganic acid (*q.v.*). The reduction of potassium permanganate soln. is a complex process involving a series of consecutive reactions between the products of the reduction, and between these products and the permanganate itself, and the decomposition of the permanganate resulting in the evolution of oxygen, a reaction influenced by catalytic effects of the products of the decomposition. A. Skrabal considered that the reduction in acidic soln. involves a *period of incubation*, during which the permanganate is reduced in accord with $Mn^{vii}=Mn^{ii}+O_2$; a *period of induction*, in which $Mn^{ii}+Mn^{vii}=Mn^{iii}$, and the change of the tervalent manganese by two side reactions: $Mn^{iii}=Mn^{ii}+Mn^{iv}$, and $Mn^{iii}=Mn^{ii}+O_2$; and there is the *terminal period*, when $Mn^{iv}=Mn^{ii}+O_2$. These reactions occur if no reducing agent is present, while in the presence of reducing agents one or more stages may be accelerated, and more permanganate may be consumed than is equivalent to the oxidation of the reducing agent. This subject has been discussed by A. V. Harcourt, A. V. Harcourt and W. Esson, R. Ehrenfeld, R. Luther, N. Schiloff, etc.— *vide supra*, permanganic acid, and manganese dioxide. The self-reduction of the permanganate is so very slow in feebly acidic and neutral soln. that they can be kept a long time when of a high degree of purity, and employed as volumetric soln. for analytical work. A. A. Maximoff studied its deoxidation in alkaline soln. F. Duran studied the absorption of **oxygen** by the solid.

E. Mitscherlich found that 100 parts of **water** at 15° dissolve 6·25 parts of the salt. Some observations on the solubility of the salt in water were reported by F. Guthrie, O. Sackur and W. Taegener, W. Herz and M. Knoch, and A. M. Patterson. W. Muthmann and O. Kuntze gave 4·184 grms. per 100 c.c. of sat. soln. at 7°. The following results are compiled from those of G. L. Voerman, E. C. Worden, and G. P. Baxter and co-workers for the percentage solubility, S:

	−0·18°	−0·58°	4°	10°	19·80°	29·80°	40°	50°	60°	75°
S	0·58	2·91	3·15	4·01	5·96	8·28	10·78	14·40	18·03	24·44

F. Flöttmann gave for the solubility at 15°, 20°, and 25° respectively 0·327, 0·391, and 0·469 mols per litre, or 4·997, 5·946, and 7·079 per cent.

P. F. Chevillot and W. F. Edwards, and R. Luboldt stated that if the aq. soln. of potassium permanganate be free from reducing agents, it can be preserved unchanged; and similar remarks apply to the crystals of the salt, for they are permanent in air. H. N. Morse and co-workers said that permanganate soln. should not be filtered through paper, but rather through asbestos; such soln. exhibit a high degree of stability, whether kept in darkness or in diffused daylight; but soln. of a high degree of purity are decomposed in direct sunlight. R. W. Oddy and J. B. Cohen also found that the stability of soln. is not perceptibly affected by exposure to light, but after 14 days the titre of the soln. was slightly less; and J. C. Bell found that only a small reduction occurred after the soln. had been kept for some months. C. Meinecke and K. Schröder found that the titre remained constant for two months with soln. whose surface was covered by a layer of vaseline oil. R. Luboldt found that aq. soln. of the purified salt were not perceptibly decomposed after being boiled for half an hour. J. O. Halverson and O. Bergeim discussed the preparation of soln. which do not vary more than 0·1 per cent. per week. The subject was discussed by O. Hackl, G. Bruhns, I. M. Kolthoff and co-workers, and W. M. Gardner and B. North. P. A. Tscheishwily found that a soln. of potassium permanganate in distilled water alone suffered no reduction in eight months; a reduction occurred after each of the first eight filtrations through asbestos, after which reduction no longer occurred on filtration; a clear filtrate could not be obtained through glass-wool. The presence of various sulphates all caused a slow reduction of the permanganate; with chrome-alum the reduction is rapid. T. Warynsky and P. A. Tscheishwily found that the decomposition of $0\cdot01M\text{-}KMnO_4$ with $\frac{1}{30}M\text{-}H_2SO_4$, in the presence of various salts used as catalysts, is accelerated in the dark, but is a retarded action in daylight. Also, in green and blue light most salts retarded the action, but in orange light a slight acceleration was observed ; the retarding effect, therefore, probably depends on the actinic rays. A rise of temp. also affects the catalytic power of salts on the reaction ; it increases the activity of the sulphates of iron, chromium, and aluminium, but retards the action of cadmium sulphate. The activity of certain catalysts, such as ferric alum, increases with the concentration. According to E. Mitscherlich, an aq. soln. of potassium permanganate, acidified with sulphuric or nitric acid, slowly evolves bubbles of oxygen gas at 30°, but with a boiling soln. the decomposition is rapid; hydrated manganese dioxide is precipitated. A. Skrabal and J. Preiss found that in the spontaneous decomposition of soln. of potassium permanganate there is a period of incubation, just as in the case of permanganic acid (q.v.). J. Holluta found that $0.004N$-$KMnO_4$ is not decomposed by long boiling, even on adding small quantities of manganese sulphate ; more dil. soln., say $0.002N$-$KMnO_4$, are slowly decomposed by boiling, possibly by the intermediate formation of $KMnO_3$, followed by the formation of K_2MnO_4 and MnO_2. The decomposition of permanganic acid, or acidified soln. of potassium permanganate, has been previously discussed. The decomposition of the permanganate in alkaline soln. was studied by R. H. Ferguson and co-workers.

TABLE II.—THE SOLUBILITY OF POTASSIUM PERMANGANATE IN SOLUTIONS OF POTASSIUM HYDROXIDE.

Temp.	H_2O	N-KOH	$2N$-KOH	$4N$-KOH	$6N$-KOH	$8N$-KOH	$10N$-KOH
0° .	0·176	0·050	0·031	0·027	0·023	0·017	0·012
10° .	0·278	0·112	0·093	0·048	0·040	0·028	0·016
(19°) 20° .	0·411	0·179	0·119	0·079	(0·074)	0·032	0·029
30° (32°) .	0·573	(0·316)	(0·213)	(0·149)	0·114	(0·062)	0·040
40° .	0·792	0·439	0·306	0·211	0·161	0·084	0·052
50° (53°) .	(1·154)	0·638	0·462	0·304	0·219	0·111	—
60° (63°) .	1·429	(0·904)	0·639	0·427	0·291	0·143	0·071
70° .	1·812	1·172	0·869	0·572	0·390	0·188	0·082
75° .	2·047	—	—	0·651	—	—	0·089
80° .	—	1·513	1·190	—	0·500	0·231	—
(83°) 84° .	—	1·655	1·352	(0·803)	0·572	—	—
90° .	—	—	—	—	0·649	0·297	—

If a soln. of potassium permanganate and conc. **potassium hydroxide** be boiled, E. Mitscherlich, R. Luboldt, and H. Aschoff observed that the liquid becomes black, then green, and it develops oxygen, forming potassium manganate. The reaction was studied by A. A. Maximoff. C. F. Schönbein observed that an excess of potassium hydroxide gradually decolorizes a soln. of potassium permanganate and a hydrated manganic dioxide is precipitated which, when treated with an acid, separates iodine from potassium iodide. C. F. Mohr, P. Thénard, R. Böttger, and C. F. Rammelsberg found that a dil. soln. of alkali-lye prepared from the hydroxide which has been fused does not change the permanganate ; and P. F. Chevillot and W. F. Edwards found that the permanganate soln. is reduced by potassium hydroxide purified by alcohol—and therefore containing organic matter—and likewise by a sodium carbonate soln. which has been frequently filtered through paper. The reduction which occurs with ordinary alkali-lye was also attributed by G. Forchhammer, and H. Aschoff to the presence of organic matter ; by G. Forchhammer, to potassium sulphide ; and by E. Bohlig, to the presence of thiosulphate. Many substances rich in oxygen were found by P. Thénard to accelerate, by contact, the action of alkali-lye on hydrated manganese dioxide, but not so, added H. Aschoff. The action of this agent has been discussed in connection with permanganic acid, and with the action of hydrogen on potassium permanganate. According to E. Mitscherlich, if a conc. soln. of the crystals of potassium permanganate in dil. alkali-lye be evaporated in vacuo, the crystals are re-formed with only a slight loss by decomposition ; but a very dil.

soln. slowly becomes green at ordinary temp. and more rapidly if the temp. be raised. In order that the change to green manganate may be complete, the quantity of aq. soln. must be sufficient to absorb the oxygen liberated in the passage of permanganate to manganate. The green soln. is reddened by acids, with the separation of hydrated manganese dioxide. O. Sackur and W. Taegener measured the solubility of potassium permanganate, expressed in mols per litre, in soln. N-KOH to $10N$-KOH, and the results are given in Table II. P. F. Chevillot and W. F. Edwards found that the permanganate soln. is also turned green by a soln. of **sodium, barium, or strontium hydroxide.** The action of a soln. of **calcium hydroxide** is slight, owing to the great dilution of the liquid. It was suggested that complex salts are formed, because in the case with barium hydroxide no barium permanganate is precipitated although that salt is virtually insoluble in water. O. Sackur and W. Taegener found the solubility, S mols per litre of sat. soln., in soln. of **potassium carbonate** to be :

K_2CO_3		$0\cdot1N$-	N-	$2N$-	$4N$-	$6N$-
	$0°$.	$0\cdot1462$	$0\cdot0629$	$0\cdot0446$	$0\cdot0270$	$0\cdot0156$
S {	$25°$.	$0\cdot4375$	$0\cdot2589$	—	$0\cdot0930$	—
	$40°$	$0\cdot7380$	$0\cdot5007$	$0\cdot3519$	—	—

and in soln. of **potassium chloride** to be :

KCl .		$0\cdot1N$-	$0\cdot5N$-	N-	$2N$-
	$0°$	$0\cdot1395$	$0\cdot0760$	$0\cdot0532$	$0\cdot0379$
S {	$25°$	$0\cdot4315$	$0\cdot3060$	$0\cdot2200$	$0\cdot1432$
	$40°$	$0\cdot7380$	$0\cdot5840$	$0\cdot4400$	$0\cdot2880$

W. Herz and F. Hiebenthal gave for the solubility, S, of potassium permanganate in n-normal soln. of various salts :

LiCl {	n	0	$0\cdot51$	$0\cdot87$	$2\cdot56$	$3\cdot81$	$4\cdot56$	
	S	$2\cdot25$	$2\cdot18$	$2\cdot09$	$1\cdot51$	$1\cdot16$	$0\cdot95$	
NaCl {	n	$0\cdot59$	$0\cdot96$	$2\cdot26$	$3\cdot35$	$4\cdot22$	$5\cdot15$	
	S	$2\cdot32$	$2\cdot29$	$2\cdot13$	$1\cdot86$	$1\cdot73$	$1\cdot53$	
NH_4Cl {	n	$0\cdot59$	$0\cdot95$	$2\cdot69$	$3\cdot78$	$4\cdot57$	$5\cdot45$	
	S	$1\cdot94$	$1\cdot75$	$1\cdot05$	$0\cdot86$	$0\cdot78$	$0\cdot72$	
$MgCl_2$ {	n	$0\cdot96$	$1\cdot92$	$4\cdot62$	$6\cdot42$	$7\cdot64$	$8\cdot10$	$9\cdot52$
	S	$2\cdot01$	$1\cdot78$	$0\cdot96$	$0\cdot64$	$0\cdot48$	$0\cdot40$	$0\cdot16$
$CaCl_2$ {	n	$1\cdot70$	$4\cdot96$	$6\cdot80$	$8\cdot10$			
	S	$2\cdot00$	$1\cdot20$	$0\cdot91$	$0\cdot80$			
$SrCl_2$ {	n	$0\cdot64$	$2\cdot48$	$3\cdot92$	$4\cdot52$	$5\cdot90$		
	S	$2\cdot27$	$1\cdot94$	$1\cdot64$	$1\cdot54$	$1\cdot36$		
KCl {	n	$0\cdot36$	$0\cdot61$	$1\cdot65$	$2\cdot32$	$2\cdot89$	$4\cdot06$	
	S	$1\cdot56$	$1\cdot30$	$0\cdot74$	$0\cdot58$	$0\cdot51$	$0\cdot40$	

for LiCl, $S=2\cdot250-0\cdot285n$; for NaCl, $S=2\cdot422-0\cdot173n$; for NH_4Cl, $S=2\cdot50-0\cdot446n$, and $S=1\cdot370-0\cdot120n$; for $MgCl_2$, $S=2\cdot250-0\cdot279n$, and $S=1\cdot700-0\cdot161n$; for $CaCl_2$, $S=2\cdot318-0\cdot188n$; and for $SrCl_2$, $S=2\cdot250-0\cdot157n$. H. M. Trimble found the percentage solubilities, S, in soln. of **potassium sulphate** and of **sodium sulphate**, at $25°$, are as follow. The soln. sat. with respect to both salts are marked with an asterisk.

K_2SO_4	$0\cdot00$	$0\cdot80$	$1\cdot98$	$5\cdot47$	$7\cdot79$	$9\cdot26^*$	$10\cdot75$	
$KMnO_4$	$7\cdot10$	$6\cdot59$	$5\cdot92$	$4\cdot52$	$3\cdot87$	$3\cdot55$	$0\cdot00$	
Sp. gr.	$1\cdot0454$	$1\cdot0483$	$1\cdot0537$	$1\cdot0730$	$1\cdot0876$	$1\cdot0979$	$1\cdot0864$	
Na_2SO_4	$0\cdot00$	$0\cdot88$	—	$7\cdot05$	$12\cdot85$	$19\cdot43$	$21\cdot04^*$	$21\cdot80$
K_2MnO_4	$7\cdot10$	$7\cdot33$	—	$7\cdot75$	$7\cdot27$	$6\cdot25$	$5\cdot91$	$0\cdot00$
Sp. gr.	$1\cdot0454$	$1\cdot0554$	—	$1\cdot1180$	—	$1\cdot2363$	—	$1\cdot2071$

The solubility of potassium permanganate in soln. of potassium sulphate decreases with increasing conc. of the sulphate. In soln. of sodium sulphate the solubility increases to a maximum with increasing conc. of sodium sulphate. The maximum solubility lies at about 6 per cent. of sodium sulphate, after which there is a slow decrease in solubility to a minimum in soln. which contain the maximum amount of sodium sulphate soluble in the presence of permanganate crystals. For the lower conc. of each sulphate, potassium sulphate acts powerfully in decreasing the solubility of potassium permanganate in soln. of sodium sulphate, whilst sodium sulphate increases its solubility in soln. of potassium sulphate to a much smaller degree.

According to C. F. Schönbein, **hydrogen dioxide** decomposes a soln. of potassium permanganate, with the separation of hydrated manganese dioxide. In neutral soln. C. Weltzien represented the reaction : $2KMnO_4 + 2H_2O_2 = 2KOH + (Mn_2O_3 + 2O_2) + 3H_2O$. L. Swiontkowsky obtained a similar result for feebly acidic soln. F. Wöhler and A. Geuther and others also found that the manganese dioxide (q.v.) also reacts with the hydrogen dioxide in acidic soln. H. Aschoff represented the initial and final stages of the reaction by $2KMnO_4 + 3H_2SO_4 + 5H_2O_2 = 2MnSO_4 + K_2SO_4 + 8H_2O + 5O_2$. B. C. Brodie said that three consecutive reactions are involved : the permanganate in alkaline soln. reacts with the alkali dioxide, forming a manganate ; the manganate then passes to hydrated manganese dioxide ; and the precipitate, in the presence of an acid, gives off oxygen and forms a manganous salt ; B. C. Brodie, and E. Schöne added that the reaction does not start at once, but once it is started it proceeds very rapidly. L. Maquenne, and R. Engel suggested that a trace of a manganous salt must first be formed, and it is this which reduces the permanganate to a manganic salt, and the latter is reduced by the hydrogen dioxide to a manganous salt, and so the cycle begins anew. The permanganate forms the manganic salt in the presence of sulphuric acid only very slowly. P. H. Segnitz found the reaction is accelerated by a soln. of a manganous salt. According to M. Martinon, if a soln. of potassium permanganate be added to an acidic soln. of hydrogen dioxide, the reaction is symbolized : $2KMnO_4 + 5H_2O_2 + 6HCl = 2MnCl_2 + 2KCl + 8H_2O + 5O_2$, whereas if the acidic soln. of hydrogen dioxide is added to the permanganate, a precipitate of hydrated manganese dioxide is formed, and the reaction is symbolized : $6KMnO_4 + 9H_2O_2 + 6HCl = 6KCl + 2H_4Mn_3O_8 + 9O_2 + 8H_2O$. This reaction also varies in character with the rate at which the hydrogen dioxide is added to the soln. If a neutral or alkaline soln. of hydrogen dioxide is added to the soln. of the permanganate, the reaction progresses in accord with $KMnO_4 + 2H_2O_2 = KOH + Mn(OH)_3 + 2O_2$. If the soln. of permanganate is very dilute and very alkaline, a small quantity of manganate is momentarily formed when hydrogen dioxide is slowly added—*vide* **4. 31, 33.** A. Gorgeu also found when hydrogen dioxide is added to a soln. of permanganate, the quantity of dioxide decomposed varies from 3 to 11 eq. per eq. of permanganate ; but when the permanganate is added to the hydrogen dioxide, there is no limit to the amount of hydrogen dioxide which is decomposed. When hydrogen dioxide is added to an alkali permanganate, the precipitate retains a considerable quantity of alkali, and a larger proportion of dioxide is required for complete decolorization. A combination of manganese dioxide and the alkali seems to be formed, and reacts readily with the hydrogen dioxide. At first a brown soln. is formed, which very readily decomposes, and which probably contains potassium permanganite. In the presence of a large excess of alkali the brown liquid is not formed. The permanganate is first converted into the green manganate, and the latter is then decolorized. J. Zawidzky gave for the speed of the reaction : $dx/dt = k(1-x)x^{-\frac{1}{2}}$, where $k = 0.119$ and 0.379 respectively at $-16°$ and $15°$. A. A. Maximoff observed that if hydrogen dioxide or the peroxide of the alkali metal be added in excess to a soln. of the hydroxide and permanganate of sodium or potassium, no manganate is formed, but a vigorous reaction, resulting in the production of manganese dioxide, takes place. The quantities of hydrogen dioxide necessary for complete deoxidation to manganate and to manganese dioxide respectively are in agreement with the theory that the reaction takes place in two consecutive stages, given for potassium permanganate by the equations $2KMnO_4 + H_2O_2 + 2KOH = 2K_2MnO_4 + 2H_2O + O_2$, and $2K_2MnO_4 + 2H_2O_2 = 4KOH + 2MnO_2 + 2O_2$. These equations hold only when the potassium hydroxide conc. is greater than about $0.5N$. If it is less than about $0.05N$, hydrated manganese dioxide is formed simultaneously with potassium manganate ; a rise of temp. has a similar effect. It is considered that the formation of a peroxide of an alkali metal is a necessary intermediate stage of the reaction. Observations on the reaction were also made by W. Ramsay, P. Thénard, M. Berthelot, A. Bach, R. T. Colgate, N. A. Tananaeff, A. Clever, and A. von Bayer and V. Villiger.

V. Thomas and P. Dupuis observed that liquid **chlorine** at its b.p. has no action on the solid permanganate; G. Gore, that liquid **hydrogen chloride** attacks the solid permanganate, making it swell up, but does not dissolve it ; J. W. Thomas, that the dry gas vigorously attacks the crystals, with the development of heat, forming chlorine, water, potassium chloride, and manganous and manganic chlorides. K. Fredenhagen studied the action of **hydrofluoric acid.** O. Ohmann, and C. Graebe found that with **hydrochloric acid** chlorine is evolved. The reaction between potassium permanganate and hydrochloric acid was studied by R. F. Weinland and P. Dinkelacker. J. Wagner thought that the reaction is catalyzed by ferric chloride, but J. Brown did not find it so. The reaction is a convenient one for making chlorine for laboratory purposes on a small scale. The reaction is represented : $2KMnO_4 + 16HCl = 2KCl + 2MnCl_2 + 8H_2O + 5Cl_2$. F. P. Venable and D. H. Jackson represent it as a two-stage reaction : $2KMnO_4 + 8HCl = 2KCl + 2MnO_2 + 4H_2O + 3Cl_2$, followed by $MnO_2 + 4HCl = MnCl_2 + 2H_2O + Cl_2$ if enough acid be present. There is a reaction with $0.00154N$-**hydrobromic acid,** but no reaction occurs with less than $0.02N$-HCl. D. Balareff and G. Kandilaroff observed that owing to adsorption barium sulphate reduces the speed of oxidation of hydrogen chloride in dil. soln. by permanganate. R. Lang observed that an excess of potassium permanganate in $5N$-sulphuric acid oxidizes **iodine, hydriodic acid,** and **iodic acid** to periodic acid. The reaction is hindered by chlorides. C. W. Hempel, M. Gröger, and W. Lindner observed that **potassium chloride and bromide** are not attacked by a boiling neutral soln. of the permanganate. M. A. Rozenberg found that an increase in the acidity of the soln. changes the reaction with a bromide from a multimolecular to a monomolecular one : $MnO_4' + 5Br' + 8H^{\cdot} = Mn^{\cdot\cdot} + 5Br + 4H_2O$. L. P. de St. Gilles found that iodine is converted into iodic acid ; and M. Gröger, that **potassium iodide** is converted into iodate—these reactions proceed best in the presence of alkali carbonate or hydro-carbonate : $KI + 2KMnO_4 + H_2O = KIO_3 + 2KOH + 2MnO_2$. M. Bobtelsky and D. Kaplan discussed the action of various salts on the reaction. The reaction is utilized in the volumetric titration of the iodides, and it was discussed by C. W. Hempel, R. Espenchied, C. Weltzien, F. L. Hahn and G. Weiler, C. F. Mohr, E. Sonstadt, S. Popoff and A. H. Kunz, E. Brücke, M. Gröger, and A. Longi and L. Bonavia. E. Müller and H. Möllering observed that in sulphuric acid soln. the reaction is complicated by the formation of an iodate, and in hydrochloric acid soln. by the formation of iodine chloride. According to E. Fürst, **chlorine dioxide** forms potassium chlorate and manganese dioxide : $KMnO_4 + 3ClO_2 + H_2O = MnO_2 + KClO_3 + 2HClO_3$. G. R. Levi and D. Ghiron found that permanganates oxidize **chlorites** to chlorates, in accord with $3ClO_2' + 2MnO_4' + H_2O = 3ClO_3' + 2MnO_2 + 2OH'$.

P. F. Chevillot and W. F. Edwards found that when solid potassium permanganate is triturated with **sulphur** partial detonation may occur, but when heated the mixture may explode. J. B. Senderens said that sulphur reduces a soln. of the permanganate at ordinary temp : $2KMnO_4 + S + 2H_2O = 2(MnO_2.H_2O) + K_2SO_4$; and J. W. Slater observed that when the mixture is boiled a sulphate is formed, while M. J. Fordos and A. Gélis added that some non-oxidized sulphur is carried along by the steam, and some dithionate may be formed. S. Cloez and E. Guignet observed that a boiling, sat. soln. of permanganate slowly oxidizes the sulphur in green powder to sulphuric acid. P. F. Chevillot and W. F. Edwards found that an excess of **hydrogen sulphide** decolorizes a soln. of the permanganate, forming potassium sulphate and precipitating pale red manganous sulphide, and also, according to H. Rose, some sulphur.   C. F. Schlagdenhauffen observed that if the permanganate be added to an aq. soln. of hydrogen sulphide, a brown precipitate is formed which rapidly turns white, and with more permanganate a clear soln. and black precipitate are formed.   According to H. B. Dunnicliff and S. D. Nijhawan, when a slow current of hydrogen sulphide is passed through a 1 per cent. soln. of potassium permanganate, the purple soln. becomes brown and a white deposit of sulphur appears round the delivery tube.   After a short time a greyish-brown solid separates without appreciable rise in temp.; this slowly changes, first to a yellow mixture of hydrated manganese dioxide, manganese sulphide, and sulphur, and finally to a pink precipitate of manganese sulphide containing much sulphur, the temp. rising rather more than 10°.   Other observations by H. B. Dunnicliff and S. D. Nijhawan are indicated in connection with hydrogen sulphide.   A. Peter, L. P. de St. Gilles, and S. Cloez and E. Guignet found that **alkali sulphides** are oxidized to sulphates, and C. F. Schlagdenhauffen added that the reaction proceeds faster if a dil. soln. of the sulphide be added to the warm soln. of permanganate.   M. Bobtelsky and D. Kaplan discussed the action of various salts on the reaction.   H. Pinsl represented the reaction : $8KMnO_4 + 3Na_2S + 4H_2O = 8KOH + 8MnO_2 + 3Na_2SO_4$.   According to M. Hönig and E. Zatzek, **alkali polysulphides** with cold soln. form trithionate and sulphur, while with warm soln. alkali sulphate and sulphuric acid are formed.   The addition to a permanganate soln. of **ammonium hydrosulphide** results in the precipitation of a rose-coloured manganese sulphide ; the reaction with sulphides was studied by L. P. de St. Gilles, A. Longi and L. Bonavia, J. W. Slater, W. R. E. Hodgkinson and J. Young, J. Mijers, J. B. Senderens, M. J. Fordos and A. Gélis, T. S. Dymond and F. Hughes, C. Luckow, M. Hönig and E. Zatzek, R. Böttger, and C. F. Schlagenhauffen.   L. P. de St. Gilles observed that most **metal sulphides** are oxidized by the permanganate ; and C. F. Schlagdenhauffen added that the reaction is complete with the sulphides of copper, calcium, zinc, bismuth, manganese, iron, and nickel, and incomplete with those of mercury, tin (ic), lead, arsenic, and antimony. P. F. Chevillot and W. F. Edwards, and H. Buignet found that **sulphur dioxide** or **sulphurous acid** acts on a soln. of permanganate, forming alkali and manganous sulphates ; M. J. Fordos and A. Gélis added that some dithionate may be formed, and that in the presence of alkali carbonates the conversion of the sulphite to sulphate is almost complete.   W. R. E. Hodgkinson and J. Young studied the reduction of the permanganate by dry sulphur dioxide.   H. P. Cady and R. Taft found the salt to be insoluble in liquid sulphur dioxide.   F. Durau studied the absorption of sulphur dioxide by the solid.   M. Hönig and E. Zatzek found that **alkali sulphites** are completely oxidized to sulphate at ordinary temp., whether in neutral or alkaline soln.   The quantity of permanganate consumed in the reaction is smaller the more dilute the soln. of the permanganate ; and the composition of the precipitate varies with the concentration of the soln. of permanganate.   This subject was discussed by M. Gröger, and W. S. Hendrixson. R. Böttger found that alkali sulphite turns permanganate soln. green, and J. Mijers added that with very dil. soln., say one part of sulphite in 100,000 parts of soln., the red permanganate soln. is coloured indigo-blue ; the red coloration returns after about 24 hrs.   When sulphurous acid is titrated with potassium permanganate under conditions where the escape of sulphur dioxide or oxidation by air is excluded, about 88 per cent. of the theoretical amount of permanganate is consumed as required by the equation : $5H_2SO_3 + 2KMnO_4 = 2KHSO_4 + 2MnSO_4 + H_2SO_4 + 3H_2O$. T. S. Dymond and F. Hughes trace this to the formation of dithionic acid.   If the reaction be $17H_2SO_3 + 6KMnO_4 = 2K_2S_2O_6 + K_2SO_4 + 6MnSO_4 + 6H_2SO_4 + 11H_2O$, then 88·2 per cent. of the oxygen required to convert all the sulphurous into sulphuric acid will be required.   The temp., acidity, and conc. of the soln. make no difference to the result.   S. Cloez and E. Guignet found that **sodium thiosulphate** is oxidized to the sulphate ; and, added L. P. de St. Gilles, the reaction is almost complete in the presence of alkali carbonates.   M. Hönig and E. Zatzek observed that in the cold the reduction of the permanganate is complete, and only independent of the concentration of the permanganate in alkaline soln.; one part of $Na_2S_2O_3.5H_2O$ consumes 1·6366 parts of $KMnO_4$, and the precipitate approximates in composition to $KH_3Mn_3O_8$; on the other hand, M. Gläser observed that with hot, conc., neutral soln. the reaction is complete; one part of $Na_2S_2O_3.5H_2O$ consumes 1·6621 parts of $KMnO_4$, and the precipitate corresponds with $KH_3Mn_4O_{10}$; A. Alander found that some tetrathionate may be formed. M. Gröger discussed the reaction. J. Mijers found that one part of sodium thiosulphate in 200,000 parts of soln. will colour a red soln. of potassium permanganate indigo-blue, but the red colour is restored when the soln. is allowed to stand for 24 hrs. M. Bobtelsky and D. Kaplan discussed the action of various salts on the reaction. The reaction was studied by S. Popoff and J. L. Whitman, S. Popoff and F. L. Chambers, T. Milobendzky, K. Schröder, W. C. Vosburgh, J. M. Hendel, R. S. McBride, W. C. Bray and G. M. McKay, and W. C. Bray and H. E. Miller. According to H. Schjerning, a mixture of sodium sulphide and thiosulphate when boiled with the permanganate soln. for 15 mins. gives a cinnamon-brown precipitate of $Mn_3O_4.nH_2O$; but with cold soln. a precipitate of hydrated manganese dioxide, $MnO_2.nH_2O$, is formed. L. P. de St. Gilles found that **alkali dithionates** are not affected by a soln. of potassium permanganate, while **alkali trithionates** are incompletely oxidized, slowly in the cold, rapidly when heated. According to P. F. Chevillot and W. F. Edwards, the crystals of permanganate dissolve in **sulphuric acid** without effervescence, forming an olive-green soln.; the decomposition of the salt in soln. takes place very slowly. If water be progressively added to the olive-green soln., the colour changes in succession to light green, orange-yellow, and scarlet. Sulphuric acid, with dilutions up to a sp. gr. 1·60, forms a red soln. from which oxygen is evolved—in a few hours with conc. acid, and in a few months with dil. acid; the liquid is thus decolorized and brown hydrated manganese oxide precipitated. As indicated above, E. Mitscherlich observed that bubbles of gas are given off slowly from a soln. of the permanganate and sulphuric acid at 30°, but rapidly when boiled; hydrated manganese dioxide is precipitated. A. Bach found that **permonosulphuric acid** is quantitatively reduced to sulphuric acid. According to A. von Bayer and V. Villiger, a sulphuric acid soln. of **persulphuric acid** and potassium permanganate is a very powerful oxidizing agent, and it is at once decolorized by benzene and by adipic and phthalic acids. B. Brauner, and J. F. Norris and H. Fay observed that **tellurous acid** is oxidized by the permanganate to telluric acid, without precipitating manganese oxide.

According to J. A. Wanklyn and W. J. Cooper, **nitrogen** is not oxidized by permanganate soln. at 100°. G. Gore, E. C. Franklin and C. A. Kraus, and H. Moissan observed that potassium permanganate is very soluble in liquid **ammonia**. P. F. Chevillot and W. F. Edwards found that ammonia is decomposed by a soln. of potassium permanganate, and nitrogen is given off. H. Rose, and S. Hoogewerff and W. A. van Dorp said that the reaction is slow with dil. soln., even when heated on a water-bath, but, added L. P. de St. Gilles, it is greatly accelerated if formic acid be present. S. Cloez and E. Guignet observed that some alkali nitrite is formed in cold soln., and this with an excess of permanganate or in hot soln. forms the alkali nitrate. H. Tamm noticed that some ammonium nitrite may be formed; and F. Jones represented the reaction: $8KMnO_4+8NH_3=4Mn_2O_3$ $+KNO_2+KNO_3+6KOH+9H_2O+3N_2$. The reaction was also studied by F. Wöhler, and J. A. Wanklyn and A. Gamgee. According to H. Rose, **ammonium salts** are not oxidized by the permanganate. W. Meyeringh found that **hydroxyl-amine salts** in the cold react with the permanganate with the evolution of nitrogen and nitric oxide, and when heated, nitric acid is formed. L. J. Simon represented the reaction with the nitrate: $2KMnO_4+5(NH_2OH.HNO_3)=2Mn(NO_3)_2+2KNO_2$ $+2N_2O+10H_2O$; and with arsenate or phosphate: $12KMnO_4+16\{(NH_2OH)_3.$ $H_3PO_4)\}=4Mn_3(PO_4)_2+6KH_2PO_4+2K_2HPO_4+2KNO_2+20N_2+3N_2O+89H_2O$. T. Curtius and F. Schrader observed that **hydrazine salts** reduce permanganate to the manganous state, and if an excess be added, a brown oxide is deposited. The oxidation of hydrazine sulphate was also studied by W. Herz, and N. A. Orloff. U. Roberto and F. Roncali, and K. Weisbrod represented the reaction: $4KMnO_4$ $+6H_2SO_4=2K_2SO_4+4MnSO_4+6H_2O+5O_2$; and $5O_2+5(N_2H_4.H_2SO_4)=10H_2O$ $+5H_2SO_4+5N_2$. J. Petersen represented the reaction: $17N_2H_4+13O=13H_2O$ $+14NH_3+10N_2$. This is also in agreement with L. Medri's results. J. A. Wanklyn and W. J. Cooper observed that **nitrous oxide** is not altered by the permanganate soln. at 100°; and P. F. Chevillot and W. F. Edwards, that **nitric oxide** precipitates hydrated manganese dioxide and forms potassium nitrate. J. A. Wanklyn and A. Gamgee found that nitric oxide is rapidly absorbed and oxidized by a cold soln. of permanganate, and the action is vigorous at 100°. B. C. Dutt and co-workers represented the reaction: $KMnO_4+NO=KNO_3+MnO_2$, with no intermediate formation of nitrous acid. L. P. de St. Gilles, G. Lunge, S. Feldhaus, and H. N. Morse and A. F. Linn also observed that in acidic soln. nitric oxide, and **nitrogen peroxide** are oxidized to nitric acid or nitrates— some nitrite may be formed. S. Feldhaus, and W. Kubel found that **nitrites** are oxidized to nitrates, but L. P. de St. Gilles said that alkaline soln. of a nitrite is not oxidized by the permanganate soln. M. Bobtelsky and D. Kaplan studied the action of various salts on the reaction with sodium nitrite. P. F. Chevillot and W. F. Edwards, and E. Mitscherlich observed that the behaviour of **nitric acid** on the permanganate resembles that of sulphuric acid. According to P. F. Chevillot and W. F. Edwards, crystals of potassium permanganate detonate vigorously when triturated with **phosphorus**; the reaction is more violent if assisted by heat. J. W. Slater said that phosphorus forms potassium phosphate when treated with the permanganate soln. at ordinary temp., and with a boiling soln. some phosphite is formed. F. Jones observed that **phosphine** is oxidized to a mixture of phosphite and phosphate; P. F. Chevillot and W. F. Edwards, that **phosphides** are oxidized to phosphates; L. P. de St. Gilles, that **hypophosphites** in alkaline soln. are not completely oxidized to phosphates; O. Kühling, that **phosphorous acid,** and **phosphites** are oxidized to phosphates; and J. W. Smith utilized the reaction for the detection of the lower oxides in phosphorus pentoxide. J. W. Slater found that **hypophosphates** are converted by permanganate to phosphates. P. F. Chevillot and W. F. Edwards found that **phosphoric acid,** of sp. gr. 1·80, dissolves potassium permanganate to form a green soln. When **arsenic** is triturated with the solid salt, the mixture detonates. J. W. Slater, and W. Foster observed that powdered arsenic is quickly oxidized by a soln. of potassium permanganate; F. Jones, that **arsine** reacts in accord with: $2KMnO_4+AsH_3=Mn_2O_3$ $+K_2HAsO_4+H_2O$; P. F. Chevillot and W. F. Edwards, that **arsenic trioxide** colours the soln. brown or brownish-yellow, and if· the conc. of the soln. be great enough, the liquid is decolorized, and a brown precipitate is formed—L. P. de St. Gilles, J. Holluta, R. Lang, O. Cantoni, F. Feigl and F. Wiener, A. Bose, W. T. Hall and C. E. Carlsón, E. H. Swift and C. H. Gregory, M. Geloso, A. Bussy, C. Reichard, A. Guyard, G. Kessler, R. Lang, W. G. Vannoy, T. Oryng, and M. Travers added that the oxidation of arsenic trioxide is complete. M. Bobtelsky and D. Kaplan studied the action of various salts on the reaction. G. Bonnet found that **potassium arsenite** precipitates a brown manganese oxide; and D. R. Hale discussed the induced reaction between potassium permanganate, sodium arsenite, and ferrous sulphate. C. F. Schlagenhauffen found that **arsenic trisulphide** is incompletely oxidized by potassium permanganate—*vide supra.* According to P. F. Chevillot and W. F. Edwards, and W. Foster, when **antimony** and solid potassium permanganate are triturated together, the metal inflames. J. W. Slater found that powdered antimony is converted into potassium antimonate by a cold or boiling soln. of potassium permanganate; F. Jones obtained the same product by the action of **stibine** ; and A. Reynoso, G. Kessler, and A. Guyard, by the action of **potassium antimonite.** A. Bussy, C. Reichard, A. Guyard, and G. Kessler found that **antimony trioxide** is oxidized; W. Pugh studied the reduction to the tervalent stage by antimonious salts in the presence of fluorides. C. F. Schlagenhauffen found that **antimony trisulphide** is incompletely oxidized by a boiling soln. of potassium permanganate, while **bismuth trisulphide** is completely oxidized under similar conditions. B. W. Gerland, and C. Friedheim found that **hypovanadates** are oxidized to vanadates. F. E. Brown and J. E. Snyder observed that **vanadium oxytrichloride,** hot or cold, has no action on potassium permanganate.

H. Zocher and H. Kautsky found that there is a faint green luminescence when potassium permanganate oxidizes oxydisilin, rhodamine, and other organic dyes. H. Moissan found that **boron** reduces a cold soln. of potassium permanganate. P. C. Ray and K. K. Chatterji studied the ternary system: potassium permanganate, **potassium fluoborate,** and water at 25°, and observed that **potassium fluoborato-permanganate,** $KBF_4.6KMnO_4$, is formed. H. Moissan and S. Smiles showed that **silicon,** prepared by sparking silene, reduces the cold soln. slowly and the hot soln. rapidly ; while **silane** behaves in a similar manner. L. Kahlenberg and W. J. Trautmann observed that when a mixture of powdered silicon and permanganate is heated over the bunsen burner, an explosion occurs. F. Pisani found that **titanous salts** are oxidized to titanic salts. According to P. F. Chevillot and W. F. Edwards, a mixture of **carbon** with solid potassium permanganate does not take fire when triturated in a mortar, but when heated the mixture burns like tinder. T. Oryng, and A. Wassermann found that potassium permanganate is readily adsorbed from aq. soln. by animal charcoal. There is first a period of rapid adsorption, followed by a slow period during which the permanganate is reduced. Acids accelerate the rate of removal of permanganate from aq. soln., and the effect increases with the conc. of the acid. S. Cloez and E. Guignet found that a boiling soln. of the permanganate slowly oxidizes the carbon in gunpowder to carbon dioxide. According to V. Meyer and M. von Recklinghausen, H. N. Morse and H. G. Byers, V. Meyer and E. Saam, and H. Hirtz and V. Meyer, the reducing action of **carbon monoxide** on soln. of potassium permanganate resembles that with hydrogen ($q.v.$) ; and G. Just and Y. Kauko, that in neutral soln. of potassium permanganate the rate of reaction is proportional to the conc. of the carbon monoxide. It was found necessary, in order to get effective mixing of the gas and soln., to rotate the reaction vessels 5000 times per minute. The conc. variations were brought about by mixing the carbon monoxide with nitrogen. The reaction in the first place occurs between one mol. of carbon monoxide and one mol. of potassium permanganate, with the probable formation of an unstable quinquevalent manganese derivative. The influence of temp. was found to be such that an increase of 10° doubled the velocity of reaction. F. Durau studied the absorption of carbon monoxide and of **carbon dioxide** by the solid. The bleaching of potassium permanganate soln. by **percarbonates** is due to a reaction which is symbolized : $5K_2C_2O_6 +8H_2SO_4+2KMnO_4=2MnSO_4+6K_2SO_4+8H_2O+10CO_2+5O_2$, and accordingly the strength of potassium percarbonate as an oxidizing agent can be determined by titration of the sulphuric acid soln. with potassium permanganate. S. Cloez and E. Guignet, and E. Donath and H. Ditz stated that **carbon disulphide** is oxidized completely to carbon dioxide and sulphuric acid by alkaline soln. of permanganate, but E. Obach showed that if the disulphide is purified, it does not act on the solid salt, or on its neutral or acidic soln. The action with the ordinary disulphide is attributed to the presence of hydrogen sulphide, which is oxidized by the permanganate. E. Allary purified carbon disulphide by treating it with a soln. of the permanganate.

Organic substances can be oxidized by potassium permanganate, and in some cases all the carbonaceous matter can be burnt to carbon dioxide and estimated as such. The wet combustion process of determining carbon was discussed by R. Warrington and W. A. Peake, C. F. Cross and E. J. Bevan, A. H. Elliott, R. Phelps, R. Finkener, R. E. and W. M. Rogers, C. Brunner, E. Ullgren, L. U. de Nardo, H. Heidenhain, H. von Jüptner, F. A. Cairns, etc. According to E. Donath and H. Ditz, oxidations with acidic permanganate soln. are less energetic than those with alkaline soln. An acidified, conc. soln. of permanganate, at a high temp., usually furnishes carbon dioxide and water, but in alkaline soln. oxalic acid is usually the final product. T. Macalpine found that hydrated manganese dioxide is formed when an alkaline soln. of permanganate is treated with **acetylene ;** and M. Berthelot, that the acetylene is oxidized to oxalic and formic acids and carbon dioxide. A. Donath and H. Ditz doubt if formic acid is produced. P. Truchot added that **ethylene** is oxidized by a neutral soln. of permanganate to formic acid and carbon dioxide ; C. Fromerz also found that ethylene is oxidized to carbon dioxide and water by an acidic soln. of permanganate, and, according to A. Steopoe, colloidal manganic hydroxide is formed. N. K. Adam and G. Jessop studied the action on compounds with ethylenic bonds. P. Truchot observed that a neutral soln. oxidizes **propylene** to formic and acetic acids. M. Berthelot found that **allylene** is oxidized by permanganate to oxalic acid, etc.; and F. and O. Zeidler, that propylene and other **olefines** also furnish oxalic acid. The subject was discussed by H. S. Davis. D. A. Howes and A. W. Nash studied the action of permanganates on the hydrocarbons ; and F. Durau, the absorption of **methane, ethane,** and **propane** byt he solid—F. Durau and V. Schnatz measured the heats of adsorption. M. Berthelot found that the **paraffin hydrocarbons** are attacked with difficulty by acidic or alkaline soln. of permanganate ; while with an acidic soln. **benzene** is oxidized to oxalic acid and possibly propionic acid; **toluene,** to benzoic acid and another product; **xylene,** slowly to toluic and terephthalic acids ; and **styrene,** to benzoic acid and carbon dioxide ; while C. Fromherz, and M. Berthelot found that **turpentine** is slowly converted into carbon dioxide and water. E. Donath and H. Ditz found that propylene, **iso- butylene,** and **amylene** yield oxalic acid. The reaction with benzene was studied by T. H. Norton, and S. Cloez and E. Guignet. E. Donath and H. Ditz observed that there is no perceptible action, but **dimethylbenzene** is readily oxidized, although toluene is not attacked. L. A. Bigelow studied the oxidizing action of permanganate on the side-chains. S. Cloez and E. Guignet found that a neutral soln. of the permanganate oxidizes **methyl alcohol** to formic acid and carbon dioxide ; S. Cloez and E. Guignet, P. F. Chevillot and W. F. Edwards, W. L. Evans and J. E. Day, H. Tamm, and T. Morawsky and J. Stingl, **ethyl alcohol** to potassium acetate, and from alkaline soln. E. T. Chapman and M. H. Smith, and E. Donath and H. Ditz obtained traces of oxalic acid. S. S. Bhat- nagar and co-workers found that the reduction of permanganate by **chloral hydrate** is accelerated by a magnetic field. T. Morawsky and J. Stingl oxidized **glycerol** to carbon dioxide and water. W. L. Evans and co-workers studied the oxidation of **ethylene and propylene glycols ; glycolaldehyde, glyoxal, glycollic acid, and glyoxylic acid.** B. V. Tronoff and L. S. Nikonova studied the oxidation of the **amines** by permanganate ; and A. Buzagh, and R. Benedikt and R. Zsigmondy, the rate of reaction with chloral hydrate. B. V. Tronoff and co-workers studied the velocity of the oxidation of alcohol by potassium permanganate. The oxida- tion of alcohol and **ether** was observed by E. T. Chapman and W. Thorp, and F. Jones; the various stages in the process, by M. Gröger ; and the catalytic effect of platinum-black, by C. F. Schönbein. B. V. Tronoff and co-workers studied the velocity of oxidation of ether. G. B. Frankforter and R. M. West, and J. Holluta and co-workers studied the reduction by **formaldehyde.** W. Eidmann, and A. Naumann found that **acetone** dissolves in a soln. of potassium permanganate. W. Herz and M. Knoch found the solubility of permanganate in aq. soln. with p per cent. acetone, expressed in S millimols—$\frac{1}{5}KMnO_4$—per 100 c.c. of soln., to be :

p .	0	10	20	40	60	70	80	90	100
S .	148·5	162·7	177·3	257·3	316·8	328·0	312·0	227·0	67·6

L. P. de St. Gilles found that oxidation of acetone does not occur with a boiling alkaline soln. of permanganate, but M. Berthelot said that it is oxidized very slowly to carbon dioxide and water. The reaction was studied by E. J. Witzemann.

E. von Cochenhausen represented the reaction: $6(CH_3.CO.CH_3)+21O_2$ $=6(CO_2H)_2.2H_2O+6CO_2$. The reaction was studied by M. Gröger. E. Donath and H. Ditz said that some oxalic acid is formed. E. S. Prschevalsky examined the action of permanganate on the phenylated fatty acids. According to L. P. de St. Gilles, in the presence of sodium carbonate a soln. of potassium permanganate oxidizes **formic acid** to carbon dioxide and water, and the alkaline soln. acts slowly when cold, rapidly when boiled. E. T. Chapman and W. Thorp said that in the presence of sulphuric acid the action is slow in the cold; L. P. de St. Gilles said that the acidic soln. does not oxidize formic acid. The mechanism of the oxidation of formic acid was discussed by N. Schiloff, J. Holluta and co-workers, W. H. Hatcher and C. R. West, and A. Skrabal and J. Preiss. An alkaline soln. of potassium permanganate was found by L. P. de St. Gilles slowly to oxidize **acetic acid.** L. Gmelin said that an acidic soln. of potassium permanganate oxidizes acetic acid very slowly, while E. Monier, O. Unverdorben, H. Rose, and E. T. Chapman and W. Thorp said that oxidation does not occur. W. Lossen represented the reaction with **sodium acetate** in alkaline soln.: $NaC_2H_3O_2+2KMnO_4=2MnO_2+(CO_2K)_2$ $+NaOH+H_2O$. A. Naumann found that potassium permanganate is soluble in **ethyl acetate,** and sparingly soluble in **methyl acetate.** B. V. Tronoff and co-workers studied the velocity of oxidation of esters. E. T. Chapman and W. Thorp also observed that **propionic acid** is not oxidized by an acidic soln. of the permanganate. E. Donath and H. Ditz observed that oxalic acid is formed in the oxidation of **butyric acid,** and also of **succinic acid.** L. P. de St. Gilles observed that in the presence of an excess of potassium carbonate, **oxalic acid** is not oxidized by potassium permanganate; M. Berthelot said that with a boiling soln. the oxidation to carbon dioxide and water proceeds slowly; T. Morawsky and J. Stingl, that in neutral soln. **potassium oxalate** is oxidized completely; and E. Fleischer represented the reaction between oxalic acid and a neutral soln. of the permanganate by: $8H_2C_2O_4+2KMnO_4=2MnC_2O_4+K_2C_2O_4+10CO_2+8H_2O$; and C. W. Hempel represented the reaction in the presence of sulphuric acid at 35° to 40° by: $2HMnO_4+5H_2C_2O_4+2H_2SO_4=2MnSO_4+10CO_2+8H_2O$. The mechanism of the reaction was discussed by A. V. Harcourt, A. V. Harcourt and W. Esson, A. Skrabal, R. Ehrenfeld, R. Luther, N. Schiloff, J. C. Witt, R. C. Banerji and N. R. Dhar, N. R. Dhar, R. P. Sanyal and N. R. Dhar, R. M. Purkayostha and N. R. Dhar, B. K. Mukerji and N. R. Dhar, A. Boutaric, G. N. Ridley, G. Scheff, M. A. Rozenberg, D. A. MacInnes, C. del Fresno, and M. Gröger. A. K. Bhattacharji and N. R. Dhar, and E. Shpolsky studied the effect of ultra-red radiations on the reaction.

The reaction between potassium permanganate and oxalic acid, $H_2C_2O_4$, in the presence of sulphuric acid, is slow at first, but progresses more quickly as time goes on, and finally proceeds with a fairly uniform velocity. It is also found that the speed of the reaction is accelerated by the presence of manganese sulphate, and if manganese sulphate be added to the mixture there is no initial acceleration. Hence it is inferred (i) that in the early stages of the reaction manganic sulphate is formed *very slowly,* in accord with: $2KMnO_4+4H_2SO_4+4H_2C_2O_4=K_2SO_4+Mn_2(SO_4)_3$ $+8H_2O+8CO_2$, and possibly, $2KMnO_4+8MnSO_4+8H_2SO_4=5Mn_2(SO_4)_3+8H_2O$ $+K_2SO_4$, and that this reaction proceeds more and more rapidly as the manganese sulphate accumulates in the system—period of induction or period of acceleration. (ii) That the manganese sulphate unites with the oxalic acid, forming a double compound supposed to be $Mn_2(SO_4)_3.H_2C_2O_4$. This reaction is supposed to proceed *too rapidly* for measurement. (iii) The double compound decomposes into manganese sulphate, carbon dioxide, and water by a reaction: $Mn_2(SO_4)_3.H_2C_2O_4 \rightarrow 2MnSO_4$ $+H_2SO_4+2CO_2$, which can be readily measured. The last two assumptions are invented to explain how the reaction in a soln. containing the eq. of $KMnO_4+7MnSO_4$ $+54H_2C_2O_4$ in mols., made up to 160 litres with water at 14°, proceeds as if it were unimolecular. Part of the soln. is removed from time to time by means of a pipette, treated with potassium iodide and sulphuric acid, and the separated iodine determined by titration with a standard soln. of sodium thiosulphate. Let x denote the amount of potassium permanganate decomposed in the soln., at the time t, and expressed in terms of the number of c.c. of thiosulphate soln. required to decolorize the iodine in the soln. withdrawn by the pipette ; then $a-x$ will represent the amount of undecomposed permanganate present in the soln. Obviously when $t=0$, $x=0$, and if $k=(1/t) \log \{a/(a-x)\}$:

t	.	0	12	25	36	46	54 minutes
$a-x$	.	53·10	37·00	24·93	27·75	13·10	10·25 c.c. " thio "
k	.	—	0·0131	0·0131	0·0132	0·0132	0·0132

Allowing for the errors of experiment, the numbers in the last line indicate that a unimolecular reaction was measured ; the assumption that the molecule of the complex salt is $Mn_2(SO_4)_3.2H_2C_2O_4$ is a guess. The inference that the unknown molecule is formed too rapidly for measurement is made because the speed at which it is formed does not interfere with the measurement of the rate at which it decomposes, as evidenced by the numbers in the above table. The inference that the manganic sulphate is formed during the early stages of the reaction between oxalic acid and potassium permanganate is based on the slow rate at which the colour of the permanganate disappears during the early stages of the titration of oxalic acid with potassium permanganate, as contrasted with the rate at which the decolorization occurs in the later stages, or when manganese sulphate is purposely added to the soln. Velocity measurements of the reaction show the same thing, for instance, with the mixture $KMnO_4+54H_2C_2O_4$ made up with water acidulated with $10H_2SO_4$ to 160 litres (14°) ; $k=(1/t) \log \{a/(a-x)\}$:

t	.	0	2	5	13	16	31	41	59 mins.
$a-x$	.	68·05	67·72	65·80	14·36	11·30	8·77	7·00	4·72 c.c. " thio "
k	.	—	0·001	0·003	0·052	0·049	0·029	0·024	0·020

The gradual increase in the speed of the reaction up to a maximum corresponds with the inference that in the early stages of the reaction something is accumulating in the system in steadily increasing quantities. The decline in the velocity constant after the maximum is reached does not agree with a unimolecular reaction. This means that there is not an indefinitely large supply of manganese sulphate available, as was the case when a large excess of this salt was purposely added to the system, and the amount of the decomposing salt decreases faster than corresponds with what would be the case with a unimolecular change ; this is because the source of supply is exhausting as the reaction progresses.

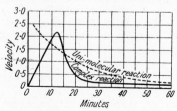

FIG. 58.—The Speed of the Reduction of Potassium Permanganate by Oxalic Acid.

The progress of the two reactions under consideration is well illustrated by Fig. 58, showing the amount of substance transformed in each reaction per unit time.

M. Bobtelsky and D. Kaplan measured the speed of decolorization of a small amount of potassium permanganate by a known excess of oxalic and sulphuric acids in the presence of various salts. The alkali chlorides exert a stronger accelerating influence than the nitrates or sulphates. The order of decreasing acceleration with the sulphates is $Li>Mg>NH_4>Na>K$. Ammonium nitrate exerts a marked acceleration, sodium nitrate is ineffective, and potassium nitrate retards the action. The action of the chlorides is the most sensitive towards changes of temp., and the action in increasing magnitude is $NH_4Cl<KCl<BaCl_2<SrCl_2<CaCl_2<MgCl_2$ $<AlCl_3$. The nitrates are feebly sensitive towards temp. changes ; and the sulphates are partly feeble and partly moderate. Salts which are sensitive towards changes of temp. are also sensitive to changes of concentration, except in the case of ammonium nitrate, which is sensitive to changes of concentration, but only feebly so with respect to temp. The order of decreasing conc. sensitive-

ness is $AlCl_3 > CdSO_4 > MgCl_2 > ZnCl_2 > ZnSO_4 > KCl > NH_4Cl > NH_4NO_3 > NaCl > (NH_4)_2HPO_4$; the salts with a feeble action are $Li_2SO_4 > MgSO_4 > K_2SO_4 > (NH_4)_2SO_4 > Na_2SO_4 > KNO_3 > NaNO_3 > CaCl_2 > SrCl_2 > BaCl_2$. According to K. Schröder, some of the oxides formed in the reduction of potassium permanganate may be reoxidized by atm. oxygen. E. Müller and H. Kogert studied the electrometric titration of oxalic acid with potassium permanganate. C. Fromherz said that an acidic soln. of potassium permanganate oxidizes **tartaric acid** to formic acid, carbon dioxide, and water : $C_4H_6O_6 + 3O = 2H_2CO_2 + 2CO_2 + H_2O$. E. Donath and H. Ditz observed the formation of some oxalic acid. The reaction was also studied by E. T. Chapman and W. Thorp, A. N. Dey and N. R. Dhar, A. K. Bhattacharji and N. R. Dhar, W. G. Vannoy, and E. Monier ; with soln. sat. with potassium hydroxide H. Rose observed that tartaric acid forms a green soln. with potassium permanganate ; and with a neutral soln. E. Fleischer found that manganous tartrate is formed, and L. P. de St. Gilles reduced the acid to carbon dioxide and water. E. Monier observed that the action with acid permanganate is very slow. S. S. Bhatnagar and co-workers found that the reaction is accelerated in a magnetic field. H. Rose found that **racemic acid** behaves like tartaric acid in the presence of an alkaline soln. of the permanganate. A. K. Bhattacharji and N. R. Dhar, and B. K. Mukerji and N. R. Dhar studied this photochemical reaction. E. Donath and H. Ditz observed that with **lactic acid** some oxalic acid is formed. A. K. Bhattacharji and N. R. Dhar studied the action of light and of ultra-red radiations on the reduction. A. N. Dey and N. R. Dhar, V. Subrahmanyan, and T. E. Friedemann and co-workers, studied the reaction. L. P. de St. Gilles showed that in acidic soln. **malic acid** is oxidized to carbon dioxide and water ; E. Monier found the reaction very slow. W. H. Hatcher and C. R. West found that formic acid occurs as an intermediate product in the oxidation of malic, maleic, oxalacetic, fumaric, malonic, tartaric, lactic, and glycollic acids and glycol. L. P. de St. Gilles observed that at 80° **citric acid** is oxidized to acetone, carbon dioxide, and water by an acidic soln. of permanganate ; A. N. Dey and N. R. Dhar, A. K. Bhattacharji and N. R. Dhar, and E. Monier also studied this reaction. C. Fromherz found that an acidic soln. of permanganate is reduced to a brown hydrated manganese oxide by **stearic acid** and **oleic acid.** E. Monier observed that a neutral and an acidic soln. of permanganate easily oxidize **tannin, gallic acid,** and **pyrogallic acid.** R. Böttger found that when tannin or gallic acid is triturated dry with potassium permanganate, the mixture inflames. P. Kubelka and E. Sövegjarto, and B. V. Tronoff and A. A. Grigorieva studied the oxidation of salts of **benzoic acid** and of other **organic acids** by permanganate ; E. M. Stoddart, **cinnamic acid ;** T. B. Douglas, **sodium thiophenolate ;** and B. V. Tronoff and A. A. Lukanin, the effect of neutral salts on the velocity of oxidation of organic substances by permanganate. S. Cloez and E. Guignet found that a neutral soln. of permanganate oxidizes **urea** with difficulty ; while J. A. Wanklyn and A. Gamgee found that with a boiling alkaline soln. urea is oxidized, yielding 22 per cent. of its nitrogen as ammonia, and in a sealed tube at 160° to 220° very little ammonia is formed and free nitrogen is produced. E. Monier found that the oxidation is very slow in acidic soln. A. Claus found that an alkaline soln. of permanganate oxidizes **uric acid** to carbon dioxide and allantoin. P. F. Chevillot and W. F. Edwards oxidized **sugar** by alkali permanganate, and E. Monier, and F. Jones found the action very slow in alkaline soln.; and S. L. Ridgway, the action on glucose in acidic soln. E. Donath observed that some oxalic acid is formed by the action of cane-sugar, grape-sugar, lactose, and dextrose. E. J. Witzemann studied the oxidation of dextrose ; C. W. R. Powell, sucrose ; S. S. Nametkin, unsaturated organic compounds ; F. Ullmann and J. B. Uzbachian, derivatives of benzoic acid ; J. Hetper, sugars, phenols, hydroxy-acids, and alcohols. Various other **organic substances** have been oxidized—e.g. with alkaline soln. of permanganates C. F. Mohr oxidized *starch*, and P. F. Chevillot and W. F. Edwards, *gum* and *paper* ; and with acidic soln. C. Fromherz oxidized gum, paper, and *wood-fibre*; G. Fester and G. Brude, paper and other organic substances; S. G. Simpson, filter-paper; and E. Monier oxidized *gum, dextrine,* and *fats*; and C. Fromherz oxidized camphor, resin, glue, and olive oil. P. F. Chevillot and W. F. Edwards found that a mixture of *lycopodium* and solid potassium permanganate takes fire when treated with sulphuric acid. D. Vorländer and co-workers found that **acyl derivatives** are oxidized readily in acidic soln., but not so easily in alkaline soln. A. W. Hofmann, I. Guareschi, and S. Cloez and E. Guignet discussed the oxidation of **organic sulphur compounds,** and E. Donath and H. Ditz found thiophene is readily attacked by a 2 per cent. alkaline soln. of permanganate. The **alkaloids** are oxidized by acidic soln. of permanganates— thus, C. Fromherz oxidized morphine; E. Monier, quinine, and caffeine; G. Kerner, quinine; E. Caventou and E. Willm, Z. H. Skraup, and O. Hesse, cinchonine; and Z. H. Skraup, cinchonidine. D. Vorländer and co-workers found that **amines** are oxidized by acidic and alkaline soln. of permanganates. J. A. Wanklyn and A. Gamgee oxidized **aniline.** Other **organic nitrogen compounds** were oxidized by acidic soln.—*e.g.* C. Fromherz oxidized *egg-albumin, fibrin,* and the red colouring matter of blood ; and D. Vitali, *animal tissue.* A. Naumann found that potassium permanganate is soluble in **benzonitrile.** R. P. Bell, and L. S. Kassel and N. K. Schaffer studied the velocity of the reaction at the liquid-liquid interface between a soln. of **benzo-o-toluidide** in benzene and an aq. soln. of potassium permanganate. According to S. Cloez and E. Guignet, **cyanogen** is oxidized by cold neutral soln. of potassium permanganate to form potassium nitrate, and similarly with **hydrocyanic acid,** which L. P. de St. Gilles oxidized to cyanic acid in alkaline soln., but he did not oxidize the hydrocyanic acid in acidic soln. K. Fredenhagen found the electrical conductivity, λ, in hydrocyanic acid to be for a mol of the salt in v litres :

v .	. 5·534	8·890	23·40	104·5	195·0	1329
λ .	. 142·1	214·1	263·5	310·5	340·2	511·0

L. Kahlenberg and H. Schlundt gave for soln. of a mol of salt in 5·5, 23·4, 104·5, and 1329 litres of liquid hydrogen cyanide the values λ=142, 264, and 311 respectively. L. P. de St. Gilles, and T. Morawsky and J. Stingl oxidized **thiocyanic acid** to cyanic and sulphuric acids in alkaline soln., and with acidic soln. E. A. Hadow, E. Erlenmeyer, and L. P. de St. Gilles oxidized thiocyanic acid to hydrocyanic acid and potassium sulphate, and similarly with **thiocyanates** in alkaline soln. M. Bobtelsky and D. Kaplan studied the action of various salts on the reaction. C. F. Schönbein, and R. C. Campbell oxidized **potassium ferrocyanide** to ferricyanide in acidic soln., and S. Cloez and E. Guignet in alkaline soln., but **potassium ferricyanide** was not changed. S. Cloez and E. Guignet found that with cold alkaline soln. **sodium nitroprusside** furnishes potassium nitrate. F. C. Calvert observed no special antiseptic properties on fungoid growths.

W. Foster found that all the common metals—*e.g.* zinc, and magnesium—reduce acidulated soln. of potassium permanganate, but dil. neutral soln. are reduced as well, even by finely divided gold, platinum, and tungsten. W. B. Giles observed that **copper** does not attack soln. of potassium permanganate, but F. Fischer, and M. C. Schuyten found that a dil. sulphuric acid soln. is readily reduced by copper. C. Friedheim, V. Meyer and M. von Recklinghausen, and W. Foster found that **silver, gold, and platinum** also do so. W. Crookes observed that hot soln. of potassium permanganate attack **magnesium** very slowly; and L. L. de Koninck found that potassium permanganate is not attacked by purified **zinc,** even in the presence of sulphuric acid, but it is attacked in the presence of ferrous salts or nitric acid. W. B. Giles also observed that zinc exerts no appreciable action on the soln. during 2 months' exposure. C. Boulanger observed the action of zinc on manganese salts. P. F. Chevillot and W. F. Edwards, W. B. Giles, D. Borar, and W. Foster found that **mercury** decolorizes a soln. of the permanganate. and is at the same time oxidized, forming, according to W. B. Giles, mercurous oxide in the cold, and mercuric oxide when boiling. A. Gawalowsky observed that in the presence of mercury a soln. of potassium permanganate gradually turns deep bluish-violet, and if potassium hydroxide be present, some potassium manganate is formed, and if only a small proportion of the alkali-lye be present, a potassium mercury manganate and a black deposit of a mercurous manganate are formed. According to A. S. Russell and D. C. Evans, all metals more electropositive than mercury, except cobalt, go rapidly into soln. as sulphates, without the accompaniment of mercury, when their amalgams are shaken with a soln. of potassium permanganate in dil. sulphuric acid. W. Crookes found that a soln. of permanganate is attacked by **aluminium** very slowly when hot, while **thallium** attacks the soln. in the cold. V. Shuleikin and X. Solovova measured the radiation of heat in the thermite reaction with aluminium. C. Boulanger observed the action of aluminium on manganese salts. W. Foster noted that the soln. is reduced by **tungsten.** M. A. Parker and H. P. Armes found that in the reduction of an acidic soln. of potassium permanganate by **iron** there is a definite relationship between the extent of the reduction and the strength of the field.

D. Nishida and K. Hirabayashi found the oxidation of **cuprous oxide** by potassium permanganate in $3N$- to $5N$-H_2SO_4, at room temp., is quantitative: $2KMnO_4 + 14H_2SO_4 + 5Cu_2O = 10CuSO_4 + 13H_2O + 2MnSO_4 + 2KHSO_4$. M. Bobtelsky and D. Kaplan studied the effect of various salts on the reaction between potassium permanganate and **silver nitrate.** D. Balareff and co-workers discussed the adsorption of permanganate by **barium sulphate.** C. W. Hempel found that a soln. of the permanganate oxidizes **mercurous salts** to mercuric salts; and E. Carstanjen, and J. E. Willm found that **thallous salts** are quantitatively oxidized—*vide infra.* In hot hydrochloric acid soln. the reaction is symbolized: $5TlCl + 2KMnO_4 + 16HCl = 5TlCl_3 + 2MnCl_2 + 2KCl + 8H_2O$. A. J. Berry did not obtain a quantitative oxidation in sulphuric acid soln. According to A. Reynoso, **stannites** are oxidized by potassium permanganate to stannates, and **plumbites** to plumbates. A. E. Haswell found that **lead salts,** in the presence of zinc or mercuric oxide, are oxidized to form lead dioxide. According to B. C. Brodie, E. T. Allen, C. F. Schönbein, and H. N. Morse and co-workers, **lead dioxide,** in the presence of nitric acid, can precipitate the manganese completely from the soln.: $2HMnO_4 + 3PbO_2 = 2MnO_2 + 3PbO + 3O_2 + H_2O$. This reaction shows why in using W. Crum's process for oxidizing manganous salt soln. to permanganate—*vide supra*—for the detection of manganese it is necessary to work with a large excess of lead dioxide and a small proportion of manganese salt. S. Cloez and E. Guignet found that precipitated and washed hydrated **chromic oxide** is converted in the cold into a chromate; while E. Bohlig found that calcined chromic oxide is similarly oxidized when the liquid is boiled. A. Reynoso, and E. Donath obtained a similar result with **chromic salts.** H. A. Fales and P. S. Roller found that the reduction of MnO_4' by $Cr^{...}$ at $25 \cdot 1°$ in sulphuric acid soln. is autocatalytic and closely resembles the reduction of the permanganate by many organic acids. There is formed a sulphuric acid complex of $Mn^{....}$ and $Mn^{...}$. Oxidation by the latter is indirect in virtue of its unimolecular disengagement from the complex and its subsequent decomposition into $Mn^{....}$, which oxidizes $Cr^{...}$ rapidly. The temp. coeff. of the unimolecular reaction is $4 \cdot 01$ between $25°$ and $35°$. $Mn^{....}$ also reacts with $Mn^{..}$, thus reverting to non-reactive $Mn^{...}$. In the interaction between $Mn^{..}$ and MnO_4' in acidic soln., the relative proportion of $Mn^{....}$ to $Mn^{...}$ increases as the ratio of $Mn^{..}$ to MnO_4' decreases. P. A. Tscheishwily found that chrome alum soln. are rapidly oxidized by permanganate. G. Forchhammer observed that **manganous carbonate** suspended in alkali-lye changes to green the red colour of a soln. of potassium permanganate, and a manganic salt is formed. M. Geloso and P. Dubois considered that the reduction of permanganates by manganous salts does not form a definite compound, but there is rather a continuous variation in the degree of oxidation of the pseudo-dioxides which are formed. Calcium carbonate neutralizes the acid which is formed, and part furnishes insoluble manganese carbonate. It also exerts a surface effect. The equation used by A. Guyard, and J. Volhard for titrating soln. of **manganous sulphate** with potassium permanganate is : $3MnSO_4+2KMnO_4+2H_2O=5MnO_2+K_2SO_4+2H_2SO_4$. Observations on the subject were made by R. T. Colgate. According to H. Baubigny, the precipitation of manganese dioxide from an acid soln. of a manganous salt by potassium permanganate depends on the acidity, on the conc. of the salts, and on the temp. The presence of the acid retards the precipitation and may even completely prevent it. The amount of manganic salt which remains dissolved increases with the conc. of the acid, but diminishes as the temp. rises. The precipitate consists solely of manganese dioxide and contains no manganic oxide. W. M. Fischer noted that the titre of a standard soln. of potassium permanganate obtained by ferrous salts with oxalates is not the same as it is with a manganous salt. E. Divers attributed the difference to the fact that the precipitate contains less oxygen than is required for manganese dioxide, owing (i) to the adsorption of some manganous salt, and (ii) to the co-precipitation of some manganic acid : $4Mn^{..}+MnO_4'+8H^{.}$ $=5Mn^{...}+4H_2O$, followed by $2Mn^{...}=Mn^{..}+Mn^{....}$; some of the manganic ions escape the latter change and react : $Mn^{...}+3OH'=Mn(OH)_3$. To neutralize any acid formed in these hydrolytic changes, zinc oxide is added ; this is said to prevent any precipitation of manganic hydroxide and adsorption of manganous salts by the precipitated manganese dioxide. E. Cahen and H. F. V. Little recommended zinc sulphate and oxide ; and B. Reinitzer and P. Conrath, sodium acetate and acetic acid ; and P. B. Sarkar and N. R. Dhar showed that almost any other cation can be employed in place of zinc, and likewise also I. M. Kolthoff, who represented the reaction : $3Mn^{..}+2MnO_4'+2H_2O=5MnO_2+4H^{.}$; or $3MnSO_4+2KMnO_4+2H_2O$ $=5MnO_2+2H_2SO_4+K_2SO_4$, as represented by A. C. Sarkar and J. M. Dutta. J. Holluta and J. Obrist found that the reaction with manganous fluoride can be symbolized : $MnO_4'+4Mn^{..}+8H^{.}=5Mn^{...}+4H_2O$. A. Gorgeu said that he never observed the evolution of oxygen or chlorine in the action of manganous chloride on potassium permanganate, but J. G. F. Druce pointed out that oxygen is evolved when a conc. soln. of manganous sulphate is added to a sat. soln. of solid potassium permanganate ; and with barium permanganate much oxygen is given off : $MnSO_4+Ba(MnO_4)_2=BaSO_4+Mn_3O_4+2O_2$; and with conc. soln. of manganous chloride and potassium permanganate, chlorine is evolved : $2MnCl_2+2KMnO_4=2KCl+4MnO_2+Cl_2$. According to J. Heyrovsky, some dwimanganese or rhenium is evolved with the chlorine. M. Bobtelsky and D. Kaplan studied the action of various salts on the reaction between potassium permanganate and manganous sulphate. The reaction was also studied by N. R. Dhar, and J. G. F. Druce. The action of **manganese dioxide** on soln. of permanganates has been discussed in connection with permanganic acid and the action of hydrogen on the permanganates. G. Rapin, and R. T. Colgate made observations on the subject.

W. C. Birch, B. Suzuki and C. Hamada, and E. Müller and H. Möllering studied the reduction of permanganate by **ferrous salts.** Y. Ono compared the simultaneous oxidation of ferrous salts and manganous salts in soln. by potassium permanganate. The ferrous salt oxidized nearly twice as fast as the manganous salt. M. Bobtelsky and D. Kaplan studied the action of various salts on the reaction ; and F. L. Hahn and M. Frommer, the electrometric titration. M. A. von Reis and F. Wiggert, and C. Winkler found that **cobaltous salts** can be oxidized to cobaltic salts by permanganate. Numerous other salts can be oxidized to a higher state of oxidation, as indicated above in connection with permanganic acid, e.g. ferrous salts, and **molybdic salts** were found by I. Macagno to be converted into molybdates. The oxidizing reactions are utilized in numerous volumetric processes of analysis. M. Berthelot also utilized permanganate as an oxidizing agent for deducing heats of oxidation, etc.

A. Gorgeu found that if a soln. of 100 grms. of potassium hydroxide, 10 grms. of potassium permanganate, and 75 grms. of water be boiled until oxygen is no longer evolved, and the soln. diluted with 150 to 200 grms. of water, and then mixed with 1 to 2 grms. of potassium permanganate, the liquid, on cooling and standing over conc. sulphuric acid, or in vacuo, deposits six-sided monoclinic plates which can be drained on porous tiles and dried at 100°. H. de Sénarmont found for the axial ratios of the crystals $a : b : c = 1.7176 : 1 : 1.3570$, and $\beta = 114° 39'$. The analysis corresponds with **potassium manganatopermanganate,** $K_2MnO_4.KMnO_4$. The crystals form a violet soln. with a 20 per cent. soln. of potassium hydroxide. Baryta-water added to the soln. gives a precipitate of barium manganate and a red soln. of potassium permanganate ; and the salt behaves towards acids like potassium manganate.

W. Muthmann obtained crystals of **rubidium permanganate,** $RbMnO_4$, from the soln. obtained by treating barium permanganate with rubidium sulphate. E. Moles and M. Crespi obtained the salt from a soln. of 5 grms. of potassium permanganate in 4·1 grms. of rubidium nitrate in 75 c.c. of water at 60° and cooled to 0°. They obtained $K = 1.566$ for the velocity of decomposition—*vide supra*, potassium permanganate. W. Muthmann found that the rhombic bipyramids have the axial ratios $a : b : c = 0.8311 : 1 : 0.6662$. T. V. Barker gave for the topic axial ratios $\chi : \psi : \omega = 4.0323 : 4.8517 : 6.4639$. For the isomorphism with the potassium salt, discussed by F. Rinne, W. Muthmann and O. Kuntze, and G. Tammann and A. Sworykin, *vide* Fig. 54. E. Moles and M. Crespi gave 3·23 for the sp. gr. ; and W. Muthmann gave 3·2348 for the sp. gr. and 63·228 for the mol. vol. The subject was discussed by A. F. Hallimond. I. I. Saslawsky gave 3·13 for the sp. gr., and calculated the contraction which occurs in the formation of the salt from its elements. E. Moles and M. Crespi found that the salt decomposes at 295° with the evolution of oxygen. W. Muthmann prepared **cæsium permanganate,** $CsMnO_4$, by the method employed for the rubidium salt ; and R. J. Meyer and H. Best, from the liquid obtained by treating silver permanganate with cæsium chloride. E. Moles and M. Crespi obtained the salt from a soln. of 3·2 grms. of potassium permanganate and 4 grms. of cæsium nitrate in 50 c.c. of water at 60° and cooled to 0°. They found $K = 1.628$ for the velocity of decomposition—*vide supra*, potassium permanganate. W. Muthmann found that the dark violet, rhombic, bipyramidal crystals have the axial ratios $a : b : c = 0.8623 : 1 : 0.6853$. T. V. Barker gave for the topic axial ratios $\chi : \psi : \omega = 4.2555 : 4.9009 : 6.7167$. W. Muthmann gave 3·5974 for the sp. gr., and 70·042 for the mol. vol. The subject was discussed by A. F. Hallimond. I. I. Saslawsky gave 3·55 for the sp. gr., and he calculated the contraction which occurs in forming the salt from its elements. E. Moles and M. Crespi gave 3·59 for the sp. gr., and found that the salt decomposes at 320° with the evolution of oxygen. W. Muthmann found that the crystals of rubidium and cæsium permanganates are isomorphous with those of potassium sulphate ; and T. V. Barker, F. Rinne, and G. Tammann and A. Sworykin discussed the isomorphism with the perchlorates. W. Muthmann found that the two salts are sparingly soluble in cold water, and freely soluble in hot water ; the solubility of the rubidium salt is between that of the potassium salt and that of the cæsium salt. A. M. Patterson gave for the solubility, S grms. in 100 c.c. of sat. soln. :

	RbMnO$_4$			CsMnO$_4$		
	2°	19°	60°	1°	19°	59°
S . .	0·46	1·06	4·68	0·097	0·23	1·25

E. Mitscherlich, and H. Aschoff obtained deliquescent **copper permanganate,** $Cu(MnO_4)_2.8H_2O$, from the soln. obtained by the action of cupric sulphate on barium permanganate. E. Moles and M. Crespi prepared the copper salt by treating a soln. of copper chloride with silver permanganate and evaporating for crystallization. The trihydrate is very deliquescent. The sp. gr. of the salt is near 2·87 ; and it decomposes with the evolution of oxygen at 75°. E. Pflüger measured the absorption spectrum of dil. soln. of the salt. I. I. Saslawsky found the sp. gr. to be 2·87, and he calculated the contraction which occurs in forming the salt from its elements. T. Klobb prepared **copper amminoperman-ganate**, which was not analyzed ; and the **copper pyridinopermanganate**, $Cu(MnO_4)_2.4C_5H_5N$. E. Mitscherlich obtained fine crystals of **silver permanganate**, $AgMnO_4$, by cooling a warm soln. of silver nitrate and potassium permanganate, but J. W. Retgers could not confirm this, and he obtained the silver salt as a black precipitate by mixing soln. of silver nitrate and potassium permanganate. E. Moles and M. Crespi, and G. Heikel used a similar process. J. Dewar and A. Scott said that the best way of making the salt is by crystallization from the soln. remaining after mixing barium permanganate and silver sulphate soln. The salt crystallizes well from hot water ; the crystals are stable and not hygroscopic. I. I. Saslawsky gave 4·27 for the sp. gr. of the salt, and he calculated the contraction which occurs in forming the salt from its elements. E. Mitscherlich found that the monoclinic prisms have the axial ratios $a : b : c = 1·4894 : 1 : 1·3703$, and $\beta = 93° 57'$. W. Büssem and K. Herrmann examined the X-radiograms of the monoclinic crystals, and found their unit cell has 4 mols., and $a = 5·66$ A., $b = 8·27$ A., and $c = 7·12$ A. The structure resembles a slightly deformed $KMnO_4$ lattice. The calculated density is 4·49. J. W. Retgers assumed that a rhombic, labile form exists. E. Moles and M. Crespi found that the sp. gr. is 4·27 ; and that the salt decomposes at 110° with the evolution of oxygen. They found $K = 0·183$ for the velocity of decomposition—*vide supra*, potassium permanganate. A. Lehmann discussed the reaction. A. Sieverts and H. Theberath represented the reaction $AgMnO_4 = AgMnO_3 + O$ at 30° and the reaction follows the rule $dx/dt = kx(a-x)$. The decomposition product, the nature of which has not been established, accelerates the reaction proportionally to its mass. The constants of the decomposition velocity of the various preparations are different. The presence of water has a very strong influence on this reaction. Dry silver permanganate decomposes very slowly, even at 50°, but small traces of water increase the decomposition velocity very much, whilst larger additions of water have little further influence. The addition of powdered pumice and the decomposition product of the reaction changes only the initial velocity. Temp. has a very marked influence on the reaction. At 0°, even in the presence of water and the decomposition product, the decomposition does not take place. At 50° the decomposition process is no longer represented by the same equation as at 30° ; the tx curves for 50° are characterized by a long, almost straight line. At 30° an increase of 20° in the temp. of reaction causes the initial velocity to increase from 12 to 20 times, the mean velocity between 19 per cent. and 38 per cent. decomposition, 6·1–7·6 times, and between 38 per cent. and 57 per cent. decomposition, 3·4–4·3 times. C. N. Hinshelwood and E. J. Bowen found a period of acceleration in the thermal decomposition of the salt. According to E. Mitscherlich, 100 parts of water dissolve 0·917 part of the salt. E. Franke found the electrical conductivity, λ, of an eq. of the salt in v litres of water at 25° to be :

v .	. 64	128	256	512	1024
λ .	. 106·3	109·4	110·9	112·0	112·7

E. Mitscherlich found that the salt can be recrystallized from moderately warm soln., but it is decomposed by boiling water. A. Gorgeu said that the salt decomposes slowly in air, and in the presence of water, being slow at ordinary temp., but faster at 100° in the presence of water. At 135° the decomposition is attended by incandescence. According to A. Gorgeu, when hydrogen dioxide is added very slowly to a sat. aq. soln. of silver permanganate, a brown precipitate forms gradually until the liquid is decolorized. The reaction is represented by the equation : $2AgMnO_4 + 3H_2O_2 = Ag_2O.2MnO_2 + 3H_2O + 3O_2$. The precipitated silver manganite is rapidly attacked by excess of hydrogen dioxide. Hydrochloric acid is oxidized by the salt to form chlorine ; it is reduced by oxalic acid, ferrous salts, and arsenious acid, losing part of the oxygen as a gas. J. Krutwig found that chlorine decomposes the warm salt vigorously, forming silver chloride, manganese dioxide, and oxygen. T. Klobb could not prepare an ammine by the direct action of ammonia, but he obtained **silver diamminopermanganate,** $AgMnO_4.2NH_3$, by adding conc. aq. ammonia to a soln. of a mol of potassium permanganate in water at 10°, and adding a mol of silver nitrate dissolved in ten times its weight of water. The crystalline precipitate is washed with ice-water and dried over calcium oxide. The violet powder consists of microscopic rhombic plates, sparingly soluble in cold water, more soluble in hot water. The salt explodes by percussion; and on exposure it gradually decomposes, with the loss of ammonia. G. Bruni and G. Levi also prepared **silver triamminopermanganate,** $AgMnO_4.3NH_3$. T. Klobb also prepared the **silver pyridinopermanganates,** $AgMnO_4.2C_5H_5N$ and $2AgMnO_4.5C_5H_5N$.

E. Mitscherlich found that no salt is precipitated when soln. of potassium permanganate and barium chloride are mixed; but E. Fleischer observed that if the mixed soln. is boiled, a reddish-violet precipitate is slowly formed, while the soln. remains violet. The precipitate can be washed with water and dried at 100°, but if the product be heated further, its colour fades, and finally becomes greyish-brown, without showing any sign of the formation of an intermediate green manganate. If the salt is mixed with 20 per cent. barium hydroxide and heated to redness, a bluish-green pigment is formed. According to L. Gmelin, an aq. soln. of potassium permanganate yields with baryta-water a violet mixture, which ultimately becomes colourless, and deposits a blue precipitate. This precipitate retains its colour when washed and dried. The blue colour suggests that it is a mixture of barium manganate and permanganate. When it is decomposed by dil. sulphuric acid, it yields permanganic acid and a precipitate of hydrated manganese dioxide. H. Aschoff, however, said that a soln. of potassium permanganate and baryta-water, when allowed to stand a long time, deposits microscopic crystals of barium manganate. E. Mitscherlich, F. Wöhler, and C. Fromherz prepared **barium permanganate,** $Ba(MnO_4)_2$, by passing carbon dioxide into water with barium manganate in suspension and evaporating the filtered soln. for crystalliza-tion—R. Böttger used hot water. H. Aschoff added that the process is slow and tedious, and the carbon dioxide is not without action on the barium permanganate which is formed. H. Aschoff obtained crystals of the permanganate from the soln. obtained when silver permanganate is treated with the calculated quantity of barium chloride. G. Rousseau and B. Bruneau treated a sat. soln. of potassium permanganate with hydrofluosilicic acid, and saturated the liquor, filtered through asbestos, with milk of baryta; the dissolution of the baryta is followed by the pre-cipitation of some barium fluosilicate. The soln. after standing half an hour is decanted and evaporated for barium permanganate. The preparation of the alkaline earth permanganates was described by R. E. Wilson and co-workers. E. Moles and M. Crespi obtained barium permanganate from a soln. of 3·62 grms. of barium chloride in 50 c.c. of water and 8 grms. of silver permanganate. The filtered soln. was evaporated for crystallization. W. Muthmann recommended the following process:

100 grms. of potassium permanganate are treated with 140 grms. of barium nitrate dissolved in 1·5 litres of boiling water, and barium hydroxide is added in portions of 20 grms. until no further evolution of oxygen takes place. The whole is then warmed until the soln. has become colourless, the precipitate of barium manganate (containing also some dioxide and carbonate) is collected, washed five times by decantation with 5 litres of boiling water, collected on the filter-pump, washed ten times more with boiling water, suspended in a litre of water, and carbon dioxide and superheated steam passed into the mixture for 10 hrs. The soln. is then filtered twice through an asbestos filter; it contains 65 to 80 grms. of barium permanganate.

E. Mitscherlich said that the acicular crystals are almost black, and are stable in air. The rhombic crystals are isomorphous with those of anhydrous sodium sulphate and selenate, as well as with silver permanganate. I. I. Saslawsky gave 3·77 for the sp. gr., and he calculated the contraction which occurs in forming the salt from its elements. E. Moles and M. Crespi found that the sp. gr. of the salt is 3·77; and it decomposes at 220° with the evolution of oxygen. The velocity constant is $K=0.088$—*vide supra*, potassium permanganate. E. Franke found the electrical conductivity, λ, of an eq. of the salt, $\frac{1}{2}Ba(MnO_4)_2$, in v litres of water at 25° to be :

v .	. 32	64	128	256	512	1024
λ .	. 87·62	93·80	98·60	101·3	105·5	107·3

C. Fromherz said that the red, aq. soln. with baryta-water forms a violet liquid, which after a time loses its alkaline reaction and on evaporation below 50° furnishes green barium manganate. According to A. Gorgeu, if hydrogen dioxide is added to a neutral soln. of barium permanganate, a brownish-yellow precipitate is formed, which contains all the barium, chiefly in the form of manganite, but with a small quantity of the manganate. If the permanganate is previously mixed with 2 to 4 eq. of barium hydroxide in soln., all the barium is precipitated in the form of the deep blue manganate on addition of hydrogen dioxide. An excess of hydrogen dioxide exerts a powerful reducing action on the manganate and a feebler action on the manganite. E. Mitscherlich prepared **strontium permanganate,** $Sr(MnO_4)_2.H_2O$, by the method employed for the barium salt ; and H. Aschoff obtained it by evaporating the soln. obtained from the action of strontium chloride on silver permanganate. I. I. Saslawsky gave 2·66 for the sp. gr., and he calculated the contraction which occurs in forming the salt from its elements. The crystals are deliquescent. E. Moles and M. Crespi obtained the salt from a soln. of 2·14 grms. of dihydrated strontium chloride and 5 grms. of silver permanganate in 25 c.c. of water. The sp. gr. is 2·75 ; and the salt decomposes at 175° with the evolution of oxygen. C. Fromherz said that the violet aq. soln. becomes pale green when treated with an excess of strontium hydroxide. E. Franke found that the electrical conductivity, λ, of a soln. of an eq. of the salt, $\frac{1}{2}Sr(MnO_4)_2$, in v litres of water at 25° is :

v .	. 64	128	256	512	1024
λ .	. 101·0	104·7	107·6	109·6	110·3

E. Mitscherlich, and H. Aschoff prepared **calcium permanganate,** $Ca(MnO_4)_2.5H_2O$, by the methods just indicated for the strontium salt. E. Delaurier also obtained it by the prolonged heating of calcium manganate in air. E. Moles and M. Crespi used the process they employed for the strontium salt. The Chemische Fabrik Griesheim-Elektron obtained by electrolyzing in a diaphragm cell a soln. of an alkali manganate or permanganate together with a non-alkali metal hydroxide or halide. I. I. Saslawsky gave 2·4 for the sp. gr., and he calculated the contraction which occurs in forming the salt from its elements. The permanganic acid formed at the anode unites with the metal hydroxide or halide. E. Delaurier said that calcium permanganate readily fuses. E. Adinolfi discussed the absorption spectrum of the salt. A. Kailan studied the action of radium rays on the permanganate. E. Franke found the electrical conductivity, λ, of a soln. of an eq. of the salt, $\frac{1}{2}Ca(MnO_4)_2$, in v litres of water at 25° to be :

v .	. 64	128	256	512	1024
λ .	. 97·21	101·4	104·9	108·8	111·7

E. Wilke-Dörfurt and H. G. Mureck prepared **calcium hexantipyrinopermanganate,** $[Ca(COC_{10}H_{12}N_2)_6](MnO_4)_2$. E. Moles and M. Crespi prepared **beryllium permanganate,** $Be(MnO_4)_2$, from a soln. of beryllium chloride and the calculated quantity of silver permanganate which, on crystallization, furnishes the *penta-hydrate*, $Be(MnO_4)_2.5H_2O$. The evolution of oxygen from the salt begins at 60°. I. I. Saslawsky calculated the contraction which occurs in forming the salt from its elements. E. Mitscherlich, and H. Aschoff also prepared **magnesium permanganate,** $Mg(MnO_4)_2.6H_2O$, from the soln. obtained by decomposing silver permanganate with magnesium chloride, or barium permanganate with magnesium sulphate. I. I. Saslawsky gave 2·18 for the sp. gr., and he calculated the contraction which occurs in forming the salt from its elements. E. Moles and M. Crespi prepared the salt by a similar method to that used for the beryllium salt, and after drying obtained crystals of the *tetrahydrate*, $Mg(MnO_4)_2.4H_2O$. The sp. gr. of the salt is 2·18 ; and it decomposes with the evolution of oxygen at 150°. The deliquescent crystals, according to A. Michael and W. W. Garner, are insoluble in chloroform, carbon tetrachloride, benzene, toluene, nitrobenzene, ether, ligroin, and carbon disulphide, but soluble in methyl alcohol, acetone, pyridine, and glacial acetic acid. The soln. in glacial acetic acid is a more active oxidizing agent for organic substances than soln. in pyridine. T. Klobb prepared **magnesium amminopermanganate,** which was not analyzed. E. Mitscherlich, T. Klobb, H. Aschoff, and C. Kupffer obtained **zinc permanganate,** $Zn(MnO_4)_2.6H_2O$, by treating barium permanganate with a soln. of zinc sulphate and evaporating the filtered liquid ; and J. F. Martenson, and G. Heikel, by treating a hot soln. of silver permanganate with a neutral soln. of zinc chloride and evaporating the filtered soln. for crystallization. E. Moles and M. Crespi obtained it as a tetra- or pentahydrate as in the case of the beryllium salt. F. Stolba obtained a soln. of the salt by adding crystalline zinc fluosilicate to a soln. of potassium permanganate. L. H. Bernagau described commercial samples with 8 to 32 per cent. insoluble matter ; and J. Biel, samples with up to 92 per cent. of zinc sulphate. The needle-like crystals are dark brown. I. I. Saslawsky gave 2·47 for the sp. gr., and calculated the contraction which occurs in forming the salt from its elements. J. F. Martenson found that the crystals can be preserved if they are free from zinc chloride, otherwise they soon begin to develop chlorine. All but one mol. of water are given off at 100° in vacuo, and the last mol. can be driven off only with the decomposition of the salt. E. Moles and M. Crespi found that the sp. gr. is 2·47 ; and that the salt decomposes at 95° with the evolution of oxygen. C. Kupffer said that the salt decomposes with the evolution of oxygen at 140° ; and T. Klobb, that the salt forms manganese dioxide when it is heated with boric oxide in a current of dry air. J. F. Martenson found that when heated in a glass tube, what appears to be a purple vapour is evolved. The salt deliquesces in moist air ; it is freely soluble in water ; and the aq. soln. can be kept a long time without decomposition. T. Klobb obtained **zinc tetramminopermanganate,** $Zn(MnO_4)_2.4NH_3$, by mixing 40 c.c. of a 50 per cent. soln. of zinc sulphate, 60 c.c. of ammonia, and 100 c.c. of a soln. of potassium permanganate saturated at 10°. The liquid is filtered rapidly, and dried in the cold over sulphuric acid. The violet crystals are deliquescent. The corresponding **zinc pyridinopermanganate,** $Zn(MnO_4)_2.4C_5H_5N$, was also prepared. C. Fromherz observed no precipitation occurs when potassium permanganate is treated with cadmium chloride. T. Klobb prepared **cadmium permanganate,** $Cd(MnO_4)_2.8H_2O$, by crystallization from a soln. of cadmium sulphate and barium permanganate ; E. Moles and M. Crespi obtained the *hexahydrate* by the method used for the beryllium salt. Its sp. gr. is 2·81 ; and it decomposes with the evolution of oxygen at 95°. The velocity constants for the decomposition are $k=0.0212$, $k_1=0.100$, and $k_2=0.111$—*vide supra*, potassium permanganate. T. Klobb obtained **cadmium tetramminopermanganate,** $Cd(MnO_4)_2.4NH_3$, from a soln. of potassium permanganate sat. with ammonia, and a cadmium salt. In a few days the black crystals form a brown mass. The salt detonates by percussion. The corresponding **cadmium pyridinopermanganate,** $Cd(MnO_4)_2.4C_5H_5N$, was also prepared.

E. Wilke-Dörfurt and H. G. Mureck prepared **aluminium hexantipyrinopermanganate,** $[Al(COC_{10}H_{12}N_2)_6](MnO_4)_3$. The action of permanganates on cerous salts has been discussed in connection with permanganic acid. F. T. Frerichs and J. L. Smith reported the formation of **didymium permanganate,** $Di(MnO_4)_3.21H_2O$, slightly soluble in water ; and similarly **lanthanum permanganate,** $La(MnO_4)_3.21H_2O$; but P. T. Cleve could not obtain either salt. E. Carstanjen found that neutral soln. of thallous sulphate and potassium permanganate form a reddish-brown precipitate consisting of thallic hydroxide and thallous permanganate. The permanganate is reduced directly to a manganous state without the formation of intermediate oxides. In very dil. soln. the thallic hydroxide predominates, and with conc. soln. **thallous permanganate,** $TlMnO_4$. J. E. Willm made some observations on this subject, and T. V. Barker said that thallous permanganate could not be prepared owing to the oxidation of the thallous salt by the permanganate. R. J. Meyer and H. Best obtained black prismatic crystals of the salt by evaporating over sulphuric acid the filtered liquid resulting from the action of a soln. of thallous sulphate on an eq. proportion of barium permanganate. The salt is liable to decompose into thallic oxide during the evaporation. C. Forchhammer obtained a brown precipitate, thought to be **lead permanganate,** $Pb(MnO_4)_2$, by treating a soln. of lead nitrate with potassium permanganate. The salt is soluble in nitric acid. E. Wilke-Dörfurt and co-workers prepared **chromic hexantipyrinopermanganate,** $[Cr(COC_{10}H_{12}N_2)_6](MnO_4)_3$; also **chromic hexamminopermanganate,** $[Cr(NH_3)_6](MnO_4)_3$; A. Werner and D. Kalkmann, and E. Wilke-Dörfurt and K. Niederer, **chromic hexacarbamidopermanganate,** $[Cr(CON_2H_4)_6](MnO_4)_3$; **chromic hexacarbamidosulphatopermanganate,** $[Cr(CON_2H_4)_6](SO_4)MnO_4$; and **chromic hexacarbamidodichromatopermanganate,** $[Cr(CON_2H_4)_6](Cr_2O_7)MnO_4$. The **molybdatopermanganates** have been discussed in connection with the molybdates.

For the **manganous permanganates** of A. Guyard, *vide supra*. C. Fromherz observed no precipitation occurs when a soln. of nickelous chloride is treated with potassium permanganate. T. Klobb obtained **nickel amminopermanganate,** as a crystalline precipitate, by dissolving a mol of potassium permanganate in the necessary quantity of water at 0°, saturating the soln. at 0° with ammonia, and adding a mol of nickel nitrate dissolved in ten times its weight of water. He also prepared **nickel pyridinopermanganate,** $Ni(MnO_4)_2.4C_5H_5N$. T. Klobb, and E. Wilke-Dörfurt and co-workers prepared **cobaltic hexamminopermanganate,** $[Co(NH_3)_6](MnO_4)_3$, or *luteocobaltic permanganate,* by mixing a warm, conc. soln. of a mol of cobaltic hexamminochloride with 12 mols of potassium permanganate ; it separates in the form of a precipitate mixed with a salt which crystallizes in hexagonal plates and is formed in greater proportion when the permanganate is not in excess. The second salt can be removed by treatment with cold water and the cobaltic hexamminopermanganate is recrystallized from water at 60°. It then forms very brilliant black tetrahedra, only slightly soluble in cold water, but more soluble in hot water, with partial decomposition. When heated it detonates, and it also explodes when struck. With hydrochloric acid it yields manganous chloride and cobaltic hexamminochloride. If a warm soln. of 8 mols of cobaltic hexamminochloride be treated with a soln. of a mol of cobaltic hexamminopermanganate, filtered rapidly, and allowed to cool, **cobaltic hexamminodichloropermanganate,** $[Co(NH_3)_6]Cl_2(MnO_4)$, separates in small black lamellæ with the form of a regular hexagon, red or brown by transmitted light. It is very unstable, and is decomposed by water with removal of the hexamminochloride, but dissolves without decomposition in a soln. of cobaltic hexamminochloride. When heated rapidly it detonates, but it does not explode on percussion. The corresponding **cobaltic hexamminodibromopermanganate,** $[Co(NH_3)_6]Br_2(MnO_4)$, is prepared in a similar manner, or by mixing warm soln. of 3 mols of potassium permanganate and a mol of cobaltic hexamminobromide. The salt furnishes hexagonal plates, which are more stable than the corresponding chloride and are not decomposed by boiling water. The salt which separates in violet hexagonal plates in the preparation of the hexamminopermanganate is **potassium cobaltic hexamminochlorodipermanganate,** $[Co(NH_3)_6]Cl(MnO_4)_2.2KCl$. It separates slowly from a cold, conc. soln. of a mol of cobaltic hexamminochloride and 3 mols of potassium permanganate. It furnishes violet hexagonal lamellæ, which dissolve freely in water, with partial decomposition into its constituents. When heated it behaves like the preceding salts. It may be regarded as a compound of cobaltic hexamminopermanganate and cobaltic hexamminochloride with potassium chloride. It can also be formed by dissolving cobaltic hexamminochloropermanganate in potassium chloride soln., or by the action of cobaltic hexamminopermanganate on a large excess of potassium chloride.

REFERENCES.

¹ C. Fromherz, *Schweigger's Journ.*, **41**. 257, 1824 ; **44**. 327, 1825 ; *Pogg. Ann.*, **31**. 677, 1834 ; E. Mitscherlich, *ib.*, **2**. 10, 1824 ; **25**. 300, 1832 ; **31**. 677, 1834 ; **32**. 8, 1834 ; P. Groth, *ib.*, **133**. 193, 1868 ; A. Kundt, *ib.*, **142**. 163, 1871 ; **145**. 67, 1872 ; G. Kessler, *ib.*, **95**. 204, 1855 ; **118**. 17, 1863 ; G. Bonnet, *ib.*, **37**. 303, 1836 ; T. J. Pearsall, *Journ. Roy. Inst.*, **2**. 49, 1831 ; *Pogg. Ann.*, **25**. 622, 1832 ; C. F. Rammelsberg, *ib.*, **128**. 169, 1866 ; *Ber.*, **8**. 232, 1875 ; J. J. Soret, *Pogg. Ann.*, **143**. 325, 1871 ; J. Müller, *ib.*, **128**. 335, 1866 ; H. Aschoff, *Ueber die Uebermangansäure und die Ueberchromsäure*, Berlin, 1861 ; *Sitzber. Akad. Berlin*, 474, 1860 ; *Pogg. Ann.*, **111**. 217, 1860 ; *Chem. News*, **4**. 103, 1861 ; *Journ. prakt. Chem.*, (1), **81**. 29, 1860 ; E. Donath, *Ber.*, **44**. 982, 1881 ; E. Donath and H. Ditz, *Journ. prakt. Chem.*, (2), **60**. 566, 1899 ; T. Morawsky and J. Stingl, *ib.*, (2), **18**. 78, 1878 ; E. von Cochenhausen, *ib.*, (2), **58**. 451, 1898 ; N. Gräger, *ib.*, (1), **96**. 169, 1865 ; R. Böttger, *Jahresb. Phys. Ver. Frankfurt*, 47, 1858 ; *Repert. Pharm.*, **6**. 247, 1867 ; *Journ. prakt. Chem.*, (1), **90**. 156, 1863 ; (2), **2**. 135, 1870 ; G. Städeler, *ib.*, (1), **103**. 107, 1868 ; R. Luboldt, *ib.*, (1), **77**. 315, 1859 ; C. F. Schönbein, *Liebig's Ann.*, **108**. 159, 1858 ; *Journ. prakt. Chem.*, (1), **41**. 231, 1847 ; (1), **75**. 99, 1858 ; (1), **77**. 276, 1859 ; (1), **78**. 162, 1849 ; (1), **103**. 316, 1868 ; F. Hoppe-Seyler, *ib.*, (1), **90**. 303, 1863 ; T. Curtius and F. Schrader, *ib.*, (2), **50**. 321, 1904 ; H. Schjerning, *ib.*, (2), **45**. 528, 1892 ; W. Kubel, *ib.*, (1), **102**. 233, 1867 ; K. Brand and J. E. Ramsbottom, *ib.*, (2), **82**. 336, 1910 ; E. Carstanjen, *ib.*, (1), **102**. 137, 1867 ; E. Obach, *ib.*, (2), **26**. 281, 1882 ; W. Muthmann, *Ber.*, **26**. 1018, 1893 ; *Zeit. Kryst.*, **22**. 540, 1894 ; W. Muthmann and O. Kuntze, *ib.*, **23**. 368, 1894 ; A. Fock, *Ber.*, **26**. 1016, 1893 ; E. Sommerfeld, *Neues Jahrb. Min.*, ii, 37, 1900 ; O. T. Christensen, *Wied. Ann.*, **19**. 257, 1883 ; *Journ. prakt. Chem.*, (2), **34**. 41, 1886 ; *Zeit. anorg. Chem.*, **24**. 203, 1900 ; R. Lorenz, *ib.*, **12**. 393, 1896 ; F. W. Skirrow, *ib.*, **33**. 25, 1902 ; G. Rudorf, *ib.*, **27**. 58, 1901 ; R. Ehrenfeld, *ib.*, **33**. 117, 1902 ; W. Herz and M. Knoch, *ib.*, **41**. 317, 1904 ; R. J. Meyer and H. Best, *ib.*, **22**. 187, 1899 ; E. Franke, *Zeit. phys. Chem.*, **16**. 475, 1895 ; P. Kubelka and E. Sövegjarto, *ib.*, **154**. 379, 1931 ; J. W. Retgers, *ib.*, **8**. 6, 1891 ; A. Hantzsch and R. H. Clark, *ib.*, **63**. 367, 1908 ; **72**. 374, 1910 ; W. Bein, *ib.*, **27**. 48, 1898 ; G. Just and Y. Kauko, *ib.*, **76**. 601, 1911 ; **82**. 71, 1913 ; W. Ostwald, *ib.*, **9**. 579, 1892 ; G. Bredig, *ib.*, **12**. 233, 1894 ; **13**. 236, 1894 ; *Compt. Rend.*, **126**. 1269, 1898 ; J. M. Lovén, *Zeit. phys. Chem.*, **17**. 376, 1895 ; J. Wagner, *ib.*, **28**. 33, 1899 ; *Massanalytische Studien*, Leipzig, 1898 ; C. M. Tessié du Motay, *Bull. Soc. Enc. Nat. Ind.*, (2), **14**. 472, 1867 ; *Dingler's Journ.*, **186**. 231, 1867 ; *L'Inst.*, **36**. 48, 1868 ; B. C. Brodie, *Proc. Roy. Soc.*, **11**. 442, 1861 ; G. Gore, *ib.*, **14**. 204, 1865 ; **20**. 140, 1873 ; **21**. 140, 1873 ; *Phil. Mag.*, (4), **29**. 546, 1865 ; W. R. E. Hodgkinson and J. Young, *B.A. Rep.*, 676, 1892 ; *Chem. News*, **66**. 199, 1892 ; E. C. Franklin and C. A. Kraus, *Amer. Chem. Journ.*, **20**. 828, 1898 ; T. H. Norton, *ib.*, **7**. 115, 1885 ; J. F. Norris and H. Fay, *ib.*, **20**. 278, 1898 ; H. N. Morse, *Ber.*, **30**. 48, 1896 ; H. N. Morse and C. L. Reese, *Amer. Chem. Journ.*, **20**. 521, 1898 ; H. N. Morse and H. G. Byers, *ib.*, **23**. 313, 1900 ; H. N. Morse, A. J. Hopkins and M. S. Walker, *ib.*, **18**. 401, 1896 ; J. C. Olsen and F. S. White, *ib.*, **29**. 253, 1903 ; H. N. Morse and A. F. Linn, *ib.*, **8**. 274, 1886 ; H. C. Jones and J. McD. Douglas, *ib.*, **26**. 428, 1901 ; L. G. Winston and H. C. Jones, *ib.*, **46**. 368, 1911 ; A. Michael and W. W. Garner, *ib.*, **35**. 267, 1906 ; C. O. Henke and O. W. Brown, *Journ. Phys. Chem.*, **24**. 608, 1920 ; G. R. White, *ib.*, **10**. 502, 1906 ; P. Henry, *Bull. Soc. Chim.*, (4), **39**. 836, 1926 ; M. A. Parker and H. P. Armes, *Trans. Roy. Soc. Canada*, (3), **18**. 203, 1924 ; D. Nishida and K. Herabayashi, *Journ. Japan. Chem. Ind.*, **26**. 1123, 1923 ; T. G. Bedford, *Proc. Roy. Soc.*, **83**. A, 459, 1910 ; W. C. D. Whetham, *ib.*, **71**. A, 332, 1903 ; E. K. Rideal and R. G. W. Norrish, *ib.*, **103**. A, 342, 366, 1923 ; C. N. Hinshelwood and E. J. Bowen, *Phil. Mag.*, (6), **40**. 569, 1920 ; G. Tammann, *Mém. Acad. St. Petersburg*, (7), **35**. 9, 1887 ; G. Heikel, *Amer. Journ. Pharmacy*, **80**. 581, 1909 ; L. H. Bernagau, *ib.*, **80**. 221, 1908 ; E. Pflüger, *Ann. Physik*, (4), **12**. 430, 1903 ; K. Fredenhagen, *Zeit. phys. Chem.*, **128**. 1, 1927 ; D. Vorländer, *Liebig's Ann.*, **354**. 251, 1906 ; D. Vorländer, G. Blau and T. Wallis, *ib.*, **354**. 251, 1906 ; A. Werner and D. Kalkmann, *ib.*, **322**. 296, 1902 ; A. Skrabal and J. Preiss, *Monatsh.*, **27**. 503, 1906 ; A. Skrabal, *Zeit. anorg. Chem.*, **42**. 1, 1904 ; **68**. 48, 1910 ; R. F. Weinland and P. Dinkelacker, *ib.*, **60**. 173, 1908 ; W. Herz and F. Hiebenthal, *ib.*, **177**. 363, 1929 ; N. Schiloff, *Ber.*, **36**. 2735, 1903 ; A. Naumann, *ib.*, **37**. 3601, 4328, 1904 ; **42**. 3795, 1909 ; **47**. 1369, 1914 ; H. C. Jenkins and H. Woolner, *U.S. Pat. No.* 1377485, 1921 ; C. J. A. Griner, *German Pat.*, *D.R.P.* 125060, 1900 ; *French Pat. No.* 300951, 1900 ; A. V. Harcourt, *Journ. Chem. Soc.*, **20**. 470, 1865 ; A. V. Harcourt and W. Esson, *Chem. News*, **10**. 171, 1864 ; *B.A. Rep.*, 29, 1865 ; *Proc. Roy. Soc.*, **14**. 470, 1865 ; *Phil. Trans.*, **156**. 193, 1866 ; **157**. 117, 1867 ; **186**. 817, 1895 ; B. C. Dutt, B. Chatterji and H. Banerji, *Proc. Chem. Soc.*, **29**. 235, 1913 ; H. Sentis, *Ann. Univ. Grenoble*, **9**. 1, 1897 ; *Journ. Phys.*, (3), **6**. 183, 1897 ; J. O. Halverson and O. Bergeim, *Journ. Ind. Eng. Chem.*, **10**. 119, 1918 ; W. M. Gardner and B. North, *ib.*, **23**. 599, 1904 ; E. Moles and M. Crespi, *Zeit. phys. Chem.*, **100**. 337, 1922 ; *Anal. Fis. Quim.*, **20**. 556, 693, 1922 ; **21**. 305 1923 ; **23**. 198, 1925 ; *Estudios acerca de los permanganatos*, Madrid, 1925 ; I. M. Kolthoff, *Pharm. Weekbl.*, **61**. 114, 337, 1924 ; I. M. Kolthoff and N. Smit, *ib.*, **61**. 241, 1924 ; F. Weckbach, *Ueber die elektrolytische Oxydation von Manganosalzen in stark saurer Lösung*, Darmstadt, 1910 ; W. Basche, *Ueber die Struktur von Verbindungen des Typus MeXO₄*, Leipzig, 26, 1926 ; W. Basche and H. Marke, *Zeit. Kryst.*, **64**. 1, 1926 ; A. Manasse, *Beiträge*

zur elektrolytische Bildung der Uebermangansäure, Heidelberg, 1903 ; A. Buzagh, *Mat. Term. Ertesito*, **40**. 134, 1923 ; J. Brock and F. Hurter, *Journ. Soc. Chem. Ind.*, **13**. 394, 1894 ; H. E. Armstrong and R. T. Colgate, *ib.*, **32**. 391, 1913 ; R. T. Colgate, *ib.*, **32**. 893, 1913 ; J. C. Bell, *ib.*, **9**. 18, 1890 ; R. W. Oddy and J. B. Cohen, *ib.*, **9**. 17, 1890 ; E. C. Worden, *ib.*, **26**. 452, 1907 ; R. M. Caven and A. Hill, *ib.*, **16**. 981, 1897 ; **17**. 124, 1898 ; J. C. Sticht, *Pharm. Viertelj*, **15**. 359, 1866 ; H. Buignet, *Journ. Pharm. Chim.*, (3), **36**. 122, 1859 ; M. J. Fordos and A. Gélis, *ib.*, (3), **36**. 113, 1859 ; C. F. Schlagdenhauffen, *ib.*, (4), **20**. 266, 1874 ; A. Bussy, *ib.*, (3), **12**. 321, 1847 ; W. Gregory, *ib.*, (2), **21**. 312, 1835 ; *Thomson's Records*, **4**. 297, 1836 ; *Liebig's Ann.*, **15**. 237, 1835 ; L. Swiontkowsky, *ib.*, **141**. 211, 1867 ; F. Wöhler and A. Geuther, *ib.*, **91**. 127, 1854 ; F. Wöhler, *ib.*, **136**. 256, 1865 ; S. Hoogewerff and W. A. van Dorp, *ib.*, **204**. 93, 1880 ; T. Salzer, *ib.*, **187**. 322, 1877 ; C. Weltzien, *Compt. Rend.*, **62**. 642, 1866 ; *Liebig's Ann.*, **120**. 349, 1869 ; O. Hesse, *ib.*, **166**, 217, 1873 ; W. Lossen, *ib.*, **148**. 174, 1868 ; F. and O. Zeidler, *ib.*, **197**. 246, 1879 ; E. Fürst, *ib.*, **206**. 75, 1881 ; F. T. Frerichs and J. L. Smith, *ib.*, **191**. 338, 1878 ; R. Espenchied, *ib.*, **114**. 255, 1860 ; R. C. Campbell, *ib.*, **28**. 52, 1838 ; W. Crum, *ib.*, **60**. 219, 1846 ; J. Volhard, *ib.*, **198**. 354, 1874 ; R. Wagner, *Chem. Centr.*, (3), **6**. 714, 1875 ; F. Bayer, *German Pat.*, *D.R.P.* 118232, 1900 ; F. Deissler, *ib.*, 105008, 1898 ; Salzbergwerk Neu-Stassfurt, *ib.*, 101710, 1898 ; Chemische Fabrik Griesheim-Elektron, *ib.*, 145368, 1903 ; O. Dieffenbach, *ib.*, 195532, 1904 ; T. Macalpine, *Brit. Pat. No.* 3381, 1899 ; C. Huggenberg, *ib.*, 13695, 1887 ; *Ber.*, **21**. 491, 1888 ; F. Ullmann and J. B. Uzbachian, *ib.*, **36**. 1797, 1903 ; H. N. Warren, *Chem. News*, **77**. 165, 1898 ; C. M. Bradbury, *ib.*, **59**. 115, 123, 136, 149, 1889 ; T. Bayley, *ib.*, **42**. 242, 1881 ; H. Tamm, *ib.*, **25**. 26, 47, 1872 ; W. Crookes, *ib.*, **15**. 204, 1867 ; E. Sonstadt, *ib.*, **26**. 173, 1872 ; W. C. Birch, *ib.*, **99**. 61, 73, 1909 ; J. Heyrovsky, *ib.*, **134**. 161, 1927 ; W. Foster, *ib.*, **39**. 131, 1879 ; **115**. 73, 1917 ; A. W. Warrington, *ib.*, **117**. 97, 1918 ; A. Bose, *ib.*, **117**. 369, 1918 ; G. N. Ridley, *ib.*, **130**. 305, 1925 ; W. B. Giles, *ib.*, **15**. 204, 1867 ; A. R. Leeds, *ib.*, **39**. 18, 1879 ; H. B. Parsons, *ib.*, **35**. 235, 1877 ; G. Forchhammer, *De mangano*, Hafnia, 1820 ; *Ann. Phil.*, **16**. 130, 1820 ; **17**. 50, 1821 ; *Overs. Danske Vid. Selsk. Forh.*, 91, 1856 ; *Lærebog : Stoffernes almindelige Kemi*, Kjöbenhaon, 381 ; 1842 ; W. Eidmann, *Ein Beitrag zur Erkenntnis des Verhaltens chemischer Verbindungen in nichtwässerigen Lösungen*, Giessen, 1899 ; J. Thomsen, *Ber.*, **6**. 1434, 1873 ; *Thermochemische Untersuchungen*, Leipzig, **3**. 271, 1883 ; K. Elbs, *Zeit. Elektrochem.*, **7**. 260, 1900 ; R. Lang, *Zeit. anorg. Chem.*, **130**. 141, 1923 ; **152**. 197, 1926 ; W. Geilmann and E. Wünnenberg, *ib.*, **159**. 271, 1927 ; D. N. Chakravarti and N. R. Dhar, *ib.*, **142**. 317, 1925 ; G. G. Stokes, *Phil. Mag.*, (4), **6**. 393, 1853 ; F. Guthrie, *ib.*, (5), **6**. 37, 1878 ; J. Conroy, *ib.*, (5), **6**. 454, 1878 ; J. A. Wanklyn and A. Gamgee, *Journ. Chem. Soc.*, **21**. 25, 1868 ; J. A. Wanklyn and W. J. Cooper, *Phil. Mag.*, (5), **6**. 288, 1878 ; (5), **30**. 431, 1890 ; C. J. W. Grieveson, *ib.*, (6), **49**. 1006, 1925 ; R. Phillip, *ib.*, (2), **1**. 313, 1827 ; E. Wiedemann, *Pogg. Ann.*, **151**. 625, 1874 ; J. Dewar and A. Scott, *Proc. Roy. Soc.*, **35**. 44, 1883 ; *Chem. News*, **47**. 98, 1883 ; H. Kopp, *Liebig's Ann. Suppl.*, **3**. 290, 1865 ; *Liebig's Ann.*, **36**. 1, 1840 ; E. Legrand, *Compt. Rend.*, **126**. 1025, 1898 ; P. Thénard, *ib.*, **42**. 382, 1856 ; **75**. 177, 1872 ; L. P. de St. Gilles, *ib.*, **46**. 624, 808, 1143, 1858 ; **47**. 554, 1858 ; *Ann. Chim. Phys.*, (3), **55**. 374, 1858 ; S. Cloez and E. Guignet, *Compt. Rend.*, **46**. 1110, 1858 ; **47**. 710, 1858 ; P. Truchot, *ib.*, **63**. 274, 1866 ; E. Monier, *ib.*, **46**. 577, 1858 ; M. V. Machuca, *ib.*, **51**. 140, 1860 ; T. L. Phipson, *ib.*, **50**. 694, 1860 ; J. Personne, *ib.*, **51**. 214, 1860 ; J. Personne and M. l'Hermite, *Journ. Pharm. Chim.*, (3), **19**. 115, 161, 1851 ; L. Maquenne, *ib.*, **94**. 795, 1882 ; E. J. Maumené, *Compt. Rend.*, **79**. 177, 1874 ; E. Caventou and E. Willm, *ib.*, **69**. 284, 1869 ; G. Rapin, *ib.*, **187**. 112, 1928 ; **188**. 1547, 1929 ; **189**. 287, 699, 1929 ; *French Pat. No.* 675477, 1929 ; V. Thomas and P. Dupuis, *Compt. Rend.*, **143**. 282, 1906 ; H. Baubigny, *ib.*, **135**. 965, 1110, 1902 ; **136**. 449, 1325, 1662, 1903 ; P. Collet, *ib.*, **183**. 1031, 1926 ; F. Pisani, *ib.*, **59**. 289, 1865 ; A. Gautier, *ib.*, **126**. 871, 1898 ; A. Baudrimont, *ib.*, **89**. 1115, 1879 ; H. Baubigny and P. Rivals, *ib.*, **124**. 859, 954, 1897 ; G. Rousseau, *ib.*, **104**, 786, 1887 ; G. Rousseau and B. Bruneau, *Bull. Soc. Chim.*, (2), **41**. 246, 1884 ; *Compt. Rend.*, **98**. 229, 1884 ; T. Klobb, *ib.*, **103**. 384, 1886 ; **118**. 1271, 1894 ; *Bull. Soc. Chim.*, (3), **3**. 508, 1890 ; (3), **11**. 605, 1894 ; M. Travers, *ib.*, (4), **37**. 456, 1925 ; P. T. Cleve, *ib.*, (2), **21**. 196, 1874 ; *Bihang. Svenska Akad.*, **2**. 7, 1871 ; A. Karlan, *Sitzber. Akad. Wien*, **133**. 477, 1924 ; E. Mulder, *Scheik. Verh. Onderzoek*, **1**. 62, 1857 ; F. Simand, *Dingler's Journ.*, **248**. 518, 1883 ; K. Chamberlain, *Nature*, **114**. 500, 1924 ; B. V. Tronoff and A. A. Lukanin, *Journ. Russ. Phys. Chem. Soc.*, **59**. 1157, 1927 ; **61**. 727, 1929 ; B. V. Tronoff, B. V. Tronoff and A. A. Lukanin, and I. I. Pavllnoff, *ib.*, **59**. 1173, 1927 ; O. Hackl, *Chem. Ztg.*, **46**. 1065, 1922 ; G. Bruhns, *ib.*, **47**. 613, 1923 ; *Zeit. anorg. Chem.*, **49**. 277, 1906 ; P. Askenasy and A. Solberg, *Nernst's Festschrift*, 53, 1912 ; P. Askenasy and S. Klonowsky, *Zeit. Elektrochem.*, **16**. 170, 1910 ; S. Klonowsky, *Ueber die Manganatschmelze und die Ueberführung von Kaliummanganat im Kaliumpermanganat auf elektrolytischen Wege*, Karlsruhe, 1910 ; O. Sackur and W. Taegener, *Zeit. Elektrochem.*, **18**. 718, 1912 ; W. Taegener, *Zur Kenntnis der wässerigen Lösungen des Kaliummanganates und des Kaliumpermanganates*, Breslau, 1913 ; F. Weigert, *Zeit. Elektrochem.*, **12**. 377, 1906 ; G. Baborovsky, *ib.*, **11**. 465, 1905 ; R. Luther, *ib.*, **12**. 596, 1906 ; H. Mark, W. Basche and E. Pohland, *ib.*, **31**. 523, 1925 ; F. C. Calvert, *Compt. Rend.*, **75**. 1015, 1872 ; *Proc. Roy. Soc.*, **20**. 197, 1872 ; *Chem. News*, **25**. 151, 157, 1872 ; J. Zawidzky, *Rocz. Chem.*, **1**. 135, 1921 ; H. S. Davis, *Journ. Ind. Eng. Chem.*, **20**. 1055, 1928 ; L. Gmelin, *Handbook of Chemistry*, London, **4**. 209, 1850 ; O. Unverdorben, *Brandes' Arch.*, **9**. 36, 1824 ; *Quart. Journ. Science*, **2**. 204, 1827 ; *Pogg. Ann.*, **7**. 322, 1826 ; O. Ohmann, *Zeit. phys. Chem. Unterr.*, **27**. 167, 1914 ; C. W. Hempel, *Liebig's Ann.*, **107**. 100, 1858 ; *Mémoire sur l'emploi de l'acide oxalique dans les dosages à liqueurs* *titrées*, Lausanne, 1853 ; F. Stolba, *Chem. Centr.*, (3), **7**. 701, 1876 ; *Sitzber. Böhm. Ges.*, 247, 1876 ; C. Kupffer, *Russ. Journ. Pharm.*, 481, 1878 ; J. F. Martenson, *ib.*, 66, 1873 ; J. Biel, *ib.*, 97, 1874 ; J. Holluta, *Zeit. anorg. Chem.*, **168**. 361, 1928 ; *Chem. News*, **100**. 266, 1909 ; *Zeit. phys. Chem.*, **101**. 34, 1922 ; **102**. 32, 276, 1922 ; **106**. 276, 324, 1923 ; **107**. 249, 333, 1923 ; **113**. 464, 1924 ; **115**. 137, 143, 1925 ; J. Holluta and N. Weiser, *ib.*, **101**. 489, 1922 ; J. Holluta and A. Mutschin, *ib.*, **150**. 381, 1930 ; J. Holluta and J. Obrist, *Monatsh.*, **41**. 555, 1920 ; J. Heslinga, *Chem. Weekbl.*, **19**. 274, 1922 ; M. Duyk, *Ann. Chim. Anal.*, **12**. 465, 1907 ; G. Wenger and H. H. Alvarez, *ib.*, **17**. 203, 1912 ; A. Steopoe, *Bull. Chim. Soc. Romana*, **28**. 83, 1925 ; *Koll. Zeit.*, **39**. 35, 1926 ; J. Oesch, *Kritisch Studien über Mangan*, Berlin, 1906 ; H. Rose, *Pogg. Ann.*, **59**. 320, 1843 ; *Handbuch der analytischen Chemie*, Braunschweig, 1. 241, 1867 ; G. L. Voerman, *Chem. Weekbl.*, **2**. 766, 1905 ; 3. 704, 1906 ; C. W. R. Powell, *Proc. Roy. Soc. New South Wales*, **48**. 223, 1914 ; E. Brücke, *Sitzber. Akad. Wien*, **74**. 428, 1877 ; *Journ. prakt. Chem.*, (1), **88**. 486, 1863 ; J. E. Purvis, *Proc. Cambridge Phil. Soc.*, **15**. 247, 1909 ; C. Meinecke and K. Schröder, *Zeit. öffentl. Chem.*, **3**. 5, 1897 ; K. Schröder, *ib.*, **16**. 270, 290, 1910 ; E. Cahen and H. F. V. Little, *Analyst*, **36**. 52, 1911 ; C. F. Mohr, *Lehrbuch der chemische-analytischen Titrirmethode*, Braunschweig, 246, 1874 ; *Zeit. anal. Chem.*, **9**. 43, 1870 ; E. Bohlig, *ib.*, **9**. 277, 1870 ; A. H. Schulze, *ib.*, **21**. 167, 1882 ; W. M. Fischer, *ib.*, **48**. 751, 1909 ; F. Feigl and F. Wiener, *ib.*, **64**. 302, 1924 ; B. Reinitzer and P. Conrath, *ib.*, **68**. 129, 1926 ; S. Feldhaus, *ib.*, **1**. 426, 1862 ; A. Alander, *ib.*, **40**. 574, 1901 ; C. Winkler, *ib.*, **7**. 48, 1868 ; **8**. 265, 420, 1869 ; E. Schöne, *ib.*, **18**. 140, 1879 ; J. Löwenthal and E. Lenssen, *ib.*, **1**. 529, 1862 ; C. Luckow, *ib.*, **32**. 53, 1893 ; C. Böhmer, *ib.*, **21**. 212, 1882 ; C. R. A. Wright and A. E. Menke, *Journ. Chem. Soc.*, **37**. 40, 1880 ; W. N. Hartley, *ib.*, **101**. 826, 1912 ; T. R. Merton, *ib.*, **99**. 637, 1911 ; A. J. Berry, *ib.*, **121**. 394, 1922 ; J. W. Thomas, *ib.*, **33**. 367, 1878 ; D. Borar, *ib.*, **99**. 1414, 1911 ; A. S. Russell and D. C. Evans, *ib.*, **127**. 2221, 1925 ; F. Jones, *Chem. News*, **37**. 37, 1878 ; *Journ. Chem. Soc.*, **29**. 841, 1876 ; **33**. 95, 1878 ; E. T. Chapman and W. Thorp, *ib.*, **19**. 477, 1866 ; E. A. Hadow, *ib.*, **11**. 174, 1858 ; E. T. Chapman and M. H. Smith, *ib.*, **18**. 301, 1867 ; **20**. 302, 1867 ; J. M. Crofts, *ib.*, **73**. 593, 1898 ; W. Ramsay, *ib.*, **79**. 1324, 1901 ; T. S. Dymond and F. Hughes, *ib.*, **71**. 314, 1897 ; H. B. Dunnicliff and S. D. Nijhawan, *ib.*, 1, 1926 ; J. W. Smith, *ib.*, **528**, 1931 ; V. Meyer and M. von Recklinghausen, *Ber.*, **29**. 2549, 1897 ; H. Hirtz and V. Meyer, *ib.*, **29**. 2828, 1896 ; W. Meyeringh, *ib.*, **10**. 1940, 1877 ; G. Lunge, *ib.*, **10**. 1075, 1877 ; A. Bach, *ib.*, **33**. 3111, 1900 ; C. Graebe, *ib.*, **35**. 43, 1902 ; E. Fleischer, *ib.*, **5**. 550, 1872 ; A. Claus, *ib.*, **7**. 227, 1874 ; A. W. Hofmann, *ib.*, **9**. 1303, 1876 ; I. Guareschi, *ib.*, **11**. 1383, 1878 ; J. Krutwig, *ib.*, **14**. 304, 1881 ; Z. H. Skraup, *ib.*, **11**. 311, 1516, 1878 ; **12**. 1104, 1879 ; *Anz. Akad. Wien*, 175, 1877 ; J. Krutwig and A. Cocheteux, *Ber.*, **16**. 1534, 1883 ; W. Herz, *ib.*, **35**. 949, 1902 ; O. Kühling, *ib.*, **33**. 2924, 1900 ; B. W. Gerland, *Proc. Manchester Lit. Phil. Soc.*, **10**. 129, 1871 ; *Chem. News*, **23**. 136, 1871 ; *Ber.*, **10**. 1513, 1877 ; C. Friedheim, *ib.*, **23**. 353, 1890 ; T. Poleck, *ib.*, **27**. 1051, 1894 ; A. Clever, *ib.*, **33**. 1506, 1900 ; A. von Bayer and V. Villiger, *ib.*, **33**. 2488, 1900 ; V. Meyer and E. Saam, *ib.*, **30**. 1933, 1897 ; R. Engel, *Bull. Soc. Chim.*, (3), **6**. 17, 1891 ; M. Martinon, *ib.*, (2), **43**. 355, 1885 ; A. Peter, *ib.*, (2), **44**. 16, 1885 ; J. B. Senderens, *ib.*, (3), **7**. 511, 1892 ; A. Guyard, *ib.*, (2), 1. 81, 92, 1864 ; A. Terreil, *ib.*, (2), **21**. 289, 1870 ; E. Allary, *ib.*, (2), **35**. 491, 1881 ; F. M. Raoult, *ib.*, (2), **46**. 805, 1886 ; H. Vignal, *ib.*, (2), **45**. 171, 1886 ; M. Hönig and E. Zatzek, *Monatsh.*, **4**. 738, 1883 ; **6**. 492, 1885 ; **7**. 48, 1886 ; M. Gläser, *ib.*, **6**. 329, 1885 ; **7**. 651, 1886 ; B. Brauner, *ib.*, **11**. 326, 1890 ; J. Mijers, *Maansbl. Natuurwet.*, 1. 79, 1871 ; J. W. Slater, *Chem. Gaz.*, **11**. 329, 1853 ; M. Gröger, *Zeit. angew. Chem.*, **7**. 13, 52, 1894 ; *Chem. Ztg.*, **18**. 639, 743, 1894 ; C. Reichard, *ib.*, **23**. 801, 1899 ; R. Benedikt and R. Zsigmondy, *ib.*, **11**. 975, 1887 ; E. Deiss, *ib.*, **34**. 237, 1910 ; W. Lindner, *Chem. Tech. Repert.*, i, 102, 1868 ; *Zeit. Chem.*, (2), **5**. 442, 1869 ; G. Kerner, *Zeit. prakt. Chem.*, (1), **108**. 182, 1869 ; *Zeit. Chem.*, (2), **5**. 593, 1869 ; E. Erlenmeyer and G. Lewinstein, *ib.*, (1), **3**. 392, 1860 ; E. Erlenmeyer, *Verh. Nat. Med. Ver. Heidelberg*, **1**. 169, 1859 ; A. Longi and L. Bonavia, *Gazz. Chim. Ital.*, **28**. i, 325, 1898 ; I. Macagno, *ib.*, **4**. 567, 1874 ; A. Gawalowsky, *Zeit. Oesterr. Apoth. Ver.*, **43**. 377, 1905 ; L. L. de Koninck, *Bull. Assoc. Chim. Belg.*, **11**. 369, 374, 1898 ; M. A. von Reis and F. Wiggert, *Zeit. angew. Chem.*, **3**. 695, 1890 ; E. Schütz, *ib.*, **24**. 1628, 1911 ; D. Vitali, *Boll. Chim. Farm.*, **43**. 493, 1904 ; L. E. Rivot, F. S. Beudant and P. A. Daguin, *Ann. Mines*, (5), **4**. 250, 1853 ; Y. Ono, *Journ. Japan. Chem. Soc.*, **44**. 726, 1923 ; G. Scheff, *Biochem. Zeit.*, **160**. 390, 1925 ; G. P. Baxter, A. C. Boylston and R. A. Hubbard, *Journ. Amer. Chem. Soc.*, **28**. 1336, 1906 ; **29**. 240, 1907 ; A. M. Patterson, *ib.*, **28**. 1734, 1906 ; A. A. Noyes and K. G. Falk, *ib.*, **34**. 454, 485, 1912 ; F. E. Brown and J. E. Snyder, *ib.*, **47**. 2671, 1925 ; F. P. Venable and D. H. Jackson, *ib.*, **42**. 237, 1920 ; H. M. Trimble, *ib.*, **44**. 451, 1922 ; S. Freed and C. Kasper, *ib.*, **52**. 4671, 1930 ; L. A. Bigelow, *ib.*, **44**. 2010, 1922 ; G. L. Clark and L. W. Pickett, *ib.*, **52**. 465, 1930 ; E. H. Swift and C. H. Gregory, *ib.*, **52**. 901, 1930 ; E. J. Witzemann, *ib.*, **38**. 150, 1916 ; **39**. 2657, 1917 ; W. L. Evans and E. J. Witzemann, *ib.*, **34**. 1086, 1912 ; W. L. Evans and H. Adkins, *ib.*, **41**. 1385, 1919 ; W. L. Evans and J. E. Day, *ib.*, **38**. 375, 1916 ; **41**. 1267, 1919 ; W. T. Hall and C. E. Carlson, *ib.*, **45**. 1615, 1923 ; J. Moir, *Trans. Roy. Soc. South Africa*, **10**. 33, 1921 ; B. V. Tronoff and L. S. Nikonova, *Journ. Russ. Phys. Chem. Soc.*, **61**. 541, 1929 ; B. V. Tronoff and A. A. Grigorieva, *ib.*, **61**. 653, 1929 ; E. M. Stoddart, *Journ. Chem. Soc.*, 1874, 1931 ; R. H. Ferguson, W. Leach and J. E. Day, *Journ. Amer. Chem. Soc.*, **53**. 126, 1931 ; S. S. Bhatnagar, R. N. Mather and R. N. Kapur, *Phil. Mag.*, (7), **8**. 457, 1929 ; G. R. Levi and D. Ghiron, *Atti Accad. Lincei*, (6), **11**. 1005, 1930 ; W. G. Vannoy, *Journ. Phys. Chem.*, **33**. 1593, 1929 ; D. R. Hale, *ib.*, **33**. 1633, 1929 ; V. Subrahmanyan, *Journ. Agric. Science*, **19**. 651, 1929 ; *Chem. News*, **139**. 262,

1929 ; T. E. Friedemann, M. Cotonio and P. A. Shaffer, *Journ. Biol. Chem.*, **73**. 335, 1927 ; E. Montignie, *Bull. Soc. Chim.*, (4), **45**. 492, 1929 ; M. Geloso and P. Dubois, *Compt. Rend.*, **189**. 296, 1929 ; C. Boulanger, *ib.*, **191**. 56, 1930 ; M. I. Belotzerkowsky, *Russ. Pat. No.* 70674, 1930 ; R. C. L. Mooney, *Phys. Rev.*, (2), **37**. 474, 1931 ; V. Chlopin and B. Nikitin, *Zeit. phys. Chem.*, **145**. 139, 1929 ; A. Wassermann, *ib.*, **149**. 223, 1930 ; V. Schuleikin and X. Solovova, *ib.*, **149**. 434, 1930 ; K. Herrmann and W. Ilge, *Zeit. Kryst.*, **71**. 47, 1929 ; G. Meslin, *Ann. Chim. Phys.*, (8), **7**. 145, 1906 ; G. Quincke, *Wied. Ann.*, **24**. 347, 1885 ; E. Shpolsky, *Nature*, **126**. 647, 1930 ; T. Ishiwara, *Science Rep. Tohoku Univ.*, **3**. 303, 1915 ; K. Honda and T. Ishiwara, *ib.*, **4**. 215, 1916 ; D. A. Howes and A. W. Nash, *Journ. Soc. Chem. Ind.*, **49**. 113, T, 1930 ; F. C. Thompson and N. Tilling, *ib.*, **43**. 37, T, 1924 ; A. Berthoud, *Helvetica Chim. Acta*, **13**. 17, 1930 ; F. Flöttmann, *Ueber Löslichkeitsgleichgewichte*, Marburg, 1928 ; *Zeit. anal. Chem.* **13**. 1, 1928 ; W. Büssem and K. Herrmann, *Zeit. Kryst.*, **74**. 458, 1930 ; H. E. Buckley, *ib.*, **73**. 443, 1930 ; **75**. 15, 1930 ; **76**. 147, 1930 ; **78**. 412, 1931 ; **80**. 238, 1931 ; K. Volz, *Zeit. ges. Textilind*, **33**. 118, 132, 1930 ; K. Schnetzler, *Phys. Zeit.*, **31**. 802, 1930 ; H. Pinsl, *Stahl Eisen*, **44**. 72, 1924 ; J. MacMullen, *Quart. Journ. Science*, **22**. 231, 1827 ; **24**. 258, 1827 ; E. Turner, *Phil. Mag.*, (2), **3**. 254, 1865 ; R. J. Kane, *Quart. Journ. Science*, **26**. 286, 1828 ; J. B. van Mons, *ib.*, **9**. 409, 1820 ; *Ann. Gen. Sciences Phys.*, **1**. 171, 1819 ; G. Fester and G. Brude, *Zeit. angew. Chem.*, **35**. 527, 1922 ; E. Langbein, *Russ. Pharm. Journ.*, **7**. 573, 1868 ; L. Wulff, *Pharm. Ztg.*, **32**. 364, 1887 ; P. Solstein, *ib.*, **32**. 659, 1887 ; R. E. Wilson, W. G. Horsch and M. A. Youtz, *Journ. Ind. Eng. Chem.*, **13**. 763, 1921 ; S. G. Simpson, *ib.*, **13**. 1152, 1921 ; P. H. Segnitz, *ib.*, **12**. 1196, 1920 ; A. Jolles, *Pharm. Centrh.*, **28**. 320, 1887 ; E. Delaurier, *Chem. News*, **20**. 240, 1869 ; *Les Mondes*, **21**. 388, 1869 ; O. Cantoni, *Ann. Chim. Appl.*, **16**. 153, 1926 ; F. Krause, *Versuche zur Oxydation von hydratischem Mangandioxyd in alkalischer Suspension*, Leipzig, 1907 ; F. A. Gooch and C. A. Peters, *Amer. Journ. Science*, (4), **7**. 461, 1899 ; F. A. Gooch and E. W. Danner, *ib.*, (3), **44**. 301, 1892 ; J. Brown, *ib.*, **19**. 31, 1905 ; *Zeit. anorg. Chem.*, **44**. 145, 1905 ; **47**. 314, 1905 ; E. Müller and H. Möllering, *ib.*, **141**. 111, 1924 ; I. I. Saslawsky, *ib.*, **146**. 315, 1925 ; J. G. F. Druce, *Chem. News*, **134**. 145, 161, 1927 ; *Journ. Chem. Soc.*, **111**. 419, 1917 ; N. A. Orloff, *Journ. Russ. Phys. Chem. Soc.*, **34**. 449, 1902 ; S. S. Nametkin, *ib.*, **55**. 70, 1924 ; E. S. Prschevalsky, *ib.*, **49**. 567, 1918 ; E. Wedekind and C. Horst, *Ber.*, **48**. 105, 1915 ; B. E. Dixon and J. L. White, *Journ. Chem. Soc.*, 1469, 1927 ; A. N. Campbell, *ib.*, **123**. 892, 2323, 1923 ; *Chem. News*, **132**. 348, 1926 ; *Trans. Faraday Soc.*, **22**. 46, 1926 ; A. J. Allamand and A. N. Campbell, *ib.*, **19**. 559, 1924 ; **20**. 376, 1925 ; E. T. Allen, *The Reaction between Lead Dioxide and Potassium Permanganate*, Baltimore, 1892 ; T. V. Barker, *Zeit. Kryst.*, **43**. 527, 1907 ; **45**. 1, 1908 ; *Journ. Chem. Soc.*, **89**. 1120, 1906 ; R. Warington and W. A. Peake, *ib.*, **38**. 6, 17, 1880 ; C. F. Cross and E. J. Bevan, *ib.*, **53**. 889, 1888 ; A. H. Elliott, *ib.*, **7**. 182, 1869 ; R. Phelps, *Zeit. anorg. Chem.*, **16**. 85, 1898 ; R. Finkener, *Mitt. Ver. Anstalt. Berlin*, 156, 1889 ; *Zeit. anal. Chem.*, **29**. 666, 1890 ; R. E. and W. M. Rogers, *Amer. Journ. Science*, (2), **5**. 352, 1848 ; (2), **6**. 110, 1848 ; C. Brunner, *Pogg. Ann.*, **95**. 379, 1855 ; E. Ullgren, *Liebig's Ann.*, **124**. 59, 1862 ; H. Heidenhain, *Techniker*, **14**. 66, 1893 ; H. von Jüptner, *Oesterr. Zeit. Berg. Hütt.*, **31**. 493, 1883 ; **34**. 67, 83, 1886 ; F. A. Cairns, *Chem. News*, **25**. 271, 1872 ; *Amer. Chem. Journ.*, **2**. 140, 1872 ; M. Geloso, *Compt. Rend.*, **171**. 1145, 1920 ; A. Boutaric, *ib.*, **160**. 711, 1915 ; T. Warynsky and P. A. Tscheishwily, *Journ. Chim. Phys.*, **6**. 567, 1908 ; P. A. Tscheishwily, *Journ. Russ. Phys. Chem. Soc.*, **42**. 856, 1910 ; **43**. 1402, 1911 ; W. Ipatieff and A. Kisseleff, *ib.*, **58**. 686, 1926 ; A. Ferguson and I. Vogel, *Phil. Mag.*, (7), **4**. 233, 1927 ; G. B. Frankforter and R. M. West, *Journ. Amer. Chem. Soc.*, **28**. 1234, 1906 ; R. S. McBride, *ib.*, **34**. 393, 1912 ; S. Popoff and J. L. Whitman, *ib.*, **47**. 2259, 1925 ; S. Popoff and F. L. Chambers, *ib.*, **45**. 1358, 1923 ; S. Popoff, J. A. Riddick and W. W. Becker, *ib.*, **52**. 2624, 1930 ; D. J. Brown and R. F. Tefft, *ib.*, **48**. 1128, 1926 ; D. J. Brown and H. A. Liebhafsky, *ib.*, **52**. 2595, 1930 ; W. C. Bray and G. M. McKay, *ib.*, **32**. 1193, 1910 ; W. C. Bray and H. E. Miller, *ib.*, **46**. 2204, 1924 ; W. C. Vosburgh, *ib.*, **44**. 2120, 1922 ; W. S. Hendrixson, *ib.*, **47**. 2156, 1925 ; H. A. Fales and P. S. Roller, *ib.*, **51**. 345, 1929 ; L. Medri, *Gazz. Chim. Ital.*, **36**. i, 373, 1906 ; E. Viterbi, *ib.*, **55**. 127, 1925 ; G. Bruni and G. Levi, *ib.*, **46**. ii, 17, 1916 ; E. Adinolfi, *Atti Accad. Lincei*, (6), **3**. 196, 1926 ; F. Zambonini, *ib.*, (5), **31**. ii, 67, 1922 ; J. Petersen, *Zeit. anorg. Chem.*, **5**. 1, 1893 ; M. Bobtelsky and D. Kaplan, *Zeit. anorg. Chem.*, **172**. 196, 1928 ; **177**. 119, 323,.1928; D. Balareff and G. Kandilaroff, *ib.*, **163**. 141, 1927 ; F. Hein and W. Daniel, *ib.*, **181**. 78, 1929 ; U. Roberto and F. Roncali, *L'Ind. Chim.*, **6**. 178, 1904 ; P. Niggli, *Zeit. Kryst.*, **75**. 228, 1930 ; F. Rinne, *ib.*, **58**. 226, 1923 ; *Centr. Min.*, 161, 1924 ; H. Grimm, *Naturwiss.*, **15**. 561, 1927 ; H. Grimm and G. Wagner, *Zeit. phys. Chem.*, **132**. 131, 1928 ; G. Wagner, *ib.*, **2**. B, 27, 1929 ; A. Sieverts and H. Theberath, *ib.*, **100**. 463, 1922 ; I. D. Götz and G. P. Pamfil, *ib.*, **109**. 165, 1924 ; E. Wilke and H. Kuhn, *ib.*, **113**. 313, 1924 ; O. Risse, *ib.*, **140**. 133, 1929 ; L. J. Simon, *Compt. Rend.*, **140**. 659, 1905 ; P. Pascal, *ib.*, **147**. 742, 1908 ; A. J. Hale, *Journ. Soc. Chem. Ind.—Chem. Ind.*, **43**. 1224, 1250, 1291, 1924 ; L. U. de Nardo, *Gion. Chim. Ind. Appl.*, **10**. 253, 1928 ; J. Hetper, *Bull. Acad. Cracovie*, 601, 1910 ; *Zeit. anal. Chem.*, **51**. 409, 1912 ; H. Kautsky and O. Neitzke, *Zeit. Physik*, **31**. 60, 1925 ; H. McCormack, *Science*, (2), **53**. 49, 1921 ; M. C. Schuyten, *Chem. Ztg.*, **20**. 129, 1896 ; H. Gombos, *Biochem. Zeit.*, **151**. 1, 7, 1924 ; R. A. Houstoun, *Proc. Roy. Soc. Edin.*, **33**. 156, 1913 ; F. Fischer, *Zeit. Elektrochem.*, **10**. 430, 1904 ; G. Grube and H. Metzger, *ib.*; **29**. 100, 1923 ; J. N. Rakschit, *ib.*, **31**. 97, 1925 ; C. del Fresno, *ib.*, **31**. 199, 1925 ; V. R. von Kurelec, *Biochem. Zeit.*, **180**. 65, 1927 ; W. W. Coblentz, *Supplementary Investigations of Infrared Spectra*, Washington, 50, 1908 ; T. Milobendzky, *Zeit. anal. Chem.*, **46**. 18, 1907 ; J. M. Hendel, *ib.*, **63**. 321, 1924 ; E. Müller and H. Kogert, *Zeit. phys. Chem.*, **136**. 437, 1928 ; O. Lehmann, *ib.*, **102**. 91, 1922 ; P. Walden, *Zeit. öffent. Chem.*, **108**. 1924 ; D. A. MacInnes, *ib.*, **130**. 217,

1927 ; Z. Stary, *ib.*, **126**. 173, 1927 ; L. Engel and W. Pauli, *ib.*, **126**. 247, 1927 ; F. L. Hahn and M. Frommer, *ib.*, **127**. 1, 1927 ; A. Hagenbach and R. Percy, *Helvetica Chim. Acta*, **5**. 454, 1922 ; W. H. Hatcher and C. R. West, *Trans. Roy. Soc. Canada*, (3), **20**. 327, 1926 ; (3), **21**. 269, 1927 ; M. A. Rozenberg, *Ukrainskii Kem. Zhurnal*, **2**. 88, 1926 ; *Science Mag. Chem. Cath. Katerinoslav*, 103, 1926 ; K. Weisbrod, *Versuche zur Reduktion von Stickoxydul, Ammonium-nitrat und untersalpetriger Säure. Oxydation von Hydrazin mit Permanganat*, Heppenheim, 1926 ; D. Balareff and N. Lukova, *Koll. Beihefte*, **32**. 304, 1931 ; D. Balareff and R. Kaischew, *Zeit. anorg. Chem.*, **167**. 237, 1927 ; D. Balareff, *ib.*, **167**. 237, 1927 ; **174**. 295, 1928 ; D. Balareff and B. Janakiewa, *ib.*, **156**. 301, 1926 ; D. Balareff, R. Kaischew and G. Kratschew, *ib.*, **168**. 154, 1927 ; R. M. Purkayostha and N. R. Dhar, *ib.*, **121**. 156, 1922 ; R. P. Sanyal and N. R. Dhar, *ib.*, **139**. 161, 1924 ; A. K. Bhattacharji and N. R. Dhar, *ib.*, **175**. 357, 1928 ; **192**. 219, 1930 ; *Journ. Phys. Chem.*, **35**. 653, 1931 ; N. R. Dhar, *Journ. Chem. Soc.*, **123**. 1856, 1923 ; B. K. Mukerji, A. K. Bhattacharji and N. R. Dhar, *Journ. Indian Chem. Soc.*, **6**. 451, 1929 ; **7**. 677, 1930 ; *Zeit. anorg. Chem.*, **192**. 219, 1930 ; *Journ. Phys. Chem.*, **32**. 1834, 1928 ; B. K. Mukerji and N. R. Dhar, *ib.*, **32**. 1308, 1928 ; **33**. 850, 1929 ; **35**. 1790, 1931 ; *Journ. Indian Chem. Soc.*, **2**. 277, 1925 ; A. N. Dey and N. R. Dhar, *Zeit. Elektrochem.*, **32**. 586, 1926 ; W. J. Müller, *ib.*, **11**. 755, 1905 ; R. C. Banerji and N. R. Dhar, *Zeit. anorg. Chem.*, **134**. 172, 1924 ; P. B. Sarkar and N. R. Dhar, *ib.*, **121**. 135, 1922 ; A. C. Sarkar and J. M. Dutta, *ib.*, **67**. 225, 1910 ; S. Roginsky and E. Schulz, *Ukraine Chem. Journ.*, **3**. 177, 1928 ; *Zeit. öffent. Chem.*, **138**. 21, 1928 ; T. Oryng, *Rocz. Chem.*, **7**. 334, 1927 ; *Zeit. anorg. Chem.*, **163**. 195, 1927 ; *Koll. Zeit.*, **11**. 169, 1912 ; A. A. Maximoff, *Zeit. anorg. Chem.*, **163**. 49, 1927 ; *Journ. Russ. Phys. Chem. Soc.*, **57**. 347, 1926 ; F. L. Hahn and G. Weiler, *Zeit. anal. Chem.*, **69**. 417, 1926 ; L. Kahlenberg and W. J. Trautmann, *Zeit. Amer. Electrochem. Soc.*, **39**. 376, 1921 ; H. M. Vernon, *Chem. News*, **66**. 104, 1892 ; E. Wedekind, *Zeit. angew. Chem.*, **37**. 87, 1924 ; G. P. Vincent, *Journ. Phys. Chem.*, **28**. 831, 1924 ; L. Kahlenberg and H. Schlundt, *ib.*, **6**. 447, 1902 ; R. P. Bell, *ib.*, **32**. 882, 1928 ; J. C. Witt, *ib.*, **26**. 435, 1922 ; N. P. Peskoff, *Koll. Zeit.*, **33**. 215, 1923 ; E. Köstermann, G. Wagner and P. Beyersdorfer, *Zeit. Elektrochem.*, **30**. 467, 1924 ; G. Tammann and A. Sworykin, *Zeit. anorg. Chem.*, **173**. 73, 1928 ; G. Tammann and H. Bredemeier, *ib.*, **144**. 64, 1925 ; N. A. Tananaeff, *ib.*, **143**. 118, 1925 ; F. A. Henglein, *ib.*, **120**. 77, 1921 ; R. Lorenz and W. Michael, *ib.*, **116**. 161, 1921 ; R. Lorenz and W. Neu, *ib.*, **116**. 45, 1921 ; M. de K. Thompson, *Chem. Met. Engg.*, **21**. 680, 1919 ; R. B. Stringfield, *ib.*, **22**. 1027, 1920 ; H. P. Cady and R. Taft, *Journ. Phys. Chem.*, **29**. 1057, 1925 ; R. E. Wilson, L. W. Parsons and S. L. Chisholm, *U.S. Pat. No.* 1453562, 1923 ; K. F. Ochs, *Ueber Oxydations- und Reduktionsketten*, Göttingen, 1895 ; J. Roudnick, *Bull. Soc. Chim. Belg.*, **38**. 147, 1929 ; A. M. Taylor, *Trans. Faraday Soc.*, **25**. 314, 856, 1929 ; A. E. Lindh, *Ark. Met. Fys.*, **18**. 14, 1924 ; *Compt. Rend.*, **172**. 1175, 1921 ; **175**. 25, 1922 ; *Zeit. Physik*, **6**. 303, 1921 ; **31**. 210, 1925 ; D. Coster, *ib.*, **25**. 83, 1924 ; O. Stelling, *ib.*, **50**. 506, 1928 ; *Zeit. öffent. Chem.*, **117**. 161, 1925 ; A. Kailan, *Anz. Akad. Wiss. Wien*, **61**. 161, 1924 ; E. Wilke-Dörfurt and R. Pfau, *Zeit. Elektrochem.*, **36**. 118, 1930 ; E. Wilke-Dörfürt, G. Balz and A. Weinhardt, *Zeit. anorg. Chem.*, **185**. 417, 1930 ; E. Wilke-Dörfurt and K. Niederer, *ib.*, **184**. 145, 1929 ; E. Wilke-Dörfurt and H. G. Mureck, *ib.*, **184**. 121, 1929 ; K. Schnetzler, *Zeit. phys. Chem.*, **14**. B, 241, 1931 ; B. Suzuki and C. Hamada, *Journ. Japan. Chem. Soc.*, **44**. 117, 1923 ; N. K. Adam and G. Jessop, *Proc. Roy. Soc.*, **112**. A, 362, 1926 ; E. Ullmann, *Zeit. Physik*, **41**. 301, 1927 ; A. F. Hallimond, *Min. Mag.*, **21**. 277, 1927 ; K. Bädecker, *Ann. Physik*, (4), **22**. 749, 1907 ; F. Streintz, *ib.*, (4), **9**. 854, 1902 ; H. Zocher and H. Kautsky, *Naturwiss.*, **11**. 194, 1923 ; L. A. Welo and A. Baudisch, *Nature*, **116**. 606, 1925 ; E. Geay, *Rev. Chim. Ind.*, **37**. 214, 318, 349, 1928 ; C. Schubert, *Beiträge zur Kenntnis der Dissoziation einiger Oxyde, Karbonate und Sulfide*, Weida i. Thür., 1910 ; W. Hempel and C. Schubert, *Zeit. Elektrochem.*, **18**. 729, 1912 ; S. Popoff and A. H. Kunz, *Journ. Amer. Chem. Soc.*, **51**. 1307, 1929 ; L. S. Kassel and N. K. Schaffer, *ib.*, **51**. 965, 1929 ; P. F. Chevillot and W. F. Edwards, *Ann. Chim. Phys.*, (2), **4**. 287, 1817 ; (2), **3**. 337, 1818 ; A. Béchamp, *ib.*, (3), **57**. 293, 1859 ; E. Bouty, *ib.*, (6), **3**. 446, 1884 ; M. Berthelot, *Bull. Soc. Chim.*, (2), **7**. 124, 1867 ; (2), **8**. 390, 1867 ; *Ann. Chim. Phys.*, (5), **5**. 318, 1875 ; H. Moissan, *ib.*, (7), **6**. 428, 1895 ; *Compt. Rend.*, **114**. 614, 1892 ; H. Moissan and S. Smiles, *Bull. Soc. Chim.*, (3), **27**. 1197, 1902 ; A. Reynoso, *Ann. Chim. Phys.*, (3), **33**. 324, 1851 ; A. Gorgeu, *Compt. Rend.*, **50**. 610, 1860 ; **110**. 958, 1890 ; **114**. 614, 912, 1892 ; *Bull. Soc. Chim.*, (3), **3**. 401, 771, 1890 ; (3), **7**. 261, 1892 ; *Ann. Chim. Phys.*, (3), **61**. 355, 1861 ; J. E. Willm, *ib.*, (4), **5**. 5, 1895 ; H. de Sénarmont, *ib.*, (3), **61**. 357, 1860 ; E. Schering, *German Pat.*, *D.R.P.* 28782, 1884 ; *Arch. Pharm.*, (2), **144**. 165, 1870 ; B. Grötzner, *ib.*, (2), 230, 1892 ; W. Reinige, *ib.*, (2), **101**. 145, 1860 ; A. E. Haswell, *Dingler's Journ.*, **235**. 387, 1880 ; **241**. 363, 1881 ; E. Desclabissac, *ib.*, **201**. 58, 1871 ; *Verh. Ver. Beförd. Gewerbefl. Preussen*, 142, 1870 ; W. Schneider, *Zeit. Physik*, **51**. 266, 1928 ; J. Bendix in A. W. Hofmann, *Bericht über die Entwickelung der chemischen Industrie*, Braunschweig, **1**. 852, 1875 ; O. Sackur and W. Taegener, *Zeit. Elektrochem.*, **18**. 718, 1912 ; A. Simon and F. Feher, *ib.*, **38**. 137, 1932 ; K. Fredenhagen, *ib.*, **37**. 684, 1931 ; R. W. Wood, *Phys. Rev.*, (2), **38**. 1648, 1931 ; R. C. Ray and K. K. Chatterji, *Journ. Chem. Soc.*, 384, 1932 ; E. Divers, *Chem. News*, **46**. 259, 1883 ; L. Delwaulle, *Compt. Rend.*, **192**. 1736, 1931 ; H. Becquerel, **102**. 106, 1886 ; T. B. Douglas, *Journ. Phys. Chem.*, **35**. 3280, 1931 ; S. L. Ridgway, *ib.*, **35**. 1984, 1931 ; F. Durau, *Zeit. phys. Chem.*, **156**. 195, 210, 1931 ; F. Durau and V. Schralz, *ib.*, **159**. 115, 1932 ; W. A. Roth and G. Becker, *ib.*, **159**. 27, 1932 ; F. Vlès and A. Simchen, *Compt. Rend.*, **193**. 581, 1931 ; H. M. Vernon, *Chem. News*, **66**. 104, 114, 141, 152, 1892 ; L. de Putnoky, *Mat. Termes Ertesits*, **47**. 732, 1930 ; L. de Putnoky and B. de Bobest, *ib.*, **47**. 751, 1930 ; W. Pugh, *Trans. Roy. Soc. South Africa*, **20**. 93, 1931.

§ 16. Manganese Fluorides

Two well-defined manganese fluorides have been prepared, namely, *manganese difluoride*, MnF_2, and *manganese trifluoride*, MnF_3; while a third fluoride, *manganese tetrafluoride*, MnF_4, can be obtained in soln. in hydrofluoric acid, and in the form of well-defined complex salts. The complex salts of manganese tetrafluoride of the type R_2MnF_6 are called *fluomanganites*, so that the complex salts of manganese trifluoride of the type R_2MnF_5 have to be called by the unfortunate term *fluohypomanganites*.

J. J. Berzelius [1] evaporated a soln. of manganous carbonate in hydrofluoric acid, and obtained small, pale amethyst-red, ill-defined crystals of **manganous fluoride,** or **manganese difluoride,** MnF_2. C. Brunner, and O. Unverdorben also prepared this salt in an analogous manner. H. Moissan and A. Venturi avoided warming the soln. during the action ; they also said that the salt is best made by dissolving manganese in dil. hydrofluoric acid contained in a silver basin, kept cool by a rapid current of cold water ; on boiling the soln., manganous fluoride is deposited as a white crystalline powder, which is collected and dried at 120°. The salt is also formed as a rose-coloured fused mass when gaseous hydrogen fluoride is passed over metallic manganese ; and it is also formed when a current of hydrogen fluoride is passed over hydrated manganese fluosilicate at 1000°. F. Röder prepared manganous fluoride, in small red needles, by melting a mixture of manganous chloride and sodium fluoride and chloride, and removing the soluble matter by leaching the product with water ; E. Defacqz also obtained manganous fluoride by melting a fluoride of an alkaline earth with manganous chloride, bromide, or iodide. The reaction is reversible, so that an excess of the fluoride is needed. P. Nuka prepared the anhydrous salt by heating the ammonium salt NH_4MnF_3 to 300° in a current of carbon dioxide.

According to H. Moissan and A. Venturi, manganous fluoride may be recrystallized from fused manganous chloride, when it forms rose-coloured prisms which, according to A. de Schulten, are isomorphous with sellaite, MgF_2. According to A. E. van Arkel, the X-radiograms of manganous fluoride correspond with the rutile or tetragonal type of space-lattice with 2 mols. per unit cell; the cell has a base $a=4.88$ A., and a height $c=3.29$ A. A. Ferrari gave $a=4.865$ A., and $c=3.284$ A., and $a:c=1:0.675$; the calculated **specific gravity** is 3.97; W. Biltz and E. Rahlfs found 3.891 for the sp. gr. at 25°/4°, and 23.88 for the mol. vol. H. Moissan and A. Venturi found the sp. gr. to be 3.98, and the **melting-point** 856° ; and A. Ferrari discussed some relations of the m.p. According to J. J. Berzelius, it is not decomposed at a red-heat. W. Herz discussed the entropy and vibration frequency. E. Petersen calculated for the **heat of neutralization** $(Mn(OH)_2,2HF_{aq.})$ $=28,064$ cals. ; and for the **heat of formation,** $(Mn,F_2,H_2O)=156.8$ Cals., while M. Berthelot obtained 155.5 Cals. ; H. von Wartenberg, 206.1 Cals. ; and K. Jellinek and R. Koop, 170.9 Cals. G. Beck studied the energy of the salt. For the anodic oxidation of the salt, *vide supra*, permanganic acid. J. Liebknecht and A. P. Wills gave 162×10^{-6} mass unit for the **magnetic susceptibility** of aq. soln. at 18°.

H. Moissan and A. Venturi found that the salt is completely reduced by **hydrogen** at 1000°, but only very slowly at 500°. K. Jellinek and A. Rugat found that in the reaction $MnF_2+H_2 \rightleftharpoons Mn+2HF$, the values of $\log (p^2{}_{HF}/p_{H_2})$ at the absolute temp. 873°, 975°, and 1073° are respectively -4.96, -4.43, and -3.99; $\log (p^2{}_{HF}/p_{H_2}p_{F_2})$, 33.12, 29.83, and 27.15; and those of $\log p_{F_2}$, -38.08, -34.26, and -31.14, where p_{F_2} is the vap. press. of the metal fluoride. According to H. Moissan and A. Venturi, dry **oxygen** acts only slowly at 400°, but at 1000° the salt is completely decomposed to form the tritatetroxide. Manganous fluoride is almost insoluble in **water.** R. H. Carter found that 100 c.c. of aq. soln. contained 0.186 grm. MnF_2 at 25°, and for the sat. soln., $p_H=7.0$. W. Biltz and E. Rahlfs prepared the *tetrahydrate* by drying it at room temp. The sp. gr. of the tetrahydrate is 2.036 at 25°/4°, and the mol. vol. 81.04. H. Moissan and A. Venturi found that if the salt be boiled with water, manganese oxyfluoride and hydrofluoric acid are first formed, but if the boiling be prolonged, a mixture of hydrated manganese fluoride and oxyfluoride is deposited ; between 1200° and 1300° steam converts manganous fluoride into manganous oxide. P. Nuka found that 100 grms. of an aq. soln. of the tetrahydrate contains 1·05 grms. of MnF_2. The salt is converted by **fluorine**—*vide infra*—into the trifluoride—slowly in the cold, rapidly when heated ; it is not attacked by **chlorine** in the cold, but at 1200° some manganous chloride is formed, but there is no evidence of the formation of a *manganese chlorofluoride*. With chlorine water, or **bromine** water, hydrofluoric acid and manganese dioxide are formed. J. J. Berzelius found that the salt is soluble in water containing **hydrofluoric acid ;** but H. Moissan and A. Venturi found that it is not perceptibly soluble in conc. hydrofluoric acid. By evaporating the aq. soln. acidified with hydrofluoric acid, F. H. Edmister and H. C. Cooper obtained crystals of **manganous pentahydroheptafluoride,** $MnF_2.5HF.6H_2O$. They are not permanent in air, but decompose with the loss of hydrogen fluoride. The crystals are rhombohedral, with prismatic cleavage, and uniaxial. The sp. gr. is 1·921. H. Moissan and A. Venturi said that cold, conc. **hydrochloric acid** dissolves manganous fluoride freely, but the dil. acid acts only slowly. When the salt is heated to 1000° in an atm. of **sulphur,** green manganous sulphide is rapidly formed ; and similarly with **hydrogen sulphide.** The salt is decomposed by sulphuric acid with the liberation of hydrogen fluoride. G. Gore, and E. C. Franklin and C. A. Kraus said that manganese fluoride is sparingly soluble in liquid **ammonia,** and H. Moissan and A. Venturi, that **manganous tritadiamminofluoride,** $3MnF_2.2NH_3$, is formed as a crystalline powder which slowly evolves ammonia ; and manganous fluoride is partially reduced when heated at 1200° in an atm. of ammonia. W. Biltz and E. Rahlfs prepared **manganese aquopentamminodifluoride,** $MnF_2.H_2O.5NH_3$, of sp. gr. 1·477 at 25°/4° ; mol. vol. 132·6 ; vap. press. 39·2 mm. at —21°, 80·0 mm. at —11°, and 173·0 mm. at 0° ; and heat of formation 9·6 Cals. Similarly, **manganese aquoamminodifluoride,** $MnF_2.H_2O.NH_3$, has a sp. gr. of 2·291 at 25°/4° ; a mol. vol. of 55·86 ; a vap. press. of 10·5 mm. at 25°, 20 mm. at 34·4°, 43·0 mm. at 46°, and 108·0 mm. at 61° ; and a heat of formation of 12·3 Cals. They also found evidence of the formation of **manganese aquohemiamminodifluoride,** $MnF_2.H_2O.\frac{1}{2}NH_3$. According to H. Moissan and A. Venturi, manganous fluoride is freely soluble in conc. **nitric acid.** Manganous fluoride is decomposed at 1000° by **boron** to form boron fluoride and manganese boride ; and by **silicon** to form manganese silicide and silicon fluoride. E. Wilke-Dörfurt and H. G. Mureck prepared **manganous hexantipyrinoborofluoride,** $[Mn(COC_{10}H_{12}N_2)_6](BF_4)_2$. J. J. Berzelius, J. C. G. de Marignac, and F. Stolba described a fluosilicate, $MnF_2.SiF_4.6H_2O$, which was formed by the action of **silicon tetrafluoride ;** J. J. Berzelius, and J. C. G. de Marignac, a fluotitanate, $MnF_2.TiF_4.6H_2O$, by the action of **titanium tetrafluoride ;** and J. C. G. de Marignac, a fluostannate, $MnF_2.SnF_4.6H_2O$, by the action of **stannic fluoride ;** and the fluozirconates $MnF_2.ZrF_4.5H_2O$ and $2MnF_2.ZrF_4.6H_2O$ by the action of **zirconium tetrafluoride.** According to H. Moissan and A. Venturi, manganous fluoride is not decomposed by **carbon** at 1200°. The salt is practically insoluble in **alcohol,** and in **ether ;** while it is but slowly dissolved by **acetic acid.** A. Naumann said that the salt is insoluble in **acetone ;** and H. Moissan and A. Venturi observed that manganous fluoride is reduced to impure metal, without incandescence, when it is heated with **sodium, potassium, magnesium,** or **aluminium.** A boiling soln. of **alkali hydroxide** forms alkali fluoride and hydrated manganese oxide. The salt is also decomposed by fused **alkali carbonate** or alkali hydroxide, and by **potassium nitrate or chlorate.** E. Defacqz found that the reaction with fused **calcium chloride** is reversible.

According to J. L. Gay-Lussac and L. J. Thénard, the white precipitate obtained by treating an aq. soln. of manganous sulphate with potassium fluoride is, according to J. J. Berzelius, **potassium manganous fluoride ;** it is said to be insoluble in

water, but freely soluble in acids. C. E. Saunders could not prepare this salt.
J. J. Berzelius also mentioned a **sodium manganous fluoride**, sparingly soluble in
water. P. Nuka prepared **ammonium manganous fluoride**, NH_4MnF_3. A sat.
soln. of the salt becomes turbid at 60° and deposits anhydrous MnF_2. At 290°
to 300°, in an atmosphere of carbon dioxide, the complex salt furnishes manganous
fluoride.

According to H. Moissan,[2] metallic manganese is attacked by fluorine at the
ordinary temp., but the reaction is limited by the formation of a layer of fluoride
on the surface of the metal. If the manganese be finely powdered, the reaction
takes place with incandescence, but the fluoride formed is partly volatilized and
decomposed, so that the product is not of constant composition. Manganous
fluoride is also attacked by fluorine, but the reaction is never complete, whilst with
manganous chloride it is difficult to expel the whole of the chlorine. With manganous iodide, however, the reaction is much more regular, and **manganese trifluoride**, or manganic fluoride, MnF_3, is produced in crystals which are pseudomorphs
after the parent iodide. The crystals have a **specific gravity** of 3·54. E. Petersen
found that the **heat of solution** is very small; and the **heat of neutralization**
$(Mn(OH)_3,3HF)=25·8$ Cals. A. Travers made this salt. H. Moissan found that
when the trifluoride is heated it decomposes, forming manganous fluoride and
fluorine; it is reduced by **hydrogen**, below redness, forming hydrogen and manganous fluorides; K. Jellinek and R. Koop studied the equilibrium in the reduction of manganic to manganous fluoride by hydrogen. According to H. Moissan,
manganic fluoride is decomposed by **oxygen** at a red-heat, forming black crystalline
manganese oxide; and it reacts with **water**, forming manganous fluoride, hydrofluoric acid, and a hydrated manganese oxide in proportions dependent on the
proportion of water employed. At ordinary temp. **chlorine** has no action on
manganese trifluoride, but when heated a ternary compound is formed; and
similarly also with **bromine**, and with **iodine**, which forms a red compound. If
heated in an atmosphere of **hydrogen chloride**, manganous chloride, hydrogen
fluoride, and chlorine are formed; and with **hydrochloric acid** a dark brown soln.
is produced which is decomposed by water. When the trifluoride is treated with
boiling **sulphur**, sulphur and manganous fluorides are formed; **hydrogen sulphide**
reacts readily at 200° with manganese trifluoride, and so do **sulphur monochloride,**
and **sulphuryl chloride ;** while **sulphuric acid** forms a dark brown soln. readily
decomposed by water; and similarly with **nitric acid.** Manganese trifluoride reacts
with **phosphorus,** at a slightly elevated temp., forming phosphorus tri- and penta-
fluorides; with **phosphorus trichloride** it yields phosphorus fluochloride; and with
phosphorus pentachloride it yields phosphorus pentafluoride. When heated with
arsenic, the reaction furnishes arsenic trifluoride. When heated with **boron,** the
reaction furnishes boron trifluoride; and with **silicon,** silicon tetrafluoride. When
manganese trifluoride is heated in a **glass** vessel, there is a violent reaction, silicon
tetrafluoride is set free, and a mixture of manganese fluoride and oxyfluoride
remains. When the salt is heated with **carbon,** carbon tetrafluoride is formed; with
carbon tetrachloride the products are manganous fluoride, chlorine, and carbon
tetrafluoride. No action was observed at 100° with **benzene, turpentine, chloroform, alcohol,** and **ether.**

O. T. Christensen, and G. Gore found that the higher manganese oxides are
attacked by hydrofluoric acid with difficulty; but J. J. Berzelius observed that
the mineral manganite, when in the form of an impalpable powder, dissolves in the
acid, forming a red soln., which, when evaporated spontaneously, furnishes dark
brown prisms which appear ruby-red by transmitted light. The powder is also
ruby-red. O. T. Christensen, and J. Nicklès obtained a similar product from a
soln. of artificially prepared manganese hemitrioxide in hydrofluoric acid. The
salt can be recrystallized from hydrofluoric acid. The analyses agree with **trihydrated manganic fluoride,** $MnF_3.3H_2O$. According to E. Müller and P. Koppe,
a fluoride of tervalent manganese is readily obtained by the action of permanganates

on a manganous salt in presence of hydrofluoric acid, the reaction being: $MnO_4'+4Mn^{..}+8H^.=5Mn^{...}+4H_2O$. The difference between the reactions in presence of hydrofluoric and sulphuric acids is due to the conversion of $Mn^{...}$ into a complex fluoride ion in the one case; then the manganese dioxide, which is insoluble in hydrofluoric acid, dissolves if a manganous salt is also present. Manganic fluoride, free from potassium, may be obtained by electrolyzing a neutral soln. of a manganous salt and dissolving the oxide precipitated at the anode in hydrofluoric acid. The difficulty of observing the end-point in presence of the pink manganic salt makes it impossible to obtain accurate results on titrating manganese with permanganate in presence of hydrofluoric acid. The reaction appears, however, to be nearly complete in a warm soln. L. von Putnoky and B. von Bobest showed that the trifluoride is a secondary product of the anodic oxidation of manganous fluoride—*vide supra*, permanganic acid. J. J. Berzelius found that the salt can be completely dissolved in a small proportion of water, but with more water, or if the clear aq. soln. be boiled, hydrolysis occurs and a basic salt is precipitated; on cooling the soln. the precipitate is redissolved. The aq. soln. gives a precipitate of hydrated manganic oxide, free from fluoride, when it is treated with ammonia; and, according to J. Nicklès, a precipitate is formed when potassium fluoride is added to the aq. soln.

F. Olsson obtained two series of complex salts of the type $RMnF_4.nH_2O$ and R_2MnF_5 by the union of manganic fluoride with an organic base—quinoline, guanidine, tetramethylammonium, dimethylamine, diethylamine, ethylamine, propylamine, and ethylenediamine. O. T. Christensen added a soln. of hydrated manganese hemitrioxide in hydrofluoric acid to a conc. soln. of ammonium fluoride, and obtained crystals of **ammonium manganic pentafluoride,** $2NH_4F.MnF_3$, or $(NH_4)_2MnF_5$. If the soln. be too dilute, evaporation may be necessary before crystallization can take place. The salt can be recrystallized from water containing ammonium fluoride or hydrofluoric acid. The dark red, almost black, prismatic crystals were also prepared by J. Nicklès, who stated that they are decomposed by heat into manganous fluoride and oxide. O. T. Christensen found that the hydrofluoric acid soln. gives a dirty red precipitate with calcium or strontium chloride, and with barium chloride, a pale red precipitate which turns violet. O. T. Christensen, and J. Nicklès also prepared **sodium manganic pentafluoride,** Na_2MnF_5, in an analogous manner. The crystals under the microscope appear to be rectangular plates. The salt is sparingly soluble in water. It melts when heated, and retains its red colour. J. Nicklès thought the salt was a compound of manganese tetrafluoride. O. T. Christensen, and J. Meyer prepared **potassium manganic pentafluoride,** $K_2MnF_5.H_2O$, by adding an excess of potassium fluoride to a filtered soln. of hydrated manganese hemitrioxide in hydrofluoric acid. The rose-red precipitate is washed with water containing hydrofluoric acid and dried on platinum. The same salt is prepared by heating manganese dioxide with potassium hydrofluoride, and by precipitation from a soln. of potassium fluoride with a soln. of manganese dioxide in hydrofluoric acid. E. Müller and P. Koppe found that by mixing, in the order given, a soln. of 8·9 grms. of manganous sulphate in 30 c.c. of water, 8 c.c. of 40 per cent. hydrofluoric acid, a soln. of 1·58 grms. of potassium permanganate in 25 c.c. of water, and one of 5·8 grms. of potassium fluoride in 20 c.c. in a platinum basin, a salt is obtained which, after washing with hydrofluoric acid and alcohol and drying in a desiccator, has the composition $2KF.MnF_3.H_2O$. According to O. T. Christensen, the salt is decomposed by water at the ordinary temp.; and also by hydrogen dioxide. Hydrochloric acid decomposes it with the production of a dark colour; when the soln. is treated with water, the soln. becomes transparent and bright yellowish-red. The salt dissolves in sulphuric acid, yielding an amethyst-coloured liquid, which becomes red on the addition of water. It forms a brown soln. with oxalic or tartaric acid and the soln. is reduced by boiling. The soln. in phosphoric acid is red. The salt is identical with the one to which J. Nicklès ascribed the formula $2KF.MnF_4$. I. Bellucci obtained the salt $K_2MnF_5.H_2O$ by the action of nitrous acid in the presence of hydrofluoric acid on either potassium permanganate or on a manganous salt, the nitrous acid acting in the former case as a reducing agent and in the latter as an oxidizing agent. The formation of this salt causes fallacious results in the determination of nitrous acid by potassium permanganate in the presence of fluoride. F. Fichter and E. Brunner observed that when a suspension of manganous fluoride in water is treated with a current of fluorine, it slowly dissolves, forming a red liquid, from which a sat. soln. of potassium fluoride precipitates the complex pentafluoride as a pink crystalline powder. There is here the possibility of a direct oxidation without the formation of an intermediate product; but the reaction is far from being complete: the formation of hydrogen dioxide can be detected from the beginning, and, moreover, we have a complicated equilibrium between manganous and manganic fluorides, hydrofluoric acid, and hydrogen dioxide, where the temp., concentration, and duration of the treatment with fluorine are of influence. Sometimes the pink colour diminishes even during the experiment. G. Wiedemann studied the magnetic properties of the potassium salt. O. T. Christensen prepared **silver manganic pentafluoride,** $Ag_2MnF_5.4H_2O$, by evaporating a mixed soln. of the component salts. The crystals are almost black, and they lose their water at 110°, along with a trace of hydrogen fluoride; **zinc manganic pentafluoride,** $ZnMnF_5.4$(and 7)H_2O, was also prepared. F. Ephraim and L. Heymann's attempts to prepare **thallous manganic pentafluoride,** analogous to the alkali salts, furnished **thallous manganosic tridecafluoride,** $5TlF.2MnF_3.MnF_2$. It is obtained by precipitating manganous acetate with ammonia and hydrogen peroxide, dissolving the well-washed precipitate in hydrofluoric acid, and adding thallous fluoride, when it forms claret-coloured prisms, decomposed by water, but soluble in cold conc. sulphuric acid or in dilute oxalic or tartaric acids to violet soln., decolorized on heating. When a soln. of manganic fluoride is added to a soln. of cobaltic chloropentamminocarbonate in hydrofluoric acid, O. T. Christensen found that **cobaltic manganese chloropentamminofluoride** is formed as a crystalline precipitate, consisting of microscopic, rectangular plates. O. T. Christensen also prepared **cobaltous manganic pentafluoride,** $CoMnF_5.4H_2O$; and **nickel manganic pentafluoride,** $CoMnF_5.4H_2O$.

According to J. Nicklès,[3] if an ethereal soln. of manganese tetrachloride be treated with hydrofluoric acid, the lower layer of brown liquor is regarded as a soln. of **manganese tetrafluoride,** MnF_4, in hydrofluoric acid; a similar soln. is formed when manganese dioxide is dissolved in hydrofluoric acid; and also by shaking potassium manganese hexafluoride, $2KF.MnF_4$, with a sat. soln. of silicon tetrafluoride in ether. The brown soln. in ether and a little water contains the tetrafluoride, and it is an energetic oxidizing agent. The brown liquid is not decomposed by the addition of a small proportion of water, but is decomposed by a larger proportion, particularly in the presence of alkali hydroxides, carbonates, or chlorides, and finely-divided hydrated manganese dioxide separates. The brown soln. decolorizes indigo, and it is decomposed by ferrous sulphate; an alcoholic soln. of lead acetate gives a brown precipitate; a soln. of brucine is reddened; aniline and naphthylamine furnish coloured derivatives; phenol is oxidized to a brown resin which is coloured green by sodium chloride; while glucose, gum, and carbohydrates are not changed. The soln. dissolves in alcohol; and ether dissolves it only in the presence of a little water. Rose-red double salts are precipitated when potassium or ammonium chloride is added to the brown soln., but sodium chloride gives a precipitate only in the presence of water. O. T. Christensen doubted the existence of the tetrafluoride so prepared. He said that the double salts are not $2RF.MnF_4$, as J. Nicklès supposed, but rather salts of the trifluoride, $2RF.MnF_3.H_2O$; but R. F. Weinland and O. Lauenstein showed that J. Nicklès was probably right. F. Fichter and E. Brunner were unable to oxidize manganous fluoride to manganese tetrafluoride by fluorine, and they added that this is analogous to the failure of E. Müller and P. Koppe to produce this salt by anodic oxidation.

R. F. Weinland and O. Lauenstein showed that potassium manganate dissolves to a violet soln. in 40 per cent. hydrofluoric acid with evolution of heat, and on evaporation the soln. yields a mixture of potassium permanganate and potassium fluomanganite. The **fluomanganites** are here considered to be salts of the hypothetical fluomanganous acid, H_2MnF_6. If potassium manganate be treated with water and carbon dioxide, potassium manganite is formed ; when dissolved in hydrofluoric acid and treated with potassium fluoride, there are deposited golden-yellow hexagonal tablets of **potassium fluomanganite,** K_2MnF_6, or *potassium manganese hexafluoride* :

$$\begin{array}{l} KF{=}F \\ KF{=}F \end{array} \!\!\!\Big\rangle Mn \!\!\Big\langle \begin{array}{l} F \\ F \end{array}$$

The hexagonal crystals have the axial ratio $a : c = 1 : 1\cdot6414$. The (0001)-cleavage is incomplete ; the corrosion figures agree with the holohedral symmetry ; the birefringence is feeble and negative. The salt turns reddish-brown when cautiously heated, and recovers its original colour on cooling ; at a higher temp. it volatilizes ; and in contact with moist air yields a violet residue, hydrogen fluoride being evolved ; whilst at a high temp. it is decomposed into oxides of manganese and potassium fluoride. It is decomposed by water, with the precipitation of hydrated manganese dioxide ; it dissolves in cold hydrochloric acid to a dark brown soln. which evolves chlorine when heated ; and when treated with cold, conc. sulphuric acid, it yields hydrofluoric acid, and with the warm acid, oxygen and ozone. With nitric acid it yields manganese nitrate and hydrofluoric acid, and no manganese goes into soln. ; this reaction distinguishes it from O. T. Christensen's complex of manganese trifluoride and potassium fluoride. The salt yields a brownish-red soln. with phosphoric acid ; it is insoluble in glacial acetic acid ; it oxidizes oxalic acid in aq. soln. ; it decolorizes indigo soln. ; and with hydrogen dioxide it yields a reddish residue, with evolution of oxygen. F. Fichter and E. Brunner observed that fluorine immediately reduces the yellow complex salt K_2MnF_6 to the red complex salt $K_2MnF_5.H_2O$. According to R. F. Weinland and O. Lauenstein, **rubidium fluomanganite,** Rb_2MnF_6, is obtained by dissolving hydrated manganese dioxide in hydrofluoric acid and adding rubidium fluoride. It furnishes yellow hexagonal tablets with the axial ratio $a : c = 1 : 1\cdot6185$, and with a feeble negative birefringence. It is quite analogous to the potassium salt. The corresponding **ammonium fluomanganite,** $(NH_4)_2MnF_6$, was obtained contaminated with the potassium salt ; while **sodium fluomanganite,** Na_2MnF_6, could not be prepared.

According to F. Wöhler, when a mixture of two parts of potassium permanganate or manganate and one part of calcium fluoride is digested with sulphuric acid in a platinum retort, a yellow vapour is evolved which in contact with moist air becomes purple. The yellow vapour corrodes glass, and is thereby resolved into silicon tetrafluoride and manganese heptoxide, which covers the glass with a brown layer and dissolves in water forming a purple soln. The yellow vapour attacks calcium chloride, which becomes hot and gives off chlorine. The yellow vapour dissolves in water, forming a soln. of hydrofluoric and permanganic acids. When the aq. soln. is evaporated, it gives off oxygen and hydrogen fluoride, and leaves a brown residue containing some manganous fluoride. The aq. soln. dissolves copper, mercury, and silver, but not gold or platinum. J. B. A. Dumas made some observations on this subject—*vide infra*, manganese tetroxychloride. F. Wöhler's product is sometimes regarded as a *manganese trioxyfluoride*, MnO_3F, but it was probably this mixture of potassium permanganate and fluomanganite contaminated with a silicon fluoride.

In addition to the potassium fluomanganite prepared first by J. Nicklès, *potassium manganese octofluoride*, $4KF.MnF_4$, was reported to be formed by the fusion of the hexafluoride, or by melting a mixture of manganese dioxide and potassium fluoride ; *potassium manganese oxytetrafluoride*, $2KF.MnOF_2$, to be formed as a rose-red precipitate by dropping manganese tetrachloride into a boiling soln. of potassium fluoride ; and *ammonium manganese oxytrifluoride*, $2NH_4F.MnOF$, to be formed by dropping manganese tetrachloride into a hot soln. of ammonium fluoride. If potassium manganese oxytetrafluoride be shaken with ether, sat. with silicon tetrafluoride, a violet-brown acid, $2HF.MnOF_2$, is said to be formed. The soln. is decolorized and decomposed by water. J. Nicklès also reported *potassium dimanganese oxyoctofluoride*, $4KF.Mn_2OF_4$, to be formed by dropping manganese trichloride in a boiling soln. of potassium fluoride. If hydrofluoric acid be added to potassium permanganate, one or other of these substances is formed and ozonized oxygen is given off. O. T. Christensén could not confirm these observations.

REFERENCES.

[1] W. Biltz and E. Rahlfs, *Zeit. anorg. Chem.*, 166. 351, 1927 ; G. Beck, *ib.*, 182. 332, 1929 ; E. Wilke-Dörfurt and H. G. Mureck, *ib.*, 184. 121, 1929 ; P. Nuka, *ib.*, 180. 235, 1929 ; K. Jellinek and A. Rugat, *ib.*, 175. 281, 1928 ; A. Rugat, *Ueber die Fluortensionen von Metallfluoriden und die chemischen Konstanten von Fluor und Fluorwasserstoff*, Marburg, 1928 ; J. H. de Boer and J. Basart, *Zeit. anorg. Chem.*, 152. 213, 1926 ; H. von Wartenberg, *ib.*, 151. 326, 1926 ; W. Herz, *ib.*, 175. 245, 1928 ; J. Liebknecht and A. P. Wills, *Ann. Physik*, (4), 1. 178, 1900 ; *Ber.*, 33. 443, 1900 ; R. H. Carter, *Journ. Ind. Eng. Chem.*, 20. 1195, 1928 ; C. Brunner, *Pogg. Ann.*, 101. 264, 1857 ; 103. 139, 1858 ; J. J. Berzelius, *ib.*, 1. 24, 197, 1824 ; A. Ferrari, *Atti Accad. Lincei*, (6), 3. 224, 1926 ; *Atti Congresso Chim. Pura Applicata*, 3. 449, 452, 1930 ; F. Röder, *Ueber Krystallinite wasserfreie Fluorbindungen*, Göttingen, 1862 ; O. Unverdorben, *Brandes' Arch.*, 9. 36, 1824 ; *Quart. Journ. Science*, 2. 204, 1827 ; *Pogg. Ann.*, 7. 322, 1826 ; K. Jellinek and R. Koop, *Zeit. phys. Chem.*, 145. 305, 1929 ; R. Koop, *Ueber heterogenes Gleichgewichte von Metallhalogeniden mit Wasserstoff bzw. Chlorwasserstoff*, Leipzig, 1929 ; H. Moissan and A. Venturi, *Compt. Rend.*, 130. 1158, 1900 ; A. de Schulten, *ib.*, 152. 1261, 1911 ; E. Defacqz, *Ann. Chim. Phys.*, (8), 1. 337, 1904 ; J. C. G. de Marignac, *ib.*, (3), 60. 288, 1860 ; *Ann. Mines*, (5), 221, 1859 ; F. H. Edmister and H. C. Cooper, *Journ. Amer. Chem. Soc.*, 42. 2419, 1920 ; *Chem. News*, 122. 27, 1921 ; A. E. van Arkel, *Rec. Trav. Chim. Pays-Bas*, 45. 437, 1926 ; C. E. Saunders, *Amer. Chem. Journ.*, 14. 127, 1892 ; E. C. Franklin and C. A. Kraus, *ib.*, 20. 828, 1898 ; G. Gore, *Proc. Roy. Soc.*, 21. 140, 1873 ; A. Naumann, *Ber.*, 37. 4329, 1904 ; E. Petersen, *Zeit. phys. Chem.*, 4. 384, 1889 ; F. Stolba, *Sitzber. Böhm. Ges. Wiss.*, 221, 1882 ; M. Berthelot, *Thermochimie*, Paris, 2. 269, 1897 ; J. L. Gay Lussac and L. J. Thénard, *Recherches physico-chimiques*, Paris, 2. 31, 1811.

[2] A. Travers, *Bull. Soc. Chim.*, (4), 37. 456, 1925 ; H. Moissan, *Compt. Rend.*, 130. 622, 1900 ; J. Nicklès, *ib.*, 65. 107, 1867 ; 67. 448, 1858 ; *Ann. Chim. Phys.*, (4), 5. 161, 1865 ; F. Ephraim and L. Heymann, *Ber.*, 42. 4456, 1909 ; E. Petersen, *Zeit. phys. Chem.*, 4. 384, 1889 ; K. Jellinek and R. Koop, *ib.*, 145. 305, 1929 ; G. Gore, *Journ. Chem. Soc.*, 22. 368, 1869 ; F. Fichter and E. Brunner, *ib.*, 1862, 1909 ; O. T. Christensen, *Journ. prakt. Chem.*, (2), 34. 41, 1886 ; (2), 35. 67, 169, 1887 ; I. Bellucci, *Gazz. Chim. Ital.*, 49. i, 209, 1919 ; 49. ii, 180, 1919 ; E. Müller and P. Koppe, *Zeit. anorg. Chem.*, 68. 160, 1910 ; F. Olsson, *ib.*, 187. 313, 1930 ; J. Meyer, *ib.*, 81. 385, 1913 ; J. J. Berzelius, *Pogg. Ann.*, 1. 1, 1824 ; G. Wiedemann, *Wied. Ann.*, 32. 452, 1887 ; L. von Putnoky and B. von Bobest, *Zeit. Elektrochem.*, 37. 156, 1931.

[3] J. Nicklès, *Compt. Rend.*, 65. 107, 1867 ; *Ann. Chim. Phys.*, (4), 5. 161, 1865 ; J. B. A. Dumas, *ib.*, (2), 36. 82, 1827 ; *Quart. Journ. Science*, 2. 475, 1827 ; F. Fichter and F. Brunner, *Journ. Chem. Soc.*, 1862, 1828 ; O. T. Christensen, *Journ. prakt. Chem.*, (2), 34. 41, 1886 ; (2), 35. 67, 169, 1887 ; R. F. Weinland and O. Lauenstein, *Zeit. anorg. Chem.*, 20. 40, 1899 ; O. Lauenstein, *Ueber Fluoiodate, Fluomanganite und über die Einwirkung von Fluorwasserstoffsäure auf Wismutsäure bezw. Kaliumbismutat*, Leipzig, 1899 ; F. Wöhler, *Pogg. Ann.*, 9. 619, 1826 ; E. Müller and P. Koppe, *Zeit. anorg. Chem.*, 68. 160, 1910.

§ 17. Manganous Chloride

J. Davy,[1] and H. Davy reported **manganese dichloride,** or **manganous chloride,** $MnCl_2$, to be formed when manganese burns in chlorine gas. J. L. Proust obtained it by evaporating a soln. of manganous chloride to dryness, and heating the dry residue, according to J. Davy, with the exclusion of air, or, according to E. Turner, in a current of hydrogen chloride. J. A. Arfvedson prepared the anhydrous salt by heating manganous carbonate in a current of hydrogen chloride, first at ordinary temp., and afterwards at a dull red-heat. H. Rose obtained it by passing chlorine over a strongly heated mixture of manganous oxide and charcoal ; and R. Weber used the carbonate in place of the oxide. F. P. Venable and D. H. Jackson obtained the chloride by passing a mixture of carbon monoxide and chlorine over manganese dioxide at 460°.

A. Scacchi observed crystals of manganous chloride in a salt-crust associated with the 1851 eruption of Vesuvius. The crystals were also observed by T. Monticelli and N. Covelli, and M. Adam called the mineral **scacchite**—after A. Scacchi. The crystals of the artificial product are, according to J. A. Arfvedson, rose-red, and they may become dirty red or brown when exposed to air, owing to the formation of higher manganese oxides. There has been some discussion on the pink colour of the manganous salts generally. C. Fromherz attributed the red colour to the presence of traces of the higher oxidation products. By repeated soln. in sulphuric or hydrochloric acid and reprecipitation with sodium carbonate they obtained a material which furnished colourless manganous chloride or sulphate ; but L. Gmelin said that the red salt cannot be decolorized by boiling with sulphurous acid, or, according to J. J. Berzelius, by treatment with hydrogen sulphide, etc. A. Brand said that colourless crystals can be obtained if the powdered salt be calcined or boiled with alcohol, ether, or a soln. of sugar and again converted into sulphate or chloride. L. Gmelin could not confirm this. F. Brandenburg obtained the red salt by preparing manganous sulphate by the action of fuming sulphuric acid containing a trace of copper on pyrolusite. F. Wöhler, and H. Schiff observed that both colourless and red crystals may be obtained from the same soln. A. Voelcker also found that the purified salt is colourless, and if traces of higher oxides are present, the salt has a reddish tint ; if the tint is not removed by treatment with a reducing agent, the coloration may be due to the presence of a trace of cobalt, which often accompanies manganese. According to J. A. Kappers, and K. J. Bayer, the green or blue tint observed by F. W. Krecke is produced by cobalt ; and A. Gorgeu said that if 8 parts of nickel per 1000 of manganese are present, the salts may be colourless. A. M. B. Burin du Buisson thought that only the anhydrous manganous salts are colourless. The subject was also discussed by J. Schwerdtfeger, and K. Reithner. According to J. H. Kastle, when the crystals of manganous chloride are cooled by liquid air, the colour may disappear altogether ; and A. Étard observed that the rose-red aq. soln. of manganous chloride is almost colourless at 240°.

An aq. soln. of manganous chloride can be prepared by dissolving the metal or manganous carbonate in hydrochloric acid. M. Faraday heated a mixture of precalcined pyrolusite and ammonium chloride slowly to dull redness, and extracted the cold product with water. If the pyrolusite is in excess, it is said that the foreign metals do not form soluble chlorides ; the pyrolusite should have been previously boiled with dil. nitric acid to remove the carbonates of the alkaline earths. J. Everitt evaporated the hydrochloric acid soln. of pyrolusite to dryness, and heated the residue until no more hydrochloric acid is evolved. H. Kolbe recommended heating the residue in a crucible at a red-heat to volatilize the ferric chloride. The residue is dissolved in water and the filtered soln. boiled with manganous carbonate to precipitate the iron and aluminium oxides. K. J. Bayer recommended treating the soln. with sodium carbonate to precipitate fractionally the iron and aluminium oxides, and with ammonium sulphide to precipitate manganous sulphide. The sulphide is then washed and dissolved in hydrochloric acid. The subject was discussed by J. A. Kappers, G. H. Zeller, H. F. Gaultier de Claubry, W. Smith, and A. Pizzi. The evaporation of the aq. soln. furnishes various hydrates, dependent on the conditions.

R. Brandes found that water at 10° can dissolve 38·33 per cent. $MnCl_2$; at 31·25°, 46·15 per cent. ; at 62·5° and at 87·5°, 55·0 per cent. ; and at 106·25°, 55·32 per cent. ; while A. Étard gave for the percentage solubility, S :

	−22°	−5°	7°	17°	35°	57°	80°	100°	140°
S	34·7	37·8	40·4	41·2	44·4	50·0	51·0	53·7	54·7

The following results for the percentage solubility are compiled from those of F. Rüdorff, A. Ditte, P. Kutznetzoff, R. Brandes, A. Étard, H. M. Dawson and P. Williams, and J. Süss :

	−5·5°	−2°	8°	25°	50°	57·85°	60°	100°	140°
S	10·5	—	38·3	43·6	49·5	51·4	52·1	53·7	54·8
	$6H_2O$			$4H_2O$			$2H_2O$		

The results are plotted in Fig. 59. W. Stortenbeker was able to obtain the **hexahydrate,** $MnCl_2.6H_2O$, only in isomorphous association with hexahydrated cobaltous chloride, but P. Kutznetzoff showed that a soln. containing 11·7 mols of water per mol of manganous chloride gives the hexahydrate when cooled to −37° and well stirred. The crystals are almost colourless, and at −2° the hexahydrate passes into the **tetrahydrate,** $MnCl_2.4H_2O$. The tetrahydrate is dimorphous and appears either as a stable or α-form, or as a labile or β-form. C. F. Rammelsberg obtained the α-tetrahydrate in rose-red crystals by the spontaneous evaporation of the aq. soln., and by cooling a hot, sat. soln. The crystals are monoclinic prisms with the axial ratios $a : b : c = 1·1525 : 1 : 0·6445$, and $β = 99° 25'$. The crystals were examined by E. H. Ducloux, and V. C. Butureanu. According to H. M. Dawson and P. Williams, the transition temp. from the α-tetrahydrate to the dihydrate is 57·85°; T. W. Richards and J. B. Churchill gave 57·7°; and T. W. Richards and F. Wrede gave 58·089°, and added that this transition temp. is a convenient fixed point for thermometry. A. Baladin discussed the contraction, and F. Ephraim, the change in vol. accompanying the formation of the salt and of its amines. J. Süss found that the transition temp. is reduced to 52·8° in the presence of potassium chloride, as shown in Fig. 59. T. Graham said that the crystals of the tetrahydrate lose two mols. of water in vacuo or over conc. sulphuric acid. J. F. John added that at 25° the crystals of the α-tetrahydrate become white and opaque ; and R. Brandes, that between 25° and 37° they give off hygroscopic water with decrepitation and become hard ; at 37·5° they become tough ; at 50°,

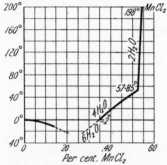

FIG. 59.—The Solubility of Manganous Chloride in Water.

semi-fluid ; and at 87·5° they form a mobile liquid which boils at 106°. If kept for some time at 100°, the α-tetrahydrate loses 3 mols. of water, leaving a white powder. A. Ditte also found that the α-tetrahydrate at 58° slowly loses water, forming the pale rose-red dihydrate, but does not melt at 120°. P. Kutznetzoff added that the soln. sat. at 58° can be cooled to 23° before the tetrahydrate begins to separate. E. M. Farrer and S. U. Pickering found that the α-tetrahydrate loses 3 mols. of water at 100°. According to J. C. G. de Marignac, when the aq. soln., sat. at say 40°, is undercooled to 10° or 0°, monoclinic, tabular crystals of β-tetrahydrate separate out. The crystals were found to have

the axial ratios $a : b : c = 1·1413 : 1 : 1·6409$, and $β = 110° 46'$. It was also prepared by P. Kutznetzoff, who observed that at 40° the crystals of the β-tetrahydrate form a crystalline powder of the dihydrate. J. C. G. de Marignac, H. M. Dawson and P. Williams, and V. C. Butureanu observed that the crystals of the β-tetrahydrate are isomorphous with those of tetrahydrated ferrous chloride. R. Brandes, and H. M. Dawson and P. Williams said that the β-tetrahydrate melts at 87·6°, and that it is more soluble in water than the α-tetrahydrate. As just indicated, the transition temp. from the α-tetrahydrate to the **dihydrate,** $MnCl_2.2H_2O$, approximates to 58°. H. Lescoeur, and A. Ditte prepared the dihydrate by saturating with hydrogen chloride a sat. aq. soln. of the tetrahydrate at 20°; and H. M. Dawson and P. Williams, by similarly treating an alcoholic soln. of the tetrahydrate at ordinary temp. H. Goldschmidt and K. L. Syngros, and H. Lescoeur obtained it by keeping the tetrahydrate in vacuo ; and C. E. Saunders, in attempting to prepare the double salts of lithium or magnesium chloride with manganous chloride, obtained the dihydrate in slender monoclinic prisms with the axial ratios $a : b : c = 1·238 : 1 :—$, and $β = 138°$ nearly. The salt resembles the tetrahydrate, but it does not lose water when dried over calcium chloride. H. M. Dawson and P. Williams observed that the dihydrate is coloured a deeper red than the tetrahydrate ; W. Müller-Erzbach, that it loses one of the mols. of water more readily than the other ; and P. Kutznetzoff, that it loses water at 170°, and when allowed to stand exposed to air for a couple of months, it forms the tetrahydrate. These results show that there are three well-defined hydrates of manganous chloride, with definite transition temp. :

$$-2° \qquad 58\ 089° \qquad 198°$$
$$MnCl_2.6H_2O \rightleftharpoons MnCl_2.4H_2O \rightleftharpoons MnCl_2.2H_2O \rightleftharpoons MnCl_2$$

Some other hydrates have been reported. K. J. Bayer said that the *pentahydrate*, $MnCl_2.5H_2O$, is formed in deliquescent, monoclinic crystals by the evaporation of an aq. soln. of manganous chloride at ordinary temp. ; but at 0°, R. Brandes always obtained the tetrahydrate. P. Sabatier also reported that when the higher hydrates are allowed to stand for some months at a summer temp. in vacuo over sulphuric acid, the *tritapentahydrate*, $MnCl_2.1\frac{3}{5}H_2O$, is formed, but H. M. Dawson and P. Williams could not confirm this observation. A. Ditte obtained crystals of a *monohydrate*, $MnCl_2.H_2O$—perhaps a misprint for the dihydrate—from a soln. of the salt in conc. hydrochloric acid—*vide infra*, E. M. Farrar and S. U. Pickering, W. Müller-Erzbach, and R. Brandes on the action of heat on the di- or tetrahydrate. The hydrates existing in aq. soln. have been discussed by H. C. Jones and co-workers.

According to E. M. Farrer and S. U. Pickering, when the tetrahydrate is heated at 200° to 230°, it loses some chlorine, while retaining a mol. of water ; and F. W. Krecke also found that the tetrahydrate loses hydrogen chloride, forming a basic chloride when heated. H. M. Dawson and P. Williams observed that the dihydrate loses its water of hydration at 198°, forming the anhydrous salt. A. Hantzsch and H. Carlsohn discussed the nature of the manganese halides. According to G. Bruni and A. Ferrari, the X-radiograms of crystals of anhydrous manganous chloride show a rhombohedral space-lattice with the axial ratio $a : c = 1 : 2\cdot34$; and A. Ferrari and co-workers gave $a = 7\cdot350$ A., $c = 17\cdot45$ A., and $a : c = 1 : 2\cdot37$. They also examined isomorphous mixtures with ferrous and cobaltous chlorides, and L. Pauling made observations on the subject. W. Klemm discussed the energy of the crystal lattice. The crystals of scacchite were observed by A. Lacroix, A. Scacchi, L. Pauling, and T. Monticelli and N. Covelli. According to H. G. F. Schröder, the **specific gravity** of the anhydrous salt is $2\cdot478$; A. Ferrari and co-workers calculated $3\cdot069$ from the X-radiograms. For the sp. gr. of the a-tetrahydrate J. F. John gave $1\cdot56$; C. H. D. Bödeker, $2\cdot01$ at 10° ; H. G. F. Schröder, $1\cdot898$ to $1\cdot928$; and G. P. Baxter and M. A. Hines, $2\cdot977$ at 25°/4°. F. Ephraim and A. Schütz, and W. Klemm discussed the molecular volume. G. T. Gerlach gave for the sp. gr. of aq. soln. of p per cent. of $MnCl_2$ at 15°/15° :

p	5	10	15	20	25	30	35	40	45
Sp. gr.	1·045	1·091	1·138	1·189	1·245	1·306	1·372	1·443	1·514

and H. M. Dawson and P. Williams gave for the sp. gr. of soln. sat. at $\theta°$, and containing S mols of $MnCl_2$ per 100 mols of water :

	25°	30°	40°	50°	57·65°	60°	70°	80°
S	11·05	11·55	12·69	14·05	15·10	15·55	15·84	16·14
Sp. gr.	1·4991	1·5049	1·5348	1·5744	1·6097	1·6108	1·6134	—

Observations on the sp. gr. of aq. soln. were also made by J. H. Long, W. Biltz, G Quincke, J. Wagner, H. C. Jones and F. H. Getman, and H. C. Jones and H. P. Bassett ; for those of A. Heydweiller, *vide infra*. B. Cabrera and co-workers gave for the concentration, C grms. of anhydrous salt per 1000 grms. of water, with soln. of sp. gr. D, $C = 2\cdot60 + 1146(D_{20}-1) - 574\cdot2(D_{20}-1)^2$; and for soln. with $C = 384\cdot2$, $D = 1\cdot4257\{1 - 0\cdot00031(\theta-20)\}$; for $C = 277\cdot0$, $D = 1\cdot2784\{1 - 0\cdot00027 \times (\theta-20)\}$; for $C = 156\cdot6$, $D = 1\cdot1437\{1 - 0\cdot00022(\theta-20)\}$; for $C = 82\cdot22$, $D = 1\cdot0724 \times \{1 - 0\cdot0019(\theta-20)\}$; for $C = 53\cdot74$, $D = 1\cdot0454\{1 - 0\cdot00018(\theta-20)\}$; for $C = 34\cdot89$, $D = 1\cdot0286\{1 - 0\cdot0017(\theta-20)\}$; and for $C = 15\cdot66$, $D = 1\cdot0120\{1 - 0\cdot00015(\theta-20) - 0\cdot0_68(\theta-20)^2\}$. According to I. Traube, the mol. **solution volumes** of the salt in 5, 20, and 40 per cent. soln. at 15°/15° are respectively $17\cdot4$, $25\cdot8$, and $29\cdot1$. A. N. Campbell examined the thesis that the sp. gr. of salt soln. can be calculated from the equation $D_N = D'_N + N(m_a + m_b)$, where D_N is the sp. gr. of the soln. with

N eq. of the salt per litre, D'_N the sp. gr. of a soln. of ammonium chloride of the same normality, and m_a and m_b are moduli for the salt in question. I. I. Saslawsky examined the relative contraction which occurs in the formation of the chloride from its elements. The **electrostriction** is the contraction in the mol. vol. of the salt on soln., that is, mol. vol. of the solid salt less its mol. vol. in soln., and it was discussed by P. Drude and W. Nernst, V. Polowzoff, F. Kohlrausch, A. B. Lamb and R. E. Lee, and G. P. Baxter and C. C. Wallace. The true soln. vol. is supposed to be represented by $M(\mu^2-1)/D(\mu^2+2)$, where μ is the refractive index for light of infinite wave-length.

Eq. per litre	0·5	0·3	0·2	0·1	0·05	0·02	0·01
Sp. gr. 15°/15°	1·02599	1·01587	1·01033	1·00507	1·00240	1·00094	1·00047
$m_{\downarrow mn} \times 10^4$	354	355	343·5	338	290	300·5	280
Electrostriction	20·4	22·3	19·75	17·85	12·45	10·8	10·45

Analyses of the anhydrous salt by R. Brandes, J. Davy, J. A. Arfvedson, and E. Turner agree with the formula $MnCl_2$; and of the tetrahydrate, by R. Brandes, T. Graham, C. F. Rammelsberg, J. C. G. de Marignac, and G. P. Baxter and M. A. Hines, with $MnCl_2,4H_2O$. The **vapour density** of the anhydrous salt, determined by J. Dewar and A. Scott, 135, is in agreement with the theoretical value, 126, for $MnCl_2$. N. Castoro calculated a **molecular weight** of 131·3 to 141·2— theoretical 126—from the f.p. of soln. of the anhydrous chloride in urethane ; and L. Rügheimer and co-workers, 129·8 from the b.p. of soln. in bismuth trichloride. G. Bruni and A. Manuelli inferred from the effect of the tetrahydrate on the f.p. of acetamide that a part of the water of crystallization remains bound to the $MnCl_2$, while with soln. in acetamide all the water separates from the $MnCl_2$.

S. Motylewsky observed that the **drop weight** of molten anhydrous chloride at its m.p. is 103 when that of a drop of water at 100° is 100. C. A. Valson found that the **capillary rise** of a normal soln. at 13° is 58·5 mm. in a tube 0·5 mm. diameter. M. Goldstein found that the capillary rise of a 17·776 per cent. soln. at 15·5° is 143·44 when that of water is 154·5. L. C. de Coppet, and F. Dreyer discussed the capillarity, and G. Tammann, the inner pressure of the soln. H. Sentis found for temp. between 16·9° and 18·4° the **surface tension,** δ dynes per cm., and the **specific cohesion,** a^2 per sq. mm., for aq. soln. with p per cent. $MnCl_2$:

p	6·60	12·49	17·76	22·56	26·90	30·85	34·42	37·81
δ	75·08	76·78	78·30	80·26	82·13	83·66	85·22	87·48
a_2	14·51	14·15	13·80	13·56	13·34	13·11	12·90	12·80

Observations on the surface tension were also made by W. H. Whatmough, and H. Piepenstock. J. C. Graham measured the rate of **diffusion** of manganous chloride in aq. soln. ; and for the **viscosity** at 25°, water unity, of N-, $0·5N$-, $0·25N$-, and $0·125N$-soln. J. Wagner observed respectively 1·2089, 1·0982, 1·0481, and 1·0230, when the respective sp. gr. are 1·0513, 1·0259, 1·0125, and 1·0063. H. C. Jones and W. R. Veazey made some observations on this subject.

J. C. G. de Marignac observed that the **specific heats** of soln. of a mol of manganous chloride in 50, 100, and 206 mols of water between 19° and 52° are respectively 0·8510, 0·9154, and 0·9526 ; and for 30 and 50 per cent. soln. between 0° and 98° A. Blümcke found the sp. hts. to be respectively 0·733 and 0·608. The subject was discussed by N. de Kolossowsky, and K. Jauch. C. Sandonnini, and A. Ferrari and A. Inganni found the **melting-point** of the anhydrous chloride to be 650°, without decomposition ; and it volatilizes at a higher temp. in a current of hydrogen chloride. A. Ferrari discussed some relations of the m.p. C. R. A. Wright and A. E. Menke found that **volatilization** occurs at a red-heat. As indicated above, R. Brandes, and H. M. Dawson and P. Williams found the m.p. of the tetrahydrate to be 87·6° ; J. B. A. Dumas made some observations on this subject. E. N. Gapon studied some relationships of the m.p. F. Rüdorff found that the **freezing-point** of aq. soln. falls 0·138° for a gram of the salt in 100 grms. of water, and it thus falls proportionally with the proportion of salt in soln. Observations were also made by L. C. de Coppet, and H. Goldschmidt and K. L. Syngros. For soln. with M mols of the salt per litre, H. C. Jones and F. H. Getman, and H. C. Jones and H. P. Bassett found **the lowering of the freezing-point** of water, $\delta\theta$, and the mol. lowering, $\varDelta$, to be :

M .	. 0·053	0·106	0·400	1·061	2·00	3·00	4·00
$\delta\theta$.	. 0·255°	0·508°	2·004°	5·965°	16·500°	31·000°	48·500°
$\varDelta$.	. 4·81	4·79	5·01	5·62	8·25	10·33	12·13

R. Salvadori, and W. Biltz made observations on this subject ; for the observations of N. Castoro, and of G. Bruni and A. Manuelli, *vide supra*. R. Salvadori found **the raising of the boiling-point** of soln. with 1·31, 3·69, and 12·89 grms. of $MnCl_2$ in 100 grms. of water to be respectively 0·12°, 0·39°, and 1·43°, and the corresponding mol. lowering to be 1·1, 1·3, and 1·4. According to C. G. Maier, the **vapour pressure,** p atm., of the anhydrous salt is :

	785·4°	882·1°	934·0°	1017·4°	1096·0°	1149·0°	1190·4°
p .	. 0·01	0·05	0·10	0·25	0·50	0·75	1·00
Q .	. —	38·30	36·02	32·52	30·61	29·58	28·78

K. Jellinek and R. Ulroth obtained for $MnCl_2+H_2 \rightleftharpoons Mn+2HCl$ at 700°, p_{HCl}/p_{H_2} $=2·02 \times 10^{-3}$, and, by extrapolation at 0°, $2·08 \times 10^{-3}$. According to G. Tammann, the **lowerings of the vapour pressure** of soln. of 8·83, 15·85, 44·45, and 66·03 grms. $MnCl_2$ in 100 grms. of water are respectively 21·9, 44·0, 147·9, and 219·0 mm. H. M. Dawson and P. Williams found the vap. press., p mm., of a sat. soln. with a solid phase of the tetrahydrate at temp. below 57·8°, and of the dihydrate above that temp.; the **dissociation pressure,** p_4 mm., of the tetrahydrate : $MnCl_2.4H_2O$ $\rightleftharpoons MnCl_2.2H_2O+2H_2O$; and the dissociation press., p_2 mm., of the dihydrate : $MnCl_2.2H_2O \rightleftharpoons MnCl_2+2H_2O$, to be :

	15·5°	20·0°	30·0°	40·0°	50·0°	57·8°	60·0°	70·5°	80·5°	90·0°
p .	7·85	9·45	17·02	28·67	46·29	62·9	64·8	110·25	172·1	262·0
p_4 .	3·50	4·06	9·31	19·28	41·72	62·83	—	—	—	—
p_2 .	—	—	—	2·9	5·9	—	13·8	26·0	38·4	73·2

H. Lescoeur also made some observations on the dissociation press. of these hydrates. C. G. Maier's values for the **heat of vaporization** of the anhydrous salt, Q cals. per mol, are indicated above. According to J. Thomsen, the **heat of formation** $(Mn,Cl_2)=112$ Cals., and, according to M. Berthelot, 112·6 Cals. M. Berthelot gave $(Mn,Cl_2,Aq.)=128·6$ Cals. ; and J. Thomsen, $(Mn,2HCl_{aq.})=49·4$ Cals., and M. Berthelot, 49·8 Cals. J. Thomsen gave $(MnCl_2,4H_2O)=14·47$ Cals. For the **heat of neutralization** J. Thomsen gave $Mn(OH)_2+2HCl_{aq.}=MnCl_{2aq.}+22·95$ Cals., and M. Berthelot, 23·7 Cals. ; M. Berthelot gave $MnCl_{2aq.}+2NaOH_{aq.}$ $=Mn(OH)_2+2NaCl_{aq.}+3·7$ Cals. ; and for the **heat of solution,** $(MnCl_2,Aq.)=16·01$ Cals. J. Thomsen gave for the heat of soln. of the tetrahydrate 1·54 Cals. ; and P. Sabatier gave for that of $MnCl_2.1\frac{3}{4}H_2O$, 9·1 Cals. at 21°. J. Perreu gave —4·56 Cals. for the limiting heat of soln. of the tetrahydrate. G. Beck studied the energy of formation. W. Herz discussed the entropy and vibration frequency ; and G. Beck, the free energy of formation of the salt ; G. Devoto and A. Guzzi gave for the free energy of formation :

	700°	750°	800°	850°	900°	950°
Free energy .	87,150	86,440	83,210	81,050	76,230	72,000 cals.

According to H. C. Jones and F. H. Getman, the **indices of refraction,** μ, of soln. with M mols of manganous chloride per litre, for the D-line, are :

M .	. 0·053	0·106	0·133	0·266	0·533	0·796	0·902
μ .	. 1·32656	1·32766	1·32829	1·33150	1·33768	1·34363	1·34588

A. N. Campbell considers that these results are affected by a constant error, because they are less than the result for water alone, viz. 1·33113 for μ_C and 1·33713 for μ_F; and he obtained :

Eq. per litre	0·5	0·3	0·2	0·1	0·05	0·02	0·01	0·005
μ_C	1·33636	1·33437	1·33327	1·33228	1·33196	1·33163	1·33147	1·33131
μ_F	1·34239	1·34044	1·33918	1·33822	1·33785	1·33756	1·33742	1·33727

These results agree with $\mu_C=1\cdot96$ and $\mu_C=2\cdot00$ for the solid chloride. C. J. W. Grieveson measured the absorption spectrum. The **flame spectrum** was described by R. T. Simmler, G. Hüfner, and J. Müller; and C. Sheard and C. S. Morris found a continuous region in the emission spectrum of manganous chloride between 5900 and 4450 A. C. J. W. Grieveson, J. von Koczkes, and S. Kato studied the absorption spectrum of dil. soln. The specific **electromagnetic rotation** of the plane of polarization was found by R. Wachsmuth to be 1·0434, and the mol. rotation, 7·3037. L. R. Ingersoll gave for Verdet's constants in angle minutes for light of wave-lengths 0·6, 0·8, 1·0, and 1·5μ respectively 0·0141, 0·0078, 0·0054, and 0·0034 for a soln. of manganous chloride of sp. gr. 1·326. H. Jahn, and G. Quincke made some observations on this subject. D. M. Yost found that the K-absorption discontinuities are the same for manganous ions in soln. or in the solid state. L. de Boisbaudran, J. R. Mourelo, and V. Klatt and P. Lenard discussed the **phosphorescence** produced by the presence of manganous salts in the oxides of various metals. R. Robl observed no fluorescence in ultra-violet light. O. Gossmann found that no ions are emitted by the salt heated below 425°. O. Stelling, D. M. Yost, S. Aoyama and co-workers, and K. Fajans studied the **X-ray absorption** ; P. Krishnamurti, the **Raman effect** ; and F. Allison and E. J. Murphy, the **magneto-optic effects.**

W. Hampe observed that molten manganous chloride is a good electrical conductor. The **electrical conductivity,** λ mhos, of aq. soln. of manganous chloride measured by J. H. Long for soln. with p per cent. of $MnCl_2$, at 18°, furnished :

p	5	10	15	20	25	28
λ	63·3	48·8	38·9	30·0	22·0	17·8

and for more dil. soln. H. Ley gave for soln. with a mol of $MnCl_2$ in v litres, at 25° :

v	32	64	128	256	512	1024
λ	100·4	104·4	108·8	111·6	115·2	118·9

A. Heydweiller gave for the sp. gr. and eq. electrical conductivity, at 18° :

	0·5N-	N-	2N-	3N-	4N-	5N-	6N-
Sp. gr.	1·02589	1·0512	1·1010·	1·1496	1·1975	1·2448	1·2917
λ	66·4	57·4	45·27	(35·7)	28·17	(21·8)	16·30

H. C. Jones and F. H. Getman, H. C. Jones and H. P. Bassett, and W. Althammer measured the mol. conductivity, μ, and H. C. Jones and A. P. West also calculated the degree of ionization, α, for temp. between 0° and 65° :

v		2	8	16	32	128	512	1024
	0°	68·14	84·98	91·79	97·4	107·0	114·1	114·9
μ	25°	121·3	156·7	169·0	181·6	202·5	216·6	216·8
	50°	—	218·0	—	288·5	329·0	357·6	374·3
	65°	—	297·9	—	355·0	406·8	444·7	465·8
	0°	59·3	74·0	79·0	84·8	93·1	99·3	100·0
α	25°	56·0	72·3	78·0	83·8	93·4	99·9	100·0
	50°	—	58·2	—	77·1	87·9	95·5	100·0
	65°	—	63·9	—	76·2	87·3	95·5	100·0

The values for the **degree of ionization** are indefinite because of the lack of a criterion to distinguish whether or not the ionization occurs in stages $MnCl_2 \rightleftharpoons MnCl' + Cl'$ and $MnCl' \rightleftharpoons Mn'' + Cl'$. There is no minimum in the conductivity or refractivity curves corresponding with the minimum observed by H. C. Jones and F. H. Getman in the f.p. curves. The phenomenon is explained by the assumption of H. C. Jones and V. J. Chambers that in conc. soln. the dissolved substance combines with the solvent with formation of hydrates, which exist in the soln. together with a small proportion of ions resulting from the electrolytic ionization of the salt, and that those substances which yield crystals containing the largest amount of water of crystallization would be expected to form the most complex hydrates in soln. The subject was discussed by W. Biltz, H. C. Jones, and A. Günther-Schulze. W. Bein calculated the **transport number** for the cations of $0.05N$-$MnCl_2$ to be 0.387 at $18°$. E. Rimbach and K. Weitzel measured the conductivity, λ, in methyl and ethyl alcohols, and in acetone, at temp. $\theta°$, between $0°$ and $45°$. The results are represented as a function of the temp. by $\lambda=\lambda_{1.5°}\{1+a(\theta-7.5)+b(\theta-7.5)^2\}$, for an eq. of the salt in v litres, where a and b are constants with the following values:

CH_3OH	v	2.451	9.832	35.79	143.2	576.1
	$\lambda\,7.5°$	12.33	19.67	26.67	35.28	47.23
	a	1.23	1.19	1.16	1.05	1.05
	b	−3.5	−1.67	0.52	1.01	−2.25
C_2H_5OH	v	1.658	9.324	37.30	55.88	223.5
	$\lambda\,7.5°$	2.389	3.263	5.301	6.085	8.948
	a	1.24	1.27	1.47	1.45	1.51
	b	−8.5	−11.2	−13.5	−10	−4.1
$CH_3CO.CH_3$	v	76.91	153.8	207.6	615.3	1231
	$\lambda\,7.5°$	9.521	10.68	11.61	12.24	12.76
	a	0.663	0.548	0.508	0.451	0.404
	b	−4.79	−10.3	−9.36	−8.48	−7.75

Observations were made by E. C. Banks and co-workers. R. Müller and co-workers observed that $0.1N$- and $0.168N$-soln. of manganous chloride at $25°$ show indefinite **decomposition potentials** of about 2 volts. G. Devoto studied the subject. The **electrolytic oxidation** of manganese salts has been discussed by N. W. Fischer, A. C. Becquerel, C. Luckow, M. Berthelot, A. Classen, A. Classen and M. A. von Reis, F. Rüdorff, A. Riche, A. Brand, L. Schucht, C. Engels, J. Köster, A. Piccini, E. Frei, K. Elbs, Badische Anilin- und Sodafabrik, F. W. Skirrow, M. G. Levi and F. Ageno, C. N. Otin, E. Grave, and G. D. van Arsdale and C. G. Maier—*vide supra*, manganese dioxide and the permanganates. M. Sem said that the electrolytic oxidation at $10°$ proceeds only to the manganic stage, and at $60°$ there is no sign of the formation of a tetrachloride. B. Neumann found the e.m.f. of the cell $Mn_nHg \mid 0.5N$-$MnCl_2 \mid$ electrolyte $\mid N$-$KCl,Hg_2Cl_2 \mid Hg$ to be -1.384 volts at room temp.—*vide supra*, the potential of manganese.

P. Théodoridès gave 110.95×10^{-6} mass unit for the **magnetic susceptibility** of the solid chloride. G. Wiedemann, and E. Wedekind said that the magnetic susceptibility of soln. of the manganous salts is greater than that of the ferric salts. The subject was studied by A. Duperior, B. Cabrera and co-workers, F. Auerbach, O. Wylach, G. Piaggesi, G. Quincke, G. Jäger and S. Meyer, A. Heydweiller, and P. Pascal. O. Liebknecht and A. P. Wills gave 117×10^{-6} to 127×10^{-6} mass unit at $18°$; T. Ishiwara, 111.8×10^{-6}; P. Théodoridès, 114.8×10^{-6}; and W. Sucksmith, 112.2×10^{-6}; B. Cabrera and A. Duperior, G. Falckenberg, and P. Théodoridès studied the effect of temp. on the susceptibility. T. Ishiwara, and K. Honda and T. Ishiwara gave:

	−178.9°	−58.7°	−22.0°	23.9°	119.7°	328.4°	428.6°	621.0°	717.4°
$\chi\times10^6$	393.0	152.5	129.7	107.0	78.6	51.3	43.2	33.5	28.0

W. L. Rolton and R. S. Troop observed no change in the surface tension of soln. of the salt under the influence of a magnetic field of $16,000$ gauss; and W. E. Garner and D. N. Jackson, no change on the mutarotation of sugar by manganous chloride in a magnetic field. S. S. Bhatnagar and co-workers observed that paramagnetic manganese salts become diamagnetic when adsorbed on charcoal, showing that adsorption is more analogous with chemical combination than admixture. G. Quincke found the magnetic susceptibility of aq. soln. to be:

Sp. gr.	1.0357	1.1209	1.1739	1.2992	1.3339	1.3695
Susceptibility$\times10^6$	5.86	19.5	28.3	49.8	56.1	58.3

and he gave 34.8×10^{-6} for a soln. in methyl alcohol of sp. gr. 1·0800 ; and for soln. in ethyl alcohol of sp. gr. 1·0258 and 1·0304 respectively 30.2×10^{-6} and 30.6×10^{-6}. B. Cabrera and A. Duperior, and J. Aharoni studied the magnetism of aq. soln., and they gave for soln. with C grms. of anhydrous salt per 1000 grms. of solvent, $C=0.3845$, the mol. susceptibility is 0·0150, and for $C=0.00582$ the mol. susceptibility is 0·149. These results agree with $4.4=X(T+\Theta)$. S. Freed and C. Kasper discussed the susceptibility of manganous ions involved in the formation of complex salts. G. Jäger and S. Meyer gave 52.4×10^{-6} for an aq. soln. with 3·55 mols per litre ; and H. du Bois, for an aq. soln. of sp. gr. 1·045, 6.82×10^{-6}. Water alone is diamagnetic, and paramagnetic if the sp. gr. exceeds this value :

Sp. gr.	0·9992	1·0010	1·0028	1·0040	1·0054	1·0087	1·0445
Susceptibility $\times 10^6$	−0·837	−0·418	−0·127	0·000	0·182	0·578	0·819

J. A. Arfvedson, and J. J. Ebelmen found that manganous chloride is not decomposed by **hydrogen** at a red-heat. K. Jellinek and co-workers studied the reduction potential of the chloride by hydrogen. W. Ipatieff and W. Kisseleff observed that hydrogen at 300° and over 150 atm. press. acts on soln. of manganous chloride, forming $MnO.H_2O$. K. Jellinek and R. Ulroth studied the reaction $MnCl_2 + H_2 \rightleftharpoons 2HCl + Mn$ at elevated temp. M. Berthelot observed that when the chloride is heated in **oxygen**, the higher manganese oxides are formed. According to J. Meyer and R. Nerlich, manganous ions are not oxidized by atm. oxygen ; nor has the presence of sodium sulphite or arsenite any influence. Manganous salts in ammoniacal or alkaline soln. are oxidized to manganic hydroxide ; thus, manganous chloride made alkaline with ammonia and mixed with ammonium chloride is oxidized by air to manganic hydroxide. In the presence of tartaric or oxalic acid, manganous salts are not precipitated by alkalies, and autoxidation takes place rapidly. In the presence of ammonia, the product is manganic hydroxide, but in the presence of sodium or potassium hydroxide, manganese dioxide is formed, probably because in presence of these stronger alkalies the complex compound is less stable, some manganous hydroxide being always present and oxidizing directly to the dioxide. Potassium and sodium manganocyanides were oxidized to manganic hydroxide, whilst soln. of a manganous salt mixed with potassium thiocyanate were not oxidized at all. V. Lenher found that when a 1 per cent. soln. of manganous chloride and about a gram of calcite were kept for a few weeks in the presence of lead, bismuth, tin, arsenic, antimony, mercury, copper, zinc, nickel, cobalt, cadmium, silver, gold, mercuric sulphide, millerite, pyrites, chalcopyrite, and zinc-blende, the first noticeable separation in the tube with the soln. and calcite alone occurred after several weeks. Lead and bismuth accelerate the reaction, producing the same effect in a few hours. All the other substances had no accelerating effect. In fact, in the case of antimony, tin, and arsenic there was a retarding action, but this was due, not to a negative catalysis, but to the reducing action of the salts of these metals which would be formed. J. Davy observed that when heated to redness in **air,** manganosic oxide is formed, while L. Gmelin added that no free chlorine is evolved, and A. Gorgeu, that an *oxychloride*, $MnCl_2.2Mn_2O_3$ is first formed ; this passes into hemitrioxide, and at a higher temp. a higher oxide is formed. I. F. Hoffmann studied the catalytic oxidation of manganous salts with tetramethyl-p-phenylenediamine as catalytic agent. W. Weldon found that when a mixture of manganous and magnesium chlorides is heated in a current of air, chlorine and magnesium manganite are formed. Manganous ions do not oxidize in acidic or neutral soln., but, as shown by J. Meyer and co-workers, soln. containing hydroxyl-ions yield hydrated manganese hemitrioxide or dioxide —*vide supra*, manganous hydroxide. C. F. Schönbein observed that paper soaked with a manganous salt becomes brown when exposed to **ozone ;** and P. Jannasch and W. Gottschalk, that a soln. of a manganous salt when treated with ozone precipitates hydrated manganese dioxide. A. Mailfert observed that there are three kinds of products : (i) conc. soln. give a brown or black precipitate of manganese dioxide provided the ozone is in excess ; (ii) a violet soln. of permanganate in soln. with a dilution not exceeding 1 : 3000 ; and (iii) a yellow or brown soln. with a dilution of from 1 : 30,000 to 1 : 600,000, and the composition of the product is Mn_3O_8 or Mn_4O_{11}. According to L. Maquenne, the precipitation by ozone must be regarded as the result of a secondary reaction between an untransformed portion of the salt and the permanganate produced by immediate oxidation. If more than 10 per cent. of sulphuric acid is present, the hydrated dioxide is no longer precipitated, and if over 30 per cent. is present, manganic sulphate is formed instead of permanganate. In very conc. soln. of manganese, precipitates are always formed; at least 50 per cent. of sulphuric acid is present; if otherwise manganic sulphate is produced.

F. Kuhlmann found that when the chloride is heated in **water** vapour, hydrogen chloride and manganese tritatetroxide are produced. The solvent action of water has been previously described. The taste of the salt is described by J. L. Proust as being saline, but not unpleasant. L. Bruner found the **hydrolysis** of soln. of manganous chloride to be too small for measurement. According to H. W. Fischer, the salt is hydrolyzed when an aq. soln. is heated to 200° in a bomb, and a dark brown precipitate is formed. A. Gorgeu observed that when an excess of a hot, conc. soln. of manganous chloride is treated with sodium carbonate and boiled half an hour, a gelatinous precipitate of the *oxychloride* $MnCl_2.2$ or $3MnO$ is formed ; and if manganese chloride be melted at a dark red-heat in the presence of steam, but with the exclusion of oxidizing gases, **manganous oxydichloride,** Mn_2OCl_2, is formed in acicular crystals which are slowly decomposed by water and alcohol. A. F. Rogers described emerald-green crystals of a manganese oxychloride, or **manganese dichlorotripermanganite,** $MnCl_2.3MnO_2.3H_2O$, or $Mn_4Cl_2O_6.3H_2O$, from the vicinity of San José, California, and the mineral was called **kempite**—after J. F. Kemp. The rhombic crystals have the axial ratios $a : b : c = 0.677 : 1 : 0.747$; the sp. gr. is 2·94 ; the hardness, 3·5 ; and the indices of refraction $\alpha = 1.684$, $\beta = 1.695$, and $\gamma = 1.698$. Kempite dissolves in hydrochloric acid with the evolution of chlorine.

According to G. Rosenthal, **hydrogen dioxide** precipitates manganese dioxide from an acetic acid soln. of a manganous salt. The reaction was studied by S. T. Orlowsky. B. C. Brodie found that in alkaline soln. hydrogen dioxide oxidizes the manganous salt to the dioxide. A. C. Robertson examined the catalytic decomposition of hydrogen dioxide by the manganous salts. For the action on permanganate, *vide supra.* S. T. Orlowsky studied the action of **sodium dioxide.** H. Kwasnick found that **barium dioxide** in a soln. of a manganous salt gives off oxygen vigorously ; the action of **lead dioxide** has been discussed in connection with the formation of permanganic acid. O. Kühling found that manganous salt soln. are slowly oxidized by **silver peroxide** and nitric acid in the cold ; a permanganate is first formed, and the soln. then becomes colourless owing to the separation of hydrated manganese dioxide. If more silver peroxide is added, the pink colour does not disappear until the soln. is heated, and finally the colour is persistent and a clear soln. of permanganate is formed.

According to H. Moissan, **fluorine** transforms manganese chloride largely into the trifluoride. V. Thomas and P. Dupuis observed that liquid **chlorine** at its b.p. does not act on manganous chloride. N. A. E. Millon observed that chlorine oxidized dil. soln. of manganous chloride to the hydrated dioxide, and A. Sobrero and F. Selmi observed a similar result occurs in darkness in the presence of alkali or alkaline earth chloride. As shown by L. F. Rivot and co-workers, F. Stromeyer, J. Schiel, H. Rose, C. R. Fresenius, and J. Volhard, chlorine oxidizes hot, dil. neutral or feebly acidic soln. of manganous salts to hydrated manganese dioxide, and even to permanganate—*vide supra* ; and H. Kämmerer, T. T. Morrell, E. Riley, S. T. Orlowsky, and P. Waage obtained similar results with **bromine.** R. F. Weinland and F. Schlegelmilch found that orange-red needles of **manganous diiodocto-**

chloride, $MnCl_2.2ICl_3.8H_2O$, are formed by passing chlorine into a suspension of **iodine** in a conc. soln. of manganous chloride. As in the case of other bivalent salts, there is a general tendency of the manganous salts to form complex anions with a feeble electro-affinity. S. T. Orlowsky studied the oxidizing action of iodine. K. Fredenhagen and G. Cadenbach, and K. Fredenhagen studied the action of **hydrofluoric acid** on manganous chloride. B. E. Dixon and J. L. White, T. J. Pearsall, E. and B. Klimenko, J. Volhard, and R. Phillips showed that a soln. of a manganous salt is oxidized by **sodium or calcium hypochlorite**—*vide supra*, potassium permanganate; E. Dèniges, by **sodium hypobromite ;** and the action was found by A. J. Balard, and J. Pelouze to be very slow with **chloric acid.** C. F. Rammelsberg, and S. R. Benedict also found that manganous salts are oxidized by **bromic acid,** and **periodic acid.** W. Ostwald observed that manganous chloride exerts a small catalytic action on the velocity of the reaction between bromic and hydriodic acids. N. Isgarischeff and S. Schapiro observed its effect on the rate of dissolution of marble. J. F. Simon, and D. Vitali found that manganous salts are oxidized by **potassium bromate** and sulphuric acid ; J. F. Simon, by hot soln., by **potassium chlorate** and sulphuric acid ; and J. B. Hannay, by potassium chlorate and nitric acid. According to J. Townsend, chlorine is formed when bricks soaked in manganous chloride are heated to $100°$–$150°$ in a current of **hydrogen chloride** and air ; and M. G. Levi and V. Bettoni studied the action of manganous chloride as a catalytic agent in H. W. Deacon's process for chlorine. M. Berthelot observed that fuming **hydrochloric acid** and oxygen added to a soln. of manganous chloride at ordinary temp. form chlorine. A. Ditte found that the solubility of manganous chloride in hydrochloric acid increases with increasing proportions of HCl ; it is greater with hot than with cold soln. ; he also added that the monohydrate crystallizes from cold soln. in the conc. acid—100 c.c. of the conc. acid dissolves 19 grms. of the salt at $12°$. M. Bobtelsky studied the catalytic effect of manganous chloride on the oxidation of hydrochloric acid by chromic acid ; and M. Bobtelsky and A. Rosenberg, the catalytic effect of Mn -ions on the oxidation of **hydrogen bromide** by chromic acid.

H. A. von Vogel observed that when manganous chloride is heated with **sulphur,** manganous sulphide is formed. A. W. Ralston and J. A. Wilkinson found that the soln. in liquid **hydrogen sulphide** is non-conducting. In the equilibrium $MnCl_2+H_2S \rightleftharpoons MnS+2HCl$, K. Jellinek and G. von Podjasky found that equilibrium occurs at $407°$ with 15 per cent. HCl by vol. ; at $506°$ with 43·5 per cent. HCl by vol. ; and at $583°$ with 72 per cent. HCl by vol. ; and he gave for the heat of the reaction $-26·030$ Cals. O. Ruff and B. Hirsch discussed the fractional precipitation of manganese as sulphide, hydroxide, and carbonate. According to H. W. F. Wackenroder, hydrogen sulphide gives no precipitate with neutral or acidic soln. of manganous salts, but with neutral acetate a little manganous sulphide may be formed. A soln. of **ammonium sulphide** gives a flesh-coloured precipitate of manganous sulphide, which is oxidized brownish-black on exposure to air, and which is insoluble in an excess of the precipitant, but soluble in dil. acids. J. Lefort and P. Thibault said that the precipitation of the sulphide is hindered by the presence of gum arabic ; J. Spiller, by the presence of alkali citrates ; and H. Rose, by the presence of pyrophosphates. The subject was discussed by A. Classen, H. How, C. R. Fresenius, and A. Terreil. A soln. of a manganous salt is not affected by **sulphur dioxide.** P. Berthier also said that **potassium sulphite** gives a precipitate when the soln. is boiled, but not so with **ammonium sulphite.** L. Meyer observed that the oxidation of sulphurous acid in air is accelerated by manganous salts more than is the case with ferrous, cobalt, nickel, zinc, cadmium, or magnesium salts. L. Meyer found it to be a good catalyst in the oxidation of sulphur dioxide. A. Vogel found that with cold, conc. **sulphuric acid** hydrogen chloride is evolved and manganous sulphate is formed. The action of **persulphates** has been discussed in connection with the formation of permanganic acid. O. W. Gibbs observed no precipitation when a manganous salt soln. is heated with **sodium thiosulphate** under press., but J. T. Norton found that a little manganous sulphide is formed. O. Brunck observed no action with **sodium hyposulphite.**

E. P. Lewis observed no phosphorescence with active **nitrogen.** G. Gore, and E. C. Franklin and C. A. Kraus stated that manganous chloride is insoluble in liquid **ammonia.** H. N. Warren noted that when the chloride is heated with ammonia a nitride is formed. H. Rose reported that ammonia unites with manganous chloride to form **manganous monamminochloride,** $MnCl_2.NH_3$; while W. Peters found that the salt at 160° forms **manganous hexamminochloride,** $MnCl_2.6NH_3$. In vacuo the hexammine loses 4 mols. of ammonia. F. Ephraim found the dissociation press., p mm., to be:

	50°	65°	70°	75.5°	80°	84°	87.5°	90.5°	91°
p . .	170	230	300	375	470	557	665	750	765

According to W. Biltz and G. F. Hüttig, anhydrous manganous chloride, at the temp. of solid carbon dioxide and alcohol, rapidly absorbs ammonia to form the white hexammine. At 76·3° the isothermal curve falls a little, and then remains horizontal until the composition approaches that of **manganous diamminochloride,** $MnCl_2.2NH_3$, the isothermal for which is 229·9°. There is then evidence of the formation of the monammine, Fig. 60. No other ammines exist under these conditions. W. Biltz and E. Birk studied the mol. vol. The dissociation press., p, and the heats of dissociation, Q Cals., are for manganous hexamminochloride, $MnCl_2.6NH_3$, at 59°, $p=218$ mm.; at 63°, $p=258$ mm.; at 76·5°, $p=495$ mm.; and the mean value of $Q=18·8$ Cals. For the diammine, at 181°, $p=65$ mm., and $Q=18·7$ Cals.; at 206°, $p=196$ mm., and $Q=18·8$ Cals.; and at 230°, $p=407$ mm., and $Q=19·1$ Cals. For the monammine, at 215°, $p=9·4$ mm., and $Q=22·1$ Cals.; at 230°, $p=28$ mm., and $Q=21·75$ Cals.; and at 278°, $p=95$ mm., and $Q=22·7$ Cals. F. Müller gave $-18°$ for the dissociation temp. of the hexamminochloride; 87° for the pentamminochloride; 240° for the diamminochloride; and over 380° for the monamminochloride. F. Ephraim, and G. L. Clark also studied the hexammine; and F. J. Garrick calculated values for the energy of co-ordination. W. Biltz and E. Rahlfs found that at still lower temp. and in contact with liquid ammonia it is possible to prepare **manganous dodecamminochloride,** $MnCl_2.12NH_3$, whose dissociation press., p mm., and heat of dissociation are at $-78·5°$ (Fig. 61), $p=29·5$ mm., and $Q=7·14$ Cals.; and at $-65°$, $p=97·5$ mm., and $Q=7·15$ Cals.; this complex breaks down into **manganous decamminochloride,** $MnCl_2.10NH_3$, which at $-78·5°$ has $p=20·5$ mm., and $Q=7·28$ Cals.; at $-65°$, $p=72$, and $Q=7·27$; at $-60°$, $p=107$, and $Q=7·28$; at $-55°$, $p=160$, and $Q=7·28$; and at $-50°$, $p=220$, and $Q=7·30$. F. Ephraim discussed the contraction in vol. attending the formation of the ammines. Neutral soln. of manganous salts with aq. ammonia give a partial precipitation of white manganous hydroxide, which is insoluble in excess of aq. ammonia and turns brown in air; if the soln. be acidic, or if ammonium salts be present, precipitation does not occur. The precipitated hydroxide dissolves in soln. of ammonium salts with the liberation of ammonia; any admixed higher oxide remains undissolved. **Ammonium salt** soln. of manganous salts deposit brown hydrated oxide on exposure to air. W. Herz discussed the equilibrium phenomena between the ammonium and manganous salts. H. Rose observed that the precipitation by ammonia is hindered by tartaric acid. C. Vincent found that **dimethylaniline** behaves like ammonia; and T. Curtius and F. Schrader, that **hydrazine hydrate** precipitates brown manganous hydroxide. H. Franzen and O. von Mayer obtained **manganous dihydrazinochloride,** $MnCl_2.2N_2H_4$; and A. Ferratini, **manganous trihydrazinochloride,** $MnCl_2.3N_2H_5Cl$, as a white crystalline powder which melts between 238° and 242°; it is sparingly soluble in cold but easily soluble in warm alcohol with partial decomposition, and it is freely soluble in water. W. Feldt prepared **manganous dihydroxylaminochloride,** $MnCl_2.2NH_2OH$, as a stable, white powder which decomposes suddenly at 150°–160°. N. Pfanner obtained **manganous hemitrihydroxylaminochloride,** $2MnCl_2.3NH_2OH.6H_2O$, by the action of manganese on an alcohol soln. of hydroxyl-amine hydrochloride. According to W. Prandtl, if a drop or two of a manganous salt soln. is added to a cold soln. of sodium nitrite in conc. hydrochloric acid, there develops a deep brownish-yellow coloration, due to the manganic chloride which is formed. Similarly, if oxalic acid is added to a soln. of sodium nitrite containing a mere trace of a manganous salt, the deep cherry-red colour of manganic oxalate appears. G. Hüfner observed that a soln. of manganous chloride absorbs **nitric oxide,** and inferred that the absorbed gas is partly united chemically with the solute, and part is dissolved in accord with Henry's law, so that the gas is more soluble in the salt soln. than it is in water alone. If v c.c. are absorbed, then a c.c. are loosely bound chemically, while b c.c. are absorbed in accord with Henry's law, $v = 2.5518 + 0.016538p$, where p mm. denotes the press. The coeff. of absorption is 0.06111. F. L. Usher, however, said that nitric oxide is indifferent towards manganous chloride in soln., and the solubility of the gas is similar to that of other inert gases, for it is less in the aq. soln. of manganous chloride than in water alone. It is difficult to prepare the gas of a high degree of purity. Manganous chloride dissolves in conc. **nitric acid,** forming a yellow soln. which soon becomes deep brown and opaque. According to A. Schlesinger, some manganic nitrate and chloride are formed, and when the soln. is boiled, a basic manganic nitrate is precipitated.

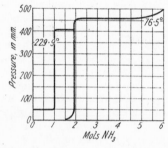

FIG. 60.—Dissociation Pressures of Manganous Hexamminochloride.

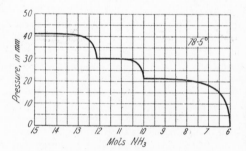

FIG. 61.—Dissociation Pressures of Manganous Dodecamminochloride.

F. W. O. de Coninck observed that when the hot soln. in sulphuric acid is mixed with nitric acid, chlorine is first given off, and then some nitrous fumes. In dil. soln. the manganous salts are not oxidized by nitric acid. L. P. de St. Gilles observed that an oxychloride is formed when manganous chloride is fused with **sodium nitrate** at 250° for a long time and the product washed with water. E. P. y Alvarez found that **pernitrates** form permanganate. H. Rose observed that heated manganous chloride is decomposed by **phosphine :** $3MnCl_2 + 2PH_3 = Mn_3P_2 + 6HCl$. H. Rose, and L. C. A. Barreswil found that when melted with syrupy **phosphoric acid** and potassium nitrate, an amethyst-blue glass is formed sensitive to 0.01 mgrm. of manganese ; for **sodium phosphate,** vide supra, the analytical reactions of manganese. H. P. Cady and R. Taft found that the chloride is insoluble in phosphoryl chloride. E. P. y Alvarez found that **perphosphates** form permanganate. R. Lang and co-workers observed that manganous salts are not in general oxidized by chromic acid or the chromates, but the oxidation is induced in the presence of **arsenites.** Thus, potassium dichromate in the presence of an arsenite oxidizes a manganous salt to a manganic salt : $Mn^{II} + Cr^{VI} + As^{III} = Mn^{III} + Cr^{III} + As^{V}$.

N. Schiloff and S. Pewsner studied the adsorption of the soln. by charcoal. J. Hoffmann prepared *manganous boroheptachloride,* $2MnCl_2.BCl_3$, by the action of chlorine on manganese boride at a red-heat. According to J. F. John, hydrated manganous chloride dissolves in **alcohol,** forming a green soln., which, according to R. Brandes, burns with a reddish flame.   R. Brandes gave for the percentage solubility, S, of manganous chloride in alcohol :

	75 per cent. alcohol				Absolute alcohol		
	10°	25°	43·75°	87·5° (b.p.)	11·25°	37·5°	76·25° (b.p.)
MnCl$_2$.	23·1	36·1	37·5	32·2	33·3	33·3	33·6 per cent.

and MnCl$_2$ crystallizes from these soln. on standing.   The solubility, S, of the tetrahydrate in 75 per cent. alcohol at 10°, 25°, 43·75°, and 87·5° (b.p.) was found to be respectively S=53, 132, 144, 100·1 per cent. MnCl$_2$.4H$_2$O.   G. C. Gibson and co-workers found the solubility of manganous chloride in methyl and ethyl alcohols, S grm. of salt per gram of alcohol, to be :

	CH$_3$OH					C$_2$H$_5$OH		
	15°	25°	35°	45°	55°	15°	35°	55°
S .	0·00190	0·00114	0·00064	0·00043	0·00029	0·00012	0·00014	0·00021

F. Bourion observed that the soln. in alcohol gives, on evaporation, rose-red crystals of the *trialcoholate*, MnCl$_2$.3C$_2$H$_5$OH, which has a sp. gr. of 1·5 at 10°, and a heat of formation of 2·36 Cals.   The alcohol is all given off between 150° and 200°. R. Brandes said that manganous chloride is insoluble in **ether.**   J. W. Döbereiner observed that the tetrahydrate is insoluble in absolute ether, and this solvent does not abstract the water of crystallization.   If 15 to 20 vols. of ether are added to a vol. of absolute alcohol sat. with MnCl$_2$, manganous chloride is completely precipitated.   R. Müller measured the solubility of manganous chloride in **pyridine.** R. Müller and co-workers, and F. Reitzenstein prepared a complex with pyridine, namely, **manganous dipyridinochloride,** MnCl$_2$.2C$_5$H$_5$N, and determined the electrical conductivity of its soln. ; and L. Pincussohn obtained the complexes MnCl$_2$.C$_6$H$_5$N.HCl and MnCl$_2$.2C$_6$H$_5$N.HCl.   According to R. B. Moore and J. Miller, the pyridine complex is more stable than the ammine.   H. Grossmann and B. Schück obtained an insoluble precipitate by adding **guanidine carbonate** to a soln. of a manganous salt.   G. A. Barbieri and F. Calzolari, and G. Scagliarini and G. Tartarini obtained a complex with **hexamethylenetetramine,** namely, MnCl$_2$.2C$_6$H$_{12}$N$_4$.10H$_2$O ; and A. Rosenheim and V. J. Meyer, a complex with **thiourea,** namely, MnCl$_2$.4CS(NH$_2$)$_2$, and he measured the conductivity of its soln. G. Bruni and A. Manuelli found that soln. of manganous chloride in **acetamide** are strongly ionized—*vide supra.*   N. Castoro examined soln. in urethane—*vide supra.*   A. Trillat observed a blue coloration is produced with **tetramethyl- diamidodiphenylmethane**—*vide supra,* analytical reactions.   Both the anhydrous salt and the tetrahydrate were found by R. Brandes to be insoluble in **turpentine.** L. Crismer studied the reactions of the manganous salts with turpentine, pinene, oil of lemons, and oil of thyme.   E. Raymond studied the action of manganese salts on the oxidation of **benzaldehyde.**   A. Naumann found that manganous chloride is insoluble in **ethyl acetate,** sparingly soluble in **methyl acetate,** and slightly soluble in **benzonitrile.**   E. Rousseau observed the polymerization of **formol** by manganous chloride in ultra-violet light.   According to O. W. Gibbs, C. R. Fresenius, and A. Classen, **oxalic acid** precipitates from concentrated but not from dilute soln. of manganous chloride crystalline manganous oxalate, which is soluble in hydrochloric or sulphuric acid, but not in oxalic acid or alcohol.   A. Villiers, and W. Sander observed that when a mixture of equal vols. of a sat. soln. of oxalic acid, 25 per cent. hydrochloric acid, and 25 per cent. nitric acid is heated, there is no evolution of gas, but if a small quantity of any manganese salt is added, there is an almost immediate reaction, with the evolution of carbon dioxide and nitrogen, and the decomposition proceeds even if heating is discontinued.   If the nitric acid is in excess, the oxalic acid is completely oxidized.   With more conc. soln. the oxalic acid is slightly decomposed even in absence of manganese, but the difference produced by the addition of manganese is very marked.   Many other compounds of the fatty group, such as glucose and saccharose, behave in the same

way. Compounds of the benzene group, on the other hand, yield chlorine substitution products instead of oxidation products ; benzene and toluene, for example,
yield chlorobenzene and chlorotoluene respectively, even at the ordinary temp.
A. Classen found that **potassium oxalate** precipitates all the manganese as oxalate,
soluble in an excess of the oxalate, and precipitated from that soln. by acetic acid.
The oxidation of oxalic acid by potassium permanganate is accelerated by the
presence of manganous salts, as shown by A. V. Harcourt, A. V. Harcourt and
W. Esson, and W. P. Jorissen and L. T. Reicher ; and likewise with the oxidation
of **tartaric acid,** as shown by J. Krutwig.   E. Darmois studied the effect of manganese chloride on the rotatory power of tartaric acid.   S. Hakomori observed
the formation of complex salts with tartaric acid and manganese salts.   According
to J. Spohr, J. H. Long, L. Kahlenberg and co-workers, and C. Kullgren, the
speed of inversion of **sugar** is accelerated by the presence of a manganous salt.
W. E. Garner and D. N. Jackson observed that the hydrolysis of aq. soln. of glucose
or sucrose, in the presence of manganous chloride, is not appreciably affected by
a magnetic field of 7000 to 8000 units. B. Köhnlein found that manganous chloride
and propyl iodide do not readily exchange their halogen atoms at 145° to 150° in
4 hrs.   R. Kuhn and K. Meyer noted how manganese salts accelerate the autoxidation of benzaldehyde, and V. K. la Mer and J. W. Temple, the autoxidation of
quinol.   A. Trillat measured the behaviour of manganous salts in acting as *inorganic
enzymes,* by measuring the volume of oxygen absorbed in a given time by a definite
quantity of gallic acid, quinol, pyrogallol, or tannin, in the presence of a manganous
salt (chloride, sulphate, or acetate) ; under these conditions the manganous salts
only become active in the presence of an alkali hydroxide or a salt of an alkaline
earth, the increase in the rate of oxidation being proportional to the quantity of
alkali hydroxide present, whilst for the same quantity of alkali hydroxide an
increase in the quantity of the manganous salt beyond a certain limit has a para-
lyzing effect.   Certain substances, such as arsenic acid, mercuric chloride, hydrocyanic acid, and hydrogen sulphide, which act as poisons on organisms, have the
effect of retarding the reaction—*vide supra,* the physiological action of manganese.
According to E. Rousseau, salts of manganese exposed to solar or ultra-violet
radiation fix the ultra-violet energy which produces photocatalytic effects in
sterilizing or activating ferments.   W. Thomson and F. Lewis studied the
action on **indiarubber.**   C. F. Rammelsberg observed that the reddish-white
precipitate produced by **potassium cyanide** in soln. of manganous salts quickly
turns brown in air ; and F. von Ittner found that the precipitate is soluble in soln.
of alkali cyanides and is decomposed by acids ; and J. Haidlen and C. R. Fresenius
noticed that if the soln. of manganous salt be poured into that of potassium cyanide,
the liquid becomes pale brownish-red and a dirty reddish-yellow precipitate is then
formed ; this dissolves to a brownish-red liquid.   Acids do not precipitate manganous
cyanide from the liquid ; but the liquid deposits hydrated manganic oxide on
exposure to air.   Observations were also made by J. H. Eaton and R. Fittig.
F. J. Otto found that **potassium ferrocyanide** gives a white precipitate with manganous salts ; it is easily soluble in hydrochloric acid, but not in an excess of
potassium ferrocyanide, ammonium chloride, and other salts.   C. H. Pfaff added
that the precipitation occurs with one part of salt in 6000 parts of water ; and
L. Blum also said that manganese can be so detected in a soln. containing 0·00004
grm. Mn.   The brownish-yellow precipitate with **potassium ferricyanide** is not
soluble in hydrochloric acid, but is decomposed by the hot acid.   Observations
were made by E. Lenssen, A. H. Allen, S. T. Orlowsky, C. N. Draper, and
S. M. Deane.   E. H. Miller and J. A. Mathews observed that $0·5N$-$MnCl_2$ gives a
white precipitate with a $0·5N$-soln. of **potassium cobaltic cyanide.**   A. Günther-
Schulze studied the basic exchange of manganous chloride and permutite.
O. C. Magistad observed that the manganese of manganous chloride and sulphate
replaces lime in **zeolites.**

J. G. Hibbs and E. F. Smith examined the action of **magnesium** on aq. or alcoholic soln. of manganous chloride, and obtained a deposit of what may have been manganese or a hydrated oxide of that element; I. Iitaka also studied the reaction. A. Terreil observed that manganous chloride explodes when it is heated with **zinc**. The action of **metals** on soln. of the salt has been discussed in connection with the metallic precipitation of manganese. Soln. of manganous salts give a white precipitate with **alkali hydroxides ;** the precipitate is not soluble in an excess of the alkali-lye, but is easily soluble in a soln. of an ammonium salt; it turns brown on exposure to air. E. Donath found that the precipitation is hindered by glycerol; and J. Lefort and P. Thibault, by gum arabic. H. Pélabon and M. Delwaulle observed that with **mercuric oxide** manganese oxides—Mn_3O_4, Mn_2O_3, and MnO_2—are formed as well as basic mercuric chlorides, depending on the conditions. E. Tiede and R. Piwonka studied the manganese-alumina phosphors. H. Rose showed that **alkali carbonates** give a white precipitate of manganous carbonate, which becomes brown if heated in air; the precipitation is incomplete in the cold or in the presence of ammonium salts; but the presence of tartaric acid makes no difference. H. Tamm, and C. R. Fresenius found that **ammonium carbonate** precipitates manganous carbonate completely from neutral soln. of manganous salts, even in the presence of ammonium salts; **potassium hydrocarbonate** gives a precipitate with conc. soln. of manganous salts; dil. soln. are rendered turbid, maybe after standing some time, but not if free carbon dioxide is in soln. For the action of the **alkaline earth carbonates,** *vide supra,* the analytical reactions of manganese. F. Wöhler, H. Barberi, and H. Rose discussed the possible formation of a manganite (*q.v.*) by the action of an ammoniacal soln. of **silver nitrate ;** S. T. Orlowsky studied the oxidizing action of silver nitrate, **mercuric nitrate,** and **copper sulphate ;** O. Kühling, the oxidizing action of **silver peroxide** to form permanganates; and A. Mailhe, and C. Rube, the action of **mercuric oxide.** H. Pélabon and M. Delwaulle represented the action of mercuric oxide when shaken with a soln. of manganous chloride : $3MnCl_2+4HgO=Mn_3O_4+2HgCl_2+2HgCl$, and with a larger proportion of mercuric oxide, manganic oxide : $2MnCl_2+3HgO$ $=Mn_2O_3+HgCl_2+2HgCl$, or manganese dioxide : $MnCl_2+2HgO=MnO_2+2HgCl$, may be formed. For the oxidizing action of bismuthates, and for the action of permanganates, *vide supra,* permanganates ; R. Lang and J. Zwerina discussed the action of **chromic acid** on manganous salts. A. D. Brokaw found that when soln. of **gold chloride,** of varying conc., are mixed with soln. of manganous chloride, of conc. varying from 0·5N- to saturation, no reaction can be detected, even after prolonged boiling. When, however, a very small amount of alkali is added to the cold mixture, manganese dioxide and gold are at once precipitated. The same result is obtained when a crystal of calcium carbonate is added to the mixture ; there is a slight effervescence, and after a few hours the crystal is covered with manganese dioxide containing flakes of gold. M. Holzmann found that hydrated manganese dioxide is precipitated by **ceric nitrate ;** and F. W. O. de Coninck, the action of **platinic chloride** in sunlight : $PtCl_4+2MnCl_2 \rightleftharpoons 2MnCl_3+PtCl_2$. O. T. Christensen found that **Fehling's soln.** is reduced by manganous salt soln.; and G. Kassner observed that the presence of manganous salts favours the oxidation of **ferrous salt** soln. by atm. air; S. T. Orlowsky found manganous salts in alkaline soln. are oxidized to manganic salts by **potassium dichromate.** The reaction was studied by R. Lang.

R. H. Brett found that the soln. of manganous hydroxide in one of ammonium chloride does not give a precipitate with hydrogen sulphide. H. Lessheim and co-workers discussed the constitution of the complex salts. According to O. Hautz, pale red monoclinic crystals of **ammonium manganous trichloride,** $NH_4Cl.MnCl_2.2H_2O$, are deposited when a mixed soln. of theoretical proportions of the component salts is evaporated. He said that the salt loses three-fourths of its water of crystallization at 100°, and that 100 parts of water dissolve 66·7 parts of the salt. A. Chassevant thought that he had prepared a similar salt. C. E. Saunders considered that there must have been a mistake in O. Hautz's analysis, because he always obtained pale pink crystals of **ammonium manganous tetrachloride,** $(NH_4)_2MnCl_4.2H_2O$, or $2NH_4Cl.MnCl_2.2H_2O$, under the conditions employed by O. Hautz. This salt was also prepared by C. E. Rice, H. W. Foote and B. Saxton, and C. von Hauer. C. E. Saunders found that the *dihydrate* usually forms radiating groups of pale pink, almost colourless crystals, which are monoclinic and have the axial ratios $a : b : c = 1.4913 : 1 : 1.4956$, and $\beta = 95° 25'$. Two of the crystal axes are almost equal in length, and this with the habit gives the crystals the appearance of a rhombic dodecahedron. The cleavage is imperfect. The salt cannot be obtained pure by recrystallization from water, since it requires an excess of manganous chloride before it deposits crystals of a high degree of purity. The salt is not deliquescent in air, nor does it give up its water of crystallization in vacuo. C. von Hauer added that the crystals lose $1\frac{1}{2}$ mols. of water at 100° and the remainder at 135°, but C. E. Saunders added that the salt has a tendency to decompose as the water is given off at 110°. At a redheat the salt loses ammonium chloride, etc., to form the tritatetrachloride. C. Hatchett found that aq. ammonia gives no precipitate with an aq. soln. of the salt. According to C. F. Rammelsberg, and A. Chassevant, the salt is a *monohydrate*, $(NH_4)_2MnCl_4.H_2O$, crystallizing in the cubic system ; S. U. Pickering also obtained a salt crystallizing in hard brown cubes which are said to be crystals of the mono-

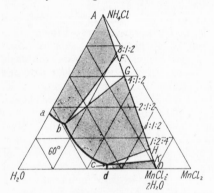

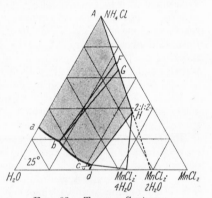

Fig. 62.—Ternary System : $MnCl_2$–NH_4Cl–H_2O at 60°.

Fig. 63.—Ternary System : $MnCl_2$–NH_4Cl–H_2O at 25°.

hydrate. On the other hand, C. E. Saunders showed that the analyses were probably made on impure salts, for he obtained no evidence of the existence of the monohydrate. E. M. Farrer and S. U. Pickering reported that **ammonium manganous hexachloride,** $4NH_4Cl.MnCl_2.3H_2O$, was formed " by crystallizing soln. of the two chlorides." The specimen analyzed probably contained ammonium chloride as impurity, for C. E. Saunders obtained no evidence of its existence. E. M. Farrer and S. U. Pickering said that this salt, on being heated in dry air, gave off water and ammonium chloride at 100° ; but even at 220°, after prolonged heating, it still retained a considerable amount of water, although the ammonium chloride had all been expelled and about 4 per cent. of the salt had been oxidized. P. de Clérmont and H. Guyot boiled manganous sulphide with an excess of ammonium chloride, and found that the filtrate deposited ammonium manganous octodecachloride, $16NH_4Cl.MnCl_2.H_2O$, but there is nothing to show that the product was a chemical individual. N. Pfanner obtained **ammonium manganous heptachloride,** $3NH_4Cl.2MnCl_2.4H_2O$, by the action of manganese on a warm aq. soln. of hydroxylamine hydrochloride ; and **ammonium manganous tetramminotridecachloride,** $9NH_4Cl.2MnCl_2.4NH_3.H_2O$. O. Lehmann recognized the formation of isomorphous mixtures in the system $MnCl_2$–NH_4Cl–H_2O, and A. Johnsen studied their crystallography ; and H. W. Foote and B. Saxton showed that the $2:1:2$-salt and ammonium chloride form two series of isomorphous mixtures with a gap between the limiting compositions of each series. F. W. J. Clendinnen and A. C. D. Rivett studied the ternary system at different temp. The results for 60° and 25° are summarized in Figs. 62 and 63. There are three well-defined zones of isomorphous mixtures represented by the shaded areas, namely, *AF*, *GH*, and *KD*, with the gaps *FG* and *HK*. The curves *ab*, *bc*, and *cd* correspond with the solubility curves of the respective series, and the intersections *b* and *c* correspond with the gaps in the series. The alleged 2 : 1 : 2-compound falls well within the second series of isomorphous mixtures *GH*. The *AD* is a section across the temp.-conc. diagram of the binary system NH_4Cl–$MnCl_2.2H_2O$ at 60°. It is doubtful if ammonium chloride forms chemical compounds with manganous chloride under these conditions and in the generally accepted sense of the words. The isotherms between 10° and 70° are shown in Fig. 64, where the percentage weights of ammonium chloride in the liquids are taken as ordinates, and the percentage weights of ammonium chloride in the dry solids, as abscissæ These curves show the relative distribution of ammonium chloride in the liquid and solid phases. The distribution isotherms divide the field into several regions. *A* and *B* are regions of the existence of homogeneous, single-phase, isomorphous mixtures ; and *C* is a heterogeneous region where solids of mean composition sepa-rate at stable equilibrium into two phases capable of existing together and with a soln. At 70° there is a considerable gap, *ab*, between the compositions of co-existing solids. With a fall of temp. the gap narrows, or the mutual solubility of ammonium chloride and manga-nous chloride dihydrate increases, showing that the formation of the solid soln. is exothermic. The composition of the solids steadily approach one another, as represented by the curve *acb* connecting the successive values of the two series of solid phases. At a temp. probably a little below 25° the regions *A* and *B* merge into one another and the two curves *ac* and *bc* join together ; *c* is clearly a (lower) critical soln. point, and below it complete miscibility is characteristic of ammonium chloride and the dihydrate within the portion of the binary system studied. Thus at 20° there is no break in the distribution curve *rst*, although there is a most distinct point of inflexion at

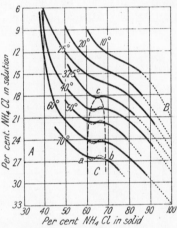

FIG. 64.—Distribution of Ammonium Chloride in Solutions of Man-ganous Chloride in the Solid and Liquid Phases.

s. At 10° the inflexion is less, although still very obvious. There are disturb-ances due to metastable phenomena at 0° and −10°. At 60° and 32·5° metastable curves have been followed well into the region *C*. As indicated above, W. Feldt prepared **hydroxylamine manganous dichloride**, $2NH_2OH.MnCl_2$, but W. Meyeringh could not obtain a double salt by using a mixed soln. of hydroxylamine chloride and manganous chloride. N. Pfanner reported a number of **ammonium man-ganous hydroxylaminochlorides**—$NH_4Cl.MnCl_2.NH_2OH.H_2O$, by the action of manganese on a cold aq. soln. of hydroxylamine hydrochloride ; $7NH_4Cl.MnCl_2.2NH_2OH.7\frac{1}{2}H_2O$, from the brown product obtained in the preparation of $3NH_4Cl.2MnCl_2.4H_2O$; $3NH_4Cl.2MnCl_2.2NH_2OH.H_2O$, by boiling soln. of $9NH_4Cl.2MnCl_2.4NH_3.H_2O$, in alcohol; G. Spacu and L. Canton prepared **ammo-nium manganous hexamminotetrachloride**, $[Mn(NH_3)_6]Cl_2.2NH_4Cl$, by the action of dry ammonia on the powdered $(NH_4)_2MnCl_4.2H_2O$. As indicated above, W. Ferratini prepared **hydrazine manganous pentachloride**, $3N_2H_5Cl.MnCl_2$.

C. E. Saunders could not prepare a compound of lithium and manganous chlorides, but when an aq. soln. of the mixed salts is concentrated, the liquid becomes green. A. Chassevant, however, found that if a cold, conc. soln. containing equivalents of lithium and manganous chlorides be allowed to crystallize, manganous chloride alone separates out; but if the soln. be concentrated on a water-bath until the rose-red liquid becomes yellowish, and then evaporated in vacuo, deliquescent crystals of **lithium manganous trichloride,** $LiCl.MnCl_2.3H_2O$, are formed. The crystals are said to be isomorphous with lithium cobaltous trichloride, $LiCoCl_3.3H_2O$. They break down into the individual chlorides when exposed to air. If the water is drawn from the crystals in vacuo, they are decomposed and the mass becomes brown. The crystals at 120° also lose water and hydrogen chloride; but the crystals can be dehydrated without decomposition in an atm. of hydrogen chloride; and the aq. soln. is stable in the presence of an excess of lithium chloride. The observations of C. Sandonnini and G. Scarpa on the f.p. of mixtures of lithium and manganous chlorides are summarized in Fig. 65. No compounds are formed. C. E. Saunders obtained some evidence of a **sodium manganous chloride,** but it was not possible to obtain the salt pure enough for analysis by cooling a hot, conc. soln. of the component salts. The impure product contained a large excess of manganous chloride. The observations of C. Sandonnini and G. Scarpa on the f.p. of mixtures of sodium and manganous chlorides are summarized in Fig. 66. There is evidence of the formation of $NaCl.MnCl_2$ and of $4NaCl.MnCl_2$. I. I. Krasikoff and I. T. Ivanoff found that 100 c.c. of a sat. soln. of sodium chloride dissolved 0·4 grm. of manganous chloride; and likewise with a

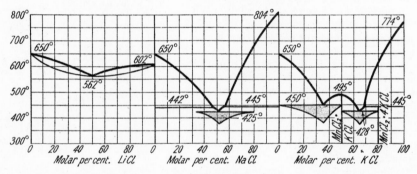

FIG. 65.—The Binary System : $MnCl_2$–LiCl.   FIG. 66.—The Binary System : $MnCl_2$–NaCl.   FIG. 67.—The Binary System : $MnCl_2$–KCl.

sat. soln. of potassium chloride at 18°. C. Sandonnini and G. Scarpa found that with a mixture of potassium and manganous chlorides (Fig. 67) there is formed **potassium manganous trichloride,** $KMnCl_3$, and also $4KCl.MnCl_2$. G. Spacu and L. Canton prepared white crystals of **potassium manganous hexamminotrichloride,** $[Mn(NH_3)_6]Cl_2.KCl$, from $KMnCl_3.2H_2O$ and dry ammonia. They also prepared the pyridine salt, $[Mn(C_5H_3N)_4]Cl_2.KCl$. According to C. E. Saunders, on adding potassium chloride to a hot, aq. soln. of manganous chloride, sufficiently concentrated to deposit crystals on cooling, much alkali chloride is dissolved, and pale pink radiating groups of crystals of a complex salt separate out as the liquid cools. Large crystals can be obtained by the spontaneous evaporation of the soln. The analysis of the salt corresponds with *dihydrated* potassium manganous trichloride, $KCl.MnCl_2.2H_2O$. The deliquescent crystals are triclinic pinacoids which have the axial ratios $a : b : c = 0.4001 : 1 : 0.3767$, and $a = 82° 59'$, $\beta = 112° 41'$, and $\gamma = 90° 53'$. Twinning occurs about the (010)-plane, and the (010)-cleavage is well defined. O. Mügge also examined the crystals which he prepared in an analogous manner. The salt is freely soluble in water, but decomposes into its component salts when the attempt is made to recrystallize it from aq. soln. It is also decomposed by hydrochloric acid, with the deposition of potassium chloride. J. Süss examined the ternary system $KCl-MnCl_2-H_2O$ at different temp., and he obtained for the percentage solubilities :

	MnCl$_2$	KCl	Solid phases
6°	40·23	—	MnCl$_2$.4H$_2$O
	35·94	9·41	MnCl$_2$.4H$_2$O ; KCl ; and KMnCl$_3$.2H$_2$O
	—	23·06	KCl
28·4°	44·46	—	MnCl$_2$.4H$_2$O
	43·28	8·66	MnCl$_2$.4H$_2$O ; and KMnCl$_3$.2H$_2$O
	38·65	13·79	MnCl$_2$.4H$_2$O ; KCl ; and K$_2$MnCl$_4$.2H$_2$O
	—	26·91	KCl
52·8°	50·14	6·01	MnCl$_2$.4H$_2$O ; MnCl$_2$.2H$_2$O ; and KMnCl$_3$.2H$_2$O
62·6°	51·86	—	MnCl$_2$.2H$_2$O
	49·95	6·67	MnCl$_2$.2H$_2$O ; and KMnCl$_3$.2H$_2$O
	44·05	12·49	KMnCl$_3$.2H$_2$O ; and K$_2$MnCl$_4$.2H$_2$O
	36·85	18·77	KMnCl$_3$.2H$_2$O ; and 4KCl.MnCl$_2$
	—	31·57	KCl

The whole of the results are plotted in Fig. 69 ; and the isothermal curve is plotted in Fig. 68. The region of stability of C. E. Saunders' complex salt, KMnCl$_3$.2H$_2$O, is indicated in Figs. 68 and 69. There is a transition temp. at 6° : MnCl$_2$.4H$_2$O, +KCl+Soln.=KMnCl$_3$.2H$_2$O+Soln. Below 6° the system contains MnCl$_2$.4H$_2$O, and above 6° it contains KMnCl$_3$.2H$_2$O ; at 28·4°, **potassium manganous tetrachloride**, K$_2$MnCl$_4$.2H$_2$O, is formed in minute, deliquescent, tetragonal pyramids

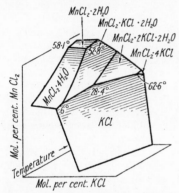

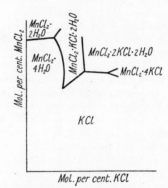

Fig. 68.—The Ternary System :
KCl–MnCl$_2$–H$_2$O.

Fig. 69.—The Ternary System :
KCl–MnCl$_2$–H$_2$O above 63°.

with the axial ratio $a:c=1:0.816$, sp. gr. 2·221, mol. vol. 140·1, and topic axial parameters $\chi=\psi=5.560$ and $\omega=4.531$. There is another transition at 62·6°, when **potassium manganous hexachloride**, 4KCl.MnCl$_2$, is formed (Figs. 68 and 69). The salt appears on C. Sandonnini and G. Scarpa's f.p. diagram, Fig. 67 ; and there is probably also a **sodium manganous hexachloride**, 4NaCl.MnCl$_2$, as indicated in Fig. 66. The potassium salt was reported by H. J. Johnston-Lavis to be a fumarole, or volcanic sublimation product, and was found in some fragmentary material ejected from Vesuvius in April, 1906. It was called **chloromanganokalite**. It appears in palé wine-yellow obtuse rhombohedra, which H. J. Johnston-Lavis and L. J. Spencer represented as hexagonal rhombohedra with the axial ratio $a:c=1:0.5801$. The deliquescent crystals are optically positive, and have a very low birefringence, and a mean refractive index of 1·59. The sp. gr. is 2·31, and the hardness 2·5. A. Lacroix thought that the crystals are pseudo-rhombohedral, and belong to the monoclinic system. J. Süss found the artificial crystals are hexagonal, with the axial ratio $a:c=1:0.594$, the topic axial parameters $\chi=7.808$ and $\omega=4.638$, sp. gr. 2·310, and mol. vol. 183·7.

According to R. Godeffroy, a pale rose-red crystalline powder is formed when a mixed soln. of manganous and rubidium chlorides is treated with conc. hydrochloric acid. The powder was regarded as anhydrous **rubidium manganous tetrachloride**, Rb$_2$MnCl$_4$, and when recrystallized from water it was said to form the trihydrate. C. E. Saunders showed that the analyses were probably made with crystals having mechanically-included water ; and that mixed soln. of the component salts in any proportions furnish crystals of the *dihydrate*, $Rb_2MnCl_4.2H_2O$. Even with a considerable excess of manganous chloride the trichloride, $RbMnCl_3$. $2H_2O$, was not obtained. The tetrachloride forms radiating groups of rose-red elongated, tabular, triclinic crystals. The crystals lose no water over calcium chloride, but all is lost at 110°. The salt is freely soluble in water, forming a neutral soln. R. Godeffroy said that a mixed soln. of cæsium and manganous chlorides deposits crystals of anhydrous **cæsium manganous tetrachloride,** Cs_2MnCl_4, when treated with conc. hydrochloric acid, and that the spontaneous evaporation of the aq. soln. gives the trihydrate, while the spontaneous evaporation of the hydrochloric acid soln. yields the hemipentahydrate. C. E. Saunders found that a mixed soln. of the component salts with an excess of cæsium chloride furnishes the *dihydrate*, $Cs_2MnCl_4.2H_2O$, in pale pink triclinic crystals which are not deliquescent in ordinary air and retain their water of crystallization when dried in a desiccator. The water of crystallization is lost at 105°. C. E. Saunders considers that R. Godeffroy's two hydrates represent the incompletely-dried dihydrate. A mixed soln. of the component salts was found by C. E. Saunders to furnish pale rose-red crystals of **cæsium manganous trichloride,** $CsMnCl_3.2H_2O$. The tabular, rhombic, bipyramidal crystals have the axial ratios $a : b : c = 0.7919 : 1 : 1.2482$, and the cleavage is parallel to the (100)-face. The salt is freely soluble in water, and it can be crystallized from its aq. soln. It loses all its water of crystallization at 105°. The salt is not deliquescent under ordinary conditions, but when powdered it loses water over calcium chloride. E. H. Ducloux discussed the crystals as a means of detecting the salt microscopically.

C. E. Saunders could not prepare **cuprous manganous chloride ;** nor could he obtain **cupric manganous chloride,** but G. André reported **copper manganous trioxydichloride,** as a *trihydrate*, $3CuO.MnCl_2.3H_2O$, to be formed by boiling for many hours freshly-precipitated cupric hydroxide with a soln. of manganous chloride (1:1). The product is washed with cold water, and dried at 100°. A. Werner represented the apple-green product by the formula $Cu_2(OH)_4.Cu(OH).MnCl_2$ with or without a mol. of water. A. Mailhe obtained the *tetrahydrate* by the action of a boiling soln. of manganous chloride on the brown hydrated oxide $4CuO.H_2O$. The green hexagonal plates are not decomposed by water—*vide supra* for $MnOCl_2$. P. A. von Bonsdorff obtained yellow rhombic prisms of **auric manganous octochloride,** $Au_2MnCl_8.8H_2O$, which are isomorphous with the magnesium salt. The octohydrate is stable in air in winter, but deliquescent in air in summer. H. Töpsöe and C. Christiansen obtained triclinic prisms of the *dodecahydrate* isomorphous with the cobalt salt.

C. E. Saunders was unable to prepare compounds of manganous chloride with the alkaline earths. A conc. soln. of mixed manganous and alkaline earth chlorides is green, as in the case of lithium chloride, but on concentration it furnishes only an impure amorphous powder. According to C. Sandonnini, no **calcium manganous chloride** is produced by fusing the component chlorides ; instead, a complete series of solid soln. is formed with a minimum at about 583° and 62 mol. per cent. of $MnCl_2$— Fig. 70. A. Ferrari and A. Inganni found that mixed crystals are formed in all proportions, and they decomposed into their components at 475°. They gave 590° for the eutectic. Similarly with **strontium manganous chloride,** which shows on the thermal diagram, Fig. 71, a minimum at 499° and 45 mol. per cent. $MnCl_2$; but with barium and manganous chlorides there are two breaks on the f.p. curves, Fig. 72— one at 540° and 52 mol. per cent. $MnCl_2$, and another at about 923°. There is a eutectic at 503° and 64 mol. per cent. $MnCl_2$. Hence it is probable that there is a **barium manganous chloride** formed which decomposes when fused. According to C. Sandonnini's f.p. curve for mixtures of manganous and magnesium chlorides, Fig. 73, there is no sign of the formation of **magnesium manganous chloride.** C. E. Saunders found that a mixed soln. of the component chlorides in 70 per cent.

alcohol, on evaporation, gives flattened, feathery crystals of **magnesium manganous hexachloride,** $MgCl_2.2MnCl_2.12H_2O$. The salt is deliquescent in air, and loses some of its water of crystallization over calcium chloride. All the water of crystallization cannot be expelled by heat without decomposition. The crystals were not defined well enough for measurement. B. Gossner obtained the hexachloride $2MgCl_2.MnCl_2.12H_2O$ from a soln. of the two component salts containing an excess

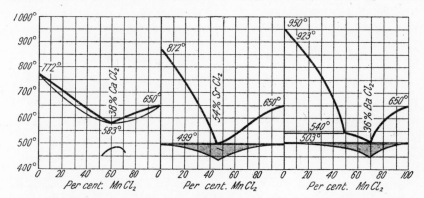

FIG. 70.—Freezing-Point Curve of the System: $CaCl_2$–$MnCl_2$.

FIG. 71.—Freezing-Point Curve of the System: $SrCl_2$–$MnCl_2$.

FIG. 72.—Freezing-Point Curve of the System: $BaCl_2$–$MnCl_2$.

of magnesium chloride. The pale red hexagonal prisms or plates have the axial ratio $a : c = 1 : 1.1649$. There is a cleavage on the (0001)-face. The birefringence is feeble and positive. The sp. gr. is 1·802. C. Sandonnini obtained no evidence of the formation of **zinc manganous chloride** on the f.p. curve, Fig. 74. The curve descends from that of manganous chloride to that of zinc chloride ; and the temp. of the eutectic coincides with the f.p. of zinc chloride. The eutectic temp. decreases

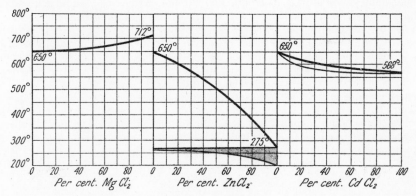

FIG. 73.—Freezing-Point Curve of the System: $MgCl_2$–$MnCl_2$.

FIG. 74.—Freezing-Point Curve of the System: $ZnCl_2$–$MnCl_2$.

FIG. 75.—Freezing-Point Curve of the System: $CdCl_2$–$MnCl_2$.

slightly with increasing amounts of manganous chloride. C. Sandonnini and G. Scarpa found that the f.p. curve of mixtures of cadmium and manganous chlorides, Fig. 75, shows a complete series of solid soln. between the f.p. of the two components. C. von Hauer evaporated spontaneously a conc. soln. of a mol of manganous chloride and 2 mols of cadmium chloride, and obtained rose-red crystals, which after many recrystallizations became almost colourless **cadmium manganous hexachloride,** $2CdCl_2.MnCl_2.12H_2O$. The crystals deliquesce in moist air, and effloresce in dry air ; they form a turbid soln. with hot water ; they lose about 10 mols. of water at 100°, and 2 more at 160°. The crystals melt at a dull red-heat. If a mixture of 2 mols. of manganous chloride and one mol. of cadmium chloride is evaporated, manganous chloride forms the first crop of crystals, and this is followed by the crystallization of the preceding complex salt. P. A. von Bonsdorff evaporated over conc. sulphuric acid a soln. of manganous chloride sat. with mercuric chloride,

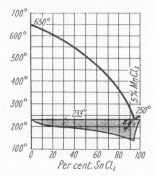

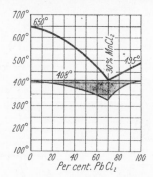

FIG. 76.—Freezing-Point Curve of the System : SnCl₂–MnCl₂.

FIG. 77.—Freezing-Point Curve of the System : PbCl₂–MnCl₂.

and obtained a crop of crystals of mercuric chloride followed by pale red rhombic columns of **mercuric manganous tetrachloride**, $HgCl_2.MnCl_2$. The crystals effloresce over conc. sulphuric acid, and deliquesce in moist air, but they are stable in moderately dry air. R. Varet said that the heat of formation from soln. of the component salts at 18° is 0·96 Cal. ; and for **mercuric manganous hexachloride**, $2HgCl_2.MnCl_2$, 1·12 Cals.

J. Kendall and co-workers observed the possible formation of **aluminium manganous chloride**, $2AlCl_3.MnCl_2$. J. Gewecke evaporated an aq. soln. of a mol of manganous chloride and 2 mols of thallic chloride, and obtained **thallic manganous octochloride**, $2TlCl_3.MnCl_2.6H_2O$, in pale rose-coloured needles, which can be purified by recrystallization. The salt is not formed in acidic soln. S. M. Jörgensen prepared **stannic manganous chloride**, or **manganous chlorostannate**, $MnSnCl_6$. $6H_2O$, by evaporating a mixed soln. of the component salts. The pale red trigonal rhombohedra have the axial ratio $a:c=1:0.5194$, and $a=112°6'$. The (101)-cleavage is marked ; and the optical character is positive. The sp. gr. is 2·215. The crystals deliquesce in moist air, and effloresce in dry air ; they lose water and stannic chloride at 100°. C. Sandonnini and G. Scarpa observed no evidence of the formation of **stannous manganous chloride** on the f.p. curve, Fig. 76 ; there is a eutectic at 233° and 95 mol. per cent. SnCl₂ ; and a similar result was obtained with respect to **lead manganous chloride**, Fig. 77, where the system has a eutectic at 408° and 70 mol. per cent. PbCl₂.

REFERENCES.

¹ J. Davy, Phil. Trans., 102. 169, 1812 ; H. Davy, ib., 101. 385, 1811 ; Elements of Chemical Philosophy, London, 275, 1812 ; J. A. Arfvedson, Afhand. Fys. Kemi Min., 6. 222, 1818 ; Ann. Phil., 7. 267, 1824 ; Schweigger's Journ., 42. 213, 1824 ; Pogg. Ann., 1. 50, 1824 ; C. F. Schönbein, ib., 77. 466, 1848 ; C. Fromherz, ib., 31. 677, 1834 ; Schweigger's Journ., 41. 257, 1824 ; 44. 327, 1825 ; F. von Ittner, Beiträge zur Geschichte der Blausäure, Freiburg, 1809 ; Schweigger's Journ., 24. 395, 1828 ; F. Brandenburg, ib., 14. 336, 1815 ; J. W. Döbereiner, Liebig's Ann., 14. 245, 1835 ; Schweigger's Journ., 63. 482, 1831 ; H. A. von Vogel, ib., 32. 51, 1821 ; A. Vogel, Sitzber. Akad. München, 639, 1860 ; Anz Gehlerte München, 16. 372, 1843 ; N. W. Fischer, Kastner's Arch., 16. 219, 1829 ; C. Hatchett, Ann. Phil., 2. 343, 1813 ; Schweigger's Journ., 14. 332, 1815 ; M. Adam, Tableau minéralogique, Paris, 70, 1869 ; H. Rose, Pogg. Ann., 20. 148, 1830 ; 24. 335, 1832 ; 27. 574, 1833 ; 105. 289, 1858 ; 101. 229, 1857 ; R. Weber, ib., 112. 619, 1861 ; J. Fellenberg, ib., 50. 76, 1840 ; J. Müller, ib., 128. 335, 1866 ; R. T. Simmler, ib., 115. 431, 1862 ; F. Rüdorff, Zeit. angew. Chem., 3. 197, 1890 ; 15. 6, 1902 ; Pogg. Ann., 116. 55, 1862 ;

C. F. Rammelsberg, *ib.*, **42**. 117, 1837 ; **55**. 66, 1842 ; **94**. 507, 1855 ; **128**. 169, 1866 ; **134**. 528, 1868 ; R. Brandes, *ib.*, **20**. 556, 1830 ; **22**. 263, 1831 ; P. A. von Bonsdorff, *ib.*, **17**. 122, 261, 1829 ; F. Wöhler, *ib.*, **41**. 344, 1837 ; *Berzelius' Jahresb.*, **11**. 186, 1832 ; T. J. Pearsall, *Pogg. Ann.*, **25**. 622, 1832 ; *Journ. Roy. Inst.*, **2**. 49, 1831 ; F. W. Krecke, *Journ. prakt. Chem.*, (2), **5**. 105, 1872 ; K. J. Bayer, *ib.*, (2), **5**. 443, 1872 ; J. Everitt, *Phil. Mag.*, (3), **6**. 193, 1835 ; *Journ. prakt. Chem.*, (1), **5**. 33, 1835 ; H. Kolbe, *ib.*, (2), **3**. 405, 1871 ; G. H. Zeller, *ib.*, (1), **5**. 33, 1835 ; *Liebig's Ann.*, **20**. 172, 1836 ; C. von Hauer, *Sitzber. Akad. Wien*, **13**. 331, 453, 1854 ; *Journ. prakt. Chem.*, (1), **63**. 436, 1854 ; T. Curtius and F. Schrader, *ib.*, (2), **50**. 321, 1894 ; M. Holzmann, *ib.*, (1), **75**. 340, 1858 ; E. Lenssen, *ib.*, (1), **80**. 408, 1860 ; C. Rube, *ib.* (1), **94**. 246, 1865 ; J. Wagner, *Zeit. phys. Chem.*, **5**. 38, 1890 ; *Wied. Ann.*, **18**. 273, 1883 ; G. Quincke, *ib.*, **24**. 347, 606, 1885 ; H. Jahn, *ib.*, **43**. 280, 1891 ; *Sitzber. Akad. Berlin*, 237, 1891 ; J. H. Long, *Journ. Amer. Chem. Soc.*, **18**. 120, 1896 ; *Wied. Ann.*, **11**. 37, 1880 ; F. Kohlrausch, *ib.*, **56**. 185, 1895 ; G. Jäger and S. Meyer, *ib.*, **83**. 83, 1897 ; *Sitzber. Akad. Wien*, **106**. 594, 623, 1897 ; **107**. 5, 1898 ; R. Wachsmuth, *Wied. Ann.*, **44**. 377, 1891 ; H. du Bois, *ib.*, **35**. 137, 1888 ; A. Blümcke, *ib.*, **23**. 161, 1884 ; W. Müller-Erzbach, *ib.*, **26**. 409, 1885 ; *Ber.*, **22**. 3181, 1889 ; J. A. Kappers, *Maandbl. Natuurwet.*, **2**. 42, 1871 ; *Ber.*, **5**. 582, 1872 ; P. Jannasch and W. Gottschalk, *ib.*, **37**. 3111, 1904 ; L. Rügheimer and E. Rudolfi, *Liebig's Ann.*, **339**. 297, 311, 1905 ; L. Rügheimer, *Ber.*, **36**. 3033, 1903 ; J. Townsend, *Brit. Pat. No.* 3483. 1874 ; *Ber.*, **9**. 648, 1876 ; E. and B. Klimenko, *ib.*, **29**. 478, 1896 ; *Journ. Russ. Phys. Chem. Soc.*, **27**. 189, 1895 ; A. Pizzi, *Ber.*, **10**. 889, 1877 ; *Gazz. Chim. Ital.*, **7**. 111, 1877 ; A. Ferratini, *ib.*, **42**. i, 138, 1912 ; L. Meyer, *Ber.*, **20**. 3058, 1887 ; J. F. John, *Ann. Phil.*. **2**. 172, 263, 1813 ; **3**. 413, 1813 ; *Gehlen's Journ.*, **3**. 452, 1807 ; **4**. 436, 1804 ; J. L. Proust, *ib.*, **3**. 429, 1807 ; *Ann. Chim. Phys.*, (1), **60**. 185, 225, 1806 ; *Mém. Savans Étrang.*, **1**. 184, 1806 ; B. C. Brodie. *Proc. Roy. Soc.*, **12**. 209, 1862 ; G. Gore, *ib.*, **21**. 828, 1898 ; E. Turner, *Trans. Roy. Soc. Edin.*, **11**. 143, 1831 ; *Phil. Mag.*, (3), **4**. 22, 96, 1828 ; A. Schlesinger, *Repert. Pharm.*, (2), **35**. 74, 1884 ; R. Godeffroy, *Ber.*, **8**. 9, 1875 ; *Arch. Pharm.*, (3), **12**. 47, 1878 ; G. Kassner, *ib.*, (2), **242**. 407, 1904 ; L. R. Ingersoll, *Journ. Amer. Opt. Soc.*, **6**. 663, 1922 ; A. Werner, *Ber.*, **40**. 4444, 1908 ; F. Ephraim, *ib.*, **45**. 1322, 1912 ; *Zeit. phys. Chem.*, **81**. 513, 1913 ; *Helvetica Chim. Acta*, **7**. 298, 1924 ; N. Isgarischeff and S. Schapiro, *Zeit. phys. Chem.*, **131**. 442, 1928 ; P. Drude and W. Nernst, *ib.*, **15**. 79, 1894 ; V. Polowzoff, *ib.*, **75**. 513, 1911 ; E. Borsbach, *Ber.*, **23**. 431, 1890 ; W. Meyeringh, *ib.*, **10**. 1946, 1877 ; W. Feldt, *ib.*, **27**. 405, 1894 ; A. Naumann, *ib.*, **42**. 3790, 1909 ; **43**. 314, 1910 ; **47**. 1369, 1914 ; H. Kämmerer, *ib.*, **4**. 218, 1871 ; E. Riley, *ib.*, **10**. 911, 1877 ; *Journ. Chem. Soc.*, **31**. 1, 1877 ; *Journ. Iron Steel Inst.*, **7**. 52, 1877 ; A. Rosenheim and V. J. Meyer, *Zeit. anorg. Chem.*, **49**. 13, 1906 ; W. Herz, *ib.*, **22**. 279, 1899 ; **175**. 245, 1928 ; L. Pincussohn, *ib.*, **14**. 388, 1897 ; F. Reitzenstein, *ib.*, **18**. 253, 1898 ; H. Saslawsky, *ib.*, **146**. 315, 1925 ; H. Franzen and O. von Mayer, *ib.*, **60**. 247, 1909 ; R. F. Weinland and F. Schlegelmilch, *ib.*, **30**. 139, 1902 ; P. Walden, *ib.*, **29**. 371, 1902 ; W. Peters, *ib.*, **77**. 137, 1912 ; *Ber.*, **42**. 4826, 1909 ; W. Prandtl, *ib.*, **49**. 1613, 1916 ; R. Müller, *ib.*, **142**. 130, 1925 ; O. Mügge, *Neues Jahrb. Min.*, ii, 91, 1892 ; E. Rousseau, *Compt. Rend. Soc. Biol.*, **91**. 1009, 1924 ; *Brit. Pat. No.* 226534, 1924 ; E. Donath, *Dingler's Journ.*, **229**. 542, 1878 ; N. de Kolossowsky, *Journ. Chim. Phys.*, **22**. 224, 1925 ; B. Gossner, *Zeit. Kryst.*, **38**. 501, 1903 ; N. Pfanner, *Ueber die Einwirkung von metallischem Mangan auf Hydroxylaminsalze*, Erlangen, 1912 ; H. P. Cady and R. Taft, *Journ. Phys. Chem.*, **29**. 1057, 1925 ; E. N. Gapon, *Journ. Chim. Phys.*, **25**. 154, 1928 ; A. R. Leeds, *Journ. Amer. Chem. Soc.*, **3**. 112, 1882 ; E. H. Miller and J. A. Mathews, *ib.*, **22**. 62, 1900 ; R. B. Moore and J. Miller, *ib.*, **30**. 593, 1908 ; J. G. Hibbs and E. F. Smith, *ib.*, **16**. 822, 1894 ; A. W. Ralston and J. A. Wilkinson, *ib.*, **50**. 358, 1928 ; P. Théodoridès, *Arch. Sciences Genève*, (5), **3**. 161, 1921 ; *Journ. Phys. Rad.*, (6), **3**. 1, 1922 ; *Compt. Rend.*, **171**. 948, 1920 ; V. C. Butureanu, *Ann. Scient. Univ.*, Jassy, **7**. 179, 1912 ; C. J. W. Grieveson, *Phil. Mag.*, (6), **49**. 1006, 1925 ; H. W. Fischer, *Untersuchungen über Metallhydroxyde*, Breslau, 1907 ; W. Ipatieff and W. Kisseleff, *Journ. Russ. Phys. Chem. Soc.*, **58**. 686, 1926 ; M. Faraday, *Journ. Science Arts*, **6**. 358, 1819 ; H. Lessheim, J. Meyer and R. Samuel, *Zeit. Physik*, **43**. 199, 1927 ; S. Aoyama, K. Kimura and Y. Nishina, *ib.*, **44**. 810, 1927 ; H. Kwasnick, *Arch. Pharm.*, (2), **229**. 573, 1891 ; L. L. de Koninck, *Bull. Assoc. Belg. Chim.*, **16**. 94, 1902 ; R. Phillips, *Phil. Mag.*, (2), **5**. 209, 1862 ; J. Süss, *Krystallization gemischter Lösungen von Manganchlorür und Kaliumchlorid*, Leipzig, 1912 ; *Zeit. Kryst.*, **51**. 252, 1912 ; H. Töpsöe in L. Gmelin and C. Kraut, *Handbuch der anorganischen Chemie*, Heidelberg, **5**. ii, 319, 1914 ; F. Müller, *Jahrb. Phil. Fac. Univ. Bern*, **2**. 80, 1922 ; C. H. Pfaff, *Handbuch der analytischen Chemie*, Altona, **2**. 400, 1821 ; J. Thomsen, *Thermochemische Untersuchungen*, Leipzig, **3**. 270, 1883 ; L. Gmelin, *Handbook of Chemistry*, London, **4**. 227, 1850 ; P. Kutznetzoff, *Journ. Russ. Phys. Chem. Soc.*, **30**. 741, 1898 ; **41**. 353, 1909 ; *Ann. Chim. Phys.*, (8), **18**. 214, 1909 ; A. J. Balard, *ib.*, (2), **57**. 225, 1834 ; G. Tammann, *Mém. Acad. St. Petersburg*, (7), **35**. 9, 1887 ; *Zeit. anorg. Chem.*, **174**. 231, 1928 ; T. W. Richards and B. Churchill, *Zeit. phys. Chem.*, **28**. 313, 1899 ; T. W. Richards and F. Wrede, *ib.*, **61**. 313, 1907 ; H. M. Dawson and P. Williams, *Journ. Phys. Chem.*, **4**. 370, 1900 ; *Zeit. phys. Chem.*, **31**. 59, 1899 ; W. Stortenbeker, *ib.*, **16**. 250, 1895 ; L. Bruner, *ib.*, **32**. 133, 1900 ; M. Goldstein, *ib.*, **5**. 239, 1890 ; H. Ley, *ib.*, **30**. 242, 1899 ; W. Bein, *ib.*, **27**. 42, 1898 ; E. Rimbach and K. Weitzel, *ib.*, **79**. 279, 1912 ; G. Hüfner, *ib.*, **59**. 416, 1907 ; F. L. Usher, *ib.*, **62**. 622, 1908 ; J. Spohr, *ib.*, **2**. 199, 1888 ; C. Kullgren, *ib.*, **41**. 407, 1902 ; W. Ostwald, *ib.*, **2**. 145, 1888 ; J. Krutwig, *ib.*, **2**. 794, 1888 ; W. P. Jorissen and L. T. Reicher, *ib.*, **31**. 142, 1899 ; F. W. O. de Coninck, *Bull. Acad. Belg.*, 730, 1902 ; 360, 1904 ; G. T. Gerlach, *Zeit. anal. Chem.*, **28**. 476, 1889 ; E. Dèniges, *ib.*, **31**. 316, 1892 ; C. Luckow, *ib.*, **8**. 24, 1869 ; **19**. 1, 1880 ; A. Brand, *ib.*, **23**. 581, 1884 ; L. Schucht, *ib.*, **22**. 492, 1883 ;

C. R. Fresenius, *ib.*, **11**. 414, 295, 1872 ; *Journ. prakt. Chem.*, (1), **82**. 267, 1872 ; J. Haidlen and
C. R. Fresénius, *Liebig's Ann.*, **43**. 132, 1842 ; J. H. Eaton and R. Fittig, *ib.*, **145**. 157, 1868 ;
F. J. Otto, *ib.*, **42**. 348, 1842 ; A. Classen, *Zeit. Elektrochem.*, **1**. 290, 1895 ; *Zeit. anal. Chem.*, **8**.
370, 1869 ; **16**. 315, 417, 1877 ; **18**. 175, 1879 ; L. Blum, *ib.*, **25**. 519, 1886 ; P. Waage, *ib.*, **10**.
206, 1871 ; *Forh. Vid. Selsk. Christiania*, **12**. 360, 1870 ; H. Goldschmidt and K. L. Syngros,
Zeit. anorg. Chem., **5**. 139, 1894 ; F. W. Skirrow, *ib.*, **33**. 25, 1902 ; A. Piccini, *ib.*, **20**. 12, 1890 ;
S. Motylewsky, *ib.*, **38**. 410, 1904 ; I. Traube, *ib.*, **8**. 34. 1895 ; O. von Mayer, *Ueber Hydrazin-
verbindungen verschiedener Metallsalze*, Heidelberg, 1907 ; J. Hoffmann, *Zeit. anorg. Chem.*, **29**.
127, 1908 ; **66**. 361, 1910 : G. P. Baxter and M. A. Hines, *ib.*, **51**. 202, 1906 ; *Journ. Amer.
Chem. Soc.*, **28**. 1560, 1906 ; L. Kahlenberg, D. J. Davis and R. E. Fowler, *ib.*, **21**. 1, 1899 ;
A. B. Lamb and R. E. Lee, *ib.*, **35**. 1667, 1913 ; F. Allison and E. J. Murphy, *ib.*, **52**. 3796, 1930 ;
S. U. Pickering, *Journ. Chem. Soc.*, **35**. 672, 1879 ; E. M. Farrer and S. U. Pickering, *Chem. News*,
53. 279, 1886 ; H. Brearley, *ib.*, **77**. 131, 1898 ; S. Kern, *ib.*, **33**. 236, 1876 ; A. H. Allen, *ib.*,
23. 290, 1871 ; C. N. Draper, *ib.*, **51**. 226, 1885 ; S. M. Deane, *ib.*, **51**. 164, 248, 1885 ; L. Crismer,
Pharm. Centrh., **32**. 438, 1891 ; K. Reithner, *Viertel. prakt. Pharm.*, **4**. 377, 1855 ; H. Kunheim,
Ueber die Einwirkung des Wasserdampfes auf Chlormetalle bei hoher Temperatur, Göttingen, 1861 ;
J. Schwerdtfeger, *Neues Jahrb. Pharm.*, **2**. 18, 30, 1864 ; A. M. B. Burin de Buisson, *Journ.
Pharm. Chim.*, (3), **28**. 345, 1855 ; G. Spacu and L. Canton, *Bull. Soc. Stiinte Cluj*, **2**. 29, 1924 ;
J. J. Berzelius, *Ars. Fysik Kemi*, **11**. 146, 1832 ; *Pogg. Ann.*, **1**. 197, 1824 ; H. F. Gaultier de
Claubry, *Bull. Soc. Enc. Nat. Ind.*, (2), **57**. 633. 1858 ; T. Graham, *Phil. Trans.*, **127**. 47, 1837 ;
Liebig's Ann., **29**. 1, 1839 ; J. C. Graham, *Zeit. phys. Chem.*, **50**. 257, 1904 ; **59**. 691, 1907 ;
A. Scacchi, *Atti Accad. Napoli*, **6**. 9, 1874 ; *Memoria sullo incendio vesuviano del mese di maggio
1855*, Napoli, 181, 1855 ; L. Palmieri, *Rend. Accad. Napoli*, **12**. 92, 1873 ; T. Monticelli and
N. Covelli, *Storia dei fenomeni del Vesuvio avvenuti negli anni 1821, 1822 e parte del 1823*, Napoli,
1823 ; *Prodromo della mineralogia vesuviana*, Napoli, 1825 ; B. D. Steele, D. McIntosh and
E. H. Archibald, *Phil. Trans.*, **205**. A, 99, 1906 ; *Zeit. phys. Chem.*, **55**. 129, 1906 ; B. Köhnlein,
Liebig's Ann., **225**. 171, 1885 ; C. Sandonnini, *Atti Accad. Lincei*, (5), **20**. i, 457, 1911 ; (5), **20**.
ii, 496, 646, 1911 ; (5), **21**. i, 208, 1912 ; (5), **21**. ii, 529, 1912 ; C. Sandonnini and G. Scarpa,
ib., (5), **20**. ii, 61, 1911 ; (5), **22**. 163, 1913 ; G. Bruni and A. Ferrari, *ib.*, (6), **4**. 10, 1926 ; *Zeit.
phys. Chem.*, **130**. 488, 1927 ; G. A. Barbieri and F. Calzolari, *Atti Accad. Lincei*, (5), **19**. ii,
584, 1910 ; A. Sella, *Mem. Accad. Lincei*, **4**. 455, 1887 ; G. Barbieri, *Gazz. Chim. Ital.*, **53**. 645,
1923 ; C. E. Rice, *Journ. Chem. Soc.*, **73**. 258, 1898 ; *Proc. Chem. Soc.*, **14**. 53, 1898 ; *Chem. News*,
77. 125, 1898 ; O. Gossmann, *Zeit. Physik*, **22**. 273, 1924 ; W. E. Garner and D. N. Jackson, *Journ.
Chem. Soc.*, **121**. 1298, 1922 ; F. P. Venable and D. H. Jackson, *Journ. Elisha Mitchell Scient.
Soc.*, **35**. 87, 1920 ; I. F. Hoffmann, *Woch. Brauerei*, **23**. 464, 1906 ; A. Lacroix, *Compt. Rend.*,
142. 1249, 1906 : *Bull. Soc. Min.*, **30**. 219, 1907 ; C. G. Maier, *Tech. Paper U.S. Bur. Mines*,
360, 1925 ; G. Falckenberg, *Zeit. Physik*, **5**. 201, 1921 ; O. Kühling, *Zeit. angew. Chem.*, **16**.
1145, 1903 ; G. Beck, *Zeit. anorg. Chem.*, **156**. 288, 1926 ; **182**. 332, 1929 ; A. Heydweiller, *ib.*,
116. 42, 1921 ; *Ann. Physik*, (4), **12**. 608, 1903 ; E. H. Ducloux, *Anal. Assoc. Quim. Argentina*,
9. 215, 1921 ; *Mikrochemie*, **2**. 108, 1924 ; H. Sentis, *Journ. Phys.*, (3), **6**. 183, 1897 ; *Ann.
Univ. Grenoble*, **9**. 1, 1897 ; A. D. Brokaw, *Journ. Ind. Eng. Chem.*, **5**. 560, 1913 ; A. Baladin,
Zeit. phys. Chem., **121**. 299, 1926 ; O. Stelling, *ib.*, **117**. 161, 1925 ; N. Schiloff and S. Pewsner,
ib., **118**. 361, 1926 ; C. Sheard and C. S. Morris, *Ohio Journ. Science*, **16**. 113, 1916 ; A. N. Camp-
bell, *Journ. Chem. Soc.*, 653, 1928 ; E. Frei, *Ueber das Verhalten der Manganosalze an der
Anode*, Giessen, 1901 ; E. P. y Alvarez, *Ann. Chim. Anal. Appl.*, **11**. 401, 1906 ; *Atti Congresso
Internaz. Chim. Appl.*, **6**. xi, 434, 1906 ; *Chem. News*, **94**. 269, 1906 ; G. D. van Arsdale and
C. G. Maier, *Trans. Amer. Electrochem. Soc.*, **33**. 109, 1918 ; R. Müller, R. Hönig and A. Konet-
schmigg, *Monatsh.*, **44**. 237, 1924 ; J. B. A. Dumas, *Quart. Journ. Science*, **2**. 475, 1827 ; *Ann.
Chim. Phys.*, (2), **36**. 82, 1827 ; P. Berthier, *ib.*, (3), **7**. 74, 1843 ; A. Günther-Schulze, *Zeit.
Elektrochem.*, **28**. 387, 1922 ; G. Rosenthal, *Dingler's Journ.*, **225**. 154, 1877 ; *Chem. News*, **36**.
147, 1877 ; H. W. Deacon, *ib.*, **22**. 157, 1870 ; *Brit. Pat. No.* 1403, 1868 ; *Journ. Chem. Soc.*, **10**.
725, 1872 ; F. Stromeyer, *Schweigger's Journ.*, **21**. 223, 1817 ; B. Cabrera and A. Duperior,
Journ. Phys. Rad., (6), **6**. 121, 1925 ; L. E. Rivot, F. S. Beudant, and P. A. Daguin, *Ann. Mines*,
(5), **4**. 221, 1853 ; J. Schiel, *Amer. Journ. Science*, (2), **15**. 275, 1853 ; O. W. Gibbs, *ib.*, (2),
37. 346, 1864 ; (2), **44**. 213, 1867 ; J. T. Norton, *ib.*, (4), **12**. 115, 1901 ; *Zeit. anorg. Chem.*,
28. 223, 1901 ; T. T. Morrell, *Amer. Chem.*, **5**. 213, 1874 ; H. Tamm, *ib.*, **3**. 145, 1872 ; D. Vitali,
Boll. Chim. Farm., **37**. 545, 1898 ; K. Fajans, *Zeit. Physik*, **50**. 531, 1928 ; J. F. Simon, *Repert.
Pharm.*, **65**. 208, 1831 ; C. H. D. Bödeker, *Die Beziehungen zwischen Dichte und Zusammensetzung bei festen und liquiden Stoffen*, Leipzig, 1860 ; H. G. F. Schröder, *Dichtigkeitsmessungen*,
Heidelberg, 1873 ; *Liebig's Ann.*, **174**. 249, 1874 ; F. Kuhlmann, *Ueber die Einwirkung des
Wasserdampfs auf Chlormetalle bei hoher Temperatur*, Göttingen, 1861 ; *Compt. Rend.*, **55**. 246,
1862 ; G. André, *ib.*, **106**. 855, 1888 ; F. Bourion, *ib.*, **134**. 555, 1902 ; E. Darmois, *ib.*, **184**. 1239,
1927 ; L. P. de St. Gilles, *ib.*, **55**. 329, 1862 ; H. Pélabon and M. Delwaulle, *Bull. Soc. Chim.*,
(4), **47**. 156, 1930 ; M. Berthelot, *Thermochimie*, Paris, **2**. 268, 1897 ; *Compt. Rend.*, **86**. 628,
1878 ; **93**. 757, 1881 ; **109**. 548, 1889 ; A. Gorgeu, *Journ. Pharm. Chim.*, (3), **37**. 253, 1860 ;
Ann. Chim. Phys., (3), **42**. 70, 1853 ; (6), **19**. 543, 1890 ; *Bull. Soc. Chim.*, (2), **49**. 668, 1888 ;
Compt. Rend., **94**. 1425, 1882 ; **97**. 1303, 1883 ; **106**. 703, 743, 1888 ; N. A. E. Millon, *Ann. Chim.
Phys.*, (3), **29**. 506, 1850 ; *Compt. Rend.*, **28**. 42, 1849 ; L. Maquenne, *ib.*, **94**. 795, 1882 ;
A. Mailfert, *ib.*, **94**. 860, 1186, 1882 ; V. Thomas and P. Dupuis, *ib.*, **143**. 282, 1906 ; J. Personne,
ib., **51**. 214, 1860 ; C. A. Valson, *ib.*, **74**. 103, 1872 ; E. Fouard, *ib.*, **142**. 796, 1906 ; A. Étard,

Ann. Chim. Phys., (7), **2**. 537, 1894 ; *Compt. Rend.*, **98**. 993, 1884 ; P. de Clérmont and H. Guyot, *ib.*, **85**. 37, 1877 ; H. Moissan, *ib.*, **130**. 622, 1900 ; L. C. de Cöppet, *ib.*, **132**. 219, 1901 ; *Ann. Chim. Phys.*, (4), **24**. 526, 1871 ; A. Terreil, *Compt. Rend.*, **45**. 652, 1857 ; *Bull. Soc. Chim.*, (2), **21**. 289, 1874 ; A. Trillat, *Compt. Rend.*, **136**. 1205, 1903 ; **137**. 922, 1903 ; **138**. 94, 274, 1904 ; L. C. A. Barreswil, *ib.*, **44**. 677, 1857 ; J. R. Mourelo, *ib.*, **128**. 1239, 1899 ; L. de Boisbaudran, *ib.*, **103**. 468, 1069, 1886 ; **104**. 1680, 1887 ; **105**. 45, 206, 1228, 1887 ; **106**. 452, 1781, 1888 ; **107**. 311, 1888 ; R. Varet, *ib.*, **123**. 422, 1896 ; A. Villiers, *ib.*, **124**. 1349, 1897 ; *Bull. Soc. Chim.*, (3), **17**. 675, 1897 ; H. W. F. Wackenroder, *Brandes' Arch.*, **16**. 114, 1825 ; J. Lefort and P. Thibault, *Pharm. Journ.*, (3), **13**. 301, 1882 ; H. How, *Chem. News*, **19**. 137, 1869 ; K. Jellinek and R. Ulroth, *Zeit. phys. Chem.*, **119**. 161, 1926 ; A. V. Harcourt, *Journ. Chem. Soc.*, **20**. 470, 1865 ; A. V. Harcourt and W. Esson, *Chem. News*, **10**. 171, 1864 ; *B.A. Rep.*, 29, 1865 ; *Proc. Roy. Soc.*, **14**. 470, 1865 ; *Phil. Trans.*, **156**. 193, 1866 ; **157**. 117, 1867 ; **186**. 817, 1895 ; H. Grossmann and B. Schück, *Zeit. anorg. Chem.*, **50**. 21, 1906 ; *Chem. Ztg.*, **30**. 1205, 1907 ; O. T. Christensen, *ib.*, **20**. 154, 1896 ; *Overs. Danske Vid. Selsk. Forh.*, 94, 1896 ; E. Wedekind, *Phys. Zeit.*, **7**. 805, 1907 ; *Ber. deut. phys. Ges.*, **4**. 412, 1907 ; B. Cabrera, E. Moles and M. Marquina, *Anal. Fis. Quim.*, **13**. 256, 1915 ; A. Duperior, *ib.*, **22**. 383, 1924 ; F. Ephraim and O. Schütz, *Helvetica Chim. Acta*, **9**. 914, 922, 1926 ; S. Kato, *Science Papers Phys. Chem. Research Tokyo*, **13**. 7, 49, 1930 ; W. L. Rolton and R. S. Troop, *Proc. Phys. Soc.*, **36**. 205, 1924 ; O. Liebknecht, *Ber.*, **33**. 443, 1900 ; *Ann. Physik*, (4), **1**. 178, 1900 ; O. Liebknecht and A. P. Wills, *Ber.*, **33**. 443, 1900 ; G. Piaggesi, *Nuovo Cimento*, (2), **4**. 247, 1903 ; G. Wiedemann, *Die Lehre von der Elektricität*, Braunschweig, **3**. 961, 1895 ; F. Auerbach in A. Winkelmann, *Handbuch der Physik*, Leipzig, **5**. ii, 227, 1905 ; P. Pascal, *Ann. Chim. Phys.*, (8), **16**. 359, 520, 1909 ; V. Klatt and P. Lenard, *Wied. Ann.*, **38**. 90, 1889 ; O. C. Magistad, *Tech. Bull. Arizona Agric. Exp. Station*, **18**. 445, 1928 ; H. J. Johnston-Lavis, *Nature*, **74**. 103, 1906 ; H. J. Johnston-Lavis and L. J. Spencer, *Min. Mag.*, **15**. 54, 1908 ; R. Robl, *Zeit. angew. Chem.*, **39**. 608, 1926 ; S. M. Jörgensen, *Danske Vid. Selsk. Forh.*, 6, 1865 ; F. Dreyer, *The Temperature of the Maximum Density of Water*, St. Petersburg, 193, 1913 ; R. H. Brett, *Phil. Mag.*, (3), **10**. 95, 1837 ; E. P. Lewis, *Phys. Rev.*, (2), **21**. 713, 1923 ; A. Johnsen, *Neues Jahrb. Min.*, ii, 93, 1903 ; S. Hakomori, *Science Rep. Tohoku Univ.*, **16**. 841, 1927 ; O. Lehmann, *Zeit. Kryst.*, **8**. 445, 1883 ; G. L. Clark, *Amer. Journ. Science*, (5), **7**. 1, 1924 ; W. Althammer, *Ueber die Beweglichkeiten der Ionen ternärer Elektrolyte*, Halle, 1913 ; W. Sander, *Ueber Mangankatalyse bei der Einwirkung von Natriumoxalat auf Quecksilber(II)-Chlorid*, Erlangen, 1930 ; J. Pelouze, *Ann. Chim. Phys.*, (3), **7**. 176, 1843 ; G. Barbieri, *Gazz. Chim. Ital.*, **53**. 645, 1923 ; R. Kuhn and K. Meyer, *Naturwiss.*, **16**. 1028, 1928 ; H. W. Foote and B. Saxton, *Journ. Amer. Chem. Soc.*, **36**. 1695, 1914 ; W. Smith, *Chem. News*, **128**. 1, 1924 ; H. N. Warren, *ib.*, **55**. 156, 1887 ; W. Biltz and G. F. Hüttig, *Zeit. anorg. Chem.*, **109**. 89, 1919 ; W. Biltz, *Ber.*, **37**. 3036, 1904 ; *Zeit. Elektrochem.*, **29**. 348, 1923 ; *Zeit. phys. Chem.*, **40**. 185, 1892 ; *Zeit. anorg. Chem.*, **130**. 93, 1923 ; **193**. 321, 1930 ; W. Biltz, K. A. Klatte and E. Rahlfs, *ib.*, **149**. 339, 1927 ; W. Biltz and E. Rahlfs, *ib.*, **149**. 145, 1925 ; **166**. 351, 1927 ; J. Meyer and R. Nerlich, *ib.*, **116**. 117, 1921 ; W. Biltz and E. Birk, *ib.*, **134**. 125, 1924 ; R. Ulroth, *Ueber die Chlortensionen von Metallchloriden und die chemischen Konstanten*, Leipzig, 1926 ; K. Jellinek and G. von Podjasky, *Zeit. anorg. Chem.*, **171**. 261, 1928 ; K. Jellinek and L. Zucker, *ib.*, **171**. 271, 1928 ; K. Jellinek and A. Rudat, *ib.*, **143**. 244, 1929 ; K. Jellinek and R. Koop, *ib.*, **145**. 305, 1929 ; A. Hantzsch and H. Carlsohn, *ib.*, **160**. 5, 1927 ; J. Meyer and W. Gulbins, *ib.*, **155**. 66, 1926 ; S. Orlowsky, *ib.*, **170**. 184, 1928 ; O. Ruff and B. Hirsch, *ib.*, **146**. 388, 1925 ; R. Lang, *ib.*, **170**. 387, 1928 ; R. Lang and J. Zwerina, *ib.*, **170**. 389, 1928 ; J. Zwerina, *Ueber einige Arsenitmethoden, insbesondere unter Anwendung der Mangansalz- und Jodkatalyse*, Brünn, 1927 ; V. Lenher, *Journ. Amer. Chem. Soc.*, **38**. 638, 1916 ; A. C. Robertson, *ib.*, **49**. 1630, 1927 ; M. Sem, *Ueber die Elektrooxydation von Manganosalzen in sauren Lösungen und einige dabei erhaltene Verbindungen*, Darmstadt, 1914 ; *Zeit. Elektrochem.*, **21**. 426, 1915 ; **23**. 98, 1917 ; W. Klemm, *ib.*, **36**. 704, 1930 ; *Zeit. phys. Chem.*, **12**. B, 1, 1931 ; A. Ditte, *Compt. Rend.*, **92**. 353, 1881 ; *Ann. Chim. Phys.*, (5), **22**. 251, 1882 ; J. J. Ebelmen, *ib.*, (3), **25**. 92, 1849 ; *Bull. Soc. Chim.*, (3), **11**. 853, 1894 ; *Ann. Chim. Phys.*, (6), **19**. 543, 1890 ; (7), **2**. 78, 1893 ; A. Sobrero and F. Selmi, *Ann. Fis. Chim.*, **1**. 40, 1850 ; *Mem. Accad. Torino*, **11**. 345, 1851 ; *Ann. Chim. Phys.*, (3), **29**. 161, 1850 ; E. Bouty, *ib.*, (6), **3**. 446, 1884 ; A. C. Becquerel, *ib.*, (2), **43**. 380, 1830 ; *Mém. Inst.*, **10**. 286, 1831 ; J. C. G. de Marignac, *Arch. Science Genève*, (2), **55**. 113, 1858 ; *Ann. Mines*, (5), **12**. 5, 1857 ; *Ann. Chim. Phys.*, (3), **60**. 288, 1860 ; A. Chassevant, *ib.*, (6), **30**. 5, 1893 ; H. Töpsöe and C. Christensen, *ib.*, (5), **1**. 25, 1874 ; *Skrift. Nat. Selsb. Kjöbenhavn*, **9**. 621, 1873 ; J. Dewar and A. Scott, *B.A. Rep.*, 597, 1881 ; *Proc. Roy. Soc.*, **35**. 44, 1883 ; *Chem. News*, **47**. 98, 1883 ; W. Weldon, *ib.*, **20**. 109, 1869 ; *B.A. Rep.*, 79, 1869 ; *Brit. Pat. No.* 2389, 1871 ; 317, 2044, 1872 ; *Laboratory*, **1**. 445, 1867 ; *Dingler's Journ.*, **201**. 354, 1871 ; *Ber.*, **8**. 168, 1875 ; *Monit. Scient.*, (3), **4**. 891, 1874 ; N. Castoro, *Gazz. Chim. Ital.*, **28**. ii, 317, 1898 ; G. Devoto and A. Guzzi, *ib.*, **59**. 591, 1929 ; R. Salvadori, *ib.*, **26**. i, 250, 1896 ; M. G. Levi and V. Bettoni, *ib.*, **35**. i, 320, 1905 ; M. G. Levi and F. Ageno, *ib.*, **37**. i, 368, 1907 ; *Atti Accad. Lincei*, (5), **15**. ii, 615, 1906 ; C. R. A. Wright and A. E. Menke, *Journ. Chem. Soc.*, **37**. 28, 1880 ; J. J. Sudborough, *ib.*, **59**. 655, 1891 ; J. B. Hannay, *ib.*, **33**. 269, 1878 ; J. Spiller, *ib.*, **10**. 110, 1857 ; B. E. Dixon and J. L. White, *ib.*, 1469, 1927 ; F. W. J. Clendinnen and A. C. D. Rivett, *ib.*, **119**. 1329, 1921 ; **123**. 1344, 1634, 1923 ; P. Sabatier, *Bull. Soc. Chim.*, (3), **1**. 88, 1889 ; (3), **11**. 547, 1894 ; A. Mailhe, *ib.*, (3), **27**. 167, 1902 ; *Ann. Chim. Phys.*, (7), **27**. 382, 1902 ; *Compt. Rend.*, **132**. 1560, 1901 ; **133**. 126, 1901 ; A. Riche, *ib.*, **85**. 226, 1877 ;

Bull. Soc. Chim., (2), **29**. 378, 1878 ; C. Vincent, *ib.*, (2), **33**. 156, 1880 ; J. H. Kastle, *Amer. Chem. Journ.*, **23**. 500, 1900 ; C. E. Saunders, *ib.*, **14**. 127, 1892 ; S. R. Benedict, *ib.*, **34**. 581, 1906 ; H. C. Jones and H. P. Bassett, *ib.*, **33**. 560, 1905 ; H. C. Jones and V. J. Chambers, *ib.*, **23**. 89, 1900 ; E. C. Franklin and C. A. Kraus, *ib.*, **20**. 828, 1898 ; H. C. Jones and F. H. Getman, *ib.*, **31**. 303, 1904 ; H. C. Jones and A. P. West, *ib.*, **34**. 357, 1905 ; **44**. 508, 1910 ; H. C. Jones, *Ber.*, **37**. 1511, 1904 ; H. C. Jones and W. R. Veazey, *Zeit. phys. Chem.*, **61**. 698, 1908 ; E. Grave, *ib.*, **177**. 513, 1911 ; B. Neumann, *ib.*, **14**. 217, 1894 ; G. Bruni and A. Manuelli, *Zeit. Elektrochem.*, **10**. 601, 1904 ; A. Classen and M. A. von Reis, *Ber.*, **14**. 1626, 1881 ; C. Engels, *Zeit. Elektrochem.*, **2**. 416, 1896 ; **3**. 306, 1897 ; J. Köster, *ib.*, **10**. 553, 1904 ; C. N. Otin, *ib.*, **15**. 386, 1909 ; Badische Anilin- und Sodafabrik, *ib.*, **11**. 853, 1905 ; *German Pat.*, *D.R.P.* 163813, 1905 ; K. Elbs, *Zeit. anorg. Chem.*, **16**. 290, 1903 ; *Zeit. Elektrochem.*, **7**. 260, 1901 ; K. Seubert and A. Schmidt, *Liebig's Ann.*, **267**. 218, 1892 ; J. Volhard, *ib.*, **198**. 332, 1879 ; G. C. Gibson, J. O. Driscoll and W. J. Jones, *Journ. Chem. Soc.*, 1440, 1929 ; J. von Koczkes, *Zeit. Physik*, **59**. 278, 1930 ; L. Pauling, *Proc. Nat. Acad.*, **15**. 709, 1929 ; J. Aharoni, *Magnetische Untersuchungen bei tiefen Temperaturen*, Leipzig, 1929 ; K. Fredenhagen, *Zeit. Elektrcchem.*, **37**. 684, 1931 ; K. Fredenhagen and G. Cadenbach, *Zeit. phys. Chem.*, **146**. 245, 1930 ; H. Piepenstock, *Ueber Oberflächenspannung wässriger Lösungen*, Münster, 1908 ; W. H. Whatmough, *Zeit. phys. Chem.*, **39**. 129, 1901 ; O. Wylach, *Untersuchungen über die Magnetisierungszahlen von Eisen und Mangansalzen*, Barmen, 1905 ; A. Ferrari and A. Inganni, *Atti Accad. Lincei*, (6), **10**. 253, 1929 ; A. Ferrari, *Atti Congresso Chim. Pura Applicata*, **3**. 449, 452, 1930 ; J. Perreu, *Compt. Rend.*, **190**. 52, 1930 ; G. Scagliarini and G. Tartarini, *Atti Accad. Lincei*, (6), **10**. 267, 1929 ; P. Krishnamurti, *Indian Journ. Phys.*, **5**. 113, 1930 ; S. Freed and C. Kasper, *Journ. Amer. Chem. Soc.*, **52**. 2632, 1930 ; A. F. Rogers, *Amer. Min.*, **9**. 66, 1924 ; *Amer. Journ. Science*, (5), **8**. 145, 1924 ; F. J. Garrick, *Phil. Mag.*, (7), **11**. 741, 1931 ; I. Iitaka, *Proc. Japan. Acad.*, **6**. 363, 1930 ; G. Devoto, *Atti Congresso Chim. Pura Applicata*, **3**. 322, 1930 ; W. Sucksmith, *Phil. Mag.*, (7), **8**. 158, 1929 ; T. Ishiwara, *Science Rep. Tohoku Univ.*, **3**. 243, 1915 ; K. Honda and T. Ishiwara, *ib.*, **4**. 215, 1916 ; A. Voelcker, *Scheik. Onderzoek Utrecht*, **3**. 526, 1846 ; *Liebig's Ann.*, **59**. 27, 1846 ; O. Hautz, *ib.*, **66**. 280, 1848 ; J. Gewecke, *ib.*, **36**. 217, 1909 ; H. Schiff, *ib.*, **118**. 365, 1861 ; **131**. 112, 1864 ; O. Brunck, *ib.*, **336**. 281, 1905 ; S. S. Bhatnagar, K. N. Mathur and P. L. Lapur, *Indian Journ. Phys.*, **3**. 53, 1928 ; I. I. Krasikoff and I. T. Ivanoff, *Mem. Belorussian State Acad. Agric.*, **4**. 238, 1927 ; *Journ. Russ. Phys. Chem. Soc.*, **60**. 561, 1928 ; S. T. Orlowsky, *ib.*, **61**. 1185, 1929 ; V. K. la Mer and J. W. Temple, *Proc. Nat. Acad.*, **15**. 191, 1929 ; M. Bobtelsky and A. Rosenberg, *Zeit. anorg. Chem.*, **182**. 74, 1929 ; M. Bobtelsky, *ib.*, **189**. 196, 1930 ; R. Lang and F. Kurtz, *ib.*, **181**. 111, 1929 ; A. Ferrari, A. Celeri and F. Giorgi, *Atti Accad. Lincei*, (6), **9**. i, 782, 1929 ; D. M. Yost, *Phil. Mag.*, (7), **8**. 845, 1929 ; E. Raymond, *Journ. Chim. Phys.*, **28**. 421, 1931 ; W. Thomson and F. Lewis, *Proc. Manchester Lit. Phil. Soc.*, **4**. 266, 1891 ; *Chem. News*, **64**. 169, 1891 ; J. Kendall, E. D. Crittenden and H. K. Miller, *Journ. Amer. Chem. Soc.*, **45**. 963, 1923 ; G. P. Baxter and C. C. Wallace, *ib.*, **38**. 70, 1916 ; H. Lescoeur, *Ann. Chim. Phys.*, (7), **2**. 78, 1893 ; E. C. Banks, E. C. Righellato and C. W. Davies, *Trans. Faraday Soc.*, **27**. 621, 1931 ; K. Jauch, *Zeit. Physik*, **4**. 441, 1921 ; W. Hampe, *Chem. Ztg.*, **11**. 1549, 1887 ; **12**. 23, 106, 122, 171, 1888 ; E. Tiede and R. Piwonka, *Ber.*, **64**. B, 2252, 1931.

§ 18. The Higher Manganese Chlorides

According to G. Forchhammer,[1] when manganese dioxide is treated with cold, conc. hydrochloric acid, a dark brown soln. is formed. The same dark liquid was mentioned by C. W. Scheele. The liquid evolves chlorine slowly at ordinary temp., but more quickly when heated, until finally the liquid appears colourless and it contains only manganous chloride in soln. If the brown soln. is largely diluted with water, it remains clear, but soon becomes turbid and deposits a copious brown precipitate of hydrated manganese dioxide admixed with other oxides. If manganese hemitrioxide be similarly treated, a similar brown soln. is formed. G. Forchhammer concluded that the brown liquid contains manganese trichloride. W. W. Fischer inferred from experiments on this subject that when the manganese oxides higher than the monoxide are treated with an excess of conc. hydrochloric acid, brown liquids are formed which contain a highly chlorinated compound of manganese, and that this product is easily resolved into manganous chloride and chlorine. When the brown liquid is diluted with water, hydrated manganese dioxide is precipitated. The soln. all have identical properties, and probably contain the same compound. W. W. Fischer inferred that the compound is **manganese tetrachloride**, $MnCl_4$; and S. U. Pickering, **manganese trichloride**, $MnCl_3$, or Mn_2Cl_6. W. W. Fischer represented the formation of the tetrachloride : $MnO_2 + 4HCl = 2H_2O + MnCl_4$, and S. U. Pickering : $2MnO_2 + 8HCl = Mn_2Cl_6$

$+Cl_2+4H_2O$. W. W. Fischer based his conclusion mainly on his observations (i) that water always precipitates a definite substance from the brown liquor containing the higher chloride ; (ii) that the precipitate is always manganese dioxide ; and (iii) that the atomic ratio of the precipitated manganese to the loosely combined chlorine of the higher chloride in the soln. is as 1 : 2. On the other hand, S. U. Pickering showed (i) that water does not precipitate a definite substance ; (ii) that the precipitate is a mixture of the dioxide and hemitrioxide in variable proportions ; and (iii) that the atomic ratio of the precipitated manganese to the available chlorine of the higher chloride in the soln. is not 1 : 2. W. W. Fischer represented the reaction with water : $MnCl_4+2H_2O$ $=MnO_2+4HCl$, and with potassium iodide : $MnCl_4+2KI=MnCl_2+2KCl+I_2$, but S. U. Pickering showed that the same result would be obtained if the higher chloride is any chloride corresponding with Mn_nCl_{2n+2}; for example, with water : Mn_2Cl_6 $+2H_2O=MnO_2+MnCl_2+4HCl$, and with potassium iodide : Mn_2Cl_6+2KI $=2MnCl_2+2KCl+I_2$. S. U. Pickering was never able to get more than half the manganese as a precipitate, and he inferred that if the equation $Mn_2Cl_6+2H_2O$ $=MnO_2+MnCl_2+4HCl$ be correct, the amount of precipitated manganese should increase if manganous chloride be added to the soln., but if the tetrachloride be treated, the amount should remain stationary. The addition of manganous chloride does increase the amount of manganese dioxide precipitated, in agreement with the trichloride hypothesis. Again, if the substance be tetrachloride, 100 per cent. of manganese should be precipitated at a low temp., and only 50 per cent. if the substance be trichloride. Actually, at 60°, only 10 per cent. was precipitated, and at a low temp., 50 per cent. H. M. Vernon favoured W. W. Fischer's hypothesis, because if the action of hydrochloric acid be in accord with $2MnO_2$ $+8HCl=Mn_2Cl_6+Cl_2+4H_2O$, half the available chlorine ought to be evolved very rapidly, especially at low temp. This is not the case, and he hence concluded that the tetrachloride is the first product of the reaction. The brown soln. of manganese dioxide in hydrochloric acid is supposed to contain much free chlorine in soln. which is given off only gradually. H. M. Vernon showed that in a current of air the soln. at −26° lost only a small quantity of chlorine, and no solid chlorine hydrate was formed. At a higher temp. the quantity of chlorine evolved increases proportionally with the temp. ; but at ordinary temp. the chlorine given off is only half that which would be expected if the trichloride were formed. L. Wacker also favoured the tetrachloride hypothesis, because when chlorine gas is passed into a soln. of manganous chloride in conc. hydrochloric acid, a brown soln. is obtained resembling that produced when manganese dioxide is dissolved in conc. hydrochloric acid ; and manganese dioxide or one of its hydrates is formed when either soln. is diluted with water. L. L. de Koninck observed that when one or two drops of nitric acid of sp. gr. 1·35 to 1·40 are added to a boiling soln. of a manganese salt in fuming hydrochloric acid, the colour of the liquid changes to a very dark green with a tinge of yellow, owing to the formation of manganese tetrachloride or possibly of a chloromanganic acid, H_2MnCl_6. This compound is very stable in hydrochloric acid ; the coloration is destroyed only by prolonged boiling. A. N. Campbell prepared the brown liquid in the anode compartment during the electrolysis of soln. of manganous chloride, and he showed by means of the ultra-microscope that it does not contain colloidal particles of manganese dioxide, but is rather a soln. of manganous chloride containing 0·0185 to 0·0188 mols of $MnCl_4$ per litre. The mode of preparing the liquid was as follows :

The electrolysis cell consisted of a rectangular glass jar containing a porous pot. The porous pot contained the anolyte of $3M$-manganous chloride, to which an eq. vol. of conc. hydrochloric acid had been added, and the main body of the cell the catholyte of ammonium chloride, containing 250 grms. of the salt per litre. Both anode and cathode were sheets of platinum foil. An anodic current density of 6 amp. per sq. dcm. was used, corresponding to a total current of 6 ampères. Current was passed for two and a half hrs., during which time the temp. rose from 18° to 47°. Rise of temp. was not prejudicial to the process. On the other hand, neither current density nor manganese concentration can be much reduced.

C. E. Rice showed that the dissociation of the chlorinated compound is reversible, for if a cooled soln. of manganous chloride be sat. with chlorine and left to stand for some days, or if a hydrochloric acid soln. of manganous chloride be left in a sealed tube with chlorine hydrate at ordinary temp., the liquid gradually darkens in colour, and this effect reaches a maximum in a few days. The result corresponds with the balanced reaction : $2MnCl_3 \rightleftharpoons 2MnCl_2 + Cl_2$. In support of the trichloride hypothesis, the brown liquid sat. with hydrogen chloride, cooled by a freezing mixture, and treated with ammonium chloride furnishes complex salts of the trichloride of the type : $2RCl.MnCl_3.nH_2O$. G. Neumann obtained similar results ; and R. J. Meyer and H. Best also favoured the trichloride hypothesis, because they obtained complex salts with pyridine and quinoline hydrochlorides from soln. of manganese dioxide in alcohol or ether sat. with hydrogen chloride. F. Olsson obtained complex salts $MnCl_3.2RCl$, when R is an organic base ; and likewise salts $MnCl_4.2RCl$. R. H. Weber found that the magnetic susceptibility of the brown soln. is of the same order as results obtained with soln. of other salts of tervalent manganese.

J. Nicklès showed that when hydrogen chloride acts on manganese dioxide suspended in dry ether, a green soln. is obtained which *variaient singulièrement* in composition, but contains manganese and chlorine in the proportion Mn : Cl $=1 : 2.58$. In one case the product agreed with $MnCl_4.12(C_2H_5)_2O.2H_2O$, but, as shown by S. U. Pickering, the same analytical data would agree with $MnCl_3.$ $12(C_2H_5)_2O.HCl.2H_2O$. J. Nicklès also obtained a product $MnCl_3.2C_5H_{11}OH.HCl.$ $8H_2O$, by similarly treating manganese hemitrioxide in the presence of amyl alcohol. According to O. T. Christensen, when chlorine is passed into absolute ether containing pure manganese peroxide in suspension and cooled by means of water, the liquid acquires after some time a violet colour so intense that it appears almost black and opaque. If the treatment with chlorine is prolonged, and the cooling insufficient, a reduction takes place, and manganous chloride gradually separates. The mixture should be shaken frequently, and kept from much light. If the dark liquid is poured off, a substance is obtained partly soluble in ether with intense violet colour ; the insoluble residue is unchanged manganese oxide. The ether poured off gives after some hours an abundant separation of manganous chloride and loses its colour. When conc. hydrochloric acid, of sp. gr. 1·19, is shaken with absolute ether, two layers are obtained, the lower a soln. of ether in hydrochloric acid, and the upper a soln. of hydrochloric acid in ether. When these are treated separately with manganese peroxide, the ethereal hydrochloric acid soln. acquires a green, whilst the hydrochloric acid containing ether acquires a violet colour. Hence the colour appears to depend on the amount of water present. O. T. Christensen concluded that when hydrochloric acid acts on manganese dioxide, manganese trichloride is formed, but at 10° more chlorine is taken up, forming the tetrachloride. Manganese hemitrioxide yielded the same chloride, $MnCl_3$, as manganese dioxide when it was treated with a soln. of hydrogen chloride in ether. The atomic ratio Mn : Cl for active chlorine in excess of that required for manganous chloride is approximately 1 : 1, in agreement with the assumption that the soln. of manganese dioxide in ether sat. with hydrogen chloride contains manganese trichloride. Freshly prepared soln. of manganese hemitrioxide in ether sat. with hydrogen chloride contain very little free chlorine. According to R. J. Meyer and H. Best, manganese oxide—Mn_2O_3, Mn_3O_4, or MnO_2—dissolves in absolute alcohol or ether saturated with hydrogen chloride, forming a green soln. of manganese trichloride which is decomposed by water and by evaporation in vacuo over sulphuric acid, so that the trichloride could not be isolated. The green soln. forms the well-defined salts with the hydrochlorides of pyridine and quinoline indicated above.

According to M. Berthelot, an aq. soln. of manganous chloride absorbs less chlorine than does water, and with the evolution of 4400 cals. instead of 3000 cals. per mol of chlorine. If, however, hydrochloric acid be present, more chlorine is absorbed, with the evolution of a greater amount of heat—namely, 9200 cals. per mol. of chlorine—and a brown soln. is formed which is supposed to contain the hydrochloride $MnCl_3.nHCl$ or $MnCl_4.nHCl$. B. Franke said that the green soln. of manganese dioxide in ether saturated with hydrogen chloride contains the acid H_2MnCl_6, which can be obtained in green, oily drops ; and that the manganous salt of this acid, $Mn(MnCl_6)$, *i.e.* Mn_2Cl_6, is present in the soln. R. J. Meyer and H. Best found no support for B. Franke's hypothesis. W. B. Holmes supposed that his work on the action of hydrogen chloride on manganese dioxide suspended in carbon tetrachloride supported the assumption that manganese tetrachloride is the first product of the reaction, although W. B. Holmes and E. V. Manuel did not consider the demonstration of the existence of the tetrachloride to be satisfactory.

According to A. Miolatti, the facts can be reconciled with the assumption that the brown soln. of manganese dioxide in conc. hydrochloric acid is a system in which there is a complex balance of reversible reactions. H. M. Vernon's observations show that both the trichloride and tetrachloride have a marked dissociation press., and that the former is less readily decomposed than the latter. Hence, the system contains $2MnCl_4 \rightleftharpoons 2MnCl_3 + Cl_2$ and $2MnCl_3 \rightleftharpoons 2MnCl_2 + Cl_2$. The hydrolytic changes $MnCl_4 + 4H_2O \rightleftharpoons Mn(OH)_4 + 4HCl$ and $MnCl_3 + 3H_2O \rightleftharpoons Mn(OH)_3 + 3HCl$ are driven back in the presence of an excess of conc. hydrochloric acid. At the same time, complex hydrochlorides are probably formed, *e.g.* $MnCl_4 + HCl \rightleftharpoons HMnCl_5$; $MnCl_4 + 2HCl \rightleftharpoons H_2MnCl_6$; as well as $MnCl_3 + HCl \rightleftharpoons HMnCl_4$; $MnCl_3 + 2HCl \rightleftharpoons H_2MnCl_5$. If any component of the complex system of balanced reactions is withdrawn by precipitation, etc., then, in accord with the mass law, the whole of the dependent equilibria are displaced until the balance is restored. The brown soln. may thus contain in soln. all three chlorides—$MnCl_2$, $MnCl_3$, and $MnCl_4$—as well as chlorine. This is supported by A. Chilesotti's observation that the electrolytic oxidation of manganous chloride does not proceed in steps $Mn^{\cdot\cdot} \rightarrow Mn^{\cdot\cdot\cdot} \rightarrow Mn^{\cdot\cdot\cdot\cdot}$, but both the changes $Mn^{\cdot\cdot} \rightarrow Mn^{\cdot\cdot\cdot}$ and $Mn^{\cdot\cdot} \rightarrow Mn^{\cdot\cdot\cdot\cdot}$ may take place. R. F. Weinland and P. Dinkelacker showed that in the action of cold, conc. hydrochloric acid on permanganates salts corresponding with R_2MnCl_6 are first formed, and then the salts R_2MnCl_5. When organic solvents are used in place of water, the balanced equilibria are displaced in favour of manganese trichloride, or else the hydrochloride of manganese trichloride is more stable than is the case with the hydrochloride of the tetrachloride.

According to W. B. Holmes, when dry hydrogen chloride is bubbled through a mixture of 5 grms. of manganese dioxide and 200 c.c. of carbon tetrachloride in a flask constantly agitated, and cooled by a mixture of ice and salt, there is formed a greenish-black solid. No manganese passes into soln., but the liquid is coloured yellow by the dissolved chlorine. The solid can be washed with a large amount of carbon tetrachloride, then with carbon disulphide containing a little ether, and dried in a desiccator over potassium hydroxide, and sulphuric acid ; it slowly decomposes on standing and chlorine and hydrogen chloride are given off. The solid is supposed to be a mixture of manganese tri- and tetrachlorides mixed with some manganous chloride. To remove the manganese trichloride the residue was washed with ether cooled with solid carbon dioxide. Two-thirds of the contained manganese trichloride is thus removed ; it was then washed with 100 c.c. of cold ether, and the analysis of the violet ethereal soln. shows that it contained manganese trichloride. About half of the original residue consists of manganese trichloride The solid could not be obtained pure enough for analysis by the evaporation of the ethereal soln. in a current of cold air, because decomposition always set in. Hence, the ethereal soln. was analyzed. Manganese trichloride is a nearly black solid with a slight green tinge, and it is immediately decomposed by water ; when the salt is heated, chlorine is evolved, and if left in a desiccator it changes into a mixture of manganous chloride and manganese tetrachloride : $Mn_2Cl_6 = MnCl_2 + MnCl_4$. It dissolves in alcohol, forming a wine-red soln. containing the tetrachloride, but if this soln. is diluted with ether and kept cold, it forms a violet soln. of the trichloride.

When the ethereal soln. of the trichloride is poured into water, only half the manganese is precipitated.

All the trichloride cannot be removed from the original residue by washing with ether, probably because of the slight decomposition of the tetrachloride. A soln. of the tetrachloride in alcohol was prepared for analysis because the solid was always contaminated with manganous chloride. Analyses agreed with the assumption that manganese tetrachloride was present in the soln. of the residue in cold absolute alcohol ; but W. B. Holmes and E. V. Manuel regard the proof of the existence of the tetrachloride to be very unsatisfactory. The solid supposed to be tetrachloride was said to be a reddish-brown solid, stable at ordinary temp. if kept dry, but it quickly decomposes on exposure to moist air. It can be kept several weeks in a desiccator without undergoing appreciable decomposition. But in a large amount of water the tetrachloride gives an immediate precipitate, probably hydrated manganese dioxide. Heated to 100° it gives off chlorine, and a residue of manganous chloride remains. When the tetrachloride is suspended in ether and kept cold, it slowly decomposes into the trichloride, imparting the characteristic violet colour to the solution. If an excess of alcohol is added to this solution, some tetrachloride is again formed. Suspended in ether with mercurous chloride it decomposes more rapidly, but all the ordinary reducing agents such as can be used in a solution nearly anhydrous cause immediate decomposition without the intermediate stage. Absolute alcohol seems to be the only solvent which will dissolve the tetrachloride without rapid decomposition. If the alcohol contains a little water the soln. is decolorized more quickly.

O. T. Christensen recommended the following process for preparing a soln. of manganese trichloride suitable for making complex salts. A mixture of 5 grms. of potassium permanganate and 50 c.c. of absolute alcohol, and an equal vol. of alcohol saturated with hydrogen chloride is shaken and cooled; chlorine and acetaldehyde are given off and a dark green soln. is formed. When the soln. is cooled by a freezing mixture, it deposits the potassium chloride. When the green ethereal or alcoholic soln. of the trichloride is treated with a little water, manganic hydroxide, $Mn(OH)_3$, is precipitated. If a sufficient excess of hydrogen chloride is present, the soln. can be boiled a short time without decomposition, but with a prolonged boiling, or evaporation in vacuo over sulphuric acid and potassium hydroxide, the soln. is decolorized. The addition of an alcoholic soln. of mercuric chloride also reduces the green soln. If the green soln. is diluted with alcohol free from hydrogen chloride, it becomes reddish-violet or reddish-brown, but the green colour is restored by adding ether. A. N. Campbell found the normal potential of quadrivalent manganese ions—assumed to be present in the brown liquid he prepared electrolytically—in the presence of bivalent manganese ions is, on the hydrogen scale, 1·465 volt at 15°. R. H. Weber studied the magnetic susceptibility of soln. of hydrated manganese dioxide in hydrochloric acid.

A. F. Rogers obtained small emerald-green crystals of a mineral with the composition of a **manganic hexoxydichloride,** $Mn_4Cl_2O_6.3H_2O$, from San José, California ; he called it **kempite**—after J. F. Kemp. The rhombic crystals have the axial ratio : $a : b : c = 0·677 : 1 : 0·747$; the sp. gr. is 2·94, the hardness 3·5, and the indices of refraction $\alpha = 1·684$, $\beta = 1·695$, and $\gamma = 1·698$. The mineral dissolves in hydrochloric acid with the evolution of chlorine.

Chlorohypomanganites.—H. Lessheim and co-workers discussed the constitution of the complex salts. According to G. Neumann, **ammonium manganic pentachloride,** $(NH_4)_2MnCl_5$, is obtained when manganese dioxide is allowed to remain for a considerable time in contact with conc. hydrochloric acid, kept cool by immersion in a freezing mixture of ice and salt, and sat. with hydrogen chloride and chlorine ; the brown soln. thus obtained, when filtered and treated with a cold soln. of ammonium chloride, yields the compound in violet-brown crystals. R. F. Weinland and P. Dinkelacker obtained the ammonium salt, $(NH_4)_2MnCl_5.H_2O$, as a reddish-black crystalline powder, by adding potassium permanganate and a conc.

soln. of ammonium chloride to a 40 per cent. aq. soln. of hydrochloric acid cooled by ice and salt; the potassium salt of the tetrachloride is precipitated, and when the mother-liquor is treated with more ammonium chloride, the salt $(NH_4)_2MnCl_5$ is precipitated. C. E. Rice obtained this salt when a mixture of 50 grms. of one of the higher manganese oxides and 250 c.c. of cold, conc. hydrochloric acid was sat. with dry hydrogen chloride while being cooled in a freezing mixture. After the mixture had stood for half an hour the clear liquor was decanted and treated with a few c.c. of a sat. acidified soln. of ammonium chloride, added drop by drop. The mixture, cooled by a freezing mixture, was again sat. with hydrogen chloride and allowed to stand half an hour. The crystals were filtered off, washed with cold, sat. hydrochloric acid, drained on a porous plate, and left for some days over soda-lime under reduced press. The analysis corresponded with $(NH_4)_2MnCl_5.H_2O$. The crystals are perfectly transparent under the microscope, transmitting a ruby-coloured light. They have a slightly pungent odour, and may be raised to a temp. of 100° without perceptible change ; above that temp., however, they evolve chlorine and water, and if heated in a current of air, leave a white residue of manganous chloride and sublimed ammonium chloride. They dissolve in hydrochloric acid, yielding a liquid resembling that from which they were obtained. Water at once decomposes them, about half the total manganese separating as hydrated higher oxide and half remaining in soln. as manganous chloride. If the complex salts of manganese tetrachloride be called *chloromanganites*, as is commonly the case, then these salts can be designated by the awkward term *chlorohypomanganites*. According to R. J. Meyer and H. Best, the green soln. of a higher oxide of manganese in absolute alcohol or ether sat. with hydrogen chloride, when treated with pyridine hydrochloride furnishes needle-like crystals of **pyridine manganic pentachloride,** $2C_5H_5N(HCl).MnCl_3$; and with quinoline hydrochloride, acicular crystals of **quinoline manganic pentachloride,** $2C_9H_7N(HCl).MnCl_3$. F. Olsson obtained a number of complexes with the chlorides of the quaternary ammonium bases.

G. Neumann, C. E. Rice, and R. F. Weinland and P. Dinkelacker prepared **potassium manganic pentachloride,** $2KCl.MnCl_3$, by the methods they employed for the ammonium salt. O. Stelling and F. Olsson studied the X-ray spectrum. R. J. Meyer and H. Best also prepared it by reducing a soln. of potassium permanganate with acetic acid with the addition of potassium acetate, and sat. the liquid with hydrogen chloride. If the soln. be only partially sat. with hydrogen chloride, *potassium manganese dodecachloride*, $5KCl.MnCl_4.MnCl_3$, is formed. C. E. Rice regarded potassium manganic pentachloride as a monohydrate, and said that the potassium and ammonium salts are isomorphous with the corresponding complex salts of ferric chloride. The other observers said that the salt is anhydrous. R. F. Weinland and P. Dinkelacker prepared **rubidium manganic pentachloride,** $2RbCl.MnCl_3$, by the process which they employed for the ammonium salt ; and similarly with R. J. Meyer and H. Best's, and R. F. Weinland and P. Dinkelacker's preparations of **cæsium manganic pentachloride,** $2CsCl.MnCl_3$. The corresponding **thallous manganic pentachloride,** $2TlCl.MnCl_3$, could not be prepared by R. J. Meyer and H. Best.

Chloromanganites.—G. Lunge and B. Zahorsky mentioned the existence of a possible **manganese oxychloride,** $MnOCl$, and G. Lunge, **manganese trioxydichloride,** $Cl-MnO_2-OCl$, in the brown liquid obtained by the action of hydrochloric acid on manganese dioxide. A. Gorgeu obtained what he regarded as **manganese hexoxydichloride,** $2Mn_2O_3.MnCl_2$, by heating manganous chloride in moist air until about half is decomposed and washing the product with water. L. P. de St. Gilles also reported **manganese enneaoxydichloride,** $3Mn_2O_3.MnCl_2$, but there is no evidence confirming the individuality of these products. R. F. Weinland and P. Dinkelacker treated calcium permanganate with 40 per cent. hydrochloric acid cooled by a mixture of ice and salt ; an aq. soln. of ammonium chloride was added, and **ammonium chloromanganite,** $(NH_4)_2MnCl_6$, crystallized out. F. Reitzenstein prepared **pyridine chloromanganite,** $2C_5H_5N.MnCl_4$, by adding pyridine to a soln. of manganese dioxide in conc. hydrochloric acid. J. G. F. Druce did not obtain **potassium manganese hexachloride,** $MnCl_4.2KCl$, or K_2MnCl_6, by passing chlorine into a soln. of potassium and manganese chlorides. R. J. Meyer and H. Best found that **potassium chloromanganite,** K_2MnCl_6, is formed as a black crystalline precipitate when an acetic acid soln. of potassium permanganate, without potassium acetate, is sat. with hydrogen chloride. R. F. Weinland and P. Dinkelacker also obtained it by a method analogous to that employed for the ammonium salt; and likewise also with **rubidium chloromanganite,** Rb_2MnCl_6. R. J. Meyer and H. Best could not obtain **thallous chloromanganite.** N. Bjerrum and G. H. Hansen could not prepare complexes with chromic chloride.

Oxychlorides.—According to J. B. A. Dumas, when a mixture of a soln. of potassium permanganate in conc. sulphuric acid is mixed with fused sodium chloride and heated to 30° or 40° in a retort, a reddish or greenish vapour is given off, and it condenses at −15° to −20°, forming a greenish-brown liquid. The vapour in contact with moist air decomposes, forming hydrochloric and permanganic acids. H. Aschoff also obtained the greenish-brown liquid by the action, under similar conditions, of sodium chloride on a soln. of manganese heptoxide in sulphuric acid. The smell of the gas recalls that of chlorine oxide, and ozone. The gas attacks the respiratory organs. E. Luck, and W. Friederichs studied the absorption spectrum. When the drops of liquid are heated on a water-bath, detonation occurs at the same temp. as with manganese heptoxide. Water attacks the liquid vigorously, forming chlorine and manganese dioxide. J. B. A. Dumas thought that he was dealing with *manganese heptachloride*; H. Aschoff's analysis corresponds with **manganese trioxychloride,** MnO_3Cl, but it may be nothing more than a soln. of chlorine or a chloride in manganese heptoxide. The product thus recalls F. Wöhler's MnO_3F, and B. Franke's $(MnO_3)_2SO_4$.

REFERENCES.

[1] C. W. Scheele, *Svenska Akad. Handl.*, **35.** 89, 177, 1774; *Abhand. Akad. Stockholm*, **36.** 95, 183, 1774; *Opuscula chemica et physica*, Lipsiæ, **1.** 227, 1788; London, 53, 1901; *Crell's Die neuesten Entdeckungen in der Chemie*, **1.** 112, 140, 1781; *Nachgelassene Briefe und Aufzeichnungen*, Stockholm, 120, 1892; G. Forchhammer, *Ann. Phil.*, **16.** 130, 1820; **17.** 50, 1821; *De mangano*, Hafnia, 1820; A. Chilesotti in R. Abegg, *Handbuch der anorganischen Chemie*, Leipzig, **4.** ii. 794, 1913; A. Miolatti, *ib.*, **2.** ii, 793, 1913; W. W. Fischer, *Journ. Chem. Soc.*, **33.** 409, 1878; S. U. Pickering, *ib.*, **35.** 654, 1879; *Phil. Mag.*, (5), **31.** 284, 1892; H. M. Vernon, *ib.*, (5), **31.** 469, 1892; *Chem. News*, **61.** 203, 1890; *Proc. Chem. Soc.*, **6.** 58, 1890; C. E. Rice, *ib.*, **14.** 53, 1898; *Chem. News*, **77.** 125, 1898; *Journ. Chem. Soc.*, **73.** 258, 1898; A. N. Campbell, *ib.*, **123.** 892, 1923; J. G. F. Druce, *ib.*, **119.** 419, 1917; S. M. Jörgensen, *Journ. prakt. Chem.*, (2), **35.** 57, 1877; B. Franke, *ib.*, (2), **36.** 31, 451, 1887; O. T. Christensen, *ib.*, **34.** 41, 1886; (2), **35.** 67, 169, 1887; *Ber.*, **16.** 2495, 1883; T. Ephraim and L. Heymann, *ib.*, **42.** 4456, 1909; F. Olsson, *Arkiv Kemi Min. Geol.*, **9.** 10, 1924; G. Lunge, *Journ. Soc. Chim. Ind.*, **11.** 882, 1892; G. Lunge and B. Zahorsky, *Zeit. angew. Chem.*, **5.** 631, 1892; L. Wacker, *Chem. Ztg.*, **24.** 285, 1900; L. L. de Koninck, *Bull. Assoc. Belg. Chim.*, **16.** 94, 1902; H. Aschoff, *Ueber die Uebermangansäure und die Ueberchromsäure*, Berlin, 1861; *Sitzber. Akad. Berlin*, 474, 1804; *Pogg. Ann.*, **111.** 217, 1860; *Journ. prakt. Chem.*, (1), **81.** 29, 1860; *Chem. News*, **4.** 103, 1841; A. Gorgeu, *Compt. Rend.*, **106.** 703, 1888; *Bull. Soc. Chim.*, (2), **49.** 669, 1888; M. Berthelot, *ib.*, (2), **35.** 661, 1881; *Compt. Rend.*, **91.** 251, 1880; *Ann. Chim. Phys.*, (5), **22.** 468, 1881; J. Nicklès, *ib.*, (4), **5.** 161, 1865; (4), **10.** 318, 1867; *Compt. Rend.*, **60.** 479, 1865; **67.** 448, 1868; L. P. de St. Gilles, *ib.*, **55.** 329, 1862; J. B. A. Dumas, *Quart. Journ. Science*, **2.** 475, 1827; *Ann. Chim. Phys.*, (2), **36.** 82, 1827; E. Müller and P. Koppe, *Zeit. anorg. Chem.*, **68.** 160, 1910; R. F. Weinland and P. Dinkelacker, *ib.*, **60.** 173, 1908; R. J. Meyer and H. Best, *ib.*, **22.** 169, 1899; H. Best, *Ueber die höheren Chloride des Mangans und Chroms*, Berlin, 1899; F. Reitzenstein, *Zeit. anorg. Chem.*, **18.** 253, 1898; N. Bjerrum and G. H. Hansen, *ib.*, **63.** 151, 1909; J. Meyer and R. Nerlich, *ib.*, **116.** 117, 1921; G. Wiedemann, *Wied. Ann.*, **32.** 452, 1887; G. Neumann, *Monatsh.*, **15.** 489, 1894; R. H. Weber, *Ann. Physik*, (4), **19.** 1056, 1906; (4), **36.** 624, 1911; W. B. Holmes, *Journ. Amer. Chem. Soc.*, **29.** 1277, 1907; W. B. Holmes and E. V. Manuel, *ib.*, **30.** 1192, 1908; F. Wöhler, *Pogg. Ann.*, **9.** 919, 1827; W. Friederichs, *Zeit. wiss. Photochem.*, **3.** 154, 1905; *Ueber Absorptionsspektra von Dämpfen*, Cöln, 1905; E. Luck, *Zeit. Chem.*, (2), **6.** 288, 1869; *Zeit. anal. Chem.*, **8.** 405, 1869; A. F. Rogers, *Amer. Journ. Science*, (5), **8.** 145, 1924; *Amer. Min.*, **9.** 66, 1924; H. Lessheim, J. Meyer and R. Samuel, *Zeit. Physik*, **43.** 199, 1927; O. Stelling and F. Olsson, *Zeit. phys. Chem.*, **7.** B, 210, 1930.

§ 19. Manganese Bromides

Anhydrous **manganese dibromide**, or **manganous bromide**, $MnBr_2$, was prepared, as a pale rose-red mass, by C. J. Löwig,[1] by the action of bromine vapour on heated manganese; and J. B. Berthemot, by heating the hydrated salt out of contact with air. A soln. of the salt was prepared by A. J. Balard by the action of bromine on manganous oxide; by J. B. Berthemot, by digesting manganese with bromine-water; and by C. J. Löwig, by dissolving manganous carbonate in hydrobromic acid. When the aq. soln. is evaporated, it furnishes a pale red powder (C. J. Löwig), or acicular crystals of the *tetrahydrate*, $MnBr_2.4H_2O$, which are coloured a deeper rose-red than the corresponding chloride (J. C. G. de Marignac). H. Lescoeur said that if the tetrahydrate is allowed to effloresce in air, it forms the *monohydrate*, $MnBr_2.H_2O$, as a rose-red powder; P. Kutznetzoff also obtained it by heating the tetrahydrate at its m.p., 64·3°. If the aq. soln. be cooled to $-14°$, or even to 0°, P. Kutznetzoff said that crystals of the *hexahydrate*, $MnBr_2.6H_2O$, are deposited. P. Kutznetzoff gave 13° for the transition temp. for the hexahydrate and tetrahydrate; and 64° for the transition temp. for the tetrahydrate and the monohydrate. The solubility data of A. Étard, when S denotes the number of grams of $MnBr_2$ in 100 grms. of soln. :

	$-21°$	7°	11°	18°	38°	52°	64°	76°	89°	97°	105°
S .	52·1	56·5	57·0	59·1	62·7	64·2	68·2	70·1	69·7	69·2	70·2

do not show the transition temp. at 13°, but there appears to be one near 70°. A. Étard's data for manganous chloride also failed to show the transition temp. satisfactorily. There appears to be a stable or α-form of the tetrahydrate which, according to J. C. G. de Marignac, is isomorphous with the α-form of the tetrahydrated chloride, and it furnishes monoclinic plates with the axial ratios $a : b : c$ $=1·1650 : 1 : 0·6483$, and $\beta=99°\ 6'$. There is also a labile or β-form of the tetrahydrate which is obtained in colourless rhombic plates by evaporating an aq. soln. of the bromide in a closed vessel. The β-form passes into the α-variety by mechanically stirring the mass; and the transformation proceeds slowly when the crystals of the α-form are allowed to stand under their mother-liquor. The β-form has a lower decomposition temp., and a larger solubility than the α-form. A. Ferrari and F. Giorgi observed that the X-radiogram of the bromide, $MnBr_2$, corresponds with a lattice of the cadmium iodide type, having $a=3·820$ A., $c=6·188$ A.; $a : c=1 : 1·62$; and density 4·549.

G. P. Baxter and M. A. Hines gave 4·385 for the sp. gr. of the anhydrous salt at 25°/4°. For A. Heydweiller's observations, *vide infra*. I. I. Saslawsky, and F. Ephraim and co-workers discussed the mol. vol., and the vol. contraction attending the formation of the salt from its elements. C. A. Valson studied the capillarity of the aq. soln.; and S. Motylewsky found the drop-weight of the molten salt at its m.p. to be 78 when that of a drop of water at 0° is 100. J. B. Berthemot said that the tetrahydrate melts in its water of crystallization and then passes into the anhydrous salt; and P. Kutznetzoff found that the m.p. of the tetrahydrate is 64·3°, at which temp. it passes into the monohydrate. C. J. Löwig, and A. Gorgeu observed that when the anhydrous salt is heated to redness in air, it loses bromine and passes into the tritatetroxide. H. Lescoeur found the vap. press. at 20° to be 5 mm. for the sat. soln.; between 5·0 and 5·1 mm. for $MnBr_2,5·1H_2O$ to $MnBr_2$, $1·5H_2O$; and over 2·3 mm. for $MnBr_2,1·05H_2O$; at 100° the vap. press. of the sat. soln. is 202 mm., for the solid tetrahydrate 200 mm., and for $MnBr_2,1·1H_2O$ 50 mm.; while at 150° the vap. press. for the hydrate between $MnBr_2,0·98H_2O$ and $MnBr_2,0·45H_2O$ is 98 to 99 mm., and for $MnBr_2,0·05H_2O$ 17 mm. A. Ferrari discussed some relations of the m.p. The vap. press., p mm., for the monohydrate is :

	20°	60°	100°	140°	150°	155°	160°
p .	5	40	200	56	99	122	156 mm.

Saturated solution	Solid monohydrate

J. Thomsen gave for the heat of formation, (Mn,Br$_2$,Aq.)=106·12 Cals.; and M. Berthelot, (Mn,Br$_{2gas}$)=114·4 Cals., and (Mn,Br$_{2liquid}$,Aq.)=107·0 Cals. In the calculations M. Berthelot used the assumption that the heats of neutralization of manganous hydroxide by the three halide acids are the same. G. Beck discussed the free energy of formation; and G. Devoto and A. Guzzi found:

	700°	750°	800°	850°	900°
Free energy .	67,600	65,180	62,780	58,980	52,220 cals.

R. Robl observed no fluorescence in ultra-violet light. B. A. Isbekoff and W. A. Plotnikoff found the sp. electrical conductivity of a 15 per cent. soln. in molten aluminium bromide to be 0·001 at 160°. A. Heydweiller gave for the sp. gr. and eq. conductivity at 18°:

	0·5N-	N-	2N-	3N-	4N-
Sp. gr. .	1·0447	1·0889	1·1763	1·2630	1·3491
λ . . .	72·4	64·7	53·54	(43·6)	35·64

W. Althammer gave for soln. with an eq. of the bromide in v litres, at 25°:

v . . .	20	40	80	160	320
λ . . .	100·4	106·1	111·5	116·6	120·3

A. Liebknecht and A. P. Wills gave for the magnetic susceptibility, of aq. soln. at 18°, 1×10^{-6} mass unit. G. Beck studied the energy of the salt. K. Jellinek and R. Ulroth found that no reaction between hydrogen and manganous bromide occurs below 770°, and that thereafter if $K = p_{H_2} p_{Br}/p^2_{HBr}$, then $\log K = -5223 T^{-1} + 0.533 \log T - 2.72$. W. Ostwald found that manganous bromide has a slight stimulating effect on the reaction between bromic and hydriodic acids; J. B. Berthemot found that with conc. sulphuric acid, hydrogen bromide and bromine are formed. G. Gore, and E. C. Franklin and C. A. Kraus observed that the salt is insoluble in liquid ammonia, but F. Ephraim prepared **manganous hexamminobromide**, MnBr$_2$.6NH$_3$, by passing ammonia over the dehydrated salt; heat is evolved, and the solid swells up. The white ammine has the dissociation press., p mm.:

	83°	90°	104°	110°	114·5°	120°	124°	128°	130·5°
p .	86	127	240	308	370	468	550	650	720 mm.

W. Biltz and E. Birk studied the mol. vol. W. Biltz and G. F. Hüttig found that when manganous bromide is treated with ammonia gas as in the case of the chloride, similar ammines are produced (Fig. 78). For the hexammine, at 107°, the dis-

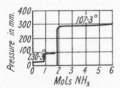

FIG. 78.—Dissociation Pressures of Manganous Hexamminobromide.

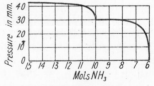

FIG. 79.—Dissociation Pressures of Manganous Decamminobromide.

sociation press., p=305, and the heat of dissociation, Q=14·26 Cals.; for **manganous diamminobromide**, MnBr$_2$.2NH$_3$, at 182°, p=13·7 mm., and Q=20·2 Cals.; at 215°, p=56·4 mm., and Q=20·4 Cals.; and at 230°, p=98·0 mm., and Q=20·5 Cals. For **manganous monamminobromide**, MnBr$_2$.NH$_3$, at 215°, p=12·3 mm., and Q=21·8 Cals.; at 230°, p=22·9 mm., and Q=21·95 Cals.; and at 278°, p=114 mm., and Q=22·5 Cals. F. Müller gave 20°–128° for the dissociation temp. of the hexamminobromide; 128° for the pentamminobromide; above 270° for the diamminobromide; and over 360° for the monamminobromide. F. Ephraim, and G. L. Clark also studied the hexammine. By working with manganous bromide in a similar way to that employed for manganous chloride, W. Biltz and E. Rahlfs were able to prepare **manganous decamminobromide**, $MnBr_2.10NH_3$; which at $-78.5°$ had $p=27.5$ mm., and $Q=7.17$ Cals.; at $-70°$, $p=61.5$, and $Q=7.16$; at $-65°$, $p=95.0$, and $Q=7.16$; at $-60°$, $p=146.5$, and $Q=7.15$; and at $55°$, $p=146.5$, and $Q=7.16$—Fig. 79. F. Ephraim discussed the vol. contraction attending the formation of the ammines. H. Grossmann obtained a complex with pyridine, $MnBr_2.6C_5H_5N$; and R. J. Meyer and H. Best, $MnBr_2.2C_5H_5N$, and $MnBr_2.2C_5H_5N(HCl)$; A. R. Leeds, a complex with aniline, $MnBr_2.2C_6H_5(NH_2)$; A. Moitessier, with phenylhydrazine, $MnBr_2.2C_6H_5(NH.NH_2)$; G. A. Barbieri and F. Calzolari, with hexamethylenetetramine, $MnBr_2.2C_6H_{12}N_4.10H_2O$. F. Ducelliez and A. Raynaud obtained a complex with ether, $MnBr_2.(C_2H_5)_2O$; G. Spacu, one with diphenyl. M. Centnerszwer found that the salt is insoluble in liquid cyanogen.

According to F. Ephraim and S. Model, manganous bromide has *eine ausserordentlich geringe Neigung* to form complex salts, and in this respect it resembles cobaltous bromide. They were unable to prepare complex salts with the bromides of potassium, sodium, ammonium, barium, and strontium. By evaporating a mixed soln. of ammonium and manganous bromides they obtained what appeared to be isomorphous mixtures of ammonium bromide and **ammonium manganous tetrabromide**, $(NH_4)_2MnBr_4.H_2O$; while a soln. of sodium and manganous bromides furnished isomorphous mixtures of manganous bromide and **sodium manganous tribromide**, $NaMnBr_3.nH_2O$. No **potassium manganous bromide** could be obtained. C. E. Saunders observed that if a hot, sat. soln. of manganous chloride be treated with potassium bromide, and allowed to cool, there are deposited crystals of potassium manganous trichloride, containing variable amounts of probably the corresponding tribromide in isomorphous mixture; and similar results were obtained when an excess of potassium chloride is added to hot, sat. soln. of manganous bromide. There is no evidence to support the hypothesis that a mixed halide is formed. F. Ephraim and S. Model prepared **calcium manganous tetrabromide**, $CaMnBr_4.4H_2O$, in pink crystals, by evaporating a conc. soln. of the component salts over conc. sulphuric acid. The salt is a little hygroscopic, and it readily decomposes into its components. The corresponding *strontium and barium manganous tetrabromides* could not be prepared. C. E. Saunders obtained **magnesium manganous hexabromide**, $MgMn_2Br_6.12H_2O$, by evaporating a soln. of 2 mols of manganous bromide and one mol of magnesium bromide in 70 per cent. alcohol. The compact masses of red crystals deliquesce in air, and do not effloresce over calcium chloride; they lose 16.27 per cent. of water at $150°$; and the salt cannot be obtained by crystallizing the aq. soln. P. A. von Bonsdorff found that a sat. soln. of the component salts furnishes pale red columns of **mercuric manganous bromide**, which are very deliquescent. R. Varet gave for the heat of formation at $17°$ of $MnBr_2.2HgBr_2$, 2.92 Cals., and for $MnBr_2.HgBr_2$, 2.48 Cals. J. Kendall and co-workers obtained evidence of the formation of **aluminium manganous bromide**, $2AlBr_3.MnBr_2$; and B. A. Isbekoff and W. A. Plotnikoff observed that manganous bromide forms a yellow soln. with aluminium bromide, and the sp. conductivity of the 15 per cent. soln. is 0.001 mho at $160°$. B. Rayman and K. Preis obtained crystals of **manganous bromostannate**, or **stannic manganous hexabromide**, $MnSnBr_6.6H_2O$, in yellow, deliquescent crystals, by evaporating a soln. of the component salts. G. Spacu and J. Dick studied complexes of manganous and stannic bromides.

According to J. Nicklès, when one of the higher manganese oxides—Mn_3O_4, Mn_2O_3, or MnO_2—is treated with ether and hydrogen bromide, a green soln. is obtained which easily decomposes and which dissolves gold. By analogy with the corresponding chloride it was thought that *manganese tribromide, or manganese tetrabromide* is present; but R. J. Meyer and H. Best doubted if the ethereal or alcoholic soln. contains a higher manganese bromide, because when treated with pyridine hydrobromide it furnishes $MnBr_2.2C_5H_6NBr$. F. Ducelliez and A. Raynaud obtained a complex with ether, $MnBr_2.(C_2H_5)_2O$, of m.p. 65° to 70°. N. Bjerrum and G. H. Hansen could not prepare complexes with chromic bromide.

REFERENCES.

[1] G. Spacu and J. Dick, *Bul. Soc. Stiinte Cluj.*, **4**. 84, 110, 1928 ; A. J. Balard, *Bibl. Univ.*, **56**. 372, 1834 ; *Journ. prakt. Chem.*, (1), **4**. 165, 1835 ; A. Liebknecht and A. P. Wills, *Ann. Physik*, (4), **1**. 178, 1900 ; C. J. Löwig, *Das Brom und seine chemischen Verhältnisse*, Heidelberg, 1829 ; *Mag. Pharm.*, **23**. 11, 1828 ; **33**. 6, 1831 ; *Pogg. Ann.*, **14**. 485, 1828 ; P. A. von Bonsdorff, *ib.*, **17**. 122, 1829 ; F. Ducelliez and A. Raynaud, *Compt. Rend.*, **158**. 576, 1914 ; *Bull. Soc. Chim.*, (4), **15**. 273, 408, 1914 ; A. Gorgeu, *ib.*, (2), **49**. 664, 1888 ; *Compt. Rend.*, **106**. 703, 1888 ; A. Moitessier, *ib.*, **124**. 1529, 1897 ; R. Varet, *ib.*, **123**. 422, 1896 ; C. A. Valson, *ib.*, **74**. 103, 1872 ; A. Étard, *ib.*, **98**. 993, 1884 ; J. Nicklès, *ib.*, **60**. 479, 1865 ; *Ann. Chim. Phys.*, **65**. 107, 1867 ; (4), **5**. 169, 1865 ; (4), **10**. 318, 1867 ; J. B. Berthemot, *ib.*, (2), **44**, 392, 1830; H. Lescoeur, *ib.*, (7), **2**. 103, 1894 ; F. Ephraim, *Helvetica Chim. Acta*, **7**. 298, 1924 ; *Ber.*, **45**. 1322, 1912 ; *Zeit. phys. Chem.*, **71**. 513, 1913 ; M. Centnerszwer, *ib.*, **39**. 217, 1902 ; *Journ. Russ. Phys. Chem. Soc.*, **33**. 545, 1901 ; P. Kutznetzoff, *ib.*, **29**. 288, 1897 ; **41**. 353, 1909 ; *Ann. Chim. Phys.*, (8), **18**. 214, 1909 ; *Zeit. anorg. Chem.*, **18**. 387, 1898 ; S. Model, *Ueber Doppelhalogenide des Zinks und Mangans*, Bern, 1911 ; F. Ephraim and S. Model, *Zeit. anorg. Chem.*, **67**. 376, 1910 ; F. Ephraim and O. Schütz, *Helvetica Chim. Acta*, **9**. 915, 922, 1926 ; W. Ostwald, *Zeit. phys. Chem.*, **2**. 145, 1888 ; R. J. Meyer and H. Best, *Zeit. anorg. Chem.*, **22**. 182, 1899 ; S. Motylewsky, *ib.*, **38**. 410, 1904 ; B. A. Isbekoff and W. A. Plotnikoff, *ib.*, **71**. 328, 1911 ; W. Biltz and E. Birk, *ib.*, **134**. 125, 1924 ; W. Biltz, *Zeit. Elektrochem.*, **29**. 348, 1923 ; *Zeit. anorg. Chem.*, **193**. 321, 1930 ; W. Biltz and G. F. Hüttig, *ib.*, **109**. 89, 1919 ; W. Biltz and E. Rahlfs, *ib.*, **148**. 145, 1925 ; K. Jellínek and R. Ulroth, *ib.*, **151**. 157, 1926 ; N. Bjerrum and G. H. Hansen, *ib.*, **63**. 151, 1909 ; I. I. Saslawsky, *ib.*, **146**. 315, 1925 ; G. Beck, *ib.*, **156**. 288, 1926 ; **182**. 334, 1929 ; A. Heydweiller, *ib.*, **116**. 42, 1921 ; G. P. Baxter and M. A. Hines, *ib.*, **51**. 202, 1896 ; *Journ. Amer. Chem. Soc.*, **28**. 1560, 1906 ; A. R. Leeds, *ib.*, **3**. 112, 1882 ; J. Kendall, E. D. Crittenden and H. K. Miller, *ib.*, **45**. 963, 1923 ; A. Ferrari, *Atti Congresso Chim. Pura Applicata*, **3**. 449, 452, 1930 ; A Ferrari and F. Giorgi, *Atti Accad. Lincei*, (6), **9**. 1134, 1929 ; G. Devoto and A. Guzzi, *Gazz. Chim. Ital.*, **59**. 591, 1929 ; G. L. Clark, *Amer. Journ. Science*, (5), **7**. 1, 1924 ; J. C. G. de Marignac, *Ann. Mines*, (5), **12**. 7, 1857 ; M. Berthelot, *Thermochimie*, Paris, **2**. 268, 1897 ; G. Gore, *Proc. Roy. Soc.*, **21**. 140, 1873 ; F. Müller, *Jahrb. Phil. Fac. Univ. Bern.*, **2**. 80, 1922 ; E. C. Franklin and C. A. Kraus, *Amer. Chem. Journ.*, **20**. 828, 1898 ; C. E. Saunders, *ib.*, **14**. 127, 1892 ; J. Thomsen, *Thermochemische Untersuchungen*, Leipzig, **3**. 271, 1883 ; H. Grossmann, *Ber.*, **37**. 564, 1254, 1904 ; R. Robl, *Zeit. angew. Chem.*, **39**. 608, 1926 ; G. A. Barbieri and F. Calzolari, *Atti Accad. Lincei*, (5), **19**. ii, 584, 1910 ; B. Rayman and K. Preis, *Liebig's Ann.*, **223**. 332, 1884 ; G. Spacu, *Bul. Soc. Stiinte Cluj.*, **4**. 210, 1928.

§ 20. Manganese Iodides

According to W. Peters,[1] the hydrated manganous iodide can be readily dehydrated in vacuo to form **manganous iodide**, MnI_2, as a pink, scaly mass ; the salt must not be heated, since it begins to give off iodine at about 80°. According to F. Ducelliez, anhydrous manganese iodide can be readily obtained by the addition of iodine to finely-divided manganese covered with anhydrous ether. A vigorous reaction occurs, which is rendered complete by gentle warming on the water-bath. Excess of iodine and iodide of iron may be removed by washing the product with ether, whilst if an excess of manganese is employed, it can be separated from the precipitated iodide by washing away the latter in a stream of ether. A. Ferrari and F. Giorgi found that the anhydrous salt has the cadmium iodide structure, and that the X-radiograms correspond with a lattice having the parameters $a=4.16$ A., and $c=6.82$ A., and a sp. gr. 5.01. The aq. soln. of the salt was prepared by J. L. Lassaigne, J. C. G. de Marignac, and H. F. Gaultier de Claubry, by dissolving manganous carbonate in hydriodic acid. The soln. furnishes pink tabular crystals of the hydrated salt, and they have, according to J. L. Lassaigne, a styptic taste. P. Kutznetzoff observed that with soln. with a mol of MnI_2 in 8 mols of water, and cooled to $-20°$, crystals of the *enneahydrate*, $MnI_2.9H_2O$, are formed. These crystals are richer in water than the mother-liquor ; and they melt at $-9.3°$. If the soln. sat. at 0° be cooled to $-5°$, deliquescent, prismatic, colourless plates of the *hexahydrate*, $MnI_2.6H_2O$, are formed ; and at $-2.7°$ deliquescent pink plates of the *tetrahydrate*, $MnI_2.4H_2O$, are formed.

These crystals are stable at ordinary temp., and they are formed by the spontaneous evaporation of the aq. soln. H. Lescoeur found the vap. press. to be 83 mm. at 100° ; H. Lescoeur also reported the *dihydrate*, $MnI_2.2H_2O$, and the *monohydrate*, $MnI_2.H_2O$, to be formed by dehydrating the tetrahydrate. The dihydrate has a vap. press. of 47 mm. at 100° ; and the monohydrate, 180 mm. at 130°—but *vide supra* for the temp. of decomposition. A. Étard said that he made some observations on the solubility of the salt. F. Ephraim and co-workers discussed the mol. vol., and the vol. contraction attending the formation of the salt. C. A. Valson studied the capillarity of the soln. H. Lescoeur found the vap. press., p mm., of the mono-, di-, and tetrahydrates and of the sat. soln. to be :

		20°	50°	60°	66°	80°	100°	110°	120°	130°	133°
	H_2O	—	—	—	—	—	—	—	130	180	198
p	$2H_2O$	—	—	—	19	—	47	91	112	—	—
	$4H_2O$	—	5	—	—	34	83	135	—	—	—
	Soln.	3·5	7	13	—	—	42·5	104	154	210	—

He also found that at 20° the vap. press. of $MnI_2.6H_2O$ to $MnI_2.4·05H_2O$ is 3·6 to 3·8 mm., that of $MnI_2.3·98H_2O$ is over 1·7 mm. ; at 100° the vap. press. of $MnI_2.4H_2O$ to $MnI_2.3·02H_2O$ is 82 to 83 mm., that of $MnI_2.2H_2O$ to $MnI_2.1·4H_2O$ is 47 mm., and that of $MnI_2.0·98H_2O$, 25 mm. ; and at 130° the vap. press. of $MnI_2.0·98H_2O$ to $MnI_2.0·6H_2O$ is 179 to 180 mm., and that of $MnI_2.0·1H_2O$, 20 mm. A. Ferrari discussed the relation of the m.p. to the space-lattice. M. Berthelot found the heat of formation $(Mn,I_{2gas})=89·8$ Cals. ; and $(Mn,I_{2solid},Aq.)=76·2$ Cals. ; J. Thomsen gave $(Mn,I_{2solid},Aq.)=75·7$ Cals. F. Ephraim and O. Schütz discussed the heat of formation. G. Devoto and A. Guzzi gave for the free energy of formation :

	650°	700°	750°	800°	850°
Free energy	50,630	48,480	46,320	45,420	43,290 cals.

E. Wedekind found that the anhydrous salt is ferromagnetic ; and A. Liebknecht and A. P. Wills gave 49×10^{-6} mass unit for the magnetic susceptibility of aq. soln.

F. Ducelliez observed that manganous iodide is a white powder. J. C. G. de Marignac said that manganous iodide becomes brown on exposure to air ; and J. L. Lassaigne, and A. Gorgeu observed that if air be excluded, the salt can be melted without decomposition, but in air, iodine and manganese oxide are formed. W. Riedel found the eq. conductivity, λ, of a soln. of an eq. of manganese iodide in v litres, at 18°, to be :

v	20	40	80	160	320	640	1280	5120	α
λ	101·13	105·89	111·09	115·18	119·94	112·37	123·55	127·32	130·6
a	0·7742	0·8108	0·8506	0·8819	0·9184	0·9370	0·9460	0·9750	100·0

The degrees of ionization, a, were also calculated ; and the transport numbers for 0·0025 to 0·005M-MnI_2 soln. were 0·6077 for the anion and 0·3923 for the cations ; and for a 0·05N-soln. respectively 0·6232 and 0·3768. The H -ion conc. of 0·05M-MnI_2 is $10^{-4·45}$, and for 0·01M-MnI_2, $10^{-4·54}$. This shows that the hydrolysis is very small. According to J. L. Lassaigne, the salt is very deliquescent. It is freely soluble in water, forming a colourless soln. which on evaporation yields white needles. The aq. soln. decomposes on exposure to air with the separation of brown flecks. P. Kutznetzoff found that when air is passed through a conc. soln. of manganese iodide or when a soln. is repeatedly evaporated, **manganous oxyiodide**, $MnI_2.MnO.6H_2O$, is formed in colourless, microscopic, birefringent needles, which gradually lose iodine at 115° to 120°. According to J. L. Lassaigne, iodine is liberated from manganous iodide by chlorine, and bromine, as well as by sulphuric acid. E. C. Franklin and C. A. Kraus found that the iodide is fairly soluble in liquid ammonia. W. Peters observed that the anhydrous salt absorbs ammonia to form **manganous hexamminoiodide**, $MnI_2.6NH_3$, and the white product loses a mol. of ammonia in vacuo. This is not taken up again when the salt is re-exposed to the gas, so that some internal change occurs. F. Ephraim gave for the dissociation press., p mm., of the hexammine :

	125·5°	135°	143·5°	149·5°	156°	162·5°	168·5°	173·5°
p .	105	150	225	280	364	475	596	720

W. Biltz and G. F. Hüttig prepared the hexamminoiodide as in the case of the hexamminochloride, Fig. 80. There was no sign of the existence of a monammine. At 154° the dissociation press. of the hexamminoiodide $p=316$ mm., and the heat of dissociation $Q=16·2$ Cals. ; and for **manganous diamminoiodide**, $MnI_2.2NH_3$, at 208°, $p=11·1$ mm., and $Q=21·6$ Cals. ; and at 215°, $p=14·6$ mm., and $Q=21·7$ Cals. F. Müller gave 35° to 172° for the dissociation temp. of the hexammine ; 172° for the pentamminoiodide ; above 200° for the diammine and the monammine.

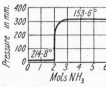

Fig. 80.—Dissociation Pressures of Manganous Hexamminoiodide.

F. Ephraim, and G. L. Clark discussed the vol. contraction attending the formation of the ammines ; and W. Biltz and E. Birk, the mol. vol. J. L. Lassaigne found that nitric acid liberates iodine from manganous iodide. P. Walden found manganous iodide to be soluble in phosphoryl chloride, and in arsenic iodide. A. R. Leeds observed that with aniline, manganous iodide forms $MnI_2.2C_6H_5(NH_2)$; A. Moitessier, that with phenylhydrazine, MnI_2. $2C_6H_5.NH.NH_2$; and G. A. Barbieri and F. Calzolari, that with hexamethylenetetramine, $MnI_2.2C_6H_{12}N_4.10H_2O$ is formed ; B. Köhnlein found that manganous iodide and propyl chloride change their halogens at 145°–150°. C. E. Saunders saturated a hot sat. soln. of manganous chloride with potassium iodide and observed that the precipitate, $KMnCl_3.2H_2O$, contained very little iodide ; and a similar result was obtained by treating manganous iodide with potassium chloride. No evidence of the formation of a mixed potassium manganous chloroiodide was obtained. A. Duboin obtained a deposit of **mercuric manganous iodide**, $5HgI_2.3MnI_2.20H_2O$, from a sat. soln. of the component iodides evaporated over sulphuric acid at 17°. The sp. gr. of the salt is 3·8.

J. L. Lassaigne observed that powdered pyrolusite with cold hydriodic acid forms a dark yellowish-red soln. which when warmed gives off iodine to form manganous iodide. J. Nicklès found that if one of the higher manganese oxides be suspended in ether and treated with hydrogen iodide, a green liquid is formed which is easily decomposed. Possibly these liquids contain a very unstable *manganese triiodide* or *tetraiodide*. According to W. Riedel, **manganese tetraiodide**, MnI_4—probably $MnI_2.I_2$—exists in soln. obtained by shaking an aq. soln. of manganous iodide with iodine at 25°. Just 2 mols. of iodine are taken up by $0·1M$-MnI_2 ; more conc. soln. take up more iodine. The eq. conductivity, λ, of the soln. of an eq. of the salt in v litres at 18° and the calculated degree of ionization, α, are :

v .	20	40	80	160	320	640	1280	5120	α
λ .	85·09	89·99	94·66	99·02	102·61	106·34	108·81	111·59	114·39
a .	0·7478	0·7866	0·8274	0·8657	0·8970	0·9296	0·9511	0·9754	—

D. Dobroserdoff observed that when a mixed conc. soln. of manganous and mercuric iodides is heated on a water-bath and allowed to stand in a desiccator over sulphuric acid, yellow prisms of **manganous mercuric hexaiodide**, $Hg_2MnI_6.6H_2O$, are formed. When roasted, manganese tritatetroxide is formed. The salt is readily separated into its components in aq. soln., with the deposition of mercuric iodide. The salt dissolves without decomposition in acetone, and in alcohol. A. Duboin obtained $3MnI_2.5HgI_2.20H_2O$ in an analogous way. The sp. gr. of the salt is 3·8. The salt dissolves freely, without decomposition, in methyl, propyl, iso-propyl, isobutyl, and allyl alcohols, in ethyl acetate and in ethyl cyanide ; it is rather less soluble in amyl, propyl, and isobutyl acetates, in acetone, in formic acid (with the precipitation of mercuric iodide), in acetic acid, in ethyl benzoate and oxalate, in butyl and amyl alcohols, and in nitrobenzene ; it is slightly soluble with decomposition in glycerol; and it is insoluble in ethyl nitrate, ethylene bromide, toluene, benzene, chloroform, carbon tetrachloride, ethyl iodide, monobromobenzene, and monochlorobenzene.

REFERENCES.

[1] W. Peters, *Ber.*, **42**. 4826, 1909; *Zeit. anorg. Chem.*, **77**. 137, 1912; P. Walden, *ib.*, **25**. 212, 1900; **29**. 371, 1902; W. Biltz and G. F. Hüttig, *ib.*, **109**. 89, 1919; W. Biltz and E. Birk, *ib.*, **134**. 125, 1924; W. Biltz, *ib.*, **193**. 321, 1930; *Zeit. Elektrochem.*, **29**. 348, 1923; E. C. Franklin and C. A. Kraus, *Amer. Chem. Journ.*, **20**. 828, 1898; C. E. Saunders, *ib.*, **14**. 127, 1892; H. Lescoeur, *Ann. Chim. Phys.*, (7), **2**. 103, 1894; B. Köhnlein, *Liebig's Ann.*, **225**. 171, 1885; P. Kutznetzoff, *Izvesta Polyt. Inst. Novotscherkask*, **2**. ii, 1, 1913; *Journ. Russ. Phys. Chem. Soc.*, **32**. 290, 1900; D. Dobroserdoff, *ib.*, **32**. 742, 1900; A. Liebknecht and A. P. Wills, *Ann. Physik*, (4), **1**. 178, 1900; F. Ephraim, *Ber.*, **45**. 1322, 1912; *Zeit. phys. Chem.*, **71**. 513, 1913; *Naturwiss.*, **7**. 49, 1919; F. Ephraim and O. Schütz, *Helvetica Chim. Acta*, **9**. 914, 922, 1926; A. R. Leeds, *Journ. Amer. Chem. Soc.*, **3**. 112, 1882; G. A. Barbieri and F. Calzolari, *Atti Accad. Lincei*, (5), **19**. ii, 584, 1910; A. Ferrari, *Atti Congresso Chim. Pura Applicata*, **3**. 449, 452, 1930; A. Ferrari and F. Giorgi, *ib.*, (6), **10**. 522, 1929; G. Devoto and A. Guzzi, *Gazz. Chim. Ital.*, **59**. 591, 1929; G. L. Clark, *Amer. Journ. Science*, (5), **7**. 1, 1924; A. Moitessier, *Compt. Rend.*, **124**. 1529, 1897; C. A. Valson, *ib.*, **74**. 103, 1872; A. Gorgeu, *ib.*, **106**. 703, 1888; *Bull. Soc. Chim.*, (2), **49**. 664, 1888; F. Ducelliez, *ib.*, (4), **13**. 815, 1913; J. Nicklès, *Ann. Chim. Phys.*, (4), **5**. 169, 1865; (4), **10**. 318, 1867; *Compt. Rend.*, **60**. 479, 1865; A. Étard, *ib.*, **98**. 993, 1884; A. Duboin, *ib.*, **142**. 1338, 1906; *Ann. Chim. Phys.*, (8), **16**. 277, 1909; M. Berthelot, *Thermochimie*, Paris, **2**. 268, 1897; J. Thomsen, *Thermochemische Untersuchungen*, Leipzig, **3**. 271, 1883; J. C. G. de Marignac, *Ann. Mines*, (5), **12**. 7, 1857; E. Wedekind, *Ber. deut. phys. Ges.*, **4**. 412, 1907; *Phys. Zeit.*, **7**. 805, 1907; J. L. Lassaigne, *Journ. Chim. Méd.*, **5**. 330, 1829; H. F. Gaultier de Claubry, *Bull. Soc. Enc. Nat. Ind.*, (3), **57**. 633, 1858; W. Riedel, *Ueber die Iodide und Polyiodide des Nickels, Kobalts und Mangans*, Halle a. S., 1913; F. Müller, *Jahrb. Phil. Fac. Univ. Bern*, **2**. 80, 1922.

§ 21. Manganese Sulphides

F. J. Müller von Reichenstein [1] described a mineral from Nagyag, Transylvania, which he called *Schwarze Blende*, and he regarded it as a Braunstein contaminated with sulphur; J. J. Bindheim also showed that it contained Braunstein, sulphur, iron, and silica; L. N. Vauquelin considered the manganese to be present in the lower stage of oxidation. A. M. del Rio described a Mexican mineral which he called *alabandina sulfurea*—after Alabanda in Caria, Asia Minor—and regarded as a compound of manganese, sulphur, and silica. D. L. G. Karsten called the mineral *Manganglanz*; C. C. Leonhard, *Braunsteinkies*; J. F. Blumenbach, *Braunsteinblende*; C. A. S. Hofmann, *Manganblende*; A. Breithaupt, *Blumenbachite*; F. S. Beudant, *alabandin*; and J. D. Dana, **alabandite**. The analyses of J. A. Arfvedson, M. H. Klaproth, J. L. Proust, and A. F. Gehlen showed that the mineral is essentially **manganese monosulphide**, or **manganous sulphide**, MnS. Other analyses were reported by C. Bergemann, A. J. Moses, and A. Raimondi. Observations on the occurrence of the mineral in the Siebenbürgen were also made by P. Groth, M. J. Ackner, V. R. von Zepharovich, K. F. Peters, A. Schrauf, R. Zahrl, and E. von Fellenberg; in Hungary, by M. J. Ackner, V. R. von Zepharovich, A. E. von Reuss, P. Groth, R. von Vivenot, and B. von Cotta and E. von Fellenberg; in Saxony, by A. Breithaupt, and A. Frenzel; in France, by A. Lacroix, and A. Bertrand; in Brazil, by G. Leonhard; in Peru, by P. y Rico, and A. Raimondi; in Mexico, by C. Bergemann, H. J. Burkart, and A. M. del Rio; in the United States, by A. J. Moses, and W. B. Smith; and in New South Wales, by A. Liversidge. Manganous sulphide was reported to be a furnace product—*e.g.* in blast-furnace slags—by J. F. L. Hausmann, J. L. H. Vogt, and H. Vogelsang. F. Wüst reported that the sulphur in pig-iron containing manganese, becomes insoluble as manganous sulphide in the metal-bath. The good development of crystals of manganous sulphide shows that they existed while the mass was still fluid; in the words of H. le Chatelier and A. Ziegler:

Le sulfure de manganèse, avant pris une symétrie cristalline, est nécessairement l'élément de première consolidation, c'est-à-dire que son point de fusion est supérieur à celui du manganèse et par suite du fer; il est donc très éloigné de celui du sulfure de fer.

K. Jellinek and J. Zakowsky attempted to determine the affinity of manganese for sulphur.   J. J. Berzelius converted the red hydrated sulphide, obtained by precipitation, into anhydrous manganous sulphide by heating it in a current of dry hydrogen sulphide ; C. Doelter, P. de Clérmont, and T. Sidot used a similar process ; and P. de Clérmont and H. Guyot dehydrated the green hydrated sulphide by heating it in dry hydrogen at 105°.   Anhydrous manganous sulphide, in more or less well-defined crystals, was prepared by J. A. Arfvedson by passing hydrogen sulphide over heated manganous oxide or sulphate so long as water is formed. C. von Hauer, F. Fouqué and A. Michel-Lévy, and J. J. Ebelmen recommended a similar process, and E. von Fellenberg used manganous carbonate.   H. Rose heated more or less oxidized manganous sulphide or sulphate mixed with sulphur in a current of hydrogen until the product had a constant weight ; and J. A. Arfvedson also heated a mixture of pyrolusite or manganous carbonate and sulphur. G. Röhl heated a mixture of manganese oxide and an excess of sulphur to incandescence in a current of hydrogen and found the product contained 96·58 per cent. MnS, 1·94 per cent. Mn_3O_4, and 1·50 per cent. S.   By repeating the operation on this product mixed with sulphur, only traces of oxide were contained in the resulting manganous sulphide. J. W. Döbereiner, and P. Berthier reduced the sulphate by carbon at a red-heat ; K. Stammer reduced the sulphate by carbon monoxide ; H. Rose, by hydrogen.   A. Voelcker heated manganite to redness in a current of carbon disulphide vapour ; and A. Gautier and L. Hallopeau observed that when the metal is similarly treated at 1400°, some carbide as well as sulphide is formed.   R. Schneider obtained good crystals by melting a mixture of manganous sulphate, potassium carbonate, and sulphur (1 : 12 : 12), extracting the soluble salts with water, and drying the product in hydrogen.   A. Mourlot reduced the sulphate by carbon in an electric furnace ; M. Picon said that the product is always contaminated with carbide, and that sulphide of a high degree of purity is best made by the action of hydrogen sulphide on the oxide at 900°.   J. Milbauer obtained the sulphide by fusing the oxide with potassium thiocyanate.   E. Wedekind and T. Veit prepared the sulphide by the action of a manganese thermite mixture on sulphur ; the action is very vigorous.   H. de Sénarmont heated a soln. of a manganous salt with alkali sulphide in a bomb-tube at 187° ; H. Baubigny left standing in a sealed tube for about a year a mixture of 1·1 grm. of neutral manganous acetate dissolved in 100 c.c. of water acidified with a few drops of acetic acid and saturated with hydrogen sulphide ; and E. Weinschenk heated in a sealed tube at 230° to 250° an aq. soln. of a manganous salt, acetic acid, and ammonium thiocyanate.   J. Milbauer obtained the amorphous sulphide by fusing a mixture of manganese oxide and potassium thiocyanate.   E. Beutel and A. Kutzelnigg studied the anodic formation of the sulphide.

G. Bruni and M. Padoa found that manganous salt soln. in dil. hydrochloric acid gave no precipitate with hydrogen sulphide even when the gas is under a great press. ; but if the soln. be treated with alkali sulphide or hydrosulphide, a precipitate is formed which, as J. F. John observed, may exhibit various colours— red, yellow, green, etc.—according to the conditions.   According to V. M. Fischer, manganous sulphide may be precipitated from a faintly acid soln. of a manganous salt by means of hydrogen sulphide if the passage of the gas be sufficiently protracted.   The precipitate obtained in this way is red or orange-red, and, depending on the degree of acidity of the soln., is either anhydrous or hydrated to a maximum of 17 per cent. of water, corresponding with the composition $MnS.H_2O$; under certain conditions it is deposited in the form of doubly refracting crystals.   Rose-coloured manganese sulphide precipitated from a soln. of a manganous salt by means of the sulphide of an alkali metal is amorphous.   The precipitate is usually flesh-coloured or pink, but if the soln. is much diluted, H. W. F. Wackenroder observed that the precipitate appears to be white for the first few moments. A. Villiers applied the term protomorphic to the condition or state in which various metal sulphides exist at the moment of their formation.   The protomorphic state is presumably equivalent to what is now called the colloidal state. O. Ruff and B. Hirsch discussed the precipitation of manganese sulphide in the presence of zinc, cadmium, and mercuric sulphides; and S. M. Kuzmeno, in the presence of zinc, iron, cobalt, and nickel sulphides. A. Terreil observed that in the presence of a large proportion of ammonium salts, the precipitate obtained with ammonium sulphide and a soln. of a manganous salt may be dirty yellow, and if much free ammonia is present, sulphur-yellow; and A. Voelcker, that a small, reddish precipitate may be produced if hydrogen sulphide is passed into a soln. of manganous acetate, particularly while the liquid is exposed to sunlight. These colorations may in part be due to impurities—sulphur, etc.—and in part to the degree of fineness of the precipitate. O. Ruff studied the precipitation in the presence of zinc salts.

Two main varieties are generally recognized, red or pink and green. The **red variety** is obtained when the precipitation is made under the conditions just indicated. U. Antony and P. Donnini recommended preparing the red sulphide by precipitation from ammoniacal soln. of manganous sulphate by ammonium sulphide, washing the product in an atm. of hydrogen sulphide, and drying it at 70° in a current of carbon dioxide. Any contamination with sulphur can be removed by washing the product with carbon disulphide. F. Seeligmann obtained it in an easily-filtered form by treating a soln. containing about half. a gram per 200 c.c. with 10 to 20 c.c. of 25 per cent. ammonia per 10 c.c., heating the liquid to 60° to 80°, adding a slight excess of ammonium sulphide, and boiling for a few minutes. F. L. Hahn also described the preparation of the red sulphide. According to L. Joulin, equimolar parts of a soln. of manganous sulphate and sodium sulphide diluted 1 : 10,000, after standing four days, contain one-fifth of the sodium sulphide still undecomposed. C. R. Fresenius said that the precipitation is incomplete if colourless or yellow ammonium sulphide is employed; but if ammonium chloride be present, the precipitation is complete; A. Terreil, and A. Classen also observed that the presence of free ammonia hinders the precipitation of manganous sulphide by ammonium sulphide. H. How, J. Spiller, and C. R. Fresenius also observed that the presence of oxalic, tartaric, or citric acid hinders the precipitation of manganese sulphide by ammonia and ammonium sulphide; while the precipitation with alkali-lye and alkali sulphide is hindered by citric acid, but not by oxalic or tartaric acid. K. Jellinek and G. von Podjasky studied the reaction $MnS+2HCl \rightleftharpoons MnCl_2+H_2S$—*vide supra*, manganous chloride; and O. F. Tower and E. E. Chapman, the formation of the sulphide in rhythmic rings.

According to C. R. Fresenius, the **green variety** of manganous sulphide can be obtained from the red in different ways. C. Meinecke obtained the green sulphide by treating an ammoniacal soln. of a manganous salt with ammonium sulphide, and boiling the mixture for some minutes. According to U. Antony and P. Donnini, if the washed precipitate of red sulphide be left in water, or better in a soln. of ammonium sulphide, for a few days, it turns green; and a similar change is brought about by heating the red powder to 300° to 320° in a current of carbon dioxide or hydrogen sulphide. J. C. Olsen and W. S. Rapalje obtained a similar result. J. T. Norton obtained the green sulphide by heating manganous sulphate with a soln. of sodium thiosulphate at 140° to 150°—the precipitation is incomplete. F. L. Hahn recommended the following process :

One hundred grams of manganese sulphate are dissolved in 300 c.c. of water. 100 c.c. of 20 per cent. ammonia soln. are sat. with hydrogen sulphide, and another 100 c.c. of the ammonia added (colourless ammonium sulphide). 30 c.c. of this liquid are saturated with sulphur at the boiling temp. and then made up to 100 c.c. with the colourless soln. (yellow ammonium sulphide). To a boiling mixture of 5 c.c. of the manganese soln., 20 c.c. of 20 per cent. ammonia, and 100 c.c. of water, are added 30 c.c. of the ammonium sulphide soln. The precipitated manganese sulphide is dark green. To this is immediately added the ammonium sulphide soln. and the warm manganese salt is added in portions, the mixture being kept almost boiling and well stirred. If the manganese salt is added too rapidly, the flesh-coloured sulphide separates ;

while V. M. Fischer recommended the following process :

Ten grams of tetrahydrated manganous chloride or a corresponding quantity of the sulphate are dissolved, together with 5 grms. of ammonium chloride, in 25 c.c. of water in an Erlenmeyer flask, 100 c.c. of 25–29 per cent. ammonia soln. being then added.   From the clear soln. thus obtained, the rose-coloured manganese sulphide is precipitated by gradual addition from a dropping funnel of 100 c.c. of cold ammonium hydrogen sulphide, prepared by saturating 2·5 per cent. ammonia soln. with hydrogen sulphide ; during the precipitation the liquid is constantly shaken.   After about fifteen minutes the rose-coloured precipitate begins to change into the green modification, the conversion being complete after some hours.   The manganous sulphide is then separated by filtration, washed with dilute ammonium hydrogen sulphide soln., and dried in a current of hydrogen at 110°.

According to A. Mickwitz and G. Landesen, the sole condition for the formation of the green salt is the presence of free ammonia before the addition of the ammonium sulphide.   If no free ammonia be present, the rose-coloured sulphide precipitated by ammonium hydrogen sulphide contains more sulphur than is required by the formula MnS, and its composition is better expressed by the formula $H_2Mn_3S_4$; in presence of free ammonia, the formula is $(NH_4)HMn_3S_4$, and this rose-coloured precipitate slowly passes into the green form, MnS, giving up $(NH_4)SH$ to the mother-liquor.   P. de Clérmont and H. Guyot studied the conditions which influence the change.   An excess of ammonium sulphide and heat favour the transformation ; while the presence of an excess of ammonium chloride hinders the change ; an excess of manganous salt or the use of sodium or potassium sulphide in different degrees of sulphuration gives the red sulphide.   F. Muck found that solid manganous chloride gives some green salt in the cold ; the sulphate gives less ; the nitrate gives only traces ;   the phosphate forms the green sulphide rapidly, so also does the oxalate. Ammonium sulphide precipitates the green sulphide from a hot ammoniacal soln. of manganous oxalate ; and a soln. of the red sulphide in ammonium oxalate gives the red sulphide when cold and the green sulphide when hot.   According to P. de Clérmont and H. Guyot, the ammoniacal soln. of manganese oxalate with an excess of ammonium sulphide in the cold gives no precipitate, but when hot, red manganous sulphide separates and it quickly turns green.   If a manganous salt be mixed for preference with potassium oxalate—ammonium oxalate and oxalic acid are less suitable —boiled, and treated with ammonia, and then with hot ammonium sulphide, a mixture of the red and green sulphides is formed, which when heated on a sand-bath becomes wholly green.   This also occurs if ammonium chloride be present. F. Muck found that some green sulphide is produced when manganous carbonate is boiled for 10 mins. with ammonium sulphide in excess, and if heated for some hours in a sealed tube all is converted into the green sulphide, but the formation of green sulphide does not occur if the carbonate be gradually heated with soln. of hydrogen sulphide or of potassium or sodium sulphide.   F. Muck, and P. de Clérmont and H. Guyot found that if the liquid in which the red sulphide is suspended be frozen, the green sulphide is formed, but A. Geuther said that this is not the case. A. Villiers obtained the green sulphide by adding a very small excess of ammonium sulphide to a very dil. soln. of manganous chloride at 0°.   He said that the precipitation of manganous sulphide in a neutral soln. saturated with ammonium and alkali salts gives a pink precipitate which does not turn green, whereas precipitation in a neutral soln. containing but a small amount of foreign salts gives a pink sulphide which slowly changes at the ordinary temp. into the green form. In order to obtain the green sulphide in the cold, any excess of acid should be first removed, the soln. diluted, made alkaline with ammonia, and ammonium hydrosulphide added.   F. Muck observed that water or a conc. soln. of hydrogen sulphide or aq. ammonia does not transform the red into green sulphide when heated under ordinary press., or when heated to 140° or 150° in a sealed tube for 4 to 5 hrs., but P. de Clérmont and H. Guyot found that the transformation does not occur if the red sulphide is heated with water for 48 hrs., but a little is changed when it is heated in water vapour at 305°, and some red sulphide is changed by the soln. of hydrogen sulphide at 220° ; and with a 20 hrs.' heating with aq. ammonia at 220° the red sulphide is turned green, but not so if ammonium chloride or quicklime be present. F. Muck observed that if the red sulphide be heated with an excess of ammonium sulphide at ordinary press., or at 140° to 150° in a sealed tube, the green sulphide is formed, but if the red sulphide be first heated with a little and then with an excess of ammonium sulphide it does not become green. P. de Clérmont and H. Guyot found that potassium and sodium sulphides do not change the red sulphide at ordinary press., or at a higher press. in a sealed tube, nor does the change occur if a little ammonium sulphide is present; potassium hydrosulphide under press. changes the red sulphide to a violet colour, and F. Muck obtained a similar result with potassium poly-sulphide. P. de Clérmont and H. Guyot observed that the red sulphide is not changed when heated to 300° with a soln. of ammonium sulphide; with ammonium carbonate, manganous carbonate is formed; with ammonium phosphate, man-ganous phosphate; and with potassium chloride, at 200°, a white compound. V. M. Fischer said that the change of red to green sulphide, which occurs in about 15 mins. in an ammoniacal soln. of ammonium sulphide in the presence of ammonium chloride, also takes place in absence of ammonium chloride, and for each con-centration of ammonia corresponding with the maximum velocity of the conversion. The latter is prevented by the presence of even a small proportion of hydroxylamine hydrochloride, and is retarded by ammonium chloride if this is added subsequently to the precipitation. The pink or red variety is also converted into the green form by trituration. The properties of the two sulphides were studied by H. B. Weiser and W. O. Milligan. They found that the change from the rose to the green manganese sulphide occurs at the b.p. in the presence of a sufficient excess of sodium sulphide. At room temp., the change readily occurs when ammonium sulphide in the presence of aq. ammonia is the precipitant. The critical conc. of the reagents for the maximum speed of the transformation is sharply defined. In the presence of ammonium hydrosulphide free from ammonia the change slowly occurs when the rose precipitate is seeded with the green one by mixing this form with the reactant before precipitation. Rapid mixing delays the change, and free ammonia is not essential. The solvent action of sodium sulphide and ammonium sulphide on the rose sulphide is an important factor in initiating and accelerating the transformation, but the absorption of ammonia by the rose precipitate acts protectively and retards the change. There is no evidence that the rose precipitate which spontaneously turns to green has the composition $(NH_4)HMn_3S_4$. The rose sulphides formed in the presence or absence of free ammonia are identical in structure, as are the light and dark green sulphides formed with sodium sulphide and ammonium sulphide respectively; the difference in colour is due to a variation in the size of the particle.

G. Landesen observed that the red precipitate obtained with a soln. of ammonium sulphide, free from ammonia, equivalent to 4·5 mols of NH_4HS per gram-atom of manganese acquires a greenish film in about 6 days, and that the subsequent change from red to green proceeds very slowly. There is, however, a more rapid change of red to orange, which is completed in about 6 months, and the dark green variety grows at the expense of the orange form. The passage from red to orange is accelerated in the presence of ammonia. The orange and red varieties are amorphous, the green form is crystalline. The reaction with manganous chloride is supposed to proceed $MnCl_2 + NH_4OH \rightarrow Mn(OH)Cl + NH_4Cl$; followed by $Mn(OH)Cl + NH_4HS$ $\rightarrow Mn(OH)(HS) + NH_4Cl$; and by $Mn(OH)(HS) \rightarrow MnS + H_2O$. Likewise with the sulphate, $2MnSO_4 + 2NH_4OH \rightarrow HO-Mn-SO_4-Mn-OH + (NH_4)_2SO_4$; $HO-Mn-SO_4$ $-Mn-OH + 2NH_4SH \rightarrow 2(HO.Mn.SH) + (NH_4)_2SO_4$; etc.

P. de Clérmont and H. Guyot found that the red sulphide after drying in vacuo contained water eq. to $MnS.H_2O$, and when dried in hydrogen at 105°, water eq. to $2MnS.H_2O$. C. R. Fresenius, and A. Classen said that the green sulphide is anhydrous; and E. Priwoznik found the green sulphide dried in vacuo has 13·39 per cent. of water, but when dried at 105° it is anhydrous. F. Muck regarded the green sulphide as an oxysulphide; and P. de Clérmont and H. Guyot observed that it

becomes anhydrous when heated in hydrogen at 105°, and it loses no more in weight
when heated to redness in a current of carbon disulphide ; when the green sulphide
has been dried in vacuo, it loses water eq. to $3MnS.2H_2O$, in dry hydrogen sulphide.
J. C. Olsen and W. S. Rapalje said that the green and red sulphides are anhydrous ;
and U. Antony and P. Donnini found that both the green and the red sulphides
dried at 70° in a current of carbon disulphide have the same composition, being
anhydrous manganous sulphides. The red variety consists of tiny, reddish, transparent crystals. U. Antony and P. Donnini, and J. C. Olsen and W. S. Rapalje
said that the green variety is crystalline. According to V. M. Fischer, green
manganous sulphide may be obtained either anhydrous or in a hydrated form,
the content of water, which varies from 0 to 17 per cent. is dependent on the
conc. of the ammonia, the presence or absence of ammonium chloride, and the
length of time during which the precipitate remains in contact with the mother-
liquor. Any hydrated green sulphide becomes anhydrous if left long enough in
the liquid. This sulphide may be obtained crystalline if the soln. is stirred during
the formation of the precipitate, or if ammonia is first added to the soln. of the
manganous salt, and ammonium hydrogen sulphide then gradually introduced.
P. de Clérmont and H. Guyot said that the green sulphide is stable, the pink
variety unstable. The difference in the properties is not due to different degrees
of hydration, for the transformation of the red to the green sulphide is not effected
by dehydrating agents like potash-lye or alcohol, but it is effected by heating
the red sulphide in a current of carbon dioxide under conditions where only 0·21
percentage loss in weight occurs. U. Antony and P. Donnini attributed the
difference in coloration and chemical properties to differences in the state of
condensation of the material, the green sulphide being more condensed than the
red variety. This is because the sp. gr. of the green variety is rather higher than
that of the red variety.

J. C. Olsen and W. S. Rapalje stated that in addition to the anhydrous red and
green sulphides, there is a *grey variety* of manganous sulphide which is highly
hydrated. The red sulphide of manganese obtained by the action of ammonium
sulphide on a neutral soln. of manganous chloride appears to be a mixture of the
grey and red sulphides in varying proportions. The red sulphide is not uniform
in composition, and contains from 4 to 14 per cent. of free sulphur and a varying
amount of water. The red variety of manganous sulphide is usually considered to
be in the amorphous or colloidal state. O. Fisseler prepared **colloidal manganous
sulphide** by adding the theoretical quantity of manganous sulphate to an aq. soln.
of sodium lysalbinate or protalbinate, and, after adding some sodium hydroxide,
passing a current of hydrogen sulphide through the liquor. The brown sol becomes
flesh-coloured. The colloidal soln. when evaporated on a water-bath and dried
in vacuo forms pale brown plates which readily form a sol with water. The sol is
milky brown by reflected light and yellowish-brown with a reddish tinge in transmitted light. P. B. Ganguly and N. R. Dhar found that in colloidal soln. sulphur
is formed. O. F. Tower and E. E. Chapman, and J. Hausmann observed that when
manganous sulphide is precipitated in jellies, *rhythmic layers* may be formed.

Native manganous sulphide is iron-black or dark steel-grey. It usually occurs
in granular aggregates ; it also occurs in cubic **crystals** with a cubic or dodecahedral
habit ; there may be **twinning** about the (111)-face. R. W. G. Wyckoff discussed
the possible space groupings for the X-radiogram of alabandite, and he concluded
that the arrangement of the atoms with either 4 or 32 chemical molecules per unit
cell is either that of the rock salt type or a tetrahedral or tetartohedral grouping
very close to this. E. J. Cuy calculated 2·61 A. for the interatomic distance.
H. B. Weiser and W. O. Milligan found the space-lattice is probably a face-
centred cube with $a=5·20$ A. The crystals were described by K. F. Peters,
F. Roll, P. Groth, A. Breithaupt, E. von Fellenberg, R. von Vivenot, A. Schrauf,
A. Bertrand, A. Lacroix, H. J. Burkart, A. J. Moses, W. B. Smith, etc. As
indicated above, U. Antony and P. Donnini found both the red and green varieties

are crystalline, but others state that the red variety is amorphous. The crystals of the mineral alabandite are like those of sphalerite, or zinc-blende, but the minerals are not isomorphous because alabandite does not possess the dodecahedral **cleavage** of zinc-blende; rather is the cubic cleavage like that of sodium chloride and magnesium oxide. T. Sidot obtained yellowish-green hexagonal prisms isomorphous with wurtzite. Hence, like zinc sulphide, manganese sulphide is dimorphous. A. Damour, and A. des Cloizeaux observed a manganiferous variety of wurtzite in some lapis-lazuli from Siberia. They called it *erythrozincite*. Crystals of the alabandite type were obtained artificially by F. Fouqué and A. Michel-Lévy, C. Doelter, A. Reis and L. Zimmermann, H. Baubigny, E. Weinschenk, H. de Sénarmont, E. Wedekind and T. Veit, R. Schneider, and A. Mourlot—*vide supra*. V. M. Fischer said that the black crystals of the green sulphide have green streaks and have the form of octahedra or icositetrahedra. A. E. van Arkel found that the **X-radiogram** shows that ferrous and manganous sulphides form ionic space-lattices. H. Ott found that the space-lattice resembles that of manganous oxide with $a=5\cdot24$ A., and the calculated density is $3\cdot98$. O. Stelling, and W. F. de Jong and H. W. V. Willems studied this subject. O. Ruff examined the effect of copper and zinc sulphides on the space-lattice; and L. Royer, parallel growths of alkali halides on manganous sulphide. The **specific gravity** of the mineral given by V. R. von Zepharovich is $3\cdot87$; by R. Zahrl, $3\cdot89$; by H. J. Burkart, $4\cdot125$; by C. Bergemann, $4\cdot036$; and by A. J. Moses, $4\cdot031$ to $4\cdot040$. A. Mourlot found that the crystals obtained in the electric furnace have a sp. gr. $3\cdot92$, and that the sulphide which had been fused had a sp. gr. of $4\cdot06$. U. Antony and P. Donnini gave $3\cdot55$ at $17°$ for the sp. gr. of the anhydrous red sulphide dried at $70°$, and $3\cdot74$ at $17°$ for the green sulphide. V. M. Fischer gave $4\cdot03$ for the sp. gr. of the crystals of the green sulphide; and $3\cdot92$ to $4\cdot06$ for the sp. gr. of alabandite. The **hardness** of alabandite is between 3 and 4. H. Fizeau found the coeff. of **thermal expansion**, a, to be $0\cdot00001519$ at $40°$, and $da/d\theta=0\cdot07217$. A. Sella gave $0\cdot1392$ for the **specific heat**; and C. T. Anderson gave for the mol. ht., C_p:

	$-213\cdot2°$	$-193\cdot9°$	$-102\cdot9°$	$-57\cdot7°$	$0°$	$23\cdot9°$
C_p	$5\cdot068$	$7\cdot467$	$11\cdot36$	$11\cdot43$	$11\cdot80$	$11\cdot93$

The results for the whole series of observations are plotted in Fig. 81. There is a sharp maximum at about $-135°$, and a break in the curve at $-126°$. Manganous sulphide is not changed when heated out of contact with air; J. J. Berzelius observed that the red sulphide gives off water when heated in a retort—*i.e.* out of contact with air—and the green sulphide is formed. P. de Clérmont and H. Guyot observed that the red sulphide is not changed when heated in a closed vessel to $300°$, and similarly with the green sulphide. N. Parravano and G. Malquori gave for the dissociation press. at $600°$, log $p_{S_2}=-19\cdot62$. M. Picon said that manganous sulphide volatilizes unchanged at $1375°$. G. Röhl observed that a sample of manganous sulphide containing $12\cdot5$ per cent.

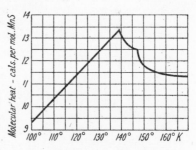

FIG. 81.—The Molecular Heat of Manganous Sulphide.

of oxide melted at $1550°$, while a preparation almost free from oxide had a **melting-point** of $1620°$; J. H. Andrew and co-workers gave $1615°$; and Z. Shibata gave $1610°$; N. Parravano and P. de Cesaris gave for the **vapour pressure** at $800°$, $4\cdot5\times10^{-18}$ atm.; at $900°$, $8\cdot3\times10^{-16}$ atm.; at $1000°$, $6\cdot6\times10^{-14}$ atm.; and at $1100°$, $2\cdot8\times10^{-12}$ atm. J. Thomsen gave $46\cdot37$ Cals.; and C. T. Anderson gave $62\cdot9$ Cals. at $25°$ for the **heat of formation** of manganous sulphide from the metal and amorphous sulphur, and with rhombic sulphur, $44\cdot39$ Cals. M. Berthelot gave for precipitated manganous sulphide, $(Mn,S)=45\cdot6$ Cals., and also

(H_2S_{soln},$Mn(OH)_{2\,precipitate}$)=10·1 Cals., and J. Thomsen, 10·7 Cals. S. Wologdine and B. Penkievitsch gave 62·901 and 70·535 Cals. for the mol. ht. of formation of MnS. J. Thomsen gave ($Mn(OH)_2$,H_2S,Aq.)=10·7 Cals. ; M. Berthelot, 10·2 Cals. ; and J. Thomsen, ($Mn(NO_3)_2$,H_2O,Aq.)= −12·2 Cals. J. Thomsen also gave $MnSO_4$,$400H_2O$ + Na_2S,$400H_2O$ = Na_2SO_4aq. + $MnS_{precipitate}$ + 7·79 Cals. ; and $Mn(NO_3)_2$aq.+H_2Saq.=$MnS_{precipitate}$+$2HNO_3$−12·26 Cals. ; and M. Berthelot gave $Mn(C_2H_3O_2)_2$aq.+Na_2Saq.=$2NaC_2H_3O_2$+$MnS_{precipitate}$+6·3 Cals. C. T. Anderson gave −64,000 cals. for the **free energy** of manganese sulphide; and 18·7 for the **entropy** at 25°. G. Beck discussed the energy of formation. O. Stelling studied the X-ray spectrum. F. Beijerinck found that the **electrical conductivity** of alabandite is negligibly small, cold or hot. W. Skey found the **electrochemical series** in sea-water to be −FeS, MnS, ZnS, SnS_2, HgS, Ag_2S, PbS, Cu_2S, FeS_2, Sb_2S_3+. E. T. Wherry observed that the crystals of alabandite make a fair **radio-detector.** E. Wedekind observed that when heated, manganous sulphide becomes strongly magnetic ; and E. Wedekind and C. Horst gave for the magnetic susceptibility of the sulphide 44·32×10^{-6} mass unit ; and G. Wistrand, 64·8×10^{-6}.

A. Mourlot observed that the crystalline or fused sulphide is less chemically active than the amorphous. The sulphide is not attacked by **hydrogen** at 1200° ; but it is inflamed by **oxygen** below a red-heat. J. Milbauer and J. Tucek considered the roasting of the sulphide in **air** to be accompanied by the reaction : R_mS_n+$2n$$SO_2$ =$R_m(SO_4)_n$+$n$$S_2$. A. Mailfert observed that **ozone** slowly converts manganese sulphide into the peroxide, with the liberation of sulphuric acid ; and some permanganic acid is simultaneously formed. The artificial sulphide turns brown in air even at ordinary temp., but the mineral is not changed by exposure to air. O. Binder noted a tendency to ignition when the artificial sulphide is dried. H. Höfer, R. von Vivenot, and H. J. Burkart have observed the natural **weathering** of the mineral to the sulphate ; and E. von Fellenberg observed that the mineral is attacked by liquids ; and A. E. von Reuss, and E. Döll observed the change of the sulphide to carbonate. J. A. Arfvedson found that when the sulphide is ignited in air, it forms manganese tritatetroxide and sulphur dioxide, the native sulphide less readily than the artificial. P. de Clérmont and H. Guyot found that the red sulphide, when dried in vacuo, becomes red-hot when exposed to air and forms sulphur dioxide, manganous sulphate, and brown manganese oxide ; while the green sulphide is more resistant to oxidation. If 10 grms. of moist green sulphide be rubbed in a mortar, the temp. rises to about 60° and steam is given off. P. W. Hofmann observed that when the sulphide is heated a few minutes in a platinum capsule, sulphur dioxide is given off, and manganous sulphate, and manganese dioxide and monoxide are formed respectively in the proportions 44·5 : 18·9 : 36·6. W. Biltz found the **solubility** of manganous sulphide in **water** to be 1·10×10^{-4} mol per litre ; O. Weigel found that for the precipitated red sulphide the solubility is 7·16×10^{-5} mol per litre at 18°, and that for the green sulphide 5·45×10^{-5} mol per litre. It is here assumed that the sulphide is completely hydrolyzed to manganous hydroxide and hydrogen sulphide. L. Bruner and J. Zawadzky calculated the **solubility product** to be 1·4×10^{-15}—the unreliability of this result turns on the uncertainty in the value for the potential of sulphur and manganese and on the state of the manganous sulphide in soln. The solubility product is probably higher than that of the sulphides of most heavy metals. This means that the conc. of the S″-ions is high in the presence of small H·-ion concentrations, and hence the sulphide is soluble even in acids of feeble strength. I. M. Kolthoff discussed the subject. O. Ruff and B. Hirsch studied the joint precipitation of zinc and manganese sulphides. A. Voelcker said that the red sulphide turns litmus blue ; and P. de Clérmont and H. Guyot, that the red sulphide is decomposed when boiled with water. H. V. Regnault represented the reaction with steam at a red-heat by $3MnS$+$4H_2O$=Mn_3O_4+$3H_2S$+H_2.

According to A. Mourlot, the crystalline sulphide is not attacked by **fluorine** in the cold, but if heated below redness the sulphide is decomposed with incandescence, while at about 350° **chlorine** attacks the sulphide which has been crystallized in the electric furnace, and sulphur monochloride is formed. E. von Fellenberg found that when ordinary synthesized manganous sulphide is heated in chlorine, it is converted into sulphur monochloride and crystalline manganous chloride. H. Rose found that the mineral is only slightly attacked when heated in chlorine, and a little sulphur monochloride is formed. A. Mourlot found that **bromine** attacks the crystalline sulphide less readily than does chlorine; and that the attack by **iodine** begins at 600°. **Hydrofluoric acid** acts on the crystalline sulphide in the cold, and so does **hydrochloric acid,** but with **hydrobromic acid** the temp. must be raised, and so also with **hydriodic acid.** F. Feigl showed that the solubility of manganous sulphide in acid is due in part to the oxidation of the sulphide to hydroxide. H. W. F. Wackenroder found that the green sulphide readily dissolves in even weak **acids,** with the evolution of hydrogen sulphide and the formation of a manganous salt. According to H. W. F. Wackenroder, red manganous sulphide is slightly soluble in a soln. of **ammonium sulphide,** but not if **ammonium polysulphide** is present; consequently, if a soln. of a manganous salt be treated with an excess of ammonium sulphide, and the filtrate from the manganous sulphide be exposed to air, or treated with a little polysulphide, manganous sulphide is precipitated—*vide supra*. A. Classen said that manganous sulphide is slightly soluble in fused sodium sulphide. P. de Clérmont and H. Guyot found that the green sulphide is not altered when it is heated with a soln. of **hydrogen sulphide** in a sealed tube at 250°. H. W. F. Wackenroder, and P. Berthier found that red manganous sulphide dissolves in an aq. soln. of **sulphur dioxide,** forming, according to C. F. Rammelsberg, sulphur and manganous thiosulphate, and, according to L. Gmelin, some manganous sulphate, but no hydrogen sulphide is evolved; A. Guérout observed that if sulphurous acid is dropped on to red manganous sulphide, hydrogen sulphide is given off, and manganous sulphite and sulphur are formed: $MnS+H_2SO_3=H_2S+MnSO_3$, and a part of the sulphur reacts with the sulphite to form thiosulphate. For W. E. Henderson and H. B. Weiser's observations on the action of sulphur dioxide, *vide* **10.** 58, zinc metasulphate. J. Milbauer and J. Tucek observed that when sulphur dioxide is passed over the heated sulphide, some sulphate is formed, but at a higher temp. the sulphate is converted into oxide. F. Förster and J. Janitzky studied the action of sulphurous acid on manganese sulphide. L. Moser and M. Behr gave 0·0056 mol per litre for the solubility in a 0·01N-soln. of **sulphuric acid** at 20°.

Aq. **ammonia** colours manganous sulphide deep yellow, forming, according to F. Muck, no ammonium sulphide, but rather a polythionate. P. de Clérmont and H. Guyot found that the green sulphide is not changed by heating it in ammonia. L. Santi observed that manganous sulphide is attacked by soln. of ammonium chloride. P. de Clérmont and H. Guyot inferred that soln. of **ammonium salts** dissolve red manganous sulphide in accord with $MnS+4NH_4Cl=2NH_4Cl.MnCl_2 +2NH_3+H_2S$. The reaction begins in the cold, and 100 c.c. of a soln. of ammonium chloride, sat. at 12°, dissolve 0·43 grm. of MnS. The green sulphide is less soluble than the red. If the soln. in excess be boiled under conditions where the hydrogen sulphide and ammonia can escape, the manganous sulphide all passes into soln.; but in a sealed tube a balanced reaction is set up. If ammonium sulphate be employed, polythionates may be found—for instance, F. Muck observed the formation of trithionate.

According to C. Tissier, a hot soln. of **boric acid** dissolves red manganous sulphide. L. Kahlenberg and W. J. Trautmann observed no reaction when a mixture of powdered silicon and the sulphide is heated over the bunsen burner, but at a higher temp. a reaction occurs. A. Mourlot found that manganous sulphide, unlike the sulphides of iron, cobalt, nickel, and chromium, is not attacked by **carbon** heated in the electric furnace for 15 mins. M. Houdard found that the diamond as well as amorphous carbon dissolves to the extent of 3·2 per cent. in molten manganous sulphide, and on cooling the carbon is rejected as graphite. M. Picon said that the heated sulphide can dissolve 15 per cent. of graphite without apparent change. N. Parravano and G. Malquori gave for the reaction $2MnS + C = 2Mn + CS_2$, at 1500°, $\log p_{CS_2} = -4 \cdot 923$. A. Wagner said that moist **carbon dioxide** rapidly attacks red manganous sulphide, liberating hydrogen sulphide, and, added P. de Clérmont and H. Guyot, the action is rapid if the temp. is raised. The red sulphide liberates hydrogen sulphide when it is treated with **acetic acid.** F. W. O. de Coninck found that **glycol** dissolves 5 per cent. of the red sulphide; and A. Naumann, that the sulphide is insoluble in **acetone.**

P. de Clérmont and H. Guyot observed that **sodium** amalgam and water do not attack the green sulphide, but do attack the red sulphide. C. H. Herty and O. S. True, and G. Röhl studied the reversible reaction with **iron,** $Fe + 2MnS \rightleftharpoons 2Mn + FeS_2$, and the formation of a complex salt, FeS.MnS. H. W. F. Wackenroder, and F. Muck observed that white manganese hydroxide is formed by a boiling soln. of **potassium hydroxide ;** and P. de Clérmont and H. Guyot, by an alcoholic soln. of potassium hydroxide in a sealed tube at 150°. P. Berthier found that an excess of molten **lead oxide** forms sulphur dioxide, lead, and a slag containing lead and manganous oxides. A. Gorgeu found that manganous sulphide reacts with many **metal salt** soln., forming the metal sulphide and a manganous salt—*e.g.* E. F. Anthon observed that manganous sulphide decomposes soln. of copper and cadmium sulphates ; silver, cobalt, and nickel nitrates ; lead acetate, and ferric chloride ; and E. Schürmann, soln. of ferrous and nickel sulphates and thallous and cobalt nitrates. According to E. Diepschlag and E. Horn, the reaction between **ferric oxide** and manganous sulphide begins at about 550°, and at 800° to 850° the reaction $MnS + 9Fe_2O_3 = MnO + 6Fe_3O_4 + SO_2$ is completed ; the reduction of the ferrosic oxide begins at about 950°, and at 1250° the reaction is $MnS + 3Fe_3O_4 = MnO + 9FeO + SO_2$. No compound, $MnO.Fe_2O_3$, was observed. They also studied the action of the sulphide on **ferrous oxide,** and on **ferrosic oxide**—*vide* iron. J. H. Andrew and co-workers studied the system with manganese sulphide and **manganese silicate** and with **ferrous silicate.** In the former, there is a eutectic at 1250° and 10 per cent. MnS ; and in the latter, one at 1055° and 10 per cent. MnS.

J. A. Arfvedson reported **manganous oxysulphide,** MnO.MnS, to be formed by heating manganous sulphate in a current of hydrogen ; K. Stammer used carbon monoxide as the reducing agent. The pale green powder is stable in air when cold, but when heated it burns to manganosic oxide ; it forms manganese sulphide when heated in hydrogen sulphide ; and it dissolves in acids, giving off hydrogen sulphide. J. Landauer said that when a manganese compound is fused with sodium thio-sulphate, a cake coloured pale green by manganous oxysulphide is formed. According to V. M. Fischer, in the presence of a large excess of sodium hydroxide, the addition of sodium sulphide to a soln. of a manganese salt gives not the rose-coloured sulphide, but a white precipitate of **manganous hexahydroxysulphide,** $MnS.3Mn(OH)_2$, or HO.Mn.O.Mn.S.Mn.O.Mn.OH. J. H. Andrew and co-workers studied the system MnO—MnS and found it to have a simple eutectic at 1285° with 50 per cent. MnS. There were limited solubilities at both ends of the curves.

P. Berthier obtained a pale brownish-red mass of **sodium manganous hepta-sulphide,** $2Na_2S.5MnS$, by heating white hot a mixture of manganous sulphate and sodium sulphate (10 : 5) in a carbon crucible. A. Voelcker prepared **sodium manganous tetrasulphide,** $Na_2S.3MnS$, by melting a mixture of dry manganous sulphate, lamp-black, and sodium carbonate (5 : 1 : 15), and, after cooling, washing out the sodium sulphide with alcohol, and the sodium sulphate by air-free water. The mass is exposed to air as little as possible during the washing operations ; and the pale red, acicular crystals are pressed between bibulous paper and dried in vacuo. The dry salt is stable in dry air, but when moist it is very readily oxidized, with the development of heat, and sometimes with inflammation. When heated on platinum foil it burns to sulphur dioxide, sodium sulphate, and manganic oxide. It is insoluble in water, alcohol, and ether ; it is freely soluble in dil. acids, with the development of hydrogen sulphide ; and with sulphurous acid sulphur is separated and manganous thiosulphate is formed. A. Voelcker prepared **potassium manganous tetrasulphide,** $K_2S.3MnS$, in dark red plates by the method which he employed for the sodium salt. It behaves very like the sodium salt, being readily oxidized in moist air, and readily burning when heated. A mixture of the salt with potassium nitrate detonates vigorously. It is insoluble in water, alcohol, and ether ; it is gradually decomposed by water with dissolved air, forming soluble potassium sulphide, sulphate, and thiosulphate, and insoluble sulphur, and hydrated manganic oxide. It is easily dissolved by acids—even acetic acid—with the liberation of hydrogen sulphide. J. Meyer and H. Bratke prepared the same salt. J. Milbauer obtained flesh-coloured crystals of a complex salt by the action of potassium thiocyanate on manganosic oxide at a bright red-heat. R. Schneider obtained **potassium manganous trisulphide,** $K_2S.2MnS$, by heating a mixture of manganous sulphate, potassium carbonate, and sulphur $(1 : 6 : 6)$ along with crystals of manganous sulphide. The crystals of the two salts can be separated by levigation. R. Schneider fused at a red-heat a mixture of dry manganous sulphate, sodium carbonate, and sulphur $(1 : 6 : 6)$, washing the cold product with air-free water, pressing between folds of bibulous paper, and drying in vacuo over conc. sulphuric acid, and obtained flesh-coloured plates and needles of **sodium manganous trisulphide,** $Na_2S.2MnS$. The moist product readily oxidizes ; and it is gradually decomposed by water. J. Milbauer obtained the complex salt, on one occasion, by fusing manganous oxide with potassium thiocyanate. According to W. Guertler and K. L. Meissner, on melting a mixture of *manganese and copper sulphides*, the mass separates into two layers, the upper consisting of manganese sulphide or of a eutectic of manganese and cuprous sulphides and the lower of pure copper or of mixed crystals of copper and manganese, according to the proportions of both metals present. Manganese has, therefore, a greater affinity for sulphur than copper, and this affinity is not modified by the addition of iron. Thus, if iron is added to a mixture of molecular proportions of cuprous sulphide with 1 atomic proportion of manganese, the mass separates into three layers, an upper layer of manganese sulphide, a middle layer of a eutectic mixture of manganese sulphide and iron, and a lower layer of copper more or less mixed with iron. W. Guertler discussed the formation of **copper manganese sulphide** in the ternary system Cu–Mn–S. According to M. Houdard, **aluminium manganous sulphide,** $Al_2S_3.MnS$, is produced when a mixture of aluminium turnings and manganese sulphide contained in a carbon boat placed in a porcelain tube is heated to dull redness for an hour in a current of hydrogen sulphide, and then the temp. is raised to a white-heat for half an hour. The product is attacked by cold water, with evolution of hydrogen sulphide and deposition of aluminium hydroxide, but the greater part, composed of brownish-yellow crystals, is insoluble. The latter is powdered and treated with acetic acid to remove aluminium sulphide. If the original mixture contains excess of manganous sulphide, the product consists of a pale golden-yellow mass throughout which green crystals of manganese sulphide are disseminated.

J. B. Hannay [2] reported a doubtful mineral which he called *plumbomanganite*. The analysis corresponded with $3MnS.PbS$, or *lead manganous tetrasulphide*. The sp. gr. was 4·01. He also obtained other doubtful minerals called *youngite*—after J. Young—representing *zinc lead manganous sulphide*, one corresponding with $6ZnS.PbS.MnS$ from the Harz ; another with $24ZnS.5PbS.5MnS$; and yet another with $10ZnS.3(MnS,FeS).2PbS$, from Ballarat, Australia. The sp. gr. ranged from 3·59 to 4·56.

A. Gautier and L. Hallopeau [3] heated rhodonite, $MnSiO_3$, in a current of the vapour of carbon disulphide at a white-heat, and obtained **manganosic sulphide,** or **manganese tritatetrasulphide,** Mn_3S_4, as an easily pulverized mass. Unlike manganous sulphide, it is easily hydrolyzed by water, with the evolution of hydrogen sulphide.

W. Haidinger described a reddish-brown or brownish-black mineral from

Kalinka, Hungary. It was discovered by K. Adler in 1846, and W. Haidinger called it **hauerite**—after J. and F. von Hauer. Analyses reported by W. Haidinger, E. Scacchi, A. Silvestri, M. Matzke, and H. de Sénarmont agree with the formula for **manganese disulphide,** MnS_2; and from the analogy with iron pyrites, P. Groth called it *manganese pyrites—Mangankies.* The Hungarian deposit was also described by L. von Cseh; Silician deposits were described by E. Scacchi, A. Silvestri, and F. de Memme; and a New Zealand deposit by S. H. Cox. H. de Sénarmont obtained manganese disulphide as an amorphous, brick-red powder, by warming a soln. of manganese sulphate and potassium polysulphide in a sealed tube at 160°. C. Doelter heated a mixture of manganese dioxide and sulphur in a current of hydrogen sulphide, and obtained crystals of artificial hauerite mixed with those of alabandite. According to L. von Cseh, the hauerite of Kalinka has been formed by solfateric action in which the vapours of sulphuric acid, hydrogen sulphide, and steam have acted on the pyroxene trachytes of that district. The deposits in the Gulf Coast salt domes were studied by A. G. Wolf, and M. A. Hanna.

Hauerite sometimes occurs in reddish-brown or brownish-black pyritohedral, cubic **crystals,** commonly in octahedra, but sometimes in globular clusters. The octahedral crystals were described by E. Onorato. The powdered mineral is brownish-red. The cubic **cleavage** is imperfect. W. H. and W. L. Bragg, P. P. Ewald and W. Friedrich, and A. E. van Arkel said that the **X-radiograms** of crystals of hauerite show that the structure is the same as those of pyrites and of cobaltite. R. W. G. Wyckoff discussed the possible groupings of atoms of manganese and sulphur in the space-lattice to form cubic crystals; $a=6\cdot111\times10^{-8}$ cm. E. J. Cuy gave 2·59 A. for the interatomic distance. P. Niggli studied the **electronic structure.** The crystals were discussed by W. Haidinger, W. H. Miller, V. Goldschmidt and K. Schröder, A. G. Wolf, and E. Scacchi, A. Silvestri, and F. de Memme. W. Haidinger gave 3·463 for the **specific gravity ;** E. Scacchi, 3·366 to 3·411; A. G. Wolf, 3·49; and A. Silvestri, 3·50 to 3·71. The **hardness** is about 4. H. Fizeau found the coeff. of **thermal expansion** to be $a=0\cdot00001111$ at 40°; and $da/d\theta=0\cdot0_7889$ per degree. G. Spezia observed that when hauerite is heated, it begins to lose sulphur at about 170°, and is ultimately converted into manganous sulphide. J. Joly said that a sublimate is formed at 450°. T. W. Case observed no cleavage in the electrical conductivity on exposing hauerite to light. R. D. Harvey, and F. Beijerinck made some indecisive observations on the **electrical conductivity** of hauerite.

According to A. Beutell and M. Matzke, when hauerite is shaken with water and **air,** a soln. of sodium carbonate, or a soln. of sodium acetate and acetic acid, it is oxidized, with the separation of free sulphur, but no sulphuric acid is formed. In this respect the mineral differs from pyrites, and it is therefore assumed that hauerite does not belong to the pyritic family of minerals—*vide supra.* M. Matzke also found that with **hydrogen dioxide** the whole of the sulphur separates as elemental sulphur. Unlike pyrite and marcasite, hauerite colours red litmus paper blue. It reacts with **hydrochloric acid,** liberating half the sulphur in the elemental form and half as hydrogen sulphide : $MnS_2+2HCl=MnCl_2+H_2S+S$. Here again hauerite behaves differently from pyrite and marcasite. According to G. Spezia, hauerite forms an explosive mixture with **potassium chlorate,** but does not react with it in the presence of water even at 100°. J. Strüver found that when crystals of hauerite are in contact with **silver,** there is slowly formed about that zone a dark film of silver sulphide : $4Ag+MnS_2=Mn+2Ag_2S$; if copper is in contact with the silver, the reaction is accelerated; **copper** in contact with hauerite also forms copper sulphide. Marcasite, pyrite, magnetic pyrites, cobaltite, and iron arsenide also react similarly with copper and silver ; but not so with stibnite. The strongest reaction occurs with sulphur alone. Hauerite, pyrite, and marcasite do not give the reaction with the **metals** zinc, tin, lead, antimony, bismuth, iron, nickel, and platinum. E. Arbeiter, and A. Beutell investigated the reaction with silver. They found that the reaction takes place without contact up to a distance of 1 cm., for sulphur is perceptibly volatile at ordinary temp. He concluded (i) that when hauerite is oxidized in air, free sulphur is formed—a similar result was obtained with arsenical pyrites, pyrite, marcasite, glaucodote, and cobaltite ; (ii) that the action of hauerite on silver is caused by free sulphur ; (iii) that the free sulphur can be distilled from the mineral in vacuo at 56° to 60°, and it becomes inactive. The activity is regained after the mineral has been re-exposed to air for 24 hrs. E. Quercigh agreed that the effect may in part be due to the vapour of sulphur produced by the decomposition of hauerite in air ; but the action may be produced when the mineral and the metal are pressed together under toluene, under conditions when it can be due neither to sulphur nor to hydrogen sulphide in the hauerite, nor to the removal of the sulphur from the mineral by toluene. He agreed with J. Strüver that the action is due to the passage of the combined sulphur of the hauerite directly to the silver or copper with which the mineral is in contact.

REFERENCES.

¹ F. J. Müller von Reichenstein, *Physikalische Arbeiten der einträchtigen Freunde in Wien*, 1. 86, 1784 ; J. J. Bindheim, *Schrift. Ges. Nat. Freunde Berlin*, 5. 452, 1784 ; M. H. Klaproth, *Beiträge zur chemischen Kenntniss der Mineralkörper*, Berlin, 3. 42, 1802 ; A. M. del Rio, *Tablas mineralogicas*, Mexico, 66, 1804 ; L. N. Vauquelin, *Ann. Mus. Hist. Nat.*, 6. 401, 1905 ; *Gehlen's Journ.*, 2. 41, 1806 ; D. L. G. Karsten, *Mineralogische Tabellen*, Berlin, 72, 1808 ; G. Leonhard, *Handwörtenbuch der topographischen Mineralogie*, Heidelberg, 385, 1843 ; C. C. Leonhard, *Systematisch-Tabellarische Uebersicht und Charakteristik der Mineralkörper*, Frankfurt a. M., 70, 1806 ; *Handbuch der Oryktognosie*, Heidelberg, 370, 1821 ; J. F. Blumenbach, *Handbuch der Naturgeschichte*, Göttingen, 1. 707, 1807 ; C. A. S. Hofmann, *Handbuch der Mineralogie*, 4. b, 197, 1818 ; R. J. Haüy, *Tableau comparatif des résultats de la cristallographie et de l'analyse chimique relativement à la classification des minéraux*, Paris, 111, 1809 ; *Traité de minéralogie*, Paris, 4. 268, 1822 ; F. S. Beudant, *Traité élémentaire de minéralogie*, Paris, 2. 399, 1832 ; A. Breithaupt, *Berg. Hütt. Ztg.*, 25. 193, 1866 ; *Mineralogische Studien*, Leipzig, 113, 1866 ; J. D. Dana, *A System of Mineralogy*, New York, 64, 1892 ; F. Mohs, *Grundriss der Mineralogie*, Dresden, 2. 592, 1824 ; P. Groth, *Die Mineraliensammlung der Universität Strassburg*, Strassburg, 30, 1878 ; V. R. von Zepharovich, *Mineralogisches Lexicon für das Kaiserthum Oesterreich*, Wien, 1. 3, 1859 ; 3. 2, 1893 ; R. Zahrl, *Berg. Hütt. Jahrb.*, 18. 344, 1870 ; K. F. Peters, *Neues Jahrb. Min.*, 665, 1861 ; E. Döll, *Verh. geol. Reichsanst. Wien*, 307, 1875 ; A. Liversidge, *The Minerals of New South Wales*, Sydney, 307, 1882 ; A. Frenzel, *Mineralogisches Lexicon für das königreich Sachsen*, Leipzig, 4, 1874 ; A. Raimondi, *Minéraux du Pérou*, Paris, 240, 1878 ; W. B. Smith, *Proc. Colorado Scient. Soc.*, 2. 155, 1887 ; A. Lacroix, *Minéralogie de la France et de ses colonies*, Paris, 2. 543, 1897 ; P. y Rico, *Anal. Esc. Min.*, 3. 61, 1883 ; H. J. Burkart, *Ber. Niederrh. Ges. Bonn*, 13. 19, 1856 ; *Neues Jahrb. Min.*, 557, 1856 ; 409, 1866 ; 828, 1867 ; A. E. von Reuss, *Jahrb. geol. Reichsanst. Wien*, 20. 521, 1870 ; R. von Vivenot, *ib.*, 19. 595, 1869 ; H. Höfer, *ib.*, 15. 240, 1865 ; 16. 1, 1866 ; J. Milbauer and J. Tucek, *Chem. Ztg.*, 50. 323, 1926 ; M. J. Ackner, *Mineralogie Siebenbürgens mit geognostischen Andeutungen*, Hermannstadt, 1855 ; B. von Cotta and E. von Fellenberg, *Die Erzlagerstätten Ungarns und Siebenbürgens*, Freiberg, 114, 1862 ; A. Bertrand, *Compt. Rend.*, 42. 1167, 1876 ; A. J. Moses, *School Mines Quart.*, 13. 236, 1892 ; H. Vogelsang, *Die Krystalliten*, Bonn, 24, 1875 ; G. Röhl, *Carnegie Mem. Iron Steel Inst.*, 4. 36, 1912 ; J. H. L. Vogt, *Die Sulfid : Silikatschmelzlösungen*, Kristiania, 1919 ; *Zur Kenntnis der Gesetze der Mineralbildung in Schmelzmassen und die neovulcanischen Ergussgesteine*, Kristiania, 1. 253, 1892 ; F. Fouqué and A. Michel-Lévy, *Synthèse des minéraux et des roches*, Paris, 307, 1882 ; E. Weinschenk, *Zeit. Kryst.*, 17. 500, 1890 ; C. Doelter, *ib.*, 11. 32, 1885 ; *Compt. Rend.*, 105. 1372, 1887 ; J. J. Berzelius, *Lehrbuch der Chemie*, Dresden, 2. i, 413, 1826 ; M. Berthelot, *Thermochimie*, Paris, 2. 269, 1897 ; J. Thomsen, *Thermochemische Untersuchungen*, Leipzig, 3. 271, 1883 ; O. Fisseler, *Ueber colloidale Verbindungen des Eisens, Mangans, und Kupfers*, Erlangen, 1904 ; F. Wüst, *Met.*, 5. 447, 1908 ; L. Gmelin, *Handbook of Chemistry*, London, 4. 218, 1850 ; N. Parravano and G. Malquori, *Gazz. Chim. Ital.*, 58. 279, 1928 ; S. M. Kuzmenko, *Ukrainskii Khem. Zhur.*, 3. 231, 1928 ; A. Voelcker, *Scheik. Onderzoek Utrecht*, 3. 526, 1846 ; *Liebig's Ann.*, 59. 35, 1846 ; E. Schürmann, *ib.*, 249. 326, 1888 ; E. Priwoznik, *ib.*, 171. 115, 1874 ; J. F. John. *ib.*, 28. 101, 1838 ; E. Wedekind, *Ber. deut. phys. Ges.*, 4. 412, 1907 ; *Phys. Zeit.*, 7. 805, 1907 ; *Zeit. Elektrochem.*, 11. 850, 1905 ; E. Wedekind and C. Horst, *Ber.*, 45. 262, 1912 ; 48. 105, 1915 ; C. Horst, *Ueber die Abhangigkeit der Magnetisierbarkeit anorganischer Verbindungen von der Wertigkeit des Hauptelementes, untersucht an den Oxyden und Sulfiden einiger Schwermetalle*, Freiburg, 1912 ; E. Wedekind and T. Veit, *Ber.*, 44. 2663, 1911 ; V. Violi, *ib.*, 10. 293, 1877 ; A. Naumann, *ib.*, 37. 4329, 1904 ; J. Landauer, *ib.*, 5. 407, 1872 ; K. J. Bayer, *Journ. prakt. Chem.*, (2), 5. 443, 1872 ; E. F. Anthon, *ib.*, (1), 10. 353, 1837 ; C. R. Fresenius, *ib.*, (1), 82. 265, 1861 ; F. Muck, *Zeit. Chem.*, (2), 5. 580, 629, 1869 ; (2), 6. 6, 1870 ; *Ber.*, 4. 446, 1877 ; A. Reis and L. Zimmermann, *Zeit. phys. Chem.*, 102. 298, 1922 ; A. Classen, *Zeit. anal. Chem.*, 8. 370, 1869 ; 16. 319, 1877 ; O. Binder, *ib.*, 47. 144,

1908; F. Seeligmann, *ib.*, **53**. 594, 1914; E. Claassen, *Amer. Chem. Journ.*, **8**. 436, 1886; C. Bergemann, *Neues Jahrb. Min.*, 394, 1857; F. Beijerinck, *Neues Jahrb. Min. B. B.*, **11**. 430, 1897; A. Geuther, *Jena. Zeit.*, **2**. 127, 1865; P. W. Hofmann, *Dingler's Journ.*, **181**. 364, 1866; R. Wagner, *ib.*, **195**. 532, 1870; F. W. O. de Coninck, *Bull. Acad. Belg.*, 359, 1905; W. Skey, *Chem. News*, **23**. 255, 1891; N. Parravano and P. de Cesaris, *Gazz. Chim. Ital.*, **47**. i, 144, 1917; W. Guertler, *Metall Erz*, **22**. 199, 1925; E. Diepschlag and E. Horn, *Arch. Eisenhüttenwesen*, **4**. 375, 1931; *Stahl Eisen*, **51**. 329, 1931; *Ueber die Umsetzungen von Eisensulfid, Mangansulfid und Kalziumsulfid mit den Oxyden des Eisens und dabei auftretende Nebenreaktionen*, Düsseldorf, 1931; O. F. Tower and E. E. Chapman, *Journ. Phys. Chem.*, **35**. 1474, 1931; C. Meinecke, *Zeit. angew. Chem.*, **1**. 3, 1888; E. Jordis and E. Schweizer, *ib.*, **23**. 577, 1910; E. Murmann, *Monatsh.*, **19**. 404, 1898; J. Milbauer, *Zeit. anorg. Chem.*, **42**. 439, 1904; K. Jellinek and G. von Podjasky, *ib.*, **171**. 261, 1928; J. T. Norton, *ib.*, **28**. 225, 1901; *Amer. Journ. Science*, (4), **12**. 115, 1901; R. W. G. Wyckoff, *ib.*, (5), **2**. 239, 1921; K. Preiss, *Zpravy Ceske Spol. Nauk*, 77, 1871; U. Antony and P. Donnini, *Gazz. Chim. Ital.*, **23**. 560, 1893; J. C. Olsen and W. S. Rapalje, *Journ. Amer. Chem. Soc.*, **26**. 1615, 1904; J. C. Olsen, E. S. Clowes and W. O. Weidmann, *ib.*, **26**. 1622, 1904; W. E. Henderson and H. B. Weiser, *ib.*, **35**. 239, 1913; E. J. Cuy, *ib.*, **49**. 201, 1927; L. Playfair and J. P. Joule, *Mem. Chem. Soc.*, **3**. 57, 1846; J. Spiller, *Journ. Chem. Soc.*, **10**. 110, 1858; Z. Shibata, *Tech. Rep. Tohoku Univ.*, **7**. 279, 1928; H. How, *Chem. News*, **19**. 137, 1869; A. Damour, *Bull. Soc. Min.*, **3**. 156, 1880; A. des Cloizeaux, *ib.*, **4**. 40, 1881; F. von Grieshammer, *Sprech.*, **43**. 153, 165, 1910; O. Stelling, *Zeit. Elektrochem.*, **34**. 520, 1928; **36**. 705, 1930; W. Biltz, *Zeit. phys. Chem.*, **58**. 288, 1907; O. Weigel, *ib.*, **58**. 293, 1907; F. L. Hahn, *ib.*, **121**. 209, 1922; L. Bruner and J. Zawadzky, *Zeit. anorg. Chem.*, **65**. 136, 1909; **67**. 454, 1910; A. Mickwitz and G. Landesen, *ib.*, **131**. 101, 1924; K. Jellinek and J. Zakowsky, *ib.*, **142**. 1, 1925; J. Meyer and H. Bratke, *ib.*, **135**. 289, 1924; O. Ruff, *ib.*, **185**. 387, 1930; G. Landesen, *ib.*, **193**. 277, 1930; L. Moser and M. Behr, *ib.*, **133**. 52, 1924; G. Beck, *ib.*, **156**. 288, 1926; F. Feigl, *ib.*, **157**. 269, 1926; O. Ruff and B. Hirsch, *ib.*, **150**. 84, 1925; **151**. 81, 1926; W. Guertler and K. L. Meissner, *Metall Erz.*, **18**. 438, 1921; V. M. Fischer, *Journ. Russ. Phys. Chem. Soc.*, **46**. 1481, 1914; C. H. Herty and O. S. True, *Blast Furnace and Steel Plant*, **13**. 492, 1925; P. B. Ganguly and N. R. Dhar, *Koll. Zeit.*, **31**. 16, 1922; A. E. van Arkel, *Physica*, **4**. 286, 1924; M. Picon, *Bull. Soc. Chim.*, (4), **41**. 189, 1927; *Compt. Rend.*, **184**. 98, 1927; G. Wistrand, *Magnetiska Susceptibiliteten hos Kvarts, Tellur och Några Holmiumföreningar*, Upsala, 1916; W. F. de Jong and H. W. V. Willems, *Physica*, **7**. 74, 1927; L. Kahlenberg and W. J. Trautmann, *Trans. Amer. Electrochem. Soc.*, **39**. 377, 1921; H. Rose, *Chem. News*, **2**. 302, 1860; *Liebig's Ann.*, **27**. 190, 1838; *Pogg. Ann.*, **42**. 540, 1837; **110**. 120, 1860; K. Stammer, *ib.*, **32**. 136, 1851; J. A. Arfvedson *Quart. Journ. Science*, **18**. 392, 1825; *Ann. Phil.*, **7**. 329, 1824; *Svenska Akad. Handl.*, 427, 1822; *Pogg. Ann.*, **1**. 50, 1824; A. Schrauf, *ib.*, **127**. 348, 1866; E. von Fellenberg, *ib.*, **50**. 76, 1840; R. Schneider, *ib.*, **151**. 449, 1874; C. F. Rammelsberg, *ib.*, **56**. 305, 1842; W. Müller, *ib.*, **127**. 404, 1866; J. W. Döbereiner, *Schweigger's Journ.*, **14**. 208, 1815; A. F. Gehlen, *ib.*, **2**. 161, 1811; L. Royer, *Bull. Soc. Min.*, **51**. 7, 1928; C. T. Anderson, *Journ. Amer. Chem. Soc.*, **53**. 476, 1931; J. L. Proust, *Journ. Phys.*, **54**. 93, 1802; **61**. 272, 1805; H. W. F. Wackenroder, *Brandes' Arch.*, **16**. 114, 1825; P. de Clérmont, *Bull. Soc. Chim.*, (3), **5**. 449, 1891; P. de Clérmont and H. Guyot, *Compt. Rend.*, **84**. 653, 1877; **85**. 37, 73, 404, 1877; **88**. 972, 1879; *Ann. Chim. Phys.*, (5), **12**. 111, 1877; *Bull. Soc. Chim.*, (3), **5**. 450, 1891; H. le Chatelier and A. Ziegler, *ib.*, (3), **27**. 1140, 1902; *Bull. Soc. Enc. Nat. Ind.*, **101**. ii, 368, 1902; A. Ziegler, *Rev. Mét.*, **6**. 459, 1909; P. Berthier, *Ann. Chim. Phys.*, (2), **22**. 247, 1823; (2), **39**. 252, 1828; H. V. Regnault, *ib.*, (2), **62**. 317, 1836; A. Mourlot, *Compt. Rend.*, **121**. 202, 1895; *Ann. Chim. Phys.*, (7), **17**. 548, 1899; L. Joulin, *ib.*, (4), **30**. 275, 1873; H. de Sénarmont, *ib.*, (3), **30**. 140, 1850; J. J. Ebelmen, *ib.*, (3), **25**. 92, 1849; A. Gorgeu, *ib.*, (3), **42**. 70, 1854; A. Gautier and L. Hallopeau, *Compt. Rend.*, **108**. 806, 1889; S. Wologdine and B. Penkievitsch, *ib.*, **158**. 498, 1914; A. Mailfert, *ib.*, **94**. 860, 1186, 1882; T. Sidot, *ib.*, **66**. 1257, 1868; H. Fizeau, *ib.*, **62**. 1101, 1133, 1866; **64**. 314, 771, 1867; H. Baubigny, *ib.*, **104**. 1372, 1887; A. Guérout, *ib.*, **75**. 1276, 1872; C. Tissier, *ib.*, **45**. 411, 1857; A. Villiers, *ib.*, **120**. 322, 1895; **159**. 67, 1914; *Bull. Soc. Chim.*, (3), **13**. 321, 1895; M. Houdard, *Compt. Rend.*, **143**. 1230, 1906; **144**. 801, 1114, 1907; A. Sella, *Nachr. Gött.*, 311, 1891; J. F. L. Hausmann, *ib.*, 226, 1855; *Beiträge zur Kenntniss krystallinischer Hüttenprodukte*, Göttingen, 1856; J. Hausmann, *Zeit. anorg. Chem.*, **40**. 110, 1904; G. Bruni and M. Padoa, *Atti Accad. Lincei*, (5), **14**. ii, 525, 1906; C. von Hauer, *Sitzber. Akad. Wien*, **25**. 124, 1857; L. Santi, *Boll. Chim. Farm.*, **43**. 673, 1904; E. T. Wherry, *Amer. Min.*, **10**. 28, 1925; H. Ott, *Zeit. Kryst.*, **63**. 222, 1926; F. Roll, *ib.*, **65**. 119, 1927; H. B. Weiser and W. O. Milligan, *Journ. Phys. Chem.*, **35**. 2330, 1931; J. H. Andrew, W. R. Maddocks and E. A. Fowler, *Journ. Iron Steel Inst.*, **125**. ii, 295, 1931; F. Förster and J. Janitzky, *Zeit. anorg. Chem.*, **200**. 23, 1931; E. Beutel and A. Kutzelnigg, *Monatsh.*, **58**. 295, 1931; I. M. Kolthoff, *Journ. Phys. Chem.*, **35**. 2711, 1931; O. F. Tower and E. E. Chapman, *ib.*, **35**. 1474, 1931; A. Terreil, *Compt. Rend.*, **45**. 652, 1857.

[2] J. B. Hannay, *Min. Mag.*, 1. 124, 152, 1877; 2. 88, 1878.

[3] W. Haidinger, *Sitzber. Akad. Wien*, 1. 101, 107, 1846; *Ber. Freunde Naturwiss.*, 2. 19, 1847; *Pogg. Ann.*, 70. 148, 1847; A. G. Wolf, *Bull. Amer. Assoc. Petr. Geol.*, 10. 531, 1926; M. A. Hanna, *ib.*, 13. 177, 1929; S. H. Cox, *Trans. New Zealand Inst.*, 14. 426, 1881; W. H. and W. L. Bragg, *X-rays and Crystal Structure*, London, 144, 1924; C. Doelter, *Zeit. Kryst.*, 11. 32, 1885; V. Goldschmidt and K. Schröder, *ib.*, 45. 214, 1908; W. H. Miller, *Introduction to Mineralogy*, London, 168, 1852; H. de Sénarmont, *Ann. Chim. Phys.*, (3), 32. 129, 1851; E. Scacchi, *Rend. Accad.*

Napoli, (2), **4**. 122, 189, 259, 1890 ; (3), **5**. 164, 1899 ; *Giorn. Min. Cryst.*, **1**. 321, 1890 ; *Riv. Min. Crist. Ital.*, **7**. 68, 1890 ; A. Silvestri, *ib.*, **7**. 68, 1890 ; E. Onorato, *Atti Accad. Lincei*, (6), **1**. 470, 1925 ; F. de Memme, *Atti Soc. Genova*, **2**. 82, 1890 ; A. E. van Arkel, *Physica*, **4**. 286, 1924 ; L. von Cseh, *Földt. Közl.*, **17**. 162, 255, 1887 ; H. Fizeau, *Compt. Rend.*, **62**. 1101, 1133, 1866 ; **64**. 314, 771, 1867 ; A. Gautier and L. Hallopeau, *ib.*, **108**. 806, 1889 ; F. Beijerinck, *Neues Jahrb. Min. B.B.*, **11**. 433, 1897 ; G. Spezia, *Atti Accad. Torino*, **43**. 354, 1908 ; J. Strüver, *Centr. Min.*, 257, 401, 1901 ; *Atti Accad. Linsei*, (5), **10**. 124, 233, 1904 ; E. Quercigh, *ib.*, (5), **24**. i, 626, 1915 ; A. Beutell, *Centr. Min.*, 758, 1913 ; 316, 411, 463, 1911 ; A. Beutell and M. Matzke, *ib.*, 270, 1915 ; M. Matzke, *Ueber die Konstitution von Zinkblende, Wurtzit, and Hauerit*, Breslau, 1914 ; *Neues Jahrb. Min.*, i, 147, 1916 ; E. Arbeiter, *Mineralogischchemische Untersuchungen an Markasit, Pyrit, und Magnetkies*, Breslau, 1913 ; R. W. G. Wyckoff, *Amer. Journ. Science*, (5), **1**. 139, 1921 ; (5), **2**. 237, 1921 ; P. P. Ewald and W. Friedrich, *Ann. Physik*, (4), **44**. 1183, 1914 ; F. Ephraim, *Ber.*, **59**. B, 790, 1926 ; R. D. Harvey, *Econ. Geol.*, **23**. 778, 1928 ; E. J. Cuy, *Journ. Amer. Chem. Soc.*, **49**. 201, 1927 ; J. Joly, *Phil. Mag.*, (6), **27**. 1, 1914 ; T. W. Case, *Phys. Rev.*, (2), **9**. 305, 1917 ; P. Niggli, *Zeit. Kryst.*, **75**. 228, 1930 ; P. Groth, *Die Mineraliensammlung der Universität Strassburg*, Strassburg, 30, 1878.

§ 22. Manganous Sulphate

C. W. Scheele [1] prepared **manganous sulphate,** $MnSO_4$, and distinguished it from all other salts. J. H. Pott, and C. F. G. H. Westfeld previously obtained the salt and confused it with alum, so that alumina was regarded as a constituent of pyrolusite. J. C. Ilsemann, and J. C. Schmeisser also confused manganous sulphate with magnesium sulphate, so that magnesia was regarded as a constituent of pyrolusite. In these cases, manganous sulphate was prepared from the soln. obtained by digesting pyrolusite with sulphuric acid. J. F. John [2] obtained a soln. of manganous sulphate by dissolving the metal in dil. sulphuric acid. It is also obtained by the action of hot sulphuric acid on manganese oxides, manganous carbonate, etc. Thus a soln. of the salt is obtained by boiling pyrolusite with dil. sulphuric acid to remove calcareous and magnesian impurities, heating the product with conc. sulphuric acid, evaporating to dryness, and gently igniting the resulting product to decompose the copper and iron sulphates. The undecomposed manganous sulphate is washed out with water. If any copper or iron salt is still present in soln., the former can be removed by hydrogen sulphide, and the latter by digesting the soln. with manganous carbonate. A. Gorgeu, A. Barreswil, G. Kassner, and F. Muck used modifications of this process. J. Milbauer obtained the sulphate by heating a mixture of pyrolusite and ferrous sulphate at 700°. If the operation be conducted in an open furnace, serious losses of sulphur trioxide occur. N. W. Fischer, and C. Klauer heated a mixture of pyrolusite and ferrous sulphate—say 1 : 4—and extracted the cold product with water to remove the manganous sulphate. C. Brunner heated a mixture of pyrolusite, sulphur, and wood-charcoal (10 : 4 : 1) for 2 hrs. ; treated the mass with dil. sulphuric acid ; extracted the soluble matter with water ; evaporated to dryness the filtrate with a little nitric acid ; heated the product to dull redness ; extracted the mass with water ; treated the filtrate with calcium carbonate in the cold ; and evaporated the filtrate—calcium sulphate first separates out, and afterwards crystals of hydrated manganous sulphate. The pentahydrate usually crystallizes from aq. soln. at ordinary temp. For R. de Forcrand's polymerides, *vide infra.*

Observations on the **solubility** of manganous sulphate were made by R. Brandes, F. Jahn, C. von Hauer, G. J. Mulder, C. E. Linebarger, etc. According to A. Étard, the solubility in water increases from 0° to about 55°, and decreases from about 55° to 145°. The increasing solubility is that of the pentahydrate ; the dihydrate separates out at 35°, and is completely insoluble at 145°. If S denotes the percentage amount of $MnSO_4$ in the soln., at $\theta°$, between $-8°$ and $57°$, $S = 30 \cdot 0 + 0 \cdot 2828\theta$; and between 57° and 150°, $S = 48 \cdot 0 - 0 \cdot 4585\theta$. F. Rüdorff gave for the percentage solubility at $-3 \cdot 35°$, $S = 19 \cdot 4$, and at $-7 \cdot 50°$, $S = 27 \cdot 9$. C. E. Linebarger gave results in great detail, but other observers have shown that something is wrong with them. F. G. Cottrell found the **eutectic temperature** is nearly $10 \cdot 5°$ for $S = 32 \cdot 2$, when the solid phases are ice and the heptahydrate. He found that the four hydrates—mono-, tetra-, penta-, and heptahydrates—can exist in aq. soln. ; and that the solubility of manganous sulphate at different temp. is as follows :

	−10°	0°	9°	15°	20°	27°	30°	50°	70°	100°
S .	32·4	34·7	37·2	37·9	38·6	**39·8**	39·4	37·3	34·2	24·9

Solid phase	$7H_2O$		$5H_2O$			H_2O		

These results are plotted in Fig. 82. F. Flöttmann found the solubility of the pentahydrate at 15°, 20°, and 25° to be respectively 3·703, 3·800 and 3·927 mols per litre, or 37·85, 38·59, and 39·554 per cent. A. Étard added that at 140°, $S=9·5$, and at 180° and 200°, S is nearly zero. According to F. G. Cottrell, there is also the unstable or labile monohydrate with a percentage solubility of 40·3 at 20°. There is also the unstable or labile tetrahydrate with a percentage solubility of 38·8 at the transition temp., 14°, between the hepta- and tetrahydrate ; and 40·80 at 40°. T. W. Richards and F. R. Fraprie gave 39·89 and 40·56 for the solubilities of the unstable tetrahydrate respectively at 30·15° and 35·00°. For R. M. Caven and W. Johnston's observations, *vide infra*, sodium manganese sulphate.

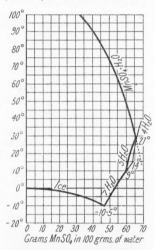

FIG. 82.—The Solubility of Manganous Sulphate in Water.

When hydrated manganous sulphate is heated to redness it forms the anhydrous salt; T. E. Thorpe and J. I. Watts found that the anhydrous salt is formed when the hydrate is heated to 280°. J. H. Krepelka and B. Réjha found that the salt is anhydrous at 450° ; and J. G. F. Druce obtained the anhydrous salt by heating the hydrate in nitrobenzene boiling at 207° ; but not in xylene boiling at 140°. Analyses in agreement with $MnSO_4$ were reported by R. Brandes, E. Turner, G. Forchhammer, and C. von Hauer. C. E. Linebarger said that the anhydrous salt is the solid phase in the presence of an aq. soln. of the salt above 117° ; but there is something wrong, because A. Étard observed that at 180° the solubility of the salt is almost zero, and that the solid phase is a pale pink, porcelain-like mass of the **monohydrate,** $MnSO_4.H_2O$. For R. de Forcrand's polymerides, *vide infra*. J. H. Krepelka and B. Réjha found that the monohydrate is stable up to nearly 200°. J. G. F. Druce obtained the monohydrate by heating the salt with toluene boiling at 110°. O. B. Kühn obtained a reddish-yellow, pulverulent deposit of the monohydrate by rapidly boiling an acidic soln. of manganous sulphate, and T. Graham, by similarly treating a neutral soln., or by drying the pentahydrate at 194° to 210° ; E. S. Larsen and M. L. Glenn, by evaporating a soln. of the sulphate on a steam-bath ; O. Pettersson, by drying the pentahydrate at 150°, and T. E. Thorpe and J. I. Watts, by drying it at 100°—*vide* Fig. 82. Analyses were reported by T. Graham, O. B. Kühn, and H. Lescoeur. According to J. von Schröckinger, reddish-white or rose-red, amorphous, stalactitic masses of the monohydrate occur as a mineral in Felsöbanya, Hungary. He called the mineral **szmikite**—after B. Szmik. The *dihydrate*, $MnSO_4.2H_2O$, does not appear as a solid phase on the solubility curve, Fig. 82. The results of W. Müller-Erzbach, and H. Bolte (Fig. 82) agreed with the existence of a dihydrate ; but W. Schieber said that it is not a chemical individual. R. Brandes said that he obtained it by melting the heptahydrate, or by boiling the hydrated salt with alcohol. T. E. Thorpe and J. I. Watts, J. Thomsen, and T. Graham used similar processes. For R. de Forcrand's polymerides, *vide infra*. R. Brandes reported the *trihydrate*, $MnSO_4.3H_2O$, to be deposited from a warm aq. soln. ; also by evaporating a soln. of the tetrahydrate in vacuo over sulphuric acid ; and by exposing the anhydrous salt in air. The trihydrate was also described by T. Graham, J. Thomsen, and T. E. Thorpe and J. I. Watts, but it does not appear as a solid phase on the solubility curve, Fig. 82, and W. Schieber denied its existence ; R. de Forcrand was unable to prove its existence. According to H. V. Regnault, the **tetrahydrate,** $MnSO_4.4H_2O$, is formed by crystallization from an aq. soln. of manganous sulphate at a gentle heat—between 20° and 30° ; or, according to J. C. G. de Marignac, between 30° and 40°. E. S. Larsen and M. L. Glenn said that the tetrahydrate is obtained by evaporating a soln. of the sulphate at 45° under reduced press. The tetrahydrate of the earlier observers—H. Kopp, G. T. Gerlach, G. J. Mulder, R. Brandes, J. F. John, E. Mitscherlich, and J. Thomsen—was possibly the over-dried pentahydrate, because the observations of T. W. Richards and F. R. Fraprie, and F. G. Cottrell show that it is an unstable hydrate (Fig. 82), and that the transition temp. of $MnSO_4.7H_2O \rightleftharpoons MnSO_4.4H_2O+3H_2O$ is nearly 14°. R. de Forcrand also prepared this salt. H. V. Regnault observed that the **pentahydrate,** $MnSO_4.5H_2O$, or *manganese vitriol,* is formed by evaporating an aq. soln. between 7° and 20° ; and J. C. G. de Marignac, by evaporating it between 15° and 20°. A. Carnot obtained it by crystallizing the aq. soln. at 15°. E. S. Larsen and M. L. Glenn obtained the pentahydrate by evaporating a soln. of the sulphate at 23° under reduced press. They call the triclinic minerals of the general formula $R_2SO_4.5H_2O$ *chalcanthites,* and describe zinc-copper-chalcanthite, iron-copper-chalcanthite, cobalt-chalcanthite, and manganese-chalcanthite. The artificial crystals are biaxial, and the indices of refraction are $\alpha=1.495$, $\beta=1.508$, and $\gamma=1.514$. The optical axial angle $2V$ is large ; the optical character negative ; and the dispersion is slight. R. Brandes made the pentahydrate by allowing the heptahydrate to stand in contact with cold alcohol ; and E. Classen, R. de Forcrand, E. Mitscherlich, and H. V. Regnault, by adding alcohol to a sat. aq. soln. of manganous sulphate and allowing the syrupy liquid to crystallize. The salt was also prepared by O. Pettersson, J. Thomsen, T. Graham, etc. The range of its stability in the presence of its aq. soln. is illustrated by Fig. 82 ; and the transition temp. of $MnSO_4.7H_2O \rightleftharpoons MnSO_4.5H_2O+2H_2O$ is nearly 9° ; and the transition temp. of $MnSO_4.5H_2O \rightleftharpoons MnSO_4.H_2O+4H_2O$ is nearly 27°. C. E. Linebarger said that the pentahydrate can exist over the range of temp. 8° to 18°, and that a *hexahydrate,* $MnSO_4.6H_2O$, can exist over a temp. range of −5° to 8° ; but this has not been verified, and W. Schieber denied its existence, and R. de Forcrand was unable to make it, although isomorphous mixtures with hexahydrated zinc sulphate are known (Fig. 82). R. Brandes, and H. V. Regnault obtained the **heptahydrate,** $MnSO_4.7H_2O$, by crystallization from the aq. soln. between −4° and 6°. A. Carnot obtained it in rhombic crystals from the aq. soln. at 6°. C. E. Linebarger said that it can exist over the temp. range of −10° to −5°. The transition temp. between it and the pentahydrate was found by F. G. Cottrell to be 9° ; and between it and the tetrahydrate, 27°—*vide* Fig. 82. R. Brandes observed that the heptahydrate loses 4.9 per cent. of water between 9° and 11° ; and 18.6 per cent. between 12.5° and 15°. It gives up 2 mols. of water to absolute alcohol ; 3 mols. to alcohol of sp. gr. 0.903 ; 4 mols. to boiling absolute alcohol ; 5 mols. to boiling 55 per cent. alcohol ; and none to cold ether. A. Carnot described a native heptahydrate, which he called **mallardite**—after E. Mallard. It was found in a silver mine near Butterfield Canon, Utah. The colourless, monoclinic crystals occur in crystalline masses with a fibrous structure. The heptahydrate thus appears to be dimorphous. E. S. Larsen and M. L. Glenn call the monoclinic minerals with the general formula $RSO_4.7H_2O$, *melanterites*—*e.g.* in a zinc-copper-melanterite the ratio Zn : Cu is between 1 : 1 and 1 : 3 and in copper-zinc-melanterite between 3 : 1 and 1 : 1. E. N. Capon and I. S. Haskes discussed hydrates of the type $[Mn,8H_2O]\cdots$, and A. Predvoditeleff and W. Blinoff, the hydrates $MnSO_4$ with $\frac{1}{2}$, 1, and $4H_2O$, revealed by their photo-electric effects.

R. Brandes described anhydrous manganous sulphate as a white, friable mass with a bitter, metallic taste ; and O. B. Kühn, the monohydrate as a pale reddish-yellow powder. H. de Sénarmont, and J. C. G. de Marignac said that the tetra-hydrate forms pale red, monoclinic plates with the axial ratios $a:b:c$ $=0.8643:1:0.5871$, and $\beta=90°$ 53'. W. Schieber said that rhombic prisms are formed between 25° and 30°. A. Carnot, and J. C. G. de Marignac said that the pentahydrate forms triclinic plates, which, according to the latter, have the axial ratios $a:b:c=0.5449:1:0.5268$, and $\alpha=113°$ 5', $\beta=109°$ 44', and $\gamma=94°$ 0'. The (001)-cleavage is incomplete, and, according to E. Mitscherlich, the crystals are isomorphous with pentahydrated cupric sulphate. S. Meyer reported that when crystallized in a magnetic field, the pentahydrate is formed in rhombic plates with the long diagonal parallel to the N : S-poles. If so, the pentahydrate is dimorphous. E. S. Larsen and M. L. Glenn found that the crystals of the penta-hydrate are triclinic, with the optical character negative ; the optical axial angle $2V$ is rather large. The trihydrate is probably monoclinic ; the optical character is negative ; and the optic axial angle $2V$ is moderately large. The monohydrate is probably monoclinic ; the optical character is positive ; and the optical axial angle $2V$ is near 90°—szmikite is probably monoclinic. A. Carnot observed that the heptahydrate forms pale red, monoclinic plates ; and H. V. Regnault added that the form of the crystals resembles that of hydrated ferrous sulphate. For iso-morphous mixtures of the hydrated manganous sulphates with those of hydrated copper, beryllium, magnesium, and zinc, vide infra, in connection with the com-plex salts. J. W. Retgers, and C. F. Rammelsberg discussed isomorphous mixtures with ferrous sulphate (q.v.) ; and E. Dittler, overgrowths with nickel and cobalt sulphates.

H. G. F. Schröder gave 2·954 to 2·975 for the **specific gravity** of anhydrous manganous sulphate ; L. Playfair, 3·386 ; C. H. D. Bödeker, 3·1 at 14° ; C. Pape, 3·192 at 16° ; O. Pettersson, 3·235 to 3·260 at 14·0° to 14·6° ; C. Lepierre, 3·14 at 12° ; and T. E. Thorpe and J. I. Watts, 3·282 at 15°. For the sp. gr. of the monohydrate, O. Pettersson gave 2·870 to 2·905 at 14·2° to 15·4° ; L. Playfair, 3·210 ; and T. E. Thorpe and J. I. Watts gave 2·845 at 15° ; while J. von Schröckinger gave 3·15 for the sp. gr. of szmikite. For the sp. gr of the dihydrate, T. E. Thorpe and J. I. Watts gave 2·526 at 15° ; and for the trihydrate, 2·356 at 15°. H. Töpsöe gave 2·261 for the sp. gr. of the tetrahydrate ; G. T. Gerlach, 2·107 at 4° ; H. Kopp, 2·092 ; and T. E. Thorpe and J. I. Watts, 2·103 at 15°. For the sp. gr. of the pentahydrate, L. Gmelin gave 1·834 ; H. Kopp, 2·087 to 2·095 ; C. Pape, 2·059 at 16° ; O. Pettersson, 2·099 to 2·107 at 15·2° to 17·6° ; T. E. Thorpe and J. I. Watts, 2·103 at 15° ; and J. L. Andreae, 2·1006 at 14·5°. Observations on the sp. gr. of aq. soln. of manganous sulphate were made by F. Fouqué, O. Schön-rock, W. Manchot and co-workers, F. Flöttmann, C. A. Valson, and P. A. Favre and C. A. Valson. G. T. Gerlach gave for the sp. gr. of soln. at 15°/15° :

$MnSO_4$	5	10	15	20	25	30	35	40	45 per cent.
Sp. gr.	1·0340	1·0690	1·1055	1·1435	1·1835	1·2255	1·2695	1·3135	1·3640

C. M. Pasea :

$MnSO_4$	0·116	0·200	0·288	0·420	0·573	0·708	0·836	1·061 per cent.
Sp. gr.	0·99982	1·00065	1·00151	1·00278	1·00431	1·00566	1·00685	1·0091

F. Flöttmann found the sp. gr. of soln. sat. at 15°, 20°, and 25° to be respectively 1·4772, 1·4866, and 1·4993 ; and J. Wagner gave for N-, 0·5N-, 0·25N-, 0·125N-, and 0·0625N-soln. the respective values 1·0728, 1·0365, 1·0179, 1·0087, and 1·0041 at 25°/4°. B. Cabrera and co-workers found that soln. with C grms. of the anhydrous salt per 1000 grms. of solvent, at $\theta°$, had, for $C=384·2$, $D=1·4547\{1-0·00026(\theta-20)\}$; for $C=277·0$, $D=1·3274\{1-0·0032(\theta-20)\}$; and for $C=201·7$, $D=1·2288\{1-0·00030(\theta-20)\}$. J. N. Rakshit calculated for the sp. gr., the **molecular volume**, and the mol. contraction of manganous sulphate, $MnSO_4.nH_2O$:

n . . .	0	1	2	3	4	5	32	42
Sp. gr. . .	3·282	2·845	2·526	2·556	2·261	2·103	1·16917	1·13615
Mol vol. . .	45·0	55·7	73·6	86·6	98·2	114·4	—	—
Mol. contr. .	—	7·3	7·4	12·4	18·8	20·6	0·8	0·07

Observations were made by W. Biltz. E. Moles and M. Crespi discussed the mol. vol. of the water of hydration. A. N. Campbell calculated the modulus for manganese, and the electrostriction as indicated in connection with manganous chloride ($q.v.$), from the sp. gr. of the aq. soln. :

Eq. per litre ..	0·5 .	0·3	0·2	0·1	0·05	0·02	0·01
Sp gr. 15°/15° .	1·03654	1·02217	1·01493	1·00733	1·00366	1·00142	1·0071
$m_{\frac{1}{2}Mn} \times 10^{-4}$.	365	365	374	364·5	342	345	320
Electrostriction	46·5	48·1	49·6	46·9	46·7	42·3	42·0

I. Traube calculated for the **molecular solution volume,** v :

$MnSO_4$.	5	10	15	20	25	30 per cent.
v . .	7·2	9·4	11·8	14·1	16·3	18·4

C. A. Valson found that the **capillary rise** of a normal soln. in a tube of 0·5 mm. diameter at 15° is 57·3 mm. ; L. C. de Coppet, and F. Dreyer also discussed the capillarity of the soln. ; and G. Tammann, the internal pressure. W. H. Whatmough measured the surface tension at 18° ; and at 15° the **surface tension,** σ dynes per cm., and **specific cohesion,** a^2 eq. mm., are :

$MnSO_4$.	0	4·77	9·10	13·06	16·68 per cent.
σ . .	73·26	73·86	74·72	75·28	75·82
a^2 . .	14·96	14·38	13·93	13·49	13·10

H. Sentis gave $\sigma=73·71$ and 74·62, and $a^2=15·07$ and 14·23 respectively for soln. with 0 and 7·81 per cent. $MnSO_4$ at 15·5°. J. Wagner gave for the **viscosity,** η (water unity), at 25° :

$MnSO_4$.	0	0·0625N-	0·125N-	0·25N-	0·5N-	N-
σ . .	7·557	7·583	7·608	7·658	7·770	7·845
η . .	1·0000	1·0158	1·0366	1·0761	1·1690	1·3640

W. H. Whatmough represented his results for the surface tension by $\sigma=7·557 +0·163N$, where N denotes the normality of the soln. J. C. Graham, and J. C. G. de Marignac measured the rate of **diffusion** of aq. soln. of manganous sulphate.

C. Pape gave 0·182 for the **specific heat** of anhydrous manganous sulphate ; and 0·338 for the pentahydrate ; while H. Kopp gave 0·323 for the pentahydrate between 17° and 46°. J. C. G. de Marignac gave for the sp. ht. of aq. soln. with $MnSO_4.nH_2O$, 0·9529, 0·9125, and 0·8440 respectively for $n=200$, 100, and 50, between 19° and 51°. S. Pagliani found the **molecular heat** to be $81+18(n-5)$. N. de Kolossowsky discussed the subject. R. Brandes observed that the **melting-point** of the heptahydrate is near 19°, and the fusion of the salt is attended by the separation of the dihydrate ; between 9° and 11° the heptahydrate loses about 4 per cent. of water, and 18·6 per cent. between 12·5° and 15°. H. Bolte, and R. Hollmann made observations on this subject—*vide infra*. W. A. Tilden gave 54° for the m.p. of the pentahydrate. T. Graham observed that if the pentahydrate is dried in air at 115°, the eq. of 3·91 mols. of water are given off, and at ordinary temp., in vacuo, over sulphuric acid, 3·25 mols. J. C. G. de Marignac found that the tetrahydrate slowly effloresces in air ; R. Brandes, that it decrepitates when heated, forming a white powder without melting, and in vacuo, over sulphuric acid, it loses a mol. of water ; and G. J. Mulder, that at ordinary temp. it loses 26·8 per cent. of water in dry air in 45 days ; at 52°, 29·3 per cent. ; at 99°, 29·9 per cent. ; at 196°, 31·1 per cent. ; and at 241°, 32·2 per cent. A. Étard found the monohydrate to be stable between 57° and 117°. E. N. Gapon studied some relationships of the m.p. K. Friedrich gave 700° for the m.p. of the anhydrous sulphate ; and there is a **transformation point** on the heating curve at 860°. According to J. L. Gay-Lussac, the anhydrous sulphate can be heated to dull redness without decomposition, but at a higher temp. it can be decomposed to form manganosic oxide. According to K. Friedrich, the decomposition of manganous sulphate commences at 1030°; G. Marchal said that decomposition can be detected at 720°; and that at 1028° the equilibrium press. is atmospheric. C. W. Davis found that at 950° manganese sulphate is completely decomposed to oxides in half an hour. The subject was studied by E. Alberts, and K. Yamamoto and K. Bito. W. Müller-Erzbach found that 3 mols. of water in the pentahydrate are easily expelled, the fourth mol. passes off at 105°, and the last mol. is retained very tenaciously. R. Hollmann observed the **vapour pressure**, p mm., of the pentahydrate to be $p=13\cdot4$ mm. at 21°. H. Lescoeur found the vap. press. of a sat. soln. to be $11\cdot3$ mm. at 20°, and 162 mm. at 60°; while the solid salt at 60° has a vap. press. of 150 to 159 mm. The vap. press. of $MnSO_4.nH_2O$, at 20°, was found to be $11\cdot5$, $11\cdot2$, and $10\cdot8$ mm. for $n=4\cdot55$, $1\cdot9$, and $1\cdot15$ respectively; $3\cdot9$ and $3\cdot0$ mm. for $n=1\cdot05$ and $1\cdot00$; and at 60°, for $n=1\cdot28$ mm. The salt which had been heated to 160° had no marked vap. press. The results at 20° do not agree with those of H. Bolte, who obtained a continuous curve which corresponded with the following selected values :

	9°	10°	12°	14°	16°	18°	20°
p	5·63	6·18	7·41	8·74	10·10	11·53	12·94

He also obtained the results shown in Fig. 83 at 14·75°; and at 20·01° for the dihydrate because of the smallness of its vap. press. at the lower temp. The vap.

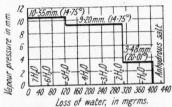

FIG. 83.—Dehydration Curve of Hydrated Manganous Sulphate.

press. of the heptahydrate is 10·5 mm. at 14·75°, and if the hexahydrate exists, its vap. press. must be the same; when the heptahydrate has lost 2 mols. of water, its vap. press. falls to 9·20 mm. at 14·75°; and there is no change as the composition of the hydrate passes from the pentahydrate to the trihydrate. The vap. press. falls to a very small value as the composition approximates to that of the dihydrate—at 20·01° the vap. press. of the dihydrate is 3·48 mm. There is no change with the monohydrate, but the last half mol. of water is retained very tenaciously because its vap. press. is too small for measurement. C. D. Carpenter and E. R. Jette found the vap. press., p mm. of mercury, of the monohydrate to be :

	25°	30·17°	35·17°	40·17°	45·14°	60·29°	65·16°
p	19·8	27·1	37·0	49·1	64·4	138·7	174·7

L. Hackspill and A. P. Kieffer studied the dehydration of the salt by heat; and K. Flick, and H. H. Willard and R. D. Fowler discussed the separation of manganese sulphate from some other sulphates by the fractional dissociation of the sulphates when heated. J. G. F. Druce discussed the creeping of the salt when its aq. soln. is evaporated.

G. Tammann found the **lowering of the vapour pressure** of water by soln. of 0·5, 1, and 2 mols. of manganese sulphate per litre to be respectively 6·0, 10·5, and 21 mm. respectively. The subject was studied by C. Dieterici, and N. Tarugi and G. Bombardini. G. T. Gerlach gave for the **boiling-point** of aq. soln. with 17·1, 32·1, 46·2, 58·9, and 68·4 (sat.) grms. of salt per 100 grms. of water respectively 100·5°, 101°, 101·5°, 102°, and 102·4°. L. Kahlenberg found the **raising of the boiling-point** of water by soln. of 0·246, 0·472, 0·957, and 1·602 mols of salt per 1000 grms. of water to be respectively 0·114°, 0·193°, 0·373°, and 0·678°. The values with over 0·25M-soln. show that at about 100° there is an inclination to form complexes whose effects are greater than those produced by ionization. For the **lowering of the freezing-point** of water L. Kahlenberg gave $-0\cdot293°$, $-0\cdot687°$, $-1\cdot399°$, and $-2\cdot591°$ for soln. with 0·1285, 0·3389, 0·7176, and 1·229 mols per

1000 grms. of water respectively; while H. C. Jones and F. H. Getman obtained for soln. with 0·08, 0·25, 0·41, 0·98, and 1·64 mols of salt per litre the respective values −0·194°, −0·510°, −0·792°, −1·898°, and −3·668°. These results are taken to show that the ionization in dil. soln. is small, and in the case of the 0·08M-soln., it amounts to about· 30 per cent. The fact that the calculated mol. depression reaches a minimum with 0·98M-soln. and then increases is supposed to indicate a hydration of the ions or of the molecules in soln. Observations were made by N. Tarugi and G. Bombardini. E. N. Gapon studied the relation between the b.p. and the sp. gr.

For the **heat of formation** J. Thomsen gave $(Mn,O_2,SO_2)=178·79$ Cals.; M. Berthelot gave $(Mn,S,2O_2,Aq.)=263·2$ Cals., and J. Thomsen, 263·7 Cals. J. Thomsen also gave $(Mn,O,H_2SO_4,Aq.)=121·25$ Cals.; $(Mn,H_2SO_{4aq.})=52·9$ Cals. For the **heat of solution** of $MnSO_4$ with 1·050H_2O, 7·726 Cals.; and 1·960H_2O, 6·305 Cals.; with 2·998H_2O, 4·156 Cals.; with 3·912H_2O, 2·454 Cals.; with 5H_2O, 0·040 Cals.; and for $MnSO_4$, 13·79 Cals. P. A. Favre and C. A. Valson made observations on the heat of soln. of the pentahydrate. W. P. Jorissen calculated for the **heat of hydration** $MnSO_4+nH_2O$, for $n=1, 2, 3,$ 4, and 5 the respective values 5·98, 1·57, 2·09, 1·91, and 2·20 Cals. For the **heat of dilution** of $MnSO_4,20H_2O$ to $MnSO_4,nH_2O$, J. Thomsen gave for $n=50, 100,$ and 200 respectively 0·532, 0·714, and 0·792 Cals. The **heat of neutralization** is $\{Mn(OH)_2,H_2SO_4,Aq\}=26·49$ Cals.; and M. Berthelot gave 27·0 Cals. G. Beck discussed the energy of formation.

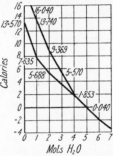

R. de Forcrand prepared what he regarded as two series of dihydrates, two series of monohydrates, and two series of anhydrous salts. Starting with the heptahydrate, the *cold series* was made by allowing it to dehydrate by efflorescence, and for the final stages, drying in vacuo over phosphoric oxide. In the *hot series* a cold, sat. soln. of the tetrahydrate was heated to 98°, and evaporated by a current of air playing on. the surface of the liquid.

FIG. 84.—The Heats of Solution of the Hydrated Manganous Sulphates.

The results are tabulated for the heat of soln., Q, of $MnSO_4.nH_2O$ prepared cold, and also hot—J. Thomsen's values are added for comparison:

n	0	0·5	1·0	1·5	2	3	4	5	7
Cold	19·620	16·300	13·740	—	9·369	5·570	1·853	−0·040	−3·251
Q { Hot	13·570	—	7·635	6·670	5·668	—	—	—	—
J.T.	13·515	—	7·610	—	6·033	3·962	2·101	−0·089	—

The heats of soln. for the hot series of salts agree with J. Thomsen's values, but for the cold series there is a marked difference from J. Thomsen's values, and the difference increases as the dehydration proceeds (Fig. 84). R. de Forcrand assumed that the anhydrous salt and hydrates of the hot series are polymerides of the corresponding salts prepared in the cold.

E. S. Larsen and M. L. Glenn found the **indices of refraction** for the pentahydrate to be $\alpha=1·495$, $\beta=1·508$, and $\gamma=1·514$; the tetrahydrate, $\alpha=1·509$, $\beta=1·518$, and $\gamma=1·522$; and the monohydrate, $\alpha=1·562$, $\beta=1·595$, and $\gamma=1·632$. The crystals of szmikite have $\alpha=1·57$, and $\beta=1·62$. According to A. N. Campbell, H. C. Jones and F. H. Getman's values for the indices of refraction are affected by a constant error, and he gave:

Eq. per litre	0·5	0·3	0·2	0·1	0·05	0·02	0·01
μ_C . .	1·33770	1·33535	1·33377	1·33253	1·33171	1·33131	1·33123
μ_F . .	1·34378	1·34141	1·33992	1·33866	1·33770	1·33731	1·33723

The calculated values for the solid are $\mu_C=1·54$ and $\mu_F=1·56$. H. C. Jones and F. H. Getman found the indices of refraction, μ, for soln. of 0·08, 0·25, 0·41, 0·98, and 1·64 mols of $MnSO_4$ per litre to be respectively 1·32750, 1·33150, 1·33575,

1·34930, and 1·36357. F. Flöttmann found the index of refraction for the D-line of soln. sat. at 15°, 20°, and 25°, the respective values 1·41120, 1·41235, and 1·41453. N. Embirikos, and P. Krishnamurti studied the Raman effect. A. Predvoditeleff and W. Blinoff found the **photoelectric activities** of the hydrates $4MnSO_4.H_2O$, and $2MnSO_4.H_2O$ to be respectively 4·25 and 1·8 times larger than the photoelectric activity of the anhydrous salt. R. Robl observed no fluorescence in ultra-violet light. H. Jahn, G. Quincke, R. Wachsmuth, and O. Schönrock made observations on the **electromagnetic rotation** in aq. soln., and found for a normal soln., 1·14, with water unity; R. Wachsmuth found that for a soln. with 17·136 grms. of $MnSO_4$ in 100 c.c. of soln., the electromagnetic rotation is 1·02904 (water unity), the sp. rotation 0·2317, and the mol. rotation 1·9433; and O. Schönrock, that for soln. with 30·819 to 41·996 grms. of $MnSO_4$ per 100 c.c. of soln., the sp. rotation is 0·3075, and the mol. rotation 2·579. L. R. Ingersoll gave for Verdet's constant for light of wave-lengths 0·6, 0·8, 1·0, and 1·25μ respectively 0·0178, 0·0101, 0·0066, and 0·0043 for soln. of manganous sulphate of sp. gr. 1·369. F. Allison and E. J. Murphy studied the magneto-optic properties; A. E. Lindh, D. Coster, and O. Stelling, the X-ray spectrum; and B. K. Mukerji and N. R. Dhar, the photosensitization of aq. soln.

E. Klein measured the **electrical conductivity,** λ, of aq. soln. with an eq. of the salt in v litres at 18°, and found :

v	0·689	1·476	2·034	3·231	4·257	5·213	6·639
λ	27·6	21·34	18·29	13·40	9·98.	7·20	4·52

Observations were also made by H. C. Jones and F. H. Getman ; while L. G. Winston and H. C. Jones obtained for the conductivity, μ, of soln. with a mol of the salt in v litres from 0° to 35°, to which are added results by H. H. Horsford and H. C. Jones for temp. from 50° to 65° :

v		4	8	32	128	512	1024	2048	4096
	0°	37·25	44·11	59·65	79·46	97·99	107·12	116·15	124·47
	25°	67·17	79·77	109·27	147·24	184·58	202·94	221·33	238·20
μ	35°	79·11	94·06	129·72	176·10	222·69	245·72	268·33	289·39
	50°	88·0	112·8	156·4	204·1	277·5	—	326·7	—
	65°	108·3	130·0	181·8	241·9	338·7	—	404·6	—
	0°	29·9	35·4	47·9	63·8	78·7	86·1	93·3	100·0
a	25°	28·2	33·5	45·9	61·8	77·5	85·2	92·9	100·0
	35°	27·3	32·5	44·8	60·8	76·9	84·9	92·7	100·0

The results for low concentrations above 35° indicate that **hydrolysis** probably occurs. R. Brandes said that the aq. soln. reddens blue litmus very faintly. W. N. Hartley showed that the absorption spectrum of dil. soln. agrees with the assumption that hydrolysis and oxidation produce colloidal $MnO(OH)_2$. M. Chanoz calculated that a 0·5N-soln. is hydrolyzed to the extent of 0·02 per cent. The percentage **degrees of ionization,** a, calculated by L. G. Winston and H. C. Jones, are indicated above. N. Tarugi and G. Bombardini studied this subject. W. Manchot and co-workers estimated the solvation of the salt in aq. soln. and found that a mol. of the salt is loaded respectively with 22·6 and 17·6 mols. of water in soln. containing 14·797, and 29·594 grms. in 100 c.c. of soln. J. B. O'Sullivan measured the H·-ion conc. of aq. soln. H. Rieckhoff and H. Zahn discussed the high-frequency conductivity of aq. soln. ; and T. Dahlblom, the relation between the conductivity and the vap. press. of the soln. O. F. Tower observed that the **electrode potential** of a manganese dioxide electrode in soln. of manganous sulphate of conc. C_{Mn}, with sulphuric acid having a H·-ion conc. of C_H, can be represented by $\pi = -0.0286 \log (C_{Mn}C_H{}^4/C_{Mn'}C_H{}^4)$, where $C_{Mn'}$ and $C_{H'}$ refer to concentrations in another soln. K. F. Ochs measured the potential of platinum and a soln. of manganous sulphate and sulphurous acid. W. Haehnel found that the curve for **decomposition voltage** of soln. of manganous sulphate has three singular points as illustrated in Fig. 86 for soln. with $[H·] = 0.1588$, and $[Mn··] = 0.1325$. M. Berthelot observed that in the **electrolysis** of dil. soln. of the salt hydrogen appears at the cathode and manganese dioxide at the anode; but with intense currents oxygen appears at the anode and manganese at the cathode. K. Elbs, and E. Frei observed that with a low acid conc., manganese dioxide is formed; with a larger acid conc., the soln. acquires a red colour; and with a still larger acid conc., manganese dioxide is no longer deposited, and all the manganese remains in soln., forming a dark red liquid. The amounts of sulphuric acid—in grms. per 100 c.c.— which prevent the separation of manganese dioxide for soln. containing M mols of $MnSO_4$ per litre, are as follow :

m		0·01	0·02	0·10	0·15	0·20	0·50	1·00
	16°	3·5	16·5	40·0	40·5	39·5	34·0	29·0
H_2SO_4	60°	27·0	37·0	59·0	59·0	58·5	54·0	45·0
	80°	44·0	54·0	70·5	58·3	68·5	58·0	—

A low temp. is favourable for the formation of permanganate; and a high acid conc. favours the formation of manganic sulphate. With lead anodes manganic acid is formed only with very dil. soln. of manganous sulphate, and with conc. soln. a brown precipitate of manganic sulphate is formed. With strongly acidic soln. of manganous sulphate some sulphate of quadrivalent manganese is formed—

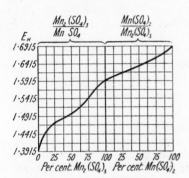

FIG. 85.—Potentials of Solutions of Manganous and Manganic Sulphates.

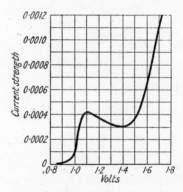

FIG. 86.—Decomposition Voltage of Solutions of Manganous Sulphate.

vide supra, permanganate. W. J. Müller observed no oxidation when zinc anodes are used, but with passive iron manganese dioxide is formed with a current density of 0·01 amp. per sq. cm. The electrolytic oxidation of manganous sulphate was studied by F. Weckbach. A. Schumrick measured the potential, E_H, of $MnSO_4$–$Mn_2(SO_4)_3$ and $Mn_2(SO_4)_3$–$Mn(SO_4)_2$ soln. using smooth platinum electrodes and MnO_2 electrodes, since platinized platinum electrodes decompose the sulphates of ter- and quadrivalent manganese. A selection from the results is illustrated by Fig. 85 with soln. in $8M$-H_2SO_4. J. Beck also studied the electrolytic oxidation of soln. of manganous sulphate. G. Grube and K. Huberich found the oxidation potentials of a soln. of 0·05 gram-atom of manganese in a litre of $15N$-H_2SO_4 at 12° are $Mn^{..} \rightarrow Mn^{...} = 1·511$ volts; $Mn^{...} \rightarrow Mn^{....} = 1·62$ volts; and $Mn^{..} \rightarrow Mn^{....} = 1·577$ volts. The potentials are dependent on the conc. of the acid, and to a far less extent on the conc. of the manganese. Increasing the conc. of the acids displaces the potentials to less positive values. The equilibrium constant for the reaction $Mn_2(SO_4)_3 \rightleftharpoons MnSO_4 + Mn(SO_4)_2$ is $K = C_{Mn^{..}} \cdot C_{Mn^{....}} / C^2_{Mn^{...}}$, and $K = 0·005032$. The value of the constant changes with the acidity and the conc. of the manganese, and with $0·05M$-$Mn_2(SO_4)_3$ in $9·1N$-H_2SO_4, about 36 per cent. is decomposed in accord with the equation, but with a $24·2N$-H_2SO_4, only 6·7 per cent., so that the reaction is displaced to the left of the equation with increasing acidity.   If K denotes the equilibrium constant, and α the percentage decomposition of manganic sulphate :

N-H_2SO_4 .	24·2	19·8	16·7	15·0	12·1	10·6	9·1
K . .	0·0013	0·0040	0·0050	0·0052	0·0127	0·0283	0·0698
α . .	6·7	11·0	12·0	13·0	18·0	25·0	36·0 per cent.

This equilibrium condition explains the abnormal behaviour of manganic sulphate on hydrolysis, for the products are manganous sulphate and hydrated oxide of quadrivalent manganese.   One product of the hydrolysis is the disulphate, $Mn(SO_4)_2$, and this is the most easily hydrolyzed component of the mixture, equilibrium is disturbed, still more manganic sulphate is hydrolyzed, so that the reaction takes place completely from left to right.   T. Swensson observed a small increase in the e.m.f. of a cell of a soln. of the salt when one electrode is exposed to light ; the subject was studied by J. Lifschitz and S. B. Hooghoudt.

P. Théodoridès found the **magnetic susceptibility** of solid manganese sulphate to be $88·72 \times 10^{-6}$ mass unit, and C. Chéneveau gave 85×10^{-6} mass unit ; for $2N$-$MnSO_4$, G. Quincke gave $29·1 \times 10^{-6}$ mass unit ; G. Jäger and S. Meyer gave for 14·83, 20·97, and 37·74 per cent. soln. the respective values 18×10^{-6}, $28·4 \times 10^{-6}$, and $56·2 \times 10^{-6}$ mass unit ; P. Pascal, 1500×10^{-5} ; G. Falckenberg gave 93×10^{-6} mass unit for an aq. soln. ; and O. Liebknecht and A. P. Wills, 100×10^{-6} mass unit.   Observations were also made by G. Piaggesi, P. Plessner, G. Falckenberg, R. H. Weber, L. C. Jackson and H. K. Onnes, P. Théodoridès, W. Albrecht, O. Wylach, P. Philipp, B. Cabrera and co-workers, and A. Heydweiller.   W. Sucksmith studied the gyromagnetic effect.   B. Cabrera and co-workers found for aq. soln. of 0·3633 and 0·01808 grm. of the anhydrous salt per 1000 grms. of solvent, mol. susceptibilities respectively 0·014981 and 0·14803, so that $4·354 = \chi(T + \Theta)$. K. Honda and T. Sone gave for the magnetic susceptibility, $\chi \times 10^6$ mass units :

$\chi \times 10^6$.	$-178°$	$-140°$	$-70°$	$0°$	$250°$	$507°$	$747°$	$1148°$
	261	183	124	94·1	55·6	38·6	30·0	14·0

H. Mosler found the temp. coeff., $\dot{a}$, of the magnetization of 13, 23, 30·1, and 40·2 per cent. of manganous sulphate to be respectively 0·00288, 0·00261, 0·00259, and 0·00255.   J. Aharoni and F. Simon observed that the susceptibility of a soln. of 106·64 grms. of $MnSO_4$ per litre expressed in arbitrary units is -1550, the susceptibility per gram for different dilutions is nearly 6·87, and when soln. and water are mixed in the following proportions by volume :

Soln. : H_2O .	1 : 0	12 : 3	12 : 15	10 : 17	7·98 : 19	6·02 : 21	4 : 23
Susceptibility	-155	-120	$-54·4$	$-38·8$	$-25·0$	$-12·4$	$-1·6$

J. A. Arfvedson found that **hydrogen** reduces red-hot manganous sulphate to form an oxysulphide.   According to W. Ipatieff and W. Kisseleff, when an aq. soln. of manganous sulphate is treated with hydrogen, at 300° and over 150 atm. press., manganese sulphide is formed.   J. A. Arfvedson found that when heated to a high temp. in **air,** this sulphate is decomposed as indicated above.   R. Brandes said that the anhydrous salt absorbs **water** with great avidity from air, forming a hard mass ; and when exposed to air it forms the trihydrate.   The solubility of the salt in water has been previously discussed.   J. H. Weibel studied the hydrolysis of the salt, and observed no separation at 150°, but at 250° a precipitate is formed. M. O. Charmandarian and E. A. Alexeeva found that manganese sulphate has a feeble catalytic effect on the decomposition of **hydrogen dioxide.**   A. Gorgeu observed that when a 20 to 25 per cent. soln. of manganous sulphate is boiled with a 2 to 3 per cent. soln. of **sodium hydroxide,** the white precipitate first formed is converted into a pink crystalline precipitate, which is not decomposed by continued washing with water, remains unaltered when exposed to air, and does not lose weight at 200°.   Its composition corresponds with **manganese oxydisulphate,** $MnO.2MnSO_4.3H_2O$.   R. Fink found that if $0·1N$-$MnSO_4$ be digested with **magnesium hydroxide** on a water-bath, 71·2 per cent. of the manganous oxide is precipitated. F. Fichter and E. Brunner observed that manganous sulphate in the presence of sulphuric acid is more readily oxidized by fluorine than is the case with manganous fluoride, presumably owing to the intervention of sulphur tetroxide in the oxidizing process. The formation of manganic sulphate, the first step, is easy to recognize, by the red colour. On continued passage of fluorine this colour changes to a brownish-red and finally to a dark brown, and the oxidizing power corresponds to a nearly complete transformation into the labile sulphate of quadri-valent manganese, $Mn(SO_4)_2$. If the concentration of the sulphuric acid is not high, hydrolysis sets in and manganese dioxide is formed; but although it is easy to obtain a yield exceeding 90 per cent., the formation of manganese dioxide is not a certain proof of the primary formation of a salt of quadrivalent manganese, for it may be formed by hydrolysis of manganic sulphate, one-half of which is reduced to manganous sulphate and subsequently re-oxidized. In order to bring the oxidation to the highest stage, permanganic acid, it is useful to have a low concentra-tion of manganous ions and a high concentration of sulphuric acid, the latter being necessary to avoid the formation of hydrogen dioxide. In these circumstances the characteristic colour of permanganate ions becomes visible the more quickly the smaller the concentration of manganous sulphate. A. B. Prescott found that very little sulphuric acid is displaced when the salt is evaporated with **hydrochloric acid.** F. Ephraim observed no addition compound with hydrogen chloride. A. B. Prescott observed that when a gram of the salt is treated with 4·035 grms. of hydrochloric acid of sp. gr. 1·153 and evaporated to dryness, 0·8 per cent. of the salt is converted to chloride.

H. Rose found that when the anhydrous sulphate is heated with **sulphur** in a current of hydrogen, or, according to A. Violi, with sulphur alone, manganous sulphide is formed: $MnSO_4 + 2S = MnS +2SO_2$; while G. Vortmann and C. Pad-berg observed that the aq. soln. is not changed by sulphur. L. Meyer observed it to be a good catalyst in the oxidation of **sulphur dioxide.** J. T. Norton found that when the soln. is heated with **sodium thiosulphate** in a sealed tube at 140° to 200°, some manganous sulphide is formed. According to C. Schultz, when a soln. of manganous sulphate in boiling, conc. **sul-phuric acid** is cooled, anhydrous, asbestos-like, prismatic crystals are formed, and at 100° crystal plates of **manganous hexa-hydrotetrasulphate,** $Mn(HSO_4)_2.2H_2SO_4$, are produced; and if sulphuric acid of sp. gr. 1·6 is employed, tabular crystals of

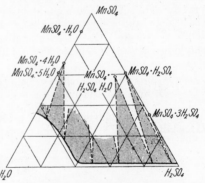

FIG. 87.—The Ternary System : $MnSO_4$–H_2SO_4–H_2O.

manganous hydrosulphate, $Mn(HSO_4)_2$, separate from the cooling soln. A. Schum-rick found that a litre of 7M-, 8M-, 10M-, and 12M-H_2SO_4 dissolves respectively 7·22, 4·00, 2·50, and 2·10 grms. of manganous sulphate. C. Montemartini and L. Losana studied the system $MnSO_4$–H_2SO_4–H_2O, and the results at 12·5°, summarized in Fig. 87, are a little uncertain as to the exact regions of the different phases. There are **manganese hydrodisulphate,** $MnSO_4.H_2SO_4$; the *monohydrate,* $MnSO_4.H_2SO_4.H_2O$; and **manganese hydrotetrasulphate,** $MnSO_4.3H_2SO_4$.

W. R. E. Hodgkinson and C. C. Trench found that when manganous sulphate is heated in a current of **ammonia** gas, the residue is an equimolar mixture of man-ganous sulphide and oxide, but no nitride is formed. G. Gore said that the anhydrous sulphate is insoluble in liquid ammonia. H. Rose found that the anhydrous sulphate absorbs dried ammonia gas very slowly to form a white powder of **manganous tetramminosulphate,** $MnSO_4.4NH_3$, which can be preserved in a sealed tube; but it loses ammonia in air, and when dissolved in water deposits manganous hydroxide. M. A. Rukazin studied the tetrammine. W. Peters, and F. Ephraim said that under the conditions indicated by H. Rose **manganous hexamminosulphate,** $MnSO_4.6NH_3$, can be formed; and when this is kept in vacuo, it passes into **manganous diamminosulphate,** $MnSO_4.2NH_3$. The monohydrated sulphate forms **manganous aquopentamminosulphate,** $MnSO_4.5NH_3.H_2O$. F. Müller gave —18° to 74° for the dissociation temp. of the hexammine; 74° for the pentammine; 180° for the diammine; and over 380° for the monammine. W. Herz studied the equilibrium between soln. of manganous sulphate and **ammonium salts**—*vide supra*, manganous hydroxide. W. Feldt observed that **hydroxylamine** forms **manganous hydroxylaminosulphate,** $MnSO_4.NH_2OH.2H_2O$, as an insoluble white powder; and N. Pfanner obtained $4MnSO_4.3NH_2OH.2H_2O$, by the action of manganese on an aq. soln. of hydroxylamine sulphate. H. Franzen and O. von Mayer found that with hydrazine and manganous sulphate there is formed **manganous dihydrazinosulphate,** $MnSO_4.2N_2H_4$. W. Manchot and co-workers found that at 25° soln. with 0, 14·194, and 29·143 grms. $MnSO_4$ per 100 c.c. dissolve respectively 53·3, 30·6, and 17·0 c.c. of **nitrous oxide** per 100 c.c.

E. Kunhein observed a reduction to sulphide when the sulphate is heated in the arc with **carbon.** According to J. L. Gay Lussac, when a mixture of manganous sulphate and carbon is heated to redness, there are formed sulphur dioxide and carbon monoxide and dioxide, as well as a mixture of manganous oxide and sulphide; and when the sulphate is heated in a current of **carbon monoxide,** manganous oxide and sulphide are formed. W. Manchot and co-workers found that at 25° soln. with 0, 14·797, and 29·594 grms. per 100 c.c. dissolve respectively 95·7, 54·8, and 31·4 c.c. of **acetylene.** R. Brandes observed that anhydrous manganous sulphate is insoluble in absolute **alcohol;** and 100 parts of 50 per cent. alcohol dissolve 2 parts of the salt; and 100 parts of alcohol of sp. gr. 0·872 dissolve 0·63 part of salt. With the heptahydrate and boiling absolute alcohol the trihydrate is formed; and a similar product is obtained by the action of absolute alcohol on the tetrahydrate. G. C. Gibson and co-workers found the solubility of manganese sulphate—*S* grm. of salt per gram of alcohol—in anhydrous alcohols to be:

		15°	25°	35°	45°	55°
S	Methyl	0·00190	0·00114	0·00064	0·00043	0·00029
	Ethyl	0·00012	—	0·00014	—	0·00021

The methyl alcohol had the sp. gr. 0·78656 at 25°/4°, and the ethyl alcohol, 0·78510. H. Schiff found that 100 parts of a sat. soln. in 0, 10, 50, and 60 per cent. alcohol

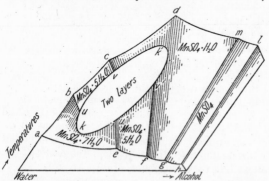

contain respectively 56·25, 51·4, 2·0, and 0·66 parts of pentahydrated manganous sulphate. When the heptahydrate is dissolved in 15 to 50 per cent. alcohol, the liquid separates into two layers; the lower layer contains less.(12 to 14 per cent.) alcohol and more (47 to 49 per cent.) salt, and the upper layer contains more (50 to 55 per cent.) alcohol and less (1·3 to 2·2 per cent.) salt. With 15 to 50 per

FIG. 88.—The Ternary System : $MnSO_4$–H_2O–C_2H_5OH.

cent. alcohol the separation takes place at ordinary temp., but with 13 to 14 per cent. or 60 per cent. or upwards of alcohol warming is necessary for the separation. F. A. H. Schreinemakers and J. J. B. Deuss studied the ternary system $MnSO_4$–H_2O–C_2H_5OH at 0°, 25°, 30°, 35°, and 50°. The diagram, Fig. 88, is characterized by a binodal surface $kuvk'v'u'$ representing the conditions for the co-existence of two liquid layers. This region extends from 5·3° to 43·5°. Usually the ternary system of salt, water, and alcohol exhibits only a minimum critical mixing temp., but in the present case there are both a minimum and a maximum critical temp. *abuku'e* represents the surface of the heptahydrate; *bcvu*, the saturation surface of the pentahydrate in contact with the liquid layer poor in alcohol, and *u'v'fe*, the pentahydrate in contact with the liquid layer rich in alcohol; which *cdmgfv'k'v* refers to the monohydrate, and *gmlh* to anhydrous manganous sulphate. The curves *eu* and *ub* refer to soln. sat. with both the hepta- and pentahydrates; *fv'* and *eu'*, to soln. sat. with both the penta- and monohydrates; and *gm*, to soln. sat. with the monohydrated and anhydrous salts. The curve *kuvk'v'u'* is derived from the following data, where concentrations are expressed in percentages :

		10°	15°	21ª	25°	30°	35°	41°	43°
Alcohol poor layer	C_2H_5OH	13·78	9·25	6·10	6·81	8·69	9·24	11·93	14·33
	$MnSO_4$	25·25	29·79	35·05	33·72	30·15	28·61	24·97	22·01
Alcohol rich layer	C_2H_5OH	37·06	44·56	53·55	53·09	45·30	41·71	34·01	31·42
	$MnSO_4$	5·44	2·79	1·10	1·23	2·40	3·44	5·86	8·51

$$\underbrace{\qquad\qquad\qquad\qquad}_{MnSO_4.5H_2O} \qquad \underbrace{\qquad\qquad\qquad\qquad}_{MnSO_4.H_2O}$$

The percentage solubilities of the hydrates of manganous sulphate in mixtures of alcohol and water are shown in Table III. E. Cuno said that the effect of temp.

TABLE III.—SOLUBILITIES OF HYDRATED MANGANOUS SULPHATE IN AQUEOUS ALCOHOL

Temp.	Water	Alcohol	$MnSO_4$	Solid phase
35°	61·4	0	38·6	$MnSO_4.H_2O$
,,	62·13	5·50	32·37	,,
,,	62·06	6·46	31·48	,,
,,	62·01	7·48	30·51	,,
,,	62·15	9·24	28·61	,,
,,	54·85	41·71	3·44	,,
,,	50·69	47·73	1·58	,,
,,	50·16	48·27	1·57	,,
30°	61·4	0	38·6	$MnSO_4.H_2O$
,,	61·43	2·26	36·31	,,
,,	61·25	5·09	33·66	,,
,,	60·78	5·96	33·26	,,
,,	61·16	8·69	30·15	,,
,,	52·31	45·20	2·49	,,
,,	44·83	54·19	0·98	,,
,,	30·95	68·97	0·08	,,
,,	9·19	90·80	0·01	,,
25°	60·7	0	39·3	$MnSO_4.5H_2O$
,,	59·47	6·81	33·72	,,
,,	45·68	53·09	1·23	,,
,,	42·05	57·39	0·56	,,
,,	23·30	76·70	0·0	$MnSO_4.H_2O$

on the composition of the two layers is small ; and that if A, W, and S respectively denote the quantities of alcohol, water, and salt in 100 c.c. of soln., the expressions suggested by G. Bodländer, namely $WS^{-\frac{1}{2}}$, and by W. Herz and M. Knoch, namely $(S+A)W/(S+A+W)$, are fairly constant for medium concentrations of alcohol. For a given quantity of salt in the soln., the electrical conductivity rapidly diminishes as the quantity of alcohol increases ; and an increase in the proportion of alcohol leads to a displacement of the maximum conductivity in the direction of soln. containing less salt. E. Darmois studied the effect of manganous sulphate on the rotatory power of tartrates. W. Eidmann, and A. Naumann found that manganous sulphate is insoluble in **acetone ;** A. W. Davidson found the sulphate to be insoluble in acetic acid ; A. Naumann, that it is insoluble in **ethyl acetate,** and in **benzonitrile ;** F. W. O. de Coninck, that 100 grms. of a sat. soln. in **glycol** contain 0·5 grm. manganous sulphate ; R. Brandes, that the salt is insoluble in absolute **ether,** and that no water of crystallization is removed by the ether ; and R. Brandes, that the salt is insoluble in boiling **turpentine,** but a mol. of water is removed from the tetrahydrate. S. Hakomori studied the action of **oxalic acid.** F. Krauss and E. Bruchhaus studied the action of the sulphate on **potassium oxalate** in light. H. Grossmann and B. Schück obtained a complex **manganous ethylenediaminosulphate,** $MnSO_4.C_2H_4(NH_2)_2.H_2O$, in triclinic prisms of sp. gr. 1·941 ; and H. Schjerning, **manganous diphenylhydrazinosulphate,** $MnSO_4.2C_6H_5NHNH_2.H_2O$, soluble in 55 parts of water at 16°. O. C. Magistad observed that the manganese of manganous sulphate will replace the calcium of zeolites.

According to V. Macri, with a few exceptions the **metal hydroxides** are not oxidized by manganous salts. H. Busch studied the adsorption of manganous salts by hydrogels of **ferric hydroxide.** When an ammoniacal soln. of **copper sulphate** and manganous sulphate is boiled, cuprous oxide is precipitated, and the supernatant, colourless liquor gradually becomes blue when exposed to air. Manganous sulphate completely precipitates silver from a hot, ammoniacal soln. of **silver nitrate.** The white precipitate formed by adding a manganous salt to an ammoniacal soln. of **mercuric nitrate** turns grey and then brown on boiling, and after treatment with sulphurous acid, or an acidified soln. of a sulphite, it leaves a heavy, brownish-grey, pulverulent deposit, which is not dissolved by dil. nitric acid, but is readily attacked by the conc. acid, forming nitrous fumes. The addition of ammonia to a soln. containing a **cobalt salt** and manganous salt yields a precipitate of manganous hydroxide which gradually becomes brown, not, however, by the direct reduction of the cobalt oxide, since the latter first undergoes peroxidation in air, and then gives up its oxygen to the manganese, especially on shaking the mixture.

J. F. John prepared **ammonium manganous disulphate,** $(NH_4)_2SO_4.MnSO_4.6H_2O$, by crystallization from a soln. of the component salts ; and C. Lepierre, by crystal-

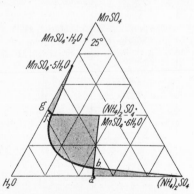

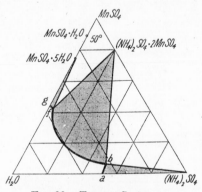

FIG. 89.—Ternary System :
$MnSO_4-(NH_4)_2SO_4-H_2O$ at 25°.

FIG. 90.—Ternary System :
$MnSO_4-(NH_4)_2SO_4-H_2O$ at 50°.

lizing an aq. soln. of ammonium manganous trisulphate. O. Aschan obtained the salt by the action of a soln. of ammonium persulphate on manganese. H. A. von Vogel observed that the hexahydrate first crystallizes from a soln. of ammonium chloride and manganous sulphate—a complex chloride remains in soln. F. A. H. Schreinemakers studied the ternary system $MnSO_4-(NH_4)_2SO_4-H_2O$ at 25° and 50°, and the results are summarized in Figs. 89 and 90. The region of stability for $(NH_4)_2SO_4.MnSO_4.6H_2O$ is shown by the shaded area over gb, Fig. 89, so that gf represents the solubility curve of pentahydrated manganous sulphate ; fb, the solubility curve of the complex salt just indicated ; and ba, the solubility curve of ammonium sulphate. R. M. Caven and W. Johnston investigated the same system at $0°$, and obtained results analogous to those at $25°$ obtained by F. A. H. Schreinemakers. It was also observed that the increase in solubility of manganous sulphate caused by ammonium sulphate at $25°$, and the decrease in solubility of ammonium sulphate caused by manganous sulphate at $25°$, are accentuated at $0°$. E. Rouyer observed evidence of the formation of this salt in soln. at $100°$. For preparing ammonium manganous disulphate the aq. soln. of the mixed salts should be evaporated between $0°$ and $25°$; the salt was also studied by M. T. Salazar and E. Moles. The results of A. Benrath are summarized in Fig. 91.

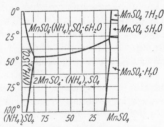

FIG. 91.—Equilibrium Conditions of Ammonium and Manganous Sulphates.

According to E. Mitscherlich, the pale pink monoclinic crystals of the salt resemble those of the magnesium salt. A. Murmann and L. Rotter gave for the axial ratios $a : b : c = 0.736 : 1 : 0.497$, and $\beta = 107° 2'$. H. G. F. Schröder found the sp. gr. to be 1.825 ; R. Krickmeyer gave 1.837 at $18°/4°$. H. A. von Vogel observed that the salt loses some water of crystallization between $75°$ and $87°$, and at a red-heat all the ammonium sulphate is expelled. N. Schiloff and B. Nekrassoff studied the adsorption of the soln. by schönite. F. Ephraim and P. Wagner found the mol. vol. to be 214.9 ; and the dissociation press. to be 400 mm. at $87°$. According to T. Graham, the heat of soln. is -9.7 Cals. T. Swensson observed a small increase in e.m.f. when an electrode in a soln. of the salt is illuminated. O. Liebknecht and A. P. Wills gave 53×10^{-6} mass unit for the magnetic susceptibility of the aq. soln. L. C. Jackson and W. J. de Haas, K. S. Krishnan, and L. C. Jackson and H. K. Onnes also examined the paramagnetism at low temp. C. Borel gave 5.91 for the dielectric constant for $\lambda = \alpha$. J. F. John found that the salt deliquesces in moist air and is freely soluble in water ; according to J. Locke, 100 parts of water at $25°$ dissolve 35.1 grms. or 0.1321 mol of the salt. In the absence of air aq. ammonia gives no precipitate with soln. of this salt.

According to C. Lepierre, if a mixture of approximately equal parts of ammonium and manganous sulphates be fused, all the water of crystallization is expelled at $200°$, and at $250°$ crystals of **ammonium manganous trisulphate,** $(NH_4)_2SO_4.2MnSO_4$, are formed. The excess of ammonium hydrosulphate is washed out by boiling in 70 per cent. alcohol. The conditions of formation in aq. soln. at $50°$ were found by F. A. H. Schreinemakers and are represented in Fig. 90. From this it follows that ammonium manganous disulphate dissociates at $50°$: $(NH_4)_2Mn(SO_4)_2.6H_2O = (NH_4)_2SO_4.MnSO_4 + \text{Solution}$; and a soln. of eq. proportions of the component salts at $50°$ furnishes crystals of ammonium manganous trisulphate. W. Lang prepared this salt in anhydrous crystals by adding excess of ammonium sulphate to a hot acid soln. of manganous sulphate ; it is decomposed by cold water into the double sulphate, $MnSO_4.(NH_4)_2SO_4$, and manganous sulphate. C. Lepierre found that the white tetrahedral crystals belong to the cubic system, and have a sp. gr. 2.56 at $14°$. The aq. soln. of this salt deposits crystals of the complex disulphate when evaporated at low temp. When heated to redness the ammonium sulphate is driven off. M. T. Salazar and E. Moles. observed no hydrolysis in the aq. soln. of ammonium manganous sulphate. According to A. Gorgeu, when an aq. soln. of the mixed sulphates is treated with ammonia, added drop by drop at $80°$, crystals of **ammonium manganous oxytrisulphate,** $(NH_4)_2SO_4.MnO.2MnSO_4.3H_2O$, are formed. The pale pink rhombic prisms are not changed by dry air, but at $180°$ water is given off, and at a dull red-heat manganous sulphate remains. The salt dissolves in water, and the soln. deposits manganous hydroxide. The salt is soluble in hydrochloric acid without coloration or the evolution of chlorine. T. Curtius and F. Schrader evaporated a mixed soln. of manganous and hydrazine sulphates, and obtained **hydrazine manganous disulphate,** $(N_2H_5)_2SO_4.MnSO_4$, as a white crystalline powder with a reddish tinge. 100 parts of water at 18° dissolve 1·67 parts of the salt. The reactions of the aq. soln. resemble those of the component salts. G. Canneri prepared **guanidine manganous disulphate,** $(CH_5N_3)_2H_2SO_4.MnSO_4.6H_2O$.

G. Calcagni and D. Marotta measured the f.p. of binary mixtures, **lithium and manganous sulphates.** The results show a simple eutectic, Fig. 92. The region a refers to a homogeneous liquid ; b, to a liquid with solid lithium sulphate ; c, .to a liquid with solid manganous sulphate ; and d, to solid β-$MnSO_4$ and β-Li_2SO_4. The corresponding curve for sodium and manganous sulphates, Fig. 93, shows the existence of two compounds—**hexasodium manganous tetrasulphate,** $3Na_2SO_4.MnSO_4$, which is unstable above 420° ; and **sodium trimanganous tetrasulphate,** $Na_2SO_4.3MnSO_4$, melting at 715°. The area b, Fig. 93, refers to liquid and solid soln. b ; c, to liquid and solid sodium manganous tetrasulphate ; d, to liquid and solid soln. d ; e, to solid soln. b and the compound $3MnSO_4.Na_2SO_4$; f, to solid soln. b and compound $MnSO_4.3Na_2SO_4$; g, to compounds $3MnSO_4.Na_2SO_4$ and $MnSO_4.3Na_2SO_4$; h, to solid soln. b and β-Na_2SO_4 ; and i, to the β-modifications of the two components. P. L. Geiger found that when the mixture of sodium chloride, manganese dioxide, and sulphuric acid employed in making chlorine is dried

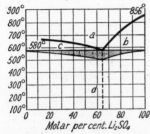

FIG. 92.—Freezing-Point Curves of the System : Li_2SO_4-$MnSO_4$.

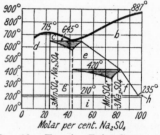

FIG. 93.—Freezing-Point Curves of the System : Na_2SO_4-$MnSO_4$.

and heated to redness, the product extracted with water, and the soln. evaporated, crystals of sodium sulphate separate out. When the mother-liquor is allowed to stand in a cool place, **sodium manganous sulphate** separates out in deliquescent crystals of the *tetrahydrate,* $Na_2SO_4.MnSO_4.4H_2O$; and the mother-liquor deposits after a long time deliquescent crystals of the *dihydrate,* $Na_2SO_4.MnSO_4.2H_2O$. O. Aschan obtained the salt by the action of sodium persulphate on manganese. M. Berthelot gave for the heat of formation $(Na_2SO_4,MnSO_4)=1·2$ Cals. ; and T. Graham, and M. Berthelot, $(MnSO_4,Na_2SO_4,Aq.)=12·0$ Cals. ; and for the heat of soln. of the dihydrate, 3·2 Cals. ; while J. Thomsen gave 13 Cals. for the heat of soln. of $Na_2Mn(SO_4)_2$. A. R. Arrott observed that the dihydrate is formed if a soln. of the constituent salts is cooled above 36·5°—say 40° to 50°. J. C. G. de Marignac could not determine the form of the crystals with certainty. If the soln. of the component salts be evaporated spontaneously at ordinary temp., J. C. G. de Marignac, A. Scacchi, and C. F. Rammelsberg obtained pale pink monoclinic crystals of the tetrahydrate with axial ratios $a : b : c=1·344 : 1 : 1·336$, and $\beta=99°$ 18′. P. L. Geiger thought that the salt is the pentahydrate ; and L. Gmelin, the hexahydrate mixed with some dihydrate. P. L. Geiger said that this salt has at first a cooling, bitter taste, which afterwards appears unpleasant and metallic. The salt reddens litmus slightly. It effloresces in warm air ; it decrepitates slightly when heated, and swells up to a white porous mass ; at a low red-heat it fuses to a light grey mass which is soluble in water ; some manganosic oxide may be left when the mass dissolves in water if the calcination temp. has been high enough. 100 parts of boiling water dissolve 98 parts of salt, and nothing separates out as the soln. cools; but if, after 24 hrs., the soln. is seeded with a crystal of the salt, there is deposited in about 3 hrs. a thick mass of sodium sulphate crystals; and the mother-liquor holds manganous sulphate in soln. F. A. H. Schreinemakers and D. J. van Prooije investigated the ternary system $MnSO_4$–Na_2SO_4–H_2O at 35°. The isotherm ab, Fig. 94, shows the composition of a soln. sat. with Na_2SO_4; bc, of a soln. sat. with hexasodium manganous tetrasulphate, $MnSO_4.3Na_2SO_4$; cd, of a soln. sat. with **sodium manganous enneadecasulphate,** $9MnSO_4.10Na_2SO_4$; and dc, of a soln. sat. with hydrated manganese sulphate, $MnSO_4.H_2O$. There was no evidence of the formation of the double salts $MnSO_4.Na_2SO_4.2H_2O$ and $MnSO_4.Na_2SO_4.4H_2O$, described by J. C. G. de Marignac, and A. Geiger. There is nothing to show whether the latter are metastable salts or mixtures when formed under conditions where Fig. 94 is applicable. The results of R. M. Caven and W. Johnston are illustrated in Fig. 95. The dotted curves refer to a temp. of 35°, the others to one of 25°. No double salt is formed at 0°; the salt $MnSO_4.Na_2SO_4.2H_2O$ is stable at 25° and 35°. The two salts were described by F. A. H. Schreinemakers and D. J. van Prooije. The near coincidence of the double salt portions at 25° and 35° shows that the solubilities of the two salts are

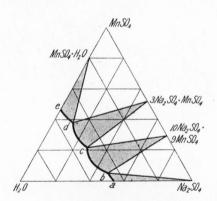

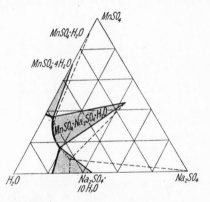

FIG. 94.—Ternary System :
$MnSO_4$–Na_2SO_4–H_2O at 35°.

FIG. 95.—Ternary System :
$MnSO_4$–Na_2SO_4–H_2O at 25° (and 35°).

nearly the same, but the solubility of the double salt at 25° is rather less than it is at 35°. At 0°, 25°, and 35° the solubility of manganese sulphate is decreased by addition of sodium sulphate. This fact is of much greater interest on more particular examination, for the solid phases are different at the different temp. The decrease is least at 25°, where the solid phase is $MnSO_4.4H_2O$, and is greatest, being much accentuated, at 35°, where the solid phase is $MnSO_4.H_2O$. An intermediate decrease is shown at 0°, where the solid phase is $MnSO_4.7H_2O$. Thus, these isotherms show the effect of addition of sodium sulphate on the solubilities of the hepta-, tetra-, and monohydrated forms of manganese sulphate. The solubility of $MnSO_4.H_2O$ at 35° is slightly greater than that of $MnSO_4.4H_2O$ at 25°. At 0° and 25° the solubility of sodium sulphate is increased by the addition of manganese sulphate. At 35°, it is much decreased by increasing quantities of manganese sulphate. Here again there is a change of solid phase from the decahydrated to the anhydrous state.

A. and H. Benrath studied the ternary system Na_2SO_4–$MnSO_4$–H_2O at 97°. The following is a selection from the results for soln., where the proportions of sodium and manganous sulphates are expressed in percentages by weight; x denotes the mol. proportion of $MnSO_4$ in the mixture, and M, the number of mols. of water per mol. of the salt mixture :

MnSO₄	0	0·68	0·69	10·42	19·25	21·41	22·81	26·48	28·49 per cent.
Na₂SO₄	29·85	22·98	29·26	17·90	14·72	13·13	11·94	2·16	0 per cent.
x	0	2·10	2·16	35·40	55·14	60·48	64·22	92·05	100·00 per cent.
M	18·56	18·00	18·48	20·41	15·89	15·54	15·24	20·80	21·08

	MnSO₄	0	0·68	0·69	10·42	19·25	21·41	22·81	26·48	28·49 per cent.

$MnSO_4$ 0   0·68   0·69   10·42   19·25   21·41   22·81   26·48   28·49 per cent.
Na_2SO_4 29·85   22·98   29·26   17·90   14·72   13·13   11·94   2·16   0 per cent.
x .   0   2·10   2·16   35·40   55·14   60·48   64·22   92·05   100·00 per cent.
M .   18·56   18·00   18·48   20·41   15·89   15·54   15·24   20·80   21·08

Solid phase : Na_2SO_4 $3Na_2SO_4.MnSO_4$ $Na_2SO_4.MnSO_4.H_2O$ $MnSO_4.H_2O$

The results are plotted in Fig. 96—the dotted curve indicates sp. gr. The solid phases include the *dihydrate*, $Na_2SO_4.MnSO_4.2H_2O$, at 97°, and **sodium manganous tetrasulphate,** $3Na_2SO_4.MnSO_4.H_2O$.
A. Benrath raised the question whether there is a limited region near 25° where the unstable tetrahydrate exists. For the stable region A. Benrath represented the equilibrium conditions of the ternary system at different temp. by Fig. 97.
A. Gorgeu prepared **sodium manganous oxytrisulphate,** $Na_2SO_4.MnO$. $2MnSO_4.4$(or 5)H_2O, by a method similar to that employed for the ammonium salt, but at 100°; it is not certain if

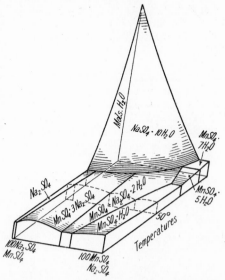

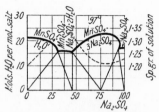

FIG. 96.—Equilibrium in the System : MnSO₄–Na₂SO₄–H₂O at 97°.

FIG. 97.—Equilibrium Diagram of the Ternary System : Na₂SO₄–MnSO₄–H₂O at Different Temperatures.

the salt is isomorphous with the salts of potassium and ammonium. The oxysulphate loses its water of crystallization at 130°.
F. R. Mallet obtained **potassium manganous disulphate,** $K_2SO_4.MnSO_4$, in reddish-white tetrahedra, by fusing a mixture of the component salts. The crystals

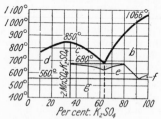

FIG. 98.—Freezing-Point Curves of the System : K₂SO₄–MnSO₄.

are stable in air. G. Carobbi and V. Caglioti could not prepare this salt ; they always obtained the 1 : 2-salt, *vide infra*. G. Calcagni and D. Marotta studied the f.p. of mixtures of potassium and manganous sulphates. A compound potassium manganous trisulphate, $K_2SO_4.2MnSO_4$, is formed, but not the disulphate. The field b, Fig. 98, refers to liquid and solid soln. b ; c, to the liquid and the trisulphate ; d, to liquid and solid soln. ; e, to solid soln. b and the trisulphate ; f, solid soln. b and β-K₂SO₄ ; g, the trisulphate and the β-form of the component sulphates.
G. J. Mulder observed that a soln. saturated at 10° with manganous sulphate and then with potassium sulphate contains 44·3 parts of K_2SO_4, and 16·7 parts of $MnSO_4$ for 100 parts of water. According to J. C. G. de Marignac, the *dihydrate*, $K_2SO_4.MnSO_4.2H_2O$, is deposited in pale pink triclinic crystals from a soln. of equimolar parts of the component salts at 40° to 50°. G. N. Wyrouboff gave for the axial ratios of the triclinic crystals of the dihydrate $a : b : c = 0·7161 : 1 : 0·4482$, and $a = 87° 50'$, $\beta = 85° 36'$, and $\gamma = 101° 29'$. H. G. F. Schröder gave for the sp. gr. of the dehydrated but not fused salt, 2·954, and for the fused salt, 3·031.

R. M. Caven and W. Johnston's study of the ternary system K_2SO_4–$MnSO_4$–H_2O at 0° is summarized in Fig. 99. The tetrahydrated complex salt crystallizes as well at 0° as it does at 25°. The isotherm at 25° is similar to that at 0°, except that it shows a more rapid increase in the solubility of the manganous sulphate with additions of potassium sulphate up to the triple point. At 25° the tetrahydrate of manganous sulphate takes the place of the heptahydrate at 0°. The isotherm of

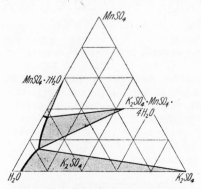

FIG. 99.—The Ternary System : K_2SO_4–$MnSO_4$–H_2O at 0°.

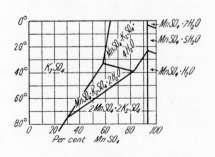

FIG. 100.—The Polytherms of the System : $MnSO_4$–K_2SO_4–H_2O.

the potassium system at 0° is different from that of the ammonium system. The range of double salt formation is greater with the ammonium system, owing (i) to the greater solubility of ammonium sulphate, and (ii) to the fact that the complex ammonium salt is hexahydrated, whereas the potassium complex salt is tetrahydrated. J. I. Pierre, C. von Hauer, A. E. H. Tutton, and J. C. G. de Marignac obtained the *tetrahydrate*, K_2SO_4. $MnSO_4.4H_2O$, in pale pink monoclinic crystals by cooling to 0° a soln. sat. at ordinary temp., or by evaporating it in vacuo at 10° to 12°. The axial ratios are $a : b : c = 1.2485 : 1 : 1.0324$, and $\beta = 95° 0'$. R. Krickmeyer gave 2.234 for the sp. gr. at 20°; and H. G. F. Schröder gave 2.13 for the sp. gr., and added that the salt can be melted at a red-heat without decomposition. F. Ephraim and P. Wagner found the dissociation press. to be 400 mm. at 84.5°. J. Thomsen gave for the heat of soln. of $K_2Mn(SO_4)_2$, 6.38 Cals.; and of $K_2Mn(SO_4)_2.nH_2O$, when $n=1$, 1.76 Cals.; when $n=2$, −2.91 Cals.; when $n=3$, −4.60 Cals.; and when $n=4$, −6.435 Cals. The differences show that there are two definite stages in the hydration. J. Thomsen gave for the heat of forma-

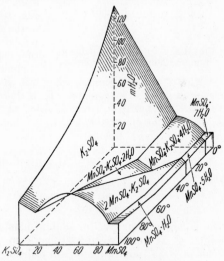

FIG. 101.—The Ternary System : $MnSO_4$–K_2SO_4–H_2O between 0° and 100°.

tion $(MnSO_4,K_2SO_4,4H_2O)=13.8$ Cals., and for $(MnSO_4,K_2SO_4)=0.990$ Cal., while M. Berthelot gave 0.800 Cal. H. de Sénarmont found the index of refraction to be 1.487. E. Mitscherlich reported a *hexahydrate* of the type $K_2Mn(SO_4)_2.6H_2O$, corresponding with analogous compounds—the schönites—with magnesium, zinc, and iron; but J. C. G. de Marignac, and A. E. H. Tutton could not verify this. O. Aschan prepared the salt by the action of a soln. of potassium persulphate on manganese. The subject was discussed by M. T. Salazar and E. Moles. A. Benrath represented the equilibrium conditions and the phases in the ternary system $MnSO_4$-K_2SO_4-H_2O, by Figs. 100 and 101. F. R. Mallet obtained **potassium manganous trisulphate,** $K_2SO_4.2MnSO_4$, in pale red tetrahedra, by melting together the component salts. The crystals are stable in air. G. Calcagni and D. Marotta's curve, Fig. 98, shows the conditions of existence of this compound, which melts at 850°. G. Carobbi and V. Caglioti also found that a molten mixture of 2 mols of manganous sulphate and a mol of potassium sulphate furnishes the 1 : 2 compound corresponding with langbeinite, $K_2SO_4.2MgSO_4$; it is also formed when the component sulphates are taken in equimolar proportions. The 1 : 2-compound was found by F. Zambonini and G. Carobbi to occur in small pink tetrahedra in stalactites of the lava cupola formed on Vesuvius in 1922. They called it **manganolangbeinite.** A. Gorgeu obtained **potassium manganous oxytrisulphate,** $K_2SO_4.MnO.2MnSO_4.3H_2O$, by the process employed for the sodium salt. It is isomorphous with the ammonium salt ; it loses its water of crystallization at 220°, and when roasted it forms potassium and manganous sulphates and manganic oxide. C. Montemartini and L. Losana studied the quaternary system K_2SO_4-$MnSO_4$-H_2SO_4-H_2O, and they observed no evidence of the formation of a quaternary salt. B. Gossner and T. Bäuerlein obtained a kind of *manganovolaite,* $[KH_5(SO_4)_3]_2[(Fe,Al)_2(OH)_3][Mn(SO_4)_4].4H_2O$.

G. N. Wyrouboff reported crystals of **rubidium manganous trisulphate,** $Rb_2SO_4.2MnSO_4$, to be formed from a soln. of equimolar parts of the component

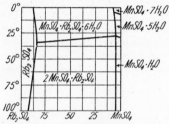

FIG. 102.—Equilibrium of Rubidium and Manganous Sulphates.

salts at 60° to 70°. F. R. Mallet obtained reddish-white tetrahedra of **rubidium manganous disulphate,** $Rb_2SO_4.MnSO_4$, from a fused mixture of the component salts. The crystals are stable in air, and are isomorphous with the corresponding potassium and thallous salts. A. Benrath's results are summarized in Fig. 102. G. N. Wyrouboff obtained crystals of the *dihydrate,* $Rb_2SO_4.MnSO_4.2H_2O$, from the mother-liquor remaining after the separation of the complex trisulphate. The rose-coloured triclinic crystals have the axial ratios $a : b : c$ =0·8250 : 1 : 0·4412, and a=89° 26′, β=90° 28′, and γ=108° 46′. Twinning occurs about the (101)-plane. F. L. Perrot obtained crystals of the *hexahydrate,* $Rb_2SO_4.MnSO_4.6H_2O$, from a soln. of the component salts. According to A. E. H. Tutton, the habit of the monoclinic crystals of the hexahydrate is tabular to short prismatic ; and the crystals have the axial ratios $a : b : c$ =0·7382 : 1 : 0·4950, and β=105° 57′. The topic axial ratios are $\chi : \psi : \omega$ =6·2542 : 8·4723 : 4·1938. The optical character is positive ; and the optic axial angles are :

	Li-line	C-line	Na-line	Tl-line	F-line
2E	109° 46′	109° 49′	109° 57′	110° 7′	110° 19′
2Va	67° 10′	67° 8′	67° 5′	67° 1′	66° 55′

The apparent angle $2E$ for sodium light increases about a degree for 50° rise of temp. F. L. Perrot gave 2·49 for the sp. gr. at 15° ; and A. E. H. Tutton found 2·459 at 20°/4°, and the mol. vol. 213·66. F. Ephraim and P. Wagner gave 211·2 for the mol. vol., and found the dissociation press. to be 400 mm. at 85·5°. R. M. Caven and J. Ferguson found the vap. press. of the rubidium salt, $MnSO_4.Rb_2SO_4.6H_2O$, to be in accord with $\log p = -7·084 + 8419T^{-1} - 1,781,000T^{-2}$. F. L. Perrot measured the indices of refraction, and A. E. H. Tutton gave for ordinary temp. :

		Li-line	C-line	Na-line	Tl-line	F-line	G-line
a		1·4741	1·4745	1·4767	1·4791	1·4821	1·4864
β		1·4781	1·4785	1·4807	1·4831	1·4860	1·4907
γ		1·4880	1·4884	1·4907	1·4933	1·4965	1·5015

so that the β-index reduced to a vacuum can be represented for wave-lengths λ as far as the F-line by $\beta=1\cdot4694+420,367\lambda^{-2}-491,200,000,000\lambda^{-4}$; and the α-index is reproduced by the same formula if $1\cdot4694$ be reduced by $0\cdot0040$, and the γ-index, if $1\cdot4694$ be increased by $0\cdot0100$. The indices at $70°$ are about $0\cdot0018$ less than those given in the table. The sp. refractions by the μ^2-formula are $0\cdot1145$, $0\cdot1153$, and $0\cdot1173$ respectively for α, β, and γ and the C-line; the mol. refractions are respectively $60\cdot14$, $60\cdot58$, and $61\cdot65$; and sp. dispersions, $\mu_G-\mu_C=0\cdot0024$, $0\cdot0025$, and $0\cdot0027$ respectively; and the mol. dispersions respectively $1\cdot29$, $1\cdot31$, and $1\cdot39$. The mol. refraction with the μ-formula are respectively $101\cdot47$, $102\cdot32$, and $104\cdot44$. The values are practically independent of temp. J. Locke found that 100 c.c. of water at $25°$ dissolve $35\cdot7$ grms. or $0\cdot0857$ mol of the salt.

A. E. H. Tutton prepared **cæsium manganous disulphate,** $Cs_2SO_4.MnSO_4.6H_2O$, by crystallization from a soln. of the component salts. The pale pink prismatic or pyramidal crystals are monoclinic with the axial ratios $a : b : c=0\cdot7274 : 1 : 0\cdot4913$, and $\beta=72° 53'$. The $(\bar{2}01)$-cleavage is perfect. The topic axial ratios are $\chi : \psi : \omega$ $=6\cdot3441 : 8\cdot7217 : 4\cdot2850$. The topical character is positive; and the optic axial angles at ordinary temp. are :

	Li-line	C-line	Na-line	Tl-line	F-line
2E	97° 22'	97° 18'	96° 57'	96° 33'	96° 0'
2Va	60° 10'	60° 7'	59° 57'	59° 46'	59° 28'

The angle $2E$ for sodium light diminishes about $2\cdot5°$ for a $50°$ rise of temp. The sp. gr. is $2\cdot7375$ at $20°/4°$; and the mol. vol. is $226\cdot59$. R. M. Caven and J. Ferguson found the vap. press. of the cæsium salt, $MnSO_4.Cs_2SO_4.6H_2O$, to be in accord with log $p=2\cdot830+2236T^{-1}-830,860T^{-2}$. F. Ephraim and P. Wagner gave $226\cdot6$ for the mol. vol.; and found the dissociation press. to be 400 mm. at $8\cdot75°$. The indices of refraction are :

	Li-line	C-line	Na-line	Tl-line	F-line	G-line
α	1·4918	1·4922	1·4946	1·4972	1·5003	1·5046
β	1·4936	1·4940	1·4966	1·4991	1·5022	1·5066
γ	1·4995	1·4999	1·5025	1·5051	1·5083	1·5129

The β-index, in vacuo, can be represented for wave-lengths λ as far as the F-line by $\beta=1\cdot4803+722,115\lambda^{-2}-4,944,600,000,000\lambda^{-4}$; the α-indices are reproduced by the same formula by reducing $1\cdot4803$ by $0\cdot0019$; and the γ-indices, by raising $1\cdot4803$ by $0\cdot0019$. Measurements at $70°$ show that the index is lowered $0\cdot0018$ by a rise of temp. of $50°$. The sp. refractions for the C-line and the μ^2-formula are $0\cdot1061$, $0\cdot1064$, and $0\cdot1075$ for α, β, and γ respectively; the mol. refractions for the C-line are respectively $65\cdot81$, $66\cdot01$, and $66\cdot68$; the sp. dispersions $\mu_G-\mu_C$ are respectively $0\cdot0022$, $0\cdot0023$, and $0\cdot0023$; and the mol. dispersions respectively $1\cdot40$, $1\cdot42$, and $1\cdot46$. The mol. refractions with the μ-formula are respectively $111\cdot62$, $112\cdot03$, and $113\cdot36$ for the C-line. The values are practically independent of temp. J. Locke found that 100 c.c. of water at $25°$ dissolve $8\cdot04$ grms. or $0\cdot157$ mol of the salt.

A. Étard reported **copper manganous disulphate,** $CuSO_4.MnSO_4.H_2O$, to be formed as a *monohydrate* from a conc. soln. of the component salts in the presence of a large excess of conc. sulphuric acid; and A. Scott, the *dihydrate*, $CuSO_4.MnSO_4.2H_2O$, in pale buff-yellow crystals, by adding sulphuric acid to a filtered soln. of the component salts. These salts are probably isomorphous mixtures. M. Schäuffele observed that manganous sulphate dissolves in a sat. soln. of copper sulphate, and conversely, and the soln. furnish isomorphous mixed crystals of varying composition. C. F. Rammelsberg noticed that a soln. with equimolar parts of pentahydrated copper sulphate and heptahydrated manganous sulphate yields triclinic crystals—the first crop of crystals has copper sulphate in excess, and the later crop, manganous sulphate in excess; while C. Weltzien observed that an isomorphous mixture of the form of pentahydrated copper sulphate is deposited from soln. with 12 times as much copper oxide as manganous oxide. J. W. Retgers, working probably at 8° to 12°, observed that triclinic crystals, resembling pentahydrated manganous sulphate, are produced with 0 to 2·18 per cent. of pentahydrated copper sulphate ; with 5·11 to 38·52 per cent. of heptahydrated copper sulphate, pale blue monoclinic crystals are formed ; and with over 91·05 per cent. pentahydrated copper sulphate, the dark blue crystals are triclinic and resemble the pentahydrated copper sulphate. R. Hollmann observed that at 21° sat. soln. of the component salts in all proportions yield only feathery aggregates of triclinic pentahydrate. He measured the vap. press. of isomorphous mixtures of the two salts : with 0 to 16·1 per cent. of copper sulphate, the vap. press. is 13·4 to 11·8 mm. ; and with 77·4 to 100 per cent. of copper sulphate, the vap. press. is 3·7 to 5·8 mm. W. Stortenbeker found that at 18° the penta-hydrate $(Cu,Mn)SO_4.5H_2O$ is formed with 0 to 10·5 and 22·9 to 100 per cent. penta-hydrated copper sulphate ; and the heptahydrate $(Cu,Mn)SO_4.7H_2O$ with 16 to 23·5 per cent. of copper sulphate. At 21°, however, a continuous series of iso-morphous mixtures of the pentahydrate is formed—Fig. 103. Below 25° the hydrates—monoclinic $MnSO_4.7H_2O$ and $CuSO_4.7H_2O$, as well as triclinic $MnSO_4.5H_2O$ and $CuSO_4.5H_2O$—are involved. Let $m7$ denote monoclinic $(Cu,Mn)SO_4.7H_2O$, and $t5$, triclinic $(Cu,Mn)SO_4.5H_2O$, and R. Hollmann's observa-tions are summarized in Fig. 104, at 0°, and Fig. 105, at 17°. The decomposition and formation of isomorphous mixtures furnishes three types of curve in which

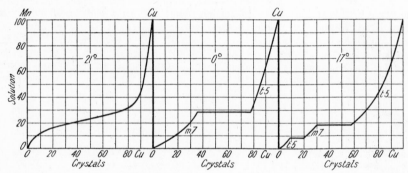

FIGS. 103, 104, and 105.—Isomorphous Mixtures of Copper and Manganous Sulphates.

the decomposition temp. for any mixture (i) lies between those of the components —*e.g.* mixtures of the heptahydrates of zinc and manganous sulphates ; (ii) reaches a maximum value—*e.g.* the heptahydrates of copper and manganous sulphates ; and (iii) has a minimum value. According to A. Recoura, a mixture of copper hydroxide and a cold aq. soln. of manganous sulphate furnishes green flocks of the composition **copper manganous oxysulphate,** $24CuO.MnSO_4.nH_2O$; and with a boiling aq. soln. of manganous sulphate, greyish-green flocks of $3CuO.MnSO_4$. nH_2O. A. Mailhe obtained $2CuO.MnSO_4.3H_2O$ from copper hydroxide and a boiling aq. soln. of manganous sulphate of medium concentration. The green isomorphous powder is dehydrated at 200° to 250°. A. Werner likewise obtained what he called the hexol salt, $3Cu(OH)_2.MnSO_4$. H. Vohl studied the isomorphous mixtures of copper sulphate and ammonium manganous sulphate.

In opposition to G. Klatzo, J. W. Retgers found that the **beryllium manganous sulphates** crystallize separately from a mixed soln. at 25°, in the form of the tetra-hydrates. P. B. Sarkar and N. Ray prepared **ammonium beryllium manganous fluosulphate,** $(NH_4)_2BeF_4.MnSO_4.6H_2O$. According to C. F. Rammelsberg, when a mixed soln. of **magnesium manganous sulphates** is evaporated, a crop of colourless crystals of the magnesium salt first appears ; the second crop of crystals has a reddish colour. The first crop contains an excess of magnesium sulphate, and the second crop an excess of manganous sulphate. A doubtful mineral from Herrengrund, Hungary, was described by A. Breithaupt, and called **fauserite**—after M. Fauser. The reddish-

or yellowish-white crystals are grouped in stalactitic forms; the brachypinacoidal cleavage is distinct; the prismatic cleavage is faint or absent; and the basal cleavage distinct. The analyses of J. Molnar correspond with $(Mg,Mn)SO_4.6H_2O$, with the ratio MnO : MgO approximately 20 : 5·5 by weight. The sp. gr. is 1·888 and the hardness 2·0 to 2·5. According to R. Ballo, and M. H. Hey, fauserite is an isomorphous mixture of magnesium and manganous sulphates, for when a mixed soln. of the component salts is allowed to crystallize between 18° and 21°, isomorphous mixtures with all proportions of the two components can be obtained. R. Hollmann said that only one series of triclinic crystals is formed, probably of the pentahydrate. H. Vohl obtained isomorphous mixtures of **ammonium magnesium manganous sulphates,** and of **potassium magnesium manganous sulphates.** Hydrated manganous sulphate was shown by C. F. Rammelsberg, W. Stortenbeker, etc., to form several series of isomorphous mixtures with hydrated zinc sulphate, although the individual salts between 0° and 39° do not form isomorphous hydrates. Thus, R. Hollmann, and R. Sahmen showed that while monoclinic heptahydrated manganous sulphate passes at about 8·8° into triclinic pentahydrate, and at about 26·6° into rhombic tetrahydrate; and rhombic heptahydrated zinc sulphate at about 38·75° forms the monoclinic hexahydrate, yet the complex series of isomorphous mixtures of the **zinc manganous sulphates** indicated in Figs. 106 to 110 is formed at the temp. indicated. Here $r7$ refers to rhombic $(Zn,Mn)SO_4.7H_2O$; $m7$, to monoclinic $(Zn,Mn)SO_4.7H_2O$; $m6$, to monoclinic $(Zn,Mn)SO_4.6H_2O$; $t5$, to triclinic $(Zn,Mn)SO_4.5H_2O$; and $r4$ to rhombic $(Zn,Mn)SO_4.4H_2O$. R. Hollmann studied the decomposition of the isomorphous

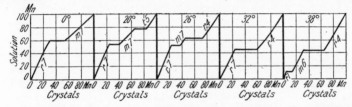

Figs. 106 to 110.—Isomorphous Mixtures of Zinc and Manganous Sulphates.

mixtures—*vide supra.* The mineral **mooreite** from Sterling Hill, New Jersey, described by L. H. Bauer and H. Berman, is clear glassy and white, and has the composition $7R(OH)_2.RSO_4.4H_2O$, where R=Mg : Mn : Zn=4 : 2 : 1; and **δ-mooreite** is bluish-white, with the composition $6R(OH)_2.RSO_4.4H_2O$, where R=Mg : Mn : Zn=5 : 3 : 4. Mooreite is monoclinic, with a perfect cleavage parallel to (010); the hardness is 3; and the sp. gr. 2·470. The optical character of the biaxial crystals is negative; the optic axial angle $2V=50°$; and the indices of refraction $\alpha=1·533$, $\beta=1·545$, and $\gamma=1·547$. Granular δ-mooreite has an imperfect cleavage; the hardness is 3; and the sp. gr. 2·665. The optical character of the biaxial crystals is negative; the optic axial angle $2V=40°$; and the indices of refraction $\alpha=1·570$, $\beta=1·584$, and $\gamma=1·585$. H. Vohl reported the formation of **ammonium zinc manganous sulphate,** $2(NH_4)_2SO_4.ZnSO_4.MnSO_4.12H_2O$; **potassium zinc manganous sulphate,** $2K_2SO_4.ZnSO_4.MnSO_4.12H_2O$; and **magnesium zinc manganous sulphate,** $MgSO_4.ZnSO_4.MnSO_4.21H_2O$.

A mineral from Lagoa Bay, South America, was regarded by J. Apjohn as a *manganous alum* and called by E. F. Glocker **apjohnite**—after J. Apjohn. It also occurs in Alum Cave, Tennessee. Its composition, according to analyses reported by J. Apjohn, R. J. Kane, H. Ludwig, W. G. Brown, and C. F. Rammelsberg, approximates **manganous aluminium sulphate,** $MnSO_4.Al_2(SO_4)_3.24H_2O$, but this result is probably influenced by an attempt to emphasize the analogy with the alums. R. M. Caven and T. C. Mitchell found the conditions of stability of this compound, $Al_2(SO_4)_3.MnSO_4.22H_2O$, at 30° to be those indicated in Fig. 111; it occurs as a solid phase in acicular crystals, between the aluminium sulphate and manganous sulphate curves. Apjohnite occurs in transparent needles with a silky lustre, and they are thought to be monoclinic; it also occurs in fibrous or asbestos-like masses, and as crusts or efflorescences. Its colour is white with a faint tinge of rose, green, or yellow. The sp. gr. is 1·782, and the hardness 1·5. It tastes like ordinary alum. A related *magneso-manganous alum* occurs in a cube near the Bushman (Bosjesman or Boschjesman) river, South Africa, and it is hence called **bushmanite,** or *boschjesmanite, bosjesmanite,* or *buschmannite.* Analyses reported by F. Stromeyer, J. L. Smith, and G. A. Kenngott agree with the formula for **magnesium manganous aluminium sulphate,** $(Mg,Mn)SO_4.Al_2(SO_4)_3.22$ or $24H_2O$. There is also a similar mineral from Maderanerthal, Switzerland, and called **keramohalite.** It also occurs at Alum Point, Utah. L. D. Gale at first regarded the Utah mineral as a manganous alum.

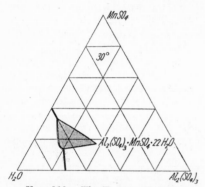

FIG. 111.—The Ternary System :
$Al_2(SO_4)_3$–$MnSO_4$–H_2O at 30°.

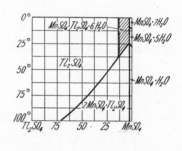

FIG. 112.—The Equilibrium of Thallous and Manganous Sulphates.

F. R. Mallet melted a mixture of manganous and thallous sulphates in equimolar proportions, and obtained reddish-white, cubic crystals of **thallous manganous disulphate,** $Tl_2Mn(SO_4)_2$. A. Benrath's results are summarized in Fig. 112. According to F. R. Mallet, the disulphate is stable in air. A. E. H. Tutton obtained well-defined crystals of the *hexahydrate,* $Tl_2Mn(SO_4)_2.6H_2O$. The holohedral, monoclinic prisms have the axial ratios $a:b:c=0.7454:1:0.4964$, and $\beta=106°$ 22'. The cleavage is parallel to the (001)-face. The topic axial ratios are $\chi:\psi:\omega=6.2134:8.3357:4.1378$. The topic axial angle $2E$ was not measurable in air, but $2V_a$ had the values :

	Li-	C-	Na-	Tl-	Cd-	F-line
$2V_a$	71° 14'	71° 16'	71° 26'	71° 41'	71° 49'	71° 59'

The sp. gr. is 3·685 at 20°/4° ; and the mol. vol. 205·62. The indices of refraction are :

	Li-	C-	Na-	Tl-	Cd-	F-line
α	1·5820	1·5826	1·5861	1·5900	1·5927	1·5959
β	1·5954	1·5960	1·5996	1·6035	1·6063	1·6096
γ	1·6041	1·6047	1·6084	1·6123	1·6152	1·6186

The general formula for β is $1.5786+832324\lambda^{-2}-3105400000000\lambda^{-4}+\cdots$ and the formula applies for the α-index if 1·5786 be reduced by 0·0135; and for the γ-index if 1·5786 is increased by 0·0088. The sp. refractions with the μ^2-formula are 0·0906, 0·0923, and 0·0934 respectively for the α-, β-, and γ-rays; likewise for the mol. refraction by the μ^2-formula respectively 68·68, 69·96, and 70·79 ; and by the μ-formula respectively 119·80, 122·55, and 124·34—the mean value being 122·23. By heating manganic chromic sulphate, A. Étard obtained a green powder of what he regarded as **manganous chromic sulphate,** $MnSO_4.Cr_2(SO_4)_3$. There are also complexes of manganous sulphate with ferric sulphate (*q.v.*), and isomorphous mixtures with ferrous sulphate (*q.v.*).

REFERENCES.

¹ C. W. Scheele, *Svenska Akad. Handl.*, **35**. 89, 177, 1774; *Abhand. Akad. Stockholm*, **36**. 95, 183, 1774; *Opuscula chemica et physica*, Lipsiæ, **1**. 227, 1788; London, 53, 1901; *Crell's Die neuesten Entdeckungen in der Chemie*, **1**. 112, 140, 1781; *Nachgelassene Briefe und Aufzeichnungen*, Stockholm, 120. 1892; J. H. Pott, *Lithogeognosia*, Potsdam, 1746; C. F. G. H. Westfeld, *Mineralogische Abhandlungen*, Göttenberg, 1767; J. C. Schmeisser, *Crell's Chem. Ann.*, ii, 39, 1789; J. C. Ilsemann, *Crell's Die neuesten Entdeckungen in der Chemie*, **4**. 24, 1782.
² J. A. Arfvedson, *Ann. Phil.*, **7**. 267, 1824; *Schweigger's Journ.*, **42**. 213, 1824; *Afhand. Fys. Kemi Min.*, **6**. 222, 1818; *Pogg. Ann.*, **1**. 50, 1824; F. Stromeyer, *ib.*, **31**. 137, 1834; A. Carnot, *Bull. Soc. Min.*, **2**. 117, 1879; *Compt. Rend.*, **88**. 1268, 1879; A. Étard, *Ann. Chim. Phys.*, (7), **2**. 587, 1894; *Bull. Soc. Chim.*, (2), **31**. 200, 1879; *Compt. Rend.*, **86**. 1400, 1878; 87. 604, 1878; **106**. 208, 1888; P. A. Favre and C. A. Valson, *ib.*, **73**. 1144, 1872; **79**. 968, 1036, 1874; C. Borel, *ib.*, **116**. 1509, 1893; L. C. de Coppet, *ib.*, **132**. 219, 1901; C. A. Valson, *ib.*, **74**. 103, 1872; M. Chanoz, *ib.*, **141**. 759, 1906; R. de Forcrand, *ib.*, **158**. 1760, 1914; **159**. 12, 1914; M. Berthelot, *ib.*, **93**. 757, 1881; *Thermochimie*, Paris, **2**. 270, 1897; L. de Boisbaudran, *Compt. Rend.*, **103**. 468, 1064, 1886; **104**. 1680, 1878; **105**. 45, 206, 1228, 1887; **106**. 452, 1781, 1888; **107**. 311, 1888; E. Darmois, *ib.*, **184**. 1239, 1927; J. R. Mourelo, *ib.*, **128**. 1239, 1899; A. Recoura, *ib.*, **132**. 1415, 1901; C. Lepierre, *ib.*, **120**. 924, 1895; *Bull. Soc. Chim.*, (3), **13**. 594, 1895; H. F. Gaultier de Claubry, *Bull. Soc. Enc. Nat. Ind.*, (2), **57**. 633, 1858; C. Brunner, *Pogg. Ann.*, **101**. 264, 1857; F. Rüdorff, *ib.*, **145**. 607, 1871; K. Stammer, *ib.*, **82**. 136, 1851; R. Brandes, *ib.*, **20**. 556, 1830; H. Rose, *ib.*, **20**. 148, 1830; *Ann. Chim. Phys.*, (2), **62**. 309, 1836; F. Brandenburg, *Schweigger's Journ.*, **14**. 346, 1815; O. B. Kühn, *ib.*, **61**. 239, 1831; L. Hünefeld, *ib.*, **53**. 121, 1828; C. Fromherz, *ib.*, **44**. 333, 1828; C. Schultz, *Ueber die wasserhaltigen und die wasserfreien sauren Salz der Schwefelsäure*, Göttingen, 1868; *Pogg. Ann.*, **133**. 137, 1868; C. F. Rammelsberg, *ib.*, **91**. 321, 1854; *Handbuch der krystallographischphysikalischen Chemie*, Leipzig, **1**. 459, 1881; *Handbuch der Mineralchemie*, Leipzig, 273, 1875; A. Barreswil, *Ann. Chim. Phys.*, (3), **17**. 53, 1846; A. Gorgeu, *Compt. Rend.*, **94**. 1425, 1882; **95**. 82, 1882; **96**. 376, 1883; *Ann. Chim. Phys.*, (3), **42**. 70, 1854; H. Lescoeur, *ib.*, (7), **4**. 213, 1895; H. V. Regnault, *ib.*, (3), **1**. 129, 1841; H. de Sénarmont, *ib.*, (3), **33**. 391, 1851; J. C. G. de Marignac, *ib.*, (5), **2**. 546, 1874; *Mém. Sciences Genève*, (1), **14**. 235, 1855; *Ann. Mines*, (5), **9**. 15, 1856; J. I. Pierre, *Ann. Chim. Phys.*, (3), **16**. 239, 1839; J. J. Ebelmen, *ib.*, (3), **22**. 213, 1848; A. Mailhe, *Action d'un oxyde ou d'un hydrate métallique sur les solutions des sels des autres métaux*, Toulouse, 1902; *Bull. Soc. Chim.*, (3), **27**. 176, 1902; *Ann. Chim. Phys.*, (7), **27**. 393, 1902; G. Charpy, *ib.*, (6), **29**. 26, 1893; P. Pascal, *ib.*, (8), **16**. 359, 520, 1909; *Compt. Rend.*, **147**. 742, 1908; F. Muck, *Zeit. Chem.*, (2), **5**. 626, 1869; W. Delffs, *ib.*, (1), **3**. 81, 1860; H. G. F. Schröder, *Dichtigkeitsmessungen*, Heidelberg, 1873; *Journ. prakt. Chem.*, (2), **19**. 266, 1870; T. E. Thorpe and J. I. Watts, *Journ. Chem. Soc.*, **37**. 113, 1880; W. N. Hartley, *ib.*, **101**. 828, 1912; F. Fichter and E. Brunner, *ib.*, 1862, 1928; L. Playfair, *ib.*, **37**. 102, 1880; A. N. Campbell, *ib.*, 653, 1928; W. A. Tilden, *ib.*, **45**. 266, 1884; A. Scott, *ib.*, **71**. 564, 1897; F. R. Mallet, *ib.*, **77**. 216, 1900; **81**. 1546, 1902; A. E. H. Tutton, *ib.*, **63**. 337, 1893; **69**. 344, 1896; *Zeit. Kryst.*, **21**. 491, 1893; **27**. 113, 1897; *Proc. Roy. Soc.*, **118**. A, 367, 1928; C. Pape, *Pogg. Ann.*, **120**. 336, 597, 1863; *Journ. prakt. Chem.*, (1), **91**. 304, 1846; T. Curtius and F. Schrader, *ib.*, (2), **50**. 311, 1894; M. Schäuffele, *Rev. Scient. Ind.*, (4), **1**. 137, 1852; *Journ. Pharm. Chim.*, (3), **21**. 81, 1852; *Journ. prakt. Chem.*, (1), **21**. 81, 1840; (1), **55**. 371, 1852; C. von Hauer, *Sitzber. Akad. Wien*, **25**. 124, 1857; *Journ. prakt. Chem.*, (1), **72**. 360, 1857; (1), **74**. 431, 1858; (1), **103**. 116, 1868; G. Klatzo, *ib.*, (1), **106**. 240, 1869; H. A. von Vogel, *ib.*, (1), **1**. 195, 1834; H. Schjerning, *ib.*, (2), **47**. 80, 1893; E. Frei, *Ueber das Verhalten der Manganosalze an der Anode*, Giessen, 1901; K. Elbs, *Zeit. angew. Chem.*, **16**. 290, 1903; *Zeit. Elektrochem.*, **7**. 260, 1900; W. Haehnel, *ib.*, **15**. 834, 1909; J. N. Rakshit, *ib.*, **32**. 276, 1926; **33**. 578, 1927; J. B. Trommsdorff, *Trommsdorff's Journ.*, **10**. 48, 1802; S. Pagliani, *Atti Accad. Torino*, **16**. 595, 717, 1881; *Nuovo Cimento*, (1), **10**. 120, 1881; G. Piaggesi, *ib.*, (2), **4**. 247, 1903; R. Ballo, *Magyar Chem. Foly.*, **13**. 17, 33, 49, 65, 81, 97, 1907; *Zeit. Kryst.*, **47**. 298, 1910; A. Schumrick, *Ueber das elektromotorische Verhalten der Oxyde des Mangans*, Halle a. S., 1912; J. Molnar, *Berg. Hütt. Ztg.*, **24**. 301, 1866; A. Breithaupt, *ib.*, **24**. 301, 1866; A. Geiger, *Die künstliche Darstellung und die Bildungsverhältnisse der Krugits*, Berlin, 1904; P. L. Geiger, *Mag. Pharm.*, **11**. 27, 1825; A. R. Arrott, *Phil. Mag.*, **24**. 502, 1846; *Mem. Chem. Soc.*, **2**. 49, 1845; R. J. Kane, *Proc. Irish Acad.*, **1**. 193, 1840; F. L. Perrot, *Arch. Sciences Genève*, (3), **25**. 675, 1891; (3), **29**. 28, 121, 1893; F. Müller, *Jahrb. Phil. Fac. Univ. Bern*, **2**. 80, 1922; A. Murmann and L. Rotter, *Sitzber. Akad. Wien*, **34**. 148, 1859; G. A. Kenngott, *Uebersichte der Resultate mineralogischer Forschungen*, Leipzig, 12, 16, 1860; E. F. Glocker, *Generum et specierum mineralium secundum ordines naturales digestorum synopsis*, Halle, 298, 1847; J. L. Smith, *Amer. Journ. Science*, (2), **18**. 379, 1854; L. D. Gale, *ib.*, (2), **15**. 434, 1853; in H. Stansburg, *An Expedition to the Valley of the Great Salt Lake of Utah*, Philadelphia, 421, 1852; B. Cabrera, E. Moles and M. Marquina, *Anal. Fis. Quim.*, **13**. 256, 269, 1915; H. Ludwig, *Arch. Pharm.*, (2), **143**. 97, 1870; G. Kassner, *ib.*, (2), **242**. 407, 1904; K. Friedrich, *Centr. Min.*, 174, 207, 1912; *Met.*, **7**. 323, 1910; F. W. O. de Coninck, *Bull. Acad. Belg.*, 359, 1905; A. B. Prescott, *Chem. News*, **36**. 178, 1877; J. F. John, *Gehlen's Journ.*, **3**. 452, 1807; **4**. 436, 1804; *Ann. Phil.*, **2**. 172, 263, 1813; **3**. 413, 1813; F. Dreyer, *The Temperature of the Maximum Density of Water*, St. Petersburg, 193, 1913; E. Mitscherlich, *Pogg. Ann.*, **11**. 323, 511, 1827; *Gesammelte Schriften*, Berlin, 317, 1896; L. Gmelin, *Hand-*

book of Chemistry, London, **4**. 240, 1850 ; E. Turner, Trans. Roy. Soc. Edin., **11**. 143, 1831 ; Phil. Mag., (2), **4**. 22, 1828 ; G. Forchhammer, Ann. Phil., **16**. 130, 1820 ; **17**. 50, 1821 ; De mangano, Hafnia, 1820 ; H. Sentis, Ann. Univ. Grenoble, **9**. 1, 1897 ; Journ. Phys., (3), **6**. 183, 1897 ; F. Fouqué, Compt. Rend., **64**. 121, 1867 ; Phil. Mag., (4), **33**. 555, 1867 ; A. Scacchi, Prodotti chimici cristallizzati spediti alla esposizione universale di pasigi, Napoli, 1867 ; Atti Ist. Napoli, (2), **4**. 79, 1867 ; E. Cuno, Ber. deut. phys. Chem., **5**. 735, 1907 ; A. Violi, Ber., **10**. 293, 1877 ; G. Vortmann and C. Padberg, ib., **22**. 2642, 1889 ; A. Naumann, ib., **37**. 4329, 1904 ; **43**. 314, 1910 ; **47**. 1370, 1914 ; R. Fink, ib., **20**. 2106, 1887 ; A. Werner, ib., **40**. 4446, 1908 ; G. Beck, ib., **156**. 288, 1926 ; **182**. 332, 1929 ; A. Heydweiller, ib., **116**. 42, 1921 ; Ann. Physik, (4), **12**. 608, 1903 ; W. Feldt, Ber., **27**. 405, 1894 ; F. Ephraim, ib., **59**. B, 1219, 1926 ; W. Peters, ib., **42**. 4826, 1909 ; Zeit. anorg. Chem., **77**. 137, 1912 ; E. Dittler, ib., **168**. 309, 1928 ; W. Eidmann, Ein Beitrag zur Erkenntnis des Verhaltens chemischer Verbindungen in nichtwässerigen Lösungen, Giessen, 1899 ; G. Gore, Proc. Roy. Soc., **21**. 140, 1873 ; **27**. 513, 1878 ; L. C. Jackson and H. K. Onnes, ib., **104**. A, 671, 1923 ; L. C. Jackson and W. J. de Haas, Proc. Acad. Amsterdam, **31**. 346, 1928 ; G. T. Gerlach, Arch. Pharm., (2), **128**. 202, 1866 ; Zeit. anal. Chem., **26**. 413, 1887 ; **28**. 466, 1889 ; Chem. Ind., **9**. 241, 1886 ; Dingler's Journ., **181**. 129, 1866 ; H. Schiff, Liebig's Ann., **118**. 365, 1861 ; H. Vohl, ib., **94**. 57, 73, 1855 ; **99**. 124, 1856 ; C. Klauer, ib., **19**. 129, 1836 ; C. Weltzien, ib., **91**. 293, 1854 ; C. M. Pasea, Trans. Roy. Soc. Canada, (3), **6**. 27, 1902 ; Zeit. phys. Chem., **42**. 509, 1903 ; W. R. E. Hodgkinson and C. C. Trench, Chem. News, **66**. 223, 1892 ; J. T. Norton. Amer. Journ. Science, (4), **12**. 115, 1901 ; Zeit. anorg. Chem., **28**. 225, 1901 ; W. Herz, ib., **22**. 279, 1899 ; O. von Mayer, Ueber Hydrazinverbindungen verschiedener Metallsalze, Heidelberg, 1907 ; H. Franzen and O. von Mayer, Zeit. anorg. Chem., **60**. 247, 1909 ; W. Herz and M. Knoch, ib., **46**. 193, 1905 ; H. Grossmann and B. Schück, ib., **50**. 21, 1906 ; W. Biltz, ib., **193**. 321, 1930 ; Zeit. phys. Chem., **58**. 288, 1907 ; I. Traube, Zeit. anorg. Chem., **8**. 34, 1895 ; H. Mosler, Der Magnetismus einiger Salzlösungen der Eisengruppe mit besonderer Berücksichtigung des Eisenchlorids, Leipzig, 1901.; Zeit. phys. Chem., **57**. 633, 1904 ; E. Moles and M. Crespi, Anales Fis. Quim., **25**. 549, 1927 ; Zeit. phys. Chem., **130**. 337, 1927 ; A. Coehn, ib., **25**. 655, 1898 ; F. A. H. Schreinemakers and J. J. B. Deuss, ib., **79**. 554, 1912 ; Proc. Acad. Amsterdam, **14**. 924, 1912 ; Chem. Weekbl., **6**. 136, 1909 ; F. A. H. Schreinemakers, ib., **6**. 131, 1909 ; F. A. H. Schreinemakers and D. J. van Prooije, Proc. Acad. Amsterdam, **15**. 1326, 1913 ; G. C. Schmidt, Ann. Physik, (4), **9**. 703, 1902 ; E. Wiedemann and G. C. Schmidt, Zeit. phys. Chem., **18**. 538, 1895 ; J. L. Andreae, ib., **76**. 491, 1911 ; R. Hollmann, ib., **37**. 204, 1901 ; **40**. 570, 1902 ; **42**. 509, 1903 ; **54**. 98, 1905 ; O. Schönrock, ib., **11**. 781, 1893 ; G. Bodländer, ib., **7**. 308, 1891 ; W. J. Müller, ib., **48**. 577, 1904 ; W. Stortenbeker, ib., **17**. 648, 1895 ; **34**. 111, 1900 ; R. Sahmen, ib., **54**. 111, 1905 ; R. Krickmeyer, ib., **21**. 67, 1896 ; J. C. Graham, ib., **50**. 257, 1904 ; **59**. 691, 1907 ; O. Stelling, ib., **117**. 161, 1925 ; Zeit. Physik, **50**. 506, 1928 ; W. H. Whatmough, Zeit. phys. Chem., **39**. 129, 1901 ; O. F. Tower, ib., **18**. 17, 1895 ; J. Wagner, ib., **5**. 31, 1890 ; J. W. Retgers, ib., **16**. 577, 1895 ; W. P. Jorissen, ib., **74**. 311, 1910 ; Chem. Weekbl., **7**. 761, 1910 ; H. Bolte, Untersuchungen über die Dissoziation einiger kristallwasserhaltigen Salzen, Halle, 1912 ; Zeit. phys. Chem., **80**. 338, 1912 ; F. Weckbach, Ueber die elektrolytische Oxydation von Manganosalzen in stark saurer Lösung, Darmstadt, 1910 ; G. Quincke, Wied. Ann., **24**. 347, 606, 1885 ; E. Klein, ib., **27**. 151, 1886 ; W. Müller-Erzbach, Ber., **22**. 3181, 1889 ; Wied. Ann., **26**. 421, 1885 ; R. Wachsmuth, ib., **44**. 377, 1871 ; F. Braun, ib., **42**. 450, 1891 ; P. Plessner, ib., **39**. 336, 1890 ; G. Jäger and S. Meyer, ib., **63**. 83, 1897 ; V. Klatt and P. Lenard, ib., **38**. 90, 1889 ; G. Tammann, Zeit. anorg. Chem., **174**. 231, 1926 ; Mém. Acad. St. Petersburg, (7), **35**. 9, 1887 ; Wied. Ann., **24**. 530, 1885 ; H. Jahn, ib., **43**. 280, 1891 ; Sitzber. Akad. Berlin, 237, 1891 ; F. Jahn, Liebig's Ann., **28**. 101, 1838 ; T. Graham, Trans. Roy. Soc. Edin., **13**. 297, 1836 ; Phil. Mag., (3), **6**. 420, 1835 ; (3), **22**. 329, 1843 ; (3), **24**. 401, 1844 ; Mem. Chem. Soc., **1**. 106, 1843 ; **2**. 51, 1845 ; J. Apjohn, ib., (2), **12**. 103, 1838 ; W. Schieber, Monatsh., **19**. 280, 1898 ; G. N. Wyrouboff, Bull. Soc. Min., **12**. 366, 1889 ; **14**. 233, 1891 ; G. Calcagni and D. Marotta, Gazz. Chim. Ital., **45**. ii, 368, 1915 ; G. Carobbi and V. Caglioti, ib., **55**. 411, 1925 ; Rend. Accad. Napoli, (3), **30**. 62, 1924 ; F. Zambonini and G. Carobbi, ib.; (3), **30**. 123, 1924 ; Gazz. Chim. Ital., **55**. 414, 1925 ; G. Canneri, ib., **55**. 611, 1925 ; C. Montemartini and L. Losana, Ind. Chimica, **4**. 199, 1929 ; K. Flick, Spannung von Metallen durch auswählende Dissoziation von Salzen in Gemischen, Darmstädt, 1929 ; P. Philipp, Untersuchungen über Magnetisierungszahlen von Salzen der Eisengrüppe und ihre Abhängigkeit von der Konzentration, Rostock, 1914 ; O. Wylach, Untersuchungen über Magnetisierungszahlen von Eisen und Mangansalzen, Barmen, 1905 ; K. Yamamoto and K. Bito, Bull. Waseda Univ. Japan, **9**. 12, 1929 ; C. W. Davis, Rep. Investigations Bur. Mines, 3033, 1930 ; M. O. Charmandarian and E. A. Alexeeva, Journ. Russ. Phys. Chem. Soc., **62**. 1677, 1930 ; N. Embirikos, Zeit. Physik, **65**. 266, 1930 ; J. Süss, Zeit. Kryst., **51**. 248, 1912 ; Krystallization gemischer Lösungen von Manganchlorür und Kaliumchlorid, Leipzig, 1912 ; J. Beck, Versuche über elektrolytische Oxydation und Reduktion, Antwerpen, 1906 ; N. Pfanner, Ueber die Einwirkung von metallischem Mangan auf Hydroxylaminsalze, Erlangen, 1912 ; R. Robl, Zeit. angew. Chem., **39**. 608, 1926 ; W. Lang, German Pat., D.R.P. 166357, 1906 ; 189178, 1908 ; L. R. Ingersoll, Journ. Amer. Opt. Soc., **6**. 663, 1922 ; W. Albrecht, Magnetochemische Untersuchungen, Elberfeld, 41, 1927 ; B. K. Mukerji and N. R. Dhar, Journ. Indian Chem. Soc., **5**. 411, 1928 ; J. B. O'Sullivan, Trans. Faraday Soc., **24**. 298, 1928 ; F. Flöttmann, Zeit. anal. Chem., **73**. 1, 1928 ; H. Busch, Ueber die Adsorption von Mangan-, Nickel-, Kobalt- u. Zink-Ion an Ferrihydroxydgel in ammoniakalischer Lösung, Worms a. Rhein, 1927 ; C. Dieterici, Ann. Physik, (4), **70**. 617,

1923; J. Milbauer, *Chem. Listy*, **20**. 389, 1926; A. E. Lindh, *Ark. Mat. Fys.*, **18**. 14, 1924; *Compt. Rend.*, **172**. 1175, 1921; **175**. 25, 1922; *Zeit. Physik*, **31**. 303, 1921; **31**. 210, 1925; D. Coster, *ib.*, **25**. 83, 1924; G. Falckenberg, *ib.*, **5**. 70, 201, 1921; P. Théodoridès, *Journ. Phys. Rad.*, (6), **3**. 1, 1922; *Arch. Sciences Genève*, (5), **3**. 161, 1921; E. S. Larsen and M. L. Glenn, *Amer. Journ. Science*, (4), **50**. 225, 1920; E. S. Larsen, *Bull. U.S. Geol. Sur.*, 679, 1921; J. Bachmann, *Chemische Abhandlungen über das Mangan*, Wien, 1829; *Zeit. Phys. Math.*, (1), **6**. 172, 1829; (2), **1**. 262, 1832; *Schweigger's Journ.*, **56**. 74, 1829; T. W. Richards and F. R. Fraprie, *Amer. Chem. Journ.*, **26**. 75, 1901; C. E. Linebarger, *ib.*, 225, 1893; H. C. Jones and F. H. Getman, *ib.*, **31**. 303, 1902; H. H. Horsford and H. C. Jones, *ib.*, **46**. 240, 1911; L. G. Winston and H. C. Jones, *ib.*, **46**. 368, 1911; J. Locke, *ib.*, **27**. 455, 1902; W. G. Brown, *ib.*, **6**. 97, 1884; F. G. Cottrell, *Journ. Phys. Chem.*, **4**. 637, 1900; L. Kahlenberg, *ib.*, **5**. 354, 1901; E. N. Gapon, *Journ. Chim. Phys.*, **25**. 154, 1928; G. J. Mulder, *Scheik. Verh. Rotterdam*, **4**. 135, 181, 1864; V. Macri, *Boll. Chim. Farm.*, **58**. 201, 1919; N. W. Fischer, *Kastner's Arch.*, **16**. 219, 1829; J. G. F. Druce, *Pharm. Journ.*, **119**. 333, 1927; H. Kopp, *Liebig's Ann. Suppl.*, **3**. 290, 1865; *Liebig's Ann.*, **36**. 1, 1840; C. H. D. Bödeker, *Die Beziehungen zwischen Dicht und Zusammensetzung bei festen und liquiden Stoffen*, Leipzig, 1860; R. Dietz, R. Funk, J. von Wrochem and F. Mylius, *Wiss. Abhand. Phys. Reichsanst.*, **3**. 428, 1900; C. Chéneveau, *Journ. Phys.*, (4), **9**. 163, 1910; O. Liebknecht and A. P. Wills, *Ann. Physik*, (4), **1**. 178, 1900; J. L. Gay Lussac, *Ann. Chim. Phys.*, (2), **63**. 433, 1836; *Journ. Mines*, **22**. 325, 405, 1807; *Arcueil Mem. Phys.*, **1**. 215, 1807; *Nicholson's Journ.*, **33**. 44, 1812; J. Thomsen, *Thermochemische Untersuchungen*, Leipzig, **3**. 176, 1883; *Ber.*, **6**. 710, 1873; *Journ. prakt. Chem.*, (2), **17**. 165, 1878; (2), **18**. 1, 1878; O. Pettersson, *Nova Acta Upsala*, **10**. 18, 1879; *Journ. prakt. Chem.*, (2), **24**. 129, 164, 293, 1881; J. von Schröckinger, *Verh. Geol. Reichsanst. Wien*, 115, 1877; *Tschermak's Mitt.*, (1), **7**. 115, 1877; *Zeit. Kryst.*, **1**. 528, 1877; *Min. Mag.*, **1**. 261, 1877; E. Classen, *Pharm. Rund.*, **5**. 35, 1887; S. Meyer, *Sitzber. Akad. Wien*, **108**. 513, 1901; *Zeit. Kryst.*, **35**. 207, 1901; K. Honda and T. Sone, *Science Rep. Tohoku Univ.*, **3**. 139, 1914; H. Töpsöe, *Arch. Sciences Genève*, (2), **45**. 223, 1872; J. H. Long, *Journ. Amer. Chem. Soc.*, **18**. 120, 1896; F. Allison and E. J. Murphy, *ib.*, **52**. 3796, 1930; G. Grube and K. Huberich, *Zeit. Elektrochem.*, **29**. 8, 1923; E. Rouyer, *Ann. Chim. Phys.*, (10), **13**. 423, 1930; *Compt. Rend.*, **183**. 46, 1926; G. C. Gibson, J. O. Driscoll and W. J. Jones, *Journ. Chem. Soc.*, 1440, 1929; A. W. Davidson, *Journ. Amer. Chem. Soc.*, **50**. 1890, 1928; J. Kendall, E. D. Crittenden and H. K. Miller, *ib.*, **46**. 963, 1923; C. D. Carpenter and E. R. Jette, *ib.*, **45**. 578, 1923; G. Marchal, *Journ. Chim. Phys.*, **22**, 324, 413, 559, 1925; N. de Kolossowsky, *ib.*, **22**. 224, 1925; R. M. Caven and J. Ferguson, *Journ. Chem. Soc.*, **125**. 1307, 1924; R. M. Caven and W. Johnston, *ib.*, 2628, 1926; 2358, 1927; 2506, 1928; *Journ. Tech. Coll. Glasgow*, **2**. 30, 1929; W. Ipatieff and W. Kisseleff, *Journ. Russ. Phys. Chem. Soc.*, **58**. 686, 1926; E. N. Gapon and I. S. Haskes, *ib.*, **58**. 1384, 1926; A. Predvoditeleff and W. Blinoff, *Zeit. Physik*, **44**. 207, 1927; T. Dahlblom, *Tek. Tid. Kemi*, **58**. 76, 1928; O. C. Magistad, *Tech. Bull. Arizona Exp. Station*, **18**. 445, 1928; L. H. Bauer and H. Berman, *Amer. Min.*, **14**. 165; 1929; F. Ephraim and P. Wagner, *Ber.*, **50**. 1088, 1917; R. H. Weber, *Ann. Physik*, (4), **36**. 624, 1911; J. H. Weibel, *Reaktionen einiger Metallsalzlösungen unter erhöhten Temperaturen und Drucken*, Zürich, 1923; L. Meyer, *Ber.*, **20**. 3058, 1887; E. Kunheim, *Ueber die Einwirkung des Lichtbogens auf Gemische von Sulfaten mit Kohle*, Berlin, 1900; P. Krishnamurti, *Indian Journ. Phys.*, **5**. 183, 1930; *Nature*, **126**. 169, 1930; L. Hackspill and A. P. Kieffer, *Ann. Chim. Phys.*, (10), **14**. 227, 1930; E. Alberts, *Ueber die Einwirkung von Gasströmen wie Kohlensäure Ammoniak, Salzsäure, Chlor, Brom, Tetrachlorkohlenstoff auf Sulfate und Sulfide*, Heidelberg, 1920; P. B. Sarkar and N. Ray, *Journ. Indian Chem. Soc.*, **6**. 987, 1929; M. T. Salazar and E. Moles, *Anal. Fis. Quim.*, **27**. 561, 1929; T. Swensson, *Lichtelektrische Untersuchungen an Salzlösungen*, Stockholm, 1919; N. Schiloff and B. Nekrassoff, *Zeit. phys. Chem.*, **118**. 79, 1926; J. Lifschitz and S. B. Hooghoudt, *ib.*, **128**. 87, 1927; K. F. Ochs, *Ueber Oxydations- und Reduktionsketten*, Göttingen, 1895; Anon., *Continental Met. Chem. Engg.*, **1**. 62, 1927; H. Rieckhoff and H. Zahn, *Zeit. Physik*, **63**. 619, 1929; A. and H. Benrath, *Zeit. anorg. Chem.*, **179**. 369, 1929; A. Benrath, *ib.*, **151**. 21, 1926; **183**. 296, 1929; **189**. 82, 1930; **195**. 247, 1931; W. Manchot, M. Jahrstorfer and H. Zepter, *ib.*, **141**. 38, 1924; F. Krauss and E. Bruchhaus, *ib.*, **189**. 53, 1930; O. Aschan, *ib.*, **194**. 139, 1930; B. Gossner and T. Bäuerlein, *Ber.*, **63**. B, 2151, 1930; J. Aharoni and F. Simon, *Zeit. phys. Chem.*, **4**. B, 175, 1929; K. S. Krishnan, *Zeit. Physik*, **71**. 137, 1931; W. Sucksmith, *Proc. Roy. Soc.*, **133**. A, 179, 1931; J. H. Krepelka and B. Réjha, *Coll. Czech. Chem. Comm.*, **3**. 517, 1931; S. Hakomori, *Science Rep. Tohoku Univ.*, **20**. 736, 1931; R. H. Hey, *Min. Mag.*, **22**. 510, 1931; H. H. Willard, *Journ. Amer. Chem. Soc.*, **54**. 496, 1932; E. N. Gapon, *Journ. Chim. Phys.*, **25**. 154, 1928; M. A. Rukazin, *Bull. Soc. Chim.*, (4), **49**. 363, 1931; N. Tarugi and G. Bombardini, *Gazz. Chim. Ital.*, **30**. ii, 405, 1900; R. M. Caven and C. Mitchell, *Journ. Chem. Soc.*, **27**. 527, 1925; J. G. F. Druce, *Chem. News*, **144**. 199, 1932.

§ 23. The Higher Manganese Sulphates—Manganic Alums

According to L. Carius,[1] manganosic oxide dissolves in cold, conc. sulphuric acid, or in an acid diluted with twice its weight of water, forming a columbine-red soln. which becomes carmine-red when diluted with water. If one part of pyrolusite is heated with 13 parts of conc. sulphuric acid until half the available oxygen is evolved, and the mass then projected into cold water, a bright red soln. is obtained. R. Phillips found that native manganic hydroxide does not dissolve in sulphuric acid under these conditions, and L. Carius obtained a similar result with dil. sulphuric acid and artificial manganic hydroxide free from manganous hydroxide ; but curiously enough, if manganous hydroxide is also present dissolution occurs, and a deep red soln. thought to contain **manganosic sulphate,** $Mn_3(SO_4)_4$, is formed. If conc. sulphuric acid acts on manganic hydroxide, manganic sulphate is formed. The red soln. of manganosic sulphate precipitates hydrated manganese dioxide when heated, and, without evolving oxygen, manganous sulphate is formed. C. Fromherz observed that reducing agents—sulphur dioxide, nitrous acid, stannous chloride, ferrous sulphate, and mercurous nitrate—decolorize the liquid and form manganous sulphate. Acetic acid, alcohol, naphtha, turpentine, lavender oil, and starch act similarly ; oxalic acid, gum, tartaric acid, and hydrochloric acid and water turn the liquid brown before decolorization ; and arsenic trioxide gives a brown precipitate. C. F. Schönbein observed the red soln. is decolorized by hydrogen dioxide.

C. F. Böhringer, W. Lang, H. Merzbach and J. F. Smith, and K. Puls considered the sulphates of ter- and quadrivalent manganese to be formed as intermediate stages in the reduction of potassium permanganate dissolved in conc. sulphuric acid. L. Carius prepared **manganic sulphate,** $Mn_2(SO_4)_3$, by triturating natural or, better, artificial manganese dioxide with conc. sulphuric acid, and heating the mush gradually to 138°. The evolution of oxygen ceases at 110°, and the mass is then greyish-violet ; at 115° to 118° it darkens in colour ; and at 138° it becomes dark green. The mixture is poured on a porous tile to remove the sulphuric acid, and the residue is rubbed in a mortar with warm, conc. nitric acid —free from nitrous acid. The acid is then removed by spreading the mixture on a porous tile, and the treatment repeated half a dozen times. The product is warmed in a porcelain basin on an oil-bath at 130° until vapours are no longer given off, and then preserved in dry, sealed tubes. Manganic hydroxide free from manganous oxide can be heated with conc. sulphuric acid at 100°, and then similarly treated. According to B. Franke, manganic sulphate can be prepared by warming a mixture of 8 grms. potassium permanganate and 100 c.c. of sulphuric acid, when some oxygen is given off, and an acid sulphate is formed. If heated to a higher temp., the mixture becomes green. The excess of sulphuric acid is removed by suction on a porous tile, and by heating the product on a sand-bath. K. Elbs, and F. Goerbig obtained the solid by the electrolysis of a soln. of manganous sulphate in $8M$-H_2SO_4 with platinum electrodes.

Manganic sulphate is a dark green, amorphous powder which can be heated to 160° without decomposition, but at a higher temp. it is decomposed into sulphuric acid, oxygen, and manganous sulphate. G. Beck gave 3·24 for the sp. gr., 122·8 for the mol. vol., and 85 Cals. for the heat of formation from the oxides. A. Chilesotti measured the e.m.f. of cells of the types : Pt | Soln.Mn^{III} +Mn^{II} | $2N$-H_2SO_4, Hg_2SO_4 | Hg, and Pt | Soln.Mn^{IV}+Mn^{III} | $2N$-H_2SO_4,Hg_2SO_4 | Hg, and calculated the normal potential $Mn^{\cdots} \rightarrow Mn^{\cdots}$ =1·55 volts ; and the normal potential for $Mn^{\cdots} \rightarrow Mn^{\cdots}$ =1·65 volts. These high values explain the powerful oxidizing action of electrolytically oxidized soln. of manganous sulphate. For G. Grube and K. Huberich's observations on the oxidation potential, and the hydrolysis, *vide supra*, manganous sulphate. R. H. Weber said that the atomic magnetism of manganic sulphate is less than 0·0115. According to L. Carius, the salt is very hygroscopic, and small quantities of the salt deliquesce in a few seconds in air to form a clear, violet soln. which soon becomes brown and turbid owing to the separation of hydrated manganese oxide. With a large proportion of water, a brownish-black mass is formed ; and with a small proportion of water, heat is developed, the mixture becomes reddish-brown, and then forms hydrated manganese oxide and sulphuric acid. B. Franke added that with water, the salt decomposes into sulphuric acid, manganous sulphate, and a mixture of manganous oxide and manganic acid ; dil. sulphuric acid forms the acid salt indicated below ; and L. Carius added that dil. acids act like water. With conc. sulphuric acid and a little water, the salt forms a reddish-brown basic salt, without much passing into soln. ; with conc. sulphuric acid, the green salt can be heated up to nearly the b.p. of the acid without decomposition, and, with the boiling acid, it gradually dissolves as manganous sulphate with the evolution of oxygen. Traces only of manganic sulphate dissolve in cold, conc. sulphuric acid to form a bluish-violet soln., and with the hot acid a violet soln. is formed. A. Schumrick found that a litre of $7M$-, $8M$-, $10M$-, $12M$-H_2SO_4 dissolves respectively 8·63, 1·74, 0·26, and 0·26 grms. of manganic sulphate. On standing, the amount 8·63 grms. in soln. is reduced to 7·20 grms. by hydrolysis and precipitation. In the presence of an excess of potassium sulphate, 0·64 grm. is dissolved. Manganic sulphate does not dissolve in cold, conc. nitric acid, but at 100° it becomes brown ; it forms a brown soln. with conc. hydrochloric acid, and chlorine is given off. It behaves towards organic substances like a mixture of manganic oxide and sulphuric acid ; the action is faster if the temp. be raised. K. F. Ochs measured the electrode potential of soln. of manganic sulphate in sulphuric acid.

B. Franke found that if 8 grms. of potassium permanganate and 100 c.c. of conc. sulphuric acid are warmed up to about 70°, not over 100°, some oxygen is evolved, and on cooling **manganic dihydrotetrasulphate,** $Mn_2(SO_4)_3.H_2SO_4.4H_2O$, separates out. The sulphuric acid is poured off, and the product washed with alcohol, and ether: The dark reddish-brown crystals lose sulphuric acid and water when heated, and form green manganic sulphate. If treated with a little water, equimolar parts of manganous sulphate, hydrated manganese dioxide, and sulphuric acid are formed. Hence, B. Franke represented the constitution of the salt by $Mn^{II}=(SO_4)_2=Mn^{IV}SO_4.H_2SO_4.4H_2O$. When treated with dil. sodium carbonate, brown manganic oxide is formed. Soln. of manganic sulphate in sulphuric acid were prepared electrolytically by E. Frei, and A. Chilesotti. A 4 per cent. soln. of manganous sulphate in sulphuric acid, of sp. gr. 1·453, was electrolyzed at 60° with a platinum anode and a current density of 4 amp. per sq. dm. The anodic liquid was contained in a porous pot. After some days, a large part of the salt separated out in tabular crystals.

C. Lepierre prepared **ammonium manganic tetrasulphate,** $(NH_4)_2SO_4.Mn_2(SO_4)_3$, or *anhydrous manganic alum*, by adding a mixture of equal vols. of nitric and sulphuric acids to ammonium manganous trisulphate, in the presence of an excess of ammonium sulphate. The crystals can be purified by successive treatment with hot, conc. sulphuric acid, glacial acetic acid, and dry ether. W. Lang prepared this salt by electrolyzing in an anode cell, lined with lead, a soln. of ammonium manganous sulphate, by a current density of 3·5 amp. per sq. cm. C. Lepierre found that the violet-brown, hexagonal crystals have a sp. gr. of 2·40 at 11° ; they are decomposed by water, forming manganic oxide ; they are insoluble in ether, benzene, and conc. sulphuric acid, but they dissolve in a mixture of equal vols. of sulphuric acid and water. When heated alone or in the mother-liquor, the salt decomposes with the evolution of sulphur dioxide and oxygen, and a soln. of ammonium manganous sulphate is formed. According to E. Mitscherlich, if pyrolusite be heated with conc. sulphuric acid, and the red soln. be treated with ammonium sulphate, the liquid furnishes dark red, octahedral crystals of what were regarded as the *tetracosihydrate,* or *ammonium manganic alum,* $(NH_4)_2SO_4.Mn_2(SO_4)_3.24H_2O$, that is, $NH_4Mn(SO_4)_2.12H_2O$; but O. T. Christensen showed that something is wrong with the inference, for the products contained not $24H_2O$ but rather 8 to $10H_2O$. Indeed, in order to prepare the manganic alum with $24H_2O$, it is necessary to work at a low temp., say —25° to —30°, for the salt is unstable at ordinary temp. and melts in its water of crystallization. The alum is obtained by dissolving 1·32 grms. of ammonium sulphate in 30 c.c. of dil. sulphuric acid (1 : 3), and mixing slowly, with stirring, with 5·36 grms. of powdered manganic acetate. The soln. is cooled in a platinum dish by means of a mixture of solid carbon dioxide and ether. The coral-red, crystalline precipitate cannot be filtered from the mother-liquor at ordinary temp., and the cold mush of crystals and mother-liquor is poured on a porous tile previously cooled by the same freezing mixture, and kept in a cooled vessel for an hour. The crystals of the ammonium manganic alum at ordinary temp. melt in a few minutes to a liquid which is almost black in colour. The salt is decomposed by water, like manganic salts in general.

According to R. J. Meyer and H. Best, if sulphuric acid be added to a soln. of potassium permanganate in acetic acid, keeping the liquid cool, **potassium manganic tetrasulphate**, $K_2SO_4.Mn_2(SO_4)_3$, or *potassium manganic alum*, is quantitatively precipitated. The crystals are washed with acetic acid, and dried over sulphuric acid, and potassium hydroxide. B. Franke obtained the same salt by adding water and potassium permanganate to the green mother-liquor obtained in the preparation of manganic dihydrotetrasulphate (*q.v.*) and warming the mixture, when oxygen is given off and reddish-brown crystals are deposited. These are separated from the mother-liquor on a porous tile ; washed with alcohol, and ether ; and dried by warming them. R. J. Meyer and H. Best found that the salt dissolves in conc. sulphuric acid, forming a violet soln. ; in moderately conc. acid, forming a red soln. ; and in dil. sulphuric acid, forming a brown soln. from which colloidal manganic hydroxide deposits. E. Pietsch and co-workers discussed the efflorescence of crystals of manganese-alum. When the salt is heated, B. Franke observed that it decomposes into manganous sulphate, sulphur trioxide, and oxygen. It is deliquescent in moist air, forming a red soln. ; and it is decomposed by water into sulphuric acid and a 1 : 1 mixture of manganous sulphate and manganic acid. E. Mitscherlich's preparation of the manganic alum is wrong, because O. T. Christensen was able to prepare the *tetracosihydrate*, $K_2SO_4.Mn_2(SO_4)_3$. $24H_2O$, or $KMn(SO_4)_2.12H_2O$, as in the case of ammonium manganic alum, from soln. cooled to a low temp. F. G. Berend described the attack of crystals of manganic alum by an ethereal soln. of ferric chloride. B. Gossner and M. Arm prepared a potassium manganic oxysulphate, analogous to voltaite, and hence called **manganivoltaite**. O. T. Christensen prepared **rubidium manganic tetrasulphate** as a *tetracosihydrate*, or *rubidium manganic alum*, $Rb_2SO_4.Mn_2(SO_4)_3.24H_2O$, or $RbMn(SO_4)_2.12H_2O$, by the method employed for the ammonium manganic alum. The salt rapidly loses water of crystallization at ordinary temp. A. Piccini electrolyzed, at 0° to 15°, a soln. of equal parts of manganous and cæsium sulphates in 15 times their weight of 25 per cent. sulphuric acid. A platinum anode was used. The cathode liquor consisted of 25 per cent. sulphuric acid and was separated by a parchment diaphragm. A coral-red, crystalline powder of **cæsium manganic tetrasulphate** as a *tetracosihydrate*, or *cæsium manganic alum*, $Cs_2SO_4.Mn_2(SO_4)_3$. $24H_2O$, was thus obtained. O. T. Christensen also prepared the salt by the process used for the ammonium manganic alum, but working at 0° to 5°. The coral-red crystals belong to the cubic system. Their refractive index for red light is 1·4466 to 1·4793. The crystals are decomposed by water with the separation of hydrated manganic oxide. They form a brown soln. with cold hydrochloric acid ; with dil. sulphuric acid they form a wine-red soln. ; and with conc. sulphuric acid, a violet-red soln. A. Piccini said that the salt melts in its water of crystallization at 40°, but it loses water below this temp. The crystals can be preserved in a closed vessel at ordinary temp., but not in air. J. L. Howe and E. A. O'Neal said that they were unable to prepare ammonium, rubidium, and cæsium manganic alums by the electrolytic process. O. T. Christensen obtained **thallous manganic tetrasulphate** as a *tetracosihydrate*, or *thallous manganic alum*, $Tl_2SO_4.Mn_2(SO_4)_3.24H_2O$, or $TlMn(SO_4)_2.12H_2O$, as a coral-red crystalline powder, by the method employed for ammonium manganic alum.

A. Étard prepared **aluminium manganic trisulphate**, $Mn_2(SO_4)_3.2Al_2(SO_4)_3$, or $MnAl(SO_4)_3$, by heating at 250° a conc. soln. of manganous and aluminium sulphates, in the theoretical proportions, with a mixture of equal vols. of sulphuric and nitric acids. The violet soln. deposits the salt in a short time as a blue crystalline precipitate which is sparingly soluble in water, and it is decomposed by that liquid. He also obtained **chromium manganic trisulphate,** $Mn_2(SO_4)_3.Cr_2(SO_4)_3$, or $MnCr(SO_4)_3$, as a green crystalline precipitate, by oxidizing manganous sulphate with chromic acid in the presence of sulphuric acid, as in the case of the aluminium manganic sulphate. If the soln. of chromium manganic sulphate be cooled before crystallization occurs, the salt crystallizes out with a mol. of sulphuric acid to form **chromium manganic trisulphatohydrosulphate,** $CrMn(SO_4)_3.H_2SO_4$, in brown plates. A similar compound with ferric sulphate (q.v.) was formed.

E. Frémy, C. F. Böhringer, W. Lang, H. Merzbach and J. F. Smith, and K. Puls regarded **manganese disulphate,** $Mn(SO_4)_2$, as well as manganic sulphate, $Mn_2(SO_4)_3$, as intermediate products of the reduction of potassium permanganate dissolved in conc. sulphuric acid. M. Sem said that soln. of manganous sulphate in dil. sulphuric acid when electrolyzed with a double anode—one plate of manganese and one of platinum—furnished a soln. of manganese disulphate. It is also said that soln. of manganous sulphate are oxidized according to the scheme : $MnSO_4 \rightarrow Mn_2(SO_4)_3 \rightarrow Mn(SO_4)_2 \rightarrow [Mn_2(SO_4)_7] \rightarrow HMnO_4$. A. N. Campbell did not observe the formation of the disulphate in his study of the electrolysis of sulphuric soln. of manganous sulphate. For G. Grube and K. Huberich's observations on the oxidation potential, and the hydrolysis of this salt, vide supra, manganous sulphate. According to F. Weckbach, the disulphate cannot be isolated, and it exists only in soln. of sulphuric acid. The Badische Anilin- und Sodafabrik found that sulphuric acid of sp. gr. 1·384 dissolves 15 per cent., and an acid of sp. gr. 1·616, 4 to 5 per cent. F. Weckbach observed that if the soln. be well cooled, crystals of $Mn_2(SO_4)_3.H_2SO_4.8H_2O$ are formed. E. Frémy obtained an acid salt of quadrivalent manganese by the action of 70 per cent. sulphuric acid on potassium permanganate ; which was for a time regarded as manganic disulphate, $Mn(SO_4)_2$. It is probably an oxysulphate. The Badische Anilin- und Sodafabrik obtained a basic salt, **manganese oxysulphate,** $MnO_2.SO_3$, or $MnO(SO_4)$, by electrolyzing a soln. of manganous sulphate in sulphuric acid, at about 60°, by means of a lead cathode in sulphuric acid ; the anode may be of lead, but if it be manganese or ferromanganese, a salt of manganese need not be dissolved in the acid, which is then used in a more concentrated state than before. In another process, a hot sulphuric acid soln. of manganous sulphate is treated with lead dioxide ; or 70 per cent. sulphuric acid is added to a mixture of potassium permanganate and sodium sulphate. The salt is obtained in the solid state by separately adding powdered manganous sulphate and potassium permanganate to hot 55 per cent. sulphuric acid ; on cooling the salt separates as a black mass. The salt and soln. are decomposed by water ; and when the sulphuric acid soln. is poured into fuming sulphuric acid, manganic sulphate is precipitated and oxygen is evolved.

According to E. Frémy, if a conc. soln. of manganous sulphate be poured into a soln. of manganese oxysulphate, hexagonal plates of a **manganese tetrasulphate,** $MnO.MnO_2.4SO_3.9H_2O$, or $MnSO_4.Mn(SO_4)_2.H_2SO_4.8H_2O$, are formed ; and also by adding alcohol to the same soln. O. T. Christensen obtained the salt by the action of sulphuric acid on manganic acetate or phosphate. According to E. Frémy, the deliquescent crystals are decomposed by heat, water, and paper, and must therefore be freed from the mother-liquor by pressure on a porous tile. The salt forms a rose-coloured soln. with dil. sulphuric acid ; it is decomposed by alkalies, and the precipitate gives up a good proportion of manganous oxide to a soln. of an ammonium salt. The salt is not therefore a manganic sulphate.

When warm and moderately conc. sulphuric acid is treated with potassium permanganate until no more salt is dissolved, and the mixture is heated, claret-red crystals of **potassium manganic henicosisulphate,** $5K_2SO_4.2Mn_5(SO_4)_8$, are formed. The crystals are washed with absolute alcohol, and ether, and dried at ordinary temp. This salt dissolves in dil. sulphuric acid to form a brown soln., and in conc. sulphuric acid to form a violet-blue soln. ; and it decomposes on heating into potassium and manganous sulphates, oxygen, and sulphur dioxide; and when treated with much water it furnishes a soln. of manganous sulphate and hydrated manganese dioxide. B. Franke represented it by the formula $Mn=(SO_4)_2=(Mn)_3=(SO_4)_2=Mn.5K_2SO_4$. N. Bjerrum and G. H. Hansen could not prepare a chromic manganic halogenosulphate like those obtained with tervalent aluminium, chromium, and iron.

REFERENCES.

[1] L. Carius, *Liebig's Ann.*, **98.** 53, 1856; C. F. Schönbein, *ib.*, **108.** 161, 1858; R. Phillips, *Phil. Mag.*, (2), **5.** 214, 1829; C. Fromherz, *Schweigger's Journ.*, **41.** 257, 1824; **44.** 327, 1825; *Pogg. Ann.*, **31.** 677, 1834; E. Mitscherlich, *ib.*, **25.** 287, 1832; *Schweigger's Journ.*, **55.** 72, 1832; B. Franke, *Journ. prakt. Chem.*, (2), **36.** 31, 168, 231, 451, 1887; E. Frémy, *Compt. Rend.*, **82.** 475, 1876; A. Mailhe, *ib.*, **132.** 1560, 1901; A. Étard, *ib.*, **86.** 1400, 1878; **87.** 603, 1878; *Bull. Soc. Chim.*, (2), **31.** 200, 1879; C. Lepierre, *ib.*, (3), **13.** 594, 1895; *Compt. Rend.*, **120.** 924, 1895; R. H. Weber, *Ann. Physik*, (4), **19.** 1056, 1906; Badische Anilin- und Sodafabrik, *Brit. Pat. No.* 17981, 1903; *U.S. Pat. No.* 837777, 1906; *German Pat.*, *D.R.P.* 163813, 1905; C. F. Böhringer, *ib.*, 117129, 1899; E. Frei, *Ueber das Verhalten der Manganosalze an der Anode*, Giessen, 1901; A. Chilesotti in R. Abegg, *Handbuch der anorganischen Chemie*, Leipzig, **4.** ii, 805, 1913; O. T. Christensen, *Ber.*, **4.** 412, 1871; *Journ. prakt. Chem.*, (2), **28.** 1, 1883; *Overs. Vid. Selsk. Förh.*, 94, 1896; *Zeit. anorg. Chem.*, **27.** 321, 1901; R. J. Meyer and H. Best, *ib.*, **22.** 169, 1899; A. Piccini, *ib.*, **17.** 355, 1898; **20.** 12, 1899; W. Lang, *German Pat.*, *D.R.P.* 166357, 1906; 189178, 1908; F. Weckbach, *Ueber die elektrolytische Oxydation von Manganosalzen in stark saurer Lösung*, Darmstadt, 1910; J. L. Howe and E. A. O'Neal, *Journ. Amer. Chem. Soc.*, **20.** 764, 1898; G. Beck, *Zeit. anorg. Chem.*, **174.** 31, 1928; M. Sem, *Ueber die Elektro-oxydation von Manganosalzen in sauren Lösungen und einige dabei erhaltene Verbindungen*, Darmstadt, 1914; *Zeit. Elektrochem.*, **21.** 426, 1915; **23.** 98, 1917; H. Merzbach and J. F. Smith, *ib.*, **7.** 455, 1901; K. Elbs, *ib.*, **7.** 260, 1900; G. Grube and K. Huberich, *Zeit. Elektrochem.*, **29.** 8, 1923; F. G. Berend, *ib.*, **35.** 582, 1929; A. N. Campbell, *Journ. Chem. Soc.*, **123.** 892, 2323, 1923; *Trans. Faraday Soc.*, **22.** 46, 1926; A. J. Allmand and A. N. Campbell, *ib.*, **19.** 559, 1923; **20.** 379, 1924; W. Lang, *Chem. Ind.*, **37.** 454, 1904; K. Puls, *Chem. Ztg.*, **25.** 263, 1901; A. Schumrick, *Ueber das elektromotorische Verhalten der Oxyde des Mangans*, Halle a. S., 1912; F. Goerbig, *Beiträge zur Kenntnis der Sulfate und Nitrate des 3-bezw. 4-wertigen Mangans*, Halle a. S., 1911; K. F. Ochs, *Ueber Oxydations- und Reduktionsketten*, Göttingen, 1895; E. Pietsch, A. Kotowsky and F. G. Berend, *Zeit. phys. Chem.*, **5.** B, 1, 1929; B. Gossner and M. Arm, *Zeit. Kryst.*, **72.** 202, 1929; N. Bjerrum and G. H. Hansen, *Zeit. anorg. Chem.*, **63.** 151, 1909.

§ 24. Manganese Carbonates

In 1782, T. Bergman [1] referred to a *magnesium acido aerëo mineralisatum*; D. G. J. Lenz, 12 years later, to *Luftsaures Braunsteinerz*; and R. J. Haüy, to *manganèse oxydé carbonaté*. These minerals were **manganous carbonate**, $MnCO_3$, and in the last part of the eighteenth century the mineral carbonate was in many cases confused with the silicate. The carbonate received many other names. Thus, A. Breithaupt called it *Rosenspat*, and *Himbeerspat*; A. G. Werner, *Mangan-spat—manganese spar—*and *Roter Braunstein*; F. Mohs, *makrotyper Parachrosbaryt*, and *isometrischer Parachrosbaryt*; and J. F. L. Hausmann, *Dichter Rotspat*, and also **rhodochrosite**—from ῥόδον, a rose, and χρώσις, colour. C. F. Jasche, and E. F. Germar called it *dialogite*—from διαλογή, doubt; and F. S. Beudant, *diallogite*. E. Dittler described pebbles of *manganodolomite* from the Enns, Upper Austria. Analyses of the mineral were reported by L. Baric and F. Tucan, C. Berge-mann, P. Berthier, A. Birnbacher, P. E. Browning, A. Bukowsky, V. C. Butureanu, G. Flink, H. von Foullon, A. Frenzel, C. L. Gruner, T. Haege, E. Hildenbrand, T. S. Hunt, C. von John, R. J. Kane, G. A. Kenngott, C. M. Kersten, L. L. de Koninck, F. Kossmat and C. von John, K. von Kraatz-Koschlau, J. A. Krenner, F. Kretschmer, G. F. Kunz, A. Lacroix, M. Lienau, H. Ludwig, E. Manasse, F. Millosevich, W. Ortloff, S. L. Penfield, P. Poni, F. Sandberger, F. Sansoni, A. Schwager and C. W. von Gümbel, M. von Sill, F. Stromeyer, V. Vesely, E. T. Wherry and E. S. Larsen, K. Zimanyi, and H. Zinkeisen. Iron carbonate is usually present; sometimes the carbonates of calcium, magnesium, and zinc; and rarely cobalt carbonate.

The *manganosiderite* of F. Bayer is a variety of siderite containing manganese carbonate ; a calcareous variety described by W. T. Roepper was called *roepperite* by G. A. Kenngott ; other calcareous varieties described by A. des Cloizeaux, J. A. Krenner, C. F. Rammelsberg, A. Bukowsky, and M. Weibull were called *manganocalcite* ; a zinciferous variety was called *zinc rhodochrosite* by E. Manasse ; and a ferruginous variety was called *ponite*—after P. Poni—by V. C. Butureanu. M. Lienau called a variety from Vielle Aure, *viellaurite* ; another variety from Vielle Aure, *torrensite* ; another variety from Vielle Aure, *lacroisite*—after A. Lacroix ; another variety from Vielle Aure, *schokoladenstein* ; and one from Huelva, *huelvite*. These five varieties of M. Lienau are probably mixtures. A. Bukowsky described large, cleavable masses of a white mineral with a rosy tinge which he called *kutnohorite* ; its composition corresponds with $7CaCO_3.5MnCO_3.FeCO_3.2MgCO_3$.

Pseudomorphs of rhodochrosite after various minerals have been examined by A. E. von Reuss, J. R. Blum, V. R. von Zepharovich, A. Frenzel, and E. Döll ; and the mode of formation of the mineral in nature has been discussed by A. Bergeat, and F. Kossmat and C. von John. Manganese carbonate imitating the mineral was prepared by H. de Sénarmont by heating a mixture of manganous chloride and calcium carbonate in a sealed tube at 150° for 18 hrs. ; by treating manganous chloride with sodium carbonate at 160° ; and by slowly driving carbon dioxide from a mixed soln. of manganous chloride and sodium hydrocarbonate saturated with carbon dioxide. The pale pink crystals so formed have a composition corresponding with $MnCO_3$. F. Hoppe-Seyler obtained microscopic rhombohedra of manganous carbonate by the action of calcium carbonate on a soln. of manganous sulphate at 200°. E. Weinschenk obtained similar crystals by heating a mixture of manganous sulphate and urea at 160° to 180° for an hour. A. de Schulten obtained small crystals whose analysis agreed with $MnCO_3$ by the action of ammonium carbonate on a soln. of manganous chloride heated on a water-bath ; and also by warming a soln. of manganous carbonate in water saturated with carbon dioxide. The anhydrous salt was also obtained by dehydrating the hydrated carbonate ; L. Joulin said that if the hydrated salt is precipitated by sodium carbonate in the cold, and dried at 60°, over quicklime, its composition is $MnCO_3$.

R. Laming, and E. Prior obtained **hydrated manganous carbonate** by treating a manganous salt soln. with ammonium carbonate ; and H. Tamm, and C. R. Fresenius noticed that even if ammonium chloride be present, the precipitation is complete. R. Laming also observed that a precipitate of manganous carbonate containing no hydroxide is produced by sodium hydrocarbonate ; and E. Prior added that the precipitation with sodium hydrocarbonate occurs only when the soln. has stood for some time, and carbon dioxide is given off. H. Moissan prepared the hydrated carbonate by adding sodium hydrocarbonate to a soln. of manganous chloride saturated with carbon dioxide, and washing the product with water saturated with carbon dioxide. According to R. Laming, if the precipitant sodium carbonate is not in excess, manganous carbonate alone is precipitated, but if an excess is employed, the precipitate loses some carbon dioxide to form sodium hydrocarbonate ; but E. Prior added that manganous carbonate alone is precipitated with or without an excess of sodium carbonate provided air be excluded, but if air be present some hydrated manganosic oxide is precipitated as well as manganous carbonate. According to A. Ure, E. Turner, and E. Prior, the composition of the precipitated carbonate, dried in vacuo, is the *hemihydrate*, $2MnCO_3.H_2O$; and if dried in air, G. Forchhammer, and E. Prior found the composition is the *monohydrate*, $MnCO_3.H_2O$. J. Lefort said that if manganous carbonate is precipitated from a hot or cold soln. of a manganous salt by alkali carbonate or hydrocarbonate, the composition is $MnCO_3.H_2O$. According to H. Rose, the precipitate obtained with soln. containing a mol of sodium carbonate and a mol of manganous sulphate, each in 10 parts of water, has the composition of $MnO.8CO_2.5H_2O$ if precipitated from cold soln., and $11MnO.10CO_2.4H_2O$ if precipitated from hot soln. ; if the two soln. contain ten times as much water, the precipitates with cold and hot soln. have the compositions respectively $9MnO.8CO_2.5H_2O$ and $6MnO.5CO_2.2H_2O$.

According to L. Joulin, when soln. of manganous chloride, sulphate, or nitrate are treated with sodium carbonate, the precipitate may be manganous hydroxide or carbonate or a mixture of the two, according to the conditions. If the manganous salt soln. be poured into the soln. of sodium carbonate at ordinary temp. with equimolar parts of the two salts and dilutions up to 1 : 200, flocculent manganous carbonate is precipitated; but with higher dilutions the precipitate will contain manganous hydroxide and this the more the greater the dilution. The filtrate contains sodium hydrocarbonate. The precipitate remains white if air be excluded, but it becomes brown on exposure to air. If the sodium carbonate be in excess and very conc. soln. are used, manganous hydroxide is formed, and this is also the case when the conc. manganous salt soln. is dropped on solid sodium carbonate; if the action occurs in vacuo, carbon dioxide is evolved, and re-absorbed by the soln. of sodium carbonate to form hydrocarbonate. If the manganous salt be in excess and conc. soln. are employed, manganous carbonate is formed; but if the dilution exceeds 1 : 500, some manganous hydroxide is formed, and this the more the greater the dilution. Only a trace of hydroxide is formed at 0° if 40 mols. of sodium carbonate are present per mol. of manganous salt; but at 100° 3 mols. of manganous carbonate per mol. of sodium carbonate must be present in order to obtain manganous carbonate alone—if equimolar proportions are present, appreciable quantities of hydroxide are formed. The formation of the precipitate occupies a certain time; with equimolar parts and a dilution of 1 : 1000, the proportions of sodium carbonate decomposed are :

	1	2	4	7	15	30 days
Na_2CO_3 decomposed .	76·85	79·88	86·56	87·28	92·67	94·90 per cent.

The speed of the reaction is retarded by reducing the concentration of the soln. ; by the presence of sodium sulphate; by reducing the temp. ; and by adding an excess of either reacting salt—*vide infra*, the hydrolysis of the carbonate. H. W. Morse observed evidence of a periodicity in the precipitation of the carbonate. W. E. Adeney reported the reduction of manganese dioxide to manganous carbonate by bacterial fermentation.

The **colour** of rhodochrosite may be various shades of pink, yellowish-grey, fawn, dark red, or brown. The powder or streak is white. The artificial crystals obtained by A. de Schulten were almost colourless. The hydrate is snow-white, tasteless, and stable in air. Distinct crystals are not common, and when they are, the form is usually rhombohedral, with more or less rounded and striated faces. Rhodochrosite occurs also in compact, granular, or cleavable masses; it may be globular or botryoidal with a more or less distinct columnar structure; and it may occur as an incrustation on other minerals. According to F. Sansoni, the **crystals** are scalenohedral and trigonal with the axial ratio $a : c = 1 : 0·81840$, while A. de Schulten gave $1 : 0·8259$, and $\alpha = 102°$ 50'. F. Rinne found that the normal angle of the (100)-face is 73° 4' 8" at 16° ; 73° 10' 14" at 115° ; and 73° 15' 38" at 212°. The axial ratio was $a : c = 1 : 0·8147$ at 16° ; and $1 : 0·8232$ at 212°. At 300° the crystals broke into pieces. N. Sundius gave 73° 2' for the cleavage angle. The (101)-**cleavage** is perfect. Observations on the crystals were made by C. F. Peters, F. Sandberger, A. des Cloizeaux, R. Nostiz, K. von Kraatz-Koschlau, S. Koch, G. Greim, A. Reis and L. Zimmermann, F. Ritter, E. Weiss, A. von Lasaulx, P. Groth, O. Luedecke, J. S. Presl, V. R. von Zepharovich, F. Millosevich, H. Berman and F. A. Gonyer, C. L. Gruner, and G. Flink. A. Lacroix found **twinning** about the (110)-plane; S. Kreutz studied the **over-growths** ; I. N. Stransky and K. Kulelieff, the growth of the crystals ; and G. Tschermak found that the **corrosion figures** resembled those of magnesite; and A. Honess, that they are like those of calcite when the crystals are treated with salt soln. and with dil. nitric acid. P. Leroux said that the mineral is pleochroic. The crystals may have **inclusions** of pyrite, wad, limonite, etc. A. Johnsen observed the (111)-plane is a **gliding plane** under a press. of 7000 atm., and K. Veit obtained a similar result at 12,000 atm. press. According to P. P. Ewald, J. Brentano and J. Adamson,

MANGANESE 435

and W. L. Bragg, the **X-radiograms** agree with a trigonal structure of the calcite-type ; and R. W. G. Wyckoff found that the length of the side of the unit rhombo-hedron is $a=6\cdot03\times10^{-8}$ cm. ; and the angle between the axes is $a=47^\circ$ $46'$; C. Mauguin gave $a=3\cdot755\times10^{-8}$ cm., and $a=77^\circ$ $59'$. M. L. Huggins, G. R. Levi, and P. Niggli discussed the electronic structure of the crystals. P. Krieger studied the X-ray diffraction patterns of the manganocalcites, and concluded that the spacing of the atomic planes varies from 3·075 A. for calcite to 2·850 A. for rhodo-chrosite. The atomic planes are therefore more closely packed in the manganese minerals ; and since the manganese and calcium atoms provide the only variables in the series, the variation is due to the replacement of calcium atoms by manganese atoms in the atomic structure. J. E. Lennard-Jones and B. M. Dent calculated the energy required to separate a mol of a crystal into its ions, and found 750 cals. G. Bilibin discussed the isomorphism of the salt.

The **specific gravity** of rhodochrosite given by T. S. Hunt is 3·25 ; V. Vesely gave 3·312 to 3·552 ; C. M. Kersten, 3·533 ; F. Stromeyer, 3·557 ; C. L. Gruner, 3·570 to 3·61 ; L. Baric and F. Tucan, 3·570 to 3·698 ; E. Madelung and R. Fuchs, 3·663 ; F. Sandberger, 3·59 ; A. Krantz, 3·660 ; O. B. Böggild, 3·666 ; and G. J. Brush and E. S. Dana, 3·76. A. de Schulten gave 3·65 for the sp. gr. of the artificial crystals. P. Krieger found the following values for the sp. gr., the refractive indices, and the spacing d_{100} of a unit rhombohedron of a series of manganocalcites :

$MnCO_3$	0	1·09	7·00	15·40	32·34	42·17	95·72 per cent.
Sp. gr.	2·715	2·724	2·824	2·856	3·021	3·143	3·710
ϵ	1·486	1·490	1·501	1·503	1·519	1·534	1·595
μ	1·658	1·662	1·672	1·680	1·713	1·721	1·817
d_{100}	3·075	3·055	3·020	3·005	2·975	2·948	2·850 A.

H. G. F. Schröder gave 3·13 for the monohydrate at 3·9°. N. Sundius examined the systems $CaCO_3$–$MnCO_3$, and $CaMg(CO_3)_2$–$Ca(Fe,Mn)(CO_3)_2$, and measured their sp. gr. The sp. gr. of manganese carbonate is 3·691. I. I. Saslawsky studied the contraction which occurs in the formation of the carbonate from its elements. The **hardness** of the crystals of rhodochrosite is given as 3·5 to 4·5 ; and F. Pfaff gave 25 for the scratching hardness on the (111)-face, and 43 on the (100)-face, when the hardness of steatite is unity. E. Madelung and R. Fuchs gave $1\cdot3\times10^{-6}$ megabars per sq. cm. for the compressibility of the carbonate. E. Jannetaz found the square root of the ratio of the **thermal conductivities** in directions parallel and vertical to the principal axis is 1·06 ; and the crystals are thermally negative.

L. Joulin studied the **dissociation pressure** of manganous carbonate ; he found that the salt dried at a low temp. in an atm. of carbon dioxide begins to decompose at 70° ; at 150° the press. of the carbon dioxide is 215 mm., which remains constant at that temp. If the salt be allowed to cool, the press. slowly returns to its initial value. Above 200° the press. rises to 2 atm., the carbonate becomes brown in colour, and no re-absorption of the gas occurs on cooling. If the carbonate be heated to 100° and allowed to cool, the press. of the gas on a second heating is less than half that attained during the first heating ; while a third heating gave virtually the same value for the press. as that obtained during the second heating. There was no exhaustion of the gas during these successive heatings, and the phenomenon is explained by assuming that the carbonate suffers an inter-molecular change which renders it more stable and more resistant towards decom-position at low temp. It must also be remembered that the carbon dioxide may be reduced by the manganous oxide, so that a complex series of equilibria is involved. Thus, $MnCO_3{\rightleftharpoons}MnO+CO_2$; $3MnO+CO_2{\rightleftharpoons}Mn_3O_4+CO$; and $2MnO+CO_2{\rightleftharpoons}Mn_2O_3$ $+CO$. W. Manchot and L. Lorenz found that the dissociation press. of manganous carbonate and the re-absorption of the carbon dioxide depend on the water-content of the specimen, and is a result of hydrolysis. The process is reproducible only with samples containing an equal proportion of water. All precipitated manganous carbonate retains water up to complete decomposition. J. Lefort's statement that the hydrate can be dehydrated at about 70° is wrong; H. Rose also noted how water is retained with great tenacity even after the carbonate has lost some carbon dioxide. W. Manchot and L. Lorenz observed that a specimen of rhodochrosite gave a lower press. than the artificial carbonate, but if moistened it reacted similarly but to a less extent. There is no evidence that a definite basic carbonate is formed. K. Friedrich and L. G. Smith found that a sample of rhodochrosite from Colorado commences to decompose at 525°, and the maximum decomposition occurs at 570°, while with a sample from Peru decomposition commences at 510° and attains a maximum at 550°. In both cases decomposition was practically complete at 700°. A. Beutell and P. Oberhoffer found that a sample from Freiburg suffered an appreciable decomposition at 300°. K. Grünberg found that the losses in weight of a sample of native manganese spar heated in a current of air were 0·45 per cent. in 3 hrs. at 300° and 360°—this loss is mainly water; 0·86 per cent. in 3 hrs. at 400°; 2·09, 9·56, and 41·60 per cent. in respectively 3, 9, and 12 hrs. at 470°; while in a current of carbon dioxide there was no loss at 360° or 400° during 3 hrs.; at 530° there was a loss of 0·13 per cent. in 12 hrs.; 0·39 per cent. in 3 hrs. at 570°; 1·59 per cent. in 3 hrs. at 590°; and 8·33 per cent. in 24 hrs.; while at 650° there was a loss of 10·58 per cent. in 3 hrs., and of 40·61 per cent. in 6 hrs. J. A. Hedvall said that dissociation begins at about 395° and is complete at 595°. With W. Nernst's theorem, O. Brill calculated for the dissociation pressure, p, of the carbonate at $T°$ K., log $p=23500/4·571T+1·75$ log $T+3·2$, so that for a dissociation press. of one atm. the calculated dissociation temp. is 359° or 632° K.; L. Joulin found 327°. According to M. Berthelot, the **heat of precipitation** of manganous carbonate from a soln. of manganous chloride by potassium carbonate is −4·0 Cals., and the precipitate is amorphous. It develops in consequence of crystallization 1·6 Cals. This value is independent of the first. If a soln. of sodium carbonate is employed, the data are respectively bomb −3·7 Cals. and 1·4 Cals. H. le Chatelier observed that in a calorimetric bomb $3MnCO_3+O =Mn_3O_4+3CO_2-27·8$ Cals. M. Berthelot calculated for the **heat of formation** of crystalline manganous carbonate $(Mn,C,3O)=208·6$ Cals.; of the amorphous carbonate, 207·0 Cals.; and of the natural carbonate, 212·7 Cals. Again, $Mn(OH)_2+CO_2+Aq. =MnCO_3+Aq.+12·0$ Cals. for amorphous carbonate, and 13·6 Cals. for the crystalline carbonate. Similarly, $CO_{2gas}+Mn(OH)_2=MnCO_{3cryst.}+H_2O+19·2$ Cals.; and $CO_{2gas}+MnO=MnCO_{3cryst.}+23·5$ Cals.; and D. Müller, 27·7 Cals., or $(Mn,C,1\frac{1}{2}O_2)=218·2$ Cals. J. Thomsen gave $(Mn,O,CO_2)=113·88$ Cals.; and $(Mn,3O,C)=181·84$ Cals.; W. A. Roth, 218·2 Cals.; and H. le Chatelier, $(MnO,CO_2) =276$ Cals.; and W. A. Roth, 279 Cals. J. C. W. Frazer and C. E. Greider gave $MnO+CO_2=MnCO_3+5·5$ Cals. G. Beck discussed the energy of formation.

The **indices of refraction** of different samples of rhodochrosite were found by P. Gaubert to range from $\omega=1·7941$ to $1·8194$, and $\epsilon=1·5946$ to $1·6023$; E. T. Wherry and E. S. Larsen, $\omega=1·817$, and $\epsilon=1·594$; W. Ortloff, $\epsilon=1·5973$; W. E. Ford, $\omega=1·8279$, and $\epsilon=1·5904$ to $1·6057$; and N. Sundius, for Na-light, $\epsilon=1·600$, and $\omega=1·816$. The subject was discussed by P. Niggli—*vide supra.* W. A. Wooster discussed the relation between the refractive index and the lattice structure. W. Ortloff gave 19·43 for the **refraction equivalent.** The **birefringence** is strong; and the **optical character** negative. A. Madelung observed a feeble **optical anomaly** with a sample of rhodochrosite. There is strong **pleochroism,** and G. F. Kunz reported a sample with the ordinary ray pink and the extraordinary ray pale yellow. W. W. Coblentz found that rhodochrosite showed maxima in the **ultrared reflection spectrum** at $6·63\mu$, $11·47\mu$, and $14·0\mu$. C. Doelter observed that the exposure of rhodochrosite to **radium radiations** has scarcely any effect on the colour. E. Engelhardt observed that some varieties have a red and others a green fluorescence under the action of **ultra-violet light.** O. Stelling studied the K-series of **X-ray absorption** ; G. Dupouy, the **magnetic properties** ; and W. Sucksmith, the **gyromagnetic effect.**

J. A. Arfvedson found that when manganous carbonate is heated in **hydrogen,** manganous oxide is formed. E. R. Schneider found that when the carbonate is heated to redness in **oxygen** it forms manganic oxide ; and F. Hoppe-Seyler, that with oxygen and steam at 200° anhydrous manganosic oxide is formed. The weathering of rhodochrosite in nature was discussed by A. Bergeat, and F. Kossmat and C. von John. A. Gorgeu observed that when the dry carbonate is heated in **air,** it primarily forms manganous oxide, which then forms a higher oxide—manganic oxide at below 425°. F. Hoppe-Seyler observed that oxygen and water-vapour at 200° transform it into manganosic oxide. A. Gorgeu found that at ordinary temp. the oxygen of air—moist or dry—gradually attacks hydrated manganous carbonate, forming manganic oxide and no higher oxide ; hence, he argued that the manganese dioxide minerals were not formed by the oxidation of the carbonate, as had been supposed by J. B. J. D. Boussingault, and L. Dieulafait. M. W. Beyerinck did not notice any particular tendency of manganous carbonate to oxidize in air, for he was able to keep an aq. suspension for years without taking any special precautions, and manganous carbonate agar-agar plates may be kept unchanged for months with free access of air. When two pieces of filter paper with a little manganous carbonate between them, and moistened with a dil. soln. of ammonium chloride and potassium phosphate, are infected with garden soil and kept at about 25°, dark brown or black spots of a manganic compound will appear on them after some days. The characteristic reactions of the manganic compound thus produced are the sudden decomposition of hydrogen dioxide and the oxidation of hydriodic acid. Bacteria and various species of mould are the cause of the oxidation. These moulds belong to very different groups of the fungi, and consist of species of the genera *Botrytes, Sporocybe, Trichocladium,* and in particular of *Mycogone.* Oxidation appears to occur as well within as without the mycelium. It could not be brought about by oxydase or peroxoxydase of different origin. H. Rose said that the carbonate begins to oxidize at 150°, and becomes dark brown at 200° ; J. Lefort found that the carbonate oxidizes at 300° ; and G. Forchhammer, at 260°. W. Reissig found that more oxygen is absorbed the longer the time the carbonate is heated in air and the higher the temp., short of 300° ; at that temp. the residue approximates $MnO.2MnO_2$. L. Joulin said that cold **water** does not decompose manganous carbonate, but if the water be boiled with the carbonate for a long time, some manganous hydroxide is formed and subsequently oxidized. J. L. Lassaigne said that hydrated manganous carbonate is insoluble in water, but it is soluble in water containing carbon dioxide in soln.—the **solubility** in 100 parts of water saturated with that gas is 0·05 part of $MnCO_3$. C. von John added that 100 parts of water dissolve 0·013 part of the carbonate, while 100 parts of water with carbon dioxide in soln. dissolve 0·026 part of carbonate. These observations are not precise enough with respect to the concentration of the carbon dioxide. According to F. Ageno and E. Valla, a litre of water at 25° dissolves 0·065 grm. of manganous carbonate. Following G. Bodländer's observations on the carbonates of the alkaline earths, and also the observations of J. Walker and W. Cormack, and of F. Auerbach and H. Pick, it follows that in aq. soln. the following equilibria are involved : $[Mn^{..}][CO_3'']=K_1$; $[H^.][HCO_3']=K_2[H_2CO_3]$, where $K_2=3\times10^{-7}$; $[H^.][CO_3'']=K_3[HCO_3']$, where $K_3=6\times10^{-11}$; and $[H_2CO_3]=K_4p$, where K_4 $=0·03388$, and the partial press. of the carbon dioxide, p, is expressed in atm. On account of the small dissociation of the HCO_3'-ions, and the almost complete dissociation of the manganese hydrocarbonate, $2K_1K_2K_4p=K_3[HCO_3']^3$; and $K_1^{\frac{1}{2}}=0·143[HCO_3']p^{-\frac{1}{2}}$. F. Ageno and E. Valla found at 25° :

p	.	.	0·8217	0·6367	0·5298	0·5228	0·3277	0·3296
S	.	.	0·003103	0·002647	0·002531	0·002240	0·002171	0·002255
$K_1^{\frac{1}{2}}$	.	.	0·000473	0·000439	0·000447	0·000397	0·000450	0·000466

The mean value for $K_1^{\frac{1}{2}}=4·45\times10^{-4}$, so that the **solubility product** of manganous carbonate at 25° is $K_1=8·83\times10^{-11}$. Water alone, at 25°, dissolves $5·659\times10^{-4}$ mol. per litre at 25°, and consequently for the hydrolysis $CO_3''+H_2O\rightleftharpoons HCO_3'$

$+OH'$, $[Mn^{..}][CO_3'']=K_1$; or $K_1/[Mn^{..}]=8\cdot83\times10^{-11}/5\cdot659\times10^{-4}=1\cdot56\times10^{-7}$; and $[HCO_3']=5\cdot659\times10^{-4}-0\cdot00156\times10^{-4}=5\cdot657\times10^{-4}$, which is virtually the same as that of $[Mn^{..}]$. This means that the degree of **hydrolysis** of manganous carbonate in aq. soln. : $MnCO_3+H_2O=Mn(OH)(HCO_3')$, is virtually 100 per cent. The soln. of manganese carbonate in water sat. with carbon dioxide contains **manganese hydrocarbonate,** $Mn(HCO_3)_2$. E. Dittler found that quartz sand adsorbs 51·74 per cent. of the manganese in soln. ; china clay, 68·73 per cent. ; compact limestone, 72·9 per cent. ; marl, 78·53 per cent. ; and chalk, 96·53 per cent. In the last case there was probably some chemical replacement of calcium by manganese. O. Haehnel found the solubilities of the manganese carbonate under a pressure of 8 and 56 atm. to be respectively 0·04 and 0·08 per cent. R. Lyden obtained for the solubility of rhodochrosite 0·0127 grm. Mn_3O_4 per 500 c.c., a value rather smaller than that usually accepted. L. Gmelin said that a boiling soln. of **potassium hydroxide** extracts carbon dioxide and forms manganous hydroxide ; a soln. of **sodium carbonate** in the presence of air was found by R. Laming to form a brown hydrated manganic oxide and sodium hydrocarbonate ; and L. Joulin added that the action is extremely slow at 0°, but rapid at 100°. J. J. Ebelmen said that manganous carbonate is no more soluble in a soln. of alkali carbonate than it is in water alone. L. Joulin found that a soln. of **sodium hydro-carbonate** changes manganous carbonate only after a few days. *Vide supra* for H. Rose's basic salts or **manganous oxycarbonates.**

F. Wöhler represented the reaction with rhodochrosite and **chlorine,** at a red-heat, by $4MnCO_3+Cl_2=MnCl_2+Mn_3O_4+4CO_2$. R. Weber noticed that the action on the hydrated carbonate is very slow at ordinary temp. As previously indicated, A. Gorgeu found that chlorine, or chlorine water, acts on manganous carbonate suspended in water, forming one of the higher oxides with the expulsion of carbon dioxide ; **bromine,** or bromine water, acts similarly but more slowly. R. Böttger obtained a similar result by the action of a boiling soln. of **calcium hypochlorite.** Manganous carbonate is soluble in **acids** generally. J. A. Arfvedson found that when the carbonate is heated to redness with twice its weight of **sulphur,** sulphur and carbon dioxides are given off and manganese sulphide, accompanied by a little oxide and sulphate, is formed ; H. Rose observed that when heated to redness with powdered sulphur in hydrogen, manganous sulphide is formed. A. Voelcker noted that **hydrogen sulphide** gives no precipitate with a soln. of manganous carbonate in carbonated water. P. de Clérmont and H. Guyot found that an excess of **ammonium sulphide** transforms manganous carbonate slowly into green manganous sulphide, while **alkali sulphides** form red manganous sulphide. C. W. Davis studied the solvent action of sulphurous acid. F. Muck did not get the same result with ammonium sulphide. E. C. Franklin and C. A. Kraus found that manganous carbonate is insoluble in liquid **ammonia.** R. H. Brett said that a soln. of the carbonate in an aq. soln. of **ammonium salts**—chloride or nitrate—does not give a precipitate with hydrogen sulphide, and G. C. Wittstein found that the freshly-precipitated carbonate is soluble in soln. of ammonium salts. H. Gold-schmidt and K. L. Syngros found that a soln. of manganous chloride and hydroxyl-amine hydrochloride forms a white precipitate with sodium carbonate ; when washed and dried, the grey powder is **manganous hydroxylaminocarbonate,** $4MnCO_3.3NH_2OH.2H_2O$, soluble in acids. According to M. Flajlot, manganous carbonate is insoluble in a soln. of **potassium cyanide.** J. Spiller found that the carbonate is not precipitated in the presence of **sodium citrate ;** and A. Naumann found that it is insoluble in **ethyl acetate.** D. Talmud and N. M. Lubman found that the flotability of manganese carbonate in **oleic acid** or mixtures of oleic acid and ammonia is a maximum for $p_H=7$. W. H. Coghill and J. B. Clemmer studied the soap flotation of rhodochrosite.

According to A. D. Brokaw, amorphous manganous carbonate reacts at once with **gold chloride** with production of the dark brown hydrated dioxide. Crystal-lized manganous carbonate acts slowly, but after a day becomes coated with the dark brown hydrated oxide and flakes of gold. F. W. O. de Coninck exposed a mixture of a soln. of 2 mols of **sodium nitrate** and a mol of manganous carbonate to light for 5 months without any reaction taking place. J. N. von Fuchs observed that the carbonate dissolves in a soln. of a **ferric salt**, giving off carbon dioxide and precipitating ferric hydroxide.

G. C. Wittstein supposed that freshly-precipitated manganous carbonate dissolved in a soln. of ammonium carbonate is present as **ammonium manganous carbonate** ; and F. Ephraim obtained the salt $(NH_4)_2CO_3.MnCO_3.4H_2O$ in microscopic prisms. W. C. Reynolds prepared **potassium manganous carbonate**, $K_2Mn(CO_3)_2.4H_2O$, by the action of a cold soln. of potassium carbonate of sp. gr. 1·53 on manganous acetate and rubbing the mixture in a mortar. Crystals of the salt are quickly formed ; they are only sparingly soluble in water. If the mixture used in the preparation be warm oxidation occurs. O. Ruff and E. Ascher studied solid soln. of *manganese and calcium carbonates*. L. H. Bauer and H. Berman found radiating groups of lathe-shaped, bluish-black needles of **zinc manganese hydroxycarbonate**, $2(Zn,Mn)CO_3.5(Zn,Mn)(OH)_2$, occurring as a mineral which they called **loseyite**—after S. R. Losey. The composition recalls that of hydrozincite, $ZnCO_3.2Zn(OH)_2$. The monoclinic crystals have the axial ratios : $a:b:c = 0.70:1:0.62$, and $\beta = 94° 30'$. The optic axial angle $2V = 64°$; the optical character is positive ; the indices of refraction are $\alpha = 1.637, \beta = 1.648,$ and $\gamma = 1.676$; the sp. gr. is 3·27 ; and the hardness about 3.

REFERENCES.

[1] T. Bergman, *Sciagraphia regni mineralis*, Lipsiæ, 1782 ; C. F. Jasche, *Kleine mineralogischen Schriften*, Sondershausen, 4, 1817 ; D. G. J. Lenz, *Versuch einer vollständigen Anleitung zur Kenntniss der Mineralien*, Leipzig, 1794 ; J. F. L. Hausmann, *Handbuch der Mineralogie*, Göttingen, 302, 1081, 1813 ; A. G. Werner, *Letztes Mineralsystem*, Freiburg, 1817 ; R. J. Haüy, *Tableau comparatif des résultats de la cristallographie et de l'analyse chimique*, Paris, 111, 1809 ; F. Mohs, *Grundriss der Mineralogie*, Dresden, 1822 ; F. S. Beudant, *Traité élémentaire de mineralogie*, Paris, 1824 ; A. Breithaupt, *Vollständiges Handbuch der Mineralogie*, Dresden, 228, 1841 ; *Pogg. Ann.*, **69**. 429, 1846 ; *Vollständiges Charakteristik der Mineralsystems*, Dresden, 67, 1832 ; E. F. Germar, *Schweigger's Journ.*, **26**. 119, 1819 ; F. Bayer, *Verh. Ver. Brünn*, 12, 1873 ; E. Manasse, *Mem. Soc. Toscana*, **27**. 76, 1911 ; R. Böttger, *Beiträge zur Physik und Chemie*, Frankfurt a. M., **2**. 12, 1841 ; O. B. Böggild, *Mineralogia Groenlandica*, Kjöbenhavn, 155, 1905 ; W. T. Roepper, *Amer. Journ. Science*, (2), **50**. 37, 1870 ; P. E. Browning, *ib.*, (3), **40**. 375, 1890 ; S. L. Penfield, *ib.*, (3), **18**. 50, 1879 ; G. F. Kunz, *ib.*, (3), **34**. 477, 1877 ; T. S. Hunt, *ib.*, (2), **28**. 134, 1859 ; G. J. Brush and E. S. Dana, *ib.*, (2), **18**. 150, 1879 ; R. W. G. Wyckoff, *ib.*, (4), **50**. 317, 1920 ; A. Honess, *ib.*, (4), **45**. 201, 1918 ; M. Lienau, *Chem. Ztg.*, **23**. 418, 1899 ; A. Krantz, *Verh. Nat. Ver. Rheinl. Westphalens*, **14**. 111, 1857 ; W. A. Roth, *Zeit. angew. Chem.*, **42**. 981, 1929 ; *Zeit. Eisenhüttenwesen*, **3**. 339, 1929 ; *Stahl Eisen*, **49**. 1763, 1929 ; A. Lacroix, *Minéralogie de la France et de ses colonies*, Paris, **3**. 626, 1905 ; *Bull. Soc. Min.*, **23**. 253, 1900 ; G. A. Kenngott, *Uebersichte der Resultate mineralogischer Forschungen*, Leipzig, 28, 1860 ; 82, 1865 ; *Neues Jahrb. Min.*, 188, 1872 ; F. Sandberger, *Pogg. Ann.*, **88**. 491, 1853 ; *Neues Jahrb. Min.*, ii, 37, 1892 ; A. Bukowsky, *Congr. Böhm. Naturf. Aertze Prag.*, 293, 1901 ; *Neues Jahrb. Min.*, ii, 338, 1903 ; C. F. Peters, *ib.*, 456, 1861 ; M. Weibull, *Tschermak's Mitt.*, (2), **7**. 110, 1885 ; C. Doelter, *ib.*, (2), **28**. 171, 1909 ; G. Tschermak, *ib.*, (2), **4**. 116, 1882 ; E. Dittler, *ib.*, (2), **36**. 164, 1924 ; C. F. Rammelsberg, *Handbuch der Mineralchemie*, Leipzig, **2**. 232, 1875 ; *Pogg. Ann.*, **68**. 511, 1846 ; R. Weber, *ib.*, **112**. 623, 1861 ; H. Rose, *Liebig's Ann.*, **80**. 237, 1873 ; *Pogg. Ann.*, **84**. 52, 1851 ; F. Wöhler, *ib.*, **27**. 627, 1833 ; H. G. F. Schröder, *ib.*, **106**. 226, 1859 ; *Dichtigkeitsmessungen*, Heidelberg, 1873 ; J. A. Krenner, *Nat. Ber. Ungarn*, **1**. 201, 1883 ; **2**. 355, 1884 ; *Zeit. Kryst.*, **8**. 242, 1884 ; **9**. 289, 1884 ; **43**. 473, 1907 ; F. Kretschmer, *Oesterr. Zeit. Berg. Hütt.*, **53**. 59, 1905 ; H. Zinkeisen, *Jahrb. Berg. Hütt. Sachsen*, 40, 1890 ; A. Schwager and C. W. von Gümbel, *Geognost. Jahrb.*, **7**. 57, 1894 ; W. Ortloff, *Zeit. phys. Chem.*, **19**. 215, 1896 ; O. Brill, *ib.*, **57**. 736, 1907 ; G. Bodländer, *ib.*, **35**. 23, 1900 ; K. von Kraatz-Koschlau, *Notizbl. Ver. Erdk. Darmstadt*, **18**. 50, 1897 ; G. Flink, *Med. Grönland*, **24**. 1, 1901 ; P. Groth, *Die Mineraliensammlung der Universität Strassburg*, 132, 1878 ; F. Millosevich, *Rend. Accad. Lincei*, (5), **15**. i, 317, 1906 ; F. Ageno and E. Valla, *ib.*, (5), **20**. ii, 706, 1911 ; T. Haege, *Die Mineralien des Siegerlandes und der abgrenzenden Bezirke*, Siegen, 1887 ; H. Quiring, *Zeit. prakt. Geol.*, **27**. 133, 1919 ; G. R. Levi, *Atti Congresso Naz. Chim. Ind.*, 257, 1924 ; V. Vesely, *Rozp. Ceske Akad.*, **31**. 9, 1922 ; M. von Sill, *Berg. Hütt. Jahrb.*, **14**. 183, 1865 ; L. Baric and F. Tucan, *Ann. Geol. Belgrad*, 129, 1925 ; P. Poni, *Mineralogie de la Roumanie*, Jassy, 57, 1900 ; L. L. de Koninck, *Bull. Acad. Belg.*, (2), **47**. 564, 1879 ; F. W. O. de Coninck, *ib.*, 691, 1909 ; O. Luedecke, *Die Minerale des Harzes*, Berlin, 334, 1896 ; G. Greim, *Die Mineralien des Grossherzogtunis Hessen*, Giessen, 24, 1895 ; A. Frenzel, *Mineralogisches*

Lexicon für das Königreich Sachsen, Leipzig, 78, 1874; V. R. von Zepharovich, *Mineralogisches Lexicon für das Kaiserthum Oesterreich*, Wien, 1. 377, 1873; 2. 274, 1873; 3. 215, 1875; *Verh. geol. Reichsanst. Wien*, 95, 1875; E. Döll, *ib.*, 95. 1875; S. Koch, *Ann. Mus. Nat. Hung.*, 20. 130, 19.3; 21. 71, 1924; J. S. Presl, *Nerostopis čili mineralogia*, Praze, 1837; E. Weiss, *Zeit. deut. geol. Ges.*, 31. 810, 1879; F. Hoppe-Seyler, *ib.*, 27. 529, 1875; A. von Lasaulx, *Sitzber-Niederrh. Ges. Nat. Bonn*, 95, 1882; K. Grünberg, *Beitrag zur Kenntnis der natürlichen kristallisierten Karbonate des Calciums, Magnesiums, Eisens und Mangans*, Leipzig, 1913; *Zeit. anorg. Chem.*, 80. 337, 1913; D. Müller, *Beiträge zur anorganischen Thermochemie mit der kalorimetrischen Bombe*, Braunschweig, 1929; C. W. Davis, *Rept. Investigations U.S. Bur. Mines*, 3024, 1930; A. Gorgeu, *Bull. Soc. Chim.*, (2), 49. 668, 1888; (3), 1. 605, 1889; *Compt. Rend.*, 106. 703, 1888; 108. 950, 1889; J. Lefort, *ib.*, 27. 268, 1847; L. Dieulafait, *ib.*, 51. 676, 1860; H. le Chatelier, *ib.*, 122. 80, 1896; J. J. Ebelmen, *ib.*, 33. 525, 1851; M. Berthelot, *ib.*, 96. 88, 1883; *Thermochimie*, Paris, 2. 270, 1897; *Ann. Chim. Phys.*, (5), 30. 543, 1883; H. de Sénarmont, *Compt. Rend.*, 28. 693, 1849; 32. 409, 1851; *Ann. Chim. Phys.*, (3), 30. 137, 1849; L. Joulin, *ib.*, (4), 30. 248, 1873; *Compt. Rend.*, 76. 558, 1873; *Bull. Soc. Chim.*, (2), 19. 338, 1873; J. B. J. D. Boussingault, *Ann. Chim. Phys.*, (5), 27. 289, 1882; P. de Clérmont and H. Guyot, *ib.*, (5), 12. 114, 1897; H. Moissan, *ib.*, (5), 21. 234, 1880; M. Flajlot, *ib.*, (3), 39. 460, 1853; *Compt. Rend.*, 36. 1090, 1853; *Ann. Mines*, (4), 3. 641, 1853; R. Nostiz, *Jahresb. Nat. Ver. Elberfeld*, 13. 59, 1912; F. Muck, *Zeit. Chem.*, (2), 5. 582, 1869; G. C. Wittstein, *Repert. Pharm.*, 57. 30, 1836; E. Weinschenk, *Zeit. Kryst.*, 17. 486, 1890; A. Madelung, *ib.*, 7. 75, 1883; F. Sansoni, *ib.*, 5. 250, 1881; W. C. Reynolds, *Journ. Chem. Soc.*, 73. 265, 1907; J. Walker and W. Cormack, *ib.*, 77. 8, 1900; J. Spiller, *ib.*, 10. 110, 1858; A. Bergeat, *Die Erzlagerstatten*, Leipzig, 1. 254, 1904; J. Thomsen, *Thermochemische Untersuchungen*, Leipzig, 3. 271, 1883; *Ber.*, 12. 2031, 1879; A. Bacovescu and E. Vlahuta, *ib.*, 42. 2638, 1909; H. Tamm, *Amer. Chemist*, 3. 145, 1872; W. Nernst, *Nachr. Gött.*, 1, 1906; H. Goldschmidt and K. L. Syngros. *Zeit. anorg. Chem.*, 5. 138, 1894; W. Manchot and L. Lorenz, *ib.*, 134. 297, 1924; A. Johnsen, *Centr. Min.*, 265, 1918; F. Rinne, *ib.*, 710, 1914; A. Beutell and P. Oberhoffer, *ib.*, 375, 1919; K. Friedrich and L. G. Smith, *ib.*, 615, 651, 688, 1912; K. Friedrich, *Met.*, 9. 409, 1912; K. Veit, *Neues Jahrb. Min. B.B.*, 45. 121, 1921; F. Pfaff, *Sitzber. Akad. München*, 3. 72, 1884; F. Auerbach and H. Pick, *Arb. Gesundheitsamte*, 38. 243, 1911; F. Ritter, *Ber. Nat. Ges. Frankfurt a. M.*, 281, 1884; E. T. Wherry and E. S. Larsen, *Journ. Washington Acad.*, 7. 365, 1917; W. E. Ford, *Trans. Connecticut Acad.*, 21. 21, 1917; P. P. Ewald, *Kristalle und Röntgenstrahlen*, Berlin, 305, 1923; C. Mauguin, *La structure des cristaux*, Paris, 247, 1924; P. Niggli, *Zeit. Kryst.*, 56. 231, 1921; 75. 228, 1930; *Lehrbuch der Mineralogie*, Berlin, 369, 1920; R. Brauns, *Chemische Mineralogie*, Leipzig, 410, 1896; E. Engelhardt, *Lumineszenzerscheinungen der Mineralien im ultravioletten Licht*, Weida i. Th., 1912; J. F. John, *Ann. Phil.*, 2. 172, 263, 1813; 3. 413, 1813; *Gehlen's Journ.*, 3. 452, 1807; 4. 436, 1804; G. Forchhammer, *Ann. Phil.*, 16. 130, 1820; 17. 50, 1821; *De mangano*, Hafnia, 1820; J. A. Arfvedson, *Afhand. Fys. Kemi*, 6. 222, 1818; *Ann. Phil.*, 7. 267, 1824; *Schweigger's Journ.*, 42. 202, 1818; E. R. Schneider, *Pogg. Ann.*, 107. 605, 1859; L. Gmelin, *Handbook of Chemistry*, London, 4. 214, 1850; J. R. Blum, *Die Pseudomorphosen des Mineralreichs*, Stuttgart, 1843; Nachträge, 4. 88, 141, 1879; H. Heymann, *Verh. Nat. Ver. Rheinl. Westfalen*, 26. 95, 1870; J. D. Dana, *A System of Mineralogy*, New York, 279, 1892; J. N. von Fuchs, *Schweigger's Journ.*, 60. 345, 1830; A. Naumann, *Ber.*, 43. 314, 1910; A. D. Brokaw, *Journ. Ind. Eng. Chem.*, 5. 560, 1913; M. W. Beyerinck, *Proc. Akad. Amsterdam*, 16. 397, 1913; W. E. Adeney, *Trans. Roy. Dublin Soc.*, (2), 6. 269, 1897; J. C. W. Frazer and C. E. Greider, *Journ. Phys. Chem.*, 29. 1099, 1925; J. E. Lennard-Jones and B. M. Dent, *Proc. Roy. Soc.*, 113. A, 673, 690, 1927; F. Ephraim, *Helvetica Chim. Acta*, 6. 920, 1923; K. Zimanyi, *Ann. Musee Nat. Hungarici*, 11. 271, 1913; E. Madelung and R. Fuchs, *Ann. Physik*, (4), 65. 289, 1921; A. des Cloizeaux, *Manuel de minéralogie*, Paris, 2. 148, 1874; *Bull. Soc. Min.*, 7. 72, 1884; A. de Schulten, *ib.*, 20. 195, 1897; *Compt. Rend.*, 122. 1352, 1896; P. Gaubert, *ib.*, 164. 46, 1917; *Bull. Soc. Min.*, 42. 88, 1919; E. Jannetaz, *ib.*, 15. 133, 1892; *Compt. Rend.*, 114. 1352, 1892; V. C. Butureanu, *Min. Mag.*, 16. 369, 1913; *Ann. Scient. Univ. Jassy*, 7. 185, 1912; *Bull. Soc. Min.*, 40. 164, 1917; E. C. Franklin and C. A. Kraus, *Amer. Chem. Journ.*, 20. 828, 1898; C. L. Gruner, *Ann. Mines*, (3), 18. 61, 1840; P. Berthier, *ib.*, (1), 6. 595, 1821; *Ann. Phil.*, 3. 573, 1821; F. Stromeyer, *Gött. Anz.*, 1081, 1843; A. Reis and L. Zimmermann, *Zeit. phys. Chem.*, 102. 296, 1922; O. Stelling, *ib.*, 117. 161, 1925; C. M. Kersten, *Berg. Hütt. Ztg.*, 5. 129, 1846; *Journ. prakt. Chem.*, (1), 37. 163, 1846; R. Wagner, *ib.*, (1), 102. 233, 1867; O. Haehnel, *ib.*, (2), 108. 187, 1924; R. J. Kane, *Journ. Dublin Geol. Soc.*, 3. 237, 1849; *Phil. Mag.*, (3), 32. 37, 1848; R. H. Brett, *ib.*, (3), 10. 95, 1837; F. Kossmat and C. von John, *Zeit. prakt. Geol.*, 13. 325, 1905; C. von John, *Jahrb. geol. Reichsanst. Wien*, 36. 344, 1883; H. von Foullon, *ib.*, 36. 344, 1883; A. E. von Reuss, *ib.*, 20. 521, 1871; *Sitzber. Akad. Wien*, 10. 44, 1853; H. Ludwig, *Arch. Pharm.*, (2), 143. 194, 1870; E. Hildenbrand, *Ver. Nat. Nassau*, 14. 434, 1860; *Liebig's Ann.*, 115. 348, 1860; A. Birnbacker, *Liebig's Ann.*, 98. 144, 1856; W. Reissig, *ib.*, 103. 27, 1857; A. Voelcker, *ib.*, 59. 35, 1846; *Scheik. Onderzoek Utrecht*, 3. 526, 1846; C. Bergemann, *Ver. Nat. Ver. Bonn*, 111, 1857; D. Talmud and N. M. Lubman, *Koll. Zeit.*, 50. 159, 1930; H. W. Morse, *Journ. Phys. Chem.*, 34. 1555, 1930; W. L. Bragg, *Proc. Roy. Soc.*, 89. A, 468, 1914; J. Brentano and J. Adamson, *Phil. Mag.*, (7), 7. 507, 1929; R. Laming, *Journ. Chim. Med.*, (3), 7. 706, 1852; J. L. Lassaigne, *ib.*, (2), 40. 329, 1829; (3), 4. 312, 1848; *Journ. prakt. Chem.*, (1), 44. 247, 1848; *Liebig's Ann.*, 68. 254, 1848; E. Prior, *Zeit. anal. Chem.*, 8. 428, 1869; C. R. Fresenius, *ib.*, 11. 425, 1872; E. Turner, *Phil. Mag.*, (2),

4. 22, 96, 1828; *Trans. Roy. Soc. Edin.*, **11.** 143, 1831; *Journ. Roy. Inst.*, **1.** 293, 1831; S. Kreutz, *Min. Mag.*, **15.** 232, 1909; A. Ure, *Quart. Journ. Science*, **13.** 1, 1822; P. Leroux, *Compt. Rend.*, **189.** 162, 1929; N. Sundius, *Tschermak's Mitt.*, (2), **38.** 175, 1925; *Geol. För. Förh. Stockholm*, **47.** 269, 1925; J. A. Hedvall, *ib.*, **47.** 73, 1925; M. L. Huggins, *Journ. Amer. Chem. Soc.*, **44.** 1841, 1922; I. I. Saslawsky, *Zeit. anorg. Chem.*, **146.** 315, 1925; G. Beck, *ib.*, **156.** 288, 1926; O. Ruff and E. Ascher, *ib.*, **185.** 369, 1930; R. Lyden, *Finska Kemi Medd.*, **34.** 72, 1925; W. W. Coblentz, *Supplementary Investigations of Infra-red Spectra*, Washington, 178, 1908; L. H. Bauer and H. Berman, *Amer. Min.*, **14.** 103, 150, 1929; P. Krieger, *ib.*, **15.** 23, 1930; H. Berman and F. A. Gonyer, *ib.*, **15.** 375, 1930; G. Bilibin, *Mem. Min. Soc. Russia*, (2), **56.** 3, 1928; I. N. Stransky and K. Kulelieff, *Zeit. phys. Chem.*, **142.** 467, 1929; W. H. Coghill and J. B. Clemmer, *Tech. Publ. Amer. Inst. Min. Eng.*, 445, 1932; W. A. Wooster, *Zeit. Kryst.*, **80.** 495, 1931; W. Sucksmith, *Proc. Roy. Soc.*, **133.** A, 179, 1931; G. Dupouy, *Ann. Physique*, (10), **15.** 495, 1931.

§ 25. The Manganese Nitrates

C. W. Scheele [1] first prepared **manganous nitrate**, $Mn(NO_3)_2$. It is obtained in soln. by dissolving manganous carbonate in nitric acid. According to J. F. John, manganese dioxide (*q.v.*) dissolves in nitric acid in the presence of reducing agents, which form some nitrous acid, or, according to C. W. Scheele, by exposing the system to sunlight, which decomposes some nitric acid into nitrous acid and oxygen. J. F. John obtained a soln. of the nitrate by dissolving the metal in hot nitric acid. J. W. Gatehouse obtained manganous nitrate by heating to 165° to 200° a mixture of manganese dioxide and ammonium nitrate. The evaporation of the aq. soln. furnishes a syrupy liquid which yields crystals of the hexahydrate. V. M. Peshkova described the preparation of the salt. A. Guyard noted the occurrence of manganous nitrate in native Chili saltpetre; and H. St. C. Deville and H. Debray found nitrates in native manganese dioxide.

J. M. Ordway found that at 25·8° the aq. soln. contains 62·4 per cent. of $Mn(NO_3)_2$ as hexahydrate. F. Rüdorff found that a soln. with 21·3 per cent. $Mn(NO_3)_2$ freezes at −10°. The following additional observations are due to R. Funk and co-workers, when the solubility S is expressed in percentages:

	−36°	−30°	−29°	−16°	0°	11°	23·5°	30°	35·5°
S	33·0	40·5	42·3	45·5	50·5	54·6	**64·6**	67·4	76·8

$\underbrace{\hspace{5cm}}_{Mn(NO_3)_2.6H_2O}$ $\underbrace{\hspace{3cm}}_{Mn(NO_3)_2.3H_2O}$

The results of R. Funk are plotted in Fig. 113. The ice-line and the solubility curve of the hexahydrate intersect at about −30°, but the **eutectic temperature** at −36° shows that a higher hydrate exists—and by analogy with the nitrates of related metals possibly a labile *enneahydrate*, $Mn(NO_3)_2.9H_2O$. J. F. John observed that the syrupy soln. crystallizes with difficulty at ordinary temp., furnishing acicular crystals, which, according to N. A. E. Millon, are those of the *hexahydrate*, $Mn(NO_3)_2.6H_2O$. A. Lührs and K. Kraut obtained the hexahydrate by evaporating the syrupy liquid over conc. sulphuric acid. Monoclinic, colourless crystals of the hexahydrate were also obtained by J. B. Hannay from its soln. in nitric acid. The crystals do not effloresce over sulphuric acid. R. Funk's Fig. 113 shows that the hexahydrate is stable between −30° and 25·8°; and

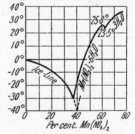

FIG. 113.—The Solubility of Manganous Nitrate.

at 25·8° water is given off owing to the formation of the *trihydrate*, $Mn(NO_3)_2.3H_2O$, so that the eutectic temp. between the tri- and hexahydrates is at 23·5°. E. Kordes discussed this eutectic mixture. A. C. Schultz-Sellack obtained the trihydrate by evaporating a soln. of the salt in conc. nitric acid in vacuo. The range of stability in aq. soln. is shown in Fig. 113. A. Ditte reported a *hemipentahydrate*, $Mn(NO_3)_2.2\frac{1}{2}H_2O$, and a *monohydrate*, $Mn(NO_3)_2.H_2O$, but the individual existence of the former has not been confirmed. A. Guntz and F. Martin obtained the monohydrate by melting the hexahydrate in its water of crystallization and evaporating the product with the continuous addition of nitric acid, drop by drop. The cooled mass on soln. in nitric acid deposits pale pink deliquescent crystals. When the monohydrate so obtained is fused in an atm. of nitric anhydride, colourless or very faint pink crystals of the *anhydrous* salt are formed. J. W. Gatehouse's process indicated above also gives the anhydrous salt. A. Guntz and F. Martin also observed that the anhydrous nitrate can be obtained by treating with manganese a dry soln. of silver nitrate in a dry, non-aqueous solvent like acetone, benzonitrile, or liquid ammonia. The nitrate so obtained may form a complex with the solvent.

According to J. M. Ordway, the **specific gravity** of the hexahydrate crystals at 21° is 1·8199, and that of the undercooled hexahydrate which has been melted is 1·8104. A. C. Oudemans found the sp. gr. of aq. soln. at 8°/4° to be :

	5	10	15	20	30	40	50	60	71
$Mn(NO_3)_2.6H_2O$	1·0253	1·0517	1·0792	1·1078	1·1688	1·2352	1·3074	1·3861	1·4811

Observations were also made by G. T. Gerlach ; and J. Wagner found for N-, 0·5N-, 0·25N-, and 0·125N-soln. of manganous nitrate at 25° the respective sp. gr. 1·0690, 1·0349, 1·0174, and 1·0093. For A. Heydweiller's observations, *vide infra*. A. N. Campbell found the sp. gr., the modulus, and electrostriction of the nitrate, as in the case of the chloride (*q.v.*), to be :

Eq. per litre .	0·573718	0·344231	0·229395	0·114744	0·057372	0·022940	0·011474
Sp. gr. at 15°/15°	1·03685	1·02226	1·01493	1·00742	1·00367	1·00160	1·00085
$m_{\frac{1}{2}Mn} \times 10^4$.	350	346	352	348	325	445	425
Electrostriction .	−11·5	−10·5	−9·9	−10·0	−12·0	+7·0	+8·0

B. Cabrera and co-workers gave for soln. with C grms. of anhydrous salt per 1000 grms. of solvent, $C=3·47+1179(D_{20}-1)-560·7(D_{20}-1)^2$, where D denotes the sp. gr. For $C=480·9$, $D=1·5430\{1-0·00052(\theta-20)\}$; for $C=384·7$, $D=1·4023\{1-0·00047(\theta-20)\}$; for $C=183·2$, $D=1·1635\{1-0·00033(\theta-20)\}$; for $C=72·38$, $D=1·0597\{1-0·00024(\theta-20)\}$; for $C=39·70$, $D=1·0313\{1-0·00021-(\theta-20)\}$; and for $C=18·84$, $D=1·0138\{1-0·00020(\theta-20)-0·0_53(\theta-20)^{20}\}$. J. Wagner gave for the **viscosities** of N-, 0·5N-, 0·25N-, and 0·125N-soln. at 25° the respective values 1·1831, 1·0867, 1·0426, and 1·0235 (water unity). C. A. Valson found for a tube 0·5 mm. diameter a **capillary rise** of 57·5 mm. at 15° for a soln. of sp. gr. 1·065. L. C. de Coppet, and F. Dreyer studied the capillarity of the soln. ; and G. Tammann, the internal pressure. J. C. Graham studied the **diffusion** of soln. of manganous nitrate. J. C. G. de Marignac found the **specific heat** of soln. with $Mn(NO_3)_2.nH_2O$, between 19° and 51°, to be 0·8320, 0·9027, and 0·9473 for soln. respectively with $n=50$, 100, and 200. K. Jauch, and N. de Kolossowsky discussed the subject. According to F. Rüdorff, the f.p. of water falls 0·116° per gram of the hydrate in 100 grms. of water. H. C. Jones and H. P. Bassett recorded a marked increase in the **lowering of the freezing-point** of soln. For small concentrations the mol. lowering corresponds with 5·55, the value for the ionization of the salt into these ions, but with more conc. soln. the high values are supposed to represent the formation of hydrates. For soln. with M mols of nitrate per litre, the lowering of the f.p. $\delta\theta$, and the mol. lowering of the f.p. Δ, are :

M . .	0·09	0·18	0·27	1·05	2·61	3·15
$\delta\theta$ . .	0·46°	0·88°	1·41°	6·77°	27·25°	38·50°
Δ . .	5·11	4·89	5·22	6·45	10·44	12·22

According to H. St. C. Deville, anhydrous manganous nitrate decomposes at 200° into manganese dioxide and nitrous vapours. F. F. Beilstein made observations on this subject. R. Funk found that the **melting-point** of the trihydrate is 35·5°, and no decomposition occurs when the salt is fused. S. Jakubsohn and M. Rabinowitsch gave 25·8° for the m.p. of the hexahydrate ; and J. L. R. Morgan and P. T. Owen, 34·81°. J. F. John noted that the hexahydrate fuses easily, and at a higher temp. it decomposes into nitric acid fumes and leaves black manganic oxide behind ; R. Funk gave 25·8° for the m.p.—Fig. 113 ; and J. M. Ordway observed that the hexahydrate melts at 25·8°, and that the **boiling-point** is 129·5°, at which temp. it slowly decomposes. E. N. Gapon studied the relation between the b.p. and the sp. gr. J. L. R. Morgan and P. T. Owen calculated the **latent heat of fusion** of the trihydrate to be 28·09 cals. per gram. H. Lescoeur observed that the **vapour pressure** of a sat. soln. of the salt at 20° is 7·4 mm. ; that of the dry hexahydrate at 20° is 3·9 mm. ; and that of the efflorescent salt, $Mn(NO_3)_2$. $3\tfrac{1}{2}H_2O$, is 2·9 mm. at 20°. The hydrate slowly dissociates at this temp. At 70° the vap. press. of the sat. soln. is about 80 mm. ; that of the partially dissociated hydrate, $Mn(OH)_2.3\tfrac{1}{2}H_2O$, is 85 mm. ; and that of the trihydrate is 30 mm. This emphasizes the chemical individuality of the trihydrate. J. Thomsen gave for the **heat of formation** of manganous nitrate, $(Mn,N_2,3O_2,6H_2O)=153·7$ Cals. ; $Mn+2HNO_{3aq.}=H_2+Mn(NO_3)_{2aq.}+117·72$ Cals. ; for the **heat of neutralization**, $Mn(OH)_{2ppt.}+2HNO_{3aq.}=Mn'(NO_2)_{2aq.}+2H_2O+23·0$ Cals. ; for the **heat of hydration**, $Mn(NO_3)_2+6H_2O=Mn(NO_3)_2.6H_2O+19·08$ Cals. ; and the **heat of solution**, $Mn(NO_3)_2.6H_2O+400H_2O$, is $-6·15$ Cals., while A. Guntz and F. Martin gave for $Mn(NO_3)_2+280H_2O$, 12·93 Cals. J. Thomsen found the **heat of dilution**, Q, for a soln. of a mol of $Mn(NO_3)_2$ in ten mols of water, with n mols of water at about 18° to be :

n .	10	15	20	50	100	200	400
Q .	0	930	1294	1528	1541	1573	1648 cals.

H. C. Jones and F. H. Getman found the **indices of refraction**, μ, of soln. with M mols of $Mn(NO_3)_2$ per litre, to be :

M .	. 0·035	0·18	0·35	0·87	1·05	2·10	3·50
μ .	. 1·32554	1·32751	1·32949	1·33643	1·33768	1·34974	1·36459

R. Wachsmuth found that a soln. of 151·2 grms. of $Mn(NO_3)_2$ per litre has a sp. **magnetic rotation** of 0·1931 (water 0·99148) and a mol. magnetic rotation 1·9205. P. Krishnamurti discussed the **Raman effect** with manganous nitrate ; and F. Allison and E. J. Murphy, the magneto-optic properties. S. Jakubsohn and M. Rabinowitsch found that the crystals of the hexahydrate had an **electrical conductivity** log $K=0·05313\theta-0·73693$ in the undercooled state. A selection of the values for the salt is :

K .	$-15°$	$-8°$	$0°$	$11°$	$23°$	$26·9°$	$40°$	$49°$
	0·0₅228	0·0₅340	0·0₅623	0·0₄1770	0·0₃1080	0·0234	0·0374	0·0439
			Solid				Molten	

The electrical conductivities, μ, of aq. soln. of a mol of manganous nitrate in v litres of water were measured by H. C. Jones and H. P. Bassett ; and H. C. Jones and A. P. West's results are as follow :

v .	. 2	8	16	32	128	512	1024
μ { 0° .	66·1	83·1	85·5	90·5	98·3	104·8	105·4
25° .	116·3	144·3	154·5	165·0	182·0	196·6	195·8
35° .	138·7	172·5	185·1	197·9	219·8	236·2	237·4
a { 0° .	62·7	78·8	81·1	83·9	93·3	99·4	100·0
25° .	59·4	73·7	78·9	84·3	93·0	99·4	100·0
35° .	58·4	72·7	78·0	83·4	92·6	99·5	100·0

The calculated values for the percentage **degree of ionization**, a, are also indicated. A. Heydweiller gave for the sp. gr. and eq. conductivity at 18° :

	0·5N-	N-	2N-	3N-	4N-	5N-	6N-	10N-
Sp. gr. .	1·03389	1·0672	1·1332	1·1981	1·2618	1·3243	1·3857	1·6215
λ .	. 66·8	58·9	47·46	37·92	30·30	23·54	17·66	4·66

H. C. Jones and H. P. Bassett discussed the hydration of the ions—*vide supra*— and E. C. Banks and co-workers, the transport numbers. O. F. Tower calculated values for the manganese dioxide electrode with soln. of manganous nitrate in nitric acid of different concentrations, and the results were found to agree with $E = -0.0286 \log (C_{Mn}C_H{}^4/C_{Mn}{}^{\cdot}C_H{}^{\cdot 4})$, where C_{Mn} refers to the conc. of the manganous ions in two soln., and C_H, the conc. of the $H^{\cdot}$-ions. L. Bruner found the **hydrolysis** in aq. soln. of manganese nitrate to be too small for measurement. W. N. Hartley showed that the absorption spectrum of dil. soln. agrees with the assumption that hydrolysis and oxidation produce colloidal $MnO(OH)_2$. K. Elbs, and E. Frei studied the **electrolysis** of soln. of manganous nitrate, and found that the anodic oxidation is similar to that with sulphate soln. without complications due to the formation of a manganic nitrate—permanganic acid and manganese dioxide being formed instead. In order to produce permanganic acid, a certain excess of free nitric acid is necessary, and a low concentration of the manganous salt. Thus, soln. with 0.001, 0.003, and 0.005 mols of $Mn(NO_3)_2$ per litre, required respectively 0.5, 12.0, and 35.0 grms. HNO_3 per 100 c.c. at 16° in order to prevent the formation of manganese dioxide; and at 60°, soln. with 0.0001, 0.0003, and 0.0006 mols of $Mn(NO_3)_2$ per litre required respectively 5, 23, and 46 grms. of nitric acid per 100 c.c. G. Jäger and S. Meyer found the **magnetic susceptibility** of aq. soln. of manganous nitrate at 18° to be 82×10^{-6} mass unit, and O. Liebknecht and A. P. Wills gave 86×10^{-6} mass unit. G. Piaggesi, R. Oppermann, P. Philipp, G. Falckenberg, A. Duperior, and B. Cabrera and co-workers made observations on this subject, and found for soln. with 0.4809 to 0.00732 grm. of anhydrous salt per 1000 grms. of solvent, the mol. susceptibilities respectively 0.0150 to 0.0148, and $4.4 = \chi(T - \Theta)$.

According to W. Ipatéeff and A. Kisseleff, when a soln. of manganous nitrate is treated with **hydrogen** at 300° and over 150 atm. press., the mineral haúsmannite, $Mn_3O_4.H_2O$, is formed; and V. Ipatéeff and B. Muromtzeff found that in quartz tubes Mn_3O_4 is formed, and in gold tubes $Mn_3O_4.H_2O$, at 190° to 240°. E. H. Westling observed that a soln. of manganous nitrate with lead dioxide furnishes manganese dioxide and lead nitrate. H. W. Hake found that when the trihydrate is exposed to air, it absorbs moisture equivalent to $Mn(NO_3)_2.16H_2O$. A. Lührs and K. Kraut found that when the soln. of manganese nitrate in **water** is evaporated on a water-bath, much hydrated manganese dioxide is deposited—particularly in sunlight. A. Gorgeu obtained the basic salt, **manganous oxynitrate**, $Mn_2O(NO_3)_2$. $3H_2O$, by mixing a boiling 60 per cent. soln. of manganous nitrate with a boiling conc. soln. of sodium carbonate, boiling for two minutes, filtering, and slowly cooling the soln. out of contact with air. The acicular crystals are dried in darkness; they turn brown in air when exposed to light; they are rapidly decomposed by water; and lose water and nitrogen oxides at 100°. The basic salt is soluble in a soln. of manganese nitrate. J. W. Thomas found that hexahydrated manganous nitrate dried in **hydrogen chloride** forms a dark brown liquid containing manganic chloride, water, chlorine, and nitric acid. E. C. Franklin and C. A. Kraus observed that anhydrous manganous nitrate is insoluble in liquid **ammonia**; and A. Guntz and F. Martin observed that **manganous enneamminonitrate**, $Mn(NO_3)_2.$ $9NH_3$, is formed in white crystals which rapidly turn brown when exposed to air and light; they are decomposed at 150°, and become incandescent when rapidly heated. In vacuo the ammine gradually loses ammonia without forming pure nitrate. The ammine is decomposed by water. W. Herz studied the equilibrium conditions of soln. of manganous nitrate in the presence of **ammonium salts**, and it is possible that a complex salt is formed. H. Franzen and O. von Mayer obtained the complex salt **manganous dihydrazinonitrate**, $Mn(NO_3)_2.2N_2H_4$. J. F. John observed that the hexahydrate is soluble in **alcohol**; and A. Guntz and F. Martin found that it is soluble in **acetone**, and **benzonitrile**, forming in the latter case the complex $2Mn(NO_3)_2.C_6H_5CN$. H. Grossmann observed that the anhydrous nitrate forms a complex, $Mn(NO_3)_2.2C_5H_5N$, with **pyridine**; G. A. Barbieri and F. Calzolari, one, $Mn(NO_3)_2.2C_6H_{12}N_4.10H_2O$, with **hexamethylenetetramine**; and J. F. Martenson, and H. Traube, one, $Mn(NO_3)_2.2K(SbO)C_4H_4O_6.H_2O$, with **potassium antimonyl tartrates**.

Complex salts of manganous nitrate with the nitrates of the alkalies, alkaline earths, and the magnesium family have not been prepared. C. di Capua's examination of the system $Mn(NO_3)_2$–$Mg(NO_3)_2$–H_2O yields no evidence of the formation of a complex salt. A. Mailhe obtained **copper manganous trioxynitrate,** 3CuO. $Mn(NO_3)_2.3H_2O$, by boiling copper hydroxide with a conc. soln. of manganous nitrate; the brown oxide $4CuO.H_2O$ also gave this compound after standing for 3 months with a cold soln. of manganous nitrate. The green powder consists of microscopic needles. The salt becomes brown when exposed to air. A. Werner regarded it as a hexol, $3Cu(OH)_6.Mn(NO_3)_2$, isomorphous with gerhardtite, $Cu(NO_3)_2 \mid 3Cu(OH)_2$. C. di Capua's study of the ternary system $Mg(NO_3)_2$–$Mn(NO_3)_2$–H_2O, Fig. 114, at 20°, gives no evidence of the formation of a **magnesium manganese nitrate.** A. Mailhe treated a hot soln. of manganous nitrate with mercuric oxide and obtained white rhombic plates of **mercuric manganous oxynitrate** as ¬ *dihydrate*, $Mn(NO_3)_2.HgO.2H_2O$. The salt is decomposed by water, with the separation of mercuric oxide. If yellow or red mercuric oxide be allowed to stand under a conc. soln. of manganous nitrate, white microscopic, hexagonal, bipyramidal prisms of the *trihydrate* are formed. The crystals acquire a black film. If mercuric oxide be dissolved in a warm soln. of manganous nitrate, and the

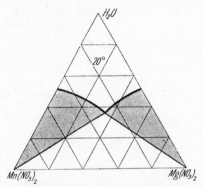

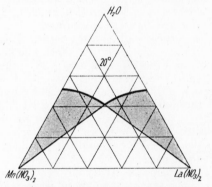

FIG. 114.—The Ternary System : $Mg(NO_3)_2$–$Mn(NO_3)_2$–H_2O at 20°.

FIG. 115.—The Ternary System : $La(NO_3)_3$–$Mn(NO_3)_2$–H_2O at 20°.

soln. cooled, white monoclinic plates of the *tetrahydrate* are formed, isomorphous with the corresponding compounds of cobalt and nickel. A. Mailhe also prepared a complex with mercuric cyanide, namely $Mn(NO_3)_2.HgCy_2$.

There is an isomorphous series of complex nitrates of some earths with the nitrates of magnesium, zinc, manganese, iron (ous), cobalt, and nickel. The general formula is $R''_3[R'''(NO_3)_6]_2.24H_2O$. The salts are hygroscopic, and lose a part of their nitric acid at 120°. T. Lange prepared **manganous cerous nitrate,** $Mn_3[Ce(NO_3)_6]_2.24H_2O$, by evaporating a mixed soln. of manganous nitrate and cerous nitrate, and alcohol. The salt was also prepared by H. Zschiesche, and G. Jantsch. A soln. of stoichiometrical proportions of the component salts is evaporated, and the salt is purified by recrystallization. The rose-red crystals are trigonal, and, according to A. Fock, have the axial ratio $a : c = 1 : 1.5775$, and $a = 79°\ 38'$. G. Jantsch gave 2.102 for the sp. gr. at 0°/4°, and 771.6 for the mol. vol. The m.p. is 83.7°. The solubility at 16° in nitric acid of sp. gr. 1.325 at 16°/4° is 0.1103 mol or 178.8 grms. per litre. A. Damour and H. St. C. Deville prepared **manganous lanthanum nitrate,** $Mn_3[La(NO_3)_6]_2.24H_2O$, in a similar way. The crystals are isomorphous with the other members of the series. C. di Capua's study of the system $Mn(NO_3)_2$–$La(NO_3)_3$–H_2O, Fig. 115, at 20° yielded no evidence of the formation of a complex salt. G. Jantsch found the sp. gr. to be 2.080 at 0°/4°; the mol. vol., 778.6; the m.p., 87.2°; and the solubility at 16° in nitric acid of sp. gr. 1.325 at 16°/4°, 0.1192 mol or 193.1 grms. per litre at 16°. G. Jantsch likewise obtained **manganous praseodymium nitrate,** $Mn_3[Pr(NO_3)_6]_2.24H_2O$, in pale yellowish-green crystals of sp. gr. 2·109 at $0°/4°$; mol. vol., 769·3 ; m.p. 81·0° ; and the solubility in nitric acid of sp. gr. 1·32 at $16°/4°$ is 0·1816 mol or 234 grms. per litre at 16°. G. Jantsch prepared **manganous neodymium nitrate,** $Mn_3[Nd(NO_3)_6]_2.24H_2O$, in similar manner. The pale violet-red crystals have a sp. gr. 2·114 at $0°/4°$; mol. vol., 771·0 ; m.p., 77·0° ; solubility at 16° in nitric acid of sp. gr. 1·325 at $16°/4°$, 0·1816 mol or 296·0 grms. per litre at 16°. G. Jantsch similarly obtained **manganous samarium nitrate,** $Mn_3[Sa(NO_3)_6]_2.24H_2O$, in reddish-yellow crystals of sp. gr. 2·188 at $0°/4°$; mol. vol., 750·3 ; m.p., 70·2° ; and solubility in nitric acid of sp. gr. 1·325 at $16°/4°$, 0·3047 mol or 500·4 grms. per litre at 16°. The great solubility of **manganous gadolinium nitrate** seemed to prevent its crystallization ; the **manganous yttrium nitrates** have not been prepared.

According to M. Holzmann, when hot or cold, conc. or dil. soln. of ceric and manganous nitrates are mixed, hydrated manganese dioxide is precipitated, and the ceric salt is reduced to the cerous state of oxidation. R. J. Meyer and R. Jacoby found that if a filtered soln. of 11 parts of manganous carbonate in nitric acid is mixed with a little water, and allowed to run slowly, with constant stirring, into a well-cooled soln. of 20 parts of ceric hydroxide in nitric acid of sp. gr. 1·4, and allowed to stand, some hydrated manganese dioxide is formed, and at the same time aggregates of dark red, tabular crystals of **manganous ceric nitrate,** $MnCe(NO_3)_6.8H_2O$, are formed. The crystals are very sensitive to moist air, and decompose with the separation of hydrated manganese dioxide. They dissolve in conc. nitric acid. A. Fock said that the trigonal crystals have the axial ratio $a : c = 1 : 1.5775$, and $\alpha = 79° 38'$; the (111)-cleavage is nearly perfect ; and the optical character is negative. R. J. Meyer and R. Jacoby observed that a mixed soln. of thorium and manganous nitrates furnishes colourless plates of **manganous thorium nitrate,** $MnTh(NO_3)_6.8H_2O$, mixed with some thorium nitrate.

G. Urbain and H. Lacombe prepared with bismuth nitrate a series of double salts with the nitrates of magnesium, zinc, manganese, cobalt, and nickel, having the general formula $3R(NO_3)_2.2Bi(NO_3)_3.24H_2O$, or $R_3[Bi(NO_3)_6]_2.24H_2O$. They are isomorphous with the corresponding complex nitrates of the rare earths. They are efflorescent in dry air, and deliquescent in moist air. They are prepared in a similar manner, and are all decomposed by water. The most unstable salt of the series is **manganous bismuth nitrate,** $Mn_3[Bi(NO_3)_6]_2.24H_2O$. It does not exist in contact with the solid phase of either constituent. The salt is pale red ; its sp. gr. is 2·42 at 16° ; it melts without decomposition at 43° to 44°. G. Jantsch found that its solubility in nitric acid of sp. gr. 1·325 at $16°/4°$ is 0·3742 mol or 657·7 grms. per litre at 16°.

C. T. Barfoed [2] was unable to prepare **manganic nitrate,** $Mn(NO_3)_3.nH_2O$, by the action of nitric acid on manganic hydroxide ; by the action of barium nitrate on manganic sulphate ; or by the action of silver nitrate on manganic chloride. M. Sem considers that he obtained manganic nitrate in soln. by the electrolytic oxidation of a soln. of manganous nitrate in fuming nitric acid, but he could not isolate the compound as such or in the form of potassium manganic nitrate. J. Meyer, however, said that the product is colloidal manganese dioxide.

REFERENCES.

[1] C. W. Scheele, *Svenska Akad. Handl.,* **35.** 89, 177, 1774 ; *Abhand. Akad. Stockholm,* **36.** 95, 183, 1774 ; *Opuscula chemica et physica,* Lipsiæ, **1.** 227, 1788 ; London, 53, 1901 ; *Crell's Die neuesten Entdeckungen in der Chemie,* **1.** 112, 140, 1781 ; *Nachgelassene Briefe und Aufzeichnungen,* Stockholm, 120, 1892 ; J. F. John, *Ann. Phil.,* **2.** 172, 263, 1813 ; **3.** 413, 1813 ; *Gehlen's Journ.,* **3.** 452, 1807 ; **4.** 436, 1804 ; J. W. Gatehouse, *Chem. News,* **35.** 118, 1877 ; E. C. Franklin and C. A. Kraus, *Amer. Chem. Journ.,* **20.** 828, 1898 ; H. C. Jones and H. P. Bassett, *ib.,* **33.** 534, 1905 ; H. C. Jones and A. P. West, *ib.,* **34.** 357, 1905 ; H. C. Jones and F. H. Getman, *ib.,* **31.** 303, 1904 ; J. M. Ordway, *Amer. Journ. Science,* (2), **27.** 14, 1859 ; A. C. Schultz-Sellack, *Zeit. Chem.,* (2), **6.** 646, 1870 ; L. Bruner, *Zeit. phys. Chem.,* **32.** 133, 1900 ; O. F. Tower, *ib.,* **18.** 17, 1895 ; J. Wagner, *ib.,* **5.** 31, 1890 ; J. C. Graham, *ib.,* **59.** 691, 1907 ; R. Wachsmuth, *Wied. Ann.,*

44. 377, 1891; G. Jäger and S. Meyer, *ib.*, **63.** 83, 1897 ; J. Thomsen, *Thermochemische Untersuchungen*, Leipzig, **3.** 271, 1883 ; C. A. Valson, *Compt. Rend.*, **74.** 103, 1872 ; N. A. E. Millon, *ib.*, **14.** 905, 1842 ; A. Gorgeu, *ib.*, **94.** 1426, 1882 ; G. Urbain and H. Lacombe, *ib.*, **137.** 568, 1903 ; A. Ditte, *ib.*, **89.** 641, 1879 ; *Ann. Chim. Phys.*, (5), **18.** 320, 1879 ; H. St. C. Deville and H. Debray, *Compt. Rend.*, **50.** 868, 1860 ; A. Damour and H. St. C. Deville, *ib.*, **43.** 976, 1856 ; *L'Inst.*, **26.** 111, 1858 ; *Proc. Verb. Soc. Philomath.*, **23**, 1858 ; H. St. C. Deville, *Ann. Chim. Phys.*, (4), **38.** 5, 1853 ; H. Lescoeur, *ib.*, (7), **7.** 423, 1896 ; A. Mailhe, *ib.*, (7), **27.** 370, 1902 ; *Compt. Rend.*, **132.** 1560, 1901 ; **133.** 126, 1901 ; **134.** 233, 1902 ; *Bull. Soc. Chim.*, (3), **25.** 790, 1901 ; (3), **27.** 176, 1902 ; J. B. Hannay, *Journ. Chem. Soc.*, **33.** 273, 1878 ; J. W. Thomas, *ib.*, **33.** 367, 1878 ; W. N. Hartley, *ib.*, **101.** 829, 1912 ; R. Funk, *Zeit. anorg. Chem.*, **20.** 403, 1899 ; *Ber.*, **32.** 100, 1899 ; R. Funk, A. Dietz, J. von Wrochem and F. Mylius, *Wiss. Abhand. Phys. Tech. Reichsanst.*, **3.** 428, 1900 ; A. C. Oudemans, *Zeit. anal. Chem.*, **7.** 419, 1868 ; G. T. Gerlach, *ib.*, **28.** 475, 1889 ; W. Herz, *Zeit. anorg. Chem.*, **22.** 279, 1899 ; R. Jacoby, *Die Doppelnitrate des Vierwerthigen Ceriums und des Thoriums*, Berlin, 1901 ; R. J. Meyer and R. Jacoby, *Zeit. anorg. Chem.*, **27.** 376, 1900 ; G. Jantsch, *ib.*, **76.** 303, 1912 ; O. von Meyer, *Ueber Hydrazinverbindungen verschieden Metallsalze*, Heidelberg, 1907 ; H. Franzen and O. von Mayer, *Zeit. anorg. Chem.*, **60.** 247, 1909 ; E. Kordes, *ib.*, **168.** 177, 1927 ; G. Tammann, *ib.*, **174.** 231, 1928 ; J. C. G. de Marignac, *Arch. Sciences Genève*, (2), **55.** 13, 1876 ; *Ann. Chim. Phys.*, (5), **8.** 410, 1876 ; F. Rüdorff, *Pogg. Ann.*, **145.** 615, 1872 ; B. Cabrera, E. Moles and M. Marquina, *Anal. Fis. Quim.*, **13.** 256, 1915 ; B. Cabrera and A. Duperior, *Journ. Phys. Rad.*, (6), **6.** 121, 1925 ; A. Guyard, *Bull. Soc. Chim.*, (2), **22.** 60, 1874 ; A. Guntz and F. Martin, *ib.*, (4), **5.** 1004, 1909 ; (4), **7.** 313, 1910 ; L. C. de Coppet, *Compt. Rend.*, **132.** 219, 1901 ; J. L. R. Morgan and P. T. Owen, *Journ. Amer. Chem. Soc.*, **29.** 1439, 1907 ; *Zeit. anorg. Chem.*, **56.** 168, 1907 ; A. Heydweiller, *ib.*, **116.** 42, 1921 ; O. Liebknecht and A. P. Wills, *Ann. Physik*, (4), **1.** 178, 1906 ; G. Piaggesi, *Nuovo Cimento*, (2), **4.** 247, 1903 ; G. A. Barbieri and F. Calzolari, *Atti Accad. Lincei*, (5), **20.** i, 119, 1911 ; N. de Kolossowsky, *Journ. Chim. Phys.*, **22.** 224, 1925 ; K. Elbs, *Zeit. angew. Chem.*, **16.** 290, 1903 ; *Zeit. Elektrochem.*, **7.** 260, 1901 ; A. N. Campbell, *Journ. Chem. Soc.*, 653, 1928 ; E. Frei, *Ueber das Verhalten der Manganosalze an der Anode*, Giessen, 1901 ; F. Dreyer, *The Temperature of the Maximum Density of Water*, St. Petersburg, 193, 1913 ; F. F. Beilstein, *Chem. Centr.*, (3), **4.** 759, 1873 ; M. Holzmann, *Journ. prakt. Chem.*, (1), **75.** 352, 1858 ; T. Lange, *ib.*, (1), **82.** 129, 1861 ; H. Zschiesche, *ib.*, (1), **107.** 65, 1869 ; C. W. G. Nylander, *ib.*, (1), **79.** 379, 1860 ; *Oefvers. Vet. Akad. Förh.*, **16.** 281, 1859 ; J. F. Martenson, *Russ. Journ. Pharm.*, **8.** 20, 1869 ; *Arch. Pharm.* (2), **188.** 198, 1869 ; A. Lührs and K. Kraut in L. Gmelin, *Handbuch der anorganischen Chemie*, Heidelberg, **2.** ii, 501, 1897 ; H. Traube, *Sitzber. Akad. Berlin*, **195.** 1895 ; *Zeit. Kryst.*, **24.** 188, 1895 ; A. Fock, *ib.*, **22.** 37, 1894 ; A. Werner, *Ber.*, **40.** 4446, 1908 : H. Grossmann, *ib.*, **37.** 564, 1254, 1904 ; F. Mylius, *ib.*, **30.** 1718, 1897 ; S. Jakubsohn and M. Rabinowitsch, *Zeit. phys. Chem.*, **116.** 359, 1925 ; *Journ. Russ. Phys. Chem. Soc.*, **57.** 251, 1925 ; W. Ipatéeff and A. Kisseleff, *Journ. Russ. Phys. Chem. Soc.*, **58.** 686, 1926 ; V. Ipatéeff and B. Muromtzeff, *Ber.*, **63.** B, 160, 1930 ; A. Duperior, *Anal. Fis. Quim.*, **22.** 383, 1924 ; G. Falckenberg, *Zeit. Physik*, **5.** 70, 1921 ; E. H. Westling, *U.S. Pat. No.* 1502079, 1924 ; H. W. Hake, *Proc. Chem. Soc.*, **12.** 34, 1896 ; *Chem. News*, **73.** 104, 1896 ; R. Oppermann, *Ueber Molekularmagnetismus und Konzentration von Lösungen paramagnetischer Salze*, Rostock, 1920 ; C. di Capua, *Gazz. Chim. Ital.*, **59.** 164, 1929 ; P. Philipp, *Untersuchungen über Magnetisierungszahlen von Salzen der Eisengruppe und ihre Abhängigkeit von der Konzentration*, Rostock, 1914 ; P. Krishnamurti, *Indian Journ. Phys.*, **5.** 1, 1930 ; F. Allison and E. J. Murphy, *Journ. Amer. Chem. Soc.*, **52.** 3796, 1930 ; E. C. Banks, E. C. Righellato and C. W. Davies, *Trans. Faraday Soc.*, **27.** 621, 1931 ; V. M. Peshkova, *Trans. Russ. Inst. Pure Chem. Reagents*, **9**, 1930 ; K. Jauch, *Zeit. Physik*, **4.** 441, 1921 ; E. N. Capon, *Journ. Chim. Phys.*, **25.** 154, 1928.

² C. T. Barfoed, in L. Gmelin and K. Kraut, *Handbuch der anorganischen Chemie*, Heidelberg, **2.** ii, 502, 1897 ; J. Meyer, *Zeit. Elektrochem.*, **22.** 201, 1916 ; M. Sem, *ib.*, **21.** 426, 1915 ; **23.** 98, 1917 ; *Ueber die Elektrooxydation von Manganosalzen in sauren Lösungen und einige dabei erhaltene Verbindungen*, Darmstadt, 1914.

§ 26. Manganous Phosphates

H. Struve[1] prepared **manganous orthophosphate**, $Mn_3(PO_4)_2$, by passing hydrogen for a long time over white-hot manganous pyrophosphate : $3Mn_2P_2O_7$ $=2Mn_3(PO_4)_2+P_2O_5$—some phosphorus, phosphine, and manganese phosphide are also formed. The anhydrous salt is produced by heating a hydrate to redness. Several hydrates have been reported. If a manganous salt soln. be treated with an excess of sodium hydrophosphate, the analyses of W. Heintz, and of E. Erlenmeyer and O. Heinrich show that the white amorphous precipitate is a *heptahydrate*, $Mn_3(PO_4)_2.7H_2O$. If manganous hydrophosphate be treated with cold water so long as it acquires an acidic reaction, acicular crystals are obtained which, according to E. Erlenmeyer and O. Heinrich, approximate to the *pentahydrate*, $Mn_3(PO_4)_2.5H_2O$, although the analytical data for the air-dried product ranges from $4\frac{1}{2}$ to $5\frac{1}{2}$ H_2O. F. Grossmann obtained the pentahydrate by the action of water on ammonium manganous phosphate. The salt was also prepared in a crystalline state by F. Ephraim and C. Rossetti. According to E. Erlenmeyer and

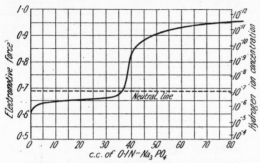

O. Heinrich, if the hepta- or pentahydrate be dried over conc. sulphuric acid, the *hemi-heptahydrate*, $Mn_3(PO_4)_2.3\frac{1}{2}H_2O$, is formed; and if heated to 100°, the *trihydrate*, $Mn_3(PO_4)_2.3H_2O$, is produced. H. J. Debray also obtained crystals of the trihydrate by heating manganous hydrophosphate with water at 100° to 140°; and also by boiling manganous carbonate with an excess of phosphoric acid. H. J. Debray also prepared the *monohydrate*, $Mn_3(PO_4)_2.H_2O$, by

FIG. 116.—Electrometric Titration of Solutions of Manganous Chloride with Sodium Phosphate.

heating the trihydrate with water in a sealed tube at 250°. H. T. S. Britton titrated electrometrically $0.02M$-$MnCl_2$ with $0.1N$-Na_3PO_4 at 20° and obtained the curve shown in Fig. 116. The phosphate began to separate when $p_H=5.76$, and it may be added that the hydroxide separation occurs when $p_H=8.43$.

F. Müllbauer obtained in Hagendorf, Bavaria, pale rose or flesh red rosettes of a *pentahydrate*, $Mn_3(PO_4)_2.5H_2O$; or rather $(Fe,Mn,Mg)_3(PO_4)_2.5H_2O$; he called the mineral **wenzelite**—after H. Wenzel. The monoclinic prisms have the axial ratios : $a:b:c=2.3239:1:2.8513$. The biaxial crystals are optically negative. G. J. Brush and E. S. Dana found a granular, massive, or crystalline mineral near Redding, Connecticut, and they called it **reddingite**. Its colour is pinkish-white, pale rose-pink, or yellowish-white. Its composition corresponds with the trihydrate, $Mn_3(PO_4)_2.3H_2O$. A little iron may replace the manganese ; and H. Berman and F. A. Gonyer gave $3(Mn,Fe)O.P_2O_5.3H_2O$. According to G. J. Brush and E. S. Dana, the crystals of reddingite are rhombic with the axial ratios $a:b:c=0.8678:1:0.9486$; the habit is octahedral, and the crystals often occur in parallel groupings. There is a distinct cleavage. The crystals of reddingite appear as if they were isomorphous with scorodite, $Fe_2(AsO_4)_2.4H_2O$, and strengite, $Fe_2(PO_4)_2.4H_2O$, although their chemical nature is different. E. H. Kraus and co-workers gave $a:b:c=0.5271:1:0.4574$. A. des Cloizeaux found that the crystals of H. J. Debray's preparation of the trihydrate resemble **hureaulite,** $H_2R''_5(PO_4)_4.4H_2O$. G. J. Brush and E. S. Dana gave 3.102 for the sp. gr. of reddingite, and 3.0 to 3.5 for the hardness. H. Berman and F. A. Gonyer gave 3.136 for the sp. gr. E. H. Kraus and co-workers gave for the indices of refraction $\alpha=1.651$, $\beta=1.656$, and $\gamma=1.683$; and H. Berman and F. A. Gonyer, $\alpha=1.655$, $\beta=1.662$, and $\gamma=1.683$, and they said that the optical character is positive, and the optic axial angle $2V=65°$. According to E. Erlenmeyer and O. Heinrich, the heptahydrate loses about $3\frac{1}{2}$ mols. of water over conc. sulphuric acid ; and about 3 mols. at 100° ; W. Heintz observed a loss of 15.90 per cent. of water between 110° and 120°. According to M. Berthelot, the heat of formation of the amorphous or colloidal orthophosphate is $(2P,4O_2,3Mn)=737.5$ Cals. ; and $2H_3PO_{4aq.}+3Mn(OH)_2$ $=Mn_3(PO_4)_2+Aq.+45.3$ Cals. K. Elbs, and E. Frei found that when a soln. of manganous carbonate in phosphoric acid is electrolyzed, manganese dioxide is formed, together with an amethyst-red soln. of manganic phosphate. G. Grube and M. Staesche found the oxidation potential of a soln. of a manganic salt in phosphoric acid involves the two changes : $2Mn'''\rightleftharpoons Mn''+Mn''''$ followed by $4Mn''''\rightleftharpoons 3Mn'''$ $+Mn'''''$. The equilibrium is affected by the conc. of the phosphoric acid and very little by the conc. of the manganese. For 0.02 gram-atom Mn in a litre of $37.8N$-H_3PO_4 at 12°, with $Mn'':Mn'''=1:1$, the oxidation potential for $Mn''\rightarrow Mn'''$ is

1·221 volts.; and for $Mn^{...}\rightarrow Mn^{....}$, 1·526 volts. The equilibrium constant K, and the percentage decomposition of manganic phosphate for $2Mn^{...}\rightleftharpoons Mn^{..}+Mn^{....}$, a, are for a soln. with 0·02 gram-atom per litre at 12° :

N-H_3PO_4	45·0	42·5	40·0	37·5	35·0	32·5	30·0
K . .	0·048	0·0076	$0·0_316$	$0·0_530$	$0·0_528$	$0·0_420$	$0·0_317$
a . .	30·0	15·0	2·4	0·35	0·33	0·89	2·6 per cent.

There is thus a maximum decomposition of the tervalent manganese phosphate in highly conc. acid, and a minimum in 30N- to 35N-H_3PO_4, and thereafter the decomposition increases slowly as the acidity increases. With the quadrivalent manganese phosphate equilibrium : $4Mn^{...}\rightleftharpoons 3Mn^{...}+Mn^{::::}$, for a soln. with 0·01 gram-atom Mn in a litre of 40·5N-H_3PO_4 at 12°, with $Mn^{....}$: $Mn^{::::}=1:1$, the oxidation potential for $Mn^{....}\rightarrow Mn^{::::}$ is 1·639 volts. The equilibrium constant, K, and the percentage decomposition of the quadrivalent manganese diphosphate, a, are for a soln. with 0·01 gram-atom Mn per litre at 12° :

N-H_3PO_4	45·0	40·0	35·0	30·0	25·0	22·5	20
K . .	$0·0_{22}21$	$0·0_{16}41$	$0·0_626$	$0·0_596$	$0·0_521$	$0·0_417$	$0·0_317$
a . .	0·0038	0·014	3·9	8·9	7·9	10	16 per cent.

As the acidity diminishes, the equilibrium shifts rapidly and continuously from left to right, so that the salt can be prepared only in highly acidic soln. Quadrivalent manganese diphosphate is a better oxidizing agent than permanganic acid, and a better reducing agent than tervalent manganic phosphate. F. Weckbach studied the electrolytic oxidation of soln. of manganous phosphate in phosphoric acid; and J. Chloupek, the potential of a platinum electrode in soln. of phosphoric acids and manganous oxide.

J. J. Berzelius found that water dissolves very little of the heptahydrate, and L. Joulin said that the salt is not decomposed by water, but F. Grossmann found that the pentahydrate suffers hydrolysis when it is shaken with water at 25°.; a limiting value was not obtained; only phosphoric acid, not manganous ions, pass into soln., so that either manganous hydroxide or a basic salt is formed as a result of the hydrolysis. F. Fichter and E. Brunner found that manganous phosphate is oxidized by fluorine to the manganic salt. C. D. Braun observed that when the heptahydrate is warmed with hydrochloric acid, a brown soln. is formed which deposits a dark brown crystalline precipitate. W. Heintz said that the phosphate is readily soluble in mineral acids, and in acetic acid. B. W. Gerland found that sulphurous acid readily dissolves the phosphate. W. Heintz observed that aq. ammonia converts it into ammonium manganous phosphate ; and J. J. Berzelius said that a boiling soln. of potassium hydroxide extracts all the phosphoric acid ; and a soln. of ammonium carbonate dissolves the phosphate, but it is re-precipitated when the soln. is boiled. According to R. H. Brett, a soln. of ammonium chloride or nitrate dissolves some phosphate ; and G. C. Wittstein observed a similar result with a soln. of ammonium sulphate or succinate. W. Heintz said that the salt is insoluble in alcohol. L. Joulin said that the heptahydrate is not decomposed by a soln. of sodium dihydrophosphate, but it is decomposed by a soln. of the hydrophosphate, forming manganous hydroxide, or, if exposed to air, hydrated manganic oxide. C. D. Braun found that lead dioxide colours the phosphate violet-grey. W. Muthmann and H. Heramhof tried the phosphate as a colouring agent for porcelain painting. W. Knaust studied the coagulation of colloidal soln. of manganese oxide peptized with phosphoric acid.

H. St. C. Deville and H. Caron heated a mixture of ammonium phosphate and an excess of manganous chloride to a bright red-heat, and extracted the cold mass with water. There remain crystals of **manganese chlorophosphate**, $Mn_3(PO_4)_2$. $MnCl_2$, or *manganese wagnerite*. If 2 parts of manganous fluoride and 5 parts of ammonium phosphate be fused with an excess of manganous chloride, and the cold mass extracted with water, there remain crystals of **manganous chlorotriorthophosphate**, $3Mn_3(PO_4)_2.MnCl_2$, or *manganese apatite*. A. Ditte melted manganous bromide with an excess of ammonium dihydrophosphate, and extracted the cold mass with hot water. Needle-like prisms of **manganous bromotriorthophosphate,** $3Mn_3(PO_4)_2.MnBr_2$, or *manganese bromoapatite* remained.

According to C. H. D. Bödeker, and E. Erlenmeyer and O. Heinrich, if a soln. of manganous sulphate be treated with a slight excess of sodium hydrophosphate, the soln. and precipitate be divided into two equal parts, and one part treated with enough nitric or hydrochloric acid just to dissolve the precipitate, and then mixed with the other part, and allowed to stand for 2 or 3 days, pale red, almost colourless, crystals of **manganous hydrophosphate,** $MnHPO_4.3H_2O$, are formed. W. Heintz obtained the same salt by adding sodium hydrophosphate to a soln. of manganous sulphate, acidulated with acetic acid until a permanent precipitate is formed. All the manganese must not be precipitated; if hydrochloric or nitric acid be employed in place of acetic acid, the precipitation is slower. After the precipitate has stood for a while it becomes granular and crystalline. This salt is also produced as a residue when an excess of pentahydrated normal phosphate is boiled with phosphoric acid. The washed precipitate becomes crystalline on standing. M. Amadori investigated the ternary system $MnO-P_2O_5-H_2O$ at 25°, and the results are summarized in Fig. 117, which shows the range of stability of

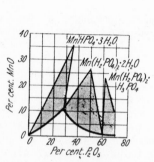

FIG. 117.—Equilibrium Conditions in the System : $MnO-P_2O_5-H_2O$ at 25°.

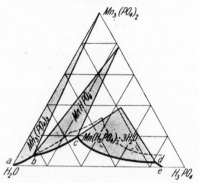

FIG. 118.—Equilibrium Conditions in the System : $Mn_3(PO_4)_2-H_3PO_4-H_2O$ at 25°.

the trihydrate. The results of G. Grube and M. Staesche in the system $Mn_3(PO_4)_2-H_3PO_4-H_2O$ at 25° are summarized in Fig. 118. The solubility curves of the solid phases are ab, for $Mn_3(PO_4)_2$; bc, for $MnHPO_4$; cd, for $Mn(H_2PO_4)_2.3H_2O$; and de, for phosphoric acid, probably $2H_3PO_4.H_2O$. The curve for 55° is dotted in Fig. 118. E. Erlenmeyer and O. Heinrich found that when the dihydrophosphate is allowed to deliquesce in moist air, or digested with one and a half vols. of water, the hydrophosphate is formed ; likewise also when the dihydrophosphate is boiled with alcohol. H. J. Debray obtained the hydrophosphate by adding alcohol to a soln. of manganous carbonate in phosphoric acid until a turbidity appears. C. H. D. Bödeker said that the crystals are tabular, right rhombic prisms, having the acute prismatic edges generally replaced by planes, so that the crystals look like hexagonal plates. C. von Haushofer said that the tabular or octahedral crystals are rhombic, with the axial ratios $a : b : c = 0.9445 : 1 : 0.9260$. The crystals lose no water in dry air over calcium chloride ; at 110°, C. H. D. Bödeker found that they lose 23·27 per cent. of water; at 110° to 120°, W. Heintz found that 22·47 per cent. is lost ; and E. Erlenmeyer and O. Heinrich, at 100°, 22·24 per cent. This water is taken up again when the crystals are exposed to air. W. Heintz found that three mols. of water are lost at 200°, and at a red-heat pyrophosphate is formed. The salt is slowly hydrolyzed by cold water, and with boiling water a soluble acid salt and an insoluble basic salt are formed. W. Heintz found that the salt is readily soluble in the strong mineral acids, but it dissolves with difficulty in acetic acid, and it is insoluble in alcohol; B. W. Gerland observed that it is readily soluble in sulphurous acid; and R. H. Brett, that when dissolved in a soln. of ammonium chloride it gives no precipitate with hydrogen sulphide. F. Fichter and E. Brunner found that when fluorine acts on a soln. of the phosphate, oxidation takes place to an extent not exceeding 66 per cent. The incomplete oxidation is again attributed to the formation of hydrogen dioxide. As permonophosphoric acid is formed by the action of fluorine on orthophosphoric acid, this oxidation may be explained by the theory that the oxidizing agent is a peroxide or peracid derived from the anion, such as sulphur tetroxide in the case of sulphates. The mineral **seamanite**—named after A. F. Seaman—is a hydrated **manganous borophosphate**, $3MnO.(B_2O_3.P_2O_5).3H_2O$, or $3MnO.B_2O_3.3H_2O$ associated with $3MnO$. $P_2O_5.3H_2O$, and it is related with reddingite. Both minerals are rhombic. E. H. Kraus gave for the axial ratios $a : b : c = 0.5195 : 1 : 0.4508$; 3.128 for the sp. gr.; 4.0 for the hardness; and for the indices of refraction, $\alpha = 1.640$, $\beta = 1.663$, and $\gamma = 1.665$—*vide supra*, reddingite.

W. Heintz prepared **manganous dihydrophosphate**, $Mn(H_2PO_4)_2.2H_2O$, by strongly heating a mixture of manganic oxide and phosphoric acid; and by allowing a soln. of normal manganous phosphate in phosphoric acid to stand for crystallization. The equilibrium conditions found by M. Amadori are indicated in Fig. 117, and by G. Grube and M. Staesche, in Fig. 118. E. Erlenmeyer and O. Heinrich obtained this salt by allowing a soln. of manganous sulphide in an excess of phosphoric acid to evaporate in a warm place. In three weeks the crystalline crust is pressed between bibulous paper, or washed with water and ether free from alcohol. A. Joly found that in the formation of the phosphate the gelatinous hydrophosphate is first precipitated, and that this gradually passes into the crystalline dihydrophosphate. According to E. Erlenmeyer and O. Heinrich, the four-sided, prismatic crystals of the dihydrophosphate are not changed by exposure to dry air, but they deliquesce in moist air, forming the hydrophosphate. The salt loses 12.61 per cent. of water at 100°, or, according to W. Heintz, 13.15 per cent. at 110°–120°, and the remaining water is expelled at a red-heat. The salt on charcoal readily fuses in the oxidizing flame of the blowpipe, giving off phosphoric acid and phosphorus in inflammable bubbles. The salt is easily soluble in water; and E. Erlenmeyer and O. Heinrich said that if the salt contains a trace of free phosphoric acid, it readily dissolves in a little water; and, added H. J. Debray, alcohol precipitates the hydrophosphate from the aq. soln. According to W. Heintz, the salt is resolved by boiling alcohol into phosphoric acid and the hydrophosphate. According to G. Viard, if 10, 20, and 100 grms. of manganous dihydrophosphate, $Mn(H_2PO_4)_2$. $2H_2O$, per 100 grms. of water at 0° be allowed to stand for many days, the mol. ratios $P_2O_5 : MnO$ in the soln. are respectively 1.06, 1.14, and 1.19; and there are 19.75, 33.39, and 97.42 grms. respectively of MnO per litre in the soln., and respectively 41.90, 76.04, and 232.05 grms. per litre of P_2O_5. The composition of the soln. thus deviates more and more from that of the original salt the greater is the proportion of dihydrophosphate employed, and it is possible to arrange that a gram of salt dissolves in 100 grms. of water without decomposition. Working at 100°, with increasing proportions of dihydrophosphate, the mol. ratio $P_2O_5 : MnO$ in the soln. increases to a maximum and then slowly decreases. If less than 20 grms. of dihydrophosphate per 100 grms. of water be used, the decomposition proceeds like that of barium or calcium phosphate at 0° or 100°, and like that of manganous dihydrophosphate at 0°. If G denotes the number of grams of $Mn(H_2PO_4)_2.2H_2O$ in 100 grms. of water; $P_2O_5 : MnO$, the ratio in soln.; MnO, grams in soln.; and P_2O_5, grams in soln.:

G	0.5	1	5	10	**20**	30	50	200	400
$P_2O_5 : MnO$	1.24	1.38	1.75	1.85	**1.88**	1.83	1.75	1.55	1.52
P_2O_5	1.926	1.56	5.43	9.87	**18.00**	26.39	41.53	106.04	133.77
MnO	2.29	4.30	19.06	36.55	**67.80**	96.75	145.27	330.12	405.95

G. Viard said that the product of the action at 100° is always **manganous dihydro-**

tetraorthophosphate, $Mn_3(PO_4)_2.2MnHPO_4.4H_2O$—M. Amadori gave $Mn_5H_2(PO_4)_5$.
$5H_2O$, which was prepared by E. Erlenmeyer and O. Heinrich by boiling manganous
hydrophosphate with water until it no longer imparts an acidic reaction to the
liquid. The rose-coloured, microscopic prisms are monoclinic, having, according
to C. von Haushofer, the axial ratios $a:b:c=1\cdot9927:1:1\cdot7122$, and $\beta=97°\ 34'$.
They lose water above 150° and do not fuse at a red-heat. A. de Schulten obtained
this salt in the form of the mineral hureaulite by adding ammonia, drop by drop,
to a soln. of phosphoric acid of sp. gr. 1·1, sat. with manganous carbonate. The
crystals have a sp. gr. 3·175 at 15°. M. Amadori also prepared **manganous hepta-
hydrotriorthophosphate,** $Mn(H_2PO_4)_2.H_3PO_4$, under the conditions illustrated by
Fig. 117. F. Ephraim and C. Rossetti prepared the acid salt $5MnO.2P_2O_5.8H_2O$
in a crystalline state.

F. Alluaud, and A. des Cloizeaux and A. Damour described a mineral from
Limoges, Huréaux commune, and it was·called **hureaulite.** The analyses of these
and samples from other localities reported by P. A. Dufrénoy, A. des Cloizeaux and
A. Damour, and G. J. Brush and E. S. Dana, correspond with the formula $5MnO$.
$2P_2O_5.5H_2O$, or $H_2Mn_5(PO_4)_4.4H_2O$, the *pentahydrate* of **manganous dihydrotetraorthophosphate.** The colour of hureaulite is orange-red, brownish-orange, rose-
violet, pale rose, grey, or nearly colourless. The streak is nearly white. The
mineral may occur in compact, scaly, or imperfectly fibrous masses, or in isolated
or grouped crystals—the groupings may be mammillary or fascicled. The short
prismatic crystals are sometimes tabular, and, according to G. J. Brush and
E. S. Dana, they are monoclinic, with the axial ratios $a:b:c=1\cdot9192:1:0\cdot5245$,
and $\beta=84°\ 1'$. The (100)- and (110)-faces may be striated. A. des Cloizeaux and
A. Damour found the sp. gr. of the yellow crystals to be 3·185, and of the red crystals
3·198 ; G. J. Brush and E. S. Dana gave 3·149 for the sp. gr. The hardness is 5.
A. des Cloizeaux and A. Damour found that the optic axial angle for yellow light is
$2H=86°\ 22'$; and as the temp. rises 100°, the angle changes 6° 34'. W. T. Schaller
described a mineral from Pala, California, which he called **palaite,** and its analysis
corresponds with the *tetrahydrate* of manganous dihydrotetraorthophosphate,
$5MnO.2P_2O_5.4H_2O$, or $H_2Mn_5(PO_4)_4.3H_2O$. Its sp. gr. is 3·14 to 3·20 ; and its
mean refractive index is 1·655.

F. J. Otto prepared **ammonium manganous phosphate,** $(NH_4)MnPO_4.H_2O$, by
boiling a mixture of a soln. of manganous chloride, hydrochloric acid, and sodium
hydrophosphate or phosphoric acid, saturating the liquid with ammonia, and
immediately corking the flask. The white hydrated manganous phosphate first
precipitated changes immediately into pearly scales of the complex salt, which are
then collected on a filter and washed with water. If air be not excluded, manganic
oxide is formed, and it imparts a reddish tinge to the salt ; but when once formed
the salt is not altered by air or by water containing air. W. Heintz prepared it by
dropping an excess of a soln. of sodium hydrophosphate into a cold, feebly ammoniacal soln. of a manganous salt and ammonium chloride. O. W. Gibbs mixed a
soln. of a manganous salt with an excess of sodium hydrophosphate, dissolved in an
excess of hydrochloric acid, heated the mixture to its b.p., saturated it with ammonia,
and boiled it for 15 mins. C. D. Braun, and F. Grossmann used an analogous
process. According to F. J. Otto, and P. Nuka, the salt forms white pearly scales,
which when heated give off ammonia and water, forming manganous pyrophosphate.
W. Heintz said that at 110° to 120° the salt loses only hygroscopic water.
F. J. Otto said that it does not dissolve in cold or boiling water, but C. R. Fresenius
found that 100 parts of cold water dissolve 0·00304 part of the salt ; and 100 parts
of boiling water, 0·00497 part. F. Grossmann observed that the salt is decomposed
by water : $3(NH_4)MnPO_4+8H_2O=NH_3+(NH_4)_2HPO_4+Mn_3(PO_4)_2.8H_2O$. A litre
of water can transform 0·3032 grm. of the salt. The proportion transformed is
reduced in the presence of sodium or ammonium hydrophosphate, ammonium
chloride, or manganous sulphate, all of which furnish ions corresponding with those
given by the substances on the right side of the above equation. The decom-

position of the salt by $0.005N$-phosphoric acid is attributed to the decrease in the phosphate ions by the acid. Acetic and carbonic acid first transform the complex salt into normal manganous phosphate, before forming the respective manganous salts. F. J. Otto found that the salt is easily soluble in acids, and when ammonia is added to the soln., manganous phosphate is precipitated, but this immediately forms ammonium manganous phosphate. O. W. Gibbs said that the salt is not soluble in aq. ammonia or soln. of ammonium salts; but C. R. Fresenius observed that 100 parts of a 1·4 per cent. soln. of ammonium chloride dissolve 0·00562 part, and since ammonia forms some manganous hydroxide, an excess of ammonia is to be avoided when manganese is precipitated as ammonium manganous phosphate in analytical work. F. J. Otto found that with a conc. soln. of potassium hydroxide, ammonia is evolved, but the salt is not decomposed by aq. ammonia, or a soln. of potassium carbonate. P. Wenger found the composition of the dried salt to correspond with the *heptahydrate*, $(NH_4)MnPO_4.7H_2O$. The solubility in water below 60° is too small for measurement by gravimetric analysis; but, expressing the solubility as S parts of $NH_4MnPO_4.7H_2O$ in 100 parts of solvent, with a soln. of 4 per cent. ammonia and 5 per cent. ammonium chloride, $S=0.0158$ at 20° and 0·0245 at 60°, while with a soln. of 4 per cent. ammonia and 10 per cent. ammonium chloride, $S=0.0375$ at 20° and 0·0543 at 60°; and with the solvents water, 5 per cent. NH_4NO_3, 5 per cent. NH_4Cl, and N-HCl:

	0°	20°	40°	60°	70°	80°
S (Water)	0·0000	0·0000	0·0000	0·0000	0·00517	0·00672
S (NH_4NO_3)	0·0206	0·0201	0·0209	0·0270	0·0281	0·0325
S (NH_4Cl)	0·0198	0·0254	0·0386	0·0384	0·0414	0·0451
S (N-HCl)	0·0116	0·0122	0·0117	0·0193	0·0191	0·0196

G. J. Brush and E. S. Dana obtained from Branchville, Connecticut, a mineral which was named **lithiophilite**—from lithium and $\phi\iota\lambda os$, a friend. Its analysis, reported by J. F. Schairer, G. J. Brush and E. S. Dana, E. S. Simpson, and S. L. Penfield, corresponds with **lithium manganous phosphate**, $LiMnPO_4$, where Mn represents bivalent manganese and iron ranging from 1 : 0·5 to 1 : 0, so that the colour varies with the proportion of iron from salmon-pink to clove-brown lithiophilite, with very little iron, to bluish-grey triphylite containing very little manganese. The colour of lithiophilite may be greenish-grey, salmon-pink, honey-yellow, yellowish-brown, and light clove-brown. It may be nearly black on the surface. The streak is colourless to greyish-white. The pleochroism is $a=$deep pink, $b=$faint pink, and $c=$pale greenish-yellow. The rhombic crystals are isomorphous with those of triphylite—*vide infra*. The optical character is negative— H. Berman and F. A. Gonyer said positive. For the index of refraction by S. L. Penfield and J. H. Pratt, *vide* triphylite. E. Sommerfeldt gave for the optic axial angle, $2V=56° 4'$, and, for Na-light, the change with temp. from $-15°$ to 19° exceeds 17° 34'. H. Berman and F. A. Gonyer gave $2V=60°$. The sp. gr. observed by G. J. Brush and E. S. Dana ranges from 3·424 to 3·432, and by S. L. Penfield, from 3·398 to 3·504. H. Berman and F. A. Gonyer gave 3·481. The hardness is 4·0 to 4·5. H. Berman and F. A. Gonyer gave for the indices of refraction $a=1.675$, $\beta=1.679$, and $\gamma=1.688$. The transformations in nature were discussed by G. J. Brush and E. S. Dana, and by F. P. Dewey. J. N. von Fuchs described a mineral from Bodenmais, Bavaria, which he named **triphylite** or rather *triphylin*— from $\tau\rho\iota s$, threefold, and $\phi\upsilon\lambda\eta$, family, in allusion to its containing three phosphates. J. J. Berzelius called a sample from Finland, *tetraphylin*; and N. G. Nordenskjöld, *perowskyn*. Analyses were reported by J. N. von Fuchs, E. P. Henderson, F. Oesten, G. C. Wittstein, C. F. Rammelsberg, S. L. Penfield, A. Lacroix, and W. Baer. The analyses agree with the formula $Li(Mn,Fe)PO_4$. As just indicated, there is a range of isomorphous lithiophilites and triphylites with almost $LiMnPO_4$ at one end of the series and $LiFePO_4$ at the other end. The colour is greenish-grey or bluish-grey, passing into the colours of lithiophilite. Triphylite usually occurs in cleavable or compact masses; the crystals are rare. The faces are uneven. G. Tschermak

found the axial ratios of the rhombic crystals to be $a : b : c = 0\cdot4348 : 1 : 0\cdot5265$.
The (001)-cleavage is perfect ; the (010)-cleavage is distinct ; and the (110)-cleavage
is interrupted. The optical character is positive ; and the optic axial angle $2H_a$ is
$74° 45'$ for red-light, and $2H_a = 79° 30'$ for blue-light. For $2V$, *vide infra*.
J. D. Dana also examined the crystals. F. Oesten gave for the sp. gr., 3·545 to
3·561 ; and S. L. Penfield, 3·482 to 3·549. The hardness is between 4 and 5.
S. L. Penfield and J. H. Pratt found for the indices of refraction of samples with
different proportions of iron, for Na-light :

FeO .	.	.	4·24	9·42	13·63	26·58	35·05 per cent.
a	.	.	—	1·676	—	1·688	—
β	.	.	1·675	1·679	—	1·692	—
γ	.	.	—	1·687	—	1·692	—
$2V$	.	.	65° 13′	62° 54′	56° 4′	$C.\ 0°$	$C.\ 120°$

M. Berthelot found that in precipitating a soln. of manganous chloride with
sodium phosphate, the colloidal precipitate rapidly becomes crystalline, forming
sodium manganous phosphate, $NaMnPO_4$, and the heat of the reaction is 7·5 Cals.
G. J. Brush and E. S. Dana described a mineral **natrophilite** consisting of sodium
manganous phosphate, $NaMnPO_4$. It occurs at Branchville, Connecticut. Its colour
is deep wine-yellow. It usually occurs in cleavable masses, and also in rhombic
crystals isomorphous with lithiophilite. Its (001)-cleavage is perfect, the (010)-
cleavage is distinct, and the (110)-cleavage is interrupted. The optical character
is positive ; the sp. gr. is 3·41 ; and the hardness 4·5 to 5·0. L. Ouvrard melted
manganous oxide with sodium pyrophosphate, sodium phosphate, or metaphosphate,
particularly in the presence of sodium chloride, and obtained rhombic prisms of
sodium manganous phosphate, $NaMnPO_4$, isomorphous with the zinc and cadmium
salts. Its sp. gr. is 3·1 at 20°. If rather less sodium pyrophosphate is employed
dendrites of **sodium manganous diorthophosphate,** $Na_4Mn(PO_4)_2$, are formed.
The sp. gr. is 2·7 at 20°. E. Cohen obtained crystals of $2Na_2HPO_4.Mn_3(PO_4)_2.7H_2O$,
as a by-product in the preparation of sodium hydrophosphate. L. Ouvrard
obtained **potassium manganous phosphate,** $KMnPO_4$, by melting an excess of
manganous oxide with potassium metaphosphate, or with potassium chloride and
sodium phosphate or pyrophosphate ; and H. Grandeau, by melting at a high
temp. a mixture of manganous hydrophosphate and an excess of potassium sulphate.
L. Ouvrard found that the rose-pink crystals are probably rhombic, and have a
sp. gr. of 3·2 at 20°. G. Grube and M. Staesche regarded manganous dihydrophosphate as a manganodiphosphoric acid, $H_4[Mn(PO_4)_2].3H_2O$. The colourless
crystals in contact with water gradually form the normal phosphate. Two salts
were prepared in stable, colourless crystals, namely **potassium manganous tri-
hydrodiphosphate,** $K_3H[Mn(PO_4)_2].5H_2O$; and **sodium manganous dihydrodi-
phosphate,** $Na_2H_2[Mn(PO_4)_2].4H_2O$.

G. J. Brush and E. S. Dana found a **calcium manganous phosphate,** $Ca_2Mn(PO_4)_2$.
$2H_2O$, at Branchville, Fairfield Co., Connecticut, and they called it **fairfieldite.**
H. Berman and F. A. Gonyer represented the composition by $(Mn,Fe)O.2CaO.$
$P_2O_5.2H_2O$. According to G. J. Brush and E. S. Dana, the colour of fairfieldite
is white, greenish-white, or pale straw-yellow ; its streak is white. It occurs in
foliated or lamellar crystalline aggregates, and in radiating or foliated masses. It
also furnishes prismatic crystals belonging to the triclinic system, with the axial
ratios $a : b : c = 0\cdot2797 : 1 : 0\cdot1976$, and $a = 102° 8\frac{2}{3}'$, $\beta = 94° 33\frac{1}{3}'$, and $\gamma = 77° 19\frac{5}{6}'$.
The (010)-cleavage is perfect, and the (100)-cleavage is distinct. The sp. gr. is 3·07
to 3·15, and the hardness 3·5. H. Berman and F. A. Gonyer gave 3·016 for the sp. gr.,
and for the indices of refraction, $a = 1\cdot640$, $\beta = 1\cdot650$, and $\gamma = 1\cdot660$; the optical
character is positive ; and the optical axial angle $2V = 86°$. F. Sandberger obtained
a variety from Zwiesel, Bavaria, which he called *leucomanganite*. S. L. Penfield
obtained **calcium manganous phosphate,** $(Ca,Mn,Fe)_3(PO_4)_2$, from the neighbourhood of Grafton, New Hampshire, and he called it **graftonite.** The mineral is also
associated with ferrous oxide. Its colour when fresh is salmon-pink, and it occurs

in monoclinic crystals with the axial ratios $a : b : c = 0.886 : 1 : 0.582$, and $\beta = 66°$. The sp. gr. is 3·672, and the hardness 5.

A hydrated **manganous aluminium phosphate** was obtained by G. J. Brush and E. S. Dana, from Branchville, Connecticut; and K. K. Landes reported it from several places in Maine. It was named **eosphorite**—$\dot{\epsilon}\omega\sigma\phi\acute{o}\rho\sigma$, dawn bearing, in allusion to the pink colour. It occurs in rose-pink, yellowish, or colourless crystals of the composition $2AlPO_4.2(Fe,Mn)(OH)_2 + 2H_2O$. The analysis reported by C. Palache and E. V. Shannon agrees with $2MnO.Al_2O_3.P_2O_5.4H_2O$. It also occurs compact. The rhombic crystals have the axial ratios $a : b : c = 0.77680 : 1 : 0.51501$; the (100)-cleavage is nearly perfect. The habit is prismatic, and the faces in the zone (100) : (010) have vertical striations. The sp. gr. is 3·11 to 3·145, and the hardness 5. The mineral is feebly pleochroic. a is colourless, β light yellow, and γ brown. The optical character is negative; the optic axial angle $2V = 50°$, and $2H = 54° 30'$. The indices of refraction $a = 1.638$, $\beta = 1.660$, and $\gamma = 1.667$. E. S. Larsen gave for the indices of refraction $a = 1.631$ to 1·633, $\beta = 1.660$ to 1·678, and $\gamma = 1.664$ to 1·684. G. J. Brush and E. S. Dana obtained a mineral from Branchville, Connecticut, which they called **fillowite**—after A. N. Fillow. Its analysis corresponds with **sodium calcium manganous ferrous phosphate**, $(Ca,Mn,Fe,Na_2)_3(PO_4)_2.H_2O$, where the ratios $Mn : Fe + Ca : Na_2 = 6 : 2 : 1$. The waxy yellow or reddish- or yellowish-brown mineral occurs in granular crystalline masses; the habit of the crystals is pseudorhombohedral. The monoclinic crystals have the axial ratios $a : b : c = 1.7303 : 1 : 1.4190$, and $\beta = 89° 50\frac{3}{4}'$. The (001)-cleavage is very distinct. The sp. gr. is 3·43, and the hardness 4·5. The same locality furnished G. J. Brush and E. S. Dana with a mineral **dickinsonite**—after W. Dickinson—whose analysis corresponds with sodium calcium manganous ferrous phosphate, $(Ca,Mn,Fe,Na_2)_3(PO_4)_2.H_2O$, with the ratios $Mn : Fe + Ca : Na_2(K_2,Li_2) = 6 : 3 : 2$. H. Berman and F. A. Gonyer gave $7(Mn,Fe)O.2(Na_2,K_2,Ca)O.3P_2O_5.H_2O$. According to G. J. Brush and E. S. Dana, dickinsonite forms olive-green, oil-green, or grass-green, slightly dichroic masses which are foliaceous, micaceous, lamellar, radiated or stellated, as well as tabular, pseudorhombohedral, monoclinic crystals with the axial ratios $a : b : c = 1.73205 : 1 : 1.19806$, and $\beta = 61° 30'$. There are triangular striations on the (001)-face, and the (001)-cleavage is perfect. The sp. gr. is 3·338 to 3·343, and the hardness, 3·5 to 4·0. The two minerals dickinsonite and fillowite are closely related and yet have many different properties. H. Berman and F. A. Gonyer found the indices of refraction to be $a = 1.648$, $\beta = 1.655$, and $\gamma = 1.662$; the optic axial angle $2V = 90°$ nearly; and the optical character is positive. L. G. Eakins, and W. P. Headden described a mineral from the vicinity of Harney City, South Dakota, and it was called **griphite**—from $\gamma\rho\acute{\iota}\phi\sigma$, an enigma. W. P. Headden represented it by the formula $5(Mn,Ca,Fe,H_2,Na_2)O.P_2O_5$. It occurs in dark brown, kidney-shaped masses, optically amorphous. Its sp. gr. is 3·401, and its hardness, 5·5. H. Berman and F. A. Gonyer described a mineral from Poland, Maine, which they called **landesite**—after K. K. Landes. The crystals are rough, with an octahedral development and a good cleavage (010). The analysis corresponds with $2Fe_2O_3.20MnO.8P_2O_5.27H_2O$. The optic angle $2V$ is large; the optical character is negative; the indices of refraction $a = 1.720$, $\beta = 1.728$, and $\gamma = 1.735$; and the pleochroism a is dark brown, β is light brown, and γ is yellow. The sp. gr. is 3·026. The mineral **triploidite,** occurring at Branchville, Connecticut, was named from triplite, and $\epsilon\tilde{\iota}\delta\sigma$, form. H. Laubmann and H. Steinmetz also found the mineral near Hagendorf, Bavaria. The American mineral was described by G. J. Brush and E. S. Dana. The composition approximates $4(Mn,Fe)O.P_2O_5.H_2O$, or $(Mn,Fe)_3(PO_4)_2.(Mn,Fe)OH$. It has a yellowish- or reddish-brown colour, but isolated crystals may vary in colour from topaz-yellow to hyacinth-red. There is a faint pleochroism. The monoclinic crystals have the axial ratios $a : b : c = 1.85715 : 1 : 1.49253$, and $\beta = 71° 46'$; F. Müllbauer gave for crystals from Hagendorf, Bavaria, $a : b : c = 1.8516 : 1 : 1.4885$, and $\beta = 108° 18'$. The crystals are striated vertically, and commonly appear in aggregates more or less fibrous and columnar; the mineral may also be more or less fibrous, and nearly compact, and massive. The (100)-cleavage is perfect. The sp. gr. is 3·697, and the hardness 4·5 to 5·0. It is soluble in acids.

A. Schwarzenberg [2] prepared anhydrous **manganous pyrophosphate** by calcining one of the hydrates; J. H. Talbot, G. Berendts, W. Heintz, C. H. D. Bödeker, and H. J. Debray, by calcining the hydrophosphate; and F. J. Otto, by calcining ammonium manganous phosphate. According to A. Schwarzenberg, and G. Vortmann, if normal sodium pyrophosphate be added to a soln. of manganous sulphate, the amorphous white *trihydrate*, $Mn_2P_2O_7.3H_2O$, is formed when the washed product is dried at 100°. C. N. Pahl discussed the possible existence of an *enneahydrate*. If it be dried at 120°, the monohydrate, $Mn_2P_2O_7.H_2O$, is formed. According to O. Andersen, the anhydrous salt forms brownish-pink, prismatic crystals composed of a great number of thin prisms in parallel intergrowth. The powder is pale pink. The axial ratios of the monoclinic crystals are $a : b : c = 0·7834 : 1 : —$, and $\beta = 74° 9'$. The (110)-cleavage is perfect, but the (001)-cleavage is poor. The sp. gr. is 3·707 at 25°/4°. F. W. Clarke gave 3·5847 at 20° and 3·5742 at 26°. There is a faint pleochroism—α being light pink, and β and γ nearly colourless with a faint yellow tinge. The optic axial angle is very large ; the optical character is positive. The refractive indices for sodium light were $\alpha = 1·695$; $\beta = 1·704$; and $\gamma = 1·710$; and the birefringence $\gamma - \alpha = 0·015$. The m.p. of the salt is 1196°, and when mixed with 75, 50, and 25 per cent. of magnesium pyrophosphate, melting at 1383°, the m.p. are respectively 1242°, 1286°, and 1340°. Hence, the crystals of manganous and magnesium pyrophosphates are isomorphous of the simple type, with no maximum or minimum (Fig. 6—1. 10, 2). The mean refractive indices of manganous and magnesium pyrophosphates are respectively 1·70 and 1·60 ; and for mixtures of manganous pyrophosphate with 75, 50, and 25 per cent. of magnesium pyrophosphate, the mean refractive indices are 1·67, 1·65, and 1·63, respectively. The complex ions $[Mn_2(P_2O_7)_3]''''''$ were studied by S. Freed and C. Kasper. G. Foëx and A. Brunet found that the coeff. of magnetization, $103·1 \times 10^{-6}$ at 16·1°, varies inversely as the temp. at −250° instead of following Curie's law. The coeff. of magnetization is constant between −80° and 485°. H. Struve found that if the pyrophosphate be heated to whiteness in hydrogen, it forms manganous orthophosphate (*q.v.*), and if heated in a carbon crucible, manganese phosphide is formed. A. Schwarzenberg said that the precipitated salt is soluble in a soln. of sodium pyrophosphate ; and H. Rose, not soluble in a soln. of manganous sulphate. C. N. Pahl added that the washed salt is sparingly soluble in a soln. of sodium pyrophosphate, but more soluble in a soln. of potassium pyrophosphate. C. D. Braun found that hydrochloric acid dissolves the salt, forming when warmed a bluish-violet liquid. A. Schwarzenberg found that the soln. in sulphurous acid when boiled forms tabular plates of what C. N. Pahl regarded as dihydropyrophosphate. A. Schwarzenberg found that the salt is decomposed by potash-lye, and C. D. Braun that when the precipitated salt is shaken with water and lead dioxide, a greyish-violet coloration appears. According to C. N. Pahl, if a soln. of the trihydrated salt in oxalic acid be evaporated, rhombic prisms of **manganous dihydropyrophosphate**, $MnH_2P_2O_7.4H_2O$, are formed ; and the same salt is produced from a soln. of the trihydrated normal salt in sulphurous acid. The dihydropyrophosphate is soluble in water. It does not melt at a red-heat.

According to K. A. Wallroth, if ammonium sodium phosphate be melted with manganous oxide, **sodium manganous pyrophosphate,** $Na_2MnP_2O_7$, is formed ; and L. Ouvrard obtained the same salt by melting an excess of sodium metaphosphate with manganous oxide, or carbonate. The prismatic crystals have a sp. gr. of 2·9 at 20°. A. Rosenheim and co-workers prepared the *tetrahydrate*, $Na_2[MnP_2O_7]$. $4H_2O$. C. N. Pahl obtained the *hemienneahydrate*, $Na_2MnP_2O_7.4\frac{1}{2}H_2O$, by adding manganous sulphate to a soln. of sodium pyrophosphate so long as the precipitate re-dissolves. If the liquid be boiled, or if it be allowed to stand 24 hrs., prismatic crystals are deposited. It melts when heated to redness. It is sparingly soluble in water. H. Rose said that the original soln. is not precipitated by ammonia or ammonium sulphide ; and C. N. Pahl, that it is not precipitated by potassium ferrocyanide. According to C. N. Pahl, if manganous pyrophosphate stands for a long time in contact with a soln. of sodium pyrophosphate, or if the mixture be warmed, sparingly-soluble crystals of **sodium manganous pentapyrophosphate,** $2Na_2P_4O_7.3Mn_2P_2O_7.24H_2O$, are formed. The salt fuses at a red-heat.

According to G. Buchner, if a 5 per cent. soln. of sodium pyrophosphate be added to a soln. of a salt of the ammonium sulphide group, a precipitate is obtained soluble in an excess of the reagent. The addition of ammonium sulphide to this soln. precipitates the metals as sulphides in the case of zinc, cobalt, nickel, and iron (ferrous and ferric), but produces no precipitate with manganese (manganous and manganic), uranium, chromium, or aluminium. When these last-mentioned soln. are heated, or allowed to stand for some time, the manganese is precipitated as pyrophosphate of manganese, ammonium, and sodium. The soln. containing aluminium and chromium become turbid if boiled and subsequently cooled ; but in the case of uranium the soln. remains clear even after boiling. If a soln. of an iron salt is precipitated by ammonium sulphide, and a soln. of sodium pyrophosphate subsequently added, the ferrous sulphide dissolves when the liquid is boiled, forming a colourless soln. which becomes dark green on cooling, and finally deposits nearly all the iron as sulphide. G. Buchner thus found that **ammonium sodium manganous pyrophosphate,** $(NH_4)NaMnP_2O_7.3H_2O$, is obtained in white crystals when a soln. of manganous sulphate is mixed with sodium pyrophosphate so that the precipitated manganous pyrophosphate re-dissolves, and the soln. treated with ammonium sulphide and allowed to stand for some time or boiled. It is also produced when manganous sulphide, precipitated from a manganous sulphate soln. by ammonium sulphide and ammonia, is dissolved in a soln. of sodium pyrophosphate and allowed to stand. The addition of sodium carbonate to the soln. gives no precipitation, but potassium hydroxide precipitates manganous hydroxide. The same salt is produced when a soln. of manganic pyrophosphate in sodium pyrophosphate is treated with ammonium sulphide and boiled or allowed to stand for some time. According to F. J. Otto, the complex salt is formed if a soln. of sodium pyrophosphate is warmed with manganous sulphate and aq. ammonia, so that the flocculent precipitate forms a yellow granular powder. This can be washed with boiling water. The salt is stable in air ; when heated it gives off water and ammonia ; conc. potash-lye also expels ammonia ; when boiled with conc. nitric acid, hydrated manganese dioxide is precipitated. The salt does not dissolve in water or alcohol, but it is easily soluble in dil. acids.

According to L. Ouvrard, if manganous oxide or carbonate be melted with an excess of potassium metaphosphate, rose-coloured prisms of **potassium manganous pyrophosphate,** $K_2MnP_2O_7$, are formed. The sp. gr. is 3·1 at 20° ; and the salt is soluble in dil. acids. C. N. Pahl obtained the *octohydrate*, $K_2MnP_2O_7.8H_2O$, by adding manganous sulphate to a soln. of sodium pyrophosphate so long as the precipitate re-dissolves, and allowing the liquid to stand for some hours. The hexagonal plates or six-sided prismatic crystals readily fuse. The syrupy soln. of manganous pyrophosphate in sodium pyrophosphate furnishes colourless, microscopic, sparingly-soluble crystals of **potassium manganous tripyrophosphate,** $2K_4P_2O_7.Mn_2P_2O_7.10H_2O$. The salt fuses at a red-heat.

R. Maddrell,[3] and T. Fleitmann prepared **manganous dimetaphosphate,** $Mn(PO_3)_2$, by treating manganous sulphate or other manganous salt with an excess of phosphoric acid at 316°. The same product was obtained by T. Fleitmann by heating the hydrate at a red-heat. The white or reddish-white powder is insoluble in water and dil. acids ; it dissolves in conc. sulphuric acid. It is decomposed when warmed with ammonium or sodium sulphide ; and when digested with sodium carbonate soln. it forms sodium dimetaphosphate. F. Warschauer regarded this salt as a tetrametaphosphate, and G. Tammann, as a trimetaphosphate. The *tetrahydrate*, $Mn(PO_3)_2.4H_2O$, was obtained by T. Fleitmann from a mixture of a conc. soln. of ammonium dimetaphosphate and an excess of manganous chloride, by adding alcohol, and allowing it to stand some time. G. Tammann gave the formula $1.5\{Mn(PO_3)_2\}.6.5H_2O$. T. Fleitmann, and A. Glatzel, by adding ammonium chloride to a soln. of manganous dimetaphosphate, obtained **ammonium manganous dimetaphosphate**, $(NH_4)_2Mn(P_2O_6)_2.4H_2O$, in efflorescent crystals. A. Glatzel found that 100 parts of water dissolved 1·205 parts of salt. All the water of crystallization is lost at 150°; and at a higher temp. ammonia and some phosphoric oxide are given off, and at a red-heat the salt fuses. The salt is easily decomposed by acids. A. Glatzel obtained similarly **potassium manganous dimetaphosphate**, $K_2Mn(P_2O_6)_2.6H_2O$, in flesh-coloured crystals; 100 parts of water dissolve 1·052 parts of salt. The salt is dissolved when boiled with conc. sulphuric acid. It loses 3 mols. of water at 100°, and the remainder at dull redness, without changing its constitution. It sinters at a higher temp. and then becomes insoluble in acids. Similarly with **sodium manganous dimetaphosphate**, $Na_2Mn(P_2O_6)_2.6H_2O$, which loses its water of crystallization at 200°; it melts at a red-heat, and then becomes insoluble in sulphuric acid. Before the calcination the salt is easily dissolved by boiling, conc. sulphuric acid.

H. Rose said that sodium trimetaphosphate gives no precipitate with soln. of manganous sulphate. F. de Carli studied the glasses formed with sodium metaphosphate. According to G. Tammann, T. Fleitmann's dimetaphosphate is **manganous trimetaphosphate**, $Mn_3(PO_3)_6$. T. Fleitmann and W. Henneberg obtained the *enneahydrate*, $Mn_3(PO_3)_6.9H_2O$, by treating a soln. of manganous chloride or sulphate with sodium trimetaphosphate. G. Tammann found that the salt melts at a red-heat, and that 100 c.c. of water at 20° dissolve 0·97 grm. of the salt. C. G. Lindboom obtained the *henahydrate*, $Mn_3(PO_3)_6.11H_2O$, in colourless triclinic prisms from a mixed soln. of sodium triphosphate and manganous chloride. The salt loses its water when heated, and does not melt below redness. It is decomposed by molten sodium carbonate; is sparingly soluble in cold and warm water; it dissolves in hydrochloric acid. The cold, aq. soln., if allowed to stand some time, or if warmed, gives a precipitate when boiled with ammonia, ammonium sulphide, sodium hydroxide, and sodium carbonate. A. Wiesler found the eq. conductivity, λ, of a soln. of $\frac{1}{6}\{Mn_2(PO_3)_6.11H_2O\}$ in v litres of water at 25° to be:

v	32	64	128	256	512	1024	2048
λ	33·6	39·7	47·8	58·0	71·3	90·3	111·7

so that $\lambda_{1024-32}=56.5$. H. Schjerning prepared **sodium manganous trimetaphosphate**, $NaMn(PO_3)_3$, from a mixture of 2 grms. of manganic orthophosphate, 3 grms. of phosphoric acid, and 10 grms. of sodium ammonium phosphate at a dull red-heat, and washing the cold mass with water. The crystals are insoluble in water and very resistant towards dil. acids and bases. The salt dissolves without decoloration in conc. phosphoric or conc. sulphuric acid. T. Fleitmann and W. Henneberg also prepared a sodium manganous trimetaphosphate as a precipitate from a mixed soln. of sodium trimetaphosphate and manganous chloride.

A. Glatzel prepared **manganous tetrametaphosphate**, $Mn_2(PO_3)_4$, by melting a mixture of manganous carbonate and phosphoric acid at dull redness. The needle-like crystals have a pale violet colour; they melt at a bright red-heat. The salt is not attacked by acids; it is decomposed by fused sodium carbonate; and is slowly decomposed in the cold by alkali sulphides. The *decahydrate*, $Mn_2(PO_3)_4.$ $10H_2O$, is obtained by mixing soln. of manganous chloride and sodium tetrametaphosphate. The pale red crystalline mass loses its water of crystallization at 200°, and melts at a bright red-heat. 100 parts of water dissolve 1·02 parts of the salt; the hydrate is sparingly soluble in acids, but dissolves in conc., boiling sulphuric acid. F. Warschauer regarded T. Fleitmann's dimetaphosphate as tetrametaphosphate.

According to H. Rose, a soln. of manganous sulphate gives a white oily precipitate when treated with sodium hexametaphosphate, and the oil dissolves in an excess of the sodium salt; ammonium sulphide precipitates manganous sulphide from the soln.; and F. J. Otto obtained a similar precipitate from the soln. in nitric acid. C. D. Braun found that it forms a reddish-violet soln. when warmed with hydrochloric acid, and a greyish-violet coloration when shaken with lead dioxide. A. Glatzel, and H. Lüdert prepared **manganous hexametaphosphate,** $3MnO.3P_2O_5$, or $Mn_3(PO_3)_6$, by allowing the turbid mixture obtained from conc. soln. of manganous sulphate and sodium hexametaphosphate to stand for some time. A rose-coloured sticky mass is obtained. It is slightly soluble in water— forming possibly a peptized soln. The colloid dries in air to form a pale rose-coloured glass, and if heated it yields a pinkish-grey powder. It melts at a red-heat.

G. Tammann reported **sodium manganous octometaphosphate,** $Na_2Mn_3(PO_3)_8$, to be formed by melting equimolar proportions of a manganous salt and ammonium sodium hydrophosphate. The pale rose cubic crystals form rosette groups. They have an anomalous birefringence. The salt is insoluble in acids—excepting conc. sulphuric acid; and is scarcely attacked by potassium sulphide during a week's action.

G. Tammann heated T. Fleitmann's ammonium dimetaphosphate to 200°, and treated the product for many weeks with an excess of a soln. of manganous sulphate, when a soln. of **manganous decametaphosphate,** $5MnO.5P_2O_5.12H_2O$, or $Mn_5(PO_3)_{10}.$ $12H_2O$, is formed. The soln. gives a flocculent precipitate when treated with water, to form a sticky mass.

M. Stange reported **sodium manganous triphosphate,** $Na_3MnP_3O_{10}.12H_2O$, to be formed when a soln. of 0·37 grm. of crystalline manganous sulphate is added to a soln. of a gram of sodium triphosphate. In about five minutes fine prismatic snow-white aggregates of crystals begin to form. The salt is sparingly soluble in water; it intumesces when heated; and becomes anhydrous at a red-heat. It melts to a colourless glass. The salt which has been fused dissolves in sulphuric acid. P. Glühmann represented the composition by $Na_3MnP_3O_{10}.6H_2O.$

REFERENCES.

[1] H. Struve, *Bull. Acad. St. Petersburg*, (3), 1. 239, 1860; *Journ. prakt. Chem.*, (1), 79. 345, 1860; R. H. Weber, *Ann. Physik*, (4), 36. 624, 1911; E. Erlenmeyer and O. Heinrich, *Liebig's Ann.*, 190. 208, 1877; W. Muthmann and H. Heramhof, *ib.*, 355. 144, 1907; C. von Haushofer, *ib.*, 190. 201, 1877; C. H. D. Bödeker, *ib.*, 69. 206, 1849; H. T. S. Britton, *Journ. Chem. Soc.*, 614, 1927; A. de Schulten, *Bull. Soc. Min.*, 27. 123, 1904; A. des Cloizeaux, *Manuel de minéralogie*, Paris, 2. 488, 1874; W. Heintz, *Pogg. Ann.*, 74. 449, 1847; K. Elbs, *Zeit. angew. Chem.*, 16. 290, 1903; *Zeit. Elektrochem.*, 7. 260, 1901; G. Grube and M. Staesche, *ib.*, 31. 362, 1925; *Zeit. phys. Chem.*, 130. 572, 1927; F. J. Otto, *Journ. prakt. Chem.*, 2. 418, 1834; *Schweigger's Journ.*, 66. 288, 1832; F. Grossmann, *Löslichkeitsverhältnisse des Manganammoniumphosphats*, Leipzig, 1904; E. Frei, *Ueber das Verhalten der Manganosalze an der Anode*, Giessen, 1901; O. W. Gibbs, *Chem. News*, 28. 51, 1873; *Amer. Journ. Science*, (2), 44. 216, 1867; G. J. Brush and E. S. Dana, *ib.*, (3), 16. 35, 114, 1878; (3), 17. 363, 1878; (3), 18. 45, 1879; (3), 39. 211, 1890; F. W. Clarke, *ib.*, (3), 14. 281, 1877; S. L. Penfield, *ib.*, (3), 13. 425, 1877; (3), 17. 226, 1879; (3), 18. 47, 1879; (4), 9. 20, 1900; S. L. Penfield and J. H. Pratt, *ib.*, (3), 50. 387, 1895; J. D. Dana, *ib.*, (2), 11. 100, 1851; J. W. Mallet, *ib.*, (2), 18. 33, 1854; F. P. Dewey, *ib.*, (3), 17. 367, 1879; H. L. Wells, *ib.*, (3), 17. 368, 1879; W. J. Craw, *ib.*, (2), 11. 99, 1851; W. P. Headden, *ib.*, (3), 41. 415, 1899; L. C. Graton and W. T. Schaller, *ib.*, (4), 20. 146, 1905; W. T. Schaller, *Bull. U.S. Geol. Sur.*, 529, 1912; L. G. Eakins, *ib.*, 60, 1890; E. S. Larsen, *ib.*, 679, 1921; F. A. Gooch and M. A. Austin, *Amer. Journ. Science*, (4), 5. 209, 260, 1898; *Zeit. anorg. Chem.*, 18. 339, 1898; M. A. Austin, *ib.*, 32. 367, 1902; *Amer. Journ. Science*, (4), 14. 156, 1902; J. Chloupek, *Coll. Czech. Chem. Comm.*, 2. 129, 1930; W. Knaust, *Chem. Erde*, 4. 529, 1930; H. Laubmann and H. Steinmetz, *Zeit. Kryst.*, 55. 523, 1920; F. Müllbauer, *ib.*, 61. 318, 1925; C. D. Braun, *Zeit. anal. Chem.*, 7. 340, 1868; G. C. Wittstein, *Repert. Pharm.*, 57. 30, 1836; *Viertelj. Pharm.*, 1. 506, 1852; J. J. Berzelius, *Lehrbuch der Chemie*, Dresden, 2. ii, 712, 1826; *Arsber. Fysik Kemi*, 15. 186, 1835; C. R. Fresenius, *Anleitung zur quantitativen Analyse*, Braunschweig, 1. 259, 1875; M. Weibull, *Zeit. Kryst.*, 32. 612, 1900; A. Renard, *Bull. Soc. Chim.*, (2), 11. 473, 1869; G. Viard, (3), 19. 749, 1898; (3), 21. 807, 1899; *Compt. Rend.*, 127. 178, 1898; 129. 412, 1899; A. Joly and E. Sorel, *ib.*, 118. 238, 1894; P. Barbier, *ib.*, 135.

1109, 1902 ; A. Joly, *ib.*, **97**. 1480, 1884 ; **98**. 1274, 1884 ; **103**. 1130, 1886 ; A. Barillé, *ib.*, **137**. 566, 1903 ; A. Ditte, *ib.*, **96**. 847, 1883 ; *Ann. Chim. Phys.*, (6), **8**. 525, 1886 ; H. J. Debray, *ib.*, (3), **61**. 434, 1860 ; L. Joulin, *ib.*, (4), **30**. 272, 1873 ; H. Grandeau, *ib.*, (6), **8**. 221, 1886 ; L. Ouvrard, *Compt. Rend.*, **106**. 1729, 1886 ; *Ann. Chim. Phys.*, (6), **16**. 314, 1889 ; H. St. C. Deville and H. Caron, *ib.*, (3), **67**. 459, 1863 ; B. W. Gerland, *Proc. Manchester Lit. Phil. Soc.*, **10**. 129, 1871 ; *Chem. News*, **23**. 136, 1871 ; *Journ. prakt. Chem.*, (2), **4**. 97, 1871 ; M. Berthelot, *Thermochimie*, Paris, **2**. 271, 1897 ; R. H. Brett, *Phil. Mag.*, (3), **10**. 95, 1837 ; T. H. Henry, *ib.*, (4), **16**. 197, 1858 ; G. Tschermak, *Sitzber. Akad. Wien*, **47**. 282, 1863 ; E. Sommerfeldt, *Neues Jahrb. Min.*, i, 152, 1899 ; F. Sandberger, *ib.*, 370, 1879 ; i, 185, 1888 ; J. R. Blum, *Lehrbuch der Oryktognosie*, Stuttgart, 537, 1847 ; F. Alluaud, *Ann. Science Nat.*, **8**. 346, 1826 ; *Ann. Chim. Phys.*, (2), **20**. 302. 1825 ; P. A. Dufrénoy, *ib.*, (2), **41**. 342, 1829 ; A. des Cloizeaux and A. Damour, *ib.*, (3), **53**. 293, 1858 ; A. Damour, *Ann. Mines*, (4), **13**. 341, 1848 ; C. W. C. Fuchs, *Journ. prakt. Chem.*, (1), **3**. 98, 1834 ; (1), **5**. 319, 1835 ; J. N. von Fuchs, *ib.*, (1), **17**. 171, 1839 ; F. Fichter and E. Brunner, *Helvetica Chim. Acta*, **12**. 214, 1929 ; C. F. Rammelsberg, *Handbuch der Mineralchemie*, Leipzig, 307, 1875 ; *Pogg. Ann.*, **85**. 439, 1852 ; F. Oesten, *ib.*, **107**. 438, 1859 ; E. S. Simpson, *Journ. Roy. Soc. West Australia*, **12**. 57, 1927 ; W. Baer, *Arch. Pharm.*, (2), **57**. 374, 1850 ; G. T. Gerlach, *Zeit. Nat. Ver. Halle*, **9**. 149, 1857 ; A. Lacroix, *Minéralogie de la France et de ses colonies*, Paris, **4**. 362, 1910 ; N. G. Nordenskjöld, *Berzelius' Jahresb.*, **15**. 212, 1835 ; J. F. Schairer, *Amer. Min.*, **11**. 101, 1926 ; E. Cohen, *Mitt. Naturw. Ver. Neuvorpommern Rügen*, **28**. 96, 1896 ; M. Amadori, *Atti Ist. Veneto*, **81**. 603, 1922 ; P. Wenger, *Étude sur la solubilité des phosphates et arséniates ammoniaco-magnésiens et du phosphate ammoniaco-manganeux*, Genève, 1911 ; F. Weckbach, *Ueber die elektrolytische Oxydation von Manganosalzen in stark saurer Lösung*, Darmstadt, 1910 ; E. P. Henderson, *Amer. Min.*, **13**. 114, 1928 ; E. H. Kraus, W. A. Seaman, and C. B. Slawson, *ib.*, **15**. 220, 1930 ; H. Berman and F. A. Gonyer, *ib.*, **15**. 375, 1930 ; K. K. Landes, *ib.*, **10**. 386, 1925 ; C. Palache and E. V. Shannon, *ib.*, **13**. 392, 1928 ; F. Ephraim and C. Rossetti, *Helvetica Chim. Acta*, **12**. 1025, 1929 ; P. Nuka, *Acta Univ. Latviensis*, **2**. 1, 1931.

  ² F. W. Clarke, *Amer. Journ. Science*, (3), **14**. 281, 1877 ; J. H. Talbot, *ib.*, (2), **50**. 244, 1870 ; S. Freed and C. Kasper, *Journ. Amer. Chem. Soc.*, **52**. 2632, 1930 ; C. D. Braun, *Zeit. anal. Chem.*, **7**. 340, 1868 ; F. J. Otto, *Schweigger's Journ.*, **66**. 288, 1832 ; *Journ. prakt. Chem.*, (1), **2**. 418, 1834 ; G. Berendts, *Beiträge zur Kenntnis der Pyrophosphate*, Berlin, 1905 ; H. J. Debray, *Ann. Chim. Phys.*, (3), **61**. 434, 1860 ; L. Ouvrard, *ib.*, (6), **16**. 315, 1889 ; G. Foëx and A. Brunet, *Compt. Rend.*, **184**. 443, 1927 ; W. Heintz, *Pogg. Ann.*, **74**. 449, 1847 ; H. Rose *ib.*, **76**. 18, 1849 ; C. H. D. Bödeker, *Liebig's Ann.*, **69**. 206, 1849 ; A. Schwarzenberg, *ib.*, **65**. 150, 1848 ; *Journ. prakt. Chem.*, (1), **46**. 247, 1849 ; *Untersuchungen über die pyrophosphorsauren Salze*, Göttingen, 1849 ; H. Struve, *Bull. Acad. St. Petersburg*, (3), **1**. 239, 1860 ; *Journ. prakt. Chem.*, (1), **79**. 345, 1860 ; C. N. Pahl, *Ber.*, **6**. 1465, 1873 ; *Bull. Soc. Chim.*, (2), **19**. 115, 1873 ; *Oefvers. Svenska Akad. Förh.*, **30**. 7, 1873 ; K. A. Wallroth, *ib.*, **40**. 3, 1883 ; *Bull. Soc. Chim.*, (2), **39**. 316, 1883 ; *Ber.*, **16**. 3659, 1883 ; G. Vortmann, *ib.*, **21**. 1104, 1888 ; G. Buchner, *Arch. Pharm.*, (3), **21**. 116, 1883 ; O. Andersen, *Journ. Washington Acad.*, **4**. 318, 1914 ; A. Rosenheim, S. Frommer, H. Gläser and W. Händler, *Zeit. anorg. Chem.*, **153**. 126, 1926.

  ³ R. Maddrell, *Phil. Mag.*, (3), **30**. 322, 1847 ; *Mem. Chem. Soc.*, **3**. 273, 1848 ; T. Fleitmann, *Pogg. Ann.*, **78**. 233, 349, 1849 ; T. Fleitmann and W. Henneberg, *ib.*, **65**. 228, 1848 ; H. Rose, *ib.*, **76**. 1, 1849 ; G. Tammann, *Zeit. phys. Chem.*, **6**. 124, 1890 ; *Journ. prakt. Chem.*, (2), **45**. 422, 425, 1892 ; H. Schjerning, *ib.*, (2), **45**. 526, 1892 ; F. J. Otto, *ib.*, (1), **2**. 418, 1834 ; *Schweigger's Journ.*, **66**. 288, 1832 ; C. G. Lindboom, *Arskr. Lunds. Univ.*, **10**. 7, 1874 ; *Ber.*, **8**. 122, 1875 ; C. Reichard, *ib.*, **27**. 1031, 1894 ; **31**. 2163, 1898 ; H. Lüdert, *Zeit. anorg. Chem.*, **5**. 36, 1893 ; A. Wiesler, *ib.*, **28**. 182, 1901 ; M. Stange, *ib.*, **12**. 454, 1896 ; F. Warschauer, *ib.*, **36**. 137, 1903 ; F. de Carli, *Atti Congres. Chim. Pura Appl.*, 1146, 1926 ; A. Glatzel, *Ueber dimeta-phosphorsaure und tetrametaphosphorsaure Salze*, Würzburg, 1880 ; *Zeit. anorg. Chem.*, **4**. 192, 1893 ; P. Glühmann, *Beitrag zur Kenntnis der Triphosphorsäure und ihrer Salze*, Berlin, 1899 ; C. D. Braun, *Zeit. anal. Chem.*, **7**. 340, 1868.

§ 27. Manganic Phosphates

O. T. Christensen [1] prepared **manganic orthophosphate**, $MnPO_4.H_2O$, by decomposing manganic acetate with phosphoric acid, but more conveniently by adding a conc. soln. of manganous nitrate in nitric acid to a hot, aq. soln. of phosphoric acid. The salt soon begins to form, with the evolution of nitrous fumes ; and it is washed with water, and dried at 100° to 110°. The greenish-grey crystalline powder slowly loses water at 300° to 400°, and rapidly at a red-heat, with the simultaneous loss of oxygen. After calcination there remains manganous pyrophosphate. A. Travers also made this salt. According to F. Fichter and E. Brunner, manganic phosphate is very stable. A conc. soln. of manganous carbonate in phosphoric acid becomes amethyst-red when it is treated with fluorine, but the oxidation is not complete. It is assumed that fluorine acts first upon the phosphoric acid, forming monoperphosphoric acid, which readily oxidizes manganous sulphate in acid soln. to manganic phosphate. J. Schmidlin and P. Massini, who first prepared monoperphosphoric acid, considered the amethyst colour to be due to permanganic acid, but spectrographic examination shows at once that the dark lines are lacking. J. Chloupek studied the potential of platinum in soln. of phosphoric acid and manganic oxide. R. H. Weber found the mol. magnetism of manganic phosphate to be 0·01084. O. T. Christensen observed that dil. nitric or dil. sulphuric acid is without action, but boiling conc. sulphuric acid forms a violet soln. which, on standing, deposits a crystalline precipitate of $Mn_2O_3.4SO_3$; conc. hydrochloric acid dissolves it slowly with the evolution of chlorine. It forms a violet soln. in molten phosphoric acid at 110°; and at 170° to 180° more of the salt is dissolved and a dark red precipitate, probably manganic hydropyrophosphate, is formed; at 220°, the red salt of H. Laspeyres is produced. H. Laspeyres observed that the red soln. is decolorized when heated in a platinum dish on a water-bath. No gas is developed, and a greenish-grey crystalline powder is deposited. It is insoluble in water. The salt, calcined at a dull red-heat or otherwise, forms chlorine when it is heated with hydrochloric acid. It dissolves in phosphoric acid at 100° to 110° forming an amethyst-blue syrupy liquid which, when concentrated on a water-bath, finally yields amethyst-blue, six-sided, birefringent plates insoluble in water. R. H. Weber studied the magnetic properties.

J. Meyer and J. Marck found that the violet colour produced when manganous salts are oxidized in the presence of phosphoric acid is due to the presence of **manganic trihydrodiorthophosphate,** $MnPO_4.H_3PO_4$, or *diphosphatomanganic acid* or **manganidiorthophosphoric acid,** $H_3[Mn(PO_4)_2]$, which has been prepared by the interaction of anhydrous manganic acetate and conc. phosphoric acid at 100°. The reddish-violet crystals are very unstable, and readily absorb moisture, forming manganic orthophosphate. The soln. in phosphoric acid is more stable, and when electrolyzed the manganese collects about the anode, showing that it is present as a complex anion. The acid furnishes a series of salts which furnish monoclinic dark red or violet crystals—excepting the guanidine salt, which is dark yellow. The guanidine salt is anhydrous, the other salts are red or violet. This difference is taken to indicate that the water of hydration is not contained in the complex anion, but is simply water of crystallization. The potassium salt is deliquescent, the other salts are stable in air; they are decomposed by hot water, depositing brown hydrated manganic hydroxide. Conc. sulphuric, phosphoric, and hydrofluoric acids form violet soln.; conc. hydrochloric acid gives a brownish-green soln. which when warmed gives off chlorine; conc. nitric acid forms a deposit of hydrated manganese dioxide; conc. acetic acid has no action. Dil. hydrochloric acid dissolves the salt; dil. nitric and sulphuric acids decompose it; oxalic acid reduces the salts to form manganous salts. The soln. in dil. phosphoric acid gradually deposit greyish-green manganic orthophosphate. Ammonium sulphide gives red manganous sulphide; sodium hydroxide or carbonate precipitates brown manganic hydroxide; and aq. ammonia gives a brown soln. of colloidal manganic hydroxide. Barium carbonate and sodium dihydropyrophosphate give a greyish-green deposit of manganic orthophosphate. The **ammonium dihydromanganidiorthophosphate,** $(NH_4)H_2[Mn(PO_4)_2].3H_2O$, is obtained by adding manganidiorthophosphoric acid to an ammoniacal soln. of ammonium chloride, or by mixing a soln. of ammonium hydrophosphate and manganidiorthophosphate. The *guanidine salt,* $(CN_3H_6)H_2[Mn(PO_4)_2]$, was prepared similarly; likewise also **lithium dihydromanganidiorthophosphate,** $LiH_2[Mn(PO_4)_2].3H_2O$; **sodium dihydromanganidiorthophosphate,** $NaH_2[Mn(PO_4)_2].nH_2O$, both as the *trihydrate* and *pentahydrate*; and **potassium dihydromanganidiorthophosphate,** $KH_2[Mn(PO_4)_2].3H_2O$. A. Yakimach also obtained this salt.

What is supposed from the analysis of R. Hermann to have been **manganic pyrophosphate** was prepared in the form of the *octohydrate,* $Mn_4(P_2O_7)_3.8H_2O$, by L. Gmelin, by the action of conc. phosphoric acid on manganosic oxide or manganese dioxide at a red-heat; H. Laspeyres worked at 100° to 110°. R. Hermann, and H. Rose used manganic oxide; H. Rose used alkali manganates or permanganates; and A. Barreswil, and F. von Kobell used manganous salts mixed with nitric acid or nitrates. The violet mass is blue when hot. It forms a columbine-red soln. with water; F. Hoppe-Seyler examined the spectrum of the aq. soln. L. Gmelin found that the aq. soln. is not decomposed by a large excess of water, but if a soln. in 6 vols. of water be allowed to stand for a few days it becomes turbid. The aq. soln. is immediately decolorized by hydrogen sulphide or sulphurous acid. R. Hermann said that if the aq. soln. is allowed to stand a long time, it deposits light brown crystalline grains, probably of hydrated manganese dioxide. The peach-coloured mass is insoluble in all acids excepting hydrochloric acid; it is decomposed by hot potash-lye. According to V. Auger, the *tetradecahydrate*, $Mn_4(P_2O_7)_3.14H_2O$, is obtained by fusing manganese nitrate with phosphoric acid at 210°, extracting the fused mass with water, and adding alcohol to the violet-coloured extract; the salt separates as a buff-coloured, crystalline precipitate which loses $10H_2O$ at 185° and the remaining $4H_2O$ at 440°. Cold soln. of alkali hydroxide extract phosphoric acid, which appears in soln. as a pyrophosphate. Sulphuric acid dissolves it with a violet colour which becomes red on dilution. Cold phosphoric acid dissolves it; from the violet soln., which becomes rapidly colourless, the phosphate $MnPO_4.H_2O$ separates. H. Schjerning found that **manganic hydropyrophosphate,** $MnHP_2O_7$, is best obtained by adding manganic orthophosphate to molten orthophosphoric acid in a platinum crucible at 220° to 230° so long as it dissolves therein, and continuing the heating for 6 to 8 hrs. with frequent stirring until the mass has become semi-solid. While still warm this product is thrown, in small portions, into cold water, the precipitate washed until free from phosphoric acid, and dried at 97°. It is pansy-coloured and of uncertain crystalline form; it undergoes oxidation when moist, and is readily decomposed by alkalies and acids, evolving chlorine with hydrochloric acid and yielding a precipitate of a higher oxide of manganese with sulphuric and nitric acids; when heated, it loses water and oxygen and is converted into manganous metaphosphate. A. Rosenheim and T. Triantaphyllides regarded $HMnP_2O_7$ as manganipyrophosphoric acid which furnishes manganipyrophosphates analogous to the corresponding chromipyrophosphates, molybdipyrophosphates, bismuthipyrophosphates, thallipyrophosphates, and ferripyrophosphates.

P. Barbier prepared **ammonium manganic pyrophosphate,** $(NH_4)MnP_2O_7$, by heating a mixture of precipitated manganese dioxide and diammonium hydrogen phosphate made up to a paste with water: a decomposition takes place, with liberation of ammonia. The product is heated with syrupy phosphoric acid until it becomes violet. On washing out with water, an insoluble, violet powder is left. This ammonium manganic pyrophosphate is decomposed by hydrochloric acid and by alkali-lye. When heated to redness it leaves a residue of manganous metaphosphate. A. Rosenheim and T. Triantaphyllides prepared the *trihydrate*, $NH_4(MnP_2O_7).3H_2O$, by the process used for the sodium salt. O. T. Christensen prepared **sodium manganic pyrophosphate,** $NaMnP_2O_7.5H_2O$, by mixing a soln. of the acetate in glacial acetic acid with sodium pyrophosphate soln.: the salt is deposited as a red crystalline precipitate. It is also prepared by treating manganic oxide with conc. hydrochloric acid, and filtering this soln. into a soln. of sodium pyrophosphate in large excess. The salt is dried at the ordinary temp. It easily loses its water of crystallization. Manganese dioxide may also be used for this preparation, and this supports the hypothesis that when treated with hydrochloric acid the dioxide does not yield the tetra- but the trichloride. A. Rosenheim and T. Triantaphyllides prepared this salt by dropping a soln. of manganic oxide in cold, conc. hydrochloric acid into a sat. soln. of sodium pyrophosphate. H. Schjerning prepared **potassium manganic pyrophosphate,** $KMnP_2O_7$, by adding a soln. of manganic orthophosphate in molten orthophosphoric acid to molten potassium nitrate; after continuing the heating for a minute or two, the melt was poured on to iron or stone and, when cold, treated with cold water. The new salt is somewhat darker than the pansy-coloured manganous hydropyrophosphate and more stable to acids and bases ; it is insoluble in water. When heated it becomes darker and then loses oxygen ; when cooled by carbon dioxide and ether it becomes much paler. A. Rosenheim and T. Triantaphyllides prepared a pale violet *pentahydrate*, $K(MnP_2O_7).5H_2O$, stable below 10°, and the *trihydrate*, $K(MnP_2O_7).3H_2O$, which is decomposed by boiling water. From it may be obtained insoluble pink **silver manganic pyrophosphate**, $Ag(MnP_2O_7).3H_2O$, and insoluble pink **barium manganic pyrophosphate**, $Ba(MnP_2O_7)_2.5H_2O$.

V. Auger prepared **manganic metaphosphate**, $Mn(PO_3)_3$, by rubbing together 200 grms. of phosphoric oxide with 100 grms. of manganese dioxide and some water. The mixture becomes hot ; the blue paste is heated until it becomes hard, and is then washed with water. H. Schjerning prepared it by heating a soln. of manganic orthophosphate in molten orthophosphoric acid at 350° until the mixture becomes pasty. It is then treated with cold water. The red crystalline product when hot is pansy-coloured, and when cold pale red. It is insoluble in water. It is very stable towards acids, but is decomposed by alkali-lye. A. Travers made this salt ; and L. Gmelin, and R. Hermann prepared the *hydrate*, $Mn(PO_3)_3.H_2O$, by heating to redness a mixture of manganosic or manganic oxide or manganese dioxide with an excess of phosphoric acid. P. Barbier obtained it by heating precipitated manganese dioxide with 4·5 times its weight of phosphoric acid soln. of sp. gr. 1·70 until nearly dry, then adding 2 more parts of phosphoric acid and heating until the mass acquires a peach-blossom colour. It is insoluble in water, but dissolves in hydrochloric acid with liberation of chlorine, and is decomposed by alkali hydroxides with separation of manganic oxide.

V. Auger and A. Yakimach prepared **ammonium manganic perphosphate**, $(NH_4)_2H_2MnP_2O_9$, by heating a soln. of a mixture of ammonium hydrophosphate and permanganate. Black rhombic crystals separate on cooling—*vide*, **8**. 50, 29.

Minerals containing manganous oxide are usually readily oxidized, and triphylite and lithiophilite are often covered with a brownish-black surface film. The *pseudotriphylite* of J. R. Blum [2] is an alteration product of triphylite occurring as an incrustation on the triphylite of Rabenstein, Bavaria. It approximates a **manganic ferric tetraphosphate**, $(Fe,Mn)_2P_4O_{19}.3H_2O$. W. P. Headden described a mineral from a tin mine in Pennington Co., South Dakota, with a similar composition. Analyses reported by C. W. C. Fuchs, and J. R. Blum approximate $4R'_3PO_4.9R''_3(PO_4)_2$. The **heterosite**—from ἕτερος, other or different—of F. Alluaud is a greenish- or bluish-grey, brown, or violet, massive mineral, from the pegmatite of Limoges, Haute Vienne. Its sp. gr. is 3·39 to 3·52, and its hardness 4 to 6. According to H. Berman, the optical character is positive ; the optic axial angle $2V$ is small ; the indices of refraction are $a=1·85$, $\beta=1·86$, and $\gamma=1·91$; the dispersion is fairly strong ; and the pleochroism a is greenish-grey, β blood-red, and γ deep purple-red. Analyses reported by P. A. Dufrénoy, J. W. Mallet, and C. F. Rammelsberg agree with the formula $(Mn,Fe)PO_4.\frac{1}{2}H_2O$—*vide* the ferric phosphates. A purple variety from Gaston Co., North Carolina, was called **purpurite** by L. C. Graton and W. T. Schaller. Its composition is similar to that of heterosite, and approximates $(Fe,Mn)_2O_3.P_2O_5.H_2O$. The sp. gr. is 3·7, and the mean index of refraction between 1·60 and 1·65. E. S. Larsen gave 1·92 for the mean index of refraction. The birefringence is strong. A. Lacroix believed that the two minerals are related like lithiophilite and triphylite, purpurite representing the members of the series with manganic phosphate predominant, and heterosite with the ferric phosphate predominant. A. Damour described a brown, massive mineral also occurring in nodules. It appears to be an impure manganic ferric phosphate from Limoges, Haute Vienne, and he called it *alluaudite*—after F. Alluaud. Its sp. gr. is 3·468 ; its hardness, 4 to 5 ; and, according to E. S. Larsen, its mean index of refraction, 1·830.

REFERENCES.

[1] O. T. Christensen, *Danske Vid. Selsk. Förh.*, 94, 1896 ; *Journ. prakt. Chem.*, (2), **28**. 1, 1883 ; A. Travers, *Bull. Soc. Chim.*, (4), **37**. 456, 1925 ; H. Laspeyres, *Journ. prakt. Chem.*, (2), **15**. 320, 1877 ; H. Schjerning, *ib.*, (2), **45**. 515, 1892 ; F. Hoppe-Seyler, *ib.*, (1), **90**. 303, 1863 ; J. Chloupek, *Coll. Czeck. Chem. Comm.*, **2**. 129, 1930 ; P. Barbier, *Compt. Rend.*, **135**. 1054, 1109, 1902 ; V. Auger, *ib.*, **133**. 94, 1901 ; V. Auger and A. Yakimach, *ib.*, **187**. 603, 1928 ; A. Barreswil, *ib.*, **44**. 677, 1857 ; G. Grube and M. Staesch, *Zeit. Elektrochem.*, **31**. 362, 1925 ; *Zeit. phys. Chem.*, **130**. 572, 1927 ; R. H. Weber, *Ann. Physik*, (4), **19**. 1056, 1906 ; (4), **36**. 624, 1911 ; J. Schmidlin

and P. Massini, *Ber.*, **43**. 1166, 1910 ; F. Fichter and E. Brunner, *Journ. Chem. Soc.*, 1862, 1928 ; F. von Kobell, *Anz. Bayr. Akad.*, **48**. 377, 1859 ; *Journ. prakt. Chem.*, (1), **76**. 415, 1859 ; H. Rose, *Pogg. Ann.*, **105**. 289, 1858 ; R. Hermann, *ib.*, **74**. 303, 1848 ; L. Gmelin, *Handbook of Chemistry*, London, **4**. 217, 1850 ; A. Rosenheim, *Zeit. anorg. Chem.*, **153**. 126, 1926 ; A. Rosenheim and T. Triantaphyllides, *Ber.*, **48**. 582, 1915 ; J. Meyer and J. Marck, *Zeit. anorg. Chem.*, **133**. 325, 1924 ; A. Yakimach, *Compt. Rend.*, **192**. 1652, 1931.
    [2] J. R. Blum, *Lehrbuch der Oryktognosie*, Stuttgart, 537, 1847 ; W. P. Headden, *Amer. Journ. Science*, (3), **41**. 415, 1899 ; C. W. C. Fuchs, *Journ. prakt. Chem.*, (1), **3**. 98, 1834 ; (1), **5**. 319, 1836 ; F. Alluaud, *Ann. Science Nat.*, **8**. 346, 1826 ; *Ann. Chim. Phys.*, (2), **30**. 302, 1825 ; P. A. Dufrénoy, *ib.*, (2), **41**. 342, 1829 ; E. S. Larsen, *Bull. U.S. Geol. Sur.*, 679, 1921 ; H. Berman, *Amer. Min.*, **12**. 170, 1927 ; J. W. Mallet, *Amer. Journ. Science*, (2), **18**. 33, 1854 ; C. F. Rammelsberg, *Handbuch der Mineralchemie*, Leipzig, 307, 1875 ; *Pogg. Ann.*, **85**. 439, 1852 ; L. C. Graton and W. T. Schaller, *Amer. Journ. Science*, (4), **20**. 146, 1905 ; A. Lacroix, *Minéralogie de la France et de ses colonies*, Paris, **4**. 362, 1910 ; A. Damour, *Ann. Mines*, (4), **13**. 341, 1848.

CHAPTER LXV

MASURIUM AND RHENIUM

§ 1. Eka-manganese, or Masurium, and Dwi-manganese, or Rhenium

THE periodic table of atomic weight had, until recently, two blanks corresponding with elements of atomic number 43 and 75, belonging to the manganese family. Following D. I. Mendeléeff's [1] nomenclature—1. 6, 4—these elements border on the transition families of Group VIII, as represented in the portion of the table :

I	.	Cr 24	Mn 25	Fe 26
II	.	Mo 42	? 43	Ru 44
III	.	W 74	? 75	Os 76

The blank corresponding with element 43 belongs to **eka-manganese,** and the next blank, corresponding with element 75, belongs to **dwi-manganese.** C. H. Bosanquet and T. C. Keeley examined a number of minerals—psilomelanes, rhodonites, rhodochrosites, and pyrolusites from various localities, polyamite, wad, manganite, and franklinite—as well as samples of manganese extracted from tobernite and from thorianite, and a Ru-Rh-Pd alloy from the Urals, by exposing them to cathode-ray bombardment in the hope of finding X-ray lines of one or more of the missing elements of the manganese family ; but not one of the minerals gave any sign of the existence of the missing elements. I. and W. Noddack and I. Tacke, O. Zvjaginstseft, W. Franke, and O. Berg and I. Tacke sought for the missing elements in a platinum earth from Russia, some osmiridium, and platinum residues, as well as in samples of columbite and tantalite. The subject was discussed by W. Prandtl, E. Rüst, and R. Swinne. In all cases, evidence of the missing elements is alleged to have been discovered. They accordingly called ekamanganese **masurium,** Ma, from Masuren in East Prussia ; and dwimanganese, **rhenium,** Re, from the German Rhine. V. Dolejsek and J. Heyrovsky considered that the evidence for dwimanganese reported by W. Noddack and I. Tacke, and O. Berg and I. Tacke is unsatisfactory. They inferred the existence of dwimanganese in some preparations of purified manganous sulphate from some irregularities in the potential-current curves ; but A. N. Campbell showed that the irregularities might also be due to the over-voltage of hydrogen. Hence, the conclusion of V. Dolejsek and J. Heyrovsky may have been right and the reasons wrong. V. Dolejsek and J. Heyrovsky said that chlorine prepared by the action of hydrochloric acid on pyrolusite contains appreciable quantities of dwimanganese as a higher volatile chloride. The subject was discussed by M. Herszfinkiel, and N. Seljakoff and M. Korsunsky.

REFERENCES.

[1] D. I. Mendeléeff, *Journ. Russ. Chem. Soc.*, **1**. 60, 1869 ; **2**. 14, 1870 ; **4**. 25, 348, 1871 ; *Liebig's Ann. Suppl.*, **8**. 130, 1872 ; *Ostwald's Klassiker*, 68, 1895 ; *The Principles of Chemistry*, London, 1892 ; *Journ. Chem. Soc.*, **55**. 634, 1889 ; C. H. Bosanquet and T. C. Keeley, *Phil. Mag.*, (6), **48**. 145, 1925 ; I. Tacke, *Zeit. angew. Chem.*, **28**. 1157, 1925 ; I. Noddack, *Zeit. Elektrochem.*, **34**. 629, 1928 ; W. Noddack, *ib.*, **34**. 627, 1928 ; I. and W. Noddack, *Metallbörse*, **20**. 621, 1930 ; *Naturwiss.*, **17**. 23, 93, 1929 ; **18**. 757, 1930 ; *Zeit. anorg. Chem.*, **181**. 1, 1929 ; **183**. 353, 1929 ; *Zeit. phys. Chem.*, **125**. 264, 1927 ; *Continental Met. Chem. Engg.*, **1**. 109, 1926 ; *Chem. News*, **134**. 257, 1927 ; W. Noddack and I. Tacke, *Naturwiss.*, **13**. 567, 1925 ; *Sitzber. Akad. Berlin*, 400, 1925 ; *Oesterr. Chem. Ztg.*, **28**. 127, 1925 ; O. Berg and I. Tacke, *ib.*, 405, 1925 ; *Naturwiss.*, **13**. 571, 1925 ; O. Berg, *Phil. Zeit.*, **28**. 864, 1927 ; V. Dolejsek and J. Heyrovsky, *Chem. Listy*, **20**. 4, 1926 ; *Rec. Trav. Chim. Pays-Bas*, **46**. 248, 1927 ; *Nature*, **116**. 782, 1925 ; J. Heyrovsky, *ib.*, **117**. 16, 1926 ; V. Dolejsek, J. G. F. Druce and J. Heyrovsky, *ib.*, **117**. 159, 1926 ; A. N. Campbell, *ib.*, **116**. 866, 1925 ; J. G. F. Druce, *Chem. News*, **131**. 273, 1925 ; *Nature*, **117**. 16, 1926 ; *Chem. Weekbl.*, **23**. 318, 497, 1926 ; *Science Progress*, **20**. 690, 1926 ; **24**. 480, 1930 ; H. Beuthe, *Zeit. Physik*, **46**. 873, 1928 ; **50**. 762, 1928 ; I. Wennerlöf, *ib.*, **47**. 422, 1928 ; E. Lindberg, *ib.*, **50**. 82, 1928 ; **56**. 402, 1929 ; F. H. Loring, *Nature*, **117**. 448, 1926 ; *Chem. News*, **132**. 101, 1926 ; F. H. Loring and J. G. F. Druce, *ib.*, **131**. 337, 1925 ; B. Polland, *Chem. News*, **133**. 409, 1925 ; *Compt. Rend.*, **183**. 737, 1926 ; M. Herszfinkiel, *ib.*, **184**. 968, 1927 ; W. Prandtl, *Ber.*, **60**. B, 621, 1927 ; *Zeit. angew. Chem.*, **39**. 1049, 1926 ; **40**. 561, 1927 ; N. Seljakoff and M. Korsunsky *Phys. Zeit.*, **28**. 478, 1927 ; E. Rüst, *Schweiss. Chem. Ztg.*, 234, 1925 ; W. F. Meggers and C. C. Kiess, *Journ. Amer. Opt. Soc.*, **12**. 417, 1926 ; R. Swinne, *Zeit. tech. Phys.*, **6**. 464, 1925 ; V. M. Goldschmidt, *Zeit. phys. Chem.*, **2**. B, 244, 1929 ; *Naturwiss.*, **17**. 134, 1929 ; W. Franke, *Ein Suche nach den Manganhomologen No.* 43 *und No.* 75, München, 1927 ; O. Zvjaginstseff, *Nature*, **118**. 261, 1926 ; C. E. St. John, *Astrophys. Journ.*, **70**. 160, 1929 ; F. Sacherl, *Chem. Listy*, **23**. 632, 1929 ; N. Schröter, *Das Rhenium*, Stuttgart, 1932 ; P. M. Tyler, *Information Circ. Bur. Mines*, 6475, 1931 ; C. Hardy, *Journ. Ind. Eng. Chem.—News*, **9**. 208, 1931 ; E. Geay, *Rev. Chim. Ind.*, **40**. 98, 1931.

§ 2. The Occurrence of Masurium and Rhenium

According to W. Noddack and I. Tacke,[1] and O. Berg and I. Tacke, columbite contains 10^{-6} to 10^{-7} part of the mixture of eka- and dwi-manganese elements in the proportion 1 : 10. Traces of ekamanganese were detected in sperrylite, gadolinite, fergusonite, and zircon ; and traces of dwimanganese in tantalite and tungstenite. W. and I. Noddack estimated that gadolinite contained 11×10^{-7} Re ; alvite, 5×10^{-7} ; gadolinite, 0 to 4×10^{-7} ; columbite, 2×10^{-7} ; tantalite, $1 \cdot 4 \times 10^{-7}$; orangite, less than 2×10^{-7} ; malacone, zircon, euxenite, risörite, blomstrandine, and fergusonite, less than 1×10^{-7} ; and traces in samarskite, monazite, and orthite. No known mineral contains more than 0·001 per cent. of rhenium.

The following proportions of rhenium in various minerals by W. and I. Noddack are to be multiplied by 10^{-6}. Alvite, 0·2 to 0·6 ; gadolinite, 0·03 to 1·1 ; hornblende, 0·002 ; muscovite, 0·01 ; orthoclase, 0·02 ; pyroxene, 0·002 ; quartz, 0·007 ; thortveitite,. 0·06 ; zircon, 0·01 to 0·05 ; columbite, 0·05 to 0·2 ; euxenite, 0·01 ; fergusonite, 0·02 ; hübnerite, 0·01 ; risörite, 0·02 ; samarskite, 0·02 ; scheelite, 0·02 ; tantalite, 0·03 to 0·08 ; wolframite, 0·02 ; chrome ironstone, 0·01 to 0·02 ; rutile 0·01 to 0·02 ; cassiterite, 0·01 ; arsenical pyrites, 0·01 ; arsenical nickel glance, 0·05 ; lead glance, 0·01 ; copper pyrites, 0·02 to 0·08 ; enargite, 0·02 ; germanite, 0·03 ; stibnite, 0·01 ; copper glance, 0·04 ; kupferschiefer, 0·03 ; magnetic pyrites, 0·02 to 0·03 ; marcasite, 0·03 ; molybdenum glance, 0·05 to 21·0 ; pentlandite, 0·01 ; pyrites, 0·01 ; lead selenide, 0·8 ; copper selenide, 0·2 ; silver glance, 0·07 ; sulvanite, 0·005 ; lead telluride, 0·01 ; troilite, 0·004 to 0·04 ; bismuth glance, 0·02 ; arsenical nickel, 0·01 ; domeykite, 0·002 ; meteoritic iron, 0·006 to 0·01 ; osmiridium, 0·01 to 1·0 ; platinum ore, 0·03 to 0·8 ; and sperrylite, 0·02. The primary sulphides have an average of 2×10^{-8} part of rhenium ; and the silicates, 1×10^{-8} part.

As a general estimate W. Noddack and I. Tacke assumed that the earth's crust contains about 10^{-13} of ekamanganese (masurium) and 10^{-12} of dwimanganese (rhenium), as well as 7×10^{-2} of manganese, and 10^{-2} of iron ; and they gave later 10^{-9} each of masurium and rhenium. F. H. Loring observed lines of the element rhenium in the X-ray spectrum of manganese phosphate. C. E. St. John said that these two elements have not yet been detected in the sun, and H. Schober discussed the subject.

REFERENCES.

[1] W. Noddack and I. Tacke, *Deut. Forsch.*, **2**. 104, 1930 ; *Zeit. phys. Chem.*, **154**. 207, 1931 ; *Zeit. angew. Chem.*, **44**. 215, 1931 ; *Zeit. anorg. Chem.*, **181**. 1, 1929 ; **183**. 353, 1929 ; *Naturwiss.*, **13**. 567, 1925 ; *Sitzber. Akad. Berlin*, 400, 1925 ; *Oesterr. Chem. Ztg.*, **28**. 127, 1925 ; O. Berg and I. Tacke, *ib.*, 404, 1925 ; *Naturwiss.*, **13**. 571, 1925 ; F. H. Loring, *Nature*, **117**. 448, 1926 ; *Chem. News*, **132**. 101, 1926 ; W. and I. Noddack, *Naturwiss.*, **17**. 23, 93, 1929 ; **18**. 757, 1930 ; *Zeit. anorg. Chem.*, **181**. 1, 1929 ; **183**. 353, 1929 ; *Zeit. phys. Chem.*, **125**. 264, 1927 ; O. Hönigschmid and R. Sachtleben, *Zeit. anorg. Chem.*, **191**. 309, 1930 ; H. Schober, *Naturwiss.*, **19**. 310, 1931 ; C. E. St. John, *Astrophys. Journ.*, **70**. 160, 1929.

§ 3. The Isolation of Masurium and Rhenium

According to W. Noddack and I. Tacke,[1] a soln. of 100 grms. of platinum earth in aqua regia was evaporated to dryness, and reduced in hydrogen. The residue of the earth, insoluble in aqua regia, was heated to redness in chlorine, and the volatile chloride dissolved in water and reduced with zinc. The products of both reductions were mixed and heated to redness in oxygen. Osmium and ruthenium tetroxides were distilled off, and on the walls of the quartz tube there collected a black film of ruthenium trioxide, a white sublimate of arsenic trioxide, and a small white deposit consisting of minute, acicular crystals. The white needles were heated in a current of hydrogen sulphide, when small spherules of molten sulphide were formed. When this product is heated in oxygen, about a milligram of small white crystals collect in the cold part of the tube. The crystals were dissolved in water, and the soln. treated with hydrogen sulphide and ammonium sulphide, which did not give a precipitate. It is assumed that the soln. contains impure ekamanganese.

According to W. Noddack and I. Tacke, the chief source of rhenium was columbite. It was treated by them as follows :

1 to 20 kgrms. of columbite were heated many hours with twice the weight of sodium hydroxide and 5 per cent. of sodium nitrate. The cooled product was exposed to air for many days and then shaken up with water to yield a 5 per cent. alkali soln. After standing, the liquid was filtered and the residue washed with 5 per cent. sodium hydroxide, NaOH. This dissolved a minimum of columbium and tantalum. The green filtrate contained manganites, and was treated with hydrogen dioxide to precipitate $MnO_2.H_2O$; and with 5 per cent. ammonium chloride, which precipitated the earthy acids and silica, titania, columbium, tantalia. The resulting filtrate of 300 litres was weakly acidified with sulphuric acid and the nitrous acid removed. A small precipitate of titanium and lead and a little silica, columbium, zirconium, tantalia, hafnia, but no rhenium came down. Hydrogen sulphide was passed in till the soln. was saturated with the gas. The sulphide precipitate was filtered off and the filtrate was treated with ammonium hydroxide and ammonium sulphide and re-acidified to 5 per cent. hydrochloric acid. These sulphides were united to the first precipitate and were heated in a stream of hydrogen to remove sulphur. The residue contained 40 per cent. Cb, Ta ; 5 per cent. Si ; 5 per cent. Ti, Zr, Hf ; 10 per cent. Fe, Co, Ni, Mn ; 30 per cent. W, Mo, Sn, V ; and 10 per cent. Cu, Pb, As, Sb, Bi, Pt, Ge, Zn, Cd ; and traces of Ir, Ru, Os. These sulphides were warmed with dilute *aqua regia*, and the sulphur and tungstic acid were filtered off. The filtrate was evaporated to drive off the nitric acid. On reduction of the residue in hydrogen there remained about one gram of substance containing 15 per cent. V ; 7, Mo ; 3, W ; 10, Pt ; 5, Pb ; 15, As ; 15, Cu ; 20, Sn, Ge, Sb, Bi ; 5, Co, Ni ; 5, Cb, Ti, Ta ; 0·2 Re. The rhenium was identified by the distinct *L*α-line. This residue was treated like the osmiridium and wolfram ores, and the alkali fusion products were treated with ammonium chloride. Conc. sulphuric acid was added to the filtrate and this was again filtered. This left Co, Ni, Cu, Pt, Bi, Nb, Ta, Sn, Ge, Sb ; Pb, W, and much V remained behind. A further hydrogen sulphide precipitation gave a preparation (0·1 grm.) containing V 20 per cent., Mo 70 per cent., As 5 per cent., Cb, Sn, and Sb 3 per cent., and Re 2 per cent. When this was dissolved in *aqua regia*, filtered, freed from HNO_3 and made 5 per cent. acid, and rapidly saturated with H_2S, most of the molybdenum was precipitated as MoS_3. This precipitate contained only a trace of rhenium. The filtrate was made alkaline with ammonium hydroxide, and ammonium sulphide was added to precipitate V, Mo, As, and all the rhenium, whilst Sb and Sn remained in soln. This sulphide (15–20 mg.) was composed of V, 85 per cent., Re, 10 per cent., Mo, 3 per cent., and As, 2 per cent. The final treatment consisted in heating the reduced substance in oxygen. Most of the rhenium was driven off as a white oxide, which sublimed on the cool parts of the tube and was extracted by cutting the tube. Gadolinite and other rare-earth minerals—monazite, cerite, orthite, malacone, zirkon, alvite, thorite, and orangite—were treated in a similar manner.

J. G. F. Druce obtained about 75 mgrms. of impure oxide of dwimanganese from crude manganese sulphate by the following process :

A soln. of 100 grms. of crude sulphate in 600 c.c. of water was treated with 50 grms. of ammonium chloride and 25 c.c. of aq. ammonia of sp. gr. 0·880, and hydrogen sulphide gas was passed in for some time. The mixture, sat. with the gas, was allowed to stand some hours before filtration. The precipitate should have included iron sulphide and an aluminium or chromium hydroxides. The filtrate was re-treated with hydrogen sulphide until there was no further precipitation. This required several filtrations before a soln was obtained which no longer gave any precipitate when sat. with the gas and allowed to stand. The filtrate and washings were allowed to stand for several days whilst still alkaline with ammonia and sat. with hydrogen sulphide to make quite sure that all manganese had been removed. The soln. was afterwards boiled for some minutes to remove excess of hydrogen sulphide and some ammonia, acidified with hydrochloric acid and evaporated to dryness. The residue was strongly heated to drive off the ammonium compounds and burn away the small quantity of sulphur formed. The final residue was dissolved in acetic acid, and ammonium oxalate in slight excess was added to precipitate the calcium present. The filtrate was evaporated to dryness and ignited strongly to drive off all ammonium compounds. The residue was dissolved in hot dil. nitric acid. The soln. was precipitated with ammonium hydroxide and the washed precipitate was dissolve in hot dil. nitric acid and evaporated to dryness again, leaving a white nitrate which was ignited to a very light brown oxide.

V. Dolejsek and J. Heyrovsky obtained a preparation of dwimanganese by introducing a small crucible containing manganese amalgam into a nearly sat. soln of manganous sulphate, and connecting the soln. with the amalgam by a piece of platinum foil. After several days the platinum foil was removed, rinsed with water and the deposit washed off with conc. hydrochloric acid. The soln. was diluted with water. Hydrogen sulphide was then passed into the liquid, and the filtered soln contained manganese with about 2 per cent. of dwimanganese. E. W. von Siemens and J. G. Halske discussed the extraction of these elements from platinum ores gadolinite, sperrylite, and molybdenite ; and W. Feit, from complex sulphid slimes.

G. Heyne and K. Moers said that the precipitation of rhenium as sulphide from soln. of its salts, and subsequent reduction of the sulphide is inconvenient, because the precipitation is not complete and the sulphide readily forms a colloid. This can be prevented by precipitating the sulphide in a pressure flask. Even then as shown by W. and I. Noddack the clear filtrate contains some rhenium. They recommend heating the rhenium concentrate in oxygen, and reducing the sublimed oxides with hydrogen. The difficulty in the condensation of the oxide cloud was overcome by passing it through a tube fitted with electrodes on the principle of F. G. Cottrell's process for the precipitation of fumes—7. 47, 3. The reduction of perrhenates, or of the oxide with hydrogen, gives good results. The separation of the perrhenate was studied by W. Feit, I. Spitzin, J. A. M. van Liempt, O. Hönig schmid and R. Sachtleben, and F. Machatschki. The process was used by W. and I. Noddack. According to G. Heyne and K. Moers, the metal can also be preci pitated from neutral or acidic soln. of its salts electrolytically. Thus, a one per cent. soln. of potassium perrhenate acidified by sulphuric acid (1 : 5), using a current density of 0·025 amp. per sq. cm., gave in 43 hrs. 0·0232 grm. of rhenium. If a higher current density is used, some blue oxide is also deposited on the cathode The metal is precipitated from conc. soln. in a colloidal form by means of hydrazine hydrochloride—a reaction studied by W. and I. Noddack, and F. Kraus and H. Steinfeld. According to G. Heyne and K. Moers, formic acid gives a blue pre cipitate of a lower oxide. No metal is precipitated by the reducing agents, stannous chloride, sulphurous acid, hydriodic acid, or formaldehyde. W. Noddack, and K. Moers showed that by heating a tungsten filament in the vapour of a rhenium halide, rhenium is deposited on the wire. The results with nickel, platinum molybdenum, and tantalum wires were not so good. The vapour of rhenium peroxide can be used in place of rhenium chloride or bromide, but the deposits are not so good.

REFERENCES.

[1] W. Noddack, *Metallw.*, **8.** 964, 1929 ; *Metallbörse*, **20.** 621, 1930 ; W. Noddack and I. Tacke, *Naturwiss.*, **13.** 567, 1925 ; *Zeit. anorg. Chem.*, **181.** 1, 1929 ; **183.** 371, 1929 ; *Sitzber. Akad. Berlin,* 400, 1925 ; *Oesterr. Chem. Ztg.*, **28.** 127, 1925 ; J. G. F. Druce, *Chem. News*, **131.** 273, 1925 ; *Nature*, **117.** 16, 1926 ; *Chem. Weekbl.*, **23.** 318, 497, 1926 ; *Ind. Chemist*, **7.** 75, 1931 ; *Science Progress*, **20.** 690, 1926 ; V. Dolejsek and J. Heyrovsky, *Rec. Trav. Chim. Pays-Bas*, **46.** 248, 1927 ; *Chem. Listy*, **20.** 4, 1926 ; *Nature*, **116.** 782, 1925 ; N. Broch, *Zeit. phys. Chem.*, **6.** B, 22, 1929 ; E. W. von Siemens and J. G. Halske, *German Pat.*, *D.R.P.* 483495, 1925 ; *Brit. Pat. No.* 317035, 1928 ; W. Feit, *Zeit. angew. Chem.*, **43.** 459, 1930 ; F. G. Cottrell, *Brit. Pat. No.* 227022, 1924 ; F. Machatschki, *Zeit. Kryst.*, **72.** 541, 1930 ; I. Spitzin, *Zeit. anorg. Chem.*, **148.** 69, 1925 ; J. A. M. van Liempt, *ib.*, **181.** 425, 1929 ; O. Hönigschmid and R. Sachtleben, *ib.*, **191.** 309, 1930 ; F. Kraus and N. Steinfeld, *ib.*, **193.** 385, 1930 ; G. Heyne and K. Moers, *ib.*, **196.** 143, 1931 ; K. Moers, *ib.*, **196.** 147, 1931 ; C. Agte, H. Alterthum, K. Becker, G. Heyne, and K. Moers, *ib.*, **196.** 129, 1931 ; *Naturwiss.*, **19.** 18, 1931 ; W. and I. Noddack, *ib.*, **17.** 23, 93, 1929 ; **18.** 757, 1930 ; *Zeit. anorg. Chem.*, **181.** 1, 1929 ; **183.** 353, 1929 ; *Zeit. phys. Chem.*, **125.** 264, 1927.

§ 4. The Physical Properties of Masurium and Rhenium

V. M. Goldschmidt [1] found that the X-radiogram of rhenium agreed with crystals in the hexagonal system having the axial dimensions $a=2\cdot765$ A., and $c=4\cdot470$, or $a:c=1:1\cdot616$; and a sp. gr. of $20\cdot53$; C. Agte and co-workers gave $a=2\cdot765$ A., $c=4\cdot470$ A., and $a:c=1:1\cdot616$; and K. Moeller gave $a=2\cdot755$ A., $c=4\cdot450$ A., and $a:c=1:1\cdot615$. G. Hägg discussed the mol. vol. V. M. Goldschmidt, and W. Noddack gave $0\cdot68$ A. for the ionic diameter. The sp. gr. of masurium is estimated to be about $11\cdot5$, and the m.p. $2300°$ K. ; while the sp. gr. of rhenium is estimated to be about 21, and the m.p. $3300°$ K. I. Noddack obtained $10\cdot4$ for sp. gr. of the reduced powder of rhenium, and calculated 20 from the weight and diameter of small fused beads. C. Agte and co-workers gave $20\cdot5$. W. Biltz and K. Meisel gave $8\cdot82$ for the at. vol. of rhenium at the absolute zero.

C. Agte and co-workers found that sintered rhenium is ductile in the cold, and when warmed it can be forged, hammered, and rolled. A piece formed as a crust on tungsten wire had a tensile strength of $50\cdot6$ kgrms. per sq. mm., and an elongation of 24 per cent. ; K. Becker found the coeff. of thermal expansion of rhenium to be $0\cdot0_5467$ perpendicular to the c-axis, and about two and a half times as great, namely $0\cdot0_41245$ in the direction of the c-axis. C. Agte and co-workers found $3440°$ to be the m.p. of rhenium. W. Noddack and I. Tacke gave $0\cdot0346$ for the sp. ht. of rhenium.

W. F. Meggers and C. C. Kiess, and W. F. Meggers discussed the **spark spectrum** of masurium ; and W. F. Meggers, and P. Zeeman and co-workers, the **arc spectrum.** There are spectral lines of wave-length $3424\cdot6$, $3451\cdot9$, $3460\cdot5$, $3464\cdot7$, $4133\cdot4$, $4136\cdot46$, $4227\cdot4$, $4394\cdot4$, $4513\cdot3$, $4522\cdot7$, $4791\cdot4$, $4889\cdot2$, $4923\cdot92$, $5271\cdot0$, $5275\cdot6$, $5834\cdot31$, $6307\cdot7$, $6321\cdot9$, and $6350\cdot7$. G. Heyne and K. Moers found that the lines furnished by $0\cdot001$ grm. of rhenium were in the ultra-violet, 2215, $2276\cdot5$, 2880, 3000, 3400, 3425, 3452, 3462, and 3465 A., and in the visible spectrum, $4889\cdot15$ A. in the blue, and $5270\cdot98$ A. and $5275\cdot57$ A. in the green. These are recommended standards in the spectral recognition of rhenium. Observations were made by W. Meidinger ; and H. Schober, and F. H. Loring discussed the possible identification of the spectral lines of rhenium with those of the sun, and of η Carinæ. H. Schober and J. Birke studied the *raies ultimes* in the arc spectrum ; P. Zeeman and co-workers, the under-water spark spectrum, and the Zeeman effect ; and W. F. Meggers, A. S. King and R. F. Bacher, the structure of the spectral lines.

According to O. Berg and I. Tacke, the **X-ray spectrum** of masurium furnishes lines $K_{\alpha 1}=0\cdot672$ A., $K_{\alpha 2}=0\cdot675$ A., and $K_{\beta 1}=0\cdot601$ A., and rhenium, lines $L_{\beta 2}=1\cdot2048$ A., $L_{\beta 3}=1\cdot216$ A., $L_{\beta 1}=1\cdot2352$ A., $L_{\alpha 1}=1\cdot4299$ A. ; and $L_{\alpha 2}=1\cdot4407$ A. It is said that these lines agree well with the values calculated respectively for elements of at. numbers 43 and 75. V. Dolejsek and J. Heyrovsky added that for the element of at. number 75, two of the β-lines of the L-series of O. Berg and I. Tacke coincide with those of tungsten ; their observed values for $L_{\beta 2}$ and $L_{\beta 3}$

coincide with the $L_{\alpha 1}$- and $L_{\alpha 2}$-lines of thallium ; and their L_α-line is indistinguishable from the $K_{\alpha 1}$-line for zinc. V. Dolejsek and J. Heyrovsky said that taking the K_β-copper line as standard, $L_{\alpha 1}=1430$, $L_{\beta 1}=1233\cdot3$, $L_{\beta 2}=1204\cdot3$, and $L_{\gamma 1}=1059$. The $L_{\alpha 1}$-line could not be measured very exactly. A. Sandström, H. Beuthe, B. Polland, I. Wennerlöf, O. Berg and I. Tacke, and I. Noddack studied the K- and L-series of rhenium ; and E. Lindberg, and H. Beuthe the M-series. H. Alterthum compared the **electronic emission** of tungsten and rhenium filaments, and represented the results in terms of $i=aT^2e^{-b/T}$, where a and b are constants. Expressing the values of a in amp. per cm. per degree :

	Re	N	Mo	Th	Zr	Hf
a	200	100	65	70	4,000	55,000
b	59,500	53,100	51,100	39,400	52,400	59,500

C. Agte and co-workers found the sp. **electrical resistance** of rhenium, R ohms per cm. cube, is four times that of tungsten :

	Ta	Pb	Re	Sr	Hf	W	Mn	Os
$R\times 10^4$	0·146	0·207	0·211	0·2475	0·326	0·059	0·044	0·095

The temp. coeff. of the resistance of rhenium between 0° and 100° is 0·00311, when the corresponding values for tungsten and osmium were respectively 0·0046 and 0·0042. They also gave for the sp. resistance, R ohms per cm. cube, and the temp. coeff., a, at $T°$ K. :

$T°$ K.	83°	243°	273°	393°	393°	2405°	2690°	2985°
$R\times 10^4$	0·0494	0·154	0·198	0·211	0·261	1·25	1·30	1·34
$a\times 10^3$	3·65	3·35	3·11	3·11	3·11	2·23	2·14	1·98

W. Meissner and B. Voigt measured the resistance down to $-271\cdot8°$, and found for the ratio, r, of the resistance, R, at the observed temp. to the resistance, R_0, at 0° ; and for the estimated ratio of the resistances, r_{red}, for the pure metals when the value of R_0 is $18\cdot9\times10^{-6}$ ohm :

	0·16°	−184·77°	−194·71°	−252·55°	−268·78°	−271·64°
r	1	0·2849	0·2474	0·110	0·110	0·109
r_{red}	1	0·1979	0·1558	0·0017	0·0017	0·0006

Observations were also made by M. le Blanc and H. Sachse. The **electrode potential** of rhenium against a normal calomel electrode, with an electrolyte of $2N\text{-}H_2SO_4$, is 0·6 volt, so that rhenium comes between copper and thallium in the electrochemical series. This is in agreement with the behaviour of these elements towards oxidizing gases. W. H. Albrecht and E. Wedekind found the **magnetic susceptibility** of rhenium to be $0\cdot046\times10^{-6}$ mass unit, a value which does not lie between those for tungsten and osmium. L. A. Sommer and P. Karlson gave 5/2 for the nuclear moment.

REFERENCES.

[1] W. Meissner and B. Voigt, *Ann. Physik*, (5), **7**. 892, 1930 ; W. Noddack and I. Tacke, *Naturwiss.*, **13**. 567, 1925 ; *Sitzber. Akad. Berlin*, 400, 1925 ; *Oesterr. Chem. Ztg.*, **28**. 127, 1925 ; I. Noddack, *Zeit. Elektrochem.*, **34**. 629, 1928 ; W. F. Meggers, *Journ. Research Bur. Standards*, **6**. 1027, 1931 ; *Journ. Franklin Inst.*, **211**. 373, 1931 ; *Phys. Rev.*, (2), **37**. 219, 1702, 1931 ; W. F. Meggers and C. C. Kiess, *Journ. Amer. Opt. Soc.*, **12**. 417, 1926 ; W. F. Meggers, A. S. King and R. F. Bacher, *Phys. Rev.*, (2), **38**. 1258, 1931 ; V. M. Goldschmidt, *Zeit. phys. Chem.*, **2**. B, 244, 1929 ; *Naturwiss.*, **17**. 134, 1929 ; W. H. Albrecht and E. Wedekind, *ib.*, **19**. 20, 1931 ; G. Hägg, *Zeit. phys. Chem.*, **12**. B, 33, 1931 ; J. G. F. Druce, *Chem. News*, **131**. 273, 1925 ; *Nature*, **117**. 16, 1926 ; *Chem. Weekbl.*, **23**. 318, 497, 1926 ; *Science Progress*, **20**. 690, 1926 ; W. Noddack, *Zeit. Elektrochem.*, **34**. 627, 1928 ; O. Berg and I. Tacke, *Sitzber. Akad. Berlin*, 405, 1925 ; *Naturwiss.*, **13**. 571, 1925 ; K. Becker, *Zeit. anorg. Chem.*, **196**. 142, 1931 ; G. Heyne and K. Moers, *ib.*, **196**. 152, 1931 ; H. Alterthum, *ib.*, **196**. 137, 1931 ; V. Dolejsek and J. Heyrovsky, *Rec. Trav. Chim. Pays-Bas*, **46**. 248, 1927 ; *Chem. Listy*, **20**. 4, 1926 ; *Nature*, **116**. 782, 1925 ; H. Beuthe, *Zeit. Physik*, **46**. 873, 1928 ; **50**. 742, 1928 ; A. Sandström, *ib.*, **65**. 632, 1930 ; B. Polland, *Chem. News*, **133**. 409, 1925 ; *Compt. Rend.*, **183**. 737, 1926 ; I. Wennerlöf, *Arkiv Mat. Astron. Fys.*, **22**. A, 8, 1930 ; *Zeit. Physik*, **47**. 422, 1928 ; E. Lindberg, *ib.*, **50**. 82, 1928 ; **56**. 402, 1929 ; F. Machatschki, *Zeit. Kryst.*, **72**. 544, 1930 ; H. Schober, *Sitzber. Akad. Wien*, **140**.

79, 1931 ; *Naturwiss.*, **19**. 310, 1931 ; H. Schober and J. Birke, *ib.*, **19**. 211, 1931 ; C. Agte, H. Alterthum, K. Becker, G. Heyne and K. Moers, *ib.*, **19**. 18, 1931 ; *Zeit. anorg. Chem.*, **196**. 129, 1931 ; W. Biltz and K. Meisel, *ib.*, **198**. 191, 1931 ; F. H. Loring, *Chem. News*, **142**. 321, 1931 ; W. Meidinger, *Zeit. Physik*, **68**. 331, 1931 ; K. Moeller, *Naturwiss.*, **19**. 575, 1931 ; L. A. Sommer and P. Karlson, *ib.*, **19**. 1021, 1931 ; P. Zeeman, J. H. Gisolf and T. L. de Brain, *Nature*, **128**. 637, 1931 ; W. Schröter, *Das Rhenium*, Stuttgart, 1932 ; O. Collenberg, *Svenska Kem. Tids.*, **43**. 265, 1931 ; M. le Blanc and H. Sachse, *Phys. Zeit.*, **32**. 887, 1931.

§ 5. The Chemical Properties of Masurium and Rhenium

According to W. Noddack and I. Tacke,[1] rhenium oxide volatilizes before molybdenum oxide. It is predicted that the oxides of masurium will be dark coloured and of the type MaO, Ma_2O_3, and MaO_2, which will be insoluble in acids, while the oxide MaO_3 will be soluble in water, forming an acid H_2MaO_4. It will also give an oxide of the type Ma_2O_7, of m.p. 350° to 400° ; Ma_2O_7 will probably be rose or yellow. Rhenium will probably form similar oxides, and Re_2O_7 will probably melt at 400° to 500°, and be pale yellow or white in colour. Both oxides will probably form monoclinic or triclinic crystals. Analogous salts will be formed. It is probable, by analogy with chromium, that neither masurium nor rhenium will form a sulphide in dil. aq. soln. J. G. F. Druce said that the crude oxide of rhenium which he prepared is soluble in warm, dil. acids, forming colourless soln., excepting the soln. of the chloride, which is slightly yellow. Soln. of alkali hydroxide precipitate rhenium hydroxide, and the precipitate is insoluble in excess. W. and I. Noddack found that rhenium oxide was soluble in a little dil. hydrochloric acid to a colourless soln. There was no precipitate on adding the hydroxides of sodium, potassium, or ammonium. Hydrogen sulphide gave no precipitate in the cold and only a slight cloudiness on warming. Addition of ammonia and ammonium sulphide caused no change. Acidifying this gave a grey precipitate soluble in ammonium sulphide with difficulty. On heating the sulphide in a stream of hydrogen it gave a black powder, either of the metal or of a lower sulphide. This burned in oxygen on warming to an oxide which sublimed as a white powder, more volatile than MoO_3. Hydrogen sulphide converted it into a grey sulphide which reformed the oxide on heating. W. Noddack observed that ammonium phosphate gives no precipitate with nitric acid soln. of rhenium ; and potassium xanthate gives a white precipitate of sulphur ; potassium thiocyanate gives a yellowish rose-coloured salt which is soluble in ether ; potassium ferrocyanide does not change visibly a soln. of rhenium salt.

According to W. Noddack, rhenium inflames in **oxygen** at 300°, forming a white tetroxide and yellow rhenium hemiheptoxide, Re_2O_7. K. Moers found that when heated in **air** to about 1000°, a film begins to form on both rhenium and tungsten, and if the air is diluted with an equal vol. of nitrogen, oxidation begins at about 1600°. The vapour of **water** in nitrogen attacks the metal at 1900°, but if heated in moist hydrogen to about 2000° the metal becomes passive towards water vapour even at 2300°. The attack then begins at 2500°.

Rhenium furnishes sublimates of rhenium chlorides when it is heated in **chlorine**, and of bromides when heated in **bromine** vapour. K. Moers observed that the metal is very little affected by **hydrofluoric acid** or by **hydrochloric acid** ; it dissolves slowly in **sulphuric acid.** Rhenium does not react with **nitrogen** when heated in that gas, and no nitride has been prepared. W. Geilmann and F. Weibke observed that **ammonia** is oxidized by hydrogen dioxide in the presence of rhenium compounds. According to K. Moers, rhenium readily dissolves in **nitric acid.** As shown by H. Tropsch and H. Kassler, rhenium does not react with **carbon** at a high temp. to form a carbide ; nor does it react with **carbon monoxide** to form a carbonyl. Carbon monoxide is reduced to methane by the action of a rhenium-copper couple. K. Moers observed that the attack of rhenium by **carbon dioxide** begins above 1600°. R. Schenk and co-workers observed that rhenium forms a carbide when heated in **methane.** K. Moers said that **mercury** does not dissolve rhenium to form an amalgam. K. Becker and K. Moers found that the **rhenium-tungsten alloys** have a solidus curve with two eutectics—one at 2892° and 50 at. per cent. rhenium, and the other at 2822° with 67 at. per cent. rhenium. There is a maximum at 3005°, corresponding with **rhenium tritaditungstide,** W_2Re_3.

The atomic weight of rhenium.—W. Noddack and I. Tacke estimated that the at. wt. of masurium, or ekamanganese, is 98 to 99·5 ; and that of rhenium, or dwi-manganese, is 187 to 188. W. and I. Noddack obtained 188·71 for the at. wt. of rhenium from analyses of the oxide, the hexachloride, and the disulphide. O. Hönigschmid and R. Sachtleben obtained a better result from the ratio $AgReO_3 : AgBr$, namely 186·31. F. Schacherl showed that the two elements belong to the manganese family. W. H. Rothery discussed the electronic structure of masurium. F. W. Aston examined the mass spectrum of rhenium by the volatilization of its chloride. The result shows that rhenium has two isotopes of at. wt. 185 and 187, in accord with the rule that complex elements of at. wt. above 9 consist of two odd mass numbers two units apart. The ratio of the relative abundance of the heavier and the lighter isotopes is 1·62 : 1. This agrees with an at. wt. of 186·22, and this value is in accord with O. Hönigschmid and R. Sachtleben's value of 186·31, the value recommended by the International Committee on Atomic Weights for 1931. The electronic structure of rhenium corresponds with (2) in the K-shell ; (2, 2, 4) in the L-shell ; (2, 2, 4, 4, 6) in the M-shell ; (2, 2, 4, 4, 6, 6, 8) in the N-shell ; (2, 2, 4, 4, 1) in the O-shell and (2) in the P-shell, or else (2, 2, 4, 4, 2) in the O-shell and (1) in the P-shell.

Reactions of rhenium of analytical interest.—K. Moers observed that the reactions of analytical interest are the precipitation of mercury or thallium perrhenates with mercury or thallium salts ; the formation of precipitates with brucine and veratrin ; and the production of brown and green colorations by treating a sulphuric acid soln. with hydroquinone. Blue needle-like crystals are precipitated by methylene blue, and cæsium salts give characteristic crystals of cæsium perrhenate. Precipitation as ammonium perrhenate gives good quantitative results. F. Krauss and H. Steinfeld recommended the precipitation of the thallium perrhenate in acetic acid soln. W. Geilmann and co-workers obtained good precipitates with nitron—*vide infra.* The ultimate spectral lines in the spectrum of rhenium furnish a good qualitative test for the presence of rhenium.

REFERENCES.

[1] W. Noddack, *Zeit. Elektrochem.*, **34**. 627, 1928 ; W. Noddack and I. Tacke, *Naturwiss.*, **13**. 567, 1925 ; *Sitzber. Akad. Berlin*, 400, 1925 ; *Oesterr. Chem. Ztg.*, **28**. 127, 1925 ; W. H. Rothery, *Phil. Mag.*, (7), **11**. 649, 1931 ; O. Hönigschmid and R. Sachtleben, *Zeit. anorg. Chem.*, **191**. 309, 1930 ; W. Geilmann and A. Voigt, *ib.*, **193**. 311, 1930 ; W. Geilmann and F. Weibke, *ib.*, **195**. 289, 1931 ; **199**. 120, 1931 ; W. Geilmann and F. W. Wrigge, *ib.*, **199**. 65, 1931 ; F. Krauss and H. Steinfeld, *ib.*, **193**. 385, 1930 ; **197**. 52, 1931 ; N. A. Puschin and P. S. Tutundzic, *ib.*, **193**. 420, 1930 ; K. Moers, *ib.*, **196**. 150, 1931 ; C. Agte, H. Alterthum, K. Becker, G. Heyne, and K. Moers, *ib.*, **196**. 129, 1931 ; G. Heyne, *ib.*, **197**. 224, 1931 ; K. Becker and K. Moers, *Metall-wortschaft*, **9**. 1063, 1930 ; F. Schacherl, *Chem. Listy*, **23**. 632, 1930 ; H. Tropsch and R. Kassler, *Ber.*, **63**. B, 2149, 1930 ; F. W. Aston, *Nature*, **127**. 591, 1931 ; *Proc. Roy. Soc.*, **132**. A, 487, 1931 ; R. Kassler, *Ber.*, **63**. B, 2149, 1930 ; J. G. F. Druce, *Chem. News.*, **131**. 273, 1925 ; **143**. 66, 1931 ; *Nature*, **117**. 16, 1926 ; *Chem. Weekbl.*, **23**. 318, 497, 1926 ; *Science Progress*, **20**. 690, 1926 ; W. and I. Noddack, *Naturwiss.*, **17**. 23, 93, 1929 ; **18**. 757, 1930 ; *Zeit. anorg. Chem.*, **181**. 1, 1929 ; **183**. 353, 1929 ; *Zeit. phys. Chem.*, **125**. 264, 1927 ; *Continental Met. Chem. Engg.*, **1**. 109, 1926 ; *Chem. News*, **134**. 257, 1927 ; J. H. Yoe, *Journ. Amer. Chem. Soc.*, **54**. 1022, 1932 ; R. Schenk, F. Kurzen and H. Wesselkock, *Zeit. anorg. Chem.*, **203**. 159, 1931.

§ 6. The Compounds of Rhenium

W. and I. Noddack [1] observed that when powdered rhenium or a lower oxide of rhenium is heated in a current of cold oxygen, a white cloud is formed which condenses to globular granules of **rhenium tetroxide,** Re_2O_8, or ReO_4 ; but if the temp. rises above 150°, some yellow oxide, R_2O_7, is formed. The product obtained by the combustion of rhenium in oxygen is contaminated with about 10 per cent. of the yellow oxide. A crystalline structure cannot be recognized in the white globules, but they refract light strongly. The white oxide is estimated to have a sp. gr. of about 8·4. When exposed to ultra-violet light the white oxide becomes yellow, and if it be warmed, it also forms the yellow oxide. The m.p. of the white oxide is in the neighbourhood of 150°, but in the melting some yellow oxide is formed. The transformation of white to yellow oxide is very rapid in vacuo. The white oxide dissolves without decomposition in water, and it is also soluble in acids, and in potash-lye or soda-lye. It is very slightly soluble in ether. When the aq. soln. is evaporated, the yellow oxide is formed. The freshly prepared aq. soln. has an acidic reaction, and with alkali-lye it forms salts. The aq. soln. of the tetroxide has the characteristics of a soln. of a peroxide—it is easily reduced ; it colours titanium salts yellow and vanadium salts brown ; and it decolorizes permanganate owing to the reduction $Re_2O_8 \rightarrow Re_2O_7$. The constitution is probably :

$$O = \begin{matrix} O \\ \diagdown \\ \diagup \\ O \end{matrix} Re-O-O-Re \begin{matrix} O \\ \diagup \\ \diagdown \\ O \end{matrix} = O$$

The dry white oxide is fairly stable. It is coloured violet by sulphur dioxide at room temp. ; and similarly also with the soln. of the white oxide in conc. sulphuric acid, and the soln. deposits a blue precipitate on standing for some time. The violet soln. is immediately decolorized when poured into water. If the violet sulphuric acid soln. is boiled, it is decolorized, and rhenium oxide is volatilized with the vapour. Hydrogen sulphide acts slowly on the aq. soln. of the tetroxide, and some sulphur is deposited ; but if the soln. be warm, rhenium sulphide is precipitated. H. V. A. Briscoe and co-workers could not confirm the existence of the tetroxide, and added that the heptoxide is the highest oxide.

An acidified soln. of the white oxide does not react with ammonium phosphate, or potassium ferrocyanide, nor does it give a coloration with potassium xanthate, and rhenium thus differs from molybdenum. The behaviour of the soln. towards potassium thiocyanate, and the greater volatility of rhenium oxide also serve to distinguish the element from molybdenum. Rhenic oxide gives no reaction with potassium iodide, and it is thus different from osmic oxide.

The yellow oxide, **rhenium heptoxide**, or **perrhenic anhydride**, Re_2O_7, is produced when rhenium burns in oxygen, or when one of the lower oxides is heated in oxygen at a temp. exceeding 150°. O. Hönigschmid and R. Sachtleben prepared it by reducing potassium perrhenate at 400° in hydrogen ; extracting the resulting black powder with water ; drying the black residue in nitrogen ; and burning it in oxygen, when the heptoxide appears as a yellow crystalline sublimate. According to W. and I. Noddack, the pale yellow oxide has a sp. gr. of 8·2 at 20°. It begins to absorb light at about 4700 A. ; the yellow colour becomes paler when it is cooled to —80°. When heated the oxide melts at 220° to form a yellow liquid, which solidifies to a yellow crystalline mass. The oxide is very volatile. It begins to sublime at 150°, *i.e.* below its m.p., in an atm. of oxygen, nitrogen, or hydrogen, to form a sublimate consisting of six-sided plates which have a high dispersion and refractive index. Small crystals sublime so rapidly that their m.p. cannot be determined. It is also difficult to measure the b.p. owing to sublimation. In a capillary tube the meniscus vanishes at about 450°, and this b.p. is greater than that at atm. press. The vapour density is 17·32 (air unity) at 520°, and the mol. wt. is therefore 490, in agreement with the formula Re_2O_7. At 800° there is some dissociation into rhenium dioxide and oxygen. W. A. Roth and G. Becker obtained —13·20 Cals. per mol. for the heat of soln. ; and 295·5 Cals. for the heat of formation of Re_2O_7 from its elements. W. and I. Noddack observed that the heptoxide is readily soluble in water, and alcohol, and less soluble in ether. The aq. soln. has an acidic reaction, and the sp. conductivity, k, and the mol. conductivity, μ, of soln. with m mols of the oxide per litre at 22° are :

m	.	0·01890	0·00945	0·00473	0·00236	0·00118	0·00059
k	.	0·006917	0·003525	0·001793	0·000904	0·000454	0·000227
μ	.	366	373	379	383	385	385

W. Feit gave for the sp. gr. of aq. soln. containing the following percentages of perrhenic acid :

$HReO_4$ 0	2·93	10·91	20·00	31·85	40·67	50·29	61·00	65·12 per cent.
Sp. gr. 1·00	1·025	1·10	1·20	1·35	1·50	1·70	2·00	2·15

The aq. soln. may contain **perrhenic acid** : $Re_2O_7 + H_2O = 2HReO_4$, or else $Re_2O_7 + H_2O = H_2Re_2O_8$. If the formula of the acid be $HReO_4$, and $m = 0·0006$, and $\mu = 325$ at 22°, the mobility of the ReO_4'-anions is 60, in agreement with the value of 69 for MnO_4' and 65 for ClO_4'. If the formula of the acid be $H_2Re_2O_8$, the calculated values of μ will be twice those just given, and the mobility of the R_2O_8''-anions will be 120. But the soln. contains no anions with a greater mobility than that of the OH'-ions. Hence, perrhenic acid is monobasic $HReO_4$. The acidity of this acid is rather less than is the case with perchloric or permanganic acids. The composition of the salts is in agreement with this formula.

If the aq. soln. be evaporated slowly to dryness, the colour becomes yellow, and ultimately the heptoxide separates out. The m.p. of the heptoxide is depressed by water. No hydrates have yet been obtained. If the heptoxide be mixed with enough water to form $R_2O_7.H_2O$, a yellow mass is formed which melts at 150°, which can be readily undercooled, and which furnishes a yellow glass. W. Geilmann and F. Weibke noted the loss by volatilization during the evaporation of aq. soln of perrhenic acid. According to W. and I. Noddack, the heptoxide is readily oxidized to the tetroxide when it is warmed in oxygen. Reducing gases like carbon monoxide or sulphur dioxide form a lower coloured oxide, slowly in the cold, rapidly when heated. At 300° hydrogen forms a bluish-black dioxide, and at 800°, metallic rhenium. In a sealed tube the heptoxide first sublimes, and it is then reduced to form a metal mirror on the walls of the tube. When heated to 300° in vacuo the heptoxide is reduced to a blue oxide. H. Hölemann observed that metal and oxide are formed during the electrolysis of feebly acidic and neutral soln. of potassium perrhenate with platinum electrodes, and a violet soln. is formed with strongly acidic soln., and with a mercury cathode and alkaline, neutral, and feebly acidic soln., rhenium amalgam and a black oxide are formed, but with strongly acidic soln., a violet soln. is produced.

The halogens chlorine, bromine, and iodine form numerous coloured compounds, studied by E. Enk, and F. Krauss and H. Steinfeld. The aq. soln. of the heptoxide, containing the relatively conc. perrhenic acid, dissolves the hydroxides of aluminium, zinc, and iron ; and also metallic zinc and iron, with the evolution of hydrogen. The oxidizing agents hydrogen dioxide and potassium permanganate have no perceptible action on the soln. Mild reducing agents have no perceptible action ; but the stronger reducing agents—like zinc dust and sulphuric acid, or hypophosphorous acid—colour the soln. of perrhenic acid. In the absence of oxygen the yellow colour is produced slowly in the cold and rapidly when heated. The yellow colour, due to the presence of rhenium trioxide, disappears when the soln. is shaken in air. Soluble thiocyanates colour cold, dil. soln. of perrhenic acid yellow, and warm soln. yellowish-red. The colouring agent is extracted by ether to form a rose-coloured ethereal soln. The cold, conc. soln. of perrhenic acid is coloured dark red and the hot soln. black. The colouring agent is extracted by ether to form a dark red ethereal soln.

Dry rhenium heptoxide reacts slowly with dry hydrogen sulphide, and at 80° rapidly, to form a black film of sulphide which to some extent protects the interior from attack. After an hour's treatment the unchanged heptoxide can be sublimed from the sulphide. If hydrogen sulphide be passed into a dil. aq. soln. of perrhenic acid, no change is perceptible, but in a few days a deposit of sulphur is formed. If the soln. be acidified with hydrochloric or sulphuric acid and treated with hydrogen sulphide, the liquid becomes yellow and slowly deposits sulphide. The presence of oxalic, tartaric, or phosphoric acids retards the deposition of the sulphide. A cold, conc. soln. of perrhenic acid when treated with hydrogen sulphide produces first a yellow coloration, and then sulphide is precipitated; if the liquid be hot, black sulphide is precipitated. If ammonia and ammonium polysulphide be added to a dil. soln. of perrhenic acid, at first no precipitate is formed; but when the liquid is acidified with hydrochloric or sulphuric acid, the liquid is coloured deep red, then grey, and a mixture of sulphur and sulphide is precipitated. If the unacidified soln. mixed with yellow ammonium sulphide be allowed to stand for some time, it becomes darker in colour and the rhenium is slowly precipitated quantitatively as sulphide. A conc. soln. of perrhenic acid when mixed with ammonia or alkali-lye and treated with a few drops of ammonium sulphide gives an immediate precipitation of black sulphide. A dil. soln. shows few characteristic reactions. The soln. are not readily reduced, and re-oxidation of the reduced yellow soln. occurs. If the soln. be evaporated to dryness with a strong reducing agent—say, hydrazine hydrochloride—a black product is obtained, probably the dioxide. J. H. Yoe found that rhenium salts give a red soln. with ammonium aurintricarboxylate, a pale yellow one with ammonia, and an almost colourless one with ammonium carbonate.

The salts, perrhenates, in acidified soln. behave like perrhenic acid. W. Geilmann and co-workers found that feebly acidified soln. of potassium perrhenate give with nitron a precipitate of nitron perrhenate, $C_{20}H_{16}N_4ReO_4$, and that the reaction is quantitative. A dil. soln. of perrhenic acid (1 grm. per litre) and a conc. soln. (20 grms. per litre) show the following reactions. Both soln. give no precipitate with soda-lye; potash-lye gives a white precipitate, soluble in water with a conc. soln. but not so with a dil. soln.; and similarly with baryta-water. Hydrochloric, nitric, sulphuric, and acetic acids have no perceptible action on conc. or dil. soln. Similarly also with hydrogen dioxide, and potassium permanganate and sulphuric acid. Sulphurous acid, hydrazine hydrochloride, hypophosphorous acid, and gallic acid give a yellow coloration which disappears when shaken in air when added to a conc. soln. of perrhenic acid, but no change occurs with dil. soln. Potassium cyanide, ferrocyanide, and ferricyanide have no perceptible influence on conc. or dil. soln.; but a conc. soln. with potassium thiocyanate gives in the cold a yellowish-red and when heated a black coloration which forms a red soln. in ether; with a dil. soln. of perrhenic acid in the cold a yellow colour is formed, in hot soln. a yellowish-red colour; and the ethereal soln. is rose-coloured. A mixture of sodium hydrophosphate and nitric acid has no perceptible influence on conc. or dil. soln. of perrhenic acid. Sodium thiosulphate in conc. soln. gives a white deposit of sulphur which becomes grey on standing, and in dil. soln. it gives a small white deposit of sulphur; and potassium xanthogenate and hydrochloric acid give similar deposits. Sodium azide and sulphuric acid, thiourea, urethane, sulphosalicylic acid, and diphenyl-sulphourea produce no perceptible change in conc. or dil. soln. Thiosincarbazide, and thiosinamine give with conc. soln. a yellow coloration which disappears on standing; with dil. soln. no change is perceptible. Potassium iodide, and sodium nitroprusside have no perceptible effect on conc. or dil. soln. Hydrogen sulphide, as indicated above, in conc. soln. produces a yellow coloration and then a grey precipitate of sulphur and sulphide, whilst with dil. soln. the yellow coloration is slowly produced and this is followed by a slow separation of a grey precipitate. With ammonia and ammonium polysulphide and conc. soln. a dark coloration slowly forms and a black sulphide separates out; with dil. soln. the reactions are similar but slower. If after the addition of ammonia and ammonium polysulphide hydrochloric or sulphuric acid be added, a conc. or dil. soln. of perrhenic acid gives an intense rose coloration, followed by the separation of a grey precipitate of sulphur and sulphide.

The aq. soln. of rhenium heptoxide has the characteristics of an acid. It dissolves metal hydroxides, and it can be neutralized by bases with the development of heat. The evaporation of these salts furnishes **perrhenates** analogous with the permanganates. The salts with colourless bases are colourless ; and those perrhenates which have been prepared are usually soluble in water. The salts are very stable, and if the base is non-volatile they can be heated to redness in oxygen without decomposition ; whilst if heated in hydrogen they are reduced to form rhenium dioxide, etc. **Sodium perrhenate,** $NaReO_4$, is obtained by neutralizing a soln. of perrhenic acid with $0.1N$-NaOH to an aq. soln., using neutral red as an indicator. The soln. furnishes colourless, six-sided plates. The salt melts in oxygen at 300°, forming a colourless liquid which does not decompose at 600°. Water dissolves about 250 grms. per litre at 20°. H. Tollert found the solubility in 89·7 per cent. alcohol to be 22·42 grms. per litre at 19·5° ; and in 99·1 per cent. alcohol, 11·14 grms. per litre at 18°. If the soln. of perrhenic acid be similarly treated with potassium hydroxide, **potassium perrhenate,** $KReO_4$, is formed as a white powder consisting of rhomboidal crystals. F. Machatschki said that the crystals are probably tetragonal bipyramids with the axial ratio $a : c = 1 : 1.5823$. N. Broch found that the X-radiogram corresponds with a tetragonal lattice isomorphous with scheelite, containing four mols. $KReO_4$, per unit lattice, and having $a = 5.615$ A., $c = 12.50$ A., and $a : c = 1 : 2.226$. The calculated density is 4·887. W. A. Roth and G. Becker found the heat of soln. to be -13.80 Cals. per mol. ; and the heat of neutralization, 13·5 Cals. per mol. of $HReO_4$. W. and I. Noddack said that the salt has a high index of refraction—F. Machatschki gave $\epsilon = 1.673$ and $\omega = 1.643$. In an atm. of oxygen the salt melts at 350°. N. A. Puschin and P. S. Tutundzic found the sp. conductivity k, the mol. conductivity μ, the transport number l of the ReO_4'-ion, and the degree of ionization a, for soln. of C mol of the salt per litre, to be :

18°	C .	0.02	0.01	0.005	0.002	0.001	0.0005	0
	$k \times 10^6$	1923	1009	519	211	108	55	—
	μ .	96.1	100.9	103.8	105.5	108.0	110.0	111.5
	l .	36.5	40.2	42.0	42.7	44.7	46.3	46.9
	a .	0.862	0.905	0.930	0.946	0.968	0.986	—
25°	$k \times 10^6$	2248	1164	596	243	124	—	—
	μ .	112.4	116.4	119.2	121.5	124.0	125.7	—
	l .	45.5	47.6	49.0	49.8	51.5	51.3	—
	a .	0.984	0.926	0.948	0.966	0.986	—	—
30°	C .	0.04	0.02	0.01	0.005	0.002	0.001	0
	$k \times 10^6$	4866	2510	1308	670	274	140	—
	μ .	121.6	125.5	130.8	134.0	137.2	140.6	141.8
	a .	0.86	0.89	0.92	0.95	0.97	0.99	—
40°	$k \times 10^6$	5736	2976	1556	799	327	167	—
	μ .	143.4	148.8	155.6	159.8	163.6	167.1	169
	a .	0.85	0.88	0.92	0.95	0.97	0.99	—

Observations on the conductivity of soln. of perrhenic acid, and of potassium perrhenate, and of the transport numbers were also made by W. A. Roth and G. Becker. W. H. Albrecht and E. Wedekind gave -0.13×10^{-6} mass unit for the magnetic susceptibility of potassium perrhenate. W. and I. Noddack found that a litre of water dissolves 12·1 grms. or 0·0415 mol at 20°. The presence of potassium hydroxide or chloride lowers the solubility. N. A. Puschin and D. Kovach found that a rise of temp. from 0° to 100° increases the solubility from 0·35 to 9·44 per cent. H. Tollert found the solubility in 89·7 per cent. alcohol to be 0·302 grms. per litre at 18·5°. F. Krauss and H. Steinfeld found that a soln. of potassium perrhenate is not reduced by sulphurous acid, or by hydrogen whilst simultaneously exposed to rays of short wave-length. It is reduced to a mixture of metal and oxide by zinc and hydrochloric acid, by sodium amalgam, or by hydrazine hydrate. The salts **rubidium perrhenate,** $RbReO_4$, and **cæsium perrhenate,** $CsReO_4$, were similarly prepared, and they are less soluble in water than the potassium salt. Likewise also with **ammonium perrhenate,** NH_4ReO_4, which furnishes white six-sided plates.

Water dissolves about 120 grms. per litre at 20°. The salt is completely decomposed when heated in oxygen, ammonia is evolved, and rhenium heptoxide sublimed. H. V. A. Briscoe and co-workers prepared **copper perrhenate,** $Cu(ReO_4)_2.4H_2O$, from a soln. of copper carbonate in perrhenic acid. The *tetrahydrate* is formed when the salt is dried over calcium chloride ; the dehydration curve has a break at 100° corresponding with the *hemihydrate* ; the green anhydrous salt is formed at 115° to 120° ; and rehydration furnishes the *pentahydrate*. Aq. ammonia or ammonia gas forms deep blue **copper tetramminoperrhenate,** $Cu(ReO_4)_2.4NH_3$, which melts and decomposes when heated. A white precipitate of **silver perrhenate,** $AgReO_4$, is formed when a soln. of silver nitrate is added to perrhenic acid. The salt appears in small, colourless, quadratic or rhomboidal plates which darken on exposure to light. Water dissolves 0·00809 mol or 3·2 grms. per litre at 20°. O. Hönigschmid and R. Sachtleben obtained it in a similar manner. The precipitate obtained by adding silver nitrate to a soln. of potassium perrhenate is contaminated with the latter salt, because both silver and potassium perrhenates are sparingly soluble. By twice recrystallizing the impure salt from its soln. in an excess of a silver nitrate soln., silver perrhenate of a high degree of purity is obtained. Like other silver salts, when silver perrhenate is melted it suffers a slight decomposition, and some rhenium oxide sublimes. According to W. and I. Noddack, if a soln. of perrhenic acid be neutralized with $0·1N$-$Ba(OH)_2$, using neutral red as indicator, and the soln. crystallized, **barium perrhenate,** $Ba(ReO_4)_2$, is formed in colourless columns or rhomboids. H. Tollert found the solubility in 89·7 per cent. alcohol to be 2·45 grms. per litre at 18·5°. Freshly-precipitated neodymium hydroxide dissolves in perrhenic acid, forming a soln. which when evaporated to dryness gives very soluble, rose-coloured **neodymium perrhenate,** $Nd(ReO_4)_3$. The corresponding **mercuric perrhenate,** $Hg(ReO_4)_2$, and **thallous perrhenate,** $TlReO_4$, have been prepared. Dark pink **cobalt perrhenate,** $Co(ReO_4)_2.5H_2O$, is formed like the copper salt. The pentahydrate yields the *trihydrate* over calcium chloride ; and further dehydration yields purple-blue anhydrous salt. It furnishes **cobalt tetramminoperrhenate,** $Co(ReO_4)_2.4NH_3$, which decomposes when heated. Pale green **nickel perrhenate,** $Ni(ReO_4)_2.5H_2O$, is similarly formed. The *pentahydrate* yields the *tetrahydrate* over calcium chloride, or at 100°, and the cream-coloured anhydrous salt is formed at 170°. The lilac **nickel hexamminoperrhenate,** $Ni(ReO_4)_2.6NH_3$, is produced by the action of ammonia, and this compound at 100° forms **nickel tetramminoperrhenate,** $Ni(ReO_4)_2.4NH_3$, which decomposes at a higher temp.

H. V. A. Briscoe and co-workers prepared rhenium dioxide ; and by reducing rhenium heptoxide with rhenium they prepared **rhenium pentoxide,** Re_2O_5. The purple-red oxide is stable in air ; it can be heated to about 300° in oxygen or in sulphur without change ; it sublimes in vacuo above 300° ; chloride gives a greenish-yellow vapour and brown solid ; dry hydrogen chloride has no action ; it is insoluble in water, and in dil. or conc. hydrochloric or sulphuric acid and in potash-lye ; it dissolves in warm dil. nitric acid, and in fused potassium hydroxide ; and it is reduced by sulphur or carbon about 300°. W. A. Roth and G. Becker gave 169 Cals. for the heat of formation of Re_2O_5 from its elements.

According to W. and I. Noddack, the characteristic compounds of rhenium just indicated contain septivalent rhenium, but in **rhenium trioxide,** ReO_3, the element is sexivalent. An aq. soln. is obtained by dissolving rhenium, rhenium sulphide, or a lower rhenium oxide in nitric acid. The yellowish-red soln. becomes pale yellow and stable when treated with alkali-lye, and it gives a precipitate with silver or barium salt. A similar soln. is produced by the action of strong reducing agents on a soln. of perrhenic acid. If rhenium powder be added to a molten alkali, a yellow mass is obtained resembling a yellow chromate. No change is perceptible when a conc. soln. of sodium rhenate is treated with soda-lye, but if the soln. be evaporated to dryness and the product be fused, a pale yellow mass is obtained. If this product be dissolved in cold water, it is decolorized, and the colourless soln.

contains sodium perrhenate. The yellow product in all these cases is either an acidic soln. of **rhenic acid,** H_2ReO_4, or a salt of that acid, namely, the **rhenates,** R'_2ReO_4. These substances are analogous with manganic acid and the manganates. The yellow soln. of rhenic acid and of its salts are very unstable ; they are immediately decolorized when warmed, and slowly when allowed to stand in the cold. The soln. of the alkali rhenates are more stable, but they too decompose slowly in the cold. The colour of the dil. acidic soln. is pale yellow, and the colour becomes more and more reddish-yellow as its concentration increases, and it is therefore assumed that **rhenic anhydride,** ReO_3, is red, even though it has not yet been isolated. The yellow soln. of the alkali salts becomes browner on standing in air, probably owing to the formation of a brown colloidal rhenium dioxide. The decolorization of the soln. in air is complete in a few hours. If the yellow alkaline soln. is dried over phosphoric oxide in vacuo, a yellow crystalline substance, probably **potassium rhenate,** K_2ReO_4, or **sodium rhenate,** Na_2ReO_4, separates out. If hydrogen sulphide be passed into the acidic or alkaline soln., a black precipitate of rhenium sulphide is formed.

If an aq. soln. of perrhenic acid be neutralized with baryta-water, using neutral red as indicator, and an equal proportion of baryta-water be added, and the soln. evaporated in vacuo over calcium chloride, and heated to 300° in a current of nitrogen, black rhenium dioxide is formed. This product is then dissolved in 5 per cent. nitric acid. The soln. is treated with soda-lye until it has an alkaline reaction, and small four-sided plates separate out. The supernatant liquor remains yellow, showing that barium rhenate is very sparingly soluble in water. The precipitated salt is **barium rhenate,** $BaReO_4$. The same salt is formed when an alkaline rhenate soln. is treated with a barium salt. Barium rhenate soon becomes dark brown on exposure to air, and finally black. The extraction of the dark brown mass with water furnishes a soln. of barium perrhenate and residual rhenium dioxide. The decomposition of the rhenate into perrhenate and rhenium dioxide : $3K_2ReO_4+2H_2O=4KOH+ReO_2+2KReO_4$, resembles the decomposition of a manganate into permanganate and manganese dioxide. The soln. of an alkali rhenate with silver nitrate gives a white precipitate of **silver rhenate,** Ag_2ReO_4. Both barium and silver rhenates are soluble in nitric acid.

When the tetroxide is reduced, the colour changes to violet, blue, and finally black, and with the heptoxide the colour becomes first blue and then black. Similarly also with soln. of these two oxides in conc. sulphuric acid. The violet oxide is produced by passing sulphur dioxide over white rhenium tetroxide ; the colour changes slowly in the cold, and rapidly at 40°. Analyses show that the violet product has a composition near Re : O=1 : 0·235, between those of ReO_3 and ReO_2 (1 : 0·1696). The violet oxide is not easily reduced by hydrogen ; no perceptible action occurs in the cold, and with careful heating the blue oxide is formed, which becomes darker and darker as the temp. of the reaction is raised. As just indicated, the black dioxide is formed at 300°, and similarly when ammonium or sodium perrhenate is treated with hydrogen. In acidic soln. all reducing agents convert the perrhenates into sexivalent salts which are yellowish-red. The dark blue oxide is produced by the action of sulphur dioxide on rhenium heptoxide, and analyses show that the composition is near Re : O=1 : 0·194, which is between that of ReO_3 and ReO_2. If either the violet or the blue oxide be heated to 300° in hydrogen, a black oxide is formed, and analyses correspond with **rhenium dioxide,** ReO_2. It is supposed that in the violet and blue oxides the quadrivalent rhenium is present as violet *rhenium perrhenate,* $Re(ReO_4)_4$, and as blue *rhenium rhenate,* $Re(ReO_4)_2$. H. V. A. Briscoe and co-workers reduced soln. of potassium perrhenate with zinc, magnesium, calcium, and Devarda's alloy in acidic soln. ; hydrazine hydrate ; and stannous chloride, and observed that the first stage of the reduction is a yellow colloidal soln.—probably the hydrated dioxide—and the final product is the *dihydrate,* $ReO_2.2H_2O$. No rhenate was detected in the products of the reduction. N. A. Puschin studied the thermal decomposition of this oxide.

The lower oxides of rhenium have a great tendency to oxidize to the yellow heptoxide, and the oxidation occurs when the dry oxides are heated in oxygen or exposed in a moist state to oxidizing agents, or even to atm. oxygen. The violet oxide is slowly oxidized and decolorized in oxygen in the cold, and rapidly when heated. If a mixture of sulphur dioxide and oxygen be passed over the white octoxide, the colour slowly becomes violet at 0°, and the speed of the reduction increases as the temp. rises to 40°, and over 50°, say at 80°, the violet coloration does not appear. Water immediately decolorizes the violet oxide. The soln. in conc. sulphuric acid is stable if air be excluded, but it is immediately decolorized if the soln. be poured into water or dil. alkali-lye, and the heptoxide can be detected in the product. The deep violet soln. in sulphuric acid is a true soln., for it retains its colour when filtered through earthenware or membrane filters. Hence it is supposed that either a rhenium perrhenate or a **rhenium sulphate**, $Re(SO_4)_2$, is formed. When the dry violet oxide is heated in hydrogen, it is easily reduced, and, at the same time, tetroxide is volatilized. The latter, collecting on the hot walls of the containing vessel, may be reduced to form a rhenium mirror.

The blue oxide is rather more stable than the violet oxide towards oxygen, and at 100° it is oxidized by oxygen. A mixture of equal parts of sulphur dioxide and oxygen rapidly colours the warm yellow heptoxide blue. At temp. exceeding 250° a residue of the heptoxide is formed. The blue soln. of the blue oxide in conc. sulphuric acid is not at once decolorized when slowly poured into water or dil. alkali-lye, but the change occurs if the soln. be allowed to stand in air for some time or if it be warmed. The addition of nitric acid decolorizes it immediately. The blue soln. in sulphuric acid contains colloidal oxide which does not pass through an earthenware or membrane filter. Hydrogen readily reduces the blue oxide to black dioxide, and finally to rhenium.

The black oxide is readily oxidized when it is warmed in oxygen. The oxidation proceeds vigorously and with the development of a pale green flame. Water, and sulphuric acid do not act on the black oxide ; hydrochloric acid acts slowly ; nitric acid immediately oxidizes it to rhenic acid ; and hydrogen at 800° reduces it to rhenium metal.

When rhenium is heated in chlorine, it forms two volatile chlorides, namely, **rhenium hexachloride,** $ReCl_6$, in brown needles, which sublime at 150° and are hydrolyzed by water, and also what is thought to be **rhenium heptachloride,** $ReCl_7$, which is green and more volatile than the hexachloride ; with bromine vapour dark-coloured, volatile **rhenium bromide,** and with iodine vapour dark, volatile **rhenium iodide** are formed. The properties of rhenium are thus intermediate between those of tungsten and osmium.

H. V. A. Briscoe and co-workers observed that **rhenium tetrachloride,** $ReCl_4$, is the primary product of heating rhenium in chlorine ; and they observed no evidence of the existence of the hexachloride and heptachloride. They prepared **potassium chlororhenate,** K_2ReCl_6, and found that it gives precipitates with silver, mercurous, and thallous salt soln., but not with soln. of lithium, barium, magnesium, zinc, manganese, cobalt, nickel, ferrous, or ferric salts. E. Enke observed that the sp. gr. is 3·34 at 15° ; that it is stable towards potassium permanganate in acidic soln. ; it is oxidized by hydrogen dioxide in alkaline soln. ; it is not affected by sulphurous or hypophosphorous acids ; and it is decolorized by zinc in acidic soln. The corresponding **cæsium chlororhenate,** Cs_2ReCl_6, and **silver chlororhenate,** Ag_2ReCl_6, are unstable. W. Manchot and co-workers said that the reduction of the chlororhenate by zinc and acid, or in sulphuric acid at a mercury cathode, furnishes evidence of the existence of tervalent rhenium ; and when oxidized by air or oxygen, quinquevalent rhenium is probably present. Acidic soln. of the chlororhenate do not bleach indigo-blue, or reduce potassium permanganate soln., but autoxidation occurs in alkaline soln.

According to F. Krauss and H. Steinfeld, when a mixture of potassium perrhenate and iodide is treated with hydrochloric acid of sp. gr. 1·18, and the mixture boiled until the evolution of iodine has ceased, the **potassium rhenium chloride,** $K_3[ReCl_6]$, is formed, and it is decomposed by a large excess of water at room temp. Similarly with **thallous rhenium chloride,** $Tl_3[ReCl_6]$, which is unstable. The salt $K_4Re_2Cl_{11}$ is also formed under similar circumstances, and it may be a mixture of K_2ReCl_5 and K_2ReCl_6. Likewise also with $Tl_4Re_2Cl_{11}$. If potassium rhenate and bromide, and hydrobromic acid are employed, **potassium rhenium bromide,** K_2ReBr_6, is formed, whilst **thallous rhenium bromide,** Tl_2ReBr_6, is obtained from a mixture of thallous rhenate and hydrobromic acid of sp. gr. 1·75. H. V. A. Briscoe and co-workers prepared **potassium rhenium iodide,** K_2ReI_6, by heating potassium perrhenate with excess of potassium iodide and aq. hydrogen iodide at the b.p. of the latter, and can be separated from the dark-coloured soln. as crystals, shining black by reflected and dark chocolate-brown by transmitted light. It can be heated to 200° without decomposition. At about 210° there is slight decrepitation, but marked liberation of iodine is not evident below about 300°. At about 300° the reaction is symbolized : $K_2ReI_6 \rightarrow 2KI + Re + 2I_2$. With a limited quantity of water, a dark violet-black soln. results, which, on dilution, changes to dark brown or black and is evidently colloidal in character. Boiling this liquid leads to flocculation and the separation of a black precipitate, which, as was anticipated, proved to be hydrated rhenium dioxide. In alcohol, or ether, either hot or cold, the crystals are only slightly soluble, but they readily dissolve in acetone, from which potassium rheni-iodide may be recrystallized with acetone of crystallization. On heating in oxygen, iodide is evolved and a black residue is left, whilst in nitrogen the decomposition takes place quantitatively to potassium iodide, metallic rhenium, and iodine.

According to W. Noddack, when rhenium oxides are reduced by carbon monoxide or sulphur dioxide, green, blue, and violet oxides are produced, which on a prolonged heating form the white and yellow oxides. The soln. of the white oxide oxidizes hydrogen sulphide to sulphur, and in the presence of acids furnishes a grey precipitate of sulphur mixed with sulphide. The precipitation is not hindered by oxalic, tartaric, or phosphoric acid, and rhenium is thus unlike tungsten. If the grey sulphide be heated in carbon dioxide at 400° to 600°, unstable black **rhenium heptasulphide,** Re_2S_7, and **rhenium trisulphide,** ReS_3, are formed ; above 600° stable black **rhenium disulphide,** ReS_2, is produced. H. V. A. Briscoe obtained the disulphide by heating rhenium to redness in an excess of sulphur in a current of hydrogen sulphide ; and by heating the heptaselenide in vacuo at a red-heat the corresponding **rhenium diselenide,** $ReSe_2$, was prepared. W. Feit observed that when hydrogen sulphide is passed into a sat. soln. of potassium perrhenate, the soln. becomes yellow, but after the gas has been passing for a day the liquid becomes brown and almost opaque. When no further change occurs, and the liquid is boiled to remove hydrogen sulphide, and then concentrated by evaporation to about one fifth its vol. at 35°, when it deposits small brown crystals ; they are a mixture of potassium perrhenate and a sulpho-salt ; with a further concentration of the soln. the crystals appear darker, and they are mixed with a dark brown precipitate of what is probably rhenium sulphide. The soln. is finally dried without a further deposit of crystals ; and the resulting dark brown mass is easily soluble in water and it behaves like a mixture of **potassium sulphoperrhenate, and oxysulpho perrhenates,** $KReO_3S$, $KReS_4$, and $KReOS_3$. When the aq. soln. of this residue is treated with $0·05N\text{-}Tl_2SO_4$, a dark brown precipitate of **thallous sulphoperrhenate** $TlReS_4$, is formed ; and when the filtrate is treated with more of the thallous sulphate soln., **thallous trioxysulphoperrhenate,** $TlReO_3S$, is formed H. V. A. Briscoe and co-workers regard Feit's thallous sulphoperrhenate, $TlReS_4$, as a mixture of rhenium sulphide and thallous perrhenate. I. R. Juza and W. Biltz gave 70·5 Cals. for the heat of formation of the disulphide between 1100° and 1200° W. Biltz and O. F. Weibke found that the precipitate obtained by the action of hydrogen sulphide on a soln. of potassium perrhenate is rhenium heptasulphide

Re_2S_7. The sample dried for 60 hrs. at 160° to 170° was a black powder which oxidized easily in air. Its X-radiogram was too feeble to distinguish from that of rhenium disulphide. Its sp. gr. was 4·866 at 25·4°, and its mol. vol. 122. H. V. A. Briscoe and co-workers add that the black powder dissociates below its m.p. It adsorbs reversibly toluene and other organic solvents, but the adsorbtivity becomes less and less as the process of adsorption and desorption is repeated. The dried heptasulphide can be spontaneously reduced in hydrogen. The red soln. obtained by the action of hydrogen sulphide on soln. of alkali perrhenate probably contain alkali sulphoperrhenate, e.g. $KReS_4$. No sulphide between ReS_2 and Re_2S_7 was observed. When a soln. of this salt is treated with hydrochloric acid, the fugitive red coloration and the separation of sulphur which occurs, show that free **trioxysulphoperrhenic acid**, $HReO_3S$, is unstable. A corresponding **rhenium heptaselenide**, Re_2Se_7, was also prepared.

REFERENCES.

[1] W. H. Albrecht and E. Wedekind, *Naturwiss.*, **19**. 20, 1931 ; W. and I. Noddack, *ib.*, **17.** 23, 93, 1929 ; **18.** 757, 1930 ; *Zeit. anorg. Chem.*, **181.** 1, 1929 ; **183.** 353, 1929 ; *Zeit. phys. Chem.*, **125.** 264, 1927 ; *Continental Met. Chem. Engg.*, **1.** 109, 1926 ; *Chem. News*, **134.** 257, 1927 ; W. Noddack, *Zeit. Elektrochem.*, **34.** 627, 1928 ; O. Hönigschmid and R. Sachtleben, *Zeit. anorg. Chem.*, **191.** 309, 1930 ; W. Geilmann and F. Weibke, *ib.*, **195.** 289, 1931 ; W. Geilmann and A. Voigt, *ib.*, **193.** 311, 1930 ; F. Machatschki, *Zeit. Kryst.*, **72.** 544, 1930 ; N. A. Puschin and P. S. Tutundzic, *Zeit. anorg. Chem.*, **193.** 420, 1930 ; F. Krauss and H. Steinfeld, *ib.*, **193.** 385, 1930 ; *Ber.*, **64.** 2552, 1931 ; N. Broch, *Zeit. phys. Chem.*, **6.** B, 22, 1929 ; H. V. A. Briscoe, P. L. Robinson and E. M. Stoddart, *Journ. Chem. Soc.*, 666, 1439, 2263, 2976, 1931 ; H. V. A. Briscoe, P. L. Robinson and A. J. Rudge, *ib.*, 2211, 3087, 3218, 1931 ; 1104, 1932 ; *Nature*, **129.** 618, 1932; N. A. Puschin and D. Kovach, *Zeit. anorg. Chem.*, **199.** 369, 1931; *Bull. Soc. Chim. Yougoslav.*, **2.** 1, 1931 ; I. R. Juza and W. Biltz, *Zeit. Elektrochem.*, **37.** 498, 1931 ; W. Biltz and F. Weibke, *Zeit. anorg. Chem.*, **202.** 3, 1931 ; E. Enke, *Ber.*, **64.** B, 791, 1931 ; W. Manchot, H. Schmid and J. Düsing, *Ber.*, **64.** B, 2905, 1931 ; W. A. Roth and G. Becker, *Zeit. phys. Chem.*, **159.** 27, 1932 ; N. A. Puschin, *Bull. Soc. Chim. Yougoslav.*, **2.** 111, 1931 ; W. Feit, *Zeit. angew. Chem.*, **44.** 65, 1931 ; *Zeit. anorg. Chem.*, **199.** 262, 271, 1931 ; H. Hölemann, *ib.*, **202.** 277, 1931 ; H. Tollert, *ib.*, **204.** 140, 1932.

CHAPTER LXVI

IRON

§ 1. The History of Iron

IRON has been known from prehistoric times. Mouldering records, decaying monuments, fabulous legends, and sibylline traditions have been examined, but no one has found out how man discovered the utility of iron, or how man first learned the art of extracting the metal from its ores. Consequently, on passing backwards into the obscure regions of antiquity, the historian reaches an epoch where truth and fable are inseparably blended, and where more or less plausible guesses take the place of positive knowledge. Max Müller,[1] E. O. von Lippmann, J. Pokorny, O. Johannsen, L. Beck, L. Wilser, O. Schrader, H. Blümner, H. Haedicke, and F. H. A. von Humboldt inferred that copper was known to the Aryan nations before their separation, because the Sanscrit term *ayas* can be traced among the different peoples—**3.** 21, 1—whereas no term for iron was employed before that separation. The names for iron are different in every one of these languages. Max Müller said :

The Sanskrit term *ayas* for copper is shared in common by the Latin and Teutonic languages—Latin, *æs*; Gothic, *aiz*; Old High-German, *êr*; Modern German, *er-z*; Anglo-Saxon, *âr*; and English, *ore*. Like the Greek χαλκός, *chalkós*, which originally meant copper, but came to mean metal in general, bronze or brass, the Latin *æs*, too, changed from the former to the latter meaning ; and we can watch the same transition in the corresponding words of the Teutonic languages. *Æs*, in fact, like Gothic, *aiz*, meant the one metal which, with the exception of gold and silver, was largely used of old for practical purposes. It meant copper whether in its pure state or alloyed, as in later times, with *tin* (bronze) and *zinc* (brass). But neither *æs* in Latin nor *aiz* in Gothic ever came to mean gold, silver, or iron. It is all the more curious, therefore, that the Sanskrit *ayas*, which is the same word as *æs* and *aiz*, should in Sanskrit have assumed the almost exclusive meaning of iron. I suspect, however, that in Sanskrit, too, *ayas* meant originally the metal, *i.e.* copper, and that as iron took the place of copper, the meaning of *ayas* was changed and specified. In passages of the *Atharva Veda* (**11.** 3) and the *Vâgasaneyisanhitâ* (**18.** 13) a distinction is made between *syâmam ayas*, dark-brown metal, and *loham* or *lohitam ayas*, bright metal, the former meaning copper, the latter iron. The flesh of an animal is likened to copper, its blood to iron. This shows that the exclusive meaning of *ayas* as iron was of later growth, and renders it more than probable that the Hindus, like the Romans and Germans, attached originally to *ayas* (*æs* and *aiz*) the meaning of the metal *par excellence*, *i.e.* copper. In Greek, *ayas* would have dwindled to *es*, and was replaced by *chalkós* ; while to distinguish the new from the old metals, iron was called Homer *sidēros*. In Latin different kinds of *æs* were distinguished by adjectives, the best known being the *æs Cyprium*, brought from *Cyprus*. Cyprus was taken possession of by the Romans in 57 B.C. *Herod* was entrusted by Augustus with the direction of the Cypriani copper-mines, and received one-half of the profits. Pliny used *æs Cyprium* and *Cyprium* by itself for copper. The popular form, *cuprum*, copper, was first used by Spartianus in the third century, and became more frequent in the fourth. Iron in Latin received the name of *ferrum*. In Gothic *aiz* stands for Greek *chalkós*, but in Old High-German *chuphar* appears as a more special name, and *êr* assumes the meaning of bronze. This *êr* is lost in Modern German, except in the adjective *ehern*, and a new word has been formed for metal in general, the Old High-German *ar-uzi*, the Modern German *erz*. As *ayas* in Sanskrit assumed the special meaning of iron, we find that in German, too, the name for iron was derived from the older name of copper. The Gothic *eisarn*, iron, is considered by J. and W. Grimm as a derivative form of *aiz*, and the same scholars conclude from this that " in Germany bronze must have been in use before iron." *Eisarn* is changed in Old High-

German to *isarn*, later to *isan*, the Modern German *eisen* ; while the Anglo-Saxon *isern* leads to *iren* and iron.

It may safely be concluded, I believe, that before the Aryan separation, gold, silver, and a third metal, *i.e.* copper, in more or less pure state, were known. Sanskrit, Greek, the Teutonic and Slavonic languages agree in their names for gold ; Sanskrit, Greek, and Latin in their names for silver ; Sanskrit, Latin, and German in their names for the third metal. The names for iron, on the contrary, are different in each of the principal branches of the Aryan family, the coincidences between the Celtic and Teutonic names being of a doubtful character. If, then, we consider that the Sanskrit *ayas*, which meant, originally, the same as Latin *œs* and Gothic *aiz*, came to mean iron ; that the German word for iron is derived from Gothic *aiz* ; and that Greek *chalkós*, after meaning copper, was used as a general name for metal, and conveyed occasionally the meaning of iron, we may conclude, I believe, that Sanskrit, Greek, Latin, and German were spoken before the discovery of iron, that each nation became acquainted with that most useful of all metals after the Aryan family was broken up, and that each of the Aryan languages coined its name for iron from its own resources, and marked it by its own national stamp, while it brought the names for gold, silver, and copper from the common treasury of their ancestral home.

In agreement with this, O. Schrader could find no primeval term for iron in Indo-German antiquity ; he thinks that iron was not known until after copper (bronze), and that the Greeks became acquainted with iron in Asia Minor and the Pontine countries in the post-Mycenic and pre-Homer times. L. Beck has suggested that *ayas* may have been a general term for metals, and then came to be applied specifically to iron, just as the Grecian χαλκός, copper, came to be employed for iron— Homer's *Odyssey* (**9.** 391) ; and, according to E. B. Tylor, in Mexico the term *tepuztli* for copper came to be applied to iron—*vide infra*. According to J. Beckmann, the Greeks, at the time of Homer, applied to steel many different names. For instance, the term ζομωμα was applied to the steeled part of an instrument ; the name χάλυψ was given to steel—from Chalybes, a people on the southern shore of the Pontus Euxinus, between Colchis and Paphlagonia ; and the term ἀδάμας was applied to articles made of steel or iron—*e.g.* the helmet of Hercules mentioned by Hesiod, in his *Theogony*, and the adamantine chains, gates, and bars mentioned by later Greek poets. It was only at a still later period that the term ἀδάμας (*adamas*) was applied to precious stones. The Romans borrowed the term *chalybs* from the Greek χάλυψ, and in consequence of the use of the term *acies* (edge) in Pliny's *Historia naturalis* (**34.** 41) H. Stephanus, J. Beckmann, and C. Salmasius suggested that the Italians adopted the term *acciajo*, the Spanish *acero*, and the French *acier* for steel. O. Johannsen, indeed, said that the term for iron in all the Indo-Germanic languages comes from the Sanscrit *ayas*. According to E. O. von Lippmann, the origin of the Latin word *ferrum* for iron is not known with certainty. The origin of the term *steel* is discussed later on.

A. H. Sayce pointed out that a Hittite text of the fourteenth century B.C. speaks of " black iron of heaven from the sky." G. F. Zimmer said that nearly all the more cultured ancient people applied to iron a term which meant a " metal or something hard from heaven." Thus, the Egyptians used *ba-en-pet*, variously written :

In the cuneiform language of Assyria and Babylonia we are told that *an-bar* or *parzillu*, meaning " the metal of heaven," was written ►⊢+ +⊢. Similarly, in the language of Sumeria and Chaldea, *barsa*, originally *barsal* or *barzel* respectively, and the Hebrew *barzel*, בַּרְזֶל, all have the same meaning. This, said G. F. Zimmer, indicates that " the metal of heaven " probably meant meteoric iron. G. Möller, and L. Beck have similar views about the early iron of Egypt and Assyria. J. Dümichen found *bia-n-ta*—metal of earth—in a late inscription at Denderah.

The term contrasted with *bia-n-pet* seems intended to distinguish terrestrial from celestial or meteoric iron. The name of the sixth or seventh Pharaoh of the first dynasty was Mibampes, and a component part of the name was *penipe*. Since the letters *b* and *p* are sometimes transposed, it is believed that *penipe* is equivalent to *benipe*, meaning the *Iron Pharaoh*, or " lover of iron," that is, a mighty patron of the industry, or a mighty warrior or swordsman. Such a name would not have been employed had iron not been known to the ancient Egyptians of the first dynasty. A later reading for this same Pharaoh is *Mer-ba-pen*, or " lover of this iron " :

G. F. Zimmer also argued with some probability that man first obtained iron from meteorites in several localities. He said :

It is easy to imagine that when a man of the Neolithic Age, searching for suitably shaped stones from which to form his weapons or tools, picked up an iron meteorite its abnormal weight attracted his keen interest. To him it was a stone which did not require chipping, but which could be altered in shape by hammering, and if the man or his associates had previous experience with copper, his fundamental metallurgical knowledge would be of distinct advantage to him. If he could work copper he might have known the use of fire, and if not, the mere rough shaping and then polishing the meteoric iron (which has a fine silver-like surface which does not easily rust) must have been a great success and the envy of his fellow-beings. The find and subsequent production from it, however crude it may have been, was such an advance upon his stone implements that his tribesmen all went to " search diligently for other things," and as meteorites, particularly the smaller ones, rarely fall alone, it was more than likely that others were found in the same locality.

A. F. Pott, and F. Lenormant said that the Greek term for iron, σίδηρος, or *sideros*, is related with *sidus*, a star, and this points to the meteoric origin of iron. The subject was discussed by O. Schrader, E. O. von Lippmann, etc. G. F. Zimmer said that the earliest hieroglyphic Egyptian term for iron was *min*,

and that at this time meteoric iron was found and used without the users knowing its origin. As soon as the users discovered whence it came, the name was altered to *ba-en-pet*, and judging from the time iron was in use, it must have taken over 2000 years to find this out This is not considered to be extraordinary when it is remembered that out of 300 iron meteorites known to-day, only ten have been seen to fall. It is also said that the inscription on the Unas showed that iron existed in Egypt before the fourth millennium B.C., and G. F. Zimmer considered that the first iron employed by the Egyptians was undoubtedly meteoric, because of its name. " In the most ancient religious texts, the Egyptians said that the firmament of Heaven was of iron, and this idea probably arose from its blue colour and from the fact that meteoric iron occasionally fell from the sky."

W. Gowland, St. J. V. Day, L. Beck, and B. H. Brough consider that the assumption that telluric and meteoric iron must have been the earliest source of the metal is unnecessary, because iron ores can be so readily reduced to metallic iron in an ordinary wood or charcoal fire. J. Percy under-estimated the difficulties which would attend the manufacture of iron by primitive workers in iron, for M. Berthelot said that the delay in the use of iron is not surprising, because however numerous the deposits of ore, the extraction of the metal by smelting is a difficult operation and one not to be performed by a people lacking some degree of trained intelligence This subject was discussed by F. M. Feldhaus, O. Schrader, M. Hoernes, I. Lippert G. Zippelius, S. Seligmann, E. Meyer, C. Brockelmann, F. Lenormant, H. Blümner F. Freise, O. Stoll, M. Gsell, and C. Faulmann.

C. H. Desch said that the history of folklore and religions favours the comparatively late origin of an Iron Age culture. The superstitions attached to the use of iron, some of which persist at the present day, and the taboos possibly imposed on it by religions, all point to the fact that iron was a newcomer and an importation into an older civilization. The common statement—by W. M. F. Petrie, T. E. Thorpe, etc.—that meteoric iron could not have been used, because it is not malleable, was shown by G. F. Zimmer to be erroneous. O. Vogel showed that in some cases natural nickeliferous iron is workable and in some cases not so. Samples of malleable meteoric iron were reported by H. A. Ward, C. U. Shepard, L. Fletcher, W. G. Owens, I. Domeyko, J. Sowerby, L. Beck, J. Johnston, A. Daubrée, J. L. Smith, W. E. Hidden, E. Cox, O. W. Huntingdon, E. H. S. Bailey, J. W. Mallet, E. Howard, H. L. Preston, G. H. Saxton, M. Donkelmann, G. Troost, O. C. Farrington, A. Goebel, E. A. de Schweinitz, O. Root, etc. The use of meteoric iron by the Esquimaux was described by J. Ross, F. Lenormant, S. Hearne, E. Sabine, C. U. Shephard, and G. F. Zimmer. G. F. Zimmer estimated that of the known samples about 99·44 per cent. are malleable and 0·56 per cent. are non-malleable. The relative weight of the evidence in favour of either hypothesis is obviously a question of temperament.

G. F. Zimmer said the idea that a bronze age followed the stone age is based on the discovery of copper and bronze utensils and weapons in ancient graves where no iron ones occur. Iron is more readily corroded than copper, and in some cases, if iron objects had decayed, the deposit of residual rust must have been obliterated by plundering. Again, iron was somewhat rare when bronze first appeared, and iron was used only in cases where bronze was not so good—say, in the cutting of harder stones. Although iron is not so suited as gold, copper, and silver for ornaments yet, according to H. Rawlinson, it was used by the ancient Chaldeans for rings and bangles, and, according to G. A. Wainwright, by the ancient Egyptians for beads, and this not necessarily because of the beauty of the metal, but rather because of its rarity—like platinum at the present day. The use of iron for rings, anklets, and other ornaments in ancient times was discussed by Pliny, in his *Historia naturalis* (**33.** 6) ; and more recently by P. S. P. Handcock, R. A. S. Macalister, G. Schweinfurth, D. Livingstone, H. Rawlinson, W. Jones, etc.

St. J. V. Day said that the term $\chi\alpha\lambda\kappa\acute{o}s$, which has been translated brass, corresponds with the Latin *æs*, and was used to signify any of the crude base metals, and the exact base metal was indicated by an adjective—*e.g.* red, black, grey, bright, etc.—to denote some peculiar or inherent quality by which the metal was known. Copper is mentioned only once in the Bible, namely, in *Ezra* (**8.** 27), but even then it does not mean pure copper, since the word *brass* is used by the translators for copper and bronze, and, indeed, all the alloys of copper. Zinc was unknown in biblical times, so that where brass occurs its really applies to copper or bronze. Pliny also confused copper and bronze. Hence, when a bronze age is spoken of, it would have been more correct to call it a copper age. St. J. V. Day continued, " the hypothesis that an Iron Age was not until long after copper and its alloys is founded on the most fragmentary and one-sided data." H. Schliemann also believed that the assumption of the sequence : stone, bronze, and iron, was not borne out by his observations in Mycenæ. According to J. G. Wilkinson, and G. Perrot and C. Chipiez, the mode of preparing bronze from tin and copper was discovered during the 5th or at the latest the 6th dynasty ; while W. M. F. Petrie found a bronze rod with 9 per cent. of tin which dated from the 4th dynasty.

Prehistoric iron was discussed by F. A. Anger, R. Behla, W. Belck, H. Bell, A. Bertholet, H. Blümner, J. G. L. Blumhof, J. Bohm, H. Braun, R. Bucholz, E. Cartailhac, K. Cermak, S. Clessin, St. J. V. Day, J. Déchelette, W. Deecke, W. Dönitz, A. Favre, F. M. Feldhaus, M. Feyerabend, E. Friedel, J. A. N. Friend and co-workers, A. Glitsch, A. Goetze, V. Gross, P. Hahnel, F. S. Hartmann, M. Hartwich, A. Hennig, M. Heydeck, H. Hilderbrand, M. Hoernes, N. O. Holst, C. Hostmann, H. Jentsch, C. Jirecek, O. Johannsen, M. Knauthe, J. H. Krause, A. Krebs, R. Krieg, S. Krzyzankiewicz, M. Kuchenbuch, P. L. B. Kupka, E. F. Lange, A. Ledebur, F. Liger, F. Lenormant, I. Lippert, G. C. F. Lisch, A. L. Lorange, J. Lubbock, L. Martinet, C. Mehlis, H. Möntefindt and co-workers, O. Montelius, M. Much, G. Müller, J. Myers,

A. Nagel, A. Norden, O. Olshausen, M. Plath, P. Putjatin, A. Quiquerez, F. Rathge
P. Reinecke, W. Ridgeway, H. Rupe, H. Rupe and F. Müller, O. Rygh, E. von Sack
A. Schlez, H. Schmidt, W. Schwartz, F. Seehars, R. A. Smith, E. Soldi, A. Stru
A. Teplouchoff, T. Turner, I. Undset, M. Viedenz, R. Virchow, M. Voss, M. Wahlbe
H. Wankel, H. Hess von Wichdorff, K. Wiegand, W. M. Williams, G. Wurmbrar
G. F. Zimmer, F. X. M. Zippe, and G. Zippelius. Analyses, etc., of ancient iron or st
were made by R. A. Hadfield, H. Garland, H. Bell, H. Hanemann, H. C. H. Carpenter a
J. M. Robertson, J. Myers, B. Neumann, J. A. N. Friend and co-workers, etc.

The use of iron in Egypt can be traced back to the pre-dynastic times. T
graves in the cemetery of El Gerzeh examined by G. A. Wainwright, a
W. M. F. Pétrie-contained some iron beads which were turned completely into ru
The graves were estimated to date from about 4000 B.C. The dates for the differe
dynasties given by W. M. F. Petrie, E. A. W. Budge, H. Brugsch, H. R. Hall, a
E. Meyer differ in some cases by as much as three centuries. Accurate dati
is said to begin about 700 B.C. An analysis of the remains of the iron beads l
C. H. Desch showed 10·9 per cent. of nickel, and this is taken to prove the meteo
origin of this iron, since, according to O. C. Farrington, meteoric iron contains 5
26 per cent. of nickel—average 7·5—whilst terrestrial iron contains only traces
nickel. A. Lucas said that the original beads may have been cut or fashioned fro
a natural sulphide, and the mineral was then slowly oxidized. According
E. B. Tylor, iron may have been made by chance in sundry places—a camp fire,
forest·fire, or even by a stroke of lightning—and thus stray pieces of metal ma
have come into use before the beginning of the iron age. Herodotus alluded to
tradition that the Dactyli discovered the art of smelting iron from the accident
burning of woods on Mount Ida in Crete ; and a similar tradition ascribed the di
covery of iron in Scythia to the reduction of the ore by forest fires. J. Déchelet
suggested that here and there, particularly in Egypt, aboriginal smelting operatio
yielded little lumps of iron, which were manufactured into small object
T. A. Rickard, however, doubted if the Egyptians had discovered how to make
pound of iron out of ore ; if they had they would have made more of it, becau
large deposits of iron were available in Egypt ; and it is not likely that a discóve
of such importance could have been kept a secret for 2500 years.

The comparative rarity of iron in the early Egyptian tombs is not likely to ha
been due to a taboo on the metal, because iron objects occur in the tomb of Tu
ankh-amen, and, according to J. H. Breasted, in a sacred inscription at Abu Sim
the god Ptah is made to say that he fashioned Rameses II (1194 B.C.) with liml
of electrum, with bones of bronze, and arms of ba-n-pet—i.e. iron. W. M. F. Petr
inferred that the beds of carboniferous strata on the ironstone in Sinai have bee
heated by eruptions of basalt and thus produced iron by the natural reduction
the ore. It is thought that the Egyptians may occasionally have found pockets c
native iron in this locality.

This evidence for the use of iron in Egypt 4000 to 3500 years before the Christia
era does not necessarily mean that the Egyptians then knew how to smelt iro
from its ores, because the iron of that early period is more likely to have fallen fro
the heavens as meteorites, and not to have been deliberately manufactured. Th
oldest known piece of iron—not steel—of any size was found in the Great Pyrami
at Gizeh in 1837 by H. Vyse ; the specimen dates from the 4th dynasty—abou
3000 B.C. It was blasted out of the solid masonry near the top of the pyramid, an
was afterwards deposited in the British Museum. T. A. Rickard believed that th
sample of iron from Gizeh is of meteoric origin, although W. Flight, and W. Gowlan
believed with H. Vyse that it is of terrestrial origin. The ancient histoŕia
Herodotus, circa 450 B.C., stated that the granite blocks employed in constructin
the Great Pyramid were shaped with iron tools, although hard rocks can b
shaped with bronze, assisted, maybe, by powdered silica—a subject discussed b
W. M. F. Petrie, and J. B. Beckmann. S. R. K. Glanville's estimate that iro
was used for industrial purposes before 3000 B.C. is considered to be ill-founded
N. T. Belaiew favours the view of C. L. Woolley that iron was smelted from its ore

by the Sumerians during the 3rd dynasty of Ur—that is, before 2200 B.C. C. L. Woolley reported finding a small furnace made with deeply fluted firebricks in the long enclosure to the courtyard close by the great Ziggurat. The furnace contained metal slag, and by it were found fragments of specular ore and some account tablets of the time of Ibi-Sin, 2208 to 2183 B.C.

J. M. Heath—*vide infra*—and R. A. Hadfield suggested that the masonry of the Egyptian pyramids was fashioned by means of iron and steel tools. H. Garland's idea is that iron tools must have been employed for the finished carvings of the Egyptian dynasty, but T. A. Rickard has pointed out that the megalithic architecture and the intricate sculpturing of the prehistoric Americans—Mitha, Mexico ; Uxmal, Yucatan ; Copan, Honduras ; and Tihuanaco, Peru—indicate that carvings of this kind can be done without the aid of iron tools. T. A. Joyce, O. H. Howard, and W. H. Holmes said that the shaping of the stones in these regions was done by means of flint, stone, or obsidian tools.

According to W. M. F. Petrie, iron did not come into general use in Egypt until about 1200 B.C. ; or, according to H. R. Hall, about 1300 B.C. ; whilst O. Montelius considered that iron made by man was rare as late as the 18th dynasty, *i.e.* 1580 to 1350 B.C. The period prior to this is called by W. M. F. Petrie the *Sporadic Iron Age*, and it includes the finds at El Gerzeh and Gizeh. There are fragments of iron picks from the Black Pyramid at Abusir, dating from the 5th dynasty, about 3000 B.C. ; a mass of iron rust from Abydos, dating from the 6th dynasty, about 2800 B.C. ; an iron spear-head, dating from the 12th dynasty, about 2200 B.C. ; an iron finger-ring and an iron sickle, found below the sphinx of Horemheb near Karnak, and dating from the 18th dynasty, about 1350 B.C. ; and an iron halbert, probably of the time of Rameses III, three knives of Ramesside, and a needle from Nubia, all about the 20th dynasty, about 1200 B.C. W. M. F. Petrie discovered a wedge of iron between two copper adzes in the temple of Abydos dating about 2800 B.C.

Iron is not mentioned in the lists of tribute collected in the 18th dynasty— 1580 to 1350 B.C.—but in the 19th dynasty iron is mentioned in the Abu Simel inscription, indicated above, as well as on a clay tablet letter from Hattushil, king of the Hittites, to Rameses II (1292 to 1225 B.C.), in which it is said : " Concerning the iron about which I sent word, there is no good quality iron in the city of Kizzu-wadni, in the house of my seal." The storing of iron under the king's seal suggests that the metal was scarce. There is a reference to scarce and costly iron in Mesopotamia in a contract made at the time of Hanimurabi—2067 to 2024 B.C. ; and in the second millennium B.C., iron in Babylonia appears to have been 15 to 20 times as valuable as copper. In the available records of the Assyrian colony at Cappadocia, 2300 B.C., there is no mention of iron, but, according to H. Winckler, the people of Kisvadra (or. Kizzuwadni) furnished Rameses II with iron. The Assyrians acquired command of the region now known as Mesopotamia about 1300 B.C. An inscription in the temple of Ammon about this time states that Menptah captured implements of iron from the Libyans ; and an inscription concerning the Pharaoh Thothmes III says that he captured iron helmets and iron spears from Waharain (Mesopotamia). A doubtful translation of some ideographic writing, 1125 to 1100 B.C., at the time of Tiglath Pileser I, an early Assyrian king contemporaneous with Nebuchadnezzar, King of Babylon, may, according to W. Ridgeway, and D. D. Luckenbill, refer to spears tipped with iron, but it may refer to something else. According to W. Ridgeway, an inscription of Ashur-nasir-pal, 885 to 860 B.C., refers to hatchets of iron (*parzillu*) and of bronze (*eru*), used for clearing a way through forests for his chariots. In this period, therefore, bronze or copper was being displaced by iron. W. Ridgeway regarded this as the earliest date of the use of iron by the Assyrians. According to W. M. F. Petrie, the iron of this period came as tribute to Assyria from Chalybes, south-east of the Black Sea. Thus, Shalmaneser II, 859–825 B.C., took iron, etc., as tribute from Chattin ; and Rimman-Nirari III, 811 to 783 B.C., took iron, etc., as tribute from Chattin,

Acharru, Tyrus, Sidon, Chumri, and Palastu.   A. Hertz said that iron was costly in the time of Tukulti Minurta I, 980 to 884 B.C. ; and an inscription of this period makes the first mention of iron tools.   Two centuries later iron had come into industrial use, as exemplified by the find, described by L. Beck, A. H. Layard, and J. Bonomi, of an accumulation of iron bars, approximating 176 tons, in a store-room among the ruins of the palace of Sargon II, 722 to 705 B.C., at Khorsabad. W. M. F. Petrie added that iron does not frequently appear in Egypt until the 22nd and 25th dynasties—*i.e.* between 945 and 718 B.C.   The heaps of iron-slag at Meroe and elsewhere in Ethiopia belong to the period succeeding 700 B.C.   The

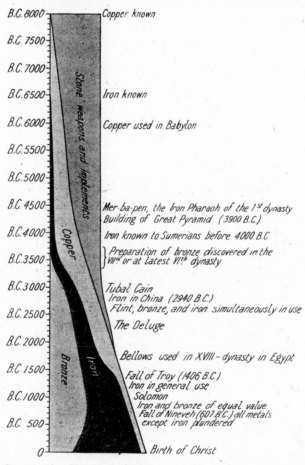

B.C.8000 — Copper known

B.C.7500 —

B.C.7000 —

B.C.6500 — Iron known

B.C.6000 — Copper used in Babylon

B.C.5500 —

B.C.5000 —

B.C.4500 — Mer-ba-pen, the Iron Pharaoh of the 1st dynasty
Building of Great Pyramid (3900 B.C.)

B.C.4000 — Iron known to Sumerians before 4000 B.C

B.C.3500 — } Preparation of bronze discovered in the VIIth. or at latest VIth dynasty

B.C.3000 — Tubal Cain
Iron in China (2940 B.C.)

B.C.2500 — Flint, bronze, and iron simultaneously in use
The Deluge

B.C.2000 —

B.C.1500 — Bellows used in XVIII - dynasty in Egypt
Fall of Troy (1406 B.C.)
Iron in general use

B.C.1000 — Solomon
Iron and bronze of equal value
Fall of Nineveh (607 B.C.) all metals

B.C. 500 — except iron plundered

0 — Birth of Christ

Stone weapons and implements   Copper   Bronze   Iron

FIG. 1.—Comparative Use of Copper, Iron, and Bronze by the Ancient World.

iron tools unearthed at Thebes belong to the time of the Assyrian invasion by Ashur-bani-pal, in 666 B.C.   Even in Neo-Babylonian days, 625 to 550 B.C., we are told that the use of copper for cart-wheel tyres shows that iron must have been scarce or else difficult to fabricate.   Many other iron objects were likewise found in the ruins of Nineveh and Babylon.   Nebuchadnezzar, 605 B.C. to 561 B.C., used iron clamps for the stone blocks employed in building a bridge over the Euphrates. Herodotus mentioned the use of iron by the Persians, and Assyrians, and also in the equipment of the army of Xerxes, who was King of Babylon from 485 to 455 B.C. Xenophon, in his *Anabasis* (5. 5), written about 400 B.C., mentioned the iron mines of the Chalybeans.   The use and manufacture of iron in Western Asia was also discussed by Marco Polo, L. W. King and H. R. Hall, A. H. Layard, J. Russegger, F. von Schwarz, and C. F. Volney ; and the use and manufacture of iron in Palestine, by L. Beck, St. J. V. Day, H. Guthe, J. Hastings, A. C. Key, R. A. S. Macalister, F. C. Movers, J. Orr, E. C. A. Riehm, D. Schenkel, G. B. Winer, and G. Zippelius.

G. F. Zimmer added that at one time iron was so rare that different nations of antiquity referred to it by talents, the same as with other precious metals. If iron had been then economically produced from its ore, it would not have been so rare ; and once the process of manufacture was discovered, the production of iron must have steadily increased, and been continuous, not sporadic, as would be the case if iron were found accidentally. W. M. F. Petrie, and others, obtained evidence that iron was freely employed for agricultural work in Egypt and Assyria about 800 B.C., and at the time of Moses iron was produced from the ore, so that the iron used in building the Great Pyramid was either telluric or meteoric, or else it was produced from the ore. The output, said G. F. Zimmer, did not at first keep pace with the demand, and the value of iron was only gradually lessened. About 607 B.C. iron had become so plentiful that in plundering the valuables at the last fall of Nineveh the iron alone was left behind. Fig. 1 represents G. F. Zimmer's idea of the comparative use of copper, iron, and bronze by the people of the ancient world, and the gradual displacement of stone by metals.

According to C. R. Conder, one of the Tel-el-Amarna tablets sent from a Hittite king to Amenshotep III—1411 to 1375 B.C.—promises iron as an extremely valuable gift. There are also an iron dagger-blade, part of an iron amuletic bracelet, and a miniature iron head-rest found in the innermost sarcophagus of Tut-ankh-amen in 1925, and described by A. Lucas, H. R. Hall, and H. Carter. These are taken to show that iron was scarce in Egypt even under the foreign domination that followed the reign of Tut-ankh-amen. These specimens of iron were considered by T. A. Rickard to be of meteoric origin, because their having resisted corrosion for so long a period is a characteristic of nickeliferous or meteoric iron. The use and manufacture of iron in Egypt were discussed by G. Belzoni, H. Blümner, St. J. V. Day, F. Delitzsch, A. Ditte, G. Ebers, A. Erman, C. Faulmann, R. Forrer, J. A. N. Friend, H. Garland, R. D. Georgi, M. Gsell, M. Hajnal, W. Heyd, M. Hoernes, F. Hommel, A. Jeremias, A. C. Key, C. B. Klunzinger, J. Lanth, O. von Lemm, R. Lepsius, H. H. Manchester, O. Olshausen, W. M. F. Petrie, R. T. Rolfe, O. Schrader, G. Schweinfurth, W. Schwenzner, E. Soldi, W. Spiegelberg, O. Stoll, A. Wiedemann, and S. Zaborowsky.

The articles on the Canaanites, chariots, iron, etc., in the *Encyclopædia Biblica* (London, 1901) have many references to the use of iron in Palestine. The old legend, referred to in *Genesis* (**4.** 22), describes how Tubal Cain was an instructor of every artificer in brass and iron, and the date approximates 3000 B.C., but since the writer of this, the earliest portion of Genesis, probably wrote about 950 B.C., he described his idea of things in the language of his own day, not long after the use of iron had been discovered. According to J. Hastings, the Hebrew text is correct ; it gives *tūbhal qayin*, but originally *tūbhal* stood alone ; *qayin* was a marginal explanation signifying artificer or smith. The affix *Cain* does not appear in the Greek version, and it is thought to have been added to *Tubal* to explain why the hero was regarded as the instructor of metal-workers. The name *Tubal* is supposed to refer to the Tibareni, mentioned by Herodotus as a people of Scythian stock dwelling in the mountains south-east of the Black Sea. Tubal appears to have been the eponymous hero or ancestor of the Tibarenian metal-workers. In the Bible—*Ezekiel* (**27.** 13)—Tubal is sometimes coupled with Meshech, who traded in " slaves and brass." Herodotus also associated the Tibareni with the Moschi (Meshki, a people of Caucasus, north of Kars). T. A. Rickard added that among their neighbours in the foothills of the Caucasus were the Chalybes, from whom the Greeks first heard of iron, which they named *Khalups*, a word, according to W. M. F. Pétrie, related to the Arabian *halaby*—tinker. Strabo refers to two tribes of Chalybes—one, living in the north-west of Armenia, was a warlike people ; and the other, living across the mountains, was a peaceful people whose principal occupation was the manufacture of iron. Even to-day it is said that in the streets of Erzeram, in the region of the source of the Euphrates, iron is worked in the old primitive way. Tubal is identified with the Assyrian Tobal, a people of Cappadocia, living in the Caucasus region, and from whom the Assyrians obtained the iron with which they went forth to conquest. In the Hebrew text of the passage in *Genesis* (4. 22) the two metals are named *bharzel* and *nehōsheth*, and these terms were translated in the Greek Septuagint as *sideros* and *chalkos* respectively. The former term refers to iron, and the latter stood for both copper and bronze. The zinc-copper alloy *brass* was unknown to the ancients of Palestine or of Greece but we are told that in Old English prior to the eighteenth century *brass* stood for any impure copper. Hence, the scholars tell us that the rendering of the passage in *Genesis* (4. 22) in modern English is " Tubal, the father of all such as forge copper and iron." *Enoch* (8. 1) also mentioned the general tradition that the first metal worker was a god, and that the fallen angel Azazel was a teacher of the art.

The Philistines entered Palestine before the Israelites, and there were numerous petty skirmishes between the two tribes. The references in *I Samuel* (13. 19–22) indicate that the Philistines were acquainted with iron, and that they kept the Israelites in ignorance of the method of working the metal. As R. A. S. Macalister pointed out, when the Philistine dominion was broken up, and David was on the throne, the use of iron became general. This is shown by the references in *I Samuel* (17. 7), *II Samuel* (12. 31), *I Chronicles* (22. 3 ; 29. 7), *II Chronicles* (2. 7), and *I Kings* (6. 7) to the armour of Goliath in his fight with David, to the building of Solomon's temple, and to the torture of the people of Rabbah. W. Ridgeway does not consider that the reference to the iron bedstead or sarcophagus of Amorite Og King of Bashan (*Deuteronomy*, 3. 11), proves that the people of Canaan were working iron when the Israelites came out of Egypt. According to J. H. Gladstone and F. J. Bliss, the excavations at Lachish, a city of the Amorites, show that iron does not appear in the remains earlier than 1250 B.C.—nearer 1000 B.C., in fact. The references in *Judges* (1. 19 ; 4. 3), *Joshua* (17. 16), and *Nahum* (2. 4), show that the Canaanites had a military advantage over the Israelites in possessing chariots of iron ; and from *Deuteronomy* (8. 9) it would appear that the Canaanites obtained their iron from the mountains of Lebanon, where smelting was conducted from early times. *Jeremiah* (15. 12) also speaks of " iron coming from the north," and J. Beckmann considers that this means " steel from the Chalybes."

The use and manufacture of iron in Western Asia were discussed by M. Firdusis, F. Freise P. Deussen, O. Schrader, E. O. von Lippmann, G. Zippelius, R. Forrer, M. Hoernes J. Hoops, H. Hanemann, E. Meyer, W. Ruge, M. I. Rostovtzeff, A. Jeremias, R. Lepsius F. Cumont, and C. Thulin.

There are many other Biblical references to iron—*e.g. Job* (19. 24 ; 20. 24 ; 41. 7), *Proverbs* (27. 17), *Jeremiah* (1. 18 ; 15. 12), *Isaiah* (60. 17), *Psalms* (18. 34, 35) and *II Samuel* (22. 35). The references in *Amos* (1. 3), *Jeremiah* (17. 1), *Isaiah* (45. 2), *Ezekiel* (4. 3), and *Micah* (4. 13) show that iron may have been known to the Hebrews and Syrians. The references in *Deuteronomy* (4. 20), *I Kings* (8. 51) and *Jeremiah* (11. 4) show that smelting furnaces were known to the later Hebrew writers. It is probable that the Israelite slaves of Egypt laboured at the iron furnaces, and the iron furnace is used as an allegorical figure expressing intense suffering. Indeed, Diodorus, in his *Bibliotheca historia* (30 B.C.), represents the labour of the slaves at the iron furnaces of Greece as the most intolerable of all tyrannies.

The archæologists have discussed whether the iron in ancient Egypt was introduced from one of the neighbouring countries of the Middle East, India, or even China, or whether the Egyptians themselves discovered the modes of extracting and treating the metal. T. A. Rickard thus summarized the available information concerning the early manufacture of iron from terrestrial ore : the art did not originate in the valley of the Nile, nor in the valley of the Euphrates, for neither was a mining region. In agreement with the myths narrated by the Greek historians, and Hebrew traditions as exemplified by the tale of Tubal, the smith, the original home of metallurgy in the ancient world was the mountainous country between the Caspian and the Black Seas. The Amorites and the Hittites, the Dactyli—mentioned by Strabo and Diodorus—the Chalybes—mentioned by Æschylus—and the Phrygians—mentioned by Herodotus—are links in the story of prehistoric metal culture. Although the first production of iron is associated with the Anatolian area, the use of the metal is connected with the extension of the Hittite power into the Syrian lowlands after 1400 B.C., and the widening use of iron was probably associated with the disintegration of the Hittite empire. According to H. Obermaier, the Assyrians obtained their metal from the Caucasus, and the Hittites brought iron into Syria. According to J. de Morgan, the tribes bordering on Armenia and Cappadocia, in the foothills of the Caucasus, discovered the art of smelting iron, where it is possible that the chance admixture of manganese may have yielded a metal of marked excellence. W. Ridgeway said that the Philistines brought iron from these countries into Palestine, and it was there that W. M. F. Petrie, in 1927, discovered the oldest specimens of undoubtedly man-made iron, for in a mound at Gerar, nine miles from Gaza, he found iron-smelting furnaces and agricultural implements, all of which had been made on the spot. These discoveries were dated by means of contemporaneous scarabs and amulets of Egyptian origin ; some iron knives are believed to go back to 1350 B.C., and the remains of the furnaces to 1194 B.C.

According to J. G. Wilkinson, the frescoes in the Egyptian tombs of Beni-Hassan (Fig. 2) show that prior to the 18th dynasty the draught in the Egyptian

FIG. 2.—Mouth Blowpipe depicted on Egyptian Tombs.

FIG. 3.—Bellows depicted on Egyptian Tombs.

metal furnaces was produced by blowpipes, and four to six men were required for the smelting operations. The mouth blowpipes were made of reeds tipped with clay, and only small pieces of metal could thus be melted. Bellows were probably introduced about the 18th dynasty. Fig. 3 is from a tomb of the period of Thothmes III, about 1500 B.C. These primitive bellows consisted of a flat pot covered with, presumably, goatskin ; there was a hole in the middle of the skin which could be closed by the heel of the operator so as to form a kind of valve ; when the valve was released by the heel, the skin was pulled up by a cord in the worker's hand. Similar bellows are used to-day by some remote tribes in India for the manufacture of iron. The primitive furnaces, or air bloomeries, were erected on high grounds in order that the wind might assist combustion. F. D. Hartland examined the remains of an ancient iron-works at Sarabit-el-Khadem, near Ayun Musa, by the Red Sea. The furnaces are thought to have been on the Catalan system, but the ore was imperfectly worked, since 53 per cent. of iron occurs in the slag-heaps. This makes it appear as if no complete smelting was employed, but only a process of fusion.

The general results show that iron was comparatively rare in Egypt until about

1300 B.C., and that before this iron was used sporadically ; only about half a dozen specimens remain to us—described by J. A. N. Friend, and H. Garland—which can be definitely shown to belong to the period prior to 1300 B.C. Although during this period the Egyptians knew how to extract iron by smelting, it was not until about 1200 B.C. and onwards that the Egyptians realized the plentiful distribution of the ore, the ease with which the metal could be extracted, and the uses to which that metal could be applied in their daily work. H. C. H. Carpenter and J. M. Robertson examined metallographically many specimens of ancient Egyptian implements, and as a result concluded that carburizing, quenching, and heat treatment generally were practised by the Egyptians many centuries before the Christian era. N. T. Belaiew pointed out that a great change in the treatment of metals in Egypt occurred in the 18th and 19th dynasties ; and that in the 19th dynasty the Egyptians were brought into contact with the Hittites and other peoples of Asia. Hence, although the Egyptians were acquainted with iron imported from Asia, they were not so well acquainted with the heat-treatment of iron. This they learned from the Hittites after the battle of Kadesh. The smelting of iron was probably begun about 1400 B.C. in the Hittite uplands between the Taurus and the Caucasus. Because of the proportion of contained nickel, it is inferred that all iron of earlier date is of meteoric origin.

According to C. Davenport, and W. Jones, legend has it that the nails used in the crucifixion of Christ were of iron, and the iron band in the Corona Ferrea, or Crown of Lombardy, was made from these very nails. There are several references to iron in the *Koran*, written in the early part of the seventh century—*e.g.* in the *Suras* (**17.** 53 ; **18.** 95 ; **22.** 21 ; **34.** 10 ; and **57.** 25). Mahomet said : " Dire evil resideth in iron as well as advantage to mankind." Herodotus made a similar statement. E. Wiedemann gave an account of the contributions of the Arabian writer Al Dimaschqui, about 1320, to the history of iron in Arabia—a subject discussed by A. von Kremer, F. Wüstenfeld, E. Meyer, W. von Gravenberch, A. Ilg, W. Heyd, and O. Stoll.

According to P. Neogi, certain passages in the *Yajuveda* indicate that iron was worked in India about 2000 B.C. Later, between 500 and 200 B.C., iron appears to have been largely used in India, more especially for warlike weapons. Probably, however, the most remarkable instance of its employment appears in a medical work describing nearly one hundred surgical instruments used for most delicate operations, which seems to show that the manufacture of steel must have been well understood. Iron swords and daggers have been unearthed from certain burial sites in Tinnevelly ; but though their exact age cannot be fixed, they are believed to have come down from prehistoric times, and specimens of third-century iron have been recovered from Buddha Gaya. According to C. von Schwarz, the manufacture of cast steel can be traced in India back to about 600 B.C., because fragments of weapons made of cast steel have been found in the Tombs of Wurri-Goan, Central India (about 500 B.C.). The metal was smelted in crucibles, and the hardened steel, called *kurs*, was transported to Damascus as raw material for the manufacture of the Damascus blades of the Middle Ages. A. K. Coomaraswamy also stated that the great antiquity of iron in India in the Vedic period is illustrated by constant references to iron in the Vedic literature, and in the latest of the four Vedas, the Atharvaveda, 1200 to 1000 B.C., iron is mentioned several times. I. E. Lester said that the use of iron between 1400 B.C. and 1000 B.C. was noted by R. C. Dutt. The old historian Herodotus stated that the Indian army of Xerxes carried arrows tipped with iron, so that iron was used for military purposes 500 B.C. The word *ondanique* which occurs in Marco Polo's travels originally referred to Indian steel, and the word is said to be a corruption of the Persian *hundwaniy.*

The Indian native processes for iron and steel were described by F. Buchanan, B. Heyne, etc.—*vide infra*, the history of the blast furnace. For a discussion on Wootz steel and Damascus steel, *vide infra.* J. M. Heath referred to the great antiquity of the iron and steel industry in India in these words :

The antiquity of the Indian process is no less astonishing than its ingenuity. We can hardly doubt that the tools with which the Egyptians covered their obelisks and temples of porphyry and syenite with hieroglyphics were made of Indian steel. There is no evidence to show that any of the nations of antiquity besides the Hindoos were acquainted with the art of making steel. The references which occur in the Greek and Latin writers on this subject served only to better their ignorance of it ; they were acquainted with the qualities and familiar with the use of steel, but they appear to have been altogether ignorant of the mode in which it was prepared from iron. The edges of cutting instruments of the ancients were all formed of alloys of copper and tin, and we are certain that tools of such an alloy could not have been employed in sculpturing porphyry and syenite. Quintus Curtius mentioned that a present of steel was made to Alexander of Macedon by Porus, an Indian chief whose country he had invaded. We can hardly believe that a matter of about 30 lbs. weight of steel would have been considered a present worthy of acceptance of the conqueror of the world had the manufacture of that substance been practised by any of the nations of the West in the days of Alexander. In view of the maritime intercourse between Egypt and the East, it appears reasonable to conclude that the steel of the South of India found its way by these routes from the country of Porus to the nations of Europe and Egypt. Consequently, the claims of India to a discovery which had exercised more influence upon the arts conducive to civilization and the manufacturing industry than any other within the whole range of human invention is altogether unquestioned.

There are numerous reports—A. Cunningham, St. J. V. Day, V. A. Smith, G. Cumming, etc.—on the famous iron pillar at Delhi, India—the *Delhi pillar*. It is 23 ft. 8 in. long, and 22 ft. is vertically above the ground ; its upper diameter is $12\frac{1}{2}$ in., and its lower diameter is $16\frac{1}{2}$ in., while its total weight is estimated to be about 6 tons. It has been stated that it dates back to 912 B.C., but later estimates give A.D. 300 as being nearer the mark. The pillar is usually said to show no symptom of rust. It bears an inscription in Sanscrit : " The triumphal pillar of Rajah Dhava, A.D. 310, who wrote his immortal fame with his sword." Numerous legends have grown about the pillar. The pillar is not now on its original site, but was moved to its present position about A.D. 1052 so as to form an adjunct to a group of temples. According to R. A. Hadfield, the analysis of the metal is : 0·080, C ; 0·046, Si ; 0·006, S ; 0·114, P ; 0·000, Mn ; 0·032, N ; and Fe, 99·720 ; the sp. gr. is 7·81 ; and Brinell's hardness, 188. The microscope reveals the presence of large grains of ferrite, with very small portions of cementite sometimes located in the ground mass and sometimes in the grain junctions.

Another iron pillar, the *Dhar pillar*, was erected at Mandu, about 22 miles from Dhar or Dhara, the ancient capital of Malava. It was probably entire in A.D. 1304, but was thrown down and broken in two by the Mohammedans ; about A.D. 1405 the larger piece was erected at Dhar. This was knocked down about 1531 and broken into two pieces. There are thus three portions scattered in the town. The total length of the whole piece must have been at least 43 ft. 4 in. The average section is $10\frac{1}{4}$ to $10\frac{1}{2}$ in., but the base is slightly bulbous and is 11 to $11\frac{1}{4}$ in. wide, 2 ft. from the end. The octagonal section is very irregular in form. The pillar has been described by V. A. Smith, H. G. Graves, R. A. Hadfield, H. Cousens, etc. R. A. Hadfield described another iron column known as *Khan Baba*, in Besh, in the Bhilsa District, Gevalior State, India ; it bears the inscription : " This Pillar was erected by a Greek called Heliodorus, son of Dion, who was an ambassador despatched by the Greek king Antialkidas to the court of an Indian Prince named Bhagabhadra, who ruled over Central India." It is believed to have been fixed about 125 B.C. There are a number of iron beams—*the Konarak beams*—from the Black Pagoda, at Konarak, in the Madras Presidency. They have been described by V. A. Smith, J. Ferguson, H. G. Graves, J. A. N. Friend and W. E. Thorneycroft, etc. The temple probably dates back to the thirteenth century, and the beams were used as supports for the lintels of the doorway, etc. The temple is in ruins, and the beams scattered about have been broken by the fall. The beams were made by welding up small blooms about 3 to 4 lbs. in weight. There are numerous slag inclusions in the metal. J. A. N. Friend and W. E. Thorneycroft gave for the analysis : 0·110, C ; 0·100, Si ; 0·024, S ; 0·015, P ; and Mn, a trace.   The Brinell's hardness is near 72.   The metal is rather more resistant to corrosion than is the case with ordinary mild steel.

The use and manufacture of iron in India were discussed by Ismail Ibn'Ati Abulfeda, R. Andrée, J. Babington, Ibn Batuta, N. T. Belaiew, I. Benzinger, S. U. Syed Ali Bilgrami, G. C. M. Birdwood, A. Bose, B. H. Brough, W. Cracroft, J. Danvers, W. Denison, F. M. Feldhaus, L. Frazer, F. Freise, J. A. N. Friend, H. G. Graves, M. Gsell, A. de Gubernatis, W. Guertler, J. M. Heath, M. Hoernes, C. Hostmann, L. Jacob, A. von Kremer, I. E. Lester, F. von Luschan, J. V. McCartney, A. McWilliam, W. Maylor, H. B. Medlicott and W. T. Blanford, O. Montelius, D. Mushet, P. Neogi, H. Oldenburg, G. G. Pearse, G. Pearson, J. Percy, B. H. B. Powell, P. W. Powlett, P. C. Ray, L. Rousselet, A. Sahlin, O. Schrader, E. Schultze, C. von Schwarz, W. V. Scudamore, P. Sonnerat, W. Sowerby, M. Taylor, T. Turner, O. Vogel, J. Wallace, H. Wilkinson, K. Woermann, B. Yaneske, and F. X. M. Zippe —*vide infra*, the history of the blast furnace.

A knowledge of Indian steel must have filtered through from India to Ceylon ; and S. M. Burrows said that Wijiya was a petty prince in the valley of the Ganges, and that he, with his followers, landed in Ceylon in 543 B.C.   The excavation of the buried cities of Ceylon, dating back to the fifth century B.C., has furnished a number of samples of iron, and A. K. Coomaraswamy, and H. Parker have described ancient processes of manufacturing iron, as well as various specimens of ancient iron and steel.   H. le ·Chatelier raised the question whether the troostite found by R. A. Hadfield in an ancient chisel represented martensite which had been transformed by spontaneous annealing during the 1500 years the specimen had been in existence.   R. A. Hadfield gave the following analyses of specimens of Sigiriya iron and steel of the fifth century :

	C	Si	S	P	Cu	Mn	Sp. gr.
Chisel . .	trace	0·12	0·003	0·28	0·090	nil	7·69
Nail . .	,,	0·11	Nil	0·32	0·119	nil	7·69
Ketta (axe) .	,,	0·26	0·22	0·34	0·012	trace	7·50

The use and manufacture of iron in Ceylon were discussed by J. Davy, R. A. Hadfield, H. Parker, L. K. Schmarda, and C. P. Thunberg.   W. Rosenhain examined the links of a chain which had probably been exposed in Ceylon to the atmosphere for 2000 years.   The relation of the Gipsies to the iron industry was discussed by R. Andrée, H. M. G. Grellmann, and J. Simson.   The use and manufacture of iron in the East Indies and vicinity were discussed by F. de Magalhaes (Magellan), P. Sonnerat, J. Crawfurd, T. Waitz, J. B. van Hasselt, M. Schulze, H. Everett, J. Moura, H. Meyer, R. Andrée, A. Schadenberg, and W. Foy ; in Sumatra, by W. Marsden, L. Horner, R. Andrée, M. Moszkowsky ; in Java, by T. S. Raffles ; in Borneo, by G. W. Earl, C. A. L. M. Schwaner, and C. Hose and W. McDougall ; in Papua, by G. W. Earl ; in Malay, by H. von Rosenberg ; in Philippines, by A. Schadenberg ; and in Polynesia, by M. Hoernes.

G. F. Zimmer said that the Chinese used iron from the time of Emperor Fo-Hi, about 2000 B.C.   At that time the aborigines of Tibet, the Miao-Tze, had iron swords and hatchets, and the Emperor Fo-Hi received tribute in supplies of iron from them.   This period is probably less remote than is here indicated, for F. R. Tegengren said that the earliest period of the use of iron in China is in 722 B.C., and in 685 B.C. copper was still being used for swords and spears, whilst iron hoes and hatchets were made of iron.   According to W. Ridgeway, the use of iron is mentioned in the *Yü Kung* dating from 2200 B.C. ; according to R. A. Smith, the province of Shan Si, in China, has yielded iron from remote times; and, according to F. Hirth, iron was used in China for agricultural purposes in 696 B.C.   Pliny, in his *Historia naturalis* (**34.** 41), said that the best iron was made by the Seres, and this is taken to have meant the Chinese.   In the thirteenth century, Marco Polo referred to the use of iron by the Chinese, and M. A. Stein found evidence of the use of iron during the eighth and ninth centuries.   The use and manufacture of iron in China were discussed by W. H. Adolph, R. Andrée, E. von Bibra, J. C. Brown, G. Chamier, M. Cremer, St. J. V. Day, F. A. Foster, F. Freise, W. Grube, M. Gsell, F. Hirth, M. Hoernes, J. Klaproth, E. Kocher, A. Ledebur,

J. Legge, F. Lenormant, E. O. von Lippmann, F. Lux, J. Markham, W. Matschoss, A. B. Middleton, O. Montelius, T. D. Morgan, M. Much, A. Pfizmaier, O. Rammstedt, T. T. Read, L. Richard, F. von Richthofen, B. Simmersbach, M. A. Stein, O. Stoll, C. P. Thunberg, O. Vogel, K. Wendt, E. Wiedemann, K. Woermann, and C. Yang and C. F. Wang.

According to W. Gowland, in Japan there were skilful workers of iron in the third or fourth century B.C. The swords are said to be " splendid examples of the work of the smith." E. Treptoff said that the oldest iron manufactured in Japan was at Sugaya in A.D. 1264. The use and manufacture of iron in Japan were discussed by R. Andrée, E. Baelz, B. H. Brough, St. J. V. Day, W. Dönitz, H. Fey, H. H. Manchester, C. P. Thunberg, and E. Treptoff ; and in Siberia, and Northern Asia, by R. Andrée, L. Cohn, M. Ebert, A. Erman, J. G. Gmelin, J. G. Georgi, B. F. J. Hermann, A. Kohn, S. Krascheninnikoff, A. Ledebur, A. von Middendorff, J. G. Müller, K. von Neumann, K. Nishio, A. E. von Nordenskjöld, P. S. Pallas, J. S. Poljäkoff, M. Radloff, J. Sievers, G. W. Steller, and E. Treptoff.

According to O. Montelius, the iron age commenced in Greece about 1500 B.C., and M. I. Rostovtzeff supposed that the iron industry was introduced by the Achæans into Greece between 1150 and 1200 B.C. The cube of iron found in 1927 at Knossos, in a Middle Minoan grave, dating from about 1800 B.C., was considered by H. R. Hall to be the " most ancient known worked iron from the Ægean area." Here again the specimen was considered as a precious metal, and is more likely to have been of meteoric origin. A similar remark also applies to the finger rings, date about 1550 B.C., found in the tombs at Pylos in the Peloponnese. J. L. Myres thinks that Herodotus may have been right in using the term *sigyunæ* for the throwing spears made wholly of iron which characterized the Iron Age culture of Cyprus in early Hellenic times. Homer, who flourished 880 B.C., was familiar with the metal ; and the Homeric Age, the period on which the *Iliad* and *Odyssey* are founded, ranges from 1400 to 1200 B.C. Both poems contain a few references to iron, and they may be taken to indicate what Homer himself thought of the use of this metal in the years to which reference is made. They prove little else. The subject was discussed by T. W. Allen, J. A. N. Friend, W. Helbig, A. Lang, V. Berard, W. Ridgeway, and H. B. Cotterill, and a collection of references is given by L. Beck—*vide infra*, the tempering of steel.

Iron was apparently on trial in Homer's time ; the Homeric swords, spears, and armour were generally of bronze, probably because, owing to poor methods of manufacture, the iron or steel weapons were unreliable and at a critical time might buckle or bend. Pausanias, in his *Periegesis* (**3.** 3, 6), in the 2nd century of our era, said that the weapons of the heroic age of Greece—*e.g.* the spear of Achilles, and the sword of Memnon—preserved in the Greek temples, were made of bronze. Iron does not appear to have replaced bronze in the manufacture of weapons of war until the sixth century B.C. L. Beck gives a number of references to iron in the *Theogony* of Hesiod, who flourished about 700 B.C. The *History* of Herodotus, written about 450 B.C., contains many references to the use of iron in Greece, Egypt, and the Near East. There are other references in Greek literature. Thus, Æschylus, in his *Prometheus* (**4.** 302 ; **6.** 712), called the Caucasus the " motherland of iron," and he praised the iron of the Chalybeans, located at the head of the Euphrates. The Greek term χάλυψ for steel takes its origin from these people. He also added that the Chalybean iron-workers are wild and inhospitable ; while Xenophon, in his *Anabasis* (**5.** 5), said that the whole race lived on the proceeds from the iron industry. E. O. von Lippmann also discussed the references to iron by Aristotle, who flourished between 384 B.C. and 322 B.C., and said :

Iron is obtained in large quantities from the ironstone of Elba and from the mines of the Chalybeans near Amisus, on the southern shore of the Black Sea. The ore is difficult to melt on account of the quantity of clay contained in it, and it is to be softened only by raising it to a great heat. Iron is of great strength and very hard, though it is said that in Cyprus there are mice which are able to gnaw it. The best and hardest of all kinds of iron known is that of the Chalybeans, that is, steel (Chalybs), and it is obtained from iron by melting it repeatedly together with certain stones in a furnace, during which process much slag is formed and a great loss in weight occurs, on account of which the product is very costly. The finished steel is hard, with a glittering surface, and resists rust ; but it is not applicable to all the purposes for which less pure iron is used. The quality is judged by the sound given out in working it on the anvil. A Sicilian trader, recognizing that iron was an indispensable commodity, once succeeded in buying up the produce of all the smelters of iron, and made a profit of 200 per cent. when a scarcity arose.

In 1871, H. Schliemann began a series of investigations at Hissarlik, the site of ancient Troy, and found the remains of several cities, possibly nine, one super posed above the other. The sixth turned out to be the Troy of Homer, dating from 1500 B.C., whilst the second dated back to 2500 B.C. From Troy, H. Schlie mann went to Mycenæ, Greece, and there he discovered evidence of a civilization contemporaneous with that of the Homeric Troy. Excavations in Crete showed that the inhabitants there attained a high stage of civilization, which reached a zenith and then passed into oblivion. The Mycenæan civilization was derived from that of Crete. J. Evans found at Knossos buried cities with indications of a bronze age above neolithic remains, and he called it the *Minoan Age*, in allusion to Minos, the legendary sea-king of Crete, mentioned in Homer's *Odyssey*. Crete was then the dominant sea-power in the Mediterranean, and this period extended from about 4000 to 1200 B.C. There was now a transitional period when iron weapons, etc., began to accompany the bronze relics. The earliest iron weapons have been found in Eastern Crete, and then they appeared in Thessaly, and later still in Athens and Tiryns. Iron swords have been here found in graves dating from 1000 B.C. The history of iron in Greece was discussed by J. Beckmann G. Beloch, H. Blümner, H. A. Boyd, R. M. Burrows, H. Chevalier, E. Curtius, F. M. Feldhaus, R. Forrer, F. Freise, L. Friedländer, M. Fuchs, M. Gercke, W. E. Gladstone, M. Gsell, H. Hanemann, M. Hoernes, J. Hoops, C. Hostmann, O. Immisch, O. Johannsen, O. Kern, C. Klinkenberg, A. Koerte, J. H. Krause, A. Lang, F. Lenormant, E. O. von Lippmann, C. A. von Lobeck, H. H. Manchester, A. H. Mauduit, E. Meyer, H. H. Montanus, O. Montelius, A. Macco, O. Olshausen, C. Pauli, K. Preisendanz, M. Regling, C. Robert, J. P. Rossignol, A. Rzach, O. Schrader, M. Sudhoff, K. Tümpel, M. Wessely, and S. Xanthoudides.

There was an advanced bronze age in Etruria, Italy, prior to 1000 B.C., and iron swords with bronze handles of this period are common in Etruscan remains. At the beginning of our era, Strabo, is his *Geographica* (5. 2), stated that iron ores were shipped from Elba for further treatment at Populonia (Piorubino)—the Sheffield of the Etruscan kingdom. The name *Elba* is said to be derived from the Greek ἔθειρα, in allusion to the flames of iron furnaces, and is said to indicate that when the Greeks discovered Elba, they found iron furnaces there at work. Virgil alluded to the inexhaustibility of the iron mines at Elba—*insula inexhaustis chalybium generoso metallis—Æneid* (10. 174)—and he added that the iron was so abundant that the soldiers sent from this neighbourhood to help Æneas were clad from head to foot in armour of iron. L. Simonin has described the remains of the bloomery hearths employed at Populonia for treating the ores from Elba. The Etruscan furnace was surrounded by blocks of sandstone, and the slag was well fused, honeycombed, black, and crystalline ; and it contained 40 per cent. of ferrous oxide. The charcoal seemed to have been derived from the oak and chestnut. The spoil-heap was over 600 yds. long, and about 7 ft. high. Diodorus Siculus also described the ironworks at Populonia. Some of the coins of ancient Populonia have the head of Vulcan with representations of hammer and tongs, thus showing the importance of the iron industry to the people there. Remains of an Etruscan ironworks have been discovered at Gheradessa on Mount Bucho al Ferro. The subject was discussed by A. Gurlt, H. Scott, and G. Dennis. T. Poech considered that the Elba mines date back to the time when iron first came into general use. Some of the discoveries in the waste-heaps go back to the Stone Age, and the weapons with which Troy and Carthage were conquered were probably made from Elba ores. F. Odernheimer said that the Elba mines were known to the Phœnicians and were subsequently worked by the Greeks and Romans. Accurate data can be traced back to 1193 A.D., when the Emperor of Germany, Henry VI, transferred his mining rights over Elba to the Republic of Pisa.

The Romans displayed little inventive genius, and what successes they obtained in the arts and crafts were due to the work of imported craftsmen—1. l, 29. There is a reference to the work in the smithy in Virgil's *Æneid* (**8.** 416) :

> As when the Cyclops, at th' Almighty nod,
> New thunder hasten for their angry god,
> Subdued in fire the stubborn metal lies ;
> One brawny smith the puffing bellows plies,
> And draws and blows reciprocating air :
> Others to quench the hissing mass prepare :
> With lifted arms they order every blow,
> And chime their sounding hammers in a row ;
> With laboured anvils Etna groans below.
> Strongly they strike ; huge flakes of flames expire :
> With tongs they turn the steel and vex it in the fire.

This shows that the Romans were familiar with steel and the method of tempering it prior to 30 B.C.—*vide infra*, the hardening of steel. There are also references to iron by other Roman poets—*e.g.* in Ovid's *Metamorphoses* (**14.** 712) ; in Horace's *Odes* (**2.** 16, 17, 51) ; and in Lucretius' *De rerum natura* (**6.** 148). Pliny, in his *Historia naturalis* (**34.** 39 to 45), *c.* A.D. 75, has collected the current lore concerning iron. He said that the art of working iron is due to Cyclops, and that other legends ascribe it to other sources. Pliny gave an account of the common types of iron ore, and the varieties of metal which they furnish. He attributed the effects of tempering (*q.v.*) to the nature of the water, and he said that the natural waters in some localities give better results than in others. He said that when the ore is fused, the metal becomes like water, and afterwards acquires a spongy, brittle texture. This is the way cast iron would behave. Pliny discussed the rusting of iron (*q.v.*), and the medicinal virtues of preparations of iron. He lamented the use of iron in the manufacture of weapons :

It is with iron that wars, murders, and robberies are effected, and this not only hand to hand, but from a distance even, by the aid of missiles and winged weapons, now launched from engines, now hurled by the human arm, and now furnished with feathery wings. This last I regard as the most criminal artifice that has been devised by the human mind ; for, as if to bring death upon man with still greater rapidity, we have given wings to iron and taught it to fly.

There are references by Diodorus, *Bibliotheca historica* (**5.** 33, 34), and by Livy, in his *Historia* (**21.** 8), to the use of iron in Spain. The history of iron in the Roman Empire and Italy was discusssed by L. Beck, J. Beckmann, H. Bell, H. Blümner, R. Forrer, F. Freise, C. Fremont, L. Friedländer, M. Gummerus, A. Gurlt, H. Hanemann, T. Haupt, J. F. L. Hausmann, M. Hoernes, J. Hoops, E. Hübner, H. Jentsch, W. Kroll, A. Ledebur, R. Marggraff, H. H. Manchester, C. Mehlis, E. Meyer, S. Mockrauer, O. Montelius, A. Morlot, B. Neumann, E. Riess, J. P. Rossignol, H. Rupe, M. Sagey, O. Schrader, H. Scott, M. Skutsch, O. Stoll, R. von Stoltzenberg, P. C. J. B. Tronson du Coudray, F. Winkelmann, and G. Wissowa.

According to R. von B. Baum, Punic and Roman tools have been found in old workings in North-West Africa, showing that there the iron-mining industry goes back to ancient times. The iron mines and the ferruginous gold of Bona are referred to by Leo Africanus. There was afterwards a period of decadence. Emir Abd-el-Kader recognized the importance of the iron-ore industry to Algiers, and the ore of Zaccar-Rharbi was there smelted in charcoal blast furnaces. According to L. Beck, the natives of Africa, Egypt excepted, extracted iron from its ores from a very remote period. The seats of the ancient iron industry are evidenced by accumulations of slag and debris, and are widely distributed in that continent. W. Gowland, and L. Beck believe that the iron at the early period must have been indigenous in Africa. R. Dart reported some results of excavations in the Mumowa caves near Broken Hill, North Rhodesia. The remains of an old smelting furnace were taken to indicate that iron was there manufactured 3000 to 4000 years ago—2070 B.C.—by a people of palæolithic culture dwelling in Central Africa. T. A. Rickard considered this to be very improbable, and that the remains are really those of foreigners versed in iron-making who established themselves for defensive purposes in the caves and made iron weapons for use against the natives.

The idea, advocated by W. E. B. du Bois, that the discovery of iron originated amongst the African negroes, and that the Egyptians acquired the art from their Ethiopian neighbours to the south or from their Libyan neighbours to the west of the Nile valley, is not probable, because the available evidence shows that the civilizations of Ethiopia and Nubia always lagged behind that of Egypt. Herodotus (2. 124) observed that :

The Ethiopian contingent of Xerxes' army was armed with long bows, on which they placed short arrows made of cane, not tipped with iron, but with stone which was made sharp, and of the kind with which we engrave seals. Besides these they had javelins, tipped with antelope's horn that had been made sharp like a lance. They also had knotted clubs.

H. Balfour thus summarized F. von Luschan's arguments in favour of the African negro as the originator of the method for extracting iron from its ores :

(1) That the high antiquity of iron-working among Negro and Bantu tribes is evidenced by its very widespread dispersal among them, and by the great degree of skill acquired by the native smiths. (2) That iron ores are very abundant in Africa, and can be collected with ease on or near the surface. (3) That some of these ores are easily reducible at a relatively low temperature, and can be, in fact, reduced in an ordinary fire. (4) That in Karagwé, Kordofan, and Usindja may be seen such open fires still used for iron smelting, and there are variations in this simple procedure which suggest stages in the evolution from the open fire to the closed kiln. If iron smelting had been introduced to the negro by an exotic people who had already considerably advanced the industry, these crude and seemingly prototypical methods would not have been adopted in the region ; and that evidence for the early stages in the progression from simple to complex should be sought for elsewhere, not in savage Africa, where, however, they seem to obtrude themselves.

It is quite possible, even probable, that the method of extracting iron from its ores was independently discovered in several different localities—say, the Caspian area, in Central Africa, etc.—and that the quest for a very first discoverer is illusive.

Diodorus (3. 13) said that the chisels used in the mining of gold in Nubia for the old Egyptian kings were made of *latomides chalkai*—*i.e.* copper or bronze— because iron was then unknown. W. M. F. Petrie and co-workers, L. W. King and H. R. Hall, and H. R. Hall do not consider it probable that the early Egyptian iron was obtained by trade from outside sources—*e.g.* the Nubians and negroes— although in the opinion of G. A. Wainwright, the art of working iron entered Egypt from Asia, and thence passed by other parts of Africa.

The use and manufacture of iron in Africa were discussed by R. Andrée, B. Ankermann, C. Arendt, J. Backhouse, S. W. Baker, H. Barth, C. V. Bellamy, J. T. Brent, T. E. Bowdich, A. E. Brehm, R. F. Burton, R. Caillié, V. L. Cameron, P. B. du Chaillu, C. C. von der Decken, A. Delegorgue, F. Dixey, J. L. Döhne, E. Dulaurier, K. Endemann, J. R. Evans, G. Fritsch, E. de Froberville, M. Guillain, W. von Harnier, M. T. von Heuglin, M. Hoernes, J. E. Holgate, E. Holub, F. Hupfeld, T. J. Hutchinson, M. Kranz, A. Lambert, J. T. Last, O. Lenz, D. Livingstone, F. von Luschan, L. Magyar, A. Mansfield, G. H. Mason, A. F. Mockler-Ferryman, G. Mollien, J. M. C. Monteiro, G. Nachtigal, S. Passarge, P. Paulitschke, J. Petherick, S. Pinto, P. Pogge, A. F. Pott, A. F. Prévost, S. Purchas, A. Raffenel, T. A. Rickard, G. Rohlfs, J. Russegger, C. Schefer, O. Schrader, O. H. Schütt, G. Schweinfurth, H. M. Stanley, P. Staudinger, G. Tessmann, J. Thomson, F. le Vaillant, T. Waitz, M. Weiss, K. Weule, and C. T. Wilson and R. W. Felkin—*vide infra*, the history of the blast furnace. The use of iron in Madagascar was discussed by W. Ellis, and G. P. Chaplin.

The cemeteries of Hallstadt, in the Austrian Tyrol, and of La Tène, in Switzerland, have furnished materials which have enabled archæologists to trace a gradual growth in culture through the bronze age to the iron age over a period from about 850 to 1 B.C. M. I. Rostovtzeff believed that the iron age in the Caspian area of the Near East dates back to 1400 B.C.; and that the Achæans arrived in Greece with a well-developed iron industry about 1200 to 1150 B.C. Hence, inquires H. Balfour :

Why is it that in the Hallstadt culture of Central Europe, which is generally considered to go back to about 850 B.C., there is unmistakable evidence of a gradual transition from bronze to iron ? Is the initiation of the iron age in Central Europe independent of its inauguration in the Near East and among the Achæans ? Or did a rudimentary knowledge of the use of iron spread westward without acquaintance with the improved types of implements and developed technique which had already been evolved farther to the east ? Or does the dating require reconsideration ?

W. Ridgeway was so impressed with the traces of the old iron industry at Hallstadt that he believed the use of iron as a metal began in Central Europe, not in Egypt or, indeed, Africa. According to V. Gross, iron was smelted near Hallstadt, Austria, and in the Bernese Jura from 2000 B.C. This subject was discussed by O. Montelius, O. Schrader, R. Forrer, M. Gsell, M. Hoernes, H. Rupe and F. Müller, O. Johannsen, J. Pokorny, J. Hoops, F. M. Feldhaus, J. Beckmann, A. Schulten, F. Freise, H. Blümner, K. Tanzer, R. Munro, H. J. E. Peake, A. Müllner, A. Quiquerez, and E. von Sacken. H. Hanemann analyzed and examined microscopically samples of iron of the La Tène period, about 500 B.C. Noricum (Noreia) —embracing Carinthia, and Styria, Görz, and Istria, in the Austrian Tyrol— was one of the earliest centres of the iron industry in Europe. It is alluded to by G. Jars, who visited Erzberg in 1758. Both Horace, in his *Epodon* (**17.** 71) and in his *Odes* (**1.** 16), and Ovid, in his *Metamorphoses* (**14.** 712), refer to the high quality of *Noric iron*. A. Macco said the iron in the neighbourhood of Krivoi Rog, Russia, was used by the ancient Greeks ; and that it is probable that the famed *Scythian iron* came from this neighbourhood.

According to R. Forrer, and J. Hoops, iron was known in Sweden 800 B.C., and, according to O. Montelius, O. Schrader, J. Hoops, J. Schlemm, and W. Tomaschek, the iron age began there about 500 B.C. There are numerous references to iron weapons and utensils in the sagas of the vikings and gods of Scandinavia and Iceland during the period between A.D. 800 and A.D. 1100— W. von Gravenberch, K. Simrock, etc. M. Wahlberg said that it is known with certainty that iron began to be manufactured in Sweden at least 500 B.C., and for about 2000 years afterwards malleable iron was produced directly from the ore— chiefly bog iron ore. The vikings were probably able to produce iron objects of large size ; thus, the iron anchor of a ship was found in a barrow of Oseberg, Sem, and described by G. Gustafson. The vikings do not appear to have had control of the method of making a thin strip of metal, like a sword, which would retain a cutting edge and not bend. This remark applies to many of the ancient iron-workers in other lands ; so that when the smith did succeed in producing a satisfactory weapon the event was celebrated in saga and legend where the fame of a sword with its own special name was recorded. D. Livingstone and others have mentioned the frequency with which the spears of the natives of Africa were bent when in use. V. Schmidt discussed the occurrence of prehistoric iron in Denmark —for Germany, etc., *vide infra*.

The inhabitants of Britain were acquainted with iron at least two centuries before our era. According to R. A. Smith :

Although there are various proofs that iron was produced in Britain centuries before the Roman occupation, no furnaces of the earliest period have been discovered ; and it is therefore probable that the ancient Britons employed the simple low hearth, resembling the Catalan furnace of the Pyrenees, which has been in use there from very remote times to our own day. The source from which Britain derived the furnace and art of extracting iron from its ore seems to have been the Mediterranean region, either the eastern Pyrenees or north-west Italy ; but it may also be reasonably held that the first iron-furnace of the Britons was derived from that used so successfully in the extraction of tin. It is important

to notice that two of the earliest sites of ironworks in Europe are situated in the Upp
Danubian region, within easy reach of the famous cemetery of Hallstadt. One is in tl
neighbourhood of Hüttenberg, in the upper basin of the Drave, Carinthia ; the second c
another tributary of the Danube, the Mur in Styria.

Julius Cæsar, in his *De bello gallico*, mentioned that when he arrived, the Britor
used brass or iron rings, determined at a certain weight, as money ; and that iro
was produced in the maritime regions. Currency bars have been found at Maider
head (Berkshire) ; Minety (Wiltshire) ; Wookey Hole, Glastonbury, and Har
Hill or Hamdon (Somerset) ; Winchester (Hampshire) ; Meon Hill and Bourtor
on-the-Water (Gloucestershire) ; Malvern and Littleton (Worcestershire) ; Hun
bury (Northamptonshire) ; Ventnor (Isle of Wight) ; Hod Hill and Spettisbur
(Dorset) ; and Holne Chase (Devonshire). The subject was discussed b
R. A. Smith, A. Lane-Fox, J. W. Hall, T. S. Ashton, R. Jenkins, J. H. Eves
R. Baker, C. W. von Siemens, T. Turner, H. Louis, C. Dawson, J. Lewis, H. Gay
thorpe, M. S. Giuseppi, W. P. Breach, H. C. Evans, T. Vickers, W. C. Symon
and J. Evans. Analyses were reported by B. H. Brough, J. Myers, and W. Gow
land. According to Julius Cæsar, the Britons at the time of the Roman conque
were famous for chariots of war drawn by two horses abreast, with a pole betwee
them. The object was to maim the enemy. When a chief died, the chariot and it
equipment were sometimes buried with him. Fragments of the iron rims of tl
wheels of some of these chariots have been found—*e.g.* in the East Riding of Yor
shire. The wheels were in some cases 3 ft. in diameter. There is no satisfactor
evidence of the use of scythed chariots. J. R. Mortimer found numerous reli
of an early iron age in the burial mounds in the district between York and Bri
lington. T. May described an iron-smelting furnace of the Roman period ɛ
Wilderspool and Stockton Heath, near Warrington. The furnace consisted of
wall covered with clay, and there were holes at the base for letting in air and allov
ing the metal to run out. For this purpose, also, the furnaces were usually place
on sloping ground. Rude bellows may have been used. C. Wilkins seems t
consider that South Wales was the original home of the iron trade of Britain. I
Roman times extensive ironworks developed in Gloucestershire. The iron reli
of early man in Britain found at Wookey Hole, near Wells, Somerset, were describe
by H. E. Balch ; they include brooches, currency bars, a sickle, an ox-shoe,
dagger, etc. A. Bulleid and H. St. G. Gray described the relics found at worl
at Glastonbury (A.D. 120). Emperor Hadrian established a works at Bath, whet
iron from the Forest of Dean was worked. G. Payne gave an account of the iro
industry which prevailed in the Weald of Kent in the sixteenth century. Ther
were furnaces, forges, or foundries at Cowden, Hawkhurst, Lamberhurst, Crar
brook, Goudhurst, Domdale, Hormoden, Tonbridge, and Biddenden. There wɛ
a rapid decline in the seventeenth century, so that in 1796 not one furnace was ɛ
work in Kent. According to S. H. Hollands, the last ironworks in the Weald
Sussex were at Ashburnham, and they were dismantled in 1828. Some of tl
present names of places recall the old industry—*e.g.* Hammer Ponds. The subje
was also discussed by M. A. Lower, and E. Straker. In 1673, J. Smith described tl
condition of the iron trade of Sussex at that time, and fears were expressed as to th
extinction of the forests to supply fuel for the 130 hammers and furnaces then in us
F. Cartwright gave an account of the history of iron in Sussex—*vide infra*. Excav
tions have been made near Richborough Castle, in the vicinity of Sandwich, Ken
which was once the site of a Roman naval station known as Rutupiæ. Many iro
relics, including brooches, bangles, rings, nails, and the iron head of an axe, wer
unearthed. Analyses of two iron nails have been made by J. A. N. Friend an
W. E. Thorneycroft. One nail contained 0·080 per cent. of carbon and 0·046 c
sulphur, no manganese, and a trace of phosphorus ; another nail had 0·070 pɛ
cent. of carbon, and no manganese, phosphorus, or sulphur. East Cliff, Folkeston
has also been identified as a Roman site, and excavations, described by S. E. W
bolt, have revealed a number of iron implements of various kinds. Some of ther

were described by J. A. N. Friend and W. E. Thorneycroft. The iron relics found
at Uriconium, near Wroxeter, Shropshire, have been described by J. P. Bushe-Fox.
The Roman iron found at Corstopitum, on the north bank of the River Tyne,
was described by H. Bell, F. Haverfield, G. Turner, R. H. Forster, and
W. H. Knowles. J. E. Stead gave for the analysis of the bloom : 0·097, C ; 0·046,
Si ; 0·025, S ; 0·044, P ; 0·049, As ; 0·010, Cu ; 0·040, Mn ; and 0·380, cinder.
H. Louis concluded that the Romans smelted the little balls of iron with charcoal,
at or near the outcrop of the local ores, and transported the cakes of spongy iron
so obtained to the town of Corstopitum to be worked up into articles of various
kinds. W. G. Collingwood and H. S. Cooper described the ancient bloomery at
Coniston ; and G. T. Lapsley described the account roll of a fifteenth-century
ironmaster in Weardale—*vide infra*. Small iron bloomery furnaces were erected at
Pontypool, South Wales, in 1425 ; and in the sixteenth century the old Sussex
ironmasters, owing to restrictive measures, migrated to South Wales and established the iron industry there. About 1577 the Lansdown MSS. says that
Richard Hanbury had " gott to his handes ij or iij iron workes there in Wales,
whereat he made much merchant iron to greate gaine." This subject was discussed
by W. Coxe, W. Llewellyn, and D. Griffiths.

According to G. F. Zimmer, and J. Lubbock, Amerigo Vespucci, who journeyed
to America between 1497 and 1504, and after whom America was named, stated
that when he first went to the La Plata region of South America, he found that
the Indians made arrow-heads and other implements out of bits of iron derived
from masses that had fallen from the sky. This is the only reference to iron occurring in the description by Amerigo Vespucci of his four voyages between 1497 and
1504 :

Their (Indians) arms are bows and arrows, very well made, save that (the arrows) are
not (tipped) with iron nor any other kind of hard metal, and instead of iron they put
animals or fishes teeth or a spike of tough wood, with the point hardened by fire.

E. B. Tylor said that the Mexicans were familiar with iron at the time of the
Spanish Conquest, and that they first called their copper and bronze *tepuztli* ; the
same word was employed as a general term for metal, and it was also applied to iron.
In order to distinguish the two metals, copper was called *red tepuztli*, and iron,
black tepuztli.

According to F. W. Putnam, the relics of the mound-builders of the Mississippi
valley include gold, silver, and copper ornaments—beads, buttons, and bracelets
—made from native metals by hammering ; and meteoric iron was fashioned into
beads, adzes, and chisels in the same way. The mound in the Turner group of
Ohio contained a piece of meteoric iron in its natural state and another piece which
had been flattened by hammering. G. F. Kunz showed that some specimens of
meteoric iron can be shaped by hammering with stone ; the Otumpa meteorite,
found in Argentine, has scars indicating where pieces have been detached ; the
Descubridora meteorite, in Mexico, has a gap in which is wedged a broken copper
chisel left there by a primitive worker ; and the Catorze meteorite, in Mexico,
likewise had a chisel of native copper wedged in a cavity in the meteorite.
W. H. Prescott pointed out that although the nations of Peru were unacquainted
with iron, they had acquired the art of cutting the hardest substances, like emeralds,
with tools of stone and copper ; similarly also with the natives of Mexico, who used
instruments of copper, with an alloy of tin, and a siliceous powder for cutting the
hardest stones. On the other hand, as pointed out by G. F. Zimmer, H. Hensoldt
has said :

When Cortez had completed the conquest of Mexico the Spaniards, among a great many
other peculiar and extraordinary observations which they made in that remarkable country,
were particularly struck and puzzled by one fact. They noticed that the Aztecs possessed
certain implements, such as knives, daggers, etc., made of iron, but it seemed that only
the most distinguished of the natives possessed such, that iron was a great rarity and was
prized higher than gold. At first the Spaniards believed that the Aztecs extracted the

metal in some crude fashion from its ore, which abounds in many parts of the country, b
they soon ascertained that this was not the case.   They found that·not a single smelti
furnace existed in the empire, and their surprise was not small when they learned that t
Aztecs were totally unacquainted with any method of extracting the iron from the o
which, indeed, they had never suspected of any kinship with the highly valued met
The question whence the Aztecs had procured the little iron they possessed became
perplexing problem to the Spaniards, which they were never able to solve.   The nativ
do not seem to have enlightened them much on the subject, for when asked they myste
ously pointed to the sky, and indicated that they obtained their iron from the regio
above.   Such assertions, no doubt, the Spaniards received with an incredulous smi
and they concluded that the Aztecs procured it by way of traffic with some other, perha
more civilized, nation which they suspected to exist and kept looking for north and sou
for more than a hundred years.   The Aztecs were quite correct ; the iron of which they h
made their implements was not fashioned from materials of this terrestrial globe, but h
come to them from the unknown regions of space.   Their iron was, in fact, of meteor
origin, like that of the Mayas of Yucatan and the Incas of Peru, of which many weapo
are still preserved in collections.

The use and manufacture of iron in America before the so-called discove
of that country by Columbus were discussed by J. de Acosta, R. Andrée, A. Bastia
L. Beck, A. de Herrera, H. Hoerens, C. Hostmann, W. H. Holmes, F. de Maga
haes (Magellan), H. H. Manchester, G. C. Musters, J. A. F. le Marquis de Nadailla
W. H. Prescott, W. Rhaleg, T. A. Rickard, and R. Virchow—*vide infra*.

There are bibliographies of the more recent developments of the iron and ste
industries [2]—Great Britain,[3] France,[4] Belgium,[5] Alsace-Lorraine and Luxen
burg,[6] and Sweden.[7]   According to L. Beck, in 1240, Philippus domus de Floreng
gave to the monks of the Abbey of Villers-Bettnach the right to mine iron or
in his lands ; and in 1260, Thierry, Lord of Hagingen (Haeges), gave to Cou
Theobald von Bar the right to mine the iron in his forests of Briey.   In 1323, a
forge served by water-power was erected near Moyeuvre.   In 1490, an ironworl
was erected at Ars-on-the-Moselle, and from these early dates the evolution
the iron industry in this region has continued up to the present time.   In Tacitu
Germania, written in the first century of our era, there are references to the use
manufacture of iron in Germany ; and, according to O. Schrader,[8] the Germa
learned the use of iron in the fourth century B.C. from the Celts.   The early man
facture of the metal in Germany was described by L. Beck, L. Lindenschmi
M. Schulz, I. Undset, etc.   Writings on the subsequent period are very numerou
In 1758, J. G. Lehmann described some iron mines in Prussia and said that
abandoned mines the iron ore grows again, so that in a few years new ore appear
but not of such good quality as the original ore.   O. Krasa observed the remai
of the smelting hearths of old Celtic ironworks at Rittershausen dating back
1000 B.C.

In connection with the development of the iron and steel industries
Finland,[9] O. Schrader reported that the West Finns owe their acquaintance wit
iron to the Germans, and the East Finns, to the Iranians.   The development
iron and steel has been studied in connection with other countries—Russia,[10] th
Balkan States,[11] the old Austria-Hungary,[12] Switzerland,[13] Italy,[14] Spain an
Portugal,[15] Australia,[16] New Zealand,[17] India,[18] Japan,[19] the United States,
Canada,[21] Cuba,[22] Brazil,[23] and Chili.[24]

In olden times iron was symbolized by ♂, the spear and shield of Mars, the G
of War, probably in allusion to its use in making weapons of war.   The term *Ma*
for iron was in common use amongst the alchemists, and it survives in such tern
as *crocus martis*, employed still in some of the older industries.   The following
R. Russell's [25] translation from the twelfth-century work, *Summa perfectionis magi*
terii, of Geber, and it gives some idea of the style of the writings of the period :

But the *Declaration* of *Mars*, and the whole *Secret* thereof, is from the *Work* of *Nature*
because it is a *Metallick Body*, very livid, a little red, pertaking of *Whiteness*, not pur
sustaining *Ignition*, fusible with no right fusion, under the *Hammer* extensible, and soundir
much.   But *Mars*, is hard to be handled, by reason of the *Impotency* of its fusion, whic
if it be made to flow by a *Medicine* changing its *Nature*, is conjoyned to *Sol* and *Luna*, an

not separated by *Examen*, without great *Industry*, but if prepared, it is conjoyned, and not separated by any *Artifice*, if the Nature of that *Fixation* be not changed by it, the Uncleanness only of the *Mars* being removed : Therefore it is a *Tincture* of *Redness* easily, but difficultly of *Whiteness*. And when it is conjoyned, it is not altered, nor doth it change the *Colour* of the *Commixtion*, but augments it in *Quantity*.

E. Wiedemann gave an account of the Arabian writer Ibn Hudail, who lived at the beginning of the eleventh century. The Arabian said that iron exists in two modifications—male and female. Steel is the male variety, soft iron the female. J. de Hammer-Purgstall, and E. Rödigfr wrote on this subject. According to J. J. Becher's *tria prima* theory—**1.** 1, 15—iron was a compound of three primitives, so that when iron appears in the ash of certain substances, it was not originally present as iron, but the iron has been synthesized, so to speak, by a readjustment of the three primitives. E. F. Geoffroy favoured the same hypothesis, but L. Lemery showed that it is very improbable. Then followed the phlogiston hypothesis, which was discarded with the advent of A. L. Lavoisier's *Traité élémentaire de chimie* (Paris, 1789), and iron came to be generally recognized as an elemental form of matter. The history of the various forms of iron associated with carbon —cast iron, steel, etc.—is outlined later on.

J. K. F. Meyer [26] reported, in 1780, that crude iron contained a new element—named *hydrosiderum*—which remained as a residue when the metal was dissolved in acid. M. Klaproth showed that the alleged element is a compound of iron and phosphorus. A similar remark applies to the *siderum* found by T. Bergman in cold short iron. G. G. Boucher thought that he had discovered a new element in the dust of a blast furnace. F. G. Ruddock confirmed this, but C. H. Jones showed that the alleged reactions correspond with those of molybdenum. J. P. Prat also reported a new element in pyrite, and he called it *lavœsium*, but the report has not been confirmed.

General observations on or references to the history of iron have been made in numerous special books or memoirs. There are :

Sixteenth-century works : G. Agricola, *De re metallica*, Basileæ, 1561 ; P. Albinus, *Meyssnische Bergkchronica*, Dresden, 134, 590 ; V. Biringuccio, *De la pirotechnia*, Venezia, 1540 ; A. Cæsalpinus, *De metallicis*, Romæ, 1596 ; H. Cardanus, *De rerum varietate*, Basileæ, 1557 ; L. Ercker, *Beschreibung Allezfürnemisten mineralischen Ertzt unnd Bergkwercks Arten*, Franckfurt a. M., 1598 ; C. Gesner, *De omni rerum fossilium genere, gemmis, lapidibus, metallis*, Tiguri, 1565 ; J. Mathesius, *Sarepta oder Bergpostill*, Nürnberg, 1564 ; N. de Monardo, *Historia de les plantas que se traen de las Indias*, Serilla, 1580 ; S. Munster, *Cosmographia*, Basel, 1544.

Seventeenth-century works : A. A. Barba, *Arte de los Metales*, Madrid, 1640 ; D. Dudley, *Metallum martis*, London, 1665 ; London, 1851 ; T. Garzoni, *La Piazza universale di tutte le professioni del mondo*, Venetia, 98, 1610 ; J. R. Glauberus, *Operis mineralis*, Amstelodami, 29, 1659 ; G. E. Löhneyss, *Bericht vom Berkwerck*, Zellerfeldt, 1617 ; S. Purchas, *His Pilgrimes*, London, 1814, 1625 ; S. Sturtevant, *Metallica*, London, 1612.

Eighteenth-century works : M. Bazin, *Traité sur l'acier d'Alsace ou l'art de convertir le fer en fonte en acier*, Paris, 1737 ; T. Bergman, *De analysi ferri*, Upsala, 1781 ; W. Blakey, *Réflexions sur les progrès de la fabrique de fer et de l'acier dans la Grande-Bretagne*, Londres, 1783 ; G. L. L. de Buffon, *Histoire des minéraux*, Paris, **2**. 341, 1783 ; B. Caryophilus, *De antiquis auri, argenti, stanni, æris, ferri, plumbique fodinis*, Viennæ, 1757 ; G. le Courtivron and E. J. Boucher, *Art des forges et fourneaux à fer*, Paris, 1762 ; F. B. de Félice, *Forges du art de fer*, Yverdan, 1777 ; J. J. Ferber, *Physikalisch-metallurgische Abhandlungen über die Gebirge und Berwerke in Ungarn, nebst Beschreibung des steirischen Eisenschmelzens und Stahlmachens*, Berlin, 1780 ; *Mineralogische und metallurgische Bemerkungen in Neuchâtel*, Berlin, 1789 ; F. A. C. Gren, *Systematisches Handbuch der gesammten Chemie*, Halle, 434, 1795 ; P. C. Grignon, *Mémoires de physique sur l'art de fabriquer le fer*, Paris, 1775 ; B. F. J. von Herrmann, *Crell's Ann. Beyträge*, **5**. 274, 373, 1791 ; **6**. 3, 1799 ; G. Herwig, *Briefe über die Bergkunde, über Eisengruben und Rohschmelzen*, Frankfurt a. M., 1789 ; *Vier Abhandlungen über Gegenstände der Bergbaukunde und Kammeralwissenschaft*, Frankfurt, 1792 ; J. von Hofmann, *Abhandlung über die Eisenhütten*, Hof, 1783 ; *Crell's Ann.*, i. 564. 1785 ; H. Horne, *Essays concerning Iron and Steel*, London, 1773 ; G. Jars, *Voyages métallurgiques*, Lyon, 1774 ; C. Linnæus, *Pluto Svecicus* (MS.), Stockholm, 1734 ; C. A. von der Monde, C. L. Berthollet and G. Monge, *Hist. Acad.*, Paris, 132, 1786 ; J. B. G. de Morveau, *Rapport sur les résultats des expériences de Clouet sur les différents états du fer pour la conversion du fer en acier fondu*, Paris, 1898 ; M. Ostmann, *Crell's Ann. Beyträge*, **6**. 194, 1799 ; C. Polhem (Polhammer), *Patriotisches Testament*, Stockholm, 1761 ; R. A. F. de Réaumur, *L'art de convertir le fer forgé en acier*, Paris, 1722 ; *An Essay on the Mystery of Steel*, London, 1771 ; G. Rinman, *Academisk Afhandling om Jernets Tilwarknings*, Upsala,

1782 ; *Crell's Ann.*, ii, 469, 1784 ; S. Rinman, *Anledninger til Kunskap om den gröfre Jern-och Stäl-Förädlingen och des Forbättrande*, Stockholm, 1772 ; *Försck till Järnets, Historia, med Tillämyning för Slögder och Handtwerk*, Stockholm, 1782 ; Berlin, 1785 ; G. F. Rippen-trop, *Crell's Ann.*, ii, 411, 506, 1796 ; B. F. Rothoff, *Academisk Afhandling i svenska Bergs-Lagfarenheten om författninger, rörande fkogarnas värd och nyttjande til bergwerkens tjenst*, Upsala, 1778 ; *Crell's Ann.*, ii, 467, 1784 ; P. Saxholm, *De ferro succecano osmund*, Upsaliæ, 1725 ; J. G. Schneider, *Analecta ad historiam rei metallicœ veterum*, Viadrum, 24, 1788 ; J. S. Schröter, *Geschichte des gediegen Eisens*, Halle, 1777 ; J. A. Scopoli, *Anleitung zur Kenntniss und Gebauch der Fossilien*, Riga, 107, 1769 ; M. Stouth, *Crell's Ann. Beyträge*, 2. i, 339, 1787 ; E. Swedenborg, *Regnum subterraneum sive minerale de ferro*, Dresdæ, 1734 ; J. F. Tölle and L. E. S. Gärtner, *Eisenhütten-Magazin*, Wernigerode, 1791 ; C. Tronson du Coudray, *Nouvelles expériences sur le fer*, Paris, 1775 ; J. G. Wallerius, *Elementa metallurgiæ speciatim chemicæ*, Holmiæ, 1768. **Nineteenth-century works :** W. de St. Ange, *Métallurgie pratique du fer*, Paris, 1838 ; A. Armengaud, *Métallurgie du fer*, Paris, 1882 ; M. Atsberg, *Die Anfänge der Eisecultur*, Berlin, 1885 ; *Berg. Hütt. Ztg.*, 45. 350, 1886 ; *Zeit. Ver. deut. Ing.*, 30. 1090, 1886 ; W. Baer, *Der Eisen*, Leipzig, 1862 ; H. Bauermann, *A Treatise on the Metallurgy of Iron*, London, 1868 ; L. Beck, *Arch. Anthropologie*, 12. 293, 1880 ; *Ann. Ver. Nassau Alterthumskunde*, 14. 317, 1877 ; *Die Geschichte des Eisens in technischer und kulturgeschtlicher Beziehung*, Braunschweig, 1884–1903 ; T. Beckert, *Leitfaden zur Eisenhüttenkunde*, Berlin, 1885 ; I. L. Bell, *Journ. Iron Steel Inst.*, 38. ii, 406, 1890 ; *Principles of the Manufacture of Iron and Steel*, London, 1884 ; R. Bergau, *Die Schmiedekunst*, Berlin, 1887 ; P. Berthier, *Traité des eseais par la voie sèche*, Paris, 1834 ; J. G. L. Blumhof, *Versuch einer Enziclopädie der Eisenhüttenkunde*, Giessen, 1821 ; *Vollständige systematische Literatur vom Eisen*, Braunschweig, 1803 ; W. Boeheim, *Handbuch der Waffenkunde*, Leipzig, 1890 ; H. Brugsch, *Berliner Vossische Ztg.*, 184, 1894 ; H. A. Bueck, *Stahl Eisen*, 3. 455, 1883 ; A. de Candolle, *Histoire des Sciences*, Genève, 1875 ; S. H. Daddow and B. Bannan, *Coal, Iron and Oil*, Pottsville, 1866 ; S. U. V. Day, *Excerpta relating to Iron*, London, 1873 ; *On the present State of some Branches of Iron Metallurgy*, Glasgow, 1868 ; E. F. Dürre, *Die Anlange und der Betrieb der Eisenhütten*, Leipzig, 1882 ; *Ueber die Constitution des Roheisens*, Leipzig, 1868 ; T. Dunlop, *American Iron Trade Manual of the leading Iron Industries of the United States*, New York, 1874 ; W. Fairbairn, *Iron : its History, Properties, and Processes of Manufacture*, Edinburgh, 1861 ; M. Faugé, *Métallurgie du fer et de l'acier*, Paris, 1896 ; L. Ferasson, *La question du fer*, Paris, 1918 ; E. Flachat, A. Barrault and J. Petiet, *Traité de la fabrication du fer*, Paris, 1846 ; W. Fordyce, *A History of Coal and Iron*, London, 1860 ; A. Frantz, *Berg. Hütt. Ztg.*, 41. 177, 197, 257, 377, 467, 557, 1882 ; L. Gages, *Métallurgie du fer*, Paris, 1898 ; J. S. Gardner, *Ironwork from the Earliest Times to the End of the Medieval Period*, London, 1892 ; A. Gillon, *Ann. Univ. Belz.*, 10. 763, 1851 ; *Des divers procédés de fabrication du fer*, Bruxelles, 1853 ; E. Glinzer, *Das Eisen, seine Gewinnung und Verwendumg*, Hamburg, 1876 ; W. H. Greenwood, *Steel and Iron*, London, 1884 ; A. Gurlt, *Die Bergbau- und Hüttenkunde*, Essen, 1877 ; C. F. A. Hartmann, *Der wohlunterrichtete Hcchofen und Hammermeister*, Weimar, 1852 ; T. L. Hasse, *Grundlinien zur Eisenhüttenkunde*, Leipzig, 1801 ; I. H. Hassenfratz, *La sidérotechnie*, Paris, 1812 ; J. F. L. Hausmann, *Jahrb. Berg. Hütt.*, 4. 141, 1821 ; C. Helson, *La sidérurgie en France et à l'étranger*, Paris, 1894 ; A. H. Hiorns, *Iron and Steel Manufacture*, London, 1889 ; E. Japing, *Die Darstellung des Eisens, und der Eisenfabrikate*, Wien, 1881 ; J. S. Jeans, *Steel : its History, Manufacture, Properties and Uses,* London, 1880 ; S. Jordan, *Album to the Course of Lectures on Metallurgy at the Central School of Arts*, London, 1878 ; *Rev. Univ. Mines*, (5), 2. 257, 1867 ; (5), 3. i, 485, 1867 ; F. Johnson, *The Iron and Steel Maker*, London, 1892 ; C. E. Jullien, *Traité théorique et pratique de la métallurgie du fer*, Paris, 1861 ; K. Karmarsch, *Geschichte der Technologie seit der Mitte der achtzehnten Jahrhunderts*, München, 1872 ; C. J. B. Karsten, *Handbuch der Eisenhüttenkunde*, Halle, 1841 ; B. Kerl, *Grundriss der Eisenhüttenkunde*, Leipzig, 1875 ; *Grundriss der Eisenprobirkunst*, Leipzig, 1875 ; A. von Kerpely, *Eisen und Stahl auf der Weltausstellung im Jahre 1878*, Leipzig, 1878 ; F. Kohn, *Iron and Steel Manufacture*, London, 1869 ; H. Kopp, *Geschichte du Chemie*, Braunschweig, 4. 137, 1847 ; W. A. Lampadius, *Die neuern Fortschritte im Gebiete der gesammten Hüttenkunde*, Freiberg, 1839 ; *Handbuch der allgemeinen Hüttenkunde*, Göttingen, 1801–1810 ; H. Landrin, *Manuel complet du maître de forges*, Paris, 1829 ; F. Laur, *Les mines et usines à l'exposition internationale de Bruxelles*, Paris, 1897 ; *Les mines et usines au XXe siècle*, Paris, 1900 ; R. Ledebur, *Handbuch der Eisenhüttenkunde*, Leipzig, 1884 ; *Stahl Eisen*, 12. 741, 1892 ; 13. 427, 1893 ; 14. 283, 1894 ; 15. 77, 856, 1895 ; 16. 857, 1896 ; 17. 862, 1897 ; 19. 28, 757, 1890 ; 23. 528, 1903 ; *Die Metalle, ihre Gewinnung und ihre Verarbeitung*, Stuttgart, 1887 ; J. P. Lesley, *The Iron Manufacturer's Guide to the Furnaces, Forges, and Rolling Mills of the United States*, New York, 1859 ; F. Liger, *La ferronnerie ancienne et moderne*, Paris, 1875 ; J. C. de Manson, *Traité du fer et de l'acier*, Strasbourg, 1804 ; F. A. von Marcher, *Beyträge zur Eisenhüttenkunde*, Klagenfurt, 1812 ; G. Mehrtens, *Eisen und Eisenkonstruktionen*, Berlin, 1887 ; *Stahl Eisen*, 7. 375, 440, 527, 608, 678, 754, 1887 ; D. Mushet, *Papers on Iron and Steel, Practical and Experimental*, London, 1840 ; W. Needham, *On the Manufacture of Iron*, London, 1831 ; H. S. Osborne, *The Metallurgy of Iron and Steel, Theoretical and Practical*, Philadelphia,

1869 ; J. Oser, *Verh. Verbreit. Naturw. Kenntnisse*, **21.** 191, 1880 ; F. Overman, *The Manufacture of Iron in all its Branches*, Philadelphia, 1850 ; J. Percy, *Metallurgy—Iron and Steel*, London, 1864 ; F. le Play, *Mémoire sur la fabrication et le commerce des fers à aciers dans le nord de l'Europe*, Paris, 1846 ; E. Röhrig, *Uebernahme und Lieferung von Eisenmaterialien*, Leipzig, 1877 ; S. B. Rogers, *An Elementary Treatise on Iron Metallurgy up to the Manufacture of Riddled Bars*, London, 1858 ; T. Scheeren, *Lehrbuch der Metallurgie*, Braunschweig, 1853 ; A. Schlink, *Gemeinfassliche Darstellung des Eisenhüttenwesens*, Düsseldorf, 1896 ; A. Schonmetzler, *Katechismus der Eisenhüttenkunde*, Wien, 1887 ; A. Schott, *Stahl Eisen*, **8.** 141, 1888 ; E. Schott, *Eisenhüttenproducte, Eisen und Stahlarbeiten bei der Wiener Austellung*, Leipzig, 1873 ; E. Schweickhardt, *Das Eisen in historischer und national-ökonomischer Beziehung*, Tübingen, 1841 ; H. Scrivenor, *A Comprehensive History of the Iron Trade throughout the World from the Earliest Records to the Present Period*, London, 1841 ; C. W. von Siemens, *Die Eisen- und Stahlindustrie*, Berlin, 1878 ; H. J. Skelton, *Economies of Iron and Steel*, London, 1891 ; R. Solly, *Extracts on the Manufacture of Iron*, Leeds, 1852 ; K. Styffe, *Bericht über die neuesten Fortschritte in Eisenhüttenwesen*, Leipzig, 1868 ; J. M. Swank, *History of the Manufacture of Iron in all Ages*, Philadelphia, 1884 and 1892 ; W. A. Tiemann, *Systematische Eisenhüttenkunde*, Nürnberg, 1801 ; F. Toldt, *Die Chemie des Eisens*, Leoben, 1898 ; W. Truran, *The Iron Manufacture of Great Britain*, London, 1855 ; P. Tunner, *Berg. Hütt. Jahrb.* Leoben, **6.** 250, 1857 ; T. Turner, *The Metallurgy of Iron and Steel*, London, 1895 ; [*The Metallurgy of Iron*, London, 1908 ;] T. Undset, *Das erste Auftreten des Eisens in Nord-Europa*, Hamburg, 1882 ; B. Valerius, *Traité théorique et pratique de la fabrication du fer*, Bruxelles, 1843 ; Paris, 1875 ; A. M. H. de Villefosse, *De la richesse minérale*, Paris, 1819 ; E. Vollhann, *Beyträge zur neuerem Geschichte des Eisenhüttenwesens*, Leipzig, 1825 ; J. J. F. Waehler, *Grundriss der Eisenhüttenkunde*, Berlin, 1806 ; T. Webster, *The Case of Josiah Marshall Heath, the Inventor and Introducer of Welding Cast Iron from British Iron*, London, 1856 ; F. Wüst, *Die Eisenhüttenkunde*, Berlin, 1899 ; H. Wedding, *Verh. Beförd. Gewerbfleisses*, **58.** 191, 1879 ; *Grundriss der Eisenhüttenkunde*, Berlin, 1871 ; *Handbuch der Eisenhüttenkunde*, Braunschweig, 1891 ; *Das Eisenhüttenwesen erläutert ın acht Vorträges*, Leipzig, 1900 ; *Stahl Eisen*, **13.** 230, 1893 ; W. M. Williams, *Iron and Steel Manufacture*, London, 1876 ; *The Chemistry of Iron and Steel Making and of their Practical Uses*, London, 1890 ; F. X. M. Zippe, *Geschichte der Metalle*, Wien, 1857 ; Y. Zoppetti, *Disegni di Forni Macchine ed Apparecchi per la Siderurgia*, Milano, 1874 ; *Ars Siderurgia*, Milano, 1883.

Twentieth-century works : T. S. Ashton, *Iron and Steel in the Industrial Revolutions*, Manchester, 1924 ; D. Baedeker, *Alfred Krupp und die Entwicklung der Gussstahlfabrik zu Essen*, Essen, 1912 ; O. Bechstein, *Prometheus*, **29.** 205, 215, 1918 ; L. Beck, in *Reallexikon der germanistischen Altertumskunde*, Stuttgart, **1.** 549, 1913 ; *Stahl Eisen*, **25.** 937, 1905 ; W. Belck, *Zeit. Ethnologie*, **42.** 15, 1910 ; *Iron Coal Trades Rev.*, **88.** 388, 1914 ; M. W. von Bernewitz, *Blast Furnace Steel Plant*, **19.** 1219, 1931 ; K. Brisker, *Dingler's Journ.*, **317.** 217, 1930 ; B. H. Brough, *Journ. Iron Steel Inst.*, **69.** i, 233, 1906 ; D. Brownlie, *Journ. Iron Steel Inst.*, **121.** i, 455, 1930 ; A. Bruening, *Die Schmiedekunst seit dem Ende der Renaissance*, Leipzig, 1902 ; J. G. Butler, *Fifty Years of Iron and Steel*, Cleveland, 1920 ; H. H. Campbell, *The Manufacture and Properties of Iron and Steel*, New York, 1903 ; F. M. Feldhaus, *Die Technik der Vorzeit der geschichtlichen Zeit unde der Naturvölker*, Leipzig, 1914 ; *Ruhmesblätter der Technik*, Leipzig, 1926 ; *Kulturgeschichte der Technik*, Berlin, 1928 ; J. Filaleta, *El Min. Mexicano*, **44.** 148, 1904 ; W. Foy, *Ethnologica*, **1.** 185, 1909 ; J. A. N. Friend, *Journ. Iron Steel Inst.—Carnegie Mem.*, **12.** 219, 1923 ; *Foundry Trade Journ.*, **26.** 159, 182, 193, 216, 1922 ; *Iron in Antiquity*, London, 1926 ; J. S. Gardner, *English Ironwork of the Seventeenth and Eighteenth Centuries*, London, 1930 ; T. Geilenkurchen, *Grundzüge der Eisenhüttenwesens*, Berlin, 1911 ; S. L. Goodale, *Chronology Iron and Steel*, Pittsburg, 1920 ; L. Guillet, *Génie Civil*, **82.** 54, 1923 ; R. A. Hadfield, *Metallurgy and its Influence on Modern Progress*, London, 1925 ; *Engg.*, **99.** 195, 1915 ; *Eng.*, **117.** 715, 1914 ; *Iron Coal Trades Rev.*, **88.** 909, 944, 987, 1914 ; A. Hasslacher, *Das Industriegebiet an der Saar und seine hauptsächlichsten Industriezweige*, Saarbrücken, 1912 ; J. A. Hedvall, *Svenska Kem. Tids.*, **30.** 183, 206, 222, 1918 ; A. H. Hiorns, *Iron and Steel*, London, 1903 ; M. Hoernes, *Die Metalle*, Wien, 1909 ; *Reallexikon der germanistischen Altertumskunde*, **1.** 549, 1913 ; W. Hoesch, *Stahl Eisen*, **26.** 1256, 1906 ; E. J. Holmyard, *Nature*, **117.** 155, 1926 ; E. von Hoyer, *Zeit. Verbands deut. Dipl. Ing.*, **3.** 136, 158, 1912 ; R. W. Hunt, *A History of the Bessemer Manufacture in America*, Chicago, 1920 ; O. Johannsen, *Geschichte des Eisens*, Düsseldorf, 1925 ; A. F. Johnson, *Iron Coal Trades Rev.*, **96.** 287, 1918 ; H. von Jüptner, *Das Eisenhüttenwesen*, Leipzig, 1912 ; W. R. Klinkicht, *Forg. Stamp. Heat Treating*, **11.** 8, 1925 ; G. von Kowalczik, *Das Eisenwerk*, Berlin, 1927 ; P. R. Kuchnrich, *Foundry Trade Journ.*, **41.** 185, 1929 ; B. de Laveleye, *Journ. Iron Steel Inst.*, **121.** i, 455, 1930 ; E. Leber, *Stahl Eisen*, **35.** 234, 1915 ; A. von Schweiger-Lerchenfeld, *Im Reiche der Zyklopen*, Wien, 1900 ; E. Lewis, *Journ. Australia Inst. Eng.*, **1.** 125, 183, 227, 1929 ; E. O. von Lippmann, *Entstehung und Ausbreitung der Alchemie*, Berlin, 1919 ; H. Lund, *Rekn. Ukeblad*, **33.** 421, 442, 1915 ; E. D. McCallum, *The Iron and Steel Industry in the United States*, London, 1931 ; T. Makemson, *Foundry Trade Journ.*, **29.** 153, 1924 ; H. H. Manchester, *Eng. Min. Journ.*, **114.** 409, 447, 495, 545, 1922 ; P. Martell, *Giesserei*, **14.** 857, 1927 ; C. Matschoss, *Beiträge zur Geschichte der Technik* *und Industrie*, Berlin, **3.** 79, 1911 ; E. Mayer, *Stahl Eisen*, **49.** 1217, 1929 ; K. Möbus, *Kritische Untersuchung der Umkehr-Walzenzugmaschine an Hand ihre geschichtlichen, Entwicklung*, Duisberg, 1927 ; A. Neuburger, *Die Technik des Altertums*, Leipzig, 1919 ; London, 1930 ; B. Neumann, *Die Metalle*, Halle a. S., 1904 ; L. Peetz, *Mitt. Aachener Bezirkver. deut. Ing.*, **3,** 1920 ; W. Reimpell, *Geschichtsblätt. Tech. Ind. Gewerbe*, **1.** 614, 1914 ; T. A. Rickard, *Eng. Min. Journ.*, **117.** 759, 1924 ; *Man and Metals*, New York, 1930 ; A. Rössing, *Geschichte der Metalle*, Berlin, 1901 ; A. Sailler, *Oesterr. Zeit. Berg. Hütt.*, **57.** 775, 1909 ; H. A. Schwartz, *American Malleable Cast Iron*, Cleveland, Ohio, 1922 ; M. von Schwarz and F. Dannemann, *Die Eisengewinnung von der ältesten Ziehen bis auf den heutigen Tag*, München, 1925 ; A. H. Sexton, *An Outline of the Metallurgy of Iron and Steel*, Manchester, 1902 ; O. Simmersbach, *Die Eisenindustrie*, Leipzig, 1906 ; J. R. Smith, *The Story of Iron and Steel*, New York, 1908 ; S. G. Smith, *Foundry Trade Journ.*, **34.** 349, 375, 1926 ; F. Somers, *Iron Trade Rev.*, **73.** 311, 389, 463, 1923 ; B. Stoughton, *The Metallurgy of Iron and Steel*, New York, 1911 ; E. Straker, *Wealdon Iron*, London, 1931 ; J. M. Swank, *Iron and Steel at the Close of the Nineteenth Century*, Washington, 1901 ; G. E. Thackray, *Trans. Amer. Soc. Steel Treating*, **6.** 443, 1924 ; *Thomas and Gilchrist 1879–1929 Bolchow and Vaugham*, Middlesbrough, 1929 ; H. P. Tiemann, *Iron and Steel*, New York, 1919 ; A. Trappen, *Stahl Eisen*, **26.** 82, 1906 ; O. Vogel, *Jahrb. Eisenhüttenwesen*, **4.** 1, 1903 ; *Prometheus*, **15.** 689, 710, 1904 ; J. B. Walker, *The Story of Steel*, New York, 1926 ; H. B. Wheatley, *Foundry Trade Journ.*, **16.** 141, 205, 1914 ; T. Wolff, *Prometheus*, **20.** 137, 154, 1909 ; F. Wüst, *Die Entwicklung der deutschen Eisenindustrie in den letzten Jahren*, Halle a. S., 1909 ; G. Zippelius, *Jahrb. Eisenhüttenwesen*, **2.** 1, 1901.

REFERENCES.

1 Ismail Ibn 'Ati Abulfeda, *Geographie* (1321), Paris, 1883 ; J. de Acosta, *Historia natural y moral de la Indias*, Madrid, **1.** 293, 1894 ; W. H. Adolph, *Scient. Monthly*, **14.** 441, 1922 ; *Chem. Met. Engg.*, **26.** 914, 1922 ; T. W. Allen, *Classical Rev.*, **19.** 359, 1905 ; **20.** 267, 1906 ; **21.** 16, 1907 ; R. Andrée, *Votive und Weihgabendes katholischen Volks in Süddeutschland*, Braunschweig, 91, 1904 ; *Die Metalle bei den Naturvölkern mit Berücksichtigung prähistorischer Verhältnisse*, Leipzig, 66, 1884 ; *Mitt. anthropol. Ges. Wien*, **14.** 97, 1884 ; F. A. Anger, *Zeit. Ethnologie*, **12.** 106, 1880 ; *Verh. Berl. Ges. Anthropologie*, 251, 466, 1884 ; B. Ankermann, *Zeit. Ethnologie*, **37.** 75, 1905 ; **42.** 307, 1910 ; C. Arendt, *Bull. Assoc. Ing. Ind. Lux.*, **9.** 478, 1909 ; T. S. Ashton, *Trans. Newcomen Soc.*, **5.** 9, 1925 ; J. Babington, *Journ. Ethnolog. Soc.*, (2), **1.** 178, 1869 ; E. Baelz, *Zeit. Ethnologie*, **39.** 299, 1907 ; E. H. S. Bailey, *Amer. Journ. Science*, (3), **42.** 385, 1891 ; R. Baker, *Iron Coal Trades Rev.*, **64.** 637, 1902 ; S. W. Baker, *The Albert N'Yanza Great Basin of the Nile, and Exploration of the Nile Sources*, London, 1866 ; H. E. Balch, *Wookey Hole, its Caves and Cave Dwellers*, London, 1914 ; H. Balfour, *Journ. Inst. Metals*, **43.** 350, 1930 ; H. Barth, *Reisen und Entdeckungen, in Nord- und Central-Afrika*, Gotha, **2.** 154, 644, 1857 ; **3.** 400, 1857 ; A. Bastian, *Die Culturländer des alten Amerika*, Berlin, **2.** 677, 1878 ; Ibn Batuta in E. Schultze, *Bibliothek denkwürdiger Reisen*, Hamburg, 63, 1911 ; R. von B. Baum, *Stahl Eisen*, **23.** 713, 1903 ; L. Beck, *Der Geschichte des Eisens in technischer und kultur-geschichtlicher Beziehung*, Braunschweig, 206, 1884 ; *Ann. Ver. Nassau Alterthumskunde*, **14.** 317, 1877 ; **15.** 124, 1879 ; *Festschrift Centralmuseums zu Mainz*, 1902 ; *Arch. Anthropology*, **12.** 92, 309, 419, 1880 ; J. Beckmann, *Beytrage zur Geschichte der Erfindungen*, Leipzig, **3.** 202, 304, 1790 ; **5.** 77, 1805 ; London, **2.** 324, 1846 ; R. Behla, *Verh. Berl. Ges. Anthropologie*, 422, 1895 ; N. T. Belaiew, *Journ. Iron Steel Inst.*, **121.** i, 449, 1930 ; *Met.*, **8.** 449, 493, 1911 ; *Journ. Inst. Metals*, **43.** 352, 1930 ; *Rev. d'Assyriologie*, **26.** 115, 1929 ; W. Belck, *Zeit. Ethnologie*, **39.** 334, 362, 379, 946, 1907 ; **40.** 45, 241, 272, 1908 ; **42.** 15, 1910 ; *Iron Coal Trades Rev.*, **88.** 388, 1914 ; H. Bell, *Journ. Iron Steel Inst.*, **85.** i, 118, 1912 ; C. V. Bellamy, *Journ. Iron Steel Inst.*, *ib.*, **66.** ii, 99, 1904 ; G. Beloch, *Riv. Filologia Intr. Class.*, **2.** 49, 1874 ; G. Belzoni, *Narrative of he Operations and Recent Discoveries within the Pyramids, Temples, Tombs, and Excavations in Egypt and Nubia*, London, 162, 1820 ; I. Benzinger, *Real Enzyklopädie des classischen Altertums*, Stuttgart, **4.** 2047, 1901 ; V. Berard, *Les Pheniciens et l'Odyssée*, Paris, 1902 ; A. Bertholet, *Zeit. Ethnologie*, **39.** 945, 1907 ; **40.** 247, 1908 ; M. Berthelot, *Chemie au Moyen Age*, Paris, **1.** 359, 1893 ; E. von Bibra, *Ueber alte Eisen- und Silber-Funde*, Nürnberg, 182, 1873 ; S. U. Syed Ali Bigrami, *Journ. Iron Steel Inst.*, **56.** ii, 65, 1899 ; G. C. M. Birdwood, *The Industrial Arts in India*, London, **2.** 3, 1880 ; J. Backhouse, *A Narrative of a Visit to the Mauritius and South Africa*, London, 377, 1844 ; W. G. Blaikie, *The Life of David Livingstone*, London, 43, 1882 ; W. P. Blake, *Amer. Journ. Science*, (3), **31.** 41, 1886 ; F. J. Bliss, *A Mound of Many Cities*, London, 135, 1894 ; H. Blümner, *Technologie und Terminologie der Gewerbe und Künste bei Griechen und Römern*, Leipzig, **4.** 67, 1887 ; J. G. L. Blumhof, *Encyclopädie der Eisenhüttenkunde*, Giessen, **2.** 339, 1817 ; J. Bohm, *Zeit. Ethnologie*, **17.** 1, 1885 ; W. E. B. du Bois, *What is Civilization ?* London, 45, 1926 ; J. Bonomi, *Nineveh and its Palaces*, London, 1852 ; A. Bose, *Stahl Eisen*, **34.** 849, 1914 ; T. E. Bowdich, *Mission from Cape Coast Castle to Ashantee ; with a Statistical Account of the Kingdom, and Geographical Notices of other parts of the Interior of Africa*, London, 1819 ; H. A. Boyd, *Amer. Journ. Archæology*, (2), **5,** 128, 1901 ; H. Braun, *Stahl Eisen*, **25.** 1195, 1905 ; W. P. Breach, *Sussex Arch. Collections*, **46.** 613, 1903 ; J. H. Breasted, *Ancient Records of Egypt*, Chicago, **3.** 177, 1906 ; A. E. Brehm, *Reisekizzen aus*

Nordost-Afrika, Jena, **1**. 209, 1855 ; J. T. Brent, *The Sacred City of the Ethiopians*, London, 211, 1893 ; *The Ruined Cities of Mashonaland*, London, 268, 1892 ; C. Brockelmann, *Geschichte der christlichen Litteraturen des Oriento*, Leipzig, 236, 1907 ; B. H. Brough, *The Early Use of Iron*, London, 1906 ; *Journ. Iron Steel Inst.*, **69**. i, 233, 1906 ; J. C. Brown, *Iron Coal Trades Rev.*, **101**. 291, 1920 ; H. Brugsch, *Religion und Mythologie der alten Aegypter*, Leipzig, 1885–1888 ; *Aegyptologie*, Leipzig, 1897 ; *Geschichte Aegyptens unter den Pharaonen*, Leipzig, 765, 1877 ; F. Buchanan, *A Journey from Madras through the Counties of Mysore, Canara, and Malabar*, London, 1807 ; M. Buchholz, *Verh. Berl. Ges. Anthropologie*, 117, 1883 ; R. Bucholz, *Verh. Berl. Ges. Anthropologie*, 503, 1890 ; E. A. W. Budge, *Egypt*, London, 54, 1925 ; *A History of Egypt*, London, 1902 ; A. Bulleid and H. St. G. Gray, *The Glastonbury Lake Village*, Glastonbury, 1911–7 ; J. H. Burkart, *Amer. Journ. Science*, (3), **7**. 75, 1874 ; R. M. Burrows, *Discoveries in Crete*, London, 208, 1907 ; *Classical Rev.*, **21**. 19, 1907 ; S. M. Burrows, *The Buried Cities of Ceylon*, Colombo, 1905 ; R. F. Burton, *The Lake Regions of Central Africa*, London, **2**. 184, 273, 311, 1860 ; J. P. Bushe-Fox, *Reports on the Research Committee of the Society of Antiquaries of of London*, **1**. 28, 1913 ; **2**. 13, 1914 ; **4**. 30, 1916 ; R. Caillié, *Journal d'un voyage à Temboctou et à Jenné dans l'Afrique Central*, Paris, **1**. 270, 1830 ; **2**. 149, 1830 ; V. L. Cameron, *Across Africa*, London, **1**. 245, 1877 ; **2**. 165, 1877 ; *Journ. Anthropol. Inst.*, **6**. 170, 1877 ; H. C. H. Carpenter, *Nature*, **123**. 906, 1929 ; H. C. H. Carpenter and J. M. Robertson, *Journ. Iron Steel Inst.*, **121**. i, 417, 1930 ; E. Cartailhac, *Verh. Berl. Ges. Anthropologie*, 424, 1891 ; H. Carter, *The Tomb of Tut-ankh-amen*, London, **2**. 248, 1927 ; *Illustrated London News*, **174**. 4, 1928 ; F. Cartwright, *Iron Coal Trades Rev.*, **75**. 736, 1907 ; K. Cermak, *Verh. Berl. Ges. Anthropologie*, 468, 1887 ; P. B. du Chaillu, *Explorations and Adventures in Equatorial Africa*, London, 90, 1861 ; G. Chamier, *Journ. Iron Steel Inst.*, **82**. ii, 319, 1910 ; G. P. Chaplin, *Iron Coal Trades Rev.*, **88**. 565, 1914 ; H. le Chatelier, *Journ. Iron Steel Inst.*, **85**. i, 180, 1912 ; H. Chevalier, *Mem. Trav. Soc. Ing. Civils*, **2**. 336, 1903 ; S. Clessin, *Corresp. Blatt deut. Ges. Anthropologie*, 55, 1876 ; L. Cohn, *Verh. Berl. Ges. Anthropologie*, 249, 1895 ; W. G. Collingwood and H. S. Cooper, *Antiquary*, **33**. 259, 1896 ; C. R. Conder, *The Tel-el-Amarna Tablets*, London, 189, 1893 ; A. K. Coomaraswamy, *Mediæval Sinhalese Art*, Broad Campden, 1908 ; H. B. Cotterill, *Ancient Greece*, London, 1913 ; H. Cousens, *Ann. Rep. Archæological Survey of India*, Calcutta, 205, 1904 ; E. T. Cox, *Amer. Journ. Science*, (3), **5**. 155, 1873 ; W. Coxe, *An Historical Tour in Monmouthshire*, London, 206, 1801 ; W. Cracroft, *Journ. Asiatic Soc. Bengal*, **1**. 150, 1832 ; J. Crawfurd, *A Descriptive Dictionary of the Indian Islands and Adjacent Countries*, London, 157, 409, 1856 ; M. Cremer, *Zeit. Berg. Hütt. Sal.*, **61**. 80, 1913 ; G. Cumming, *In the Himalayas and on the Indian Plains*, London, 1898 ; F. Cumont, *Les religions orientales dans le paganisme romain*, Paris, 1909 ; A. Cunningham, *Archæological Survey of India*, Simla, 1871 ; E. Curtius, *Griechische Geschichte*, Berlin, **1**. 138, 1887 ; J. Danvers, *Journ. Soc. Arts*, **41**. 602, 1893 ; R. Dart, *Nature*, **126**. 321, 1930 ; A. Daubrée, *Compt. Rend.*, **66**. 572, 1868 ; C. Davenport, *Jewellery*, London, 65, 1905 ; J. Davy, *An Account of the Interior of Ceylon and of its Inhabitants*, London, 261, 1821 ; C. Dawson, *Sussex Arch. Collections*, **46**. 1, 1902 ; St. J. V. Day, *The Prehistoric Use of Iron and Steel*, London, 1877 ; *On some Evidences as to the Early Use of Iron*, Edinburgh, 1871 ; *On the High Antiquity of Iron and Steel*, London, 1875 ; *Nostrand's Eng. Mag.*, **11**. 481, 1874 ; *Proc. Phil. Soc. Glasgow*, **7**. 476, 1871 ; **8**. 235, 1873 ; J. Déchelette, *Manuel d'Archéologie*, Paris, **2**. 513, 541, 1910 ; C. C. von der Decken, *Reisen in Ostafrika*, Leipzig, **2**. 17, 1871 ; W. Deecke, *Monatsbl. Ges. Pommersche Geschichte*, **11**. 87, 1906 ; A. Delegorgue, *Voyage dans l'Afrique Australe*, Paris, **2**. 30, 1847 ; F. Delitzsch, *Babel und Bibel*, Leipzig, 1905 ; W. Denison, *Journ. Ethnolog. Soc.*, (2), **1**. 198, 1869 ; G. Dennis, *The Cities and Cemeteries of Etruriens*, London, 1848 ; *Die Städte und Begräbnis plätze Etruriens*, Leipzig, 390, 1852 ; C. H. Desch, *B.A. Rep.*, 437, 1928 ; *Journ. Iron Steel Inst.*, **94**. ii, 350, 1916 ; E. Desor, *Die Pfahlbauten des Neuenburger Sees*, Frankfurt a. M., 1866 ; P. Deussen, *Allgemeine Geschichte der Philosophie*, Leipzig, 1894 ; A. Ditte, *Le Mois Scient. Inst.*, 132, 1900 ; F. Dixey, *Mining Mag.*, **23**. 213, 1920 ; J. L. Döhne, *Zulu-Kafir Dictionary*, Cape Town, 89, 1857 ; W. Dönitz, *Verh. Berl. Ges. Anthropologie*, 122, 1887 ; I. Domeyko, *Compt. Rend.*, **81**. 597, 1875 ; M. Donkelmann, *Ann. Chim. Phys.*, (2), **13**. 111, 1820 ; J. Dümichen, *Historische Inschriften*, Leipzig, **2**. 56, 1869 ; E. Dulaurier, *Journ. Asiatique Soc.*, (4), **8**. 143, 1846 ; G. W. Earl, *Journ. Asiatic Soc. Great Britain*, **4**. 178, 1837 ; *The Native Races of the Indian Archipelago*, London, 76, 1853 ; G. Ebers, *Zeit. Aegyptosprache Alterthumkunde*, **9**. 19, 1871 ; M. Ebert, *Reallexikon der Vorgeschichte*, **3**. 356, 1924 ; W. Ellis, *Three Visits to Madagascar*, London, 264, 1858 ; K. Endemann, *Zeit. Ethnologie*, **6**. 25, 1874 ; A. Erman, *Ges. Anthropologie*, 180, 1888 ; *Aegypten und aegyptisches Leben im Altertum*, Tübingen, **2**. 611, 1887 ; *Arch. Sciences Russ.*, **1**. 314, 1841 ; *Zeit. Ethnologie*, **2**. 386, 1870 ; A. J. Evand, *Prehistoric Tombs of Knossos*, London, 1906 ; *Archæologia*, **59**. 391, 1905 ; H. C. Evans, *Foundry Trade Journ.*, **35**. 321, 505, 1927 ; J. Evans, *The Coins of the Ancient Britons*, London, 41, 1864 ; J. R. Evans, *Eng. Min. Journ.*, **122**. 179, 1926 ; H. Everett, *Journ. Asiatic Soc.—Straits*, **1**. 20, 1878 ; J. H. Evesy, *Foundry Trade Journ.*, **38**. 109, 1928 ; O. C. Farrington, *Field Museum Publ. Geol. Series*, 3, 1916 ; *Amer. Journ. Science*, (4), **29**. 350, 1910 ; C. Faulmann, *Illustrierte Culturgeschichte*, Wien, 1881 ; A. Favre, *Arch. Sciences Genève*, (2), **37**. 97, 1870 ; *Zeit. Ethnologie*, **2**. 129, 1870 ; F. M. Feldhaus, *Die Technik der Vorzeit, der geschichtlichen Zeit und der Naturvölker*, Leipzig, 1914 ; J. Ferguson, *Illustrations of Ancient Architecture in Hindustan*, London, 1847 ; H. Fey, *Stahl Eisen*, **50**. 598, 1930 ; M. Feyerabend, *Verh. Berl. Ges. Anthropologie*, 257, 1890 ; M. Firdusis, *Schah- Nameh*, Berlin, **1**. 47, 1890 ; L. Fletcher, *An Introduction to the Study of Meteorites*, London, 1904 ; *Min. Mag.*, **7**. 179, 287,

1887; **9.** 107, 149, 1890; **14.** 28, 1904; W. Flight, *Journ. Chem. Soc.*, **41.** 140, 1882; W. M. Foote, *Amer. Journ. Science*, (4), **3.** 65, 1897; (4), **8.** 153, 1899; R. Forrer, *Real-Lexikon der prähistorischen, klassischen und frühekristlichen Altertümer*, Stuttgart, 1907; *Urgeschichte des Europäerns*, Stuttgart, 1908; R. H. Forster and W. H. Knowles, *Corstopitum*, Newcastle, 1910; F. A. Foster, *Amer. Machinist*, **51.** 345, 1919; W. Foy, *Chem. Ztg.*, **32.** 973, 1908; *Verh. Ges. deut. Naturf. Aerzte*, **80.** ii, 208, 1908; *Ethnologica*, **1.** 185, 1909; L. Fraser, *Iron and Steel in India*, Bombay, 1919; F. Freise, *Erzbergbau*, **2.** 663, 761, 779, 820, 1906; **3.** 20, 76, 93, 1907; *Geschichte der Bergbau und Hüttentechnik*, Berlin, 1908; C. Fremont, *Génie Civil*, **90.** 198, 1927; E. Friedel, *Die Stein-, Bronze-, und Eisen-Zeit in der Mark Brandenburg*, Berlin, 32, 1878; *Corresp. Blatt Deut. Ges. Anthropologie*, 11, 1880; *Verh. Berl. Ges. Anthropologie*, 372, 1879; 41, 1880; L. Friedländer, *Darstellungen aus der Sittengeschichte Roms*, Leipzig, 1910; J. A. N. Friend, *Iron in Antiquity*, London, 1926; *Trans. Worcestershire Nat. Club*, 2, 1919; *Journ. Iron Steel Inst.—Carnegie Mem.*, **12.** 219, 1923; *Journ. Iron Steel Inst.*, **120.** ii, 343, 1930; J. A. N. Friend and W. E. Thorneycroft, *Metal Ind.*, **25.** 257, 1924; *Journ. Iron Steel Inst.*, **110.** ii, 313, 1924; **112.** ii, 225, 1925; G. Fritsch, *Die Eingeborenen Süd-Afrika's*, Breslau, 71, 434, 1873; E. de Froberville, *Bull. Soc. Géogr.*, (3), **8.** 322, 1847; M. Fuchs, *Ikonographie der Planeten*, München, 2. 508, 1909; H. Garland, *Ancient Egyptian Metallurgy*, London, 97, 1927; H. Gaythorpe, *Barrow Naturalists Field Club*, **17.** 1, 1903; J. G. Georgi, *Bemerkungen einer Reise im russischen Reich*, St. Petersburg, **1.** 115, 127, 260, 308, 1775; R. D. Georgi, *Polular Science Monthly*, **67.** 687, 1905; M. Gercke, *Mitt. Geschichte Med. Naturwiss.*, **3.** 341, 1907; M. S. Giuseppi, *Surrey Arch. Collections*, **17.** 28, 1902; J. H. Gladstone, *Nature*, **57.** 594, 1898; Diodorus, *Bibliotheca Historica*, **5.** 13, c. 30 B.C.; W. E. Gladstone, *The Time and Place of Homer*, London, 46, 1876; S. R. K. Glanville, *Journ. Egypt. Arch.*, **14.** 191, 1928; A. Glitsch, *Verh. Berl. Ges. Anthropologie*, 486, 1884; J. G. Gmelin, *Reise durch Sibirien*, Göttingen, **1.** 280, 407, 1751; A. Goebel, *Bull. Acad. St. Petersburg*, (3), **19.** 544, 1874; A. Goetze, *Zeit. Ethnologie*, **32.** 202, 1900; W. Gowland, *Metals of Antiquity*, London, 1912; *Journ. Anthropological Inst.*, 285, 1912; W. von Gravenberch, *Wigalois*, Berlin, 1819; H. G. Graves, *Chem. Ztg.*, **36.** 594, 1912; *Journ. Iron Steel Inst.*, **85.** i, 187, 1912; **85.** i, 188, 1912; H. M. G. Grellmann, *Die Zigeuner*, Leipzig, 60, 1783; D. Griffiths, *Journ. Soc. Chem. Ind.—Chem. Ind.*, **50.** 431, 1931; J. and W. Grimm, *Deutsches Wörterbuch*, Leipzig, **3.** 1076, 1862; V. Gross, *Zeit. Ethnologie*, **38.** 996, 1906; H. Grosse, *Zeit. Ethnologie*, **41.** 72, 1909; S. Groves, *Iron Steel Mag.*, **10.** 193, 300, 1905; W. Grube, *Geschichte der chinesischen Litteratur*, Leipzig, 1909; *Religion und Kultur der Chinesen*, Leipzig, 1910; M. Gsell, *Eisen, Kupfer und Bronze bei den alten Aegyptern*, Karlsruhe, 1910; *Mitt. Geschichte Med. Naturwiss.*, **6.** 362, 1910; A. de Gubernatis, *Mythologie des plantes*, Paris, 1878–1882; W. Guertler, *Internat. Zeit. Metallogr.*, **5.** 129, 1914; M. Guillain, *Documents sur l'histoire, la géographie et le commerce de l'Afrique orientale*, Paris, **1.** 205, 224, 1856; M. Gummerus, *Real Enzyklopädie des classischen Altertums*, Stuttgart, **9.** 1441, 1916; A. Gurlt, *Eisen- und Stahlgewinnung bei den Römern*, Siegen, 1881; *Rev. Univ. Mines*, (2), **19.** 293, 1886; G. Gustafson, *Osebergfundet*, Kristiania, 1917; H. Guthe, *Kurzes Bibelwörterbuch*, Tübingen, 147, 432, 1903; R. A. Hadfield, *Iron Age*, **89.** 55, 1912; *Iron Trade Rev.*, **77.** 1333, 1925; *Proc. Roy. Soc.*, **86.** a, 94, 1912; *Journ. Iron Steel Inst.*, **85.** i, 134, 156, 173, 1902; **120.** ii, 345, 1930; *Journ. Soc. Chem. Ind.—Chem. Ind.*, **44.** 1029, 1925; H. Haedicke, *Mitt. Geschichte Med. Naturwiss.*, **12.** 271, 1913; P. Hahnel, *Verh. Berl. Ges. Anthropologie*, 23, 1877; M. Hajnal, *Banyaszati es Kohaszati Lepok*, **40.** 218, 1907; H. R. Hall, *The Cambridge Ancient History*, Cambridge, **1.** 656, 1923; *Man*, **3.** 147, 1903; *Aegean Archæology*, London, 177, 1915; *The Oldest Civilization of Greece*, London, 198, 1901; *The Civilization of Greece in the Bronze Age*, London, 252, 1928; J. W. Hall, *Trans. Newcomen Soc.*, **5.** 1, 1925; P. S. P. Handcock, *Archæology of the Holy Land*, London, 210, 1916; H. Hanemann, *Internat. Zeit. Metallog.*, **4.** 248, 1913; *Oesterr. Zeit. Berg. Hütt.*, **62.** 183, 1914; *Mitt. Geschichte Med. Naturwiss.*, **12.** 271, 1913; *Stahl Eisen*, **51.** 67, 104, 1931; W. von Harnier, *Reise am oberen Nil*, Darmstadt, 50, 1866; F. D. Hartland, *Proc. Soc. Antiquarians*, (2), **5.** 328, 1872; F. S. Hartmann, *Verh. Berl. Ges. Anthropologie*, 235, 1874; M. Hartwich, *Verh. Berl. Ges. Anthropologie*, 222, 1887; J. B. van Hasselt, *Zeit. Ethnologie*, **8.** 171, 1876; J. Hastings, *A Dictionary of the Bible*, Edinburgh, **4.** 821, 1909; T. Haupt, *Berg. Hütt. Ztg.*, **47.** 41, 51, 61, 95, 107, 123, 141, 161, 179, 189, 199, 1888; J. F. L. Hausmann, *Commentarium de arte ferri conficiendi veterum, inprimis Græcorum et Romanorum*, Göttingae, 1819; F. Haverfield, *Journ. Iron Steel Inst.*, **85.** i, 133, 1912; S. Hearne, *A Journey from Prince of Wales's Fort in Hudson's Bay to the Northern Ocean*, London, 169, 1795; J. M. Heath, *Journ. Roy. Asiatic Soc.*, **5.** 390, 1839; W. Helbig, *Das homerische Epos aus dem Denkmalern erläutet*, Leipzig, 330, 1887; A. Hennig, *Zeit. Ethnologie*, **11.** 303, 1879; H. Hensoldt, *Amer. Geol.*, **4.** 28, 73, 1889; B. F. J. Hermann, *Mineralogische Reisen in Sibirien*, St. Petersburg, **3.** 102, 1801; A. de Herrera, *Zwölfter Teil der neuen Welt*, Frankfurt, 20, 126, 1623; A. Hertz, *L'Anthropologie*, **35.** 75, 1925; M. T. von Heuglin, *Reise in das Gebiet des weisses Nil und seiner westlichen Zuflüsse*, Leipzig, 196, 1869; W. Heyd, *Geschichte des Levante—Handels im Mittelalter*, Stuttgart, **1.** 183, 1879; **2.** 497, 1879; M. Heydeck, *Verh. Berl. Ges. Anthropologie*, 363, 1877; B. Heyne, *Tracts Historical and Statistical on India*, London, 1814; W. E. Hidden, *Amer. Journ. Science*, (3), **32.** 304, 1886; (4), **9.** 367, 1900; H. Hildebrand, *Das heidnische Zeitalter in Schweden*, Hamburg, 1873; *Arch. Anthropologie*, **8.** 278, 1875; J. R. Hill, *Cassier's Eng. Monthly*, **47.** 275, 1915; F. Hirth, *The Ancient History of China, to the East of the Chou Dynasty*, New York, 203, 1908; M. Hoernes, *Natur- und Urgeschichte der Menschen*, Wien, 2. 297, 1909; *Die Metalle*, Wien, 2. 291, 1909; *Reallexikon der germanistischen Altertumskunde*, **1.** 549

1913; **2**. 366, 1915; **3**. 126, 1916; *Kultur der Unzeit*, Leipzig, **2**. 11, 1917; J. E. Holgate, *Journ. Iron Steel Inst.*, **117**. i, 209, 1928; *Journ. Chem. Soc. South Africa*, **28**. 155, 1928; **29**. 2, 1928; S. H. Hollands, *Antiquary*, **32**. 198, 1896; W. H. Holmes, *Archæological Studies*, Chicago, 276, 1895; *Ann. Rept. Smithsonian Inst.*, 723, 1903; N. O. Holst, *Tek. Tids.*, **42**. 46, 1912; E. Holub, *Mitt. geogr. Ges. Wien*, (2), **12**. 283, 321, 1879; F. Hommel, *Geschichte des alten Morgenlandes*, Leipzig, 1912; J. Hoops, *Real-Lexikon der germanistischen Altertumskunde*, Strassburg, 1911; L. Horner, *Tijds. Ind. Taal-Land-Volkenkunde*, (4), **1**. 371, 1861; C. Hose and W. McDougall, *The Pagan Tribes of Borneo*, London, **1**. 193, 1912; C. Hostmann, *Studien zur vorgeschichlichen Archäologie*, Braunschweig, 120, 1890; *Arch. Anthropol.*, **8**. 278, 1875; **9**. 197, 1876; **10**. 418, 1878; **12**. 442, 1880; *Verh. Berl. Ges. Anthropologie*, 185, 1876; E. Howard, *Phil. Trans.*, **92**. 206, 211, 1802; O. H. Howard, *Arch. Journ.*, **49**. 7, 1892; E. E. Howell, *Amer. Journ. Science*, (3), **40**. 223, 1890; E. Hübner, *Real Enzyklopädie des classischen Altertums*, Stuttgart, **3**. 1890, 1899; C. Hülsen, *ib.*, **6**. 2171, 1909; F. H. A. von Humboldt, *Versuche über den politischen Zustand des Königreichs Neuspanien*, Tübingen, **4**. 8, 1813; *Vues des Cordillères*, Paris, **1**. 314, 1816; *Kosmos*, Stuttgart, 1850; O. W. Huntingdon, *Proc. Amer. Acad.*, **25**. 229, 1890; F. Hupfeld, *Mitt. deut. Schutzgebieten*, **12**. 175, 1899; T. J. Hutchinson, *Impressions of Western Africa*, London, 192, 1858; A. Ilg, *Beiträge zur Geschichte der Kunst und der Kunsttechnik aus mittelhochdeutschen Dichtungen*, Wien, 131, 1892; O. Immisch, *Lexikon der griechischen und römischen Mythologie*, Leipzig, **2**. 1587, 1897; L. Jacob, *Journ. Roy. Asiatic Soc.—Ceylon*, **7**. 98, 1848; G. Jars, *Voyages metallurgiques*, Lyon, **1**. 30, 1774; R. Jenkins, *Trans. Newcomen Soc.*, **4**. 102, 1924; **6**. 42, 1925; *Eng.*, **140**. 575, 1925; H. Jentsch, *Verh. Berl. Ges. Anthropologie*, 387, 1885; 588, 1886; 721, 1887; 52, 123, 1888; 566, 1893; *Die prähistorischen Alterthümer aus dem Stadtund Landkreise Guben*, Guben, 1886; *Die prähistorischen Altertümer der Gymnasialsammlung*, Guben, 1886; *Verh. deut. Ges. Anthropologie*, 435, 1888; A. Jeremias, *Handbuch der altorientalischen Geisteskultur*, Leipzig, 1913; F. B. Jevons, *Journ. Hellenic Studies*, **13**. 25, 1923; C. Jirecek, *Archäolog. Mitt. Oesterr. Ungarn.*, **10**. 43, 129, 1886; O. Johannsen, *Arch. Geschichte Naturwiss. Technik*, **3**. 365, 1918; *Zeit. angew. Chem.*, **31**. 149, 1918; *Geschichte des Eisens*, Düsseldorf, 9, 1925; *Prähist. Zeit.*, **9**. 176, 1917; **8**. 165–168, 1917; J. Johnston, *Ottawa Naturalist*, **20**. 51, 1906; W. Jones, *Finger Ring Lore*, London, 303, 1877; *Crowns and Coronations*, London, 366, 1883; T. A. Joyce, *Mexican Archæology*, London, 141, 1914; G. W. A. Kahlbaum, *Gedenkschrift*, Leipzig, 127, 1909; *Mythos und Naturwissenshaft*, Leipzig, 1898; O. Kern, *Real Enzyklopädie des classischen Altertums*, Stuttgart, **4**. 2018, 1901; A. C. Key, *Mining Journ.*, **66**. 627, 659, 734, 822, 1896; L. W. King and H. R. Hall, *Egypt and Western Asia in the Light of Recent Discoveries*, London, 112, 1907; 116, 1910; C. Klinkenberg, *Mitt. Geschichte Med. Naturwiss.*, **15**. 339, 1916; J. Klaproth, *Nord. Blätt. Chem.*, **1**. 229, 1817; C. B. Klunzinger, *Bilder aus Oberägypten, der Wüste und dem Rothen Meere*, Stuttgart, 13, 1877; M. Knauthe, *Verh. Berl. Ges. Anthropologie*, 680, 1887; E. Kocher, *Stahl Eisen*, **41**. 9, 1921; A. Koerte, *Mitt. deut. Archæol. Athen*, **24**. 19, 1899; A. Kohn, *Zeit. Ethnologie*, **10**. 461, 1878; M. Kranz, *Natur- und Kultur-Leben der Zulus*, Wiesbaden, 66, 1880; A. Krascheninnikoff, *Opisanie Zemli Kamtschatki*, Lemgo, 223, 1766; J. H. Krause, *Pyrgoteles*, Halle, 124, 1856; A. Krebs, *Die vorrömische Metallzeit in östlichen Westfalen*, Leipzig, 1925; A. von Kremer, *Culturgeschichte des Orients unter den Chalifen*, Wien, **1**. 79, 1875; **2**. 284, 1875; R. Krieg, *Korresp. Blatt. gesamt. Ver. deut. Geschichte*, **62**. 280, 1914; W. Kroll, *Arch. Religionswissenschaft*, Beiblatt, **8**. 29, 1905; S. Krzyzankiewicz, *Untersuchungen vorgeschichtlicher Eisenfunde*, Basel, 1909; M. Kuchenbuch, *Zeit. Ethnologie*, **7**. 31, 1875; G. F. Kunz, *Amer. Journ. Science*, (3), **31**. 145, 1886; (3), **33**. 233, 1887; (3), **34**. 471, 1887; P. L. B. Kupka, *Zeit. Ethnologie*, **47**. 404, 1915; A. Lambert, *Le Jour du Monde*, **3**. 373, 1861; A. Lane-Fox, *Archæologia*, **46**. 435, 1877; A. Lang, *Rev. Archéologique*, **7**. 280, 1906; *Homer and his Age*, London, 1906; E. F. Lange, *Assoc. Under Managers and Foremen*, Manchester, 1900; J. Lanth, *Allgem. Ztg.*, 182, 1868; G. T. Lapsley, *Colliery Guardian*, **78**. 176, 1899; J. T. Last, *Proc. Geogr. Soc.*, (2), **5**. 586, 1883; *Die Metalle*, Jena, 1906; A. H. Layard, *Nineveh and its Remains*, London, **1**. 40, 1849; A. Ledebur, *Stahl Eisen*, **19**. 757, 1899; **21**. 841, 1901; **4**. 633, 1884; *Glaser's Ann.*, 16. 191, 1885; J. Legge, *The Chinese Classics*, London, **3**. i, 121, 1865; J. G. Lehmann, *Geographiæ subterraneæ*, Berlin, 1759; O. von Lemm, *Mitt. Geschichte Med. Naturwiss.*, **7**. 485, 1908; F. Lenormant, *Die Anfänge der Cultur*, Jena, **1**. 46, 58, 1875; *Die Geheinwissenschaften Asiens. Die Magie und Wahrsagekunst der Chaldäer*, Jena, 1878; O. Lenz, *Skizzen aus Westafrica*, Berlin, 35, 374, 1878; R. Lepsius, *Abh. Berlin Akad.*, 29, 92, 120, 1871; *Ueber die Götter der vier Elemente bei den Aegyptern*, Berlin, 1856; *Der Metalle in den aegyptischen Inschriften*, Berlin, 1872; *Verh. Berlin Ges. Anthropologie*, 63, 1873; I. E. Lester, *Iron Coal Trades Rev.*, **83**. 561, 1911; *Journ. Iron Steel Inst.*, **85**. i, 180, 1912; *Proc. Staffs Iron Steel Inst.*, **27**. 2, 1911; J. Lewis, *Ironmonger*, **138**. 447, 1911; F. Liger, *La ferronnerie ancienne et moderne ou monographie du fer et de la serrurierie*, Paris, 1873; L. Lindenschmit, *Handbuch der deutschen Alterthumskunde*, Braunschweig, 1, 1880; I. Lippert, *Kulturgeschichte der Menschheit*, Stuttgart, 224, 1887; E. O. von Lippmann, *Arch. Geschichte Naturwiss.*, 233, 1910; *Stahl Eisen*, **30**. 1099, 1910; *Entstehung und Ausbretung der Alchemie*, Berlin, 628, 1919; *Abhandlungen und Vorträge zur Geschichte der Naturwissenschaften*, Leipzig, **2**. 265, 1913; G. C. F. Lische, *Andeutungen über die norddeutschen Grabalterthümer aus der vorchristlichen zeit überhaupt*, Rostock, 1837; D. Livingstone, *Missionary Travels and Researches in South Africa*, London, 402, 1857; 557, 1899; *Narrative of an Expedition to the Zambesi and its Tributaries*, London, 113, 1865; W. Llewellyn, *Arch. Cambrensis*, (3), **9**. 291, 1863; (4), **11**. 222, 1880; C. A. von Lobeck, *Aglaophamus*, Königsberg, 1829; A. Lorange, *Zeit. Ethnologie*, **7**. 245, 330, 1875; A. L. Lorange, *Den* yngre Jernalders Svaerd, Bergen, 1889 ; H. Louis, Archœclogia Æliana, 265, 1910 ; Journ. Iron Steel Inst., 85. i, 129, 1912 ; 129. i, 29, 1929 ; M. A. Lower, Trans. Fed. Inst. Min. Eng., 14. 701, 1896 ; J. Lubbock, Prehistoric Times, London, 1865 ; A. Lucas, Ancient Egyptian Materials, London, 97, 1926 ; D. D. Luckenbill, Ancient Records of Assyria and Babylonia, Chicago, 1. 247, 1927 ; F. von Luschan, Zeit. Ethnologie, 39. 381, 1907 ; 41. 22, 49, 1909 ; Verh. deut. Kolonialkongress., 166, 1902 ; F. Lux, Stahl Eisen, 33. 545, 590, 1913 ; R. A. S. Macalister, A History of Civilization in Palestine, Cambridge, 60, 1921 ; Excavation of Gezer, London, 1912 ; J. V. McCartney, Blast Furnace, 11. 140, 1923 ; A. Macco, Zeit. prakt. Geol., 6. 139, 1898 ; A. MacWilliam, Journ. Iron Steel Inst., 102. ii, 159, 1920 ; F. de Magalhaes (Magellan) in A. Pigafetta, Voyage Arcund the World, Cleveland, 2. 41, 1906 ; or in G. M. Towle, The Story of Magellan, or the First Voyage Round the World, London, 1891 ; L. Magyar, Reisen in Südafrika, Leipzig, 376, 1859 ; J. W. Mallet, Amer. Journ. Science, (3), 2. 10, 1871 ; H. H. Manchester, Eng. Min. Journ., 115. 889, 1923 ; 114. 409, 447, 495, 545, 1922 ; A. Mansfield, Urwald Dokumente, Berlin, 113, 1908 ; R. Marggraff, Ueber das Vorkommen und die Bedeutung bronzener und eiserner Vögel auf römischen und germanischen Begräbnisstätten, Berlin, 1874 ; J. Markham Journ. Geog. Soc., 40. 217, 1870 ; W. Marsden, Reise nach Ostindien und China, Leipzig, 361, 1783 ; L. Martinet, Le Berry préhistorique, Paris, 1878 ; G. H. Mason, Life with the Zulus of Natal, South Africa, London, 164, 1855 ; W. Matschoss, Tech. Wirtschaft, 6. 396, 1913 ; Stahl Eisen, 33. 1084, 1913 ; A. H. Mauduit, Emploi de l'aurain à défaut de fer chez le plupart des peuples, Paris, 1844 ; Appendices du livre intitulé : Découvertes dans la Troade et dans les traductions d'Homère, Paris, 1846 ; T. May, Warrington's Roman Remains, Warrington, 1904 ; Iron Coal Trades Rev., 71. 427, 1905 ; W. Maylor, Proc. Inst. Civil Eng., 126. 383, 1896 ; H. B. Medlicott and W. T. Blanford, Rev. Anthropol., (2), 3. 299, 1880 ; A Manual of the Geology of India, Calcutta, 1879 ; C. Mehlis, Corresp. Blatt. deut. Ges. Anthropologie, 16, 1876 ; 72, 1878 ; 147, 149, 1883 ; Fels zum Meer, 2. 202, 1884 ; E. Meyer, Geschichte des Altertums, Stuttgart, 1913 ; 1. 68, 1907 ; Reich und Kultur der Chetiter, Berlin, 1914 ; H. Meyer, Blätter aus meinem Reisetagebuche, Leipzig, 275, 1883 ; A. von Middendorff, Reise in den äussersten Norden und Osten Sibiriens, St. Petersburg, 4. 1557, 1875 ; A. B. Middleton, Iron Coal Trades Rev., 86. 853, 1913 ; A. F. Mockler-Ferryman, Up the Niger, London, 212, 1892 ; S. Mockrauer, Verh. deut. Ges. Anthropologie, 276, 1880 ; G. Mollien, Reise in das Innere von Afrika nach den Quellen des Senegal und Gambia, Berlin, 137, 284, 349, 1820 ; H. Möntefindt, Zeit. Ethnologie, 45. 1003, 1913 ; H. Möntefindt, H. Nicolai and A. Schlez, Zeit. Ethnologie, 45. 83, 1913 ; G. Möller, Die Metallkunst der alten Aegypter, Berlin, 13, 1925 ; H. H. Montanus, Montana Rund., 4. 1202, 1244, 1922 ; J. M. C. Monteiro, O Muata Cazembe e os povos Maraveo, Chévas, Muizas, Muembas, Lundas e outros da Africa austral, Lisboa, 1854 ; Zeit. allgem. Erkunde, 6. 268, 1856 ; O. Montelius, Geschichte für Technik, Industrie und Gewerbe, Berlin, 1. 246, 1914 ; Prähistorische Ztg., 5. 290, 1913 ; Journ. Iron Steel Inst., 58. ii, 514, 1900 ; Man, 5. 12, 1905 ; La civilisation primitive en Italie depuis l'introduction des métaux Stockholm, 1895, 1910 ; Corresp. Blatt. deut. Ges. Anthropologie, 31. 142, 1900 ; Berg. Hütt. Ztg., 59. 518, 1900 ; Les débuts de l'âge de fer, Paris, 1907 ; Zeit. Ethnologie, 42. 955, 1910 ; J. de Morgan, Journ. Asiatique, 203. 117, 1923 ; T. D. Morgan, Iron Age, 83. 386, 1909 ; A. Morlot, Jahrb. geol. Reichsanst. Wien, 1. 199, 1856 ; J. R. Mortimer, Forty Years' Researches in British and Saxon Burial Mounds of East Yorkshire, Hull, 1905 ; M. Moszkowsky, Zeit. Ethnologie, 40. 230, 1908 ; J. Moura, Rev. Ethnographie, 1. 435, 1882 ; F. C. Movers, Das. phönizische Alterthum, Berlin, 2. ii, 67, 1856 ; M. Much, Mitt. Anthropolog. Ges. Wien, 9. 214, 1880 ; G. Müller, Monatsbl. Ges. Pommersche Geschichte, 8. 17, 1894 ; J. G. Müller, Bull. Acad. Russ., 6. 540, 1742 ; 8. 24, 101, 188, 231, 1763 ; Max Müller, Lectures on the Science of Language, London, 2. 255, 1882 ; A. Müllner, Berg. Hütt. Jahrb., 53. 205, 355, 1905 ; 54. 361, 1906 ; 56. 51, 66, 1908 ; 58. 67, 89, 1910 ; 60. 81, 174, 1912 ; 61. 138, 343, 1913 ; Zeit. Oesterr. Ing. Arch. Ver., 62. 684, 1910 ; Oesterr. Zeit. Berg. Hütt., 55. 53, 68, 1907 ; 56. 94, 1908 ; 57. 53, 61, 1909 ; 58. 67, 79, 1910 ; 61. 138, 343, 1913 ; Geschichte des Eisens in Inner-Oesterreich von der Urzeit bis zum Anfange, Wien, 1908 ; J. Munro, The Lake Dwellings of Europe, London, 516, 542, 545, 1890 ; D. Mushet, Phil. Trans., 95. 163, 1805 ; Nicholson's Journ., 11. 221, 1805 ; Papers on Iron and Steel, London, 1840 ; G. C. Musters, Unter den Patagoniern, Jena, 112, 177, 1873 ; J. Myers, Journ. Soc. Chem. Ind., 41. 133, T, 1922 ; J. L. Myres, B.A. Rep., 664, 1908 ; G. Nachtigal, Sahara und Sudan, Berlin, 1. 451, 1879 ; 2. 168, 666, 1881 ; J. A. F. le Marquis de Nadaillac, Bull. Soc. Anthropol., (3), 6. 431, 1883 ; A. Nagel, Verh. Berl. Ges. Anthropologie, 28, 1888 ; P. Neogi, Journ. Roy. Soc. Arts, 63. 43, 1914 ; Bull. Indian Assoc. Cult. Science, 12, 1914 ; A. Neuburger, Die Technik des Altertums, Leipzig, 1919 ; London, 1930 ; B. Neumann, Zeit. Elektrochem., 29. 175, 1923 ; Arch. Eisenhüttenwesen, 1. 241, 1927 ; K. von Neumann, Globus, 26. 347, 1874 ; K. Nishio, Trans. Amer. Min. Eng., 43. 54, 1912 ; A. Norden, Jernkontorets Ann., (2), 81. 265, 1926 ; A. E. von Nordenskjöld, Die Umsegelung Asiens und Europas auf der Volga, Leipzig 2. 93, 1882 ; H. Obermaier, Der Mensch der Vorzeit, Wien, 1912 ; F. Odernheimer, Zeit. angew. Chem., 11. 193, 1898 ; Stahl Eisen, 18. 631, 1898 ; H. Oldenberg, Die Lehre der Upanischaden, Göttingen, 240, 1898 ; O. Olshausen, Geschichtsblätter Tech. Ind. Gewerbe, 3. 112, 1916 ; Prähistorische, Ztg., 6. 1, 1916 ; Zeit. Ethnologie, 22. 30, 1890 ; 37. 85, 1905 ; 39. 691, 1907 ; 41. 60, 86, 1909 ; Baltische Studien, 35. 396, 1885 ; Verh. Berl. Ges. Anthropologie, 321, 1885 ; 19, 1893 ; 500, 504, 1897 ; J. Orr, The International Standard Bible Encyclopœdia, Chicago, 3. 1402, 1925 ; W. G. Owens, Amer. Journ. Science, (3), 43. 423, 1892 ; P. S. Pallas, Bull. Acad. Russ., 20. 170, 308, 410, 1776 ; Reise durch verschredene Provinzen des Russischen Reichs, St. Petersburg, 1771 ; Voyages en Sibérie, Berne, 1. 203, 437, 1791 ; 2. 189, 421, 1791 ;

S. Purchas, *His Pilgrimes*, London, 927, 1171, 1625 ; Mungo Park, *Travels in the Interior Districts of Africa*, London, 1799 ; *The Journal of a Mission to the Interior of Africa*, London, 1805 ; H. Parker, *Journ. Roy. Asiatic Soc.—Ceylon*, **8**. 39, 1884 ; **8**. 61, 1884 ; S. Passarge, *Adamanua*, Berlin, 246, 469, 1895 ; C. Pauli, *Lexikon der griechischen und römischen Mythologie*, **4**. 787, 1909–15 ; P. Paulitschke, *Ethnolographie Nordost Afrika*, Berlin, 1893 ; A. von Pauly and G. Wissowa, *Real Enzyklopädie des classischen Altertums*, Stuttgart, **5**. 2142, 1905 ; G. Payne, *Archæologia Cantiana*, **21**. 308, 1895 ; *Notes Queries*, (8), **8**. 325, 1895 ; H. J. E. Peake, *The Bronze Age and the Celtic World*, London, 118, 1922 ; G. G. Pearse, *Journ. Ethnolog. Soc.*, (2), **1**. 211, 1869 ; G. Pearson, *Phil. Trans.*, **85**. 322, 1795 ; J. Percy, *Metallurgy Iron and Steel*, London, 873, 1864 ; G. Perrot and C. Chipiez, *Histoire de l'art dans l'antiquité*, Paris, **1**. 829, 1882 ; **3**. 921, 1885 ; *History of Art in Phoenicia*, London, 1885 ; J. Petherick, *Egypt, the Soudan, and Central Africa*, London, 394, 1861 ; W. M. F. Petrie, *Nature*, **120**, 56, 1927 ; *Ancient Egypt*, London, 12, 1915 ; *Journ. Iron Steel Inst.*, **85**. i, 184, 1912 ; *The Arts and Crafts of Ancient Egypt*, London, 1909 ; *Gerar*, London, 14, 1928 ; W. M. F. Petrie, G. A. Wainwright and E. Mackay, *The Labyrinth Gerzeh, and Mazchuneh*, London, 15, 1912 ; A. Pfizmaier, *Die chinesische Lehre von den Kriesläufen und Luftarten*, Wien, 41, 1866 ; S. Pinto, *Wanderung quer durch Afrika, vom Atlantischen zum Indischen Ozean*, Leipzig, **1**. 117, 1881 ; **2**. 31, 1881 ; M. Plath, *Verh. Berl. Ges. Anthropologie*, 371, 1897 ; T. Poech, *Oesterr. Zeit. Berg. Hütt.*, **51**. 365, 1903 ; P. Pogge, *Beiträge zur Entdeckungsgeschichte Afrika*, Berlin, **3**. 238, 1880 ; J. Pokorny, *Mitt. Geschichte Med. Naturwiss.*, **14**. 195, 1915 ; **15**. 314, 1916 ; *Zeit. vergleich. Sprachforsch.*, **46**. 202, 1914 ; J. S. Poljäkoff, *Schrift. Akad. St. Petersburg*, **30**. 2, 1877 ; *Arch. Anthropologie*, **11**. 323, 1879 ; Marco Polo, *Voyages and Travels*, London, **1**. 94, 1903 ; A. F. Pott, *Etymologische Forschungen auf dem Gebiete der Indogermanischen Sprachen mit besonderem Bezug auf die Lautumwandlung im Sanskrit, Grieschen, Lateinischen, Littanischen und Gothischen*, Lemgo, 127, A, 1833 ; *Zeit. Volkerpsychlogie*, **2**. 120, 1861 ; B. H. B. Powell, *Handbook of the Economic Products of the Punjab*, Roorkee, Lahore, 1868 ; P. W. Powlett, *Gazetteer of Ulwar*, London, 1879 ; K. Preisendanz, *Arch. Religionswissenschaft*, **16**. 548, 1913 ; W. H. Prescott, *The Conquest of Peru*, London, 1847 ; *The Conquest of Mexico*, London, 1843 ; H. L. Preston, *Amer. Journ. Science*, (4), **5**. 269, 1898 ; A. F. Prévost, *Histoire générale des voyages*, Paris, **5**. 172, 1748 ; P. Putjatin, *Verh. Berl. Ges. Anthropologie*, 335, 1893 ; F. W. Putnam, *Amer. Antiquarian Soc.*, **2**. 354, 1883 ; *Peabody Museum Reports*, **3**. 1, 1884 ; A. Quiquerez, *Monuments de l'ancien évêché de Bâle*, Porrentruy, 1866 ; *Notice historique et statistique sur les mines, les foréts et les forges de l'ancien évêché de Bâle*, Paris, 1866 ; *Mitt. Antiquar. Ges. Zürich*, 17, 1871 ; M. Radloff, *Verh. Berl. Ges. Anthropologie*, **88**, 1871 ; 430, 1882 ; A. Raffenel, *Nouveau voyage dans le pays des nègres*, Paris, **1**. 56, 1856 ; T. S. Raffles, *The History of Java*, London, **1**. 172, 1817 ; O. Rammstedt, *Apoth. Ztg.*, **24**. 209, 1909 ; F. Rathgen, *Verh. Gewerbefl. Abhand.*, **91**. 241, 1912 ; *Chem. Ztg.*, **56**. 703, 1903 ; *Stahl Eisen*, **23**. 955, 1903 ; H. Rawlinson, *Five Great Monarchies of the Ancient Eastern World*, London, **1**. 98, 1862 ; P. C. Ray, *A History of Hindu Chemistry*, London, **1**. 60, 84, 1902 ; T. T. Read, *Trans. Amer. Inst. Min. Eng.*, **43**. 351, 1912 ; *Iron Age*, **108**. 451, 1921 ; M. Regling, *Real Enzyklopädie des classischen Altertums*, Stuttgart, **7**. 970, 1912 ; M. Reil, *Beiträge zur Kenntnis des Gewerbes im hellenistischen Aegypten*, Leipzig, 1913 ; P. Reinecke, *Festschrift zur Feier des 50- jährigen Bestehens des römische-germanischen Centralmuseums zu Mainz*, Mainz, 53, 1902 ; *Verh. Berl. Ges. Anthropologie*, 230, 1898 ; W. Rhaleg, *Achter Teil Americæ*, Franckfurt, 8, 1624 ; L. Richard, *Comprehensive Geography of the Chinese Empire and Dependencies*, Shanghai, 53, 125, 151, 402, 1908 ; T. A. Rickard, *Journ. Iron Steel Inst.*, **120**. ii, 323, 1929 ; *Nature*, **126**. 788, 1930 ; *Journ. Inst. Metals*, **43**. 297, 1930 ; *Man before Metals*, New York, 1931 ; F. von Richthofen, *China*, London, **2**. 150, 411, 1882 ; W. Ridgeway, *The Early Age of Greece*, Cambridge, **1**. 617, 1901 ; B. A. Rep., 9, 30, 1896 ; 644, 1907 ; *Eng. Min. Journ.*, **62**. 101, 1896 ; *Journ. Hellenic Studies*, **16**. 114, 1896 ; *Proc. Brit. Acad.*, **4**. 121, 1909 ; *Ironmonger*, **147**. 61, 1914 ; E. C. A. Riehm, *Handwörterbuch des biblischen Alterthums*, Leipzig, **1**. 371, 1893 ; E. Riess, *Real Enzyklopädie des classischen Altertums*, Stuttgart, **1**. 45, 90, 1894 ; C. Robert, *ib.*, **7**. 1421, 1912 ; S. Roeder in W. H. Roscher, *Lexikon der griechischen und römischen Mythologie*, Leipzig, **4**. 777, 1909–15 ; G. Rohlfs, *Quer durch Afrika*, Leipzig, **2**. 207, 1875 ; R. T. Rolfe, *Metal Ind.*, **31**. 191, 1927 ; **32**. 321, 369, 1928 ; O. Root, *Amer. Journ. Science*, (2), **14**. 439, 1852 ; H. von Rosenberg, *Der malayische Archipel*, Leipzig, 210, 1878 ; W. Rosenhain, *Trans. Faraday Soc.*, **9**. 132, 1914 ; J. Ross, *A Narrative of a Second Voyage in Search of a North-West Passage*, London, 1835 ; J. P. Rossignol, *Les métaux dans l'antiquité*, Paris, 1863 ; L. Rousselet, *Rev. Anthropol.*, **2**. 61, 1878 ; M. I. Rostovtzeff, *A History of the Ancient World*, Oxfora, **1**. 109, 1926 ; W. S. Routledge, *With a Prehistoric People*, London, 84, 1910 ; W. Ruge, *Real Enzyklopädie classischen Altertums*, Stuttgart, **3**. 2100, 1899 ; H. Rupe, *Verh. Naturf. Ges. Basel*, **21**. 25, 1910 ; *Mitt. Geschichte Med. Naturwiss.*, **5**. 86, 1906 ; H. Rupe and F. Müller, *Verh. Naturf. Ges. Basel*, **21**. 108, 1916 ; J. Russegger, *Reisen in Europa, Asien und Afrika*, Stuttgart, **1**. ii, 544, 1843 ; *Arch. Min. Geognos. Berg. Hütt.*, **10**. 761, 1837 ; **11**. 125, 1838 ; O. Rygh, *Geographiæ subterraneæ*, 286, 1878 ; A. Rzach, *Real Enzyklopädie des classischen Altertums*, Stuttgart, **8**. 1223, 1912 ; E. Sabine, *Quart. Journ. Science*, **7**. 79, 1819 ; E. von Sacken, *Das Grabfeld von Hallstall in Oberösterreich und dessen Alterhümer*, Wien, 1868 ; M. Sagey, *Ann. Mines*, (2), **4**. 121, 1828 ; A. Sahlin, *Stahl Eisen*, **33**. 265, 1913 ; C. Salmasius, *Epistolis*, Lugduni Batavorum, **4**. 97, 1656 ; G. H. Saxton, *Proc. Asiatic Soc. Bengal*, 64, 1870 ; A. H. Sayce, *Man.*, **21**. 164, 1921 ; A. Schadenberg, *Zeit. Ethnologie*, **12**. 137, 1880 ; **17**. 9, 1885 ; C. Schaefer, *Bibliothéque de voyages anciens*, Paris, **1**. 84, 1895 ; D. Schenkel, *Bibel Lexikon*, Leipzig, **4**. 207, 1872 ; J. Schlemm, *Wörterbuch zur Vorges-*

chichte, Berlin, 132, 1908 ; A. Schlez, *Fundber. Schwaben Altertümer*, Stuttgart, **13**. 30, 1905 ; H. Schliemann, *Mykenä*, Leipzig, 183, 1878 ; *Mycenæ*, London, 1878 ; *Ilias*, Leipzig, 674, 1881 ; *Corresp. Blatt dent. Ges. Anthrop.*, 9, 1879 ; H. Schmidt, *Zeit. Ethnologie*, **38**. 456, 1906 ; **43**. 582, 1911 ; V. Schmidt, *Compt. Rend. Assoc. Franc.*, 333, 1889 ; 214, 223, 1890 ; L. K. Schmarda, *Reise um die Erde*, Braunschweig, **1**. 421, 1861 ; O. Schrader, *Die Metalle*, Jena, 1906; *Sprachvergleichung und Urgeschichte*, Jena, 220, 1883 ; 2. i. 58, 1906 ; *Reallexikon der indogermanischen Altertumskunde*, Stuttgart, 1901 ; *Sprachvergleichung und Urgeschichte*, Jena, 1907 ; O. H. Schütt, *Beiträge zur Entdeckungsgeschichte Afrika's*, Berlin, **4**. 128, 1881 ; A. Schulten, *Real Enzyklopädie des classischen Altertums*, Stuttgart, **8**. 2004, 1912 ; E. Schultze, *Arch. Geschichte Naturwiss. Technik*, **2**. 350, 1910 ; M. Schulze, *Verh. Berl. Ges. Anthropologie*, 213, 1880 ; *Verh. Berl. Ges. Anthropologie*, 119, 1877 ; C. A. L. M. Schwaner, *Borneo*, Amsterdam, **1**. 109, 1853 ; C. von Schwarz, *Journ. Iron Steel Inst.*, **56**. ii, 89, 1899 ; *Stahl Eisen*, **21**. 337, 391, 1901 ; *Zeit. Berg. Hutt. Steiermark*, **11**. 1, 1879 ; F. von Schwarz, *Turkestan, die Wiege der indogermanischen Völker*, Freiburg, i. Br., 396, 1900 ; W. Schwartz, *Verh. Berl. Ges. Anthropologie*, 88, 1881 ; 539, 1882; G. Schweinfurth, *The Heart of Africa*, London, 81, 124, 1873 ; *In Herzen von Afrika*, Leipzig, i, 224, 1874 ; ii, 115, 1874 ; *Zeit. Ethnologie*, **5**. 18, 1875 ; **37**. 84, 1905 ; *Verh. Berl. Ges. Anthropologie*, 294, 1884 ; E. A. de Schweinitz, *Amer. Journ. Science*, (4), **1**. 208, 1896 ; W. Schwenzner, *Mitt. Geschichte Med. Naturwiss.*, **15**. 51, 1916 ; H. Scott, *Journ. Iron Steel Inst.*, **47**. i, 141, 1895 ; W. V. Scudamore, *Iron and Steel Work in the Bombay Presidency*, Bombay, 1907 ; J. Seehars, *Verh. Berl. Ges. Anthropologie*, 786, 1889 ; **189**. 1898 ; S. Seligmann, *Der böse Blick*, Berlin, 1910; C. U. Shepbard, *Amer. Journ. Science*, (2), **4**. 74, 1847 ; (2), **21**. 213, 1856 ; (3), **30**. 208, 1860 ; (2), **42**. 250, 1866 ; (3), **26**. 336, 1882 ; C. W. von Siemens, *Journ. Iron Steel, Inst.*, **12**. ii, 413, 1897 ; J. Sievers, *Briefe aus Sibirien an seine Lehrer*, St. Petersburg, 197, 1796 ; B. Simmersbach, *Oesterr. Zeit. Berg. Hütt.*, **61**. 343, 1913 ; L. Simonin, *Ann. Mines*, (5), **14**. 557, 1859 ; K. Simrock, *Amelungenlied*, Stuttgart, **1**. 59, 1863 ; J. Simson, *A History of the Gipsies with Specimens of the Gipsy Language*, London, 234, 1865 ; M. Skutsch, *Real Enzyklopädie des classischen Altertums*, Stuttgart, **6**. 742, 1909 ; J. L. Smith, *Amer. Journ. Science*, (2), **47**. 385, 1869 ; J. Smith, *England's Improvement Revived in a Treatise of all Manners of Husbandry and Trade by Land and Sea*, London, 1673 ; R. A. Smith, *A Guide to the Antiquities of the Bronze Age*, London, 2, 1920 ; *A Guide to the Antiquities of the Early Iron Age*, London, 1, 1905 ; *Proc. Soc. Antiquities*, **20**. 179, 1905 ; (2), **27**. 69, 1915 ; V. A. Smith, *Journ. Roy. Asiatic Soc.*, 11, 1897 ; 143, 1898 ; *Journ. Iron Steel Inst.*, **85**. i, 158, 1912 ; E. Soldi, *Bull. Soc. Anthropologie*, (3), **4**. 34. 1881 ; *L'Art Egyptien d'après les derrières découvertes*, Paris, 1879 ; P. Sonnerat, *Voyages aux Indes Orientales et la Chine*, Paris, 1782 ; J. Sowerby, *Exotic Mineralogy*, London, **2**. 133, 1817 ; W. Sowerby, *Proc. Inst. Civil Eng.*, **16**. 82, 1857 ; *Rec. Govt. India (Home)*, 18, 1856 ; *Rec. Govt. India (Public Works)*, 26, 1859 ; *Kumaon Iron Works*, Serampone, 1860 ; W. Spiegelberg, *Rec. Trav. Phil. Arch. Egypt. Assyr.*, **26**. 166, 1904 ; H. M. Stanley, *Through the Dark Continent*, London, 1878 ; P. Staudinger, *Verh. Berl. Ges. Anthropologie*, 505, 1892 ; J. E. Stead, *Journ. Iron Steel. Inst.*, **85**. i, 129, 1912 ; M. A. Stein, *Ruins of Desert Cathay*, London, 275, 352, 1912 ; G. W. Steller, *Beschreibung von dem Lande Kamtschatka*, Frankfurt, 247, 320, 1774 ; H. Stephanus, *Hypomneses de gallica lingua*, Lugduni Batavorum, **8**. 152, 1582 ; O. Stoll, *Das Geschlechtsleben in der Völkerpsychologie*, Leipzig, 1908 ; R. von Stoltzenberg, *Verh. deut. Ges. Anthropologie*, 251, 268, 1892 ; E. Straker, *Wealdon Iron*, London, 1931 ; A. Struck, *Verh. Berl. Ges. Anthropologie*, 539, 1898 ; M. Sudhoff, *Arch. Religionswissenschaft*, **10**. 290, 1907 ; W. C. Symons, *Illustrated Archæologist*, **2**. 89, 1895 ; K. Tanzer, *Abh. Ber. deut. Museums*, **2**. 85, 1930 ; M. Taylor, *Journ. Ethnolog. Soc.*, (2), **1**. 157, 1869 ; F. R. Tegengren, *The Iron Ores and Iron Industry of China*, Peking, ii, 297, 1924 ; C. A. Tellen, *Verh. Berl. Ges. Anthropologie*, 476, 1890 ; A. Teplouchoff, *Arch. Anthropologie*, **12**. 220, 1880 ; G. Tessmann, *Beiträge zur Geschichte der Technik und Industrie*, Berlin, **11**. 95, 1921 ; J. Thomson, *To the Central African Lakes and Back*, London, 1. 372, 1881 ; 2. 281, 1881 ; T. E. Thorpe, *Proc. Phil. Soc. Glasgow*, **8**. 164, 1872 ; C. Thulin, *Real Enzyklopädie des classischen Altertums*, **10**. 1139, 1917 ; C. P. Thunberg,. *Reise durch einen Theil von Europa, Afrika und Asien*, Berlin, **2**. ii, 226, 1794 ; *Svenska Akad. Handl.*, **5**. 70, 1784 ; W. Tomaschek, *Real Enzyklopädie. des classischen Altertums*, **3**. 1044, 1899 ; E. Treptoff, *Jahrb. Berg. Hütt.*, 149, 1904 ; *Der Altjapanische Bergbaie und Hüttenbetrieb*, Freiberg, 1904 ; P. C. J. B. Tronson du Coudray, *Mémoire sur la manière dont on extrait en Corse le fer de la mine d'Elbe*, Paris, 1775 ; G. Troost, *Amer. Journ. Science*, (2), **5**. 351, 1848 ; I. Tsing, *Record of the Buddhist Religion in India*, Oxford, 1896 ; K. Tümpel, *Real Enzyklopädie des classischen Altertums*, Stuttgart, **4**. 2058, 1901 ; G. Turner, *Journ. Iron Steel Inst.*, **85**. i, 131, 1912 ; T. Turner, *Journ. Iron Steel Inst.*, **44**. ii, 162, 1893 ; **63**. i, 295, 1903 ; E. B. Tylor, *Anthropology*, London, 1881 ; *Anahuac : or Mexico and the Mexicans*, London, 140, 1861.; I. Undset, *Zeit. Ethnologie*, **23**. 14, 1891 ; *Corresp. Blatt. deut Ges. Anthropologie*, **12**. 131, 1881 ; **13**. 61, 1882 ; F. le Vaillant, *Voyage dans l'intérieur de L'Afrique per le Cap Bonne Espérance*, Paris, 1790 ; Amerigo Vespucci, *Lettera delle Isole Nuouamente Trouate*, Florence, 1505 ; T. Vickers, *Metal Ind.*, **25**. 527, 1924 ; M. Viedenz, *Verh. Berl. Ges. Anthropologie*, 133, 1881 ; R. Virchow, *Verh. Berl. Ges. Anthropologie*, 262, 1876 ; 144, 1877 ; *Corresp. Blätt. deut. Ges. Anthropologie*, 9, 1875 ; *Verh. Berl. Ges. Anthropologie*, 96, 1880 ; 419, 1881 ; 545, 1887 ; 425, 1890 ; O. Vogel, *Ber. Allgem. Bergmannstag*, 305, 1904 ; *Iron*, **37**. 470, 1891 ; *Zeit. angew. Chem.*, **29**. 509, 1916 ; *Chem. Ztg.*, **32**. 393, 1908 ; **33**. 507, 1909 ; *Stahl Eisen*, **28**. 780, 1908 ; **29**. 1097, 1909 ; **36**. 685, 1916 ; C. F. Volney, *Reise nach Syrien und Aegypten*, Jena, ii, 324, 1788 ; M. Voss,

Verh. Berl. Ges. Anthropologie, 97, 1876 ; H. Vyse, *Operations carried on at the Pyramids of Gizeh*, in 1837, London, **1**. 276, 1840 ; M. Wahlberg, *Baumaterialenkunde*, **2**. 141, 1898 ; *Schwedische Mag.*, **1**. 445, 1868 ; G. A. Wainwright, *Cairo Scient. Journ.*, **8**. 177, 1914 ; *Rev. Archeol.*, (4), **19**. 255, 1912 ; *Bull. Soc. Geog. Cairo*, **9**. 183, 1919 ; T. Waitz, *Anthropologie der Naturvölker*, Leipzig, **5**. 133, 1865 ; J. Wallace, *Cassier's Mag.*, **24**. 220, 1903 ; H. Wankel, *Prähistorische Eisenschmelz- und Schmedestätten in Mähren*, Wien, 1879 ; *Mitt. Anthropol. Ges. Wien*, **8**. 289, 1879 ; *Arch. Anthropologie*, **12**. 270, 1880 ; *Corresp. Blatt. deut. Ges. Anthropologie*, **13**. 54, 1882 ; H. L. Ward, *Proc. Roch. Acad. Science*, **4**. 79, 1902 ; H. A. Ward, *Amer. Journ. Science*, (4), **23**. i, 1907 ; M. Weiss, *Zeit. Ethnologie*, **41**. 111, 1909 ; K. Wendt, *Stahl Eisen*, **51**. 1, 1931 ; M. Wessely, *Ephesia Grammata*, Wien, 1886 ; K. Weule, *Mitt. deut. Schutzgebieten*, **12**. 1, 1908 ; S. E. Wibolt, *Roman Villa Site, East Cliff*, Folkestone, 1924 ; *Roman Folkestone*, London, 1925 ; H. Hess von Wichdoriff, *Zeit. Ethnologie*, **36**. 237, 1904 ; A. Wiedemann, *Jahrb. Ver. Alterthumsfreunden Rheinlands*, **99**. 14, 1896 ; E. Wiedemann, *Geschichtsblätter Tech. Ind. Gewerbe*, **3**. 193, 1913 ; *Ueber die Uhren im Bereich der islamische Kultur*, Halle, 1915 ; *Ber. deut. phys. Ges.*, (3), **9**. 364, 1907 ; *Beiträge zur Geschichte der Naturwissenschaft*, Erlangen, 1902 ; K. Wiegand, *Verh. Berl. Ges. Anthropologie*, 595, 1897 ; C. Wilkins, *The History of the Iron, Steel, Tinplate, and other trades of Wales*, Merthyr Tydfil, 1903 ; J. G. Wilkinson, *Manners and Customs of the Ancient Egyptians*, London, **3**. 241, 339, 1837 ; H. Wilkinson, *Journ. Roy. Asiatic Soc.*, **5**. 383, 1839 ; W. M. Williams, *Iron*, **32**. 566, 1888 ; L. Wilser, *Deutsche Vorzeit Berlin-Steglitz*, 25, 1917 ; C. T. Wilson and R. W. Felkin, *Uganda and the Egyptian Soudan*, London, **1**. 147, 1882 ; H. Winckler, *Vorderasien im zweiten Jahrtausend*, Berlin, 1913 ; G. B. Winer, *Biblisches Realwörterbuch*, Leipzig, i, 97, 1820 ; ii, 448, 1820 ; F. Winkelmann, *Limesblatt*, 34, 1902 ; G. Wissowa, *Real Enzyklopädie des classischen Altertums*, Stuttgart, **2**. 1472, 1896 ; K. Woermann, *Geschichte der Kunst*, Leipzig, 1915 ; C. L. Woolley, *Antiquaries' Journ.*, **5**. 391, 1925 ; F. Wüstenfeld, *Das Heerwesen der Muhammedauer*, Göttingen, 27, 1880 ; G. Wurmbrand, *Corresp. Blatt deut. Ges. Anthropologie*, 150, 1877 ; *Arch. Anthropologie*, **11**. 401, 1879 ; S. Xanthoudides, Εφημερις Αρχαιολογικη, Athens, 22, 1904 ; B. Yaneske, *Journ. Iron Steel Inst.*, **115**. i, 181, 767, 1927 ; C. Yang and C. F. Wang, *School Mines Quart.*, **33**. 164, 1912 ; G. F. Zimmer, *Cassier's Eng. Monthly*, **47**. 14, 87, 1915 ; *Journ. Iron Steel Inst.*, **94**. ii, 306, 1916 ; F. X. M. Zippe, *Geschichte der Metalle*, Wien, 115, 1857 ; G. Zippelius, *Jahrb. Eisenhüttenwesen*, **2**. 1, 1903 ; *Mitt. Geschichte med. Naturwiss.*, **1**. 168, 1902.

[2] L. Gmelin, *Handbuch der anorganischen Chemie (Eisen)*, Berlin, 1929.

[3] W. G. Armstrong, *The Industrial Resources of the Tyne, Wear, and Tees*, Newcastle, 1864 ; J. O. Arnold, *British and German Steel Manufacture*, Oxford, 1915 ; T. S. Ashton, *Trans. Newcomen Soc.*, **5**. 9, 1925 ; L. Beck, *Stahl Eisen*, **26**. 861, 932, 1123, 1906 ; A. R. Bell, *Machinery*, **11**. 185, 1905 ; I. L. Bell, *B.A. Rep.*, 730, 1863 ; *Eng.*, **91**. 22, 1901 ; *Our Foreign Competitors in the Iron Trade*, Newcastle, 1868 ; G. C. Bond, *Iron Coal Trades Rev.*, **108**. 426, 1924 ; C. Broling, *Anteoknigar under en resa i England*, Stockholm, 1817 ; Giessen, 1825 ; B. H. Brough, *Feilden's Mag.*, **4**. 42, 1901 ; R. Buchanan, *Ironmonger*, **121**. 11, 1907 ; H. Bumby, *Journ. Iron Steel Inst.*, **60**. 9, 1901 ; W. Bund, *Iron Coal Trades Rev.*, **83**. 607, 1911 ; W. H. Butlin, *Journ. Iron Steel Inst.*, **23**. i, 188, 1883 ; A. Campion, *Eng. Rev.*, **25**. 117, 1911 ; L. Coste, and A. Perdonnet, *Mémoirs métallurgiques sur le traitement des minérais de fer, d'étain, et de plomb en Angleterre*, Paris, 1830 ; L. Crell, *Crell's Ann.*, ii, 29, 1784 ; C. Dawson, *Sussex Arch. Coll.*, **46**. i, 1903 ; St. J. V. Day, *The Iron and Steel Industries of Scotland*, Edinburgh, 1876 ; M. C. Delany, *The Historical Geography of the Wealden Iron Industry*, London, 1921 ; D. Dudley, *Metallum martis*, London, 1665 ; *Journ. Iron Steel Inst.*, **5**. ii, 215, 1872 ; P. A. Dufrénoy, *Sur l'emploi de l'air chaud dans les usines à fer de l'Écosse et de l'Angleterre*, Paris, 1834 ; London, 1836 ; P. A. Dufrénoy and J. B. A. L. L. E. de Beaumont, *Voyage métallurgique en Angleterre*, Paris, 273, 1827 ; L. Eck and M. Chunchul, *Karsten's Arch.*, **22**. 691, 1848 ; **23**. 777, 1850 ; H. C. Evans, *Foundry Trade Journ.*, **35**. 321, 505, 1927 ; J. J. Ferber, *Mineralogische und technologische Bemerkungen auf einer Reise durch verschiedene Provinzen in England und Schottland*, Mietau, 1778 ; J. K. Fischer, *Tagebuch einer im Jahr 1814 gemachten Reise über Paris nach London und einigen Falnkstädten Englands*, Aarau, 1816 ; W. Fordyce, *A History of Coal, Coke, and Iron*, London, 1860 ; W. G. Fossick, *History of the Iron Trade*, London, 1877 ; W. J. Foster, *Iron Coal Trades Rev.*, **90**. 471, 1915 ; I. Gjers, *Journ. Iron Steel Inst.*, **3**. ii, 202, 1871 ; N. W. Griffiths, *Iron and Steel Manufacters of Great Britain*, London, 1883 ; S. Griffiths, *Guide to the Iron Trade of Great Britain*, London, 1873 ; L. E. Gruner and C. Lan, *État présent de la métallurgie du fer en Angleterre*, Paris, 1862 ; R. A. Hadfield, *Eng.*, **99**. 195, 1915 ; J. N. Hall, *Trans. Newcomen Soc.*, **5**. 1, 1925 ; F. W. Harbord, *Journ. Soc. Chem. Ind.*, **28**. 867, 1909 ; F. W. Harbord and E. F. Law, *Stahl Eisen*, **44**. 1422, 1924 ; F. H. Hatch, *The Iron and Steel Industry of the United Kingdom under War Conditions*, London, 1920 ; J. Henderson, *Proc. Lincoln Iron Steel Inst.*, **1**. 121, 1920 ; F. Hendrichs, *Deut. Metallind. Ztg.*, **16**. 1627, 1667, 1900 ; J. S. Jeans, *Pioneers of the Cleveland Iron Trade*, Middlesbrough, 1876 ; W. T. Jeans, *Creators of the Age of Iron*, London, 1884 ; R. Jenkins, *Trans. Newcomen Soc.*, **4**. 102, 1924 ; **5**. 140, 575, 1925 ; **6**. 42, 1926 ; *Eng.*, **131**. 502, 1921 ; **134**. 572, 1922 ; H. B. Johnson, *Iron Steel Trades Journ.*, 33, 1902 ; J. F. W. Johnston, *Economy of a Coal-field*, Durham, 1838 ; D. Jones, *Journ. Iron Steel Inst.*, **48**. ii, 8, 1895 ; B. Jordan, *Bull. Soc. Enc. Nat. Ind.*, **69**. 275, 1870 ; D. W. Kemp, *Notes on Early Iron Smelting in Sutherland*, Edinburgh, 1887 ; G. H. Kinahan, *Trans. North England Inst. Min. Mech. Eng.*, **54**. 108, 1904 ; E. Künzer, *Sammlung. Berg. Hütt. Abhand.*, 82, 1911 ; G. T. Lapsley, *Colliery Guardian*, **78**. 176, 1899 ; K. Lewis, *Ironmonger*, **138**. 447, 1911 ; J. Lloyd, *Early History of Old*

South Wales Iron Works, London, 1906 ; M. A. Lower, *Historical and Archæological Memoir on the Iron-Works of the South-East of England*, London, 1854 ; *Contributions to Literature*, London, 1834 ; R. R. Mabson, *Fifty Years' History of the British Iron Trade*, London, 1881 ; W. I. Macadam, *Proc. Soc. Antiquaries Scotland*, **21.** 89, 1887 ; *Notes on the Ancient Iron Industry of Scotland*, Edinburgh, 1886 ; W. Macfarlane, *Journ. West Scotland Iron Steel Inst.*, **9.** 115, 1904 ; H. H. Manchester, *Eng. Min. Journ.*, **116.** 152, 1923 ; P. Mantoux, *La révolution industrielle au XVIIIe siècle*, Paris, 1906 ; *Edin. Rev.*, **205.** 125, 1907 ; E. P. Martin, *Eng.*, **99.** 407, 1905 ; J. Mayer, *Journ. Iron Steel Inst.*, **5.** 11, 28, 1872 ; L. Meachem, *Trans. Fed. Inst. Min. Eng.*, **6.** 554, 1893 ; R. Meade, *Iron Industries of the United Kingdom*, London, 1882 ; J. von Dalem Meermann, *Reisen durch Grossbritannien und Irland*, Nürnberg, 1789 ; A. B. Middleton, *Iron Coal Trades Rev.*, **70.** 1354, 1905 ; T. Mitchell, *Monmouthshire Iron Steel Trade*, Newport, 1904 ; H. G. Nichols, *Iron-making in the Forest of Dean*, London, 1866 ; *Arch. Journ.*, **17.** 225, 1860 ; H. Niebuhr, *Die Reorganisation der englischen Eisenindustrie*, Berlin, 1923 ; A. N. Palmer, *John Wilkinson and the Old Bersham Ironworks*, Wrexham, 1899 ; G. Payne, *Archæologie Cantiana*, **21.** 308, 1895 ; *Notes, Queries*, (8), **8.** 325, 1895 ; C. M. Pepper, *British Iron and Steel Industry, and Luxemburg Iron and Steel wages*, Washington, 1909 ; G. R. Porter, *On the Progress, Present Amount and Probable Future Condition of the Iron Manufacture of Great Britain*, London, 1847 ; *B.A. Rep.*, **99,** 1847 ; R. G. Rice, *Arch. Journ.*, **152.** 158, 1895 ; J. Riley, *Journ. Iron Steel Inst.*, **28.** ii, 398, 1885 ; E. Roberts, *Iron Coal Trades Rev.*, **80.** 767, 1910 ; T. B. Rogerson, *Journ. West Scotland Iron Steel Inst.*, **14.** 4, 1907 ; F. J. Rowan, *Journ. Iron Steel Inst.*, **28.** ii, 376, 1885 ; H. Saemann, *Stahl Eisen*, **46.** 436, 1926 ; L. F. Salzman, *English Industries of the Middle Ages*, Oxford, 1924 ; S. Smiles, *Industrial Biography—Iron Workers and Tool Makers*, London, 1863 ; M. Stentz, *Zeit. Berg. Hütt. Sal.*, **3.** 81, 1856 ; E. Straker, *Wealdon Iron*, London, 1931 ; E. T. Svedenstierna, *Reise durch einen Theil von England und Schottland*, Marburg, 1811 ; W. C. Symons, *Illustrated Archæologist*, **2.** 89, 1895 ; W. Truran, *The Iron Manufacture of Great Britain, Theoretically and Practically considered, including Descriptive Details*, London, 1855 ; G. Turner, *Scotia*, **1.** 2, 1907 ; *Ironmonger*, **120.** 530, 1906 ; **122.** 616, 1907 ; **126.** 332, 1909 ; **128.** 226, 1909 ; M. Weber, *Berg. Hütt. Ztg.*, **42.** 555, 565, 1883 ; H. B. Wheatley, *Journ. Soc. Arts*, **61.** 961, 977, 1913 ; G. Wilkie, *The Manufacture of Iron in Great Britain*, London, 1857 ; C. Wilkins, *The History of the Iron Steel Tinplate and other Trades of Wales*, Merthyr Tydvil, 1903.

⁴ P. Anglès d'Auriac, *L'état actuel et l'avenir de l'industrie sidérurgique dans le departement du nord*, Paris, 1910 ; *L'évolution de la sidérurgie française*, Paris, 1912 ; *Bull. Soc. Ind. Min.*, (5), **1.** 445, 593, 1912 ; G. Arth and P. Lejeune, *Rev. Mét.*, **2.** 789, 1905 ; J. F. d'Aubuisson, *Arch. Bergbau Hütt.*, **16.** 107, 1827 ; *Ann. Science Nat.*, **6.** 488, 1825 ; L. Babu, *Ann. Mines*, (9), **15.** 357, 1899 ; A. Bitton, *Une fonderie de fer des invasions saxonnes en Bas-Poitou*, La Roche-sur-You, 1905 ; P. C. J. B. Tronçon du Coudray, *Mémoire sur la manière dont on extraît en Corse le fer de la mine d'Elbe*, Paris, 1775 ; Leipzig, 1786 ; L. Dary, *Bull. Soc. Ind. Min.*, (5), **3.** 397, 551, 1913 ; A. Desloges, *Les forges de Normandie—origine de la fabrication du fer en Normandie*, Verneuil, 1904 ; P. F. de Dietrich, *Description des gîtes de minérai des forges et des salines des Pyrénées*, Paris, 1786 ; P. Dunaime, *Étude sur l'industrie du fer dans le nord des Ardennes françaises*, Paris, 1908 ; J. François, *Recherches sur le gisement et le traitement direct des minérais de fer dans les Pyrénées et particulièrement dans l'Ariège, suivies de considérations historiques, économiques et pratiques sur le travail du fer et de l'acier dans les Pyrénées*, Paris, 1843 ; L. Guillet, *Rev. Mét.*, **18.** 1, 1921 ; O. Johannsen, *Stahl Eisen*, **39.** 299, 1919 ; S. Jordan, *Journ. Iron Steel Inst.*, **14.** ii, 316, 1878 ; **36.** ii, 10, 1889 ; J. Levainville, *L'industrie du fer en France*, Paris, 1922 ; M. Lévêque, *Bull. Soc. Ind. Min.*, (5), **9.** 5, 1916 ; P. Picot de Lapeirouse, *Traité sur les mines de fer et les forges du Comté de Foix*, Toulouse, 1786 ; F. Miltoun, *Iron Trade Rev.*, **61.** 819, 1917 ; A. Pawlowsky, *La métallurgie du fer dans le Nord et l'Est envahis*, Paris, 1921 ; E. Pelouze, *L'art du maître de forges*, Paris, 1828 ; L. Pillet and H. Will, *Examen analytique de l'usine de Decazeville*, Paris, 1832 ; H. Pinget, *Journ. Iron Steel Inst.*, **58.** ii, 39, 1900 ; F. le Play, *Ann. Mines*, (4), **9.** 113, 209, 1848 ; A. Porlier, *Rev. Mét.*, **2.** 793, 1905 ; T. Richard, *Quelques idées sur l'exploitation des bois et la fabrication du fer en Corse*, Paris, 1840 ; M. de Reffye, *Rev. d'Archéologie*, (2), **10.** 337, 1864 ; *Les armes d'Alise*, Paris, 1864 ; A. Vicaire, *Bull. Soc. Ind. Min.*, **10.** 31, 1909 ; A. M. H. de Villefosse, *Recherches statistiques sur l'état actuel des usines à fer de la France*, Paris, 1827 ; *Ann. Mines*, (1), **8.** 649, 1823 ; *Arch. Bergbau Hütt.*, **17.** 103, 1828 ; *Mémoire sur l'état actuel des usines à fer de la France*, Paris, 1826 ; M. Villot, *Ann. Mines*, (9), **9.** 205, 1896 ; Xavier de la Sainte, *Ferrum*, Paris, 1906.

⁵ A. de Balascheff, *Notice sur l'exploitation du fer en Belgique*, Paris, 1841 ; S. Bleekrode, *De Ijzerslappen in Nederland en de Ijzerbereadig in vroegeren Tijd*, Amsterdam, 1857 ; J. Deby, *Journ. Iron Steel Inst.*, **6.** 391, 1873 ; A. Delmer, *The Belgian Iron and Steel Industry*, London, 1925 ; A. Gillon, *Journ. Iron Steel Inst.*, **46.** ii, 7, 1894 ; L. Greiner, *Journ. Iron Steel Inst.*, **99.** i, 33, 1919 ; A. Gurlt, *Die Bergbau- und Hüttenkunde eine gedrängte Darstellung der geschichtlichen und kunstmässigen Entwickelung des Bergbaues und Hüttenwesens*, Essen, 1879 ; G. Hottenger, *L'ancienne industrie de fer en Lorraine*, Nancy, 1928 ; E. de Laveleye, *Journ. Iron Steel Inst.*, **88.** 8, 1913 ; *Stahl Eisen*, **33.** 1573, 1913 ; *Eng.*, **113.** 353, 1911 ; *Rev. Univ. Mines*, **57.** 67, 1913 ; M. Martell, *Tech. Blätt. deut Bergwerks Ztg.*, **16.** 113, 1915 ; M. de Nimal, *Monit. Intérêts Matériel*, **63.** 4673, 4507, 4565, 4601, 4733, 4764, 1913 ; **64.** 125, 1914 ; T. Soparth and T. M. Smith, *Reports on the Ironworks at Couvin in Belgium*, London, 1846 ; V. Tahon, *Rev. Univ. Mines*, **30.** 67, 1911 ; J. Tranquoy, *Des progrès de la fabrication du fer dans le pays de Liége*, Liége, 7, 1894.

[6] L. Beck, *Stahl Eisen*, **25**. 937, 1905 ; P. F. de Dietrich, *Crell's Ann.*, ii, 84, 1789 ; *Description des gîtes de minérai, forges, salines, verreries, träfileries, fabriques de fer blanc, porzelaine, faïance, etc., de la haute et basse Alsace*, Paris, 1789 ; E. Gréau, *Le fer en Lorraine*, Paris, 1908 ; *Bull. Soc. Ind. l'Est*, 58, 1908 ; A. Koch, *Zeit. Bergrecht*, **15**. 176, 1874 ; M. Limpack, *Colliery Guardian*, **70**. 399, 1895 ; A. Knaff, *Rev. Tech. Luxembourgeoise*, **22**. 61, 1930 ; C. M. Pepper, *British Iron and Steel Industry and Luxemburg Iron and Steel Wages*, Washington, 1909 ; J. B. Soisson, *Stahl Eisen*, **27**. 1373, 1907 ; *Bull. Assoc. Ing. Ind. Lux.*, **7**. 66, 1907 ; A. Somme, *La Lorraine métallurgique*, Paris, 1930 ; M. Ungehauer, *Die Entwicklungsgeschichte der Luxemburgischen Eisenindustrie im 19-ten Jahrkundert*, Luxemburg, 1910 ; *Bull. Assoc. Ing. Ind. Lux.*, **9**. 134, 148, 163, 178, 1909 ; **10**. 12, 31, 53, 80, 107, 1910 ; J. Wagner, *La sidérurgie luxembourgeoise*, Paris, 1921 ; A. Weyhmann, *Stahl Eisen*, **31**. 1873, 1911 ; *Jahrb. Ges. lothring. Geschichte*, 17, 1905 ; 22, 1911 ; *Geschitchte der älteren lothringischen Eisenindustrie*, Metz, 1905.

[7] R. Akerman, *On the Present State of Iron Manufacture in Sweden*, London, 1876 ; *Berg. Hütt. Ztg.*, **41**. 271, 1882 ; *Journ. Iron Steel Inst.*, **54**. ii, 7, 1898 ; *Stahl Eisen*, **18**. 876, 1898 ; T. Althin, *Jernkontorets Ann.*, (2), **81**. 6, 1926 ; A. J. Backlin, *Iron Trade Rev.*, **44**. 1031, 1909 ; I. Barthen, *Iron Age*, **93**. 252, 1914 ; O. Blanck, *Der Mineralreichthum der schwedischen Provinz Norrbotten und das Eisensteinlager Gellivara*, Stockholm, 1866 ; F. Böbert, *Karsten's Arch.*, **9**. 627, 1836 ; P. Bonde, *Iron Trade Rev.*, **65**. 1046, 1919 ; H. Braune, *Jernkontorets Ann.*, (2), **59**. 1, 1904 ; H. Cornell, *ib.*, (2), **74**. 317, 1919 ; J. Curle, *Proc. Soc. Antiquaries Scotland*, **29**. 292, 1895 ; A. Dulk, *Die schwedischen Lappmarken*, **46**. 261, 288, 1873 ; I. Durcher, *Berg. Hütt. Ztg.*, **16**. 7, 28, 59, 65, 92, 102, 113, 125, 149, 193, 261, 269, 285, 301, 361, 373, 381, 389, 421, 1857 ; J. von Ehrenworth, *Das Eisenhüttenwesen Schwedens*, Leipzig, 1885 ; O. Evenstad, *Praktische Abhandlung, von den Sumpf- und Morasteinsensteinen in Nowegen*, Göttingen, 1801 ; G. Flugare, *On Svenska Jern-och, Stälförädlingens tillväxt i sednare tider*, Upsala, 1788 ; A. Grabe, *Jernkontorets Ann.*, (2), **77**. 5, 1922 ; F. Grönning, *Reise in die schwedischen Bergwerke*, Giessen, 1781 ; J. F. L. Hausmann, *Reise durch Skandinavien in den Jahren 1806 und 1807*, Göttingen, 1814 ; J. Head, *Journ. Iron Steel Inst.*, **45**. i, 47, 1894 ; B. F. J. von Hermann, *Ueber die beste Methode, Eisen zu schmelzen und zu schmieden*, St. Petersburg, 1784 ; S. G. Hermelin, *Försöktill Mineral Historiaöfver Lappmarken och Vesterbotten*, Stockholm, 1804 ; A. Johansson and A. Wahlberg, *Stahl Eisen*, **47**. 62, 1927 ; P. Johnsson, *Industritidningen Nord.*, **42**. 121, 133, 1914 ; **46**. 129, 267, 278, 1918 ; J. Larsson, *Jernkontorets Ann.*, (2), **77**. 7, 1922 ; K. Leo, *Berg. Hütt. Ztg.*, **62**. 109, 1903 ; H. Lundbohm, *Journ. Iron Steel Inst.*, **54**. ii, 111, 1898 ; C. M. Maedge, *Ueber den Ursprung der ersten Metalle des See- und Sumpfverhüttung der Bergwerksindustrie und ihrer ältesten Organisation in Schweden*, Jena, 1916 ; M. Meyer, *Beiträge zur genauern Kenntnis des Eisenhüttenwesens in Schweden*, Berlin, 1829 ; P. Nicou, *Bull. Soc. Ind. l'Est*, 65, 1908 ; J. Nihlén, *Jernkontorets Ann.*, (2), **82**. 679, 1927 ; A. Norden, *ib.*, (2), **81**. 265, 1926 ; C. Polhem, *Svenska Akad. Handl.*, **2**. 28, 1741 ; J. G. A. Rhoden, *Trans. Newcomen Soc.*, F. 17, 1926 ; *Eng.*, **142**. 668, 1926 ; S. Rönnow, *Jernkontorets Ann.*, (2), **77**. 5, 1922 ; E. Schepperus, *De ferri confectione ejusque usu vario*, Upsala, 1725 ; L. Strippelmann, *Die Eisenerzlagerstätten Schwedens*, Prag, 1873 ; E. T. Svedenstjerna, *Tal om Svenska Jernhandteringen i äldne och nyare tider*, Strengnas, 1810 ; M. B. Swederus, *Jernkontorets Ann.*, (2), **58**. 1, 1903 ; (2), **59**. 235, 470, 1904 ; (2), **65**. 23, 1910 ; P. R. von Tunner, *Das Eisenhuttenwesen in Schweden*, Freiberg, 1858 ; C. D. af Uhr, *Bericht von einem Probeschmelzen auf Roheisen auf der Björnhütte*, Rudolfstadt, 1818.

[8] P. Albinus, *Meyssnische Bergk Chronica*, Dresden, 134, 1590 ; R. R. Angerstein, *Zeit. Ver. Tech. Ind. Solingen*, **6**. 33, 1926 ; M. Ansorge, *Erzbergbau*, **3**. 20, 1907 ; J. O. Arnold, *British and German Steel Metallurgy*, Oxford, 1915 ; I. von Arnoldi, *Geschichte der Oranien-Nassauischen Länder und ihrer Regenten*, Coblentz, **3**. 22, 1816 ; G. D. Baedeker, *Alfred Krupp und die Entwicklung des Gusstahlfabrik zu Essen*, Essen, 1889 ; E. Bayle, *Ann. Mines*, (4), **5**. 457, 1844 ; J. P. Becher, *Mineralogische Beschreibung des Oranien-Nassauischen Landes*, Marburg, 1789 (Reprint Dittenburg, 1902) ; L. Beck, on Matschoss, *Beiträge zur Geschichte der Technik und Industrie*, **3**. 86, 1911 ; *Stahl Eisen*, **29**. 337, 384, 1909 ; *Die Geschichte des Eisens*, Braunschweig, 1884–1903 ; *Ann. Ver. Nassau-Altertumskunde*, **33**. 210, 1903 ; **37**. 228, 1907 ; O. Behre, *Bergwirtschaftl. Mitt.*, **2**. 237, 1911 ; W. Berdrow, *Alfred Krupp*, Berlin, 1926 ; L. Bickell, *Die Eisenhütten des Klosters Haine*, Marburg, 1889 ; *Berg. Hütt.*, 36, **51**. 38, 1892 ; L. Bittner, *Das Eisenwesen in Innerberg-Eisenerz bis zur Gründurg de Innerberger Hauptgewerkschaft im Jahre 1625*, Wien, 1901 ; J. G. L. Blumhof, *Einige Beyträge zur älteren Geschichte des Eisenbergbaues und Hüttenwesens am Harze*, Braunschweig, 1803 ; J. G. L. Blumhof and J. G. Stuenkel, *Beobachtungen auf einer Fussreise besonders in Rüchsicht auf Eisenhüttenwerke*, Freyberg, 1800 ; F. Böcking, *Glückauf*, **31**. 749, 1895 ; N. Bömmels, *Natur Kultur Eifelver*, **7**. 1925 ; O. A. Bormann, *Zur Entstehung und Entwicklung des metallverarbeitenden Industrie*, M. Gladbach, 1925 ; B. Schulz-Briesen, *Stahl Eisen*, **31**. 1019, 1096, 1903 ; W. Brügmann, *Journ. Iron Steel Inst.*, **62**. ii, 10, 1902 ; *Zeit. Ver. deut. Ing.*, **27**. 416, 470, 1883 ; H. A. Bueck, *Stahl Eisen*, **8**. 670, 1888 ; H. Calvör, *Acta historico-chronologico-mechanica circa metallurgiam in Hercunia Superiori*, Braunschweig, 1763 ; F. L. von Canerin, *Beschreibung der vorzüglichsten Bergwerke in Hessen, an dem Haarz und in dem Saalfeldischen*, Frankfurt a. M., 43, 1767 ; W. Cartellieri, *Die Eisenindustrie au der Saar*, Saarbrücken, 1929 ; L. W. Cramer, *Vollständige Nachricht von dem Hollerter Zuge einem wichtigen Eisensteinwerke*, Freyberg, 1793 ; *Vollständige Beschreibung des Berg-Hütten- und Hammerwesens in den Nassau-Usingischen Ländern*, Frankfurt a. M., 1805 ; L. von Crell, *Crell's Ann.*, ii, 58, 1799 ; R. Cronau, *Geschichte der Solinger Klingenindustrie*,

Leipzig, 1885 ; W. Däbritz, in C. Matschoss, *Beiträge zur Geschichte der Technik und Industrie* Berlin, **15**. 13, 1925 ; R. M. Daelon, *Journ. Iron Steel Inst.*, **62**. ii, 46, 1902 ; M. Danz, *Geschicht des Bergbaues und der Metallindustrie im westlichen Teil des Thüringer Waldes und Geschicht der Eisenbergwerke Stahlberg, und Mommel in der Hersscheft Schmalkalden*, Thüringen, 1893 E. Decken, *Der landessherrliche Eisenhammer Lippoldsberg*, Cassel, 1920 ; P. Dieffenbach, *Arch hessische Geschichte*, **4**. 303, 1843 ; M. Dobers and E. Althaus, *Die königliche Friedrichshütte be Tarnowitz in Ober-Schlesien*, Berlin, 1886 ; C. Doenges, *Stahl Eisen*, **27**. 1341, 1907 ; F. F. von Ducker, *Berggeist*, **16**. 531, 1871 ; F. W. Dünkelberg, *Glückauf*, **49**. 1358, 1913 ; W. von Dyck *Darstellungen aus der Geschicht der Technik*, München, 1906 ; L. Eck, *Karsten's Arch.*, **21**. 504 1847 ; E. Eicken, *Stahl Eisen*, **23**. 1245, 1903 ; G. Einecke, *Der Eisenerzbergbau und der Eisen hüttenbetrieb an der Lahn, Dill, und in den berachbaren Revieren*, Jena, 1907 ; W. Engels an A. Legers, *Aus der Geschichte der Remscheider und Bergischen Werkzeug- und Eisen-industrie* Remscheid, 1928 ; M. Esch, *Werk*, **2**. 199, 1922 ; H. Eulenberg, *Zeit. Ver. deut. Ing.*, **31**. 1150 1887 ; *Zeit. Berg. Hütt. Sal.*, **44**. 75, 1896 ; F. A. A. Eversmann, *Uebersicht des Eisen- und Stahl Erzeugung auf Wasserworken in den Ländern zwischen Lahn und Lippe*, Dortmund, 1804 H. Fechner, *Zeit. Berg. Hütt. Sal.*, **40**. 279, 1892 ; **48**. 279, 1900 ; **49**. 1, 383, 487, 1901 ; **50**. 221 499, 691, 1902 ; F. M. Feldhaus, *Welt der Technik.*, 203, 1907 ; A. Delvaux de Fenffe, *De la situa tion de l'industrie du fer en Prusse (Haute-Silésie)*, Liège, 1844 ; J. J. Ferber, *Bergmännische Nachrichten von den markwürdigsten mineralischen gegenden der Herzoglich-Zweybrückischen Chur-Pfälzischen Wild- und Rheingräflichen und Nassauischen Ländern*, München, 1776 ; *Beo bachtungen in den sächsischen Gebürgen*, Mietau, 1778 ; M. Förster, *Tech. Mitt.*, **6**. 417, 1913 ; F. Forcher von Ainbach, *Zeit. Hist. Ver. Steiermark*, **5**. 1, 1907 ; W. A. Frantz, *Uebersicht der Eisenindustrie und des Eisenverkehrs, Deutschlands*, 1860–69, Leipzig, 1872 ; F. Freise, *Berg wirtscheffl. Mitt.*, **4**. 121, 1913 ; *Zeit. prakt. Geol.*, **15**. 11, 1907 ; J. A. N. Friend, *Journ. Iron Steel Inst.—Carnegie Mem.*, **12**. 267, 1923 ; H. Frobenius, *Alfred Krupp*, Dresden, 1898 ; K. Geisler, in C. Matschoss, *Beiträge zur Geschichte der Technik und Industrie*, Berlin, 1924– 1926 ; O. Gerhard, *Die Eisengiesserei-Industrie des Siegerlandes in ihrer Entwicklung und Lage*, Giessen, 1916 ; G. Gerlach, *Die wissenschaftliche Entwicklung des Eisenhüttenwesens an der Lahn und Dill im* 19 *Jahrhundert*, Stuttgart, 1911 ; A. Geyer, *Stahl Eisen*, **27**. 1412, 1907 ; J. F. Gmelin, *Beyträge zur Geschichte des teutschen Bergbaus*, Halle a. S., 1783 ; G. Goldstein, *Verh. Gewerbefl.*, **87**. 175, 307, 415, 475, 528, 1908 ; **88**. 51, 77, 1909 ; R. Gontermann, *Entwicklung ind Bedeutung der Stegerländer Spezialhochöfen*, Giessen, 1927 ; A. Gouvy, *Bull. Soc. Ind. l'Est*, 35, 1903 ; La *Métallurgie du fer et de l'acier dans les provinces du Rhin et de la Westphalie*, Nancy, 1903 ; *État actuel des industries du fer et de l'acier dans les provinces du Rhin et de la Westphalie*, Paris, 1903 ; *Mém. Trav. Soc. Ing. Civil*, 59, 1903 ; W. Greiling, *The German Iron and Steel Industry*, London, 1925 ; M. Grentzen, *Zeit. Berg. Hütt. Sal.*, **52**. 201, 1904 ; W. Grevel, *Die Anfänge der Gussstahl fabrikation im Stift Essen*, Essen-Ruhr, 1881 ; *Glückauf*, **20**. 66, 1884 ; J. Günther, *Zeit. Ver. Tech. Ind.* Solingen, **7**. 23, 1927 ; H. Haedicke, *Stahl Eisen*, **6**. 517, 1886 ; J. R. Häfner, *Die sechs Kantonen der vormaligen Herrschaft Schmalkalden in historischer, topographischer und statistischer Hinsicht*, Schmalkalden, 1908 ; H. Hanemann, *Internat. Zeit. Metallog.*, **4**. 248, 1913 ; A. Hasslacher, *Literatur über das Industriegebiet an der Saar*, Saarbrücken, 1879 ; *Beiträge zur älteren Geschichte des Eisenhüttenwesens im Saargebiete*, Berlin, 1896 ; *Zeit. Berg. Hütt. Sal.*, **44**. 75, 1896 ; J. F. L. Hausmann, *Ueber den gegenwärtigen Zustand und die Wichtigkeit des Hanno verischen Harzes*, Göttingen, 1832 ; A. Heinrichsbauer, *Deut. Bergwerks Ztg.*, **25**. 1, 1924 ; F. Hendrichs, in C. Matschoss, *Beiträge zur Geschichte der Technik und Industrie*, Berlin, **15**. 262, 1925 ; H. Hermann, *Oesterr. Berg. Hütt. Zeit.*, **56**. 526, 1908 ; E. Herwig, *Beschreibung des in der Herrschaft, Schmalkalden üblichen Eisenschmelzens und Schmiedens*, Franckfurt a. M., 1778 ; H. G. Heymann, *Mont. Ztg.*, **40**. 337, 1904 ; R. B. Hodgson, *Iron Coal Trades Rev.*, **68**. 751, 1904 ; R. L. Honemann, *Die Alterthümer des Harzes*, Clausthal, 1756 ; J. Horn, *Das. Metall.*, 178, 200, 223, 1914 ; A. Ilg, *Beiträge zur Geschichte der Kunst und der Kunsttechnik aus mittel hochdeutschen Dichtungen*, Wien, 1892 ; M. Illies, in C. Matschoss, *Beiträge zur Geschichte der Technik und Industrie*, Berlin, **3**. 79, 1911 ; O. Ismer, *Glückauf*, **52**. 219, 1916 ; E. Jacobs, *Zeit. Harz. Ver. Geschichte*, **13**. 250, 1880 ; E. A. Jäferschmid, *Bemerkungen über einige metallische Fabriken der Grafschaft Mark*, Dorlach, 1788 ; E. Jagsch, *Stahl Eisen*, **31**. 1535, 1911 ; E. Jüngst, *Glückauf*, **49**. 1426, 1913 ; J. H. Jung, *Kuhrpfälz. phys. ökon. Ges.*, 160, 1777 ; W. Jutzi, *Krupp* 1812–1912, Köhn, 1912 ; C. J. B. Karsten, *Metallurgische Reise durch einen Theil von Baiern und durch die süddeutschen Provinzen Oesterreichs*, Halle a. S., 1921 ; R. Keibel, *Aus hundert Jahren deutscher Eisen- und Stahlindustrie*, München, 1915 ; B. Kerl, *Der Communion-Unterharz*, Freiberg, 1853 ; E. Klapschke, *Stahl Eisen*, **7**. 258, 1887 ; F. Klein, *Stahl Eisen*, **11**. 705, 787, 1891 ; A. Knaff, *Beiträge zur Geschichte der Eisenindustrie an der mittleren Sieg*, Düsseldorf, 1910 ; *Rev. Tech. Lux.*, **12**. 164, 1920 ; K. Knapmann, *Abh. Staatswiss. Sominar Münster*, 2, 1907 ; *Stahl Eisen*, **27**. 1862, 1907 ; C. Knetsch, *Zeit. Ver. Hennebergische Geschichte*, 16, 1911 ; G. Koepper, *Das Gussstahlwert Fried. Krapp und Seine Entslekung*, Essen, 1898 ; B. Koxmann, *Die Entwicklung und Zukunff der Rheinish-Westfälischen Eisenindustrie*, Berlin, 1902 ; *Zeit. Ver. deut. Ing.*, **32**. 907, 1888 ; *Stahl Eisen*, **8**. 133, 1888 ; O. Krasa, *Stahl Eisen*, **51**. 1287, 1931 ; H. Kruse, in C. Matschoss, *Beiträge zur Geschichte der Technik und Industrie*, Berlin, 1918 ; F. Kunze, *Erzbergbau*, 155, 1907 ; B. Kuske, *Kölner Tech. Blätter*, 18, 1919 ; C. Kuzniar, *The Upper Silesian Iron Industry and Polish Ore*, London, 1921 ; M. Landgraber, *Tech. Blätt. Berwerks Ztg.*, **14**. 113, 121, 129, 1924 ; J. G. Lehmann, *Geographiœ subterraneœ*, Berlin, 1759 ; H. Lemberg, *Die Eisen und Stahlwerke des niederrheinisch-westfälischen Industriebezirks*, Dortmund, 1897 ; *Die Eisen- und Stahlwerke, Machinenfabriken und Giesserien des niederrheinisch-westfälischen Industriebezirks,* Dortmund, 1899 ; K. L. Ley, *Zur. Geschichte und ältesten Entwicklung der Siegerländer Stahl- und Eisenindustrie,* Munster i. W., 1906 ; L. Lindenschmit, *Handbuch der deutschen Alterthumskunde,* Braunschweig, 1880 ; J. Lowag, *Montan Ztg.,* **113**. 29, 1905 ; F. W. Lurmann, *Stahl Eisen,* **29**. 89, 1909 ; P. Martell, *Giesserei Ztg.,* **6**. 339, 369, 1910 ; E. Mathesius, *Verh. Beförd. Gewerbfleiss.,* **91**. 35, 1911 ; C. Matschoss, *Zeit. Ver. deut. Ing.,* **66**. 581, 1922 ; *Bergwirtschefl. Mitt.,* **3**. 219, 1912 ; *Beiträge zur Geschichte der Technik und Industrieh* Berlin, 1925 ; C. Mehlis, *Studien zur ältesten Geschichte der Rheinlande,* Leipzig, 1883 ; M. Metayer, *Les progrès de la sidérurgie allemande,* Paris, 1903 ; C. Meuskins, *Sammlung Berg. Hütt. Abhand.,* **78**, 1911 ; K. F. Mosch, *Zur Geschichte des Bergbaues in Deutschland,* Liegnitz, 1829 ; F. C. G. Müller, *Krupp's Steel Works,* London, 1898 ; A. Müllner, *Berg. Hütt. Jahrb.,* **53**. 205, 355, 1905 ; **54**. 361, 1906 ; **56**. 51, 66, 1908 ; **58**. 67, 79, 1910 ; **60**. 81, 174, 1912 ; **61**. 228, 1913 ; *Oesterr. Berg. Hütt. Zeit.,* **55**. 53, 68, 1907 ; **56**. 51, 66, 94, 1908 ; **57**. 53, 61, 1909 ; **58**. 67, 79, 1910 ; **61**. 138, 343, 1913 ; *Zeit. Oesterr. Ing. Arch. Ver.,* **62**. 684, 1910 ; K. Nebe, *Ein denwürdiges Erzeugnis aus Siegerländer Stahl,* Siegerland, **3**. 155, 1918 ; B. Neumann, *Zeit. Elektrochem,* **29**. 175, 1923 ; W. Neumeister, *Staats Sozial. Forsch.,* 150, 1910 ; B. Osann, *Giesserei Ztg.,* **18**. 119, 1921 ; F. C. Philippson, *Der Freihandel in Eisen und seine Gegner,* Berlin, 1876 ; *Ver. Förd. Freihänd. Blätt.,* 6, 1879 ; *Geschichte Heinrichs des Löwen, Herzogs von Baiern und Sachsen und der welfischen und Staufischen Politik seiner Zeit,* Leipzig, 1867 ; A. Pistor, in C. Matschoss, *Beiträge zur Geschichte der Technik und Industrie,* Berlin, 1919 ; *Thüringen in Wort und Bild,* Leipzig, **2**. 383, 1902 ; F. Preiss, *Deut. Export Rev.,* **14**. 261, 1915 ; J. C. Quantz, *Praktische Abhandlung über die Eisen- und Stahlmanipulation in der Herrschaft Schmalkalden,* Nürnberg, 1799 ; W. Quast, *Die Entwicklung der Eisenindustrie im Sauerland,* Köln, 1928 ; O. R. Redlich, *Jahrb. Eisenhüttenwesen,* **3**. 6, 1902 ; J. Reichert, in C. Matschoss, *Beiträge zur Geschichte der Technik und Industrie,* Berlin, **2**. 236, 1910 ; K. Reinhardt, *Journ. Iron Steel Inst.,* **71**. iii, 36, 1906 ; H. von Remagen, *Eisen Ztg.,* **22**. 388, 1901 ; W. Remy, *Stahl Eisen,* **34**. 1625, 1914 ; M. Rentrop, *Sauerländischer Gebingsbote,* **25**. 66, 1917 ; K. Rieger, *Deut. Metallind. Ztg.,* **35**. 505, 1919 ; S. Rieger, *Oester. Berg. Hütt. Zeit.,* **60**. 519, 544, 557, 1912 ; H. Riegler, *Eisenproduktion auf dem Weltmarkt während des Krieges unter besonderer Brücksichtigung Deutschlands,* Berlin, 1919 ; W. Riemann, *Beschreibung des Bergreviers Wetzlar,* Bonn, 71, 1878 ; W. Ritter, *Zeit. Ver. deut. Ing.,* **51**. 1395, 1907 ; R. Rotacker, *Giesserei Ztg.,* **22**. 342, 1925 ; P. Russwurm, *Glückauf,* **43**. 163, 1907 ; J. Schäffler, *Stahl Eisen,* **30**. 1478, 1930 ; J. Schall, *Geschichte des königlichen württembergischen Hüttenworkes Wasseralfingen,* Stuttgart, 1896 ; C. Scheffner, *Entwicklung und gegenwärtoger Stand des Hüttenwesens im königreich Sachsen,* Freiberg, 1905 ; M. Schiffner, *Stahl Eisen,* **24**. 609, 1904 ; P. Schmid, *Geschichte der Eisenwerke in Laufach im Spessart,* 1469, 1775, 1925 ; Aschaffenburg, 1925 ; A. Schmidt, *Erzbergbau,* **3**. 67, 1907 ; 311, 1907 ; O. Schrader, *Die Metalle,* Jena, 1906 ; M. Schultz, *Arch. Bergbau Hüttenwesen,* **4**. 229, 1821 ; **5**. 95, 1822 ; M. Schulz, *Verh. Berl. Ges. Anthropologie,* 213, 1880 ; E. Schroedter, *Journ. Iron Steel Inst.,* **36**. i, 112, 1889 ; R. Seidel, *Zeit. Berg. Hütt. Sal.,* **44**. 373, 1896 ; *Die königliche Eisengiesserei zu Gleuoitz,* Berlin, 1896 ; O. Simmersbach, *Die Begründung des oberschlesischen Eisenindustrie unter Preussens Königen,* Kattowitz, 1911 ; *Sammlung Berg. Hütt. Abhand.,* **74**, 1911 ; L. Sinzheimer, *Der volkswirtschaftliche Charakter der technischen Entwicklung des deutschen Eisenhüttengewerbes,* München, 1892 ; F. Sommer, in C. Matschoss, *Beiträge zur Geschichte der Technik und Industrie,* Berlin, 1922 ; F. Sondermann, *Geschichte der Eisenindustrie in Kreise Olpe,* Münster i. W., 1907 ; J. G. Stünkel, *Beschreibung der Eisenbergwerke und Eisenhütten aus Harz,* Göttingen, 1803 ; A. Stüwer, *Wirtschaftsfragen der Gegenwart,* Düsseldorf, 1925 ; *Die Entwicklung der Eisenindustrie in Düsseldorf,* Düsseldorf, 1925 ; C. A. Tellen, *Verh. Berl. Ges. Anthropologie,* 476, 1890 ; H. Tenge, *Stahl Eisen,* **32**. 905, 1912 ; A. Thun, *Die Industrie am Niederrhein und ihre Arbeiter,* Leipzig, 1879 ; A. Tille, *Der Ruckgang der südwestlichen Eisen, werke in der Eisenindustrie des deutschen Zollgebietes,* Saarbrücken, 1908 ; F. Titz, *Stahl Eisen;* **29**. 2041, 1909 ; A. Trappen, *Stahl Eisen,* **26**. 82, 1906 ; I. Undset, *Zeit. Ethnologie,* **23**. 14, 1891 ; U. von Unger, *Karsten's Arch.,* **25**. 261, 1853 ; E. Virmond, *Geschichte der Eifeler Eisenindustrie;* Schleiden, 1896 ; O. Vogel, *Stahl Eisen,* **18**. 534, 1110, 1898 ; **29**. 1913, 1909 ; **35**. 453, 1915 ; G. Voigtmann, *Mittelalterliche Geschützfabrikation im vormaligen Fürstentum Nassau-Villenberg-Siegen,* 1905 ; E. Voye, *Geschichte der Industrie im Märkischen Sauerlande,* Hagen, 1908 , L. Wachler, *Geschichte des ersten Jahrhunderts der königlichen Eisenhüttenwerke zu Malapane,* Glogau, 1856 ; *Betrachtung über die jetzige Lage des Hochofenbetriebes in Oberschlesien,* Oppeln, 1858 ; *Die Eisenerseugang Niederschlesiens und der Grafschaft Glatz,* Oppeln, 1848 ; P. Weber, *Die Bau- und Kundstdenkmäler im Regierungsbezirk, Cassel,* Marburg, 1913 ; H. Wedding, *Johann Friedrich Wedding,* Berlin, 1899 ; *Journ. Iron Steel Inst.,* **18**. ii, 451, 1880 ; **38**. ii, 491, 1890 ; *Stahl Eisen,* **24**. 756, 1904 ; *Zeit. Harz Ver. Geschichte,* **14**. 1, 1881 ; H. Wenck, *Hessische Landesgeschichte mit einem Urkundenbache,* Franckfurt, 1803 ; M. Wendriner, *Jahrb. Eisenhüttenwesen,* **5**. 5, 1904 ; H. H. von Wichdorff, *Zeit. Ethnologie,* **36**. i, 237, 1904 ; W. Wick, *Die wirtschaftliche Entwicklung des Eisenhüttenwesens an der Lahn und Dill im 19 Jahrhundert,* Stuttgart, 1911 ; J. H. Willekopp, *Crell's Ann. Beytträge,* **3**. 323, 1787 ; J. J. Winkelmann, *Gründliche und varhafte Beschreibung der Fürstenthümer Hessen und Hersfeld,* Bremen, 1697 ; D. Winter, *Werkmeister Ztg.,* 325, 1907 ; E. Wittich, *Zeit. Berg. Hütt. Sal.,* **53**. 556, 1905 ; A. Woltmann and F. Frölich, *Die Gutehoffnungshütte Oberhausen, Rheinland,* Düsseldorf, 1910 ; G. Württenberger, *Karsten's Arch.,* **25**. 235, 1853 ; F. Wüst, *Die Einwirklung der deutschen Eisenindustrie in den letzten Jahren,* Halle a. S., 1909 ; E. Zivier, *Stahl Eisen,* **34**. 310, 1914.

[9] L. Menander, *Historico delineatio officinarum ferrariarune in magno ducatu Finnlandiæ*, Abo, 1746; O. Schrader, *Die Metalle*, Wien, 1906; *Real-Lexikon der indogermanischen Altertumskunde*, Stuttgart, 1901; *Sprachvergleichung und Urgeschichte*, Jena, 1883; J. Hoops, *Real-Lexikon der germanischen Altertumskunde*, Strassburg, 1911; G. W. A. Kahlbaum, *Mythos und Naturwissenschaft*, Leipzig, 1898; I. Castren, *Kleine Schriften*, St. Petersburg, 288, 1862. [10] H. Bauerman, *Journ. Iron Steel Inst.*, **53**. i, 134, 1898; W. D. Beloff, *Gorny Journ.*, **5**. 80, 1902; *Stahl Eisen*, **22**. 469, 1902; P. Blossfeld, *Beiträge zur Industrie Rigas*, Riga, 1912; A. Eversmann, *Arch. Scient. World Russ.*, **9**. 495, 1851; B. F. J. von Hermann, *Versuch einer mineralogischen Beschreibung des uralischen Erzgebirges*, Berlin, 1789; E. Holtz, *Die Grundlagen der Russischen Eisenindustrie*, Berlin, 1903; G. Kamensky, *Journ. Iron Steel Inst.*, **48**. ii, 70, 1895; S. Kern, *Journ. Iron Steel Inst.*, **20**. ii, 80, 1881; G. Klöber, *Glaser's Ann.*, **87**. 38, 1920; M. Koltowsky, *Arch. Scient. World Russ.*, **9**. 504, 1851; N. Labzin, *Stahl Eisen*, **14**. 1019, 1894; K. Lisenko, *Arch. Scient. World Russ.*, **6**. 337, 1848; P. Martell, *Giesserei Ztg.*, **4**. 310, 1907; *Riga. Ind. Ztg.*, 213, 1907; *Oesterr. Zeit. Berg. Hütt.*, **56**. 153, 1907; J. E. Norbery, *Ueber die Produktion des Roheisens in Russland, und über eine neue Schmelzmethode in sogenannten Stürzöfen*, Freiberg, 1805; P. S. Pallas, *Reise, durch verschiedene Provinzen des Russischen Reichs*, St. Petersburg, 1771; J. W. Revillon, *Iron Coal Trades Rev.*, **90**. 245, 1915; F. Sandelin, *Stahl Eisen*, **34**. 1309, 1914; O. Simmersbach, *Montana Rund.*, **7**. 596, 630, 1915; P. R. von Tunner, *O sowremennom sostojanii scheljesnoff promyschlennosti Rossii*, St. Petersburg, 1871; M. Tschewkin and A. Osersky, *Arch. Scient. World Russ.*, **11**. 509, 1852; F. Wenzel, *Arch. Scient. World Russ.*, **9**. 480, 1851.
[11] F. Freise, *Arch. Geschichte Naturwiss. Tech.*, **5**. 241, 1914; *Erzbergbau*, 761, 779, 820, 1906; *Zeit. Berg. Hütt. Sal.*, **50**. 199, 1907; A. Muzet, *Bull. Soc. Ind. Min.*, **15**. 139, 1911; O. Vogel, *Stahl Eisen*, **34**. 1387, 1914.
[12] G. Arduino, *Raccolta de memoire chimico-mineralogische, metallurgiche, e orittografiche, Venezia*, 1775; A. M. Balling, *Jahrb. Berg. Akad. Leoben*, **17**. 212, 1867; K. Balling, *Die Eisenerzeugung in Böhmen, geschichtlich statistisch und nach ihrem gegenwärtigen Betriebe, dargestellt sowie mit kritischen Bemerkungen begleitet*, Prag, 1849; H. Bauermann, *Journ. Iron Steel Inst.*, 75, iii, 27, 1907; M. Behmann, *Prometheus*, **29**. 430, 439, 1918; L. Bittner, *Jahrb. Eisenhüttenwesen*, 2. 2, 1901; B. von Cotta, *Die Lehre von den Erzlagerstätten*, Freiberg, 360, 1855; O. von Keil-Eichenthurn, *Stahl Eisen*, **45**. 808, 1925; C. d'Elvert, *Zur Geschichte der Bergbaues und Hüttenwesens in Mähren Oesterreichische-Schesien*, Brünn, 1866; J. J. Ferber, *Physikalisch-metallurgische Abhandlungen über die Gebirge und Bergwerke in Ungarn*, Berlin, 1780; M. Gerbel, *Balkan Rev.*, 1. 250, 1914; G. Göth, *Verdernberg in der neusten Zeit.*, Wien, 1839; B. F. J. von Hermann, *Reisen durch Oesterreich, Steyermark, Kärnten, Krain, Italien Tyrol, Salzburg, und Baiern*, Wien, 1783; *Beschreibung, der Methode durch welche der Brescianer Stahl verfestigt wird*, Wien, 1782; E. Heyrowsky, *Stahl Eisen*, **19**. 672, 1899; O. von Hingenau, *Das Bessemern in Oesterreich*, Wien, 1865; C. F. Hollunder, *Tagebuch einer metallurgisch-technologischen Reise durch Mähren, Böhmen einer Theil von Deutschland und der Niederlande*, Nürnberg, 1824; C. J. B. Karsten, *Metallurgische Reise durch einen Theil von Baiern und durch die süddentschen Provinzen Oesterreich*, Halle a. S., 1821; W. Kestranek, *Stahl Eisen*, **35**. 818, 1915; *Journ. Iron Steel Inst.*, **75**. iii, 10, 1907; F. Kupelweiser, *Oesterr. Zeit. Berg. Hütt.*, 34, 1886; G. Kyrle, *Oesterr. Monatsschr. Berg. Hütt.*, 1. 256, 282, 1920; D. A. Louis, *Journ. Iron Steel Inst.*, **52**. ii, 193, 1897; J. Lowag, *Oesterr. Zeit. Berg. Hütt.*, **49**. 129, 1901; *Allgem. Berg. Zeit.*, 27, 1900; *Mont. Rund.*, **5**. 677, 1913; **6**. 53, 91, 1914; **7**. 10, 43, 74, 112, 142, 173, 1915; F. A. von Marcher, *Notizen und Bemerkungen über den Betrieb der Hochöfen und Rennwerke zur Verschmelzung der Eisenerze*, Klagenfurt, 1811; F. Marian, *Berg. Hütt. Ztg.*, **4**. 297, 1845; *Mitt. Ver. Ermunt. Gew. Böhmen*, 4. 543, 1844; P. Martell, *Centr. Hütt. Walzwerke*, **18**. 8, 1914; A. Müllner, *Geschichte des Eisens in Inner-Oesterreich von der Urzeit bis zum Anfange des XIX Jahrhunderts*, Wien, 1908; *Oesterr. Zeit. Berg. Hütt.*, **55**. 53, 68, 1907; **56**. 94, 1908; **57**. 53, 61, 1909; **58**. 67, 79, 1910; **61**. 138, 343, 1913; *Zeit. Oesterr. Ing. Arch. Ver.*, **62**. 684, 1910; *Berg. Hütt. Jahrb.*, **53**. 205, 355, 1905; **54**. 361, 1906; **56**. 51, 66, 1908; **60**. 81, 174, 1912; **61**. 278, 1913; F. Munichsdorfer, *Geschichte des Hüttenberger Erzberges*, Klagenfurt, 1870; A. Nechleba, *Montana Rund.*, **6**. 569, 1914; V. I. Pantz and A. J. Atzl, *Versuch einer Beschreibung, der vorzüglichsten Berg- und Hüttenwerke des Herzogthume Steyermark*, Wien, 1814; S. Rieger, *Oesterr. Zeit. Berg. Hütt.*, **60**. 519, 544, 557, 571, 589, 1912; E. K. Runtscheiner, *Zeit. Oesterr. Ing. Arch. Ver.*, **82**. 316, 1930; J. F. Schmidt von Bergenhold, *Uebersichtliche Geschichte des Bergbau und Hüttenwesens im Königreiche Böhmen von den ältesten bis auf die neuesten Zeiten*, Prag, 1873; J. Schmut, *Berg. Hütt. Jahrb.*, **52**. 251, 1905; D. G. Schreber, *Beschreibung, der Eisen-Berg-, und Hüttenwerke zu Eisenärz in Steyermark*, Königsberg, 1772; P. Tunner, *Oesterr. Berg. Hütt. Jahrb.*, **3**. 281, 293, 307, 1853; **6**. 81, 129, 176, 1857; *Die Zukunft der österreichischen Eisenwesens insbesondere der Roheisen-Erzeugung*, Wien, 1869; *Journ. Iron Steel Inst.*, **23**. ii, 426, 1882; J. W. Valvasor, *Die Ehre des Hertzogthums Crain*, Laybach, 1689; H. Wankel, *Bilder aus der Mährischen Schweiz und ihrer Vergangenheit*, Wien, 1882; A. Wehmann, *Zeit. Bergrecht*, **53**. 84, 1912; G. A. Wille, *Crell's Ann. Beyträge*, ii, 21, 1786; iv, 9, 1786; G. Zimmermann, *Die tschechoslowakische Eisenindustrie in ihren Beziehungen zu Volks- und Weltwirtschaft*, Eger, 1931.
[13] R. Durrer, *Untersuchungen zur Klärung der Frage der elektrischen Verhüttung schweizerischer Eisenerz*, Dusseldorf, 1924; O. Hedinger, *Die Geschichte der Eisenindustrie im Jura und die Gesellschaft der Ludwig von Roll'schen Eisenwerke*, Gerlefingen, 1923; A. Münch, *Jahresb. Hist.*

Ges. Aargau, **24**. 15, 1893 ; P. Plattner, *Geschichte des Bergbau's der östlichen Schweiz*, Chur, 1878 ; J. H. Zemek, *Giesserei Ztg.*, **4**. 210, 244, 1907.

[14] L. Adami, *I combustibili fossili i materiali refrattari e l'industria siderurgica*, Roma, 1884 ; E. Audibert, *Ann. Mines*, (4), **1**. 613, 1842 ; *Karsten's Arch.*, **18**. 316, 1844 ; G. Baldraggo, *Costituzione metallifera della Sardegna*, Turin, 1854 ; C. de Castro, *Rass. Mineraria*, **20**. 265, 1909 ; L. Dompé, *Rass. Mineraria*, **21**. 23, 1910 ; M. Fitzner, *Ber. Handl. Ind.*, **22**. 4, 10, 1915 ; *Giesserei*, **2**. 123, 148, 162, 169, 1915 ; N. Garella, *Ann. Mines*, (3), **16**. 3, 1839 ; *Karsten's Arch.*, **18**. 289, 1844 ; O. Johannsen, *Stahl Eisen*, **31**. 1960, 1911 ; E. Jüngst, *Glückauf*, **51**. 878, 1915 ; *Stahl Eisen*, **35**. 962, 1915 ; G. Ponzi, *Delle miniere di ferro e degli stabilimenti per la manifattura del medesimo nello stato Pontificio*, Roma, 1846 ; L. Simonin, *Ann. Mines*, (5), **14**, 557, 1858.

[15] P. de Alzola, *Journ. Iron Steel Inst.*, **50**. ii, 5, 1896 ; H. Braune, *Oesterr. Zeit. Berg. Hütt.*, **53**. 153, 1905 ; *Uber eine schnelle Methode für die Bastimmurg, des Stickstofsgehaltes, in Eisen und Stahl und eine Untersuchung von prähistorischen Eisen aus Castaneda (Sud-Graubünden)*, Basel, 1905 ; J. T. Dillon, *Travels through Spain*, London, 1780 ; W. von Eschwege, *Karsten's Arch.*, **8**. 185, 1835 ; J. G. Hemas, *Notes sobre la fabricacion de aceros en España*, Madrid, 1884 ; O. R. Kuhn, *Eng. Min. Journ.*, **121**. 367, 1926 ; C. Muthuon, *Journ. Mines*, **2**. 1, 1795 ; M. Pernollet, *Ann. Mines*, (4), **8**. 595, 1845 ; F. le Play, *ib.*, (3), **5**. 175, 209, 1834.

[16] W. Baragwanath, *Ann. Rept. Soc. Mines Victoria*, 66, 1910 ; E. Lewis, *Journ. Australia Inst. Eng.*, **1**. 125, 1929 ; J. Plummer, *Mining World*, **23**. 493, 1905.

[17] J. A. Heskett, *Journ. Iron Steel Inst.*, **101**. i, 201, 1920.

[18] R. H. Mahon, *Report on the Manufacture of Iron and Steel in India*, Simla, 1899 ; R. D. Oldham, *Report of the Examination of the Districts in the Damoodah Valley and Burbhoom producing Iron Ore*, Calcutta, 1856 ; *Report on the Government Iron Works in Kumaon*, Calcutta, 1859 ; D. Smith, *Coal and Iron Districts in Bengal*, Calcutta, 1856 ; W. Sowerby, *Mineral Deposits in Kumaon and the Experimental Iron-Smelting Operations at Dechouree*, Calcutta, 1836 ; D. H. Williams, *Geological Report on the Kymore Mountains, the Ramghur Coalfields and on the Manufacture of Iron*, Calcutta, 1852—*vide supra*.

[19] S. Hattori, *Proc. World's Eng. Congr. Tokyo*, **33**. 43, 1931 ; H. Yoshikawa, *ib.*, **33**. 163, 1931 ; S. Unotoro, *ib.*, **33**. 255, 1931.

[20] W. H. Adams, *Journ. Iron Steel Inst.*, **40**. ii, 233, 1891 ; *Trans. Amer. Inst. Min. Eng.*, **20**. 196, 1891 ; P. Barnes, *The Present Technical Condition of the Steel Industry of the United States*, Washington, 1885 ; G. Baum, *Glückauf*, **44**. 217, 663, 697, 736, 769, 865, 969, 1908 ; I. L. Bell, *Notes of a Visit to Coal and Iron Mines and Ironworks in the United States*, Newcastle, 1875 ; *On the American Iron Trade and its Progress during Sixteen Years*, Edinburgh, 1892 ; *Journ. Iron Steel Inst.*, **8**. 80, 1875 ; J. Berkinbone, *Min. Ind.*, **10**. 399, 1901 ; *Trans. Amer. Inst. Min. Eng.*, **21**. 473, 1893 ; **42**. 222, 1911 ; M. W. Bernewitz, *Blast Furnace Steel Plant*, **19**. 1219, 1931 ; K. Bruce, *Virginia Iron Manufacture in the Slave Era*, New York, 1931 ; J. Bowron, *Iron Age*, **94**. 1124, 1184, 1914 ; C. S. Boyer, *Early Forges and Furnaces in New Jersey*, Philadelphia, 1931 ; H. M. Boylston, *Fuels Furnaces*, **4**. 193, 1926 ; *Mineral Ind.*, **37**. 349, 1928 ; E. P. Buffet, *Amer. Machinist*, **25**. 406, 1902 ; **27**. 240, 354, 1904 ; *Eng. Min. Journ.*, **85**. 309, 1908 ; J. G. Butler, *Iron Trade Rev.*, **77**. 425, 481, 1925 ; *Blast Furnace Steel Plant*, **6**. 1, 1918 ; *Fifty Years of Iron and Steel*, Cleveland, 1922 ; O. Cary, *Iron Age*, **74**. 28, 1904 ; T. S. Casey, *Iron Age*, **85**. 938, 1910 ; H. S. Chamberlain, *Iron Trade Rev.*, **56**. 176, 198, 1915 ; E. F. Cone, *Iron Age*, **94**. 254, 1914 ; H. Corning, *Yearbook Amer. Iron Steel Inst.*, **18**. 135, 1928 ; W. C. Cronemeyer, *Iron Age*, **85**. 997, 1910 ; W. F. Durfee, *Popular Science Monthly*, **39**. 729, 1891 ; W. Firmstone, *Trans. Amer. Inst. Min. Eng.*, **3**. 152, 1875 ; **38**. 124, 1906 ; **40**. 459, 1907 ; *Berg. Hütt. Ztg.*, **34**. 201, 1875 ; *Oesterr. Zeit. Berg. Hütt.*, **34**. 817, 1886 ; B. F. French, *History of the Iron Trades of the United States from 1621 to 1857*, New York, 1858 ; J. Fritz, *Journ. Franklin Inst.*, **148**. 437, 1899 ; *Trans. Amer. Inst. Min. Eng.*, **24**. 594, 1895 ; H. George, *North Amer. Rev.*, **144**. 86, 1887 ; C. D. Godfrey, *Mech. Eng.*, **35**. 127, 1915 ; J. Goostray, R. F. Harrington and M. A. Hosmer, *Trans. Amer. Inst. Min. Eng.*, **71**. 404, 1925 ; J. M. Hartman, *Iron Trade Rev.*, **35**. 32, 1902 ; *Eng. News*, **47**. 348, 1902 ; E. W. Hassler, *Amer. Manufacturer*, **68**. 325, 356, 1901 ; W. Hawdon, *Journ. Iron Steel Inst.*, **78**. iii, 28, 1908 ; J. A. Herrick, *Iron Age*, **49**. 202, 1892 ; C. F. Himes, *Journ. Franklin Inst.*, **156**. 413, 1903 ; H. H. Hopkins, *Blast Furnace Steel Plant*, **18**. 1451, 1930 ; R. W. Hunt, *Iron Trade Rev.*, **49**. 606, 1911 ; E. J. S. Jeans, *American Industrial Conditions and Competition*, London, 1902 ; W. R. Jones, *Journ. Iron Steel Inst.*, **19**. i, 129, 1881 ; **20**. ii, 370, 1881 ; J. D. Kase, *Eng. Min. Journ.*, **59**. 559, 1895 ; W. Kennedy, *Amer. Manf.*, **68**. 1, 1901 ; W. P. Kibbee, *Iron Age*, **57**. 1474, 1896 ; J. D. Knox, *Iron Trade Rev.*, **67**. 919, 1920 ; O. Kreutzberg, *Iron Trade Rev.*, **75**. 157, 284, 1924 ; A. A. Lambing, *Proc. Hist. Soc. Western Pennsylvania*, 1, 1893 ; C. Larsen, *Amer. Manufacturer*, **66**. 486, 1900 ; A. Ledebur, *Stahl Eisen*, **20**. 266, 1920 ; H. Levy, *Die Stahlindustrie der Vereinigten Staaten von Amerika*, Berlin, 1905 ; H. W. Lewis, *Iron Trade Rev.*, **53**. 459, 1913 ; J. A. Mathews, *Forg. Stamp. Heat Treating*, **9**. 288, 1923 ; *Journ. Ind. Eng. Chem.*, **18**. 913, 1926 ; T. D. Morgan, *Iron Age*, **80**. 1057, 1908 ; W. Neumeister, *Staats-Sozialwiss. Forsch.*, 150, 1910 ; H. St. Osborn, *The Metallurgy of Iron and Steel*, Philadelphia, 1869 ; E. C. Pechin, *Trans. Amer. Inst. Min. Eng.*, **24**. 877, 1895 ; R. Peters, *Iron Trade Rev.*, **89**. 111, 1919 ; *Iron Age*, **89**. 1047, 1907 ; *Two Centuries of Iron Smelting in Pennsylvania*, Philadelphia, 1921 ; W. B. Phillips, *Iron Age*, **89**. 14, 141, 1912 ; *Iron Making in Alabama*, Montgomery, 1896 ; *Rept. Alabama Geol. Survey*, 7, 1898 ; O. S. Pike, *Amer. Machinist*, 606, 1905 ; F. Popplewell, *Some Modern Conditions and Recent Developments in Iron and Steel Production in America*, Manchester, 1906 ; T. W. Robinson, *Journ. Iron Steel*

Inst., **116.** ii, 13, 1927 ; H. M. Roche and J. C. Stoddard, *Iron Trade Rev.*, **57.** 171, 183, 1915 ; H. Saemann, *Stahl Eisen*, **46.** 436, 1926 ; A. Sauveur, *Chem. Met. Engs.*, **23.** 633, 1921 ; E. Schrödter, *Stahl Eisen*, **34.** 1075, 1914 ; E. D. Shuster, *Historical Notes on the Iron and Zinc Mining in Sussex County*, New Jersey, 1927 ; T. G. Smith, *Journ. Iron Steel Inst.*, **5.** ii, 102, 1872 ; A. N. Somers, *Bull. Amer. Steel Assoc.*, **39.** 43, 1906 ; A. Spies, *Cassiers' Mag.*, **7.** 65, 1895 ; J. M. Swank, *History of the Manufacture of Iron in All Ages and particularly in the United States*, Philadelphia, 1884 ; *Twenty Years of Progress in the Manufacture of Iron and Steel in the United States*, Washington, 1892 ; *Mineral Resources of the United States*, Washington, 1901 ; *Amer. Manufacturer*, **67.** 332, 1900 ; *Iron Age*, **73.** 12, 1904 ; R. H. Sweetzer, *Mining Met.*, **12.** 450, 1931 ; F. W. Taussig, *The Iron Industry in the United States*, Boston, 1900 ; G. S. Thackray, *Trans. Amer. Soc. Steel Treating*, **6.** 443, 1924 ; S. Thomas, *Trans. Amer. Inst. Min. Eng.*, **29.** 901, 1900 ; P. von Tunner, *Das Eisenhüttenwesen der Vereinigten Staaten von Nord-Amerika*, Wien, 1877 ; R. C. Wright, *Iron Trade Rev.*, **79.** 1417, 1926.

²¹ J. H. Bartlett, *The Manufacture, Consumption, and Production of Iron and Steel in Canada*, Montreal, 1885 ; J. Birkinbine, *Journ. Canada Min. Inst.*, **5.** 218, 1902 ; *Iron Trade Rev.*, **45.** 247, 1909 ; G. C. Mackenzie, *Ann. Rept. Bur. Mines, Toronto*, **17.** 190, 1909 ; H. S. Pool, *Trans. Mining Soc. Nova Scotia*, **2.** 144, 1894.

²² B. Simmersbach, *Oesterr. Zeit. Berg. Hütt.*, **61.** 75, 1913.

²³ O. A. Derby, *Eng. Min. Journ.*, **88.** 1112, 1909 ; F. Freise, *Materialen zur Geschichte des brasilianischen Bergbaue*, Leipzig, **2.** 462, 1910 ; H. K. Scott, *Journ. Iron Steel Inst.*, **61.** 1, 237, 1902 ; Anon., *Eng. Min. Journ.*, **67.** 201, 1898.

²⁴ J. Brüggen, *Mitt. deut. südamer. Inst.*, 229, 1914 ; A. Hartwig, *ib.*, 12, 1915 ; C. Vattier, *Journ. Iron Steel Inst.*, **86.** ii, 320, 1912.

²⁵ J. J. Becher, *Experimentum chymicum*, Francofurti, 1671 ; E. F. Geoffroy, *Mém. Acad.*, 362, 1705 ; 176, 1707 ; Ibn Hudail, *Cod. Arab.* 881 *B*, *München* ; L. Lemery, *Mém. Acad.*, 411, 1706 ; 376, 1708 ; N. Lemery, *Cours de Chymie*, Paris, 156, 1679 ; J. de Hammer-Purgstall, *Journ. Asiatique*, (5), **3.** 66, 1854 ; E. Rödigfr, *Zeit. deut. Med. Ges.*, **14.** 489, 1866 ; R. Russell, *The Works of Geber*, London, 81, 1678 (reprinted London, 1928) ; E. Wiedemann, *Ber. deut. phys. Ges.*, **9.** 364, 1907.

²⁶ T. Bergman, *De analysi ferri*, Upsala, 1781 ; G. G. Boucher, *Chem. News*, **76.** 99, 182, 1898 ; C. H. Jones, *Chem. News*, **76.** 171, 1898 ; M. H. Klaproth, *Schrift. Ges. Nat. Freunde Berlin*, **9.** 71, 1789 ; J. K. F. Meyer, *Schrift. Ges. Nat. Freunde Berlin*, **2.** 334, 1781 ; **3.** 380, 1782 ; *Crell's Ann.*, **2.** 195, 1784 ; J. P. Prat, *Le Monde Pharm.*, 1, 1877 ; F. G. Ruddock, *Chem. News*, **76.** 118, 1898.

§ 2. The Occurrence of Iron

Gold is for the mistress, silver for the maid,
Copper for the craftsman, cunning at his trade.
" Good," said the Baron, sitting in his hall,
" But iron—cold iron—is master of them all."—OLD TALE.

Metallic iron occurs free in nature, but it is comparatively rare. This might be anticipated on account of the readiness with which the metal is oxidized in moist air. Combined iron is exceedingly common, occurring as it does in hundreds of minerals—oxides, hydrated oxides, carbonates, silicates, sulphides, etc. It occurs frequently in smaller proportions in various rocks, particularly those containing amphiboles, pyroxenes, micas, and olivine. It is so common, indeed, that an extraordinary number of rocks and minerals owe their tints—particularly when fired—to the presence of a small proportion of admixed iron compounds, and that R. J. Haüy [1] could say with truth that when Nature takes up her brush, iron oxide is almost always on her palette. W. Spring discussed the coloration of soils by ferruginous matter—*vide infra*, ferric oxide. C. M. Smyth discussed the abstraction of oxygen from the air by the iron in the earth's crust.

According to G. Tammann, the results of seismographic observations agree with the assumption that the earth's crust can be roughly divided into three layers, or rather, a core and two shells, namely :

	Thickness (Kilometres)	Density	Composition
Silicate layers	0 to 1500	2·9	$(Al_2O_3, Fe_2O_3, FeO, CaO, MgO, K_2O, Na_2O).1\cdot5SiO_2$
Sulphide layer	1500 to 2900	5·6	$FeS, Fe_3P, FeO, Fe, SiO_2$
Metal core	2900 to 6370	9·6	Fe, 88 ; Ni, 8 ; (Fe : SP), 3 ; rare metals, 1 per cent.

According to F. W. Clarke, in the outer crust, iron ranks fourth in the list of elements arranged in the order of their relative abundance in the earth's lithosphere. The order is : oxygen, 46·46 per cent. ; silicon, 27·61 per cent. ; aluminium, 8·07 per cent. ; iron, 5·06 per cent. ; and calcium, 3·64 per cent. ; or, taking the average of the hydrosphere and lithosphere, O, 49·20 ; Si, 25·67 ; Al, 7·50 ; Fe, 4·71 ; and Ca, 3·39. Consequently, iron is outranked only by oxygen, silicon, and aluminium, and is closely followed by calcium—cf. Table I. For the average composition of the igneous rocks F. W. Clarke and H. S. Washington gave O, 46·59 ; Si, 27·72 ; Al, 8·13 ; Fe, 5·01 ; and Ca, 3·63 ; whilst J. H. L. Vogt gave O, 47·2 ; Si, 28·0 ; Al, 8·00 ; Fe, 4·5 ; and Ca, 3·5 ; and W. Vernadsky, O, 49·7 ; Si, 26·0 ; Al, 7·45 ; Fe, 4·2 ; and Ca, 3·25. It is further supposed, from the density of the earth, that iron is much more abundant towards the centre of the globe, and that if estimates could be made for the whole earth, iron would occupy a more prominent position in the list. According to A. E. Fersman, taking the atomic proportions, the order is O, 53·81 ; H, 17·18 ; Si, 15·85 ; Al, 4·76 ; Na, 1·80 ; Mg, 1·67 ; Ca, 1·44 ; Fe, 1·30 ; and K, 1·04 per cent. W. Lindgren estimated the relative natural abundance of some commercial metals, with gold unity, to be :

Al	Fe	Mn	Ni	Cu	Zn	Pb	Ag
15,680,000	8,800,000	16,000	46,000	15,000	8,000	4,000	20

Considering the oxidized elements, F. W. Clarke gave for the percentage composition of the lithophere :

	Igneous rocks	Shale	Sandstone	Limestone	Weighted Average
SiO_2	59·14	58·10	78·33	5·19	59·08
Al_2O_3	15·34	15·40	4·77	0·81	15·23
Fe_2O_3	3·08	4·02	1·07	0·54	3·10
FeO	3·80	2·45	0·30	—	3·72
CaO	5·08	3·11	1·16	42·57	5·10
MgO	3·49	2·44	5·50	7·89	5·10
Na_2O	3·84	1·30	0·45	0·05	3·71

W. and I. Noddack and O. Berg gave for the absolute abundance of the elements in the earth's crust : Fe, $4·7 \times 10^{-2}$; Co, $1·8 \times 10^{-6}$; Ni, $1·8 \times 10^{-5}$; and Cu, $1·0 \times 10^{-4}$. A. von Antropoff estimated the atomic percentage to be :

	Stellar atmospheres	Earth's crust	Whole earth	Silicate meteorites
Si	5·7	16·20	9·58	11·2
Na	5·7	2·02	0·97	0·6
Al	3·6	4·95	2·66	1·1
Fe	2·5	1·48	46·37	5·92
Mn	0·36	0·035	0·06	—

The subject was also discussed by V. M. Goldschmidt, E. Herlinger, O. Hahn, J. Joly, L. de Launay, F. W. Clarke, H. S. Washington, G. Berg, R. A. Sonder, R. Wildt, and P. Niggli.

The relative distributions of ferric and ferrous oxides in British and American igneous rocks are, according to A. Harker :

	Fe_2O_3	FeO
British igneous rocks	5·34	2·40
American igneous rocks	2·65	3·35

Iron occurs native as a terrestrial mineral, but it is so scarce and unimportant that it is regarded as a mineralogical curiosity. Minute grains of native iron occur in many eruptive rocks—particularly basalts. They were first demonstrated by T. Andrews [2] in the basalt of Antrim, Ireland. The iron gave a precipitate of copper when placed in a soln. of copper sulphate ; and A. von Lasaulx found that the particles of iron also reduce a soln. of cadmium borotungstate, producing violet-blue patches in the liquid. Several of the specimens of meteoric iron which have been discovered may be really of terrestrial origin. G. F. Zimmer has discussed the reports of S. Hearne, J. Ross, R. E. Peary, J. S. Steenstrup,

D. C. Clavering, and I. I. Hayes on the meteoric origin of the iron employed by the Eskimos for making arrow-heads, spear-heads, knives, etc. In 1870, A. E. Nordenskjöld discovered a remarkable deposit of iron at Ovifak, Disco Island, Greenland. In some cases masses of iron up to 20 tons in weight have weathered out like boulders from the basalt, and lenticular and disc-like pieces of metal, still uncorroded, were embedded in the mass. The iron was at first thought to be meteoric, but the evidence points the other way. The iron phosphide, schreibersite, common to many meteorites, is absent ; J. S. Steenstrup showed that native iron is abundantly disseminated through the basalt of that region ; A. Daubrée obtained pellets of iron by fusing a native chrome spinel with carbon, and he showed that beds of lignite occur on the island, and graphite is associated with native iron ; while H. Moissan observed that the iron contained granules of graphite, and amorphous carbon. All this favours the view that the iron has been reduced by carbonaceous matters on its way up from below. On the other hand, the iron is not always found in basalts or peridotites penetrating carbonaceous strata. E. B. de Chancourtois may be right in assuming that the iron has come up from great depths to teach us that the earth's interior is rich in uncombined metals. The suggestion of C. Winkler, and E. Weinschenk that the iron and nickel have been brought up from below as carbonyls is not so probable, because these gases are so unstable at elevated temps.; and C. Winkler observed no evidence of occluded carbon monoxide. The Disco Island occurrences have also been discussed by G. Tschermak, T. Nicolau, A. Schwantke, R. Nauckhoff, W. Wahl, C. Benedicks, J. L. Smith, S. Meunier, A. G. Nathorst, and A. E. Törnebohm. C. Winkler gave an analysis of a weathered sample ; and analyses reported by G. Forchhammer, J. Lorenzen, F. Wöhler, A. Daubrée, N. Wyssotzky, E. T. Allen, W. J. Taylor, W. H. Melville, E. Cohen, J. S. Steenstrup, J. W. Mallet, G. S. Jamieson, G. C. Hoffmann, R. A. A. Johnston, A. Damour, W. Skey, A. A. Inostzanzeff, A. E. Kupffer, W. Irmer, J. G. Neumann, and J. L. Smith show the presence of up to 95·15 per cent. Fe ; up to 2·55 per cent. Ni ; up to 0·93 per cent. Co ; up to 0·48 per cent. Cu ; up to 3·72 per cent. S ; up to 3·11 per cent. C ; and up to 4·18 per cent. SiO_2. J. D. Dana reported :

Fe	Ni	Co	Ca	P	S	Cl
94·71	2·25	0·63	0·24	1·82	0·29	0·06 per cent.

Native iron may also be of secondary origin. There are several reports where the iron has been reduced from its combinations. Thus, J. B. Tyrrell [3] observed masses of iron 15 to 20 lbs. in weight which have been formed during the burning of beds of lignite in contact with ironstone. The subject was discussed by A. Schwantke, P. Jeremejeff, J. Hector, G. vom Rath, G. H. F. Ulrich, J. von Szabo, W. H. Melville, G. C. Hoffmann, A. de Lapparent, J. G. Bornemann, T. G. Bonney and E. Aston. E. T. Allen found iron in borings in sedimentary rocks in Missouri near beds of coal ; A. E. Kupffer found iron under peat, and it had been formed by the reduction of bog iron ore. A. A. Inostzanzeff cited a case of naturally-reduced iron near Vladivostok ; M. Sidorenko, one at Gruschewka, Russia ; G. C. Hoffmann, one at St. Joseph Island, Lake Huron ; and E. Priwosnik, one at Shotley Bridge, England. The subject was discussed by J. F. L. Hausmann, F. M. Stapff, G. A. Kenngott, O. Vogel, and A. Reuss. J. F. Bahr found iron mixed with limonite and organic matter in petrified wood. The iron was called **sideroferrite,** and was supposed to have been produced by the decomposition of some salt of iron by the organic matter of wood.

There are reports of some specimens of native iron which may be really meteoric, and of meteoric iron which may be terrestrial. E. Hussak [4] found particles of native iron in an auriferous gravel in Brazil ; A. Daubrée and S. Meunier, in the gold washings at Berezovsk, Urals ; and W. Skey, in the drift of the Gorge River, New Zealand. In addition to the cases mentioned above, native iron has been reported to occur in basalts, trap rocks, dolerites, magnetites, etc., of Great Britain,[5] France,[6] Italy,[7] Sweden,[8] Spain,[9] Germany,[10] Russia,[11] Africa,[12] Japan,[13] Canada,[14] United States,[15] Mexico,[16] Greenland [17]—*vide supra*—Brazil,[18] Australia,[19] and New Zealand.[20] The structure of native iron was discussed by C. Benedicks,[21] A. Schwantke, H. Fleissner, W. Eitel, W. Irmer, F. Hornstein, and K. Oebbeke and M. Schwarz.

Iron occurs also as an extra-terrestrial element. The spectra of the sun, and some of the hottest stars were shown by J. von Fraunhofer,[22] G. Kirchoff, J. N. Lockyer, C. E. Moore and H. N. Russell, C. Young, H. N. Russell, H. von Klüber, A. Secchi, H. A. Vogel, G. Rayet, J. N. Lockyer and F. E. Baxandall, A. Cornu, J. Parry, P. W. Merrill, E. M. Lindsay, C. G. Abbot, H. A. Rowland, S. Albrecht, C. E. St. John, M. N. Saha, S. A. Mitchell, H. M. Vernon, H. Deslandres, R. Furnhjelm, H. Ludendorff, J. Wilsing, H. Ebert, F. J. M. Stratton, G. E. Hale, G. E. Hale and co-workers, C. Fabry and H. Buisson, C. H. Payne, C. H. Payne and C. P. Chase, T. Dunham, J. Stebbins, W. S. Adams, W. C. Rufus, C. D. Shane, J. Storey, W. H. Wright, G. F. Paddock, E. P. Waterman, A. de Gramont, J. Hartmann, and F. McClean to indicate the presence of this element is those remote regions. H. von Klüber discussed the occurrence of lines of iron in the spectrum of the solar protuberances ; E. A. Fath, of spiral nebulæ ; and F. S. Hogg, and H. von Klüber, of comets ; F. E. Wright, and B. Lyot found no evidence of the effects of iron in polarized light of the moon ; but S. Mohorovicic included iron amongst the lunar elements. Meteorites are usually highly ferruginous, and contain metallic iron—**meteoric iron.**

Iron occurs in the metallic state in most meteorites ; it may form the entire mass ; or it may occur as a spongy, cellular matrix with imbedded grains of silicates ; or in grains or scales disseminated in a stony matrix. A. Daubrée [23] applied the term **siderites** or **holosiderites** to meteorites of iron. These meteorites consist of iron alone or of iron associated with occasional veins of troilite, graphite or diamond, schreibersite, daubreelite, or lawrencite. When the Widmanstätten structure is absent, A. Brezina called them **ataxites.** The meteorites with a more or less spongy mass or network of iron, with embedded grains of chrysolite or other silicates, were called **siderolites** or **syssiderolites.** A. Brezina applied the term *siderolithites* to those with the iron network, and he considered two varieties—*mesosiderite* and *grahamite* ; and he applied the term *lithosiderites* to those consisting almost wholly of nickel-iron, which he subdivided into *siderophyrs* and *pallasites.* A. Daubrée called the stony meteorites **sporadosiderites,** where the iron is more or less disseminated through the stony mass, and according to the relative abundance of the disseminated iron the sporadosiderites were called **polysiderites,** or **oligosiderites,** or **cryptosiderites ;** and if no iron was present, **asiderites.** G. Rose called the stony meteorites with rounded spherical grains of enstatite or chrysolite, **chondrules**—χόνδρος, a spherule—and when the structure is more or less radiating, **chondrites ;** and when free or almost free from iron, they were called *achondrites.* N. S. Maskelyne used the term *siderite* for meteoric iron, *siderolite* for lithosiderite and siderolite, and *aërolites* for chondrites and achondrites—the term " siderite " is in regular use for native ferrous carbonate. The subject has been discussed by C. von Reichenbach, G. F. Zimmer, G. Tschermak, M. E. Wadsworth, and C. U. Shephard, as well as in numerous monographs, catalogues of museum collections, etc.

E. Cohen, *Meteoritenkunde*, Stuttgart, 1894–1905 ; S. Meunier, *Les météorites*, Paris, 1884 ; O. Buchner, *Die Meteoriten in Sammlungen ihre Geschichte, mineralogische und chemische Beschaffenheit*, Leipzig, 1863 ; L. Fletcher, *Introduction to the Study of Meteorites*, London, 1888 ; O. C. Farrington, *Handbook and Catalogue of the Meteorite Collection*, Chicago, 1903 ; *Meteorites : their Structure, Composition, and Terrestrial Relations*, Chicago, 1916 ; G. Tschermak, *Die Meteoriten des kaiserlichkoniglichen mineralogischen Museums*, Wien, 1872 ; A. Daubrée, *Les météorites et la constitution du globe terrestre*, Paris, 1886 ; *Expérience synthétique relative aux météorites*, Paris, 1866 ; W. Flight, *A Chapter in the History of Meteorites*, London, 1887 ; E. A. Wülfling, *Die Meteoriten in Sammlungen und ihre Litteratur nebst einem Versuch, den Tauschwert der Meteoriten zu bestimmen*, Tübingen, 1897 ; G. vom Rath, *Die Meteoriten des naturhistorischen Museums der Universität Bonn*, Bonn, 1875 ; K. Vrba, *Meteoritensammlung des Museums des Königreichs Böhmen in Prag*, Prag, 1904 ; A. Brezina, *Meteoritenstudien*, Bonn, 1881 ; F. Berwerth, *Tschermak's Mitt.*, (2), **22.** 189, 1904 ; *Verzeichnis der Meteoriten in kaiserlich und königlich naturhistorischen Hofmuseums*, Wien, 1903 ; W. Bruhns, *Verzeichnis der Meteoriten des mineralogischen und petrologischen Instituts von Strassburg*, Strassburg, 1903 ; F. W. Clarke, *The Meteorite Collection in the U.S. National Museum*, Washington, 1889 ; A. del Castillo, *Catalogue descriptive des météorites du Mexique*, Paris, 1889 ; M. F. Fouqué and M. Lévy, *Expériences synthétiques relative à la reproduction artificielle de météorites*, Paris, 1881 ; C. P. Harris, *Chemical Constitution and Chronological Arrangement of Meteorites*, Göttingen, 1859 ; H. Laspeyres, *Die Meteoritensammlung der Universität Bonn*, Bonn, 1895 ; C. F. Rammelsberg, *Ueber die Meteoriten und ihre Beziehung zur Erde*, Berlin, 1872 ; A. Purgold, *Die Meteoriten des mineralogischen Museums in Dresden*, Dresden, 1882 ; G. Rose, *Systematische Eintheilung der Meteoriten*, Berlin, 1865 ; H. A. Ward, *Check List of all known Meteorites*, Chicago, 1897 ; *Catalogue of the Ward-Coonley Collection of Meteorites*, Chicago, 1904 ; C. Klein, *Meteoritensammlung der königlichen Friedrich Wilhelm Universität zu Berlin*, Berlin, 1904 ; C. von Schreiber, *Beyträge zur Geschichte und Kenntniss meteorischer Stein- und Metallmassen und der Erscheinungen, welche deren Niederfallen zu begleiten pflegen*, Wien, 1820 ; E. King, *Remarks concerning Stones said to have Fallen from the Clouds*, London, 1796 ; G. Dewalque, *Ann. Soc. Géol. Belg.*, **32.** 15, 1905.

There are references in the *Bible* to falls of meteorites—*e.g. Joshua* (**10.** 11), *Psalms* (**18.** 13), *Acts* (**19.** 35)—and in several of the ancient Greek and Latin writers

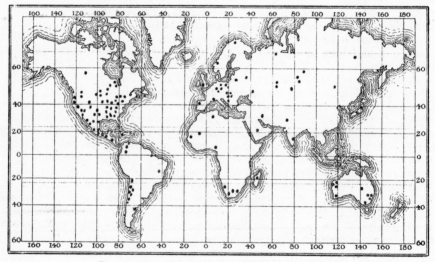

FIG. 4.—Localities of Known Falls of Meteorites.

—*e.g.* Pliny, *Historia naturalis* (**2.** 58, and **37.** 51, 52, 61). E. F. F. Chladni [24] compiled tables in 1803 and 1815 ; and in 1860, P. A. Kesselmayer listed 647 falls between 1984 B.C. and A.D. 1860. Numerous other lists of known falls of meteorites have been prepared, and G. F. Zimmer's has represented the known localities in the map, Fig. 4. Recent lists of the known falls have been also compiled by E. Cohen, F. Berwerth, and H. Michel. F. Berwerth has calculated that the number falling on the earth at the present time is about 900 per annum. Allowing for the unknown falls and for the meteorites lost in the oceans, the earth is being well peppered with them every day. P. Kropotkin estimated that 146,000,000 small meteorites reach the earth annually, but they are so small that it would take 100,000 years for their dust to raise the surface of the globe a single inch. N. S. Maskelyne observed that the lighter surface of the meteorites is blown away as dust as the meteorite passes through our atmosphere, and in some cases the meteorite itself deflagrates with a more or less violent explosion, to form not a single meteorite but rather a shower of fragments and dust. A. von Lasaulx discussed the nature of meteoric dust.

The first chemical analysis of meteoric iron was made in 1802 by E. Howard [25] ; and in the next year M. H. Klaproth found that nickel was present in the meteorite from Agram. In 1815, F. Stromeyer observed the presence of cobalt, and in 1833, copper. The copper was confirmed by J. L. Smith. A. Laugier found chromium ; J. J. Berzelius, phosphorus ; C. T. Jackson, chlorine ; A. Liversidge, J. C. H. Mingaye, and J. E. Whitfield and G. P. Merrill, gold, and the platinum metals ; and S. Tennant, graphite—M. Eroféeff and P. Latschinoff observed diamonds in the meteorite of Novo-Urei, Russia ; W. Will and J. Pinnow, in that of Carcote, Chile ; and G. A. Koenig and A. E. Foote, in that of the Canyon Diablo, Arizona—discussed by C. Friedel, F. E. Mallard and A. Daubrée, and H. Moissan. In all, the following elements have been detected in meteorites : Na, K, Rb, Cu, Ag, Au, Ca, Sr, Ba, Mg, Zn, Al, C, Si, Pb, P, As, V, S, Cr, Tl, Mn, Fe, Co, Ni, Ir, Pt, Pd, and Ru. J. Lunt, A. P. Forjaz, and W. Crookes established the presence of some of these elements spectroscopically. A. W. Wright, T. Graham, W. Flight, J. W. Mallet, and R. T. Chamberlin observed that 0·97 to 47·13 vols. of gas may be occluded in meteoric iron, and that the occluded gas has from 14·54 to 85·68 per cent. of hydrogen ; 0·12 to 43·29 of carbon dioxide ; 4·46 to 71·05, carbon monoxide ; 1·54 to 17·66, nitrogen ; and up to 4·55, methane. W. Ramsay and co-workers, F. Paneth and co-workers, and H. D. Campbell and J. L. Howe found argon and helium amongst the occluded gases. R. J. Strutt, and T. T. Quirke and L. Finkelstein observed that many samples of meteoric iron are radioactive ; and F. Paneth, D. Urry and W. Koeck measured the helium and radium contents of a number of meteorites, and made estimates of their age.

The average of 318 analyses of meteoric iron was calculated by O. C. Farrington and the results are here shown with the average previously given for the Greenland terrestrial iron :

	Fe	Ni	Co	Cu	Cr	P	S	C	Cl	
Meteoric .	90·85	8·52	0·59	0·02	0·01	0·17	0·04	0·03	—	per cent.
Terrestrial	94·71	2·25	0·63	0·24	—	1·82	0·29	—	0·06	per cent.

The results are said to agree as closely as individual analyses of meteoric iron. F. W. Clarke has emphasized the chemical and mineralogical analogy between meteorites and the earth itself. F. Berwerth and H. Michel have compiled the results of 415 analyses of meteoric iron made [26] during the past century. According to O. C. Farrington,. " the most striking feature brought out by the analyses is the relation between chemical composition and structure." This seems to be definite and general. All the meteorites of hexahedral structure have a nearly uniform composition, whilst amongst the octahedral meteorites fineness of structure increases with increase of nickel. Practically, the members of all the classes conform in composition to the average. G. P. Merrill found the average percentage of metallic iron in stony meteorites to be 11·98, and of ferrous oxide, 14·58, and 1·15 per cent. of metallic nickel ; and O. C. Farrington gave for all meteorites :

Fe	O	Ni	Si	Mg	S	Ca	Co
72·6	10·10	6·50	5·20	3·80	0·49	0·46	0·44

Al	Na	P	Cr	K	C	Mn	Etc.
0·39	0·17	0·14	0·09	0·04	0·04	0·03	0·05

I. and W. Noddack's results are indicated in Table I, which shows F. W. Clarke and H. S. Washington's estimates of percentage proportions of the elements in the earth's crust, and F. Behrend and G. Berg's estimates of the percentage proportions of the elements in stony meteorites, in meteoric iron, and in troilite, as well as the relative abundance of the atoms when the value for oxygen is unity.

TABLE I.—THE DISTRIBUTION OF THE ELEMENTS IN THE EARTH'S CRUST AND IN METEORITES.

Element.	Earth's crust.	Meteorites. Stony.	Iron.	Troilite.	Atomic proportions.
H	$8\cdot8\times10^{-3}$	—	—	—	—
He	$4\cdot2\times10^{-9}$	—	—	—	—
Li	$5\cdot0\times10^{-5}$	$5\cdot0\times10^{-6}$	—	—	$2\cdot7\times10^{-5}$
Be	$5\cdot0\times10^{-6}$	$1\cdot0\times10^{-5}$	+	—	$4\cdot2\times10^{-5}$
B	$1\cdot4\times10^{-5}$	0	+	—	—
C	$8\cdot7\times10^{-4}$	$3\cdot4\times10^{-4}$	$3\cdot9\times10^{-4}$	—	$1\cdot9\times10^{-3}$
N	$3\cdot0\times10^{-4}$	0	$1\cdot0\times10^{-5}$	—	$1\cdot9\times10^{-5}$
O	$4\cdot942\times10^{-1}$	$4\cdot204\times10^{-1}$	—	—	$1\cdot0$
F	$2\cdot7\times10^{-4}$	+	—	—	—
Ne	$5\cdot0\times10^{-9}$	—	—	—	—
Na	$2\cdot64\times10^{-2}$	$7\cdot18\times10^{-3}$	—	—	$1\cdot2\times10^{-2}$
Mg	$1\cdot94\times10^{-2}$	$1\cdot590\times10^{-1}$	$3\cdot2\times10^{-4}$	—	$2\cdot5\times10^{-1}$
Al	$7\cdot51\times10^{-2}$	$1\cdot61\times10^{-2}$	$4\cdot0\times10^{-5}$	—	$2\cdot4\times10^{-2}$
Si	$2\cdot575\times10^{-1}$	$2\cdot143\times10^{-1}$	$8\cdot0\times10^{-3}$	—	$3\cdot0\times10^{-1}$
P	$1\cdot2\times10^{-3}$	$5\cdot06\times10^{-4}$	$1\cdot47\times10^{-3}$	$3\cdot05\times10^{-3}$	$2\cdot2\times10^{-3}$
S	$4\cdot8\times10^{-4}$	$2\cdot01\times10^{-2}$	$3\cdot6\times10^{-4}$	$3\cdot43\times10^{-1}$	$4\cdot0\times10^{-2}$
Cl	$1\cdot88\times10^{-3}$	$9\cdot04\times10^{-4}$	—	—	$1\cdot0\times10^{-3}$
A	$3\cdot6\times10^{-6}$	—	—	—	—
K	$2\cdot4\times10^{-2}$	$2\cdot63\times10^{-3}$	—	—	$2\cdot6\times10^{-3}$
Ca	$3\cdot39\times10^{-2}$	$1\cdot92\times10^{-2}$	$5\cdot0\times10^{-4}$	—	$1\cdot9\times10^{-1}$
Sc	$7\cdot5\times10^{-7}$	$1\cdot1\times10^{-4}$	+	—	$9\cdot5\times10^{-5}$
Ti	$5\cdot8\times10^{-3}$	$2\cdot10\times10^{-3}$	$4\cdot0\times10^{-5}$	—	$1\cdot7\times10^{-3}$
V	$1\cdot6\times10^{-4}$	$3\cdot0\times10^{-4}$	$6\cdot2\times10^{-6}$	$4\cdot5\times10^{-5}$	$2\cdot3\times10^{-4}$
Cr	$3\cdot3\times10^{-4}$	$5\cdot0\times10^{-3}$	$2\cdot4\times10^{-4}$	$1\cdot20\times10^{-3}$	$4\cdot0\times10^{-3}$
Mn	$8\cdot0\times10^{-4}$	$2\cdot05\times10^{-3}$	$3\cdot0\times10^{-4}$	$4\cdot6\times10^{-4}$	$1\cdot6\times10^{-3}$
Fe	$4\cdot7\times10^{-2}$	$1\cdot276\times10^{-1}$	$9\cdot02\times10^{-1}$	$6\cdot11\times10^{-1}$	$5\cdot9\times10^{-1}$
Co	$1\cdot8\times10^{-5}$	$1\cdot81\times10^{-4}$	$5\cdot47\times10^{-3}$	$2\cdot08\times10^{-3}$	$2\cdot7\times10^{-3}$
Ni	$1\cdot8\times10^{-4}$	$2\cdot01\times10^{-3}$	$8\cdot46\times10^{-2}$	$2\cdot88\times10^{-2}$	$4\cdot2\times10^{-2}$
Cu	$1\cdot0\times10^{-4}$	$1\cdot55\times10^{-6}$	$3\cdot05\times10^{-4}$	$4\cdot20\times10^{-4}$	$3\cdot9\times10^{-4}$
Zn	$5\cdot7\times10^{-5}$	$3\cdot40\times10^{-6}$	$1\cdot15\times10^{-4}$	$1\cdot53\times10^{-3}$	$1\cdot3\times10^{-4}$
Ga	$1\cdot0\times10^{-9}$	+	$1\cdot3\times10^{-5}$	+	$5\cdot0\times10^{-6}$
Ge	$3\cdot0\times10^{-11}$	$3\cdot3\times10^{-5}$	$2\cdot36\times10^{-4}$	$1\cdot15\times10^{-3}$	$1\cdot7\times10^{-4}$
As	$5\cdot5\times10^{-6}$	$2\cdot0\times10^{-5}$	$3\cdot6\times10^{-4}$	$1\cdot02\times10^{-3}$	$1\cdot9\times10^{-4}$
Se	$2\cdot5\times10^{-8}$	+	+	$8\cdot4\times10^{-4}$	$4\cdot2\times10^{-5}$
Br	$6\cdot0\times10^{-6}$	$1\cdot0\times10^{-6}$	—	—	$5\cdot0\times10^{-7}$
Kr	$2\cdot0\times10^{-11}$	—	—	—	—
Rb	$3\cdot4\times10^{-5}$	$4\cdot5\times10^{-6}$	0	0	$2\cdot0\times10^{-6}$
Sr	$1\cdot7\times10^{-4}$	$7\cdot2\times10^{-5}$	+	—	$3\cdot2\times10^{-5}$
Y	$5\cdot5\times10^{-5}$	$3\cdot4\times10^{-5}$	+	—	$1\cdot5\times10^{-5}$
Zr	$2\cdot3\times10^{-4}$	$1\cdot0\times10^{-4}$	$8\cdot0\times10^{-6}$	—	$4\cdot2\times10^{-5}$
Nb	$4\cdot0\times10^{-8}$	$2\cdot0\times10^{-6}$	$1\cdot0\times10^{-6}$	—	$1\cdot1\times10^{-6}$
Mo	$7\cdot2\times10^{-6}$	$2\cdot5\times10^{-6}$	$1\cdot66\times10^{-5}$	$1\cdot10\times10^{-5}$	$6\cdot0\times10^{-6}$
Ma	—	—	+	+	—
Ru	$2\cdot3\times10^{-13}$	0	$2\cdot39\times10^{-5}$	$4\cdot20\times10^{-6}$	$6\cdot1\times10^{-6}$
Rh	$9\cdot0\times10^{-13}$	0	$5\cdot0\times10^{-6}$	$1\cdot0\times10^{-6}$	$1\cdot3\times10^{-6}$
Pd	$8\cdot5\times10^{-13}$	0	$1\cdot9\times10^{-5}$	$4\cdot5\times10^{-6}$	$4\cdot6\times10^{-6}$
Ag	$4\cdot0\times10^{-8}$	0	$3\cdot2\times10^{-6}$	$2\cdot1\times10^{-5}$	$1\cdot5\times10^{-6}$
Cd	$1\cdot1\times10^{-7}$	—	$8\cdot0\times10^{-6}$	$3\cdot0\times10^{-5}$	$2\cdot9\times10^{-6}$
In	$9\cdot0\times10^{-9}$	—	+	$8\cdot0\times10^{-7}$	$2\cdot7\times10^{-8}$
Sn	$6\cdot0\times10^{-6}$	$4\cdot0\times10^{-6}$	$1\cdot02\times10^{-4}$	$1\cdot61\times10^{-3}$	$7\cdot3\times10^{-5}$
Sb	$2\cdot3\times10^{-7}$	$1\cdot0\times10^{-7}$	$2\cdot0\times10^{-6}$	$7\cdot8\times10^{-6}$	$7\cdot3\times10^{-7}$
Te	$6\cdot0\times10^{-19}$	—	—	$1\cdot7\times10^{-5}$	$5\cdot0\times10^{-7}$
I	$6\cdot0\times10^{-8}$	+	—	—	—
Xe	$2\cdot4\times10^{-11}$	—	—	—	—
Cs	$7\cdot0\times10^{-7}$	$1\cdot0\times10^{-7}$	—	—	$2\cdot9\times10^{-8}$
Ba	$4\cdot7\times10^{-4}$	$2\cdot0\times10^{-5}$	+	—	$5\cdot6\times10^{-6}$
La	$6\cdot0\times10^{-6}$	+	—	—	—
Ce	$2\cdot7\times10^{-5}$	$4\cdot0\times10^{-6}$	+	—	$1\cdot1\times10^{-6}$
Pr	$4\cdot0\times10^{-6}$	+	—	—	—
Nd	$1\cdot7\times10^{-5}$	$3\cdot0\times10^{-6}$	—	—	$7\cdot9\times10^{-7}$
Sm	$6\cdot0\times10^{-6}$	$3\cdot0\times10^{-6}$	—	—	$7\cdot7\times10^{-7}$

TABLE I (*continued*).

Element.	Earth's crust.	Meteorites.			
		Stony.	Iron.	Troilite.	Atomic proportions.
Eu	$2 \cdot 0 \times 10^{-7}$	$+$	$-$	$-$	$-$
Gd	$6 \cdot 0 \times 10^{-6}$	$+$	$+$	$-$	$-$
Tb	$1 \cdot 0 \times 10^{-6}$	$+$	$-$	$-$	$-$
Dy	$6 \cdot 0 \times 10^{-6}$	$+$	$-$	$-$	$-$
Ho	$1 \cdot 0 \times 10^{-6}$	$+$	$-$	$-$	$-$
Er	$5 \cdot 0 \times 10^{-6}$	$+$	$-$	$-$	$-$
Tm	$1 \cdot 0 \times 10^{-6}$	$+$	$-$	$-$	$-$
Yb	$6 \cdot 0 \times 10^{-6}$	$+$	$-$	$-$	$-$
Cd	$1 \cdot 4 \times 10^{-6}$	$+$	$-$	$-$	$-$
Hf	$2 \cdot 0 \times 10^{-5}$	$1 \cdot 0 \times 10^{-6}$	$+$	$-$	$2 \cdot 1 \times 10^{-7}$
Ta	$1 \cdot 2 \times 10^{-8}$	$7 \cdot 0 \times 10^{-7}$	$1 \cdot 0 \times 10^{-6}$	$-$	$3 \cdot 0 \times 10^{-7}$
W	$5 \cdot 5 \times 10^{-5}$	$1 \cdot 8 \times 10^{-5}$	$8 \cdot 1 \times 10^{-6}$	$+$	$4 \cdot 7 \times 10^{-6}$
Re	$-$	$8 \cdot 0 \times 10^{-10}$	$8 \cdot 2 \times 10^{-9}$	$1 \cdot 0 \times 10^{-9}$	$1 \cdot 3 \times 10^{-9}$
Os	$6 \cdot 0 \times 10^{-12}$	$-$	$8 \cdot 8 \times 10^{-6}$	$1 \cdot 0 \times 10^{-5}$	$1 \cdot 4 \times 10^{-6}$
Ir	$3 \cdot 0 \times 10^{-12}$	0	$2 \cdot 3 \times 10^{-6}$	$5 \cdot 0 \times 10^{-7}$	$3 \cdot 2 \times 10^{-7}$
Pt	$8 \cdot 0 \times 10^{-11}$	$8 \cdot 3 \times 10^{-8}$	$1 \cdot 77 \times 10^{-5}$	$3 \cdot 0 \times 10^{-6}$	$2 \cdot 3 \times 10^{-6}$
Au	$1 \cdot 0 \times 10^{-9}$	0	$1 \cdot 4 \times 10^{-6}$	$4 \cdot 5 \times 10^{-7}$	$1 \cdot 9 \times 10^{-7}$
Hg	$2 \cdot 7 \times 10^{-8}$	$-$	$-$	$+$	$-$
Tl	$8 \cdot 5 \times 10^{-10}$	$-$	$+$	$3 \cdot 0 \times 10^{-7}$	$5 \cdot 6 \times 10^{-9}$
Pb	$8 \cdot 0 \times 10^{-6}$	$5 \cdot 0 \times 10^{-6}$	$5 \cdot 3 \times 10^{-5}$	$7 \cdot 1 \times 10^{-4}$	$2 \cdot 1 \times 10^{-5}$
Bi	$3 \cdot 4 \times 10^{-8}$	$-$	$5 \cdot 0 \times 10^{-7}$	$2 \cdot 0 \times 10^{-6}$	$1 \cdot 0 \times 10^{-7}$
Th	$2 \cdot 5 \times 10^{-5}$	$2 \cdot 0 \times 10^{-6}$	$+$	$-$	$3 \cdot 3 \times 10^{-7}$
U	$5 \cdot 0 \times 10^{-8}$	$+$	$+$	$-$	$-$

TABLE II.—THE COMPOSITION OF GASES OCCLUDED IN METEORITES.

	Meteorite.	H_2S.	CO_2.	CO.	CH_4.	H_2.	N_2.	Total.
Stony.	Guernsey, Ohio	—	1·80	0·13	0·06	0·95	0·05	2·99
	Pultusk, Poland	—	1·06	0·06	0·06	0·52	0·04	1·75
	Pultusk, Poland	—	2·34	0·19	0·27	0·64	0·09	3·54
	Parnallee, India	—	2·13	0·04	0·05	0·36	0·04	2·63
	Weston, Conn.	—	2·83	0·08	0·04	0·46	0·08	3·49
	Iowa County, Iowa	—	0·88	0·05	—	1·45	0·12	2·50
	Kold Bokkeveld	—	23·49	0·61	0·82	0·10	0·21	25·23
	Dhurmsala, India	—	1·59	0·03	0·10	0·72	0·03	2·51
	Mocs	—	1·25	0·07	0·09	0·45	0·07	1·94
	Orgueil	$\left\{ \begin{array}{c} SO_2 \\ 48 \cdot 03 \end{array} \right\}$	7·40	1·14	0·87	—	0·33	57·87
	Allegan, Mich.	trace	0·21	0·19	0·01	0·08	trace	0·49
	Estacado, Texas	trace	0·24	0·25	0·03	0·31	0·01	0·84
	Average	4·00	3·77	0·24	0·20	0·50	0·09	8·80
Iron.	Lenarto	—	0·13	0·00	—	2·44	0·28	2·85
	Augusta Co., Va.	—	0·31	1·21	—	1·14	0·51	3·17
	Tazewell Co., Tenn.	—	0·46	1·31	—	1·35	0·05	3·17
	Shingle Springs, Cal.	—	0·13	0·12	—	0·67	0·05	0·97
	Cross Timbers, Tex.	—	0·11	0·19	—	0·99	—	1·29
	Dickson County, Tex.	—	0·29	0·34	—	1·57	—	2·20
	Arva, Hungary	—	5·92	31·91	—	8·57	0·73	47·13
	Cranbourne, Australia	—	0·04	1·13	0·16	1·63	0·63	3·59
	Rowton, Shropshire	—	0·33	0·47	—	4·96	0·62	6·38
	Toluca, Mexico	trace	0·12	1·32	0·04	0·27	0·10	1·85
	Average	—	0·78	3·80	0·02	2·36	0·30	7·26
	Average (not Arva)	—	0·21	0·67	0·02	1·67	0·24	2·83

R. T. Chamberlin [27] compiled Table II from the observations of A. W. Wright, J. Dewar and G. Ansdell, R. T. Chamberlin, T. Graham, J. W. Mallet, and W. Flight on the gases occluded in meteorites. The nickel influences the structure. It may also account for the change from a hexahedral to an octahedral structure, since the irons with hexahedral structure have the lowest percentage of nickel. The percentage of nickel in iron meteorites as a whole, as shown by reliable analyses, lies between 5 and 26 per cent. Cobalt in iron meteorites rarely exceeds 1 per cent. No constant relation in amount appears to exist between it and nickel, although, perhaps, as a rule it is higher with higher nickel. Analyses of meteoric iron always show iron, nickel, cobalt, copper, and phosphorus, and in most cases sulphur, carbon, and silicon. F. Paneth, and F. Paneth and W. D. Urry found up to 36.15×10^{-6} c.c. of helium in meteoric iron.

The structure of the nickel-iron meteorites is discussed in connection with the iron-nickel alloys. In connection with these alloys, the relationship of **kamacite,** with over 7 per cent. nickel, **taenite,** with over 27 per cent. nickel, and **plessite,** a mixture of kamacite and taenite, is described. The structure of meteorites after polishing and etching shows that there are roughly three types : (i) Those with an octahedral structure are called **octahedrites.** They have two sets of parallel lines at right angles to one another, which gives rise to the so-called Widmanstätten structure or lines. The lines are produced by the alloys kamacite, taenite, and plessite. (ii) Those with a cubic structure or cleavage are called **hexahedrites.** They have lines intersecting at 120°. (iii) Those with an interrupted or indistinct structure are called **ataxites.**

The *phosphorus* in meteoric iron, forming **schreibersite** and **rhabdite,** is discussed in connection with the phosphides ; the *sulphur,* forming **troilite,** in connection with the sulphides, FeS ; the *carbon,* forming graphite or **cliftonite,** and carbides —**cementite,** or **cohenite**—in connection with the carbides, and the structure of iron and steel ; the *chromium,* forming chromite, and **daubreelite,** $FeS.Cr_2S_3$, in connection with the iron sulphides ; the *chlorine,* as **lawrencite,** in connection with ferrous chloride ; and the *silicon,* forming **moissanite,** SiC, in connection with silicon—there are also many ferruginous *silicates* present, *e.g.* plagioclase, pyroxene, olivine, etc.

Many of the specimens analyzed also had their sp. gr. taken. O. C. Farrington said that the sp. gr. of meteoric iron is between 7·6 and 7·9. Since the sp. gr. of purified iron is 7·85, it will be increased by that of nickel (8·8) according to the proportion of the latter. It will be decreased by accessory minerals such as troilite, FeS, of sp. gr. 4·7 ; schreibersite, Fe_3P, of sp. gr. 6·5 ; graphite, of sp. gr. 2·2 ; and oxidized ingredients, as well as by increasing porosity. C. Benedicks [28] discussed the electrical conductivity ; P. N. Laschtschenko and W. J. Iwanis, and P. N. Tschirwinsky, the passivity ; and H. H. Nininger, the oxidation of meteorites. F. Paneth and co-workers measured the relative proportions of helium and radium in meteorites, and calculated that the ages of meteorites ranged from 100 to 2600 million years. The solidification data indicate that these meteorites originated in our solar system. There have been observations by N. F. Belaiew, [29] C. Benedicks, F. Berwerth, W. Fränkel and G. Tammann, W. Guertler, H. Moissan, F. Osmond and G. Cartaud, F. Rinne, and F. Rinne and H. E. Boeke on the synthesis of meteoric iron—*vide infra.*

The list of minerals containing combined iron as an essential constituent is extensive. Comparatively few of the following minerals are of commercial importance. The industrially-important minerals, so far as the extraction of iron is concerned, include : (i) The magnetite group of ferrosic oxides ; (ii) The hæmatite group of anhydrous ferric oxides ; (iii) The limonite group of hydrated ferric oxides —*e.g.* limonite and brown iron ores ; (iv) The iron carbonate group—*e.g.* siderite ; (v) The iron silicate group—*e.g.* thuringite, chamosite, and glauconite ; and (vi) The iron sulphide group—*e.g.* pyrite and pyrrhotite. Some of these groups are of importance only under special conditions—*e.g.* in central Bohemia and Thuringia chamosite and thuringite are worked commercially; and glauconite has been tried as a subsidiary to the recovery of its potash. The ferruginous minerals are exceedingly common, and a list would include the majority of known minerals. The following list includes those in which iron is usually considered to be always present :

Acmite, $Na_2Fe_2(SiO_3)_4$. **Actinolite**—a variety of grünerite. **Adelpholite**—weathered mossite. **Aegirite,** $Na_2Fe_2(SiO_3)_4$. **Ænigmatite,** $2(Na_2,Fe)O.2SiO_2$. **Almandine,** $3FeO.$ $Al_2O_3.3SiO_2$. **Amaranite,** $Fe_2O_3.2SO_3.7H_2O$. **Amesite**—a ferruginous chlorite. **Ammoniojarosite,** $(NH_4)_2SO_4.3Fe_2O_3.3SO_3.6H_2O$. **Anapaite,** $FeCa_2(PO_4)_2.4H_2O$. **Andradite,** $3CaO.$ $Fe_2O_3.3SiO_2$. **Andrewsite,** $4Fe_2O_3.2FeO.2CuO.3P_2O_5.7H_2O$. **Ankerite,** $2CaCO_3.MgCO_3.$ $FeCO_3$. **Anophorite**—a variety of arfvedsonite. **Anthophyllite,** $(Mg,Fe)SiO_3$. **Aphrosiderite**—a variety of cronstedtite. **Arfvedsonite**—$Na_2O.FeO.4SiO_2$. **Argentojarosite,** $Ag_2SO_4.3Fe_2O_3.3SO_3.6H_2O$. **Argillaceous iron ore**—vide clay ironstone. **Arizonite,** $Fe_2O_3.3TiO_2$. **Arrojadite**—a complex ferrous manganous phosphate, $4R'_3PO_4.9R''_3(PO_4)_2$. **Arsenic,** $FeS_2.FeAs_2$. **Arsenical mundic,** $FeS_2.FeAs_2$. **Arsenical pyrites,** $FeS_2.FeAs_2$. **Arseniosiderite,** $6CaO.4Fe_2O_3.3As_2O_5.9H_2O$. **Arsenoferrite,** $FeAs_2$. **Astrolite,** $(Fe,Al)(Na,K)$-$SiO_3.H_2O$. **Awaruite**—an alloy of iron and nickel—q.v. **Babingtonite**—a variety of hypersthene. **Baldaufite,** $Fe_3(PO_4)_2.3H_2O$. **Barkevicite**—a ferruginous amphibole. **Barnhardite,** $2Cu_2.S.Fe_2S_3$. **Barrandite**—hydrogel of ferric phosphate. **Bartholomite**—more or less dehydrated ferronatrite. **Beraunite,** $FePO_4.2Fe_2(PO_4)(OH)_3.4H_2O$. **Berlauite**—a leptochlorite. **Berthierite,** $FeS.Sb_2S_3$. **Beudantite,** $2PbO.3Fe_2O_3.As_2O_5.2SO_3.6H_2O$. **Bianchite,** $FeZn_2(SO_4)_3.18H_2O$. **Bilinite,** $FeSO_4.Fe_2(SO_4)_3.24H_2O$. **Bixbyite,** $FeO.MnO_2$. **Blackband**—a carbonaceous ferrous carbonate. **Blakeite**—an early name for coquimbite. **Blue iron earth**—an earthy variety of vivianite. **Bog ore**—hydrated ferric oxide. **Borgströmite,** $Fe_2O_3.SO_3.3H_2O$. **Borickite,** $2CaO.5Fe_2O_3.2P_2O_5.16H_2O$. **Bornite**—a sulphide of iron and copper. **Bosphorite,** $3Fe_2O_3.2P_2O_5.17H_2O$—colloidal. **Boryckite,** $CaO.$ $2Fe_2O_3.P_2O_5.7H_2O$. **Botryogen**—essentially ferric sulphate, or $2MgO.Fe_2O_3.4SO_3.15H_2O$. **Brandisite,** $12(Mg,Ca,Fe)O.6(Al,Fe)_2O_3.5SiO_2.H_2O$. **Bronzite**—a variety of hypersthene. **Brush ore**—a variety of limonite. **Cacoxenite,** $2Fe_2O_3.P_2O_5.12H_2O$. **Calcioferrite,** $7FeO.$ $2P_2O_5.2H_2O$. **Canbyite**—a ferruginous clay. **Carminite,** $3PbO.5Fe_2O_3.6As_2O_5$. **Carphosiderite,** $3Fe_2O_3.4SO_3.9H_2O$. **Castanite,** $Fe_2O_3.2SO_3.8H_2O$. **Cataphorite**—a ferruginous amphibole. **Catarinite**—an alloy of nickel and iron Fe_2Ni. **Chalcodite**—a variety of stilpomelane. **Chalcopyrite**—vide copper pyrites. **Chalcopyrrhotin,** $Cu_2S.3Fe_2S_3.2FeS$. **Chalcosiderite,** $3Fe_2O_3.CuO.2P_2O_5.8H_2O$. **Chalmersite,** $CuFe_2S_3$. **Chalybite**—vide spathic ore. **Chalypite**—a compound of iron and carbon. **Chamosite**—an iron silicate. **Chenevixite,** $3CuO.Fe_2O_3.As_2O_5.3H_2O$. **Childrenite**—hydrated phosphate of iron and aluminium. **Chloritoid,** $(Fe,Mg)O.Al_2O_3.SiO_2.H_2O$. **Chloropal**—a ferruginous clay. **Chloropite**—a variety of delessite. **Christophite**—a ferruginous sphalerite, $(Fe,Zn)S$. **Chrome iron ore**—vide chromite. **Chromite,** $FeO.Cr_2O_3$. **Chromitite,** $Fe_2O_3.Cr_2O_3$. **Chromoferrite**—vide chromite. **Clementite**—a ferruginous heptochlorite. **Clay ironstone**—an impure ferrous carbonate. **Cleveland ironstone**—a variety of clay ironstone. **Clinochlor**—a ferruginous chlorite. **Clinophæite**—an impure voltaite. **Clintonite,** $10(Mg,Cu)O.5(Al,Fe)_2O_3.$ $4SiO_2.3H_2O$. **Cobalt-nickel pyrites,** $(Fe,Co,Ni)S_2$. **Cockscomb pyrites**—a variety of marcasite. **Codazzite,** $(Ca,Mg,Fe,Ce)CO_3$. **Cohenite,** $(Fe,Co,Ni)_3C$. **Columbite,** or niobite. **Copiapite,** $3Fe_2O_3.8SO_3.27H_2O$, or else $2Fe_2O_3.5SO_3.18H_2O$. **Copper pyrites,** $Cu_2S.FeS_2$. **Copperas,** $FeSO_4.7H_2O$. **Coquimbite**—a hexagonal form of $Fe_2(SO_4)_3.9H_2O$. **Corkite,** $2PbO.3Fe_2O_3.P_2O_5.2SO_3.6H_2O$. **Coronadite,** $(Mn,Pb,Fe,Zn,Cu)_2Mn_3O_7$. **Corundophilite**—a ferruginous orthochlorite. **Cossyrite**—a variety of ænigmatite. **Crichtonite,** $FeTiO_3$. **Crocidolite**—a variety of riebeckite. **Cronstedtite,** $4FeO.2Fe_2O_3.3SiO_2.4H_2O$. **Crossite**—a variety of riebeckite. **Cubanite,** $CuS.Fe_2S_3$. **Cube ore**—vide iron sinter. **Daphnite,** $27FeO.$ $10Al_2O_3.18SiO_2.28H_2O$. **Daubréelite,** $FeS.Cr_2S_3$. **Delafossite,** $CuFeO_2$. **Delessite**—a ferruginous leptochlorite. **Derbylite,** $2FeSbO_3.5TeTiO_3$. **Destinezite,** $2Fe_2O_3.2SO_3.P_2O_5.12H_2O$. **Diadochite,** $2Fe_2O_3.P_2O_5.2SO_3.2H_2O$. **Dietrichite**—an impure ferric alum. **Dimagnetite,** Fe_3O_4. **Douglasite,** $FeCl_2.2KCl.2H_2O$. **Dufrenite,** $Fe_2(OH)_3PO_4$. **Durdenite,** $Fe_2O_3.$ $3TeO_2.4H_2O$. **Ekmanite**—a variety of cronstedtite. **Ekonorite,** $3Fe_2O_3.2P_2O_5.8H_2O$. **Emmonsite**—hydrated ferric tellurite. **Enophite**—a weathered chlorite. **Eosphorite**—a variety of childrenite rich in manganese. **Epichlorite**—a variety of leptochlorite. **Epigenite,** $4Cu_2S.3FeS.As_2S_5$. **Epiphanite**—a variety of leptochlorite. **Erubescite**—vide bornite. **Erythrosiderite,** $2KCl.FeCl_3.H_2O$. **Esmeraldaite,** $Fe_2O_3.4H_2O$. **Eukampite**—a variety of leptochlorite. **Euralite**—a variety of cronstedtite. **Fayalite,** $2FeO.SiO_2$—vide iron olivine. **Ferberite,** $FeO.WO_3$. **Ferriallophane,** $(Fe,Al)_2O_3.SiO_2.5H_2O$. **Ferrisymplesite,** $3Fe_2O_3.$ $2As_2O_5.13H_2O$. **Ferritungstite,** $Fe_2O_3.WO_3.6H_2O$. **Ferronatrite,** $Na_3Fe(SO_4)_3.3H_2O$. **Ferropallidite,** $FeSO_4.H_2O$. **Ferrotellurite,** $FeO.TeO_3$. **Ferrovanite,** $2Fe_2O_3.2V_2O_5.5H_2O$. **Fibroferrite,** $Fe_2O_3.2SO_3.10H_2O$. **Flajolotite**—hydrogel ferric phosphate. **Fosterite,** $2(Mg,Fe)O.$ SiO_2. **Foucherite**—like borychite and picite. **Franklinite**—vide zincite. **Gadolinite,** FeO $2BeO.Y_2O_3.2SiO_2$. **Ganomatite**—colloidal ferric arsenate. **Gastaldite**—a variety of glaucophane. **Geikielite,** $(Mg,Fe)O.TiO_2$. **Gillespite,** $FeO.BaO.4SiO_2$. **Gillingite**—a ferruginous clay. **Glaucodote,** $(Co,Fe)AsS$. **Glauconite**—an iron silicate. **Glaucophane,** $Na_2O.(Al,Fe)_2O_3.4SiO_2$.

Glockerite, $2FeO.Fe_2O_3.SO_3.6H_2O$. Goethite, $Fe_2O_3.H_2O$. Graftonite, $(Fe,Mn,Ca)_3(PO_4)_2$. Gramenite—a ferruginous clay. Grengesite—a variety of delessite. Grünerite, $FeO.SiO_2$. Gudmundite, FeSbS. Halotrichite, $FeSO_4.Al_2(SO_4)_3.24H_2O$. Hæmatite—crystals of ferric oxide. Hæmatophanite, $Pb(Cl,OH)_2.4PbO.2Fe_2O_3$. Hastingsite—a variety of riebeckite. Hedenbergite, $FeO.CaO.2SiO_2$. Hercynite, $FeO.Al_2O_3$. Hetopazote, or heterosite, Fe_2O_3. $P_2O_5.H_2O$. Hisingerite, $Fe_2O_3.2SiO_2.2H_2O$. Hoeferite, $2Fe_2O_3.3SiO_2.7H_2O$. Hollandite, $(Mn,Ba,K_2,H_2)MnO_5.n(Mn,Fe,Al)_4(MnO_5)_3$. Holmquistite—a variety of glaucophane. Homitite, $3CaO.FeO.B_2O_3.2SiO_2$. Horse-flesh ore—vide bornite. Hudsonite—a variety of glaucophane. Hversalt, an impure halotrichite. Hydrogoethite, $3Fe_2O_3.4H_2O$. Hydrohæmatite—vide turgite. Hydrotroilite, $FeS.nH_2O$. Hystatite, $FeTiO_3$. Ihleite, Fe_2O_3. $3SO_3.12H_2O$. Ilmenite, $FeO.TiO_2$. Ilmenorutile, $FeCb_2O_6.4TiO_2$. Ilvaite—see lievrite. Iron glance—vide specular ore. Iron, native. Iron olivine, Fe_2SiO_4. Iron pyrites—vide pyrites. Iron sinter, $2FeAsO_4.Fe(OH)_3.5H_2O$. Iozite, FeO. Janosite—a rhombic form of $Fe_2(SO_4)_3.9H_2O$. Jarosite, $K_2SO_4.3Fe_2O_3.4SO_3.6H_2O$. Iron tourmaline, $8FeO.6Al_2O_3$. $3B_2O_3.12SiO_2.4H_2O$. Jollyite—a ferruginous clay. Josephinite—an alloy of iron and nickel—q.v. Kakoxen, $2Fe_2O_3.P_2'O_5.12H_2O$. Kamasite—an alloy of iron and nickel —q.v. Kibdelophane, $FeTiO_3$. Kidney ore, Fe_2O_3. Knebetite, $2(Fe,Mn)SiO_3$. Koninck-ite, $FePO_4.3H_2O$. Kornelite, $Fe_2O_3.3SO_3.7\frac{1}{2}H_2O$. Kraurite, $2Fe_2O_3.P_2O_5.3H_2O$. Krausite, $K_2SO_4.Fe_2(SO_4)_3.2H_2O$. Kremersite, $KCl.NH_4Cl.FeCl_3.H_2O$. Kreuzbergite —a ferric aluminium phosphite. Lagonite, $Fe_2O_3.3B_2O_3.3H_2O$. Lake ore—vide bog ore. Laterite—similar to limnite. Lausenite, $Fe_2(SO_4)_3.6H_2O$. Lavenite, $Na_2O.2(Mn,Ca,Fe)O$. $2(ZrO,F).4SiO_2$. Lawrencite—ferrous chloride. Lazulite, $(Mg,Fe)O.Fe_2O_3.P_2O_5.H_2O$. Lehnerite, $Fe_7(OH)_2(PO_4)_4.5H_2O$. Lepidocrocite—fibro-scaly goethite. Leucopyrite, $FeAs.FeAs_2$. Lievrite, $2CaO.4(Fe,Mn)O.Fe_2O_3.4SiO_2.H_2O$. Lillite—a variety of stilpo-melane. Limnite, $Fe_2O_3.3H_2O$. Limonite, $2Fe_2O_3.3H_2O$. Liskeardite—hydrated arsenate of iron and aluminium. Lodestone—vide magnetite. Löllingite, $FeAs_2$. Looking-glass ore—vide specular ore. Lossenite, $2PbO.9Fe_2O_3.6As_2O_5.SO_3.33H_2O$. Ludlamite, $7FeO.2P_2O_5$. $9H_2O$. Ludwigite, $(Fe,Mg)O.Fe_2O_3.B_2O_3$. Mackensite, $Fe_2O_3.SiO_2.2H_2O$. Maghemite —native ferromagnetic ferric oxide. Magnesioferrite, $MgO.Fe_2O_3$. Magnetic pyrites, $4FeS$. Fe_3S_4. Magnetite, Fe_3O_4. Magnetoferrite, $2PbO.3Fe_2O_3$. Metachroite — resembles chamosite. Magnetoplumbite, $2(Pb,Mn)O.3Fe_2O_3$. Magnoferrite—vide magnesioferrite. Manganhedenbergite—a variety of hedenbergite. Marcasite, FeS_2. Margarite—a basic $Ca_2(Al,Fe)$-silicate. Marmatite, FeS.4ZnS. Martite, Fe_2O_3. Masrite—an impure ferric alum. Mazapilite, $3CaO.2Fe_2O_3.2As_2O_5.6H_2O$. Melanolite—a variety of leptochlorite. Melano-tekite, $2PbO.Fe_2O_3.2SiO_2$. Melanterite—vide copperas. Melnikowite, $FeS_2.nH_2O$. Menac-canite—vide ilmenite. Mesitite, $FeCO_3.2MgCO_3$. Metavauxite, $FeO.Al_2O_3.P_2O_5.4H_2O$. Metavoltine—a hydrated voltaite. Micaceous iron ore, Fe_2O_3. Minette—a hydrated Fe_2O_3. Mingueite—a variety of stilpomelane. Mispickel—vide arsenical pyrites. Molysite, $FeCl_3$. Moravite—a variety of cronstedtite. Moronolite—a variety of jarosite. Mossite, $(Fe,Mn)O$. $(Cb,Ta)_2O_5$. Müllerite—a ferruginous clay. Mundic—vide pyrites. Narsarsukite, $3Na_2O$. $(Fe,F)O.12SiO_2.2TiO_2$. Natrojarosite, $Na_2SO_4.3Fe_2O_3.3SO_3.6H_2O$. Needle ironstone—vide goethite. Neptunite, $(Na,K)_2O.(Fe,Mn)O.4SiO_2.TiO_2$. Niobite, $FeO.Cb_2O_5$. Nontro-nite, $Fe_2O_3.3SiO_2.5H_2O$. Nordmarkite—impure staurolite. Ochre—a variety of limonite. Octibbehite—an alloy of iron and nickel. Olivine, Fe_2SiO_4,Mg_2SiO_4. Onegite—vide goethite. Orileyite, $(Cu_2,Fe)_3(As,Sb)_2$. Orthochlorite, $2(Mg,Fe)O.Al_2O_3.SiO_2.2H_2O$ plus $3(Mg,Fe)O$. $2SiO_2.2H_2O$. Osannite—a variety of riebeckite. Ottrelite, $(Fe,Mn)O.Al_2O_3.2SiO_2.H_2O$. Oxalite, $2FeO.C_2O_3.3H_2O$. Pacite, $FeS_2.4FeAs_2$. Paravauxite, $5FeO.4Al_2O_3.5P_2O_5$. $26H_2O+21H_2O$; or $FeO.Al_2O_3.P_2O_5.5H_2O$. Pattersonite—a variety of leptochlorite. Pelhamite—a variety of chlorite. Pennine—a ferruginous orthochlorite. Pentlandite, $2FeS.NiS$. Pharmaco-siderite—vide iron sinter. Phillipite, $CuSO_4.Fe_2(SO_4)_3.nH_2O$—probably a mixture. Phosphoferrite, $7FeO.2P_2O_5.2H_2O$. Phosphophyllite, $3R_3(PO_4)_2.2Al(OH)SO_4$. $9H_2O$, where R represents Fe,Mg,Ca,K_2. Phosphosiderite, $2FePO_4.7H_2O$. Picite, $8FePO_4$. $6Fe(OH)_3.27H_2O$. Pinguite, $2Fe_2O_3.6SiO_2.Aq$. Pisanite, $(Fe,Cu)SO_4.7H_2O$. Pistomesite, $FeCO_3.MgCO_3$. Pitticite—an arsenical sinter. Plagiocitrite—an impure voltaite. Plano-ferrite, $Fe_2O_3.SO_3.15H_2O$. Plinthite—a ferruginous clay. Plumboferrite, $(Pb,Fe,Cu)O.Fe_2O_3$. Plumbojarosite, $PbSO_4.3Fe_2O_3.3SO_3.6H_2O$. Prochlorite—a ferruginous orthochlorite. Pseudobrookite, $Fe_2O_3.3TiO_2$. Puddle ore, Fe_2O_3. Pyroxlerite—a variety of leptochlorite. Purpurite—hydrogel ferric phosphate. Pyroaurite, $Fe(OH)_3.3Mg(OH)_2.3H_2O$. Pyroxmangite, $(Fe,Mn)SiO_3$. Pyrrhotite—vide magnetic pyrites. Quenstedtite, $Fe_2(SO_4)_3.10H_2O$. Quetenite, $MgO.Fe_2O_3.3SO_3.12H_2O$. Red fossil ore, Fe_2O_3. Red hæmatite—a generic name for anhydrous Fe_2O_3; and it is also given to turgite. Red ochre—vide turgite and red hæmatite. Reinite, FeO. WO_3. Rhabdite, $(Ni,Fe)_3P$. Rhodonite, $2(Mn,Fe)O.2SiO_2$. Rhomboclase, $[Fe(OH)_2]_2(HSO_4)_2$. $6H_2O$. Rhodusite—a variety of riebeckite. Rhönite—a variety of ænigmatite. Richellite, a ferric fluophosphate. Richterite—a variety of arfvedsonite. Riebeckite, $Na_2O.Fe_2O_3$. $4SiO_2$ mixed with $FeO.SiO_2$. Rinneite, $FeCl_2.3KCl.NaCl$. Roemerite, $FeSO_4.Fe_2(SO_4)_3$. $12H_2O$. Röpperite, $2(Fe,Mn,Zn,Mg)O.SiO_2$. Roscnerite, $(Fe,Mn,Ca)_2Al(OH)(PO_4)_2.2H_2O$. Rubinglimmer—vide goethite. Rogersite—an early name for lausenite. Rubrite, $MgSO_4$. $Fe_2(SO_4)_3.18H_2O$. Ruddle, Fe_2O_3. Rumfite—a variety of cronstedtite. Salmonsite—hydrogel ferric phosphate. Salvadorite, $(Cu,Fe)SO_4.7H_2O$. Sammet-blende—a velvety variety of goethite. Sarcopside, $2(Fe,Mg,Mn,Ca)_3(PO_4)_2.(Fe,Mg,Mn,Ca)F_2$. Schafarzikite,

FeO.P$_2$O$_3$. **Schreibersite,** (Fe,Ni)$_3$P. **Schuchardtite**—a variety of chlorite. **Scorodite,** FeAsO.2H$_2$O. **Senaite,** (Fe,Mn,Pb)O.TiO$_2$. **Shining ore**—micaceous iron ore. **Sicklerite,** (Li,H)$_2$O.6MnO,Fe$_2$O$_3$.4P$_2$O$_5$.H$_2$O. **Siderazote,** Fe$_2$N. **Siderite**—*vide* spathic ore. **Sidero-chrome**—*vide* chromite. **Sideroferrite**—metallic iron present in petrified wood. **Sidero-natrite,** 2Na$_2$O.Fe$_2$O$_3$.4SO$_3$.7H$_2$O. **Sider-plesite,** 2FeCO$_3$.MgCO$_3$. **Siderotile,** FeSO$_4$.5H$_2$O. **Sienna,** Fe$_2$O$_3$.Aq. **Sitaparite,** 9Mn$_2$O$_3$.4Fe$_2$O$_3$.MnO.3CaO. **Sjögrufvite**—hydrogel ferric phosphate. **Skemmatite,** 3MnO$_2$.2Fe$_2$O$_3$.6H$_2$O. **Slavikite,** (Na,K)$_2$SO$_4$.2Fe$_5$(OH)$_3$(SO$_4$)$_6$. 63H$_2$O. **Smith ore**—a variety of limonite. **Souesite**—an alloy of iron and nickel—*q.v.* **Spathic ore,** FeCO$_3$. **Soear pyrites**—a variety of marcasite. **Specular iron ore,** Fe$_2$O$_3$. **Sphæro-siderite**—a variety of clay ironstone. **Stainerite,** (Co,Fe,Al)$_2$O$_3$.H$_2$O. **Stannite,** Cu$_2$S.FeS.SnS$_2$. **Staurotite,** 4FeO.9Al$_2$O$_3$=8SiO$_2$.H$_2$O. **Steatargillite**—a variety of lepto-chlorite. **Strengite,** FePO$_4$.2H$_2$O. **Sternbergite,** Ag$_2$S.Fe$_2$S$_3$.2FeS. **Stilpnomelane,** 2(Fe,Mg)O.(Fe,Al)$_2$O$_3$.5SiO$_2$.3H$_2$O. **Striegovite**—a variety of cronstedtite. **Symplesite,** 3FeO.As$_2$O$_3$.8H$_2$O. **Szechenyite**—a variety of glaucophane. **Tænite**—an alloy of iron and nickel—*q.v.* **Talc-chlorite**—a variety of leptochlorite. **Tantalite,** FeO.Ta$_2$O$_5$. **Tapiolite,** FeO.Ta$_2$O$_5$. **Taramellite,** 4BaO.FeO.2Fe$_2$O$_3$.10SiO$_2$. **Taranakite,** like kehoeïte. **Tauriscite,** FeSO$_4$.7H$_2$O. **Thraulite**—a ferruginous clay. **Thuringite**—an iron silicate. **Titanic iron ore,** FeTiO$_2$. **Trevorite,** NiO.Fe$_2$O$_3$. **Triphyllite,** Li(Fe,Mn)PO$_4$. **Triplite,** 3(Fe,Mn)O.P$_2$O$_5$. (Fe,Mn)F$_2$. **Triploidite,** 4(Mn,Fe)O.P$_2$O$_5$.H$_2$O. **Tripuhite,** 2FeO.Sb$_2$O$_5$. **Troilite,** FeS. **Tur-gite,** 2Fe$_2$O$_3$.H$_2$O. **Uddevalite,** FeTiO$_2$. **Unghwarite**—a ferruginous clay. **Urusite,** is sideronatrite. **Valleriitc,** Cu$_2$Fe$_4$S$_7$. **Vauxite,** 4FeO.2Al$_2$O$_3$.3P$_2$O$_5$.24H$_2$O+3H$_2$O, or FeO.Al$_2$O$_3$.P$_2$O$_5$.6H$_2$O. **Venasquite,** FeO.Al$_2$O$_3$.3SiO$_2$.H$_2$O. **Viridite,** 4FeO.2SiO$_2$.3H$_2$O. **Vivianite,** Fe$_2$(PO$_4$)$_2$.8H$_2$O. **Voltaite,** 3FeSO$_4$.Fe$_2$(SO$_4$)$_3$.9H$_2$O. **Vonsenite,** 4(Mg,Fe)O. Fe$_2$O$_3$.3B$_2$O$_3$. **Vredenburgite,** 2Fe$_2$O$_3$.3Mn$_3$O$_4$. **Weinbergerite,** Na$_2$O.6FeO.Al$_2$O$_3$.8H$_2$O. **Wenzelite,** (Fe,Mn,Mg)$_2$(PO$_4$)$_2$. **White iron pyrites**—*vide* marcasite. **Willcoxite**—a variety of heptochlorite. **Wolframite,** (Fe,Mn)WO$_4$. **Wood iron ore**—a variety of limonite. **Xantholite**—an impure staurolite. **Xanthophyllite,** 14(Mg,Ca,Fe)O.8Al$_2$O$_3$.5SiO$_2$.4H$_2$O. **Xantho-siderite,** Fe$_2$O$_3$.2H$_2$O. **Xanthoxenite**—basic ferric phosphate. **Yukonite,** (Ca$_3$. Fe$_2$)As$_2$O$_8$.2Fe(OH)$_3$.5H$_2$O. **Zincite,** (Mn,Fe)O.Fe$_2$O$_3$. **Zwieselite**—a ferruginous triplite.

The more important supplies of iron ore are sedimentary deposits, including replacement and residual deposits. E. C. Eckel [30] estimated that 10·7 per cent. were formed by direct or indirect igneous action; 26·2 per cent., by superficial weathering and chemical action; and 63·1 per cent., by direct sedimentary deposition.

I.—The igneous deposits include those which are found as original constituents of a mass of igneous rocks, but E. C. Eckel added that none at present worked in the United States can with certainty be ascribed to this group. The titani-ferous magnetites, however, are generally supposed to be of magmatic origin. The subject was discussed by G. Berg.

II.—The sedimentary deposits include those in which the iron derived from the decay or weathering of a pre-existing rock has been transformed by running water either in suspension or in solution, and afterwards deposited by simple sedimenta-tion, by evaporation, by chemical action, or by organic agencies, discussed by J. M. van Bemmelen—*vide* limonite. The sedimentary ores of the Rhine area, Middles-brough, Belgium, France, Alabama, and Nova Scotia are of this character. The sedimentary rocks formed by the transportation of matter suspended in running water appear as transported concentrates, usually magnetite, along stream beds and sea beaches—*vide infra*, limonite. Deposits in which the iron is carried largely or entirely in solution by surface waters and afterwards deposited as a precipitate from the solution, include (1) *spring deposits*, which have been formed from spring-waters at their point of issue; (2) *bog deposits*, appearing as brown ores, pyrite, or carbonate in swamps or lakes; (3) *basin deposits*, in which the iron ore has been deposited in a completely or partially enclosed sea-basin by evapora-tion, chemical action, or organic agencies. The basin deposits include (i) the carbonate ores; (ii) iron silicate ores like the glauconites reported as forming extensive areas over the present ocean bed, and which are illustrated by the green sand deposits of New Jersey and the silicate ores of Thuringia, discussed by E. R. Zalinsky, C. Schmidt, and A. Lacroix; and (iii) the iron oxide ores exemplified by the Clinton ores of the United States, the Wabana ores of Newfoundland, the minette ores of Lorraine and Luxembourg, and the Minas Geraes ores of Brazil.

III.—Replacement ores have been formed by the deposition of an iron mineral in a pre-existing mass of rock. The iron has been carried to the place of deposition in solution—hot or cold. The ferruginous waters may have been ascending or descending, and it may form (i) *cavity or pore deposits* by filling spaces pre-existing in the mass of rock ; (ii) *normal replacement deposits*, in which a mass of pre-existing rock has been replaced by an iron mineral, *e.g.* when soln. of iron salts act on limestones—*vide infra*, iron carbonates ; (iii) *secondary concentration deposits*, in which a low-grade ore has been enriched by the subsequent deposition of iron ;. and (iv) *contact replacement deposits*, in which a mass of pre-existing rock has been replaced by an iron mineral deposited from heated solutions set in action by local igneous intrusions.

IV.—Alteration ores.—These ores include (1) *Gossan deposits*, formed by the surface alteration of a pre-existing deposit of iron sulphide, discussed by H. M. Chance, E. Newton, J. W. Gruner, and T. S. Lovering ; and (2) *residual deposits*, formed during the decay or solution of a ferruginous rock, leaving the iron ore behind or newly formed *in situ*, *e.g.* lateritic ores—studied by H. Harrassowitz.

An idea of the geographical distribution of the commercially important ores of iron can be gathered from the map, Fig. 5. There are a number of works specially

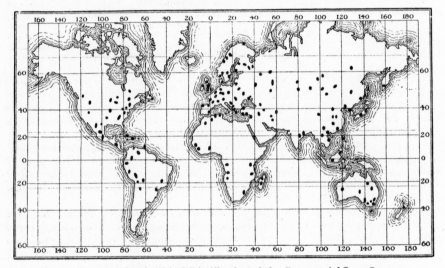

FIG. 5.—Geographical Distribution of the Commercial Iron Ores.

devoted to this subject,[31] and the official geographical reports of many countries contain much data.

Europe.—In **Great Britain** [32] there are the carbonate ores of the Mesozoic rocks of Yorkshire, Lincolnshire, and Northamptonshire. They include the oolitic siderite of Cleveland, the deposit in Lincolnshire, which is continued in a less well-developed form in Leicestershire, the deposit of Rutland and Oxford, that in Northampton, and an analogous deposit in Inverness. There are immense deposits of carbonate or clay ironstone ores associated with the coal-measures, and which crop out in various parts, ranging from Newcastle-on-Tyne to South Wales ; they are mined extensively in Staffordshire and Scotland. The South Wales deposits were discussed by J. D. Kendall, H. Louis, S. Vivian, and M. Morgans. The South Wales and Scottish deposits are outliers, and some of these ores—*e.g.* those of Northumberland—are carboniferous, but they do not belong to the coal-measures. There are hæmatite and magnetite ores in Cumberland and Lancashire, where they are associated with the carboniferous limestone. There are lodes of red hæmatite of minor importance in Cornwall and Devon ; pockets of brown ore in Gloucester ; veins of spathic ore in Somerset ; pisolitic ores in Carnarvon (North Wales) ; and bedded oolitic ores in Wiltshire and Kent. There are many other deposits which are of lesser importance or only of minor interest—

the Forest of Dean deposits, for instance, were discussed by J. W. Watson, and H. R. Insole and C. Z. Bunning. R. W. Dron described the iron ores of Shetland. The pisolitic, residual ores at Antrim in **Ireland** were discussed by H. Louis, C. H. Williams, W. Peile, A. McHenry, E. St. J. Lyburn, J. D. Kendall, E. Hull, C. S. Parnell, G. V. du Noyer, G. A. J. Cole, H. P. T. Rohleder, R. Tate and J. S. Holden, G. Kinahan, J. F. Hodges, and P. Argall. Clay ironstone occurs near Lough Allen and in Kilkenny county; while magnetite occurs at Ballycog. In **France,**[33] the region embracing the Lorraine-Luxemburg area is perhaps the most important iron district in Europe. The French portion of the deposits includes those of the Aumetz-Arsweiler Plateau, Fentsch, the Longwy basin—Hussigny, and Saulnes—the Briey basin—Orne, Landres, and Tucquegnieux—the Nancy basin, and the Crusnes basin—Grand-Rimont, Mercy-le-Hunt, and Audun-le-Roman. There are hæmatite and carbonate ores in western France, thus the Normandy deposits at May, Urville, St. Rémy, La Ferrière, Halouze and Larchamp, Dilette, etc.—the Anjou deposits—e.g. at Segré—the Brittany deposits—e.g. at Rougé and Nozay. There are also deposits in southern France—principally in the department of Pyrénées Orientales. In **Luxemburg,**[34] in Lorraine basin, there are the phosphatic minette ores—at Esch-sur-l'Alzette, Belvaux, Differdange, and Rodange. In **Belgium,**[35] there are a few low-grade deposits of hæmatite, but Belgium imports its main supplies from Spain, Sweden, and Germany. The principal iron mines are north of the Meuse valley—near Vedrin, Marchovelette, and Houssois. There is brown ore in the Campine district and also carbonate ore in the coal-measures of north-eastern Belgium. In **Holland,**[36] there are small deposits of bog ore in Groningen, Overyssel, and Gelderland. In **Portugal,**[37] there are small deposits not well developed. In **Spain,**[38] the most extensive deposits are near Moncorvo in Tras-os-Montes, Alemtejo in Odemira, and Porto de Moz in Estremadura. There are large deposits, some of which supply the demands of the British Bessemer steel process. There are hæmatite and carbonate ores associated with the cretaceous limestones of Bilbao, in the province of Vizcaya. There are brown hæmatites in the province of Lugo; and high-grade carbonates and hæmatites at Astorga and other parts of the province of Leon; while the provinces of Oviedo, Huelva, Sevilla, Almeria, Gerona, Murcia, Guipuzcoa, Navarra, Huesca, Pamplona, Logrono, Burgos, Segovia, Badajoz, Malaga, Granada, Santander, Saragossa, Teruel, and Guadalajara possess more or less important ores. When the ores of the Lorraine-Luxemburg region were ceded to France, at the conclusion of the 1914–18 war, **Germany**[39] lost about two-thirds of her estimated iron resources. The most extensive of the remaining deposits are in the Siegerland district of southern Westphalia and other parts of the east Rhine area—Dill-Lahn district, the regions of Taunus, Vogelsberg, Westerwald, Spessart, and Bergischer-Kalkberg. There are also iron ores in the Weser district, in the cretaceous rocks on the north of the Harz mountains, and the Salzgitter-Ilsede, the Harz mountains, Kellerwald-Sauerland, the Lower Hesse, Bentheim-Ochtrup-Ottenstein area, the Teutoburger Forest area; in the western Rhine area—near Aachen, and on the Soonwald; at Schmiedelberg in Silesia; at Amberg, Hollfeld, and Kressenberg in Bavaria; and in Würtemberg-Gieslingen, and Aalen. There are also deposits of bog iron in north and central Germany. In **Poland,**[40] there are low-grade spathic ores in the Czenstochau district of old Poland; brown ores in the Radom district—at Ilsha, Konsk, etc. There are also deposits in the districts of Warsaw, Kalisch, Wielun, Sieradz, Konin, etc. In **Czechoslovakia,**[41] there are extensive deposits in central Bohemia—Nucitz, Zditz, Krusnahora, Riesengebirge, and Erzgebirge; in the Szepes-Gömör area on the southern slopes of the Carpathian mountains in Ruthenia; on the east of March valley in the Sudetic mountains in Moravia; and there are old workings in the north-east Carpathians—in Zaros, Zemplen, Ung, and Bereg. In **Bulgaria,**[42] there are small deposits only of local importance at Blagoovest, Rudin-Kamak, Spassenije, and Kremikova. There are some deposits of iron ore in **Albania.**[43] In **Jugoslavia,**[44] there are deposits in Bosnia at Vares—Snireka, Drozkovats, Brezik, Slatina, Potoci, Borak, and Ponikva—and at Javorik near Ljubia—Stari Rieka, Adamusa, Drenovats, Stari Majdan, Sanski Most, Jazevats, Prevja, and Keska Ruda; in Serbia, brown iron ore is mined at Majdanpek, and there are deposits in the Kapaonik and the Zlalibor mountains—Mokra Gora, Mataruge, Massuritsa, Gevranitsa, Gare, Ruplje, Jabukovats, Lebeta, Korbeovats, Rupusite, and the Venchac mountains; in Serbian Macedonia there are deposits of brown ore at Babuna, hæmatite in the Osogov mountains, spathic ore at Dobrovo, and magnetite at Sredorek and Sracin; in Slovenia there are deposits near Assling, Jauerburg, Belshitsa, Lepene, Kropp, Kranz, Radovljitsa, Seisenberg, Weixelburg, Sittich, Ruppertshof, Nassenfuss, Jablanza, Thurmanhart, Treffen, Gonobits, Slemen, Seitz, Sallach, Schelesmo, and Preszka; in Dalmatia there are unimportant deposits near Bibenik, Kamenar, Ivine Vodice, and Kotlenitse; in Montenegro there are unworked deposits near Piperska and at Sozina; in Croatia there are deposits in the Velebit mountains, near Topusko, Gospits, Breslinats, Samobor, and Gjurmanets; and in Slavonia, at Poszega, Pleternitsa, Podvinij, Sibinj, and Sirats. In **Rumania,**[45] there is an iron industry centred in Banat—Resicza, Tvinova, Petrosz, and in the Bihar mountains; and there are deposits in Hunyad between Ruszkica and Also-Telek, between Gyalar and Also-Telek, and near Erdöhat, Aranyos, Batrina, and Kudzsir. There are deposits in Szeklerland, and in Suceava, Muscel, Gorji, Tulcea, Braila, and Mehedinti in old Rumania. In **Switzerland,**[46] there are deposits in

Fricktal, in Mount Chemin, at Chamoson, the Erzegg-Planplatten area, in the Delémont basin, and at Gonzen. Switzerland has hitherto depended for her iron on imports from Germany. In **Austria**,[47] there are important deposits of siderite and limonite at Erzberg in Styria, and at Donnersalpe, Glanzberg, and Polster in the Erzberg area ; there are also deposits at Hüttenberg in Carinthia, and on the left bank of the Danube about 45 miles from Vienna. The iron ore deposits of **Hungary**,[48] before the adjustment after the 1914–18 war, were described by L. von Loczy and C. von Papp. In **Italy**,[49] the mines at Elba have furnished the greatest part of the output. The ore is high-grade, and low in phosphorus. There are deposits in Piedmont—Val d'Aosta, Traversella, Cogne, Liconi, Larcinaz, Colona, Carlo Muta, and Montchalet ; in Sardinia—San Leone, and La Murra ; in Lombardy—in the Brembana valley ; in central Italy—La Tolfa, and the coastal regions of Tuscany from Monte Atsicco, in the Versilia district, and the north to Monte Argentario, and in the south to Orbetello district ; in south Italy—at Stilo, etc. ; and in Sicily—near Messina. In **Greece**,[50] there are important chromiferous or manganiferous iron ores in the Laurium peninsula, near Lake Kopais—at Lokris, Thebes, and Karditza in the province of Boitio ; and at Tsouka, Lutzi, and Pavlorada in the province of Lokris—at Politka on the island of Euboea ; at the Skyros mine west of the island of Skyros ; near Spathi on the island of Zea ; and on the islands Cerigo, Thermia, Seriphos, and Cyclades. In **Turkey**,[51] some iron ore occurs near Rodosto, and some magnetite near Samakov. Specimens of micaceous iron ore have been reported from **Cyprus**.[52] In **Russia**,[53] there are many important deposits of iron ore. There are important deposits in the Krivoi Rog basin in south Russia, and adjoining these are those of Lichmandeoskaja, the Sheltaja River district, at Korssak-Mogila in the Taurida district, and those in the peninsula of Kertch, in the Crimea. In central Russia there are deposits at Lipetsk in the Government of Tamboff ; at Priklon, Slobina, Motmos, and Pessotschnaia in the Government of Vladimir ; about Koschatinsky, and Duminitschsky in the Government of Kaluga ; about Krapivno, and Bogorodizk in the Government of Tula ; at Istijnsky and Syntulsky in the Government of Riasan ; about Liwny, and Kromy in the Government of Orel. In the north Urals there are deposits near Bogoslovsky, near the Kolonja River, at Kutinskojoe, and at Voronzov. In the central Urals there are deposits near Kiselovsky, Troitsk, Cora Blagodat, Gora Wyssokaja, in the Alapaievsk district at Blagonadeshvoi, in the Neviansk district at Magorno Staroborowsko, Pitschuginsko, Reschewsko, Schwedsko, and Schuralinsko ; in the Bilimbaievsky district at Ilmosko, and on the western slopes of the Bjelaja and Penkowaja mountains ; and there are deposits at Versk-Isetsk. In the south Urals there are deposits in the Kussinskaia and Achtenskoje areas, in the Slatoust mining district, in the Komarowskaia area—at Karabijskoje, and Lemesinsky—in the group of hills of Magnitnaia Gora, in the Tscherdynsky district of the Government of Perm, and in the district of Glasowsky, and Slobodsky of the Government of Viatka. There are deposits in the Powenez area of the Government of Olonetz, and in the Jarensk area of the Government of Vologada. In **Finland**[54] there are iron ore deposits on the island of Jussarö, in the Porkonen-Pahtavaara area in Kittilä ; at Juvakaisenmaa ; and at Suojarvi. There are extensive deposits of bog ore in the lake country of central Finland ; and titaniferous iron ore at Välimaki, on the north-eastern shore of Lake Lagoda. Iron has been produced in **Sweden**[55] for centuries ; it was one of the most important centres in the later Middle Ages, since it had many accessible deposits of rich ore, an abundance of forests of coniferous wood as fuel, and ready access for transport. There are deposits of phosphatic ores situated mainly north of the Arctic Circle in the province of Norrbotten—including the Kiiruna and Gellivaara ore fields—at Kiirunavaara, Gellivaara, Malmberg, Luossavaara, Svappavaara, Leveäniemi, Mertainen, Ekströmsberg, Nakerivaara, Ylipäasnjarka, Tuolluvaara, Laukkujärvi, Altavaara, Painirova, etc., the Ruoutevare deposit, and one in the Vallatj mountains. In central and southern Sweden there are the important mining areas of Lomberg, East and West Ormberg, and also the deposits of Persberg, Norberg, Dannemora, Taberg, Herräng, Strippa, Strässa, etc. In **Norway**,[56] the main ores are not of the usual type. The country has low-grade ores which require concentrating for export. The ores for concentration occur at Sydvaranger, Fiskefjord, Blokken, Gullesfjord, and Oksfjord ; there are also the Dunderland, Dunderford deposits—Urtvand, Vesteraali, Finkaataenget, Stensundtjern, Björhei, Urtfjeldmo, Strandfjord, and Nävernäs. There are also iron ore deposits near Ranenfjord, Fuglestrand, Seljelid, Elsfjord, Davemoen, Forsland, Sörovaagen, Risöen, Mosjöen, Dolstadaasen, Beieren, Naeverhaugen, Madstukrogan, Ofotenfjord, Haafjeld, Strand, Bervik, Kleven, Lenvik, Osmark, Narvik, Rombakfjord, Gratangen, Lavangen, Generalhaugen, Storhaugen, Loukostjokka, Sorreisen, Rollö, Andorgö, Dyrö, Tromsösund, Möllendalsakseln, Solliskaret, Kalvebaeklien, Solligangen, Langgangen, etc. Rich ores of magnetite and specular ore, ready for shipping without concentration, occur on the islands of Vesteraalen, Lofoten, Vestvaagö, and Gimsö, Oestvaago, Melövaer, Bjarkö, and Hindö. There are deposits near Beitstadfjord, Oelve, and Söftesdtad, west of Lake Nisservand, and between Arendal and Kragerö—Klodeberg, Braasted, and the Längo and Gomö islands. North of Kragerö are the so-called Fehn Mines, and towards the east there are deposits at Myrestö, Storemyr, Barmen, Narverud, etc. There are also deposits at Mistberg, and Skreia, north of Christiania. There are several small chrome iron ore deposits in Norway, and titaniferous ores at Koldal, Kyland, Storgangen, Blaafjeld, Laksedal, Rödsand, Surendalsfjord, Heindalen, Gusja, Rödsaeter, Meisingset, Lesjeskogen, Söholt, Solnördal, Oerien, Röddal, Sökelven, Vanelven, Sördalen, Sellenvold, Löland, Lavikdal, Lindaas, Radö, Askeland, Lyseknappen, Lofoten, Vesteraalen, Langö, Oexnes, Flakstadö, etc.   There is also a deposit on **Spitzbergen**.[57]   There are iron deposits in the north-western peninsular of **Iceland**.[58]

Asia.—In **Palestine**,[59] a red and brown hæmatite occurs in the Ajlun district east of the River Jordan, between the Rivers Jabbok and Wâdi Radjib.   In **Syria**,[60] some iron has been found at Anatolia in **Asia Minor**.[61]   In **Mesopotamia**,[62] iron ore occurs in the Sergusa Hills, north of Amadia; there are deposits east of Amadia, and in the Dohuk district, and in the valleys of the Bohtan and Tigris.   In **Arabia**,[63] deposits of red oxide are worked at Ras-el-Kheimah, and small deposits occur in the province of Yemen, and on the island of Dalmah.   In **Persia**,[64] there is a deposit of red oxide on the island of Ormuz, and workable deposits of hæmatite in the Bishneh and the Durdur districts.   In **Turkey-in-Asia**,[65] there are deposits of iron ore in Anatolia, Ayasmand, Aidin, Brusam, and Adana.   Rich mineral deposits occur in Armenia, and Kurdistan—*e.g.* Diarbekr, Van, Bitlis, and Trebizond.   In **Transcaucasia**,[66] there are numerous deposits but no coal, and transport is difficult.   There is ore in the province of Kutais, Georgia—at Khamuli, Artirn, Ubissi, Shrosha, Tchabakh, and Kédabek—Mont Bdak-Burum, the province of Terek, near Lenkoran, near Poti, and near Dashkesan.   There are several deposits of pyrites in Georgia.   In the **Aden**,[67] and the vicinity some iron ores occur in varying amounts in the basalts and quartz-trachytes. In **India**,[68] in Assam, there is clay ironstone in the Abor Hills, and in the Khasi Hills the natives manufactured iron many years ago.   There is iron ore near Jaipur, Manipur, and in the Mikir Hills ; and in Bengal, at Biher, and Orissa.   Deposits of laterite occur in the Rajmahal and Mallarpur areas, and they were at one time the chief sources of the native iron industry about Birbhum.   There are iron ores in the Raniganj, Mayurbhanj, Gurumai-shini, Okampad, Badampahar, Pol Lahara, Singhbhum, Bonai, Keonjhar, Hazaribagh, Manbhum, and Palamau.   In Bombay there are ores in the districts of Almedabad, Kaira, Panch Mahals, Surat, Bijapur, Ratnagiri, Rewa Kantha, and Sind.   In Burma there are ores in the states of Mandalay, Shan, and Khesi Mansam.   In the Central India Agency there are deposits in the Bijawar series—*e.g.* Bundelkland—in Gwalior—*e.g.* Bagh, Par Hill, Mangor, and Santow—in Indore—*e.g.* Barwai, Chikitimodri, Karondia, Mendikhaira, Nandnia, and between Bain and Sendrani—and in the valley of the Ken River in Punna, and in the Son valley in Rewah.   The Central Provinces is the chief centre for iron-smelting in small, indigenous blast-furnaces.   There are iron ores in the Drug (including Raipur) district—*e.g.* Dondi-Lohara, in the western hills of Kairagarh, near Jurlakhar in Nandgron, at Chutrala, Kumi, and Basantapur in Thakurtola, and at Worarland.   There are ores in the Jubbulpore district—near Khumbi, Bjeragogarh, Agaria, Sihora, Mansakra, Ghogra, Imalia, Jauli, Kanhwara Hills, Lora Hill, and Saroli ; in the Chanda district—near Asola, Bissi, and the hills of Chamoursi, Dewalgaon, Lohara, Poser, Pipalgaon ; in the district of Narsinghpur at Omarpani ; and in the district of Nimar.   In Hyderabad iron ore occurs in the Bidar district, south of Kaliani ; and Konasamudram in the Nizamabad district is said to have been one of the localities where steel for the famous Damascus sword-blades was manufactured.   Iron ore also occurs in the Warangal district, and the Singarenni coalfield.   In Madras iron ores occur in the districts of Arcot, Bellary, Coimbatore, Godaveri, Kistna, Kurnool, Malabar, Nellore, Salem, Trichinopoly, and Vizagapatam.   Large quantities of ore also occur in the Mysore state in the Bababudan Hills of Kadur district, in the Channagiri, Channarayapatina, and Malvalli.   Hæmatite occurs in the districts of Bannu and Hazara of the North-West Frontier Province.   In the Punjab there are deposits between the Jumna and Ravi rivers ; in the Patiala state between Chhapri and Jannpur, and near Dhanota and Sohla.   In Rajputana there are deposits in the states of Alwar at Rajgarh, and Jaipur near Nimla. In the United Provinces there are ores in Kumaon, Dechauri, Khurpa Tal, and Naini Tal. In Goa there are deposits which are a continuation of those in the Ratnagiri district of Bombay.   In **Ceylon**,[69] the iron ores are widely distributed but in relatively small quanti-ties near Pulmoddai, Tirukkovil, Kiribatgala, Ampitiya, Hanguranketa, Nuwara Eliya, Badulla, and Bandarawela.   There are deposits in **Burma**,[70] at Twinnge, north-east of Thondaung.   In the **Malay States**,[71] there are extensive deposits at Pondok Tanjong, near Dungun in Trengganu, about Kuala Kuantan in Pahang, in Kuala Batu Pahat in Johore, and on Kedah Peak in Kedah.   In **Borneo**,[72] there are deposits of limonite on Tagoho Hill, British North Borneo.   Clay ironstone occurs in Labuan, etc.   There are ores in Tanah Laut, near Tambaga, the island of Seboekoe, or Sebuku, and Pulu Laut ; in Western Borneo there is clay ironstone in the state of Palo—on the islands of Bessi and Karimata, near Batu Bessi, Kapuas, Kandarwangan, Padjilu, and between Siluas and Sidin ; and in Eastern Borneo, at Kusan, and Kutei.   Iron was also formerly manufactured in Borneo, but the industry virtually succumbed to the competition with European iron about the middle of last century.   Iron ores are widely distributed in Sarawak—par-ticularly at Ridjang.   In Brunei iron ores occur in the basin of the River Barram ; in Sabah near Kudat, on the hills between Tunder Batu and Punguh, and near Pinunguh. In **Siam**[73] in ancient times there was much iron mining and smelting, but at present very little is done.   In **Celebes**,[74] there are deposits in the Lacona district ; and in **Sumatra**,[75] there are large deposits in the Lampong district. In **Timor,** iron ore occurs in Laleia, Portuguese Timor, and chrome iron ore in Dutch Timor. There are occurrences on the **Lesser Sunda Islands,**[76] *e.g.* Flores. There are deposits of magnetite and hæmatite on the **Philippine Islands** [77] in the eastern cordillera of Luzon—in the Bulacan province, at Santa Inez, Rizal province, on the margin of the Mambulao-Paracale district in Camarines, etc. There are lateritic ores in the Surigao province, Mindanao Island. In **Hong Kong** [78] and territory there are the Ma-On-Shan deposit, and occurrences north-west of Tide Cove, between Kam-Tin and Tsin-Wan, and north-west and south of the Lan-Tau Island. In **French Indo-China,**[79] there are deposits of iron ore at Cu-van, and Thai-Nguyen in Tonking; at Phnome-Dek in Cambodia; in the provinces of Vinh, Quang-tri, Quang-Ngai, Quang-Nam, and Ha-Tinh. There are deposits of chrome ore at Van-Am, and Nui-Nua in Thanh-Hoa; and titaniferous iron ore at Pagoda Point. There are reports of iron ore in **Thibet,**[80] particularly near Chiamdo. In **China,**[81] iron ore ranks next in importance to coal, the most important mineral. The largest iron mines are at Huangshihkang, and Wuchang in Tayeh, Hupel province, where a good quality hæmatite is treated. In the province of Shansi the deposits are somewhat irregular in quality and are suited to native methods of working, but not to modern blast-furnace work on a large scale. In the province of Manchuria ore is worked ort a commercial scale at Penchihu or Penhsihu, and native methods have been employed at Tiehling; there are deposits near Lishan, Aushan, Haicheng, Fushun, Hsiuyen, Kirin, and Sansing. In the province of Anhui there is a large mine at Taochung, and there are mines in the Tungling district. In the province of Shantung there are deposits at Paoshan, Chefoo, and Chungpuchwang. There are iron ore deposits in the provinces of Shensi, Chihli, Kiangsu, Honam, Szechuan, Yunnan, Kewichow, Hunan, Kiengsi, Chekiang, Fukien, Kwantung, Kwangsi, and Mongolia. There are deposits of iron and coal in the north of **Manchuria.**[82] There are numerous iron ore deposits in **Japan** [83]; there are magnetite ores in the districts or prefectures of Adzumadake (Aomori); Rogi, Kebaraichi, Kamaishi, and Hitokabe (Iwate); Kamichuka (Fukushima); Kamo, and Higashi-Kambara (Niigata); Nakakosaka (Toschigi); Kahiru (Fukui); Mikato (Hiogo); Dorogawa (Nava); and Yanagigaura (Oita). There are micaceous iron ores at Sennin, and Omoye (Iwate); Okuzu (Akita); Aone (Miyagi); Narabara (Fukushima); Akadani, and Sodeyama (Niigata); and Ito (Shimane). There are red iron ores at Yonai, Asahishi, Isogozawa, and Yanagawa (Iwate); Aki, Anani, Soahji, Konotani, and Oyashiki (Kochi). The brown iron ores of Japan occur at Abuta, and Wakatasapu (Hokkaido); Kotaki, Naone, and Taro (Iwate); Yanahara (Okayama); Takata (Hiroshima); Ofuku (Yamaguchi); Hirao (Oita); Kawatana (Saga); Maski (Miyazaki); and Makisone and Makurasaki (Kagoshima). Iron sand occurs in the provinces of Izumo and Iwami (Shimane); Hoki (Tottori); Aki and Bingo (Hiroshima); Bitchu, Bizen, and Mimasaka (Okayama); Rikuchu (Iwate); Ugo (Akita); Mutsu and Hokkaido (Aomori). The principal pyrite mines are at Limori (Wakayama); Yanahara and Hisagi (Okayama); Takara (Yamanashi); Kucho (Yehime); and Kamaishi (Iwate). In **Corea,**[84] there are mines in the provinces of Wheng-hai, Kokai, Phyöng-an, Heian-nan, and Keiki. Iron ores occur abundantly in **Siberia.**[85] In western Siberia there are deposits in the Tomsk region. There are regions at Gurevskoe, at Altai, at Abakanskoe in the Minuoinsk region, near Karkaralinsk, and near Tyumen in the Tobolsk province. In eastern Siberia there are deposits near Bratski-Ostrog, in the valleys of the Yenisei River and its tributaries, in the valleys of the Upper Lena and Kirenga, near Misosvk, and on the Tsagan-Khuntei range. Iron ore is found in the Nerchinsk district—*e.g.* at Baleginsk, or Balyazinsk. Iron ore is abundant around Yakutsk. There are deposits in the provinces of Amur, Maritime, and Anadyr. There are deposits at Bielaya-Gora, and at Sergievsk, Sudzukhe, Olginsk, Kamehatka, and north of Russian Sakhlin.

Africa.—In **Morocco,**[86] there are ores supposed to be of minor importance near Oudjda, Djebel Hadrid, the valley of the Oum er Rebra, the Atlas region, Ida ou Mahmoud, the valley of the Segsaoua, Immingount, Djebel Figuermi, and Tagelt, all under French influence; and near Melilla, under Spanish influence. In **Algeria,**[87] in the department of Oran, there are deposits near Sebabna, Rar-el-Maden, in the Beni-Saf region, at Kristel, and a few smaller places. In the department of Algiers there are rich ores between Cape Ténès and Cherchel, at Djebel Hadid, Temoulga, Rouina, Zaccar, Miliana, in the Blida district, near Fondouk, and at Aïn Oudrer. In the department of Constantine there are deposits between the Soumman and Agrioum valleys, in the neighbourhood of Filfila, in the Aïn Mokra region west of Bône, Ouenza, and Bou Kadra. In **Tunisia,**[88] there are deposits in the Nefzas region, at Douaria, Raz-er-Radjel, Djerissa, Slata, in the Harraba and Bou Jaber mountains, at Djebel Onk, and near Kef. In **Egypt,**[89] in south-west Sinai, there are ores near Wadi Malha, Wadi Halliq, Nasb, and Wadi Baba. In south-east Sinai there are ores at Wadi Um Agraf. There are ores in the north-east desert on the seaward slope of the northern Gallala range, in the Red Sea hills, in the hills about Wadi Abu Marwat, and in the Wadi Abu Jerida; in the south-east desert in Wadi Suegat, and near El Ranga. In the western desert oasis there are ores near Bahariâ, and at Gebel Ghorabi (Raven Hill). The Nubian sandstone is highly ferruginous. There are some deposits of iron in **Syria.**[90] In the **Sudan,**[91] there are deposits in the Tokar region, in the province of

Bahr-el-Ghazal, the Upper Nile, and Mongalla, near Wadi Halfa, Kerma, and Dongola. The natives of south and west Sudan have smelted iron by primitive methods for many years. Iron ore is widely distributed throughout **Abyssinia**.[92] The deposits in the province of Tigré, in the hills around Addis Abbaba (Addi-Abbas) and the Enarea region are worked by the natives. Deposits have been reported in the Harrar (Harar) district at Hamoressa, Gobeli-Amoressa, Giarso, and near Boubassa. In **Kenya**,[93] formerly the British East Africa Protectorate, iron ore has been reported near the eastern border of the northern frontier district, and near Buttelu. Iron ores—particularly limonite—are abundant in **Uganda**,[94] *e.g.* near Kigezi, and Tororo. In **Tanganyika**,[95] formerly German East Africa, there are deposits on the west of the Hundussi mountains near Morogoro, in the districts of Upangua, Ruanda, and other places between Victoria Nyanza and the north of Lake Tanganyika have been worked by the natives; so also with deposits south-west of Karissimbi, the Mutare mountains, and west Ruanda. There are laterite deposits west of the Muscha mountains, and at Karambo, west of the Muwissi mountains, in the Jassenunu Mountain Pass, on the Kumutana mountain, etc. Iron ore occurs on the Kinga or Livingstone mountains, on the Liganga hills, in the Mahenge district, and in the Mkatta steppe. There are rich deposits near Karema. In the **Nyasaland**[96] protectorate, the ores are chiefly hæmatite and magnetite. There are deposits on the Mangui hill, the Ponkonyoma valley, the Sumbu district, the Namitawa Hills, north of the Northern Rukuru River, east of Panyanole in the Namalundo district, and the Malingundi Hill. In Cabo Delgado, or **Portuguese Nyasaland**,[97] iron ore has been reported about the Lujenda and Rovuma rivers. In **Madagascar**,[98] iron ore occurs abundantly—*e.g.* in the Ambatolaona region, and deposits of titaniferous ore in the Betsiriry region, and north of Tamatave. In **Mozambique**,[99] or Portuguese East Africa, there are deposits of iron ore in the Tete district, in the Manica region with its centre at Massikessi, or Macequece. There are here evidences of extensive ancient workings—particularly in the Inyamukarakara valley. Deposits have also been found on the sides of the Lusite valley, and the district of Mafusi. In **Swaziland**,[100] there are siliceous iron ores in the neighbourhood of Rigg's Peak, and near the border with Transvaal. In **Rhodesia**,[101] deposits of magnetite occur in the north, and there are laterite deposits near Lek Bangweolo. In the south there are pisolitic limonite deposits on the surface, and ironstone in the Kalahari, Karoo, and Lomagundi regions. Banded ironstone, etc., occurs between Gwelo and Umvuna, near Que Que, Shangani, and Sabi valley, and chromiferous or titaniferous magnetite occurs near Selukwe, Umvukwe, Lalapanzi, and Belingwe. According to A. J. C. Molyneaux, the iron outcrops in Zambesia were worked extensively by the ancients. In the **Transvaal**,[102] there are beds of titaniferous iron ore near Onderstepoort, at Maguet Heights in the district of Lydenburg, and in the Magalakwin valley. Chrome iron ore occurs midway between Lydenburg and Pietersburg, near Ohrigstad. Magnetite quartzites occur near Pretoria, Potchefstroom, Airlie, Isberg, Lulukop, and Ermelo. Hæmatites occur near Malelane, Middleburg, Pullenshoop, Boschmanskop, Lyttleton junction, the Waterberg district, Crocodile River district, Donkerpoort, North Rustenburg district, and between Rhenosterfontain and Kromdraai. In **Cape Province**,[103] iron ore occurs in the beds extending 270 miles from the Prieska division to Bechuanaland. In **Natal**,[104] there are siliceous iron ores in the north part of the Uryheid district, in Zululand, and at Isibudeni ; and titaniferous magnetite in the Tugela valley. There are limonite, hæmatite, and magnetite ores north-east of Dundee, at Doornberg, near Mount Kelly, and at Sweetwaters. There are surface deposits of pisolitic iron ore on the plateau west of Alverstone, the eastern slope of Hathorn's Hill, the townlands of Pietermaritzburg. In **South-west Africa**,[105] there are deposits north-west of Kalkfeld, west of Kaokoveld, south of Great Namaqualand, in Bastardland, and east of Keetmanshoop. In **Angola**,[106] a Portuguese possession, iron has been found in the valley of the Lukalla, and in Bailundo. There is also iron ore in **Portuguese Guinea**,[107] some of which has been worked by the natives on the Corubal River ; likewise in Madeira iron ore occurs near Ponta do Sol. Iron ores are widely distributed in the **Belgian Congo**.[108] There are deposits near Katanga, near the Lualaba River, in the Kasei region on the northern slopes of the Angolan plateau, and in the Welle region on the north-east plateau. There are also deposits in the Maniema and Lake Kivu region. In the **French Congo**,[109] or French Equatorial Africa, iron ore has been reported in the region south of the Niari, on the right bank of the Jue or Djoue River, between Brazzaville and the sea, as well as farther south near Boko Congo. In the **French Cameroon**,[110] formerly German Kamerun, iron ore occurs near the Sanaga River, and near Yabasei ; also in Laka, and in the Mandara mountains. In **French West Africa**,[111] laterite occurs in French Guinea and in Ivory Coast ; titaniferous magnetite, and hæmatite occur in Dahomey. In Togoland massive hæmatite occurs at Banyeli, in the Sokede-Bassari district. Lateritic iron ore is abundant in Upper Senegal and Niger. Hæmatite occurs in the Yatenga district, and on the banks of the Bakhoy in the Mandingo district. Iron ore is said to occur in the Tagant and Ijil districts in Mauritania, where traces of native workings have been found. In **Spanish Guinea**,[112] there are ores in the regions of the Muni and Utamboni rivers, and on the island of Fernando Po. In **Nigeria**,[113] there are important deposits on Mount Patti, and others in the northern part of Bassa province—*e.g.* Assadam ; in the Mumuye country in the Muri province. There are deposits at Panguru, east of Bauchi, Okuruku, in the Kabba province, and there are iron ores at Atika, Anamu, Bangedde, between Jakura and Wa, Okeli, Ogein, Akwi, 'and Ojerami. In northern Nigeria there are deposits at Oyo in the province of Lagos, and near Iseyin and Odo Ogun, west of Oyo ; also on the hill-slopes between Bali and Bamenda. In the **Gold Coast,**[114] the clay ironstone east of the River Volta has been smelted by the natives at Dagomba, Pampamba, Buem, Kotokori, Gurma, and Mossi. There are also deposits about Akpafu, Togoland. In the negro republic, **Liberia,** the iron ores are in some cases worked by natives. Deposits occur near Monrovia, at Cape Mount, in the Finley mountains, and near Careysburg. Nearly all the inland territory remains unexplored. In **Sierra Leone,**[115] there are lateritic ores along the inner margin of the coastal plain—near Devil's Hole, Waterloo, between Freetown and Tombo, and over a large part of the Koinadugu plateau. Titaniferous magnetite occurs on the western side of the Bathurst Mountain. In **Gambia** iron has been found in the cliffs of Kossoun, and Sami Tenda, the Kossema plateau, and the hills of Medina and Eda.

In **Greenland,**[116] telluric iron ores have been reported at Disco.

North America.—In **Canada,**[117] there are numerous deposits of iron—magnetite, titaniferous magnetite, ilmenite, hæmatite, limonite, and siderite. In *Nova Scotia,*[118] there are deposits in the Nictaux-Torbrook area, in the vicinity of Clementsport, Margarets-ville, north of Middleton, between Chute and Young Coves south-west of Mount Hanley, and north of Annapolis. There are also deposits in the Hants County in the Goshen and Rocky Brook areas ; in the Colchester County in the areas of Brookfield, Clifton, and Londonderry ; in the Pictoci County in the Sutherland-Meikelfield area and on the South McLellan Mountain : in the Antigonish County in the Arisaig district, near Brown's Mountain, at Lochabar, North Lochabar, Pinkie Town, Soldiers Grant copper mine, Ireland, Polson Lake, McNaughton Brook, Polson Brook, and Caledonia Mills. In the Guysborough County hæmatite has been reported at Erinville, Atwater, Guysborough, Moon Point, and Bigsby Head. Magnetite and hæmatite have been found in Kings County and Digby County. In Cape Breton County there are deposits on the Coxheath Hills, between Sydney and East Bay, at Loran Harbour, Grand Mira, and the Barachois area. In Inverness County there are deposits on the slopes of Skye Mountain, and at Iron Brook, at Campbell's Brook, at Logan Glen, and at Upper Glencoe. In Richmond County a deposit of specular hæmatite and magnetite occurs at Robinson Cove. In *New Brunswick,*[119] the deposits of iron ore are rather poor. There are occurrences in the counties of Gloucester, Carleton, Charlotte, Northumberland, Queens, St. John, and Sunbury. In *Quebec,*[120] iron ore was mined and smelted under the French régime in the eighteenth century. In the Argentenil County magnetite occurs near Grenville ; in Compton County, near Spalding ; in Gaspé County, on Gaspé peninsula ; in Megantic County, near Leeds ; in Ottawa County, near Hull, Ottawa City, and Templeton ; in Pontiac County, near Chats Falls ; in Beauce County, between the Plante and Gallway rivers, and near Beauceville ; in Lake St. John County, on the Alma Island, near Kenogami, and Bourget ; in Saguenay County, near the Bay of Seven Islands, the Natashquan and St. John rivers, and on the north shore of the St. Lawrence ; in St. Maurice County, near St. Boniface de Shawinigan ; in Terrebonne County, near Beresford ; in Charlevoix County, near St. Urbain, and Baie St. Paul ; in Wolfe County, Ham Township, Bersimis, Moisie, Mingan, and Natashqwan ; and in Ungava, in Long Islands, Belcher Islands, Nastapokan Islands, Hopewell Islands, and along the Koksoak and Hamilton rivers. In *Ontario,*[121] the production of iron ore exceeds that of any other Canadian province. In the Rainy River district there are outcrops of magnetite and pyrrhotite along the Atikokan River between Kawene and Atikokan, on Hunter's Island near Knife, Cypress, This Man's and Jasper Lakes, near Watten, Halkirk, and the Seine Bay ; in the Kenora district, along the Winnipeg River between the Lake of the Woods and English River, west of Lake St. Joseph, near Lake Minnitaki, Dryden, and Bending and Keewatin Lakes. In the Patricia district, near Lac Seul, Lake St. Joseph, and Sutton Mill Lakes. In Thunder Bay district there are deposits on the Mattawin Iron Range, near Kashaboiwe, Loon Lake area, the Onaman Iron Range, and west of Windejokan Lake ; in the Algoma district there are deposits north-west of Michipicoten harbour, the Brant Lake property, the Alice property, Algoma, near Deroche, Bellevue, Aweres, Macdonald Meredith, and Aberdeen. In the Sudbury district there are deposits near Nemegos, the Woman River area, Ridout, north-west of Lake Sahkatawichtah, Wakami, Groundhog River area, and Moose Mountain. In the Timiskaming district there are deposits in the Mattagami River area, the Opasatika River area, near Munro, Warden, Leonard, Boston, Otto, Dack, and Letchford. In the district of Nipissing there are three iron ranges at the north-eastern arm of Lake Timagami, near Matagama Point, Austin Bay, east of Emerald Lake, and Huron Mountain west of Lake Manitopeepagee. In Haliburton district there are deposits near Lutterworth, Snowdon, Glamorgan, and Monmouth, in Peterborough County, near Anstruther, Belmont, near Crow Lake, and Chandos ; in Hastings County, near Carlow, Faraday, Dungannon, Mayo, Wollaston, Coehill, Tudor, Gilmour, Marmora, and Madoc ; in Renfrew County near Grattan, Blithfield, Calabogie, and McNab ; in Frontenac County, near South Canonto, Palmerston, and Bedford ; in Lanark County, near Levant, Darling, White Lake, Dal-housie, South Sherbrooke, Christie's Lake, and Bathurst ; and Leeds County, near North Crosby, and South Crosby about Mud Lake. No important deposits of iron ore have been found in *Manitoba*,[122] but iron ore has been found north of the Riding Mountain, and in the Assiniboine valley, about Knee Lake, Rice Lake, and Star Lake, and Black Island on Winnipeg Lake. In *Saskatchewan*,[123] there is a deposit south-east of Black Bay, Lake Athabaska. In *Alberta*,[124] there are many deposits, but none has been found of sufficient size to warrant commercial development—*e.g.* along the Red Deer River, the Peace River, Athabaska valley, north of Lake Athabaska, north-east of Black Bay, at Tsu Lake, near Red Creek, Blairmore, and Sheep River near Calgary. In *British Columbia* [125] very little iron ore has been produced. In Vancouver and adjacent islands there are deposits up Nixon Creek near Cowichan Lake ; near Port Renfrew, or Port San Juan ; Malahat Mountains ; the Shawnigan Lake slope ; on Salt Spring Island, and south-west of Vancouver Island. In the Alberni Mining Division there are claims located near Anderson Lake, Uchicklesit Bay, Tzartos or Copper Island, near Clifton Point, Santa Maria Island, near Cape Beale, and Broughton Range ; in the Clayoquot Mining Division, near Head Bay, Kennedy Lake, Hesquiat Harbour, and Maggie Lake ; in the Quatsino Mining Division, near Coal Harbour ; in the Nanaimo Mining Division, near Nimkish Lake, and north of the Quinsam River ; on Texada Islands, extending from Raven Bay to Pocohontas, and to Sturt Bay ; on Queen Charlotte Islands—Graham, Louise, and Moresby ; in the Atlin Mining Division, on Rant Mountain ; in the Skeena Mining Division, on Iron Mountain ; in the Omineca Mining Division, near the head-waters of Summit Creek ; in the Bella Coola Division, on the north of Rivers inlet ; in the Clinton Mining Division, in the Taseko valley, the Schwartz valley, the Frank Gott valley, and the Iron Creek valley; in the Lillooet Mining Division, near Pemberton Meadows ; in the Ashcroft Mining Division, east of Thompson River near Lytton, and at the head of Nelson Creek ; in the Kamloops Mining Division, at Cherry Bluff ; in the Nicola Mining Division, near Nicola ; in the Nelson Mining Division, near Kitchener ; and in the Fort Steel Mining Division, at Bull River, Lamb Creek, and Sand Creek. There are many varieties of iron ore in **Newfoundland** [126] ; two of the largest iron mines in the world are situated on the north-western shore of Bell Island, in Conception Bay.

The **United States** [127] iron industry dates from the early years of the seventeenth century. E. C. Eckel divided the country into four groups for convenience in considering the production of iron ore.

I. *The Lake Superior Region* [128] includes the states of Minnesota, Michigan, Wisconsin, and Iowa. In the Vermilion district, north-east Minnesota, there are ores near Tower, Soudan, and Ely ; in the Mesabi Range, also in Minnesota, west of Lake Superior, deposits occur near the towns of Biwabik, Eveleth, Virginia, Chisholm, Hibbing, Nashwauk, and Coleraine ; in the Cuyuna district there is an area 65 miles long and from less than a mile to 9 miles in width extending south-west from the west of Dulmuth. The Gogebic Range is south of Lake Superior and extends in Michigan and Wisconsin. The most important part of the iron ore district is in Michigan, although two-thirds of the formation extends into Wisconsin. The Menominee Range includes Iron Mountain and Norway, and it lies wholly in Michigan. The Marquette Range extends from Marquette on Lake Superior to Lake Michigan, and it lies wholly in the state of Michigan. There is a deposit of iron ore near Wankon in Allamakee County, Iowa.

II. *The Southern Region* [129] includes the states of Alabama, Georgia, North and South Carolina, Virginia, West Virginia, Tennessee, Kentucky, Maryland, Arkansas, Louisiana, Missouri, and Texas. The main source of supply of iron ore of the Southern States is the red oolitic ores or the so-called Clinton hæmatite. The ores resemble the minette ore of the Lorraine-Luxemburg area in type, but they have a different geological age. The Birmingham district is situated in the valley region of Alabama, on the east side of the Coosa coalfield, and the Warrior coalfield on the north-west. The area covered is 75 miles in length and 10 miles in width. Birmingham City is near the centre of this area. E. C. Eckel estimates that there are about a thousand million tons of red iron ore in Alabama. In the Chattanooga-Attalla region the red ore has been worked in mines extending from Attalla and Gadsden (Alabama) northwards to Chattanooga. In the Tennessee-Virginia region the red ore extends north-east across Tennessee from Chattanooga to Cumberland Gap, where it enters Virginia. In the Appalachian valley district brown iron ores occur as scattered deposits. There is a productive belt beginning in Vermont and following the boundary of that state and of New York. The belt continues along the borders of New York State with Massachusetts and Connecticut, and after a barren interval reappears in eastern Pennsylvania, when there is another barren stretch and the ore reappears in south-west Virginia and runs across Tennessee and Georgia into Alabama. In the Tennessee River drainage area there is a region where brown iron ores occur in north-west Alabama, middle Tennessee, and western Kentucky. The area is drained by the Tennessee River and its main tributaries. In north-eastern Texas there are many deposits of brown iron ore in a triangular region approximating 10,000 sq. miles. It is bounded on the north by an irregular line from Sulphur Fork, Cass Co., extending west and south through Dangerfield, Morris Co., to a little south of Quitman, Wood Co. ; on the west it extends southwards irregularly through the west side of Smith Co., the east side of Van Zandt Co., and Henderson Co., the centre of Anderson Co., west of Palestine, and south-westerly to the Brazos River near Hearne. The southern limit crosses the Trinity River near Crockett, the

Neches River near Augusta, and the Sabine River, north-east of Sabine Co. The crystal-line rock area east of the Appalachian valley includes magnetites, specular hæmatites, and brown ores. It includes the magnetites of Cranberry, North Carolina; the magnetites and hæmatite of Pittsville and Rocky Mount, Virginia; the magnetites of Carter Co., Tennessee; and the brown gossan ores of Ducktown, Tennessee; deposits of magnetites in Llano Co. and Mason Co., Texas. There are titaniferous and non-titaniferous magnetites in the west of North Carolina. The deposits of iron ore in Louisiana consist mainly of limonite.

III. *The North-Eastern Region* [130] includes the states of New York, Vermont, New England, New Jersey, Pennsylvania, Indiana, and Ohio. There is the Adirondack region, which includes deposits of magnetite. It approximates 12,000 sq. miles, and is situated in the north-east of New York State. There is also a deposit of titaniferous magnetite in the north-east corner of Rhode Island. The New Jersey and New York highlands include a belt of magnetites extending in Putnam Co. and Orange Co., New York State, and north-eastern New Jersey. The north-eastern states region includes brown iron ores which occur in western New England, south-eastern New York, northern New Jersey, and south-western Pennsylvania. The south-eastern Pennsylvania region contains magnetites. It includes a belt passing through New Jersey and across south-eastern Pennsylvania. New York and Pennsylvania regions of the Clinton red ores extend from the central part of New York State to the Niagara River, and continue for some distance beyond into Ontario, Canada. The Western Adirondacks includes a series of deposits of red hæmatites extending along the western flank of the Adirondack region in St. Lawrence Co., and Jefferson Co., New York. The Ohio and Pennsylvania carbonate ores are associated with the carboniferous rocks of western Pennsylvania and Ohio.

IV. *The Western Region* [131] includes the eleven states lying to the west of the eastern boundaries of Montana, Wyoming, Colorado, and New Mexico—that is, these four states along with California, Nevada, Washington, Arizona, Utah, Idaho, and Oregon, in all about one-third of the total area of the United States—but it produces only about 2 per cent. of the total output of the country. Most of that is from the Hartville region, Wyoming; the deposits of iron ore are situated in Laramie Co., near Guernsey. There are large deposits of iron ore in Iron Co., southern Utah. There are two mining areas, Iron Springs in the north of the state and Pinto Iron in the south. Some iron ores have been mined in Colorado and New Mexico, but the productive areas are approaching exhaustion. The iron ore deposits in the remaining states—California, Nevada, Washington, Idaho, Oregon, and Montana—have not been exploited to any great extent. The known deposits are numerous but small. There are the iron sands on the Pacific Beach described by D. T. Day, and H. V. Winchell. The iron ore deposits in **Alaska** [132] have not received much attention. There are deposits near Nome, Seward Peninsula; on Hinchinbrook and Knight Islands, Prince William Sound; and near Haines, Sitka district.

Very large deposits of iron ore occur in **Cuba.** [133] On the south coast, in the district about Santiago City, high-grade ores have been regularly worked since 1884. The ores are magnetite and hæmatite and they are chiefly worked at Sevilla, Firmeza, Daiquirri, and Berraco. On the north coast there are deposits of brown iron ore. In the Oriente Province, formerly Santiago de Cuba Province, at the eastern end of the island, there are the Mayari and Moa ore fields, from the former of which is obtained the so-called *Mayari iron.* The following is reported to represent the composition of typical Mayari pig-iron:

C	Mn	P	S	Ni,Co	Cr	V	Ti	Cu	Si
4·67	0·90	0·047	0·011	1·30	2·66	0·05	0·18	0·035	0·80%

In the south of the Oriente Province there are deposits in the Daiquirri area and in the Firmeza district; while in the Camaguey Province there are ore deposits in the Cubitas area north of the Camaguey City. In **Hayti** and **San Domingo,** [134] beds of limonite have been reported; beds of limonite also occur in **Porto Rico,** [135] east of Mayaguez. Specimens of hæmatite and magnetite have been found in the Northern Range of **Trinidad,** [136] and there are deposits in the Maraccas valley; red oxide in the district of Oropuche West; and a brown ferruginous sandstone in La Brea. The iron in the rocks of **Bermudas** [137] was discussed by W. L. R. Emmet.

There are numerous deposits of iron ore in **Mexico** [138]; only a few of them have been closely examined or worked. There are the Cerro de Mercado, or the Iron Mountain, north of Durango; Las Truchas and Calvaric in the state of Michoacan; El Mamey in the state of Colina; Las Vegas, near Vera Cruz; near Monterey in the state of Nuevo Leon; Monclova in the state of Coahuila; and Tequesquite on the isthmus of Tehuantepec. In **Honduras,** [139] high-grade magnetic ore occurs at Agalteca, and deposits of iron ore occur in the district of Petoa, in the department of Santa Barbara. In **Nicaragua,** [140] there are large deposits of iron ore in the Pis-Pis district. In **Costa Rica,** [141] there is a large deposit of iron sand on the Atlantic side of the republic.

South America.—In **British Guiana,** [142] magnetic ironstone occurs in the district of Aruka Yarakita in the north-west; and ilmenitic black sands occur in many other places. In **Dutch Guiana,** [143] a laterite ore occurs in the Donderbary Mountains. In **Brazil,** [144] there are important iron ore deposits in Minas Geraes. The area contains massive hæmatite, specular hæmatite, and laminated micaceous hæmatite, with some conglomerates, as well as stream and gravel ores which require concentration. There are deposits at Pico d'Itabira do Matto Dentro, Pico d'Itabira do Compo, Santa Barbara, the central part of the state of Goyaz, the San Francisco region of the state of Bahia, and the Corumba district of the state of Matto Grosso. Magnetite occurs in the coastal region of Sao Paulo, Parana, and Santa Catharina. In **Paraguay**,[145] iron ore is said to be abundant; there is limonite between the Apa and Aquidaban rivers ; magnetite and hæmatite at Quiquio, Caapucu, and San Miguel. In **Uruguay**,[146] deposits of iron ore have been reported at Zapucay, San Juan, and at Piedra del Gigante in Minas. In **Argentina**,[147] a deposit of titaniferous magnetite occurs ; but the known deposits are few and inferior. Magnetite occurs west of Albigasta in the Sierra de Ancasti, and east of Cerro Lacco in the province of Los Andes ; and magnetite sands at Necochea and other parts of the Atlantic coast. In **Bolivia**,[148] iron ore has been reported in the province of Santa Ana. In **Chile**,[149] there are many deposits. The best known is the Tofo deposit in the province of Coquimbo, and in the same province there are deposits near Juan Soldado, Romeral, Pleito, Zapallo, Pejerreyes, Ovalle, and Illapel. In the Antofagasta province there are deposits near Potrero, north of Teltal ; and in the province of Atacama there are deposits near Vallenar—*e.g.* Algarrobo, Ojes de Agua, and Chanar Quemada—and deposits near Chanaral, Copiapo, Tierra Amarilla, and the Cristales district. In **Peru**,[150] the development of the iron ore has been handi-capped by the lack of suitable transport. There are deposits at Marcona, Huacravilca, Aija, and Callaycancha. In **Colombia**,[151] there are small, inaccessible deposits near Amaga, Medellin, Antiquia, Bogota, and Zipaquisa. In **Venezuela**,[152] there are deposits at Manoa, at the foot of the Imataca mountains, the Sierra de Imataca, and Piacoa, up the Orinoco.

Australasia.—In **Queensland**,[153] there is a large deposit at Mount Leviathan, or the Black Mountain, Mount Pisa, Mount Philip, Fountain Range, Mount Lucy, Iron Island, Olsen's Caves, Kabra, Mount Morgan, Iron Gully, Alma Creek, Pleasant Creek, Kroombit, Degalgil, Many Peaks, Glassford, Cania, Spring Creek, Gold Diggings, Cabbage Tree, Riverston, Rolleston, Pittsworth, Biggenden, Mount Perry, Eastern Creek, and Mount Isa. In **New South Wales**,[154] there are deposits of iron ore at Coombing Park near Carcoar, Cadia, Mittagong district, and Chalybeate Springs. There are magnetite deposits in the Gulgong district, the Cowra district, Broula Range, the Wallerawang district, the Goulburn district, and Congwarrah in Beresford county. There are clay band ores in the upper coal measures in the Wallerawang and Lithgow districts, Capertee and Carlo's Gap district, at Rix Creek, Ravensworth, Westbrook Creek, and Illawarra district. There are basaltic iron ores in the neighbourhood of Mittagong, Bowral, Wingello, Capertee, between Moss Vale and Sutton Forest, and in the New England district. There are miscellaneous deposits in Milbang, Argyle county, near Gobondery, Talbragar in Bligh county, Goulburn, Bherweree in St. Vincent county, Walli, Lyndhurst, Hampton, and Kenilworth, Marulan Molong district, Wyaldra in Phillip county, in the districts of Newbridge, Blayney, Orange, Rylstone, Cudgegong, and Piper's Flat, and Wallerawang. There are titaniferous deposits north-west of Port Stephens, and aluminous deposits at Wingello. In **Victoria**,[155] there are deposits of iron ore on the south-western slope of Mount Nowa, Mount Tara, Alberton West, Mirboo, Leongatha, San Remo, Grantville, Sandstone Island, Mount Major, and the Whitfield district. In **South Australia**,[156] there are deposits at Iron Knob and Iron Monarch, west-south-west from Port Augusta, near Williamstown, near Victoria Harbour, Mount Jagged, Koolka, near Quorn, south of Mingary, Oodla Wirra, and Moonta. In **West Australia**,[157] there are lenticular lodes of hæmatite with quartz gangue associated with crystalline schists and allied rocks on the Koolan and Cockatoo Islands, Yampi Sound, around Kimberley, Pilbara, Ashburton—Mount Edith, Murchison district, Weld Range, Wilgie Mia, Mounts Taylor, Hale, Matthews, Yarrameedee, and Gould, Gabanintha east of Nannine, Edjudina and south-west of Lake Raeside, Mount Mason, Mount Gibson, and Southern Cross. There are lodes of goethite forming the weathered portions of pyrites and pyrrhotite beds with magnetite and ferruginous silicates at Mount Caudan and Koolyanobbing. There are superficial deposits of brown iron ores with a gangue of gibbsite, clay, or quartz forming masses associated with ferruginous laterites at Clackline, Waterfall, and Comet Vale. There are also soft, porous deposits of bog ore of recent origin along the southern and western coastline of the state, and also on the eastern side of Herdsman Lake. In **Tasmania**,[158] in the Beaconsfield district, there are deposits on Brandy Creek, Sugar Loaf, Mount Vulcan, Scott's Hill, and Barnes' Hill. In Dial Range and along Penguin Creek there is non-magnetic red hæmatite, and also in the Iron Cliff lode. There is the Blythe River iron ore deposit of red hæmatite ; the Rutherford iron lode of red hæmatite ; the Long Plain iron ore ; the Zeehan deposits ; and Nelson River deposits. Iron ore is known to occur in **Papua**,[159] in the Mount Louis area ; and also near the Kebenau River in **New Guinea** [160]—formerly Kaiser Wilhelmsland. H. Cayley-Webster mentioned a native iron-forge which he found in the Kei Islands. The bellows consisted of two bamboo cylinders 3 ft. high, with bunches of feathers on sticks to form the pistons. There are also good deposits of iron ore in the French island of **New Caledonia**.[161] There are a number of deposits of iron ore in **New Zealand**,[162] but only that at Parapara, near the north-west corner of the South Island is worked ; and there are beds of iron sand on or near the coast in many localities of the western coast of the North Island. There are deposits of minor importance at Waitangi River, North Auckland, at Cape Kerr, and in the Greymouth area. There are also small deposits at Kawakawa, and Mount Royal, Palmerston. Chrome iron ore is reported on the Dun Mountain, near Croixelles, and near Milford Sound.

The world's production of pig-iron has risen enormously in the past quarter of a century. It was, in metric tons :

1800	1820	1840	1860	1880	1890
480,000	880,000	2,750,000	7,430,000	18,490,000	27,580,000
1900	1906	1910	1917	1920	1925
40,330,000	58,650,000	65,300,000	69,637,224	79,325,884	75,692,728

The results for 1925 in more detail are :

Great Britain	6,261,700	Luxemburg	2,325,929
Austria	373,921	Sweden	455,253
Belgium	2,502,352	India	886,602
France	9,797,719	China	363,780
Czechoslovakia	1,148,000	Japan	684,923
Germany	9,929,413	Corea	100,323
Finland	—	Australia	439,419
Italy	527,612	New Zealand	1,289
Holland	107,400	South Africa	—
Poland	309,596	Canada	596,475
Rumania	63,258	United States	36,700,566
Norway	86,542	Mexico	48,593
Hungary	91,810	Brazil	70,000
Russia	1,295,108		
Jugoslavia	3,439	Total .	75,692,728
Spain	521,658		

E. C. Eckel[163] gave the results indicated in Tables III and IV for the output in metric

TABLE III.—THE WORLD'S PRODUCTION OF PIG-IRON.
(In Millions of Tons)

Year.	United States.	Germany and Luxemburg.	Great Britain.	France.	Russia.	Austria and Hungary.	Belgium.	Canada.	Sweden.	Spain.	Italy.	Other countries.	Total.
1800	0·060	0·02	0·20	0·06	0·04	0·01	0·02	—	0·02	—	—	0·05	0·48
1820	0·02	0·04	0·40	0·14	0·10	0·03	0·04	—	0·03	—	—	0·08	0·88
1840	0·29	0·15	1·40	0·35	0·19	0·06	0·10	—	0·06	—	—	0·15	2·75
1860	0·82	0·60	3·83	0·90	0·34	0·18	0·32	—	0·19	—	—	0·25	7·43
1880	3·84	2·73	7·75	1·73	0·45	0·46	0·61	—	0·41	0·09	0·02	0·40	18·49
1900	13·79	8·38	8·96	2·67	2·85	1·43	1·00	0·09	0·52	0·09	—	0·65	40·33
1910	27·30	14·56	10·01	3·97	2·98	2·01	1·82	0·71	0·59	0·37	0·21	0·60	65·13
1920	36·92	6·15	8·03	3·38	0·13	0·13	1·10	1·00	0·68	0·25	0·11	1·86	79·32

TABLE IV.—COMPARISON OF THE WORLD'S METAL OUTPUT AND VALUES (E. C. Eckel).

Metal.	Output—metric tons.	Output—percentage tonnage.	Output—percentage value.	Selling price per ton—iron unity.
Iron .	65,300,000	95·62	46·2	1
Lead .	1,139,700	1·67	3·5	4
Copper	836,900	1·23	12·0	20
Zinc	816,600	1·19	4·5	8
Tin .	115,700	0·17	4·3	52
Aluminium	43,800	0·06	0·7	24
Nickel	34,500	0·040	0·8	46
Silver	7,437	0·011	6·3	1,200
Mercury	4,100	0·006	0·3	90
Gold .	704	0·001	21·4	40,000

tons, percentages of the world's metal output by tonnage, percentages of the world's metal output by value, and the selling prices per ton, with iron unity as basis. S. G. Koon's estimate of the world's production of pig-iron, in thousands of gross tons, is indicated in Table V ; and of steel ingots and castings, in thousands of

TABLE V.—THE WORLD'S PRODUCTION OF PIG-IRON.

	1913.	1921.	1923.	1928.	1929.
United States	30,966	16,688	40,361	38,156	42,614
Canada	1,015	616	909	1,039	1,090
Great Britain	10,260	2,616	7,440	6,611	7,580
France	5,126	3,392	5,380	10,097	10,439
Belgium	2,445	858	2,114	3,825	3,970
Luxemburg	—	955	1,384	2,724	2,906
Italy	424	75	265	539	664
Spain	418	244	402	565	709
Sweden	732	314	297	396	484
Germany	19,000	7,719	4,857	11,804	13,401
Austria	2,344	220	337	457	450
Czechoslovakia	—	534	738	1,569	1,643
Poland	—	437	512	684	699
Hungary	—	70	123	286	350
Russia	4,563	112	295	3,274	4,018
Japan	236	642	784	1,508	1,750
China	150	126	260	400	250
India	204	371	614	1,051	1,000
Australia	47	352	330	420	333
Saar Territory	1,371	1,131	1,005	1,936	2,088
Netherlands	—	—	—	210	256
Miscellaneous	200	149	200	—	—
World total	77,813	37,437	68,197	86,760	95,900

gross tons, in Table VI. Over 95 million tons of iron per annum are being turned

TABLE VI.—THE WORLD'S PRODUCTION OF STEEL INGOTS AND CASTINGS.

	1913.	1921.	1923.	1928.	1929.
United States	31,301	19,744	44,944	51,544	56,433
Canada	1,043	669	884	1,239	1,380
Great Britain	7,664	3,703	8,482	8,520	9,655
France	4,614	3,010	5,029	9,387	9,666
Belgium	2,428	752	2,260	3,870	4,039
Luxemburg	1,315	742	1,182	2,510	2,702
Italy	919	689	1,124	1,910	2,115
Spain	238	394	456	734	929
Sweden	582	208	267	576	683
Germany	18,632	9,837	6,204	14,517	16,246
Austria	2,585	354	500	637	630
Czechoslovakia	—	903	984	1,992	2,145
Poland	—	841	1,114	1,437	1,398
Hungary	785	163	290	478	526
Russia	4,181	311	578	4,246	4,723
Japan	300	830	944	1,519	2,100
China	100	47	130	300	50
India	—	183	215	440	600
Australia	—	209	200	439	348
Saar Territory	2,047	935	981	2,040	2,174
Miscellaneous	100	100	200	—	—
World total	74,687	44,624	76,968	109,789	118,213

out of the blast-furnaces of the world, and the output is increasing. The prices of a standard blast-furnace iron—Derbyshire No. 3 foundry cast iron—varied in Manchester during 1922–29 from £5 7s. 11d. to £3 8s. 0d. per ton.

Obviously this enormous output has made the curious wonder how long available supplies of ore will last. Estimates have been made of the world's reserve stocks of available iron in different countries—neglecting, of course, the unknown but assumed internal core. Pessimistic estimates like those of A. E. Törnebohm, in 1910, say that if the consumption increases hereafter as fast as it did between 1893 and 1906, the available ten billion tons of ore with which he credits the world will be exhausted in about 40 years. If so, there is a prospect of an immediate iron famine, at which Burns might well have said :

> And forward though I canna see
> I guess and fear.

There are also optimistic estimates, like that of E. C. Eckel, who considers that A. E. Törnebohm's estimates are twenty times too low ; and that of H. M. Howe, who considers that the supply is incalculable, because as the richer ores become exhausted, poorer ores will be available, until " a large bed of 4 per cent. ore, perhaps even 2·5 per cent. ore, will become a veritable bonanza." Rock with 2·5 per cent. of gold is an extraordinarily valuable ore, and rock with 2·5 per cent. of copper is treated to-day as copper ore. This subject has also been discussed by F. Beyschlag, H. E. Boker, H. H. Campbell, J. F. Kemp, P. Krusch, L. de Launay, W. Oechelhäuser, G. Mehrtens, D. Forbes, J. Deby, R. Akermann, and A. Lindmann. The pessimistic estimate of A. E. Törnebohm was perhaps responsible for the collection of data for different countries by different experts for the International Geological Congress held at Stockholm in 1910, and these reports were collected in the publication *The Iron Ore Resources of the World*, Stockholm, 1910. H. Sjögren summarized in Table VII the various estimates, expressed in millions of metric tons, of the reserves for different countries ; and M. Roesler's results are summarized in Table VIII.

TABLE VII.—SUMMARY OF THE WORLD'S IRON ORE RESERVES (H. Sjögren).
(In millions of metric tons.)

Continent.	Actual.		Potential.	
	Iron Ore.	Metal Iron.	Iron Ore.	Metal Iron.
Europe . . .	12,032	4,733	41,029	12,085
America . . .	9,855	5,154	81,822	40,731
Australia . . .	136	74	69	37
Asia . . .	260	156	457	283
Africa . . .	125	75	Billions	Billions
Totals . .	22,408	10,192	123,377	53,136

Iron is a constituent of most natural waters, but it is present in very small proportions. The presence of iron can be readily detected in oceanic waters, and also in the salts obtained by the evaporation of these waters. Observations were made by J. Usiglio,[164] A. Goebel, J. Roth, W. Dittmar, R. Quinton, A. F. von Sass, S. Robinet and J. Lefort, E. von Bibra, E. H. Ducloux, G. Forchhammer, and F. J. Malaguti and co-workers. C. Schmidt gave 0·0012 grm. ferrous carbonate per litre for the Baltic Sea, and A. Goebel, 0·0067 grm. per litre ; C. Schmidt, 0·0016 grm. per litre for the White Sea ; J. Usiglio, 0·003 grm. per litre for the Mediterranean Sea ; C. Schmidt, 0·0029 to 0·0065 grm. per litre for the Indian Ocean ; C. Schmidt, 0·0039 grm. per litre for the Red Sea, and 0·0049 for the South Sea ; C. Schmidt, 0·0019 to 0·0022 grm. per litre for the Atlantic Ocean ;

T. E. Thorpe and E. H. Morton, 0·0050 grm. per litre for the Irish Sea. Deep-sea deposits—manganese nodules, phosphatic concretions, red and marine clays, glauconite, and other sediments—reported by J. Murray and A. F. Renard,[165] L. W. Collet, etc., show that considerable proportions of iron may be present. Thus, F. W. Clarke gave 8·66 per cent. of Fe_2O_3 and 0·84 per cent. of FeO in the red clay.

At the beginning of this era Pliny, in his *Historia naturalis* (**35.** 52), says that *alumen* turns black when treated with pomegranate juice or nut-galls. The reaction was also mentioned by Dioscorides, in his *De materia medica*, a contemporary of Pliny, and by Paracelsus,[166] who employed the reaction as a test for iron in mineral water. R. Boyle showed that a soln. of an iron salt is blackened by decoctions of nut-galls, pomegranate, logwood, and other astringent vegetable matters. F. Hoffmann, and T. Bergman also used the reaction as a test for iron

TABLE VIII.—SUMMARY OF THE IRON ORE RESERVES OF EUROPE (M. Roesler).
(In millions of metric tons.)

	Known.	Probable.	Possible.	Total.	Per cent.
France . . .	1,790·0	1,053·6	1,526·0	4,369·6	35·2
United Kingdom . .	317·5	464·3	1,472·3	2,254·1	18·2
Sweden . . .	442·9	376·1	729·6	1,548·6	12·5
German Republic .	255·6	207·4	911·7	1,374·7	11·1
Spain . . .	353·1	116·3	148·9	618·3	5·0
Central Russia . .	140·0	180·0	204·1	524·1	4·2
Norway . . .	85·8	56·4	330·1	472·3	3·8
Russia (Ukraine) . .	71·0	131·0	142·0	344·0	2·8
Czechoslovakia .	22·3	84·8	58·6	165·7	1·3
Ural Region . .	52·3	60·8	47·8	160·9	1·3
Poland . . .	11·2	50·6	69·2	131·0	1·1
Austria . . .	76·7	9·5	30·0	116·2	0·9
Luxemburg . . .	60·0	21·0	—	81·0	0·7
Greece . . .	18·0	18·0	22·5	58·5	0·5
Belgium . . .	2·5	14·1	23·2	39·8	0·3
Portugal . . .	8·2	16·2	12·5	36·9	0·3
Jugoslavia . . .	9·5	8·0	16·0	33·5	
Caucasus . . .	6·2	6·2	18·6	31·0	
Finland . . .	3·6	11·4	1·9	16·9	
Rumania . . .	2·5	8·5	4·0	15·0	0·8
Italy . . .	5·5	3·3	—	8·8	
Switzerland . .	1·2	—	2·2	3·4	
Bulgaria . . .	—	0·7	—	0·7	
Totals . .	3,735·6	2,898·2	5,771·2	12,405·0	100·0

in mineral waters; and A. S. Marggraf detected iron in rain-water, snow-water, and different mineral waters by a soln. of potassium ferrocyanide.

The waters of most rivers contain some iron salt in solution. Thus, H. St. C. Deville [167] found it in the waters of the Rhine near Strassburg; R. Finkener, the Spree; H. St. C. Deville, the Loire and the Seine; J. F. Hodges, in Loch Neagh; E. J. Maumené, the Vesle; T. Graham and co-workers, the Thames; H. Wurtz, the Delaware; and C. Schmidt, the Dwina.

The so-called **chalybeate waters,** or *ferruginous waters*, or *steel-waters* contain not less than 0·06 grm. of iron salts per litre, and the iron is probably present as ferrous hydrocarbonate, $Fe(HCO_3)_2$, although it may be reported in analyses as ferric oxide. In illustration of chalybeate waters containing much carbon dioxide and but a small proportion of soluble salts, R. Kremann [168] reported the waters of Altwasser; those of Württemberg, reported by H. von Fehling; Brückenar, by J. Scherer; Chateldon, by J. P. Bouquet; Frewalde, by W. Lasch; Hofgeismar, Kurhessen, by H. A. L. Wiggers; Langenschwalbach, by R. Fresenius; Liebenstein, Thuringia, by E. Reichardt, J. von Liebig, and M. W. Thüring; the Ambros-quelle and Karolquelle, Marienbad, by W. F. Gintl; Niederlangenau, Glatz, by T. Poleck; Rabbia (antica fonti), by J. Zehentner; Radeberg, by W. Stein and C. Bley; Reinerz, by R. Woy; Royat, Puy-de-Dôme, by L. Moissenet, J. Lefort, J. L. Lassaigne, and A. Duboin; Saratoga, New York, by C. F. Chandler and F. A. Cairns, A. H. Chester, and L. R. Milford; Schandau, by H. W. F. Wacken-roder and E. Reichardt; Schwendi-Kaltbad, Canton Oberwalden, by P. A. Bolley and M. Schultz; Spaa, by E. Gérard and H. Chaurin; and Steben, by F. von Gorup-Besanez, and E. Reichardt.

There are also chalybeate waters containing a relatively large proportion of carbon dioxide as well as of sodium carbonate and sulphate in soln. For instance, the waters of Bartfeld, examined by C. von Hauer [169]; Birresborn, by H. Vohl, and H. Fresenius; Fideris and Graubünden, by G. Nussberger; Flinsberg, Silesia, by T. Poleck; Kochl, Bayern, by M. Pettenkofer; Radein, by J. Holm; and Vals-les-Baines, by G. A. C. de C. de Castelnau, L. P. U. le Verrière, and O. Henry. Chalybeate waters may also contain, in addition, relatively large proportions of calcium carbonate and sulphate. For instance, the waters of Antogast, reported by R. Bunsen [170]; Bad Elster, Saxony, by A. Goldberg; Carlsbad, by J. Roth; Contrexeville, Dept. Vogesen, by O. Henry, L. Dieulafait, and L. Moissenet; Driburg, by R. Fresenius, and H. A. L. Wiggers; Freyersbach, Schwarzwald, by K. Birnbaum, and R. Bunsen; Fairhaven Springs, Missouri, by P. Schweitzer; Göppingen, Württemberg, by H. von Fehling and C. Hell; Griesbach, by G. Rupp, and R. Bunsen; Krynica, Galicia, by H. Dietrich; Langenau, by F. von Gorup-Besanez; Lippa, by M. Say; Mittagong, by J. C. H. Mingaye; O jo Caliente. New Mexico, by W. F. Hillebrand, and W. Lindgren; Petersthal, Baden, by J. Nessler; Pyrmont, by C. Neuberg, F. J. Hugi, and R. Fresenius; Recoara, by G. Bizio, and P. Spica; Rippolsdau, by R. Bunsen, and H. Will; Santa Moritz, by A. Husemann, A. von Planta and A. Kekulé, E. Bosshard, F. P. Treadwell, and W. Gambel; Schuls, Graubünden, by A. von Planta; Vichy, France, by J. Bouquet; and Wildungen, by R. Fresenius. Yet another class of chalybeate waters contains ferrous sulphate—for instance, the waters of Alexisbad, examined by T. Pusch,[171] and H. Bley; Mitterbad, Tyrol, by L. von Barth and R. Wegscheider, and J. C. Wittstein; Ronneby, Sweden, by N. O. Hamberg; and Roufrage, by J. C. Essener. The radioactivity of the waters of some German iron springs has been discussed by A. Simon and K. Kötschau.

Other chalybeate waters have been reported—e.g. at Kaiserqueele, Aachen, by V. Monheim [172]; Actos, Greece, by J. Landerer; Berlin, by O. A. Ziurek; Bohrloch, Zwickau, by C. M. Kersten; Bibra, by M. Papp; Cusset, by O. Henry, and J. P. Bouquet; Doberau, by F. Schultze; Dornawatra, by C. von John, and C. von Hauser and C. von John; Dorna-Kadreny, Bukowina, by P. Pribram and F. Langer, and P. Pribram; Dinan, Côtes-du-Nord, by F. J. Malaguti; Aix-les-Bains, by E. Bonjeau; Dürkheim, R. Bunsen and G. Kirchhoff, and H. Laspeyres; Karlsbrunn, Silesia, by E. Ludwig; Kreis Witebsk, by C. Schmidt; Pont-à-Mousson, by L. Grandeau; Missouri zinc region, by C. P. Williams; Mountain View Mine, Montana, by W. F. Hillebrand; Paramo de Ruiz, New Granada, by L. Lewy; Pressburg, Hungary, by P. Weselsky and A. Bauer; Rockbridge Co., Virginia, by M. B. Hardin; Rome, by F. Manganini; Rastenburg, by E. Ludwig; Savoy, by E. Wilm; Stolykin, by C. Schmidt; Sour Spring, Tuscarora, by T. S. Hunt; Stettin, by R. Fresenius; Trefriw, Wales, by T. Carnelley; Trentschein-Teplitz, by C. von Hauer; Weinheimer, by G. Müller; Wien-Raaber Eisenbahn, by P. Weselsky; Wiesau, by E. von Gorup-Besanez; Saitama (Japan), by S. Yoshimura; and Zeche Johann, near Steele, by W. von der Marck. Many of the chalybeate waters also contain arsenic.[173] For instance, those of Alumwell, Missouri, reported by P. Schweitzer; Burtscheider Quelle, by R. Wildenstein; Egypt, by F. Raspe; St. Etienne, by X. Landerer; Levico, by E. Ludwig and R. von Zeynek; Orsola, South Tyrol, by C. F. Eichleiter; Roncegno, by R. Nasini and co-workers, and M. Gläser and W. Kalmann; Shoal Creek, Missouri, by W. F. Hillebrand; Srebrenica, Bosnia, by E. Ludwig; and Vöslau, by H. Siegmund and P. Juhacz, and M. Bamberger and A. Landsiedel. There are also ferruginous waters of volcanic origin. For instance, the waters of California geysers, Sonoma Co., reported by T. Price [174]; Cove Creek, Utah, by W. T. Lee; Paramo de Ruiz, Colombia, by J. B. J. D. Boussingault; Pozzuoli, Italy, by S. de Luca; Brook Sungi Pait, Java, by F. A. Flückiger; Popocatapetl, by J. Lefort; Hot Lake, White Island, N.Z., by C. du Ponteil, W. Skey, and J. S. Maclaurin; and the Lakes of Taal volcano, Philippine Islands, by J. Centeno, G. F. Becker, and R. F. Bacon.

There are numerous reports on the natural waters of different countries.[175] The behaviour of ferrous carbonate in carbonic acid soln. is analogous to that of calcium carbonate. Deposits are formed around chalybeate springs, and stalactites are formed as in the case of calcium carbonate soln., only the ferrous carbonate is not very stable, and it readily changes to limonite—*vide infra*, ferrous carbonate, and limonite. The *iron sinter* or deposit near a chalybeate spring in Death Gulch, Yellowstone National Park, contained, according to W. H. Weed [176]:

SiO_2	Fe_2O_3	Al_2O_3	SO_3	H_2O and Organic matter
1·37	63·03	0·08	8·35	26·94 per cent.

The work of water in helping to distribute iron on the surface of the globe has been discussed by A. Daubrée,[177] V. M. Goldschmidt, W. Lindgren, and H. S. Washington. F. W. Clarke estimated that the average iron content of the rivers of the world, calculated as $(Fe,Al)_2O_3$, is only 4·76 per cent. of the total mineral content; and, added E. S. Moore and J. E. Maynard, this would be precipitated almost immediately by the electrolytes in sea-water, if present in the river in the colloidal form. According to W. Lindgren, the **iron cycle** in nature is somewhat as follows. Igneous rocks average about 6 per cent. of ferrous and ferric oxides, and in the more basic rocks 12 to 16 per cent. may be present. These rocks form the raw material from which nature manufactures commercial iron ore. Iron oxides, particularly magnetite, sink in the magmas to form strongly ferriferous rocks, even massive magnetite, usually accompanied by the faithful companions titanium, phosphorus, and vanadium. These differentiation products are sometimes brought to the surface as masses in the rocks or as dikes. Magnetite is also, though rarely in quantities, brought up by underground waters, that is, in pegmatite dikes. Much more abundantly it is carried up as the vapour of a salt, probably in combination with halogens. Absorbed by limestones, it takes the form of magnetite, pyrrhotite, and pyrite in contact with metamorphic deposits. Carried up by underground waters, it is deposited as veins and replacement deposits as pyrite, pyrrhotite, and other sulphides or as arsenides. In all these forms it makes deposits of economic importance, the sulphides and the apatite-magnetite mixtures being utilized only lately as metallurgical methods improved. These " hypogene " deposits may be contrasted with those formed by processes whose home is in or near the surface.

Meteoric waters circulating in the crust dissolve the iron of the rocks and when overloaded deposit it below as sulphides or carbonates—a process rarely of great economic importance. Surface waters oxidize all rocks in the zone of weathering and, particularly in the basic rocks, they find a suitable raw material for their concentrating action. Magnetite is washed down to form " black sand." All rocks are decomposed, yielding soluble iron salts easily oxidized or hydrolyzed to the ultimate sub-aerial product, ferric hydroxides. A large part of the iron of the rocks remains thus *in situ*, or is carried a little way maybe to replace limestone. Colloidal processes are at work in the weathered rocks, and they concentrate the scattered limonite to deposits of some importance. A smaller part stays in soln., as bicarbonates or sulphate, and is carried to the sea, there to give rise to new iron deposits. The continuous stream of soluble iron salts which reaches the shores from ferriferous regions of rock decay is largely precipitated by complex reactions in the sea-water, in part biochemical, to form silicates (glauconite, chamosite) or carbonate (siderite), or hæmatite, the precipitate usually assuming the oolitic texture. In the littoral muds rich in animal ooze there is often enough sulphur to cause an abundant precipitation of colloidal iron sulphides, which later crystallize as pyrite or marcasite. In muddy waters rich in vegetable substances siderite may be precipitated, which later appears in the coal seams as " black bands." Epochs of uplift subject the hardened sediments again to limonitic alteration and soln., and the products are again swept to the sea.

Besides these major cycles there are minor paths of circulation, usually of biochemical nature. The plants need organic iron compounds, which they absorb from the soil, and after their death the iron returns to the soil ; or land animals, man included, feed on plants, absorbing their iron. Meat-eating animals, including man, feed on the plant-eating species, and obtain their iron from them or from the blood of other carnivorous beings. Similar cycles are in operation in the sea, but for marine inhabitants iron is less of a necessity than for those of the land. Essentially the secondary iron deposits are products of the land or the shores. There seems to be very little iron in the sea-water, perhaps $0.00x$ per cent. in the dissolved salts. It seems to be very readily removed, as in the case of phosphorus.

According to H. Harrassowitz, humic acids carry away alumina and ferric oxide from regions that are continually damp, thereby concentrating the silica ; and if humic acids be absent, the alumina and ferric oxide are moderately concentrated in mixed gels of silica, alumina, and ferric oxide ; whilst in regions alternately wet and dry, poor in humic acids, alumina and ferric oxide are strongly concentrated. Desert lands, free from humic acids, are enriched in silica and ferric oxide, whilst in the alternately wet and dry steppes, rich in humic acids, the silica, alumina, and ferric oxide form gels and are not transported.

G. Tissandier [178] observed particles of meteoric iron in atmospheric dust, and they could be separated by means of a magnet. The composition of atmospheric dust was discussed by J. A. Udden, E. E. Free, and A. Ditte. A. Bergeat named ferric chloride amongst the sublimation products of fumaroles.

About 1702, L. Lemery [179] observed that iron is present in the ashes of many plants. He said :

On s'apercevra que dans ce moment beaucoup de particules du charbon se hérissent et seront attirées par le couteau, s'y attachant de même que la limaille de fer s'attache à l'aimant. Cette expérience moutre que le charbon de miel contient du fer.

E. F. Geoffroy supposed that the iron was synthesized from its primal elements during the calcination, but L. Lemery showed that the iron is only separated, not synthesized, during the process. In 1747, V. Menghini discovered the presence of iron in blood.

Iron is one of the important elements concerned with enzymes and the living organism ; it is one of the component elements of hæmaglobin, which contains 0.43 per cent. of iron. This subject was discussed by N. Scharoff,[180] A. B. Macallum, A. N. Richards, J. Barcroft, L. Maquenne and R. Cerighelli, etc. The body of man is said to contain one or two parts of iron per 10,000, and the blood, according to I. Novi, about 5 parts in 10,000. The iron content of the liver was discussed by A. Guillemonat, and A. Guillemonat and L. Lapicque. G. Bunge found the proportion varied from 1.0 to 35.5 mgrms. per 100 grms. of liver in dogs and cats. According to A. Dastre, the liver of invertebrates can take up iron preferentially, so that the liver of the cephalopods contains 25 times more iron than the rest of the body. E. Auscher and L. Lapicque found that the spleen contains insignificant quantities of iron, except in pathological states, where the red corpuscles of the blood deposit hydrated ferric oxide, $2Fe_2O_3.3H_2O$. A. Guillemonat and G. Delamare observed that the lymphatic glands of various animals contain traces up to 0.38 part per 1000—after inanition the proportion decreases, and after splenectomy it increases. G. Bunge found 0.72 per cent. Fe_2O_3 in ash of a new-born dog, and 0·12 per cent. in the ash of dog's milk, and he argued that the fœtus receives a store of iron through the maternal placenta previous to birth. Similar results were obtained with young cats, rabbits, and guinea-pigs. H. M. Fox and H. Ramage found iron to be present in the tissues of all the polychætes examined, and the evidence indicates that iron is a universal constituent of protoplasm.

According to A. B. Macallum, iron firmly combined is a constant constituent of animal and vegetable chromatin, and of nucleoli. The chromophilous substance in ferment-forming cells contains iron, and the cytoplasm of protozoan organisms, which probably also secretes ferments, contains an iron compound. According to G. Bunge, the iron in the yellow colouring matter of eggs is due to a nuclein, which during incubation normally furnishes hæmaglobin. Iron does not enter the organism when introduced as inorganic salts of iron, because these salts are not assimilated. In the stomach they produce chlorides, which in the intestine form hydrated oxide or carbonate, and finally sulphide, in which form the iron appears in the fæces. It is not the same with some ferruginous organic compounds, a subject discussed by G. Bunge, H. F. Hendrix, and A. Jacquet. According to A. Guillemonat and L. Lapicque, a healthy man excretes from the intestines about 20 or 30 mgrms. of iron in 24 hrs., but normal urine contains only traces of iron— P. Figaroli found that about a milligram per diem is excreted by man; while A. Dastre, and L. Lapicque said that the bile gives off about 5 mgrms. per day.

Iron is not an essential component of the chlorophyll of vegetables, but, according to A. Meyer, plants cannot produce normal chlorophyll in the absence of iron; and, according to S. Winogradsky, and J. L. Raulin, Aspergillus niger can develop 900 times faster in the presence of iron compounds. According to A. B. Macallum, a compound of iron is present in the chromophilous substance of the cytoplasm of the fungi. The non-nucleated bacteria, owing to their minuteness, have, with one exception, given little evidence of the presence of an organic iron compound; but the chromophilous portion of the central substance of the cyanophyceæ contains iron; and iron is also present in the peripheral granules formed of cyanophycin. Iron is precipitated from soil soln. in arable land, and it is taken up by the roots of plants, which sometimes cause a decolorization of the soil in their vicinity, as indicated by A. Daubrée—vide infra, limonite.

REFERENCES.

[1] R. J. Haüy, Traité de minéralogie, Paris, 4. 3, 1801; F. W. Clarke, The Data of Geochemistry, Washington, 1924; F. W. Clarke and H. S. Washington, Proc. Nat. Acad., 8. 108, 1922; The Composition of the Earth's Crust, Washington, 1924; H. S. Washington, Bull. Nat. Research Council, 2. ii, 30, 1926; Amer. Journ. Science, (4), 38. 90, 1914; (5), 9. 351, 1925; (5), 12. 272, 1926; Journ. Washington Acad., 14. 435, 1924; Trans. Amer. Inst. Min. Eng., 39. 735, 1908; Proc. Nat. Acad., 1. 574, 1915; Journ. Franklin Inst., 190. 777, 1920; F. W. Clarke and G. Steiger, Journ. Washington Acad., 4. 58, 1914; J. H. L. Vogt, Zeit. prakt. Geol., 6. 225, 314, 377, 413, 1898; 7. 10, 274, 1899; 14. 223, 1906; W. Lindgren, Econ. Geol., 18. 419, 1923; Mineral Deposits, New York, 14, 1913; V. M. Goldschmidt, Videnskapsselskapets Schrift., 11, 1922; 3, 1923; Zeit. Elektrochem., 28. 411, 1922; Der Stoffwechsel der Erde, Kristiania, 1922; W. Vernadsky, Essai de minéralogie descriptive, St. Petersburg, 1. 121, 740, 1914; La geochimie, Paris, 16, 1924; Centr. Min., 758, 1912; A. Harker, Geol. Mag., (4), 6. 220, 1899; W. Spring, Rec. Trav. Chim. Pays-Bas, 17. 202, 1898; A. E. Fersmann, Bull. Acad. St. Petersburg, (6), 6. 367, 1912; G. Tammann, Zeit. anorg. Chem., 131. 96, 1923; 134. 269, 1924; E. Herlinger, Fortschr. Min., 12. 253, 1927; A. von Antropoff, Sitzber. Nat. Hist. Ver. Rheinlande, 1, 1926; O. Hahn, Naturwiss., 14. 159, 1926; W. and I. Noddack and O. Berg, ib., 13. 568, 1925; J. Joly, The Surface History of the Earth, Oxford, 1925; P. Niggli, Geochemie und Konstitution der Atomkerne, Helsingfors, 50, 1928; Die leichtflüchtigen Bestandteile im Magma, Leipzig, 5. 1920; Naturwiss., 9. 463, 1921; G. Berg, Vorkommen und Geochemie der mineralischen Rohstoffe, Leipzig, 1929; R. A. Sonder, Zeit. Kryst., 57. 611, 1923; Zeit. anorg. Chem., 192. 257, 1930; L. de Launay, Rev. Gén. Sciences, 15. 386, 1904; C. M. Smyth, Journ. Geol., 13. 319, 1905; R. Wildt, Zeit. Physik, 54. 856, 1929.

[2] T. Andrews, B.A. Rep., 34, 1852; Chem. Gaz., 10. 416, 1852; A. von Lasaulx, Ber Niederrh. Ges. Bonn, 100, 1882; A. E. Nordenskjöld, Geol. Mag., (1), 8. 570, 1871; (1), 9. 72, 460, 516, 1872; Akad. Förh. Stockholm, 1058, 1870; 1, 1871; Journ. Geol. Soc., 28. 44, 1872;

Zeit. deut. geol. Ges., **23**. 738, 1871 ; J. S. Steenstrup, *Compt. Rend.*, **77**. 464, 1873 ; **116**. 677, 1893 ; *Ved. Medd. Kopenhagen*, 295, 1875 ; *Zeit. deut. geol. Ges.*, **23**. 745, 1871 ; **28**. 225, 1876 ; **35**. 695, 1883 ; *Neues Jahrb. Min.*, **91**, 1877 ; *Congr. Internat. Anthropologie Bruxelles*, 24, 2, 1872 ; *Min. Mag.*, **1**. 143, 1877 ; **6**. 1, 1884 ; *Geol. För. Förh. Stockholm*, **14**. 312, 1892 ; J. Lorenzen, *Min. Mag.*, **6**. 14, 1884 ; *Congr. Internat. Anthropologie Bruxelles*, 1, 1872 ; *Medd. Grönland*, 135, 1883 ; J. L. Smith, *Ann. Chim. Phys.*, (5), **16**. 452, 1879 ; *Bull. Soc. Min.* **1**., 90, 1878 ; A. Daubrée, *Études synthétiques de géologie expérimentale*, Paris, 515, 555, 574, 1879 ; *Compt. Rend.*, **74**. 1542, 1872 ; **75**. 240, 1872 ; **84**. 66, 1877 ; **85**. 1256, 1877 ; **87**. 512, 911, 929, 1878 ; A. Damour, *ib.*, **84**. 478, 1877 ; H. Moissan, *ib.*, **116**. 1269, 1893 ; S. Meunier, *ib.*, **89**. 215, 794, 924, 1879 ; E. B. de Chancourtois, *Bull. Soc. Géol.*, (2), **29**. 210, 1872 ; J. D. Dana, *A System of Mineralogy*, New York, 28, 1892 ; C. Winkler, *Ber. Sächs. Ges. Wiss.*, **52**. 9, 1900 ; *Zeit. Kryst.*, **37**. 286, 1903 ; *Oefvers. Akad. Förh. Stockholm*, **58**. 495, 1901 ; E. Weinschenk, *Compt. Rend. Congr. Géol. Internat.*, **8**. i, 447, 1900 ; W. Skey, *Trans. New Zealand Inst.*, **18**. 401, 1885 ; S. Hearne, *A Journey from the Prince of Wales's Fort in Hudson's Bay to the Northern Ocean*, London, 1795 ; J. Ross, *A Voyage of Discovery to Baffin's Bay*, London, 114, 1819 ; G. F. Zimmer, *Journ. Iron Steel Inst.*, **94**. ii, 306, 1916 ; R. E. Peary, *Northward on the Great Ice*, London, 2. 612, 1898 ; D. C. Clavering, *Edin. Phil. Journ.*, **9**. 21, 1830 ; I. I. Hayes, *Amer. Journ. Science*, (2), **42**. 249, 1866 ; W. J. Taylor, *ib.*, (3), **24**. 294, 1887 ; W. H. Melville, *ib.*, (3), **43**. 510, 1892 ; E. T. Allen, *ib.*, (4), **4**. 99, 1897 ; G. S. Jamieson, *ib.*, (4), **19**. 413, 1905 ; G. C. Hoffmann, *ib.*, (4), **19**. 319, 1905 ; *Ann. Rep. Canada Geol. Sur.*, 1, 1892 ; F. Wöhler, *Anz. Gött. Gel.*, 197, 1872 ; *Neues Jahrb. Min.*, 832, 1879 ; G. Tschermak, *Tschermak's Mitt.*, (1), **1**. 107, 1871 ; W. Wahl, *ib.*, (2) **26**. 56, 1907 ; R. Nauckhoff, *ib.*, (1), **4**. 109, 1874 ; *Akad. Handl. Stockholm*, **1**. 6, 1872 ; A. G. Nathorst, *Geol. För. Förh. Stockholm*, **4**. 203, 1879 ; A. E. Törnebohm, *Bihang. Oefvers. Akad. Stockholm*, **5**. 10, 1879 ; *Neues Jahrb. Min.*, 173, 1879 ; G. Forchhammer, *Danske Vid. Selskr. Forh.*, 1, 1854 ; *Pogg. Ann.*, **93**. 155, 1854 ; E. Cohen, *Medd. Grönland*, **15**. 302, 1897 ; *Ann. Naturhist. Hofmuseums*, **7**. 146, 1892 ; *Meteoritenkunde*, Stuttgart, **1**. 138, 1894 ; J. W. Mallet, *Chem. News*, **44**. 189, 1881 ; R. A. A. Johnston, *Summary Rep. Canada Geol. Sur.*, 257, 1911 ; A. A. Inostzanzeff, *Trav. Soc. Imp. Nat. St. Petersburg*, **35**. 21, 1907 ; A. E. Kupffer, *Ann. Russ. Inst. Mines*, 318, 1908 ; W. Irmer, *Verh. Senkenberg Naturf. Ges.*, **37**. 104, 1920 ; W. Eitel, *ib.*, **37**. 148, 1920 ; J. G. Neumann, *Jahresb. geol. Reichsanst.*, **8**. 355, 1857 ; N. Wyssotzky, *Mém. Russ. Com. geol.*, **62**. 106, 667, 1913 ; A. Schwantke, *Sitzber. Akad. Berlin*, 853, 1906 ; *Sitzber. Beförderung Naturwiss. Marburg*, 126, 1913 ; T. Nicolau, *Medd. Grönland*, 215, 1901 ; *Neues Jahrb. Min.*, i, 182, 1903 ; C. Benedicks, *Met.*, **8**. 65, 1911.

³ J. B. Tyrrell, *Amer. Journ. Science*, (3), **33**. 73, 1887 ; E. T. Allen, *ib.*, (4), **4**. 99, 1897 ; W. H. Melville, *ib.*, (3), **43**. 508, 1892 ; *Bull U.S. Geol. Sur.*, 113, 1893 ; A. E. Kupffer, *Ann. Russ. Inst. Mines*, 318, 1908 ; A. Daubrée and S. Meunier, *Compt. Rend.*, **113**. 172, 1892 ; G. C. Hoffmann, *Eng. Min. Journ.*, **52**. 240, 1891 ; *Amer. Journ. Science*, (4), **19**. 319, 1905 ; *Rep. Canada Geol. Sur.*, 9, 1906 ; A. A. Inostzanzeff, *Trav. Soc. Imp. Nat. St. Petersburg*, **35**. 21, 1907 ; *Zeit. Kryst.*, **50**. 61, 1911 ; E. Priwosnik, *Oesterr. Zeit. Berg. Hütt.*, **58**. 327, 1910 ; A. Schwantke, *Centr. Min.*, 65, 1901 ; *Neues Jahrb. Min. B.B.*, **18**. 460, 1904 ; M. Sidorenko, *Schrift. Neuruss. Naturf. Ges.*, **25**. 71, 1903 ; *Neues Jahrb. Min.*, i, 13, 1906 ; P. Jeremejeff, *Proc. Russ. Min. Soc.*, **30**. 444, 1893 ; J. Hector, *Nature*, **35**. 513, 1887 ; G. vom Rath, *Sitzber. Niederrh. Ges. Bonn*, 289, 1887 ; G. H. F. Ulrich, *Journ. Geol. Soc.*, **43**. 3, 1887 ; **46**. 124, 619, 1890 ; T. G. Bonney and E. Aston, *ib.*, **52**. 452, 1896 ; A. de Lapparent, *Fer natif et météorites*, Paris, 1897 ; O. Vogel, *Chem. Ztg.*, **31**. 1181, 1907 ; J. von Szabo, *Földt. Közl.*, **21**. 97, 135, 1891 ; J. G. Bornemann, *Pogg. Ann.*, **88**. 145, 1853 ; J. F. Bahr, *Oefvers. Akad. Handl. Stockholm*, 100, 1851 ; *Journ. prakt. Chem.*, (1), **54**. 194, 1851 ; *Pogg. Ann.*, **88**. 325, 1853 ; J. F. L. Hausmann, *Handbuch der Mineralogie*, Göttingen, **2**. 40, 1847 ; F. M. Stapff, *Zeit. deut. geol. Ges.*, **18**. 130, 1866 ; G. A. Kenngott, *Uebersichte der Resultate Mineralogischer Forschungen*, Wien, 156, 1859 ; A. Reuss, *Sitzber. Akad. Wien*, **25**. 541, 1858.

⁴ E. Hussak, *Bol. Comm. Geogr. Geol. San Paulo*, 7, 1890 ; A. Daubrée and S. Meunier, *Compt. Rend.*, **113**. 172, 1891 ; W. Skey, *Trans. New Zealand Inst.*, **18**. 401, 1885.

⁵ T. Clark, *Journ. Roy. Inst. Cornwall*, **10**. 396, 1891 ; M. F. Heddle, *Min. Mag.*, **5**. 150, 1884 ; W. Flight, *An Introduction to the Study of Meteorites*, London, 66, 1908.

⁶ E. de Beaumont, *Compt. Rend.*, **72**. 187, 1871 ; L. Moissenet, *ib.*, **73**. 761, 1871 ; J. A. H. Lucas, *Tableau méthodique des espèces minéraux*, Paris, 1. 307, 1806 ; 2. 357, 1813 ; R. J. Haüy, *Traité de minéralogie*, Paris, 3. 533, 1822 ; *Journ. Phys.*, **60**. 340, 1805 ; P. A. Dufrénoy, *Traité de minéralogie*, Paris, 2. 438, 1845 ; A. Lacroix, *Minéralogie de la France et de ses colonies*, Paris, 2. 392, 1897 ; J. F. L. Hausmann, *Handbuch der Mineralogie*, Göttingen, 2. 39, 1847 ; F. Gonnard, *Minéralogie du Département du Puy-de-Dôme*, Paris, 156, 1876.

⁷ A. Sella, *Compt. Rend.*, **112**. 171, 1891.

⁸ J. F. Bahr, *Oefvers. Akad. Handl. Stockholm*, 100, 1851 ; *Ann. prakt. Chem.*, (1), **54**. 194, 1851 ; *Pogg. Ann.*, **88**. 325, 1853 ; F. M. Stapff, *Zeit. deut. geol. Ges.*, **18**. 130, 1866 ; A. G. Högbom, *Zeit. Kryst.*, **53**. 408, 1914 ; C. J. B. Karsten, *Handbuch der Eisenhüttenkunde*, Berlin, 2. 12, 1841 ; J. F. L. Hausmann, *Handbuch der Mineralogie*, Göttingen, 2. 40, 1847.

⁹ F. Navarro, *Geol. Centr.*, **7**. 184, 1905 ; *Bol. Soc. Esp. Hist. Nat.*, **4**. 429, 1904.

¹⁰ F. Zirkel, *Lehrbuch der Petrologie*, Leipzig, 2. 893, 1894 ; J. G. Lehmann, *Einleitung in einige Theile der Bergwissenschaft*, Berlin, 59, 1751 ; J. G. Bornemann, *Pogg. Ann.*, **88**. 148, 1853 ; C. J. B. Karsten, *Handbuch der Eisenhüttenkunde*, Berlin, 2. 13, 1841 ; F. Rinne, *Neues Jahrb. Min.*, ii, 61, 1906 ; J. Beckenkamp, *Sitzber. Phys. Med. Ges. Würzburg*, 51, 1903 ;

B. Cramer, *Schrift. Ges. Nat. Freunde, Berlin*, **2**. 294, 1799 ; W. G. Lettsom, *Phil. Mag.*, (4), **4**. 335, 1852 ; K. A. Neumann, *Jahrb. geol. Reichsanst.*, **8**. 351, 1857 ; J. G. Neumann, *ib.*, **8**. 354, 1857 ; G. G. Pusch, *Zeit. Min.*, **1**. 533, 1826 ; F. A. Reuss, *Sitzber. Akad. Wien*, **25**. 541, 1858 ; P. Partsch, *ib.*, **1**. 20, 1848 ; C. Zerrenner, *ib.*, **11**. 462, 1853 ; G. A. Kenngott, *Uebersichte der Resultate mineralogischer Forschungen*, Wien, 157, 1859 ; F. F. Hornstein, *Centr. Min.*, **276**, 1907 ; H. von Payr, *Jahresber.*, 677, 1858 ; A. Brezina, *Ann. Naturhist. Hofmuseums*, 274, 1896 ; J. Molnar, *Haidinger's Ber.*, **3**. 412, 1848 ; V. R. von Zepharovich, *Mineralogisches Lexicon für das Kaiserthum Oesterreich*, Wien, **1**. 138, 501, 1859 ; **3**. 90, 1893 ; G. A. Koch, *Erdelyi Muz. Eokon. Kolosvar*, 259, 1878 ; K. von Seebach, *Zeit. deut. geol. Ges.*, **12**. 189, 1860 ; *Centr. Min.*, 640, 1910 ; A. Schwantke, *ib.*, 65, 1901.

[11] F. Zirkel, *Lehrbuch der Petrologie*, Leipzig, **2**. 868, 1894 ; A. Lagorio and St. Pfaffius, *Tschermak's Mitt.*, (2), **8**. 483, 1887 ; St. Pfaffius, *Pamietnik Fyzyograficzny*, 31, 1886 ; *Neues Jahrb. Min.*, ii, 75, 1888 ; C. Grewingck and C. Schmidt, *ib.*, i, 29, 1884 ; G. Rose, *Reise nach dem Ural, dem Altai, und dem kaspischen Meere*, Berlin, **1**. 161, 1837 ; C. Grewingck, *Arch. Naturk. Liv. Esth. Kurlands*, 9, 1882 ; N. Wisotzky, *Mém. Russ. Com. Géol.*, **62**. 106, 1913 ; A. Daubrée and S. Meunier, *Compt. Rend.*, **113**. 172, 1891 ; G. A. Erman, *Erman's Arch.*, **1**. 314, 1841 ; **5**. 183, 1847 ; *Proc. Russ. Min. Soc.*, 74, 1842 ; 167, 1844.

[12] A. A. Hayes, *Amer. Journ. Science*, (2), **21**. 153, 1856 ; J. D. Dana, *A System of Mineralogy*, New York, 16, 1868 ; W. F. W. Herschel, *Phil. Mag.*, (4), **14**. 32, 1839.

[13] M. Chikashige and T. Hiki, *Zeit. anorg. Chem.*, **77**. 197, 1912 ; *Mem. Coll. Science Kyoto*, **5**. 1, 1912.

[14] J. D. Dana, *A System of Mineralogy*, New York, 29, 1892 ; G. C. Hoffmann, *Ann. Rep. Geol. Sur. Canada*, **6**. 23, 1895 ; *Trans. Roy. Soc. Canada*, (3), **8**. 39, 1890 ; *Geol. Nat. Hist. Canada*, **3**. 39, 1892.

[15] J. D. Dana, *A System of Mineralogy*, New York, 29, 1892 ; F. A. Genth, *Proc. Amer. Phil. Soc.*, **11**. 443, 1873 ; *Amer. Journ. Science*, (2), **28**. 246, 1859 ; J. W. Mallet, *Chem. News*, **44**. 189, 1881 ; G. H. Cook, *Ann. Rep. New Jersey Geol. Sur.*, 56, 1874 ; G. Troost, *Neues Jahrb. Min.*, 42, 1838 ; W. H. Melville, *Amer. Journ. Science*, (3), **43**. 509, 1892 ; C. Palache, *ib.*, (5), **12**. 136, 1926 ; E. T. Allen, *ib.*, (4), **4**. 99, 1897 ; G. W. Hawes, *ib.*, (3), **13**. 33, 1877 ; C. A. Lee, *ib.*, (1), **12**. 154, 1827 ; W. Burrall, *ib.*, (1), **12**. 154, 1827 ; S. Read, *ib.*, (2), **5**. 292, 1848 ; C. U. Shephard, *ib.*, (1), **12**. 155, 1827 ; (2), **43**. 28, 1867 ; E. E. Howell, *ib.*, (4), **25**. 49, 1908 ; A. Kromeyer, *Arch. Pharm.*, (2), **110**. 11, 1862 ; J. F. L. Hausmann, *Handbuch der Mineralogie*, Göttingen, 39, 1847 ; G. P. Merrill, *Proc. U.S. Nat. Museum*, **43**. 595, 1912 ; *Eng. Min. Journ.*, **95**. 350, 1913 ; J. Birkinbine, *Trans. Amer. Inst. Min. Eng.*, **24**. 616, 1894.

[16] H. J. Burkart, *Neues Jahrb. Min.*, 402, 1866 ; *Ber. Niederrh. Ges. Bonn*, 72, 1865 ; A. del Castillo, *Catalogue descriptive des météorites du Mexique*, Paris, 1, 1889 ; A. Brezina, *Die Meteoritensammlung des mineralogischen Hofkabinetes*, Wien, 117, 1885 ; *Die Meteoritensammlung des kaiserlich königlichen naturhistorischen Hofmuseums*, Wien, 274, 1896 ; L. Fletcher, *Min. Mag.*, **9**. 174, 1892.

[17] O. B. Böggild, *Medd. Grönland*, **74**. 9, 1927.

[18] I. Domeyko, *Elementos de mineralojia*, Santiago, 138, 1879 ; A. Daubrée, *Compt. Rend.*, **84**. 482, 1877 ; **85**. 1255, 1877 ; E. B. de Chancourtois, *Bull. Soc. Géol.*, (3), **5**. 110, 1877 ; O. A. Derby, *Amer. Journ. Science*, (3), **29**. 33, 496, 1885 ; L. F. Gonzaga de Campos, *ib.*, (3), **36**. 157, 1888 ; *Meteoritos Brasileiros*, Rio de Janeiro, 1888 ; S. Meunier, *Les météorites*, Paris, 102, 1884 ; E. A. Wulfling, *Die Meteoriten*, Tübingen, 307, 1897 ; E. Cohen, *Meteoritenkunde*, Stuttgart, **1**. 111, 1894 ; C. J. B. Karsten, *Handbuch der Eisenhüttenkunde*, Berlin, **2**. 12, 1841 ; E. Hussak, *Bol. Comm. Geogr. Geol. San Paulo*, 7, 1890 ; W. L. von Eschwege, *Pluto Brasiliensis*, Berlin, 583, 1833.

[19] W. M. Foote, *Amer. Journ. Science*, (4), **37**. 391, 1914.

[20] W. Skey, *Trans. New Zealand Inst.*, **18**. 401, 1885 ; *Journ. Geol. Soc.*, **43**. 3, 1887 ; *Amer. Journ. Science*, (3), **33**. 244, 1887.

[21] C. Benedicks, *Met.*, **8**. 65, 1911 ; H. Fleissner, *Stahl Eisen*, **30**. 1333, 1910 ; A. Schwantke, *Sitzber. Akad. Berlin*, 853, 1906 ; W. Eitel, *Verh. Senkenberg Naturf. Ges.*, **37**. 148, 1920 ; W. Irmer, *ib.*, **37**. 91, 1920 ; F. Hornstein, *Verh. Ges. Naturf.*, ii, 176, 1905 ; *Centr. Min.*, 276, 1907 ; K. Oebbeke and M. Schwarz, *Zeit. Metallkunde*, **12**. 505, 1920.

[22] R. Furnhjelm, *Astron. Nachr.*, **192**. 117, 1912 ; H. Ludendorff, *ib.*, **192**. 123, 1912 ; J. von Fraunhofer, *Denks. Akad. München*, 5. 193, 1817 ; M. N. Saha, *Phil. Mag.*, (6), **40**. 472, 1920 ; G. Kirchhoff, *Abhand. Akad. Berlin*, 63, 1861 ; 227, 1863 ; J. N. Lockyer, *Phil. Trans.*, **164**. 479, 805, 1874 ; *Proc. Roy. Soc.*, **28**. 157, 1878 ; **60**. 475, 1897 ; **86**. 78, 1911 ; *Compt. Rend.*, **92**. 904, 1884 ; *Nature*, **19**. 197, 225, 1879 ; J. Parry, *ib.*, **45**. 253, 1892 ; A. Cornu, *Ann. Scient. École Norm.*, (2), **9**. 21, 1880 ; *Journ. École Polyt.*, **53**. 175, 1883 ; F. McClean, *Monthly Notices Roy. Astron. Soc.*, **49**. 386, 1889 ; J. N. Lockyer and F. E. Baxandall, *ib.*, **65**. 1, 1902 ; **74**. 548, 1905 ; H. A. Rowland, *Preliminary Table of Solar Spectrum Wave-lengths*, Chicago, 1898 ; *Astrophys Journ.*, **1**. 29, 130, 222, 295, 377, 1895 ; **2**. 45, 109, 188, 306, 360, 1895 ; **3**. 141, 201, 356, 1896 ; **4**. 106, 278, 1896 ; **6**. 11, 1897 ; S. A. Mitchell, *ib.*, **71**. 1, 1930 ; C. E. St. John, *ib.*, **70**. 160, 1929 ; J. Wilsing, *Sitzber. Akad. Berlin*, 426, 1899 ; H. A. Vogel, *ib.*, 905, 1882 ; H. Ebert, *Astron. Nachr.*, **162**. 193, 1903 ; W. S. Adams, A. H. Joy and N. L. Humason, *Publ. Astron. Soc. Pacific*, **34**. 175, 1922 ; G. F. Paddock, *ib.*, **30**. 244, 1918 ; G. E. Hale, F. Ellermann and J. A. Parkhurst, *Publ. Yerkes Obs.*, **2**. 253, 1903 ; G. E. Hale and W. S. Adams, *Astrophys. Journ.*, **25**. 75, 1907 ; G. E. Hale, *ib.*, **28**. 315, 1908 ; C. E. Moore and H. N. Russell, *ib.*, **68**. 151,

1928; H. N. Russell, *Mount Wilson Contr.*, 383, 1929; *Astrophys. Journ.*, **63**. 1, 1926; **70**. 11, 1929; S. Albrecht, *ib.*, **41**. 333, 1915; **72**. 65, 1930; C. Fabry and H. Buisson, *Compt. Rend.*, **148**. 1240, 1909; H. Deslandres, *ib.*, **141**. 409, 1905; G. Rayet, *ib.*, **67**. 756, 1868; A. Secchi, *ib.*, **70**. 905, 1870; A. de Gramont, *ib.*, **150**. 37, 1910; **172**. 893, 1921; *Séances Soc. Franc. Phys.*, **14**. 5, 1911; C. St. John, *Proc. Nat. Acad.*, **2**. 226, 1916; J. Hartmann, *Astron. Mitt. Göttingen*, 19, 1916; P. W. Merrill, *Astrophys. Journ.*, **56**. 457, 1922; **58**. 195, 1923; **63**. 13, 1926; **69**. 330, 1929; P. W. Merrill and C. G. Burwell, *ib.*, **71**. 285, 1930; E. M. Lindsay, *Nature*, **124**. 94, 1929; H. von Klüber, *Zeit. Physik*, **44**. 481, 1927; *Das Vorkommen der chemischen Elemente im Kosmos*, Leipzig, 1931; C. Young, *The Sun*, London, 1892; C. G. Abbot, *The Sun*, London, 1912; F. J. M. Stratton, *Astronomical Physics*, London, 1925; *Ann. Solar Phys. Obs. Cambridge*, **4**. 1, 1920; C. H. Payne, *Stellar Atmospheres*, Cambridge, 1925; *Proc. Nat. Acad.*, **11**. 192, 1925; C. H. Payne and C. P. Chase, *Circ. Harvard Coll. Obs.*, 300, 1927; E. P. Waterman, *Bull. Lick Obs.*, 243, 1913; J. Stebbins, *ib.*, 41, 1903; C. D. Shane, *ib.*, 10, 1920; W. H. Wright, *ib.*, 14, 1924; E. A. Fath, *ib.*, 149, 1908; *Astrophys. Journ.*, **33**. 58, 1911; **37**. 198, 1913; T. Dunham, *Contr. Princeton Univ. Obs.*, 9, 1929; W. C. Rufus, *Publ. Astron. Obs. Univ. Michigan*, **2**. 103, 1915; J. Storey, *Monthly Not. Astron. Soc.*, **81**. 141, 1920; F. S. Hogg, *Journ. Astron. Soc. Canada*, **23**. 55, 1929; B. Lyot, *Ann. Obs. Paris*, **8**. 1, 1929; F. E. Wright, *Proc. Nat. Acad.* **13**. 535, 1927; S. Mohorovicic, *Archiv. Hem. Farm.*, **1**. 95, 1927; H. M. Vernon, *Chem. News*, **61**. 51, 1890.

²³ A. Daubrée, *Compt. Rend.*, **65**. 6, 1867; *Les météorites*, Paris, 1884; G. Rose, *Sitzber. Akad. Berlin*, 29, 1863; G. F. Zimmer, *Journ. Iron Steel Inst.*, **94**. ii, 306, 1916; A. Brezina, *Verh. Ges. Naturf. Aerzte Nürnberg*, 167, 1893; N. S. Maskelyne, *Phil. Trans.*, **160**. 189, 1870; **161**. 359, 1871; *B.A. Rep.*, 188, 1862; C. von Reichenbach, *Pogg. Ann.*, **107**. 155, 1859; C. U. Shephard, *Amer. Journ. Science*, (2), **43**. 22, 1867; G. Tschermak, *Sitzber. Akad. Wien*, **71**. 661, 1875; **75**. 151, 1877; **88**. 347, 1883; M. E. Wadsworth, *Mem. Mus. Zool. Cambridge*, 11, 1884.

²⁴ D. Urry and W. Koeck, *Zeit. Elektrochem.*, **36**. 727, 1930; A. von Lasaulx, *Zeit. Kryst.*, **5**. 307, 1881; E. Cohen, *Meteoritenkunde*, Stuttgart, 1894–1905; F. Berwerth, *Forts. Min. Kryst. Petrog.*, **1**. 257, 1911; **2**. 227, 1912; **3**. 245, 1913; **5**. 265, 1916; H. Michel, *ib.*, **7**. 245, 1922; E. F. F. Chladni, *Gilbert's Ann.*, **15**. 307, 1803; **50**. 225, 1815; N. S. Maskelyne, *Phil. Trans.*, **160**. 189, 1870; **161**. 359, 1871; *B.A. Rep.*, 188, 1862; G. F. Zimmer, *Journ. Iron Steel Inst.*, **94**. ii, 306, 1916; P. Kropotkin, *Nineteenth Century*, **46**. 934, 1899; P. A. Kesselmayer, *Ueber den Ursprung der Meteorsteine*, Senkenberg, 1860; *Abh. Senkenberg, Nat. Ges.*, 313, 1861; *Pogg. Ann.*, **120**. 506, 1863.

²⁵ O. C. Farrington, *Publ. Columbian Museum*, 120, 1907; 151, 1911; *Amer. Min.*, **5**. 57, 1920; F. W. Clarke, *The Evolution and Disintegration of Matter*, Washington, 1924; *The Data of Geochemistry*, Washington, 40, 1924; F. Berwerth and H. Michel, in C. Doelter, *Handbuch der Mineralchemie*, Leipzig, **3**. ii, 574, 1926; E. Howard, *Phil. Trans.*, **92**. 168, 1802; W. Flight, *ib.*, **173**. 893, 896, 1883; *Proc. Roy. Soc.*, **33**. 343, 1882; T. Graham, *ib.*, **15**. 502, 1866; J. W. Mallet, *ib.*, **20**. 365, 1871; R. J. Strutt, *ib.*, **77**. 480, 1906; M. H. Klaproth, *Sitzber. Akad. Berlin*, 21, 1803; *Beiträge zur chemischen Kenntnis der Mineralkörper*, Berlin, **4**. 99, 1807; F. Paneth, W. D. Urry and W. Koeck, *Nature*, **125**. 490, 1930; F. Stromeyer, *Gött. Gel. Anz.*, 204, 1816; 369, 1833; J. L. Smith, *Amer. Journ. Science*, (2), **49**. 332, 1870; H. D. Campbell and J. L. Howe, *ib.*, (4), **15**. 469, 1903; A. W. Wright, *ib.*, (3), **11**. 257, 1876; (3), **12**. 257, 1876; T. T. Quirke and L. H. Finkelstein, *ib.*, (4), **44**. 237, 1917; C. T. Jackson, *ib.*, (1), **34**. 335, 1838; G. A. Koenig and A. E. Foote, *ib.*, (3), **42**. 413, 1891; A. Laugier, *Liebig's Ann.*, **4**. 363, 1817; J. J. Berzelius, *Pogg. Ann.*, **27**. 128, 1832; S. Tennant, *Phil. Mag.*, **25**. 182, 1806; A. Liversidge, *Proc. Roy. Soc. New South Wales*, **36**. 341, 1902; J. C. H. Mingaye, *Journ. Washington Acad.*, **10**. 314, 1920; J. E. Whitfield and G. P. Merrill, *Mem. Nat. Acad.*, **14**. 7, 1916; W. Ramsay and M. W. Travers, *Proc. Roy. Soc.*, **70**. 445, 1897; W. Ramsay, *Nature*, **52**. 224, 1895; *Compt. Rend.*, **120**. 1049, 1895; H. Moissan, *ib.*, **116**. 288, 1893; A. P. Forjaz, *ib.*, **173**. 1170, 1921; C. Friedel, *ib.*, **115**. 1037, 1892; F. E. Mallard and A. Daubrée, *ib.*, **114**. 812, 1892; J. Lunt, *South African Journ. Science*, **11**. 243, 1915; W. Will and J. Pinnow, *Ber.*, **23**. 345, 1890; M. Erofééff and P. Latschinoff, *Journ. Russ. Phys. Chem. Soc.*, **20**. 185, 1888; W. Crookes, *Phil. Trans.*, **207**. A, 411, 1920; *Chem. News*, **119**. 45, 53, 61, 1919; R. T. Chamberlin, *The Gases in Rocks*, Washington, 1908.

²⁶ P. A. von Holger, *Zeit. Phys. Math.*, (1), **7**. 129, 1830; (1), **8**. 279, 1830; A. Wehrle, *ib.*, (2), **3**. 222, 1835; C. U. Shepard, *Proc. Amer. Assoc.*, **3**. 152, 1850; *Amer. Journ. Science*, (1), **16**. 217, 1829; (1), **36**. 81, 1839; (1), **43**. 354, 1842; (2), **15**. 1, 366, 1853; (2), **17**. 334, 1854; (2), **4**. 76, 1847; (2), **43**. 385, 1867; (2), **47**. 230, 1869; (3), **3**. 438, 1872; (3), **12**. 119, 1876; (3), **19**. 381, 1880; (3), **26**. 338, 1883; (3), **29**. 469, 1885; W. Tassin, *Ann. Rep. Smithsonian Inst.*, 670, 1901; *Proc. Nat. Museum*, **25**. 11, 1902; **27**. 955, 1904; **28**. 213, 1905; **32**. 35, 1907; *Amer. Journ. Science*, (4), **25**. 49, 107, 1908; H. A. Ward, *ib.*, (3), **45**. 153, 1893; (3), **49**. 53, 1895; (4), **5**. 135, 1898; (4), **7**. 233, 1899; (4), **8**. 225, 1899; (4), **9**. 283, 400, 1899; (4), **12**. 453, 1901; (4), **15**. 316, 396, 1902; (4), **17**. 283, 1903; (4), **19**. 240, 1905; (4), **23**. 1, 1907; *The Ward-Coonley Collection of Meteorites*, Chicago, 1900; *Popular Science Monthly*, **61**. 351, 1904; *Proc. Rochester Acad.*, **2**. 171, 1893; **4**. 67, 137, 1902; H. L. Preston, *ib.*, **2**. 151, 1893; *Journ. Geol.*, **10**. 518, 1902; *Amer. Journ. Science*, (3), **44**. 163, 1892; (4), **5**. 62, 269, 1898; (4), **15**. 395, 1902; (4), **9**. 201, 1900; H. A. Newton, *ib.*, (3), **45**. 152, 1893; (4), **3**. 1, 1897; L. G. Eakins, *ib.*, (3), **46**. 283, 1894; A. O. Derby, *ib.*, (3), **49**. 101, 1895; *Arch. Mus. Nac. Rio de Janeiro,*

9. 87, 1897 ; A. Lacroix, *Bull. Soc. Min.*, **28**. 70, 1906 ; *Bull. Soc. l'Ouest de France*, **6**. 81, 1907 ;
A. Brezina, *Proc. Amer. Phil. Soc.*, **43**. 211, 1904 ; *Danske Vid. Selsk. Skrif.*, **4**. 113, 1910 ; *Neues
Jahrb. Min.*, ii, 207, 1910 ; *Misc. Rep. West Australia Geol. Sur.*, 47, 1914 ; *Oesterr. Illust. Ztg.*,
842, 1905 ; *Oesterr. Zeit. Berg. Hütt.*, **38**. 355, 1890 ; *Sitzber. Akad. Wien*, **113**. 577, 1905 ;
A. Brezina and E. Cohen, *ib.*, **113**. 89, 1905 ; *Jahr. Ver. Nat. Würtemberg*, **58**. 292, 1903 ;
C. Klein, *Studien über Meteoriten*, Berlin, 1906 ; D. M. Barringer and B. C. Tilghman, *Proc. Amer.
Acad.*, 1905 ; D. M. Barringer, *ib.*, **57**. 861, 1906 ; W. N. Hartley, *Journ. Chem. Soc.*, **89**. 1566,
1906 ; R. Meli, *Boll. Soc. Geol. Ital.*, **25**. 887, 1906 ; F. Rinne and H. E. Booke, *Neues Jahrb.
Min. Festband*, 227, 1907 ; L. L. Fermor, *Rec. Geol. Sur. India*, **35**. 68, 79, 1907 ; *Journ. Wash-
ington Acad.*, **2**. 230, 1912 ; W. A. Wahl, *Zeit. anorg. Chem.*, **69**. 52, 1911 ; C. R. Keyes, *Australian
Min. Standard*, **44**. 411, 1910 ; W. A. D. Rudge, *Proc. Roy. Soc.*, **90**. A, 19, 1914 ; J. S. Vanick,
Trans. Amer. Soc. Steel Treating, **7**. 171, 1925 ; G. Troost, *Amer. Journ. Science*, (1), **38**. 254,
1840 ; (1), **49**. 342, 1845 ; (2), **5**. 351, 1848 ; W. P. Blake, *ib.*, (3), **31**. 44, 1886 ; W. G. Owens, *ib.*,
(3), **43**. 423, 1892 ; H. W. Nichols, *ib.*, (4), **19**. 242, 1905 ; W. Mariner and L. M. Hoskins, *ib.*,
(4), **5**. 136, 1898 ; (4), **9**. 201, 1900 ; J. L. Smith, *ib.*, (2), **19**. 161, 1855 ; (2), **30**. 240, 1860 ;
(2), **31**. 265, 1861 ; (2), **38**. 385, 1862 ; (2), **42**. 218, 1866 ; (2), **43**. 280, 425, 1867 ; (2), **47**. 271,
385, 1869 ; (2), **49**. 33, 1870 ; (3), **2**. 335, 1871 ; (3), **5**. 108, 1873 ; (3), **7**. 392, 1874 ; (3), **10**.
351, 1875 ; (3), **13**. 213, 1877 ; J. L. Smith and J. B. Mackintosh, *ib.*, (3), **20**. 324, 1880 ;
J. Steinmann, *ib.*, (1), **19**. 384, 1847 ; J. W. Mallet, *ib.*, (3), **2**. 13, 1871 ; (3), **28**. 287, 1884 ;
(3), **33**. 59, 1887 ; (4), **21**. 347, 1905 ; F. P. Venable, *ib.*, (3), **40**. 63, 162, 312, 1890 ; C. H. Rockwell, *ib.*, (1), **46**. 402, 1844 ; H. N. Stokes, *ib.*, (3), **50**. 252, 1895 ; (4), **1**. 252, 1896 ; J. M. Davison,
Journ. Geol., **10**. 518, 1902 ; *Proc. Rochester Acad.*, **1**. 87, 1890 ; *Amer. Journ. Science*, (3), **42**.
64, 1891 ; (3), **49**. 53, 1895 ; (4), **7**. 4, 1899 ; (4), **13**. 467, 1902 ; (4), **17**. 383, 1904 ; (3), **44**.
164, 1892 ; J. B. Mackintosh, *ib.*, (3), **20**. 74, 1880 ; (3), **30**. 238, 1885 ; (3), **31**. 147, 462, 1886 ;
(3), **32**. 306, 1886 ; (3), **33**. 225, 1887 ; N. F. Lupton, *ib.*, (3), **29**. 233, 1886 ; M. L. McItwain,
ib., (3), **36**. 277, 1888 ; G. F. Kunz, *ib.*, (3), **40**. 312, 1891 ; (4), **19**. 396, 1905 ; E. E. Howell,
Proc. Rochester Acad., **1**. 86, 1890 ; *Trans. New York Acad.*, **9**. 197, 1892 ; *Amer. Journ. Science*,
(3), **40**. 223, 1891 ; (3), **44**. 415, 1892 ; (3), **50**. 252, 1895 ; E. E. Howell, W. F. Hillebrand and
G. P. Merrill, *ib.*, (3), **47**. 430, 1893 ; W. M. Foote, *ib.*, (3), **42**. 413, 1892 ; (3), **43**. 64, 1892 ;
(4), **3**. 65, 1897 ; (4), **8**. 153, 415, 1899 ; (4), **34**. 437, 1912 ; (4), **37**. 391, 1914 ; (4), **39**. 80,
1915 ; W. E. Hidden, *ib.*, (4), **9**. 367, 1899 ; K. S. Howard, *ib.*, (4), **21**. 186, 1905 ; (4), **22**. 55,
1906 ; (4), **23**. 379, 1907 ; T. L. Watson, *ib.*, (4), **36**. 165, 1913 ; B. S. Burton, *ib.*, (3), **12**. 439,
1870 ; E. A. Schweinitz, *ib.*, (4), **1**. 208, 1896 ; G. P. Merrill, *ib.*, (4), **2**. 149, 1896 ; (4), **23**.
224, 1906 ; (4), **35**. 509, 1913 ; (5), **3**. 335, 1922 ; (4), **27**. 469, 1908 ; (5), **5**. 63, 175, 1923 ;
Chem. News, **126**. 63, 1923 ; *Eng. Min. Journ.*, **95**. 320, 1913 ; *Proc. Amer. Phil. Soc.*, **65**.
119, 1926 ; *Bull. Amer. Geol. Soc.*, **27**. 50, 1916 ; *Proc. U.S. Nat. Museum*, **24**. 907, 1902 ;
61. 4, 1922 ; (4), **24**. 192, 1901 ; **32**. 241, 1907 ; **33**. 595, 1912 ; **34**. 325, 1913 ; **48**. 503, 1915 ;
Bull. U.S. Nat. Museum, 149, 1930 ; *Smithsonian Miss. Coll.*, **60**. 1, 1912 ; G. P. Merrill and
W. Jassin, *Amer. Journ. Science*, (4), **21**. 356, 1905 ; *Smithsonian Miss. Coll.*, **50**. 203, 1907 ;
Proc. U.S. Nat. Museum, **28**. 213, 1905 ; **31**. 505, 1906 ; G. P. Merrill and H. N. Stokes, *Proc.
Washington Accad.*, **2**. 41, 1901 ; F. W. Taylor, *Proc. Amer. Acad.*, **8**. 3, 1856 ; *Amer. Journ.
Science*, (2), **22**. 374, 1856 ; (2), **24**. 294, 1857 ; (3), **28**. 300, 1884 ; D. Fisher and C. G. Allmen-
dinger, *ib.*, (3), **34**. 383, 1887 ; D. Olmsted, *ib.*, (1), **48**. 388, 1845 ; A. A. Hayes, *ib.*, (1), **48**.
153, 1845 ; C. T. Jackson, *ib.*, (1), **34**. 335, 1838 ; (2), **36**. 261, 1863 ; (2), **47**. 281, 1867 ; (3),
4. 495, 1872 ; B. Silliman and T. S. Hunt, *ib.*, (2), **2**. 372, 1846 ; E. V. Shannon, *ib.*, (5), **3**. 335,
1922 ; W. M. Thornton, *ib.*, (4), **36**. 165, 1913 ; E. Everhart, *ib.*, (5), **3**. 215, 1922 ; F. A. Cairns,
ib., (3), **5**. 21, 1873 ; M. Dickman and J. B. Mackenzie, *ib.*, (4), **29**. 350, 1910 ; J. P. Santos, *ib.*,
(3), **15**. 337, 1878 ; G. F. Kunz and E. Weinschenk, *ib.*, (3), **43**. 65, 424, 1892 ; E. Weinschenk,
Neues Jahrb. Min., ii, 57, 1890 ; *Amer. Journ. Science*, (3), **43**. 425, 1892 ; P. Berthier, *ib.*,
(3), **15**. 20, 1853 ; E. H. S. Bailey, *ib.*, (3), **42**. 386, 1891 ; G. J. Brush, *ib.*, (2), **36**. 153, 1863 ;
N. S. Manross, *ib.*, (2), **15**. 22, 1853 ; W. Haidinger, *ib.*, (3), **32**. 144, 1861 ; C. Palache, *ib.*,
(5), **12**. 136, 1926 ; M. H. Klaproth, *Sitzber. Akad. Berlin*, 21, 1803 ; *Beiträge zur chemischen
Kenntniss der Mineralkörper*, Berlin, **4**. 99, 1807 ; **6**. 306, 1815 ; R. B. Riggs, *Bull. U.S. Geol.
Sur.*, 8, 1887 ; *Amer. Journ. Science*, (3), **30**. 312, 1885 ; O. C. Farrington, *Publ. Columbian
Museum*, 1, 1895 ; 283, 1902 ; 101, 1905 ; 3, 1907 ; 120, 1907 ; 151, 1911 ; *Journ. Geol.*, **5**.
126, 1898 ; *Amer. Journ. Science*, (4), **11**. 60, 1900 ; (4), **14**. 38, 1902 ; (4), **15**. 71, 1903 ; (4),
17. 329, 1904 ; (4), **21**. 86, 1906 ; (4), **22**. 303, 1906 ; (4), **29**. 250, 1910 ; *Popular Science
Monthly*, **58**. 429, 1901 ; *Journ. Amer. Folklore*, 199, 1900 ; *Iron Coal Trades Rev.*, 69. 1269,
1904 ; *Geol. Series Field Columbian Museum*, **3**. 2, 111, 165, 1907 ; **5**. 1, 1914 ; *Meteorites*,
Chicago, 1916 ; *Amer. Min.*, **5**. 57, 1920 ; W. S. Chapman, *Trans. Roy. Soc. Adelaide*, **25**. 1,
1901 ; A. A. Koch, *Bull. Amer. Geol. Soc.*, **14**. 104, 1903 ; J. E. Whitfield, *Proc. U.S. Nat.
Museum*, **43**. 595, 1912 ; **51**. 325, 447, 1916 ; **61**. 1, 1922 ; **62**. 18, 1923 ; *Proc. Rochester Acad.*,
4. 65, 148, 1902 ; *Amer. Journ. Science*, (3), **33**. 500, 1887 ; (3), **34**. 472, 1887 ; (3), **36**. 276,
1888 ; (3), **37**. 391, 440, 1889 ; (4), **3**. 66, 1897 ; (4), **8**. 154, 1899 ; (4), **15**. 469, 1903 ; (4), **39**.
80, 1915 ; (5), **5**. 53, 175, 1923 ; *Mem. Nat. Acad.*, **14**. 4, 1916 ; W. S. Clark, *On Metallic Meteorites*, Göttingen, 42, 1852 ; H. E. Clarke and H. L. Bowman, *Min. Mag.*, **16**. 35, 1911 ;
E. H. Ducloux and F. Pastore, *Rev. Fac. Cienc. Quim.*, **6**. 13, 1930 ; J. N. Lockyer, *Proc. Roy.
Soc.*, **55**. 139, 1894 ; H. F. Ulrich, *ib.*, **53**. 54, 1893 ; G. Hindrichs, *Compt. Rend.*, **118**. 1418,
1893 ; E. Goldsmith, *Journ. Franklin Inst.*, **164**. 369, 1908 ; *Proc. Acad. Philadelphia*, 373,
1893 ; W. H. Hobbs, *Bull. Amer. Geol. Sur.*, **14**. 97, 1903 ; H. P. Gurney, *Trans. Inst. Min.*

Eng., **24**. 274, 1903; E. von Fellenberg, *Centr. Min.*, 152, 1900; O. Vogel, *Stahl Eisen*, **16**. 442, 491, 536, 1896; A. G. Högbom, *Bull. Geol. Inst. Upsala*, **5**. 132, 1902; *Zeit. Kryst.*, **53**. 408, 1914; G. Schweder, *Ann. Géol. Min. Russ.*, **4**. 10, 1902; E. Fraas, *Zeit. Ver. deut. Ing.*, **46**, 129, 1902; R. C. Hills, *Eng. Min. Journ.*, **63**. 382, 1897; *Proc. Colorado Scient. Soc.*, **5**. 2, 1896; **6**. 30, 1897; F. Eberle, *Mining World*, **23**. 279, 1905; D. R. Grantham and F. Oates, *Min. Mag.*, **22**. 487, 1931; K. Buss, *Naturw. Ver. Osnabrück*, **21**. 1, 1929; L. F. Navarro, *Bol. Soc. Espan. Hist. Nat.*, **29**. 19, 1929; *Trans. Soc. Espan. Hist. Nat.*, **15**. 859, 1929; W. F. Petterd, *Rept. Sec. Mines, Tasmania*, 353, 1901; G. A. Goyder, *Trans. Roy. Soc. South Australia*, **25**. 14, 1902; T. Cooksey, *Rec. Australian Museum*, **3**. 51, 1898; R. T. Baker, *Journ. Roy. Soc. New South Wales*, **34**. 81, 1900; E. van den Brock, *Proc. Verb. Soc. Géol. Belg.*, **10**. 63, 1899; G. E. Linck, *Ann. Naturh. Hofmus.*, **13**. 103, 1899; C. Hödlmoser, *Tschermak's Mitt.*, (2), **18**. 513, 1899; J. A. Antipoff, *Bull. Acad. St. Petersburg*, (5), **9**. 91, 1898; E. B. y Casanoves, *Act. Soc. Espancl. Hist.*, **33**, 1899; E. Artini and G. Melzi, *Rend. Ist. Lombardo*, **31**. 983, 1899; *Société d'esplorazione commerciale in Africa*, Milan, 1899; J. M. Davidson, *Proc. Rochester Acad.*, **3**. 201, 1900; F. W. Clarke, *Bull. U.S. Geol. Sur.*, 168, 1901; 228, 1904; F. Smycka, *Zeit. Kryst.*, **34**. 707, 1900; W. Ramsay, *Compt. Rend.*, **120**. 1049, 1895; W. Ramsay and L. H. Borgström, *Bull. Comm. Géol. Finlande*, 12, 1902; L. H. Borgström, *Trans. Astron. Soc. Canada*, 69, 1904; *Bull. Comm. Géol. Finlande*, 14, 1904; 34, 1912; F. Berwerth, *Wiss. Mitt. Bosnia Hersegovina*, **8**. 409, 1902; *Festschr. Naturwiss. Ver. Wien*, 29, 1907; *Ann. Naturh. Hofmus.*, **18**. 6, 1903; *Tschermak's Mitt.*, (2), **25**. 179, 511, 1906; M. Neff and A. Stocky, *Program. Czech. Gymn. Mähr-Ostrau*, 1, 1899; M. A. Goebel, *Bull. Acad. St. Petersburg*, (3), **19**. 544, 1874; A. Patera, *Oester. Blatt. Lit.*, 169, 1847; O. Hildebrand, *Mitt. Nat. Ver. Neuvorpommern Rügen*, **34**. 2, 1902; **35**. 4, 1903; *Jahrb. Ver. Vaterland Württemberg*, **58**. 292, 1902; R. A. A. Johnston, *Bull. Min. Canada Geol. Sur.*, 15, 1915; R. A. A. Johnston and H. V. Ellswerth, *Trans. Roy. Soc. Canada*, (3), **15**. 69, 1921; H. E. Clarke and H. L. Bowman, *Min. Mag.*, **15**. 350, 1910; *Nature*, **79**. 148, 1908; W. F. Denning, *ib.*, **80**. 128, 1909; G. T. Prior, *Min. Mag.*, **15**. 312, 1909; **16**. 274, 1912; **17**. 22, 127, 1914; **18**. 1, 26, 152, 173, 1918; **19**. 163, 1921; **20**. 134, 1923; C. L. Edholm, *ib.*, **17**. 33, 1914; L. Fletcher, *ib.*, **7**. 125, 179, 1887; **8**. 258, 1889; **12**. 167, 1899; **13**. 1, 1901; *ib.*, **15**. 147, 1908; *Nature*, **66**. 577, 1902; **74**. 490, 1906; *Proc. Roy. Soc.*, **55**. 142, 1894; W. H. Milligan, *Nature*, **66**. 577, 1902; F. F. Sharpless, *Amer. Geologist*, **18**. 270, 1896; N. H. Winchell, *ib.*, **14**. 389, 1890; **17**. 173, 234, 1893; **18**. 267, 1894; **20**. 316, 1898; **36**. 250, 1905; *Compt. Rend.*, **122**. 681, 1898; A. Löwe, *Neues Jahrb. Min.*, 199, 1849; E. Geinitz, *ib.*, 609, 1876; M. Boeking, *ib.*, 51, 1856; C. von Bonhorst, *ib.*, 372, 1888; C. Fischer, i, 227, 1889; F. von Sandberger, *ib.*, ii, 173, 1889; M. Halbach, *ib.*, 230, 1907; J. Fahrenhorst, *Ann. South African Mus.*, **2**. 1, 14, 1900; *Ann. Naturh. Hofmus.*, **15**. 43, 76, 353, 371, 380, 1900; O. Koestler, *ib.*, **6**. 144, 1891; E. Manteuffel, *ib.*, **6**. 149, 1891; **7**. 133, 1892; G. S. Stanley, *South African Journ. Science*, **10**. 5, 1914; E. Cohen, *Mitt. Nat. Ver. Neuvorpommern Rügen*, **32**. 1, 1900; **33**. 14, 29, 1901; **35**. 3, 57 1903; **36**. 84, 98, 1903; *Sitzber. Akad. Berlin*, 76, 386, 1035, 1897; 19, 306, 607, 1898; 1122, 1900; *Medd. Grönland*, **15**. 293, 1898; *Ann. South African Museum*, **2**. 9, 21, 1900; *Amer. Journ. Science*, (4), **15**. 254, 1902; *Meteoritenkunde*, Stuttgart, **3**. 217, 1905; *Neues Jahrb. Min.*, i, 254, 1897; 227, 1889; *Ueber das Meteoreisen im Monadal bei Grjotli zwischen Skiaker und Stryn, Norwegen*, Christiania, 1899; *Ann. Naturh. Hofmus.*, **6**. 131, 1891; **7**. 101, 143, 1892; **9**. 97, 1894; **12**. 42, 119, 1897; **13**. 118, 473, 1898; **15**. 74, 351, 1900; E. Cohen and E. Weinschenk, *ib.*, **6**. 142, 158, 1891; E. Cohen and B. von Manteuffel, *ib.*, **7**. 131, 1892; **9**. 104, 1894; E. Cohen and O. Hildebrand, *Mitt. Nat. Ver. Neuvorpommern Rügen*, **33**. 13, 1902; **34**. 87, 1903; E. Cohen and J. Fahrenhorst, *ib.*, **31**. 39, 1900; W. F. Alexejeff, *Proc. Russ. Min. Soc.*, **2**. 30, 470, 1893; *Sitzber. Akad. Berlin*, 76, 1047, 1897; 19, 1898; *Amer. Journ. Science*, (2), **7**. 449, 1849; *Ann. Naturh. Hofmus.*, **12**. 121, 1897; **13**. 47, 118, 131, 147, 479, 1898; **14**. 138, 150, 1898; F. Scherer and O. Sjöström, *Vid. Selsk. Skrift.*, 1, 1900; *Mitt. naturwiss. Ver. Neupommern*, **30**. 1, 1899; **31**. 63, 1900; *Ann. Naturh. Hofmus.*, **12**. 55, 1897; F. Scherer, *ib.*, **9**. 114, 1894; **15**. 387, 1900; O. Sjöstrom and J. Fahrenhorst, *ib.*, **12**. 43, 1897; C. Anderson and J. C. H. Mingaye, *Rec. Australian Museum*, **10**. 49, 1913; J. C. H. Mingaye, *Proc. Roy. Soc. New South Wales*, **27**. 82, 1893; *Journ. Washington Acad.*, **10**. 314, 1920; *Eng. Min. Journ.*, **56**. 501, 1893; *Rep. Australasian Assoc.*, **9**. 162, 1902; *Records Geol. Sur. New South Wales*, **7**. 305, 1904; **9**. 1, 1916; H. P. White, *ib.*, **7**. 312, 1904; G. W. Card, *ib.*, **5**. 49, 1897; **7**. 218, 1903; O. B. Böggild, *Medd. Grönland*, **74**. 9, 1927; C. Friedheim, *Sitzber. Akad. Berlin*, 345, 1889; J. R. Gregory, *Nature*, **47**. 90, 1893; J. Torrey and E. H. Barbour, *ib.*, **42**. 136, 1890; W. Will and J. Pinnow, *ib.*, **41**. 428, 1889; *Ber.*, **23**. 345, 1890; P. G. Melikoff and W. Krschischanowsky, *ib.*, **32**. 11, 1899; *Oesterr. Zeit. Berg. Hütt.*, **45**. 174, 1892; P. G. Melikoff, *Journ. Russ. Phys. Chem. Soc.*, **28**. 114, 299, 307, 1899; P. G. Melikoff and C. Schwalbe, *Ber.*, **25**. 234, 1892; P. Melikoff and P. Pissarjeffsky, *ib.*, **27**. 1293, 1893; S. M. Losanitsch, *ib.*, **25**. 876, 1892; G. de P. Cotter, *Records Geol. Sur. India*, **42**. 265, 1912; E. Prizwoznik, *Berg. Hütt. Jahrb.*, **38**. 399, 1890; *Oesterr. Zeit. Berg. Hütt.*, **40**. 465, 1892; G. Bontschew, *Periodicesko Spisanie*, **71**. 373, 1910; G. Trottarelli, *Gazz. Chim. Ital.*, **20**. 611, 1890; G. D. Kislakowsky, *Bull. Soc. Moscou*, **4**. 187, 1891; O. Nordenskjöld, *Compt. Rend.*, **116**. 677, 1893; *Neues Jahrb. Min.*, i, 138, 1892; B. Doss, *ib.*, i, 71, 1892; R. Prendel, *ib.*, i, 33, 1895; S. W. J. Smith, *Phil. Trans.*, **208**. A, 21, 1908; M. Lugeon, *Geol. Centr.*, 6. 325, 1905; F. Rinne, *ib.*, **3**. 499, 1906; F. Behrend and G. Berg, *Chemische Geologie*, Stuttgart, 1927; F. W. Clarke and H. S. Washington, *Proc. Nat. Acad.*, **8**. 108, 1922; *The Composition of the Earth's Crust*, Washington, 1924; I. and W. Noddack,

Naturwiss., **17**. 757, 1920 ; A. M. Miller, *Eng. Min. Journ.*, **75**. 154, 1903 ; *Science*, (2), **18**. 243, 1904 ; H. Laspeyres and E. Kaiser, *Zeit. Kryst.*, **24**. 458, 493, 495, 1895 ; F. Paneth, *Zeit. Elektrochem.*, **36**. 727, 1930 ; A. Castello, *Iron Age*, **55**. 1167, 1895 ; A. F. Renard, *Bull. Acad. Belg.*, (3), **31**. 654, 1896 ; S. B. Mirat, *Bull. Soc. Chim.*, (3), **15**. 1070, 1897 ; J. F. Spencer, *Min. Mag.*, **22**. 271, 1930 ; C. Palache and F. A. Gonyer, *Amer. Min.*, **15**. 388, 1930 ; F. Paneth and W. D. Urry, *Zeit. phys. Chem.*, **152**. 127, 1931 ; C. B. Hasselberg, *Oefvers. Vet. Akad. Stockholm*, **56**. 131, 1901 ; H. Jimeno, *Bol. Soc. Espian. Hist. Nat.*, 215, 1901 ; W. C. Jenkins and E. L. Rhead, *Monthly Notices Astron. Soc.*, **75**. 92, 1914 ; O. Buchner, *Die Feuermeteore insbesondere der Meteoriten, historisch und naturwissenschaftlich betrachtet*, Giessen, 144, 1859 ; *Die Meteoriten in Sammlungen, ihre Geschichte, mineralogische und chemische Beschaffenheit*, Leipzig, 1863 ; T. L. Phipson, *Meteors, Aerolites, and Falling Stars*, London, 94, 1867 ; A. Liversidge, *Proc. Roy. Soc. New South Wales*, **16**. 31, 1882 ; **36**. 34, 241, 341, 1902 ; **37**. 240, 1903 ; *Chem. News*, **88**. 233, 1903 ; *Amer. Journ. Science*, (4), **14**. 466, 1902 ; H. D. Campbell and J. L. Howe, *ib.*, (4), **15**. 469, 1902 ; L. C. Glenn, *ib.*, (4), **17**. 215, 1903 ; J. J. Berzelius, *Pogg. Ann.*, **27**. 118. 1833 ; **32**. 135, 1834 ; A. Duflos and N. W. Fischer, *ib.*, **72**. 475, 1847 ; H. Wichelhaus, *ib.*, **118**. 631, 1863 ; C. Bergmann, *ib.*, **100**. 246, 1857 ; C. von Reichenbach, *ib.*, **94**. 250, 1861 ; E. Uricoecher, *ib.*, **41**. 252, 1854 ; *Journ. prakt. Chem.*, (1), **63**. 317, 1854 ; M. Böcking, *Pogg. Ann.*, **46**. 243, 1855 ; W. P. Riddell, *Trans. Acad. St. Louis*, **1**. 623, 1860 ; H. A. Prout, *ib.*, **1**. 711, 1860 ; J. P. Calogeras, *Rev. Scient.*, **50**. 591, 1893 ; I. Domeyko, *Elementos de mineralojia*, Santiago, 1879 ; *Compt. Rend.*, **81**. 597, 1875 ; H. Moissan, *ib.*, **116**. 1269, 1893 ; **121**. 483, 1895 ; **139**. 776, 1904 ; **140**. 227, 405, 1905 ; *Ann. Chim. Phys.*, (8), **5**. 174, 1905 ; *Chem. News*, **90**. 295, 1904 ; S. Meunier, *Bull. Soc. Inst. Nat. d'Autun*, **6**. 17, 1893 ; *Amer. Journ. Science*, (4), **10**. 250, 1900 ; *La Nature*, **30**. 19, 1902 ; *Compt. Rend.*, **104**. 872, 1887 ; **109**. 875, 976, 1889 : **116**. 257, 1151, 1893 ; **117**. 257, 1893 ; **128**. 1130, 1899 ; **130**. 566, 1900 ; **131**. 869, 1900 ; **132**. 441, 501, 1901 ; **134**. 755, 1902 ; **153**. 785, 1911 ; **154**. 1739, 1912 ; G. Stefanesco, *ib.*, **112**. 450, 1891 ; C. Friedel, *ib.*, **115**. 1037, 1892 ; **116**. 224, 1893 ; J. Gouyat, *ib.*, **155**. 916, 1912 ; A. Damour, *ib.*, **66**. 569, 1868 ; J. B. J. D. Boussingault, *ib.*, **74**. 1287, 1872 ; M. de Rivero and J. B. J. D. Boussingault, *Ann. Chim. Phys.*, (2), **25**. 442, 1924 ; A. Duflos, *ib.*, (2), **84**. 61, 1848 ; J. C. Booth, H. Garret and M. Blair, *Journ. Amer. Mus.* **9**. 242, 1909 ; *Proc. Amer. Acad.*, **27**. 875, 1905 ; N. Zenzen, *Geol. För. Förh. Stockholm*, **52**. 366, 1930 ; A. Leonhardt, *Zeit. Kryst.*, **66**. 449, 1928 ; F. A. Genth, *Proc. Amer. Acad.*, **14**. 366, 1886 ; *Amer. Journ. Science*, (2), **17**. 239, 1854 ; (2), **20**. 119, 1855 ; (3), **12**. 42, 1876 ; (3), **13**. 214, 1877 ; *Neues Jahrb. Min.*, ii, 42, 1889 ; R. E. Peary, *Northward over the Great Ice*, London, **2**. 553, 1898 ; 600, 1898 ; J. E. Stead, *Journ. Iron Steel Inst.*, **91**. i, 140, 1915 ; H. B. Nason, *Journ. prakt. Chem.*, (1), **71**. 123, 1857 ; H. Müller, *ib.*, (1), **79**. 25, 1860 ; C. A. Joy, *Liebig's Ann.*, **86**. 39, 1853 ; W. Eberhard, *ib.*, **46**. 286, 1855 ; E. Pugh, *ib.*, **48**. 383, 1856 ; C. Martius, *ib.*, **115**. 92, 1860 ; W. P. Headden, *Proc. Colorado Scient. Soc.*, **9**. 79, 1908 ; S. W. Cramer, *Trans. New Jersey Acad.*, **9**. 197, 1890 ; L. G. Eakins, *Proc. Colorado Scient. Soc.*, **2**. 15, 1886 ; *Amer. Journ. Science*, (3), **39**. 59, 395, 1890 ; (3), **40**. 226, 1890 ; (3), **43**. 424, 1892 ; (3), **44**. 416, 1892 ; (3), **46**. 283, 1893 ; E. Dittler, *Tschermak's Mitt.*, (2), **34**. 272, 1917 ; J. von Siemaschko, *ib.*, (2), **9**. 87, 1891 ; J. F. John, *Journ. Chem. Phys.*, **32**. 253, 1821 ; L. Häpke, *Abh. Nat. Ver. Bremen*, **8**. 517, 1884 ; J. S. Agraz, *Bol. Soc. Geol. Mexicana*, 9, 1909 ; H. W. Nichols, *Publ. Geol. Field Museum*, **1**. 308, 1902 ; **3**. 4, 175, 1910 ; J. Auerbach, *Neues Jahrb. Min.*, 362, 1863 ; *Sitzber. Akad. Wien*, **49**. 497, 1864 ; E. Ludwig, *Denks. Akad. Wien*, **31**. 194, 1871 ; C. F. Rammelsberg, *Pogg. Ann.*, **74**. 443, 1848 ; **84**. 153, 1851 ; *Sitzber. Akad. Berlin*, 440, 1870 ; 37, 1873 ; C. Klein, *ib.*, **114**. 987, 1904 ; R. Knauer, *ib.*, 607, 1899 ; A. Lindner, *ib.*, 35, 151, 1904 ; W. O. Huntington, *Proc. Amer. Acad.*, **17**. 229, 1890 ; **18**. 1, 204, 1891 ; **23**. 251, 1896 ; H. Baumhauer and F. Seelheim, *Arch. Néerl.*, (1), **2**. 376, 1867 ; M. van der Boom Mesch, *ib.*, (1), **1**. 468, 1866 ; L. E. Rivot, *Ann. Mines*, (5), **6**. 554, 1854 ; F. Guild, *Mineralogy of Arizona*, Easton, Pa., 22, 1910 ; E. O. Hovey, *Ann. New York Acad.*, **22**. 335, 1912 ; A. R. Ledoux, *ib.*, **8**. 186, 1891 ; R. Mazelius, *Bull. Upsala Geol. Inst.*, **9**. 229, 1910 ; G. E. Lichtenberger, *Sitzber. Iris Dresden*, 4, 1873 ; A. Kolb, *Jahresb. Naturh. Ges. Nürnberg*, 1, 1920 ; E. S. Simpson, *Bull. West Australian Geol. Sur.*, 26, 1907 ; 48, 1912 ; 59, 1914 ; *Misc. Rep. West Australia Geol. Sur.*, 47, 1914 ; E. S. Simpson and H. Bowley, *ib.*, 47, 1919 ; F. Wöhler and W. Wicke, *Gött. Nachr.*, 364, 1863 ; F. Wohler, *ib.*, **82**. 243, 1852 ; M. Chikashige and T. Hiki, *Mem. Coll. Science Kyoto*, **5**. 1, 1912 ; *Zeit. anorg. Chem.*, **77**. 197, 1912 ; S. R. Brinkley, *Mem. Nat. Acad.*, **19**. 5, 1922 ; N. Sokolowsky, *Arch. Kunde Russ.*, **1**. 317, 1841 ; M. Uwanow, *ib.*, **1**. 723, 1841 ; J. Laspeyres, *Zeit. Kryst.*, **17**. 586, 1897 ; **24**. 494, 1895 ; C. L. Vlaanderen, *Natuurk. Tids. Nederl. Ind.*, **29**. 298, 1867 ; E. H. Ducloux, *Rev. Mus. de la Plata*, (2), **15**. 84, 1908 ; W. S. Chapman, *Ann. Rep. South Australian School Min.*, 227, 1900 ; W. Flight, *Phil. Trans.*, **173**. 894, 1883 ; *Proc. Roy. Soc.*, **33**. 343, 1882 ; W. N. Hartley and H. Ramage, *A Spectroscopic Analysis of Iron Meteorites*, Dublin, 1898 ; *Scient. Proc. Roy. Dublin Soc.*, **8**. 703, 1898 ; H. A. Miers, *Science Prog.*, **7**. 349, 1898 ; *Industries Iron*, **23**. 337, 1897 ; W. H. Brewer, *Proc. Amer. Assoc. Science*, **4**. 36, 1851 ; T. Wada, *Minerals of Japan*, Tokyo, **2**. 30, 1906 ; K. Jimbo, *ib.*, **2**. 30, 1906 ; T. Wakimiza, *Beiträge Min. Japan*, 145, 1912.

[27] W. Flight, *Phil. Trans.*, **173**. 893, 896, 1882 ; J. Dewar and G. Ansdell, *Proc. Roy. Inst.*, **11**. 332, 541, 1886 ; A. W. Wright, *Amer. Journ. Science*, (3), **9**. 294, 459, 1875 ; (3), **11**. 253, 1876 ; (3), **12**. 165, 1876 ; (3), **21**. 209, 1886 ; T. Graham, *Proc. Roy. Soc.*, **15**. 502, 1867 ; J. W. Mallet, *ib.*, **20**. 365, 1872 ; R. T. Chamberlin, *The Gases in Rocks*, Washington, 1908 ; O. C. Farrington, *Publ. Columbian Museum*, i, 1895 ; 283, 1902 ; 101, 1905 ; 3, 1907 ; 120, 1907 ;

151, 1911; *Journ. Geol.*, **5.** 126, 1898; *Amer. Journ. Science*, (4), **11.** 60, 1900; (4), **14.** 38, 1902; (4), **15.** 71, 1903; (4), **17.** 329, 1904; (4), **21.** 86, 1906; (4), **22.** 303, 1906; (4), **29.** 250, 1910; *Popular Science Monthly*, **58.** 429, 1901; *Journ. Amer. Folklore*, 199, 1900; *Iron Coal Trades Rev.*, **69.** 1269, 1904; *Geol. Series Field Columbian Museum*, **3.** 2, 111, 165, 1907; **5.** 1, 1914; *Meteorites*, Chicago, 1916; *Amer. Min.*, **5.** 57, 1920; F. Paneth, *Zeit. Elektrochem.*, **36.** 727, 1930; F. Paneth and W. D. Urry, *Zeit. phys. Chem.*, **152.** 127, 1931.
    [28] P. N. Laschtschenko and W. J. Iwanis, *Nachr. Don. Polytech.*, **4.** 27, 1915; P. N. Tschirwinsky, *Zeit. Kryst.*, **57.** 643, 1923; C. Benedicks, *Internat. Zeit. Metallog.*, **9.** 105, 1917; H. H. Nininger, *Trans. Kansas Acad. Science*, **32.** 63, 1929; F. Paneth, W. D. Urry, and W. Koeck, *Nature*, **125.** 490, 1930; F. Paneth and W. D. Urry, *Zeit. phys. Chem.*, **152.** 127, 1931.
    [29] N. F. Belaiew, *Ann. Russ. Tech. Soc.*, **1.** 1, 1909; C. Benedicks, *Rev. Mét.*, **8.** 85, 1911; *Nova Acta Upsala*, (4), **2.** 10, 1910; F. Berwerth, *Sitzber. Akad. Wien*, **114.** 345, 1905; *Journ. Iron Steel Inst.*, **75.** iii, 37, 1907; H. Moissan, *Le four électrique*, Paris, 1897; *Compt. Rend.*, **140.** 185, 1905; W. Guertler, *Zeit. phys. Chem.*, **74.** 428, 1910; W. Fränkel and G. Tammann, *Zeit. anorg. Chem.*, **60.** 416, 1908; F. Rinne, *Neues Jahrb. Min.*, i, 122, 1905; F. Rinne and H. E. Boecke, *Neues Jahrb. Min. Festband*, 227, 1907; F. Osmond and G. Cartaud, *Rev. Mét.*, **1.** 69, 1904.
    [30] E. C. Eckel, *Iron Ores : Their Occurrence, Valuation, and Control*, New York, 31, 1914; *Eng. Min. Journ.*, **96.** 1, 1913; *Iron Trade Rev.*, **43.** 228, 1908; F. F. Osborne, *Econ. Geol.*, **23.** 724, 1926; F. W. Clarke, *The Data of Geochemistry*, Washington, 1924; A. Bencke, *Oesterr. Berg. Hütt. Zeit.*, **62.** 297, 1914; P. Krusch, *Zeit. prakt. Geol.*, **18.** 165, 1910; **21.** 506, 1913; J. H. L. Vogt, *Chem. Ztg.*, **18.** 642, 1894; *Om dannelse af zernmalmfore-komster*, Christiania, 1892; *Zeit. prakt. Geol.*, **8.** 233, 370, 1900; **9.** 9, 180, 289, 327, 370, 1901; **14.** 217, 1906; **15.** 86, 1907; H. Stremme, *ib.*, **18.** 18, 1910; S. F. Emmons, *Ann. Rep. Smithsonian Inst.*, 309, 1905; *Zeit. prakt. Geol.*, **18.** 5, 1910; *Bull. Amer. Geol. Soc.*, **15.** 1, 1904; *Trans. Amer. Inst. Min. Eng.*, **30.** 177, 1901; *Mining Scient. Press.*, **100.** 739, 1910; W. H. Emmons, *Bull. U.S. Geol. Sur.*, 529, 1913; P. P. Pyatnitzkil, *Trans. Inst. Econ. Min. Geol.*, **9.** 1924; E. Posnjak and H. E. Merwin, *Amer. Journ. Science*, (4), **47.** 311, 1919; O. A. Derby, *ib.*, (4), **25.** 213, 1908; R. B. Sosman and J. C. Hostetter, *Trans. Amer. Inst. Min. Eng.*, **58.** 409, 433, 1917; H. M. Chance, *Canada Mining Journ.*, **29.** 402, 1908; *Trans. Amer. Inst. Min. Eng.*, **86.** 408, 1908; H. P. Gillette, *ib.*, **34.** 710, 1903; P. Frazer, *ib.*, **35.** 298, 308, 1904; *Eng. Min. Journ.*, **86.** 408, 1908; E. Newton, *Bull. Exp. Station Minnesota School Mines*, **5.** 1918; J. W. Gruner, *Econ. Geol.*, **17.** 407, 1922; **25.** 697, 1930; T. S. Lovering, *ib.*, **18.** 523, 1923; A. Lacroix, *Minéralogie de la France et de ses colonies*, Paris, 1. 401, 1893; A. C. Lane, *Journ. Canada Min. Inst.*, **9.** 210, 1907; *Mining World*, **31.** 413, 1909; *Eng. Min. Journ.*, **63.** 542, 1897; C. Schmidt, *Zeit. Kryst.*, **11.** 601, 1886; J. F. Kemp, *Mineral Ind.*, **11.** 632, 1903; **15.** 781, 1906; *Ore Deposits of the United States and Canada*, New York, 1900; *Canada Min. Journ.*, **34.** 543, 1913; *Mineral Ind.*, **11.** 632, 1903; *Ann. New York Acad.*, **17.** 632, 1907; *Science*, (2), **23.** 14, 1906; *Econ. Geol.*, **2.** 1, 1907; E. R. Zalinsky, *Neues Jahrb. Min. B.B.*, **19.** 40, 1904; G. A. Waller, *Rep. Australasian Assoc.*, 205, 1903; C. C. Swanson, *Summary Rep. Canada Dept. Mines*, 106, 1924; R. van Audel, *Rev. Gén. Sciences*, **36.** 671, 1925; **38.** 14, 1927; A. Sachs, *Centr. Min.*, 40, 1904; J. P. Kimball, *Amer. Geol.*, **8.** 352, 1891; *Amer. Journ. Science*, (3), **42.** 231, 1891; A. Irving, *Proc. Geol. Assoc.*, **12.** 227, 1891; *Yale Science Monthly*, 1, 1906; R. A. F. Penrose, *Eng. Min. Journ.*, **59.** 341, 1894; *Journ. Geol.*, **2.** 288, 1894; F. D. Power, *Trans. Australasian Inst. Min. Eng.*, **4.** 1, 1897; H. Höfer, *Oesterr. Zeit. Berg. Hütt.*, **47.** 157, 1899; R. Beck, *Lehre von den Erzlagerstätten*, Berlin, 1901; W. H. Weed, *Bull. Amer. Geol. Soc.*, **11.** 179, 1902; F. Gillman, *Trans. Inst. Min. Met.*, **20.** 447, 1911; J. M. Maclaren, *Mining Journ.*, **72.** 752, 1902; J. W. Gregory, *ib.*, **79.** 583, 617, 1905; *Chem. News*, **94.** 141, 154, 1906; E. B. Wilson, *Mines Minerals*, **24.** 527, 1904; J. Park, *Eng. Min. Journ.*, **79.** 799, 896, 1905; A. Lakes, *ib.*, **79.** 1226, 1905; R. W. Raymond, *ib.*, **80.** 961, 1905; F. J. Fohs, *ib.*, **81.** 553, 1905; V. H. Winchell, *ib.*, **84.** 1067, 1907; *Amer. Geol.*, **10.** 277, 1892; V. Acker, *Bany. Koh. Lapola*, **38.** 201, 1905; C. H. Smyth, *Journ. Geol.*, **13.** 319, 1905; O. Stutzer, *Zeit. Berg. Hütt. Sal.*, **54.** 301, 1905; A. Schierl, *Einteilung der Erzlagerstätten*, Mährisch-Ostrau, 1905; H. Potonié, *Der Erzbergbau*, **2.** 448, 1906; M. Rottand, *ib.*, **3.** 96, 117, 1907; L. Cayeux, *Génie Civil*, **48.** 366, 1905; *Compt. Rend.*, **142.** 716, 895, 1906; L. Demaret, *Ann. Mines Belg.*, **11.** 541, 1906; B. Baumgärtel, *Oberharzer Gangbilder*, Leipzig, 1907; G. Schreckenthal, *Chem. Erde*, **6.** 51, 1930; J. E. Spurr, *Rass. Min.*, **29.** 1, 21, 1908; *Econ. Geol.*, **2.** 781, 1907; *Trans. Amer. Inst. Min. Eng.*, **33.** 288, 1903; J. E. Stead, *Proc. Cleveland Inst. Eng.*, 75, 1910; A. Sachs, *Centr. Min.*, 40, 1904; W. L. Uglow, *Econ. Geol.*, **21.** 352, 1926; T. Read, *ib.*, **1.** 101, 1905; T. M. Broderick, *ib.*, **14.** 353, 1919; F. Behrend, *Zeit. prakt. Geol.*, **32.** 81, 102, 1924; F. Rose, *ib.*, **16.** 497, 1908; J. Bellinger, *ib.*, **11.** 237, 1903; K. Hummel, *Glückauf*, **60.** 765, 1924; *Metall Erz*, **18.** 577, 1921; E. C. Harder, *Prof. Paper U.S. Bur. Mines*, 113, 1919; W. H. Goodchild, *Trans. Inst. Min. Met.*, **28.** 274, 1919; *Mining Mag.*, **18.** 20, 75, 131, 1918; **19.** 135, 188, 1918; J. D. Kendall, *Trans. Canada Min. Inst.*, **21.** 293, 1918; W. B. Phillips, *Iron Age*, **81.** 1788, 1856, 2008, 1907; J. T. Singewald, *Zeit. prakt. Geol.*, **21.** 279, 1913; *Mining Scient. Press*, **114.** 733, 1917; *Zeit. prakt. Geol.*, **21.** 279, 1913; *Eng. Min. Journ.*, **92.** 22, 1911; V. Novaresse, *Russ. Min.*, **20.** 113, 1904; J. M. Campbell, *Mining Mag.*, **17.** 67, 120, 1917; C. L. Dake, *Trans. Amer. Min. Eng.*, **53.** 106, 116, 1915; R. C. Allen, *ib.*, **63.** 188, 1919; W. P. Jenny, *ib.*, **33.** 445, 1903; K. von Mücke, *Glückauf*, **50.** 1397, 1914; E. Schulz, *ib.*, **50.** 207, 1914; H. Wölbling, *ib.*, **45.** 1, 1909; **46.** 1437, 1910; **47.** 1437, 1911; G. Köhler, *ib.*, **44.** 729, 1908; R. C. Wells, *Bull. U.S. Geol. Sur.*, 609, 1915; F. H. Hatch, *Trans. Inst. Min. Met.*, **23.** 41, 232, 1914; C. R. Keyes, *Trans. Amer. Inst. Min. Eng.*, *ib.*, **30.** 323, 1901;

42. 917, 1910; L. de Launay, *Bull. Soc. Ind. Min.*, (5), **9**. 220, 1913; *Compt. Rend. Soc. Ind. Min.*, 220, 1913; *Ann. Mines*, (9), **12**. 119, 1897; (10), **19**. 461, 1911; *Compt. Rend.*, **135**. 406, 1903; **138**. 225, 1904; *Rev. Gén. Sciences*, **15**. 386, 1904; R. van Aubel, *ib.*, **36**. 671, 1925; **38**. 14, 1927; G. E. Collins, *Proc. Colorado Scient. Soc.*, **10**. 211, 1913; *Canada Mining Journ.*, **34**. 480, 1913; C. A. Stewart, *Eng. Min. Journ.*, **90**. 513, 1910; T. A. Rickard, *ib.*, **75**. 402, 661, 776, 845, 1903; W. Dieckmann, *Zeit. prakt. Geol.*, **20**. 385, 1912; E. Harbort, *Neues Jahrb. Min.*, i, 179, 1903; *Zeit. prakt. Geol.*, **19**. 219, 1911; **20**. 385, 1912; F. Klockmann, *ib.*, **12**. 73, 1904; F. Peters, *Rev. Min.*, **63**. 472, 481, 509, 1912; F. L. Ransome, *Econ. Geol.*, **6**. 325, 1911; *Mining Eng. World*, **35**. 286, 1911; W. H. Herdsman, *Journ. Iron Steel Inst.*, **83**. i, 476, 1911; *Journ. West Scotland Iron Steel Inst.*, **18**. 18, 41, 1911; W. Lindgren, *Trans. Amer. Inst. Min. Eng.*, **30**. 578, 1902; *Mining World*, **31**. 1111, 1909; *Econ. Geol.*, **1**. 47, 1905; **2**. 745, 1908; H. Johansson, *Geol. För. Förh. Stockholm*, **26**. 143, 1907; **29**. 258, 1908; C. Hart, *Mining Met.*, **10**. 468, 1929; G. Tschermak, *Ver. Verbreit. Naturwiss. Kenntnisse*, **4**. 177, 1864; C. K. Leith, *Econ. Geol.*, **7**. 662, 1912; **26**. 274, 1931; *Trans. Canada Min. Inst.*, **15**. 532, 1912; A. Schmidt, *Sammlung Berg. Hütt. Abh.*, 25, 1908; R. Klemm, *Centr. Min.*, 90, 1928; W. R. G. Atkins, *Proc. Roy. Dublin Soc.*, **19**. 455, 1930; G. E. Allan and J. Brown, *Proc. Edin. Roy. Soc.*, **33**. 69, 1912; F. L. Nason, *Trans. Amer. Inst. Min. Eng.*, **24**. 121, 1893; **43**. 291, 1913; *Eng. Min. Journ.*, **51**. 693, 1891; G. F. Becker, *ib.*, **78**. 743, 1904; F. L. Garrison, *ib.*, **78**. 258, 470, 1904; G. Bleicher, *Compt. Rend.*, **114**. 590, 1892; E. M. Mumford, *Journ. Chem. Soc.*, **103**. 645, 1913; F. Posepny, *Trans. Amer. Inst. Min. Eng.*, **23**. 197, 1893; M. Boehmer, *ib.*, **34**. 449, 1904; W. M. Bouron, *ib.*, **36**. 587, 1905; C. R. van Hise, *ib.*, **30**. 27, 1900; *Monog. U.S. Geol. Sur.*, 47, 1904; G. Gürich, *Zeit. prakt. Geol.*, **8**. 173, 1899; L. Loewe, *ib.*, **9**. 341, 1900; E. Bodifée, *ib.*, **15**. 309, 1907; R. Delkeskamp, *ib.*, **12**. 289, 1903; O. Erschan, *ib.*, **15**. 56, 1907; *Finske Vet. Oefvers.*, 1, 1906; J. M. van Bemmelen, *Zeit. anorg. Chem.*, **32**. 315, 1899; *Arch. Néerl.*, (2), **4**. 19, 1901; A. Strahan, W. Gibson, T. C. Cantrell, R. L. Sherlock and H. Dewey, *Special Rep. Mem. Geol. Sur.*, 13, 1920; B. H. Brough, *Journ. Soc. Arts*, **48**. 673, 1900; C. Riemann, *Stahl Eisen*, **22**. 278, 1902; L. Blum, *ib.*, **21**. 1285, 1901; **31**. 922, 1911; *Rev. Univ. Mines*, **57**. 241, 1901; H. Sjögren, *Wermländska Ann.*, 1, 1905; L. Rollier, *Viertelj. Nat. Ges. Zürich*, 150, 1905; E. K. Soper, *Eng. Min. Journ.*, **92**. 897, 947, 1911; P. B. McDonald, *ib.*, **96**. 208, 1913; G. W. Miller, *Min. Eng. World*, **36**. 515, 1911; T. E. Savage and C. S. Ross, *Amer. Journ. Science*, (4), **41**. 187, 1916; C. W. Drysdale, *Mem. Canada Geol. Sur.*, 77, 1915; G. Berg, *Metallwirtschaft*, **9**. 1, 1930; H. Harrassowitz, *Zeit. angew. Chem.*, **43**. 185, 1930.

³¹ J. D. Kendall, *The Iron Ores of Great Britain and Ireland*, London, 1893; E. C. Eckel, *Iron Ores—their Occurrence, Valuation, and Control*, New York, 1914; A. E. Törnebohm, *Glückauf*, **41**. 1542, 1905; H. E. Boker, *ib.*, **47**. 420, 457, 491, 1911; F. Beyschlag, P. Krusch and J. H. L. Vogt, *Die Lagerstätten der nutzbaren Mineralien und Gesteine*, Stuttgart, 1913; F. Beyschlag, *Ber. prakt. Geol. Internat. Kongress Bergbau Düsseldorf*, 13, 1910; *Zeit. prakt. Geol.*, **18**. 209, 1910; A. Lindemann, *ib.*, **18**. 217, 1910; J. F. Kemp, *School Mines Quart.*, **20**. 323, 1899; *Zeit. prakt. Geol.*, **18**. 220, 1910; L. de Launay, *ib.*, **18**. 224, 1910; *Gîtes minéraux et métallifères*, Paris, 1913; H. H. Campbell, *Iron Age*, **99**. 51, 1917; P. Krusch, *Zeit. Berg. Hütt. Sal.*, **62**. 176, 1914; W. Lindgren, *Mineral Deposits*, New York, 1913; Anon., *Imperial Mineral Resources Bureau*, London, 1922; E. C. Harder and F. T. Eddingfield, *Eng. Min. Journ.*, **109**. 1060, 1920; H. Harrassowitz, *Zeit. angew. Chem.*, **43**. 185, 1930; G. Berg, *Metallwirtschaft*, **9**. 1, 1930; C. K. Leith, *Iron Ore Reserves*, Washington, 1907; L. Demaret, *Bull. Assoc. Ing. Liége*, **23**. 63, 1899; A. S. Cushman, *Journ. Franklin Inst.*, **171**. 345, 1911; A. Selwyn-Brown, *Eng. Mag.*, **42**. 41, 213, 1911.

³² J. D. Kendall, *The Iron Ores of Great Britain and Ireland*, London, 1893; *Colliery Guardian*, **28**. 1, 1874; **32**. 657, 1876; *Trans. Manchester Geol. Soc.*, **13**. 231, 1876; **17**. 292, 1884; **35**. 105, 1886; *Journ. Geol. Soc.*, **32**. 180, 1876; *Trans. Fed. Inst. Min. Eng.*, **7**. 650, 1893; *Trans. North England Inst. Min. Mech. Eng.*, **28**. 109, 1879; **30**. 27, 1881; **35**. 145, 1886; C. Parkin, *ib.*, **27**. 131, 1878; I. L. Bell, *ib.*, **14**. 109, 1864; T. F. Brown, *ib.*, **23**. 197, 1874; J. Marley, *ib.*, **5**. 165, 1857; **13**. 17, 1864; **19**. 193, 1870; J. Bewick, *Geological Treatise of the district of Cleveland in North Yorkshire, its Ferruginous Deposits, Lias, and Oolites, with some Observations on Ironstone Mining*, London, 1861; *Trans. North England Inst. Min. Mech. Eng.*, **6**. 15, 1858; N. Wood, *ib.*, **7**. 85, 1859; J. Daglish and R. Howse, *ib.*, **24**. 23, 1875; E. W. Binney, *Proc. Manchester Lit. Phil. Soc.*, **8**. 423, 1848; **7**. 55, 1868; W. Brockbank, *ib.*, **8**. 51, 1869; E. A. Walford, *Journ. Roy. Soc. Arts*, **65**. 654, 1927; *Iron Coal Trades Rev.*, **95**. 386, 1917; G. C. Bond, *ib.*, **108**. 426, 1924; W. McDonald, *ib.*, **110**. 434, 1925; Anon., *ib.*, **101**. 204, 1920; **108**. 265, 1924; G. A. Moon, *Geological Notes on Iron Ores*, Whitehaven, 1868; H. B. Woodward, *B.A. Rep.*, 760, 1893; J. Phillips and R. Barker, *ib.*, 106, 1858; J. Phillips, *Journ. Geol. Soc.*, **14**. 84, 1858; R. Tate and J. S. Holden, *Phil. Mag.*, (4), **40**. 73, 1870; *Journ. Iron Steel Inst.*, **2**. i, 460, 1871; *Journ. Geol. Soc.*, **26**. 151, 1870; S. Sharp, *ib.*, **26**. 354, 1870; **29**. 225, 1873; J. W. Judd, *Geology of Rutland*, London, 1875; *Journ. Geol. Soc.*, **26**. 326, 1870; J. S. Gardner, *ib.*, **35**. 214, 1879; J. E. Cross, *ib.*, **31**. 115, 1875; J. F. Blake and W. H. Huddleston, *ib.*, **33**. 260, 1877; W. H. Huddleston, *Proc. Geol. Assoc.*, **4**. 123, 1874; **11**. 108, 1889; J. C. Greenwell, *Trans. Manchester Geol. Soc.*, **5**. 248, 1866; S. H. Blackwell, *The Iron Making Resources of the United Kingdom*, London, 1853; S. Haughton, *On the Iron Ores of Carnarvonshire*, Dublin, 1854; E. Hull, *Iron Coal Trades Rev.*, **40**. 35, 1890; *Geology of the Country around Woodstock*, London, 1859; C. S. Parnell, *The Echo*, Dec. 18, 1890; W. H. Mills, *Trans. Fed. Inst. Min. Eng.*, **2**. 28, 1891; J. L. Shaw, *Proc. Inst. Mech. Eng.*, **363**,

1880; *Journ. Iron Steel Inst.*, **64**. ii. 197, 1903; *Trans. Fed. Inst. Min. Eng.*, **3**. 580, 1892; J. M. Main, *ib.*, **8**. 31, 1895; J. Prentice, *ib.*, **12**. 435, 447, 1896; C. E. Hawkins, *ib.*, **13**. 605, 1898; Anon., *Proc. Geol. Assoc.*, **12**. 172, 1891; A. McHenry, *ib.*, **14**. 129, 1895; J. Smith, *Industries Iron*, **16**. 22, 1894; *Proc. Glasgow Geol. Soc.*, **10**. 133, 1894; G. Kinahan, *Trans. Manchester Geol. Soc.*, **22**. 458, 1893; C. H. Williams, *ib.*, **22**. 518, 1893; W. Peile, *ib.*, **22**. 522, 1893; B. Dawkins, *ib.*, **22**. 501, 1893; G. C. Greenwell, *ib.*, **22**. 553, 1893; J. S. Martin, *ib.*, **23**. 162, 1895; A. L. Steavenson, *Journ. Iron Steel Inst.*, **44**. ii, 45, 1893; H. W. Hughes, *ib.*, **48**. ii, 22, 1895; D. Jones, *ib.*, **48**. ii, 8, 1895; H. Bumby, *ib.*, **60**. ii, 9. 1901; J. Randall, *Colliery Guardian*, **68**. 668, 714, 757, 803, 1894; R. Richardson, *ib.*, **76**. 1029, 1898; E. St. J. Lyburn, *ib.*, **84**. 967, 1902; H. C. Sorby, *ib.*, **93**. 30, 1907; F. Rutley, *Geol. Mag.*, **2**. 227. 1895; O. Curtz, *Jernkontorets Ann.*, **52**. 268, 1897; E. Riley and R. H. Harland, *Ironmonger*, **88**. 119, 1899; R. F. Percy, *Trans. Inst. Min. Eng.*, **22**. 30, 1901; A. E. Pratt, *ib.*, **16**. 328. 1907; F. W. Rudler, *A Handbook to a Collection of the Minerals of the British Isles*, London, 1905; C. Fox-Strangways, *The Geology of the Leicestershire and South Derbyshire Coalfield*, London, 112, 1907; W. G. Fearnsides, *B.A. Rep.*, 510, 1908; R. W. Dron, *Proc. Geol. Soc. Glasgow*, **13**. 165, 1908; *Iron Coal Trades Rev.*, **75**. 1945, 1907; R. M. Kendrick, *ib.*, **94**. 409, 603, 1917; G. Fliegel, *Glückauf*, **47**. 1801, 1911; H. P. T. Rohleder, *Stahl Eisen*, **47**. 638, 1927; E. Grateau, *Génie Civil*, **2**. 47, 1863; T. Ainsworth, *Chem. News*, **24**. 104, 1871; P. Würzburger, *Journ. Iron Steel Inst.*, **7**. 287, 1874; J. T. Woodhouse, *ib.*, **3**. ii, 27, 1871; G. Dove, *ib.*, **10**. ii, 318, 1876; **12**. ii, 316, 1877; *Proc. Inst. Mech. Eng.*, 413, 1885; J. W. Watson, *Geologist*, **1**. 217, 265, 1858; **2**. 241, 1859; W. W. Smyth, *ib.*, **1**. 306, 1858; *Trans. Roy. Geol. Soc. Cornwall*, **7**. 332, 1860; *Iron Ores of Great Britain*, London, 1856; *Iron Ores of the Shropshire Coal Field and of North Staffordshire*, London, 1862; H. B. Allin-Smith, *Bull. U.S. Dept. Commerce*, 133, 1923; Anon., *Mining Journ.*, **146**. 728, 1924; M. S. Birkett, *Tech. Publ. Amer. Inst. Min. Eng.*, 268, 1930; M. C. Delany, *The Historical Geography of the Wealden Iron Industry*, London, 1921; J. A. Watson, *Journ. Soc. Chem. Ind.*, **49**. 88, T, 1930; J. H. Collins, *Mining Mag. Rev.*, **1**. 77, 1872; *Miner's Assoc. Cornwall Devon*, 1, 1873; M. Morgans, *Trans. South Wales Inst. Eng.*, **6**. 78, 1868; *Proc. Cardiff Naturalists Soc.*, **3**. 79, 1870; J. Morgan, *Journ. Geol. Soc.*, **25**. 255, 1869; N. Bryant, *Rep. Roy. Cornwall Polyt. Soc.*, 38, 1871; H. R. Insole and C. Z. Bunning, *Journ. Brit. Soc. Mining Students*, **6**. 70, 1881; E. Jüngst, *Glückauf*, **51**. 42, 1915; S. Vivian, *Trans. Cardiff Nat. Soc.*, **3**. 80, 1872; *Trans. South Wales Inst. Eng.*, **14**. 48, 1884; R. Moore, *Trans. Inst. Scot. Soc. Arts*, **6**. 11, 1864; *Proc. South Wales Inst. Eng.*, **3**. 239, 1863; T. Joseph, *ib.*, **12**. 381, 1881; R. W. Atkinson, *ib.*, **37**. 537, 1922; C. E. de Rance, *Geol. Mag.*, (1), **10**. 64, 1873; W. E. Walker, *Trans. Inst. Min. Eng.*, **25**. 292, 1903; *Colliery Guardian*, **81**. 401, 1901; J. B. Jukes, *The Iron Ores of South Staffordshire*, London, 1858; A. Campion, *Eng. World*, **25**. 119, 1911; E. Rogers, *The Iron Ores of South Wales*, London, 1861; A. H. Green, *Geology of the Yorkshire Coalfield*, London, 1878; B. Holgate, *Proc. Geol. Polyt. Soc. West Riding Yorkshire*, **6**. 137, 1876; P. McBeth, *Trans. Mining Inst. Scotland*, **3**. 130, 1881; T. Beesley, *Geology of the Neighbourhood of Banbury*, London, 1872; R. Tate and J. F. Blake, *The Yorkshire Lias*, London, 1877; G. Barrow, *Proc. Cleveland Inst. Eng.*, 180, 1880; T. Allison, *ib.*, 157, 1882; G. V. du Noyer, *Belfast Field Club*, **5**. 21, 1868; J. de Lazurtegui, *La reunion del Instituto del Hierro y del Acero*, Bilbao, 1903; A. Weiskopf, *Berg. Hütt. Ztg.*, **63**. 149, 1904; P. Argall, *Proc. Roy. Dublin Soc.*, **3**. 151, 1883; J. F. Hodges, *Iron*, **19**. 442, 1882; G. A. J. Cole, *The Interbasaltic Rocks of North-East Ireland*, Dublin, 1912; F. H. Hatch, *Geol. Mag.*, (6), **6**. 391, 1919; *Report on the Sources of Production of Iron and other Metalliferous Minerals*, London, 1918; *Iron Coal Trades Rev.*, **98**. 795, 1919; *Journ. Iron Steel Inst.*, **97**. i, 71, 1918; C. J. Homer, *ib.*, **8**. 562, 1875; H. K. Scott, *Iron Coal Trades Rev.*, **98**. 723, 1919; W. Thorneycroft, *Trans. Edin. Geol. Soc.*, **10**. 196, 1913; J. Cadman, *Trans. Federated Inst. Min. Eng.*, **22**. 99, 1901; **26**. 106, 1904; *Journ. Iron Steel Inst.*, **61**. i, 433, 1902; A. Strahan, W. Gibson, T. C. Cantrill, R. L. Sherlock and H. Dewey, *Special Rep. Mem. Geol. Sur.*, 13, 1920; T. C. Cantrill, R. L. Sherlock and H. Dewey, *ib.*, 9, 1919; B. Smith, *ib.*, 8, 1919; T. F. Sibly, *ib.*, 10, 1927; R. Meade, *The Coal and Iron Industries of Great Britain*, London, 1882; D. R. Rankin, *Trans. Highland Agric. Soc.*, (2), **8**. 88, 1843; M. Brand, *Trans. Inst. Min. Eng.*, **25**. 256, 1903; A. H. Stokes, *Economic Geology of Derbyshire*, London, 1878; *Trans. Chesterfield Inst. Eng.*, **6**. 60, 1878; H. Louis, *The Iron Ore Resources of the World*, Stockholm, **2**. 623, 1910; L. de Launay, *Gîtes minéraux et métallifères*, Paris, **2**. 484, 1913; M. MacGregor, G. W. Lee and G. V. Wilson, *Mem. Geol. Sur. Scotland*, 11, 1920; G. W. Lee and S. S. Buckman, *ib.*, 1, 1920; R. G. Carruthers and C. H. Dinham, *ib.*, 1, 1907.

[33] H. Coquand, *Bull. Soc. Géol.*, (2), **6**. 328, 1849; S. Jordan, *Journ. Iron Steel Inst.*, **14**. ii, 316, 1878; **36**. ii, 10, 1889; P. St. C. Deville, *Ann. Mines*, (11), **13**. 416, 1928; V. Charrin, *Génie Civil*, **93**. 403, 1928; **98**. 196, 1931; A. J. Reynaud, *Iron Age*, **120**. 540, 1927; J. Seigle, *Journ. Iron Steel Inst.*, **115**. i, 53, 1927; A. Nerreter, *Stahl Eisen*, **43**. 585, 625, 659, 686, 1923; *Iron Coal Trades Rev.*, **106**. 982, 1923; A. H. Brooks and M. F. la Croiz, *Bull. U.S. Geol. Sur.*, 703, 1920; A. Pawlowsky, *Le minerai et les mines de fer en France*, Paris, 1926; *La métallurgie du fer dans le nord et l'est envahis*, Paris, 1921; J. François, *Recherches sur le gisement et le traitement direct des minerais de fer dans les Pyrénées*, Paris, 1843; F. Wandesleben, *Berg. Hütt. Ztg.*, **49**. 81, 1890; *Stahl Eisen*, **10**. 677, 1890; M. D. Danton, *ib.*, **12**. 319, 1892; *Bull. Soc. Ind. Min.*, (4), **5**. 311, 1891; A. Bordeaux, *ib.*, (5), **14**. 49, 1918; E. Fuchs and L. de Launay, *Traité des gîtes minéraux et métallifères*, Paris, **1**. 677, 1893; M. Lebreton, *Ann. Mines*, (9), **6**. 281, 1894;

G. Vieira, *ib.*, (9), **7**. 560, 1895 ; W. Schilling, *Stahl Eisen*, **15**. 139, 1895 ; F. Greven, *ib.*, **18**. 1, 1898 ; A. Sömme, *La Lorraine métallurgique*, Paris, 1930 ; G. Rolland, *Compt. Rend.*, **126**, 285, 1898 ; **132**. 444, 1901 ; *Compt. Rend. Internat. Cong. Geol.*, 664, 1901 ; *Stahl Eisen*, **18**. 218, 1898 ; W. Albrecht, *ib.*, **19**. 305, 354, 1899 ; A. Laeroix, *Compt. Rend.*, **128**. 1467, 1899 ; D. P. Oehlert, *ib.*, **146**. 515, 1908 ; J. Rick, *Zeit. Ver. deut. Ind.*, **43**. 1367, 1899 ; H. Ansel, *Zeit. prakt. Geol.*, **9**. 81, 1901 ; F. Laur, *Étude complète du bassin ferrifère de Briey et de la formation ferrugineuse, Lorraine*, Paris, 1901 ; F. Villain, *Compt. Rend. Soc. Ind. Min.*, 182, 1901 ; *Le gisement de minerai de fer oolithique de la Lorraine*, Paris, 1902 ; *Bull. Soc. Ind. Mulhouse*, **75**. 55, 1905 ; *Notice sur l'exposition collective des mines de fer du bassin de Briey*, Nancy, 1905 ; *Bull. Soc. Ind. l'Est*, 223, 1900 ; *Ann. Mines*, (10), **1**. 113, 1902 ; O. Lang, *Berg. Hütt. Ztg.*, **61**. 161, 1902 ; *Glückauf*, **39**. 649, 1902 ; *Stahl Eisen*, **19**. 714, 1899 ; L. Rollier, *Viertelj. Nat. Ges. Zürich*, 1270, 1905 ; *Stahl Eisen*, **25**. 1500, 1901 ; E. C. Eckel, *Iron Age*, **124**. 1667, 1703, 1929 ; *Eng. Min. Journ.*, **127**. 392, 1929 ; C. W. Oliver, *Colliery Engg.*, **7**. 60, 1930 ; R. Pitaval, *Echo Mines*, **34**. 947, 1907 ; Comité des Forges de France, *La sidérurgie française 1864–1914*, Paris, 1920 ; P. Nicou and C. Schlemberger, *Ann. Mines*, (10), **7**. 249, 1905 ; P. Nicou, *Bull. Soc. Ind. Min.*, (5), **5**. 441, 1909 ; *Journ. Iron Steel Inst.*, **90**. ii, 131, 1914 ; **104**. ii. 15, 1921 ; *Les ressources de la France en minerais de fer*, Paris, 1911 ; *The Iron Ore Resources of the World*, **1**. 4, 1910 ; V. M. Dondelinger, *ib.*, **1**. 43; 1910 ; L. van Werveke, *Zeit. prakt. Geol.*, **9**. 396, 1901 ; E. Bellanger, *La Nature*, **40**. 9, 1911 ; *Ann. Mines*, (10), **20**. 452, 1911 ; H. Carnot, *ib.*, (8), **18**. 1, 1890 ; L. Bailly, *Rev. Mét.*, **2**. 335, 1905 ; **3**. 1, 1906 ; *Iron Coal Trades Rev.*, **73**. 2013, 1906 ; *Ann. Mines*, (10), **7**. 5, 1905 ; A. de Grossouvre, *ib.*, (8), **10**. 311, 1886 ; C. E. Heurteau, *ib.*, (10), **11**. 613, 1907 ; R. Masse, *ib.*, (10), **1**. 581, 1902 ; L. Pralon, *ib.*, (9), **19**. 125, 1901 ; F. Rigaud, *ib.*, (7), **14**. 9, 1878 ; A. Stouvenot, *Ann. Mines*, (11), **9**. 57, 1920 ; M. Langrogne and M. Bergerat, *ib.*, (11), **10**. 5, 95, 175, 1920 ; M. Villot, *ib.*, (9), **9**. 205, 1896 ; M. Coiznard, *ib.*, (9), **18**. 489, 1900 ; M. Etienne, *ib.*, (10), **4**. 550, 1903 ; A. Bigot, *Rev. Gén. Sciences*, **24**. 258, 346, 1913 ; E. F. Burchard, *Min. Resources U.S. Geol. Sur.*, i, 557, 1918 ; L. Cayeux, *Le minerai de Lorraine*, Paris, 1918 ; *Les minerais de fer oolithiques de France*, Paris, 1909 ; *Iron Coal Trades Rev.*, **74**. 206, 1907 ; *Bull. Soc. Ind. Min.*, **41**. 134, 1918 ; *Compt. Rend.*, **142**. 716, 1906 ; **170**. 1456, 1920 ; **173**. 117, 121, 1921 ; *Rev. Ind. Min.*, 117, 121, 1921 ; *Rev. Mét.*, **8**. 117, 1911 ; **10**. 336, 1913 ; *Rev. Univ. Mines*, (6), **19**. 61, 1923 ; F. Schmidt, *ib.*, (3), **55**. 43, 1901 ; N. de Mercey, *Bull. Soc. Géol.*, **28**. 793, 1900 ; *Compt. Rend.*, **127**. 1245, 1898 ; G. Vandeville, *Rev. Univ. Mines*, **27**. 109, 1909 ; L. Ferasson, *La question du fer*, Paris, 1918 ; L. Guillet, *Bull. Soc. Ing. Civils*, 208, 1908 ; *Journ. Iron Steel Inst.*, **104**. ii, 73, 1921 ; A. Guillain, *ib.*, **104**. ii, 59, 1921 ; W. Kohlmann, *Iron Coal Trades Rev.*, **80**. 1001, 1910 ; *Stahl Eisen*, **22**. 493, 552, 1273, 1304, 1902 ; **31**. 413, 469, 544, 1911 ; *Journ. Iron Steel Inst.*, **62**. ii, 384, 1902 ; V. Metz, *Stahl Eisen*, **10**. 677, 1890 ; K. Frecke, *Glückauf*, **46**. 4, 1910 ; M. Lynch, *Iron Trade Rev.*, **60**. 924, 1917 ; F. Miltoun, *ib.*, **32**. 1311, 1918 ; J. de Maulde, *Les mines de fer et l'industrie métallurgique dans le Département du Calvados*, Caen, 1916 ; M. Peyre, *Bull. Soc. Ind. Min.*, (2), **13**. 5, 1884 ; M. Autissier, *ib.*, (5), **15**. 298, 1919 ; A. Dreux, *ib.*, (5), **10**. 20, 1914 ; L. Davy, *ib.*, (4), **14**. 19, 1911 ; *Rév. Mét.*, **8**. 779, 1911 ; L. Hoffmann, *Zeit. prakt. Geol.*, **4**. 68, 1896 ; *Glückauf*, **35**. 640, 1899 ; *Echo de Mines*, 5527, 1899 ; *Stahl Eisen*, **16**. 945, 988, 1896 ; *Verh. Ver. Rheinlands, Westfalens*, **55**. 109, 1898 ; O. R. Kuhn, *Blast Furnace Steel Plant*, **14**. 158, 1926 ; A. Nicolas, *Arts Métiers*, 261, 1921 ; Anon., *Glückauf*, **56**. 163, 1920 ; *Génie Civil*, **76**. 418, 1920 ; *Board Trade Journ.*, **107**. 89, 1921 ; *Iron Coal Trades Rev.*, **97**. 517, 1918 ; A. H. Brooks, *Eng. Min. Journ.*, **109**. 1065, 1920 ; T. Callot, *ib.*, **87**. 1221, 1909 ; A. C. Spencer, *Trans. Amer. Inst. Min. Eng.*, **61**. 130, 1918 ; S. Paige, *ib.*, **61**. 135, 1918 ; H. H. Campbell, *Iron Age*, **96**. 168, 188, 1915 ; M. Kreuzkarn, *Erzbergbau*, 184, 1910 ; F. Hoppe, *Bihang. Jernkontorets Ann.*, 7, 1903 ; J. G. Junger, *Rev. Univ. Mines*, (6), **19**. 265, 1892 ; S. Meunier, *Bull. Soc. Géol.*, (4), **2**. 250, 1903 ; E. W. Benecke, *Mitt. Geol. Landesanst. Elsass-Lothr.*, **5**. 139, 1903.
  [34] W. Kohlmann, *Stahl Eisen*, **31**. 413, 469, 544, 1911 ; J. W. Pearse, *Trans. Inst. Min. Eng.*, **25**. 586, 1903 ; C. Lemaire, *L'Age de Fer*, **36**. 626, 1920 ; A. H. Brooks and M. F. la Croix, *Bull. U.S. Geol. Sur.*, 703, 1920 ; E. Faber, *La métallurgie du Luxembourg*, Luxemburg, 1927 ; Anon., *Glückauf*, **57**. 1145, 1921 ; V. M. Dondelinger, *The Iron Ore Resources of the World*, Stockholm, **1**. 43, 1910 ; K. Limpach, *Stahl Eisen*, **21**. 965, 1901 ; A. Pirard, *Rev. Univ. Mines*, **55**. 108, 1901.
  [35] G. Lespineaux, *The Iron Resources of the World*, Stockholm, **2**. 662, 1910 ; L. Greiner, *Journ. Iron Steel Inst.*, **99**. i, 33, 1919 ; A. Delmer, *Ann. Mines Belg.*, **17**. 853, 1912 ; **18**. 325, 1913 ; K. Heilhack, *Glückauf*, **54**. 261, 373, 1918 ; B. Schuz-Briesen, *ib.*, **41**. 37, 1905 ; *Iron Coal Trades Rev.*, **70**. 263, 1904 ; G. Lambert, *Découverte d'un puissant gisement de minerais de fer*, Bruxelles, 1904 ; A. H. Brooks and M. F. la Croix, *Bull. U.S. Geol. Sur.*, 703, 1920.
  [36] Anon., *Iron Coal Trades Rev.*, **98**. 412, 1919 ; W. Gill, *Journ. Iron Steel Inst.*, **50**. ii, 36, 1896 ; G. A. F. M. Molengraaff, *The Iron Ore Resources of the World*, Stockholm, **2**. 645, 1910 ; Anon., *Iron Coal Trades Rev.*, **98**. 412, 1919 ; W. H. D. Jongh, *De Ing.*, 644, 1918 ; M. Pernollet, *Ann. Mines*, (4), **9**. 35, 1846 ; (4), **10**. 253, 1856 ; (4), **16**. 3, 1849 ; *Bull. Soc. Géol.*, **4**. 522, 1847 ; J. Miles, *Iron Coal Trades Rev.*, **108**. 22, 823, 1924.
  [37] J. P. Comes, *Iron Resources of the World*, Stockholm, **1**. 95, 1910 ; M. Werneke, *Zeit. prakt. Geol.*, **10**. 151, 1902 ; J. Ahlburg, *ib.*, **15**. 183, 1907 ; **15**. 196, 1907 ; P. Bresson, *Bull. Soc. Ind. Min.*, (5), **17**. 19, 1920 ; J. M. do Rego Lisma, *Algumas palavras sobre las d'adaptaçao da industria sidurigica em Portugal*, Lisbon, 1890 ; R. Fisher, *Trans. Fed. Inst. Min. Eng.*, **10**. 124, 1896 ; A. Klautzsch, *Zeit. prakt. Geol.*, **9**. 323, 1901 ; F. W. Foote and R. S. Ransom, *Eng. Min. Journ.*, **106**. 47, 1918 ; R. von Zwerger, *Untersuchungen über die Bauwürdigkeit der*

Eisenerzlagerstätten auf dem Cabeco da Mua und der Serra Reboredo in Portugal (Provinz Tras-os-Montes), Freiburg i. Br., 1929.
³⁸ J. D. Kendall, *The Iron Ores of Great Britain and Ireland*, London, 265, 1893; *Trans. Federated Inst. Min. Eng.*, **3**. 604, 1892; *Revista Minera*, **44**. 201, 1893; N. Preus, *ib.*, **50**. 440, 1899; J. Hereza, *ib.*, **53**. 295, 1902; A. Lasala, *ib.*, **54**. 49, 1903; B. G. Iribarne, *ib.*, **53**. 591, 1902; **54**. 1, 1903; F. Gascue, *ib.*, **41**. 35, 49, 65, 83, 105, 117, 1890; **42**. 86, 1891; Anon., *Mining Journ.*, **60**. 1455, 1890; J. Piey Allue, *ib.*, **42**. 377, 1891; R. Oviol, *ib.*, **43**. 177, 1892; Anon., *Amer. Manf.*, **50**. 19, 1892; I. Parga and D. Lorenzo, *Anal. Fis. Quim.*, **28**. 353, 1930; J. Balzola, *Journ. Iron Steel Inst.*, **118**. ii, 15, 1928; A. P. Wilson, *ib.*, **46**. ii, 182, 1894; J. de Lazurtegui, *Ensayo sobre la cuestion de los minerales de Hierro*, Ayer, Hoy, y Mañana, Bilbao, 1910; E. F. M. Gutierrez, *La industria siderurgica en España*, Madrid, 1892; V. Delport, *Iron Trade Rev.*, **83**. 829, 918, 1928; F. Foldt, *Stahl Eisen*, **13**. 603, 642, 1893; Oesterr. *Zeit. Berg. Hütt.*, **41**. 184, 1893; M. Mettrier, *Ann. Mines*, (9), **6**. 280, 1894; E. Schrödter, *Stahl Eisen*, **16**. 265, 1896; A. Kaysser, *ib.*, **18**. 373, 662, 1898; J. W. Spencer, *Journ. Iron Steel Inst.*, **49**. i, 304, 1896; P. de Alzola, *ib.*, **50**. ii, 5, 1896; R. W. Barrington, *Mineral Ind.*, **5**. 371, 1897; A. Mitinsky, *Gorni Journ.*, **82**. 327, 1906; C. H. Fritzsche, *Glückauf*, **65**. 1229, 1929; J. A. Jones, *Trans. Inst. Min. Eng.*, **18**. 279, 1899; **20**. 438, 1901; *Iron Coal Trades Rev.*, **72**. 705, 1901; J. E. de Echeverria and F. Gujelmo, *La minas de hierro de la Provincia de Vizcaya*, Bilbao, 1901; E. F. Dürre, *Die Hochofenbetriebe am Ende des XIX Jahrhunderts*, Berlin, 12, 1901; F. D. Adams, *Trans. Amer. Inst. Min. Eng.*, **28**. 649, 1901; *Journ. Canada Min. Inst.*, **4**. 196, 1902; A. Schöppe, *Berg. Hütt. Ztg.*, **60**. 455, 1901; A. Klautzsch, *Zeit. prakt. Geol.*, **9**. 323, 1901; F. Fircks, *ib.*, **14**. 142, 233, 1906; R. S. Lozano, *Bol. Comision Mapa geol. España*, **26**. 205, 1902; L. Mallada, *ib.*, **26**. 152, 1902; F. Illingworth, *Contract Journ.*, **47**. 799, 1902; B. H. Brough, *Cassier's Mag.*, **23**. 697, 1902; R. F. Arias, *Asturias Industrial*, Gijon, 1903; A. Gascon, *Los criaderos de hierro de Burguillos*, Madrid, 1904; C. H. M. Trayner, *Iron Coal Trades Rev.*, **73**. 1177, 1905; H. A. McBride, *Mines Minerals*, **31**. 577, 1911; *Rev. Min.*, **7**. 373 1904; E. Bourson, *Rev. Univ. Mines*, (2), **4**. 648, 1880; M. John, *Glückauf*, **46**. 2002, 2045, 1911; G. Prus, *Génie Civil*, **5**. 145, 1884; M. Demay, *Ann. Mines*, (12), **5**. 137, 1924; C. Estep, *Iron Trade Rev.*, **68**. 219, 1921; P. H. Sampelayo, *Bol. Inst. Geol. España*, **41**. 1, 1920; F. Gillman, *Trans. Inst. Min. Met.*, **20**. 447, 1910; R. Pilz, *Zeit. prakt. Geol.*, **16**. 177, 1908; I. de Goenaga, *Revista Min.*, **34**. 296, 328, 355, 447, 459, 1883; R. de la Sota, *ib.*, **54**. 247, 1903; J. M. Palacios, *ib.*, **56**. 176, 1905; R. M. de Rotaeche, *ib.*, **77**. 93, 1926; M. Roesler, *Bull. U.S. Geol. Sur.*, 706, 1921; O. Putz, *Erzbergbau*, **3**. 408, 1907; A. de Sierra, *Bol. Inst. Geol. España*, **36**. 239, 1915; **41**. 408, 1920; W. Harnickell, *Stahl Eisen*, **49**. 536, 1929; A. Bourbon, *Rev. Ind. Min.*, 245, 1928; F. C. Roberts, *Iron Age*, **119**. 494, 571, 1927; Anon., *Iron Coal Trades Rev.*, **114**. 219, 1927; L. G. Ros, *ib.*, **108**. 630, 1924; M. Kayser, *Zeit. Berg. Hütt. Sal.*, **77**. 64, 1929; M. Pondal and D. Lorenzo, *Anal. Fis. Quim.*, **28**. 353, 1930; H. Wedding, *Verh. Ver. Beförd. Gewerbfleisses*, **75**. 293, 1896; L. de Adaro and G. Junquera, *Mem. Inst. Geol. Espan.*, **2**. 1, 1916; V. Kindelan and R. Manuel, *ib.*, **3**. 1, 1918; J. G. Haggard, *Foreign Office Rep.*, 3458, 1905; Anon., *Iron Coal Trades Rev.*, **105**. 150, 1922; J. Ahlburg, *Zeit. prakt. Geol.*, **15**. 183, 1907; P. Grosch, *ib.*, **20**. 201, 1912; C. Schmidt and H. Preiswerk, *ib.*, **12**. 225, 1904; R. de Yarza, *Compt. Rend. Cong. Géol. Internat.*, 297, 1910; G. H. Bulmer, *Proc. Inst. Civil Eng.*, **159**. 312, 1905; E. Dann, *Stahl Eisen*, **33**. 1181, 1232, 1913; M. Teichgräber, *ib.*, **24**. 332, 1904; P. Fabrega, *Mining Journ.*, **82**. 5, 44, 78, 114, 1907; *Rev. Min.*, **58**. 266, 284, 1907; **60**. 147, 187, 207, 219, 1909; D. R. Guardiola, *Bol. Minero*, **7**. 225, 1904; *Rev. Min.*, **60**. 486, 1909; D. A. Eleicegui, *ib.*, **60**. 521, 1909; *Bol. Min.*, **7**. 225, 1904; S. T. y Codina, *Gaceta Min. Cataluna*, **4**. 177, 1904; A. Gounot, *Bull. Soc. Ind. Min.*, (4), **3**. 749, 1904; C. John, *Glückauf*, **46**. 2002, 2045, 1910; O. Simmersbach, *ib.*, **41**. 1377, 1905; V. de Ysassi, *Trans. Amer. Inst. Min. Eng.*, **53**. 84, 1915; E. Mackay-Heriot, *Eng. Min. Journ.*, **76**. 510, 1903; O. R. Kuhn, *ib.*, **121**. 367, 1926; A. E. Carlton, *ib.*, **88**. 715, 1909; H. H. Campbell, *Iron Age*, **98**. 248, 1916; Anon., *Mining Journ.*, **104**. 4, 1914; E. S. Moore, *Trans. Canada Inst. Min. Met.*, **30**. 347, 1927; L. M. Vidal, *The Iron Ore Resources of the World*, Stockholm, **1**. 49, 1910; L. Barreiro, *Iron Age*, **116**. 680, 1925; O. Berggren, *Jernkontorets Ann.*, **114**. 355, 1930; J. Hesemann, *Abh. prakt. Geol. Bergwirtsch.*, **10**. 1, 1927.
³⁹ E. E. W. Baumler, *Verh. Nat. Hist. Ver. Bonn*, **27**. 158, 1870; *Zeit. Berg. Hütt. Sal.*, **17**. 426, 1869; A. Hasslacher, *ib.*, **44**. 75, 1896; O. Stutzer, *ib.*, **54**. 301, 1906; G. Berg, *Jahrb. Preuss. Geol. Landesanst.*, 201, 1902; H. Bucking, *ib.*, 12, 1892; H. Loretz, *ib.*, 10, 1892; 120, 1884; P. Krusch, *ib.*, 2, 1908; *Stahl Eisen*, **42**. 1705, 1922; *Glückauf*, **54**. 261, 1918; *Zeit. prakt. Geol.*, **15**. 129, 1907; H. Pohl, *ib.*, **30**. 133, 1922; F. Beyschlag, *ib.*, **5**. 337, 1897; *Jahrb. Preuss. Geol. Landesanst.*, 329, 1888; *Zeit. prakt. Geol.*, **5**. 337, 1897; *Glückauf*, **33**. 307, 1897; G. Einecke and W. Köhler, *Arch. Preuss. Geol. Landesanst. Lagerstätt.*, 1, 1910; *The Iron Ore Resources of the World*, Stockholm, **2**. 671, 1910; G. Einecke, *Mitt. Ges. wirthschaft. Ausbildung*, **2**, 1907; W. Bornhardt, *ib.*, 1910; W. Müller, *Ueber die Erzlagerstätten in der Umgebung von Berggiesshübel*, Leipzig, 1890; A. W. Stelzner, *Das Eisenerzfeld von Naeverhaugen*, Freiberg, 1890; B. Gerlach, *Stahl Eisen*, **11**. 613, 1891; L. Bickell, *Die Eisenhütten des Klosters Haina*, Marburg, 1890; A. Buchrucker, *Stahl Eisen*, **11**. 911, 1891; E. Schrödter, *ib.*, **16**. 265, 1896; B. Kosmann, *Die Entwickelung und Zukunft der Rheinisch-Westfälischen Eisenindustrie*, Berlin, 1902; *Stahl Eisen*, **18**. 357, 623, 1898; O. Vogel, *ib.*, **18**. 1110, 1898; G. B. Riemann, *ib.*, **22**. 278, 1902; *Zeit. prakt. Geol.*, **2**. 50, 1894; C. Geiger, *Stahl Eisen*, **27**. 592, 1907; F. von Sandberger, *Neues Jahrb. Min.*, ii, 37, 1892; F. Kretschmer, *Oesterr. Zeit. Berg. Hütt.*, **42**. 167, 186, 1894; *Centr. Min.*, 289, 321, 1901; C. Gaebler, *Zeit. Berg. Hütt. Sal.*, **42**. 157, 1894; J. Boehm, *ib.*, **53**. 259, 1905; W. von

Gümbel, *Ber. Bayr. Akad.*, 293, 1894 ; G. Stockfleth, *Glückauf*, **30.** 1791, 1855, 1894 ; *Verh. Ver. preuss. Rheinlande*, **52.** 1, 1895 ; O. Luedecke, *Die Minerale des Harzes*, Berlin, 1896 ; A. Keita, *Glückauf*, **34.** 436, 1898 ; E. Kaiser, *Verh. Nat. Ver. Rheinlande*, **54.** 78, 1898 ; H. Metzel, *Zeit. prakt. Geol.*, **6.** 273, 1898 ; J. Bellinger, *ib.*, **11.** 68, 231, 1903 ; F. Krekeler, *ib.*, **38.** 53, 1930 ; W. Petersson, *Jernkontorets Ann.*, **54.** 1, 1899 ; G. Koehler, *Berg. Hütt. Ztg.*, **58.** 217, 1899 ; E. Knackstedt, *ib.*, **61.** 169, 181, 1902 ; M. Dérer, *Bany. Koh. Lapok*, **36.** 34, 1903 ; A. Denckmann, *Jahrb. Geol.*, 1, 1906 ; R. Russwurm, *Glückauf*, **43.** 163, 1907 ; M. Dieckmann, *Erzbergbau*, **3.** 231, 1907 ; R. Goebel, *ib.*, **4.** 454, 481, 1908 ; K. Fickenscher, *Berg. Hütt. Rund.*, **10.** 57, 1913 ; W. Rothmann, *Zur Frage der Eisen- und Manganerzversorgung der deutschen Industrie*, Jena, 1921 ; Anon., *Bergbau*, 685, 1919 ; E. Frohwein, *Beschreibung des Bergreviers Dillenburg*, Bonn, 1885 ; F. Harbort, *Zeit. prakt. Geol.*, **19.** 219, 1911 ; *Neues Jahrb. Min.*, i, 179, 1903 ; E. R. Zalinsky, *Neues Jahrb. Min. B.B.*, **19.** 40, 1904 ; B. Turley, *Berg. Hütt. Ztg.*, **49.** 120, 1890 ; H. Voltz, *Die Bergwerks- und Hüttenverwaltung des oberschlessischen Industriebezirks*, Kattowitz, 1892 ; T. Wiese, *Das Vorkommen von oolitschen Roteisensteinen im Wesergebirge bei Minden*, Giesen, 1903 ; *Zeit. prakt. Geol.*, **11.** 217, 1903 ; K. Masling, *ib.*, **19.** 361, 1912 ; C. Blomeke, *ib.*, **2.** 414, 1894 ; M. Bodifée, *ib.*, **15.** 309, 1907 ; C. R. L. Chelius, *ib.*, **12.** 53, 356, 1904 ; R. Delkeskampf, *ib.*, **11.** 265, 1903 ; K. Ermisch, *ib.*, **12.** 160, 1904 ; R. Fluhr, *Die Eisenerzlagerstätten Würtembergs und ihre volkswirtschaftliche Bedeutung*, Berlin, 1907 ; *Zeit. prakt. Geol.*, **16.** 1, 1908 ; E. Haarmann, *ib.*, **17.** 343, 1909 ; C. Hatzfeld, *ib.*, **14.** 361, 1906 ; M. Krahmann, *Stahl Eisen*, **24.** 1245, 1904 ; *Zeit. prakt. Geol.*, **12.** 329, 1904 ; F. Krecke, *ib.*, **12.** 384, 1904 ; H. Lotz, *ib.*, **15.** 251, 1907 ; *Zeit. deut. geol. Ges.*, **54.** 139, 1902 ; K. Schlegel, *ib.*, **54.** 24, 1902 ; K. Hummel, *Zeit. prakt. Geol.*, **30.** 69, 1922 ; **35.** 17, 38, 1927 ; O. Friz, *ib.*, **14.** 256, 1906 ; H. Pohl, *ib.*, **30.** 133, 1922 ; E. Harbort and A. Mestwerdt, *ib.*, **21.** 199, 1913 ; A. Rothpletz, *ib.*, **21.** 249, 1913 ; J. Ahlburg, *Stahl Eisen*, **39.** 29, 62, 1919 ; *Zeit. prakt. Geol.*, **19.** 59, 1911 ; A. Vierschilling, *ib.*, **18.** 393, 1910 ; M. Priehäusser, *ib.*, **17.** 104, 1909 ; E. Jüngst, *ib.*, **43.** 993, 1907 ; A. Schmidt, *Die Mineralien des Fichtelgebirge*, Bayreuth, 1903 ; *Die nordbayrischen Eisen und Manganvorkommen*, Mattowitz, 1913 ; *Berg. Hütt. Rund.*, **9.** 293, 1913 ; *Erzbergbau*, **2.** 666, 1906 ; **3.** 67, 1907 ; *Glückauf*, **43.** 1034, 1907 ; E. S. Briesen, *ib.*, **40.** 361, 1904 ; M. Willert, *ib.*, **44.** 304, 1908 ; E. A. Scheibe, *ib.*, **59.** 530, 556, 582, 606, 1923 ; M. Kipper, *ib.*, **44.** 1101, 1907 ; F. Klockmann, *Stahl Eisen*, **28.** 1913, 1908 ; *Zeit. prakt. Geol.*, **12.** 73, 1904 ; E. Köbrich, *Stahl Eisen*, **34.** 393, 445, 1914 ; H. Macco, *ib.*, **23.** 613, 1903 ; O. Simmersbach, *ib.*, **14.** 968, 1894 ; F. G. Bremme, *ib.*, **16.** 755, 1896 ; H. Rentzsch, *ib.*, **23.** 617, 620, 1903 ; F. R. Eickhoff, *ib.*, **29.** 97, 1909 ; F. Kollmann, *ib.*, **6.** 787, 1886 ; W. Kollmann, *ib.*, **18.** 593, 1898 ; W. Venator, *ib.*, **27.** 127, 1907 ; Anon., *ib.*, **27.** 25, 533, 1907 ; O. Krupp, *ib.*, **31.** 486, 1911 ; *Glückauf*, **47.** 114, 160, 201, 1911 ; E. Holzapfel, *ib.*, **46.** 341, 1910 ; R. Schreiter, *Jahrb. Berg. Hütt.*, **93.** 195, 1919 ; J. Lowag, *Oesterr. Zeit. Berg. Hütt.*, **50.** 608, 623, 635, 1902 ; F. Miltoun, *Iron Trade Rev.*, **60.** 1030, 1917 ; Anon., *Iron Age*, **102.** 582, 1918 ; H. Münster, *Zeit. prakt. Geol.*, **13.** 242, 413, 1905 ; W. Resow, *ib.*, **16.** 305, 1908 ; F. Rose, *ib.*, **16.** 497, 1908 ; L. von Werveke, *ib.*, **3.** 97, 1895 ; **4.** 68, 1896 ; Anon., *ib.*, **14.** 62, 1906 ; H. Niebuhr, *Stahl Eisen*, **48.** 1672, 1928 ; Anon., *ib.*, **48.** 609, 1928 ; H. Willing, *ib.*, **48.** 609, 1928 ; *Iron Coal Trades Rev.*, **110.** 349, 1925 ; H. C. Estep, *Iron Trade Rev.*, **72.** 727, 1923 ; A. Heinrichsbauer, *Stahl Eisen*, **44.** 96, 1924 ; H. Hess von Wichdorff, *ib.*, **28.** 529, 1908 ; H. Schneiderhöhn, *Mitt. Inst. Eisenforsch.*, **3.** 9, 1921 ; **5.** 79, 1924 ; *Stahl Eisen*, **44.** 19, 1924 ; W. Raabe, *Die Eisenerzvorkommen zwischen Bingerbrück und Stromberg*, Berlin, 1927 ; *Mitt. Inst. Eisenforsch.*, **9.** 177, 1927 ; J. Hesemann, *Die devonischen Eisenerz des Mittelharzes*, Halle (Saale), 1927 ; H. Haf, *Stahl Eisen*, **42.** 1417, 1922 ; *Zeit. prakt. Geol.*, **50.** 77, 1922 ; R. Seemann, *Abhand. Nathist. Ges. Nürnberg*, **22.** 91, 1925 ; *Zeit. prakt. Geol.*, **33.** 104, 1925 ; K. Oebbeke, *Bayer. Ind. Gewerbefl.*, **46.** 363, 1914 ; M. Barbier, *Rev. Ind. Min.*, 449, 469, 484, 513, 1929 ; E. A. Ehmann, *Chem. Erde*, **6.** 117, 1930.

⁴⁰ M. Pernollet, *Ann. Mines*, (5), **13.** 89, 1858 ; J. Couharevitch, *Rev. Univ. Mines*, **19.** 265, 1892 ; J. Milewsky, *Journ. Ind. Eng. Chem.—News*, **8.** 14, 1930 ; B. Schapira, *Iron Trade Rev.*, **70.** 599, 1922 ; *Stahl Eisen*, **69.** 1411, 1921 ; M. Roessler, *Bull. U.S. Geol. Sur.*, 706, 1921 ; F. Bartonec, *Oesterr. Zeit. Berg. Hütt.*, **54.** 645, 1906 ; **63.** 726, 1914 ; S. Doborzynsky, *Geol. Centr.*, **2.** 262, 686, 1902 ; E. Tietze, *Jahrb. Geol. Reichsanst.*, **37.** 423, 1887 ; I. Lewinsky, *Metall Erz*, **18.** 631, 1921 ; *Rev. Gen. Sciences*, **32.** 634, 1921 ; A. Gerke, *Bergbau*, 606, 621, 637, 653, 1919 ; *Glückauf*, **55.** 977, 997, 1017, 1919 ; W. Pawlica, *Bull. Géol. Pologne*, **1.** 1, 1920 ; C. Kuzniar, *Compt. Rend. Géol. Pologne*, **2.** 1922.

⁴¹ B. Schapira, *Iron Trade Rev.*, **57.** 962, 976, 1921 ; *Journ. Iron Steel Inst.*, **75.** iii, 266, 1907 ; *Iron Coal Trades Rev.*, **68.** 962, 976, 1921 ; M. Roesler, *Bull. U.S. Geol. Sur.*, 706, 1921 ; K. A. Weber, *Glückauf*, **50.** 1193, 1914 ; F. H. Hatch, *Report on the Sources and Production of Iron and other Metalliferous Ores used in the Iron and Steel Industry*, London, 1918 ; L. de Launay, *Gites minéraux et métallifères*, Paris, **2.** 470, 1913 ; V. Uhlig, *The Iron Ore Resources of the World*, Stockholm, 143, 1910 ; L. von Loczy and K. von Papp, *The Iron Ore Resources of the World*, Stockholm, **1.** 198, 1910 ; F. Katzer, *Oesterr. Zeit. Berg. Hütt.*, **53.** 390, 1905 ; L. von Schmidt, *ib.*, **50.** 219, 1902 ; F. Kretschmer, *Jahrb. Geol. Reichsanst.*, **49.** 29, 1899 ; **52.** 353, 1902 ; E. Tietz, *ib.*, **51.** 317, 1901 ; F. W. Voit, *ib.*, **50.** 695, 1900 ; K. A. Weber, *Glückauf*, **50.** 1193, 1238, 1914 ; P. Chlebus, *Montan. Rund.*, **12.** 145, 161, 180, 1920 ; R. d'Andrimont, *Ann. Soc. Géol. Belg.*, **30.** 123, 1904 ; A. Kriz, *The Iron and Steel Industry in Czechoslovakia*, Prague, 1930 ; G. Behaghel, *Die Eisen- und Manganerz Osteuropas*, Leipzig, 1922 ; M. Palfy, *Magyar Kir. Földt.*, **26.** 1, 1924.

⁴² H. Beck, *Jahrb. geol. Reichsanst.*, **53.** 473, 1904 ; C. von John and C. F. Eichheiter, *ib.*, **53.** 499, 1904 ; H. K. Scott, *Trans. Inst. Min. Met.*, **22.** 597, 1912 ; A. Galocsy, *Bany. Koh.*

Lapok, **41.** 201, 1907 ; F. Kovai, *Zeit. Chem. Ind.,* 6, 1900 ; R. Helmhacker, *Berg. Hütt. Ztg.,* **54.** 83, 1895 ; M. Roesler, *Bull. U.S. Geol. Sur.,* 706, 1921 ; L. Vankoff, *The Iron Ore Resources of the World,* Stockholm, **1.** 331, 1910 ; H. K. Scott, *Trans. Inst. Min. Met.,* **22.** 611, 1913 ; A. Muzet, *Bull. Soc. Ind. Min.,* **15.** 113, 1911 ; D. A. Wray, *Mining Mag.,* **30.** 73, 1924 ; K. A. Weber, *Cassier's Mag.,* **46.** 211, 1914 ; A. Schmitter, *Berg. Hütt. Ztg.,* **52.** 279, 1893.

⁴³ F. Nowack, *Montan Rund.,* **16.** 695, 1924 ; D. A. Wray, *Mining Mag.,* **32.** 329, 1925.

⁴⁴ D. A. Wray, *The Geology and Mineral Resources of the Serb-Croat-Slovene State,* London, 1921 ; *Mining Mag.,* **26.** 154, 1922 ; F. Katzer, *Geologischer Führer durch Bosnien,* Sarajevo, 1903 ; *Die Eisenerzlagerstätten Bosniens und der Hercegovina,* Sarajevo, 1910 ; *Jahrb. Berg. Hütt.,* **48.** 99, 1900 ; **58.** 1, 1910 ; **59.** 25, 180, 1911 ; *Oesterr. Zeit. Berg. Hütt.,* **59.** 229, 1911 ; *The Iron Resources of the World,* Stockholm, **1.** 299, 1910 ; M. Nottmeyer, *ib.,* **1.** 311, 1910 ; R. Helmhacker, *Berg. Hütt. Ztg.,* **55.** 138, 1896 ; A. Götting, *ib.,* **60.** 237, 1901 ; A. Habets, *Ann. Assoc. Ing. École Liége,* **17.** 686, 1904 ; B. Baumgärtel, *Tschermak's Mitt.,* (2), **23.** 393, 1905 ; F. Nowack, *Montan Rund.,* **16.** 695, 1924 ; G. G. Smith, *Eng. Min. Journ.,* **110.** 705, 1920 ; M. Letzous, *Iron Coal Trades Rev.,* **101.** 446, 1920 ; E. M. Butler, *ib.,* **103.** 168, 1921 ; A. Muzet, *Bull. Soc. Ind. Min.,* **15.** 113, 1911 ; E. Kittl, *Jahrb. geol. Reichsanst.,* **53.** 515, 1903 ; C. von John and C. F. Eichleiter, *ib.,* **53.** 499, 1904 ; H. Beck, *ib.,* **53.** 473, 1903 ; J. Hörnhager, *Oesterr. Zeit. Berg. Hütt.,* **51.** 87, 104, 1903 ; B. A. Wendeborn, *Zeit. prakt. Geol.,* **20.** 266, 1912 ; F. Czermak, *ib.,* **33.** 175, 1925 ; A. Bordeaux, *Rev. Univ. Mines,* **30.** 260, 1895 ; F. Poech, *L'industrie minérale de Bosnie-Herzegovine,* Wien, 1900 ; C. Rauscher, *Montan Ztg.,* 9. 463, 1902 ; Anon., *Montan Rund.,* **20.** 63, 1923.

⁴⁵ M. Roessler, *Bull. U.S. Geol. Sur.,* 706, 1921 ; J. von Papp, *The Iron Resources of the World,* Stockholm, **1.** 248, 1910 ; F. Nopcsa, *Jahrb. Ungar. geol. Anst.,* **14.** 93, 1905 ; C. M. Paul and B. Walther, *Jahrb. geol. Reichsanst.,* **26.** 261, 1876 ; P. Poni, *Ann. Univ. Jassy,* **1.** 15, 1900 ; W. Schöppe, *Zeit. prakt. Geol.,* **18.** 309, 1910 ; H. Quiring, *ib.,* **27.** 133, 1919 ; K. A. Weber, *Glückauf,* **50.** 1193, 1238, 1914 ; K. von Mücken, *Glückauf,* **50.** 1397, 1914 ; J. von Halavats, *Oesterr. Zeit. Berg. Hütt.,* **39.** 91, 102, 1891 ; N. G. Caranfil, *Génie Civil,* **77.** 533, 1920.

⁴⁶ Anon., *Journ. Soc. Chem. Ind.,* **39.** 185, R, 1920 ; *Eng. Min. Journ.,* **113.** 169, 1922 ; M. von Isser, *Oesterr. Zeit. Berg. Hütt.,* **44.** 200, 1895 ; A. Bordeaux, *Rev. Univ. Mines,* **43.** 1, 1898 ; H. Heim, *ib.,* **50.** 110, 1900 ; *Viertelj. Nat. Ges. Zürich,* **45.** 183, 1901 ; *Geol. Centr.,* **1.** 740, 1901 ; *Stahl Eisen,* **23.** 1361, 1903 ; H. B. de Florin, *Der. Erzbergbau,* 387, 1905 ; H. Fehlmann, *Die Fricktaler Eisenerz,* Bern, 1921; B. Helbling, *Oesterr. Zeit. Berg. Hütt.,* **51.** 169, 1903 ; A. Wencelius, *Berg. Hütt. Ztg.,* **62.** 541, 629, 1902 ; **63.** 217, 1903 ; W. Hotz, *Zeit. prakt. Geol.,* **17.** 29, 1909 ; C. Schmidt, *ib.,* **11.** 205, 1903 ; O. Wilhelm, *ib.,* **30.** 149, 1922 ; Anon., *Schweiz. Bauztg.,* 44, 1920 ; C. Viola, *Rass. Min.,* **19.** 113, 1903 ; T. G. Bonney, *Journ. Geol. Soc.,* **59.** 55, 1903.

⁴⁷ M. Roesler, *Bull. U.S. Geol. Sur.,* 706, 1921 ; F. Kupelweiser, *Zeit. Oesterr. Ing. Arch. Ver.,* **45.** 313, 1893 ; A. Jugoviz, *Illustrirter Führer auf der Bahnlinie Eisenerz Vordernberg,* Wien, 1894 ; R. Helmhacker, *Montan Ztg.,* **5.** 249, 1898 ; M. Schrey, *Glaser's Ann.,* **42.** 141, 1898 ; W. Petersson, *Jernkontorets Ann.,* **54.** 1, 1899 ; J. Melion, *Montan Ztg.,* **9.** 131, 1902 ; U. Söhle, *Carinthia,* **2.** 159, 1902 ; V. Neumann, *Tschermak's Mitt.,* (2), **20.** 258, 1901 ; F. Rose, *Zeit. Berg. Hütt. Sal.,* **53.** 205, 1905 ; J. Ahlburg, *ib.,* **55.** 463, 1907 ; O. Friedrich, *Berg. Hütt. Jahrb.,* **77.** 131, 1929 ; T. F. von Hassler, *Montan Ztg.,* **14.** 338, 1907 ; H. Haberfelner, *Berg. Hütt. Jahrb.,* **76.** 87, 1928 ; B. Schapira, *Iron Trade Rev.,* **67.** 717, 1920 ; **68.** 962, 976, 1921 ; F. Katzer, *Verh. geol. Reichsanst.,* 193, 1904 ; *Oesterr. Zeit. Berg. Hütt.,* **53.** 390, 1905 ; *Berg. Hütt. Jahrb.,* **57.** 173, 1909 ; **58.** 202, 1910 ; J. Lowag, *Glückauf,* **30.** 1217, 1893 ; **35.** 163, 1899 ; *Berg. Hütt. Ztg.,* **62.** 277, 1903 ; *Allgem. Berg. Zeit.,* **27.** 1900 ; *Montan Ztg.,* **5.** 249, 1898 ; **8.** 5, 1901 ; **16.** 372, 446, 1909 ; **17.** 200, 1910 ; R. Beck and T. Döring, *Tschermak's Mitt.,* (2), **26.** 481, 1907 ; G. Oelwein, *Montan Ztg.,* **16.** 186, 1909 ; H. Bauerman, *Journ. Iron Steel Inst.,* **75.** iii, 27, 1907 ; A. Aigner, *Die Mineralschätze der Steiermark,* Wien, 169, 1907 ; O. Nagel, *Iron Age,* **94.** 482, 1914 ; Anon., *Journ. Iron Steel Inst.,* **75.** iii, 280, 1907 ; W. Kestranck, *ib.,* **75.** iii, 10, 1907 ; J. Blass, *Zeit. prakt. Geol.,* **8.** 369, 1900 ; F. Ryba, *ib.,* **9.** 337, 1900 ; R. Canaval, *Montan Rund.,* **22.** 21, 53, 1930 ; *Zeit. prakt. Geol.,* **16.** 479, 1908 ; *Jahrb. Berg. Hütt.,* **52.** 145, 1904 ; *Carinthia,* **2.** 12, 1903 ; *Bergbaue Steiermarks,* Leoben, 1904 ; W. A. Humphrey, *Jahrb. geol. Reichsanst.,* **55.** 349, 1905 ; C. V. John and C. F. Eichleiter, *ib.,* **53.** 480, 1903 ; C. F. Eichleiter, **57.** 403, 1907 ; **45.** 13, 1895 ; C. von John, *ib.,* **57.** 419, 1907 ; K. A. Redlich, *Zeit. prakt. Geol.,* **38.** 121, 1930 ; *Berg. Hütt. Jahrb.,* **55.** 267, 1908 ; *Jahrb. geol. Reichsanst.,* **53.** 285, 1903 ; **55.** 267, 1907 ; E. Döll, *Verh. geol. Reichsanst.,* 457, 1895 ; J. T. Singewald, *Eng. Min. Journ.,* **92.** 22, 1911 ; E. Teitze, *Jahrb. geol. Reichsanst.* Wien, **51.** 317, 1903 ; F. Kretschmer, *ib.,* **52.** 353, 1904 ; *Jahrb. geol. Reichsanst.,* **47.** 54, 1897 ; **57.** 21, 1907 ; *Centr. Min.,* 304, 1906 ; J. Hörhager, *Oesterr. Zeit. Berg. Hütt.,* **51.** 87, 104, 337, 352, 1903 ; J. Taffanel, *Ann. Mines,* (10), **4.** 24, 1903 ; D. A. Wray, *Mining Mag.,* 329, 1925 ; E. Priwoznik, *Berg. Hütt. Jahrb.,* **38.** 402, 1890 ; **40.** 458, 1892 ; *Montan Ztg.,* **9.** 463, 1902 ; F. Kerner, *ib.,* **10.** 295, 1903 ; A. Irmler, *Hornicke a hutnicke listy,* 22, 1902 ; V. Uhlig, *The Iron Ore Resources of the World,* Stockholm, **1.** 143, 1910 ; F. Hemprich, *Montan Ztg.,* **18.** 52, 1911 ; Anon., *Montan Rund.,* **20.** 677, 1928 ; L. Jahne, *ib.,* **22.** 1, 1930 ; F. Schwarz, *Berg. Hütt. Jahrb.,* **78.** 104, 1930.

⁴⁸ L. von Loczy and C. von Papp, *The Iron Ore Resources of the World,* Stockholm, **1.** 177, 1910 ; Anon., *Montan Rund.,* **10.** 47, 522, 547, 1918 ; K. A. Weber, *Glückauf,* **50.** 1193, 1914 , A. Götting, *Berg. Hütt. Ztg.,* **60.** 323, 1901 ; A. Vendl, *Foldt. Közl.,* **43.** 911, 958, 1912 ; A. Liffa; *ib.,* **38.** 276, 1911 ; *Zeit. Kryst.,* **48.** 441, 1911 ; W. Schöppe, *Zeit. prakt. Geol.,* **18.** 309, 1911 ; H. Arlt and M. Scheffer, *Glückauf,* **46.** 489, 1910 ; J. Balas, *Banyaszati es Kohaszati Lapok,* 144,

1910 ; E. Howard, *Board Trade Journ.*, **68**. 312, 1909 ; K. von Papp, *Jahrb. unger. geol. Anst.*, **62**, 1906 ; *Die Eisenerz- und Kohlenvorräte des Ungarischen Reiches*, Budapest, 1919 ; F. W. Voit, *Jahresb. geol. Reichsanst. Wien*, **50**. 695, 1902 ; F. Kossmet and C. von John, *Zeit. prakt. Geol.*, **13**. 305, 1905 ; C. von John and C. F. Eichleiter, *ib.*, **45**. 13, 1895 ; **53**. 499, 1904 ; K. A. Redlich, *ib.*, **53**. 285, 1904 ; *Bergbau Steiermarkes*, Leolen, 1904 ; F. Katzer, *Verh. geol. Reichsanst. Wien*, **193**, 1904 ; R. d'Andrimont, *Ann. Soc. Géol. Belg.*, **30**. 123, 1904 ; Anon., *Glückauf*, **27**. 61, 1891 ; J. Loczka, *Math. Naturwiss. Ber. Ungarn*, **8**. 99, 1892 ; K. Jahn and M. Hassak, *Vegytani Lapok*, **1**. 43, 1892 ; A. R. von Kerpely, *Stahl Eisen*, **16**. 932, 1896 ; M. Milosevies, *ib.*, **16**. 886, 1896 ; H. Wedding, *ib.*, **22**. 13, 1902 ; D. A. Lewis, *Journ. Iron Steel Inst.*, **52**. ii, 193, 1897 ; C. von John and C. F. Eichleiter, *Jahrb. geol. Reichsanst.*, **47**. 749, 1898 ; H. Ullmann, *Montan Ztg.*, **6**. 115, 1899 ; G. Adolph, *ib.*, **9**. 108, 1902 ; K. Schafarzik, *Földt. Közl.*, **31**. 1, 1902 ; *Zeit. Zentralver. Bergbau Betriebsleiter*, 341, 1911 ; L. von Schmidt and L. Litschauer, *Oesterr. Zeit. Berg. Hütt.*, **50**. 219, 1902 ; *Bany. Koh. Lapok*, 330, 1901 ; F. Nopcsa, *Mitt. Jahrb. Ungar. Geol. Anstalt*, **14**. 93, 1906 ; H. Böckh, *ib.*, **14**. 63, 1906 ; *Stahl Eisen*, **25**. 1269, 1905 ; W. Viebig, *Glückauf*, **42**. 9, 1906 ; I. Vitalis, *Bany. Koh. Lapok*, **64**. 486, 511, 1931.

⁴⁹ G. Aichino, *The Iron Ore Resources of the World*, Stockholm, **1**. 95, 1910 ; C. Capacci, *L'Industria*, **20**. 760, 1906 ; *Journ. Iron Steel Inst.*, **84**. ii, 412, 1911 ; A. Martelli, *Atti Accad. Lincei*, (5), **21**. i, 803, 1912 ; C. Martelli and T. Sotgia, *Journ. Iron Steel Inst.*, **108**. ii, 125, 1923 ; G. E. Falck, *ib.*, **108**. ii, 11, 1923 ; R. Catani, *ib.*, **84**. ii, 215, 353, 1911 ; L. Testa, *ib.*, **84**. ii, 364, 1911 ; H. Scott, *ib.*, **49**. ii, 141, 1895 ; A. P. Wilson, *ib.*, **47**. ii, 182, 1894 ; W. Jervis, *The Mineral Resources of Central Italy*, London, 1868 ; *I tesori sotterranei dell'Italia*, Torino, 1873–89 ; R. Rohrer, *Tschermak's Mitt.*, (2), **15**. 184, 1896 ; A. Ciampi, *Journ. Iron Steel Inst.*, **84**. ii, 398, 1911 ; G. la Valle, *ib.*, **84**. ii, 409, 1911 ; G. Calvi, *ib.*, **84**. ii, 380, 1911 ; L. Dompé and F. S. Pucci, *ib.*, **84**. ii, 239, 1911 ; A. Bonacossa, *Geol. Centr.*, **2**. 232, 1902 ; T. G. Bonney, *Journ. Geol. Soc.*, **59**. 55, 1903 ; A. Crida, *Met. Ital.*, **3**. 231, 1911 ; M. Duenkel, *Zeit. Berg. Hütt. Sal.*, **50**. 666, 1902 ; B. Lotti, *Rass. Min.*, **15**. 33, 1901 ; *Boll. Ministero Agric.*, **5**. 557, 1906 ; *Zeit. prakt. Geol.*, **15**. 62, 1907 ; F. C. Müller, *ib.*, **20**. 209, 1912 ; V. Novaresse, *ib.*, **10**. 179, 1902 ; M. Priehauser, *ib.*, **17**. 104, 1909 ; F. Peters, *Rev. Univ. Mines*, **39**. 97, 1912 ; F. Poech, *Oesterr. Zeit. Berg. Hütt.*, **51**. 365, 1903 ; G. Martin, *ib.*, **51**. 329, 1903 ; G. Ristori, *Atti Soc. Toscana*, **20**. 60, 1904 ; V. Sevieri, *Rass. Min.*, **14**. 101, 1900 ; G. Castelli, *ib.*, **55**. 46, 1921 ; **63**. 101, 1925 ; M. Bentz, *Bergwirtschaftlische Mitt.*, 277, 1914 ; E. Cortesse, *Rass. Min.*, **35**. 49, 124, 1911 ; M. Nentien, *Ann. Mines*, (9), **12**. 231, 1897 ; J. Stockfleth, *Stahl Eisen*, **17**. 534, 1897 ; E. Odernhermer, *Zeit. angew. Chem.*, **11**. 193, 1898 ; *Stahl Eisen*, **18**. 631, 1898 ; A. H. d'Escailles, *Mining Journ.*, **68**. 1090, 1112, 1898 ; P. Toso, *Boll. Com. Geol. Ital.*, **8**. 216, 1898 ; E. Cortese, *Descrizione geologica della Calabria*, Rome, 1895 ; A. Edvi-Illes, *L'industrie des mines de fer et hauts fourneaux de Hongrie*, Budapest, 1900 ; E. Manasse, *Proc. Soc. Toscana*, **12**. 21, 1901 ; G. Ristori, *Atti Soc. Toscana*, **20**. 60, 1906 ; M. Duenke, *Zeit. Berg. Hütt. Sal.*, **50**. 666, 1902 ; F. Millosevich, *Rend. Accad. Lincei*, (5), **16**. i, 884, 1908 ; F. Peters, *Publ. Assoc. Ing. École Mines Mons*, **5**. 378, 1911 ; *Rev. Univ. Mines*, (4), **39**. 112, 1912 ; C. Crema, *Min. Ital.*, **4**. 3, 1920 ; Anon., *Iron Coal Trades Rev.*, **107**. 413, 1923 ; **108**. 50, 1924.

⁵⁰ L. de Launay, *Ann. Mines*, (9), **13**. 157, 1898 ; L. Rohrer, *Montan Ztg.*, **17**. 5, 1910 ; H. K. Scott, *Journ. Iron Steel Inst.*, **87**. i, 447, 1913 ; A. P. Wilson, *ib.*, **47**. ii, 182, 1894 ; W. H. Cottrell, *Mining Journ.*, **75**. 661, 1904 ; M. Roessler, *Bull. U.S. Geol. Sur.*, 706, 1921 ; K. Vallindas, *Geol. Centr.*, **9**. 425, 1907 ; 'H ὕησος Σέριφος, Athens, 1907 ; A. Cordella, *La Grèce, géologique et minéralogique*, Paris, 1878 ; *Ann. Mines*, (10), **2**. 478, 1902 ; E. Schrödter, *Stahl Eisen*, **16**. 265, 1896 ; M. Nottmeyer, *The Iron Resources of the World*, Stockholm, **1**. 343, 1910 ; D. A. Wray, *Mining Mag.*, **32**. 329, 1925 ; W. H. Cottrell, *Min. Journ.*, **75**. 661, 1904 ; A. McDonnell, *ib.*, **84**. 9, 1908 ; *Board Trade Journ.*, **57**. 377, 1907 ; J. Deprat, *Étude géologique de l'île d'Eubée*, Besançon, 1904 ; R. Lepsius, *Geologie von Attika*, Berlin, 1893 ; A. Habets, *Rev. Univ. Mines*, **21**. 129, 1908 ; N. Bonanos, *ib.*, **21**. 139, 1908 ; Anon., *Iron Trade Rev.*, **53**. 624, 1913.

⁵¹ L. Dominian, *Eng. Min. Journ.*, **78**. 184, 1905 ; M. Nottmeyer, *The Iron Resources of the World*, Stockholm, **1**. 352, 1910 ; E. Coulant, *ib.*, **1**. 359, 1910 ; G. M. Edwards, *Trans. Inst. Min. Met.*, **23**. 192, 1913 ; E. Nowack, *Zeit. prakt. Geol.*, **36**. 108, 1928.

⁵² W. R. Dunstan, *Bull. Imp. Inst.*, **4**. 208, 1907.

⁵³ P. Kovaloff, *Iron Age*, **104**. 1247, 1919 ; P. M. Zamyatin, *Mineral. Tzvetnuie Met.*, **4**. 512, 1929 ; P. Trasenster, *Bull. Assoc. Ing. Liége*, 11, 1890 ; A. Ernst, *Geognostische und bergbauliche Skizzen über die Kaukasusländer*, Freiberg, 1, 1891 ; *Die Mineralischen Bodenschülze des Donezgebietes*, Hanover, 1893 ; *Oesterr. Zeit. Berg. Hütt.*, **42**. 582, 1894 ; P. A. Schemjatschensky, *Trudy Peterbourgskago Obstehestra Ertestvoispytatelj*, **20**. 1, 1892 ; *Geol. Centr.*, **2**. 685, 1902 ; A. Stuckenberg, *Materialy dia Geologii Rossii*, **13**. 53, 1892 ; P. Gladkij, *Russ. Mining Journ.*, **50**. 96, 1892 ; A. Potozoff, *Bull. Ural Soc.*, **12**. 58, 1892 ; A. Saitzew, *Mém. Com. Russ. Geol.*, **13**. 83, 1892 ; J. Couherevitch, *Rev. Univ. Mines*, **19**. 265, 1892 ; E. Fuchs and L. de Launay, *Traité des gîtes minéraux et métallifères*, Paris, **1**. 664, 738, 1893 ; P. G. Rubin and A. N. Pokhvisneff, *Sci. Mag. Met. Catheder Driepropetrovsk*, **1**. 1, 1929 ; F. Thiess, *Zeit. Berg. Hütt. Sal.*, **41**. 68, 1893 ; **55**. 608, 1907 ; R. Helmhacker, *Stahl Eisen*, **14**. 943, 1894 ; G. Berg, **18**. 39. 189, 1919 ; H. Fritsche, *Bull. Soc. Imp. Moscow*, 381, 1893 ; K. Johansson, *Jernkontorets Ann.*, **49**. 174, 1895 ; J. Cordeweener, *Contribution à l'étude de la crise industrielle du Donetz*, Brussels, 1902 ; G. Kamensky, *Journ. Iron Steel Inst.*, **48**. i, 70, 1895 ; *Colliery Guardian*, **76**. 28, 1898 ; D. Ghambashidze, *Mineral Resources of Georgia and Caucasia*, London, 1919 ; H. Klein, *Die südrussische Eisenindustrie*, Düsseldorf, 1920 ; *Stahl Eisen*, **38**. 238, 1918 ; C. Palgen, *La métallurgie du fer et*

de l'acier en Russie, Louvain, 1896 ; J. Kowarsky, *Stahl Eisen*, **16**. 229, 860, 1896 ; J. Thieme, *ib.*, **18**. 611, 717, 1898 ; M. von Tittler, *ib.*, **21**. 519, 1901 ; S. V. Konstantoff, *Trans. Russ. Scient. Tech. Min. Congress*, **6**. 41, 1928 ; H. Louis, *Notes on the Iron Industry of the Urals*, Newcastle-on-Tyne, 1898 ; *Trans. Fed. Inst. Min. Eng.*, **14**. 368, 1898 ; A. Macco, *Zeit. prakt. Geol.*, **6**. 139, 1898 ; H. B. C. Nitze, *Journ. Franklin Inst.*, **147**. 442, 1899 ; C. S. Smith, *Board Trade Journ.*, **63**. 317, 1909 ; M. Glasenapp, *Riga Ind. Ztg.*, **73**, 1899 ; M. Verstraete, *L'Oural*, Paris, 1899 ; M. Bayard, *Ann. Mines*, (9), **15**. 505, 1899 ; F. Kovar, *Zeit. Kryst.*, **31**. 525, 1899 ; A. G. Brophy, *Mining Journ.*, **75**. 659, 1904 ; L. Podgajetzky, *Stahl Eisen*, **24**. 1010, 1904 ; A. Gouvy, *Trans. Soc. Ing. Civils*, **70**. 762, 1917 ; *Trans. Inst. Min. Eng.*, **59**. 418, 1920 ; T. H. Preston, *Mining Mag.*, **14**. 197, 1916 ; **23**. 98, 1920 ; J. Birkinbine, *Ann. Rep. U.S. Geol. Sur.*, **16**. iii, 21, 1895 ; M. Roessler, *ib.*, **16**. 706, 1921 ; V. Gudkov, *Mining Met.*, **2**. 10, 1921 ; K. Bogdanowitsch, *Geol. Centr.*, **3**. 485, 1903 ; *Stahl Eisen*, **32**. 990, 1912 ; *The Iron Ore Resources of the World*, Stockholm, **1**. 363, 516, 1910 ; W. Weyrauch, *Das Eisen in Russland*, Leipzig, 1920 ; H. Bauermann, *Journ. Iron Steel Inst.*, **53**. i, 134, 1898 ; K. Faeber, *Metallbörse*, **21**. 1444, 1931 ; S. H. Ball and B. Low, *Eng. Min. Journ.*, **103**. 403, 1917 ; M. Rhodes, *Mining Journ.*, **84**. 546, 1908 ; C. R. King, *Eng. Mag.*, **48**. 481, 1915 ; J. H. Grout, *Ind. World*, 990, 1908 ; M. Neumark, *Stahl Eisen*, **21**. 62, 1901 ; M. Gubkin, *ib.*, **43**. 889, 1923 ; A. Schepowalnikoff, *Geol. Centr.*, **2**. 547, 1902 ; **3**. 327, 1903 ; W. Taressenko, *ib.*, **2**. 322, 1901 ; C. Simonowitsch, *ib.*, **4**. 208, 1903 ; A. Lewitzky, *ib.*, **3**. 641, 1902 ; P. Javoroffsky, *ib.*, **3**. 644, 1902 ; D. Bogdanoff, *ib.*, **3**. 6, 1903 ; N. Karakasch, *ib.*, **2**. 136, 1902 ; J. Kobetzky, *ib.*, **3**. 8, 35, 1903 ; A. Krosnopolsky, *ib.*, **3**. 36, 1903 ; *Ann. Géol. Min. Russ.*, **5**. 109, 1902 ; J. Samojloff, *Proc. Russ. Min. Soc.*, **329**. 1901 ; *Zeit. prakt. Geol.*, **11**. 301, 1903 ; *Geol. Centr.*, **1**. 358, 1901 ; L. Piotrowsky, *ib.*, **3**. 35, 1903 ; S. Doborzynsky, *ib.*, **2**. 262, 686, 1902 ; M. Schymanowsky and P. Rubin, *ib.*, **3**. 36, 1903 ; R. Zeidler, *ib.*, **3**. 5, 1903 ; M. Winda, *Nachr. Bergwerke Bewasserung Kaukasus*, **3**, 1900 ; *Geol. Centr.*, **3**. 36, 1903 ; A. Terpigoreff, *ib.*, **3**. 6, 1903 ; *Zeit. prakt. Geol.*, **13**. 115, 116, 1905 ; K. Futterer, *ib.*, **5**. 193, 1897 ; W. Friz, *ib.*, **13**. 60, 1905 ; L. Koniouchevsky, *Mém. Com. Géol.*, 21, 1906 ; *Geol. Centr.*, **4**. 310, 1904 ; E. Fedoroff and W. Nikitin, *ib.*, **2**. 326, 1902 ; H. J. Freyn, *Blast Furnace Steel Plant*, **18**. 90, 99, 1930 ; F. Loweinson-Lessing, *Ann. Polyt. St. Petersburg*, **5**. 12, 1906 ; *Zeit. Kryst.*, **36**. 653, 1902 ; *Geol. Centr.*, **8**. 411, 1906 ; **12**. 170, 1909 ; L. Ouspensky, *ib.*, **3**. 36, 1903 ; N. Smirnoff, *ib.*, **12**. 171, 1909 ; M. Bayard, *Ann. Mines*, (9), **15**. 505, 1899 ; A. P. Head, *The South Russian Iron Industry*, London, 1902 ; *Journ. Soc. Arts*, **51**. 75, 1903 ; N. Besborodko, *Neues Jahrb. Min. B.B.*, **34**. 783, 1912 ; T. von Gorecky, *Zeit. prakt. Geol.*, **11**. 148, 1903 ; C. Monkofsky, *Rev. Univ. Mines*, **12**. 72, 1905 ; S. Popoff, *Zeit. Kryst.*, **52**. 606, 1913 ; B. Simmersbach, *Oesterr. Zeit. Berg. Hütt.*, **62**. 253, 272, 288, 303, 1914 ; F. Thiess, *ib.*, **55**. 608, 1907 ; L. Mrazec and L. Duparc, *ib.*, **51**. 711, 735, 1903 ; *Compt. Rend.*, **136**. 1409, 1903 ; N. Sokoloff, *Bull. Com. Geol. Russ.*, **19**. 407, 1900 ; J. Morozewicz, *Tschermak's Mitt.*, (2), **23**. 113, 225, 1904 ; *Trans. Inst. Min. Eng.*, **29**. 679, 1904 ; *Ann. Géol. Min. Russ.*, **5**. 114, 1902 ; V. Nikitin, *Mém. Com. Géol.*, 22, 1907 ; W. Schockley, *Trans. Amer. Inst. Min. Eng.*, **39**. 274, 1908 ; Anon., *Mining Journ.*, **126**. 495, 515, 529, 1919 ; **154**. 615, 1926 ; *Iron Age*, **104**. 1247, 1919 ; *Iron Coal Trades Rev.*, **107**. 119, 1923 ; J. W. Revillon, *ib.*, **90**. 245, 1915 ; W. Leist and A. D. Archangelsky, *Zeit. prakt. Geol.*, **32**. 11, 1924 ; M. Roidot, *Rev. Ind. Min.*, 644, 1922 ; 75, 1923 ; J. Demaret-Freson, *Les minerais de fer de Krivoï-Rog*, Bruxelles, 1903 ; F. Gervais, *Giorny Journ.*, 73, 1907 ; H. K. Scott, *Journ. Iron Steel Inst.* **87**. i, 447, 1913 ; P. P. Pyatnitzkil, *Trans. Inst. Econ. Min. Pet. Moscow*, 9, 1924 ; S. A. M. Bresgunow, *Stahl Eisen*, **47**. 973, 1927 ; L. Schapiro, *Iron Trade Rev.*, **71**. 647, 1922 ; M. Martschenko, *Rev. Met.*, **21**. 121, 1924 ; A. W. Richards, *Electrician*, **85**. 539, 1920.

[54] J. J. Sederholm, *Eng. Min. Journ.*, **113**. 157, 1922 ; Anon., *Mining Journ.*, **87**. 375, 1909 ; *Zeit. prakt. Geol.*, **15**. 294, 1907 ; G. Berg, *Glückauf*, **52**. 45, 1916 ; G. A. Aartovaara, *Ann. Acad. Fennicæ*, **2**. 1, 1910 ; *Stahl Eisen*, **30**. 1109, 1910 ; A. F. Tiegerstedt, *Bull. Fennia Geog. Soc.*, **14**. 8, 1898 ; *Eng.*, **91**. 673, 1901 ; O. Trüstedt, *Bull. Comm. Géol. Finlande*, **19**. 1, 1907 ; *The Iron Resources of the World*, Stockholm, **1**. 547, 1910 ; P. Martell, *Zeit. Berg. Hütt. Maschinenbau*, **26**. 155, 1907 ; O. R. Kuhn, *Eng. Min. Journ.*, **124**. 291, 329, 1927 ; Anon., *Journ. Roy. Soc. Arts*, **68**. 506, 1920 ; *Stahl Eisen*, **38**. 948, 1918 ; *Mining Journ.*, **87**. 375, 1909.

[55] H. Sundholm, *Blad för Bergshandteringens Vanner*, Oerebro, 1909 ; *Jernkontorets Ann.*, **53**. 85, 1898 ; H. Wedding, *Verh. Ver. Beförd. Gewerbfleisses*, **77**. 37, 1898 ; *Stahl Eisen*, **13**. 802, 1893 ; *Die phosphorhaltigen Eisenerze Schwedens und ihre Bedeutung für die deutsche Eisenindustrie*, Berlin, 1898 ; *Zeit. Berg. Hütt. Sal.*, **18**. 662, 1898 ; P. Geimer, *Gewinnung und Beförderung der Eisenerze aus der nordschwedishen Gruben von Gellivare und Kiruna*, Düsseldorf, 1927 ; A. Vosmaer, *Stahl Eisen*, **10**. 185, 299, 306, 1890 ; N. Kjellberg, *Jernkontorets Ann.*, **45**. 350, 1891 ; A. Sjögren, *Wermländska Bergmannaföreningens Annaler*, Filipstad, 14, 1899 ; *Jernkontorets Ann.*, **48**. 13, 1893 ; A. Dellwik, *ib.*, **60**. 259, 1906 ; Anon., *Stahl Eisen*, **12**. 9, 1892 ; W. Tiemann, *ib.*, **15**. 217, 1895 ; *Zeit. Ver. deut. Ing.*, **39**. 542, 1895 ; H. von Post, *Geol. För. Förh. Stockholm*, **12**. 491, 1892 ; E. Fuchs and L. de Launay, *Traité des gites minéraux et métallifères*, Paris, **1**. 714, 1893 ; P. von Tunner, *Das Eisenhüttenwesen in Schweden*, Freiberg, 1898 ; G. Nordenström, *L'industrie minière de la Suède*, Stockholm, 1897 ; *Journ. Iron Steel Inst.*, **54**. ii, 35, 1898 ; J. de Lazurtegui, *Espana*, **1**. 2, 1898 ; J. Hammer, *Tek. Tids.*, **28**. 240, 1898 ; D. A. Louis, *Eng. Mag.*, **16**. 610, 1898 ; **17**. 632, 1899 ; J. Mauerhofer, *Oesterr. Zeit. Berg. Hütt.*, **47**. 313, 328, 1899 ; H. V. Tiberg, *Affärswärlden*, **3**. 28, 1903 ; *Berg. Hütt. Ztg.*, **62**. 307, 1903 ; J. Hereza, *Affärswärlden*, 50, 1903 ; A. Törnebohm, *ib.*, **5**. 275, 1904 ; A. Bygden, *Bull. Geol. Inst. Upsala*, **6**. 92, 1906 ; F. König, *Zeit. Oesterr. Ing. Arch. Ver.*, **58**. 386, 1906 ; F. Henriksen, *Oesterr. Zeit. Berg. Hütt.*,

54. 168, 1906 ; G. Bene, *Bany. Koh. Lapok*, **39.** 533, 1906 ; N. Hedberg, *Jernkontorets Ann.*, **62.** 67, 1907 ; G. G. Bring, *ib.*, **114.** 64, 1930 ; W. Petersson, *ib.*, **62.** 238, 1907 ; **108.** 193, 1924 ; *Tek. Tids.*, **37.** 74, 1907 ; *Oesterr. Zeit. Berg. Hütt.*, **51.** 742, 1903 ; *Congress. Internat. Géol.*, **11.** 29, 1910 ; *Stahl Eisen*, **27.** 1571, 1907 ; *Journ. Iron Steel Inst.*, **114.** ii, 95, 1926 ; J. H. L. Vogt, *Iron Coal Trade Rev.*, **85.** 315, 1912 ; B. Granigg, *Montan Rund.*, 845, 926, 1912 ; B. H. Strom, *Eng. Min. Journ.*, **105.** 381, 1930 ; M. Roessler, *Bull. U.S. Geol. Sur.*, 706, 1921 ; R. Akerman, *Journ. Iron Steel Inst.*, **54.** ii, 7, 1898 ; L. L. Fermor, *ib.*, **84.** ii, 113, 1911 ; W. H. Herdsman, *ib.*, **83.** i, 476, 1911 ; H. Lundbohm, *ib.*, **54.** ii, 111, 1898 ; *Undersökningen rörande Jernmalmstillgangarne* Stockholm, 1898 ; *Congress. Internat. Géol.*, **11.** 5, 1910 ; H. Lundbohm and W. Petersson, *The Iron Resources of the World*, Stockholm, 2. 553, 1910 ; *Engg.*, **84.** 326, 1907 ; *Trans. Amer. Inst. Min. Eng.*, **38.** 766, 1907 ; *Congress. Internat. Géol.*, **11.** 29, 1910 ; A. G. Högbom, *ib.*, **11.** 4, 1910 ; A. Johansson, *Jernkontorets Ann.*, **114.** 623, 1930 ; C. S. Osborne, *Iron Coal Trades Rev.*, **67.** 808, 1903 ; *Mines Minerals*, **24.** 111, 1904 ; *Journ. Lake Superior Min. Inst.*, **9.** 94, 1903 ; H. Arlt, *Glückauf*, **47.** 765, 1911 ; M. Kukuk, *ib.*, **47.** 820, 861, 905, 1911 ; M. Spackeler, *ib.*, **45.** 473, 509, 545, 594, 632, 669, 1909 ; B. Neumann, *ib.*, **44.** 1177, 1908 ; O. Hecker, *ib.*, **44.** 1351, 1908 ; *Zeit. Berg. Hütt. Sal.*, **52.** 61, 1904 ; R. Bärtling, *Zeit. prakt. Geol.*, **16.** 89, 1908 ; O. Stutzer, *ib.*, **14.** 65, 137, 140, 1906 ; *Monatsh. deut. geol. Ges.*, 135, 1907 ; *Berg. Hütt. Rund.*, **3.** 273, 1907 ; *Journ. Iron Steel Inst.*, **74.** ii, 106, 1907 ; J. Head, *ib.*, **45.** i, 47, 1894 ; H. Bauerman, *ib.*, **55.** i, 55, 1899 ; H. Johannsen, *Geol. För. Förh. Stockholm*, **32.** 239, 1910 ; *Proc. World's Eng. Congr. Tokyo*, **33.** 31, 1931 ; *Congress. Internat. Géol.*, **30.** 32, 1910 ; J. Birkinbine, *Iron Age*, **85.** 986, 1910 ; A. Zsigmondy, *Bany. Koh. Lapok*, **36.** 305, 1902 ; *Oesterr. Zeit. Berg. Hütt.*, **51.** 279, 300, 1903 ; R. A. Daly, *Origin of the Iron Ores at Kiruna*, Stockholm, 1915 ; P. A. Geijer, *Igneous Rocks and Ores of Kirunavaara, Luossavaara, and Tuollavaara*, Stockholm, 1910 ; *Econ. Geol.*, **5.** 699, 1910 ; *Sveriges Geol. Undersökning Arsbok*, **12.** 5, 1918 ; *Geol. För. Förh. Stockholm*, **33.** 21, 1912 ; **34.** 727, 1912 ; *Neues Jahrb. Min.*, ii, 437, 1913 ; *Jernkontorets Ann.*, (2), **79.** 243, 1924 ; *Zeit. prakt. Geol.*, **21.** 247, 1913 ; E. Malm, *Bihang Jernkontorets Ann.*, **16.** 167, 1915 ; H. Ereding, *Berg. Hütt. Ztg.*, **62.** 3, 17, 35, 45, 69, 1903 ; B. Simmersbach, *Oesterr. Zeit. Berg. Hütt.*, **62.** 253, 272, 1914 ; P. de Celsis, *Revista Min.*, **53.** 547, 1902 ; L. de Launay, *Ann. Mines*, (10), **4.** 49, 109, 1903 ; P. Nicou, *ib.*, (10), **14.** 221, 341, 1908 ; (10), **19.** 85, 174, 249, 1911 ; (11), **4.** 107, 181, 255, 1923 ; *Les minerais suédois et l'industrie sidérurgique allemande pendant la guerre*, Paris, 1921 ; W. G. Miller, *Canada Min. Journ.*, **31.** 591, 1910 ; B. Kjellberg, *Jernkontorets Ann.*, (2), **76.** 147, 1921 ; N. H. Magnusson, *Sveriges Geol. Undersökning*, 13, 1929 ; E. Kinander, *Journ. Iron Steel Inst.*, **114.** ii, 13, 1926 ; A. Johansson and A. Wahlberg, *ib.*, **114.** ii, 51, 1926 ; L. Nordenfelt, *Journ. Chem. Met. Soc. South Africa*, **25.** 315, 1925 ; J. G. A. Rodin, *Eng.*, **142.** 136, 168, 1926 ; Anon., *Blast Furnace Steel Plant*, **13.** 173, 1925 ; A. B. Sloane, *Jernkontorets Ann.*, (2), **79.** 601, 1924 ; H. V. Winchell, *Min. Scient. Press.*, **102.** 35, 1911 ; W. F. Wilkinson, *Trans. Inst. Min. Met.*, **13.** 489, 1904 ; O. R. Kuhn, *Eng. Min. Journ.*, **124.** 291, 329, 1927 ; C. W. Boise, *ib.*, **110.** 53, 1920 ; G. Brandl, *Stahl Eisen*, **44.** 110, 1924 ; A. Bloch, *Zeit. prakt. Geol.*, **31.** 81, 100, 1923 ; W. Lindgren, *Trans. Amer. Inst. Min. Eng.*, **61.** 120, 1918 ; J. W. Revillon, *Iron Coal Trades Rev.*, **90.** 245, 1915 ; C. R. King, *Eng. Mag.*, **48.** 481, 1915 ; C. Sahlin, *Jernkontorets Ann.*, **64.** 122, 1910 ; E. D. Winslow, *Chem. Met. Engg.*, **8.** 164, 1910.

56 G. Henriksen, *On the Iron Ore Deposits in Sydvaranger, Finmarken, Norway*, Christiania, 1902 ; *The Iron Ore Deposits of Dunderland*, Upsala, 1894 ; E. Fuchs and L. de Launay, *Traité des gîtes minéraux et métallifères*, Paris, 1. 714, 1893 ; *Les gisements de minerai de fer de Sydvaranger*, Paris, 1904 ; *The Iron Ore Deposits at Sydvaranger*, Christiania, 1904 ; *Sundry Geological Problems*, Christiania, 1906 ; *Geological Notes*, Christiania, 1910 ; *Oesterr. Zeit. Berg. Hütt.*, **52.** 232, 1904 ; W. Petersson, *Geol. För. Förh. Stockholm*, **15.** 45, 1894 ; H. Sjögren, *ib.*, **15.** 55, 140, 1893 ; *Trans. Inst. Min. Eng.*, **38.** 766, 1907 ; W. Tiemann, *Zeit. Ver. deut. Ing.*, **39.** 542, 1895 ; *Stahl Eisen*, **15.** 217, 233, 1895 ; L. Possehl, *ib.*, **15.** 424, 1895 ; H. T. Newbigin, *Trans. Fed. Inst. Min. Eng.*, **15.** 154, 1898 ; F. Svenonius and W. Petersson, *Jernkontorets Ann.*, **55.** 215, 1900 ; *Iron Coal Trades Rev.*, **61.** 78, 123, 1900 ; *Glückauf*, **36.** 620, 658, 1900 ; O. Vogel, *Stahl Eisen*, **20.** 530, 590, 1900 ; *Norwegen als Eisen erzeugendes Land*, Düsseldorf, 1900 ; H. C. Carpenter, *Eng. Min. Journ.*, **70.** 372, 1900 ; K. Huldt, *Mining Journ.*, **71.** 1013, 1900 ; C. E. Wegmann, *Zeit. prakt. Geol.*, **34.** 17, 1926 ; H. Everding, *Berg. Hütt. Ztg.*, **62.** 3, 17, 33, 45, 57, 69, 1903 ; B. A. Wendeborn, *ib.*, **63.** 597, 1904 ; P. A. Geijer, *Geol. För. Förh. Stockholm*, **33.** 312, 1911 ; H. L. Geissel, *Eng. News*, **43.** 276, 1900 ; L. de Launay, *Ann. Mines*, (10), **4.** 49, 109, 1903 ; P. Nicou, *ib.*, (10), **19.** 85; 177, 249, 1911 ; H. Louis, *Journ. Iron Steel Inst.*, **61.** i, 416, 1902 ; J. Head, *ib.*, **45.** i, 47, 1894 ; B. Simmersbach, *Zeit. Berg. Hütt. Sal.*, **53.** 19, 1905 ; H. H. Smith, *Mining Journ.*, **86.** 325, 1909 ; *Trans. Inst. Min. Met.*, **32.** 35, 1922 ; M. Lund, *Tek. Ugeblad*, **127.** 1904 ; W. F. Wilkinson, *Trans. Inst. Min. Met.*, **13.** 489, 1904 ; D. E. Woodbridge, *Eng. Mag.*, **43.** 9, 1912 ; *Eng. Min. Journ.*, **91.** 1255, 1910 ; **92.** 260, 1911 ; O. R. Kuhn, *ib.*, **124.** 291, 329, 1927 ; O. Falkenberg, *Metall Erz*, **18.** 631, 1921 ; Anon., *Engg.*, **90.** 383, 1910 ; **93.** 481, 1912 ; J. H. L. Vogt, *Norges Geol. Undersökelse*, 51, 1910 ; 85, 1919 ; *Zeit. prakt. Geol.*, **4.** 78, 1896 ; **11.** 9, 24, 59, 180, 289, 327, 1903 ; **12.** 1, 1904 ; **14.** 60, 1906 ; **15.** 62, 1907 ; **18.** 59, 1910 ; *The Iron Resources of the World*, Stockholm, 2. 605, 1910 ; *Norges Geol. Undersög. Aalog*, 3, 1905 ; *Salten og Ranen*, Kristiania, 1895 ; *Arch. Math. Naturvid. Kristiania*, **10.** 1, 1890 ; *Stahl Eisen*, **14.** 790, 1894 ; *Rev. Univ. Mines*, **30.** 96, 1895 ; W. C. Brögger and J. H. L. Vogt, *Berg. Hütt. Ztg.*, **54.** 106, 1895 ; S. Fosilie, *Norges Geol. Undersoekelse*, 126, 1925 ; Anon., *Iron Coal Trades Rev.*, **99.** 229, 1919 ; A. Udling, *ib.*, **84.** 161, 1912 ; M. Wiull, *ib.*, **76.** 1781, 1907 ; W. Lindgren,

Trans. Amer. Inst. Min. Eng., **61**. 120, 1918; J. Birkinbine, *Iron Age*, **85**. 986, 1910; E. F. Gray, *Board Trade Journ.*, **67**. 540, 1909; A. W. Stelzner, *Berg. Hütt. Ztg.*, **50**. 180, 1891; H. J. Blatt, *Stahl Eisen*, **47**. 502, 1927.

⁵⁷ M. Conway, *Geogr. Journ.*, **53**. 83, 1919; Anon., *Engg.*, **104**. 496, 1917.

⁵⁸ Anon., *Ironmonger*, **172**. 105, 1920.

⁵⁹ G. S. Blake, *The Mineral Resources of Palestine and Transjordania*, Jerusalem, 35, 1930.

⁶⁰ I. M. Toll, *Eng. Min. Journ.*, **112**. 846, 1921; Anon., *Board Trade Journ.*, **61**. 550, 1907.

⁶¹ K. E. Weiss, *Zeit. prakt. Geol.*, **9**. 249, 1901; C. Schmeisser, *ib.*, **14**. 186, 1906; F. Frech, *Glückauf*, **51**. 381, 412, 438, 464, 1915; G. M. Edwards, *Trans. Inst. Min. Met.*, **23**. 192, 1913.

⁶² Anon., *Iron Coal Trades Rev.*, **115**. 131, 1927.

⁶³ O. H. Little, *Geography and Geology of Makalla (South Arabia)*, Cairo, 135, 1925.

⁶⁴ K. Fatch, *Rev. Univ. Mines*, (8), **1**. 270, 1929; A. F. Stahl, *Chem. Ztg.*, **17**. 1910, 1893; R. Helmhacker, *Eng. Min. Journ.*, **66**. 38, 1898; H. Winklehner, *Oesterr. Zeit. Berg. Hütt.*, **47**. 645, 1899; E. Vredenburg, *Mem. Geol. Sur. India*, **31**. 291, 1901; E. Böhme, *Stahl Eisen*, **48**. 1577, 1928; G. E. Pilgrim, *Report on the Minerals of Economic Value investigated in the Provinces of Fars and Kerman in Southern Persia*, Simla, 1919; *Mem. Geol. Sur. India*, **26**. iv, 144, 1908; M. Nottmayer, *The Iron Ore Resources of the World*, Stockholm, **2**. 895, 1910; Anon., *Oesterr. Zeit. Berg. Hütt.*, **52**. 705, 1904.

⁶⁵ F. Beyschlag, *Zeit. prakt. Geol.*, **26**. 81, 1918; H. A. Karajian, *Mineral Resources of Armenia and Anatolia*, New York, 1920; W. F. Thomas, *Trans. Amer. Inst. Min. Eng.*, **28**. 208, 1898; N. M. Penzer, *Mining Mag.*, **21**. 220, 1919.

⁶⁶ D. Ghambashidze, *Mineral Resources of Georgia and Caucasia*, London, 1919; V. Babet, *Richesses Minières*, Paris, 1920; J. A. Phillips and H. Louis, *Ore Deposits*, London, 550, 1896.

⁶⁷ Anon., *Rec. Geol. Sur. India*, **38**. 313, 1910.

⁶⁸ J. Kirsopp, *The Near East*, **16**. 179, 205, 231, 1919; A. Bose, *Journ. Iron Steel Inst.*, **89**. i, 528, 1914; T. H. Hughes, *Records India Geol. Sur.*, **7**. 25, 1874; H. C. Jones, *ib.*, **54**. 203, 1922; **64**. 111, 1930; P. N. Bose, *ib.*, **20**. 167, 1887; **26**. 161, 1893; **31**. 167, 1904; **33**. 55, 1905; *General Rep. Geol. Sur. India*, 43, 1898; C. S. Middlemiss, *ib.*, 20, 1898; E. Vrendenburg and L. L. Fermor, *ib.*, 14, 1903; E. Vrendenburg, *ib.*, **31**. 108, 1904; **34**. 313, 1906; T. H. de la Touche, *Bibliography of Indian Geology and Physical Geography*, Calcutta, 1918; V. Ball, *Mem. India Geol. Sur.*, **15**. 112, 1880; J. C. Brown and A. M. Heron, *ib.*, **44**. ii, 1, 1923; J. C. Brown, *Rec. India Geol. Sur.*, **61**. 180, 1928; *Mining Mag.*, **24**. 339, 1921; **25**. 11, 1921; *Rec. Indian Geol. Sur.*, **47**. 137, 1916; L. L. Fermor, *ib.*, **34**. 128, 1907; **43**. 18, 1913; **50**. iv, 268, 1919; **53**. iii, 239, 1921; E. L. G. Clegg, *ib.*, **74**. 1112, 1924; S. K. Roy, *Proc. Indian Science Congress*, **15**. 288, 1928; V. S. Swanimathan, *ib.*, **15**. 287, 1928; T. H. Holland, *Board Trade Journ.*, **60**. 426, 1908; *Sketch of the Mineral Resources of India*, Calcutta, 1908; *Trans. Min. Geol. Inst. India*, 34, 1907; *The Iron Resources and Iron Industries of the Southern Districts, Madras Presidency*, Calcutta, 1892; *Mem. Geol. Sur. India*, **30**. 111, 1901; *Records Geol. Sur. India*, **32**. 51, 1904; *The Iron Ore Resources of the World*, Stockholm, **2**. 901, 1910; F. H. de la Touche, *ib.*, **2**. 904, 1910; C. K. Leith, *Foundry Trade Journ.*, **34**. 259, 1926; Anon., *Bull. Imp. Inst.*, **24**. 737, 1926; *Iron Coal Trades Rev.*, **108**. 515, 1924; J. F. Spedding, *Eng. Min. Journ.*, **113**. 403, 1922; A. Sahlin, *Ironmonger*, **123**. 159, 1908; R. B. Foote, *Records Geol. Sur. India*, **25**. 1, 1897; S. A. Bilgrami, *Journ. Iron Steel Inst.*, **56**. ii, 65, 1899; R. H. Mahon, *ib.*, **56**. ii, 83, 1899; R. D. Oldham, *Mem. Geol. Sur. India*, **31**. 1, 1901; T. L. Walker, *ib.*, **33**. 19, 1903; H. H. Hayden, *ib.*, **36**. 1, 1904; *The Geology of Spiti, with parts of Bashahr and Rupshu*, London, 1904; C. R. von Schwarz, *Stahl Eisen*, **21**. 333, 391, 1901; *Journ. Iron Steel Inst.*, **56**. ii, 89, 1899; F. J. Stephens, *Trans. Inst. Min. Met.*, **12**. 192, 1902; J. W. Evans, *Rec. Mysore Geol. Dept.*, **1**. 11, 1902; A. Primrose, *ib.*, **3**. 210, 1904; W. F. Smeeth, *ib.*, **5**. 17, 1906; V. S. S. Iyer, *ib.*, **3**. 240, 1904; E. W. Wetherell, *Mem. Mysore Geol. Dept.*, **2**. 33, 1905; **3**. 1, 1906; H. K. Slater, *ib.*, **6**. 5, 1907; H. and F. J. Warth, *Chem. News*, **87**. 256, 1903; E. P. Martin and H. Louis, *Agric. Reg.*, 3, 1904; J. C. Scott, *Journ. Soc. Arts*, **53**. 623, 1905; V. S. S. Iyer, *Report on the Mineral Resources of the Kalabasti Zamindary*, Madras, Bangalore, 1906; E. Krenkel, *Zeit. prakt. Geol.*, **38**. 81, 1930; R. Mather, *Journ. Soc. Arts*, **75**. 600, 1927; A. P. Som, *Blast Furnace Steel Plant*, **14**. 250, 274, 1926; J. V. McCartney, *ib.*, **11**. 140, 1923; C. P. Perin, *Yearbook Amer. Iron Steel Inst.*, 281, 1920; C. M. Weld, *Econ. Geol.*, **10**. 435, 1915.

⁶⁹ W. R. Dunstan, *Reports on Results of the Mineral Survey of Ceylon*, Calcutta, 1904; *Miscellaneous Colonial Reports*, 37, 1906.

⁷⁰ J. C. Brown, *Rec. Geol. Sur. India*, **47**. ii, 137, 1916; H. C. Jones, *ib.*, **64**. 111, 1930; J. C. Brown and A. M. Heron, *Mem. Geol. Sur. India*, **44**. ii, 1, 1923.

⁷¹ J. B. Scrivenor, *Eng. Min. Journ.*, **114**. 239, 1922; *The Geology of Malayan Ore Deposits*, London, 1928; A. B. Snow, *Mining Journ.*, **72**. 465, 1902; *Iron Coal Trades Rev.*, **64**. 902, 1902.

⁷² T. Posewitz, *Borneo : its Geology and Mineral Resources*, London, 1892; J. W. Evans, *The Iron Ore Resources of the World*, Stockholm, **2**. 989, 1910; G. A. F. Molengraaff, *ib.*, **2**. 993, 1910.

⁷³ A. W. Smyth, *Notes of a Journey on the Upper Makong, Siam*, London, 14, 1895; Anon., *Iron Coal Trades Rev.*, **108**. 172, 1924.

⁷⁴ Anon., *Iron Age*, **104**. 300, 1919; *Journ. Roy. Soc. Arts*, **68**. 747, 1920; **70**. 157, 1922; A. C. Kruijt, *Bijdr. Ned. Indie*, **9**. 148, 1903; A. L. ter Braake, *Eng. Min. Journ.*, **115**. 1158, 1923; W. Dieckmann, *Die Infenieur*, **34**. 782, 1919; C. K. Leith, *Foundry Trade Journ.*, **34**. 259, 1926.

[75] P. Müller-Herrings, *Glückauf*, **51**. 913, 937, 961, 985, 1915 ; J. Elbert, *Zeit. prakt. Geol.*, **17**. 509, 1909.
[76] Anon., *Eng. Min. Journ.*, **114**. 504, 1922.
[77] F. Rinne, *Zeit. prakt. Geol.*, **10**. 115, 1902 ; F. A. Dalburg and W. E. Pratt, *Iron Coal Trades Rev.*, **90**. 474, 1915 ; *Philippine Journ. Science*, **9**. 201, 1914 ; J. F. Springer, *Iron Trade Rev.*, **58**. 77, 1916 ; D. T. Day, *Eng. Mag.*, **17**. 242, 1899 ; E. C. Smith, *Mines Minerals*, **25**. 199, 1905 ; W. D. Smith and P. R. Fanning, *Iron Coal Trades Rev.*, **84**. 49, 1912 ; W. E. Pratt, *Trans. Amer. Inst. Min. Eng.*, **53**. 90, 1916 ; *Philippine Journ. Science*, **10**. 323, 1915 ; W. E. Pratt and V. E. Lednicky, *ib.*, **10**. 335, 1915 ; F. T. Eddingfield, *ib.*, **9**. 263, 1914 ; G. I. Adams, *ib.*, **5**. 106, 1910 ; *Mining World*, **33**. 463, 1909 ; H. D. McCaskey, *Report on a Geological Reconnaissance of the Iron Region of Angat, Bulacan*, Manila, 1903 ; *Bull. Philippine Mining Bur.*, 3, 1903 ; J. F. Kemp, *The Iron Ore Resources of the World*, Stockholm, **2**. 983, 1910 ; H. Nishihara, *Eng. Min. Journ.*, **119**. 717, 1925 ; Anon., *Mining Journ.*, **127**. 474, 1922 ; E. Glasser, *ib.*, **75**. 616, 1904 ; Anon., *Min. Eng. World*, **42**. 1116, 1915 ; G. F. Becker, *Mines Minerals*, **19**. 109, 1899 ; M. Goodman, *Mineral Resources of the Philippine Islands*, Manila, 1909.
[78] C. M. Weld, *Trans. Amer. Inst. Min. Eng.*, **50**. 236, 1914.
[79] Anon., *Mining Mag.*, **21**. 307, 1919 ; **22**. 113, 1920 ; G. Dupouy, *Études minéralogiques sur l'Indochine française*, Paris, 1913 ; E. Fuchs, *Ann. Mines*, (8), **2**. 185, 1882 ; E. Beauverie, *Bull. Soc. Ind. Min.*, **14**. 446, 1911 ; H. Charpentier, *ib.*, **4**. 615, 1905.
[80] W. W. Rockhill, *The Land of the Lamas*, London, 1891 ; L. A. Waddell, *Lhasa and its Mysteries*, London, 1891 ; H. Bower, *Diary of a Journey Across Tibet*, London, 1894 ; M. S. Welby, *Through Unknown Tibet*, London, 1898.
[81] B. P. Torgasheff, *The Mineral Industry of the Far East*, Shanghai, 1930 ; W. Smith, *A Geographical Study of Coal and Iron in China*, Liverpool, 1927 ; K. Wendt, *Stahl Eisen*, **51**. 1, 1931 ; V. K. Ting, *Mining Mag.*, **17**. 188, 1917 ; *The China Year Book—1921–22*, Peking, 1922 ; Anon., *Iron Coal Trades Rev.*, **101**. 555, 1920 ; **103**. 978, 1921 ; *Iron Age*. **107**. 328, 1921 ; C. Y. Wang, *Journ. Assoc. Chinese Amer. Eng.*, **6**. 5, 1925 ; *The Mineral Resources of China*, Tientsin, 1922 ; *Trans. Amer. Inst. Min. Eng.*, **61**. 130, 1917 ; *Yearbook Amer. Iron Steel Inst.*, 341, 1923 ; W. A. Wong, *Eng. Min. Journ.*, **109**. 239, 1920 ; H. A. Andresen, *Iron Coal Trades Rev.*, **99**. 632, 1919 ; M. Raby, *Bull. Econ. Indo-Chine*, 444, 1923 ; F. R. Tegengren, *The Iron Ores and Iron Industry of China*, Peking, 1923 ; *Mem. Geol. Sur. China*, 1, 1921 ; 2, 1923 ; W. Wen-hao, *ib.*, 1, 1919 ; L. W. Hoyt, *Iron Trade Rev.*, **72**. 227, 303, 1923 ; *Iron Coal Trades Rev.*, **107**. 126, 156, 198, 1923 ; H. L. Hsueh, *ib.*, **116**. 938, 1928 ; T. T. Read, *Eng. Min. Journ.*, **85**. 1296, 1908 ; *Commerce Rep. U.S. Dept.*, 7, 1922 ; *Trans. Amer. Inst. Min. Eng.*, **43**. 3, 1912 ; *The Iron Ore Resources of the World*, Stockholm, **2**. 915, 1910 ; W. H. Schockley, *ib.*, **34**. 841, 1903 ; C. M. Weld, *ib.*, **44**. 27, 1912 ; **50**. 236, 1914 ; H. F. Bain, *ib.*, **61**. 132, 1918 ; M. S. Welby, *Through Unknown Tibet*, London, 365, 1898 ; J. G. H. Glass, *B.A. Rep.*, 871, 1900 ; C. Bernard, *Echo Mines*, **27**. 1063, 1899 ; C. Y. Hsieh and C. C. Liu, *Bull. Geol. Sur. China*, 9, 1927 ; T. O. Chu and C. C. Li, *ib.*, 6, 1924 ; C. C. Liu and J. C. Chao, *Preliminary Report on the Geology and Mineral Resources of Kiangsu*, Pekin, 1924 ; K. Nishizawa, *Mining Journ.*, **103**. 1004, 1913 ; *Journ. Roy. Soc. Arts*, **58**. 935, 1910 ; **61**. 1018, 1913 ; H. Murakami, *Geology of the An-Shan Iron Mine District, South Manchuria*, Dairen, 1922 ; E. C. Baber, *Travels and Researches in Western China*, London, 1882 ; M. Brucher, *Glückauf*, **60**. 759, 789, 811, 840, 1924 ; A. Hosie, *Three Years in Western China*, London, 1890 ; F. F. von Richthofen, *Letters to the Shanghai Chamber of Commerce*, Shanghai, 1903 ; C. K. Leith, *Foundry Trade Journ.*, **34**. 259, 1926 ; O. R. Kuhn, *Iron Trade Rev.*, **76**. 215, 1924 ; A. Bordeaux, *Bull. Soc. Ind. Min.*, (5), **10**. 10, 1914 ; *Rev. Univ. Mines*, (5), **5**. 235, 1914 ; F. Lux, *Stahl Eisen*, **33**. 545, 599, 1913 ; A. J. Seltzer, *Mining Scient. Press*, **100**. 546, 1909 ; C. E. Heurteau, *Ann. Mines*, (10), **6**. 107, 1904 ; A. Berteaux, *ib.*, (10), **11**. 156, 1907 ; J. C. Brown, *Records Geol. Sur. India*, **61**. 180, 1928 ; *Mem. Geol. Sur. India*, **47**. i, 1, 1920 ; M. Duclos, *Colliery Guard.*, **75**. 304, 1898 ; *La mission Lyonnaise d'exploration commerciale en Chine*, Lyons, 1898 ; G. Leinung, *Stahl Eisen*, **18**. 221, 1898 ; *Zeit. prakt. Geol.*, **6**. 67, 1898 ; A. Dieseldorff, *ib.*, **7**. 206, 1899 ; P. Dahms, *Geol. Centr.*, **5**. 677, 1904 ; H. Lantenois, *Ann. Mines*, (10), **11**. 415, 1907 ; K. Nishizawa, *Journ. Soc. Arts*, **58**. 935, 1910 ; C. C. Wang, *Bull. Geol. Sur. China*, 10, 1928 ; L. W. Hoyt, *Iron Trade Rev.*, **72**. 227, 303, 1923 ; *Iron Coal Trades Rev.*, **107**. 126, 156, 198, 1923 ; P. F. Kohlhaas, *Blast Furnace Steel Plant*, **11**. 37, 1923 ; K. E. Humbert, *Iron Age*, **112**. 461, 534, 598, 1923.
[82] E. E. Ahnert, *Mem. Geol. Sur. China*, 7, 1929 ; Anon., *Iron Coal Trades Rev.*, **118**. 610, 1929 ; H. Fromm, *Stahl Eisen*, **45**. 979, 1925.
[83] K. Inoaye, *The Iron Ore Resources of the World*, Stockholm, **2**. 927, 1910 ; T. Mukai, *Stahl Eisen*, **18**. 541, 1898 ; P. Jordan, *Ann. Mines*, (9), **14**. 530, 1898 ; O. Vogel, *Mining Journ.*, **70**. 32, 1900 ; A. Selwyn-Brown, *Eng. Mag.*, **40**. 568, 1910 ; C. K. Leith, *Foundry Trade Journ.*, **34**. 259, 1926 ; H. Nishihara, *Eng. Min. Journ.*, **114**. 239, 1922 ; M. Striebeck, *Zeit. Berg. Hütt. Sal.*, **59**. 287, 1911 ; C. E. Heurteau, *Ann. Mines*, (10), **6**. 106, 1904 ; G. S. Herrick, *Iron Age*, **121**. 55, 1928 ; H. C. Huggins, *Iron Coal Trades Rev.*, **106**. 641, 1923 ; E. Kothny, *Stahl Eisen*, **43**. 777, 813, 1923 ; *Iron Age*, **112**. 1317, 1591, 1658, 1923 ; L. P. Sidney, *Iron Age*, **106**. 1045, 1920 ; F. Baare, *Stahl Eisen*, **49**. 1470, 1929 ; K. Tsuru, *Rept. Ryojun Coll. Eng.*, **1**. 143. 1931 ; M. Watanabe, *Science Rep. Tohoku Univ.*, **3**. 101, 1927.
[84] K. Inoaye, *The Iron Ore Resources of the World*, Stockholm, **2**. 973, 1910 ; C. F. Wang, *Blast Furnace Steel Plant*, **6**. 109, 1918 ; *Trans. Amer. Inst. Min. Eng.*, **59**. 395, 1918 ; Anon., *Mining Journ.*, **85**. 545, 1909 ; W. F. Collins, *Eng.*, **147**. 486, 1929.

[85] P. Polevoi, *Mining Mag.*, **23**. 178, 1920 ; Anon., *L'Age de Fer*, **36**. 590, 1920 ; *Iron Coal Trades Rev.*, **101**. 442, 1920 ; A. G. Marshall, *Iron Coal Trades Rev.*, **87**. 88, 1913 ; A. Bordeaux, *Rev. Univ. Mines*, (4), **38**. 203, 1912 ; W. Hotz, *Zeit. prakt. Geol.*, **17**. 268, 1909 ; A. A. Inostrancew, *Trav. Sec. Nat. St. Petersburg*, **35**. 21, 1909.

[86] R. von B. Baum, *Stahl Eisen*, **23**. 713, 1903 ; H. Bartsch, *ib.*, **49**. 1487, 1929 ; C. de Kalb, *Mining Met.*, **6**. 563, 1925 ; O. R. Kuhn, *Eng. Min. Journ.*, **123**. 803, 1927 ; L. Barreiro, *Ingen. Constr.*, **2**. 9, 1924 ; L. Joleaud, *Bull. Soc. Enc. Nat. Ind.*, **119**. 417, 1920 ; W. Dieckmann, *Zeit. prakt. Geol.*, **20**. 385, 1912 ; F. Klockmann, *ib.*, **21**. 202, 1913 ; M. Brun, *Bull. Soc. Ind. Min.*, (5), **10**. 350, 1914 ; E. Brumder, *Glückauf*, **50**. 1509, 1533, 1553, 1914 ; L. Adaro and A. del Valle, *Rev. Min.*, **61**. 133, 1910 ; M. Simon, *Ann. Mines*, (10), **13**. 269, 1908 ; Anon., *Iron Age*, **117**. 986, 1926 ; *Iron Coal Trades Rev.*, **101**. 586, 1920 ; L. de Launay, *Les richesses minérales de l'Afrique*, Paris, 164, 1903 ; C. Rubio y Munoz, *Bol. Inst. Geol. España*, (2), **12**. 1, 1911 ; A. del Valle and P. F. Iruegas, *ib.*, (2), **18**. 159, 1917 ; A. del Valle, *Zone oriental du Maroc. Region de Guelaya*, Madrid, 1926 ; P. Geijer, *Econ. Geol.*, **22**. 537, 1927 ; *Jernkontorets Ann.*, **111**. 111, 1927 ; O. R. Kuhn, *Eng. Min. Journ.*, **123**. 803, 1927.

[87] E. Dietz, *Rev. Univ. Mines*, **17**. 165, 1899 ; *Stahl Eisen*, **19**. 669, 1899 ; R. Chudeau, *Rev. Gén. Sciences*, **15**. 703, 1904 ; P. Nicou, *The Iron Ore Resources of the World*, Stockholm, **2**. 999, 1910 ; *Zeit. prakt. Geol.*, **17**. 498, 1909 ; M. Simon, *Ann. Mines*, (9), **9**, 563, 1896 ; (10), **7**. 575, 1905 ; (10), **13**. 13, 269, 1908 ; (10), **17**. 524, 1910 ; M. Dussert, *ib.*, (11), **1**. 69, 135, 1912 ; *Étude sur les gisements de fer de l'Algerie*, Paris, 1912 ; M. Pernollet, *Ann. Mines*, (4), **8**. 595, 1845 ; H. Carnot, *ib.*, (8), **18**. 1, 1890 ; M. Tingry, *ib.*, (9), **8**. 184, 1895 ; M. Sergère, *ib.*, (9), **8**. 188, 1895 ; M. Poncelet, *ib.*, (9), **16**. 221, 1899 ; (10), **17**. 531, 1910 ; G. Baum, *Stahl Eisen*, **23**. 713, 1903 ; G. B. Traverso, *Rass. Min.*, **19**. 98, 1903 ; Anon., *Iron Age*, **117**. 986, 1926 ; *Iron Coal Trades Rev.*, **87**. 538, 1913 ; C. T. Grellet, *Amer. Manf.*, **54**. 735, 1894 ; L. de Launay, *Les richesses minérales de l'Afrique*, Paris, 164, 1903 ; R. von B. Baum, *Stahl Eisen*, **23**. 713, 1903 ; P. Cazeneuve, *Bull. Soc. Enc. Nat. Ind.*, **109**. 444, 1907 ; O. R. Kuhn, *Eng. Min. Journ.*, **123**. 803, 1927 ; E. Schrödter, *Stahl Eisen*, **16**. 265, 1896 ; M. Clère, *ib.*, **88**. 460, 1909 ; L. Joleaud, *Bull. Soc. Enc. Nat. Ind.*, **119**. 417, 1920 ; B. Simmersbach, *Zeit. prakt. Geol.*, **29**. 27, 1921 ; L. Gentil, *Étude géologique du bassin de la Tafna*, Alger, 1903 ; J. Blayae, *Esquisse géologique du bassin de la Seybouse*, Alger, 1912 ; P. Geijer, *Econ. Geol.*, **22**. 537, 1927 ; *Jernkontorets Ann.*, **111**. 111, 1927.

[88] P. Nicou, *Bull. Soc. Ind. Min.*, (5), **5**. 441, 1909 ; *The Iron Ore Resources of the World*, Stockholm, **2**. 1003, 1910 ; O. R. Kuhn, *Eng. Min. Journ.*, **123**. 803, 1927 ; M. Clère, *ib.*, **88**. 460, 1909 ; E. J. L. Berkeley, *Board Trade Journ.*, **56**. 137, 1907 ; **58**. 178, 1907 ; E. Fuchs and L. de Launay, *Traité des gîtes minéraux et métallifères*, Paris, **1**. 721, 1893 ; *Les richesses minérales de l'Afrique*, Paris, 164, 1903 ; A. Prost, *Ann. Mines*, (9), **15**. 533, 1899 ; R. von B. Baum, *Stahl Eisen*, **23**. 713, 1903 ; L. Joleaud, *Bull. Soc. Enc. Nat. Ind.*, **119**. 417, 1920 ; H. Arlt, *Glückauf*, **49**. 1129, 1169, 1913 ; B. Granigg, *Oesterr. Zeit. Berg. Hütt.*, **57**. 739, 755, 779, 793, 1909 ; A. J. McInierny, *Iron Coal Trades Rev.*, **65**. 1439, 1902 ; G. B. Traverso, *Rass. Min.*, **19**. 98, 1903 ; H. Carnot, *Ann. Mines*, (8), **18**. 1, 1890 ; K. Roberty, *L'Industrie Extractive en Tunisie*, Tunis, 1908 ; M. Solignac, *Compt. Rend.*, **191**. 107, 1930 ; L. Pervinquière, *Étude géologique de la Tunisie centrale*, Paris, 1903 ; L. Berthon, *L'industrie en Tunisie*, Tunis, 1922 ; L. Berthon and M. Solignac, *Comm. Congres. Géol. Internat. Madrid*, 101, 1926 ; P. Fourmarier, *Ann. Soc. Géol. Belg.*, **45**. 3, 1923 ; P. Geijer, *Econ. Geol.*, **22**. 537, 1927 ; *Jernkontorets Ann.*, **111**. 111, 1927.

[89] W. F. Hume, *The Distribution of Iron Ores in Egypt*, Cairo, 1909 ; *The Iron Ore Resources of the World*, Stockholm, **2**. 1009, 1910 ; *Topography and Geology of South-Eastern Sinai*, Cairo, 1906 ; T. Barron and W. F. Hume, *Topography and Geology of the Eastern Desert of Egypt*, Cairo, 1902 ; J. Ball, *A Description of the First or Aswan Cataract of the Nile*, Cairo, 1907 ; Anon., *Board Trade Journ.*, **61**. 550, 1908.

[90] I. M. Toll, *Eng. Min. Journ.*, **112**. 846, 1921.

[91] A. J. McInierny, *Iron Coal Trades Rev.*, **65**. 1439, 1902 ; S. C. Dunn and G. W. Grabham, *The Iron Ore Resources of the World*, Stockholm, **2**. 1021, 1910 ; A. Hébert, *Compt. Rend.*, **140**. 163, 1907.

[92] W. F. Hume, *The Iron Ore Resources of the World*, Stockholm, **2**. 1016, 1910.

[93] L. de Launay, *Les richesses minérales de l'Afrique*, Paris, 164, 1903.

[94] J. W. Evans, *The Iron Ore Resources of the World*, Stockholm, 2, 1029, 1910.

[95] W. Koert, *The Iron Ore Resources of the World*, Stockholm, **2**. 717, 1910 ; C. Gagel, *Glückauf*, **45**. 1029, 1909 ; F. Tornau, *ib.*, **43**. 382, 1907 ; *Monatsb. deut. geol. Ges.*, 67, 1907 ; K. Schmeisser, *Glückauf*, **38**. 1268, 1902 ; *Colliery Guardian*, **85**. 187, 1903.

[96] R. A. Farquharson, *First Report on the Geology and Mineral Resources of British Somaliland*, London, 1924 ; O. R. Kuhn, *Eng. Min. Journ.*, **123**. 803, 1927.

[97] Anon., *Handbook of Portuguese Nyasaland*, London, 1920.

[98] L. de Launay, *Les richesses minérales de l'Afrique*, Paris, 164, 1903 ; A. Lacroix, *Les richesses minérales de Madagascar*, Paris, 1913 ; *Rev. Scient.*, **2**. 257, 1913 ; J. Goursat, *Ann. Mines*, (11), **16**. 5, 77, 1929 ; L. Pelatan, *Rev. Univ. Mines*, **52**. 278, 1901 ; Anon., *Bulletin Économique de Madagascar*, Tananarive, 1, 1919 ; 2, 1920 ; *Iron Coal Trades Rev.*, **85**. 827, 1912 ; E. Bonneford, *Bull. Soc. Ing. Civil*, (7), **1**. 95, 1913 ; O. R. Kuhn, *Eng. Min. Journ.*, **123**. 803, 1927.

⁹⁹ Anon., *Manual of Portuguese East Africa*, London, 1920.

¹⁰⁰ Anon., *Special Reports to the Mineral Resources Bureau*, Mbabane, 1920.

¹⁰¹ R. M. W. Swan, *The Ruined Cities of Mashonaland*, London, 349, 1892; A. J. C. Molyneaux, *Bulawayo Chronicle*, Sept. 12, 1903; O. R. Kuhn, *Eng. Min. Journ.*, **123**. 803, 1927; J. S. Diller, *Min. Resources U.S. Geol. Sur.*, i, 29, 1913; F. P. Mennell, *The Iron Ore Resources of the World*, Stockholm, **2**. 1051, 1910; H. J. van der Byl, *Journ. Soc. Arts*, **77**. 500, 1929; *Iron Coal Trades Rev.*, **118**. 329, 356, 1929; Anon., *Journ. Chem. Met. Min. South Africa*, **27**. 174, 1927; *Mining Journ.*, **139**. 804, 1922; *Eng.*, **137**. 144, 1924; J. H. Holden, *Foundry Trade Journ.*, **29**. 28, 1924; G. H. Blenkinsop, *Iron Coal Trades Rev.*, **102**. 468, 1921; E. Bury, *ib.*, **103**. 435, 1921; H. Schneiderhöhn, *Arch. Eisenhüttenwesen*, **4**. 269, 1930.

¹⁰² F. W. Harbord, *Iron Coal Trades Rev.*, **80**. 839, 1910; F. W. Harbord and T. G. Trevor, *Rep. Transvaal Govt. Min. Eng.*, 1910; F. H. Hatch, *The Geology of South Africa*, London, 266, 1905; A. L. Hall, *Bull. Geol. Sur. Mines Dept. South Africa*, 1, 1911; *Trans. Geol. Soc. South Africa*, **12**. 41, 1909; *Rep. Geol. Sur. Transvaal*, 73, 1906; G. H. Stanley, *South African Journ. Ind.*, **1**. 307, 1917; **3**. 627, 1920; A. L. Hall and C. J. N. Jourdan, *ib.*, **2**. 1118, 1919; L. de Launay, *Les richesses minérales de l'Afrique*, Paris, 164, 1903; P. A. Wagner, *The Iron Ore Deposits of the Union of South Africa*, Pretoria, 1928; *Trans. Geol. Soc. South Africa*, **23**. 118, 1921; A. W. Rogers, *The Iron Ore Resources of the World*, Stockholm, **2**. 1067, 1910; G. A. F. Moldengraaff, *ib.*, **2**. 1059, 1910; *Géologie de la république Sud-Africane du Transvaal*, Paris, 1901; H. Kynaston, *Rep. Geol. Sur. Transvaal*, 35, 1906.

¹⁰³ A. W. Rogers, *The Iron Ore Resources of the World*, Stockholm, 1910; *South Africa Engg.*, **24**. 2, 1915; A. L. du Toit, *ib.*, **24**. 1, 1915; D. F. Forsyth and R. Dunlop, *ib.*, **24**. 27, 1915; O. R. Kuhn, *Eng. Min. Journ.*, **123**. 803, 1927; Anon., *Bull. Imp. Inst.*, **18**. 82, 1920; *Iron Coal Trades Rev.*, **103**. 100, 1921; T. N. Dewar, *ib.*, **120**. 604, 642, 1930; H. Schneiderhöhn, *Stahl Eisen*, **51**. 68, 1931; E. Krenkel, *Naturwiss.*, **17**. 57, 1929.

¹⁰⁴ F. H. Hatch, *Iron Coal Trades Journ.*, **87**. 45, 1910; *Report on the Mines and Mineral Resources of Natal*, London, 1910; Anon., *Eng.*, **138**. 594, 1924; H. Kynaston, *Rep. Geol. Survey Natal*, 19, 1913; G. H. Stanley, *South African Journ. Ind.*, **1**. 307, 1917; **3**. 627, 1920; J. P. Hamilton, *Trans. Fed. Inst. Min. Eng.*, **3**. 884, 1892.

¹⁰⁵ C. Guillemain, *Zeit. prakt. Geol.*, **18**. 138, 1910; P. A. Wagner, *Mem. Geol. Sur. Union South Africa*, 7, 1916; W. Koert, *The Iron Ore Resources of the World*, Stockholm, **2**. 1045, 1910; Anon., *Bull. Imp. Inst.*, **13**. 233, 1915; **24**. 536, 1926; C. Dantz, *Mitt. deut. Schutzgeb.*, **15**. 139, 1903; H. Schneiderhöhn, *Metall Erz*, **18**. 225, 266, 1921; K. Schmeisser, *Glückauf*, **38**. 1268, 1902; *Colliery Guardian*, **85**. 187, 1903.

¹⁰⁶ G. Castelli, *Rass. Min.*, **62**. 101, 125, 1925.

¹⁰⁷ Anon., *Peace Handbooks of the Foreign Office*, London, **19**. 25, 1920.

¹⁰⁸ X. Stainier, *Trans. Fed. Inst. Min. Eng.*, **15**. 491, 1898; Anon., *Manual of Belgian Congo*, London, 1920; S. H. Ball and M. K. Shaler, *Trans. Amer. Inst. Min. Eng.*, **41**. 210, 1910; J. Cornet, *Rev. Univ. Mines*, **28**. 217, 1894.

¹⁰⁹ G. F. J. Preumont, *Ann. Mines*, (10), **7**. 575, 1905; L. Brustier, *ib.*, (11), **3**. 137, 1923; L. de Launay, *Les richesses minérales de l'Afrique*, 164, 1903; J. Cornet, *The Iron Ore Resources of the World*, Stockholm, **2**. 1037, 1910; M. Barrat, *Ann. Mines*, (9), **7**. 458, 1895.

¹¹⁰ K. Schmeisser, *Glückauf*, **38**. 1268, 1902; *Colliery Guardian*, **85**. 187, 1903; L. Brustier, *Ann. Mines*, (12), **3**. 137, 1923.

¹¹¹ K. Schmeisser, *Glückauf*, **38**. 1268, 1902; *Colliery Guardian*, **85**. 187, 1903; E. Ackermann, *Chem. Ztg.*, **30**. 62, 1906; W. Koert, *Erzbergbau*, **4**. 80, 1907; *The Iron Ore Resources of the World*, Stockholm, 1910; Anon., *Bull. Imp. Inst.*, **13**. 410, 1915; *London Foreign Office Historical Handbooks*, 105, 110, 1920; F. Hupfeld, *Mining Journ.*, **70**. 501, 1899.

¹¹² Anon., *Peace Handbooks of the Foreign Office*, London, **20**. 37, 1920.

¹¹³ H. Clifford, *Special Report to the Mineral Resources Bureau*, London, 1921; C. Guillemain, *Abh. Pruss. Geol. Landesanst.*, 62, 1909; W. R. Dunstan, *South African Engg.*, **12**. 5, 1909; *Eng.*, **101**. 465, 1906.

¹¹⁴ K. Schmeisser, *Glückauf*, **38**. 1268, 1902; *Colliery Guardian*, **85**. 187, 1903; *Zeit. prakt. Geol.*, **14**. 73, 1905; O. R. Kuhn, *Eng. Min. Journ.*, **123**. 803, 1927; W. Koert, *Glückauf*, **41**. 1640, 1905.

¹¹⁵ F. Dixey, *Rep. Geol. Sur. Sierra Leone*, 1919; *Mining Mag.*, **23**. 213, 1920.

¹¹⁶ O. B. Böggild, *Medd. Grönland*, **32**. 625, 1906.

¹¹⁷ J. E. Woodman, *Iron Ore Occurrences in Canada*, Ottawa, 1909; E. Haanel, *The Iron Ore Resources of the World*, Stockholm, **2**. 721, 1910; C. K. Leith, *Econ. Geol.*, **3**. 276, 1908; *Canada Mining Journ.*, **29**. 370, 1908; *Bull. Canada Mining Inst.*, **2**. 75, 1908; R. A. Parker, *Eng. Min. Journ.*, **54**. 561, 1892; W. W. Russell, *ib.*, **54**. 627, 1892; **55**. 28, 74, 122, 170, 1893; T. D. Ledyard, *Amer. Manf.*, **65**. 187, 1899; J. S. Jeans, *Iron Coal Trades Rev.*, **68**. 1456, 1491, 1904; Anon., *Bull. Imp. Inst.*, **24**. 94, 1926; G. A. Young, *Canada Geol. Sur.—Econ. Geol.*, 1, 1926; *Bull. Canada Geol. Sur.*, 1085, 1909; G. C. Hoffman, *ib.*, 958, 1907; S. J. Cook, *Canada Mining Journ.*, **48**. 524, 1927; R. G. E. Leckie, *ib.*, **11**. 155, 1892; E. S. Moore, *Bull. Canada Inst. Min. Met.*, 209, 1925; J. G. Morrow, *Rept. on Iron Ore*, 14, 1924; A. H. A. Robinson, *Mineral Industries of Canada*, Ottawa, 1924; G. C. Hoffmann, *Ann. Rept. Geol. Sur. Canada*, **7**. 16, 1896; G. C. Mackenzie, *Iron Steel Canada*, **5**. 136, 1922; E. Lindeman and L. L. Bolton, *Mines Branch Canada Dept. Mines*, 217, 1917; J. A. Dresser, *Mem. Canada Geol. Sur.*, 22, 1914; M. Mena, *Bull. Soc. Ind. Min.*, (5), **5**. 483, 1909; E. C. Harder, *Bull. Canada Geol. Sur.*, 1085, 1909;

E. Kraynik, *Glückauf*, **45.** 915, 959, 995, 1085, 1909 ; J. Birkinbine, *Canadian Min. Rev.*, **8.** 129, 1890 ; W. R. Nursey, *Iron Coal Trades Rev.*, **60.** 783, 1899 ; C. F. Just, *Journ. Soc. Arts*, **53.** 442, 1905 ; W. R. Lang, *Rep. Ontario Bur. Mines*, **14.** 1, 1905.
  [118] H. Louis, *Proc. Trans. Novia Scotia Inst. Nat. Science*, **5.** 47, 1897 ; D. Weatherbe, *ib.*, **10.** 350, 1902 ; J. E. Woodman, *Annual Report Department of the Interior*, Nova Scotia, 1907 ; *Summary Rep. Canadian Dep. Mines*, 1, 1909 ; H. Fréchette, *ib.*, 7, 1912 ; T. C. Denis, *ib.*, 58, 1909 ; T. Cantley, *Iron Coal Trades Rev.*, **83.** 392, 1911 ; E. Sjostedt, *Proc. Mining Soc. Nova Scotia*, **1.** 8, 1893 ; J. G. Donald, *Eng. Min. Journ.*, **57.** 250, 1894 ; E. Gilpin, *The Iron Ores of Nova Scotia*, Montreal, 1891 ; *Trans. Canadian Soc. Civil Eng.*, **5.** 97, 1892 ; *Trans. Fed. Inst. Min. Eng.*, **7.** 566, 1893 ; *Journ. Canada Mining Inst.*, **1.** 193, 1896 ; *Trans. Nova Scotia Inst. Science*, **4.** 167, 1893 ; **9.** 10, 1896 ; **11.** 89, 1905 ; L. W. Bailey, *Ann. Rept. Geol. Sur. Canada*, **9.** M, 5, 1898 ; G. B. Cowlam, *Iron Coal Trades Rev.*, **61.** 116, 1900 ; *Colliery Guardian*, **80.** 136, 1900 ; A. P. Low, *Eng. Mag.*, **19.** 205, 1900 ; W. F. C. Parsons, *Canada Mining Rev.*, **26.** 152, 1906 ; A. B. Willmott, *Journ. Canada Min. Inst.*, **7.** 257, 1904 ; *Eng. Min. World*, **35.** 336, 1911 ; C. K. Leith, *Econ. Geol.*, **3.** 276, 1908 ; *Canada Min. Journ.*, **29.** 370, 1908 ; *Bull. Canada Min. Inst.*, 2, 1908 ; E. Kraynik, *Stahl Eisen*, **29.** 265, 1909 ; F. W. Gray, *Iron Steel Canada*, **11.** 4, 1928 ; R. Dunn, *Canada Min. Journ.*, **43.** 896, 1923 ; A. W. G. Wilson, *Rept. Canada Dep. Mines*, 597, 1924.
  [119] W. E. Anderson, *Board Trade Journ.*, **65.** 280, 1909 ; G. A. Young, *Canada Mining Journ.*, **35.** 339, 1914 ; *Summary Rep. Canada Geol. Sur.*, 217, 1909 ; B. F. Haanel, *Summary Rept. Canada Mines Dept.*, 109, 1909 ; T. C. Denis, *ib.*, 58, 1909 ; J. E. Hardman, *Canada Mining Journ.*, **29.** 303, 336, 1908 ; *Bull. Canada Mining Inst.*, **2.** 139, 1908.
  [120] A. P. Low, *Rep. Canada Geol. Sur.*, 923, 1906 ; J. A. Dresser, *Mem. Canada Geol. Sur.*, 22, 1914 ; F. Cirkel, *Report on Iron Ore Deposits along Ottawa and Gatineau Rivers*, Ottawa, 1909 ; E. Lindeman, *Bull. Canada Dept. Mines*, 2, 1910 ; G. C. Mackenzie, *ib.*, 145, 1912 ; R. W. Ellis, *Bull. Geol. Sur. Canada*, 977, 1907 ; J. T. Donald, *Eng. Min. Journ.*, **58.** 224, 1894 ; A. M. Lamb, *ib.*, **84.** 1160, 1907 ; C. R. Mickle, *Journ. Canada Mining Inst.*, **5.** 256, 1902 ; C. K. Leith, *Mining World*, **34.** 488, 1910 ; *Econ. Geol.*, **5.** 227, 1910 ; T. C. Denis, *Canada Min. Journ.*, **33.** 442, 1911 ; P. E. Dulieux, *ib.*, **33.** 450, 1911 ; *Trans. Canada Min. Inst.*, **16.** 351, 1913 ; *Met. Ital.*, **8.** 758, 1916 ; D. E. Woodbridge, *Eng. Min. Journ.*, **112.** 251, 1921 ; A. H. A. Robinson, *Investigations Min. Resources Canada Geol. Sur.*, 42, 1924 ; B. F. Haanel, *Summary Rept. Canada Dept. Mines*, 109, 1909 ; P. H. Griffin, *Trans. Amer. Inst. Min. Eng.*, **21.** 974, 1893 ; J. Obalsky, *ib.*, **21.** 781, 1893 ; **28.** 283, 1901 ; *Journ. Canada Min. Inst.*, **4.** 91, 1901 ; F. Hille, *ib.*, **6.** 245, 1903 ; S. H. Boright, *ib.*, **6.** 411, 1903.
  [121] C. K. Leith, *Econ. Geol.*, **5.** 188, 1910 ; *Mining World*, **34.** 488, 1910 ; C. R. van Hise and C. K. Leith, *Monog. U.S. Geol. Sur.*, 52, 1911 ; F. Hille, *Journ. Canada Mining Inst.*, **5.** 49, 1902 ; **6.** 245, 1903 ; *Report on the Examination of some Iron Ore Deposits in the Districts of Thunder Bay and Rainy River*, Ottawa, 1908 ; *Rept. Canada Dept. Mines*, 1, 1908 ; R. Bell, *ib.*, 87, 1892 ; *Rept. Ontario Bur. Mines*, **21.** ii, 65, 1912 ; M. B. Baker, *ib.*, **20.** i, 214, 1911 ; *Rept. Canada Dept. Mines*, 20, 1911 ; E. Lindeman, *Canada Mining Journ.*, **29.** 393, 1908 ; *Rept. Canada Dept. Mines*, 184, 254, 303, 1914 ; F. Cirkel, *ib.*, 1, 1909 ; J. McLeish, *ib.*, 349, 1915 ; *Bull. Ontario Dept. Mines*, 79, 1910 ; *Chrome Iron Ore Deposits in the Eastern Townships*, Ottawa, 1909 ; *Report on the Iron Ore Deposits along the Ottawa (Quebec) Side*, Ottawa, 1909 ; M. E. Wilson, *Rep. Geol. Sur. Canada Dept. Mines*, 1160, 1912 ; A. W. G. Wilson, *Mem. Dept. Mines Geol. Sur.*, 1, 1910 ; A. P. Coleman and W. G. Miller, *Iron Age*, **68.** 9, 1903 ; A. P. Coleman, *Trans. Canada Mining Inst.*, **1.** 1, 1896 ; *Eng. Min. Journ.*, **84.** 116, 1907 ; *Econ. Geol.*, **1.** 521, 1906 ; *Ann. Rep. Canada Bur. Mines*, **10.** 128, 1902 ; **16.** 105, 1908 ; **17.** 136, 1909 ; *Canada Mining Journ.*, **34.** 573, 1913 ; W. L. Goodwin, *ib.*, **32.** 600, 1911 ; W. H. Collins, *Summary Rep. Canada Geol. Sur.*, 81, 1906 ; *Rept. Geol. Sur. Canada*, 1075, 1909 ; *Bull. Canada Geol. Sur.*, 992, 1908 ; 1059, 1909 ; W. H. Collins, T. T. Quirke, and E. Thomson, *Mem. Canada Geol. Sur.*, 147, 1926 ; J. L. Tanton, *Summary Rep. Canada Geol. Sur.*, C, 1, 1923 ; C, 1, 1924 ; J. E. Gill, *ib.*, C, 28, 1924 ; G. A. Young, *ib.*, E, 1. 1921 ; R. C. Wallace, *Bull. Canada Inst. Min. Met.*, 164, 1925 ; *Trans. Canada Inst. Min. Met.*, **28.** 303, 1925 ; F. A. Jordan, *Canada Mining Journ.*, **33.** 807, 1912 ; W. A. Parks, *Proc. Roy. Soc. Arts*, **73.** 898, 1925 ; E. L. Bruce, *Rept. Ontario Bur. Mines*, **31.** 8, 1922 ; E. S. Moore, *Econ. Geol.*, **5.** 25, 28, 1910 ; *Ann. Rep. Canada Bur. Mines*, **16.** 136, 1907 ; **34.** 1, 1925 ; *Eng. Min. Journ.*, **110.** 396, 1920 ; D. E. Woodbridge, *ib.*, **112.** 251, 1921 ; A. H. A. Robinson, *Summary Rep. Canada Dept. Mines*, 542, 1920 ; G. E. Edwards, *Mining Eng. World*, **38.** 333, 1913 ; R. E. Hore, *ib.*, **37.** 1040, 1912 ; H. Fréchette, *Summary Rept. Canada Dept. Mines*, 82, 1909 ; B. F. Haanel, *ib.*, 109, 1909 ; A. B. Willmott, *Journ. Canada Mining Inst.*, **7.** 1, 1904 ; *Bull. Canada Mining Inst.*, **2.** 91, 1908 ; *Rept. Bur. Mines Ontario*, 91, 1902 ; N. L. Leach, *ib.*, **2.** 149, 1908 ; J. J. Bell, *Rept. Ontario Bur. Mines*, **14.** 1, 1905 ; *Eng. Min. Journ.*, **85.** 805, 1908 ; T. D. Ledyard, *Trans. Amer. Inst. Min. Eng.*, **19.** 28, 1890 ; *Eng. Min. Journ.*, **55.** 322, 1893 ; W. Molin, *ib.*, **54.** 484, 1892 ; W. G. Miller, *Trans. Canada Min. Inst.*, **4.** 265, 1901 ; *Canada Mining Rev.*, **14.** 40, 1895 ; W. E. H. Carter, *ib.*, **24.** 35, 1905 ; W. H. Merritt, *Trans. Fed. Inst. Min. Eng.*, **10.** 301, 1896 ; F. J. Pope, *Berg. Hütt. Ztg.*, **58.** 556, 1899 ; *Trans. Amer. Inst. Min. Eng.*, **29.** 372, 1900 ; P. Thompson, *Eng. Min. Journ.*, **81.** 719, 1905 ; A. Goetz, *ib.*, **93.** 1090, 1912 ; S. D. Mills, *Canada Mining Rev.*, **25.** 119, 1906 ; E. T. Cookill, *Ann. Rep. Canada Bur. Mines*, **16.** 55, 1907 ; R. C. Campbell-Johnston, *Mining Journ.*, **123.** 760, 1918.
  [122] R. C. Wallace, *Trans. Canada Mining Inst.*, **22.** 329, 1919.

[123] E. Haanel, *The Iron Ore Resources of the World*, Stockholm, 2. 721, 1910 ; E. L. Derby, *Mining Congress Journ.*, 15. 731, 1929.
[124] J. A. Allan, *Iron Steel Canada*, 3. 185, 1920 ; *Annual Report of the Mineral Resources of Alberta*, Edmonton, 1920 ; J. B. Tyrrell, *Ann. Rep. Geol. Sur. Canada*, 150, E, 1886 ; R. G. McConnell, *ib.*, 5. 63, D, 1890 ; R. W. Ellis, *Summary Rept. Dept. Mines, Canada*, 63, 1914 ; F. J. Alcock, *ib.*, 154, 1916.
[125] E. Lindeman, *Iron Ore Deposits of Vancouver and Texada Islands*, Ottawa, 1910 ; R. G. McConnell, *Mem. Canada Geol. Sur.*, 58, 1914 ; G. M. Dawson, *Rep. Canada Geol. Sur.*, 1, 1886 ; 1, 1889 ; C. W. Drysdale, *Mem. Canada Geol. Sur.*, 77, 1915 : L. Reinecke, *ib.*, 79, 1915 ; G. A. Young and W. L. Uglow, *Econ. Geol. Canada Geol. Sur.*, 3. 1926 ; W. L. Uglow, *Econ. Geol.*, 21. 352, 1926 ; W. Blakemore, *Journ. Canada Mining Inst.*, 5. 76, 1902 ; H. V. Ellsworth and J. F. Walker, *Summ. Rep. Geol. Sur. Canada*, 230, 1926 ; J. Ashworth, *Iron Coal Trades Rev.*, 93. 183, 1916 ; A. Halsey, *Stahl Eisen*, 19. 1135, 1899 ; W. C. Cronemayer, *Industries Iron*, 27. 130, 1899 ; R. C. C. Johnston. *Mining Journ.*, 123. 760, 1918 ; A. B. Willmott, *Min. Eng. World*, 35. 336, 1911 ; E. Jacobs, *Canada Mining Journ.*, 30. 655, 1910 ; R. W. Seelye, *Iron Trade Rev.*, 46. 515, 1909 ; H. C. Estep, *ib.*, 44. 33, 1909 ; J. D. Mackenzie, *Summary Rep. Canada Geol. Sur.*, 1, 1915 ; 1869, 1921 ; C. H. Clapp, *ib.*, 94, 1909 ; W. M. Brewer, *Eng. Min. Journ.*, 69. 526, 1900 ; H. M. Lamb, *Eng. Mag.*, 20. 399, 1901 ; *Rep. Minister Mines B.C.*, 241, 1919 ; C. K. Leith, *Bull. U.S. Geol. Sur.*, 285, 1906 ; *Econ. Geol.*, 3. 276, 1908 ; J. P. Kimball, *Eng. Min. Journ.*, 65. 159, 1898 ; *Amer. Geol.*, 19. 225, 1898.
[126] J. P. Howley, *Journ. Canadian Min. Inst.*, 12. 149, 1909 ; *Iron Coal Trades Rev.*, 80. 377, 1919 ; *The Iron Ore Resources of the World*, Stockholm, 2. 749, 1910 ; *Colliery Guardian*, 72. 1063, 1896 ; A. O. Hayes, *Mem. Canada Geol. Sur.*, 78, 1915 ; *Min. Met.*, 9. 361, 1928 ; *Econ. Geol.*, 24. 687, 1929 ; 23. 44, 1931 ; A. E. Outerbridge, *Journ. Franklin Inst.*, 144. 165, 1897 ; M. A. Macpherson, *Iron Coal Trades Rev.*, 59. 346, 1899 ; C. A. Meissner, *Journ. Canada Min. Inst.*, 2. 66, 1899 ; *Journ. Min. Soc. Nova Scotia*, 7. 55, 1903 ; W. Scott, *Eng. Min. Journ.*, 70. 155, 1899 ; H. B. C. Nitze, *Mines Minerals*, 20. 413, 1900 ; W. R. Nursey, *Iron Coal Trades Rev.*, 60. 1085, 1899 ; L. P. Gratacap, *Mining World*, 23. 525, 1906 ; J. McLeish, *Canada Dept. Mines*, 349, 1915 ; E. Lindemann and L. L. Bolton, *Canada Dept. Mines*, 217, 1917 ; B. S. Stephenson, *Iron Trade Rev.*, 45. 651, 1909 ; T. Cantley, *Iron Age*, 96. 1285, 1915 ; *Journ. Canadian Min. Inst.*, 14. 31, 1911 ; R. E. Chambers, *ib.*, 1. 41, 1896 ; *Canada Mining Journ.*, 41. 241, 1920 ; *Iron Age*, 57. 808, 1896 ; O. R. Kuhn, *ib.*, 117. 1264, 1926 ; A. Hasebrink, *Glückauf*, 62. 553, 1926 ; Anon., *Iron and Steel Canada*, 8. 237, 1925 ; D. E. Woodbridge, *Eng. Min. Journ.*, 123. 397, 1927 ; D. J. Davies, *Trans. Amer. Inst. Min. Eng.*, 34. 114, 1924 ; *Canada Min. Journ.*, 41. 821, 1920 ; *Trans. Inst. Min. Met.*, 34. 114, 1924 ; J. B. Gilliatt, *Trans. Canada Inst. Min. Met.*, 27. 616, 1924 ; H. A. Wilson. *Journ. West Scotland Iron Steel Inst.*, 26. 50, 1919 ; B. Symons, *Mining Journ.*, 99. 1051, 1912 : *Eng. Min. Journ.*, 91. 1008, 1911.
[127] J. F. Kemp, *The Ore Deposits of the United States*, New York, 1893 ; *The Iron Ore Resources of the World*, Stockholm, 2. 755, 1910 ; E. C. Eckel, *Iron Ores : their Occurrence, Valuation, and Control*, New York, 1914 ; *Mineral Resources of the United States*, Washington, 1. 51, 1908 ; D. E. Woodbridge, *Iron Age*, 119. 1658, 1720, 1927 ; O. R. Kuhn, *ib.*, 114. 1204, 1248, 1285, 1924 ; E. F. Burchard, *Min. Resources U.S. Geol. Sur.*, i, 168, 1911 ; J. L. W. Birkinbine, *Journ. Franklin Inst.*, 110. 429, 1888 ; *Iron Trade Rev.*, 48. 49, 1910 ; F. W. Clarke, *Bull. U.S. Geol. Sur.*, 419, 1909 ; C. W. Hayes, *ib.*, 394, 1909 ; P. C. Warman, *ib.*, 215, 1903 ; J. M. Hill and W. Lindgren, *ib.*, 507, 1912 ; E. C. Harder, *Bull. U.S. Geol. Sur.*, 666, 1918 ; *Trans. Amer. Inst. Min. Eng.*, 58. 453, 1917 ; *Min. Resources U.S. Geol. Sur.*, i, 81, 1908 ; R. W. Raymond and W. R. Ingalls, *Bull. Amer. Inst. Min. Eng.*, 249, 1909 ; J. P. Lesley, *The Iron Manufacturers' Guide*, New York, 1859 ; T. Dunlap, *American Iron Trade Manual*, New York, 1874 ; T. S. Hunt, *Journ. Iron Steel Inst.*, 37. ii, 628, 1890 ; S. F. Emmons, *Trans. Amer. Inst. Min. Eng.*, 24. 755, 1893 ; R. C. Allen, *ib.*, 43. 188, 1919 ; J. T. Singewald, *Bull. U.S. Bur. Mines*, 64, 1913 ; G. H. Ashley, *Proc. Eng. Soc. West Pennsylvania*, 37. 1, 1921 ; Z. Jeffries, *Tech. Paper Amer. Inst. Min. Eng.*, 331, 1930.
[128] M. Crowell and M. Murray, *The Iron Ores of Lake Superior*, Cleveland, Ohio, 1917 ; J. F. Wolff, *Trans. Amer. Inst. Min. Eng.*, 56. 142, 1916 ; T. L. Joseph, E. P. Barrett, and C. E. Wood, *ib.*, 71. 372, 1927 ; C. Zapffe, *Mining World*, 34. 585, 1910 ; *Trans. Amer. Inst. Min. Eng.*, 71. 372, 1925 : 75. 346, 1927 ; C. Zapffe and W. A. Barrows, *ib.*, 44. 3, 1912 ; C. P. McCormack, *ib.*, 71. 386, 1925 ; R. W. Raymond and W. R. Ingalls, *ib.*, 40. 44, 1909 ; J. D. Kendall, *Trans. Canadian Min. Inst.*, 21. 172, 199, 1918 ; G. A. Hewett, *Proc. Lake Superior Mining Inst.*, 14. 1, 1910 ; E. Newton, *Bull. Minnesota School Mines*, 5, 1918 ; H. H. Campbell, *Iron Age*, 99. 51, 1917 ; G. A. Thiel, *Eng. Min. Journ.*, 118. 735, 1924 ; 121. 687, 1926 ; L. E. Ives, *ib.*, 99. 443, 1915 ; C. A. Cheney, *ib.*, 99. 1113, 1915 ; E. P. McCarty, *ib.*, 100. 400, 1915 ; L. O. Kellog, *ib.*, 96. 863, 1199, 1913 ; 97. 7, 83, 695, 749, 1035, 1093, 1914 ; E. F. Burchard, *Mineral Resources U.S. Geol. Sur.*, 1, 1919 ; *Bull. U.S. Geol. Sur.*, 340, 1908 ; 400, 1909 ; 620, 1915 ; E. C. Kreutzberg, *Iron Trade Rev.*, 69. 1207, 1223, 1285, 1921 ; W. S. Bayley, *Amer. Journ. Science*, (3), 46. 176, 1894 ; *Proc. Amer. Assoc. Adv. Science*, 49. 189, 1901 ; *Monog. U.S. Geol. Sur.*, 46, 1903 ; J. M. Clements, *ib.*, 45, 1903 ; C. K. Leith, *Econ. Geol.*, 1. 47, 1905 ; 2. 145, 1906 ; 26. 274, 1931 ; *Trans. Amer. Inst. Min. Eng.*, 36. 101, 1905 ; *Bull. U.S. Geol. Sur.*, 213, 1902 ; J. M. Clements, H. L. Smyth, W. S. Bayley and C. R. van Hise, *ib.*, 36, 1899 ; C. R. van Hise, W. S. Bayley and H. L. Smyth, *ib.*, 28, 1897 ; T. B. Brooks, *Rep. Michigan Geol. Sur.*, 1. 1, 1873 ; J. L. Spurr, *The Iron-Bearing Rocks of the Mesabai Range in Minnesota*, Min-

neapolis, 1894 ; *Bull. Minnesota Geol. Sur.*, 10, 1894 ; *Amer. Geol.*, **29**. 345, 1903 ; R. Hurd, *Iron Ore Manual*, St. Paul, Minn., 1911 ; W. W. J. Croze, *Mining World*, **33**. 717, 1910 ; G. E. Edwards, *ib.*, **28**. 65, 1907 ; **30**. 693, 1909 ; C. A. Blatchley, *Eng. Min. Journ.*, **109**. 702, 1920 ; P. B. McDonald, *ib.*, **87**. 902, 1912 ; **92**. 210, 1912 ; **96**. 208, 335, 1913 ; *Mining World*, **34**. 887, 1911 ; W. J. Miller, *Econ. Geol.*, **14**. 509, 1919 ; J. T. Stark, *ib.*, **24**. 528, 1929 ; T. M. Broderick, *ib.*, **12**. 419, 1917 ; **15**. 422, 1920 ; F. S. Adams, *ib.*, **5**. 729, 1910 ; **6**. 60, 156, 1911 ; E. C. Harder and A. W. Johnston, *Bull. U.S. Geol. Sur.*, 660, 1917 ; C. R. van Hise and C. K. Leith, *ib.*, 360, 1909 ; C. R. van Hise and W. S. Bayley, *The Marquette Iron-bearing District of Michigan*, Washington, 1897 ; C. R. van Hise, *Iron Age*, **67**. 12, 1902 ; *Amer. Journ. Science*, **37**. 32, 1889 ; (3), **43**. 116, 1892 ; *Ann. Rept. U.S. Geol. Sur.*, **21**. iii, 305, 1901 ; *Journ. Geol.*, **13**. 89, 1905 ; D. E. Woodbridge, *Iron Age*, **76**. 1756, 1905 ; **77**. 26, 420, 1906 ; **87**. 1080, 1911 ; **93**. 15, 1914 ; *Mines Minerals*, **20**. 206, 1900 ; *Eng. Min. Journ.*, **79**. 74, 122, 170, 266, 319, 365, 466, 557, 602, 698, 892, 1905 ; **84**. 775, 1908 ; R. C. Allen, *Mining Eng. World*, **41**. 625, 1914 ; W. N. Smith, *Mining World*, **22**. 206, 1905 ; E. A. Smith, *Iron Trade Rev.*, **52**. 25, 1913 ; H. E. Birkinbine, *ib.*, **45**. 247, 1909 ; H. Engelbach, *Compt. Rend. Soc. Ind. Min.*, 374, 1913 ; G. Baum, *Glück-auf*, **44**. 697, 1908 ; C. W. Shannon, *Indiana Dept. Geol.*, **31**. 299, 1908 ; J. W. Beede and C. W. Shannon, *ib.*, **31**. 383, 1908 ; H. R. Mussey, *Columbia Univ. Studies*, 23, 1905 ; R. A. F. Penrose, *Rep. Geol. Sur. Arkansas*, **1**. 124, 1892 ; A. F. Foerste, *Amer. Journ. Science*, (3), **41**. 28, 1891 ; C. H. Smyth, *ib.*, (3), **43**. 487, 1892 ; G. M. Schwartz, *Amer. Min.*, **15**. 243, 1930 ; *Eng. Min. Journ.*, **116**. 409, 1923 ; A. B. Parsons, *ib.*, **117**. 157, 203, 1924 ; N. H. Winchell, *Bull. Amer. Geol. Soc.*, **23**. 317, 1912 ; *Amer. Manuf.*, **50**. 200, 329, 1891 ; *Ann. Rept. Geol. Sur. Minnesota*, **17**. 1, 1890 ; *Trans. Fed. Inst. Min. Eng.*, **13**. 493, 1898 ; *Iron Trade Rev.*, **28**. 11, 1896 ; *Amer. Geol.*, **10**. 169, 1892 ; **20**. 154, 1902 ; N. H. and H. V. Winchell, *The Iron Ores of Minnesota*, Minnesota, 1891 ; J. W. Gruner, *Econ. Geol.*, **25**. 697, 837, 1930 ; *Bull. Minnesota Geol. Sur.*, 19, 1924 ; F. F. Grout and T. M. Broderick, *ib.*, 17, 1920 ; M. C. Lake, *Canada Min. Journ.*, **47**. 866, 1926 ; *Mining Met.*, **7**. 325, 1926 ; F. L. Nason, *Yearbook Amer. Iron Steel Inst.*, **12**. 168, 1922 ; G. A. St. Clair, *ib.*, **87**, 97, 1913 ; J. D. Dana, *Amer. Journ. Science*, (3), **39**. 67, 1890 ; W. D. Dwight, *ib.*, (3), **39**. 150, 1890 ; G. W. Goetz, *Trans. Amer. Inst. Min. Eng.*, **19**. 59, 1890 ; J. Birkinbine, *The Distribution of the Lake Superior Iron Ores*, Washington, 1904 ; *Trans. Amer. Inst. Min. Eng.*, **27**. 519, 1897 ; J. E. Jopling, *ib.*, **27**. 541, 1897 ; C. M. Boss, *ib.*, **27**. 978, 1897 ; *Amer. Manf.*, 50. 376, 1892 ; H. V. Winchell and J. T. Jones, *Trans. Amer. Inst. Min. Eng.*, **21**. 951, 1893 ; E. W Griffin, *Iron Age*, **47**. 276, 1891 ; C. F. Howe, *ib.*, **48**. 895, 1892 ; R. D. Irving, *Amer. Journ. Science*, (3), **32**. 255, 1886 ; T. E. Savage and C. S. Ross, *ib.*, (4), **41**. 187, 1916 ; B. A. Ludgate, *Bull. Amer. Iron Steel Assoc.*, **25**. 1, 1892 ; *Iron*, **38**. 490, 1892 ; S. D. Mills, *Iron Age*, **48**. 743, 1891 ; E. C. Pechin, *ib.*, **48**. 1031, 1891 ; J. L. Peyton, *ib.*, **48**. 1079, 1891 ; E. C. Moxham, *Amer. Manuf.*, **50**. 18, 1892 ; O. J. Abell, *Iron Trade Rev.*, **42**. 95, 659, 1908 ; H. C. Estep, *ib.*, **58**. 179, 1916 ; R. D. Irving and C. R. van Hise, *The Penokee Iron-Bearing Series of Michigan and Wisconsin*, Washington, 1894 ; *Bull. U.S. Geol. Sur.*, 19, 1892 ; W. S. Gresley, *Journ. Geol. Soc.*, **51**. 98, 1895 ; H. Wedding, *Stahl Eisen*, **16**. 7, 1896 ; H. Macco, *ib.*, **24**. 69, 1904 ; *Zeit. prakt. Geol.*, **12**. 48, 1904 ; S. Calvin, *Ann. Rep. Iowa Geol. Sur.*, **4**. 1, 1895 ; A. P. Head, *Proc. South Staffs Inst. Iron Steel Works Managers*, 100, 1898 ; A. P. Coleman, *Eng. Min. Journ.*, **72**. 385, 1901 ; *Iron*, **73**. 103, 1902 ; P. M. Ostrand, *ib.*, **105**. 269, 1918 ; S. W. Beyer, *ib.*, **73**. 275, 1902 ; R. T. Rose, *Proc. Lake Superior Mining Inst.*, **10**. 88, 1905 ; *Eng. Min. Journ.*, **78**. 343, 1905 ; S. Weidman, *ib.*, **78**. 309, 1905 ; *Iron Age*, **50**. 1271, 1892 ; *Trans. Amer. Inst. Min. Eng.*, **21**. 644, 1893 ; *Wisconsin Eng.*, **9**. 31, 1905 ; *Bull. Wisconsin Geol. Sur.*, 13, 1904 ; U. S. Grant, *Mining Journ.*, **10**. 175, 1904 ; E. J. Carlyle, *Journ. Canada Mining Inst.*, **7**. 1, 1904 ; A. L. Carnahan, *Mining World*, **23**. 468, 1905 ; M. P. Youngs, *ib.*, **24**. 300, 1906 ; A. Oppel, *Der Erzbergbau*, 700, 1906 ; O. W. Wilcox, *Journ. Geol.*, **14**. 243, 1906 ; F. D. de Vaney and J. B. Clemmer, *Rep. Investigations U.S. Bur. Mines*, 3045, 1930 ; C. E. Abbot, *Mining World*, **26**. 65, 1907 ; *Eng. Min. Journ.*, **83**. 601, 1907 ; *Proc. Lake Superior Min. Inst.*, **12**. 116. 1907 ; H. Nordquist, *Bihang Jernkontorets Ann.*, **70**. 383, 1907 ; R. Meeks, *Eng. Min. Journ.*, **84**. 193, 1907 ; W. O. Hotchkiss, *ib.*, **108**. 443, 501, 537, 577, 1919 ; S. A. Mahon and T. B. Counselman, *ib.*, **130**. 519, 1930 ; F. F. Grout, *Econ. Geol.*, **14**. 452, 1919 ; E. Stebinger, *Bull. U.S. Geol. Sur.*, 540, 1914 ; F. T. Thwaites, *ib.*, 540, 1914.

¹²⁹ E. F. Burchard, C. Butts and E. C. Eckel, *Bull. U.S. Geol. Sur.*, 400, 1909 ; E. F. Burchard and C. Butts, *Bull. U.S. Geol. Sur.*, 400, 1910 ; E. F. Burchard, *ib.*, 260, 1905 ; 315, 1907 ; 340, 1908 ; 380, 1909 ; 620, 1915 ; 795, 1927 ; *Iron Age*, **119**. 847, 1927 ; *Trans. Amer. Inst. Min. Eng.*, **40**. 75, 1908 ; *Bull. Tennessee Geol. Sur.*, 16, 1913 ; 16, 1914 ; P. N. Moore, *Rep. Kentucky Geol. Sur.*, **4**. 241, 1878 ; W. B. Caldwell, *ib.*, **5**. 251, 1880 ; R. P. Jarvis, *Rep. Resources Tennessee*, **2**. 9, 1912 ; C. H. Gordon and R. P. Jarvis, *ib.*, **2**. 12, 1912 ; S. W. McCallie, *Bull. Georgia Geol. Sur.*, 10, 1900 ; 17, 1908 ; J. T. Singewald, *Tech. Publ. Amer. Inst. Min. Eng.*, 197, 1929 ; *Rep. Maryland Geol. Sur.*, **9**. iii, 123, 1911 ; *Econ. Geol.*, **4**. 530, 1910 ; E. C. Eckel, *Iron Trade Rev.*, **43**. 228, 1908 ; **44**. 28, 1909 ; **52**. 77, 1913 ; *Iron Age*, **76**. 478, 1905 ; *Eng. Mag.*, **30**. 518, 1906 ; *Bull. U.S. Geol. Sur.*, 260, 1905 ; 285, 1906 ; 400, 1910 ; C. Butts, *ib.*, 470, 1912 ; F. W. Clarke, *ib.*, 90, 1893 ; B. K. Emerson, *ib.*, 159, 1899 ; C. Leith, *ib.*, 213, 1903 ; C. K. Leith and W. N. Smith, *ib.*, 225, 1904 ; R. J. Holden, *ib.*, 285, 1906 ; W. C. Phalen, *Econ. Geol.*, **1**. 660, 1906 ; *Bull. U.S. Geol. Sur.*, 340, 1908 ; E. C. Harder, *ib.*, 380, 1909 ; 430, 1910 ; C. W. Hayes and E. C. Eckel, *ib.*, 213, 1903 ; J. E. Kemp, *The Iron Ore Resources of the World*, Stockholm, 1910 ; A. H. Sawyer, *Eng. Min. Journ.*, **98**, 49, 1914 ; J. E. Spurr, *ib.*, **123**. 363, 1927 ; T. Linton, *ib.*, **96**. 1153, 1913 ; W. R. Crane, *Iron Ore Mining Practice in Birmingham District, Alabama*,

Washington, 1926 ; *Development, Mining and Handling of Ore in the Birmingham District, Alabama*, Washington, 1927 ; *Tech. Paper U.S. Bur. Mines*, 377, 1926 ; *Trans. Amer. Inst. Min. Eng.*, 72. 157, 1925 ; *Eng. Min. Journ.*, 79. 274, 1904 ; W. Kennedy, *Rep. Texas Geol. Sur.*, 2. 7, 1891 ; *Trans. Amer. Inst. Min. Eng.*, 24. 258, 862, 1895 ; T. H. Aldrich, *ib.*, 71. 304, 1925 ; S. Whinery, *ib.*, 44. 25, 1912 ; E. C, Moxham, *ib.*, 21. 133, 1892 ; E. Higgins, *Eng. Min. Journ.*, 86. 1043, 1083, 1150, 1908 ; 87. 1, 1909 ; J. E. Johnson, *ib.*, 76. 231, 1903 ; G. L. Pultz, *ib.*, 88. 345, 1909 ; J. J. Porter, *Manf. Record*, 51. 717, 749, 788, 1907 ; 54. 54, 1910 ; 56. 55, 1912 ; L. L. Wittich, *Mines Minerals*, 33. 227, 1912 ; J. S. Grasty, *ib.*, 50. 550, 1906 ; W. M. Chauvenet, *Rept. Tenth Census U.S.A.*, 15. 289, 351, 1886 ; B. L. Johnson and C. H. Warren, *Amer. Journ. Science*, (4), 25. 1, 1907 ; *Econ. Geol.*, 13. 419, 1918 ; L. C. Johnson, *U.S. House Document*, 195, 1888 ; R. A. F. Penrose, *Rept. Arkansas Geol. Sur.*, 1. 1, 1892 ; *Bull. Amer. Geol. Soc.*, 3. 44, 1892 ; H. B. C. Nitze, *Bull. North Carolina Geol. Sur.*, 1, 1893 ; *Eng. Min. Journ.*, 53. 447, 1892 ; *Trans. Amer. Inst. Min. Eng.*, 21. 260, 1892 ; M. H. Chance, *ib.*, 29. 224, 1031, 1899 ; F. L. Nason, *Rep. Missouri Geol. Sur.*, 1, 1892 ; *Report on Iron Ores*, Jefferson City, 1892 ; *Rep. Pennsylvania Geol. Sur.*, 1, 1878 ; E. F. Dumbel, *Rep. Texas Geol. Sur.*, 1, 1891 ; *Eng. Min. Journ.*, 72. 104, 1901 ; R. D. George, *Geology and Natural Resources of Colorado*, Boulder, Colorado, 1927 ; W. S. Bayley, *Econ. Geol.*, 16. 142, 1921 ; 18. 362, 1923 ; *Bull. U.S. Geol. Sur.*, 735, 1922 ; S. Paige, *ib.*, 430, 1910 ; 450, 1911 ; S. Paige and A. C. Spencer, *ib.*, 450, 1911 ; E. F. Burgess, *ib.*, 540, 1914 ; S. E. Doak, *Eng. Min. Journ.*, 111. 386, 1921 ; S. M. Ball, *ib.*, 88. 200, 1909 ; P. B. McDonald, *Iron Trade Rev.*, 55. 759, 790, 1914 ; S. Norton, *ib.*, 46. 345, 1909 ; A. M. Peter, *Journ. Ing. Eng. Chem.*, 6. 479, 1914 ; E. L. Lull, *Iron Age*, 90. 1423, 1912 ; J. M. Cameron, *Mines Minerals*, 32. 42, 1911 ; E. M. Kindle, *ib.*, 285, 1906 ; J. J. Traver, *Journ. U.S. Assoc. Charcoal Iron Workers*, 8. 331, 1890 ; C. R. Boyd, *Eng. Min. Journ.*, 49. 171, 1890 ; J. B. Killibrew, *ib.*, 51. 695, 1891 ; W. H. Ruffner, *Iron Age*, 44. 959, 1890 ; E. C. Pechin, *ib.*, 45. 809, 1890 ; *Journ. Iron Steel Inst.*, 37. ii, 318, 1890 ; *Eng. Min. Journ.*, 51. 264, 322, 349, 1891 ; 52. 333, 1891 ; 54. 150, 1892 ; W. M. Brewer, *Mineral Ind.*, 4. 391, 1896 ; *Eng. Min. Journ.*, 55. 77, 1893 ; 63. 16, 1897 ; W. B. Phillips, *ib.*, 56. 448, 1893 ; 61. 113, 134, 159, 1896 ; *Iron-making in Alabama*, Montgomery, 1896 ; *Iron Age*, 48. 61, 1892 ; 81. 1788, 1856, 2008, 1908 ; 82. 381, 632, 1909 ; 89. 141, 1912 ; *Proc. Eng. Soc. Western Pennsylvania*, 18. 64, 1902 ; R. H. Couper, *Eng. Min. Journ.*, 69. 738, 1899 ; F. M. Stapff, *Berg. Hütt. Ztg.*, 50. 311, 319, 1891 ; G. R. Johnson, *Trans. Amer. Inst. Min. Eng.*, 20. 96, 173, 1891 ; S. F. Emmons, *ib.*, 24. 755, 1894 ; A. Winslow, *ib.*, 24. 634, 1894 ; C. Catlett, *ib.*, 29. 84, 1900 ; T. L. Watson, *ib.*, 34. 643, 1904 ; H. S. Williams, *Amer. Journ. Science*, (3), 48. 325, 1894 ; *Trans. Amer. Inst. Min. Eng.*, 16. 921, 945, 1894 ; W. Kennedy, *ib.*, 24. 258, 1894 ; E. J. Schmitz, *ib.*, 26. 97, 1896 ; C. W. Hayes, *ib.*, 30. 403, 1901 ; M. C. Wilson, *Proc. Alabama Ind. Scient. Soc.*, 4. 60, 1895 ; J. W. Castleman, *ib.*, 9. 13, 1899 ; C. Haller, *Stahl Eisen*, 17, 439, 1897 ; J. P. Kimball, *Amer. Geol.*, 19. 225, 1898 ; *Eng. Min. Journ.*, 65. 166, 1898 ; H. V. Maxwell, *ib.*, 78. 590, 1905 ; E. R. Judd, *ib.*, 83. 567, 1907 ; E. A. Smith, *Iron Age*, 66. 1, 1901 ; *Iron Trade Rev.*, 52. 25, 1913 ; J. T. Singewald and C. Milton, *Year Book Trans. Amer. Inst. Min. Eng.*, 330, 1929 ; P. Wooton, *Min. Eng. World*, 37. 489, 1912.

[130] J. F. Kemp, *Ann. Rep. U.S. Geol. Sur.*, 19. iii, 277, 1899 ; *The Iron Ore Resources of the World*, Stockholm, 1910 ; *Eng. Min. Journ.*, 79. 897, 1905 ; *Trans. New York Acad.*, 13. 76, 1895 ; *Trans. Amer. Inst. Min. Eng.*, 27. 146, 1897 ; A. L. Holley, *ib.*, 6. 226, 1878 ; J. J. Rutledge, *ib.*, 39. 1057, 1908 ; 40. 134, 1909 ; W. Kelly, *ib.*, 40. 854, 1910 ; J. Birkinbine, *ib.*, 18. 747, 1890 ; *Iron Age*, 54. 796, 858, 1894 ; *Journ. U.S. Assoc. Charcoal Iron Workers*, 8. 322, 1870 ; R. J. Colony, *The Magnetite Iron Deposits of South-Eastern New York*, Albany, 1923 ; J. P. Kimball, *Amer. Journ. Science*, (3), 40. 155, 1891 ; C. H. Smyth, *ib.*, (3), 43. 487, 1892 ; H. J. Detwiller, *Iron Age*, 48. 528, 1892 ; S. S. Knight, *ib.*, 64. 11, 1899 ; H. H. Slock, *Trans. Amer. Inst. Min. Eng.*, 20. 369, 1892 ; W. H. Hoffman, *ib.*, 21. 513, 1892 ; E. F. Durfre, *ib.*, 24. 830, 1893 ; F. L. Nason, *ib.*, 24. 121, 1893 ; *Yearbook Amer. Iron Steel Inst.*, 12. 168, 1922 ; *Econ. Geol.*, 17. 633, 1922 ; W. P. Blake, *ib.*, 17. 770, 1891 ; J. E. Wolff, *Annual Report of the State Geologist*, New Jersey, 359, 1894 ; J. E. Wolff and A. H. Brooks, *Eng. Min. Journ.*, 63. 40, 1897 ; *Bull. Amer. Geol. Soc.*, 8. 397, 1897 ; W. O. Crosby, *Tech. Quart.*, 14. 162, 1902 ; *Amer. Geol.*, 29. 233, 1903 ; J. H. Ganbery, *Eng. Min. Journ.*, 81. 889, 986, 1905 ; R. B. Brinsmade, *ib.*, 82. 493, 1906 ; C. W. Shannon, *Indiana Dept. Geol.*, 31. 299, 1908 ; J. W. Beede and C. W. Shannon, *ib.*, 31. 385, 1908 ; S. Norton, *Iron Trade Rev.*, 46. 345, 1909 ; E. C. Kreutzberg, *ib.*, 69. 1207, 1223, 1285, 1921 ; 75. 157, 284, 1924 ; W. G. Imhoff, *Blast Furnace Steel Plant*, 4. 553, 1916 ; C. A. Blatchly, *Eng. Min. Journ.*, 109. 702, 1920 ; W. J. Miller, *Econ. Geol.*, 14. 509, 1919 ; F. R. Koeberlin, *ib.*, 4. 713, 1909 ; E. C. Harder, *ib.*, 5. 599, 1910 ; W. H. Hobbs, *ib.*, 2. 153, 1907 ; D. H. Newland and N. V. Hansell, *Eng. Min. Journ.*, 82. 863, 1906 ; D. H. Newland, *Iron Age*, 82. 1376, 1908 ; *Econ. Geol.*, 2. 763, 1907 ; *Trans. Amer. Inst. Min. Eng.*, 40. 165, 1909 ; *Bull. New York State Museum*, 116, 119, 1908 ; 102, 1916 ; D. H. Newland and C. A. Hartnagel, *ib.*, 123, 1908 ; J. C. Smock, *ib.*, 7, 1889 ; H. P. Whitlock, *ib.*, 107, 1907 ; I. H. Ogilvies, *ib.*, 96, 1906 ; J. T. Singewald, *Bull. U.S. Bur. Mines*, 64, 1913 ; T. E. Singewald and C. Milton, *Tech. Publ. Amer. Inst. Min. Eng.*, 197, 1929 ; C. M. Holmgren, *Bihang. Jernkontorets Ann.*, 15. 221, 1914 ; C. H. Warren, *Amer. Journ. Science*, (4), 25. 24, 1908 ; M. E. Wadsworth, *Bull. Museum Comp. Zool. Harvard Coll.*, 7, 1881 ; 1, 1884 ; D. MacVichie, *Trans. Amer. Inst. Min. Eng.*, 74. 163, 1927 ; W. Kelly and H. S. Chamberlain, *ib.*, 40. 855, 1909 ; J. M. Clarke, *Ind. World*, 5, 1908 ; W. S. Bayley, *Iron Age*, 89. 141, 1912 ; *Rep. Geol. Sur. New Jersey*, 8. 7, 1910 ; C. S. Clark, *Iron Trade Rev.*, 56. 617, 1915 ; B. S. Stephenson,

ib., **45**. 371, 416, 1910 ; D. F. Morgan, *ib.*, **42**. 335, 1908 ; A. C. Spencer, *Mines Minerals*, **27**. 182, 1907 ; *Mining Mag.*, **10**. 377, 1904 ; *Bull. U.S. Geol. Sur.*, 315, 1907 ; 359, 1908 ; S. Paige, *ib.*, 381, 1909 ; C. Butts, *ib.* 279, 1906 ; J. P. Lesley and E. V. d'Invilliers, *Ann. Rep. Pennsylvania Geol. Sur.*, **2**. 532, 1885 ; *Proc. Iron Steel Inst.*, 369, 1890 ; F. Prime, *Rept. Pennyslvania Geol. Sur.*, 1, 1878 ; F. S. Witherbee, *Yearbook Amer. Iron Steel Inst.*, **6**. 328, 1916 ; E. C. Eckel, *Eng. Min. Journ.*, **78**. 432, 1905 ; **79**. 897, 1905 ; *Iron Ores : their Occurrence, Valuation and Control*, New York, 1914 ; *Bull. U.S. Geol. Sur.*, 260, 1905 ; W. C. Phalen and L. Martin, *ib.*, 447, 1911 ; G. C. Stoltz, *Eng. Min. Journ.*, **85**. 1091, 1908 ; **92**. 809, 1911 ; E. Higgins, *ib.*, **86**. 1150, 1908 ; G. H. Ashley, *ib.*, **93**. 683, 1912 ; A. H. Hubbel, *ib.*, **110**. 658, 1920 ; L. O. Kellogg, *ib.*, **96**. 863, 1065, 1913 ; F. S. Mills, *ib.*, **85**. 1193, 1908 ; P. B. McDonald, *ib.*, **95**. 689, 1913 ; C. F. Taylor and W. M. Booth, *ib.*, **94**. 893, 1912 ; T. C. Hopkins, *Mines Minerals*, **21**. 97, 1901 ; *Bull. Amer. Geol. Soc.*, **2**. 475, 1903 ; C. R. Fettke, *School Mines Quart.*, **33**. 382, 1912 ; C. A. Stewart, *ib.*, **29**. 283, 1908 ; W. H. Callahan and W. H. Newhouse, *Econ. Geol.*, **24**. 403, 1929.

[131] E. C. Eckel, *Iron Ores : their Occurrence, Valuation, and Control*, New York, 1914 ; J. F. Kemp, *The Iron Ore Resources of the World*, Stockholm, 1910 ; *Ann. New York Acad.*, **16**. 353, 1905 ; *Zeit. prakt. Geol.*, **13**. 71, 1905 ; R. Chauvenet, *Trans. Amer. Inst. Min. Eng.*, **18**. 266, 1890 ; G. O. Smith and B. Willis, *ib.*, **30**. 356, 1116, 1901 ; H. M. Chance, *ib.*, **30**. 987, 1901 ; **31**. 318, 1901 ; T. Tonge, *Iron Coal Trades Rev.*, **41**. 234, 1890 ; J. W. Nesmuth, *Iron Age*, **47**. 1077, 1890 ; D. T. Day, *ib.*, **73**. 25, 1905 ; H. V. Winchell, *ib.*, **73**. 31, 1905 ; F. C. Lincoln, *Mining Districts and Mineral Resources of Nevada*, Nevada, 1923 ; F. F. Chisholm, *Mineral Resources of the United States*, Washington, 34, 1890 ; W..E. Hidden and J. B. Mackintosh,' *Amer. Journ. Science*, (3), **41**. 439, 1891 ; W. Irelan, *Rept. State Mineralogist California*, **11**. 1, 1893 ; J. J. Crawford, *Report of the State Mineralogist*, Sacramento, **12**. 325, 1894 ; E. P. Snow, *Eng. Min. Journ.*, **60**. 320, 1895 ; W. S. Tangier, *Amer. Journ. Science*, (4). **16**. 334, 1903 ; D. Maguire, *Mines Minerals*, **25**. 408, 1905 ; N. H. Darton, *Prof. Paper U.S. Geol. Sur.*, 32, 1905 ; G. D. James, *Eng. Min. Journ.*, **80**. 914, 1906 ; N. W. Emmens, *Mining Mag.*, **13**. 109, 1906 ; T. S. Lovering, *Bull. U.S. Geol. Sur.*, 811, 1929 ; D. F. Campbell, *Mining Scient. Press*, **93**. 603, 1906 ; J. Dern, *Mines Minerals*, **27**. 251, 1907 ; D. T. Day and R. H. Richards, *Min. Resources U.S.A.*, 1175, 1905 ; D. T. Day and J. A. Edman, *Bull. U.S. Geol. Sur.*, 315, 1907 ; J. B. Umpleby, *Eng. Min. Journ.*, **104**. 1140, 1917 ; G. J. Young, *Eng. Min. Journ.*, **119**. 209, 1925 ; C. M. Rolker, *Trans. Amer. Inst. Min. Eng.*, **14**. 266, 1886 ; D. MacVichie, *ib.*, **74**. 163, 1925 ; W. B. Devereux, *ib.*, **12**. 638, 1885 ; E. P. Jennings, *ib.*, **35**. 338, 1904 ; **44**. 14, 1912 ; G. O. Smith and B. Willis, *ib.*, **30**. 356, 1910 ; C. K. Leith and E. C. Harder, *Bull. U.S. Geol. Sur.*, 338, 1908 ; C. K. Leith, *ib.*, 229, 1904 ; 285, 1906 ; S. Paige, *ib.*, 381, 1909 ; L. G. Westgate, *ib.*, 715, 1920 ; E. F. Burchard, *ib.*, 821, 1931 ; J. S. Diller, *ib.*, 213, 1903 ; 260, 1905 ; 353, 1908 ; E. C. Harder, *ib.*, 380, 1906 ; 430, 1910 ; 503, 1912 ; E. C. Harder and J. L. Rich, *ib.*, 430, 1910 ; J. M. Boutwell, *ib.*, 225, 1904 ; W. S. T. Smith, *ib.*, 91, 1903 ; A. R. Schultz, *ib.*, 543, 1914 ; S. H. Ball, *ib.*, 308, 1907 ; 315, 1907 ; *Prof. Paper U.S. Geol. Sur.*, 63, 1908 ; E. Stebinger, *Iron Trade Rev.*, **53**. 363, 1913 ; *Bull. U.S. Geol. Sur.*, 540, 1914 ; B. S. Butler, *Prof. Paper U.S. Geol. Sur.*, 111, 1920 ; G. R. Mansfield, *Bull. U.S. Geol. Sur.*, 803, 1929 ; *Prof. Paper U.S. Geol. Sur.*, 152, 1927 ; H. W. Hoots, *ib.*, 151, 1929 ; J. Birkinbine, *Ann. Rep. U.S. Geol. Sur.*, **19**. vi, 62, 1898 ; *Iron Age*, **67**. 19, 1902 ; W. E. Upham, *Mining Scient. Press*, **102**. 521, 1911 ; L. E. Aubury, *Bull. California State Min. Bur.*, 38, 1906 ; J. A. Snedaker, *Eng. Min. Journ.*, **79**. 313, 1905 ; C. R. Keyes, *ib.*, **78**. 632, 1904 ; E. Y. Dougherty, *ib.*, **123**. 765, 1927 ; D. P. Rohlfing, *ib.*, **115**. 716, 1923 ; J. Sanders, *ib.*, **92**. 1191, 1911 ; A. R. Townsend, *ib.*, **85**. 307, 1908 ; F. M. Endlich, *Rep. Hayden Geol. Sur.*, 204, 1877 ; C. C. Jones, *Eng. Min. Journ.*, **87**. 785, 1909 ; *Mines Minerals*, **31**. 574, 1911 ; *Trans. Amer. Inst. Min. Eng.*, **53**. 306, 1915 ; H. G. Shaw, *Min. Ind.*, 149, 1893 ; B. Prescott, *Econ. Geol.*, **3**. 465, 1908 ; J. C. Jones, *ib.*, **8**. 247, 1913 ; F. Lerch, *Iron Trade Rev.*, **37**. 49, 1904 ; B. T. Putnam, *U.S. Rep. Tenth Census*, **15**. 469, 1886 ; S. Shedd, *Rep. Washington Geol. Sur.*, **1**. 215, 1902 ; *The Iron Ores of Washington*, Washington, 1903 ; B. W. Vallat, *Proc. Colorado Scient. Soc.*, **8**. 315, 1907 ; *Eng. Min. Journ.*, **85**. 399, 1908 ; J. T. Singewald, *Econ. Geol.*, **7**. 560, 1912.

[132] A. Knopf, *Bull. U.S. Geol. Sur.*, 442, 1910 ; U. S. Grant and D. F. Higgins, *ib.*, 443, 1910 ; H. M. Eakin, *ib.*, 622, 1915 ; 699, 1919 ; P. S. Smith, *ib.*, 783, A, 1926 ; A. H. Brooks, *ib.*, 394, 1909 ; 480, 1911 ; 714, 1921 ; 755, 1924 ; 773, 1925 ; A. C. Gill, *ib.*, 742, 1922 ; R. S. Knappen, *ib.*, 797, 1929 ; W. C. Mendenhall and F. C. Schroder, *Prof. Paper U.S. Geol. Sur.*, 15, 1903 ; W. C. Mendenhall, *ib.*, 41, 1905.

[133] C. K. Leith and W. J. Mead, *Trans. Amer. Inst. Min. Eng.*, **42**. 90, 1911 ; C. W. Hayes, *ib.*, **42**. 109, 1911 ; J. E. Little, *ib.*, **42**. 152, 1911 ; W. Lindgren and C. P. Ross, *ib.*, **53**. 40, 1915 ; J. S. Cox, *ib.*, **42**. 73, 1912 ; R. A. de Yarza, R. S. Lozano and V. Kindelan, *Rev. Minera*, **62**. 495, 1911 ; J. L. de Corral, *ib.*, **62**. 457, 1911 ; D. E. Woodbridge, *Canada Min. Journ.*, **32**. 738, 1911 ; O. R. Kuhn, *Eng. Min. Journ.*, **121**. 607, 1926 ; J. F. Kemp, *The Iron Ore Resources of the World*, Stockholm, 2. 793, 1910 ; *Trans. Amer. Inst. Min. Eng.*, **51**. 3, 1916 ; M. Roesler, *ib.*, **56**. 77, 1917 ; C. M. Weld, *ib.*, **40**. 299, 1909 ; **61**. 124, 1918 ; H. Souder, *ib.*, **35**. 308, 1904 ; A. C. Spencer, *Bull. U.S. Geol. Sur.*, 340, 1918 ; *Trans. Amer. Inst. Min. Eng.*, **42**. 1031, 1911 ; *Eng. Min. Journ.*, **72**. 633, 1901 ; J. T. Singewald and B. le R. Miles, *ib.*, **101**. 587, 1916 ; E. S. Murias, *ib.*, **114**. 197, 1922 ; C. W. Hayes, T. W. Vaughan and A. C. Spencer, *Report on a Geological Reconnaissance of Cuba*, Washington, 77, 1901 ; Anon., *Iron Age*, **90**. 530, 1912 ; R. Cabrera, *Journ. Franklin Inst.*, **146**. 26, 1898 ; B. Orton, *Tek Tids.*, **42**. 74, 88, 98, 1912 ; *Stahl Eisen*, **34**. 1731, 1914 ; J. S. Cox, *Eng. Mag.*, **16**. 745, 1898 ;

R. P. Porter, *Iron Age*, **64.** 3, 1899 ; *Iron Trade Rev.*, **32.** 12, 1899 ; P. M. Tyler, *Iron Age*, **111.** 275, 1923 ; D. T. Day, *ib.*, **66.** 16, 1903 ; *Eng. Mag.*, **17.** 242, 1899 ; F. F. Chisholm, *Proc. Colorado Scient. Soc.*, **3.** 259, 1891 ; D. A. Willey, *Eng. Mag.*, **44.** 867, 1913 ; W. L. Cummings and B. L. Miller, *Trans. Amer. Inst. Min. Eng.*, **42.** 116, 1912 ; *Iron Trade Rev.*, **48.** 964, 1911 ; J. P. Kimball, *Amer. Journ. Science*, (3), **28.** 416, 1884 ; *Trans. Amer. Inst. Min. Eng.*, **13.** 613, 1885 ; C. Catlett, *ib.*, **38.** 358, 1907 ; Anon., *Iron Age*, **80.** 421, 1907 ; **81.** 1149, 1908 ; T. H. Graham, *ib.*, **44.** 997, 1890 ; E. B. Wilson, *Mines Minerals*, **31.** 245, 1911 ; B. B. Lawrence, *Journ. Canada Min. Inst.*, **13.** 100, 1911 ; J. F. C. Abelspies, *Iron Coal Trades Rev.*, **78.** 1002, 1909 ; H. Wedding, *Iron Age*, **49.** 607, 1892 ; *Stahl Eisen*, **12.** 545, 1892.

[134] J. F. Kemp, *The Iron Ore Resources of the World*, Stockholm, 796, 1910 ; *Eng. Min. Mag.*, **112.** 458, 1921 ; E. M. de Garston, *Mining Journ.*, **83.** 682, 1909 ; J. Levainville, *Ann. Géogr.*, **31.** 87, 1922.

[135] C. R. Fettke and B. Hubbard, *Iron Trade Rev.*, **63.** 210, 1918 ; *Trans. Amer. Inst. Min. Eng.*, **61.** 97, 1920 ; C. R. Fettke, *ib.*, **70.** 1024, 1924 ; S. H. Hamilton, *Eng. Min. Journ.*, **88.** 518, 1909 ; W. F. Willoughby, *Bull. U.S. Bur. Census*, 6, 1904 ; Anon., *Mining Journ.*, **75.** 616, 1903 ; B. Low, *Eng. Min. Journ.*, **128.** 5, 1929.

[136] A. P. Cathedral, *Bull. Imp. Inst.*, **10.** 641, 1912 ; J. Cadman, *Trans. Inst. Min. Eng.*, **35.** 453, 1908.

[137] W. L. R. Emmet, *Journ. Maryland Acad.*, **1.** 235, 1930.

[138] L. C. Espinosa, *Bol. Min.*, **5.** 563, 1918 ; E. Glennie, *ib.*, **10.** 246, 1920 ; D. E. A. Charlton, *Eng. Min. Journ.*, **112.** 455, 1921 ; *Iron Trade Rev.*, **64.** 1097, 1919 ; T. F. Witherbee, *Trans. Amer. Inst. Min. Eng.*, **32.** 156, 1902 ; J. L. W. Birkinbine, *ib.*, **41.** 167, 1910 ; O. C. Farrington, *Eng. Min. Journ.*, **78.** 345, 1905 ; *Geol. Series Field Pub. Columbian Museum*, 5, 1904 ; K. Thomas and J. E. Kelly, *Eng. Min. Journ.*, **118.** 976, 1924 ; E. Ordonez, *Eng. Min. Journ.*, **90.** 665, 1910 ; *The Iron Ore Resources of the World*, Stockholm, **2.** 781, 1910 ; E. Halse, *Mining Journ.*, **82.** 310, 1907 ; O. R. Kuhn, *Blast Furnace Steel Plant*, **15.** 74, 112, 1927 ; M. F. Rangel and A. Terrones, *Eng. Min. Journ.*, **112.** 168, 1921 ; C. W. Botsford, *ib.*, **89.** 223, 1910 ; J. de D. Villarello and E. Bose, *Min. Mexicano*, **42.** 121, 1903 ; M. F. Rangel, *ib.*, **42.** 289, 1903 ; J. G. Aguillera, *Trans. Amer. Inst. Min. Eng.*, **32.** 497, 1903 ; A. Alzate, *Ann. Mexicanos*, **1.** 14, 1904 ; R. T. Hill, *Eng. Mag.*, **4.** 743, 1892 ; *Amer. Journ. Science*, (3), **45.** 111, 1893 ; M. D. Barriga, *Mining Journ.*, **77.** 455, 1905 ; A. Capilla, *Mem. Soc. Cient. Antonio Alzate*, **19.** 341, 1905 ; L. Jerome, *Journ. Board Trade*, **49.** 506, 1905.

[139] Anon., *Eng. Min. Journ.*, **93.** 173, 1912 ; **95.** 926, 1913 ; **97.** 140, 1914 ; **112.** 458, 1921 ; *U.S. Comm. Rep.*, 1684, 1920.

[140] L. Garbrecht, *Eng. Min. Journ.*, **109.** 791, 1920.

[141] F. C. Nicholas, *Mining World*, **24.** 723, 1905.

[142] J. W. Evans, *The Iron Ore Resources of the World*, Stockholm, **2.** 309, 1910.

[143] F. W. Voit, *Zeit. prakt. Geol.*, **30.** 17, 1922.

[144] E. Hussak, *Zeit. prakt. Geol.*, **14.** 329, 1906 ; *Neues Jahrb. Min.*, ii, 296, 1894 ; F. Katzer, *Zeit. prakt. Geol.*, **12.** 57, 1904 ; *Oesterr. Zeit. Berg. Hütt.*, **46.** 500, 1898 ; O. Wilson, *Chem. Met. Engg.*, **26.** 631, 697, 745, 1922 ; H. K. Scott, *Journ. Iron Steel Inst.*, **61.** i, 237, 1902 ; *Eng. Min. Journ.*, **74.** 680, 1902 ; A. L. Gottschalk, *ib.*, **44.** 123, 1916 ; W. Jones, *ib.*, **95.** 1208, 1913 ; G. E. Anderson, *ib.*, **88.** 81, 1909 ; E. Teixeira, *ib.*, **124.** 730, 1927 ; C. K. Leith and E. C. Harder, *Econ. Geol.*, **6.** 670, 1911 ; E. C. Harder, *Trans. Amer. Inst. Min. Eng.*, **50.** 143, 1915 ; **61.** 116, 1918 ; *Econ. Geol.*, **9.** 101, 1914 ; E. C. Harder and R. T. Chamberlin, *Journ. Geol.*, **23.** 341, 385, 1915 ; J. T. Richards, *Mining Journ.*, **72.** 253, 1902 ; N. A. V. Paulson, *Chem. Met. Eng.*, **25.** 1057, 1921 ; W. Pothmann, *Glückauf*, **55.** 601, 625, 1919 ; E. C. Eckel, *Iron Ores : their Occurrence, Valuation, and Control*, New York 303, 1914 ; Gonzaga de Campos, *The Iron Ore Resources of the World*, Stockholm, **2.** 811, 1910 ; O. A. Derby, *Min. Eng. World*, **35.** 485, 1911 ; *Amer. Journ. Science*, (3), **41.** 311, 1891 ; (4), **12.** 211, 1902 ; *The Iron Ore Resources of the World*, Stockholm, **2.** 813, 1910 ; Anon., *Iron Trade Rev.*, **52.** 459, 685, 1913 ; R. Stappenbeck, *Mining Journ.*, **154.** 886, 1926 ; F. M. de Souza, *Iron Coal Trades Rev.*, **97.** 381, 1918 ; *Rev. Mét.*, **14.** 758, 1917 ; G. Chalmers, *Iron Age*, **92.** 243, 1913 ; T. Gatham, *Zeit. prakt. Geol.*, **21.** 234, 1913 ; P. Ferrand, *Rev. Umb. Mines*, **23.** 396, 1894 ; A. Stange, *Mining World*, **34.** 445, 1910 ; I. Bolstad, *Bihang. Jernkontorets Ann.*, 230, 1930 ; S. Waessmann, *Direccion Gen. Minas Buenos Aires*, 62, 1929 ; J. P. Calogeras, *As Minas do Brazil e Sua Legislaçao*, Rio de Janeiro, **2.** 5, 1905 ; P. de Oliveira, *Echo Mines*, **57.** 686, 1929 ; *Mineral Resources of Brazil*, Rio de Janeiro, 1930 ; W. B. Chaplin, *Board Trade Journ.*, **55.** 568, 1907 ; J. B. Elgar, *Cassier's Mag.*, **41.** 540, 1912 ; T. Gathmann, *Zeit. prakt. Geol.*, **21.** 234, 1913 ; F. M. de S. Aguilar, *Iron Coal Trades Rev.*, **97.** 381, 1918 ; W. S. Schurz, *Iron Trade Rev.*, **70.** 1861, 1868, 1922 ; *Iron Coal Trades Rev.*, **105.** 155, 1922 ; S. G. Irving, *ib.*, **120.** 680, 1930.

[145] B. L. Miller and J. L. Singewald, *Mineral Deposits of South America*, London, 1918.

[146] R. Marstrander, *Eng. Min. Journ.*, **99.** 484, 1915 ; *Min. Mag.*, **14.** 315, 1916 ; C. Guillemain, *Zeit. prakt. Geol.*, **18.** 189, 1911 ; N. A. Lannefors, *Direccion Gen. Minas Buenos Aires*, 61, 1929.

[147] G. Bodenbender, *Anal. Agric. Republic Argentina*, **1.** 1, 1906 ; S. Waessman, *Publ. Direccion Geol. Gen. Minas*, 70, 1930 ; Anon., *Eng.*, **130.** 474, 1920 ; B. L. Miller and J. T. Singewald, *Mineral Deposits of South America*, London, 1918 ; L. Brackebusch, *Zeit. Berg. Hütt. Sal.*, **41.** 15, 1893 ; R. Stappenbeck, *Bol. Minas*, 19, 1918 ; Anon., *Mining Journ.*, **131.** 872, 1920 ; *The Iron Ore Resources of the World*, Stockholm, **2.** 826, 1910 ; *Zeit. prakt. Geol.*, **18.** 67, 1910 ;

H. D. Hoskold, *Mémoire général sur les mines dans la république Argentine*, Buenos Aires, 188, 1889; P. T. Vignal, *Anal. Soc. Cient. Argentina*, (2), **91**. 105, 1931; E. H. Ducloux, *ib.*, (2), **91**. 247, 1931.

¹⁴⁸ J. F. Kemp, *The Iron Ore Resources of the World*, Stockholm, **2**. 803, 1910; C. Sanjines, *Min. Scient. Press*, **104**. 376, 1912.

¹⁴⁹ C. Vattier, *Mém. Soc. Ing. Civils*, **19**. 552, 1902; *Journ. Iron Steel Inst.*, **86**. ii, 320, 1912; *Les mines de fer et la sidérurgie dans l'Amérique du sud et principalement au Chili*, Paris, 1911; *Bull. Soc. Ing. Civil*, **45**. 37, 1892; **64**. 159, 1911; *Trans. Amer. Inst. Min. Eng.*, **43**. 570, 1912; *L'avenir de la métallurgie du fer au Chili*, Paris, 1890; Anon., *Rev. Minera*, **71**. 547, 1920; *Iron Trade Rev.*, **52**. 459, 1913; *Iron Age*, **93**. 1456, 1914; *Min. Eng..World*, **41**. 523, 1914; *Mining Journ.*, **128**. 44, 1920; *Eng. Min. Journ.*, **112**. 454, 1921; C. A. Buck, *ib.*, **97**. 82, 1914; **99**. 145, 1915; M. Wiener, *Ann. Mines*, (9), **13**. 676, 1898; F. Gautier, *Chili et Bolivie*, Paris, 82, 1906; O. Wilson, *Chem. Met. Engg.*, **26**. 631, 697, 745, 1922; J. F. Kemp, *The Iron Ore Resources of the World*, Stockholm, **2**. 805, 1910; R. Stappenbeck, *Mining Journ.*, **154**. 816, 1926; J. Daniels, *Mining Met.*, **7**. 200, 1926; G. M. Slight, *Iron Coal Trades Rev.*, **115**. 295, 1927; B. A. Russell, *Trans. Mining Inst. Scotland*, **32**. 13, 1909; F. Wüst, *Bol. Min. Soc. Nac. Chile*, **43**. 381, 1931; C. H. Fritzsche, *Stahl Eisen*, **51**. 541, 1931; *Der Eisenerzbergbau in Chile und Aussichten einer heimischen Eisenhüttenindustrie*, Düsseldorf, 1931.

¹⁵⁰ J. J. Bravo, *Eng. Min. Journ.*, **111**. 263, 1921; J. Daniels, *Min. Met.*, 200, 1926; E. I. Duenas, *Bol. Cuerp. Ing. Min. del Peru*, 53, 1907; 87, 1918; L. Pflücker, *Mining Journ.*, **80**. 269, 1907; *Bol. Cuerp. Ing. Min. del Peru*, 36, 1906; P. C. Venturo, *ib.*, 8, 1904; *Los Yacimientos de Fierro de Tambo Grande*, Lima, 1904; J. F. Kemp, *The Iron Ore Resources of the World*, Stockholm, **2**. 803, 1910; R. Stappenbeck, *Mining Journ.*, **154**. 816, 1926; C. P. Jimenez, *Rev. Min.*, **72**. 549, 568, 577, 1921; O. Wilson, *Chem. Met. Engg.*, **26**. 631, 697, 745, 1922.

¹⁵¹ B. L. Miller and J. T. Singewald, *Mineral Deposits of South America*, London, 1918; Anon., *U.S. Commerce Rep.*, 263, 1920; *Stahl Eisen*, **40**. 898, 1920; J. F. Kemp, *The Iron Ore Resources of the World*, Stockholm, **2**. 801, 1910; I. A. Manning, *Mining Eng. World*, **38**. 387, 1913.

¹⁵² Anon., *Iron Trade Rev.*, **52**. 685, 1913; *Iron Age*, **45**. 286, 1890; B. L. Miller and J. T. Singewald, *Mineral Deposits of South America*, London, 534, 1918; S. Norton, *Bull. Amer. Iron Steel Assoc.*, 1, 1890; *Iron Age*, **52**. 931, 1893; D. E. A. Charlton, *Eng. Min. Journ.*, **112**. 458, 1921; *Iron Age*, **106**. 15, 1920; *Journ. Ind. Eng. Chem.*, **8**. 555, 1916; E. P. Burchard, *Tech. Publ. Amer. Inst. Min. Eng.*, 295, 1930; *Econ. Geol.*, **25**. 549, 1930; G. Zuloaga, *ib.*, **25**. 99, 1930; J. F. Kemp, *The Iron Ore Resources of the World*, Stockholm, **2**. 802, 1910; R. Stappenbeck, *Mining Journ.*, **154**. 816, 1926.

¹⁵³ B. Dustand, *Rec. Geol. Sur. Queensland*, 2, 1905; *Queensland Govt. Mining Journ.*, **18**. 425, 1917; *The Iron Ore Resources of the World*, Stockholm, **2**. 843, 1910; *Publ. Queensland Geol. Sur.*, 265, 1920; I. C. Ball, *ib.*, 194, 1904; K. M. Grant, *Iron Coal Trades Rev.*, **74**. 55, 1907; J. Findlay, *Iron Trade Rev.*, **44**. 37, 1908; Anon., *Iron Steel Canada*, **3**. 207, 1920; C. L. Baker, *Trans. Amer. Inst. Min. Eng.*, **66**. 42, 1922; Anon., *Mining Mag.*, **24**. 214, 1921; E. C. St. Smith, *Queensland Govt. Mining Journ.*, **15**. 354, 1918.

¹⁵⁴ A. Liversidge, *Trans. Roy. Soc. New South Wales*, **25**. 234, 1892; *Mines Min. Stat. New South Wales*, 98, 1875; J. E. Carne, *Ann. Rept. Dept. Mines, New South Wales*, 147, 1893; *Chrome Iron Ore*, Sydney, 1898; *Mem. Geol. Sur. New South Wales*, 6, 1908; J. A. Watt, *Ann. Rep. Dept. Mines Agric., New South Wales*, 184, 1897; E. F. Pittman, *The Iron Ore Resources of the World*, Stockholm, **2**. 947, 1910; *Ann. Rep. Dept. Mines, New South Wales*, 128, 1902; T. W. E. David, *ib.*, 240, 1892; C. S. Wilkinson, *ib.*, 212, 1891; *Official Report of the International Exhibition of Mining and Metallurgy*, Sydney, 1890; L. F. Harper, *Bull. New South Wales Geol. Sur.*, 4, 1923; C. L. Baker, *Trans. Amer. Inst. Min. Eng.*, **66**. 42, 1922; *Mining Mag.*, **20**. 150, 1919; J. B. Jaquet, *Ann. Rept. Dept. Mines, New South Wales*, 70, 1904; *The Iron Ore Deposits of New South Wales*, Sydney, 1901; *Colliery Guardian*, **80**. 553, 1900; *Mem. Geol. Sur. New South Wales*, 2, 1901; C. A. Sussmilch, *Journ. Australia Inst. Eng.*, 1..144, 1929; J. S. Mitchell, *Colliery Guardian*, **61**. 502, 1891; W. S. Dun, *Records Geol. Sur. New South Wales*, **6**. 183, 1899.

¹⁵⁵ O. A. L. Whitelaw, *Records Geol. Sur. Victoria*, **4**. ii, 162, 1920; H. C. Jenkins, *Rep. Dept. Mines Victoria*, 1, 1901; J. Dennant, *Rec. Geol. Sur. Victoria*, **1**. 36, 1903; A. E. Kitson, *The Economic Rocks and Minerals of Victoria*, Melbourne, 1906; A. M. Howitt, *Chem. Eng. Min. Rev.*, **12**. 370, 1920; J. W. Gregory, *Iron Coal Trades Rev.*, **67**. 1080, 1903; *The Iron Ore Resources of the World*, Stockholm, **2**. 875, 1910; C. L. Baker, *Trans. Amer. Inst. Min. Eng.*, **66**. 42, 1922.

¹⁵⁶ H. Y. L. Brown, *The Iron Ore Resources of the World*, Stockholm, **2**. 837, 1910; *Mining Records South Australia*, 1, 1905; J. L. Pearson, *Bull. S. Australia Dept. Mines*, 1, 1927; D. Baker, *Proc. Eng. Soc. West Pennsylvania*, **43**. 225, 1927; *Yearbook Amer. Iron Steel Inst.*, 34, 1922; W. Aitkinson, *Colliery Guardian*, **66**. 149, 1893; C. L. Baker, *Trans. Amer. Inst. Min. Eng.*, **66**. 42, 1921; R. L. Jack, *Bull. South Australia Geol. Sur.*, 9, 1922; J. B. Austin, *Mining Journ.*, **62**. 775, 1892.

¹⁵⁷ A. G. Maitland, *Bull. West Australia Geol. Sur.*, 16, 1905; 23, 1906; *Ann. Progress Rep. West Australia*, 1, 1906; *Mem. Geol. Sur. West Australia*, 1, 1919; *The Iron Ore Resources of the World*, Stockholm, **2**. 829, 1910; A. G. Maitland and A. Montgomery, *Bull. Geol. Sur. West Australia*, 50, 1912; E. S. Simpson and C. G. Gibson, *ib.*, 30, 1907; A. Montgomery, *The Iron Ore Deposits of Yampi Sound*, Perth, 1920; C. G. Gibson, *Bull. Geol. Sur. West*

Australia, 14, 1904; C. L. Baker, *Trans. Amer. Inst. Min. Eng.*, **66**. 42, 1922; Anon., *Mining Mag.*, **20**. 150, 1919; J. B. Wilson, *Eng. Min. Journ.*, **89**. 724, 1909; D. Clark, *West Australian Min. Met.*, 199, 1904; H. P. Woodward, *Mining Handbook to the Colony of Western Australia*, Perth, 87, 1894; Ann. *Rept. Govt. Geol.*, 1888–89, 25, 1890.

¹⁵⁸ W. H. Twelvetrees and A. McIntosh, *Min. Resources Tasmania Geol. Sur.*, 6, 1919; W. H. Twelvetrees, *The Iron Ore Resources of the World*, Stockholm, **2**. 881, 1910; *Rep. Tasmania Geol. Sur.*, 1, 1903; D. Jones, *Trans. Australian Inst. Min. Eng.*, **5**. 117, 1898; H. Lavers, *Proc. Australasian Inst. Min. Met.*, 43, 1921; C. L. Baker, *Trans. Amer. Inst. Min. Eng.*, **66**. 42, 1922; Anon., *Mining Mag.*, **20**. 159, 1919; W. G. Dauncey, *Proc. Roy. Soc. Tasmania*, 49, 1897.

¹⁵⁹ E. R. Stanley, *Geology of Papua*, Melbourne, 44, 1924.

¹⁶⁰ H. Cayley-Webster, *Through New Guinea and the Cannibal Countries*, London, 182, 1898.

¹⁶¹ E. Glasser, *Ann. Mines*, (10), **4**. 299, 397, 1903; (10), **5**. 111, 1904; W. M. Davis, *Proc. Nat. Acad.*, **4**. 275, 1915; H. J. Jensen, *Proc. Pan-Pacific Societies Congress*, **2**. 1832.

¹⁶² J. M. Bell, *Bull. New Zealand Geol. Sur.*, 3, 1907; *The Iron Ore Resources of the World*, Stockholm, **2**. 891, 1910; *Trans. Australasian Inst. Min. Eng.*, **13**. 79, 1910; *New Zealand Mines Record*, **11**. 240, 335, 1908; W. Donovan, N. L. Wright and R. P. Wilson, *Journ. Soc. Chem. Ind.*, **36**. 292, 1917; W. S. Lecky, *Electrochemist*, **2**. 54, 1902; E. M. Smith, *Journ. Iron Steel Inst.*, **49**. i, 65, 1896; H. P. Washbourn, *Eng. Min. Journ.*, **69**. 588, 1899; C. C. Longridge, *Mining Journ.*, **81**. 522, 1906; J. A. Heskett, *Iron Coal Trades Rev.*, **113**. 390, 1926; W. Donovan, *New Zealand Journ. Science Tech.*, **6**. 140, 1923; V. W. Aubel, *Trans. Amer. Inst. Min. Eng.*, **63**. 266, 1919; G. J. Binns, *Trans. Fed. Inst. Min. Eng.*, **4**. 59, 1893.

¹⁶³ A. E. Törnebohm, *Tek. Tids.*, **35**. 73, 1905; *Zeit. angew. Chem.*, **18**. 1179, 1905; *Glückauf*, **41**. 1542, 1905; F. H. Hatch, *Geol. Mag.*, (6), **57**. 504, 1920; M. Fourment, *Rev. Met.*, **22**. 170, 1925; A. Redlich, *Berg. Hütt. Jahrb.*, **72**. 1, 1924; W. Oechelhäuser, *Vergleichende Statistik der Eisenindustrie aller Länder und Erörterung ihrer ökonomischen Lage im Zollverein*, Berlin, 1852; G. Mehrtens, *Stahl Eisen*, **7**. 485, 1887; D. Forbes, *Journ. Iron Steel Inst.*, **6**. 197, 445, 1873; **7**. 174, 410, 1874; **8**. 260, 581, 1875; **9**. i, 171, 1876; I. L. Bell, *ib.*, **37**. ii, 406, 1890; J. Deby, *ib.*, **10**. ii, 525, 1876; **11**. i, 213, 1877; R. Akerman, *ib.*, **14**. ii, 359, 1878. There are reports in nearly all the volumes of the *Journ. Iron Steel Inst.* for subsequent years. A. Marcus, *Die grossen Eisen- und Metallkonzerne*, Leipzig, 1929; L. Demaret, *Les principaux gisements de minerais de fer du monde*, Bruxelles, 1902; H. Kreusser, *Eisen sein Vorkommen und seine Gewinnung*, Weimar, 1893; A. S. Cushman, *Journ. Franklin Inst.*, **171**. 345, 1911; C. K. Leith, *Trans. Amer. Inst. Min. Eng.*, **63**. 194, 1916; *Proc. World's Eng. Congr. Tokyo*, **33**. 1, 1931; *Iron Ore Reserves*, Washington, 1907; E. C. Harder, *Eng. Min. Journ.*, **109**. 1060, 1920; Comité des Forges de France, *Tableaux statistiques sur la production minière et sidérurgique des principaux pays 1864–1913*, Paris, 1914; S. G. Koon, *Mineral Ind.*, **37**. 298, 1928; **38**. 340, 1930; R. Schlenker, *Die Eisenindustrie in der Welt unter Berücksichtigung des internationalen Eisenpaktes*, Jena, 1927; H. B. Vanderblue and W. L. Crum, *The Iron Industry in Prosperity and Depression*, New York, 1927; C. Nattan-Larrier, *La production sidérurgique de l'Europe continentale et l'entente internationale de l'acier*, Paris, 1928; H. K. Scott, *Proc. Cleveland Inst. Eng.*, 69, 1923; J. Percy, *Metallurgy—Iron and Steel*, London, 1864; O. R. Kuhn, *Iron Age*, **110**. 211, 1922; *Eng. Min. Journ.*, **122**. 84, 1926; *Blast Furnace Steel Plant*, **14**. 2, 1926; H. M. Howe, *Atlantic Monthly*, **105**. 827, 1910; *The Metallography of Steel and Cast Iron*, New York, 12, 1916; E. C. Eckel, *Iron Ores : Their Occurrence, Valuation and Control*, New York, 1914; F. Beyschlag, *Ber. Internat. Kongress Bergbau Düsseldorf*, 13, 1910; *Zeit. prakt. Geol.*, **18**. 209, 1910; A. Lindmann, *ib.*, **18**. 217, 1910; J. F. Kemp, *ib.*, **18**. 220, 1910; L. de Launay, *ib.*, **18**. 224, 1910; *Les réserves mondiales en minerais de fer*, Paris, 1910; H. E. Boker, *Glückauf*, **47**. 420, 457, 499, 1911; H. H. Campbell, *Iron Age*, **99**. 51, 1917; M. Roesler, *Bull. U.S. Geol. Sur.*, 706, 1921; P. Krusch, *Zeit. Berg. Hütt. Sal.*, **62**. 176, 1914; H. Sjögren, *The Iron Ore Resources of the World*, Stockholm, **1**. 18, 1910; H. Sundholm, *Jernkontorets Ann.*, (2), **83**. 459, 1928; G. de Geer, *ib.*, (2), **83**. 7, 1928.

¹⁶⁴ T. E. Thorpe and E. H. Morton, *Liebig's Ann.*, **158**. 122, 1878; *Chem. News*, **21**. 182, 1870; E. H. Ducloux, *Anal. Soc. Cient. Argentina*, **54**. 62, 1902; C. Schmidt, *Bull. Acad. St. Petersburg*, (3), **24**. 231, 1878; *Mélanges Phys. Chim.*, **10**. 594, 1877; J. Usiglio, *Ann. Chim. Phys.*, (3), **27**. 92, 172, 1849; F. J. Malaguti, J. Durocher and M. Sarzeau, *ib.*, (3), **28**. 129, 1850; G. Forchhammer, *Phil. Trans.*, **155**. 203, 1865; J. Roth, *Allgemeine und chemische Geologie*, Berlin, **1**. 490, 1879; W. Dittmar, *Challenger Reports—Physics and Chemistry*, London, **1**. 1, 1884; R. Quinton, *L'eau de mer*, Paris, 221, 1904; A. F. von Sass, *Journ. prakt. Chem.*, (1), **98**. 251, 1866; (1), **99**. 480, 1866; A. Goebel, *Pogg. Ann. Ergbd.*, 1. 187, 1842; *Bull. Acad. St. Petersburg*, (2), **4**. 131, 1861; H. Struve, *ib.*, (1), **4**. 130, 1861; E. von Bibra, *Liebig's Ann.*, **77**. 98, 1851; S. Robinet and J. Lefort, *Compt. Rend.*, **62**. 436, 1866.

¹⁶⁵ J. Murray and A. F. Renard, *Challenger Reports—Deep-Sea Deposits*, London, 1891; L. W. Collet, *Les dépôts marines*, Paris, 1908; L. W. Collet and G. W. Lee, *Compt. Rend.*, **142**. 999, 1906; J. B. Harrison and A. J. J. Brown, *Journ. Geol. Soc.*, **51**. 313, 1895; W. A. Caspari, *Proc. Roy. Soc. Edin.*, **30**. 183, 364, 1910; J. Y. Buchanan, *ib.*, **18**. 131, 1891; K. Nattarer, *Monatsh. Chem.*, **14**. 624, 1893; **15**. 530, 1894; **20**. 1, 1899; A. and H. Strecker, *Liebig's Ann.*, **95**. 177, 1855; E. Bödeker, *ib.*, **302**. 43, 1893; K. Andrée, *Geol. Rund.*, **3**. 324, 1912; C. K. Leith, *Monog. U.S. Geol. Sur.*, 43, 1903; L. Cayeux, *Contributions à l'étude micrographique des terrains sédimentaires*, Paris, 1897; *Mém. Soc. Geol. Nord*, **4**. 163, 1897; C. W. von Gümbel, *Sitzber. Akad. München*, **16**. 417, 1886; **26**. 545, 1896; D. S. Calderon, D. F. Chaves and P. del Pulgar,

Anal. Soc. Espan. Hist. Nat., **23**. 8, 1894 ; F. W. Clarke, *The Data of Geochemistry*, Washington, 518, 1924.

[166] R. Boyle, *The Usefulness of Experimental Philosophy*, Oxford, 1671 ; F. Hoffmann, *De methodo examinandi aquas salubres*, Lugduni Batavorum, 1708 ; T. Bergman, *De minerarum docimasia humida*, Upsala, 1780 ; A. S. Marggraf, *Mém. Acad. Berlin*, **7**. 131, 1751 ; Paracelsus, *Bücher und Schriften des edlen, hochgelahrten, und bewehrten philosophi medici, Philippi Theophrasti Bombast von Hohenheim Paracelsi genannt*, Bale, 1589.

[167] H. St. C. Deville, *Ann. Chim. Phys.*, (3), **23**. 42, 1848 ; E. J. Maumené, *Compt. Rend.*, **31**. 270, 1850 ; T. Graham, W. A. Miller, and A. W. Hofmann, *Journ. Chem. Soc.*, **4**. 375, 1851 ; C. Schmidt, *Bull. Acad. St. Petersburg*, (3), **20**. 154, 1874 ; J. F. Hodges, *Chem. News*, **30**. 103, 1874 ; R. Finkener, *Vorarbeiten zu einer Zukünftigen Wasserversorgung der Stadt Berlin*, Berlin, 347, 349, 1871 ; H. Wurtz, *Amer. Journ. Science*, (2), **22**. 124, 1856.

[168] H. von Fehling, *Jahrb. Württemberg. Natw. Ger.*, **13**. 113, 1857 ; R. Kremann, in E. Doelter, *Handbuch der Mineralchemie*, Leipzig, **3**. i, 894, 1918 ; J. Scherer, *Liebig's Ann.*, **99**. 257, 1856 ; J. von Liebig, *ib.*, **63**. 221, 1847 ; F. von Gorup-Besanez, *ib.*, **79**. 50, 1851 ; **89**. 222, 1854 ; J. P. Bouquet, *Ann. Chim. Phys.*, (3), **42**. 278, 1854 ; W. Lasch, *Journ. prakt. Chem.*, (1), **63**. 321, 1854 ; R. Fresenius, *ib.*, (1), **64**. 335, 1855 ; T. Poleck, *ib.*, (1), **52**. 353, 1851 ; H. A. L. Wiggers, *Dribergs neueste chemische Analyse. Nebst einer Einleitung und balneologischen Bemerkungen von A. T. Brück*, Osnabrück, 1860 ; *Pharm. Centrb.*, **25**. 934, 1854 ; *Balneologische Ztg.*, **1**. 5, 1854 ; E. Reichardt, *Arch. Pharm.*, (3), **2**. 124, 1873 ; H. W. F. Wackenroder and E. Reichardt, *ib.*, (2), **35**. 278, 1843 ; (2), **71**. 22, 1852 ; M. W. Thüring, *ib.*, (2), **98**. 257, 1859 ; W. Stein and C. Bley, *ib.*, (2), **119**. 1, 1864 ; J. Zehentner, *Zeit. Ferdinandeums*, (3), **57**. 303, 1913 ; R. Woy, *Zeit. öffent. Chem.*, **17**. 181, 1911 ; L. Moissenet, *Ann. Mines*, (5), **17**. 7, 1860 ; J. Lefort, *Journ. prakt. Chim.*, (3), **31**. 84, 1857 ; J. L. Lassaigne, *Journ. Chim. Méd.*, (3), **5**. 489, 1849 ; A. Duboin, *Compt. Rend.*, **128**. 1469, 1899 ; E. Gérard and H. Chaurin, *ib.*, **157**. 302, 1913 ; C. F. Chandler and F. A. Cairns, *Amer. Chemist*, **1**. 347, 1871 ; **3**. 164, 1873 ; **4**. 186, 1874 ; A. H. Chester, *ib.*, **2**. 296, 1872 ; L. R. Milford, *Journ. Ind. Eng. Chem.*, **4**. 593, 1912 ; **5**. 24, 557, 1913 ; **6**. 552, 1914 ; P. A. Bolley and M. Schultz, *Zeit. Schweiz. Polyt.*, **4**. 83, 84, 1859 ; W. F. Gintl, *Journ. prakt. Chem.*, (2), **24**. 25, 1881.

[169] C. von Hauer, *Jahrb. geol. Reichsanst.*, **9**. 137, 1859 ; H. Vohl, *Ber.*, **8**. 611, 1875 ; **9**. 20, 1876 ; H. Fresenius, *Journ. prakt. Chem.*, (2), **14**. 61, 1876 ; J. Holm, *Heilmittel Revue*, **8**. 12, 1880 ; M. Pettenkofer, *Arch. Pharm.*, (2), **55**. 180, 1848 ; G. A. C. de C. de Castelnau, *Ann. Mines*, (8), **13**. 530, 1888 ; L. P. U. le Verrière, *ib.*, (8), **13**. 537, 1888 ; O. Henry, *Rep. Chim. Appl.*, **1**. 282, 1859 ; *Bull. Acad. Imp. Méd.*, **22**. 1079, 1857 ; G. Nussberger, *Schweiz. Wochenschr. Chem. Pharm.*, **51**. 149, 1902 ; T. Poleck, *Journ. prakt. Chem.*, (1), **52**. 353, 1851.

[170] R. Bunsen, *Zeit. anal. Chem.*, **10**. 39, 1871 ; O. Henry, *Journ. Pharm. Chim.*, (3), **35**. 250, 1859 ; L. Dieulafait, *Compt. Rend.*, **95**. 999, 1882 ; J. C. H. Mingaye, *Proc. Roy. Soc. New South Wales*, **26**. 73, 1892 ; L. Moissenet, *Ann. Mines*, (5), **17**. 7, 1860 ; R. Fresenius, *Journ. prakt. Chem.*, (1), **79**. 385, 1860 ; (1), **95**. 151, 1865 ; (1), **98**. 321, 1866 ; F. J. Hugi, *ib.*, (1), **42**. 464, 1847 ; H. A. L. Wiggers, *Arch. Pharm.*, (2), **102**. 215, 1860 ; A. Husemann, *ib.*, (3), **97**. 395, 1869 ; F. P. Treadwell, *ib.*, (3), **26**. 314, 1889 ; W. Gambel, *Sitzber. Bayr. Akad.*, **1**, 1893 ; A. Goldberg, *Ber. Naturw. Ges. Chemnitz*, **15**. 74, 108, 1904 ; K. Birnbaum, *Ber.*, **17**. 1614, 1884 ; J. Bouquet, *Ann. Chim. Phys.*, (3), **42**. 304, 1854 ; H. von Fehling and C. Hell, *Jahrsb. Württemberg. Natw.*, **37**. 153, 1881 ; P. Schweitzer, *Rep. Missouri Geol. Sur.*, **3**. 174, 1892 ; G. Rupp, *Zeit. angew. Chem.*, **4**. 448, 1891 ; H. Dietrich, *Tschermak's Mitt.*, (2), **3**. 439, 1881 ; F. von Gorup-Besanez, *Liebig's Ann.*, **89**. 225, 1854 ; H. Will, *ib.*, **61**. 181, 1847 ; A. von Planta and A. Kekulé, *ib.*, **90**. 316, 1854 ; A. von Planta, *ib.*, **109**. 157, 1859 ; J. Roth, *Allgemeine und chemische Geologie*, Berlin, **1**. 569, 1879 ; M. Say, *Sitzber. Akad. Wien*, **13**. 457, 1854 ; J. Nessler, *Sandberger's geol. Beschr. Sect. Oppenau*, 16. 29, 1863 ; C. Neuberg, *Zeit. Bahn. Klim.*, **5**. 561, 1913 ; G. Bizio, *Atti Ist. Veneti*, (3), **9**. 104, 273, 325, 1882 ; P. Spica and G. Schiavon, *Gazz. Chim. Ital.*, **32**. i, 63, 75, 1902 ; P. Spica, *ib.*, **22**. i, 354, 1892 ; *Boll. Chim. Farm.*, **37**. 385, 1898 ; W. F. Hillebrand, *Bull. U.S. Geol. Sur.*, 113, 1893 ; W. Lindgren, *Econ. Geol.*, **5**. 22, 1910 ; E. Bosshard, *Chem. Centr.*, (4), **4**. 1039, 1892.

[171] T. Pusch, *Arch. Pharm.*, (2), **140**. 1, 1869 ; H. Bley, *ib.*, (2), **82**. 129, 1855 ; L. von Barth and R. Wegscheider, *Wien. Klin. Wochenschr.*, 8, 1891 ; A. Simon and K. Kötschau, *Zeit. anorg. Chem.*, **168**. 129, 1927 ; J. C. Wittstein, *Vierteljahr. Pharm.*, **1**. 47, 1852 ; N. O. Hamberg, *Journ. prakt. Chem.*, (1), **80**. 325, 1860 ; J. C. Essener, *Bull. Soc. Chim.*, (3), **7**. 480, 1892.

[172] M. Papp, *Zeit. Naturw. Halle*, **78**. 353, 1907 ; V. Henry, *Journ. Pharm. Chim.*, (3), **13**. 5, 1848 ; (3), **29**. 413, 1855 ; F. J. Malaguti, *ib.*, (3), **44**. 381, 1863 ; J. P. Bouquet, *Ann. Chim. Phys.*, (3), **42**. 278, 1854 ; L. Grandeau, *ib.*, (3), **60**. 479, 1860 ; F. Schultze, *Arch. Pharm.*, (2), **116**. 176, 1863 ; C. von John, *Verh. geol. Reichsanst*, 208, 1876 ; J. Landerer, *Vierteljahr. Pharm.*, **7**. 34, 1858 ; C. P. Williams, *Amer. Chemist*, **7**. 246, 1877 ; C. von Hauser and C. von John, *Jahrb. geol. Reichsanst.*, **25**. 197, 1875 ; P. Pribram and F. Langer, *Jahrb. Bukow. Landesmus.*, **11**. 9, 1903 ; W. F. Hillebrand, *Bull. U.S. Geol. Sur.*, 113, 1893 ; E. Bonjeau, *Bull. Soc. Chim.*, (3), **23**. 405, 1900 ; E. Ludwig, *Journ. prakt. Chem.*, (1), **104**. 360, 1868 ; *Tschermak's Mitt.*, (2), **4**. 273, 1882 ; P. Weselsky and A. Bauer, *Sitzber. Akad. Wien*, **29**. 585, 1858 ; F. Manganini, *Gazz. Chim. Ital.*, **17**. 517, 1887 ; C. Schmidt, *Bull. Acad. St. Petersburg*, (3), **11**. 315, 1867 ; (3), **12**. 1, 1868 ; R. Fresenius, *Chem. Centr.*, (3), **15**. 423, 1884 ; *Zeit. Mineralw. Fabrik*, **1**. 20, 1884 ; T. Carnelley, *Proc. Manchester Lit. Phil. Soc.*, **14**. 59, 1875 ; *Mem. Manchester Lit. Phil. Soc.*, **5**. 256, 1876 ; *Chem. News*, **31**. 27, 1875 ; G. Müller, *Neues Jahrb. Pharm.*, **3**. 205, 1855 ; E. von

Gorup-Besanez, *Liebig's Ann.*, **119**. 240, 1861 ; P. Weselsky, *Sitzber. Akad. Wien*, **54**. 34, 1866 ; O. A. Ziurek, *Vorarbeiten zu einer Zukunftigen Wasserversorgung der Stadt Berlin*, Berlin, 263, 1871 ; H. Laspeyres, *Zeit. deut. geol. Ges.*, **20**. 191, 1868 ; C. M. Kersten, *Neues Jahrb. Min.*, 728, 1846 ; *Journ. prakt. Chem.*, (1), **35**. 257, 1845 ; W. von der Marck, *Correspbl. Ver. Rheinlande Westphalen*, **3**. 86, 1867 ; R. Bunsen and G. Kirchhoff, *Pogg. Ann.*, **113**. 358, 1860 ; V. Monheim, *Correspbl. Nat. Hist. Ver. Bonn*, **1**. 60, 1865 ; C. von Hauer, *Sitzber. Akad. Wien*, **69**. 72, 1874 : E. Wilm, *Bull. Soc. Chim.*, (2), **29**. 294, 1878 ; M. B. Hardin, *Amer. Chem.*, **4**. 247, 1874 ; T. S. Hunt, *Geology of Canada*, Ottawa, 545, 1847 ; L. Lewy, *Compt. Rend.*, **78**. 461, 1874 ; R. Pribram, *Viertelj prakt. Pharm.*, **15**. 182, 1866.

[173] F. Raspe, *Heilquellen Analysen*, Dresden, 1885 ; J. Landerer, *Vierteljahr. Pharm.*, **7**. 34, 1858 ; R. Wildenstein, *Journ. prakt. Chem.*, (1), **85**. 100, 1862 ; T. L. Phipson, *Chem. News*, **60**. 67, 1889 ; E. Ludwig, *Tschermak's Mitt.*, (2), **11**. 303, 1890 ; E. Ludwig and R. von Zeynek, *Wien. Klin. Wochenschr.*, **11**. 634, 1898 ; C. F. Eichleiter, *Jahrb. geol. Reichsanst.*, **57**. 529, 1907 ; R. Nasini, M. G. Levi and F. Ageno, *Gazz. Chim. Ital.*, **39**. ii, 481, 1909 ; M. Gläser and W. Kalmann, *Ber.*, **21**. 1687, 2879, 1888 ; H. Siegmund and P. Juhacz, *Sitzber. Akad. Wien*, **14**. 216, 1854 ; M. Bamberger and A. Landsiedel, *Monatsh.*, **19**. 114, 1899 ; P. Schweitzer, *Rep. Missouri Geol. Sur.*, **3**. 131, 1892 ; W. F. Hillebrand, *Bull. U.S. Geol. Sur.*, 113, 1893 ; S. Yoshimura, *Journ. Japan. Geol.*, **8**. 269, 1931.

[174] T. Price, *Trans. Tech. Soc. Pacific Coast*, **5**. 48, 1888 ; W. T. Lee, *Bull. U.S. Geol. Sur.*, 315, 1907 ; J. B. J. D. Boussingault, *Ann. Chim. Phys.*, (5), **2**. 80, 1874 ; S. de Luca, *Compt. Rend.*, **70**. 408, 1870 ; J. Lefort, *ib.*, **56**. 909, 1863 ; F. A. Flückiger, *Mitt. Naturf. Ges. Bern*, 17, 1862 ; C. du Ponteil, *Liebig's Ann.*, **96**. 193, 1855 ; W. Skey, *Trans. New Zealand Inst.*, **10**. 423, 1877 ; J. S. Maclaurin, *Proc. Chem. Soc.*, **27**. 10, 1911 ; J. Centeno, *Estudio geologico del volcan de Taal*, Madrid, 1885 ; G. F. Becker, *Ann. Rep. U.S. Geol. Sur.*, **21**. iii, 49, 1901 ; R. F. Bacon, *Philippine Journ. Science*, **1**. 433, 1906 ; **2**. 115, 1907.

[175] E. Jacquot and E, Willm, *Les eaux minérales de la France*, Paris, 1894 ; E. Guyon, *Études sur les eaux thermales de la Tunisie*, Paris, 1864 ; M. Hanriot, *Les eaux minérales de l'Algérie*, Paris, 1911 ; F. Raspe, *Heilquellen Analysen*, Dresden, 1885 ; J. K. Crook, *The Mineral Waters of the United States*, New York, 1899 ; A. C. Peale, *Bull. U.S. Geol. Sur.*, 32, 1886 ; F. A. Gooch and J. E. Whitehead, *ib.*, **47**. 1888 ; E. Orton, *Ann. Rep. U.S. Geol. Sur.*, **19**. iv, 633, 1898 ; W. H. Norton, *Ann. Rep. Iowa Geol. Sur.*, **6**. 117, 1896 ; J. H. Shepherd, *Bull. South Dakota Agric. Exp. Station*, 41, 1895 ; J. C. Branner, *Ann. Rep. Arkansas Geol. Sur.*, **1**. 1, 1891 ; E. H. S. Bailey, *Ann. Rep. Kansas Geol. Sur.*, **7**. 1, 1902 ; P. Schweitzer, *Ann. Rep. Missouri Geol. Sur.*, **3**. 1, 1892 ; S. W. McCallie, *Bull. Georgia Geol. Sur.*, 20, 1913 ; A. C. Lane, *Paper U.S. Geol. Sur.—Water Supply*, 31, 1899 ; G. A. Waring, *ib.*, 338, 1914 ; 418, 1917 ; W. Anderson, *Mineral Springs and Health Resorts of California*, San Francisco, 1892 ; R. T. Elsworthy, *Bull. Canada Mines Dept.*, 20, 1918 ; L. de Launay, *Recherche captage et aménagement des sources thermominérales*, Paris, 1899 ; A. Carnot, *Ann. Mines*, (8), **7**. 79, 1885 ; (9), **6**. 355, 1894 ; (9), **16**. 33, 1899 ; A. Raimondi, *El Peru estudios min. Geol.*, **4**. 235, 1902 ; L. Darapsky, *Aguas minerales de Chile*, Valparaiso, 1890 ; E. H. Ducloux, *Rev. Mus. la Plata*, **14**. 9, 1907 ; **16**. 51, 1909 ; E. A. y Casariego and J. de Vera y Gomez, *Estudio descriptivo de algunas manantiales minerales de Filipinas*, Manila, 1893 ; A. Liversidge, W. Skey and G. Gray, *Rep. Australasian Assoc.*, 87, 1898 ; R. Ishizu, *The Mineral Springs of Japan*, Tokyo, 1915 ; O. Aschan, *Finska Kem. Medd.*, **40**. 22, 1931 ; S. Yoshimura, *Japan. Journ. Geol.*, **8**. 269, 1931.

[176] W. H. Weed, *Amer. Geologist*, **7**. 48, 1891.

[177] A. Daubrée, *Les eaux souterraines*, Paris, 1887 ; H. S. Washington, *Journ. Franklin Inst.*, **190**. 757, 1920 ; V. M. Goldschmidt, *Der Stoffwechsel der Erde*, Leipzig, 1922 ; W. Lindgren, *Mineral Deposits*, New York, 1913 ; *Econ. Geol.*, **18**. 419, 434, 1923 ; E. S. Moore and J. A. Maynard, *ib.*, **24**. 365, 1929 ; F. W. Clarke, *The Data of Geochemistry*, Washington, 119, 1924 ; H. Harrassowitz, *Zeit. angew. Chem.*, **43**. 185, 1930 ; C. R. Sturdevant, *Scient. Amer. Suppl.*, **85**. 14, 30, 1918.

[178] G. Tissandier, *Les poussières de l'air*, Paris, 49, 1877 ; J. A. Udden, *Journ. Geol.*, **2**. 318, 1894 ; E. E. Free, *Science*, (2), **29**. 423, 1909 ; *Bull. U.S. Dept. Agric.—Dept. Soils*, 68, 1911 ; A. Ditte, *Rev. Scient.*, (5), **2**. 709, 1904 ; A. Bergeat, *Abhand. Bayr. Akad.*, **20**. 193, 1899.

[179] W. Lemery, *Cours de chimie*, Paris, 874, 1730 ; E. F. Geoffroy, *ib.*, 362, 1705 ; 176, 1707 ; L. Lemery, *ib.*, 411, 1706 ; 376, 1708 ; V. Menghini, *De Bononiensi scientiarum et artium Instituto atque Academia Commentarii*, Bononiensis, **2**. iii, 475, 1747.

[180] J. Barcroft, *The Respiratory Function of the Blood*, Cambridge, 1928 ; N. Scharoff, *Das Eisen als das thätige Prinzip der Enzyme und der lebendigen Substanz*, Jena, 1902 ; A. B. Macallum, *Proc. Roy. Soc.*, **50**. 277, 1892 ; **57**. 261, 1895 ; A. N. Richards, *Lancet*, ii, 1495, 1900 ; M. Martz, *Province Méd. Lyon*, **13**. 39, 1899 ; L. Lapicque, *Observations et expériences sur les mutations organiques du fer chez les vertébrés*, Paris, 1897 ; *Bull. Soc. Biol.*, (9), **2**. 669, 1880 ; H. M. Fox and H. Ramage, *Nature*, **126**. 682, 1930 ; A. Guillemonat and G. Delamare, *Compt. Rend. Soc. Biol.*, **53**. 897, 1901 ; A. Guillemonat, *Bull. Soc. Biol.*, (10), **4**. 32, 1897 ; A. Guillemonat and L. Lapicque, *ib.*, (10), **4**. 345, 1897 ; *Arch. Physiol.*, **8**. 843, 1896 ; E. Auscher and L. Lapicque, *ib.*, (5), **8**. 390, 1896 ; A. Dastre, *ib.*, (5), **3**. 136, 1891 ; G. Bunge, *Zeit. Physiol. Chem.*, **9**. 49, 1885 : **13**. 399, 1889 ; **16**. 173, 1892 ; **17**. 63, 78, 1892 ; H. F. Hendrix, *Arch. Méd. Belg.*, (3), **22**. 467, 1882 ; A. Jacquet, *Semaine Méd.*, **21**. 49, 1901 ; P. Figaroli, *Rend. Assoc. Méd. Chir. Parma*, **1**. 241, 1900 ; S. Winogradsky, *Hot. Ztg.*, **46**. 261, 1888 ; A. Daubrée, *Ann. Mines*, (4), **10**. 55, 1846 ; J. L. Raulin, *Études chimiques sur la végétation*, Paris, 1870 ; A. Meyer, *Lehrbuch der Agriculturchemie*, Heidelberg, **1**. 263, 1871 ; L. Maquenne and R. Cerighelli, *Compt. Rend.*, **173**. 273, 1921.

§ 3. The Extraction of Iron

While man has had to do little more than purify gold as it occurs in nature, it has been necessary for him, so to speak, to create iron. When one considers that the art of working this metal, which combines so many industrial processes, which triumphs over so many difficulties and obstacles, and which makes use so ingeniously of fire to conquer iron, goes back to the remotest antiquity, to beyond the flood, one is disposed to regard the first thought about this wonderful art as a sort of inspiration.—R. J. Haüy.

In the most primitive form of extracting iron from its ores, a mixture of the ore and charcoal was heated. The impurities formed a scoria or slag, and the remainder of the ore was reduced to a tough, porous, pasty mass of iron. The iron was withdrawn in porous blocks, called blooms, and these were put into another furnace and strongly heated. The iron was taken out and hammered into a compact mass so as to drive out any scoriaceous matters. The earliest furnaces had a natural draught, and they were generally erected on high grounds, in order that the wind might assist combustion. This method is used even to-day in some parts of Africa. C. V. Bellamy,[1] for instance, thus described the process carried out in west Africa, in the hinterland of Lagos :

The ore used is a siliceous hæmatite occurring in shale. It is roasted, and then pulverized in a wooden mortar. The pounded ore is then washed by women. A hole is dug in the ground about 2 feet deep and filled with water. In this, a woman stands and washes the ore in a tray about 18 inches in diameter. It is then subjected to a further and more careful washing by a second woman, seated on the ground near by. The ore is then conveyed to the furnace in a smelting shed, of which there are eleven in the village. Each shed is about 25 feet long and 16 feet wide, with a doorway at each end. The walls are built of clay, and are from 4 to 6 feet high. They are not carried up to the roof, but a space is left all round for light and ventilation. From the ground to the ridge of the roof the height is 25 feet. The furnace is in the centre of the shed. It is built of clay, and occupies a circular space 7 feet in diameter. Its height is 3 feet 9 inches. Opposite one of the doorways a depression in the floor gives access to the furnace. The dome of the furnace is bound round by a rope of twisted vines. In the centre of the bottom of the furnace is an aperture 3 inches in diameter which communicates with a short tunnel below the floor of the shed, to which access is obtained by a pit inside the shed. The shed also contains a small kiln for firing the earthenware tuyères, and an ore-bin, both being made of clay. The process of smelting occupies 36 hours, draught being supplied by nine pairs of earthenware pipes. These are only rudely shaped by hand around a stick, and but partly baked. The average diameter of each pipe is 1·4 inch. Selected slag from each successive smelting is used as flux. It is run off by opening the orifice in the bottom of the furnace. For removing the bloom, the clay seals over the six apertures are broken up, the earthenware pipes removed and thrown aside, and the doorway of the furnace opened. The contents of live charcoal are raked out, and the 70-lb. bloom removed in a red-hot state by a loop of green creeper. Subsequently it is broken up, with the aid of a stone, into convenient sizes and sold to smiths. The metal produced in this way is a natural forged steel, which by reheating by the native smith is brought down to a tool steel with one per cent. of carbon.

The frescoes in Egyptian tombs show that prior to the 18th dynasty they produced a draught in their furnaces by blowpipes, and four to six men are shown so engaged in melting metal. Drawings of furnaces with the draught worked by bellows appear on the frescoes of the 18th dynasty. The iron-smelting furnaces of Populonia, and those reconstructed by T. May from the remains at Wilderspool, near Warrington, and dating from about A.D. 410, consisted essentially of a cavity with a wall and covering of clay, with holes at the base for admitting a draught and for withdrawing the metal. They were usually built on sloping ground, and the remains show that coal was used with the charcoal for smelting. There is no proof that bellows were employed ; nor is there any proof that cast iron was produced in one furnace and converted into malleable iron or steel in another. The plant consisted of a kiln for roasting the ores, a smelting furnace, and a smith's forge. Minute samples of metal collected in a fluid state on the furnace bottom, but the smelting furnace yielded blooms of spongy iron. The fusion of the iron in the furnace, owing to the formation of cast iron, must occasionally have occurred when the temperature was higher than what was usually obtained. This, for example, explains Pliny's statement indicated above, *mirumque cum excoquatur vena modo liquari ferrum*. A. Ure thus described the Indian method of extracting iron and manufacturing steel :

The manner in which iron ore is melted and converted into wootz or Indian steel by the natives of the present day is probably the very same as was practised at the time of the invasion of Alexander, and is a uniform process from the Himalaya Mountains to Cape Comerin. The furnace or bloomery in which the ore is smelted is from four to five feet high ; it is somewhat pear-shaped, being about five feet wide at the base and one foot at the top ; it is built entirely of clay, so that a couple of men may finish its erection in a few hours and have it ready for use the next day. There is an opening in front about one foot or more in height which is built up with clay at the commencement and broken down at the end of each smelting operation. The bellows are usually made of a goat's skin which has been stripped from the animal without ripping open the part covering the belly. The apertures of the legs are tied up and a nozzle of bamboo is fastened into the opening formed by the neck. The orifice at the tail is enlarged and distended by two slips of bamboo ; these are grasped in the hand and kept close together in making the stroke for the blast ; in the return stroke they are separated to admit the air. By working a bellows of this kind with each hand making alternate strokes, a tolerably uniform blast is produced ; the bamboo nozzles from the bellows are inserted into tubes of clay, which pass into the furnace. The furnace is filled with charcoal, and lighted coal being introduced before the nozzles, the mass in the interior is soon kindled. As soon as this is accomplished a small portion of the ore, previously moistened with water to prevent it from running through the charcoal, but without any flux whatever, is laid on the top of the coals and covered with charcoal to fill up the furnace. In this manner ore and fuel are supplied, and the bellows are urged for three or four hours, when the process is stopped, the temporary wall in front broken down, and the bloom removed with a pair of tongs from the bottom of the furnace.

In converting the iron into steel the natives cut it into pieces to enable it to pack better into the crucible, which is formed of refractory clay mixed with a quantity of charred husks of rice. It is seldom charged with more than a pound of iron, which is put in with the proper weight of dried wood chopped small, and both are covered with one or two green leaves (the proportion being in general ten parts of iron to one of wood and leaves). The mouth of the crucible is then stopped with a handful of tempered clay, rammed in very closely to exclude the air. As soon as the clay-plugs of the crucible are dry, from twenty to twenty-four of them are built up in the form of an arch in a small blast-furnace ; they are kept covered with charcoal and subjected to heat urged by a blast for about two-and-a-half hours, when the process is considered to be complete. The crucibles are now taken out of the furnace and allowed to cool ; they are then broken and the steel is found in the form of a cake rounded by the bottom of the crucible. Rude as the whole appears to be, yet to gain that point must have been the result of considerable experience. The formation of the bellows—the composition of the crucibles—the charging of the furnaces and crucibles —all tell of observation and experience.

The method as practised by the native smiths of Uganda is depicted in Figs. 6 to 8 by G. H. Davis. A hole is dug in the ground and lined with clay (Fig. 6) ; on this is placed a bed of charcoal; then burnt grass, reeds, etc., for lighting the furnace. About the hole is built a stack with lumps from ant-hills as refractory. Inside this is a lining of iron ore ; and charcoal is placed in the interior. The furnace is fed with air from bellows. The furnace illustrated by Fig. 7 is operated by five sets of bellows worked by hand, as illustrated in the diagram. A plan of the smelting-furnace is shown in Fig. 8. The subject was also discussed by F. Dixey, and R. G. Cumming. According to T. Turner, S. A. Bilgrami, E. P. Martin and H. Louis, R. B. Foote, C. Lemaire, J. T. Last, L. Guillemain, W. S. Routledge, I. E. Lester, R. A. Hadfield, T. H. Holland, C. von Schwarz, H. L. Stokes, J. Danvers, F. H. Wynne, F. W. Reid, G. Braecke, H. D. McCaskey, F. Hupfield, A. Ledebur, R. A. Dart and N. del Grande, E. Fuchs and E. Saladin, an analogous process was used in India, etc. H. Louis

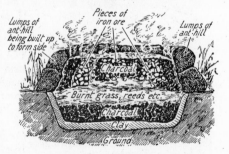

FIG. 6.—Bed of Primitive Uganda Iron Furnace.

and E. P. Martin, and F. H. Wynne described various forms of bellows used in India. Some observations on the early extraction of iron were made by P. Berthier, F. L. von Cancrin, C. Combes, M. Gazeran, F. J. von Gerstner,

Fig. 7.—Iron-Smelting in Uganda.

A. Gurlt, J. F. L. Hausmann, A. Ledebur, F. A. von Marcher, L. B. Guyton de Morveau, T. E. Norburg, T. A. Rickard, G. H. Rivius, B. Valerius, and C. M. Weld.

The Catalan process of extracting iron was formerly practised in the province of Catalonia, north of Spain, and also about Ariège, south of France. The furnace was used in the seventeenth century in Navarre, and Guipuzcoa in Spain, and it consisted of a shallow, oval cavity or hearth forming a kind of inverted truncated cone. A tuyère projected downwards and inwards over the middle of one of the long sides of the oval. The blast was supplied by two bellows working alternately.

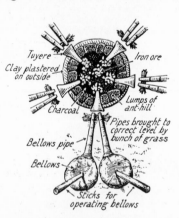

Fig. 8.—Plan of Uganda Smelting-Furnace.

Various modifications in size and shape were introduced from time to time, and about the end of the seventeenth century the *trompe* was introduced for supplying a continuous blast of air, in localities where a fall of water from a height of a few yards was available. The theory of the *trompe* was discussed by G. B. Venturi [2] in 1800, and observations on the subject were made by M. Thibaud and M. Tardy, J. F. d'Aubuisson, and G. Magnus. The Catalan forge, or *la forge Catalane*, consists essentially of a furnace, a blowing machine, and a heavy hammer. It was described by T. Richard, J. François, and J. Percy. A general idea of the furnace will be obtained from Fig. 9. The so-called *Corsican furnace* was employed in Corsica from a remote period, and a few were in use in 1828. It was little more than a black-smith's forge—Fig. 10. It was described by M. Sagey,[3] J. M. Muthuon, L. Cordier, P. C. J. B. Tronson du Coudray, and J. H. Hassenfratz.

In former times a bloomery smelting-furnace was much used in Sweden, Norway, and Finland, and it came to be called the *osmund furnace*—so named from the Swedish term *åfsumd, åfsmundtz,* or *osmund* for the bloom produced in this kind of furnace. The furnace was an oblong, rectangular cavity to receive the lump of reduced iron ; there was a large opening at the side through which the lump of iron, or bloom, was extracted, and which during the working of the furnace was temporarily built up with stones. The inner lining of the furnace was a refractory rock,

FIG. 9.—Catalan Furnace.

FIG. 10.—Corsican Furnace.

and the space between this and the timber casing on the outside was filled with earth. The calcined ore was smelted with charcoal, and the resulting bloom was forged as required. The furnace was described by E. Swedenborg,[4] A. Wahlberg, A. Wehrle, P. R. von Tunner, R. Gontermann, M. Meyer, J. Percy, L. J. Igelström, C. J. B. Karsten, etc. The blast was obtained by two bellows worked by a treadle.

A **bloom** is an ingot of iron or steel or a pile of puddled bars which, by passing through a set of rollers, has been reduced to a thick bar and left for further rolling when required for use ; it also refers to a mass of iron which has undergone the first hammering—R. Plott, and M. Ray. The term is also applied to the ball or mass of iron from the puddling furnace which is to be hammered or shingled into a bloom— A. Ure. A **bloomary** or **bloomery** is the first forge through which the metal passes after it has been melted from the ore, and in which it is made into blooms—M. Lister.

FIG. 11.—The Osmund Furnace.

According to Notes and Queries (**8.** 27, 1907), the term *bloma* was in use *ante* 1000 A.D., as indicated in T. Wright and R. P. Wülcker's *Anglo-Saxon and Old English Vocabularies* (London, **1.** 141, 1884), *ante* 1000 ; and in J. Mirkus' *Liber Festivalis*, published at the beginning of the fifteenth century. In this book it is said that devils made " blomes of brennyng yerne " at St. Brendan.

V. Biringuccio represented the pre-Roman smelting-furnace by Fig. 12 ; and it is supposed to date from the time of Hesiod. It was fired with wood. The remains of one in Jura are described by R. Schaur. It was built anew after each smelting. The so-called *Stückofen* resembled two osmund furnaces, one inverted above the other—Fig. 13. They were at one time in operation in various parts of Europe—Carniola, Carinthia, Syria, Hungary, etc. The larger furnaces were 10 to 16 ft. in height, and the blast was operated by bellows worked by a water-wheel. The product was a lump of unfused malleable iron—up to about 6 cwts. in weight. This was cut into parts or *Stücke*, which was then hammered in the usual manner. This furnace is considered to be the forerunner of the modern blast-furnace. G. Jars, C. J. B. Karsten, J. Percy, G. Agricola, L. Beck, J. C. Quantz, O. Krasa, and others have described the operation of these furnaces. The conditions in the *Stückofen* were so favourable to the formation of that highly carburized, relatively fusible product known as cast iron, that when it was obtained it had to be subjected to a process of decarburization before it could be worked under the hammer. Indeed, the carburized iron was virtually a new metal, which could be readily cast into any desired shape and size.

J. J. Becher [5] is sometimes regarded as the discoverer of cast iron, but it is very doubtful if any one can be credited with the discovery of this material. Stove-plates appear to have been one of the earliest forms of iron-castings ; and, according to A. Schrödter, they were made at Nassau in 1474 ; and, according to A. Kippen-berger, at Eifel in 1497. J. Schwank said cannon for artillery were made from cast iron in 1544 ; and J. Goostray and co-workers, between 1520 and 1854, when rifled cannon appeared. According to O. Johannsen, observations on the subject were made by K. Brunner in 1547. L. Bickel stated that the earliest recorded date for the working of cast iron in the Haina monastery, Hessen, is 1555, but the working of the iron foundries goes back much earlier. For instance, an inventory of guns belonging to the Prince of Hessen is dated 1544. M. A. Lower suggested that cast iron was probably made in Sussex about the middle of the fourteenth century. P. Buchanan said that R. Hogge made a cast-iron cannon at Bucksteed, Sussex, in 1543. Cast iron was imported into England about 1500,

Fig. 12.—Pre-Roman Iron-Smelting Furnace.   Fig. 13.—Primitive *Stückofen*.

and a large iron gun weighing 10,500 lbs. was cast in London in 1516 ; and, according to H. A. Dillon, two large cast-iron cannon were brought to London from Ireland during the reign of Henry VII. W. Treptoff has reviewed the use of cast iron for making cannon in the Middle Ages.

The development of the cast iron industry has been discussed by H. Alker, L. Beck, L. Bickel, K. Bimler, P. G. H. Boswell, O. Brandt, E. Bremer, R. Buchanan, C. E. Dana, P. Desbief, J. F. Daubuisson, W. Erben, O. Erlinghagen, A. Faber, J. Fernie, F. A. Foster, J. P. Frey, C. A. Gerhard, J. Goostray and co-workers, A. Guettier, J. H. von Hefner-Alteneck, C. F. Himes, A. Hirsch, J. E. Hurst, R. Jenkins, O. Johannsen, H. Kalakuzky, E. C. Kreutzberg, J. Laissus, A. Ledebur, K. Lind, V. Lohse, K. Luthmer, T. Makemson, G. Malkowsky, P. Martell, C. F. P. von Martius, W. Mathesius, S. Miller, C. Pardun, H. Pudor, B. Rathgen, M. Rotacker, H. Schmitz, E. Schneegans, J. Schwank, R. Siedel, K. Sipp, S. G. Smith, W. A. Tiemann, A. Thiele, W. H. Uhland, O. Vogel, and L. van Werveke.

The size of the furnace for making iron was gradually increased to save fuel and to reduce the cost of manufacture ; at the same time it was noticed that the accidental production of cast iron became increasingly frequent, because the iron remained a longer time in contact with the fuel—charcoal—and it thus became more highly carburized. For a time the *Stückofen* was used for producing both the malleable iron blooms and molten cast iron. The furnaces which replaced the *Stückofen* were called *Bauerofen*, *Blaseofen*, or *Blauofen*. The furnaces were at first exactly like the *Stückofen*, and the name referred to the product, not to the construction. Eventually cast iron was virtually the only direct product ; and, as is the case at the present time, it was obtained in the blast-furnace. The *blast-furnace* came to be called the *Hochofen* in Germany, and *le haut fourneau* in France. According to J. M. Swank,[6] the blast-furnace originated in the Rhine provinces about the beginning of the fourteenth century, and in 1340 one was built at Marche-les-Dames, Belgium. The evolution of the blast-furnace in Styria was described by J. Arduino, L. Beck, J. M. Bineau, L. Bittner, J. J. Ferber, H. Frontault, G. Göth, O. Johannsen, F. Kupelweiser, A. H. Leobner, F. A. von Marcher, A. von Muchar, A. Müllner, F. Münichdorfer, V. Ignaz von Pantz and A. J. Atzl, I. Prandstetter, M. Robert, A. Schauenstein, and R. Schaur. Many others have written on the history of blast-furnaces, either in general or in reference to particular localities. According to A. Müllner, the iron industry has been active in Central Austria for over 2600 years, and occupied so important a position in the middle of the fifteenth century that England sent to Austria for teachers for her iron industry.

Just as crude metal was extracted from the ore by fire, so was it found that by another application of the same purifying agent the crude metal could be converted into malleable iron. In the modern method for extracting iron from its ores, cast iron is first produced, and this product is employed as a starting-point for the manufacture of iron and steel. What was formerly an accidental and abnormal defect is now the regular and normal product.

In the sixteenth century the ironworks in England were consuming the forests to make charcoal fuel at such a rate that it was feared that there would be a scarcity of wood for fuel and shipbuilding. According to J. Nicholl,[7] in the reign of Elizabeth Acts of Parliament were passed to restrict the use of timber as fuel in the manufacture of iron. A patent was granted to S. Sturtevant in 1611 by James I for the use of " sea-coale or pit-coale " in the extraction of iron, but the patent was " cancelled and made voyde by reason of his standing outlawed at the time of the grant." In 1613 his privileges were transferred to J. Rovenzon, but he did not make the use of this fuel a success ; and similar remarks apply to the patents of W. Gomeldon, F. de Blewston, and E. Jorden. About 1620, however, D. Dudley did succeed in substituting pit-coal for charcoal in the smelting of iron ; he obtained a patent for the process in 1619, and gave an account of his labours, but not the process, in his *Metallum martis*, published in 1665. Between 1652 and 1658 Oliver Cromwell granted patents to W. Astell and co-workers for the use of pit- or sea-coal as fuel in the blast-furnace, but both attempts also failed. It is thought, but not definitely known, that the success of D. Dudley was due to his using coke in place of raw coal. R. Plot mentions an unsuccessful attempt to smelt iron with coal in 1685. H. Powle described the smelting of iron with charcoal as fuel in blast-furnaces in the Forest of Dean, in 1676, and the subsequent conversion of the cast iron into malleable iron in an open-hearth finery using sea-coal as fuel ; J. Collier, and J. Sturdy described the process in use in Lancashire at the end of the seventeenth century. D. Dudley does allude to the making of char—according to T. Turner, that is coke—from sea-coal. The art was lost after the death of D. Dudley, so that in 1685 R. Plot said :

They have a way of charring the coal in all particulars the same as they do wood. The coal thus prepared they call *cokes*, which conceives as strong a heat almost as charcoal itself, and is fit for most uses, but for melting, fining, and refining of iron, which it cannot be brought to do, although attempted by the most skilful and curious artists.

About 1735, J. H. Darby tried to smelt iron with a mixture of raw coal and charcoal, but without success ; he then tried the use of coke made by treating pit-coal as charcoal burners treat wood, and succeeded. The substitution of coke for charcoal then grew apace. Only in very special circumstances is charcoal now employed—*e.g.* in out-of-the-way places where the output is small, timber cheap, and coal dear ; or where a specially pure metal is desired, as at Ulverston, Lancashire, described by W. J. MacAdam. Hence, the furnace charge employed in 1887 was virtually the same as that employed in 1738. D. H. Wood reviewed the history of iron-founding in the Midlands (England).

The subject was discussed by J. F. d'Aubuisson de Voisins, L. Bittner, G. Göth, S. L. Goodale and J. Speer, H. Illies, O. Johannsen, W. A. Lampadius, F. W. Lürmann, E. Mauer and W. Bischof, A. Müllner, F. Münichsdorfer, V. I. von Pantz and A. J. Atzl, I. Prandstetter, A. Schauenstein, C. Schinz, E. Vollhann, and H. Wedding.

With bituminous coal most of the hydrocarbon gases are given off before the reduction of the ore is accomplished, and accordingly they do very little chemical work in reducing the ore. Heat is required for the decomposition of the coal, so that the extra fuel consumption gives an enriched exit gas. Anthracite coal gives but a relatively small yield of hydrocarbon gases, and more nearly approaches coke in this respect. Anthracite coal has been used in blast-furnaces in South Wales and in Eastern Pennsylvania. Attempts to melt iron by using a gaseous fuel—say natural gas—as a source of heat, while the reduction proper is effected by solid carbon were made in this direction by J. T. Wainwright, but the results were not satisfactory. Actually, in modern practice, at least 75 per cent. of the available energy in the solid fuel employed is utilized. Charcoal is still employed as a fuel in the production of the so-called Swedish iron, and the modern procedure was described by J. A. Leffler. The use of peat coke was discussed by I. I. Granikoff and M. A. Pavloff.

According to M. P. Rossigneux, when coke began to replace charcoal in the smelting of iron, the furnaces were low, of small capacity, and worked with a cold blast. A light, porous coke resembling charcoal was desirable, because in such furnaces the hard coke would descend to the level of the tuyères, suffering very little change. In taller furnaces, of large capacity, worked with a hot blast, a hard, compact coke is needed in order to resist the weight of the heavy furnace charge. The density of the coke is greater the higher the coking temp., and the more dense the coke the less the fuel consumption, since less carbon is attacked by the carbon diɔ de of the furnace gases. This was demonstrated by I. L. Bell. The blast-furnace coke must be strong enough to sustain without crushing the burden in the furnace ; it must be porous enough to allow it to be penetrated by the hot blast ; and it should burn with very little ash. The properties of good blast-furnace coke were discussed by S. Weill,[8] J. H. Darby, C. L. Bell, D. A. Louis, G. D. Cochrane, etc.

The substitution of coke for charcoal in the smelting of iron rendered necessary blowing machines of increasing power, and the introduction of steam power enabled engineers readily to cope with the demands of the iron smelters. This subject was discussed by C. J. B. Karsten,[9] J. Percy, D. E. Roberts, A. von Ihering, J. Kitson, E. Baur, A. Greiner, R. H. Rice, etc. In 1828, J. B. Neilson patented the use of the hot blast, and J. Percy said that " the use of the hot blast greatly cheapened the production of iron, and it is thus to be regarded as one of the most important improvements ever made in metallurgy." A few years later, in 1835, virtually every ironworks in Scotland was using the hot blast. According to E. Baur, and E. Herzog, A. C. W. F. von Faber du Faur utilized the hot blast in 1832. J. B. Neilson's invention, said H. Marten, appeared directly to contradict general experience, because all furnace managers agreed that the produce per furnace was more in winter than in summer, and hence it was concluded that the colder the blast the better the yield. Attempts were even made to cool the blast in summer by passing it over cold water, but a result contrary to expectation was observed. The conclusion was shown by H. Marten, and J. Percy to ignore two vital factors : (i) the air in summer is much more humid than it is in winter ; and (ii) in hot weather the blowing engines will deliver a smaller weight of oxygen in a given time, unless they are worked at a faster speed.

The moisture in the gas was thought at one time to be advantageous, because the hydrogen formed by the dissociation of the steam is so powerful a reducing agent; but I. L. Bell showed that no advantage is obtained by raising the moisture content of the blast. W. H. Fryer, on the contrary, showed that the desiccation of the blast would increase the production, and decrease the fuel costs. J. Gayley proposed to freeze out the moisture by an ammonia refrigeration apparatus. The subject was discussed by C. A. Meissner, B. Osann, E. H. Lewis, F. Krull, E. Jantzen, W. Mathesius, J. B. Miles, N. M. Langdon, M. Drees, E. S. Cook, C. Aldendorff, J. Vajk, E. de M. Campbell, H. Bonte, W. Schmidhammer, A. Lindner, C. von Linde, L. Grabau, E. C. Heurteau, H. le Chatelier, J. E. Johnson, G. Jones, F. A. Daubiné and E. V. Roy, W. McConnachie, and J. von Ehrenwerth. The last-named showed that the advantage of drying the blast is greater the lower the temp. of the blast, and the higher the temp. of the waste gases at which the furnace previously worked. The use of oxygen in the dry blast was discussed by A. Brunighaus, F. W. Davis, M. Derclaye, J. Seigle, R. Schenck, H. Blome, G. Trasenster, and C. A. Edwards.

The hot blast was discussed by H. Marten, T. Clark, L. F. Gjers and J. H. Harrison, W. McConnachie, F. T. Merbach, J. Percy, W. Truran, D. Mushet, I. L. Bell, C. Cochrane, etc. The methods of heating the hot blast employed by J. B. Neilson were described by H. Marten. In 1833, A. C. W. F. von Faber du Faur invented a hot-blast stove which was heated by the combustion of the waste gases from the blast-furnace; but the method was not successful until applied by J. P. Budd in 1845. In 1860, E. A. Cowper applied the regenerative principle and burnt the waste gases in order to supply the necessary heat. There are many designs for the checker bricks for the hot stove, and also many modifications of the principle, discussed by T. Whitwell, T. Massicks, W. Crooke, B. J. Hall E. Disdier, L. F. Gjers and J. H. Harrison, A. J. Boynton, W. Mathesius, S. G. Valentine, R. S. Moore, G. Jones, M. A. Pavloff, and A. Spannagel.

The ends of the pipes or tuyères employed for delivering the blast of air into the furnace rapidly deteriorate unless they are efficiently protected, and particularly so when a hot blast is employed. The term *tuyère* is often spelt *twyer*, and, according to R. Plot,[10] older and corrupt spellings are *tue-iron, tuiron*, and *tuarn*. J. Percy said that the protection of the tuyère by cooling it with water was first applied by Mr. Condie, shortly after the introduction of the hot blast. In this tuyère, generally called the *Scotch tuyère*, a wrought-iron pipe, through which cold water circulates, is embedded and coiled about a short, hollow, conical nozzle of cast iron. Numerous modifications of the principle have been described by F. H. Lloyd, T. W. Plum, H. Wedding, H. Pilkington, A. K. Rees, J. E. Stead, J. S. Hollings, F. L. Grammer, etc.

There are differences of opinion as to the most economical size and shape of the blast-furnace; and there are numerous descriptions of the blast-furnaces in different works available.[11] The subject is also discussed in many special books. There are also many labour-saving devices in connection with the mechanical handling of materials—conveying charges to the top of the blast-furnace, its introduction to the hoppers, and transfer to the furnace itself.

Ores can sometimes be worked in the blast-furnace without any preliminary treatment; in other cases the ore must be subjected to some preparatory process. Hand-picking to separate earthy and shaly matters may suffice; in some cases it is necessary to crush the ore into pieces the size of an egg. The sizing of the ore depends on its nature. A porous ore, for instance, can be used in larger lumps than a dense, compact ore, since it is more readily penetrated by the reducing gases. Systems of concentrating the ore can be employed only in special cases, on account of their cost. In some places the magnetic iron sands or tailings are washed by hand, but only on a moderate scale. Ore-washing in some of the United States works has been described by G. R. Johnson,[12] M. F. Ortin, and S. C. McLanahan. The concentration of ores by magnetic separators was proposed by A. Chenot[13] in 1854, and the electromagnetic and electrostatic separation has been discussed by H. C. McNeill, H. Louis, W. A. Anthony, C. Jones, G. Prus, H. Wedding, T. Turner, etc.

Hæmatite ore was once concentrated at Norburg, Sweden, by screening the crushed ore, which was then graded, and the fines were briquetted with about 10 per cent. of lime before smelting.[14] Finely-divided ores have also been briquetted with tarry matters. W. Hutchinson and F. W. Harbord [15] proposed incorporating fine ores with molten blast-furnace slag. Ores in a fine state of subdivision are not suited for smelting in the ordinary blast-furnace because of the resistance they offer to the passage of the blast. Finely-divided ores are best smelted in blast-furnaces which are not very tall, and only a low-press. blast is employed. This subject was discussed by H. Louis, J. Gayley, E. Moffart, A. Thielen, etc.

In some cases the ore is weathered in heaps for months or years. The hard shale of argillaceous ironstone so treated crumbles to powder, and allows the iron ore to be separated by hand-picking. Certain sulphureous ores may also have their pyrites oxidized to sulphate and so washed away. Hydrated ores may be calcined or roasted to drive off water of hydration ; carbonate ores, to drive off carbon dioxide ; sulphide ores, to convert sulphides to oxides, and so eliminate the sulphur—at the same time some arsenic may be driven off ; ferrous ores, to convert ferrous to ferric oxide with ferrous ores liable to form too fusible a slag, which rapidly attacks the furnace lining ; and carbonaceous ores, like the black band ores, to drive off carbonaceous matter, which prevents a proper fusion of the materials in the blast-furnace. The subject was discussed by S. G. Valentine.[16] The roasting or calcination may be performed in open heaps or in special kilns.

The blast-furnace is a long cylindrical shaft fed at the top with ore, fuel, and flux, and supplied with the air necessary for the combustion of the fuel at the bottom. The function of the blast-furnace is to reduce the iron oxides to the metallic state, and at the same time convert the impurities into a fusible slag. Both molten iron and slag are discharged at the bottom of the furnace, whilst the waste gases pass away at the top. The materials employed in the blast-furnace charge are (i) the iron ore, containing essentially ferric oxide, (ii) the flux—generally limestone, and (iii) the fuel—charcoal or coke. A mixture of these materials is continually introduced at the top so that the interior is kept nearly full, while slag, or *cinder*, and cast iron accumulate in a molten state in the hearth at the bottom. The slag or cinder flows out over the dam, while the molten iron accumulates below. The iron is allowed to escape at intervals through the tapping hole. The solid contents of the furnace are gradually and continuously descending, while air blown in through the tuyères ascends to the top and is carried away in pipes as blast-furnace gas. The oxygen of the air impinges on the incandescent fuel, where it burns to carbon dioxide ; this is immediately reduced to carbon monoxide. The ferric oxide is reduced partly by the carbon monoxide and partly by the carbon to form metallic iron. Higher up, the limestone is decomposed into carbon dioxide and calcium oxide. The temp. of the furnace is greatest near the tuyères, where the maximum combustion occurs, and decreases as the distance upwards increases. The reduced iron near the lower part of the furnace becomes highly carburized, and forms cast iron, which melts and trickles down to the hearth. The iron ore contains more or less impurities—silica, alumina, etc.—and the ash of the fuel contains more or less earthy matters. The iron is associated with the earthy, and other impurities whose nature is such that usually they readily fuse when they have entered into combination with lime. The limestone of the charge " draws " some silicon, sulphur, manganese, and alumina—but not phosphorus —from the melting iron. There is thus formed a frothy slag. Nearly all the phosphorus, much of the sulphur, three-quarters of the manganese, and some silicon remain with the molten iron. The molten slag trickles down to the hearth, and helps to protect the surface of the molten metal from any decarburization under the influence of the oxidizing blast.

The weight of materials entering the blast-furnace is from seven to nine times the weight of the iron produced, and more than half the weight of materials entering the furnace is atm. air supplied by its blast. No solids are formed in the furnace working under normal conditions, since all the solids charged into the furnace are converted into molten slag and molten iron. The charge and products per ton of iron are approximately :

CHARGE			Cwts.	PRODUCTS				Cwts.
Calcined ironstone	.	.	48	Iron	.	.	.	20
Limestone	.	.	12	Slag	.	.	.	30
Coke	.	.	20	Waste gases	.	.	.	130
Air	.	.	100					
Total	.	.	180	Total	.	.	.	180

The following description (Fig. 14) of the blast-furnace of one of the largest steel plants in the United States, namely, that at Gary, on the southern shore of

FIG. 14.—Blast-Furnace in Circuit with Four Hot-Blast Stoves.

Lake Michigan, is based on that given by J. B. Walker.[17] The height of the blast-furnace is 90 ft., and the diameter 25 ft. It makes 550 tons of iron every 24 hrs. It is built of steel, like a large upright steam boiler, and is lined with firebricks. The lower and hottest portion is surrounded with hollow bronze bricks filled with rapidly flowing water to keep them cool. The blast passes up through 1500 tons of *burden*, which is at first arranged in alternate layers of ore, coke, and limestone, put in at the top so as to be porous enough to allow a free passage for the ascending gases driven upwards by the blast. The coke, ore, and limestone from the store bins are carried by electrically operated lorries to the furnace skip, of which there are two to each furnace. The skips run up an inclined railway to the charging platform at the top of the blast-furnace. Each trip of a skip is made in 60 seconds, and its average load is 7000 lbs. of ore, 6000 lbs. of limestone, and 3600 lbs. of coke. On its arrival at the top of the furnace the skip automatically discharges its load into a hopper. Within the furnace are two cones. The contents of the skip fall upon the first cone or bell, A, which is then lowered so that the materials fall on the second or lower cone, B. The upper cone, A, is then elevated to seal the exit, and the lower cone, B, is lowered so as to discharge the materials into the furnace. This arrangement prevents any escape of the furnace gases.

The furnace once started is kept going continuously until repairs are necessary. Some furnaces have a record of several years' continuous operation. The temp. near the top is about 200°. The chemical action of the up-rushing blast of gas is to remove about 90 per cent. of the oxygen in the ore and transform it into particles of finely-divided spongy iron, which retain their shape as the charge descends until the iron is melted. The temp. of the charge increases as it descends, and at about 430° the spongy iron begins to take up carbon from the coke. There is an opposing chemical action tending to remove carbon from the iron. The iron takes up several times its own volume of carbon, and when the temp. of the descending charge has attained about 900° the iron sponge no longer expands. The iron with its dissolved carbon continues its descent and begins to melt. While these changes are going on, the limestone unites with the siliceous and aluminous constituents of the ore and with the ashes of the coke. The slag also melts and trickles down with the molten iron through the incandescent coke. The molten mixture collects at the bottom, so that the molten slag floats on the molten iron. The coke contains 88 per cent. of carbon, and the burning of the incandescent coke by the hot blast completes the fusion of iron and slag in the lower part of the furnace. The slag is drawn off at regular intervals from the *cinder notch*, C, and run into large ladles ; it is then hauled away to be crushed and utilized in the cement mills. The molten iron, containing about 3·5 or 4 per cent. of carbon, is drawn off separately from the *iron notch*, D, about every four hours. About 100 tons of pig-iron are obtained at one draw, which occupies about a quarter of an hour. The molten metal is transferred to the Bessemer converters or to the open-hearth furnaces to be transformed into steel. The blast is stopped for a moment to re-plug the notch. When the mass of material in the furnace is relieved of the supporting influence of the upward blast, it sinks a little.

The air required for combustion enters the furnace just above the hearth at press. of about 18 lbs. per sq. in., and then passes through a series of water-cooled tuyères. The hot furnace gases are led by a large pipe from the top of the furnace into a dust-catcher, and after being cleaned in a washer, they are passed through the hot-stoves. There are four hot-stoves to each furnace. The stoves are cylindrical plate-steel structures filled with a honeycomb of firebricks. As the gases enter two of the stoves a certain amount of air is fed in with them, and the burning gas, passing through the stoves, raises the firebricks inside to a high temp. When the proper heat is attained, the gases are deflected into an adjoining pair of stoves, while cold air from the blowing engines is made to enter at the bottom of the two stoves which have just been heated, and in passing through the honeycomb of firebrick the air takes up the heat previously given up by the furnace gases, and thus enters the blast-furnace at a high temp. Part of the heat carried off by the waste gases of the blast-furnace is thus returned. The two right-hand stoves in the diagram are represented as being heated by the burning gases, which are led in and ignited at the bottom, while the valves from the cold-air pipe are closed. At the top of these two stoves the valves opening to the hot-blast pipe are closed and the products of the burning gases pass into the atmosphere through the two smoke-stacks above the stoves. At the same time the valves opening from the cold-air duct at the bottom of the two left-hand stoves are open, while the corresponding gas valves just above them are closed. The valves controlling the smoke-stacks are closed, and the valves opening to the hot-blast pipes are open. The nature of the slag is controlled by the proportion of limestone which is added, and that, in turn, is determined by the character of the siliceous impurities associated with the ferric oxide in the iron ore. In some cases where the ore is non-aluminous a certain proportion of an aluminous ore analogous to bauxite, or an argillaceous ore, may be added.

This subject has been discussed by L. Blum,[18] G. Bontemps, O. Boudouard, O. Bowles, C. Braubach, G. Gredt, H. Wedding, S. E. Bretherton, C. Brisker, E. V. Britzke and co-workers, D. H. Brown, H. Burchartz and O. Bauer, R. Chauvenet, T. P. Colclough, A. L. Day and E. S. Shepherd, C. Dichmann, E. Diepschlag and H. Fliegenschmidt, E. Diepschlag and L. Treuheit, C. Dralle, K. Endell, E. Faust, A. L. Feild and co-workers, H. Fleissner, J. E. Fletcher, O. R. Foster, J. Fournet, O. Glaser, W. Grosse and W. Dinkler, L. Gruner, A. Guttmann, W. Harnickell and R. Durrer, A. Harpf and co-workers, F. Hartmann and A. Lange, J. F. L. Hausmann, E. A. Hersam, C. H. Herty and J. M. Gaines, G. Hilgenstock, E. Hollmann, W. G. Imhoff, C. E. Ireland, I. E. Johnson, J. L. Joseph and co-workers, C. J. B. Karsten, O. von Keil and P. Kettler, B. Kerl, E. Kochs and co-workers, B. Kosmann, T. Kuroda, A. Ledebur, R. S. McCaffery and co-workers, W. Mathesius, C. von Mayrhoffer, C. Méne, A. Michel, W. Mrazek, A. Mund and co-workers, B. Neumann, H. Passow, J. J. Porter, G. A. Rankin and F. E. Wright, R. Rieke, P. Rohland, J. Sarek, S. Schleicher, E. S. Shepherd and co-workers, O. Simmersbach, M. Simonis, L. G. Smith, M. Theusner, A. E. Uehling, A. de Vathaire, J. H. L. Vogt, H. Wedding, C. E. Wood and T. L. Joseph, and E. Zimmermann.

In some cases calcareous iron ores can be associated with siliceous ores to produce a self-fluxing mixture. The brown ores, known as minette, occurring in the Rhenish provinces are self-fluxing ;. while some Styrian ores are highly basic and require an acidic flux—like quartz, sand, etc. M. Paschke and E. Jung discussed slags for highly aluminous ores—e.g. those from Mayari. For acidic ores, where limestone is employed as a flux, there have been claims that it is more economical to employ caustic lime ; that is, the limestone is calcined before it is introduced into the blast-furnace, instead of leaving the calcination of the limestone to be done in the furnace. The desulphurizing properties of limestone were discussed by T. Turner, J. E. Stead, etc. H. von Jüptner considered that a state of equilibrium is established in the partition of sulphur between the slag and the metal, and that the partition favours the slags with the highest basicity—vide infra, sulphur. T. Turner found that calcium sulphide tends to separate from the slag and to solidify last. R. Moldenke used fluorspar ; and E. H. Saniter employed quicklime mixed with calcium chloride as desulphurizing agent ; and E. J. Ball and A. Wingham found that fused potassium cyanide has a desulphurizing action. Magnesian limestones are sometimes used. R. S. McCaffery and co-workers discussed the viscosity of magnesian slags. F. C. Calvert applied a patent for the use of chlorine, or hydrochloric acid, or hypochlorite in the blast-furnace, introduced preferably in the form of sodium chloride along with the charge. The object was to remove phosphorus and sulphur, which united with sodium to form a slag. J. Percy reported no advantage accrued from the use of this nostrum. G. Kassel found the ferrous oxide combined as ferrous silicate is not reduced by the blast-furnace gases, and one function of strong bases like lime may be to drive the ferrous oxide from the silicate slag and so prevent undue losses. The proportion of ferrous oxide in the slags of the old Roman furnaces in the south of England was so great that the slags have been re-smelted for iron. Most of the oxide of manganese present in the ore is reduced and alloys with the iron—vide infra, manganese-iron alloys—but, according to C. H. Ridsdale, the manganese is partitioned between the iron and the slag, somewhat as follows :

Mn	in iron	0–5	5–10	10–15	15–20	20–25	25–30	50–70	70–85 per cent.
	in slag	1·0	1·5	2·0	2·5	3·0	3·5	4·0	4·5 per cent.

J. Percy has quoted the results of experiments made at Ekaterinburg, in the Urals; at Ougrée, in Belgium ; and at Dowlais and Ebbw Vale, in Wales ; and observations have also been made by L. Eck, C. Schinz, G. D. Cochrane, I. L. Bell,

C. Wood, etc. According to T. Turner, the advantages and disadvantages attending the use of quicklime are so evenly balanced that quicklime is not likely to displace limestone except when small furnaces are used, or where the gaseous products are abnormally great. R. H. Sweetser, and R. H. Lee discussed the use of barium oxide ; M. Paschke and E. Jung, alumina ; F. Petry, magnesia ; and R. M. Keeney, fluorspar. K. Iwase and M. Fukushima studied the influence of siliceous matters on the reducibility of iron ores. The adjustment of the furnace charge for particular ores has been discussed by W. C. Roberts-Austen, C. A. M. Bolling, H. C. Jenkins, A. Wingham, F. F. Amsden, W. Macfarlane, W. Mrazek, F. Toldt, B. Platz, L. Blum, F. Wittmann, S. P. Bjerregaard, etc. G. Lunde and T. von Fellenberg noted the occurrence of iodine in the slag.

In 1728, J. Payne,[19] and in 1813, J. Mander and co-workers patented processes for utilizing blast-furnace slag for making bricks, quarries, tiles, etc. The utilization of slag for levelling and reclaiming waste land, as road metal, as railway ballast, for sewage filter beds, for making bricks, paving blocks, cements, etc., has a large literature of its own. The waste heat of the slag has been utilized for evaporating pans,[20] and in the generation of low-press. steam. Slag may be granulated by allowing it to trickle into cold water, and if a jet of steam be blown into the molten slag, *slag-wool* is formed, and this is used as a non-inflammable material for packing.

Many collections of analyses of blast-furnace slags have been reported by B. Kerl,[21] A. Ledebur, J. Percy, A. von Kerpely, C. F. Rammelsberg, E. Riley, W. H. Miller, G. Lindauer, H. Pilkington, J. H. L. Vogt, I. L. Bell, C. E. Schafhäutl, B. Platz, F. Kupelwieser, H. Rathke, etc. With charcoal as fuel the composition ranges from about 45 to 65 per cent. silica, 5 to 10 per cent. alumina, and 30 to 45 per cent. bases. In A. Ledebur's collection the silica ranges from 40·95 to 66·90 ; the alumina, 3·33 to 8·70 ; the magnesia, 0·57 to 16·32 ; the lime, 17·00 to 31·23 ; the manganous oxide, 0·85 to 4·09 ; the ferrous oxide, 0·79 to 2·70 ; the potash and soda, 0·32 to 3·83 ; and the calcium sulphide, 0·38 to 2·10. While with coke as fuel the silica ranges from 30 to 35 per cent., the alumina, 10 to 15 per cent., and the bases, 50 to 55 per cent. In A. Ledebur's collection the silica ranges from 23·59 to 47·94 ; the alumina, 7·14 to 24·69 ; the magnesia, 1·09 to 18·30 ; the lime, 30·80 to 47·20 ; the manganous oxide, 0·19 to 4·91 ; the ferrous oxide, 0·21 to 1·60 ; the potash and soda, 0·50 to 2·35 ; and the calcium sulphide, 1·33 to 9·08. According to G. Lunde and T. von Fellerberg, all common varieties of iron and steel contain 0·1 to 1·10 mgrm. of iodine per kilogram—average 0·1 to 0·15 mgrm. per kgrm. P. Berthier, E. Riley, and J. Percy emphasize how rarely is phosphoric oxide found in blast-furnace slags, although the 0·15 to 3·51 per cent. found by E. Riley was considered to be exceptional, and was due to the imperfect reduction of the iron. C. C. von Leonhard found samples with high proportions of phosphoric acid. The reduction of phosphoric oxide to form iron phosphide was discussed by N. Kjellberg, and G. Hilgenstock. The reduction of some silicon which alloys with the iron as silicide was discussed by A. Lampen. H. Bansen investigated the conditions of the materials at the lower stages of their descent through the furnace.

Although the materials are introduced into the blast-furnace in layers, the layers are broken up as the charge descends. The way the materials are distributed in the descending charge was found by F. Brabant [22] to be dependent on the shape and size of the furnace, and more particularly on the diameter of the mouth and the diameter of the charging cone. The subject was also studied by I. L. Bell, T. L. Joseph and co-workers, I. Bohm, T. J. Ess, B. V. Vuistavkin and co-workers, E. C. Evans and co-workers, E. Cotel, A. Peters, J. R. Young and R. C. Irving, R. A Hacking, S. P. Kinnay, A. Siegel, C. C. Furnas and T. L. Joseph, R. H. Richards and R. W. Lodge, and E. C. Pechin. A cone of relatively large diameter gives an accumulation of coarse material in the centre, so that the ascending gases pass more readily up the centre than up the sides, where the finer material tends to accumulate. If a very marked separation occurs, the finer ore may be imperfectly reduced, and the smelting is then irregular. If the bell is relatively narrow, the centre is finer and the outside coarse, when the smelting is irregular and the furnace lining is unduly worn. L. E. Grüner found the solid charge descended at the rate of about 20 ins. per hour, but in some modern furnaces T. Turner said its rate of descent is not infrequently 5 ft. per hour. G. Bulle, J. Stöcker and G. Bulle, C. C. Furnas and T. L. Joseph, R. H. Sweetser, W. Lennings, H. Bansen, E. Bertram, S. P. Kinney, etc., studied the effect of variations in the grain-size of the charges.

Estimates of the *temperature* in different parts of the blast-furnace were made by J. J. Ebelmen [23] about 1844, and later by P. von Tunner and R. Richter, S. P. Kinney, G. Eichenberg, A. Wagner, F. Kupelwieser, M. Jungst, P. Rheinländer, H. Allen, L. Rinman, and L. Rinman and B. Fernquist. According to H. le Chatelier, the highest temp. of the blast-furnace is in front of the tuyères, and it is about 1930°, and the first part of the tappings of grey cast iron had a temp. of 1400°, while the last and hottest portions had a temp. of 1570°—Swedish white cast iron melts at 1135°, and grey cast iron at 1220°. Again, according to I. L. Bell, the waste gases from a modern blast-furnace burning coke vary from 150° to 270°; the lower temp. corresponds with the introduction of fresh ore. The greatest variations are due to irregularities in the charging. The temp. curve for a furnace 75 ft. high, indicated in Fig. 15, is based on the observations of F. Clements—*cf.* also Fig. 16.

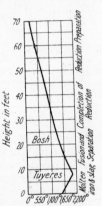

FIG. 15. — Temperature Zones of Blast-Furnace.

According to L. E. Grüner, the average rate of ascent of the gases in the blast-furnace approximates about 20 ins. per second, but with some modern furnaces T. Turner said that the speed of ascent is much greater. Numerous analyses have been made of the gases emitted at the top of the blast-furnace, and also of the gases at different levels in the furnace. The division of the furnace into specific zones of reaction has been based on these analyses. There are, of course, no hard-and-fast lines of demarcation between these zones, but certain reactions are favoured in particular regions of temp. Reports on the composition of the gases have been discussed by R. Bunsen,[24] R. Bunsen and L. Playfair, J. J. Ebelmen, T. Scheerer and C. Langberg, J. Stoecker, G. Heine, J. J. Berzelius, L. Ledebur, W. van Vloten, A. Jaumain, B. Osann, L. E. Grüner, F. Kupelwieser and R. Schöffel, R. Schöffel, L. Rinman, L. Rinman and B. Fernquist, A. Tamm, F. W. Lürmann, E. Bellani, M. Levin and H. Niedt, W. Hawdon, H. von Jüptner, P. von Tunner, P. von Tunner and R. Richter, I. L. Bell, J. E. Stead, J. Percy, H. Wedding, P. Gredt, and C. Stöckmann. According to A. Ledebur, the following analyses may be regarded as typical of the exit gases :

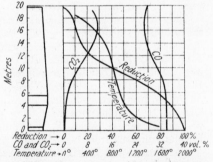

FIG. 16.—The Changes of Temperature and of the Composition of the Gases at Different Levels in the Blast-Furnace.

		N₂	CO	CO₂	H₂	CH₄
Charcoal fuel	vol.	56·7–57·6	23·1–25·5	14·7–15·3	1·7–4·3	0·5–0·8
	wt.	53·3–55·0	22·1–23·8	22·3–22·4	0·1–0·3	0·3–0·4
Coke fuel	vol.	59·0–62·8	23·5–31·0	5·3–13·8	0·1–2·1	0·4–2·2
	wt.	55·0–61·5	21·9–30·1	8·1–20·2	0·01–0·1	0·2–1·9

Observations on the distribution of the gases in the blast-furnace have been made by M. Levin and H. Niedt, H. Niedt, N. Metz, W. A. Schlesinger, M. Zyromsky,

S. P. Kinney and co-workers, C. Aldendorff, F. Lange, G. Eichenberg and P. Ober-
hoffer, G. Bulle, F. Sauerwald, H. Lent, R. Franchot, H. Koppers, P. Reichardt,
H. H. Meyer, F. Wust and P. Wolff, W. Lennings, and R. Schenck. The results of
S. P. Kinney are summarized in Figs. 16 and 17.

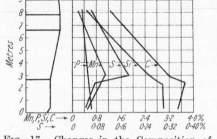

FIG. 17.—Changes in the Composition of
the Metal at Different Levels in the Blast-
Furnace.

A little *hydrogen* is found in the gases
in all parts of the furnace; it originates
from the moisture in the air-blast and in
the raw materials: $C+H_2O=CO+H_2$;
and, according to N. Metz, $CO+H_2O$
$=CO_2+H_2$. According to W. Müller, the
hydrogen begins to reduce iron oxides at
about 277°. The subject was discussed
by W. van Vloten, B. Osann, and W. Lennings. Not only methane, but, as shown
by the analyses of R. Bunsen and L. Playfair, and others, unsaturated hydrocarbons
may also be present. J. J. van Laar discussed the relation between the working
temp. of the furnace and the temp. of the blast necessary for a given fuel consumption provided that no carbon dioxide is present in the exit gases.

Small quantities of *hydrogen sulphide* also occur in blast-furnace gases. G. Hilgen-
stock found that the sulphur content of the gas did not exceed 0·06 per cent. The
subject was discussed by T. L. Joseph, H. Wedding, and F. Wüst and P. Wolff.
The desulphurizing action of slags was discussed by L. Blum, R. Bolling, H. L. Diehl,
F. Firmstone, O. R. Forster, C. Frick, H. Geiger, C. H. Herty, G. Hilgenstock,
O. Johannsen, J. E. Johnson, T. L. Joseph and co-workers, A. Killing, S. P. Kinney,
A. Ledebur, L. M. Lindemann, R. S. McCaffery and J. F. Oesterle, A. McCance,
F. Muck, B. Osann, E. H. Saniter, R. Schäfer, E. Schulz, O. Simmersbach,
G. J. Snelus, J. E. Stead, N. B. Wittmann, C. E. Wood and T. L. Joseph, and F. Wüst
and P. Wolff—*vide infra*, the action of sulphur on iron. The action of *silicon* or
silica in the blast-furnace was discussed by I. Bohm,[25] S. L. Goodale, H. C. Green-
wood, H. Hanemann, F. Lange, A. Ledebur, H. H. Meyer, G. Tammann and
G. Bätz, H. von Wartenberg, F. Wüst, and F. Wüst and A. Schüller—*vide infra*,
the action of silicon on iron. The behaviour of *titanium* in the blast-furnace was
discussed by E. Bahlsen,[26] R. Durrer, J. Head, J. A. Heskett, J. F. Kemp,
A. J. Rossi, O. Simmersbach, and O. Vogel—*vide infra*, the action of titanium on
iron. The behaviour of phosphorus was discussed by I. Bohm,[27] W. Mathesius,
H. H. Meyer, S. Stein, W. van Vloten, and F. Wüst—*vide infra*, the action of phosphorus on iron. Blast-furnace gases may contain varying quantities of *ammonia*;
and G. Hilgenstock observed 0·06 grm. of ammonia per cubic metre of gas.
A. E. Fletcher, H. Allen, F. W. Paul, and A. Gillespie discussed the recovery of
tar and ammonia from blast-furnace gases.

R. Bunsen and L. Playfair[28] observed 1·34 per cent. of cyanogen in the lower
part of a blast-furnace; H. Wedding thought that some mistake had been
made, but W. Haufe and H. von Schwarze observed that cyanogen may be formed
under the conditions which prevailed in the blast-furnace. In 1826, P. Berthier
observed impure potassium carbonate in the hottest part of a blast-furnace at
Merthyr Tydvil, and he inferred that it was derived from the ironstone employed.
Possibly the substance collected by P. Berthier also contained cyanate, but not
suspecting its presence, he failed to detect it. K. Jurisch noted the occurrence
of hydrogen cyanide in blast-furnace gases. M. Desfosses observed that potassium
cyanide is readily formed when nitrogen is passed over charcoal at a red-heat—
the alkali, of course, was present as an integral part of the charcoal. G. Townes,
and W. Hempel have confirmed this observation. J. Dawes obtained a patent for
collecting potassium cyanide from iron-smelting furnaces by the introduction of a
pipe near the tuyères of the furnace. J. C. L. Zinken and C. Bromeis, H. von Jüptner,

C. J. A. Scheerer, J. Müller, L. Eck, A. Gillespie, H. Braune, A. K. von Kerpely, W. McConnachie, C. A. Meissner, C. Catlett, R. Franchot, F. Lange, S. P. Kinney, A. Lefebvre, S. P. Kinney and E. W. Guernsey, W. Haufe and H. von Schwarze, R. Peters, and J. Redtenbacher discussed the occurrence of potassium cyanide in iron-smelting furnaces ; R. Bunsen and L. Playfair collected a considerable quantity of potassium cyanide from a blast-furnace at Alfreton. W. C. Roberts-Austen discussed the part possibly played by cyanides in the reduction of the ore ; J. Percy, and I. L. Bell consider that this is very small. H. Braune, and H. le Chatelier emphasized the fact that the formation of too much cyanide in the lower part of the furnace lowers the quality of the product, since nitrogen is absorbed by the iron from cyanides, but not from atm. air—*vide* nitrogen and iron. H. Kinder showed that besides being derived from the decomposition of carbon monoxide, the carbon found in the refractory linings of bricks may be due to the presence of cyanates of alkali metals in coke and ore : $K_2CO_3+N_2+4C=2KCN+3CO$, and $KCN+CO_2=KCNO +CO$; and with steam, and carbon dioxide, $2KCNO+CO_2+H_2O=K_2CO_3+2HCN +O_2$; and the latter in contact with particles of iron in the brick furnishes carbon, hydrogen, and nitrogen. These results were discussed by H. Ditz. F. W. Lürmann found that the alkali cyanides also act deleteriously on the linings of blast-furnaces.

The furnace gas carries along with it a fine flue-dust, which settles along the track of the gases as a white or yellowish-white powder. Numerous analyses have been reported by E. Ebermayer,[29] B. H. Thwaite, B. Kerl, J. Pattinson, P. von Tunner, A. von Kerpely, A. Engelhardt, G. Leuchs, H. Wedding, J. Percy, F. W. Lürmann, A. Ledebur, R. M. Colles, V. le Vrärier, W. B. Phillips, C. Pradel, and C. F. Rammelsberg. J. Percy quoted the analysis :

CaSO$_4$	MnO	CaO	MgO	K$_2$O	Al$_2$O$_3$	Fe$_2$O$_3$	SiO$_2$
4·42	1·77	2·30	1·13	1·80	8·43	47·05	30·33 per cent.

This is of no particular use. Sometimes, however, a relatively large proportion of potash salt is present, which can be removed by lixiviation with water. The following is quoted by A. Ledebur :

NH$_4$CyS	NaCl	KCl	MgCl$_2$	NH$_4$Cl	FeCl$_2$	MnCl$_2$	CaSO$_4$	K$_2$SO$_4$	SiO$_2$	Fe$_2$O$_3$	H$_2$O
0·69	13·02	19·26	10·95	6·59	0·54	0·10	5·27	31·14	0·64	1·47	9·92 per cent.

C. Bolin found a grey material in a blast-furnace at Eisenerz with constituents corresponding with :

KCy	KOCy	KCl	K$_2$CO$_3$	Na$_2$CO$_3$	Insoluble
26·52	2·09	2·83	40·59	10·72	17·36 per cent.

E. Priwoznik found that dust of a blast-furnace of the Austrian Alpine Co. contained :

KCy	KOCy	KSCy	K$_4$FeCy$_6$	Fe	Total K
0·08	0·69	0·24	7·86	6·86	35·29 per cent.
0·003	0·03	0·01	0·42	26·05	6·61

The occurrence of potassium salts in the flue-dust of blast-furnaces has been discussed—**2**. 20, 5.

The collection of analyses by F. W. Lürmann shows wide variations, and there may be present, in addition, sulphides or oxides of tin, lead, zinc, copper, silver, aluminium, antimony, thallium, manganese, iron, calcium, and magnesium ; also chlorides, sulphur, and carbonaceous matters. C. H. Lündström reported bismuth in the blast-furnaces at Finshytte; L. Blum, J. J. Porter, M. Paschke, and F. W. Lürmann, zinc oxide ; I. A. Baar, I. L. Bell, F. Bicheroux, I. Bohm, W. D. Brown, F. W. Davis, M. Derclaye, J. E. Fletcher, R. Forsythe, L. Gruner, O. F. Hudson, J. E. Johnson, H. von Jüptner, A. Korevaar, A. Ledebur, R. Lorenz, W. Mathesius, H. H. Meyer, M. von Schwarz, A. H. Sexton, O. Simmersbach, B. Stoughton, H. Thaler, and T. Turner, manganese oxide ; W. Heike, lead and copper ; A. Ledebur, silver ; R. von Seth, and O. Vogel, vanadium ; E. D. Campbell, copper, nickel, and cobalt; J. Pattinson and J. E. Stead, W. Mathesius, and O. Simmersbach, arsenic; A. Ledebur, antimony; and L. Blum, chlorides.

The recovery of the potassium salts from blast-furnace gases was discussed 2. 20, 4. The cleaning of the gas from dust is a problem in chemical engineering; and so also is the utilization of the waste-gas as a gaseous fuel. As an example of what can be done the following, according to J. B. Walker, represents the practice at Gary :

Part of the "waste gases" poured out of the blast furnace are employed for heating the hot stoves; for raising steam in batteries of boilers; for operating gas engines for running the furnace blowers; and also other gas engines for operating generators for the supply of power and light. The twelve blast furnaces at Gary produce 40,300,000 c. ft. of gas every hour. Of this amount 30 per cent. is used in heating the hot stoves; 7·5 per cent. is used in the steam-power plant; 2·5 per cent. is used in the primary washers for the hot-blast stoves, and in the secondary washers to clean the gas before it passes to the gas holders; 15 per cent. is used by the blowing engines; and the remaining 45 per cent. is available for running the gas engines in the electric power station. The purified gas has an average heating value of 90 B.T.U. per c. ft., and it is estimated that two and a half times as much can be derived from a given quantity of gas with gas engines as can be secured with boilers and steam engines. The blast furnace gas at Gary serves to operate fifty-seven 2500 to 3000 horse-power gas-driven generators and blowing engines.

As indicated above, the molten metal from the blast-furnace may be run directly into ladles and conveyed to converters or mixers to be made into steel; it may also be run into ladles and conveyed to machines where it is cast in iron moulds or chills. The old method of casting is to run the metal from the furnace to the depressions or moulds in the sand floor of the so-called pig-beds. The channel along which the iron ran to feed the moulds and the moulds bear a fanciful resemblance to a litter of sucking pigs; the runner was called the *sow*, and the iron in the moulds, *pigs*. Hence the term *pig-iron*. The pig-iron cast in sand moulds is also called

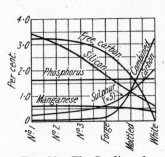

FIG. 18.—The Grading of Cleveland Pig-Iron.

sand-cast pig, and that cast in metal moulds or chills is called *chill-cast pig*, and where machine casting is employed, *machine-cast pig*. The rate of cooling of sand-cast pig is sufficiently constant to enable a trained eye to obtain a rough indication of the proportion of contained silicon from the appearance of the fractured surface. Thus, a grey open fracture indicates a high silicon content, whilst a white fracture corresponds with a low proportion of silicon. The appearance of the fracture also gives a rough indication of the proportions of free and combined carbon, in that a grey iron is high in free carbon and low in combined carbon, whilst a white iron is low in free carbon and high in combined carbon. The indications are not so reliable with pig-iron cast in iron moulds, where the cooling is faster and more irregular.

One way of classifying pig-iron is based on the relation of free or graphitic to combined carbon. If much of the carbon be "free," the iron is called **grey pig-iron**; and if much combined carbon be present, **white pig-iron**; intermediate varieties furnish **mottled pig-iron.** The following analyses will illustrate the difference between the three varieties of pig-iron :

	Grey	Mottled	White
Combined carbon .	0·90	1·80	3·00 per cent.
Free carbon . .	2·8	1·40	0·10 per cent.

The grey and mottled varieties may be further subdivided. Pig-irons, too, are often graded according to their source, because certain districts work a specially pure or a specially foul ore, and this gives the iron from these districts characteristic properties—good or bad. Another system of classification is based on analysis. For example, T. Turner [30] represented the analyses of different grades of Cleveland pig-irons by Fig. 18. The percentage of sulphur is multiplied by 5 for the sake of clarity. All the samples from the Forest of Dean contained traces of copper. Another system of classification is based according to use. These different forms of iron-carbon alloys with over 2 per cent. of carbon are also called **cast iron**—*vide infra*, nomenclature. Cast iron is not malleable, nor can it be welded. It is used for casting articles—stoves and ornamental iron—which with ordinary usage are not likely to be subjected to shocks. Cast iron is the starting-point for the manufacture of wrought iron and steel. The so-called *foundry iron* for remelting includes foundry pig, malleable-iron pig, and charcoal iron. Foundry iron usually has sulphur below 0·05 per cent., and manganese up to about 2·5 per cent. or even more, and silicon up to 3 per cent. or even more. H. Allen said that foundry iron is generally not so grey as Bessemer pig-iron, and that the limits of composition for average qualities are :

Free C	Combined C	Silicon	Sulphur	Phosphorus	Manganese
2·19–3·85	0·06–0·75	1·71–3·19	0·01–0·05	0·61–1·77	0·26–1·68 per cent.

According to H. Littlehales, the term *bloom* is the earliest known name for the mass of metal obtained by smelting iron ore. *Bloom* is mentioned in many documents of the Anglo-Saxon period, and it was in use for some centuries. In the fifteenth century the term *sow* was sometimes used in place of *bloom*; and just as in the fifteenth century *sow* ousted the term *bloom*, so in the early part of the sixteenth century the term *pig* displaced the term *sow* for the lump of iron from the ore. The old casting bed consisted of a main channel with smaller channels at the side. It has been accordingly suggested that the casting of metal in the main channel was known as *sow*, and the castings in the smaller channels as *pigs*. Actually, however, documentary evidence makes it probable that the term *pig* properly belongs to one period and *sow* to another.

The pig-iron produced with charcoal as fuel is usually made in blast-furnaces of smaller dimensions than when coke is used, and the product is usually of a higher degree of purity than ordinary pig-irons. For instance, the limits of composition of six grades of Swedish pig-iron, made with charcoal, range from :

Free C	Combined C	Silicon	Sulphur	Phosphorus	Manganese
3·29–4·19	0·29–0·86	0·02–1·38	0·01–0·03	0·01–0·05	0·06–2·46 per cent.

W. Danielsen said that good Swedish charcoal iron has less than 1·25 per cent. of slag, and that the range of composition for :

	C	Mn	Si	P	S
Finished iron	0·02–0·06	tr.–0·10	0·02–0·04	0·04–0·07	0·005–0·010 per cent.
Melting bars	0·06–0·14	0·04–0·10	0·02–0·04	0·015–0·022	0·005–0·010 per cent.

Forge pig-iron for puddling, etc., has a higher proportion of combined and a smaller proportion of free carbon, and accordingly it has a whiter fracture. It is usually produced at a lower temp. than the greyer varieties of iron. The limits of composition for average qualities are :

Free C	Combined C	Silicon	Sulphur	Phosphorus	Manganese
1·75–2·97	0·33–0·89	0·99–3·75	0·04–0·34	0·04–3·05	0·06–2·25 per cent.

A still lower grade of pig-iron with a mottled fracture has the limits of composition varying between :

Free C	Combined C	Silicon	Sulphur	Phosphorus	Manganese
1·07–2·55	1·25–2·31	0·70–1·79	0·10–0·30	0·02–1·50	0·14–1·13 per cent.

whilst the lowest grade of ordinary classes of pig-iron is white in fracture and very brittle, with limits of composition varying between :

Free C	Combined C	Silicon	Sulphur	Phosphorus	Manganese
0 to 0·88	2·28–3·50	0·38–1·59	0·15–0·36	0·03–1·40	0·19–1·10 per cent.

The steel-making irons include the so-called Bessemer pig-iron for conversion into steel by the acid process. The composition of a grey Bessemer pig-iron was :

Free C	Combined C	Silicon	Sulphur	Phosphorus	Manganese
3·43	0·33	2·51	0·02	0·04	0·48 per cent.

The pig-iron used for the basic Bessemer process or the Thomas-Gilchrist process has sulphur below 0·2 per cent., silicon below 1 per cent., phosphorus 1·5 to 3·0 per cent., and manganese about 1·5 to 2·5 per cent. The so-called low phosphorus pig-iron, used for making steel with an extra small proportion of phosphorus, has under 2 per cent. of silicon, below 0·03 per cent. of sulphur, below 0·03 per cent. of phosphorus, and below 1 per cent. of manganese ; and basic pig-iron—white or mottled—has less than 1 per cent. of silicon, less than 0·05 per cent. of sulphur, less than 1 per cent. each of phosphorus and manganese. The so-called ferro-alloys include ferromanganese, ferrosilicon, silicon spiegels, etc. T. E. Holgate gave :

	Free C	Combined C	Silicon	Sulphur	Phosphorus	Manganese
Ferro-silicons }	0·55–2·40	0·11–0·35	8·54–17·80	0·041–0·078	0·047–0·115	1·07–3·25 per cent.
Silicon-spiegels }	0·33–1·13	0·29–1·85	10·74–15·94	—	0·074–0·095	19·64–24·36 per cent.
Ferro-manganese }	4·27–6·31		0·11–1·12	—	0·078–0·175	8·11–87·92 per cent.

A. Kayser found 0·07 to 0·29 per cent. of calcium, and 0·03 to 0·38 per cent. of magnesium in pig-iron from Bilbao. A. Ledebur found in Hungarian pig-iron : total carbon, 3·500 per cent. ; Si, 1·480 ; P, 0·123 ; S, 0·007 ; Sb, 0·001 ; Sn, 0·003 ; Pb, 0·005 ; Cu, 0·265 ; Cr, 0·012 ; Ni, 0·041 ; Mn, 2·440 ; and Ti, 0·039 ; and in Upper Silesian pig-iron : total carbon, 2·518 per cent. ; Si, 0·292 ; P, 2·360 ; S, 0·117 ; As, 0·006 ; Sb, 0·001 ; Pb, 0·002 ; Cu, 0·099 ; Cr, 0·073 ; Ni, 0·016 ; Mn, 0·792 ; Ti, 0·056 ; Co, 0·011 ; and V, 0·072 ; A. Pourcel gave for a French pig-iron : C, 2·257 ; Si, 3·265 ; P, 0·459 ; S, 0·036 ; Mn, 0·388 ; Al, 0·028 ; Cr, 0·027 ; V, 0·012 ; Cu, 0·009 ; Ni, and Co, 0·035 ; As, 0·015 ; Sb, 0·011 ; Ca, 0·072 ; Mg, 0·100 ; and Ti, 0·025. W. N. Hartley and H. Ramage observed indium, gallium, thallium, and molybdenum in iron ores. Observations on the grading and composition of pig-irons were made by T. Turner, K. Daeves, G. L. Luetscher, E. Adamson, A. Pourcel, H. Pilkington, I. L. Bell, H. P. Tiemann, J. E. Johnson, E. A. Kebler, etc. G. Bätz discussed the extraction of iron pyrites from the ores.

In localities where carbonaceous fuel is costly and cheap water-power is available, it has been found possible to generate electricity and use it as a source of heat for smelting iron. There has been quite a number of methods suggested for the **electrical smelting of iron ores.** These are described in various books on electric furnaces.[31] The following description of the smelting plant near Domnarfvet, Sweden, was furnished me by Mr. Harold Almquist when visiting the plant in Sweden. He said : The essential difference between the electrical process and the blast-furnace process is that the fuel required for heating and melting in the blast-furnace is replaced by electrical energy. In the electric smelting-furnace only that quantity of charcoal or coke required for reducing the ore is charged into the furnace. No air is blown into the furnace, so that the combustion of the carbon can be effected only by the oxygen of the ore. The differences in design and operation between an ordinary blast-furnace and an electric smelting-furnace are due to these conditions. A section through the furnace is represented in Fig. 19. The shaft and hopper arrangements at the top are similar to those of a blast-furnace. The furnace can be charged in any convenient way. The lower part, or hearth, differs from that of an

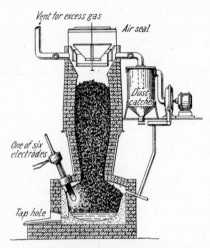

FIG. 19.—Electric Smelting-Furnace.

ordinary blast-furnace. It consists of a large crucible the walls of which are connected with the shaft of the circular roof or arch. Four to eight electrodes are inserted in the arch, and they have a diameter of 60 to 70 cms., dependent on the capacity of the furnace. The current is brought to the electrodes by copper busbars so as to allow a load of ·2 amps. per sq. mm. The high-tension lines outside are connected to switches, etc., in a high-tension switchroom behind the furnace, and thence coupled to transformers, which bring down the voltage to 60 or 100 volts. The transformers stand as near as possible to the furnace and are connected with the same by the busbars.

Gas is drawn from the furnace at the top of the shaft and cleaned in the usual way. Part of it is again blown into the furnace through tuyères placed around the upper part of the hearth mantle, thus directing the cold gas into the interspace formed between the arch and the incline of the furnace charge. A certain quantity of gas is therefore always circulating in the furnace. The proper circulation of the gas is a very important factor for the successful working of the furnace. The gas cools the roof and thereby increases its life ; it also distributes the heat and ensures the progress of the chemical reactions evenly between hearth and shaft. The formation of gas in an electric furnace is naturally considerably less than in a blast-furnace where about three times as much carbon is burnt. The heat carried by the gas from the hearth up through the shaft, as well as its ability to produce chemical reactions, is therefore less in an electric furnace than in a blast-furnace. This is counterbalanced by the gas circulation. The carbon dioxide of the gas is immediately reduced to carbon monoxide, which higher up the shaft is again oxidized during the reduction of the ore.

The operation of the electric smelting-furnace is very sensitive and requires careful attention. For instance, the amount of carbon in the charge must be exactly adjusted to the oxygen of the ore. If too much carbon is used, the excess cannot be burnt off, and it accumulates in the hearth, thereby producing a " hot run." On the other hand, if insufficient carbon is employed, the reduction will be incomplete, and the furnace will " run cold."

The iron ore employed at Domnarfvet is the well-known Grängesberg magnetite mixed with some hæmatite and apatite ; its composition is : Fe_3O_4, 65·00 per cent. ; Fe_2O_3, 20·00 ; MnO, 0·30 ; MgO, 2·00 ; CaO, 4·00 ; Al_2O_3, 1·80 ; SiO_2, 4·50 ; and P_2O_5, 2·40. The pig-iron produced has the composition :

Carbon	Silicon	Manganese	Phosphorus	Sulphur
2·70	0·80	1·20	2·00	0·01 per cent.

The slag has the composition :

FeO	MnO	MgO	CaO	Al_2O_3	SiO_2	P_2O_5
1·00	2·90	10·00	42·00	7·10	34·00	0·90 per cent.

The analysis of the furnace gas is :

CO_2	CO	H_2	N	Hydrocarbons
20–25	60–65	10–15	1·0–1·5	The rest per cent.

The gas from the electric furnace is in consequence considerably richer than ordinary blast-furnace gas, and this is an appreciable item on the credit side of the electric furnace account. The excess of gas has been estimated at about 500 cubic metres per ton of pig-iron, and it can be utilized as a fuel in metallurgical furnaces, for heating boilers, etc.

The fuel or reducing agent in the electric smelting-furnace is charcoal. The difficulties with coke are its low electrical resistance and high density, and there is a tendency for it to graphitize on the high-temp. zone about the electrodes. The electric smelting-furnace can be used with good economy only when the electric power is cheap. If the price per kilowatt-year exceeds about £4, the other items in the production costs must be low if the electric furnaces are to compete with blast-furnaces using coke at the ordinary price.

G. Tammann and G. Bätz,[32] G. Tammann and C. F. Grevemeyer, G. Bogitch, F. Sauerwald, and G. Kassel studied the extraction of iron from silicate ores ; and the extraction of iron from silicates by the electrolysis of the fused ore has been discussed by F. Sauerwald and G. Neuendorff ; and from pyrites, by G. Ongaro, R. D. Pike and co-workers, F. A. Eustis, and M. Guédras. J. Reese, C. Adams, M. Boistel, and S. L. Madorsky studied the manufacture of iron by the reduction of molten iron oxide by hydrogen.

REFERENCES.

[1] C. V. Bellamy, *Journ. Iron Steel Inst.*, **66.** ii, 99, 1904 ; T. Turner, *ib.*, **44.** ii, 162, 1893 ; S. A. Bilgrami, *ib.*, **56.** ii, 65, 1899 ; E. P. Martin and H. Louis, *Agric. Ledger*, 3, 1904 ; *Journ. Iron Steel Inst.*, **66.** ii, 456, 1904 ; **119.** i, 29, 1929 ; T. A. Rickard, *ib.*, **120.** ii, 323, 1930 ; R. A. Hadfield, *ib.*, **85.** i, 134, 1912 ; A. Ure, *Dictionary of Arts, Manufactures, and Mines*, London, **3.** 764, 1867 ; G. H. Davis, *The Graphic*, **110.** 719, 1924 (I am indebted to the publishers for permission to base Figs. 6 to 8 on the drawings there given) ; T. May, *Iron Coal Trades Rev.*, **71.** 427, 1905 ; A. Gurlt, *Die Roheisenerzeugung mit Gas, oder die Verhüttung der Eisenerze mit indirecter Benutzung der Brennmateriales*, Freiberg, 1856 ; P. Berthier, *Ann. Mines*, (1), **7.** 377, 1822 ; *Arch. Bergbau Hüttenwesen*, **7.** 323, 1823 ; L. B. Guyton de Morveau, *Obs. Phys.*, **2.** 450, 1773 ; *Crell's Ann.*, ii, 157, 1784 ; F. Stibold, *ib.*, ii, 257, 1787 ; M. Gazeran, *ib.*, ii, 326, 1793 ; *Ann. Chim. Phys.*, (1), **7.** 97, 1790 ; (1), **31.** 113, 1799 ; F. J. von Gerstner, *Drei Abhandlungen ; Worin besteht der Unterschied zwischen Roheisen aus Hohenöfen und geschmeidigern Eisen aus Frischherden ?* Leipzig, 1799 ; F. L. von Cancrin, *Kurzgefasste ganz neue Lehren weiman aus jedem Eisenerz das best möglichste seinem Urstoff eigene Eisen erhalten kann*, Halle a. S., 1800 ; J. F. L. Hausmann, *Gött. gelehrte Anz.*, 664, 1815 ; G. H. Rivius, *Der furnembsten notwendigsten der gantzen Architectur angehörigen mathematischen und mechanischen künst eygentlicher Bericht und vast klare verstendliche Unterrichtung zu rechtem verstandt der Lehr Vitruvii*, Nurnberg, 1547 ; B. Valerius, *Traité théoretique et pratique de la fabrication de la fonte*, Freiberg, 1851 ; C. Combes, *Ann. Mines*, (1), **9.** 329, 1824 ; *Arch. Bergbau Hüttenwesen*, **9.** 465, 1825 ; F. A. von Marcher, *Beyträge zur Eisenhüttenkunde*, Klagenfurt, 1805 ; T. E. Norburg, *Ueber die Produktion des Roheisens in Russland und über eine neue Schmelzmethode im sogenannten Sturzofen*, Freiberg, 1805 ; J. V. Day, *On the Past and Present of Iron Smelting*, Edinburgh, 1873 ; L. Guillemain, *Kolonialan Rund.*, 1, 1909 ; *Die Eisenindustrie der eingeborenen Kameruns*, Berlin, 1909 ; W. S. Routledge, *Nature*, **79.** 148, 1910 ; Anon., *Eng.*, **62.** 376, 1891 ; C. M. Weld, *ib.*, **102.** 332, 1906 ; *Iron Age*, 668, 1905 ; J. T. Bent, *The Ruined Cities of Mashonaland*, London, 268, 1892 ; *The Sacred City of the Ethiopians*, London, 211, 1893 ; T. H. Holland, *Record Indian Geol. Sur.*, **25.** 135, 1892 ; *Handbook Imperial Institute*, London, **8.** 16, 1892 ; H. L. Stokes, *Westminster Gaz.*, March 13, 1893 ; J. Danvers, *Journ. Soc. Arts*, **41.** 602, 1893 ; J. T. Last, *Journ. Roy. Inst. British Architects*, (3), **1.** 635, 1894 ; C. Lemaire, *Rev. Univ. Mines*, 28, 283, 1895 ; G. Braecke, *ib.*, **59.** 229, 1903 ; F. von Richthofen, *China*, London, 2. 150, 411, 1882 ; *Iron Coal Trades Rev.*, **57.** 732, 1898 ; S. Hedin, *Through Asia*, London, **1.** 257, 1898 ; J. Duclos, *Amer. Manf.*, **62.** 296, 1898 ; W. Kennedy, *ib.*, **68.** 1, 1901 ; X. Stainer, *Trans. Inst. Min. Eng.*, **15.** 499, 1898 ; F. H. Wynne, *ib.*, **26.** 231, 1904 ; J. M. Nisbet, *Cassier's Mag.*, **15.** 433, 1898 ; A. Ledebur, *Stahl Eisen*, **19.** 757, 1899 ; **21.** 842, 1901 ; R. G. Cumming, *Five Years' Hunting in South Africa*, Edinburgh, 59, 1902 ; F. W. Reid, *Hardware Trade Journ.*, 84, 1903 ; I. E. Lester, *Proc. Staffs Iron Steel Inst.*, **27.** 2, 1911 ; R. B. Foote, *Mem. Geol. Sur. India*, **25.** 191, 1896 ; F. Dixey, *Mining Mag.*, **23.** 213, 1920 ; H. D. McCaskey, *Eng. Min. Journ.*, **76.** 780, 1903 ; C. von Schwarz, *Zeit. Berg. Hütt. Ver. Steiermark*, 1, 1879 ; *Zeit. österr. Ing. Arch. Ver.*, **44.** 189, 1892 ; *Stahl Eisen*, **21.** 209, 277, 337, 1901 ; F. Hupfeld, *ib.*, **20.** 347, 1900 ; *Mitt. deut. Schutzgebieten*, 4, 1899 ; E. Fuchs and E. Saladin, *Ann. Mines*, (8), **2.** 287, 1882 ; R. A. Dart and N. del Grande, *Trans. Roy. Soc. South Africa*, **19.** 397, 1931.

[2] T. Richard, *Études sur l'art d'extraire immédiatement le fer de ses minerais sans convertir le métal en fonte*, Paris, 1838 ; J. François, *Recherches sur le gisement et le traitement direct des minerais de fer dans les Pyrénées, particulièrement dans l'Ariège*, Paris, 1843 ; J. Percy, *Metallurgy—Iron and Steel*, London, 278, 1864 ; J. F. d'Aubuisson, *Ann. Chim. Phys.*, (2), **32.** 327, 1826 ; *Journ. Mines*, **38.** 155, 1815 ; *Ann. Mines*, (2), **4.** 236, 1828 ; M. Thibaud and M. Tardy, *ib.*, (1), **8.** 595, 1823 ; G. Magnus, *Sitzber. Akad. Berlin*, 135, 1848 ; *Phil. Mag.*, (4), **1.** 1, 1851 ; *Pogg. Ann.*, **80.** 1, 1850 ; *Ann. Chim. Phys.*, **66.** 234, 1856 ; G. B. Venturi, *Bull. Soc. Philomath.*, **2.** 60, 1797 ; *Nicholson's Journ.*, **3.** 13, 59, 1800.

[3] M. Sagey, *Ann. Mines*, (2), **4.** 121, 1828 ; J. H. Hassenfratz, *La sidérotechnie*, Paris, 1812 ; *Das wichtigste aus der Eisenhüttenkunde*, Leipzig, 1822 ; J. M. Muthuon, *Traité des forges dites catalanes*, Turin, 1808 ; L. Cordier, *Journ. Mines*, **27.** 181, 1810 ; P. C. J. B. Tronson du Coudray, *Mémoire sur la manière dont on extrait en Corse le fer de la mine de l'Elbe*, Upsala, 1774 ; Paris, 1775.

[4] V. Biringuccio, *De la Pirotechnica*, Venetia, 1540 ; R. Schaur, *Stahl Eisen*, **49.** 489, 1929 ; E. Swedenborg, *Regnum subterraneum sive minerale de ferro*, Dresdæ, **1.** 119, 1734 ; A. Wehrle, *Lehrbuch der Probir- und Hüttenkunde*, Wien, **2.** 116, 1834 ; J. Percy, *Metallurgy—Iron and Steel*, London, 320, 1864 ; M. Meyer, *Beiträge zur genaueren Kenntniss des Eisenhüttenwesens, in*

Schweden, Berlin, 1829 ; R. Plott, *The Natural History of Staffordshire*, Oxford, 1679 ; M. Ray, *Iron Work*, London, 1674 ; M. Lister, *Phil. Trans.*, **17**. 865, 1693 ; A. Ure, *A Dictionary of Arts, Manufactures, and Mines*, London, 1875 ; P. R. von Tunner, *Das Eisenhüttenwesen in Schweden*, Freiberg, 1858 ; L. J. Igelström, *Några ord om Finlands Bergshandtering*, Stockholm, 1851 ; C. J. B. Karsten, *Handbuch der Eisenhüttenkunde*, Halle, **3**. 34, 1841 ; G. Jars, *Voyages métallurgiques*, Lyon, **1**. 37, 1774 ; J. C. Quantz, *Praktische Abhandlung über die Eisen- und Stahlmanipulation in der Herrschaft Schmalkalden*, Nürnberg, 28, 1799 ; J. M. Swank, *History of the Manufacture of Iron in all Ages*, Philadelphia, 1902 ; A. Wahlberg, *Baumaterialienkunde*, **2**. 141, 1898 ; G. Agricola, *De re metallica*, Basileæ, 1561 ; L. Beck, *Die Geschichte des Eisens in technischer und kulturgeschichtlicher Beziehung*, Braunschweig, 1884 ; M. A. Lower, *Contributions to Literature, Historical, Antiquarian, and Metrical*, London, 98, 1854 ; H. A. Dillon, *Archæologia*, **51**. 168, 1888 ; R. Gontermann, *Entwicklung und Bedeutung der Siegerländer Spezialhochöfen*, Giessen, 1927 ; W. Quast, *Die Entwicklung der Eisenindustrie im Sauerland*, Köln, 1928 ; O. Krasa, *Stahl Eisen*, **51**. 1287, 1931.

⁵ R. Buchanan, *Ironmonger*, **121**. 11, 1907 ; *Iron Age*, **95**. 460, 1915 , W. Treptoff, *Zeit. Ver. deut. Ing.*, **51**. 373, 486, 1907 ; J. J. Becher, *Närrische Wersheit und wise Narrheit*, Franckfurt, 1682 ; H. Alker, *Giesserei*, **9**. 227, 1922 ; J. Laissus, *ib.*, **9**. 207, 1922 ; G. Malkowsky, *ib.*, **2**. 133, 1915 ; L. Beck, *Stahl Eisen*, **14**. 285, 884, 1894 ; *Oesterr. Zeit. Berg. Hütt.*, **42**. 240, 1894 ; L. Beck, in C. Matchoss, *Beiträge zur Geschichte der Technik und Industrie*, Berlin, **2**. 83, 1910 ; V. Lohse, *ib.*, **2**. 90, 1910 ; L. Bickel, *Die Eisenhütten des Klosters Haine*, Marburg, 1889 ; *Berg. Hütt. Ztg.*, **51**. 38, 1892 ; P. Desbief, *ib.*, **18**. 167, 1859 ; J. Fernie, *ib.*, **16**. 55, 61, 1857 ; K. Bimler, *Eisen Ztg.*, **35**. 113, 1914 ; P. G. H. Boswell, *Comparison of British and American Foundry Practice*, London, 1922 ; O. Brandt, *Zur Geschichte der deutschen Eisengiessereien*, Düsseldorf, 1921 ; E. Bremer, *Foundry*, **56**. 541, 1928 ; J. E. Hurst, *ib.*, **56**. 699, 746, 759, 793, 1928 ; J. P. Frey, *ib.*, **42**. 216, 1914 ; E. C. Kreutzberg, *ib.*, **51**. 973, 1923 ; T. Makemson, *Foundry Trade Journ.*, **29**. 153, 1924 ; O. Erlinghagen, *Krupp's Monatsh.*, **6**. 85, 1925 ; C. E. Dana, *Proc. Amer. Phil. Soc.*, **50**. 147, 1911 ; J. F. Daubuisson, *Journ. Mines*, **14**. 455, 1803 ; W. Erben, *Zeit. hist. Waffenkunde*, **7**. 85, 118, 1916 ; B. Rathgen, *ib.*, **8**. 343, 1920 ; *Stahl Eisen*, **40**. 148, 1920 ; **46**. 254, 1926 ; *Das Geschütz in Mittelalter*, Berlin, 1928 ; F. A. Foster, *Amer. Machinist*, **51**. 345, 1910 ; C. A. Gerhard, *Ber. Berlin Acad.*, 60, 1781 , J. Goostray, R. F. Harrington and M. A. Hosmer, *Trans. Amer. Inst. Min. Eng.*, **71**. 404, 1925 ; *Stahl Eisen*, **45**. 1614, 1925 ; A. Guettier, *De la fonderie, telle qu'elle existe aujourd'hui en France et de ses nombreuses applications à l'industrie*, Angers, 1844 ; *De l'emploi pratique et raisonné de la fonte de fer dans les constructions*, Paris, 1861 ; J. H. von Hefner-Alteneck, *Eisenwerke oder Ornamentik der Schmiedekunst des Mittelalters und der Renaissance*, Frankfurt a. M., 1861 ; C. F. Himes, *Journ. Franklin Inst.*, **156**. 413, 1903 ; R. Jenkins, *Eng.*, **124**. 493, 1917 ; **125**. 311, 445, 486, 492, 1918 ; **126**. 52, 1918 ; O. Johannsen, *Arch. Geschichte Naturwiss.*, **3**. 365, 1912 ; **5**. 127, 1915 ; **7**. 165, 245, 313, 1916 ; **8**. 66, 1918 ; *Stahl Eisen*, **37**. 184, 1917 ; **39**. 1457, 1625, 1919 ; *Korresp. Blatt. Gesamtver. deut. Geschichte*, **63**. 260, 1915 ; *Zeit. hist. Waffenkunde*, **8**. 1, 1918 ; H. Kalakuzky, *Russ. Artillery Journ.*, **7**, 1869 ; *Monstre-Geschütze der Vorzeit*, Cassel, 1870 ; A. Kippenberger, *Cicerone*, **18**. 307, 1926 ; *Die Kunst der Ofenplatten*, Düsseldorf, 1928 ; A. Ledebur, *Dingler's Journ.*, **258**. 171, 1885 ; *Stahl Eisen*, **5**. 121, 1885 ; **9**. 219, 1889 ; **11**. 219, 1891 ; K. Luthmer, *ib.*, **47**. 1048, 1927 ; W. Mathesius, *ib.*, **47**. 888, 1927 ; K. Sipp, *ib.*, **47**. 1085, 1927 ; A. Schrödter, *ib.*, **34**. 1075, 1914 ; O. Vogel, *ib.*, **37**. 400, 521, 610, 1917 ; **38**. 165, 262, 1101, 1210, 1918 ; **39**. 1617, 1919 ; **40**. 869, 1920 ; K. Lind, *Mitt. Central-Commision Erforschung Erhaltung Kunst.*, (2), **7**. 66, 1881 ; P. Martell, *Giesserei Ztg.*, **9**. 249, 1912 ; S. Miller, *ib.*, **22**. 352, 1925 ; H. Pudor, *ib.*, **1**. 419, 452, 1904 ; M. Rotacker, *ib.*, **22**. 342, 1925 ; C. F. P. von Martius, *Kastner's Arch.*, **9**. 491, 1825 ; C. Pardun, *Deut. Bergwerks Ztg.*, **25**. 5, 1924 ; H. Schmitz, *Berliner Eisenkunstguss*, München, 1917 ; *Giesserei*, **9**. 207, 1922 ; E. Schneegans, *ib.*, **10**. 223, 1923 ; **12**. 486, 1925 ; J. Schwank, *Zeit. Ver. Hess. Geschichte*, **26**. 22, 1891 ; R. Seidel, *Die königliche Eisengiesserei zu Gleiwitz*, Berlin, 1896 ; S. G. Smith, *Foundry Trade Journ.*, **34**. 349, 375, 1926 ; W. A. Tiemann, *Abhandlung über die Förmerei und Giesserei auf Eisenhütten*, Nürnberg, 1803 ; A. Thiele, *Krupp's Monatsh.*, **1**. 185, 1920 ; W. H. Uhland, *Handbuch für den praktischen Maschinen-Constructeur*, Leipzig, **3**. 1, 1886 ; A. Hirsch, *Rev. Tech. Luxembourgeoise*, **21**. 25, 69, 1929 ; L. van Werveke, *ib.*, **21**. 49, 1929 ; A. Faber, *ib.*, **19**. 159, 1927 ; A. J. Sexton, *Proc. Glasgow Phil. Soc.*, **30**. 284, 1899 ; F. Büttgenbach, *Rev. Univ. Mines*, **36**. 241, 1897 ; L. Babu, *Ann. Mines*, (9), **15**. 357, 1899 ; M. A. Lower, *Trans. Fed. Inst. Min. Eng.*, **14**. 701, 1896 ; H. A. Dillon, *Archæologia*, **51**. 168, 1888.

⁶ C. L. Althans, *Karsten's Arch.*, **12**. 259, 1826 ; **13**. 207, 1826 ; M. Schäffer, *ib.*, **8**. 429, 1835 ; L. Eck, *ib.*, **21**. 504, 1847 ; **23**. 661, 1850 ; U. von Unger, *ib.*, **25**. 261, 1853 ; M. Brand, *ib.*, **25**. 560, 1853 ; M. Stengel, *ib.*, **13**. 232, 1826 ; M. Wachler, *ib.*, **4**. 419, 1832 ; **7**. 191, 554, 1834 ; P. Berthier, *Journ. Mines*, **27**. 196, 1810 ; W. A. Bone, *Nature*, **122**. 728, 1928 ; E. W. Hulme, *ib.*, **122**. 728, 1928 ; N. Bornonii, *Vandoperani nagæ*, Basileæ, 1533 ; E. Swedenborg, *Beskrifning öfver Masugnar och theras Bläsninger Manuscript*, 1719, *Novaskogs Arkiv.*, **10**. 201, 1903 ; D. Thélaus, *Metallurgical works on the Roasting of Ores*, Upsala, 1757 ; G. le Compasseur de Crégui-Monfort de Courtioron and E. J. Boucher, *L'art des forges et fourneaux à fer*, Paris, 1762 ; J. P. F. G. Duhamel, *Mém. Acad.*, 456, 1786 ; *Crell's Ann.*, ii, 67, 1794 ; *Ann. Mines*, (1), **2**. 129, 1817 ; J. C. Garnej, *Handeldning uti Svenska Masmästeriet*, Stockholm, 1791 ; F. A. von Marcher, *Beyträge zur Eisenhüttenkunde*, Klagenfurt, 1805 ; *Notizen und Bemerkungen über den Betrieb der Hochöfen und Renwerke zur Verschmelzung der Eisenerze*, Klagenfurt, 1811 ;

P. L. Voltz, *Ann. Mines*, (3), **4**. 77, 1833 ; P. A. Dufrénoy, *ib.*, (3), **4**. 431, 1833 ; L. Gruner, *ib.*, (7), **2**. 1, 1872 ; (7), **12**. 472, 1877 ; J. V. Herder, *Abhandlung und Beschriebung der vorzüglichtsen Apparathe der Erwärmung der Gebläseluft auf den Hüttenwerken in Deutschland, England, Frankreich, der Schweiz und Schweden*, Freyberg, 1840 ; R. Gontermann, *Entwicklung und Bedeutung der Siegerländer Spezialhochöfen*, Darmstadt, 1927 ; T. F. Merbach, *Die Anwendung der erwarmten Gebläseluft im Gebiete der Metallurgie*, Leipzig, 1840 ; E. A. Cowper, *Civil Eng. Architect's Journ.*, **23**. 277, 297, 315, 1860 ; *Journ. Iron Steel Inst.*, **24**. ii, 76, 1883 ; *Stahl Eisen*, **3**. 611, 1883 ; *Dingler's Journ.*, **158**. 104, 198, 1860 ; G. M. Hunter, *ib.*, **226**, 590, 1877 ; *Polytech. Rev.*, **99**, 1877 ; F. Lürmann, *Zeit. Ver. deut. Ing.*, **19**. 354, 1875 ; *Stahl Eisen*, **16**. 801, 891, 1896 ; J. Arduino, *Sammlung einiger mineralogisch- chymisch- metallurgisch und oryktographischer Abhandlungen*, Dresden, 193, 1778 ; L. Beck, *Die Geschichte des Eisens*, Braunschweig, 1898 ; L. Bittner, *Das Eisenwesen in Innerberg-Eisenerz*, Wien, 1901 ; G. Göth, *Vordernberg in der neuesten Zeit.*, Wien, 1839 ; O. Johannsen, *Geschichte des Eisens*, Düsseldorf, 1924 ; F. Kupelweiser, *Stahl Eisen*, **49**. 498, 1929 ; A. von Muchar, *Geschichte der Steiermark*, Gratz, 1874 ; A. Müllner, *Geschichte des Eisens in Innerösterreich von der Urzeit bu zum Anfange*, Wien, 1909 ; F. Münichdorfer, *Geschichte des Hüttenberger Erzberges*, Klagenfurt, 1870 ; *Oesterr. Berg. Hütt. Zeit.*, **55**. 53, 68, 1907 ; **56**. 94, 1908 ; **57**. 53, 61, 1909 ; **58**. 67, 79, 1910 ; **61**. 138, 343, 1913 ; *Zeit. Oesterr. Ing. Arch. Ver.*, **62**. 684, 1910 ; *Berg. Hütt. Jahrb.*, **53**. 205, 355, 1905 ; **54**. 361, 1906 ; **60**. 81, 174, 1912 ; **61**. 278, 1913 ; V. Ignaz von Pantz and A. J. Atzl, *Versuch einer Beschreibung der vorzüglichsten Berg- und Hüttenwerke des Herzogthums Steyermark*, Wien, 1814 ; I. Prandstetter, *Aufschwung und Niedergang des Vordernberger Holzkohlen-Hochofen betriebes*, Berlin, 1914 ; A. Schauenstein, *Denkbuch des österreichischen Berg- und Hüttenwesens*, Wien, 1873 ; R. Schaur, *Stahl Eisen*, **49**. 489, 1929 ; S. J. V. Day, *The Iron and Steel Industries of Scotland*, Edinburgh, 1876 ; W. Firmstone, *Oesterr. Zeit. Berg. Hütt.*, **34**. 817, 1886 ; H. Wedding, *Stahl Eisen*, **11**. 675, 1891 ; G. Rasch, *ib.*, **47**. 634, 1927 ; M. Theobald, *ib.*, **40**. 268, 1920 ; P. Capito, *ib.*, **46**. 1394, 1926 ; A. Ledebur, *ib.*, **11**. 219, 1891 ; E. Buttgenbach, *ib.*, **16**. 983, 1896 ; A. Schmitthenner, *ib.*, **33**. 444, 1913 ; F. Lange, *ib.*, **35**. 33, 71, 1915 ; O. Vogel, *ib.*, **17**. 745, 1897 ; **18**. 534, 1898 ; **33**. 25, 1913 ; **35**. 22, 1915 ; O. Simmersbach, *ib.*, **16**. 1005, 1896 ; *Technische Fortschritte im Hochofenwesen*, Kattowitz, 1906 ; G. Jones, *Journ. Iron Steel Inst.*, **78**. iii, 59, 1908 ; H. Braune, *Jernkontorets Ann.*, (2), **59**. 1, 1904 ; A. Grabe, *ib.*, (2), **77**. 5, 1922 ; O. von Friesen, *ib.*, (2), **77**. 62, 1922 ; R. C. Heaslett, *Blast Furnace*, **11**. 34, 1923 ; C. Longenecker, *Iron Trade Rev.*, **79**. 568, 721, 1926 ; H. R. Simmonds, *ib.*, **79**. 839, 1926 ; *Iron Age*, **118**. 947, 1277, 1926 ; A. H. Sexton, *Eng. Min. Journ.*, **59**. 536, 1895 ; J. M. Swank, *The History of the Manufacture of Iron in All Ages*, Philadelphia, 1902 ; J. J. Ferber, *Physikalisch-metallurgische Abhandlung*, Berlin, 1780 ; M. Robert, *Méthode pour laver et fondre les mines de fer, relativement à leurs différentes espèces*, Paris, 1757 ; J. M. Bineau, *Ann. Mines*, (3), **13**. 131, 1838 ; H. Frontault, *Essai sur la transformation de la métallurgie au bois dans l'Ariège*, Paris, 1871 ; A. H. Leobner, *Berg. Hütt. Jahrb.*, **48**. 47, 1900 ; F. B. de Félice, *Forges du art de fer*, Yverdon, 1777.

[7] J. Nicholl, *Some Account of the Worshipful Company of Ironmongers*, London, 1851 ; J. Evelyn, *Sylva, or a Discourse on Forest Trees, and the Propagation of Timber*, London, 1664 ; J. Sturdy, *Phil. Trans.*, **17**. 695, 1693 ; J. F. d'Aubuisson de Voisins, *Journ. Mines*, **14**. 455, 1803 ; H. Wedding, *Verh. Gewerbfl.*, **78**. 257, 1899 ; E. Vollhann, *Beyträge zur neueren Geschichte des Eisenhüttenwesens*, Eichstadt, 224, 1825 ; H. Illies, in C. Matschoss, *Beiträge zur Geschichte der Technik und Industrie*, Berlin, 3. 79, 1911 ; W. A. Lampadius, *Handbuch der allgemeinen Hüttenkunde*, Göttingen, 1870 ; G. Göth, *Vordernberg in der neuesten Zeit*, Wien, 1839 ; L. Bittner, *Das Eisenwesen im Innerberg-Eisenerz bis zur Gründung der Innerberger Hauptgewerkschaft*, Wien, 1901 ; S. L. Goodale and J. Speer, *Chronology of Iron and Steel*, Pittsburg, 1920 ; O. Johannsen, *Arch. Geschichte Naturwiss.*, **3**. 365, 1912 ; **5**. 127, 1915 ; **8**. 66, 1918 ; F. W. Lürmann, *Stahl Eisen*, **16**. 801, 1896 ; R. Schaur, *ib.*, **49**. 489, 1929 ; E. Mauer and W. Bischof, *ib.*, **50**. 477, 1930 ; A. Müllner, *Geschichte des Eisens in Inneröstrereich*, Wien, 1909 ; F. Münichsdorfer, *Geschichte des hüttenberger Erzberges*, Klagenfurt, 1870 ; V. I. von Pantz and A. J. Atzl, *Versuch einer Beschreibung der vorzüglichsten Berg- und Hüttenwerke des Herzogthums Steyermark*, Wien, 1814 ; I. Prandstetter, *Aufschwung und Niedergang des Vordernberger Holzkohlen-Hochofenbetriebes*, Berlin, 1914 ; C. Schinz, *Dokumente betreffend des Hohofen zur Darstellung von Roheisen*, Berlin, 1868 ; A. Schauenstein, *Denkbuch des österreichischen Berg- und Hüttenwesens*, Wien, 1873 ; J. Collier, *Mem. Manchester Lit. Phil. Soc.*, **5**. 109, 1798 ; R. Buchanan, *Ironmonger*, **121**. 11, 1907 ; J. Rovenzon (Robinson), *A Treatise of Metallica*, London, 1613 ; *Brit. Pat. No.*, May 15, 1613 ; S. Sturtevant, *Metallica*, London, 1611 ; *Brit. Pat. No.*, Feb. 29, 1611 ; W. Gomeldon, *ib.*, 26, 1623 ; E. Jorden, *ib.*, 61, 1632 ; F. de Blewston, *ib.*, 198, 1677 ; W. Astell, J. Copley and F. Crofts, *ib.*, 38, 1627 ; E. Dudley, *ib.*, 18, 1619 ; D. Dudley, G. Horsey, D. Ramsey and R. Foulke, *ib.*, 117, 1638 ; D. Dudley, *Metallum martis : or Iron made with Pit-coale, Sea-coale, and with the same Fuell to Melt and Fine Imperfect Metalls, and Refine Perfect Metalls*, London, 1665 ; *Journ. Iron Steel Inst.*, **5**. ii, 227, 1872 ; R. Plot, *The Natural History of Staffordshire*, Oxford, 1686 ; H. Powle, *Phil. Trans.*, **12**. 931, 1676 ; H. Schrivenor, *A Comprehensive History of the Iron Trade throughout the World from the Earliest Records to the Present Time*, London, 1841 ; W. J. MacAdam, *Trans. Inverness Scient. Soc.*, **3**. 256, 1887 ; J. T. Wainwright, *Journ. Iron Steel Inst.*, **35**. i, 294, 1889 ; T. Turner, *ib.*, **85**. i, 203, 1912 ; G. D. Cochrane, **97**. i, 141, 1918 ; J. H. Darby, *ib.*, **53**. i, 44, 1898 ; C. L. Bell, *ib.*, **65**. i, 188, 1904 ; D. A. Louis, *ib.*, **64**. ii, 293, 1903 ; H. Louis, *ib.*, **119**. i, 29, 1929 ; J. Kitson, *ib.*, **35**. i, 19, 1889 ; A. Greiner, *ib.*, **57**. i, 109, 1900 ; M. P. Rossigneux, *ib.*, **39**. i, 301, 1891 ; I. L. Bell,

ib., **40**. ii, 187, 1891 ; S. Weill, *Bull. Soc. Enc. Nat. Ind.*, **107**. 557, 1905 ; A. von Ihering, *Proc. Inst. Civil Eng.*, **112**. 432, 1892 ; J. Percy, *Metallurgy—Iron and Steel*, London, 387, 1864 ; D. E. Roberts, *Proc. Inst. Mech. Eng.*, 375, 1906 ; R. H. Rice, *Trans. Amer. Inst. Min. Eng.*, **50**. 90, 1914 ; D. H. Wood, *Foundry Trade Journ.*, **40**. 269, 1929 ; J. A. Leffler, *Proc. World's Eng. Congr. Tokyo*, **33**. 79, 1931 ; I. I. Granikoff, *Vestn. Metallopromychl*, **11**. 105, 1931 ; *Chim. Ind.*, **26**. 335, 1931 ; M. A. Pavloff, *Domez*, 12, 1930.

⁸ O. Simmersbach and G. Schneider, *Grundlagen der Kokschemie*, Berlin, 1930 ; O. Simmersbach, *Stahl Eisen*, **33**. 512, 1913 ; F. W. Hinrichsen, *Die Chemie der Kohle*, Leipzig, 1916 ; F. Muck, *Die Chemie der Steinkohle*, Leipzig, 1916 ; A. Korevaar, *Combustion in the Gas Producer and the Blast Furnace*, London, 1924 ; *Stahl Eisen*, **43**. 431, 948, 1565, 1923 ; **46**. 1258, 1926 ; W. Mathesius, *Die physikalischen und chemischen Grundlagen des Eisenhüttenwesens*, Leipzig, 1924 ; *Iron Trade Rev.*, **60**. 1234, 1917 ; *Gewerbfl.*, **108**. 163, 1929 ; *Stahl Eisen*, **43**. 907, 1923 ; H. Strache and R. Lant, *Kohlenchemie*, Leipzig, 1924 ; F. Häusser and R. Bestehorn, *Gesammelte Untersuchungen über die Verbrennlichkeit von Hüttenkoks in technischer Körnung*, Halle a. S., 1926 ; *Ber. Ges. Kohlentech.*, **1**. 345, 1926 ; H. le Chatelier, *Leçons sur le carbone*, Paris, 1926 ; *Le chauffage industriel*, Paris, 53, 1920 ; R. Mezger and F. Pistor, *Die Reaktionfähigkeit des Kokses*, Halle a. S., 1927 ; *Gas Wasserfach*, **69**. 1061, 1926 ; G. Agde and H. Schmitt, *Theorie der Reduktionsfähigkeit von Steinkohlenkoks auf Grund experimenteller Untersuchungen*, Halle a. S., 1928 ; *Ber. Chemikeraus Eisenhüttenleute*, 50, 1927 ; *Stahl Eisen*, **47**. 1477, 1927 ; *Zeit. angew. Chem.*, **40**. 1003, 1027, 1927 ; *Gas Wasserfach*, **70**. 1000, 1927 ; G. Agde, *Feuerungstech.*, **15**. 301, 1927 ; A. Rosli, *Studien über die Entgasung und Reaktionsfähigkeit verkokter Brennstoffe*, Zürich, 1924 ; G. A. Brender, A. Brandis and J. W. le Nobel, *Het Gas*, **47**. 37, 1927 ; I. L. Bell, *Journ. Iron Steel Inst.*, **27**. i, 57, 72, 1885 ; **40**. ii, 187, 1891 ; C. S. Gill, *ib.*, **116**. ii, 91, 1927 ; J. H. Darby, *ib.*, **53**. i, 44, 1898 ; C. L. Bell, *ib.*, **65**. i, 188, 1904 ; D. A. Louis, *ib.*, **64**. ii, 293, 1903 ; G. D. Cochrane, *ib.*, **97**. i, 141, 1918 ; L. Levêque, *Bull. Soc. Ind. Min.*, **5**. 433, 1906 ; S. Weill, *Bull. Soc. Enc. Nat. Ind.*, **107**. 557, 1905 ; C. J. Ramsburg and F. W. Speer, *Journ. Franklin Inst.*, **183**. 391, 1917 ; *Mech. Eng.*, **39**. 405, 1917 ; A. Baille-Barelle, *Génie Civil*, **76**. 435, 1920 ; G. W. Hewson, *Iron Coal Trades Rev.*, **96**. 371, 1918 ; R. Bulmer, *ib.*, **115**. 265, 1927 ; *Bull. Brit. Cast Iron Research*, 19, 1927 ; O. W. Rice, *Iron Trade Rev.*, **68**. 423, 1921 ; W. Diamond, *Foundry Trade Journ.*, **35**. 448, 1927 ; A. C. Fieldner and J. D. Davis, *Fuels Furnaces*, **5**. 1181, 1927 ; J. D. Davis, *Iron Coal Trades Rev.*, **117**. 262, 1928 ; J. D. Davis and D. A. Reynolds, *Journ. Ind. Eng. Chem.*, **20**. 617, 1928 ; H. Krueger, *Giesserei Ztg.*, **24**. 487, 1927 ; J. Gwosdz, *Ueber die von Wasserdampf an glühender Kohle*, Berlin, 1918 ; *Verh. Gewerbfl.*, **97**. 33, 55, 1918 ; *Stahl Eisen*, **38**. 661, 1918 ; *Giesserei Ztg.*, **26**. 578, 1929 ; O. Huppert, *ib.*, **27**. 35, 1930 ; *Zeit. Ver. deut. Ing.*, **13**. 1293, 1929 ; M. W. Travers, *Journ. Soc. Chem. Ind.*, **46**. 128, T, 1927 ; Y. Oshima and Y. Fukuda, *Journ. Soc. Chem. Ind. Japan*, **31**. 288, 1928 ; A. E. Taylor, *Gas World*, **88**. 18, 1928 ; H. Hock and M. Paschke, *Arch. Eisenhüttenwesen*, **3**. 99, 1930 ; B. Hofmeister, *ib.*, **3**. 559, 1930 ; H. Jungbluth and K. Klapp, *Giesserei*, **16**. 761, 787, 1929 ; *Krupp's Monatsh.*, **10**. 105, 1929 ; B. Osann, *Giesserei*, **16**. 421, 1929 ; *Stahl Eisen*, **42**. 301, 1922 ; J. E. Lose, *Yearbook Amer. Iron Steel Inst.*, 79, 1927 ; D. Sillars, *Journ. West. Scotland Iron Steel Inst.*, **32**. 52, 1925 ; J. H. Jones, J. G. King and F. S. Sinnatt, *The Reactivity of Coke*, London, 18, 1927 ; *Journ. Iron Steel Inst.*, **117**. i, 145, 1928 ; P. Bardenheuer and G. Thanheiser, *Mitt. Inst. Eisenforschung*, **5**. 13, 1924 ; O. Ruff, *Zeit. anorg. Chem.*, **38**. 793, 1930 ; W. Durrer, *Stahl Eisen*, **37**. 1052, 1917 ; F. Wüst, *ib.*, **30**. 1715, 1910 ; **41**. 1258, 1921 ; W. van Vloten, *ib.*, **13**. 26, 1893 ; C. Flössel, *ib.*, **42**. 382, 1922 ; A. Wagner, *Ber. Kokereiaus. Eisenhüttenleute*, 22, 1925 ; *Stahl Eisen*, **41**. 1577, 1921 ; **44**. 104, 1924 ; *Zeit. Ver. deut. Ing.*, **69**. 531, 1925 ; H. Koppers, *ib.*, **34**. 585, 1914 ; **41**. 1173, 1254, 1921 ; **42**. 297, 382, 569, 1288, 1922 ; **43**. 948, 1557, 1923 ; *Giesserei*, **9**. 411, 423, 1922 ; *Kopper's Mitt.*, **4**. 11, 175, 1922 ; H. H. Hollings, *Journ. Iron Steel Inst.*, **113**. i, 285, 1926 ; *Stahl Eisen*, **42**. 1287, 1922 ; A. Osten, *ib.*, **42**. 1287, 1922 ; C. Zix, *ib.*, **42**. 588, 1284, 1922 ; J. Becker, *ib.*, **43**. 479, 1923 ; H. Bähr, *Ber. Hochofenaus. Eisenhüttenleute*, 63, 1923 ; *Stahl Eisen*, **44**. 1, 39, 42, 694, 1924 ; O. Wehrheim, *ib.*, **44**. 1005, 1074, 1105, 1138, 1924 ; C. Bulle, *ib.*, **45**. 1058, 1925 ; P. Oberhoffer and E. Piwowarsky, *ib.*, **46**. 1311, 1926 ; L. Nettenbusch, *ib.*, **47**. 669, 1927 ; W. A. Roth, *ib.*, **48**. 1442, 1928 ; H. A. Brassert, *Blast Furnace Steel Plant*, **4**. 834, 1915 ; *Stahl Eisen*, **36**. 2, 30, 61, 119, 394, 1916 ; **43**. 44, 69, 1923 ; W. Thörner, *ib.*, **4**. 513, 594, 1884 ; 6. 71, 1886 ; F. Häusser, *ib.*, **43**. 903, 1566, 1923 ; **45**. 878, 1925 ; *Gluckauf*, **59**. 699, 1923 ; *Ber. Kokereiaus. Eisenhüttenleute*, 22, 1925 ; *Ber. Ges. Kohlentech.*, **1**. 265, 1926 ; H. Bansen, *Stahl Eisen*, **47**. 1483, 1927 ; F. Lange, *ib.*, **38**. 307, 1928 ; G. Holthaus, *ib.*, **45**. 1131, 1925 ; **46**. 33, 1926 ; M. Schlipköter, *ib.*, **42**. 300, 1922 ; F. Heyd, *ib.*, **42**. 298, 1922 ; M. Tigerschiöld, *ib.*, **42**. 297, 1922 ; A. W. Belaen, *Tech. Paper Bur. Mines*, 50, 1913 ; F. P. Dewey, *Trans. Amer. Inst. Min. Eng.*, **12**. 111, 1884 ; J. Fulton, *ib.*, **12**. 212, 1884 ; A. R. Powell and S. W. Parr, *ib.*, **63**. 674, 1919 ; G. S. J. Perrott and S. P. Kinney, *ib.*, **69**. 543, 1923 ; G. S. J. Perrott and R. A. Sherman, *Proc. Eng. Soc. West Pennsylvania*, **39**. 351, 1923 ; *Iron Age*, **115**. 1043, 1925 ; R. A. Sherman and S. P. Kinney, *ib.*, **111**. 1839, 1923 ; R. A. Sherman and J. Blizard, *Trans. Amer. Inst. Min. Eng.*, **69**. 526, 1923 ; P. H. Royster and T. L. Joseph, *ib.*, **70**. 224, 1924 ; T. L. Joseph, P. H. Royster and S. P. Kinney, *Proc. Eng. Soc. West Pennsylvania*, **41**. 428, 1926 ; S. P. Kinney, *Blast Furnace Steel Plant*, **13**. 243, 1925 ; T. L. Joseph, *Rep. Investigations Bur. Mines*, 2604, 1924 ; H. P. Howland, *Trans. Amer. Inst. Min. Eng.*, **56**. 339, 1917 ; W. H. Blauvelt, *ib.*, **56**. 371, 1917 ; R. H. Sweetser, *Iron Age*, **117**. 477, 1926 ; W. A. Haven, *ib.*, **110**. 695, 1922 ; *Stahl Eisen*, **42**. 1787, 1922 ; H. H. Berger, *ib.*, **43**. 857, 1923 ; *Krupp's Monatsh.*, **4**. 57, 1923 ; E. R. Sutcliffe and E. C. Evans,

Engg., **115**. 603, 638, 664, 1923 ; *Journ. Iron Steel Inst.*, **107**. i, 27, 79, 1923 : *Blast Furnace Steel Plant*, **10**. 427, 1922 ; F. W. Sperr and D. L. Jacobson, *ib.*, **11**. 314, 378, 426, 1923 ; A. Thau, *Gluckauf*, **58**. 1010, 1922 ; *Stahl Eisen*, **43**. 1127, 1136, 1923 ; H. Bunte and A. Kölmel, *Gas Wasserfach*, **65**. 592, 1922 ; H. Bunte and W. Fitz, *ib.*, **67**. 241, 1924 ; H. Bunte, *ib.*, **69**. 192, 217, 1926 ; E. Diepschlag, *Stahl Eisen*, **44**. 496, 1924 ; E. Diepschlag and F. Habert, *Ber. Hochofenaus. Eisenhüttenleute*, 59, 1923 ; F. Heyd, F. Schreiber, G. Agde and F. Recke, *Brenn-stoff Chem.*, **4**. 339, 1923 ; F. Schreiber, *ib.*, **4**. 273, 1923 ; F. Fischer, P. K. Breuer and H. Broche, *ib.*, **4**. 33, 1923 ; H. Broche, *ib.*, **4**. 343, 1923 ; D. J. W. Kreulen, *ib.*, **10**. 128, 148, 168, 288, 1929 ; W. K. Lewis, *Journ. Ind. Eng. Chem.*, **15**. 502, 1923 ; D. Perietzeano, *Rev. Mét.*, **21**. 624, 1924 ; J. P. Arend and J. Wagner, *ib.*, **21**. 585, 1924 ; R. Wigginton, *Fuel Science Pract.*, **4**. 3, 47, 93, 139, 183, 229, 275, 325, 371, 417, 461, 503, 1925 ; W. T. K. Braunholtz, G. M. Nave and H. V. A. Briscoe, *ib.*, **8**. 414, 1928 ; S. W. Parr and W. D. Staley, *ib.*, **7**. 540, 1928 ; R. A. Dengg, *ib.*, **7**. 152, 1928 ; I. Zerzog, *Giesserei Ztg.*, **22**. 477, 528, 535, 1925 ; J. Follmann, *Feuerungstech.*, **15**. 205, 1927 ; F. G. Hoffmann, *ib.*, **17**. 225, 1929 ; *Brennstoff Chem.*, **10**. 287, 1929 ; H. S. Taylor, *Proc. Roy. Soc.*, **108**. A, 105, 1925 ; G. M. Schwab and E. Pietsch, *Zeit. Elektrochem.*, **35**. 135, 573, 1929 ; *Zeit. phys. Chem.*, **1**. B, 385, 1928 ; P. Pietsch, A. Kotowsky and G. Berend, *ib.*, **5**. B, 1, 1929 ; T. F. E. Rhead and R. V. Wheeler, *Journ. Chem. Soc.*, **99**. 1140, 1911.

⁹ T. B. Mackenzie, *Life of J. B. Neilson, F.R.S., Inventor of the Hot Blast*, Glasgow, 1928 ; J. B. Neilson, *Brit. Pat. No.* 5701, 1828 ; *Report of the Trial before the Lord President of the Court of Session and a Special Jury, of the Issues in the Conjoined Actions of Suspension and Interdict, and Count, Reckoning, Payment, and Damages, at the instance of James Beaumont Neilson, of Glasgow, Engineer, and others, against William Baird and Company, of the Garthsherry Iron-Works, for Infringement of the Hot-blast Patent*, Edinburgh, 1843 ; *Report of Trial before Baron Parke and Special Jury for Infringement of the Hot Blast Patent by Harford*, Edinburgh, 1841 ; *Report of Trial before Lord Justice Clark Hope for Infringement of Hot Blast Patent by Hausehill Coal and Iron Co.*, Edinburgh, 1842 ; H. Marten, *Proc. Inst. Mech. Eng.*, 62, 1859 ; J. Percy, *Metallurgy —Iron and Steel*, London, 389, 394, 1864 ; T. Clark, *On the Application of the Hot Blast in the Manufacture of Cast-Iron*, Edinburgh, 1835 ; *Trans. Roy. Soc. Edin.*, **13**. 373, 1836 ; *Phil. Mag.*, (3), **10**. 329, 1837 ; F. T. Merbach, *Die Anwendung der erwärmten Gebläseluft im Gebiete der Metallurgie*, Leipzig, 1840 ; W. Truran, *The Iron Manufacture of Great Britain, Theoretically and Practically Considered*, London, 1862 ; T. W. Robinson, *Trans. Amer. Inst. Min. Eng.*, **17**. 282, 1889 ; **36**. 759, 1906 ; R. W. Raymond, *ib.*, **36**. 763, 1906 ; **37**. 228, 1907 ; E. S. Cook, *ib.*, **39**. 705, 1909 ; *Iron Age*, **81**. 53, 1908 ; D. Mushet, *Experiments upon Hot Blast Cast and Malleable Iron at the Milton Iron Works, Yorkshire*, London, 1843 ; *Papers on Iron and Steel*, London, 348, 1840 ; R. Plot, *The Natural History of Staffordshire*, Oxford, 128, 1686 ; C. Cochrane, *Proc. Inst. Mech. Eng.*, 124, 1883 ; I. L. Bell, *Chemical Phenomena of Iron Smelting*, Newcastle-on-Tyne, 1871 ; *Principles of the Manufacture of Iron and Steel*, London, 1884 ; *Journ. Iron Steel Inst.*, **44**. ii, 242, 1893 ; F. W. Lürmann, *ib.*, **38**. ii, 754, 1890 ; *Ber. Hochofen Komm. Ver. deut. Eisenhüttenleute*, 18, 1911 ; *Stahl Eisen*, **10**. 766, 1890 ; E. Baur, *ib.*, **24**. 562, 1904 ; O. Simmers-bach, *ib.*, **29**. 283, 1909 ; A. C. W. F. von Faber du Faur, *Ann. Mines*, (4), **1**. 433, 1842 ; J. P. Budd, *Brit. Pat. Nos.* 9495, 10475, 11078, 1845 ; E. A. Cowper, *Proc. Inst. Mech. Eng.*, 54, 1860 ; *Brit. Pat. No.* 1404, 1857 ; *Journ. Soc. Chem. Ind.*, **12**. 311, 1893 ; *Journ. Iron Steel Inst.*, **24**. ii, 576, 1883 ; *Proc. South Staffs Iron Steel Inst.*, **1**. 1, 1883 ; W. J. Hudson, *ib.*, **7**. 108, 1891 ; C. A. Meissner, *Iron Age*, **77**. 771, 872, 1906 ; *Trans. Amer. Inst. Min. Eng.*, **37**. 201, 1906 ; E. de M. Campbell, *ib.*, **36**. 765, 1906 ; N. M. Langdon, *ib.*, **40**. 614, 1909 ; J. W. Richards, *ib.*, **36**. 745, 1905 ; C. B. Dudley, *ib.*, **36**. 792, 1905 ; W. Mathesius, *Stahl Eisen*, **25**. 266, 1905 ; **36**. 695, 749, 1916 ; *Trans. Amer. Inst. Min. Eng.*, **51**. 794, 1915 ; S. G. Valentine, *ib.*, **50**. 90, 1914 ; B. Osann, *Iron Age*, **78**. 798, 1906 ; *Stahl Eisen*, **25**. 73, 214, 1905 ; **26**. 784, 844, 1381, 1906 ; **29**. 1781, 1909 ; C. A. Edwards, *Iron Coal Trades Rev.*, **86**. 92, 1913 ; *Proc. Cleveland Inst. Eng.*, 83, 1912 ; W. H. Fryer, *ib.*, 16, 69, 1890 ; *Journ. Iron Steel Inst.*, **39**. i, 360, 1891 ; J. Dawson, *ib.*, **74**. ii, 223, 238, 1907 ; J. Gayley, *Trans. Amer. Inst. Min. Eng.*, **35**. 746, 1925 ; *Proc. Eng. Soc. West. Pennsylvania*, **28**. 277, 1912 ; *Stahl Eisen*, **24**. 1289, 1904 ; **25**. 645, 1905 ; *Iron Age*, **87**. 308, 1911 ; **89**. 52, 1912 ; *Chem. Met. Engg.*, **11**. 71, 1913 ; *Journ. Iron Steel Inst.*, **66**. ii, 274, 1904 ; **67**. i, 256, 1905 ; A. K. Reese, *ib.*, **106**. ii, 9, 1922 ; E. H. Lewis, *ib.*, **116**. ii, 43, 1927 ; **119**. i, 29, 1929 ; *Iron Coal Trades Rev.*, **80**. 4, 1910 ; F. A. Daubiné and E. V. Roy, *Bull. Soc. Ind. Min.*, **11**. 397, 479, 1909 ; *Journ. Iron Steel Inst.*, **83**. i, 28, 1911 ; M. Drees, *Stahl Eisen*, **25**. 158, 410, 1905 ; **29**. 1430, 1602, 1909 ; A. Wagner, *ib.*, **40**. 1397, 1920 ; **50**. 122, 1930 ; C. Schwarz, *ib.*, **42**. 1385, 1424, 1456, 1519, 1922 ; H. Schmalenbach, *ib.*, **34**. 305, 1914 ; R. Schenck, *ib.*, **44**. 521, 1924 ; W. Schmidhammer, *ib.*, **24**. 1372, 1904 ; L. Grabau, *ib.*, **25**. 162, 213, 1905 ; C. von Linde, *ib.*, **25**. 3, 7, 1905 ; A. Lindner, *ib.*, **25**. 215, 1905 ; C. Zix, *ib.*, **25**. 154, 1905 ; **45**. 434, 1925 ; H. Bonte, *ib.*, **26**. 1381, 1906 ; J. Vajk, *ib.*, **27**. 346, 1907 ; C. Aldendorff, *ib.*, **28**. 474, 1908 ; F. Wüst, *ib.*, **30**. 1715, 1910 ; H. Blome, *ib.*, **35**. 1028, 1915 ; E. Jantzen, *ib.*, **36**. 825, 1916 ; E. Heyd, *ib.*, **42**. 298, 1922 ; H. Dressler, *ib.*, **45**. 180, 1925 ; P. Reichardt, *ib.*, **47**. 1448, 1927 ; G. B. Waterhouse, *Met. Mag.*, **37**. 186, 1910 ; J. E. Johnson, *Mech. Eng.*, **36**. 188, 1915 ; *Journ. Iron Steel Inst.*, **71**. iii, 404, 429, 1906 ; *Trans. Amer. Inst. Min. Eng.*, **38**. 901, 1912 ; *Met. Chem. Engg.*, **13**. 429, 1915 ; B. F. Burman, *ib.*, **13**. 624, 1915 ; C. D. Abell, *Foundry Trade Journ.*, **43**. 247, 1930 ; M. Derclaye, *Rev. Univ. Mines*, (6) **15**. 1, 1922 ; *Rev. Mét.*, **20**. 830, 1923 ; M. Preusler, *Ital. Eisere*, 827, 1921 ; R. A. Jaques, *Met. Ital.*, **19**. 446, 1927 ; J. Seigle, *Rev. Mét.*, **20**. 481, 1923 ; **21**. 260, 1924 ; E. C. Heurteau, *ib.*, **1**. 651, 1904 ; H. le Chatelier, *ib.*, **1**. 633, 1904 ; C. J. B. Karsten, *Mitt. Ges. Berlin*, **3**. 29, 1838 ; *Karsten's Arch.*, **12**. 520, 1839 ;

E. Dewaey, *Calcul du lit de fusion des hauts-fourneaux*, Paris, 1927 ; C. Frankenstein, *Di[e] Erzeugung von Eisen und Stahl*, Berlin, 1927 ; W. Lennings, *Gestell- und Rastuntersuchung eine[s] Hochofens unter besonderer Berücksichtigung der Verbrennungsverhältnisse vor den Blasformen*, Düsseldorf, 1928 ; E. Herzog, *Stahl Eisen*, **37**. 102, 129, 1917 ; *Die Arbeiten und Erfindungen Faber du Faurs auf dem Gebiete der Winderhitzung und der Gasfeuerung*, Halie a. S. 1914 ; F. W. Davis, *Rep. Investigations Bur. Mines*, 2502, 1923 ; *Chem. Met. Engg.*, **29**. 264, 272, 276, 1923 ; *Iron Steel Eng.*, **1**. 339, 1924 ; *Iron Trade Rev.*, **73**. 1619, 1923 ; A. E. Maccoun, *ib.*, **56**. 1167, 1255, 1915 ; **57**. 28, 1915 ; J. B. Miles, *Iron Age*, **89**. 1022, 1912 ; *Iron Coal Trades Rev.*, **84**. 635, 1912 ; D. E. Roberts, *Proc. Inst. Mech. Eng.*, 375, 1909 ; F. Krull, *Zeit. Ver. deut. Ing.*, **70**. 907, 1926 ; A. von Ihering, *Proc. Inst. Civil Eng.*, **112**. 432, 1892 ; J. Kitson, *Journ. Iron Steel Inst.*, **35**. i, 19, 1889 ; A. Greiner, *ib.*, **57**. i, 109, 1900 ; R. H. Rice, *Trans. Amer. Inst. Min. Eng.*, **50**. 90, 1914 ; J. von Ehrenwerth, *ib.*, **87**. i, 124, 1913 ; E. Walsh, *ib.*, **31**. i, 392, 1887 ; T. Whitwell, *ib.*, **1**. 206, 1869 ; **3**. ii, 217, 1871 ; T. Massicks, *ib.*, **22**. ii, 602, 1882 ; W. Crooke, *ib.*, **38**. ii, 340, 1890 ; B. J. Hall, *ib.*, **49**. i, 20, 1896 ; E. Disdier, *ib.*, **55**. i, 130, 1899 ; L. F. Gjers and J. H. Harrison, *ib.*, **57**. i, 154, 1900 ; **62**. ii, 282, 1902 ; A. Spannagel, *ib.*, **90**. ii, 232, 1914 ; G. Trasenster, *ib.*, **88**. ii, 226, 1913 ; R. S. Moore, *ib.*, **80**. ii, 150, 1909 ; W. A. Bone and R. V. Wheeler, *ib.*, **73**. i, 126, 1907 ; G. Jones, *ib.*, **80**. ii, 144, 1909 ; A. J. Boynton, *Year-book Amer. Iron Steel Inst.*, 358, 1916 ; M. A. Pavloff, *Blast-Furnaces and Hot Blast Stoves*, St. Petersburg, 1910 ; W. A. Haven, *Blast Furnace Steel Plant*, **18**. 85, 1930 ; P. Rheinländer, *Stahl Eisen*, **50**. 205, 1930 ; *Arch. Eisenhüttenwesen*, **3**. 487, 1930 ; J. Stöcker, *Stahl Eisen*, **50**. 249, 1930 ; E. Wengel, *ib.*, **49**. 126, 1929 ; J. E. Fletcher, *Iron Steel Ind. British Foundryman*, **3**. 101, 133, 1930 ; P. A. Dufrénoy, *On the Use of Hot Air in the Iron Works of England and Scotland*, London, 1836 ; C. F. A. Hartmann, *Ueber den Betrieb der Hohöfen und Cupolöfen, mit erhitzter gebläseluft*, Cuedlinburg, 1834 ; F. Cabrol, *French Pat. No.* 10191, 1835 ; *Notice sur l'application de l'appareil à gaz carbonés à l'un des hauts-fourneaux des usines de la Compagnie de l'Aveyron*, Paris, 1837 ; C. Schinz, *Researches on the Action of the Blast Furnace*, London, 1870 ; B. Valérius, *Handbuch der Roheisenfabrikation in Belgien*, Freiberg, 1851 ; B. Thompson, *Brit. Pat. No.* 12722, 1849 ; R. Akerman, *Studien über die Wärmeverhaltnisse des Eisenhohofenprozesses mit besonders Berücksicht auf den hierbei geübten Einfluss des erhitzten Windes*, Leipzig, 1872 ; F. Clerf, *Journ. West Scotland Iron Steel Inst.*, **37**. 51, 1930 ; J. B. Fortune, *Fuel Economist*, **4**. 563, 1929 ; E. J. Bailey, *Fuel Economy Rev.*, **8**. 35, 1929 ; T. Geilenkischen, *Verwendungen von Kalt erblasenem Roheisen zu der Flusseisendarstellung*, Hörde, 1904 ; S. D. Mills, *Journ. U.S. Assoc. Charcoal Iron Workers*, **8**. 306, 1889 ; A. Gouvy, *Mem. Soc. Ing. Civils*, 453, 1905 ; A. Pourcel, *Génie Civil*, **47**. 234, 1905 ; E. Lemaire, *ib.*, **47**. 214, 1905 ; A. Lodin, *Bull. Comité Forges France*, 2528, 1905 ; L. Levêque, *Rev. Mét.*, **2**. 471, 1905 ; G. Ekman, *Tek. Tids.*, **35**. 251, 1905 ; A. Steinbart, *Iron Age*, **77**. 1032, 1905 ; J. W. Richards, *Electrochem. Met. Ind.*, **4**. 129, 383, 1905 ; O. Monnett, *Power*, **30**. 382, 1908 ; W. McConnachie, *Iron Steel Ind.*, **4**. 223, 1931 ; *Blast Furnace Steel Plant*, **18**. 1827, 1930 ; A. Brunighaus, *Stahl Eisen*, **45**. 737, 1925.

[10] R. Plot, *The Natural History of Staffordshire*, Oxford, 128, 1686 ; J. Percy, *Metallurgy— Iron and Steel*, London, 428, 1864 ; H. Pilkington, *Proc. South Staffs Iron Steel Inst.*, 2. 1, 1891 ; T. W. Plum, *Journ. Iron Steel Inst.*, **13**. i, 299, 1878 ; H. Wedding, *ib.*, **38**. ii, 515, 1890 ; A. K. Rees, *ib.*, **97**. i, 151, 1918 ; J. S. Hollings, *ib.*, **98**. ii, 217, 1918 ; J. E. Stead, *ib.*, **97**. i, 157, 1918 ; F. H. Lloyd, *ib.*, **8**. 241, 1875 ; *Proc. Inst. Mech. Eng.*, 350, 1876 ; F. L. Grammer, *Trans. Amer. Inst. Min. Eng.*, **34**. 608, 1903.

[11] S. Rinman, *Geschichte des Eisens mit Anwendung für Künstler und Handwerker*, Liegnitz, 1814–19 ; C. J. B. Karsten, *Handbuch der Eisenhüttenkunde*, Halle a. S., 1816 ; B. Kerl, *Handbuch der metallurgischen Hüttenkunde*, Leipzig, 1864 ; *Grundriss der Eisenhüttenkunde*, Leipzig, 1875 ; I. L. Bell, *Chemical Phenomena of Iron Smelting*, London, 1872 ; *Principles of the Manufacture of Iron and Steel*, London, 1884 ; *Mineral Ind.*, **4**. 415, 1896 ; *Journ. Iron Steel Inst.*, **1**. 37, 1869 ; **13**. i, 17, 1878 ; **21**. ii, 534, 1882 ; **23**. i, 119, 1883 ; **32**. ii, 74, 1887 ; **38**. ii, 406, 1890 ; **44**. ii, 219, 1893 ; P. Oberhoffer, *Das technische Eisen*, Berlin, 1925 ; B. Tieman, *Iron and Steel*, New York, 1919 ; H. M. Boylston, *An Introduction to the Metallurgy of Iron and Steel*, London, 1928 ; *Fuels Furnaces*, **4**. 695, 1926 ; W. Mathesius, in A. Binz, *Chemische Technologie in Einzeldarstellungen*, Leipzig, 1924 ; W. A. Lampadius, B. F. J. von Hermann and H. K. Schindler, *Drey Abhandlungen über Roh- und Frischeisen*, Leipzig, 1799 ; J. C. Garnej, *Abhandlung vo n Bau und Betrieb der Hohöfen*, Freyberg, 1800 ; F. A. A. Eversmann, *Uebersicht der Eisen- und Stahlerzeugung*, Dortmund, 1804 ; A. Wagner and G. Bulle, *Stahl Eisen*, **49**. 1860, 1929 ; *Arch. Eisenhüttenwesen*, **3**. 391, 1929 ; B. Osann, *ib.*, **2**. 137, 1928 ; *Lehrbuch der Eisenhüttenkunde*, Leipzig, 1923–6 ; *Stahl Eisen*, **24**. 437, 501, 1904 ; **25**. 523, 1169, 1231, 1300, 1905 ; **26**. 336, 441, 1906 ; **48**. 1402, 1928 ; V. G. Kotelnikoff, *Journ. Russ. Met. Soc.*, **5**. 5, 1929 ; N. Noveseloff, *ib.*, 341, 1929 ; S. Stein, *Ber. Niederrh. Ges. Nat. Bonn*, 66, 1894 ; A. G. McKee and W. A. Haven, *Trans. Amer. Soc. Mech. Eng.*, **52**. 13, 1930 ; N. B. Wittmann, *Trans. Amer. Inst. Min. Eng.*, **18**. 427, 1890 ; B. F. Fackenthal, *ib.*, **18**. 379, 1890 ; E. Dowd, *ib.*, **20**. 270, 1891 ; F. W. Gordon, *ib.*, **21**. 349, 1892 ; *Journ. Iron Steel Inst.*, **43**. ii, 422, 1892 ; E. S. Cook, *U.S. Assoc. Charcoal Iron Workers*, **8**. 303, 1889 ; *Iron Age*, **94**. 202, 1914 ; J. C. Ford, *U.S. Assoc. Charcoal Iron Workers*, **8**. 272, 1889 ; J. Gayler, *Trans. Amer. Inst. Min. Eng.*, **21**. 253, 1892 ; **24**. 779, 1894 ; *Journ. Iron Steel Inst.*, **37**. ii, 18, 1890 ; *Le dévelopment des hauts-fourneaux Américains*, Liége, 1891 ; *Iron Age*, **45**. 253, 1890 ; J. L. White, *ib.*, **46**. 406, 445, 1890 ; R. Hunt, *ib.*, **46**. 630, 1890 ; *Cassier's Mag.*, **21**. 3, 1902 ; J. Wister, *Iron Age*, **51**. 246, 1893 ; F. F. Amsden, *ib.*, **67**. 9, 1891 ; E. C. Pechin, *ib.*, **48**. 494, 1892 ; P. Gredt, *Stahl Eisen*, **10**. 598, 1890 ; P. Zetzsche, *ib.*, **10**. 853,

1890; H. H. Weinlig, *ib.*, **11**. 619, 1891; F. Wüst, *ib.*, **48**. 1273, 1928; W. Hawdon, *Colliery Guardian*, **61**. 363, 1891; *Journ. Iron Steel Inst.*, **23**. i, 101, 1883; **45**. i, 78, 1894; E. F. Dürre, *Chem. Ztg.*, **22**. 309, 1898; *Oesterr. Zeit. Berg. Hütt.*, **46**. 672, 1898; *Zeit. Ver. deut. Ing.*, **38**. 258, 1893; *Hochofen Betriebe am Ende des XII Jahrhunderts*, Berlin, 1901; F. W. Lürmann, *Stahl Eisen*, **7**. 163, 480, 569, 1887; **12**. 221, 336, 1892; **17**. 168, 1060, 1891; **26**. 1363, 1906; *Iron Coal Trades Rev.*, **75**. 734, 1907; F. C. G. Müller, *Stahl Eisen*, **12**. 969, 1892; H. van Vloten, *ib.*, **12**. 114, 1892; **13**. 26, 1893; **14**. 834, 1894; J. T. Erpf, *ib.*, **12**. 336, 1892; C. Blauer, *ib.*, **15**. 704, 1895; W. Colquhoun, *Proc. South Wales Inst. Eng.*, **17**. 247, 1892; A. Wingham, *Journ. Iron Steel Inst.*, **42**. i, 233, 1892; E. de Billy, *Ann. Mines*, (9), **2**. 67, 1892; G. Bresson, *ib.*, (9), **2**. 5, 1892; H. Webb, *Trans. Manchester Assoc. Eng.*, **37**. 66, 1892; C. C. Furnas and T. L. Joseph, *Tech. Publ. Amer. Inst. Min. Eng.*, 249, 1929; *Tech. Paper Bur. Mines*, 476, 1930; V. Deshayes, *Génie Civil*, **21**. 147, 1892; R. G. Leckie, *Canada Min. Journ.*, **11**. 155, 1892; B. Viswanath, *Mining Met.*, **11**. 332, 1930; J. Hörhager, *Berg. Hütt. Jahrb.*, **41**. 1, 1893; C. af Geijerstam, *Jernkontorets Ann.*, **48**. 136, 1893; J. Logerwall, *ib.*, **49**. 259, 1895; G. Unden, *ib.*, **49**. 114, 1895; C. Sjögren, *ib.*, **49**. 87, 1895; E. Sjostedt, *Trans. Mining Soc. Nova Scotia*, **1**. 8, 1893; W. Stein, *ib.*, **2**. 75, 1894; R. E. Chambers, *ib.*, **3**. 68, 1895; P. H. Griffin, *Trans. Amer. Inst. Min. Eng.*, **21**. 974, 1892; E. C. Potter, *ib.*, **23**. 370, 1893; *Journ. Iron Steel Inst.*, **31**. i, 163, 1887; **38**. ii, 55, 1890; J. Head, *Trans. Amer. Inst. Mech. Eng.*, 224, 1893; A. P. Head, *Journ. Soc. Arts*, **51**. 81, 1903; A. J. Rossi, *Journ. Iron Steel Inst.*, **42**. i, 409, 1892; W. J. Foster, *ib.*, **65**. i, 311, 1904; S. P. Bjerregaard, *Iron Age*, **52**. 609, 1893; J. W. Thomas, *ib.*, **55**. 387, 1895; A. Sahlin, *ib.*, **65**. 14, 1900; *Iron Coal Trades Rev.*, **60**. 1229, 1900; **64**. 1381, 1901; J. Birkinbine, *Engg. Mag.*, **9**. 483, 1895; *Annual Report of the Bureau of Industrial Statistics*, Pennsylvania, 1844; A. H. Sexton, *Eng. Min. Journ.*, **59**. 536, 1895; *Eng. Rev.*, **10**. 7, 1904; T. Jung, *Zeit. Ver. deut. Ing.*, **39**. 679, 1895; F. Clements, *Blast Furnace Practice*, London, 1929; *Journ. Iron Steel Inst.*, **101**. i, 125, 1920; M. A. Pavloff, *Atlas of Designs concerning Blast Furnace Practice*, Ekaterinoslav, 1902; *Calcul du lit de fusion des hauts-fourneaux*, Paris, 1924; *The Determination of the Dimensions of Blast Furnaces and Open-Hearth Furnaces*, Leningrad, 1925; *Blast Furnaces and Hot Blast Stoves*, St. Petersburg, 1910; *Iron Age*, **84**. 618, 1909; *Eng.*, **107**. 493, 1909; **109**. 65, 1910; *Abmessungen von Hoch und Martenöfen*, Leipzig, 1928; W. McConnachie, *Blast Furnace Steel Plant*, **18**. 1827, 1930; *Iron Steel Ind.*, **4**. 223, 1931; B. Igevsky, *Blast Furnace Practice*, Karkoff, 1904; *Rev. Mét.*, **2**. 842, 1905; H. H. Campbell, *The Manufacture and Properties of Iron and Steel*, New York, 1903; H. M. Howe, *Eng. Min. Journ.*, **86**. 507, 1908; *Iron, Steel, and Other Alloys*, Boston, Mass., 1903; J. J. Morgan, *Blast Furnace Practice*, London, 1909; R. Forsythe, *The Blast Furnace and the Manufacture of Pig Iron*, New York, 1908; T. Turner, *Journ. West Scotland Iron Steel Inst.*, **10**. 40, 1903; *Proc. Staffs Iron Steel Inst.*, **18**. 15, 1903; *Metallurgy of Iron*, London, 1915; J. E. Johnson, *Iron Age*, **83**. 468, 1908; *Trans. Amer. Inst. Min. Eng.*, **36**. 434, 1905; *Blast Furnace Construction in America*, New York, 1917; *The Principles, Operation, and Products of the Blast Furnace*, New York, 1918; *Chem. Met. Engg.*, **12**. 451, 497, 1914; *Journ. Iron Steel Inst.*, **71**. iii, 404, 1906; W. W. Hollings, *ib.*, **102**. ii, 91, 1920; R. Hawson, *ib.*, **24**. ii, 585, 1883; B. Samuelson, *ib.*, **31**. i, 91, 1887; W. Brügmann, *ib.*, **62**. ii, 10, 1902; H. C. Jenkins, *ib.*, **39**. i, 151, 1891; *Iron Trade Rev.*, **96**. 354, 1918; *Journ. Iron Steel Inst.*, **61**. i, 296, 1902; **65**. i, 311, 1904; G. Jones, *ib.*, **78**. iii, 59, 1908; A. Baar, *ib.*, **88**. ii, 273, 1913; N. Kapp, *ib.*, **90**. ii, 104, 1914; F. Bainbridge, *ib.*, **121**. i, 97, 1930; J. Gjers, *ib.*, **2**. i, 202, 1871; T. Whitwell, *ib.*, **13**. i, 197, 1878; P. von Tunner, *ib.*, **22**. ii, 561, 1882; C. H. Bagley, *Proc. Cleveland Inst. Eng.*, 10, 1890; E. J. W. Richards and T. Lewis, *ib.*, 151, 1909; R. Sharp, *ib.*, 128, 1914; H. G. Scott, *ib.*, 120, 1918; S. S. Hartranet, *Trans. Amer. Inst. Min. Eng.*, **30**. 573, 1900; F. L. Grammer, *Journ. Iron Steel Inst.*, **66**. ii, 404, 1904; *Trans. Amer. Inst. Min. Eng.*, **34**. 88, 608, 1903; **35**. 124, 1905; D. Baker, *ib.*, **35**. 244, 553, 1905; *Iron Trade Rev.*, **49**. 1551, 1911; T. F. Witherbee, *Trans. Amer. Inst. Min. Eng.*, **35**. 575, 1905; C. P. Linville, *ib.*, **41**. 268, 1910; R. H. Lee, *ib.*, **20**. 269, 1891; **47**. 344, 1913; R. P. Roberts, *ib.*, **46**. 445, 1913; H. P. Howland, *ib.*, **56**. 339, 1917; A. E. Maccoun, *Proc. Eng. Soc. West Pennsylvania*, **30**. 935, 1915; *Yearbook Amer. Iron Steel Inst.*, 29, 1915; G. W. Vreeland, *ib.*, 100, 1916; J. G. West, *ib.*, 50, 1918; *Blast Furnace Steel Plant*, **6**. 289, 323, 1918; G. D. Cochrane, *Proc. Inst. Mech. Eng.*, 164, 1863; 589, 1888; J. G. Beckton, *ib.*, 249, 1864; T. B. Rogerson, *Journ. West Scotland Iron Steel Inst.*, **7**. 153, 167, 1900; T. B. Rogerson and W. Buchanan, *ib.*, **21**. 15, 1914; J. Kennedy, *Proc. Eng. Soc. West Pennsylvania*, **23**. 1, 1907; *Iron Age*, **60**. 2, 1897; E. B. Cook, *Chem. Met. Engg.*, **8**. 251, 1910; J. W. Richards, *ib.*, **8**. 18, 1910; *Metallurgical Calculations*, New York, 1910; D. E. Roberts, *Proc. South Wales Inst. Eng.*, **28**. 279, 374, 1913; *Iron Coal Trades Rev.*, **85**. 455, 1912; W. H. Buckley, *Trans. Manchester Assoc. Eng.*, 193, 1920; H. Pilkington, *Proc. South Staffs Iron Steel Inst.*, **2**. 1, 1891; A. G. McKee, *Iron Trade Rev.*, **85**. 1369, 1929; *Blast Furnace Steel Plant*, **17**. 1805, 1929; R. H. Sweetser, *ib.*, **18**. 1824, 1828, 1930; *Trans. Amer. Inst. Min. Eng.*, **44**. 105, 1912; R. H. Sweetser and S. P. Kinney, *Iron Steel Eng.*, **6**. 575, 1929; S. P. Kinney, *ib.*, **6**. 579, 1929; *Tech. Paper U.S. Bur. Mines*, 442, 1929; G. Bulle, H. Bansen and G. Eichenberg, *Arch. Eisenhüttenwesen*, **3**. i, 169, 241, 325, 1929; *Stahl Eisen*, **49**. 1760, 1929; F. Lange, *ib.*, **35**. 33, 71, 1915; R. Franchot, *Min. Met.*, **7**. 368, 1926; M. de Aguinaga, *Ing. Construccion*, **7**. 82, 1929; L. E. Gruner, *Études sur les hauts-fourneaux*, Paris, 1872; London, 1872; A. von Kerpely, *Die Anlage und Einrichtungen der Eisenhütten*, Leipzig, 1873; *Zeit. Verg. Ver. Kärnten*, **10**. 199, 1878; W. A. Lyttle, *Metallurgical Patents*, London, 1875; A. de Vathaire, *Construction et conduite des hauts-fourneaux et fabrication des diverses fontes*, Paris, 1885; H. F. Lichte, *Das*

Roheisen und seine Darstellung durch den Hochofenbetrieb, Hanover, 1907 ; J. T. Wainwright, *Method of Operating a Blast Furnace for making Steel from Impure Ore and Fuel*, Chicago, 1893 ; W. G. Gillhausen, *Untersuchungen über die Warme- und Stoffbalanz beim Hochofen*, Aachen, 1910; T. D. West, *Metallurgy of Cast Iron*, Cleveland, 1897 ; H. Mehner, *Verh. Ver. Beförd. Gewerbfleisses*, **84**. 75, 1905 ; O. Simmersbach, *Sammlung Berg. Hütt. Abh.*, 3, 1906 ; *Stahl Eisen*, **17**. 307, 1057, 1897 ; **18**. 79, 1898 ; **21**. 1090, 1901 ; **23**. 163, 1903 ; **26**. 262, 319, 289, 463, 1906 ; **27**. 1197, 1907 ; **29**. 611, 1909 ; **34**. 827, 1914 ; *Berg. Hütt. Rund.*, **227**, 1907 ; H. von Jüptner, *Beiträge zur Theorie der Eisenhüttenprozesse*, Stuttgart, 1907 ; *Sammlung technischer Forschungsergebnisse*, Leipzig, 1921 ; *Grundriss der Siderologie*, Leipzig, 1902–4 ; C. Brisker, *Berechnung und Untersuchung des Eisenhochofens*, Halle a. S., 1909 ; *Stahl Eisen*, **21**. 1346, 1901 ; **28**. 391, 1908 ; I. Binder, *Der praktische Hochofenbetrieb*, Halle a. S., 1910 ; Harbison Walker, *A Study of the Blast Furnace*, Pittsburg, Pa., 1911 ; W. de St. Ange, *Metallurgie pratique du fer*, Paris, 1835 ; F. Clerf, *Journ. West Scotland Iron Steel Inst.*, **37**. 51, 1930 ; K. Rummel and G. Neumann, *Arch. Eisenhüttenwesen*, **3**. 531, 1929 ; O. Petersen, *Stahl Eisen*, **49**. 785, 1929 ; H. Hoff, *Hochofenanlage*, Leipzig, 1926 ; *Stahl Eisen*, **49**. 613, 1929 ; W. Mathesius, *ib.*, **43**. 873, 907, 1923 ; **49**. 1220, 1929 ; R. W. Miller, *Blast Furnace Steel Plant*, **17**. 1054, 1929 ; *Röhrenind.*, **22**. 200. 1929 ; C. R. Kuzell, *Mining Congress Journ.*, **16**. 375, 1930 ; A. Ledebur, *Berg. Hütt. Ztg.*, **36**. 277, 1877 ; *Met. Rev.*, 377, 1877 ; *Stahl Eisen*, **7**. 310, 1887 ; *Handbuch der Eisenhüttenkunde*, Leipzig, 1906; J. Henderson, *Journ. Chem. Met. Min. Soc. South Africa*, **30**. 233, 1930 ; J. Saconney, *Rev. Mét.*, **10**. 1289, 1913 ; F. B. Richards, *Iron Trade Rev.*, **29**. 17, 1896 ; F. E. Bachman, *ib.*, **29**. 7, 1896 ; *Iron Age*, **83**. 1438, 1909 ; G. R. Johnson, *Iron Trade Rev.*, **26**. 138, 1895 ; **29**. 9, 1896 ; E. W. Richards, *Proc. Inst. Mech. Eng.*, 107, 1896 ; H. V. Tiberg, *Oesterr. Zeit. Berg. Hütt.*, **43**. 604, 1895 ; F. Büttgenbach, *ib.*, **44**. 141, 1896 ; R. Welcke, *ib.*, **44**. 135, 1896 ; J. Lowag, *ib.*, **49**. 129, 1901 ; H. Tholander, *Oesterr. Zeit. Berg. Hütt.*, **52**. 124, 1904 ; *Jernkontorets Ann.*, **40**. 163, 1896 ; E. G. Odelstjerna, *ib.*, **50**. 169, 1896 ; *Berg. Hütt. Ztg.*, **55**. 25, 1896 ; *Tek. Tids.*, **34**. 165, 1904 ; E. Schrödter, *Die Deckung der Erzbedarfes der deutschen Hochöfen*, Düsseldorf, 1895 ; G. Teichgräber, *Stahl Eisen*, **16**. 632, 1896 ; H. von Schwarze, *ib.*, **45**. 609, 1925 ; A. Wolsky, *ib.*, **16**. 706, 869, 911, 1896 ; K. Sorge, *ib.*, **12**. 268, 1892 ; M. Bansen, *ib.*, **50**. 668, 1930 ; A. Gouvy, *ib.*, **21**. 680, 1901 ; E. Langheinrich, *ib.*, **21**. 953, 1901 ; E. Lamoureux, *ib.*, **24**. 387, 1904 ; E. Bernard, *Rev. Univ. Mines*, **35**. 64, 1896 ; M. Pierronne, *Stahl Eisen*, **21**. 165, 1901 ; *Rev. Univ. Mines.*, **39**. 81, 1897 ; *Bull. Soc. Ind. Min.*, (4), **1**. 489, 1902 ; *Rev. Mét.*, **2**. 663, 1905 ; J. Smeysters, *Rev. Univ. Mines*, **52**. 196, 1901 ; *Ann. Mines Belg.*, **10**. 113, 1905 ; J. L. Stevenson, *Eng.*, **82**. 25, 80, 1896 ; **94**. 248, 321, 347, 386, 474, 1902 ; 1900. 177, 1905 ; *The Designing and Equipment of Blast Furnaces*, London, 1902; *Blast Furnace Calculations and Tables for Furnace Managers and Engineers*, London, 1906 ; F. H. Crockard, *Eng. Mag.*, **22**. 493, 1902 ; H. L. Haldeman, *Amer. Manfr.*, **59**. 154, 1896 ; C. Larsen, *ib.*, **48**. 257, 1901 ; C. Dantin, *Génie Civil*, **41**. 373, 1902 ; O. O. Laudig, *Trans. Amer. Inst. Min. Eng.*, **26**. 269, 1896 ; F. Firmstone, *ib.*, **39**. 227, 1909 ; **40**. 459, 1909 ; E. G. Spilsbury, *ib.*, **25**. 452, 1896 ; **27**. 452, 1897 ; *Iron Age*, **59**. 15, 1897 ; J. Fritz, *ib.*, **58**. 1089, 1896 ; *Eng. News*, **36**. 381, 1896 ; *Trans. Amer. Soc. Mech. Eng.*, **18**. 40, 1897 ; A. C. Johnson, *Eng. News*, **45**. 248, 1901 ; G. J. Snelus, *Journ. Iron Steel Inst.*, **50**. ii, 104, 1896 ; E. de Billy and E. Julhiet, *Bull. Soc. Enc. Nat. Ind.*, (5), 2. 47, 1897 ; P. T. Grath, *Eng. Mag.*, **21**. 571, 1901 ; *Eng. News*, **46**. 59, 1901 ; A, Pourcel, *Rev. Gén. Sciences*, **7**. 465, 510, 1896 ; J. Kowarsky, *Amer. Manfr.*, **59**. 731, 1896 ; J. Sevieri, *Rass. Min.*, **18**. 179, 1903 ; G. A. Waterhouse, *Iron Age*, **80**. 1591, 1907 ; G. Rocour, *Étude sur l'équilibre calorifique du haut-fourneau*, Liége, 1898 ; A. Korevaar, *Combustion in the Gas Producer and in the Blast Furnace*, London, 1924 ; *Iron Coal Trades Rev.* **110**. 577, 1925 ; J. Tomkins, *Colliery Guardian*, **76**. 622, 1899 ; A. Edvi-Illes, *L'Industrie des mines de fer et hauts fourneaux de Hongrie*, Budapest, 1900 ; F. Poech, *L'Industrie minérale de Bosnie-Herzegovine*, Wien, 1900 ; L. Gages, *Foyers métallurgiques*, Paris, 1901 ; J. Demaret-Freson, *Hauts fourneaux au bois*, Charleroi, 1903 ; *Les hauts fourneaux Américains*, Bruxelles, 1903 ; *Les hauts fourneaux d'Almaznaia*, Bruxelles, 1903 ; F. Stille, *Oesterr. Zeit. Berg. Hütt.*, **30**. 5, 1902 ; G. Martin, *Stahl Eisen*, **22**. 67, 1902 ; A. Brezgunoff, *ib.*, **21**. 914, 984, 1901 ; *Gorny Journ.*, **1**. 1900 ; 73, 1901 ; E. Langheinrich, *Stahl Eisen*, **21**. 1097, 1168, 1220, 1294, 1901 ; E. Bahlsen, *ib.*, **21**. 1213, 1901 ; C. Waldeck, *ib.*, **23**. 670, 1903 ; A. Sattmann, *ib.*, **23**. 1224, 1903 ; D. P. Shuler, *ib.*, **24**. 157, 1904 ; H. Macco, *ib.*, **24**. 148, 1904 ; B. Kunz, *ib.*, **24**. 624, 1904 ; M. Kirdoff, *ib.*, **25**. 240, 368, 1905 ; P. Thomas, *ib.*, **26**. 598, 1906 ; J. M. Hartman, *Iron Trade Rev.*, **33**. 42, 1902 ; *Iron Age*, **48**. 541, 1892 ; **49**. 257, 1892 ; **50**. 322, 1892 ; J. B. van Brussel, *Iron Trade Rev.*, **41**. 535, 1907 ; J. J. Porter, *ib.* **42**. 33, 191, 1908 ; **43**. 433, 1912 ; F. Stark, *Zeit. Ver. deut. Ing.*, **46**. 1976, 1902 ; **47**. 1161, 1903 ; J. Nebelung, *ib.*, **47**. 1559, 1625, 1903 ; F. Frölich, *ib.*, **51**. 1055, 1907 ; A. Chepoffabnikoff, *Gorny Journ.*, 248, 1901 ; J. Karpinsky, *ib.*, 320, 1901 ; H. Braune, *Warmländske Berg. Ann.*, 51, 1901 ; *Jahrb. Eisenhüttenwesen*, 2. 253, 1903 ; W. F. Keiser, *Iron Coal Trades Rev.*, **76**. 1780, 1902 ; C. H. Ridsdale, *ib.*, **75**. 1854, 1907 ; *Proc. Cleveland Inst. Eng.*, 12, 1908 ; H. Wedding, *Stahl Eisen*, **12**. 1029, 1892 ; *Verh. Ver. Beförd. Gewerbfl.*, 199, 1904 ; B. A. N. Murti, *Bull. Myson Eng. Assoc.*, **8**. 48, 1930 ; C. E. Heurteau, *Ann. Mines*, (10), **6**. 102, 1904 ; A. Gounot, *L'Ingegneria Ferroviaria*, 2. 56, 1905 ; D. E. Woodbridge, *Eng. Min. Journ.*, **78**. 226, 1903 ; L. Lewis, *ib.*, **82**. 1201, 1906 ; B. Stoughton, *ib.*, **84**. 145, 206, 307, 347, 1907 ; F. Carlson, *Iron Trade Rev.*, **40**. 711, 1907 ; *Bihang Jernkontorets Ann.*, 223, 1907 ; W. Konspassewitsch, *Berg. Hütt. Ztg.*, **63**. 630, 1904 ; C. Haening, *Eisen Ztg.*, **28**. 52, 296, 1907 ; *Giesserei Ztg.*, **3**. 371, 1906 ; F. Schroeder, *ib.*, **4**. 202, 227, 1907 ; *Oesterr. Zeit. Berg. Hütt.*, **55**. 365, 380, 1907 ; L. Fortunate, *ib.*, **55**. 1, 18, 34, 44, 58, 70, 81, 1907 ; G. Latinak, *Bany. Koh. Lapok*, **39**.

203, 1906 ; F. Logeling, *Rev. Univ. Mines*, (8), **2**. 368, 1929 ; J. P. Dovel, *Blast Furnace Steel Plant*, **18**. 113, 1930 ; W. A. Haven, *ib.*, **18**. 85, 1930 ; W. McFarlane, *Trans. Min. Geol. Inst. India*, **1**. 147, 1908 ; H. L. Hannover, *Tek. Tids.*, **36**. 261, 1907 ; J. A. Leffler, *ib.*, **36**. 184, 1907 ; **63**. 347, 1908 ; H. Carlsson, *ib.*, **36**. 125, 1907 ; G. D. Drummond, *Journ. Canada Min. Inst.*, **10**. 442, 1907 ; J. G. Parmlee, *ib.*, **11**. 111, 1908 ; H. E. Wright, *Proc. Cleveland Inst. Eng.*, **8**, 1929 ; *Iron Coal Trades Rev.*, **118**. 527, 1929 ; *Journ. Iron Steel Inst.*, **101**. i, 179, 1920 ; H. Jäger, *Stahl Eisen*, **27**. 339, 1907 ; E. Kraynik, *ib.*, **29**. 265, 1909 ; F. Fröhlich, *ib.*, **30**. 436, 1910 ; G. Jantzen, *ib.*, **46**. 681, 1924 ; C. Zix, *ib.*, **46**. 1049, 1926 ; R. Capito, *ib.*, **46**, 1394, 1926 ; E. Zimmermann, *ib.*, **46**. 833, 1926 ; J. von Ehrenwerth, *Oesterr. Zeit. Berg. Hütt.*, **56**. 229, 301, 1908 ; Z. Bielsky, *ib.*, **57**. 479, 491, 1909 ; F. C. Coleman, *Iron Trade Rev.*, **43**. 767, 1908 ; B. E. V. Luty, *ib.*, **48**. 10, 1911 ; R. T. Kent, *ib.*, **42**. 931, 1907 ; *Iron Age*, **81**. 1591, 1907 ; C. M. Ripley, *Ores Metals*, **20**. 343, 1908 ; L. B. Orchard, *Canada Min. Journ.*, **29**. 36, 1908 ; S. G. Moore, *Board Trade Journ.*, **60**. 498, 1908 ; J. E. Carne, *Eng. Min. Journ.*, **85**. 601, 1908 ; A. Gradenwitz, *ib.*, **87**. 836, 1909 ; J. L. Pultz, *ib.*, **88**. 345, 1909 ; R. Jordan, *Rev. Mét.*, **21**. 127, 223, 1924 ; O. V. de Gaigne, *Eng. News*, **61**. 163, 1909 ; T. Good, *Cassier's Mag.*, **37**. 3, 1910 ; A. Wagner, *Rev. Tech. Luxembourgeoise*, **19**. 15, 1927 ; *Fuel Economist*, **3**. 301, 381, 456, 513, 1928 ; H. Groeck, *Zeit. Ver. deut. Ing.*, **54**. 307, 1910 ; W. Landris, *Chem. Met. Engg.*, **8**. 231, 1910 ; R. A. Hacking, *Metallurgia*, **1**. 195, 235, 1930 ; **2**. 99, 1930 ; M. Derclaye, *Rev. Univ. Mines*, (8), **4**. 106, 1930 ; *Rev. Mét.*, **25**. 1, 120, 1928 ; J. Sarek, *Journ. Iron Steel Inst.*, **122**. ii, 43, 1930 ; R. V. McKay, *Yearbook Amer. Iron Steel Inst.*, 85, 1914 ; *Iron Age*, **93**. 1386, 1443, 1914 ; M. P. G. Hillman, *Yearbook Amer. Iron Steel Inst.*, 441, 1914 ; H. A. Brassert, *ib.*, 15, 1914 ; *Iron Age*, **93**. 1338, 1578, 1914 ; **94**. 92, 153, 178, 1914 ; J. F. Shadgen, *ib.*, **108**. 456, 1921 ; L. Delville, *Rev. Ing. Index Téch.*, **25**. 199, 1920 ; **26**. 261, 1921 ; A. Anderson, *Trans. Amer. Soc. Steel Treating*, **1**. 312, 1921 ; A. Gandini, *Giorn. Chim. Ind. Appl.*, **3**. 494, 1921 ; R. S. McCaffery and R. G. Stephenson, *Tech. Publ. Amer. Inst. Min. Eng.*, 384, 1931.

 [12] S. C. McLanahan, *Iron Age*, **45**. 631, 1890 ; *U.S. Pat. No.* 419790, 1890 ; G. R. Johnson, *Trans. Amer. Inst. Min. Eng.*, **24**. 34, 1894 ; A. Wagner, *Stahl Eisen*, **51**. 217, 1931 ; M. F. Ortin, *Trans. Russ. Tech. Min. Congr.*, **8**. 7, 19-8.

 [13] C. Jones, *Trans. Amer. Inst. Min. Eng.*, **19**. 289, 1891 ; *Journ. Iron Steel Inst.*, **38**. ii, 671, 1890 ; G. Prus, *ib.*, **39**. i, 273, 1891 ; H. C. McNeill, *ib.*, **56**. ii, 18, 1899 ; H. Wedding, *ib.*, **70**. ii, 116, 1906 ; *Die magnetische Aufbereitung von Erzen*, Berlin, 1898 ; *Verh. Ver. Beförderung*, 263, 1898 ; 154, 1899 ; *Stahl Eisen*, **26**. 76, 1906 ; E. W. Davis, *Mining Met.*, **11**. 518, 1930 ; F. D. de Vaney and S. R. B. Cooke, *Bull. School Mines Univ. Missouri*, **11**. 3, 1930 ; C. M. Ball, *Trans. Amer. Inst. Min. Eng.*, **19**. 187, 1891 ; J. C. Fowle, *ib.*, **19**. 62, 1891 ; W. A. Anthony, *Cassier's Mag.*, **13**. 433, 1898 ; H. Louis, *Journ. West Scotland Iron Steel Inst.*, **19**. 206, 1912 ; M. Venström, *Eng. Min. Journ.*, **46**. 437, 1888 ; *Journ. U.S. Assoc. Charcoal Workers*, **8**. 105, 1889 ; J. Birkinbine, *ib.*, **8**. 107, 1889 ; G. W. Pickard, *U.S. Pat. Nos.* 827115, 827116, 1906 ; T. Turner, *The Metallurgy of Iron*, London, 80, 1915 ; A. Chenot, *Brit. Pat. No.* 658, 1854 ; W. Phillips, *Trans. Amer. Inst. Min. Eng.*, **25**. 399, 1895 ; H. A. J. Wilkens and H. B. C. Nitze, *ib.*, **26**. 351, 1089, 1896 ; G. Gromier, *Bull. Soc. Ind. Min.*, **7**. 465, 1893 ; C. Blömecke, *Oesterr. Zeit. Berg. Hütt.*, **46**. 148, 1898 ; S. Farbaky, *ib.*, **46**. 182, 1898 ; E. Primosigh, *ib.*, **47**. 271, 1899 ; C. Bugge, *ib.*, **55**. 102, 1907 ; C. Rosambert, *ib.*, **22**. 503, 1902 ; H. Bumby, *ib.*, **22**. 457, 1902 ; W. Svensson, *Berg. Hütt. Ztg.*, **58**. 259, 1899 ; H. Smits, *Stahl Eisen*, **20**. 1186, 1900 ; H. Ostwald, *ib.*, **31**. 22, 1911 ; R. Lanner, *ib.*, **32**. 576, 1912 ; F. O. Schnelle, *Verh. Ver. Beförderung*, 183, 1902 ; G. W. Petersson, *Eng. Min. Journ.*, **83**. 889, 1907 ; R. Sharp, *Iron Steel Ind.*, **5**. 103, 1931 ; E. Rothelius, *Jernkontorets Ann.*, **116**. 1, 1932.

 [14] A. Granström, *Jernkontorets Ann.*, **34**. 304, 1889.

 [15] W. Hutchinson and F. W. Harbord, *Brit. Pat. No.* 2747, 1891 ; H. Louis, *Cassier's Mag.*, **28**. 227, 1905 ; *Journ. West Scotland Iron Steel Inst.*, **19**. 206, 1912 ; *Journ. Iron Steel Inst.*, **65**. i, 40, 1904 ; A. Thielen, *ib.*, **38**. ii, 49, 1890 ; J. Gayley, *ib.*, **38**. ii, 73, 1890 ; E. Moffart, *ib.*, **35**. i, 300, 1889 ; H. Wedding, *Stahl Eisen*, Wien, 1903 ; N. V. Hansell, *Iron Trade Rev.*, **44**, 323, 364, 1909 ; *Journ. Iron Steel Inst.*, **60**. ii, 344, 1909 ; *Iron Age*, **89**. 710, 1912 ; G. W. Maynard, *ib.*, **88**. 1349, 1911 ; J. Gayley, *ib.*, **89**. 73, 1912 ; E. Schumacher, *ib.*, **86**. 1330, 1910 ; A. Johannsson, *Stahl Eisen*, **29**. 462, 1909 ; *Journ. Iron Steel Inst.*, **79**. i, 514, 1909 ; *Jernkontorets Ann.*, **63**. 400, 1908 ; R. Goebel, *Stahl Eisen*, **28**. 323, 1908 ; **29**. 240, 1909 ; H. E. Dünkelberg, *ib.*, **29**. 551, 1909 ; F. Witte, *ib.*, **30**. 755, 1910 ; G. Franke, *ib.*, **30**. 1060, 1900 ; G. Gröndal, *ib.*, **31**. 537, 1539, 1911 ; *Mining World*, **26**. 360, 1908 ; *Journ. Iron Steel Inst.*, **73**. i, 382, 1907 ; **78**. iii, 507, 1908 ; *Iron Trade Rev.*, **49**. 29, 1911 ; C. Bolin, *Tek. Tids.*, 99, 1909 ; A. Kumpfmiller, *Ueber Sulfit-Zellstoff-Ablange*, München, 1909 ; *Stahl Eisen*, **29**. 2011, 1909 ; A. Weiskopf, *Monit. Rund.*, 1248, 1297, 1912 ; *Stahl Eisen*, **31**. 1097, 110, 1911 ; **33**. 276, 319, 1913 ; E. Holzhüter, *ib.*, **31**. 1539, 1911 ; K. Sorge, *ib.*, **33**. 139, 1913 ; E. Dreves, *ib.*, **33**. 1366, 1913 ; R. Durrer, *ib.*, **36**. 1231, 1916 ; J. Mehrtens, *ib.*, **32**. 135, 1912 ; B. Osann, *ib.*, **32**. 465, 649, 739, 1912 ; **33**. 1236, 1913 ; W. J. Bartsch, *ib.*, **33**. 1238, 1913 ; C. Brisker, *ib.*, **34**. 412, 457, 1914 ; E. Jantzen, *ib.*, **34**. 1047, 1914 ; A. Beilstein, *ib.*, **34**. 41, 100, 1914 ; O. Höhle, *ib.*, **34**. 1135, 1914 ; O. Kippe, **34**. 1164, 1914 ; M. Zeidler, *ib.*, **25**. 321, 1905 ; B. C. Klugh, *Iron Trade Rev.*, **96**. 835, 1915 ; G. Barrett and B. Rogerson, *Journ. Iron Steel Inst.*, **96**. ii, 7, 1917 ; K. Endell, *Mitt. Inst. Eisenforsch.*, **3**. 37, 1921 ; *Metall Erz*, **18**. 169, 1921 ; M. Biernbaum, *ib.*, **19**. 1, 1922 ; M. Benecke, *Erzbergbau*, 20, 1912 ; B. Haas, *Eisen Ztg.*, 57, 1914 ; J. Savelsberg, *German Pat.*, *D.R.P.* 210742, 1909 ; H. V. Schiefer, *Iron Age*, **108**. 1141, 1921 ; J. Wilborgh, *Journ. Iron Steel Inst.*, **56**. ii, 8, 1899 ; A. L. Colby, *ib.*, **71**. iii, 358, 1906.

[16] S. G. Valentine, *Journ. Iron Steel Inst.*, **36**. ii, 333, 1889 ; W. J. Taylor and N. M. Langdon, *ib.*, **32**. ii, 232, 1887 ; *Trans. Amer. Inst. Min. Eng.*, **9**. 306, 1880 ; A. E. Pratt, *Trans. Inst. Min. Met.*, **16**. 328, 1907 ; R. Akerman, *Om jernmalmers Rostning*, Stockholm, 1897 ; *Das Rösten der Eisenerze*, Leipzig, 1880 ; F. Kupelweiser, *Berg. Hütt. Jahrb.*, **16**. 373, 1867 ; L. E. Gruner, *Ann. Mines*, (7), **9**. 540, 1876 ; J. Birkinbine, *Trans. Amer. Inst. Min. Eng.*, **12**. 361, 1884 ; R. Tholander, *Iron*, **8**. 194, 258, 355, 418, 482, 546, 578, 642, 706, 770, 834, 1876 ; **9**. 36, 99, 163, 226, 291, 387, 483, 515, 579, 1877 ; *Experimentelle Untersuchungen über die Reduktion von Eisenerzen und die Wirkung der Röstung auf Magneteisensteine und Hämatite*, Wien, 1878 ; O. Davis and C. Colby, *Eng. Min. Journ.*, **56**. 665, 1894 ; S. Jordan, *Rev. Univ. Mines*, (3), **31**. 1, 1895 ; H. Wedding, *Verh. Ver. Beförderung*, 368, 1895 ; 185, 1899 ; *Journ. Iron Steel Inst.*, **50**. ii, 116, 1896 ; J. Zemann, *Tech. Blätt.*, 149, 1870 ; *Dingler's Journ.*, **198**. 32, 1870 ; J. Jacobi, *ib.*, **201**. 245, 1871 ; *Bayr. Ind. Gewerbefl.*, 187, 1871 ; F. Gautier, *Berg. Hütt. Ztg.*, **35**. 8, 1876 ; R. J. W. Lent, *Oesterr. Zeit. Berg. Hütt.*, **61**. 326, 1913 ; F. Stridsberg, *Tech. Tids.*, 36, 1907 ; R. Goebel, *Erzbergbau*, 122, 1907 ; G. O. Petersson, *Stahl Eisen*, **25**. 1201, 1905 ; C. Brisker, *ib.*, **32**. 867, 1912 ; W. Mathesius, *ib.*, **32**. 1502, 1912 ; R. Ludwig, *Bihang. Jernkontorets Ann.*, **12**. 989, 1911 ; W. J. Willis, *Iron Coal Trades Rev.*, **85**. 1020, 1912 ; M. Pavloff, *Abmessungen von Hoch- und Martinöfen*, Leipzig, 1928 ; *Calcul du lit de fusion des hauts-fourneaux*, Paris, 1923 ; W. Harnickell, *Beiträge zur Röstung und Aufbereitung der Siegländer Spateisensteine*, Breslau, 1912 ; *Stahl Eisen*, **32**. 1949, 1912 ; **33**. 1735, 1913 ; J. Ruhrmann, *ib.*, **46**. 1118, 1926 ; E. Fournier, *Rev. Ind. Min.*, **235**. 435, 1930 ; T. L. Joseph and E. P. Barrett, *Tech. Publ. Amer. Inst. Min. Eng.*, 372, 1930.

[17] J. B. Walker, *Scientific American*, **130**. 28, 109, 162, 234, 310, 396, 1924 ; **131**. 98, 174, 252, 324, 398, 1924 ; **132**. 246, 317, 388, 1925. I am indebted to the publishers for permission to use the descriptive matter and diagram. The diagram, etc., were subsequently published by J. B. Walker, *The Story of Steel*, New York, 36, 1926 ; G. T. Franklin, *Journ. Chem. Education*, **8**. 143, 1931 ; H. Günther, *Der Wegdes Eisens vom Erz zum Stahl*, Stuttgart, 1925.

[18] B. Kerl, *Handbuch der metallurgischen Hüttenkunde*, Freiberg, **1**. 810, 1861 ; E. Faust, *Arch. Eisenhüttenwesen*, **1**. 119, 1927 ; *Stahl Eisen*, **47**. 1871, 1927 ; J. Percy, *Metallurgy—Iron and Steel*, London, 518, 1864 ; C. Schinz, *Researches on the Action of the Blast Furnace*, London, 151, 1870 ; G. D. Cochrane, *Proc. Inst. Mech. Eng.*, 589, 1888 ; *Journ. Ind. Steel Inst.*, **36**. ii, 388, 1889 ; I. L. Bell, *ib.*, **46**. ii, 38, 1894 ; *Proc. Inst. Mech. Eng.*, 612, 1888 ; C. Wood, *Journ. Iron Steel Inst.*, **46**. ii, 62, 1894 ; P. Gredt, *Stahl Eisen*, **9**. 756, 1889 ; *Journ. Iron Steel Inst.*, **36**. ii, 412, 1889 ; H. C. Jenkins, *ib.*, **39**. i, 151, 1891 ; A. Wingham, *ib.*, **42**. i, 233, 1892 ; J. E. Stead, *ib.*, **42**. ii, 223, 1892 ; **43**. i, 48, 1893 ; H. von Jüptner, *ib.*, **58**. ii, 276, 1900 ; **61**. i, 304, 1902 ; E. H. Saniter, *ib.*, **42**. ii, 216, 1892 ; **43**. i, 67, 1893 ; E. J. Ball and A. Wingham, *ib.*, **41**. i, 102, 1892 ; T. P. Colclough, *ib.*, **107**. i, 267, 1923 ; F. F. Amsden, *ib.*, **39**. i, 369, 1891 ; C. S. Gill, *ib.*, **116**. ii, 91, 1927 ; *Gas World—Coke section*, **87**. 127, 1927 ; H. O. Hofman, *ib.*, **29**. 682, 1899 ; W. Macfarlane, *Proc. South Staffs Iron Steel Inst.*, **15**. 23, 1899 ; L. Eck, *Karsten's Arch.*, (2), **25**. 436, 1852 ; T. Turner, *The Metallurgy of Iron*, London, 239, 1915 ; *Journ. Soc. Chem. Ind.*, **24**. 1142, 1905 ; S. E. Bretherton, *Eng. Min. Journ.*, **86**. 483, 1908 ; L. G. Smith, *ib.*, **90**. 1260, 1910 ; W. C. Roberts-Austen, *An Introduction to the Study of Metallurgy*, London, 256, 1902 ; C. Méne, *Compt. Rend.*, **63**. 608, 1866 ; C. J. B. Karsten, *Pogg. Ann.*, **99**. 229, 1840 ; *Journ. prakt. Chem.*, (1), **20**. 373, 1840 ; J. Fournet, *Ann. Chim. Phys.*, (3), **4**. 370, 1842 ; H. Wedding, *Ausführliches Handbuch der Eisenhüttenkunde*, Braunschweig, **3**. 878, 1906 ; G. Bontemps, *Phil. Mag.*, (3), **35**. 440, 1849 ; *B.A. Rep.*, 34, 1849 ; *Journ. prakt. Chem.*, (1), **49**. 175, 1850 ; C. A. M. Bolling, *Compendium der metallurgischen Chemie*, Bonn, 1882 ; *Berg. Hütt. Jahrb.*, **17**. 211, 1867 ; C. von Mayrhoffer, *ib.*, **10**. 277, 1860 ; W. Mrazek, *ib.*, **18**. 282, 1867 ; **19**. 375, 1868 ; S. P. Bjerregaard, *Iron Age*, **52**. 609, 1893 ; F. Toldt, *Oesterr. Zeit. Berg. Hütt.*, **42**. 15, 1892 ; B. Osann, *Stahl Eisen*, *ib.*, **22**. 155, 1036, 1902 ; **23**. 870, 1903 ; **34**. 1450, 1914 ; A. Michel, *ib.*, **47**. 696, 1927 ; F. Wittmann, *ib.*, **24**. 14, 1904 ; C. Dichmann, *ib.*, **31**. 749, 1911 ; G. Hilgenstock, *ib.*, **29**. 1480, 1909 ; W. Mathesius, *ib.*, **24**. 1001, 1904 ; **28**. 1121, 1908 ; J. Sarek, *ib.*, **50**. 1622, 1930 ; M. Simonis, *ib.*, **27**. 739, 1907 ; W. Grosse and W. Dinkler, *ib.*, **47**. 448, 1927 ; W. Harnickell and R. Durrer, *Ferrum*, **13**. 113, 1916 ; *Stahl Eisen*, **37**. 221, 1917 ; E. Hollmann, *ib.*, **39**. 57, 91, 1919 ; B. Kosmann, *ib.*, **12**. 270, 1892 ; H. Passow, *ib.*, **25**. 1128, 1905 ; B. Neumann, *ib.*, **30**. 1505, 1910 ; **38**. 953, 1918 ; K. Zulkowsky, *ib.*, **27**. 1062, 1098, 1907 ; P. Rohland, *ib.*, **27**. 661, 1907 ; O Simmersbach, *ib.*, **38**. 135, 1918 ; C. Braubach, *ib.*, **42**. 1750, 1922 ; W. Kosfeld, *ib.*, **49**. 245, 1929 ; E. Zimmermann, *ib.*, **46**. 833, 1926 ; G. Kassel, *Journ. Soc. Chem. Ind.*, **25**. 1099, 1906 ; C. H. Ridsdale, *Notes on Iron and Steel Manufacture*, Middlesbrough, 43, 1889 ; F. C. Calvert, *Brit. Pat. No.* 13793, 1851 ; C. H. Herty and J. M. Gaines, *Bull. U.S. Dept. Commerce*, 308, 1929 ; G. Mars, *Ueber den Einfluss der Tonerde auf die Eigenschaften der Sehlacken in den Stahlschmelzöfen*, Düsseldorf, 1928 ; E. V. Britzke, A. N. Krestovnikoff and I. B. Chmanenkoff, *Min. Suir. Tzvetnuie Met.*, 359, 1929 ; F. Hartmann and A. Lange, *Arch. Eisenhüttenwesen*, **3**. 615, 1930 ; *Stahl Eisen*, **50**. 517, 1930 ; B. Platz, *ib.*, **11**. 1, 1891 ; **12**. 2, 1892 ; E. J. Janitzky, *Yearbook Amer. Iron Steel Inst.*, 417, 1929 ; A. J. Rossi, *Iron Age*, **48**. 970, 1891 ; **49**. 342, 1892 ; J. J. Porter, *Trans. Amer. Inst. Min. Eng.*, **44**. 201, 1912 ; *Iron Age*, **79**. 404, 1907 ; R. H. Lee, *ib.*, **85**. 516, 1909 ; R. H. Sweetser, *ib.*, **85**. 259, 1909 ; R. Akerman, *Jernkontorets Ann.*, (2), **44**. 315, 1889 ; *Trans. Amer. Inst. Min. Eng.*, **22**. 265, 1893 ; F. Firmstone, *ib.*, **24**. 198, 1894 ; **81**. 1700, 1908 ; O. R. Foster, *ib.*, **29**. 562, 1899 ; E. A. Hersam, *ib.*, **31**. 340, 1901 ; A. E. Uehling, *Proc. Alabama Ind. Scient. Soc.*, **4**. 24, 1894 ; *Erzbergbau*, 19, 1911 ; T. T. Reed, T. L. Joseph and P. H. Royster, *Rep. Investigations U.S. Bureau Mines*, 2560,

1923; *Iron Trade Rev.*, **74**. 288, 1924; *Iron Coal Trades Rev.*, **108**. 176, 1924; A. L. Feild and P. H. Royster, *Tech. Paper Bur. Mines*, 187, 189, 1917; A. L. Feild, *ib.*, 157, 1916; R. Moldenke, *Iron Trade Rev.*, **31**. 11, 1899; D. H. Brown, *Electrochem. Met. Ind.*, **5**. 174, 1907; R. Chauvenet, *ib.*, **10**. 36, 104, 1912; **12**. 626, 1914; B. F. Burman, *ib.*, **14**. 256, 1916; *Chemical Arithmetic and Calculation of Furnace Charges*, Philadelphia, 1912; H. Fleissner, *Eisenhochofenschlacken ihre Eigenschaften und ihre Verwendung*, Halle, 1912; *Oesterr. Zeit. Berg. Hütt.*, **58**. 75, 91, 104, 122, 140, 158, 169, 186, 1910; A. Harpf, M. Langer and H. Fleissner, *ib.*, **57**. 709, 727, 746, 762, 1909; J. F. L. Hausmann, *Gött. Ver. Berg. Freunde*, **6**. 355, 1854; C. Dralle, *Chem. Ztg.*, **24**. 1132, 1900; E. Kochs and F. Seyfert, *Zeit. angew. Chem.*, **14**. 719, 1901; E. Kochs, *ib.*, **19**. 2122, 1906; L. Blum, *Ferrum*, **9**. 138, 1914; **13**. 33, 1916; *Stahl Eisen*, **21**. 1024, 1901; J. E. Fletcher, *Proc. Staffs Iron Steel Inst.*, **31**. 77, 1916; *Iron Coal Trades Rev.*, **92**. 364, 1918; *Journ. Iron Steel Inst.*, **103**. i, 105, 1921; *Foundry Trade Journ.*, **29**. 395, 429, 1924; E. Diepschlag and H. Fliegenschmidt, *Centr. Hütt. Walzwerke*, **31**. 551, 567, 587, 1927; E. Diepschlag and L. Treuheit, *Giesserei*, **18**. 705, 1931; O. Bowles, *Rolling Mill Journ.*, **5**. 87, 167, 247, 1931; J. E. Johnson, *Trans. Amer. Inst. Min. Eng.*, **44**. 123, 1912; *Ferrum*, **11**. 20, 1914; *Met. Chem. Engg.*, **14**. 363, 1916; O. von Keil and P. Kettler, *Ber. Hochofenaus. Ver. Eisenhüttenleute*, 62, 1923; H. Salmang and F. Schick, *Untersuchungen über die Verschlakung feuerfester Stoffe*, Düsseldorf, 1930; F. Schick, *Untersuchungen über die Korrosionskraft und die Konstitution der Eisenhüttenschlacken*, Aachen, 1930; G. Geijer, *Bihang Jernkontorets Ann.*, **15**. 135, 1914; R. M. Keeney, *Min. Scient. Press.*, **109**. 335, 1914; C. Brisker, *Berechnung und Untersuchung des Eisenhochofens*, Halle, 1915; *Stahl Eisen*, **27**. 1205, 1907; C. E. Wood and T. L. Joseph, *Tech. Publ. Trans. Amer. Inst. Min. Eng.*, 181, 1929; T. L. Joseph, S. P. Kinney and C- E. Wood, *ib.*, 112, 1928; *Tech. Paper U.S. Bur. Mines*, 425, 1928; A. Knight, *Journ. Birmingham Met. Soc.*, **8**. 209, 1922; S. Schleicher, *Gesetzmässigkeiten in der Zusammensetzung bauscher Siemens-Martin-Schlacken*, Düsseldorf, 1930; R. Grün, *Thermische Untersuchungen an Hochofenschlacker*, Düsseldorf, 1925; *Der Hochofenzement und seine Verwendung*, Berlin, 1929; R. S. McCaffery, J. F. Oesterle and O. O. Fritsche, *Tech. Publ. Amer. Inst. Min. Eng.*, 383, 1931; R. S. McCaffery, J. F. Oesterle and L. Schapiro, *ib.*, 19, 1927; *Stahl Eisen*, **47**. 508, 1927; R. S. McCaffery and J. F. Oesterle, *ib.*, **45**. 592, 1925; *Yearbook Amer. Iron Steel Inst.*, 285, 1924; R. S. McCaffery, *Iron Age*, **114**. 1130, 1924; *Iron Trade Rev.*, **75**. 1161, 1924; G. Lunde and T. von Fellenberg, *Zeit. anorg. Chem.*, **165**. 225, 1927; K. Iwase and M. Fukushima, *Kinzoku no Kenkyu*, **7**. 524, 1930; T. Kuroda, *Tetsu-to-Hagane*, **17**. 118, 1931; J. H. L. Vogt, *Die Sulfid-Silikat-Schmelzlösungen*, Kristiania, 1919; *Jernkontorets Ann.*, (2), **60**. 1, 1905; B. Kalling, *ib.*, (2), **79**. 283, 1924; O. Glaser, *Arch. Eisenhüttenwesen*, **2**. 73, 1929; F. Hartmann and A. Lange, *ib.*, **3**. 615, 1930; G. A. Rankin and F. E. Wright, *Zeit. anorg. Chem.*, **92**. 213, 1915; *Amer. Journ. Science*, (4), **39**. 1, 1915; A. L. Day and E. S. Shepherd, *ib.*, (4), **22**. 265, 1906; E. S. Shepherd, *Journ. Ind. Eng. Chem.*, **3**. 211, 1911; *Zeit. anorg. Chem.*, **71**. 19, 1911; W. G. Imhoff, *Iron Age*, **118**. 210, 547, 612, 1926; C. E. Ireland, *ib.*, **114**. 1131, 1924; A. Ledebur, *Handbuch der Eisenhüttenkunde*, Leipzig, **1**. 199, 1902; *Zeit. Berg. Hütt.*, **13**. 64, 1881; M. Theusner, *Met.*, **5**. 657, 1908; R. Rieke, *Sprech.*, **40**. 593, 610, 625, 1905; O. Boudouard, *Journ. Iron Steel Inst.*, **67**. i, 339, 1905; *Stahl Eisen*, **25**. 1351, 1905; H. Burchartz and O. Bauer, *ib.*, **37**. 626, 646, 1917; *Mitt. Materialprüfungsamt*, **34**. 157, 1916; K. Endell, *Ber. Hochofenkomm. Ver. Eisenhüttenleute*, 34, 1914; L. Gruner, *Études sur les hauts-fourneaux, suivies d'une notice sur les appareils à air chaud*, Paris, 39, 1873; A. de Vathaire, *Ann. Mines*, (6), **4**. 224, 1874; A. Guttmann, *Die Verwendung der Hochofenschlacke im Baugewerbe*, Düsseldorf, 1919; *Ber. Ausschusses Hochofenschlacke Ver. Eisenhüttenleute*, 5, 1925; 7, 1926; *Stahl Eisen*, **46**. 1423, 1481, 1926; **47**. 1047, 1927; A. Mund, J. Stoecker and W. Eilender, *ib.*, **51**. 1449, 1931; M. Paschke and E. Jung, *Arch. Eisenhüttenwesen*, **5**. 1, 1931; F. Petry, *Der Einfluss des Magnesiumoxyds auf die Reduktions- Oxydations- und Kohlungsvorgänge beim Eisen*, Münster, 1929.

[19] J. Mander, A. Manby and J. Vernon, *Ann. Phil.*, **2**. 157, 1814; *Brit. Pat. No.* 3705, 1813; J. Payne, *ib.*, 505, 1728; J. T. Chance, *ib.*, 1985, 1855; W. Hawdon, *Proc. Inst. Mech. Eng.*, 70, 1892; J. Head, *ib.*, 240, 1893; J. E. Stead, *Journ. Iron Steel Inst.*, **31**. i, 405, 1887; C. Wood, *ib.*, **6**. 186, 1873; **12**. ii, 443, 1877; C. von Schwarz, *ib.*, **57**. 141, 1900; **76**. 137, 1908; E. H. Lewis, *ib.*, **101**. i, 111, 1920; R. Zsigmondy, *Dingler's Journ.*, **284**. 233, 1892; F. W. Lürmann, *Zeit. Architekten Hannover*, **13**. 297, 1867; *Zeit. Ver. deut. Ing.*, **12**. 32, 1867; **19**. 185, 1875; M. Paulovich, *Oesterr. Zeit. Berg. Hütt.*, **41**. 333, 1891; L. Tetmajer, *Notizblatt. Ziegler*, **23**. 79, 1887; A. Prost, *Ann. Mines*, (8), **16**. 158, 1889; G. Jantzen, *Verh. Ver. Beförderung*, **82**. 19, 1903; *Stahl Eisen*, **23**. 36, 1903; T. Klehe, *Zeit. angew. Chem.*, **18**. 933, 1905; O. Schwabe, *ib.*, **18**. 1265, 1905; O. Vogel, *Stahl Eisen*, **18**. 178, 1898; H. Eger and E. Cramer, *ib.*, **25**. 711, 1905; C. Canaris, *ib.*, **24**. 813, 1904; H. Passow, *ib.*, **23**. 878, 1903; **25**. 1128, 1905; A. Birk, *ib.*, **20**. 886, 1900; C. Steffens, *ib.*, **20**. 1170, 1900; M. Kämmerer, *ib.*, **19**. 1087, 1899; E. May, *ib.*, **18**. 205, 320, 1898; A. Guttmann, *Die Verwendung der Hochofenschlacke im Baugewerbe*, Düsseldorf, 1919; H. Detienne, *Rev. Univ. Mines*, (3), **39**. 237, 1897; B. Osann, *Die Giesserei*, **16**. 772, 1929.

[20] I. L. Bell, *Brit. Pat. No.* 17564, 1888; *Journ. Soc. Chem. Ind.*, **33**. 594, 1914.

[21] C. E. Schafhäutl, *Proc. Inst. Civil Eng.*, **8**. 117, 1849; J. Percy, *Metallurgy—Iron and Steel*, London, 497, 1864; A. Ledebur, *Handbuch der Eisenhüttenkunde*, Leipzig, **2**. 221, 1906; F. Kupelwieser, *Das Hüttenwesen auf der Weltausstellung zu Philadelphia*, Wien, 1877; B. Kerl, *Grundriss der Eisenhüttenkunde*, Leipzig, 168, 1875; B. Platz, *Stahl Eisen*, **12**. 3, 1892; A. von Kerpely, *Die Anlage und Einrichtungen der Eisenhütten*, Leipzig, 1873; *Ungarns Eisensteine*

und Eisenhüttenerzeugnisse, Wien, 84, 1877 ; W. H. Miller, *B.A. Rep.*, 351, 1847 ; C. F. Rammels-berg, *Handbuch der Mineralchemie*, Leipzig, 731, 1860 ; E. Riley, *Trans. Soc. Engineers*, 45, 1862 ; G. Lindauer, *Compendium der Hüttenchemie mit besonderer Anwendung auf die Metallurgie des Eisens*, Prag, 278, 1861 ; C. C. von Leonhard, *Hüttenerzeugnisse und andere auf künstlichem Wege gebildete Mineralien als Stützpunkte geologischer Hypothesen*, Stuttgart, 175, 1858 ; A. Neuburger, *Sitzber. Ver. Beförd. Gewerbfleisses*, **84**. 81, 1905 ; C. Matignon, *L'électrométallurgie des fontes, fers, et aciers*, Paris, 1906 ; J. B. C. Kershaw, *The Electric Furnace in Iron and Steel Production*, London, 1907 ; E. Haanel, *Electrothermic Processes for the Smelting of Iron Ores and the Making of Steel*, Ottawa, 1904 ; *Report on the Experiments made at Sault St. Marie, Ontario, in the Smelting of Canadian Iron Ores by the Electrothermic Process*, Ottawa, 1907 ; *Report on the Investigation of an Electric Shaft Furnace, Domnarfvet, Sweden*, Ottawa, 1909 ; J. Escard, *L'électrosidérurgie*, Paris, 1908 ; W. Rodenhauser and J. Schoenawa, *Elektrische Oefen in der Eisenindustrie*, Leipzig, 1911 ; B. Naumann, *Elektrometallurgie des Eisens*, Halle a. S., 1907 ; E. Stassano, *Electrothermic Process for the Reduction of Iron Ores*, Ottawa, 1904 ; H. Harmet, *Treatise on the Electrometallurgy of Iron*, Ottawa, 1904 ; G. Tammann and G. Bätz, *Zeit. anorg. Chem.*, **151**. 129, 1926 ; P. Geimer, *Stahl Eisen*, **43**. 681, 1923 ; J. Seigle, *Bull. Soc. Ind. Min.*, (5), **14**. 109, 1918 ; (5), **17**. 5, 1920 ; P. Berthier, *Ann. Mines*, (3), **14**. 113, 1838 ; F. C. Wrightson, *Chem. Gaz.*, **7**. 478, 1849 ; H. Pilkington, *Proc. South Staffs Iron Steel Inst.*, **3**. 4, 1887 ; J. H. L. Vogt, *Jernkontorets Ann.*, **60**. 1, 1905 ; I. L. Bell, *Principles of the Manufacture of Iron and Steel*, London, 169, 1884 ; N. Kjellberg, *Dingler's Journ.*, **287**. 207, 1893 ; *Jernkontorets Ann.*, **47**. 191, 1892 ; G. Hilgenstock, *Stahl Eisen*, **4**. 2, 1884 ; A. Lampen, *Journ. Amer. Chem. Soc.*, **28**. 846, 1906 ; H. Bansen, *Arch. Eisenhüttenwes.*, **3**. 241, 1929 ; H. Rathke, *Untersuchungen über die mechanisch-technologischen Eigenschaften und den Zerfall von Hochofen schlacken*, Breslau, 1931.

²² F Brabant, *Journ. Iron Steel Inst.*, **32**. ii, 283, 1887 ; E. C. Pechin, *ib.*, **34**. ii, 235, 1888 ; I. L. Bell, *Principles of the Manufacture of Iron and Steel*, London, 124, 1884 ; R. H. Richards and R. W. Lodge, *Trans. Amer. Inst. Min. Eng.*, **16**. 149, 1888 ; T. F. Witherbee, *ib.*, **38**. 387, 1907 ; T. Turner, *The Metallurgy of Iron*, London, 161, 1915 ; L. E. Grüner, *Études sur les hauts-fourneaux, suivies d'une notice sur les appareils à air chaud*, Paris, 1873 ; *Studies of Blast Furnace Phenomena*, London, 1873 ; H. Bansen, *Arch. Eisenhüttenwes.*, **1**. 245, 1927 ; E. Bertram, *ib.*, **1**. 19, 1927 ; G. Bulle, *ib.*, **1**. 161, 1927 ; **3**. 169, 1929 ; *Stahl Eisen*, **48**. 329, 368, 433, 1928 ; Ber. *Hochofenaussch. Ver. deut. Eisenhüttenleute*, 93, 1928 ; J. Stöcker and G. Bulle, *ib.*, 78, 1926 ; W. Lennings, *Gestellund Rastuntersuchung eines Hochofens unter besonderer Berücksichtigung der Verbrennungsverhältnisse vor den Blasformen*, Düsseldorf, 1927 ; C. C. Furnas and T. L. Joseph, *Tech. Pub. Amer. Soc. Min. Eng.*, 249, 1929 ; 476, 1930 ; S. P. Kinney, *Fuel*, **9**. 307, 309, 1930 ; *Blast Furnace Steel Plant*, **18**. 472, 1930 ; **19**. 407, 1931 ; *Iron Steel Inst.*, **3**. 201, 1930 ; *Tech. Paper U.S. Bur. Mines*, 397, 1926 ; 459, 1930 ; A. Wagner, *Stahl Eisen*, **46**. 1005, 1926 ; **50**. 122, 1930 ; G. Teichgräber, *ib.*, **22**. 77, 1902 ; R. Durrer, *ib.*, **46**. 328, 1926 ; W. Mathesius, *ib.*, **49**. 1220, 1919 ; E. V. Britzke, A. N. Krestovnikoff and I. B. Chmanenkoff, *Min. Suir. Tzvet. Met.*, 359, 1929 ; F. B. Richard, *Iron Trade Rev.*, **28**. 14, 1895 ; R. H. Sweetser, *Blast Furnace Steel Plant*, **18**. 1824, 1828, 1930 ; *Mining Met.*, **11**. 423, 1930 ; P. H. Royster and T. L. Joseph, *Trans. Amer. Inst. Min. Eng.*, **70**. 224, 1924 ; S. P. Kinney, P. H. Royster and T. L. Joseph, *Tech. Paper U.S. Bur. Mines*, 391, 1926 ; T. L. Joseph, P. H. Royster and S. P. Kinney, *Proc. Eng. Soc. Western Pennsylvania*, **41**. 428, 1926 ; *Blast Furnace Steel Plant*, **12**. 246, 254, 274, 1924 ; **14**. 15, 24, 1926 ; *Engg.*, **116**. 667, 1923 ; J. W. Richards, *Met. Chem. Engg.*, **8**. 18, 1910 ; E. B. Cook, *ib.*, **8**. 251, 1910 ; J. E. Johnson, *Met. Chem. Engg.*, **14**. 363, 443, 464, 520, 642, 1916 ; **15**. 21, 69, 1916 ; A. L. Feild, *ib.*, **14**. 377, 1916 ; G. W. Vreeland, *Yearbook Amer. Iron Steel Inst.*, **6**. 106, 1916 ; *Iron Age*, **97**. 1332, 1916 ; F. Wüst and W. P. Rutten, *Stahl Eisen*, **43**. 1540, 1923 ; M. Derclaye, *Rev. Univ. Mines*, (7), **1**. 146, 1924 ; *Rev. Mét.*, **21**. 315, 396, 450, 1924 ; K. Hofmann, *Trans. Amer. Electrochem. Soc.*, **51**. 323, 1927 ; G. Eichenberg, *Arch. Eisenhüttenwesen*, **3**. 1, 1929 ; G. Lunde and T. von Fellen-berg, *Zeit. anorg. Chem.*, **165**. 225, 1927 ; M. A. Vernon, *Fuel Econ. Rev.*, **10**. 48, 1931 ; E. C. Evans and F. J. Bailey, *Journ. Iron Steel Inst.*, **117**. i, 53, 1928 ; E. C. Evans, L. Reeve, and M. A. Vernon, *ib.*, **123**. i, 95, 1931 ; *Engg.*, **131**. 807, 1931 ; E. Cotel, *Rev. Mét.*, **28**. 375, 1931 ; A. Peters, *Chim. Ind.*, **25**. 1327, 1931 ; R. A. Hacking, *Metallurgia*, **3**. 27, 183, 196, 1931 ; J. R. Young and R. C. Irving, *Proc. Australasian Inst. Min. Met.*, **79**. 215, 1930 ; A. Siegel, *Arch. Eisenhüttenwesen*, **4**. 557, 1931 ; T. J. Ess, *Iron Steel Eng.*, **8**. 173, 1931 ; B. V. Vuistavkin, M. M. Katok and I. A. Ostashkevich, *Domez*, 12, 1930 ; I. Bohm, *Jernkontorets Ann.*, **116**. 19, 1932.

²³ P. Rheinländer, *Arch. Eisenhüttenwesen*, **3**. 487, 1929 ; *Temperatur messungen am Hochofen*, Düsseldorf, 1930 ; *Stahl Eisen*, **50**. 205, 1930 ; J. J. Ebelmen, *Ann. Mines*, (4), **5**. 19, 1844 ; (4), **20**. 409, 1851 ; P. von Tunner and R. Richter, *Jahrb. osterr. Bergakad.*, **9**. 281, 296, 1860 ; H. le Chatelier, *Compt. Rend.*, **114**. 470, 1892 ; I. L. Bell, *Proc. Cleveland Inst. Eng.*, 25, 1892 ; F. Büttgenbach, *Berg. Hütt. Ztg.*, **54**. 231, 1895 ; S. Norton, *Iron Age*, **55**. 818, 1893 ; F. Clements, *Journ. Iron Steel Inst.*, **101**. i, 125, 1920 ; M. Jungst, *Zeit. Berg. Hütt. Sal.*, **19**. 68, 1871 ; F. Kupelwieser, *Jahrb. österr. Bergakad.*, **21**. 232, 1871 ; L. Rin-man, *Berg. Hütt. Ztg.*, **36**. 94, 1877 ; L. Rinman and B. Fernquist, *ib.*, **24**. 257, 1865 ; J. H. L. Vogt, *Zeit. Kryst.*, **18**. 669, 1890 ; M. Paulovitch, *Oester. Zeit. Berg. Hütt.*, **39**. 333, 347, 1891 ; F. Todt, *ib.*, **41**. 201, 1893 ; H. Allen, *Eng.*, **96**. 84, 1903 ; S. P. Kinney, *Blast Furnace Steel Plant*, **19**. 407, 1931 ; *Rep. U.S. Bur. Mines*, 2978, 1929 ; *Iron Coal Trades Rev.*, **120**. 318, 1930 ; *Fuel*, **9**. 115, 1930 ; G. Eichenberg, *Arch. Eisenhüttenwesen*, **3**. 325, 1929 ; H. Lent, *Stahl Eisen*, **45**. 1149, 1925 ; A. Wagner, *ib.*, **46**. 1005, 1926 ; *Blast Furnace Steel Plant*, **14**. 505, 1926 ; A. Michel, *Stahl*

Eisen, **47**. 696, 1927 ; L. E. Gruner, *Études sur les hauts-fourneaux, suivies d'une notice sur les appareils à air chaud*, Paris, 1873 ; *Studies of Blast Furnace Phenomena*, London, 1873 ; T. Turner, *The Metallurgy of Iron*, London, 1915.

[24] R. Bunsen and L. Playfair, *B.A. Rep.*, 142, 1845 ; 170, 1846 ; *Report on the Gases evolved from Iron Furnaces with reference to the Theory of the Smelting of Iron*, London, 1903 ; *Journ. Pharm.*, **14**. 441, 1848 ; *Journ. γrakt. Chem.*, (1), **42**. 266, 1847 ; R. Bunsen, *Liebig's Ann.*, **32**. 325, 1839 ; *Pogg. Ann.*, **46**. 192, 1839 ; T. Scheerer and C. Langberg, *ib.*, **60**. 489, 1843 ; J. J. Ebelmen, *Ann. Mines*, (3), **20**. 395, 1841 ; (4), **5**. 24, 1844 ; (4), **19**. 117, 1851 ; A. Jaumain, *ib.*, (7), **20**. 323, 1881 ; L. E. Grüner, *ib.*, (7), **20**. 336, 1881 ; *Études sur les hauts-fourneaux, suivies d'une notice sur les appareils à air chaud*, Paris, 1872 ; *Studies of Blast Furnace Phenomena*, London, 1873 ; P. von Tunner and R. Richter, *Jahrb. österr. Bergakad.*, **9**. 281, 1860 ; P. von Tunner, *ib.*, **10**. 491, 1860 ; **15**. 109, 1865 ; R. Schöffel, *ib.*, **21**. 188, 1871 ; F. Kupelwieser and R. Schöffel, *Berg. Hütt. Ztg.*, **32**. 169, 1873 ; L. Rinman, *ib.*, **36**. 94, 1877 ; L. Rinman and B. Fernquist, *ib.*, **24**. 257, 1865 ; G. Heine, *ib.*, **1**. 809, 1842 ; A. Tamm, *Jernkontorets Ann.*, **35**. 135, 1880 ; *Iron*, **13**. 674, 706, 739, 771, 803, 1879 ; **14**. 2, 67, 98, 131, 1879 ; **16**. 23, 46, 310, 400, 418, 1880 ; **17**. 22, 58, 1881 ; F. W. Lürmann, *Stahl Eisen*, **18**. 247, 1898 ; **19**. 473, 1899 ; **21**. 1154, 1901 ; *Zeit. Ver. deut. Ing.*, **26**. 266, 1882 ; E. Bellani, *Oesterr. Zeit. Berg. Hütt.*, **24**. 444, 1876 ; B. Osann, *Arch. Eisenhüttenwesen*, **1**. 673, 1928 ; *Stahl Eisen*, **21**. 906, 1901 ; **36**. 210, 1916 ; **48**. 860, 1928 ; C. Waldeck, *ib.*, **23**. 670, 1903 ; G. Bulle, *ib.*, **48**. 433, 1928 ; C. Aldendorff, *ib.*, **33**. 1526, 1528, 1913 ; W. A. Schlesinger, *ib.*, **31**. 1182, 1911 ; P. Gredt, *ib.*, **10**. 591, 1890 ; H. Lent, *ib.*, **45**. 1149, 1925 ; **47**. 1332, 1927 ; M. Levin and H. Niedt, *ib.*, **31**. 2135, 1911 ; *Met.*, **8**. 515, 555, 1911 ; H. Niedt, *Untersuchungen über die Zusammensetzung des Gasstromes in Hochofen*, Berlin, 1911 ; M. Levin, *Ferrum*, **11**. 261, 1914 ; R. Schenck and W. Heller, *Stahl Eisen*, **25**. 1121, 1905 ; R. Schenck, *Zeit. anorg. Chem.*, **166**. 146, 1927 ; *Deut. Forschung*, 3, 1928 ; *Zeit. angew. Chem.*, **24**. 1077, 1904 ; I. L. Bell, *The Principles of the Manufacture of Iron and Steel*, London, 1884 ; J. E. Stead, *Proc. Inst. Mech. Eng.*, 138, 1883 ; *Journ. Iron Steel Inst.*, **42**. ii, 233, 1892 ; **43**. i, 48, 1893 ; W. Hawdon, *ib.*, **23**. i, 101, 1883 ; C. Stöckmann, *Die Gase des Hochofens und der Siemensgeneratoren*, Ruhrort, 20, 1876 ; A. Ledebur, *Stahl Eisen*, **14**. 336, 1894 ; *Handbuch der Eisenhüttenkunde*, Leipzig, **2**. 277, 1906 ; H. Wedding, *Ausführliches Handbuch der Eisenhüttenkunde*, Braunschweig, **3**. 200, 1906 ; J. Percy, *Metallurgy—Iron and Steel*, London, 430, 1864 ; W. Müller, *Pogg. Ann.*, **136**. 51, 1869 ; **144**. 609, 1872 ; T. Turner, *The Metallurgy of Iron*, London, 161, 1915 ; H. Bansen, *Arch. Eisenhüttenwesen*, **3**. 241, 1929 ; S. P. Kinney, *Rept. Investigations U.S. Bur. Mines*, 2978, 2979, 1929 ; *Journ. Iron Steel Inst.*, **115**. 1, 136, 1927 ; *Stahl Eisen*, **47**. 1331, 1927 ; *Tech. Paper Bur. Mines*, 397, 442, 1929 ; *Iron Coal Trades Rev.*, **120**. 318, 1930 ; *Iron Steel Eng.*, **6**. 579, 1929 ; S. P. Kinney, P. H. Royster and T. L. Joseph, *Rep. Investigations Bur. Mines*, 2747, 1926 ; *Journ. Iron Steel Inst.*, **116**. ii, 516, 1927 ; *Stahl Eisen*, **47**. 361, 1927 ; *Tech. Paper Bur. Mines*, 391, 1927 ; T. L. Joseph, S. P. Kinney and C. E. Wood, *ib.*, 425, 1928 ; C. E. Wood and T. L. Joseph, *Tech. Publ. Amer. Inst. Min. Eng.*, 181, 1929 ; *Stahl Eisen*, **49**. 1093, 1929 ; R. S. McCaffery and J. F. Oesterle, *ib.*, **44**. 181, 1924 ; *Trans. Amer. Inst. Min. Eng.*, **69**. 606, 1923 ; J. E. Johnson, *ib.*, **44**. 123, 1912 ; *Stahl Eisen*, **33**. 1331, 1913 ; O. R. Forster, *ib.*, **21**. 1203, 1901 ; *Trans. Amer. Inst. Min. Eng.*, **29**. 562, 1899 ; F. Firmstone, *ib.*, **24**. 498, 1894 ; *Stahl Eisen*, **14**. 967, 1894 ; T. L. Joseph, *ib.*, **45**. 436, 1925 ; *Trans. Amer. Inst. Min. Eng.*, **71**. 453, 1925 ; W. H. Watkinson, *Journ. West Scotland Iron Steel Inst.*, **2**. 137, 1895 ; H. von Jüptner, *Oesterr. Zeit. Berg. Hütt.*, **43**. 430, 501, 522, 1895 ; J. J. van Laar, *Chem. Weekbl.*, **22**. 367, 1925 ; A. S. Keith, *Proc. Cleveland Inst. Eng.*, 203, 1896 ; B. H. Thwaite, *Journ. Iron Steel Inst.*, **60**. ii, 149, 1901 ; *Iron Coal Trades Rev.*, **54**. 169, 1897 ; **56**. 732, 1898 ; J. H. Ashby, *ib.*, **57**. 594, 1898 ; C. T. Jung, *Stahl Eisen*, **17**. 180, 1897 ; J. Herman, *Western Chemist Metallurgist*, **1**. 145, 1906 ; A. Greiner, *Journ. Iron Steel Inst.*, **53**. i, 21, 1898 ; W. Galbraith, *On the Utilization of Blast-Furnace Gases by means of a Gas-Engine*, Glasgow, 1898 ; *Journ. West Scotland Iron Steel Inst.*, **5**. 49, 65, 1898 ; F. Zeyringer, *Stahl Eisen*, **19**. 664, 1899 ; W. van Vloten, *ib.*, **13**. 26, 1893 ; G. Hilgenstock, *ib.*, **5**. 422, 1885 ; **11**. 798, 1891 ; **13**. 49, 168, 455, 461, 1893 ; F. Wüst and P. Wolff, *ib.*, **25**. 585, 1905 ; O. Simmersbach, *ib.*, **18**. 19, 1898 ; **23**. 163, 1903 ; O. Johannsen, *ib.*, **33**. 69, 1913 ; L. M. Lindemann, *ib.*, **35**. 1265, 1915 ; A. Killing, *ib.*, **42**. 968, 1922 ; F. Muck, *ib.*, **6**. 468, 1886 ; H. L. Diehl, *ib.*, **41**. 845, 1921 ; E. Kraynik, *ib.*, **25**. 1437, 1905 ; J. Stoecker, *ib.*, **49**. 1927, 1929 ; H. Hubert, *Ann. Mines Belg.*, **2**. 233, 1898 ; *Utilization directe des gaz des hauts-fourneaux pour la production de la force motrice*, Paris, 1901 ; R. H. Sweetser, *Trans. Amer. Inst. Min. Eng.*, **28**. 608, 1898 ; E. Disdier, *Journ. Iron Steel Inst.*, **55**. i, 130, 1899 ; P. Mortier, *Compt. Rend. Soc. Ind. Min.*, **54**. 1899 ; L. H. Jacoupy, *Rev. Ind.*, 279, 289, 1899 ; V. Thering, *Journ. Gasbeleucht.*, **42**. 225, 1899 ; E. Meyer, *Zeit. Ver. deut. Ing.*, **43**. 488, 483, 1899 ; J. Körting, *ib.*, **43**. 554, 1899 ; B. Donkin, *Eng.*, **88**. 509, 561, 568, 1899 ; C. Dellwik, *Journ. Iron Steel Inst.*, **57**. i, 119, 1900 ; J. Deschamps, *Les grands moteurs à gaz et l'utilization des gaz de haut-fourneau*, Paris, 1901 ; J. Seigle, *Compt. Rend.*, **178**. 1426, 1924 ; J. J. Berzelius, *Jahresb. Chem.*, **20**. 72, 1840 ; M. Zyromsky, *Compt. Rend. Ind. Min.*, 574, 1911 ; G. Eichenberg and P. Oberhoffer, *Arch. Eisenhüttenwesen*, **1**. 617, 1928 ; *Stahl Eisen*, **48**. 1079, 1928 ; P. Reichardt, *ib.*, **47**. 1494, 1927 ; F. Lange, *ib.*, **37**. 261, 1927 ; H. Koppers, *ib.*, **41**. 1254, 1921 ; H. H. Meyer, *ib.*, **49**. 1059, 1929 ; F. Sauerwald, *Physikalische Chemie der metallurgischen Reaktionen*, Berlin, 127, 1930 ; R. Franchot, *Min. Met.*, **7**. 368, 1924 ; **8**. 55, 146, 1927 ; *Tech. Paper Amer. Inst. Min. Eng.—Iron Steel*, 25, 1929 ; W. Lennings, *Arch. Eisenhüttenwesen*, **1**. 549, 1928 ; *Stahl Eisen*, **48**. 1077, 1928 ; *Gestell- und Rastuntersuchung eines Hochofens unter Besonderer Berücksichtigung der Verbrennungsverhältnisse vor den Blas-formen*, Aachen, 1927 ;

O. Boudouard, *Ann. Chim. Phys.*, (7), **24**. 12, 1901; N. Metz, *Stahl Eisen*, **33**. 93, 1913; *Studien über die im Hochofen zwischen den Eisenerzen und Gasen obwaltenden Verhältnisse*, Berlin, 1912; L. Blum, *Stahl Eisen*, **33**. 1077, 1913; *Ferrum*, **10**. 225, 1913; *Zeit. anal. Chem.*, **27**. 451, 1888; E. Schulz, *Beiträge zur Verhüttungen schwefelhaltiger Kiesabbrände im Hochofen*, Breslau, 1912; *Stahl Eisen*, **32**. 1254, 1370, 1912; R. Schäfer, *ib.*, **33**. 68, 1913; *Ferrum*, **10**. 129, 1913; *Ueber den Schwefel bei der Roheisendarstellung*, Berlin, 1912; A. McCance, *ib.*, **97**. i, 253, 1918; E. H. Saniter, *ib.*, **43**. i, 73, 1893; G. J. Snelus, *ib.*, **43**. i, 77, 1893; B. Bolling, *Iron Age*, **81**. 160, 1908; H. Geiger, *Blast Furnace Steel Plant*, **16**. 1201, 1208, 1928; C. Frick, *Chem. Ztg.*, **53**. 317, 1929; H. Allen, *Fielden's Mag.*, **9**. 1, 1903; F. W. Paul, *Journ. West Scotland Iron Steel Inst.*, **5**. 4, 1898; A. Gillespie, *Trans. Inst. Eng. Shipbuilders Scotland*, **39**. 187, 1897; *Cassier's Mag.*, **13**. 354, 1897; A. E. Fletcher, *Annual Report on Alkali Works*, London, **28**. 12, 1891; N. B. Wittman, *Trans. Amer. Inst. Min. Eng.*, **36**. 820, 1905.
²⁵ H. C. Greenwood, *Journ. Chem. Soc.*, **93**. 1483, 1908; *Stahl Eisen*, **47**. 1793, 1927; F. Lange, *ib.*, **35**. 35, 1915; F. Wüst, *ib.*, **48**. 1274, 1928; F. Wüst and A. Schüller, *ib.*, **23**. 1128, 1903; H. von Wartenberg, *ib.*, **45**. 476, 1925; *Zeit. anorg. Chem.*, **142**. 335, 1925; H. H. Meyer, *Mitt. Inst. Eisenforschung*, **9**. 273, 1927; *Stahl Eisen*, **47**. 1793, 1927; A. Ledebur, *ib.*, **14**. 810, 1894; *Handbuch der Eisenhüttenkunde*, 561, 1902; G. Tammann and G. Bätz, *Zeit. anorg. Chem.*, **151**. 129, 1926; S. L. Goodale, *Blast Furnace Steel Plant*, **10**. 274, 367, 1922; I. Bohm, *Tekn. Tids.*, **58**. 9, 1928; H. Hanemann, *Ueber die Reduktion von Silizium aus Tiegelmaterialien durch geschmolzenes kohlehaltiges Eisen*, Berlin, 1909.
²⁶ E. Bahlsen, *Stahl Eisen*, **22**. 326, 1902; R. Durrer, *ib.*, **40**. 938, 1920; O. Simmersbach, *ib.*, **34**. 672, 1914; A. J. Rossi, *ib.*, **16**. 310, 1896; *Iron Age*, **57**. 354, 464, 1896; *Rev. Mét.*, **22**. 121, 193, 1925; J. Head, *Journ. Iron Steel Inst.*, **45**. i, 47, 1894; J. A. Heskett, *ib.*, **101**.·201, 1920; J. F. Kemp, *School Mines Quart.*, **20**. 323, 1899; **21**. 56, 1900; O. Vogel, *Ferrum*, **14**. 177, 1917.
²⁷ I. Bohm, *Tekn. Tids.*, **58**. 9, 1928; H. H. Meyer, *Mitt. Inst. Eisenforschung*, **9**. 273, 1927; W. van Vloten, *Stahl Eisen*, **14**. 834, 1894; W. Mathesius, *ib.*, **6**. 637, 1886; S. Stein, *ib.*, **14**. 786, 1894; F. Wüst, *ib.*, **48**. 1274, 1928; G. Hilgenstock, *ib.*, **5**. 422, 1885; H. Allen, *Fielden's Mag.*, **9**. 1, 1903; F. W. Paul, *Journ. West Scotland Iron Steel Inst.*, **5**. 4, 1898; A. Gillespie, *Trans. Inst. Shipbuilders Scotland*, **39**. 187, 1897; *Cassier's Mag.*, **13**. 354, 1857; A. E. Fletcher, *Annual Report on Alkali Works*, London, **28**. 12, 1891.
²⁸ P. Berthier, *Ann. Mines*, (1), **13**. 101, 1826; C. A. Meissner, *Proc. Alabama Ind. Scient. Soc.*, **4**. 68, 1895; M. Desfosses, *Journ. Pharm. Chim.*, (2), **14**. 280, 1828; *Ann. Chim. Phys.*, (2), **38**. 158, 1828; J. Dawes, *Brit. Pat. No.* 6948, 1835; T. Clark, *Trans. Roy. Soc. Edin.*, **13**. 373, 1836; *Phil. Mag.*, (3), **10**. 329, 1837; J. C. L. Zinken and C. Bromeis, *Pogg. Ann.*, **55**. 89, 1842; *Journ. Prakt. Chem.*, (1), **25**. 246, 1842; J. Redtenbacher, *Liebig's Ann.*, **47**. 150, 1843; J. Percy, *Metallurgy—Iron and Steel*, London, 445, 1864; G. Townes, *B.A. Rep.*, **52**. 1841; H. Kinder, *Stahl Eisen*, **32**. 231, 1912; **40**. 756, 1920; H. Ditz, *ib.*, **32**. 1659; W. Hempel, *Ber.*, **23**. 3390, 1890; C. J. A. Scheerer, *Lehrbuch der Metallurgie*, Berlin, **2**. 18, 1848; J. Müller, *Bergwerksfreund*, **5**. 285, 1843; L. Eck, *Karsten's Arch.*, **24**. 286, 1851; R. Peters, *Berg. Hütt. Ztg.*, **17**. 243, 1858; W. C. Roberts-Austen, *An Introduction to the Study of Metallurgy*, London, 294, 1902; H. Braune, *Stahl Eisen*, **45**. 581, 1925; *Tek. Tids.*, **33**. 45, 1905; *Oesterr. Zeit. Berg. Hütt.*, **53**. 153, 1905; *Journ. Iron Steel Inst.*, **67**. i, 646, 1905; I. L. Bell, *ib.*, **2**. i, 81, 1871; *Principles of the Manufacture of Iron and Steel*, London, 214, 1884; H. le Chatelier, *Rev. Mét.*, **2**. 497, 1905; F. W. Lürmann, *Stahl Eisen*, **12**. 336, 1892; W. McConnachie, *Chem. Age—Met. Section*, **22**. 21, 1930; *Blast Furnace Steel Plant*, **19**. 9,55, 1931; *Iron Steel Ind.*, **4**. 396, 1931; A. K. von Kerpely, *Zeit. Berg. Ver. Kärnten*, **10**. 199, 1878; J. Whiting, *Trans. Amer. Inst. Min. Eng.*, **20**. 280, 1891; P. Gredt, *Berg. Hütt. Ztg.*, **54**. 79, 1895; G. M. F. Arth, *Dingler's Journ.*, **206**. 24, 1895; S. P. Kinney and E. W. Guernsey, *Journ. Ind. Eng. Chem.*, **17**. 670, 1925; *Tech. Paper U.S. Bur. Mines*, 390, 1926; S. P. Kinney, *Iron Age*, **120**. 95, 1927; A. H. Sexton, *Proc. Glasgow Phil. Soc.*, **27**. 122, 1896; R. Hamilton, *Journ. West Scotland Iron Steel Inst.*, **9**. 125, 1902; *Journ. Soc. Chem. Ind.*, **35**. 663, 1916; K. Jurisch, *Chem. Ztg.*, **30**. 393, 1906; C. Catlett, *Iron Coal Trades Rev.*, **93**. 154, 1916; F. Lange, *Stahl Eisen*, **37**. 361, 1917; W. Haufe and H. von Schwarze, *Arch. Eisenhüttenwesen*, **1**. 453, 1928; *Stahl Eisen*, **48**. 201, 1928; R. Bunsen and L. Playfair, *B.A. Rep.*, 142, 1845; 170, 1846; *Journ. prakt. Chem.*, (1), **42**. 266, 1847; *Journ. Pharm.*, **14**. 441, 1848; *Report on the Gases evolved from Iron Furnaces with reference to the Theory of the Smelting of Iron*, London, 1903; H. Wedding, *Ausführliches Handbuch der Eisenhüttenkunde*, Braunschweig, **3**. 249, 1906; R. Franchot, *Min. Met.*, **7**. 368, 1926; B. 55, 364, 1927; *Iron Age*, **119**. 1769, 1927; **120**. 289, 1927; *Trans. Amer. Inst. Min. Eng.*, **62**. 237, 1925; H. von Jüptner, *Chem. Ztg.*, **9**. 890, 1885; A. Lefebvre, *Rev. Univ. Mines*, (8), **5**. 157, 1931; A. Gillespie, *Trans. Inst. Shipbuilders Scotland*, **39**. 187, 1897; *Cassier's Mag.*, **13**. 354, 1897.
²⁹ F. W. Lürmann, *Stahl Eisen*, **16**. 955, 1896; **18**. 260, 1898; **22**. 898, 1902; G. Leuchs, *Journ. prakt. Chem.*, (1), **104**. 186, 1868; A. Engelhardt, *Bergwerksfreund.*, **2**. 472, 1840; H. Wedding, *Ausführliches Handbuch der Eisenhüttenkunde*, Braunschweig, **3**. 384, 1906; J. Percy, *Metallurgy—Iron and Steel*, London, 472, 1864; C. Bolin, *Tek. Tids.*, **34**. 24, 1904; H. Littlehales, *Foundry Trade Journ.*, **30**. 80, 1924; C. H. Lündström, *Jernkontorets Ann.*, (2), **45**. 312, 1890; W. Schmidhammer, *Stahl Eisen*, **13**. 640, 1893; O. Hahn, *ib.*, **17**. 55, 1897; A. Ledebur, *ib.*, **4**. 640, 1884; **17**. 482, 1897; *Handbuch der Eisenhüttenkunde*, Leipzig, **2**. 290, 1906; P. von Tunner, *Jahrb. österr. Bergakad.*, **15**. 97, 1865; B. Kerl, *Grundriss der Eisen-*

hüttenkunde, Leipzig, **1**. 807, 1875.; J. Pattinson, *B.A. Rep.*, 49, 1863 ; *Berg. Hütt. Ztg.*, **22**. 439, 1863 ; E. Ebermayer, *ib.*, **17**. 394, 1858 ; A. von Kerpely, *ib.*, **24**. 419, 1865 ; *Zeit. Berg. Ver. Kärnten*, **10**. 199, 1878 ; C. F. Rammelsberg, *Lehrbuch der chemischen Metallurgie*, Berlin, 138, 1850 ; J. B. Walker, *The Story of Steel*, New York, 1926 ; B. H. Thwaite, *Journ. Iron Steel Inst.*, **63**. i, 246, 1903 ; R. M. Colles, *Journ. Iron Steel Inst.—Carnegie Mem.*, **18**. 53, 1929 ; V. le Vrärier, *Génie Civil*, **26**. 164, 1895 ; W. B. Phillips, *Proc. Alabama Ind. Scient. Soc.*, **4**. 64, 1895 ; A. H. Sexton, *An Outline of the Metallurgy of Iron and Steel*, Glasgow, 62, 1902 ; *Journ. West Scotland Iron Steel Inst.*, **2**. 112, 1895 ; R. Hamilton, *ib.*, **9**. 125, 157, 1902 ; L. Blum, *Stahl Eisen*, **17**. 984, 1897 ; **33**. 1356, 1913 ; C. Pradel, *Bull. Soc. Nat. Agric.*, **59**. 299, 1899 ; J. J. Porter, *Iron Age*, **73**. 10, 1904 ; *Trans. Amer. Inst. Min. Eng.*, **38**. 448, 1907 ; *Stahl Eisen*, **24**. 1359, 1904 ; E. Priwoznik, *Berg. Hütt. Jahrb.*, **53**. 396, 1906 ; E. D. Campbell, *Journ. Iron Steel Inst.*, **68**. ii, 371, 1905 ; R. K. Meade, *Met. Chem. Engg.*, **17**. 78, 1917 ; J. S. Grasty, *ib.*, **19**. 434, 1918 ; J. G. Dean, *ib.*, **19**. 439, 1918 ; F. W. Bruckmiller, *ib.*, **19**. 447, 1918 ; L. Bradley, *ib.*, **19**. 457, 1918 ; R. A. Berry and D. N. McArthur, *Journ. Soc. Chem. Ind.*, **37**. 1, T, 1918 ; *Iron Coal Trades Rev.*, **96**. 88, 1918 ; K. M. Chance, *ib.*, **96**. 58, 1918 ; N. H. Gellert, *Iron Age*, **105**. 355, 1919 ; *Blast Furnace Steel Plant*, **7**. 334, 1919 ; W. H. Ross and A. B. Merz, *Journ. Ind. Eng. Chem.*, **14**. 302, 1922 ; W. McConnachie, *Journ. West Scotland Iron Steel Inst.*, **34**. 79, 1927 ; W. Danielsen, *Min. Met.*, **5**. 569, 1924 ; M. Paschke, *Arch. Eisenhüttenwesen*, **1**. 387, 1928 ; L. Gruner, *Métallurgie du fer*, Paris, 168, 1862 ; I. L. Bell, *Principles of the Manufacture of Iron and Steel*, London, 165, 1864 ; O. F. Hudson, *Iron and Steel*, London, 17, 1913 ; B. Osann, *Lehrbuch der Eisenhüttenkunde*, Leipzig, 448, 1923 ; R. Forsythe, *The Blast Furnace and the Manufacture of Pig Iron*, New York, 200, 1922 ; F. Bicheroux, *Principles de sidérurgie*, Paris, 46, 1924 ; A. Korevaar, *Combustion in the Gas Producer and Blast Furnace*, London, 124, 1924 ; T. Turner, *The Metallurgy of Iron*, London, 170, 1908 ; B. Stoughton, *The Metallurgy of Iron and Steel*, New York, 528, 1923 ; W. Mathesius, *Die physikalischen und chemischen Grundlagen des Eisenhüttenwesens*, Leipzig, 222, 1916 ; *Stahl Eisen*, **32**. 1502, 1912 ; H. von Jüptner, *Hochofentheorie*, Leipzig, 114, 1921 ; M. von Schwarz, *Eisenhüttenkunde*, Leipzig, **1**. 85, 1924 ; H. H. Meyer, *Mitt. Inst. Eisenforschung*, **9**. 273, 1927 ; O. Simmersbach, *Stahl Eisen*, **37**. 502, 844, 919, 1917 ; I. A. Baar, *ib.*, **45**. 438, 1925 ; W. Heike, *ib.*, **35**. 313, 1915 ; O. Vogel, *ib.*, **16**. 615, 1896 ; H. Thaler, *ib.*, **34**. 1481, 1914 ; *Experimentelle Untersuchung des Siegerländer Spiegeleisen Hochofens*, Breslau, 1914 ; I. Bohm, *Tek. Tids.*, **58**. 9, 1928 ; J. E. Johnson, *Chem. Met. Engg.*, **13**. 636, 700, 1915 ; R. Lorenz, *Zeit. anorg. Chem.*, **92**. 35, 1915 ; W. D. Brown, *Blast Furnace Steel Plant*, **13**. 236, 1925 ; M. Derclaye, *Rev. Mét.*, **21**. 315, 396, 450, 1924 ; F. W. Davis, *Iron Age*, **112**. 717, 1923 ; J. E. Fletcher, *Iron Coal Trades Rev.*, **92**. 364, 1916 ; R. von Seth, *Metall Erz*, **22**. 219, 1925 , *Jernkontorets Ann.*, (2), **79**. 561, 1924 ; J. Pattinson and J. E. Stead, *Journ. Iron Steel Inst.*, **34**. ii, 171, 1888.

[30] H. Allen, *Metallurgical Manual of Iron and Steel*, London, 148, 1911 ; *Iron Trade Rev.*, **40**. 419, 589, 741, 1004, 1906 ; **41**. 61, 227, 430, 1907 ; E. Adamson, *Trans. Manchester Assoc. Eng.*, 129, 1905 ; T. Turner, *Journ. Iron Steel Inst.*, **39**. i, 119, 1891 ; *The Metallurgy of Iron*, London, 279, 1915 ; H. Pilkington, *Proc. South Staffs Inst. Iron Steel*, **5**. 84, 1890 ; I. L. Bell, *Principles of the Manufacture of Iron and Steel*, London, 1884 ; T. E. Holgate, *Proc. South Staffs Inst. Iron Steel*, **4**. 1, 1888 ; J. E. Stead, *Journ. Iron Steel Inst.*, **43**. i, 153, 1893 ; H. P. Tiemann, *Iron and Steel*, New York, 342, 1919 ; J. E. Johnson, *Chem. Met. Engg.*, **15**. 530, 588, 642, 683, 1916 ; *Amer. Machinist*, **23**. 342, 1899 ; E. A. Kebler, *Iron Trade Rev.*, **42**. 1183, 1908 ; H. Dickmann, *Bibliographie über die Darstellung des Roheisens im elektrischen Ofen*, Düsseldorf, 1921 ; M. Orthey, *Met.*, **4**. 78, 1907 ; G. Bätz, *Ueber die Gewinnung von Eisen aus Silikaten und Pyrite*, Göttingen, 1925 ; L. Houghton, *Foundry*, **29**. 109, 1907 ; C. H. Kain, *Foundry Trade Journ.*, **41**. 403, 422, 1929 ; N. Lilienberg, *Bihang Jernkontorets Ann.*, **4**. 202, 1903 ; N. Kjellberg, *Jernkontorets Ann.*, (2), **44**. 389, 1890 ; W. N. Hartley and H. Ramage, *Proc. Roy. Soc.*, **60**. 35, 393, 1896 ; *Journ. Iron Steel Inst.*, **52**. ii, 182, 1897 ; A. Gouvy, *Berg. Hütt. Jahrb.*, **39**. 1, 1891 ; E. Priwoznik, *ib.*, **38**. 406, 1890 ; **40**. 466, 1892 ; **50**. 437, 1902 ; **53**. 390, 1905 ; W. B. Phillips, *Proc. Alabama Ind. Soc.*, **6**. 15, 1897 ; W. H. Brannon, *ib.*, **6**. 11, 1896 ; C. F. Eichleiter, *Jahrb. geol. Reichsanst.*, **47**. 751, 1898 ; G. L. Luetscher, *ib.*, **47**. 1058, 1891 : **48**. 17, 1891 ; *Journ. Iron Steel Inst.*, **40**. ii, 245, 1891 ; O. Simmersbach, *Correspondenz Ver. deut. Eisengiessereien*, 117, 1897 ; *Die Eisenindustrie*, Leipzig, 48, 1907 ; N. L. Goodwin, *Journ. Soc. Chem. Ind.*, **21**. 743, 1902 ; Anon., *Chem. Ztg.*, **15**. 1493, 1891 ; H. Wedding, *ib.*, **20**. 425, 1896 ; M. Eckwaldt, *Giesserei Ztg.*, **5**. 16, 1908 ; J. M. Hartman, *Journ. Franklin Inst.*, **134**. 132, 1892 ; R. Fluhr, *Zeit. prakt. Geol.*, **16**. 1, 1908 ; A. Kayser, *Oesterr. Zeit. Berg. Hütt.*, **40**. 256, 1892 ; R. Volkmann, *ib.*, **41**. 656, 1893 ; J. Parry and J. J. Morgan, *Industries*, **14**. 90, 1893 ; W. Schilling, *Stahl Eisen*, **15**. 134, 1895 ; A. Ledebur, *ib.*, **14**. 810, 1894 ; B. Osann, *ib.*, **22**. 1035, 1902 ; T. Jung, *ib.*, **15**. 663, 1895 ; K. Daeves, *ib.*, **51**. 202, 1931 ; J. Kowarsky, *ib.*, **16**. 863, 1896 ; F. Wüst, *ib.*, **17**. 1008, 1897 ; H. O. Goldschmidt, *ib.*, **18**. 368, 1898 ; O. Thallner, *ib.*, **19**. 914, 1899 ; M. Neumark, *ib.*, **21**. 112, 1901 ; A. Helfenstein, *ib.*, **41**. 1481, 1572, 1921 ; C. von John and C. F. Eichleiter, *Jahrb. geol. Reichsanst.*, **45**. 21, 1896 ; L. J. Igelström, *Zeit. Kryst.*, **26**. 94, 1896 ; T. D. West, *Amer. Machinist*, **23**. 428, 1900 ; A. Pourcel, *Rev. Gen. Sciences*, **7**. 465, 510, 539, 1896 ; W. W. Taylor, *Iron Trade Rev.*, **31**. 7, 1899 ; H. Littlehales, *Foundry Trade Journ.*, **30**. 80, 1924 ; W. Danielsen, *Min. Met.*, **5**. 569, 1924.

[31] J. N. Pring, *The Electric Furnace*, London, 174, 1921 ; E. Haanel, *Trans. Faraday Soc.*, **2**. 120, 1906 ; **5**. 306, 1909 ; *Report on the Canadian Commission on the Electrothermic processes*

for Smelting Iron Ores, Ottawa, 1904 ; *Stahl Eisen*, **35**. 531, 1905 ; **37**. 1256, 1907 ; *Report on the Experiments made at Sault St. Marie, Ontario*, Ottawa, 1907 ; *Report on the Investigation of an Electrical Shaft Furnace at Domnarfvet, Sweden*, Ottawa, 1907 ; *Electrochem. Ind.*, **4**. 265, 1906 ; *Iron Steel Mag.*, **11**. 401, 1906 ; *Iron Age*, **84**. 831, 1909 ; *Trans. Amer. Electrochem. Soc.*, **15**. 25, 1909 ; *Trans. Canada Soc. Civil Eng.*, **19**. 103, 1907 ; C. Vattier, *Mém. Soc. Ing. Civils*, **19**, 1903 ; J. B. C. Kershaw, *Elect. World*, **51**. 856, 1908 ; *The Electric Furnace in Iron and Steel Production*, London, 1907 ; *Electrothermal Methods of Iron and Steel Production*, London, 1913 ; *Elect. Rev.*, **42**. 793, 842, 1903 ; *Elect. Mag.*, 181, 1904 ; *Cassier's Mag.*, **30**. 23, 1906 ; **32**. 26, 1907 ; *Iron Trade Rev.*, **39**. 31, 1906 ; **40**. 30, 1907 ; **50**. 41, 1912 ; *Eng. Mag.*, **34**. 261, 1908 ; G. Garnier, *Mois Scient.*, 3, 1903 ; M. Ruthenberg, *Electrochemist Metallurgist*, **2**. 12, 1902 ; *Iron Age*, **70**. 5, 1902 ; *Trans. Amer. Electrochem. Soc.*, **2**. 93, 1903 ; **4**. 9, 1903 ; **18**. 185, 1910 ; R. Pitaval, *Compt. Rend. Soc. Ind. Min.*, 273, 1901 ; *Congrès Internat. Liége*, **1**. 307, 1905 ; A. Gerard, *L'Ind. Electrochim.*, **3**. 7, 1899 ; E. Hubon, *Mem. Soc. Ing. Civils*, **52**. 424, 1899 ; H. Flodin and E. G. T. Gustafsson, *Swedish Pat. No.* 66671, 1929 ; E. G. T. Gustafsson, *U.S. Pat. No.* 1751083, 1930 ; D. T. Waby, *Elect. World*, **94**. 326, 1929 ; O. Webr, *Chem. Listy*, **22**. 101, 1928 ; T. F. Baily, *Elect. World*, **71**. 780, 1918 ; *Tech. Publ. Amer. Inst. Min. Eng.*, 296, 1930 ; *Iron Age*, **125**. 726, 1930 ; F. H. Daniels, *ib.*, **58**. 635, 1896 ; H. Harmet, *Compt. Rend. Soc. Ind. Min.*, 85, 1902 ; *Electrochemist Metallurgist*, **2**. 93, 1902 ; F. W. Harbord, *Trans. Faraday Soc.*, **1**. 140, 1905 ; *Electrochem. Ind.*, **3**. 218, 1905 ; F. W. Harbord and E. Haanel, *ib.*, **2**. 486, 1904 ; F. Wright, *Electric Furnaces and their Industrial Applications*, London, 1904 ; *Trans, Canadian Soc. Civil Eng.*, **19**. 103, 1907 ; W. Rodenhauser, *Elect. Kraftbetriebe Bahnen*, **10**. 281, 1912 ; **11**. 561, 1913 ; W. Rodenhauser and J. Schoenawa, *Elektrische Oefen in der Eisenindustrie*, Leipzig, 1911 ; *Electric Furnaces in the Iron and Steel Industry*, New York, 248, 1920 ; A. Stansfield, *Met. Chem. Engg.*, **20**. 630, 1919 ; **27**. 941, 1923 ; *Eng. Min. Journ.*, **107**. 224, 1919 ; *Fuels Furnaces*, **7**. 87, 251, 1929 ; *Iron Coal Trades Rev.*, **98**. 287, 1919 ; *Trans. Canadian Soc. Civil Eng.*, **7**. 157, 1906 ; *Journ. Canada Min. Inst.*, **10**. 129, 1908 ; **11**. 180, 1909 ; *Bull. Canada Min. Inst.*, **87**. 706, 1919 ; *Canadian Min. Journ.*, **33**. 448, 1912 ; *Rep. Canada Dept. Mines*, 344, 1915 ; *Bull. Columbia Dept. Mines*, 2, 1919 ; *The Electric Furnace*, Toronto, 1907 ; New York, 1914 ; *Cassier's Mag.*, **49**. 97, 1916 ; R. S. Hutton, *Journ. Soc. Chem. Ind.*, **24**. 589, 1905 ; *Engg.*, **82**. 779, 1906 ; *Iron Coal Trades Rev.*, **73**. 1264, 1906 ; B. Neumann, *Stahl Eisen*, **24**. 682, 761, 821, 883, 944, 1904 ; **31**. 1010, 1911 ; **32**. 1409, 1912 ; **35**. 1152, 1915 ; *Elektrometallurgie des Eisens*, Halle a. S., 1907 ; *Die technische Gewinnung von Eisen und Stahl im elektrischen Ofen*, Braunschweig, 1910 ; *Met. Ital.*, **8**. 248, 1916 ; F. J. Moffett, *The Electric Furnace*, London, 1921 ; J. W. Richards, *Metallurgical Calculations*, New York, **2**. 403, 1907 ; *Proc. Eng. Soc. West Pennsylvania*, **27**. 125, 1911 ; **28**. 83, 1913 ; *Iron Coal Trades Rev.*, **80**. 738, 1910 ; *Tech. Quart.*, **17**. 22, 1904 ; *Chem. Met. Engg.*, **5**. 165, 1907 ; **7**. 253, 1909 ; **10**. 289, 1912 ; **22**. 61, 1920 ; *Journ. Franklin Inst.*, **164**. 443, 1907 ; **165**. 47, 1908 ; **169**. 131, 1910 ; *Trans. Amer. Electrochem. Soc.*, **12**. 81, 1907 ; **15**. 53, 1909 ; **21**. 403, 1912 ; H. H. Noble, *ib.*, **11**. 16, 383, 1913 ; M. Oesterreich, *Stahl Eisen*, **33**. 305, 1913 ; **36**. 1059, 1916 ; *Chem. Met. Engg.*, **16**. 509, 1917 ; G. Arnou, *Lumière Électr.*, **16**. 269, 1911 ; *Rev. Mét.*, **7**. 1190, 1910 ; A. E. Greene and F. S. Macgregor, *Chem. Met. Engg.*, **5**. 367, 1907 ; *Trans. Amer. Electrochem. Soc.*, **12**. 65, 1907 ; R. Moldenke, *Iron Trade Rev.*, **31**. 12, 1898 ; *Chem. Met. Engg.*, **5**. 207, 1907 ; G. L. Simpson, *Trans. Amer. Electrochem. Soc.*, **57**. 435, 1930 ; *Bull. Canada Min. Inst.*, **87**. 709, 1919 ; *Iron Coal Trades Rev.*, **68**. 173, 605, 1904 ; E. Stassano, *German Pat.*, *D.R.P.* 141512, (1898) 1903 ; *L'Électricien*, **32**. 65, 82, 1906 ; *Nuovo Processo elettro-metallurgico par l'Estrazione del Ferro dai suoi Minerali*, Roma, 1899 ; *Ueber die gegenwärtige Lage und Zukunft des thermo-elektrischen Hüttenwesens im allgemeinen und der thermoelektrischen Eisenindustrie im besonderen*, Turin, 1906 ; *Elektrotech. Zeit.*, **18**. 19, 1911 ; *Trans. Amer. Electrochem. Soc.*, **15**. 63, 1909 ; *Electrochem. Ind.*, **6**. 315, 1908 ; **7**. 107, 1909 ; *Rev. Mét.*, **5**. 575, 1908 ; *Brit. Pat. No.* 11604, 1898 ; *Riv. Minera*, **51**. 116, 1899 ; A. Lindblad, *Iron Coal Trades Rev.*, **82**. 838, 1911 ; G. K. Elliot, *Trans. Amer. Electrochem. Soc.*, **35**. 175, 1919 ; **41**. 21, 1923 ; C. J. West, *ib.*, **38**. 365, 1920 ; W. E. Cahill, *ib.*, **41**. 99, 1922 ; S. H. Eckmann, *Electrician*, **70**. 389, 1912 ; H. Etchells, *ib.*, **81**. 734, 1918 ; A. H. Marshall, *ib.*, **80**. 550, 1918 ; A. Grönwall, *Tek. Tids.*, **43**. 145, 1913 ; *Tek. Ukeblad*, **36**. 601, 1918 ; **41**. 164, 1923 ; **42**. 16, 1924 ; *Stahl Eisen*, **42**. 460, 1922 ; *Bihang Jernkontorets Ann.*, **8**. 296, 1907 ; A. Grönwall, A. Lindblad, and O. Stålhane, *ib.*, **8**. 296, 1907 ; J. Crawford, *Met. Chem. Engg.*, **11**. 383, 1913 ; E. Fornander, *Värmländska Bergsmann. Ann.*, 36, 1913 ; *Iron Coal Trades Rev.*, **86**. 955, 1913 ; P. G. Angew, *Elect. Rev.*, **64**. 100, 1914 ; K. G. Frank, *Proc. Amer. Inst. Elect. Eng.*, **34**. 2547, 1915 ; A. H. W. Aten, *Chem. Weekbl.*, **17**. 433, 441, 450, 461, 482, 493, 508, 1920 ; E. S. Bardwell, *Iron Age*, **106**. 973, 1920 ; E. F. Cone, *ib.*, **109**. 485, 1917 ; A. Redlich, *Schweiz. Bauztg.*, **77**. 249, 1921 ; J. Baumann, *Chem. Ztg.*, **48**. 699, 1924 ; J. L. McYardley, *Blast Furnace Steel Plant*, **12**. 532, 1924 ; **13**. 21, 30, 1925 ; H. L. Hatt, *Iron Trade Rev.*, **68**. 149, 1921 ; E. Guarini, *L'état actuel de l'électrométallurgie du fer et de l'acier*, Paris, 1905 ; *Scient. Amer. Suppl.*, **58**. 23895, 23904, 23918, 1904 ; P. Grillet, *La métallurgie du fer*, Paris, 1919 ; C. A. Keller, *Traitement électrothermique du fer et de l'acier*, Paris, 1906 ; *French Pat. No.* 405277, 1908 ; 19358, 1913 ; *Contribution à l'étude des fours électriques, appliqués à la fabrication des fers et aciers*, Grenoble, 1909 ; *Journ. Iron Steel Inst.*, **63**. i, 161, 1903 ; *Trans. Amer. Electrochem. Soc.*, **15**. 87, 1909 ; **37**. 189, 1920 ; *Tech. Moderne*, 361, 423, 1919 ; E. Lecron, *ib.*, 177, 1921 ; P. Ferchland, *Die englischen elektrochemischen Patente*, Halle a. S., 1907 ; *Die elektrochemischen Patentschriften der Vereinigten Staaten von Nord-Amerika*, Halle a. S., 1913 ; A. Thorne,

P. C. Farup and J. H. L. Vogt, *Forelöbig Industriberetning*, Kristiania, 1909; *Tek. Ukeblad*, **32.** 20, 1914; **56.** 419, 1919; J. H. L. Vogt, *Jernmalm og Jernverk saerlig om elektrisk Jernmalsmelting*, Kristiania, 1918; *Tek. Ukeblad*, **21.** 303, 1903; *Iron Coal Trades Rev.*, **86.** 340, 1913; *Norges Geol. Undersökelse*, 85, 1918; *Stahl Eisen*, **40.** 368, 702, 1920; H. Ponthière, *Traité d'électrométallurgie*, Paris, 1910; F. Regelsberger, *Elektrometallurgie*, Leipzig, 1910; H. Vigneron, *Électrochimie et électrométallurgie*, Paris, 1911; L. Puccinelli, *I forni electrici nella siderurgia*, Turin, 1913; K. Hofmann, *Zeit. angew. Chem.;* **38.** 1085, 1925; D. Wilkinson, *Foundry*, **50.** 143, 1922; A. J. Rossi, *Iron Age*, **70.** 5, 1902; *Electrochem. Ind.*, **3.** 53, 1905; *Trans. Amer. Electrochem. Soc.*, **7.** 199, 1905; J. L. Cawthon, *ib.*, **41.** 45, 1922; H. Goldschmidt, *Zeit. Elektrochem.*, **9.** 647, 660, 1903; **10.** 529, 1904; *Electrician*, **52.** 163, 1903; *Electrochem. Ind.*, **1.** 461, 1903; *Stahl Eisen*, **24.** 787, 1904; L. Höwenstein, *Giesserei Ztg.*, **1.** 651, 1904; W. McClure, *English Rev.*, **11.** 335, 1904; G. Miami, *Met. Ital.*, **1.** 17, 1910; E. A. Sjostedt, *Met. Chem. Engg.*, **8.** 8, 1910; L. J. Barton, *ib.*, **23.** 270, 1922; *Iron Age*, **111.** 269, 1923; B. D. Enlund, *Jernkontorets Ann.*, (2), **66.** 400, 1911; G. Herlin, *ib.*, (2), **77.** 99, 1922; (2), **78.** 132, 1923; B. Kalling, *ib.*, (2), **74.** 413, 1919; I. Hole, *Tek. Ukeblad*, **32.** 161, 1914; W. Olssön, *ib.*, **32.** 566, 1914; H. Batt, *ib.*, **42.** 67, 1924; *La Vie Tech.*, 84, 1926; C. Svensson, *Tek. Ukeblad*, **41.** 8, 1923; F. B. Grimes, *ib.*, **41.** 200, 1923; B. Giersten, *ib.*, **41.** 103, 1923; U. Koren, *ib.*, **41.** 299, 1923; B. Raeder, *ib.*, **41.** 239, 1923; H. Kalpers, *Dingler's Journ.*, **341.** 177, 1926; *Stahl Eisen*, **40.** 437, 1920; E. Demenge, *Génie Civil*, **33.** 205, 220, 1898; G. S. Schaller, *Trans. Amer. Foundrymen's Assoc.*, **33.** 510, 1926; F. von Kügelgen, *Zeit. Electrochem.*, **9.** 516, 1903; J. Neuberg, *Bull. Science Assoc. Élèves Écoles*, **6.** 169, 1904; A. Stiévenant, *ib.*, **14.** 91, 161, 219, 379, 1912; P. L. T. Héroult, *Electrochem. Ind.*, **2.** 408, 1904; *Trans. Amer. Electrochem. Soc.*, **6.** 129, 1904; *French Pat. No.* 733040, 1903; C. de Coussergues, *Rev. Mét.*, **20.** 422, 1923; M. Mathieu and M. Sutter, *ib.*, **22.** 477, 489, 1925; F. Cirkel, *Stahl Eisen*, **26.** 868, 1369, 1906; K. Dornhecker, *ib.*, **41.** 1881, 1921; **42.** 854, 1357, 1922; W. Steubing and A. Kirschbaum, *ib.*, **44.** 467, 1924; K. P. Grigorowitsch, *ib.*, **46.** 377, 1926; K. Christen, *ib.*, **49.** 769, 1929; M. Wintermeyer, *Elektrotech. Anz.*, **40.** 612, 1923; R. Kunz, *Ber. Stahlwerksaus, Ver. Eisenhüttenleute*, 61, 1921; L. Grimshaw, *Iron Trade Rev.*, **40.** 954, 1907; R. V. Sawhill, *ib.*, **61.** 437, 1917; G. Hooghwinkel, *Electrician*, **65.** 307, 1910; N. Henry, *L'Électricien*, **38.** 132, 1909; H. Nathusius, *Giesserei*, **16.** 993, 999, 1929; C. Brisker, *Stahl Eisen*, **30.** 1049, 1910; W. Conrad, *ib.*, **30.** 1076, 1910; C. Flössel, *ib.*, **42.** 464, 1922; P. Seehaus, *ib.*, **42.** 461, 1922; J. Bronn, *ib.*, **41.** 881, 1040, 1921; **42.** 854, 1922; C. Hering, *Met. Chem. Engg.*, **8.** 471, 1910; J. Herlenius, *ib.*, **24.** 108, 1921; W. L. Anderson, *ib.*, **26.** 312, 1922; G. Kroupa, *Oesterr. Zeit. Berg. Hütt.*, **59.** 502, 515, 1911; R. von Seth, *Tek. Tids.*, **52.** 808, 1922; J. Forssell, *ib.*, **59.** 605, 619, 640, 1929; F. R. Eichhoff, *Stahl Eisen*, **27.** 47, 1907; *Die elektrische Erzeugung von Stahl und Eisen*, Berlin, 1914; *Zeit. angew. Chem.*, **27.** 166, 1914; A. Hiorth, *Heat Balance for A. Hiorth's Electrical Blast Furnace*, Kristiania, 1914; *Some Remarks on Iron Smelting*, Kristiania, 1912; *Eng. News*, **16.** 196, 1907; *Eisen. Ztg.*, **28.** 420, 657, 658, 1907; *Tek. Ugeblad*, **25.** 81, 1907; M. Lorentzen, *ib.*, **25.** 98, 1907; **36.** 563, 1918; **41.** 72, 123, 228, 435, 1928; **42.** 268, 1924; A. Helland, *Norsk. Tids. Haandvœerk*, **13.** 82, 1907; *Glückauf*, **42.** 1384, 1419, 1443, 1469, 1519, 1552, 1582, 1619, 1644, 1907; E. Hammarström, *Tek. Tids.*, **36.** 33, 1907; H. Allen, *Mech. Eng.*, **19.** 39, 1907; *Cassier's Mag.*, **27.** 358, 1905; A. Pourcel, *Génie Civil*, **49.** 232, 1907; E. C. Ibbotson, *Journ. Iron Steel Inst.*, **71.** iii, 397, 1906; B. Osann, *Stahl Eisen*, **28.** 654, 1908; R. Durrer, *Untersuchungen zur Klärung der Frage der elektrischen Verhüttung schweizerischer Eisenerze*, Düsseldorf, 1924; *Iron Trade Rev.*, **70.** 827, 1922; *Stahl Eisen*, **41.** 753, 1039, 1153, 1921; **42.** 463, 1922; **43.** 662, 1923; **44.** 465, 748, 1924; **45.** 10, 1925; *Schweiz. Bauztg.*, **76.** 241, 1920; R. L. Phelps, *Min. Scient. Press.*, **95.** 87, 1907; T. H. Holland, *Trans. Min. Geol. Inst. India*, 9, 1907; F. Laur, *Echo Mines*, **31.** 968, 1904; C. A. Hansen, *ib.*, **7.** 270, 1909; *Electrochem. Ind.*, **7.** 206, 1909; F. Louvrier, *Mining Journ.*, **83.** 651, 1908; *Electrochem. Met. Ind.*, **7.** 159, 1909; **11.** 710, 1913; L. François and L. Tissier, *Rev. Tech. Luxembourgeoise*, **25.** 469, 695, 1904; G. Gin, *ib.*, **566.** 1065, 1904; *Trans. Amer. Electrochem. Soc.*, **11.** 291, 1907; J. Wright, *Cassier's Mag.*, **26.** 24, 1904; W. Troeller, *Prometheus*, **15.** 561, 1904; J. Härden, *Iron Coal Trades Rev.*, **73.** 2012, 1902; *Electrician*, **68.** 467, 1912; *Page's Weekly*, **12.** 1279, 1908; *Tek. Tids.*, **41.** 21, 1911; *Trans. Met. Chem. Engg.*, **12.** 444, 1914; *Trans. Faraday Soc.*, **4.** 120, 1908; *Chem. Met. Engg.*, **7.** 16, 1909; **12.** 82, 223, 444, 1914; R. Catani, *ib.*, **7.** 268, 1909; *Met. Ital.*, **7.** 212, 1915; *L'Industria*, **23.** 82, 135, 1909; *Stahl Eisen*, **29.** 277, 1909; *Journ. Iron Steel Inst.*, **84.** ii, 215, 1911; *Trans. Amer. Electrochem. Soc.*, **15.** 159, 1909; A. F. Schneider, *Mining Mag.*, **10.** 109, 1904; F. Peters, *Glückauf*, **42.** 1015, 1906; A. Minet, *Le four électrique*, Paris, 1905; *Eng. Mag.*, **27.** 796, 1904; *Trans. Faraday Soc.*, **4.** 88, 1904; E. A. Ashcroft, *ib.*, **4.** 134, 1909; E. Frasenster, *Rev. Univ. Mines*, (4), **21.** 252, 1909; B. Blount, *Journ. Soc. Arts*, **52.** 743, 753, 767, 1904; A. Neuburger, *Handbuch der praktischen Elektrometallurgie*, München, 1907; *Berg. Hütt. Ztg.*, **62.** 481, 493, 1903; *Zeit. angew. Chem.*, **20.** 97, 1907; *Glaser's Ann.*, **63.** 199, 215, 1909; A. Neuburger and A. Minet, *Mining Journ.*, **76.** 672, 1904; **77.** 672, 1905; *Rev. Minera*, **56.** 85, 1905; G. Gallo, *ib.*, **28.** 117, 1907; C. le Chatelier, *Rev. Mét.*, **4.** 85, 1908; W. Schmidhammer, *Oesterr. Zeit. Berg. Hütt.*, **52.** 613, 1904; A. Pummer, *ib.*, **55.** 105, 125, 1907; J. von Ehrenwerth, *ib.*, **56.** 1, 21, 1908; *Elektrotech. Zeit.*, **31.** 331, 1910; *Zeit. Ver. deut. Ing.*, **63.** 442, 1919; L. Katona, *Bany. Koh. Lapok*, **39.** 285, 1906; R. H. Wolff, *Iron Age*, **77.** 1990, 1906; K. Pietrusky, *Chem. Zeit.*, **4.** 433, 1905; T. H. Norton, *Ind. World*, 8, 1908; J. Elwell, *ib.*, 3, 1909; W. Mason, *Elect. Rev.*, **79.** 190, 1923; G. L. Casey, *ib.*, **76.** 500, 1920; O. Frick, *Jernkontorets Ann.*, (2), **59.** 333, 1905;

Met. Chem. Engg., **9**. 631, 1911 ; J. J. Smith, *ib.*, **9**. 624, 1911 ; J. Thibeau, *Rev. Univ. Mines*, **15**. 206, 1906 ; D. T. Day, *Iron Age*, **76**. 1742, 1905 ; O. Stromberg, *ib.*, **82**. 1868, 1908 : W. McA. Johnson, *ib.*, **90**. 450, 1912 ; *Met. Chem. Engg.*, **12**. 165, 1914 ; W. McA. Johnson and G. N. Sieger, *ib.*, **11**. 504, 563, 1913 ; A. Lodyguine, *Trans. Amer. Electrochem. Soc.*, **7**. 157, 1905 ; E. F. Kern, *ib.*, **13**. 103, 1908 ; *Met. Chem. Engg.*, **6**. 242, 1908 ; L. D. Farnsworth, *ib.*, **6**. 326, 1908 ; T. D. Robertson, *Trans. Amer. Electrochem. Soc.*, **20**. 375, 1911 ; *Mech. Eng.*, **28**. 815, 1911 ; *Electrician*, **70**. 501, 1912 ; A. Stewart, *Eng. Rev.*, **14**. 219, 1906 ; G. de Geer, *ib.*, **24**. 429, 1921 ; M. Mariani, *Rev. Mét.*, **4**. 84, 1906 ; H. Cassel, *Mining Journ.*, **85**. 113, 1909 ; J. Hess, *Zeit. Elektrochem.*, **12**. 231, 1906 ; F. Müller, *ib.*, **13**. 108, 1907 ; R. W. van Norden, *Journ. Elect. Power Gas*, **29**. 453, 1912 ; *Elect. Rev.*, **61**. 1134, 1912 ; *Met. Chem. Engg.*, **11**. 17, 1913 ; W. Gillett, *Metals Alloys*, **1**. 671, 1930 ; W. Lister, *Foundry Trade Journ.*, **43**. 165, 1930 ; E. J. Ljungberg, *Iron Coal Trades Rev.*, **87**. 799, 1913 ; *Iron Age*, **92**. 1392, 1913 ; *Journ. Iron Steel Inst.*, **80**. ii, 9, 1909 ; B. Igewsky, *ib.*, **76**. i, 155, 1908 ; B. Blount, *Trans. Conference Inst. Civil Eng.*, 110, 1907 ; T. S. Anderson, *Eng. Min. Journ.*, **83**. 1231, 1907 ; J. Tyssowsky, *ib.*, **90**. 269, 1910 ; L. Campredon, *Centr. Hütt. Walzwerke*, 454, 1907 ; W. Steel, *Giesserei Ztg.*, **4**. 78, 1907 ; K. von Kerpely, *ib.*, **22**. 213, 328, 1925 ; **23**. 33, 1926 ; *Iron Age*, **117**. 760, 1926 ; *Stahl Eisen*, **45**. 2004, 1925 ; F. C. Perkins, *Mining World*, **30**. 535, 1909 ; A. H. Martin, *ib.*, **33**. 365, 1910 ; S. Herlin, *Jernkontorets Ann.*, (2), **77**. 99, 1922 ; (2), **78**. 132, 1923 ; *Stahl Eisen*, **43**. 1431, 1923 ; L. Yungström, *Bihang Jernkontorets Ann.*, **10**. 739, 1900 ; M. Guédras, *Giorn. Chim. Ind. Appl.*, **3**. 58, 1921 ; G. Ongaro, *ib.*, **3**. 288, 1921 ; E. R. Taylor, *Mech. Eng.*, **25**. 131, 1910 ; *Trans. Amer. Electrochem. Soc.*, **16**. 229, 1909 ; *Iron Age*, **85**. 1202, 1910 ; *Iron Trade Rev.*, **46**. 141, 1910 ; *Trans. Amer. Inst. Chem. Eng.*, **2**. 280, 1909 ; F. E. Carcano, *Atti Assoc. Elettrotech. Ital.*, **14**. 201, 1910 ; *Met. Ital.*, **1**. 5, 1910 ; *Electrochem. Ind.*, **7**. 155, 1909 ; P. M. Bennie, *Chem. Met. Engg.*, **5**. 75, 1907 ; *Trans. Amer. Electrochem. Soc.*, **15**. 35, 1909 ; *Iron Age*, **85**. 216, 1910 ; *Proc. Eng. Soc. West. Pennsylvania*, **26**. 487, 1911 ; *Iron Coal Trades Rev.*, **37**. 63, 1904 ; **81**. 276, 1910 ; P. Farup, *ib.*, **81**. 367, 1910 ; **90**. 57, 1915 ; J. A. Leffler, *Tek. Tids.*, **134**. 5, 1922 ; *Bihang Jernkontorets Ann.*, **8**. 302, 1907 ; *Engg.*, **109**. 131, 1915 ; *Jernkontorets Ann.*, (2), **66**. 222, 243, 1911 ; (2), **68**. 1, 1913 ; (2), **70**. 199, 1915 ; (2), **71**. 46, 1917 ; (2), **72**. 46, 1917 ; *Engg.*, **100**. 131, 1915 ; **104**. 621, 1917 ; *Iron Coal Trades Rev.*, **82**. 957, 1911 ; **95**. 65, 1917 ; **110**. 510, 1925 ; *Chem. Met. Engg.*, **10**. 71, 1912 ; J. A. Leffler and E. Nyström, *Bihang Jernkontorets Ann.*, **7**. 378, 1906 ; *Jernkontorets Ann.*, (2), **66**. 407, 423, 1911 ; (2), **67**. 248, 1912 ; *Iron Coal Trades Rev.*, **84**. 996, 1912 ; G. Odquist, *ib.*, **87**. 992, 1913 ; *Tek. Tids.*, **44**. 24, 1914 ; J. Lyman, *Trans. Amer. Electrochem. Soc.*, **19**. 193, 1911 ; *Iron Age*, **87**. 322, 1911 ; J. A. Knesche, *Iron Trade Rev.*, **48**. 65, 1911 ; H. J. Hanson, *ib.*, **53**. 1003, 1913 ; A. Helfenstein, *Stahl Eisen*, **41**. 1481, 1572, 1921 ; *Iron Coal Trades Rev.*, **88**. 505, 1914 ; *Foundry Trade Journ.*, **16**. 269, 1914 ; S. Rice, *Min. Eng. World*, **36**. 811, 1912 ; P. Nicou, *Bull. Soc. Ind. Min.*, (5), **3**. 589, 1913 ; *Rev. Univ. Mines*, (4), **37**. 127, 1912 ; *Rev. Mét.*, **9**. 209, 1911 ; *Ann. Mines*, (2), **3**. 133, 255, 1913 ; *Le haut-fourneau électrique*, Paris, 1913 ; A. Beielstein, *Stahl Eisen*, **33**. 1270, 1913 ; **34**. 1172, 1914 ; H. A. de Fries, *Chem. Met. Engg.*, **25**. 193, 1921 ; D. A. Lyon, *ib.*, **6**. 139, 1908 ; **11**. 15, 1913 ; *Trans. Amer. Electrochem. Soc.*, **15**. 39, 1909 ; *Journ. Franklin Inst.*, **177**. 187, 1914 ; *Rev. Electrochimie*, **7**. 210, 1913 ; D. A. Lyon, R. M. Keeney and J. F. Cullen, *The Electric Furnace in Metallurgical Work*, Washington, 1916 ; D. A. Lyon and R. M. Keeney, *Chem. Met. Engg.*, **11**. 577, 1913 ; *Bull. U.S. Bur. Mines*, 77, 1914 ; *Trans. Amer. Electrochem. Soc.*, **24**. 119, 1913 ; R. C. Gosrow, *ib.*, **41**. 109, 1922 ; *Iron Trade Rev.*, **74**. 982, 991, 1924 ; *Chem. Met. Engg.*, **27**. 490, 1922 ; *Foundry*, **49**. 242, 311, 1923 ; *Journ. Electricity*, **47**. 265, 1921 ; E. F. Burchard, *Min. Resources U.S. Geol. Sur.*, i, 1, 1911 ; C. van Langendonck, *Iron Age*, **94**. 478, 1914 ; I. Barthen, *ib.*, **93**. 252, 1914 ; F. Hodson and M. Sem, *ib.*, **113**. 1585, 1924 ; F. Hodson, *Chem. Met. Engg.*, **25**. 881, 1921 ; M. Sem, *Tek. Ukeblad*, **41**. 37, 103, 1923 ; O. Meyer, *Geschichte des Elektroeisens mit besonderer Berücksichtigung der zu seiner Erzeugung bestimmten elektrischen Oefen*, Berlin, 1914 ; M. Georges, *Elektrische Oefen*, Leipzig, 1914 ; G. Tysland, *Tek. Ukeblad*, **42**. 339, 251, 1924 ; L. M. Lindeman, *Stahl Eisen*, **35**. 1265, 1915 ; L. Lyche, *ib.*, **43**. 110, 1923 ; J. O. Boving, *Iron Age*, **93**. 1268, 1914 ; *Iron Coal Trades Rev.*, **94**. 601, 1917 ; H. Styri, *ib.*, **98**. 43, 1918 ; *Trans. Amer. Electrochem. Soc.*, **32**. 129, 1918 ; R. Turnbull, *ib.*, **34**. 143, 1918 ; **41**. 59, 1923 ; *Bull. Canada Min. Inst.*, **46**. 2, 1908 ; *Trans. Amer. Electrochem. Soc.*, **32**. 119, 1917 ; **34**. 143, 1919 ; *Iron Coal Trades Rev.*, **95**. 671, 1917 ; *Iron Age*, **102**. 1026, 1918 ; *Met. Chem. Engg.*, **17**. 459, 1917 ; **20**. 178, 1919 ; J. Escard, *Rev. Gén. Sciences*, **29**. 366, 1918 ; *Les fours électriques et leurs applications industrielles*, Paris, 1905 ; *L'Électrométallurgie du fer et de ses alliages*, Paris, 1920 ; *Les fours électriques industriels et les fabrications électrothermiques*, Paris, 1919 ; G. Stig, *Tek. Ukeblad*, **37**. 51, 1910 ; **66**. 151, 1919 ; *Chem. Met. Engg.*, **23**. 29, 1920 ; J. Bibby, *Proc. Cleveland Inst. Eng.*, 83, 1918 ; *Iron Coal Trades Rev.*, **47**. 719, 1918 ; **48**. 611, 1919 ; *Eng.*, **127**. 513, 1919 ; *Trans. Amer. Electrochem. Soc.*, **41**. 63, 1922 ; C. E. Williams and C. E. Sims, *Tech. Paper U.S. Bur. Mines*, 418, 1928 ; *Journ. Franklin Inst.*, **205**. 575, 1928 ; C. E. Williams, C. E. Sims and C. A. Newall, *ib.*, **43**. 191, 1923 ; W. Borchers, *Elektrometallurgie*, Leipzig, 1902 ; *Die elektrischen Oefen*, Halle a. S., 1920 ; *Stahl Eisen*, **25**. 631, 689, 1905 ; **31**. 706, 1911 ; H. von Jüptner, *Die Reduktion der Eisenerze im elektrischen Oefen*, Leipzig, 1924 ; A. Coutagne, *Rev. Mét.*, **17**. 450, 1920 ; *La fabrication des ferro-alliages, fontes électriques et metaux spéciaux*, Paris, 1924 ; T. J. Ess, *Iron Steel Eng.*, **8**. 173, 1931.

[32] G. Tammann and C. F. Grevemeyer, *Zeit. anorg. Chem.*, **136**. 114, 1924 ; G. Tammann and G. Bätz, *ib.*, **151**. 129, 1926 ; G. Bätz, *Ueber die Gewinnung von Eisen aus Silikaten und Pyrite*, Göttingen, 1925 ; F. Sauerwald and G. Neuendorff, *Zeit. Elektrochem.*, **31**. 643, 1925 ; **34**. 199,

1926 ; G. Neuendorff, *Ueber die Schmelzflusselektrolyse von Eisen, Chrom, und Mangan*, Breslau, 1927 ; G. Ongaro, *Giorn. Chim. Ind. Appl.*, **3**. 288, 1921 ; M. Guédras, *ib.*, **3**. 58, 1921 ; G. Kassel, *Stahl Eisen*, **26**. 1322, 1906 ; S. L. Madorsky, *Journ. Ind. Eng. Chem.*, **23**. 99, 1931 ; M. Boistel, *French Pat. No.* 92020, 1871 ; J. Reese, *Brit. Pat. No.* 1223, 1886 ; *U.S. Pat. No.* 55710, 1886 ; C. Adams, *ib.*, 121226, 1871 ; G. Bogitch, *Compt. Rend.*, **184**. 883, 1927 ; R. D. Pike, G. H. West, L. V. Steck, R. Cummings, and B. P. Little, *Tech. Paper Amer. Inst. Min. Eng.*, 268, 1930 ; F. A. Eustis, *Chem. Met. Engg.*, **27**. 684, 1922 ; F. Sauerwald, *Zeit. Elektrochem.*, **38**. 76, 1932.

§ 4. The Chemical Reactions in the Blast-Furnace, and in the Reduction of Iron Oxides

In general, the reactions in the blast-furnace, near the tuyères, involve the oxidation of carbon : $C+O_2=CO_2$; $2CO_2=2CO+O_2$; $2C+O_2=2CO$; for R. Bunsen and L. Playfair [1]—*vide supra*—found that the oxygen of the blast is burned in the immediate vicinity of the tuyères, forming carbon monoxide. As a result, no free oxygen or carbon dioxide occurs in the gases ascending from the hearth into the boshes. W. van Vloten's analyses correspond with :

Oxygen	Carbon dioxide	Carbon monoxide	Hydrogen	Nitrogen
0	0	34	2	64 per cent.

Higher up still, the ferric oxide is reduced by the carbon monoxide : Fe_2O_3+3CO $=2Fe+3CO_2+4.6$ cals. There are thus two zones when heat is generated in the blast-furnace : (i) near the tuyères, where carbon is oxidized to the monoxide, and (ii) higher up, where the ferric oxide is reduced. I. L. Bell found that the relative proportions of carbon and oxygen in the gases, per 100 parts of nitrogen, at different heights above the tuyères, were :

Height	.	0	6	12	25	37	50	60	76.5 feet
Carbon	.	26.8	25.2	24.6	23.9	24.1	23.8	24.0	27.5
Oxygen	.	36.5	33.7	33.3	32.6	33.1	32.4	33.9	41.6

C. R. A. Wright emphasized that there is a complex play of reactions involving different oxides of iron, and carbon, and carbon monoxide and dioxide ; while E. Baur and A. Glässner showed that at atm. press. FeO and Fe_3O_4, carbon, CO, and CO_2, can exist side by side at 647°, and the three solids at 685° ; above 685° carbon and iron can exist together, and below 647° carbon and ferrosic oxide. Iron in contact with a gas rich in carbon monoxide below 647° is oxidized and carbon is deposited, while above 680° no carbon is deposited from the gas. C. Zix studied the deposition of carbon. The equilibrium conditions and the work of E. Baur and A. Glässner are discussed by P. Mahler.

According to L. Mond, the temp. of the blast-furnace is never low enough to permit the formation of iron carbonyls. There is also the endothermal decomposition of the limestone in the body of the furnace to be considered, when the temp. is between 566° and about 810°. At the high temp. in the vicinity of the tuyères there also occurs the reduction of silica : $SiO_2+2C=2CO+Si$; of manganous oxide : $MnO+C=Mn+CO$; and of phosphoric oxide : $P_2O_5+5C=5CO+2P$; all of which are favoured by the presence of iron, which alloys with the manganese, silicon, and phosphorus. These three reactions are of minor importance in the study of the equilibrium conditions in the furnace. G. Charpy and L. Jacqué found the barium and calcium sulphates begin to be reduced at 600°, and the process is rapid at 900° to 950°. Reduction by the metal alone results in the sulphurization of the iron. I. L. Bell showed that under ordinary conditions the part played by hydrogen in the reduction of iron ore is relatively unimportant ; and that from thermochemical principles the use of hydrogen or of water vapour, which would yield hydrogen by decomposition in the furnace, offers no particular advantage. The equilibrium conditions with hydrogen and the iron oxides are discussed below.

T. Turner showed that the theoretical minimum amount of carbon required to produce one unit of iron approximates :

Reduction of ferrric oxide . . . 4·84
Carbon required for generating heat . 0·30
Carburization of iron . . . . 0·60—Total 5·82 units

I. L. Bell, T. Turner, S. P. Kinney and co-workers, W. Mathesius, J. E. Johnson, A. Morette, P. Geimer, E. Maurer, N. Metz, H. Thaler, H. le Chatelier, M. Levin, E. Pierre, F. A. Kjellin, B. Osann, P. Anglès d'Auriac, M. Zyromsky, W. D. Brown, G. Tobin, W. Lennings, G. Eichenberg and P. Oberhoffer, W. G. Gillhausen, K. Hofmann, G. Godin, C. P. Linville, P. Farup, J. M. Clay, L. Lévêque, H. Riesenfeld, W. J. Foster, F. T. Sisco, B. Stålhane, W. McConnachie, F. Mulet, F. Logeling, H. von Jüptner, R. A. Hacking, F. Wüst, E. Richarme, H. Kamura, G. Rocour, E. A. Uehling, T. Weill, H. Mehner, A. Wagner and co-workers, J. Seigle, M. Derclaye, R. Franchot, J. Lilot, K. Mühlbradt, H. Bansen, P. Reichardt, R. H. Sweetser, A. Michel, I. Bohm, G. Bulle, A. Michel, P. H. Emmett, F. C. Howard, T. L. Joseph, H. H. Meyer, O. C. Ralston, E. C. Evans and F. J. Bailey, F. Clements, L. E. Gruner, F. Brabant, and many others have drawn up heat balance sheets of the blast-furnace.

Expressing the results in hundredweights or cwt. calories, H. Allen gave per ton of hot-blast pig-iron :

HEAT BALANCE OF BLAST-FURNACE PER TON OF IRON.

Combustion C to CO_2 . .	40,240	Reduction of iron . .	37,680
Combustion C to CO (less lime-		Carbon deposited from CO	1,800
stone effect) . . .	31,800	Evaporation water in coke	1,024
Heat introduced by blast .	12,289	Expulsion CO_2 from lime-	
	———	stone	3,345
Total heat supplied . .	84,329	Reduction CO_2 to CO .	3,840
		Decomposition H_2O in blast	1,479
		Fusion of iron . . .	6,600
		Fusion of slag . . .	7,188
		Reduction silica . .	4,384
		[Heat appropriated by	
		furnace . . .	67,340]
		Escaping CO_2 . . .	1,385
		Escaping CO . . .	3,576
		Escaping hydrogen . .	30
		Escaping nitrogen . .	7,111
		Escaping water . .	1,673
		[Heat lost in escaping	
		gases . . .	13,775]
		Heat lost by tuyère water .	1,293
		Heat not utilized . .	16,989
		Total heat . . .	84,329

The subject was discussed by H. Bansen,[2] J. F. Barkley, W. A. Bone and co-workers, E. Bormann, W. D. Brown, G. Bulle, B. F. Burman, F. Clements, R. Durrer, G. Eichenberg and co-workers, E. C. Evans, E. C. Evans and E. J. Bailey, A. L. Feild, K. Feist, J. B. Fortune, C. C. Furnas, W. G. Gillhausen, L. Gruner, R. Hahn, H. P. Howland, T. C. Hutchinson, J. E. Johnson, A. Korevaar, F. Lange, O. O. Laudig, W. Lennings, M. Levin and J. Wesselmann, A. Liebreich, L. Mathesius, W. Mathesius, E. Maurer, M. A. Morette, K. Mühlbradt, B. Osann, A. K. Reese, P. Reichardt, J. W. Richards, P. H. Royster and co-workers, R. Schenck, O. Simmersbach, H. Thaler, G. Tobin, W. Trinks, P. W. Uhlmann, A. Wagner, A. Wagner and G. Bulle, H. Wedding, F. Werndl, H. E. Wright, and F. Wüst.

The system : Fe-O-H.

—For the reduction of ferric oxide, Fe_2O_3, to ferrosic oxide, Fe_3O_4, and to iron, vide infra. In the light of later knowledge the observations of J. L. Gay-Lussac,[3] H. V. Regnault, H. Debray, and W. Müller indicate that the reaction between steam and iron is a reversible process. H. St. C. Deville studied the application of the law of mass action in the equilibrium between ferrosic oxide, iron, steam, and hydrogen : $Fe_3O_4 + 4H_2 \rightleftharpoons 4H_2O + 3Fe$. The equilibrium constant can be written $K_3 = [H_2O]/[H_2]$, where it is assumed that the solid phase is a mixture of Fe and Fe_3O_4. Analogous results were obtained by approaching the state of equilibrium from both directions. The values of K_3 derived from these experiments are :

	200°	265°	360°	440°	670°	920°
K_3. .	0·0491	0·0688	0·1188	0·1758	0·5410	0·6590

If p_1 be the press. of the water vapour, and p_2 that of the hydrogen, the values for the constant K_3 will be :

	200°		400°	
p_1	4·6	9·7	4·6	10·1
p_2	95·9	195·3	25·8	57·9
K_3	0·048	0·049	0·178	0·174

Hence, if water vapour be passed over iron, the ratio p_1/p_2 is greater than the constant $K_3 = p_1/p_2$, and chemical change will go on until the iron is converted into oxide ; when hydrogen is passed over the oxide, the ratio p_1/p_2 is less than the above constant, and consequently the oxide will be reduced. At about 1500°, K_3 is nearly unity, so that if a mixture of equal proportions of water vapour and hydrogen be passed over either the metals or the oxide at this temp., no chemical change will occur. G. Preuner repeated the experiments under somewhat similar conditions and obtained $K_3 = 0.687$ at 900° ; 0·781 at 1025° ; and 0·860 at 1150°. Observations were also made by G. Chaudron, L. Wöhler and W. Prager, G. Gallo, L. Wöhler and O. Balz, W. Krings and J. Kempkens, and E. Schreiner and F. B. Grimnes. In the early experiments there was no assurance what particular oxide (or oxides) was concerned in the reaction. H. St. C. Deville at first supposed that the solid phase is Fe_4O_5 ; G. Preuner, a mixture of Fe and Fe_3O_4 ; and O. Sackur, an oxide between Fe and FeO. E. Schreiner and F. B. Grimnes obtained results in good agreement with the assumed reaction : $Fe + H_2O \rightleftharpoons FeO + H_2$; they found discrepancies between their results obtained at higher temp. and those of other workers. The thermodynamical values of the equilibrium constant are higher than the observed results, and this is attributed to the formation of solid soln. between iron and ferrous oxide. G. Chaudron showed that in all probability the ferrous oxide formed at a high temp. is decomposed : $4FeO = Fe + Fe_3O_4$ below 570°, so that under these conditions it is assumed that ferrosic oxide is the oxide in equilibrium with iron. At 570° the three solids Fe, FeO, and Fe_3O_4 are in equilibrium ; and above that temp. the equilibrium curve has two branches, corresponding with the equilibria : $Fe + H_2O \rightleftharpoons FeO + H_2$ and $3FeO + H_2O \rightleftharpoons Fe_3O_4 + H_2$; below 570° there is only one system involved : $4FeO = Fe_3O_4 + Fe$. This subject was discussed by A. Smits and J. M. Bijvoet—vide infra, ferric oxide. P. P. Fedotéeff and T. N. Petrenko found that the product of the oxidation of iron by steam at 1000° to 1100° changes continuously in composition from ferrous oxide to ferrosic oxide, although at any given time only one solid phase is present. It thus seems that both isomorphous mixtures and solid soln. of the oxides must be formed. The first effect of the steam is probably to form a layer of ferrous oxide on the surface of the metal, and this is quickly oxidized to ferrosic oxide, which is reduced to the ferrous state again by the neighbouring metal, after which oxidation again occurs, and so on. E. D. Eastman and R. M. Evans measured the equilibrium constants $[H_2O]/[H_2]$, namely K_1 for the system involving Fe : FeO, and K_2 for the system involving FeO : Fe_3O_4. The results were :

	700°	750°	800°	850°	900°	950°	1000°
K_1	0·584	0·645	0·706	0·765	0·822	0·879	0·937
K_2	1·45	2·11	2·98	4·16	5·50	7·08	9·12

These corresponding curves, Fig. 22, intersect near 570°, below which temp. ferrous oxide is unstable with respect to ferrosic oxide and iron. Fig. 20 shows the percentage of hydrogen with respect to these equilibria at different temp. G. Chaudron's values for the equilibrium constants are not in close agreement with those of other workers, excepting perhaps those of J. B. Ferguson. The observations of L. Wöhler and co-workers, K. Hofmann, K. M. Tigerschiöld, A. McCance, W. Biltz and H. Müller, S. L. Madorsky, W. E. Jominy and D. W. Murphy, W. P. Fishel and J. F. Wooddell, B. Neumann and G. Köhler, J. B. Ferguson, C. H. Herty, P. H. Emmett and J. F. Schultz, J. Thibeau, P. Farup, E. Schreiner and F. B. Grimnes, P. van Groningen, and E. D. Eastman and R. M. Evans are in very fair agreement for the values of the equilibrium constants. The thermal value of the reaction : $Fe+H_2O=FeO+H_2$, calculated by G. Chaudron, is 6·6 Cals. per mol at room temp. and 3·8 Cals. at 700° ; K. M. Tigerschiöld gave 9·0 Cals. at 17° ; L. Wöhler and R. Günther obtained 3·9 Cals., and P. van Groningen, 4·1 Cals. The thermal value of the reaction : $3FeO+H_2O$ =$Fe_3O_4+H_2$, calculated by G. Chaudron, is 19 Cals. per mol at room temp., and 11·6 at 650° ; K. M. Tigerschiöld gave 14·8 Cals. at 17° ; L. Wöhler and R. Günther, 14·4 Cals. ; and P. van Groningen, 15·7 Cals. The thermal value of the reaction : $3Fe+4H_2O=Fe_3O_4$ $+4H_2$, calculated by G. Chaudron, is 38·8 Cals. per mol at room temp., and 40 Cals. at 500° ; K. M. Tigerschiöld gave 41·8 Cals. at room temp. ; L. Wöhler and R. Günther, 37·2 Cals.; and P. van Groningen, 28·0 Cals. K. M. Tigerschiöld calculated for the thermal value of the reaction : $3Fe_2O_3+H_2=2Fe_3O_4+H_2O$, 5450 to 8000 Cals. at 17°. The thermal value of the reaction : $3Fe+4H_2O=Fe_3O_4+4H_2O$, is 38,480 cals. at 17° -

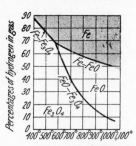

FIG. 20.—Chemical Equilibrium Curves.

when calculated from the heats of formation of ferrosic oxide and of water. G. Preuner's value, calculated from the equilibrium constants, is 11,900 cals. at 960°. A discussion of these reactions from other points of view by O. Hahn, F. Haber, C. H. Herty, F. S. Tritton and D. Hanson, etc., is resumed in connection with the ferrous and ferric oxides. The study of the equilibrium conditions gives no information on the speed of the reactions. For H. Kamura's observations on the rate of reduction of ferric oxide by hydrogen, *vide infra*. The subject was investigated by S. Mita, and B. Stålhane and T. Malmberg.

The system : Fe-O-C.—As early as 1869, I. L Bell [4] recognized the working of the mass law in the reduction of iron from its oxides by the furnace gases of the blast-furnace. He said : " Iron oxide can only be completely reduced by carbon monoxide when an excess of that gas is present." He also pointed out the complex nature of the conditions of equilibrium which must subsist between iron, carbon monoxide, carbon dioxide, carbon, and iron oxides of various kinds, at different temp. Observations were also made on the reaction by W. Müller, R. Akerman, R. Akerman and C. G. Särnström, A. Stansfield, H. le Chatelier, A. B. Kinzel and J. J. Egan, P. Pingault, E. Bauer, B. Stålhane and co-workers, H. Fleissner and F. Duftschmid, C. Svensson, G. Grönal, B. Kalling and G. Lilljekvist, S. Reiner and W. Feldmann, F. Glaser, R. H. Sweetser, H. Tholander, B. Kosmann, L. Mathesius, C. Schinz, J. Wiborgh, M. Mayer and J. Jakoby, K. Arndt and G. Schraube, H. Tutsya, F. E. Rhead and R. V. Wheeler, E. Terres and A. Pongracz, C. C. Furnas and G. G. Brown, E. Scheil and E. H. Schulz, R. Schenck, G. Bodländer, K. Stammer, P. Schützenberger, H. St. C. Deville, A. Ledebur, A. Guntz, L. E. Gruner, J. J. Ebelmen, L. Rinman and B. Fernquist, F. Kupelwieser and R. Schöffel, I. Bohm, W. G. Gillhausen, P. H. Royster and co-workers, H. H. Meyer, N. Metz, G. Bulle and W. Lennings, G. Bulle, G. Eichenberg and P. Oberhoffer, M. L. Becker, E. Jänecke, J. Klärding, H. Dünwald and C. Wagner, W. Krings, N. A. Kostuileff, and F. Wüst.

F. Wüst, W. P. Fishel and J. F. Wooddell observed higher proportions of carbon dioxide than correspond with the equilibrium value at 800° to 1100°. P. Farup discussed the catalytic action of iron ores in decomposing carbon monoxide. In the ternary system with carbon, oxygen, and iron, K. Iwase, and T. Watase said that there are the following systems to be considered : (1) Fe_2O_3+3CO =$2Fe+3CO_2$; (2) $Fe_2O_3+3C=3CO+2Fe$; (3) $3Fe_2O_3+CO=2Fe_3O_4+CO_2$; (4) $Fe_3O_4+CO=3FeO+CO_2$; (5) $Fe_3O_4+4CO=3Fe+4CO_2$; (6) $FeO+CO$ =$Fe+CO_2$; (7) $FeO+C=Fe+CO$; (8) $3FeO+5CO=Fe_3C+4CO_2$; and (9) $3Fe+2CO=Fe_3C+CO_2$. Reactions (2) and (7) are irreversible ; reactions (4) and (6) are incompatible with (5). I. Braithwaite noticed that at a dull red-heat ferric oxide is completely transformed into ferrosic oxide by the action of carbon monoxide : $3Fe_2O_3 + CO = 2Fe_3O_4 + CO_2$. W. A. Bone and co-workers obtained the results summarized in Fig. 21. With up to about 11 per cent. of deoxidation there is the irreversible reaction $3Fe_2O_3 + CO \rightarrow 2Fe_3O_4 + CO_2$; with between 11 and about 30 per cent. deoxidation the reversible reaction $Fe_3O_4 + CO \rightleftharpoons 3FeO + CO_2$ occurs ; and with between 30 and 85 per cent. deoxidation the reaction is $FeO + CO \rightleftharpoons CO_2 + Fe$. In the blast-furnace, of course, above the region where the limestone decomposes, carbon dioxide is being poured into the gaseous system, with its consequent effect on the equilibrium relations of the reversible reactions.

E. Baur and A. Glässner measured the equilibrium constant in the reaction $FeO + CO \rightleftharpoons Fe + CO_2$, and obtained for $K_1 = [CO]/[CO_2]$:

	550°	680°	750°	850°	900°
K_1	1·78	1·44	1·56	2·12	2·51

The curve, Fig. 20, has a minimum, while for the reaction $Fe_3O_4 + CO = 3FeO + CO_2$ the curve has a maximum. They obtained for $K_2 = [CO]/[CO_2]$:

	450°	550°	650°	750°	850°	950°
K_2	0·852	0·786	0·587	0·439	0·351	0·299

The results when plotted furnish the curves in Fig. 21. The curves represent equilibrium lines in connection with the corresponding oxides and iron. According to

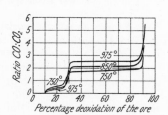

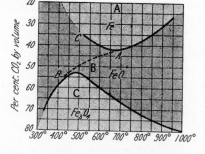

FIG. 21.—The Progress of the Step-by-Step Reduction of Ferric Oxide.

FIG. 22.—Equilibrium in Systems with Iron, Iron Oxides, and Carbon Monoxide and Dioxide.

H. W. B. Roozeboom, each system involves three components—Fe, C, and O—and three phases, two solids—Fe and FeO or FeO and Fe_3O_4, respectively—and a gas. Each system is therefore bivariant, so that, at any given temp., the mixture of gases exerts a definite press. and has a definite composition. The equilibrium curves in the system with the three components—Fe, C, and O—studied by E. Baur and A. Glässner thus divide the whole area of the diagram into three regions : A with iron ; B with ferrous oxide ; and C with ferrosic oxide. The results of E. Baur and A. Glässner indicate that above 600° equilibrium was probably attained, but the observed variations below this temp. make it doubtful if sufficient time had been allowed owing to the slowness of the reaction. The observations of R. Schenck and co-workers, H. J. van Royen, and M. Levin make it probable that the upper curve, Fig. 22, should be in the direction AB, Fig. 22, rather than in the direction AC. The minimum reported by E. Baur and A. Glässner at 650° has not been confirmed by other observers— E. Terres and A. Pongracz, R. Schenck and co-workers, E. D. Eastman, H. J. van Royen, M. Levin and H. Niedte, S. Hilpert and F. Beyer, G. Chaudron, F. E. C. Scheffer, and P. van Groningen. Rather do the curves assume the form of Fig. 21—vide ferrous oxide—and it is analogous to the curves deduced for the steam-iron equilibrium. G. Chaudron, and P. van Groningen place the quadruple point at 570°, and here iron and ferrous and ferrosic oxides can exist beside the gas phase ; below 570° the reaction proceeds : $Fe_3O_4+4CO \rightleftharpoons 3Fe+4CO_2$; and above 570°, in accord with $Fe_3O_4+CO \rightleftharpoons 3FeO+CO_2$, and $FeO+CO \rightleftharpoons Fe+CO_2$. According to H. Semiller, expressing the concentrations of the gases in percentages, and the total pressure at equilibrium by p mm. :

		552°	556°	561°	596°	619°	651°	662°
[CO]	.	53·7	53·4	53·6	55·5	56·8	57·9	58·4
[CO_2]	.	46·3	46·6	46·4	44·5	43·2	42·1	41·6
p	.	129·7	136·9	142·2	296·4	411·3	570·9	662·0
K_1	.	1·160	1·146	1·155	1·247	1·315	1·375	1·404

The values of E. Baur and A. Glässner, R. Schenck and co-workers, M. Levin, H. J. van Royen, V. Falcke, E. Terres and A. Pongracz, G. Chaudron, and A. Matsubara were averaged by E. D. Eastman and R. M. Evans with the following results :

		600°	700°	750°	800°	850°	900°	950°	1000°
K_1	.	0·871	0·678	0·608	0·552	0·505	0·466	0·432	0·403
K_2	.	1·15	1·68	2·02	2·40	2·79	3·24	3·67	4·17

L. Wöhler and R. Günther obtained for the three constants $\log K_1 = -854T^{-1} +0·666$; $\log K_2 = -3143T^{-1}+3·398$; and $\log K_3 = -1480T^{-1}+1·411$; and they calculated from G. Chaudron's data $\log K_1 = -742T^{-1}+0·44$; $\log K_2 = -2632T^{-1} +2·68$; and $\log K_3 = -1510T^{-1}+1·36$. P. van Groningen gave $\log K_1 = -897T^{-1} +0·68$; $\log K_2 = -3435T^{-1}+3·67$; and $\log K_3 = -532T^{-1}+1·42$. K. Hofmann calculated from E. D. Eastman's data with the steam and iron reaction $\log K_1 = -954T^{-1}+0·57$; and $\log K_2 = -2900T^{-1}+3·15$; and from E. D. Eastman's data for the CO_2 and iron equilibrium, $\log K_1 = -834T^{-1}+0·636$; and $\log K_2 = -3237T^{-1} +3·509$. L. Wöhler and O. Balz, and K. M. Tigerschiöld calculated values for the constant K_4 with Fe_3O_4 and Fe_2O_3 as the solid phases : $3Fe_2O_3+H_2 = 2Fe_3O_4+H_2O$ —a system also studied by P. van Groningen, and H. Kamura. For the Fe→FeO equilibrium—i.e. $FeO+CO \rightleftharpoons Fe+CO_2$—with $K_1 = [CO_2]/[CO]$, E. D. Eastman gave $\log K_1 = 949T^{-1}-1·140$; A. McCance, $\log K_1 = 675T^{-1}-0·87$; K. Hofmann, $\log K_1 = 949T^{-1}-1·140$; P. van Groningen, $\log K_1 = 1000T^{-1}-1·16$; K. M. Tigerschiöld, $\log K_1 = 217·7T^{-1}+0·5 \log T -0·0006348(T-600)-1·708$; and R. R. Garran, $\log K_1 = 868T^{-1}-1·055$; as well as $\log K_1 = 4160T^{-1}+9·51 \log T -0·00121T -31·680$. For the FeO→$Fe_3O_4$ equilibrium—i.e. $Fe_3O_4+CO \rightleftharpoons 3FeO+CO_2$— with $K_2 = [CO_2]/[CO]$, E. D. Eastman gave $\log K_2 = -1645T^{-1}+1·925$; A. McCance, $\log K_2 = -1304T^{-1}+1·68$; and $\log K_2 = -1304T^{-1}+1·68$; K. Hofmann, $\log K_2 = -1645T^{-1}+1·935$; P. van Groningen, $\log K_2 = -1600T^{-1}+1·92$; K. M. Tigerschiöld, $\log K_2 = -715·6T^{-1} + 0·5 \log T - 0·000564(T-600) - 0·735$; and R. R. Garran, $\log K_2 = -1434T^{-1}+1·723$, as well as $\log K_2 = -3440T^{-1}-7·91 \log T +0·00161T+25·860$. For the Fe→$Fe_3O_4$ reaction—$Fe_3O_4+4CO \rightleftharpoons 3Fe+4CO_2$ —K. Hofmann gave $\log K_3 = 261T^{-1}-0·325$; and P. van Groningen, $\log K_3 =354T^{-1}-0·39$. K. M. Tigerschiöld observed that at 450°, $K_3 = 0·91$, and at 500°, 0·89 ; and for the quadruple point, where there are the co-existing phases Fe, FeO, Fe_3O_4, and gas, he gave 534° ; while A. McCance gave 503°, for here $K_1 =K_2=K_3=1$. According to I. Braithwaite, and R. Akerman and C. G. Särnström, the reaction $3Fe_2O_3+CO = 2Fe_3O_4+CO_2$ is practically complete at a dull red-heat ; and A. Matsubara showed that the reaction is irreversible, due, it is supposed, to the high dissociation press. of the ferric oxide. K. M. Tigerschiöld came to the same conclusion, but K. Iwase regarded the question as an open one. The reaction was also studied by H. Groebler and P. Oberhoffer.

R. R. Garran's curves are expressed in percentages ; for the FeO→Fe_3O_4 reaction :

	600°	700°	800°	900°	1000°	1100°	1200°	1300°
[CO]	43·7	35·3	28·2	22·4	18·1	14·8	15·5	—
[CO_2]	56·3	64·7	71·8	77·6	81·9	85·2	87·5	—

and for the Fe→FeO reaction :

	600°	700°	800°	900°	1000°	1100°	1200°	1300°
[CO] .	—	59·5	65·0	69·3	72·7	75·0	76·5	77·1
[CO$_2$] .	—	40·5	35·0	30·7	27·3	25·0	23·5	22·9

According to A. Smits and J. M. Bijvoet, the equilibrium $Fe_3O_4+H_2 \rightleftharpoons 3FeO+H_2O$ can be resolved into $2Fe_3O_4 \rightleftharpoons 6FeO+O_2$, and $2H_2O \rightleftharpoons 2H_2+O_2$, while the equilibrium $Fe_3O_4 +CO \rightleftharpoons 3FeO+CO_2$ can be resolved into $2Fe_3O_4 \rightleftharpoons 6FeO+O_2$, and $2CO_2 \rightleftharpoons 2CO+O_2$. The pT-diagram for the case studied in connection with the action of hydrogen on ferric oxide (q.v.), shows that the 3-phase lines $FeO+Fe_3O_4+G$, and $Fe_2O_3+Fe_3O_4+G$ do not intersect in stability points, Fig. 23. Here the two 3-phase lines—two solid phases and vapour—intersect without inverse melting taking place. Fig. 24 represents the case where the two

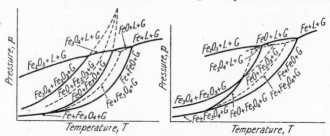

FIGS. 23 and 24.—Pressure-temperature Equilibria for Carbon Monoxide and the Iron Oxides.

lines intersect in stable points. Here the 3-phase line Fe_3O_4+L+G is metastable. For the system: $Fe+CO_2 \rightleftharpoons FeO+CO$, and $2CO_2 \rightleftharpoons 2CO+O_2$, log p_0 =log K_p-2 log K, where p atm. refers to CO_2, and $K=p_{CO}/p_{CO_2}$. For the carbon dioxide equilibrium, with the thermal value $-133,000$ cals. at 800°, log $K_p = 29,100T^{-1}+\log T+5\cdot8$. Taking W. Reinders' values for log K_p, the values of log K_p, and log K_3 at different temp., log $P_{O_2}=\log K_p -2$ log K_3; likewise for log K_2 it follows that log $P_{O_2}=\log K_p-2$ log K_2 for $3FeO+CO_2 \rightleftharpoons Fe_3O_4+CO$; and for log K'_3 it follows that log $P_{O_2}=\log K_p-2$ log K_3 for $3Fe+4CO_2 \rightleftharpoons Fe_3O_4+4CO$. The values are as follow :

	400°	500°	550°	600°	700°	800°	900°
log K_p	−34·6	−28·9	−26·7	−24·6	−21·1	−18·3	−15·9
log K_1	—	—	−0·01	−0·06	0·18	0·27	0·34
log P_{O_2}	—	—	−26·7	−24·7	−21·5	−18·8	−16·6
log K_2	—	—	−0·11	−0·17	−0·29	−0·39	−0·49
log P_{O_2}	—	—	−26·5	−24·3	−20·5	−17·5	−14·9
log K_3	−0·16	−0·05	—	—	—	—	—
log P_{O_2}	−34·3	−28·8	—	—	—	—	—

The equilibrium conditions between iron and its oxides, and carbon monoxide and dioxide are not completely described by Fig. 25, because carbon may be formed : $2CO \rightleftharpoons C+CO_2$. It is therefore necessary to superpose on Fig. 25 the effects of this reaction on the results. W. A. Bone and co-workers studied the reduction of iron ores by carbon monoxide at temp. below 700°, where the equilibria are metastable. The reactions involved are : $3Fe_2O_3+CO=2Fe_3O_4+CO_2$, which is exothermic and irreversible ; and the reversible reactions : $Fe_3O_4+CO \rightleftharpoons 3FeO +CO_2\pm5\cdot4$ Cals., and $FeO+CO \rightleftharpoons Fe+CO_2\pm2\cdot6$ Cals. Free carbon was not deposited in appreciable quantities on the reduced ore until reduction had progressed so far that all the higher oxides had been reduced to Fe_3O_4 at 550° or a lower temp., or to FeO at 600° or a higher temp., and a small portion of either oxide had been reduced to iron, which then catalyzed the reaction $2CO \rightleftharpoons CO_2+C+39$ Cals. The higher the temp., the less the tendency for carbon deposition. The deposition of carbon at low temp. proceeds slowly at 275°, and its optimum temp. is 450°, but it does not occur in the absence of a suitable catalyzing surface. Iron, and ferrosic and ferrous oxides are powerful promoters of carbon deposition at temp. up to between 650° and 700°, but at higher temp. the phenomenon becomes inappreciable until nearly 90 per cent. of the ore is reduced, when it again becomes prominent. The carbon deposition in a blast-furnace may occur between 275° and 700°, and it may result in the impregnation of the ore with carbon, or the carbon may envelop the granules of ore, or both impregnation and envelopment may occur. The impregnated carbon is a more powerful reducing agent at 750° than is the case with carbon monoxide. If carbide is formed, it is conditioned by the presence of free iron in a system containing both oxides of carbon and an ore undergoing reduction.

The data of O. Boudouard, at atm. press., are summarized by the curve DE, Fig. 25. The systems represented to the left of the shaded region refer to those in which no carbon is formed, whereas the shaded areas refer to systems in which, for equilibrium, some carbon is formed. Thus the system represented by the point a is not in stable equilibrium with respect to carbon, and that element will be deposited until the system acquires the state represented by b. The whole area for systems with the three components—Fe, C, and O—is thus divided by the equilibrium curves into six regions, namely A with iron ; A' with iron and carbon ; B with ferrous oxide ; B' with ferrous oxide

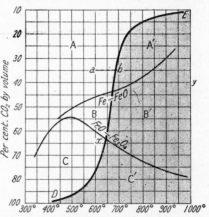

FIG. 25.—Equilibria in the System with Iron, Iron Oxides, Carbon Monoxide and Dioxide, and Carbon.

and carbon ; C with ferrosic oxide ; and C' with ferrosic oxide and carbon. The point x involves the solid phases Fe, FeO, and carbon ; and y, the solid phases Fe_3O_4, FeO, and carbon. R. Schenck and co-workers found the equilibrium press., p mm., of the gas in the system with the solid phases : iron, ferrous oxide, and carbon—(i) amorphous carbon from carbon monoxide, and (ii) from sugar charcoal, as well as (iii) graphite, were :

(i)			(ii)			(iii)		
455°	596°	670°	408°	560°	647°	500°	660°	755°
p . 27	296	858	5·6	161·7	750·1	12·3	129	574

The results with Fe_3O_4, FeO, and amorphous carbon as solid phases are :

	528°	535°	551°	560°	568°	581°
p . .	121	129	175	303	430	699

They represent the results by the curves shown in Fig. 25. The ferrous oxide used in these experiments was prepared from ferrous oxalate, and it is possible that it was contaminated with carbon or carbide. A. Gautier and P. Clausmann observed that in the prolonged action of carbon monoxide on iron some carbon and carbide are formed : 3Fe +28CO=Fe_3O_4+16C+12CO$_2$. H. C. H. Carpenter and C. C. Smith found that at 650° carbon monoxide reacts with iron, forming a carbide, and that the production of the carbide is inhibited if enough carbon dioxide be also present, and it is favoured by the presence of hydrogen. S. Hilpert and T. Dieckmann observed that when iron oxide is reduced by carbon monoxide, the product at 850° contained carbon ; and between 720° and 800° the deposition of carbon was accelerated, presumably by the formation of unstable carbides. Free carbon was not observed until the product

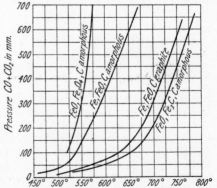

FIG. 26.—Equilibrium in Systems with Iron, Iron Oxides and Carbide, Carbon, and Carbon Monoxide and Dioxide.

attained a composition eq. to Fe_3C with 6·6 per cent. of carbon. R. Schenck discussed the equilibrium $3Fe+2CO\rightleftharpoons Fe_3C+CO_2$; and also the reduction with methane involving $3Fe+CH_4\rightleftharpoons Fe_3C+2H_2$. The subject was studied by G. Tammann and A. Sworykin, F. Wüst, and W. Gluud and co-workers. V. Falcke found carbon is formed as a separate phase only when iron is treated for a long time in a current of carbon monoxide. This result is supposed to vitiate the results of R. Schenck indicated in Fig. 26. V. Falcke observed no reaction between carbon and ferrous oxide in an evacuated tube below 650°; and above this temp. different varieties of carbon acted at different speeds—amorphous carbon reacted with extreme slowness. V. Falcke also measured the equilibrium constants between carbon monoxide and different varieties of iron. If $K=[CO]^2/[CO_2]$ in the reaction $CO_2+C\rightleftharpoons 2CO$, when press. are expressed in atm.:

	$K_{600°}$	$K_{700°}$
Purified iron	0·230	1·57
Iron preheated in CO at 600°	0·146	1·27
Graphite and commercial FeO	0·115	1·18
Graphite and FeO from Fe	—	0·87
Calculated from free energies	0·080	0·965

The calculated values are due to E. D. Eastman. E. Terres and A. Pongracz inferred from the action of carbon dioxide on iron that carbon, and a solid soln. of ferrous and ferrosic oxides are formed. A. Matsubara studied the action of carbon monoxide on iron oxides, and found that the iron was carburized, forming an iron carbide as a separate phase; and his curves agree closely with those of W. A. Bone and co-workers for temp. of 750°, 850°, and 975°. A. Johansson and R. von Seth studied the equilibria in the reaction $3Fe+2CO\rightleftharpoons Fe_3C+CO_2$ between 700° and 1100°, and found that at about 700° the equilibria coincided with those of R. Schenck, but not at higher temp. R. Schenck supposed that the carbon press. of cementite is always greater than that of elementary carbon, but this is true only below 800°; above that temp. the carbon press. of cementite is lower. The

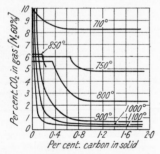

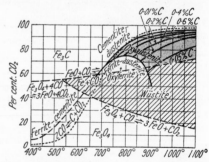

FIG. 27.—Equilibria in the System: $3Fe+2CO\rightleftharpoons Fe_3C+CO_2$ at different temperatures.

FIG. 28.—Equilibria in the Systems with Iron, Iron Oxides, Carbon, and Carbon Monoxide and Dioxide.

results are summarized in Figs. 27 and 28. The results in the first diagram refer to a press. of 40 per cent. of mixed carbon monoxide and dioxide and 60 per cent. of nitrogen; while the results in Fig. 28 have been calculated for a press. of the mixed carbon monoxide and dioxide equal to one atm. G. Chaudron noted that the curves $FeO–Fe_3O_4$ and $Fe–FeO$ meet at 570° to 580°. U. Hofmann and E. Groll showed that with carbon monoxide free from oxygen and iron prepared from the carbonyl, graphite and ferrosic oxide and a little carbide are formed below 450°; graphite and ferrous oxide and a little carbide and ferrosic oxide between 450° and 650°; graphite and carbide, but no ferrous or ferrosic oxide, above 655°. With purified ferric oxide and carbon monoxide, ferrosic oxide and carbide were formed at 275° and 320°; some unknown lines in the X-radiograms were attributed to the carbide Fe_2C. The subject was discussed by R. Schenck and co-workers, W. Reinders, W. Reinders and P. van Groningen, K. Jellinek and A. Diethelm, K. Iwase and T. Watase, H. C. H. Carpenter and C. C. Smith, V. Falcke and co-workers, A. McCance, and K. Hofmann. M. L. Becker found that between 650° and 1000° graphite is stable with respect to iron carbide, for the vap. press. of the carbon vapour of iron carbide is higher than that of carbon alone, and the gas in equilibrium with iron carbide plus saturated solid soln. is richer in carbon monoxide than is the case with graphite at the same temp. A. Matsubara, and A. Johansson and R. von Seth considered the carbon vap. press. of the carbide to be lower, not higher, than that of graphite at temp. exceeding 800°—*vide infra*, the decarburization of cast iron.

H. Nippert found that the constant $K=[CO]^2/[CO_2]$ for the action of carbon monoxide on iron is higher for purified iron than for carburized iron ; and the

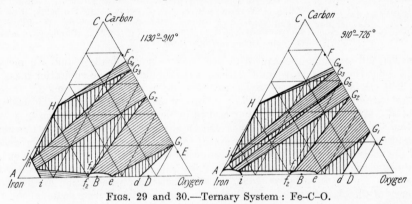

FIGS. 29 and 30.—Ternary System : Fe–C–O.

results with nickeliferous iron are lower than for carburized iron, and these results are taken to be the true equilibrium values, for the reaction is accelerated when nickel is present. R. Schenck, and J. Müller studied the effect of the presence of magnesia, and of silica on the equilibrium conditions ; R. Schenck and co-workers, the influence of alumina, manganese oxide, lime, beryllia, cobalt, and nickel ; and R. Schenck and co-workers, and P. van Groningen, the effect of other impurities.

K. Iwase and T. Watase attempted to represent the relations in the ternary system at 1130°–910° and 910°–726° by Figs. 29 and 30. Hence, B denotes FeO ; D, Fe_3O_4 ; E, CO_2 ; F, CO ; and H, Fe_3C ; while G_1, G_2, G_3, G_4, and G_5 represent mixtures of carbon monoxide and dioxide. The area $Ajhgi$ represents Fe ; f_2igh_1, Fe+FeO ; Hjh, Fe+Fe_3C ; HG_4G_3, Fe_3C ; G_1de, FeO +Fe_3O_4 ; G_2f_1g, FeO+Fe , G_3hH, Fe+Fe_3C ; $G_1ef_1G_2$, FeO ; G_2ghG_3, Fe ; and CkG_4, Fe_3C+C. E. Jänecke also represented results with the ternary system Fe–O–C by triangular diagrams. According to R. Schenck, the equilibrium conditions at a constant temp. below 700° can be represented diagrammatically by Fig. 31 ; the reactions : $2CO \rightleftharpoons CO_2+C$ (curve 5) ; $FeO+CO \rightleftharpoons Fe+CO_2$ (curve 3) ; $3FeO+5CO \rightleftharpoons Fe_3C+4CO_2$ (curve 2) ; $3Fe+2CO$

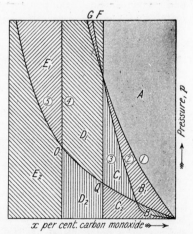

FIG. 31.—Diagrammatic Representation of the Equilibrium Curves involving Fe, FeO, Fe_3O_4, C, CO_2, and CO, below 700°.

$\rightleftharpoons Fe_3C + CO_2$ (curve 1); and $Fe_3O_4 + CO \rightleftharpoons 3FeO + CO_2$ (curve 4), are involved. The curves, Fig. 31, divide the area into 12 fields.

The reactions which take place in the different fields are : *Field A*—$3Fe + 2CO = Fe_3C$ $+ CO_2$; $3FeO + 5CO = Fe_3C + 4CO_2$; $FeO + CO = Fe + CO_2$; $Fe_3O_4 + CO = 3FeO + CO_2$; and $2CO = C + CO_2$. *Field B_1*—$Fe_3C + CO_2 = 3Fe + 2CO$; $3FeO + 5CO = Fe_3C + 4CO_2$; $FeO + CO = Fe + CO_2$; $Fe_3O_4 + CO = 3FeO + CO_2$; and $2CO = C + CO_2$. *Field B_2*—the first four reactions of B_1 apply here, and in addition $C + CO_2 = 2CO$. *Field C_1*—$Fe_3C + CO_2$ $= 3Fe + 2CO$; $Fe_3C + 4CO_2 = 3FeO + 5CO$; $FeO + CO = Fe + CO_2$; $Fe_3O_4 + CO = 3FeO$ $+ CO_2$; and $2CO = C + CO_2$. *Field C_2*—the first four reactions for the field C_1 apply here, and in addition $C + CO_2 = 2CO$. *Field D_1*—$Fe_3C + CO_2 = 3Fe + 2CO$; $Fe_3C + 4CO_2 = 3FeO$ $+ 5CO$; $Fe + CO_2 = FeO + CO$; $Fe_3O_4 + CO = 3FeO + CO_2$; and $2CO = C + CO_2$. *Field D_2*— the first four reactions for the field D_1 apply here, and in addition $C + CO_2 = 2CO$. *Field E_1*—$Fe_3C + CO_2 = 3Fe + 2CO$; $Fe_3C + 4CO_2 = 3FeO + 5CO$; $Fe + CO_2 = FeO + CO$; $3FeO$ $+ CO_2 = Fe_3O_4 + CO$; and $2CO = CO_2 + C$. *Field E_2*—the first four reactions for the field E_1 apply here, and in addition $C + CO_2 = 2CO$. *Field F*—$3Fe + 2CO = Fe_3C + CO_2$; $3FeO$ $+ 5CO = Fe_3C + 4CO_2$; $Fe + CO_2 = FeO + CO$; $Fe_3O_4 + CO = 3FeO + CO_2$; and $2CO$ $= C + CO_2$. *Field G*—$3FeO + 5CO = Fe_3C + 4CO_2$; $Fe_3C + 4CO_2 = 3FeO + 5CO$; $Fe + CO_2$ $= FeO + CO$; $Fe_3O_4 + CO = 3FeO + CO_2$; and $2CO = C + CO_2$. *Field H*—$3Fe + 2CO$ $= Fe_3C + CO_2$; $Fe_3C + 4CO_2 = 3FeO + 5CO$; $Fe + CO_2 = FeO + CO$; $3FeO + CO_2 = Fe_3O_4$ $+ CO$; and $2CO = C + CO_2$—*vide infra*, ferrous oxide.

The end-products are cementite and carbon in the fields A and F; metallic iron and carbon in fields B_1 and C_1, without the simultaneous precipitation of carbon in fields B_2 and C_2; ferrous oxide with carbon in the fields D_1 and G; ferrous oxide without carbon in the field D_2; ferrosic oxide with carbon in the fields E_1 and H; and ferrosic oxide without carbon in the field E_2. Consequently, at any given temp., any of the four solids can be obtained as a stable phase by simple variations of the composition and press. of the gas phase. If the temp. be raised, all the fields are modified, the curvatures of the boundary lines alter, and the curves are displaced to the right. If, then, a third dimension, temp., be included in the diagram, the resulting figure would be a geometrical representation of the whole theory of the blast-furnace. The subject is discussed from other points of view in connection with ferrous oxide and also ferric oxide.

R. Schenck continued : Unlike the other solid phases, cementite is stable only in fields where carbon monoxide is labile and subject to decomposition into carbon and carbon dioxide. Consequently, cementite is not formed from carbon and the metal, and the only cementing agent which can form the tritacarbide directly is carbon monoxide. Cementite, however, can be formed by the action of carbon on ferrous oxide in field B. Solid carbon can act as a cementing agent if it is not in the formation of cementite as a separate phase, but in the formation of a solid soln. of this substance with metallic iron. If the temp. for the formation of the solid soln. falls inside the field C_2, the field in which at temp. below 770° metallic iron is the only stable solid phase, the reaction $Fe_3C + CO_2 \rightleftharpoons 3Fe + 2CO$ becomes reversible. The composition of the solid soln. is dependent on the press. and composition of the gas, and this is also the case for the reaction $FeO + CO \rightleftharpoons Fe$ (containing Fe_3C) $+ CO_2$. H. Tutsya observed that in the ferric oxide and carbon monoxide reaction X-radiograms show that the reduction proceeds $Fe_2O_3 \rightarrow Fe_3O_4$ $\rightarrow FeO \rightarrow Fe_3C$. The deposition of carbon was also studied by W. A. Bone and co-workers, A. Ledebur, and M. L. Becker.

The equilibrium conditions between the oxides of iron and of carbon have been fairly well established by the work of R. Schenck, but the mechanism of the reaction between the oxides of carbon and iron resulting in the formation of the iron carbides and carbon is not so clear. It is doubtful if the reaction $2CO \rightleftharpoons C + CO_2$ progresses directly at temp. below 680°; it is more likely that the free carbon is indirectly formed as a consequence of the decomposition of an iron carbide. As just indicated, R. Schenck assumed that cementite, *i.e.* iron tritacarbide, is the solid phase. According to U. Hofmann, although cementite is always present when a separation of carbon has taken place, yet it is improbable that the carbon is produced by the decomposition of the cementite, because if that compound be heated for 2 hrs. below 450° in nitrogen no decomposition can be detected, but if the cementite be formed from carbon monoxide under similar conditions, ten times as much carbon is produced as could be obtained by the decomposition of the cementite. H. Tutsya assumed that the carbon is here formed by the reaction $2CO=C+CO_2$, catalyzed by the cementite, but (i) U. Hofmann showed that the properties of the resulting carbon make this improbable ; (ii) R. Schenck could not determine the state of equilibrium of the reaction below 680° ; and (iii) the equilibrium proportions of carbon dioxide measured by U. Hofmann and E. Groll are always less than those required on the assumption that the carbon is produced by the reaction $2CO=C+CO_2$.

W. Gludd and co-workers, and F. Fischer and H. Bahr observed that at low temp., between 275° and 320°, the separation of carbon proceeds very slowly, and the X-radiogram shows that the space-lattice of what is thought to be iron hemicarbide, Fe_2C, appears, provided the temp. is below 400°. It is therefore assumed that the hemicarbide decomposes rapidly in the vicinity of 400°. S. Hilpert first assumed the existence of higher carbides than the tritacarbide. The X-ray spectral lines of the hemicarbide agree with those observed by R. Brill and H. Mark for $FeCy_2$; and with those observed by A. Mittasch and E. Kuss for an unknown carbide. U. Hofmann and E. Groll also observed the presence of the space-lattice of the assumed hemicarbide associated with that of ferrosic oxide in the decomposition products of ferric oxide by carbon monoxide between 275° and 320°. H. Tutsya did not detect the presence of this carbide, but he is thought to have worked at too high a temp., for U. Hofmann and E. Groll observed that the decomposition per hour, using 0·2 grm. of iron and a rapid current of carbon monoxide, results in the separation of :

	250°	320°	420°	450°	500°
Carbon	0·5	1·6	26·0	55·0	77·0 mgrms.

These data are considered to represent the speed of decomposition of the hemicarbide, and they are also taken to correspond with the rate at which carbon is produced in the action of carbon monoxide on iron below 400°. No evidence of the formation of the hemicarbide was observed in the action of a slow current of carbon monoxide on iron at 510°—only ferrosic oxide, carbon, iron, and cementite were formed ; but at 585° only iron, carbon, and cementite were present; no ferrosic oxide could be detected. With a rapid current of carbon monoxide, at 450° to 700°, the quantity of carbon dioxide formed is below that required for equilibrium, and only iron and cementite were present in the solid phase. No decomposition of cementite was observed at 450° for 2 hrs. in an atm. of nitrogen ; but when kept at the temp. of its formation for 2 hrs. the cementite was completely decomposed into carbon and iron. The general conclusion of U. Hofmann and E. Groll is that at these low temp. the carbon produced by the action of carbon monoxide on iron or on ferrosic oxide is a result of the formation and subsequent decomposition of iron hemicarbide.

E. Baur and A. Glässner calculated for the thermal value of the reaction $Fe+CO_2 \rightleftharpoons FeO+CO$, −8724 cals. at 835° ; hence the formation of carbon monoxide is favoured by a rise of temp. They found for the reaction $Fe_3O_4+CO \rightleftharpoons 3FeO+CO_2$, −5176 cals. at 765°, and +6563 cals. at 400°. G. Bodländer gave for the free energy of the reduction of ferrous oxide by carbon : $-34,950+35·26T-4·58 \log p_{CO}$. S. Hilpert said that this reaction begins at 240° and that the product of the reaction is carbonaceous. For the reaction $Fe+CO_2=FeO+CO$, G. Chaudron calculated the heat of formation to be −3·4 Cals. per mol at 17°, and −2·0 Cals. at 650° ; and K. M. Tigerschiöld gave −1·8 Cals. at 17°. G. Chaudron gave for the reaction $3FeO+CO_2=Fe_3O_4+CO$, 9·0 Cals. per mol at 17°, and 6·8 Cals. at 650° ; whilst K. M. Tigerschiöld gave 4·0 Cals. at 17°. G. Chaudron gave for the reaction $3Fe+4CO_2=Fe_3O_4+4CO$, −1·2 Cals. per mol at 17°, and −2·0 Cals. at 650°, whilst K. M. Tigerschiöld gave 1·4 Cals. at 17°. K. M. Tigerschiöld gave >16·25 to <18·8 Cals. per mol. for the thermal value of the reaction $3Fe_2O_3+CO =2Fe_3O_4+CO_2$ at 17°. The thermal values of these reactions were also discussed by H. le Chatelier, P. van Groningen, and E. D. Eastman. H. L. Maxwell and A. Hayes gave $3\alpha\text{-Fe}+C_{graphite}=Fe_3C_{solid}+19\cdot163$ Cals. at 650° ; and 19·161 Cals. at 700°. U. Hofmann and E. Groll calculated for the reaction $3Fe+4CO_2=Fe_3O_4+4CO$, —5380 cals. ; and for $Fe_3O_4+6CO=Fe_3C+5CO_2$, —41,850 cals.

The simultaneous action of hydrogen and carbon monoxide in the quaternary system Fe–O–C–H was discussed by G. Chaudron, E. D. Eastman and R. M. Evans, K. Hofmann, and R. Schenck. The results of these observations have been applied by W. Reinders, T. H. Byrom, L. Guillet, F. H. Willcox, D. Sillars, E. Bertram, G. Bulle, A. Michel, B. Osann, C. Zix, H. Bansen, M. Levin, F. Wüst, I. Bohm, S. P. Kinney, H. H. Meyer, W. van Vloten, G. S. J. Perrott and S. P. Kinney, H. A. Brassert, W. Lennings, K. Hofmann, A. Wagner, F. Kupelweiser and R. Schöffel, H. Kinder, J. E. Johnson, W. Mathèsius, F. Clements, F. A. Kjellin, E. G. Odelstjérna, G. W. Vreeland, A. K. Reese, W. G. Imhoff and co-workers, F. T. Sisco, E. Diepschlag and K. Feist, A. L. Boegehold, J. E. Fletcher, R. Schenck and co-workers, K. Iwase and T. Watase, H. Mehner, W. A. Bone and co-workers, N. Metz, H. Kamura, L. E. Gruner, H. J. van Royen, etc., to bring out the nature of the reactions involved in the reduction of iron ores in the blast-furnace. The relative ease of the reducibility of iron ores was discussed by H. Tholander,[5] B. Bogitch, E. A. Uehling, O. Simmersbach, B. Stålhane and T. Malmberg, J. Klärding, H. Seigel, S. Sugimoto, G. Yamada, M. Kawaguchi, R. H. Sweetser and S. P. Kinney, R. Baake, A. Weiskopf, A. D. Elbers, and J. Wiborgh. The greater the density, the less readily is the ore reduced ; ores which are porous after they have lost their volatile matter are readily reduced. C. H. Desch emphasized that the formation of a film of impervious carbon on ore may hinder the reduction. H. Braune discussed the work done by nitrogen reactions in the blast-furnace, and added that cyanogen is the substance from which iron most readily takes up carbon in the blast-furnace—*vide supra*.

The disintegration of firebricks is associated with the action of carbon monoxide about the ferric oxide, etc., present as " iron spots " in the materials, resulting in the deposition of carbon in the interior of the firebricks. This may be attended by a bursting or shattering of the firebricks. The subject was discussed by E. Diepschlag and K. Feist,[6] A. T. Green and co-workers, R. P. Heuer, H. K. Mitra and A. Silverman, C. E. Nesbitt and M. L. Bell, B. M. O'Harra and W. J. Darby, B. Osann, S. M. Phelps, and P. Rischbieth.

REFERENCES.

[1] W. van Vloten, *Stahl Eisen*, 12. 114, 1892 ; I. L. Bell, *Chemical Phenomena in Iron Smelting*, London, 1872 ; *Principles of the Manufacture of Iron and Steel*, London, 76, 1884 ; *Journ. Iron Steel Inst.*, 44. ii, 219, 1893 ; F. Clements, *ib.*, 101. i, 125, 1920 ; W. J. Foster, *ib.*, 61. i, 296, 1902 ; *Proc. Staffs Iron Steel Inst*, 24. 3, 1907 ; G. Rocour, *Étude sur l'équilibre calorifique du haut-fourneau*, Liége, 1898 ; *Rev. Univ. Mines*, 42. 1, 1898 ; L. E. Gruner, *Studies of Blast Furnace Phenomena*, London, 1873 ; *Études sur les hauts-fourneaux, suivies d'une notice sur les appareils à air chaud*, Paris, 1873 ; R. Bunsen and L. Playfair, *B.A. Rep.*, 142, 1845 ; 170, 1846 ; C. R. A. Wright, *Proc. Roy. Inst.*, 7. 248, 1875 ; *Pharm. Journ.*, 4. 966, 1006, 1043, 1874 ; R. Schenk, *Zeit. Elektrochem.*, 10. 397, 1904 ; F. Brabant, *Rev. Univ. Mines*, 9. 133, 1890 ; B. Osann, *Arch. Eisenhüttenwesen*, 1. 673, 1928 ; 2. 137, 1928 ; *Stahl Eisen*, 21. 1277, 1901 ; 22. 258, 1902 ; 32. 465, 649, 739, 1912; 36. 210, 477, 530, 1916 ; A. Gouvy, *ib.*, 22. 294, 1902 ; N. Metz, *ib.*, 33. 93, 1913 ; E. Baur and A. Glässner, *Zeit. phys. Chem.*, 43. 354, 1903 ; L. Mond, *Journ. Chem. Soc.*, 59. 604, 1090, 1891 ; T. Turner, *The Metallurgy of Iron*, London, 211, 1915 ; H. Allen, *Metallurgical Manual of Iron and Steel*, London, 165, 1911 ; *Eng.*, 96. 84, 1903 ; W. W. Davis, *Journ. Amer. Foundrymen's Assoc.*, 12. 47, 1903 ; *Mech. Eng.*, 12. 370, 1903 ; E. A. Uehling, *Journ. Franklin Inst.*, 159. 117, 1905 ; G. Tobin, *Blast Furnace Steel Plant*, 15. 114, 1927 ; P. Mahler, *Rev. Mét.*, 1. 493, 1904 ; T. Weill, *ib.*, 1. 627, 1904 ; H. Mehner, *Gleichgewichtszustande bei der Reduktion der Eisenerze*, Berlin, 1905 ; E. Pierre, *Rev. Univ. Mines*, (6), 7. 301, 1920 ; E. Richarme, *Bull. Soc. Ind. Min.*, (5), 5. 83, 1906 ; F. Mulet, *ib.*, (5), 14. 12, 1918 ; A. Wagner and G. Bulle, *Arch. Eisenhüttenwesen*, 3. 391, 1929 ; A. Wagner, *Blast Furnace Steel Plant*, 17. 81, 1929 ; *Stahl Eisen*, 50. 122, 1930 ; B. Stålhane, *ib.*, 49. 1835, 1929 ; *Jernkontorets Ann.*, (2), 84. 95, 1929 ; B. Stålhane and T. Malmberg, *ib.*, (2), 85. 1, 1930 ; C. P. Linville, *Trans. Amer. Inst. Min. Eng.*, 50. 547, 1910 ; W. Mathesius, *ib.*, 56. 376, 1917 ; *Iron Age*, 99. 1494, 1917 ; *Die physikalischen*

und Chemischen Grundlagen des Eisenhüttenwesens, Leipzig, 1916; *Stahl Eisen*, **33**. 1465, 1517, 1913; **34**. 866, 1914; **42**. 873, 907, 1922; H. Thaler, *ib.*, **34**. 1481, 1914; *Berg. Hütt. Rund.*, **12**. 61, 69, 1916; P. Geimer, *Stahl Eisen*, **43**. 681, 1923; **46**. 173, 1926; K. Mühlbradt, *ib.*, **47**. 1813, 1927; R. A. Hacking, *Metallurgia*, **1**. 195, 235, 1930; **2**. 27, 1930; F. Logeling, *Rev. Univ. Mines*, (8), **2**. 368, 1929; M. Derclaye, *ib.*, (7), **8**. 270, 1925; *Rev. Mét.* **23**. 1, 1926; **25**. 195, 1928; G. Godin, *ib.*, (7), **9**. 237, 266, 1926; J. Lilot, *ib.*, (7), **11**. 10, 1926; W. McConnachie, *Iron Coal Trades Rev.*, **119**. 980, 1929; S. P. Kinney, *Tech. Paper U.S. Bur. Mines*, 397, 1926; S. P. Kinney, P. H. Royster and T. L. Joseph, *ib.*, 391, 1927; *Rep. Investigations*, 2747, 1926; *Engg.*, **116**. 667, 1923; *Trans. Amer. Inst. Min. Eng.*, **69**. 543, 1923; R. Franchot, *ib.*, **71**. 463, 565, 1926; *Proc. Internat. Conf. Bituminous Coal*, 544, 1926; *Min. Met.*, **7**. 368, 1926; **8**. 55, 146, 1927; *Fuels Furnaces*, **5**. 1451, 1927; *Yearbook Amer. Iron Steel Inst.*, 135, 1927; *Tech. Publ. Trans. Amer. Inst. Min.*, 170, 1929; C. Zix, *Rev. Tech. Luxembourgeoise*, **21**. 97, 119, 1929; *Stahl Eisen*, **25**. 154, 1905; **45**. 434, 1925; E. Maurer, *Arch. Eisenhüttenwesen*, **1**. 331, 1927; *Stahl Eisen*, **48**. 7, 1928; W. Lennings, *ib.*, **48**. 1077, 1928; *Iron Coal Trades Rev.*, **117**. 729, 1928; *Arch. Eisenhüttenwesen*, **1**. 549, 1928; G. Eichenberg and P. Oberhoffer, *ib.*, **1**. 613, 1928; *Gestell- und Rastuntersuchung eines Hochofens unter besonderer Berücksichtigung der Verbrennungs-verhältnisse vor den Blasformen*, Aachen, 1927; *Stahl Eisen*, **48**. 1076, 1928; R. D. Pike, *Journ. Ind. Eng. Chem.*, **20**. 1356, 1928; H. von Jüptner, *Berg. Hütt. Jahrb.*, **68**. 1, 1920; *Zeit. phys. Chem.*, **100**. 231, 1922; G. Charpy and L. Jacqué, *Compt. Rend.*, **188**. 473, 1929; H. Riesenfeld, *Kohle Erz*, 5, 1907; L. Lévêque, *Bull. Soc. Ind. Min.*, (4), **5**. 433, 1907; A. Morette, *ib.*, (5), **5**. 217, 1914; J. M. Clay, *Iron Trade Rev.*, **42**. 1090, 1908; K. Hofmann, *Trans. Amer. Electro-chem. Soc.*, **51**. 91, 1927; P. H. Emmett, *ib.*, **51**. 207, 1927; H. Kamura, *ib.*, **51**. 413, 1927; W. G. Gillhausen, *Stahl Eisen*, **30**. 1956, 1910; M. Levin, *ib.*, **32**. 232, 1912; *Nernst's Festschrift*, 252, 1912; F. Wüst, *Stahl Eisen*, **46**. 1213, 1926; **48**. 505, 1273, 1928; *Mitt. Inst. Eisenforsch.*, **8**. 117, 1926; *Iron Coal Trades Rev.*, **114**. 480, 1927; *Journ. Iron Steel Inst.*, **116**. ii, 91, 1927; *Rev. Tech. Luxembourgeoise*, **20**. 81, 1928; W. D. Brown, *Met. Chem. Engg.*, **8**. 663, 1910; J. E. Johnson, *ib.*, **13**. 634, 718, 787, 833, 905, 954, 1918; **14**. 38, 77, 210, 235, 266, 318, 1916; **16**. 17, 1917; M. Zyromsky, *Compt. Rend. Soc. Ind. Min.*, 574, 1911; P. Anglès d'Auriac, *ib.*, 576, 1911; H. le Chatelier, *Rev. Mét.*, **9**. 513, 1912; J. Seigle, *ib.*, **18**. 81, 1921; **20**. 195, 481, 1923; **26**. 12, 1929; *Rev. Univ. Mines*, (7), **2**. 96, 1923; *Rev. Ind. Min.*, 241, 1926; *Compt. Rend.*, **178**. 1426, 1924; F. A. Kjellin, *Bihang Jernkontorets Ann.*, **13**. 1, 1912; F. Hodson, *Chem. Met. Engg.*, **25**. 881, 1921; F. T. Sisco, *Trans. Amer. Soc. Steel Treating*, **7**. 363, 1925; H. Bansen, *Rev. Mét.*, **25**. 614, 1929; *Arch. Eisenhüttenwesen*, **1**. 245, 1927; G. Bulle, *ib.*, **1**. 161, 1927; *Blast Furnace Steel Plant*, **17**. 425, 435, 1929; P. Reichardt, *Rev. Mét.*, **25**. 521, 1928; *Stahl Eisen*, **47**. 1494, 1927; *Arch. Eisenhüttenwesen*, **1**. 77, 1927; A. Michel, *Giesserei Ztg.*, **24**. 567, 1927; *Iron Coal Trades Rev.*, **45**. 88, 1927; *Iron Age*, **120**. 535, 1927; *Stahl Eisen*, **47**. 696, 1927; I. Bohm, *Jernkontorets Ann.*, (2), **111**. 145, 1927; R. H. Sweetser, *Tech. Publ. Amer. Inst. Min. Eng.*, 11, 1927; F. C. Howard, *Iron Age*, **122**. 271, 1928; T. L. Joseph, *Fuels Furnaces*, **6**. 635, 1928; H. H. Meyer, *Mitt. Inst. Eisenforsch.*, **10**. 107, 1928; *Stahl Eisen*, **49**. 1059, 1929; O. C. Ralston, *Iron Oxide Reduction Equilibria*, Washington, 1929; *Bull. U.S. Bur. Mines*, 296, 1929; P. Farup, *Tids. Kemi Berg.*, **6**. 1, 15, 1926; E. C. Evans and F. J. Bailey, *Journ. Iron Steel Inst.*, **117**. i, 53, 1928; N. A. Kostuileff, *Domez*, 8, 1930; P. Farup, *Iron Coal Trades Rev.*, **81**. 367, 1910.

² J. E. Johnson, *The Principles, Operation, and Products of the Blast Furnace*, New York, 1918; *Chem. Met. Engg.*, **14**. 210, 266, 464, 520, 1916; **15**. 21, 69, 127, 1916; A. Feild, *ib.*, **14**. 377, 1916; B. F. Burman, *ib.*, **13**. 624, 1915; L. Mathesius, *Studie über die Reduzierbarkeit von eisenerzen in stromenden Gazen*, Berlin, 1913; *Stahl Eisen*, **34**. 866, 1914; W. Mathesius, *Die physikalischen und chemischen Grundlagen des Eisenhüttenwesens*, Leipzig, 1916; *Ferrum*, **12**. 16, 1915; **13**. 172, 1916; *Iron Trade Rev.*, **60**. 1234, 1917; *Stahl Eisen*, **31**. 1380, 1545, 1911; **33**. 1465, 1517, 1518, 1522, 2074, 1913; **36**. 695, 749, 1916; **37**. 149, 202, 1052, 1917; **43**. 873, 907, 910, 1923; B. Osann, *ib.*, **13**. 986, 1893; **22**. 1033, 1101, 1902; **36**. 477, 530, 1926; **37**. 645, 1917; **46**. 1795, 1926; **48**. 1082, 1928; *Arch. Eisenhüttenwesen*, **1**. 101, 1928; *Lehrbuch der Eisenhüttenkunde*, Leipzig, **1**. 671, 1923; H. Bansen, *Wärmewerlkeit Wärme- und Gasfluss, die physikalischen Grundlagen metallurgischer Verfahren*, Düsseldorf, 14, 1929; *Arch. Eisenhüttenwesen*, **1**. 245, 1928; **3**. 241, 1930; *Rev. Mét.*, **25**. 614, 1928; *Stahl Eisen*, **39**. 493, 1919; **46**. 1558, 1926; **47**. 1007, 1927; **49**. 1760, 1929; **50**. 807, 1930; W. G. Gillhausen, *ib.*, **30**. 1956, 1910; *Met.*, **7**. 421, 458, 467, 524, 1910; L. Gruner, *Ann. Mines*, (7), **2**. 1, 1872; (7), **4**. 224, 1873; F. Clements, *Blast Furnace Practice*, London, 1929; *Journ. Iron Steel Inst.*, **101**. i, 121, 1920; E. C. Evans and E. J. Bailey, *ib.*, **117**. i, 53, 1928; E. C. Evans, *Fuel Economy Rev.*, **4**. 18, 1925; M. Levin and J. Wesselmann, *Ferrum*, **11**. 261, 1914; M. Levin, *ib.*, **13**. 125, 1916; **14**. 15, 1917; R. Hahn, *Stahl Eisen*, **47**. 1572, 1672, 1927; G. Eichenberg, *Arch. Eisenhüttenwesen*, **3**. 1, 1930; G. Eichenberg and R. Hahn, *ib.*, **2**. 207, 1929; G. Eichenberg and P. Oberhoffer, *ib.*, **1**. 613, 1928; P. Reichardt, *ib.*, **1**. 77, 1928; C. C. Furnas, *Blast Furnace Steel Plant*, **17**. 807, 1929; H. P. Howland, *Trans. Amer. Inst. Min. Eng.*, **56**. 339, 365, 1917; O. O. Laudig, *ib.*, **26**. 269, 1061, 1896; A. Wagner and G. Bulle, *Arch. Eisenhüttenwesen*, **3**. 391, 1930; *Stahl Eisen*, **49**. 1860, 1929; A. Wagner, *ib.*, **40**. 1397, 1930; G. Bulle, *ib.*, **48**. 433, 1928; *Arch. Eisenhüttenwesen*, **1**. 161, 1928; J. W. Richards, *Stahl Eisen*, **30**. 1266, 1910; *Internat. Kongr. Bergbau*, **5**. ii, 130, 1910; *Metallurgical Calculations*, New York, **2**. 1, 1907; R. Durrer, *Stahl Eisen*, **37**. 1052, 1917; F. Wüst, *Ber. Internat. Kongr. Bergbau*, **5**. 228, 1910; *Stahl Eisen*, **30**. 1715, 1910; **31**. 953, 1382, 1911; **32**. 389, 1912; **46**. 1219, 1926;

47. 1008, 1927; **48.** 1286, 1928; *Met.*, **7.** 403, 1910; **8.** 385, 1911; E. Maurer, *Arch. Eisen-hüttenwesen*, **1.** 331, 1928; *Stahl Eisen*, **48.** 7, 1928; H. Thaler, *ib.*, **40.** 317, 1920; O. Simmersbach, *ib.*, **24.** 1007, 1904; **31.** 1543, 1911; **33.** 1522, 1913; **37.** 561, 1927; K. Feist, *ib.*, **44.** 311, 1924; F. Werndl, *ib.*, **31.** 1543, 1911; E. Bormann, *ib.*, **45.** 2041, 2085, 1925; F. Lange, *ib.*, **38.** 305, 1918; R. Schenck, *ib.*, **35.** 509, 1925; A. Liebreich, *ib.*, **37.** 154, 1917; K. Mühlbradt, *ib.*, **47.** 1813, 1927; H. Wedding, *Ausführliches Handbuch der Eisenhüttenkunde*, Braunschweig, **3.** 323, 1906; W. Lennings, *Arch. Eisenhüttenwesen*, **1.** 562, 1928; *Stahl Eisen*, **48.** 1079, 1928; J. B. Fortune, *Fuel Economist*, **4.** 247, 1929; M. A. Morette, *Compt. Rend. Soc. Ind. Min.*, 217, 455, 1914; W. A. Bone, R. A. Hadfield and A. Hutchinson, *Journ. Iron Steel Inst.*, **100.** 11, 1919; A. K. Reese, *ib.*, **106.** 9, 1922; W. Trinks, *Blast Furnace Steel Plant*, **10.** 451, 1922; S. P. Kinney, P. H. Royster and T. L. Joseph, *ib.*, **12.** 274, 1924; W. D. Brown, *ib.*, **13.** 236, 1925; G. Tobin, *ib.*, **15.** 114, 1927; P. W. Uhlmann, *ib.*, **15.** 177, 1927; A. Korevaar, *Combustion in the Gas Producer and in the Blast Furnace*, London, 1924; J. F. Barkley, *Tech. Paper Bur. Mines*, 401, 1927; H. E. Wright, *Iron Coal Trades Rev.*, **118.** 527, 1929; T. C. Hutchinson, *Journ. Iron Steel Inst.*, **78.** iii, 38, 1908; A. Anjou, *Jernkontorets Ann.*, **114.** 86, 1931.

³ H. St. C. Deville, *Compt. Rend.*, **70.** 1105, 1201, 1870; **71.** 30, 1871; H. Debray, *ib.*, **45.** 1019, 1857; **88.** 1341, 1879; G. Chaudron, *ib.*, **159.** 237, 1914; *Rev. Ann. Chim. Phys. Met.*, **21.** 467, 1924; *Chim. Ind.*, **8.** 959, 1922; *Ann. Chim. Phys.*, (9), **16.** 221, 1921; J. L. Gay-Lussac, *ib.*, (2), **1.** 37, 1816; H. V. Regnault, *ib.*, (2), **62.** 372, 1836; W. Müller, *Pogg. Ann.*, **129.** 459, 1866; **133.** 336, 1868; **144.** 626, 1872; G. Preuner, *Zeit. phys. Chem.*, **47.** 385, 1904; L. Wöhler and W. Prager, *Zeit. Elektrochem.*, **23.** 199, 1917; L. Wöhler and O. Balz, *ib.*, **27.** 406, 1921; L. Wöhler and R. Günther, *ib.*, **29.** 276, 1923; K. Hofmann, *Stahl Eisen*, **45.** 1709, 1751, 1857, 1925; *Zeit. Elektrochem.*, **31.** 172, 1925; *Zeit. angew. Chem.*, **38.** 715, 1058, 1085, 1925; *Zeit. anorg. Chem.*, **31.** 173, 1925; B. Neumann and G. Köhler, *ib.*, **34.** 232, 1928; E. Schreiner and F. B. Grimnes, *Zeit. anorg. Chem.*, **110.** 311, 1920; E. D. Eastman, *Journ. Amer. Chem. Soc.*, **44.** 975, 1922; E. D. Eastman and R. M. Evans, *ib.*, **46.** 888, 1924; P. H. Emmett and J. F. Schultz, *ib.*, **52.** 4268, 1930; J. Thibeau, *Rev. Univ. Mines*, (6), **6.** 313, 1925; (6), **7.** 25, 74, 155, 186, 1925; P. van Groningen, *Evenwichten in de Stelsels Ijzer-Koolstof-Zuurstof en Ijzer-Waterstof-Zuurstof*, Delft, 1921; J. B. Ferguson, *Journ. Washington Acad.*, **13.** 275, 1923; *Canadian Chem. Met.*, **7.** 175, 1923; H. Kamura, *Journ. Iron Steel Inst.*, **112.** ii, 279, 1925; A. Smits and J. M. Bijvoet, *Proc. Akad. Amsterdam*, **21.** 386, 1918; K. M. Tigerschiöld, *Jernkontorets Ann.*, (2), **78.** 67, 1923; H. Tholander, *ib.*, (2), **29.** 60, 1894; W. Krings and J. Kempkens, *Zeit. anorg. Chem.*, **183.** 225, 1929; J. Kempkens, *Ueber die Löslichkeit des Sauerstoffs im festen Eisen*, Aachen, 1930; J. Beyer, *Studien über die Gleichgewichtsbedingungen zurischen Wasserstoff-Wasserdampf-Gemischen und Eisenoxyden*, Berlin, 1911; O. Sackur, *Die chemische Affinität und ihre Messungen*, Braunschweig, 64, 1908; W. Reinders, *Chem. Weekbl.*, **15.** 186, 1918; A. McCance, *Trans. Faraday Soc.*, **21.** 181, 1926; F. Wüst and P. Rütten, *Mitt. Inst. Eisenforsch. Düsseldorf*, **5.** 5, 1924; *Stahl Eisen*, **43.** 154, 1923; F. Wüst, *ib.*, **47.** 963, 1927; *Zeit. anorg. Chem.*, **188.** 143, 1930; S. Mita, *Journ. Ferrous Met. Japan*, **31.** 1067, 1929; P. P. Fedotéeff and T. N. Petrenko, *Zeit. anorg. Chem.*, **157.** 165, 1926; G. Gallo, *Ann. Chim. Applicata*, **17.** 27, 1927; W. E. Jominy and D. W. Murphy, *Journ. Ind. Eng. Chem.*, **23.** 384, 1931; *Trans. Amer. Soc. Steel Treating*, **18.** 19, 1930; C. H. Herty, *Bull. Carnegie Inst. Pittsburg*, 34, 1927; F. Haber, *Zeit. anorg. Chem.*, **38.** 5, 1904; O. Hahn, *Zeit. phys. Chem.*, **44.** 513, 1903; **48.** 735, 1904; F. S. Tritton and D. Hanson, *Journ. Iron Steel Inst.*, **110.** ii, 85, 1924; W. Biltz and H. Müller, *Zeit. anorg. Chem.*, **163.** 257, 1927; S. L. Madorsky, *Journ. Ind. Eng. Chem.*, **23.** 99, 1931; B. Stålhane and T. Malmberg, *Jernkontorets Ann.*, 2, **65.** 609, 1930; W. P. Fishel and J. F. Wooddell, *Trans. Amer. Soc. Steel Treating*, **11.** 730, 1927; P. van Groningen, *Evenwichten in de Stelsels Ijzer-Koolstof-Zuurstof en Ijzer-Waterstof-Zuurstof*, Delft, 1921.

⁴ W. Müller, *Pogg. Ann.*, **144.** 617, 1872; K. Stammer, *ib.*, **82.** 136, 1851; H. le Chatelier, *Ann. Mines*, (8), **13.** 164, 1888; I. L. Bell, *Journ. Chem. Soc.*, **22.** 203, 1869; *Journ. Iron Steel Inst.*, **1.** 85, 1871; *Chemical Phenomena of Iron and Steel Smelting*, London, 1872; *B.A. Rep.*, 62, 1869; *Principles of the Manufacture of Iron and Steel*, London, 1884; C. Schinz, *Dokumente, betreffend den Hochofen zur Darstellung von Roheisen*, Berlin, 57, 1868; S. Reiner and W. Feldmann, *Mitt. Luxemb. Berg. Hütt.*, **1.** 121, 1925; R. H. Sweetser, *Min. Met.*, **11.** 423, 1930; L. Mathesius, *Untersuchungen über die Reduzierbarkeit von Eisenerzen in strömenden Gasen*, Berlin, 1913; *Stahl Eisen*, **34.** 866, 1924; B. Kosmann, *ib.*, **8.** 586, 1888; C. Zix, *ib.*, **25.** 156, 1905; **45.** 434, 1925; **49.** 1198, 1929; W. van Vloten, *ib.*, **13.** 26, 1893; F. Wüst, *ib.*, **30.** 1715, 1910; **46.** 1215, 1926; **47.** 905, 955, 964, 1008, 1927; **48.** 505, 1093, 1273, 1928; *Journ. Iron Steel Inst.*, **116.** ii, 65, 1927; *Met.*, **7.** 403, 1910; H. Fleissner and F. Duftschmid, *Berg. Hütt. Jahrb.*, **74.** 42, 1926; H. von Jüptner, *Zeit. Phys. Chem.*, **100.** 231, 1922; *Zeit. Elektrochem.*, **12.** 815, 1906; *Berg. Hütt. Jahrb.*, **68.** 1, 1920; *Beiträge zur Theorie der Eisenhüttenprozesse*, Stuttgart, 1907; E. Diepschlag and K. Feist, *Feuerfest Ofenbau*, **4.** 133, 1928; B. Kalling and G. Lilljekvist, *Bergwetenskap*, 1, 1926; *Tekn. Tidskr.*, **56.** 1, 1926; E. G. Odelstjerna, *ib.*, **45.** 132, 1915; M. Mayer and J. Jakoby, *Journ. Gasbeleucht.*, **52.** 282, 1909; F. E. Rhead and R. V. Wheeler, *Journ. Chem. Soc.*, **97.** 2178, 1910; **99.** 1140, 1911; H. Bansen, *Arch. Eisenhüttenwesen*, **3.** 241, 1930; B. Osann, *ib.*, **2.** 137, 1929; *Stahl Eisen*, **21.** 1277, 1901; **22.** 258, 1902; **28.** 1784, 1908; **32.** 465, 739, 1912; **42.** 302, 1922; **48.** 1081, 1928; H. A. Brassert, *ib.*, **43.** 73, 1923; H. Kinder, *ib.*, **32.** 231, 1912; T. H. Byrom, *ib.*, **56.** 145, 1916; *Journ. Iron Steel Inst.*, **92.** ii, 106, 113, 1915; G. S. J. Perrott and S. P. Kinney, *Trans. Amer. Inst. Min. Eng.*, **69.** 543, 584, 1923; W. Mathesius, *ib.*, **51.** 194, 1916; F. Kupelweiser and R. Schöffel,

Berg. Hütt. Ztg., **32.** 169, 1873 ; F. A. Kjellin, *Bihang Jernkontorets Ann.*, **13.** 1, 1912 ; J. E. Johnson, *Chem. Met. Engg.*, **13.** 536, 634, 718, 787, 1915 ; **14.** 210, 266, 363, 642, 1916 ; **15.** 69, 127, 1916 ; G. W. Vreeland, *Iron Age*, **97.** 1332, 1916 ; W. G. Imhoff and D. E. Ackermann, *ib.*, **115.** 203, 1925 ; W. G. Imhoff, *ib.*, **121.** 1686, 1928 ; **122.** 203, 393, 1928 ; F. H. Wilcox, *Bull. Bur. Mines*, 130, 1917 ; F. Clements, *Journ. Iron Steel Inst.*, **101.** i, 125, 1920 ; A. K. Reese, *ib.*, **106.** ii, 9, 44, 1922 ; D Sillars, *Journ. West Scotland Iron Steel Inst.*, **32.** 52, 1925 ; F. T. Sisco, *Trans. Amer. Soc. Steel Treating*, **7.** 363, 1925 ; E. Bertram, *Arch. Eisenhüttenwesen*, **1.** 19, 1928 ; A. Michel, *Giesserei Ztg.*, **24.** 567, 1927 ; A. L. Boegehold, *Trans. Amer. Foundrymen's Assoc.*, **37.** 91, 1929 ; J. E. Fletcher, *Bull. Brit. Cast Iron Research Assoc.*, **25.** 147, 1929 ; O. Boudouard, *Bull. Soc. Chim.*, (3), **21.** 269, 463, 465, 712, 1899 ; (3), **23.** 137, 1900 ; (3), **25.** 227, 282, 484, 833, 1901 ; *Ann. Chim. Phys.*, (7), **24.** 5, 1901 ; *Compt. Rend.*, **131.** 1206, 1900 ; **140.** 40, 1905 ; **141.** 252, 1905 ; *Génie Civil*, **47.** 235, 1905 ; L. Guillet, *ib.*, **78.** 104, 126; 151, 169, 190, 1921 ; W. Reinders, *Chem. Weekbl.*, **15.** 180, 1918 ; *Versl. Akad. Amsterdam*, **25.** 10, 1916 ; *Proc. Akad. Amsterdam*, **19.** 175, 1916 ; W. Reinders and P. van Groningen, *Rec. Trav. Chim. Pays-Bas*, **40.** 701, 1921 ; P. van Groningen, *Evenwichten in de Stelsels Ijzer-Koolstof-Zuurstof en Ijzer-Waterstof-Zuurstof*, Delft, 1921 ; F. E. C. Scheffer, *Versl. Akad. Amsterdam*, **25.** 600, 1916 ; W. Krings, *Zeit. anorg. Chem.*, **201.** 188, 1931 ; H. Groebler and P. Oberhoffer, *Stahl Eisen*, **47.** 1985, 1927 ; K. Jellinek and A. Diethelm, *Zeit. anorg. Chem.*, **124.** 225, 1922 , J. Müller, *Das System Eisen-Kohlenstoff-Sauerstoff bei höheren Temperaturen mit besonderer Berücksichtigung der Bodenkörperfrage*, Münster, 1927 ; W. Gluud, K. V. Otto and H. Ritter, *Ber.*, **62.** B, 2483, 1929 ; *Ber. Ges. Kohlentech.*, **3.** 40, 1930 ; R. Brill and H. Mark, *Zeit. phys. Chem.*, **133.** 443, 1928 ; A. Mittasch and E. Kuss, *Zeit. Elektrochem.*, **34.** 159, 1928 ; G. Eichenberg and P. Oberhoffer, *Arch. Eisenhüttenwesen*, **1.** 613, 1927 ; J. Klärding, *ib.*, **5.** 129, 1931 ; G. Bulle, *ib.*, **3.** 169, 1930 ; *Stahl Eisen*, **46.** 441, 1926 ; **48.** 433, 1928 ; G. Bulle and W. Lennings, *Ber. Hochofenaussch. Ver. Eisenhüttenleute*, 78, 1926 ; A. Wagner, *ib.*, 75, 1926 ; *Stahl Eisen*, **50.** 122, 1930 ; W. Lennings, *Arch. Eisenhüttenwesen*, **1.** 549, 1928 ; *Iron Coal Trades Rev.*, **117.** 729, 1928 ; *Stahl Eisen*, **48.** 1077, 1928 ; *Gestell- und Rastuntersuchung eines Hochofens unter besonderer Berücksichtigung der Verbrennungsverhältnisse vor den Blasformen*, Düsseldorf, 1927 ; C. G. Särnström, *Tek. Tids.*, **23.** 61, 1893 ; J. Wiborgh, *ib.*, **17.** 3, 1887 ; A. Guntz, *Bull. Soc. Chim.*, (3), **3.** 275, 1892 ; F. Schlagdenhauffen and C. Paget, *Compt. Rend.*, **128.** 309, 1899 ; P. Schützenberger, *Traité de chimie générale*, Paris, **2.** 475, 1880 ; A. Ledebur, *Berg. Hütt. Ztg.*, **36.** 278, 1877 ; *Met. Rev.*, 377, 1877 ; W. J. Hudson, *Proc. South Staffs Iron Steel Works Managers*, 84, 1894 ; J. J. Ebelmen, *Ann. Mines*, (3), **20.** 395, 1841 ; (4), **5.** 24, 1842 ; C. C. Furnas and G. G. Brown, *Journ. Ind. Eng. Chem.*, **20.** 507, 1928 ; L. Rinman and B. Fernquist, *Undersokningar rorande Masugnsgasernas kemiska sammansätning pression och temperatur*, Stockholm, 1862 ; S. P. Kinney, *Journ. Iron Steel Inst.*, **116.** ii, 78, 1927 ; *Blast Furnace Steel Plant*, **13.** 243, 1925 ; *Stahl Eisen*, **46.** 441, 1926 ; *Tech. Paper Bur. Mines*, 397, 1926 ; P. H. Royster, S. P. Kinney and T. L. Joseph, *Blast Furnace Steel Plant*, **12.** 246, 254, 274, 1924 ; *Rep. Investigations Bur. Mines*, 2747, 1926 ; *Tech. Paper Bur. Mines*, 391, 1927 ; H. H. Meyer, *Mitt. Inst. Eisenforsch.*, **9.** 273, 1927 ; **10.** 107, 1928 ; *Stahl Eisen*, **48.** 1786, 1928 ; W. P. Fishel and J. F. Wooddell, *Trans. Amer. Soc. Steel Treating*, **11.** 730, 1927 ; U. Hofmann and B. Groll, *Zeit. anorg. Chem.*, **191.** 414, 1930 ; U. Hofmann, *Ber.*, **61.** B, 1180, 2183, 1928 ; A. B. Kinzel and J. J. Egan, *Tech. Publ. Amer. Inst. Min. Eng.*, 230, 1929 ; H. Tutsya, *Bull. Japan Inst. Phys. Chem. Research*, **8.** 609, 1929 ; *Science Papers Inst. Phys. Chem. Research Tokyo*, **10.** 69, 1929 ; E. Bauer, *Themen der physikalischen Chemie*, Leipzig, 1910 ; H. Koppers, *U.S. Pat. No.* 1746705, 1930 ; J. Thibeau, *Rev. Univ. Mines*, (7), **6.** 313, 1925 ; (7), **7.** 25, 74, 155, 186, 1925 ; A. Stansfield, *Trans. Amer. Electrochem. Soc.*, 217, 1927 ; C. H. Herty, *Rep. Investigations U.S. Bur. Mines*, 3054, 1930 ; K. Hofmann, *Stahl Eisen*, **45.** 1709, 1751, 1857, 1925 ; *Zeit. angew. Chem.*, **38.** 721, 1058, 1085, 1925 ; *Zeit. Elektrochem.*, **31.** 172, 1925 ; E. Terres and A. Pongracz, *ib.*, **25.** 386, 1919 ; L. Wöhler and R. Günther, *ib.*, **29.** 276, 1923 ; L. Wöhler and O. Balz, *ib.*, **27.** 406, 1921 ; L. Wöhler and W. Prager, *ib.*, **23.** 199, 1917 ; A. Smits, *ib.*, **18.** 1081, 1918 ; A. Smits and L. K. Wolff, *Zeit. phys. Chem.*, **45.** 199, 1903 ; *Proc. Akad. Amsterdam*, **4.** 417, 1902 ; A. Smits and J. M. Bijvoet, *ib.*, **21.** 386, 1918 ; E. Baur and A. Glässner, *Stahl Eisen*, **23.** 556, 1903 ; *Zeit. phys. Chem.*, **43.** 354, 1903 ; O. Hahn, *ib.*, **42.** 705, 1903 ; **44.** 513, 1903 ; G. Charpy, *Compt. Rend.*, **137.** 120, 1903 ; P. Pingault, *ib.*, **192.** 45, 1931 ; H. St. C. Deville, *ib.*, **59.** 874, 1864 ; A. Gautier and P. Clausmann, *ib.*, **151.** 16, 355, 1910 ; G. Chaudron, *ib.*, **159.** 237, 1914 ; **172.** 152, 1921 ; *Rev. Mét.*, **21.** 462, 1924 ; *Ann. Chim. Phys.*, (9), **16.** 221, 1921 ; R. Schenck, H. Franz and H. Willekie, *Zeit. anorg. Chem.*, **181.** 1, 1929 ; R. Schenck and H. Wesselkock, *ib.*, **184.** 39, 1929 ; R. Schenck and T. Dingmann, *ib.*, **166.** 114, 1927 ; R. Schenck and H. Nippert, *ib.*, **167.** 260, 1927 ; H. Nippert, *Ueber die Beziehungen verschiedener Kohlenstoffmodifikationen*, Breslau, 1913 ; R. Schenck and F. Zimmermann, *Ber.*, **36.** 445, 1903 ; F. Zimmermann, *Met. Chem. Engg.*, **8.** 182, 1910 ; *Stahl Eisen*, **25.** 758, 1905 ; R. Schenck and W. Heller, *Ber.*, **38.** 2132, 1905 ; *Stahl Eisen*, **25.** 1121, 1905 ; *Engg.*, **81.** 471, 1906 ; W. Heller, *Beiträge zur Theorie des Eisenhochofenprozesses*, Marburg, 1905 ; H. Semiller, *Die Reduktionsprozesse im Eisenhochofen*, Marburg, 1906 ; R. Schenck, H. Semiller and V. Falcke, *Ber.*, **40.** 1704, 1907 ; R. Schenck, T. Dingmann, G. Hub, M. S. C. Kirscht and A. Kortengräber, *Zeit. anorg. Chem.*, **206.** 73, 1932 ; R. Schenck, *Arch. Eisenhüttenwesen*, **1.** 483, 1927 ; *Stahl Eisen*, **48.** 199, 1928 ; *Zeit. Metallkunde*, **20.** 93, 1928 ; *Physikalische Chemie der Metalle*, Halle a. S., 137, 1909 ; *Zeit. anorg. Chem.*, **164.** 145, 313, 1927 ; **166.** 113, 1927 ; **167.** 254, 315, 1927 ; **182.** 97, 1929 ; *Deut. Forschung*, 3, 1928 ; *Stahl Eisen*, **43.** 155, 1923 ; **46.** 665, 1926 ; **48.**

15, 1928; *Zeit. Elektrochem.*, **10**. 397, 1904; **12**. 218, 1906; **24**. 248, 1918; **34**. 399, 1928; R. Schenck, T. Dingmann, P. H. Kirscht and A. Kortengräber, *Zeit. anorg. Chem.*, **206**. 73, 1932; R. Schenck, F. Kurzen and H. Wesselkock, *ib.*, **206**. 273, 1932; R. Schenck, W. Riess and E. O. Brüggemann, *Zeit. Elektrochem.*, **38**. 562, 1932; G. Bodländer, *Zeit. Elektrochem.*, **8**. 839, 1902; V. Falcke and W. Fischer, *ib.*, **32**. 194, 1926; F. Fischer and H. Bahr, *Gesammelte Abh. Kenntnis Kohle*, **8**. 265, 1927; V. Falcke, *Zeit. Elektrochem.*, **21**. 37, 1915; **22**. 121, 1916; **27**. 268, 1921; **33**. 1, 1927; **34**. 393, 1928; *Ber.*, **46**. 743, 1913; S. Hilpert, *ib.*, **42**. 4575, 1909; **48**. 1281, 1915; S. Hilpert and F. Beyer, *ib.*, **44**. 1618, 1911; S. Hilpert and T. Dieckmann, *ib.*, **48**. 1281, 1915; A. Matsubara, *Trans. Amer. Inst. Min. Eng.*, **67**. 3, 1922; *Zeit. anorg. Chem.*, **124**. 39, 1922; *Stahl Eisen*, **43**. 241, 1923; I. Braithwaite, *Chem. News*, **72**. 211, 1895; H. W. B. Roozeboom, *Die heterogenen Gleichgewichte*, Braunschweig, **1**. 26, 33, 1901; M. Levin, *Met.*, **8**. 606, 1911; *Stahl Eisen*, **32**. 232, 1912; *Nernst's Festschrift*, 252, 1912; K. Arndt and G. Schraube, *ib.*, 46, 1912; M. Levin and H. Niedt, *Stahl Eisen*, **31**. 2135, 1911; *Met.*, **8**. 515, 555, 1911; W. G. Gillhausen, *ib.*, **7**. 421, 1910; H. C. H. Carpenter and C. C. Smith, *Journ. Iron Steel Inst.*, **98**. ii, 139, 1918; I. Bohm, *ib.*, **116**. ii, 83, 1927; *Stahl Eisen*, **47**. 1955, 1927; **48**. 1085, 1928; *Jernkontorets Ann.*, (2), **82**. 145, 1927; H. Kamura, *Trans. Amer. Inst. Min. Eng.*, **71**. 549, 1925; *Trans. Amer. Electrochem. Soc.*, **51**. 305, 1927; *Journ. Iron Steel Inst.*, **112**. ii, 279, 1925; A. Johansson and R. von Seth, *ib.*, **114**. ii, 295, 1926; H. J. van Royen, *Experimentelle Untersuchung über das System Fe, FeO, C, CO und CO₂ und Betrachtungen über die chemischen Vorgänge im Hochofen vom Standpunkte der Affinitätslehre*, Bonn, 1911; E. D. Eastman, *Journ. Amer. Chem. Soc.*, **44**. 975, 1922; E. D. Eastman and R. M. Evans, *ib.*, **46**. 888, 1924; H. L. Maxwell and A. Hayes, *ib.*, **48**. 584, 1926; L. E. Gruner, *Mémoire sur le dédoublement de l'oxyde de carbone sous l'action combinée du fer métallique et des oxydes de ce métal*, Paris, 1872; *Compt. Rend.*, **73**. 28, 1871; *Der Hochofen*, Wiesbaden, 96, 1875; H. Mehner, *Ueber Gleichgewichtszustände bei der Reduktion der Eisenerze*, Berlin, 1905; N. Metz, *Stahl Eisen*, **33**. 93, 1913; *Studien über die im Hochofen zwischen den Eisenerzen und Gasen obwaltenden Verhältnisse*, Düsseldorf, 1912; R. R. Garran, *Trans. Faraday Soc.*, **24**. 201, 1928; A. McCance, *ib.*, **21**. 176, 1925; *Journ. Iron Steel Inst.*, **99**. i, 437, 1919; K. M. Tigerschiöld, *Jernkontorets Ann.*, (2), **78**. 67, 1923; H. Tholander, *ib.*, (2), **29**. 60, 1874; B. Stålhane, *ib.*, (2), **84**. 95, 1929; B. Stålhane and T. Malmberg, *ib.*, (2), **85**. 1, 1930; G. Grönal, *ib.*, (2), **67**. 158, 1912; C. Svensson, *ib.*, (2), **78**. 200, 1923; R. Akerman and C. G. Särnström, *ib.*, (2), **37**. 329, 1882; *Berg. Hütt. Ztg.*, **37**. 16, 1883; *Stahl Eiser*, **3**. 140, 1883; R. Akerman, *ib.*, **3**. 157, 1883; W. A. Bone, L. Reeve and H. L. Saunders, *Journ. West Scotland Iron Steel Inst.*, **35**. 50, 1928; *Engg.*, **123**. 564, 1927; **129**. 647, 1930; *Metallbörse*, **17**. 1295, 1351, 1927; *Iron Coal Trades Rev.*, **120**. 754, 1930; *Journ. Iron Steel Inst.*, **115**. i, 127, 1927; **121**. i, 35, 1930; M. L. Becker, *ib.*, **112**. ii, 239, 1925; **121**. i, 337, 1930; E. Schreiner and F. B. Grimnes, *Zeit. anorg. Chem.*, **110**. 311, 1920; F. Glaser, *ib.*, **36**. 21, 1903; E. Scheil and E. H. Schulz, *ib.*, **188**. 290, 1930; G. Tammann and A. Sworykin, *ib.*, **170**. 62, 1928; E. Jänecke, *ib.*, **178**. 73, 1929; **204**. 257, 1932; K. Iwase and T. Watase, *Osaka Celebration Kyoto*, 185, 1927; G. Takahashi, *Science Rep. Tohoku Univ.*, **15**. 157, 1926; K. Iwase, *ib.*, **15**. 511, 1926; H. Dünwald and C. Wagner, *Zeit. anorg. Chem.*, **199**. 321, 1931; N. A. Kostuileff, *Domez*, 8, 9, 1930; P. Farup, *Iron Coal Trades Rev.*, **81**. 367, 1910.

⁵ H. Tholander, *Berg. Hütt. Jahrb.*, **26**. 55, 1878; *Jernkontorets Ann.*, **29**. 1, 1874; J. Wiborgh, *ib.*, **52**. 280, 1897; B. Bogitch, *Rev. Mét.*, **25**. 247, 1928; E. A. Uehling, *Journ. Franklin Inst.*, **159**. 117, 1905; C. H. Desch, *Foundry Trade Journ.*, **44**. 105, 1931; O. Simmersbach, *Stahl Eisen*, **24**. 1007, 1904; H. Braune, *Tek. Tids.*, **33**. 45, 1905; *Oesterr. Zeit. Berg. Hütt.*, **53**. 153, 1905; O. Weiskopf, *Stahl Eisen*, **24**. 1225, 1905; A. D. Elbers, *Amer. Manf.*, **37**. 732, 795, 1904; J. Klärding, *Reduktionscharakteristik einiger Eisenerze*, Düsseldorf, 1931; H. Siegel, *Reduktionsversuche an Minette-Eisen und Sintergut*, Düsseldorf, 1931; *Arch. Eisenhüttenwesen*, **4**. 557, 1931; E. Sugimoto, *Proc. World's Eng. Congr. Tokyo*, **33**. 325, 365, 1929; M. Kawaguchi, *ib.*, **33**. 99, 1931; G. Yamada, *ib.*, **33**. 497, 1929; R. H. Sweetser and S. P. Kinney, *ib.*, **33**. 429, 1931; B. Stålhane and T. Malmberg, *Jernkontorets Ann.*, **113**. 95, 1929; **114**. 1, 1930; R. Baake, *Stahl Eisen*, **51**. 1277, 1931.

⁶ E. Diepschlag and K. Feist, *Feuerfest*, **4**. 133, 1928; A. T. Green, H. Ellerton and W. Hugill, *Bull. Brit. Refractories Research Assoc.*, **24**. 47, 1931; **25**. 14, 1931; B. Osann, *Stahl Eisen*, **27**. 1626, 1907; B. M. O'Harra and W. J. Darby, *Journ. Amer. Cer. Soc.*, **6**. 904, 1923; S. M. Phelps, *ib.*, **7**. 716, 1924; H. K. Mitra and A. Silverman, *ib.*, **11**. 278, 1928; R. P. Heuer, *ib.*, **12**. 30, 1929; C. E. Nesbitt and M. L. Bell, *Brick Clay Rev.*, **62**. 1042, 1923; P. Rischbieth, *Zeit. phys. Chem. Unten.*, **44**. 22, 1931.

§ 5. The Manufacture of Wrought Iron

Wrought iron is iron which has been produced in a pasty condition below its m.p.; it contains a relatively low proportion of carbon and other impurities. It is associated with a small proportion of slag, which is originally present in the metal as granules, or separate particles, but when rolled into strips or bars the granules are elongated so as to impart a fibrous structure to the metal. Wrought iron melts at about 1500°, it can be welded, and is ductile when cold. It is not appreciably hardened when quenched from a red-heat in water. It thus differs from both steel and cast iron—*vide infra*, nomenclature. In the old methods for extracting iron from its ores, wrought iron was nearly always the direct product—*vide supra*, the extraction of iron. The open-hearth processes of the Romans in Britain, the primitive processes used by the natives of India and Africa, and the old Catalan forge process, as well as the American bloomery process, all yield a mass or bloom of what might be called spongy wrought iron. Charcoal fuel is employed. If coke were used, the metal in that state has a great avidity for any sulphur present, and the finished metal becomes red-short. The iron produced in the old osmund furnaces, the small blast-furnaces of India (H. Harris,[1] A. R. Roy, C. von Schwarz, and E. Stöhr), China (T. T. Read, and A. B. Middleton), Madagascar (G. P. Chaplin), Persia (J. Robertson), and West Africa (C. V. Bellamy, G. A. Schweinfurth, T. T. Read, and C. V. Bellamy), as well as in some of the taller *Stückofens* of Europe, yielded wrought iron. The blooms produced in the early process with a stationary hearth were described by C. Husgafvel, G. Agricola, V. Biringuccio, L. Beck, B. Osann, T. A. Rickard, E. Swedenborg, L. Beck, etc.

A. Chenot obtained wrought iron without smelting the ore by the direct reduction of hæmatite mixed with about one-fifth its weight of charcoal by heating it in retorts. The process was discussed by P. R. von Tunner, M. Baills, A. Gurlt, E. Grateau, and J. Percy, but it could not compete against the cheaper process of smelting for cast iron, and subsequently converting the cast iron into wrought iron. Other proposals of a similar nature, but more or less modified, were made by C. Adams, W. Arthur, O. Daube, M. Baills, A. E. Bellford, W. F. Berner, T. S. Blair, Bulls Iron and Steel Co., Ltd., W. N. Clay, C. Otto, R. M. Daelen, A. Dickenson, E. F. Fleischer, G. Günther, J. I. Hawkins, H. Leobner, W. Henderson, W. Ivanoff, J. H. Johnson, H. A. Jones, P. Justice, J. Leinberger, S. Lucas, W. Mills, W. Moore, D. Mushet, W. E. Newton, C. Otto, F. Projahn, C. S. Quillard, J. Renton, I. Rogers, A. Sattmann and A. Homatsch, E. Servais and P. Gredt, C. W. von Siemens, F. von Siemens, O. Simmersbach, O. Thieblemont, O. Thiel, F. Uchatius, G. A. Whipple, F. Yates, etc., where the heating was done in reverberatory rotary furnaces. These also came to nothing. Modifications devised by T. S. Blair, C. Adams, and H. H. Eames have been worked at Pittsburg, and they have been described by J. A. Hunt, J. Ireland, J. von Ehrenwerth, A. Ledebur, A. L. Holley, and H. von Jüptner.

The production of the so-called *spongy iron*—*vide infra*—has been discussed by E. P. Barrett,[2] P. M. Bonnerup, E. Edwin, B. Kalling and G. Lilljequest, B. Stoughton, N. K. G. Tholand, G. B. Waterhouse, M. Wiberg, P. E. Williams and co-workers, etc. ; and there are numerous proposals described in the records of the Patent Offices. Here the iron is formed at a temp. below its m.p. The so-called *synthetic iron* or *direct process iron* has been discussed by E. P. Barrett,[3] L. P. Basset, W. Baukloh and R. Durrer, A. E. Bourcoud, E. Bremer, E. W. Davis, K. Dornhecker, J. von Ehrenwerth, P. H. Emmett, H. Fleissner and F. Duftschmid, H. Flodin, E. Fornander, A. Gandini, A. Gurlt, H. Groebler and P. Oberhoffer, A. Groenwalt, G. Gröndal, E. G. T. Gustafsson, H. Harris, F. Hodson and O. Smalley, G. Hooghwinkel, R. E. Hore, E. Houbaer, C. Husgafvel, K. Iwase and M. Fukusima, K. Iwase, M. Fukusima and S. Mitsukuri, K. Iwase and Y. Saito, H. Kamura, K. Klöpper, J. D. Knox, H. Lang, J. A. Leffler, H. Leobner, T. Levoz, V. Lindt, C. Longenecker, P. Longmuir, S. L. Madorsky, H. H. Meyer, O. Meyer and W. Eilender, J. W. Moffat, R. H. Monk and R. J. Traill, I. Moscicki, C. E. Parsons, D. Perietzeanu, C. P. Perin, J. W. Ramsay, T. T. Read, S. E. Sieurin, J. K. Smith, H. Stamm, B. Stålhane, W. F. Sutherland, R. J. Traill and W. R. McClelland, G. B. Waterhouse, R. Whitfield, J. G. Wiborgh, L. Wickenden, C. E. Williams, E. P. Barrett and B. M. Larsen, F. Wüst, etc. There are numerous patents described in the records of the Patent Office.

The exact date is unknown when, in the Middle Ages, tall blast-furnaces were regularly used for the production of cast iron, and the cast iron was subsequently purified in special furnaces so as to convert it into malleable wrought iron. At first one refining hearth was employed, and where the metal was required of still greater purity a second was used. The manufacture of iron wire by drawing was described by Theophilus,[4] who wrote in the eleventh century. In 1676, H. Powle thus described the conversion of cast or pig iron into malleable or wrought iron as practised in the ironworks of the Forest of Dean :

From these furnaces (high blast-furnaces) they bring their sows and pigs of iron to their forges. These are of two sorts, though standing together under the same roof : one they call their Finery, the other the Chafery. Both of them are open hearths, on which they place great heaps of sea-coal, and behind them bellows, like those of the furnaces, but nothing near so large. Into the Finery they first put their pigs of iron, placing three or four of them together behind the fire, with a little of one end thrust into it. Where, softening by degrees, they stir and work them with long bars of iron, till the metal runs together into a round mass or lump, which they call a half-bloom. This they take out, and giving it a few strokes with their sledges, they carry it to a great weighty hammer, raised likewise by the motion of a water-wheel, where applying it dexterously to the blows, they presently beat it out into a thick, short square. This they put into the Finery again, and heating it red hot, they work it out under the same hammer, till it comes into the shape of a bar in the middle with two square knobs in the ends. Last of all, they give it other heatings in the Chafery, and more workings under the hammer, till they have brought their iron into bars of several shapes and sizes, in which fashion they expose them to sale.

The refining hearths were at first very simple, but they gradually became more and more complex, owing to modifications being introduced to suit local conditions. The open hearth refinery was called in Germany the *Frischofen* or *Frischherden*. There are some in use in Styria and a few other localities. They have been described by P. R. von Tunner, J. W. Hall; A. Wigand, J. Percy, F. Maresch, G. Jars, E. Thirria, E. Audibert, S. Homfray, F. Botischeff, F. Overmann, M. Stengel, M. Wachler, R. Akerman, and J. von Ehrenwerth. The pig-iron is melted on the hearth, which contains charcoal and the so-called hammer slag or iron scale—mainly ferrosic oxide, Fe_3O_4. Air is also blown in at the same time, and the iron is freely sprinkled with slag. The iron is decarburized by the joint action of the air blast and the oxidizing slag. It is possible to obtain wrought iron or steel by suitable modifications of the process.

In 1784, H. Cort [5] patented a process in which the decarburization and purification were conducted in a reverberatory furnace with a hollow bottom, so as to contain the metal in a fluid state. Patents closely related to that of H. Cort were obtained by T. and G. Cranage, in 1766, and by P. Onions, in 1783. At first white pig-iron was treated in furnaces with a siliceous bottom. This lining was rapidly attacked, and renewals were costly. The process was called *dry puddling*. The process was also wasteful of iron, for only 70 per cent. yields were in some cases obtained. The dry puddling process was described by T. Beddoes, J. Percy, V. Couailhac, C. Hartmann, J. M. Bineau, L. Ansiaux and L. Masion, St. J. V. Day, C. W. von Siemens, A. A. Fesquet, C. Otto, H. Scrivenor, T. Turner, etc. S. B. Rogers is said to have introduced the "iron bottom" about 1818 ; and there are references to the subject in the patents of R. Gardner, in 1642, and W. Taylor, in 1793. The introduction of old bottom-material, consisting mainly of iron silicate and ferrosic oxide, produced more slag, and hence it was called *wet puddling*, but the yields were greater—amounting in some cases to 90 per cent. J. Hall is generally credited with the introduction of the modern *pig-boiling process* into works practice. The name is applied to wet puddling in allusion to the vigorous bubbling or "boiling" of the molten metal owing to the formation of carbon monoxide by the oxidation of the carbon in the iron by the oxides in the furnace bottom. The gas burns with a blue flame at the surface of the metal. The jets of flame are called *puddlers' candles*, also called sulphur, in allusion to the colour of the flame.

The puddling process has been discussed by L. Beck, R. Biedermann, G. A. C. Bremme, J. G. Danks, C. H. Desch, M. Düber, H. Fehland, F. Sauvage, R. Smith, C. D. af Uhr, and A. Gounot. The operation of puddling has been described in detail by J. Percy, T. Turner, etc. The diagrams, Figs. 32 and 33, of a puddling-furnace were given by J. Percy. The pig-iron is placed on the bed of the furnace, and melted down by the heat from the firemouth, F. The operation requires about half an hour, and during this operation most of the silicon and manganese, as well as a large proportion of phosphorus, is eliminated. The molten metal is allowed to " clear " for about 10 minutes, during which nearly all the silicon and manganese are eliminated and more phosphorus is removed. During the clearing the metal is well stirred by means of a bar bent at right angles inserted in the aperture d,

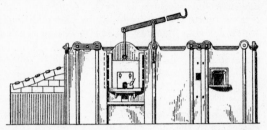

FIG. 32.—Outside Elevation of Puddling-Furnace.

Fig. 32. The whole charge thus is exposed to the action of the fettling and cinder, and to some extent to the oxidizing action of the air. The furnace-draught is then diminished, and a smoky flame is produced. The metal is also vigorously stirred so that it comes in contact with the cinder. This is the so-called boiling stage. The violence of the reaction gradually diminishes, and in about half an hour the *balling-up stage* begins. Here the puddler works the iron into cakes of metal of a convenient size for subsequent treatment. The balling occupies about 20 minutes. The balls, approximately 80 lbs. in weight, are withdrawn from the furnace and hammered to remove much of the slag. The bloom of iron which results is then rolled to form *puddled bars* of wrought iron. J. Hall thus summarized the process of puddling :

First, charge the furnace with good forge pig-iron, adding, if required, a sufficiency of flux—increasing or diminishing the same in proportion to the quality and nature of the pig-iron used. Secondly, melt the iron to a boiling or liquid constituency. Thirdly, clear the iron thoroughly before dropping down the damper. Fourthly, keep a plentiful supply of fire on the grate. Fifthly, regulate the draught of the furnace by the damper. Sixthly, work the iron into one mass before it is divided into balls ; when thus in balls, take the whole to the hammer as quickly as possible, after which roll the same into bars for mill purposes.

The different oxidizing agents, or *fettling*, employed in the puddling-furnace consist of the so-called *hammer-slag* or cinder obtained from the compression of the puddle-balls. It is a ferrous silicate containing ferrosic oxide. The object of the

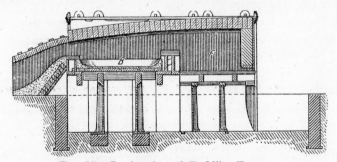

FIG. 33.—Section through Puddling-Furnace.

" flux " is to provide a bath of liquid cinder into which the globules of cast iron may trickle as the metal melts. The sides of the cavity of the furnace bottom consist of *bull-dog*, obtained by calcining tap-cinder. Bull-dog is a ferrous silicate containing more ferrosic oxide than hammer slag. The so-called *blue billy* or *purple ore* is also used ; it is a by-product obtained in the oxidation of iron pyrites in the manufacture of sulphuric acid. Compact lumps of ferrosic oxide are used for making the sides of the basin in which the metal is melted. This material may be the tap-cinder obtained by working a mill furnace with an oxide bottom, or it may be obtained by calcining a suitable iron ore. The puddler prepares the bed and introduces about $4\frac{1}{2}$ cwts. of pig-iron for another run. The *tap-cinder* or ferrous silicate slag produced in the puddling-furnace includes the " boilings " which splashes over the fore-plate during the heating, and the " tappings " which is removed at the end of the process. The former alone contains " shots " of metallic iron. T. Turner gave :

	Fe_2O_3	FeO	SiO_2	P_2O_5
Boilings . . .	6·94	62·61	19·45	6·32 per cent.
Tappings . .	12·90	64·62	15·47	3·91 per cent.

T. Turner thus described the process of what might be called the differential oxidation of the impurities in cast iron :

If a globule of cast iron be melted in the air, and then exposed to a blast of air or oxygen, it will be observed that the impurities are not the only substances that are oxidized. It is true that, under very special conditions, either the carbon or the silicon may be separately oxidized. But on performing the experiment above indicated it will be found that the iron itself is oxidized in about the same relative proportion as the other elements, and the result is that practically a layer of impure magnetic oxide of iron is formed outside the globule, while the portion of metal that is left is of nearly the same composition as the original iron. If the cinder be allowed to run away as rapidly as it is formed, ultimately the whole of the iron would be converted into magnetic oxide, and the last particle of cast iron so removed would have nearly the same composition as the original metal. In this case oxidation has taken place, but no purification has resulted. If, now, the same experiment be tried, but the fluid oxide be allowed to remain and to cover the fused metal, the oxidation of the iron will proceed very little further ; a reducing action will then be commenced whereby the silicon, carbon, and other easily oxidizable elements will be removed, but at the same time a corresponding weight of iron will be returned to the globule from the surrounding slag. But if, thirdly, a globule of cast iron be covered with magnetic oxide of iron to protect it from the air and to supply the necessary cinder, and it be then strongly heated, it will be found that the globule has not lost in weight, but has become distinctly heavier during the process. It is scarcely necessary to say that the waste which takes place during reheating or remelting corresponds to the first condition above given. The oxide runs away as it is formed, and this is an example of waste of iron pure and simple. The only redeeming feature is that sometimes the oxide produced may be of value for other purposes. The early open-hearth processes for producing wrought iron in fineries, and the original method of puddling, resemble the second case, for part of the iron is wasted to produce the cinder needed to remove the impurities from the remainder of the metal. The larger the proportion of these impurities, the greater will be the loss of iron necessary to make the required cinder, and for this reason a comparatively pure iron is needed, in order to obtain the least waste, while at best the waste is comparatively great. A deficiency of fluid cinder in the early stages of ordinary puddling or " pig boiling " has an exactly similar effect, and leads to waste for the same reasons. In the modern method of working, on the other hand, the object is to imitate the conditions of the third case previously supposed.

I. L. Bell represented the effect of puddling on the composition of cold-blast pig-iron by the following analyses :

	Carbon	Silicon	Sulphur	Phosphorus
Pig-iron . . .	3·656	1·255	0·033	0·565 per cent.
Finished iron . .	0·226	0·109	0·012	0·064 per cent.

H. von Jüptner gave for the composition of blooms made from charcoal and coke pig-irons, and of the wrought irons produced from them :

			C	Si	Mn	S	P	Cu	Fe
Bloom	Charcoal	(i)	0·207	0·108	0·644	0·005	0·033	tr.	98·892 per cent.
		(ii)	0·287	0·132	0·587	0·005	0·037	tr.	99·822 per cent.
	Coke	(iii)	0·116	0·169	0·628	0·006	0·068	0·003	99·870 per cent.
		(iv)	0·281	0·207	0·706	0·018	0·121	0·004	98·391 per cent.
Wrought iron	Charcoal	(i)	0·121	0·074	0·573	0·004	0·021	tr.	99·103 per cent.
		(ii)	0·127	0·094	0·538	0·006	0·027	tr.	99·154 per cent.
	Coke	(iii)	0·101	0·069	0·581	0·005	0·048	0·003	98·586 per cent.
		(iv)	0·120	0·133	0·658	0·012	0·104	0·003	98·586 per cent.

The slags contained in the blooms and wrought irons had the compositions :

		Slag in Blooms			Slag in Wrought Iron		
		SiO_2	Fe_2O_3	MnO	SiO_2	Fe_2O_3	MnO
Charcoal	(i)	0·018	0·189	0·011	0·040	0·156	0·009
	(ii)	0·018	0·189	0·005	0·042	0·188	0·004
Coke	(iii)	0·012	0·101	0·009	0·054	0·095	0·005
	(iv)	0·018	0·242	0·012	0·048	0·319	0·017

Some of the properties and the manufacture of wrought iron were described by W. Richards, J. Aston, J. Kitson, E. Matheson, and F. L. Garrison. D. S. Price and E. C. Nicholson noticed how quickly the silicon is eliminated during the oxidation of pig-iron, even before a sensible amount of carbon has been removed. The theory of the process was also discussed by J. Percy. The changes in composition at different stages of the puddling were described by F. C. Calvert and R. Johnson, C. Lan, and L. Cubillo. The observations of A. E. Tucker on the relative rates of the differential oxidation of the chief impurities in cast iron are summarized in Fig. 34. H. Bauerman also said that the impurities are removed in the order : silicon, manganese, phosphorus, and lastly sulphur. The oxidation of the impurities is due in part to the oxygen of the air, and in part, as emphasized by G. J. Snelus, to the ferric oxide, but, as shown by L. Cubillo, the main oxidation is due to the ferrosic oxide in the fettling. Indeed, C. W. von Siemens said that the removal of the silicon and carbon from pig-iron in the ordinary pig-boiling process is entirely due to the molten iron oxide, and that an equivalent amount of iron is at the same time produced and

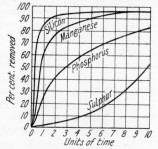

FIG. 34.—Progress of Refining during the Puddling of Cast Iron.

added to the bath. The gain of iron is, however, lost in subsequent stages of the process. Each unit of silicon in the pig-iron which is oxidized by ferrosic oxide introduced 2·8 times its weight of iron, or three parts of iron is produced for each unit of silicon oxidized to silica. T. Turner favoured the same hypothesis. L. E. Gruner suggested that ferrous oxide acts as a carrier of oxygen from the atmosphere to the impurities in the cast iron.

J. Percy assumed that the phosphorus is present in the iron as iron phosphide, and since when molten pig-iron is cooled the portions which solidify last are richest in phosphorus, there is a tendency for the phosphide in the balled iron in the bath of cinder to separate by liquation or sweating. The observations of G. J. Snelus, J. E. Stead, and T. Turner have shown that the elimination of phosphorus is due to its oxidation to phosphate by the iron oxide, partly during the melting stage and partly during the quiescent stage which precedes the boil. Once the metal has become granular, the elimination of phosphorus almost entirely ceases. The presence of silicon and of an excess of manganese retards the elimination of phosphorus. Sulphur is present in the iron and also in the slag as iron sulphide, and virtually no sulphur is eliminated as sulphur dioxide; consequently, it appears as if the iron sulphide is shared between the iron and slag in accord with the partition law. J. E. Stead observed that in slags, iron sulphide and oxide exist side by side without interaction. The chemistry of the subject has been discussed by H. Louis, F. A. Matthewman and A. Campion, P. M. Macnair, A. Jung, F. T. Sisco, J. Kollmann, K. List, A. Schilling, M. Drassdo, and F. Gouvy.

Various substances have been proposed as additions during the puddling process to hasten the elimination of impurities. A. Guenyveau, and J. Nasmyth proposed introducing steam as well as atm. air into the puddling-furnace, and, according to J. Percy, G. Parry obtained some success in the desulphurization and dephosphorization of pig-iron by this process. It was assumed that sulphur escapes as hydrogen sulphide and the phosphorus as phosphine, but this has not been proved. J. Payne suggested the use of " the ashes of wood and other vegetables, all kinds of glass and sandever (*i.e.* glass gall), common salt and rock salt, argile, kelp, and pot ash, and slagg or cinders from iron furnaces and forges " ; J. Wood, " lime, kelp, and soaper's waste " ; J. Goodyer, " common salt and other saline substances " ; D. Mushet, and S. B. Rogers, " unslaked lime, salt, nitre, and manganese oxide " ; and R. Richter, and G. Faller, litharge. J. Gibbons also recommended limestone, but J. Percy added that it is liable to make the iron red-short and rotten. Good results, however, were obtained by A. E. Tucker, and H. A. Webb. J. D. M. Stirling patented the use of tin for increasing the hardness of the finished metal ; and G. Allan described the effect of aluminium. Few of these or other additions have been successful, and none is regularly employed to any great extent.

In J. Aston's modification the pig-iron is melted in a cupola, the molten metal is refined in a bessemer converter, and a slag of the proper composition is prepared in an open-hearth furnace. The mechanical disintegration of the iron, and the incorporation of it with the slag are attained by pouring a charge of the molten refined iron into a bath of the molten slag. The squeezing of the ball of iron into a convenient form for working involves no new principle, nor does the mechanical working of the squeezed iron into a form suitable for handling in subsequent operations. The process and product were examined by H. S. Rawdon and co-workers. There is very little difference in the composition, structure, density, mechanical properties, and resistance to corrosion between wrought iron prepared by hard-puddling and that obtained by J. Aston's process. The subject was discussed by W. von Gutmann and H. Esser, and A. Mitinsky.

Improvements in the puddling-furnace, principally in the direction of gas-firing, have been proposed by J. Head, O. Springer, J. A. Detmold, P. Onions, H. de Simencourt and S. H. Blackwell, A. Raze, B. Kosmann, E. Laudron, E. Goedicke, F. Siemens, G. Pietzka, and H. Wedding ; A. le Play described the Carinthian process of puddling with wood as fuel. Other processes of making wrought iron have also been proposed by J. Aston, D. E. Roberts, E. Bonehill, A. M. Byers, A. H. Beale and co-workers, etc. F. L. Garrison, O. Murisier, etc., described furnaces with movable hearths. Methods of mechanical puddling have been discussed by W. H. Tooth, J. S. Jeans, J. P. Roe, S. Danks, J. Head, P. F. Nursey, W. Yates, J. I. Williams, F. H. Dechant, H. D. Hibbard, S. Jordan, R. Howson, H. Kirk, G. Hofer, E. F. Smith, J. T. Jones, J. A. Jones, P. Roberts, J. Lester, A. Spencer, G. J. Snelus, J. J. Bodmer, F. A. Paget, T. Gidlow, etc. This appears to be largely an engineering problem. Attempts to obtain iron directly from the ore in reverberatory furnaces were discussed by E. W. Davis, E. Laudron, H. Leobner, C. Otto, and C. R. von Schwarz.

REFERENCES.

¹ C. Husgafvel, *Jernkontorets Ann.*, **42**. 85, 1887 ; *Stahl Eisen*, **9**. 35, 121, 1889 ; *German Pat.*, *D.R.P.* 37178, 1886 ; G. Agricola, *De re metallica*, Basileæ, 1561 ; V. Biringuccio, *De la Pirotechnia*, Venetia, 1540 ; L. Beck, *Die Geschichte des Eisens*, Braunschweig, 1884 ; *Stahl Eisen*, **15**. 77, 1895 ; *Iron Age*, **55**. 652, 702, 810, 911, 1895 ; E. Swedenborg, *Om Järnet* (reprint), Stockholm, 1923 ; B. Osann, *Lehrbuch der Eisenhüttenkunde*, Leipzig, 1926 ; O. Johannsen, *Geschichte des Eisens*, Düsseldorf, 1925 ; S. Rinman, *Försök till Järnets Historia*, Stockholm, 1782 ; C. J. B. Karsten, *Handbuch der Eisenhüttenkunde*, Halle a. S., 1826 ; Berlin, 1841 ; B. Kerl, *Handbuch der metallurgischen Hüttenkunde*, Freiberg, 1855 ; J. Robertson, *Architects Journ.*, **3**. 296, 1840 ; *Ann. Mines*, (3), **18**. 667, 1840 ; H. Wedding, *Zeit. Berg. Hütt. Sal.*, **24**. 481, 1876 ; *Stahl Eisen*, **11**. 110, 1891 ; A. Wahlberg, *ib.*, **17**. 730, 1897 ; F. Wüst, *ib.*, **46**. 1214, 1926 ; P. R. von Tunner, *Das Eisenhüttenwesen der Vereinigten Staaten von Nordamerika*, Wien, 58, 1887 ; *Oester. Zeit. Berg. Hütt.*, **4**. 415, 1856 ; *Zeit. Berg. Hütt. Ver. Stiermark*, 253, 1881 ; N. Haltzoff, *Gorny Journ.*, 517, 1887 ; A. Brand, *Verh. Gewerbfl.*, **79**. 197, 1900 ; J. A. Hunt, *Journ. Iron Steel Inst.*, **34**. ii, 252, 1888 ; **36**. ii, 423, 1889 ; W. N. Clay, *Brit. Pat. No.*, 7518, 1837 ; 8459, 1840 ; A. Chenot, *ib.*, 1587, 1588, 1589, 1590, 1856 ; E. Grateau, *Rev. Univ. Mines*, (1), **6**. 1, 1859 ; H. H. Eames, *U.S. Pat. No.* 391034, 1888 ; F. Yates,

Iron and Steel; on some Points of Economy in their Manufacture, London, 1860; J. Percy, *Metallurgy—Iron and Steel*, London, 335, 1864; J. Ireland, *Journ. Iron Steel Inst.*, **13.** i, 47, 1878; T. A. Rickard, *ib.*, **120.** ii, 323, 1929; C. W. von Siemens, *ib.*, **6.** i, 84, 253, 1873; **11.** i, 345, 1877; *Journ. Roy. Soc. Arts*, **24.** 93, 1876; *Journ. Chem. Soc.*, **26.** 661, 1873; J. Renton, *U.S. Pat. No.* 11838, 1854; C. S. Quillard, *ib.*, 2394, 1841; A. Dickenson, *ib.*, 5013, 1847; G. A. Whipple, *ib.*, 9715, 1853; *Amer. Polyt. Journ.*, **2.** 161, 1853; A. L. Holley, *Trans. Amer. Inst. Min. Eng.*, **8.** 321, 1880; **10.** 274, 1882; A. Sattmann and A. Homatsch, *ib.*, **23.** 3, 1893; T. Egleston, *ib.*, **8.** 515, 1880; *Berg. Hütt. Ztg.*, **40.** 49, 1881; M. Baills, *Ann. Mines*, (7), **15.** 229, 1879; J. von Ehrenwerth, *Oester. Zeit. Berg. Hütt.*, **39.** 545, 1891; W. Schmidhammer, *ib.*, **54.** 489, 1906; H. von Jüptner, *ib.*, **42.** 237, 1894; A. Ledebur, *Stahl Eisen*, **16.** 576, 1896; A. Gurlt, *Die Roheisenerzeugung mit Gas oder die Verhüttung der Eisenerze mit indirekter Benutzung des Brennmaterials*, Freiberg, 1857; *Berggeist*, 56, 1859; 256, 1863; H. Leobner, *Berg. Hütt. Jahrb.*, **50.** 1, 1902; C. Otto, *Chem. Ztg.*, **26.** 181, 1902; *German Pat.*, *D.R.P.* 86875, 1896; 141567, 1903; E. Stöhr, *Berg. Hütt. Ztg.*, **22.** 116, 1863; C. von Schwarz, *Zeit. Berg. Hütt. Ver. Steiermark*, **11.** 1, 1879; N. Lilienberg, *ib.*, **13.** 255. 1881; G. A. Schweinfurth, *Stahl Eisen*, **20.** 347, 1900; H. Harris, *Proc. South Staffs Iron Steel Inst.*, **38.** 42, 1923; G. P. Chaplin, *Iron Coal Trades Rev.*, **88.** 565, 1914; A. B. Middleton, *ib.*, **86.** 853, 1913; T. T. Read, *Hardware Trade Journ.*, 84, 1903; *Iron Age*, **108.** 451, 1921; A. R. Roy, *ib.*, **90.** 764, 1912; C. V. Bellamy, *Journ. Iron Steel Inst.*, **66.** 99, 1904; *Stahl Eisen*, **24.** 1395, 1904; R. Akerman, *Jernkontorets Ann.*, (2), **23.** 264, 1868; A. Grabe, *ib.*, (2), **77.** 5, 1922; I. Rogers, *Scient. Amer.*, (2), **6.** 310, 1862; J. H. Johnson, *Brit. Pat. No.* 1115, 1863; S. Lucas, *ib.*, 1869, 1791; 1730, 1854; D. Mushet, *ib.*, 2447, 1800; J. I. Hawkins, *ib.*, 7142, 1836; A. E. Bellford, *ib.*, 1454, 1855; F. Uchatius, *ib.*, 2189, 1855; W. E. Newton, *ib.*, 851, 1856; W. Henderson, *ib.*, 1728, 1863; C. Adams, *German Pat.*, *D.R.P.* 56195, 1890; G. Günther, *ib.*, 76043, 1894; E. Servais and P. Gredt, *ib.*, 89179, 1896; P. Justice, *ib.*, 2717, 1877; H. A. Jones, *ib.*, 90961, 1897; J. Leinberger, *ib.*, 147531, 1904; W. Mills, *ib.*, 88844, 1896; R. M. Daelen, *ib.*, 154578, 1904; Bulls Iron and Steel Co., Ltd., *ib.*, 22993, 1882; W. Arthur, *ib.*, 28220, 1883; O. Thieblemont, *ib.*, 28223, 1884; T. S. Blair, *ib.*, 65684, 1892; W. F. Berner, *ib.*, 76646, 1894; O. Thiel, *ib.*, 109177, 1900; W. Ivanoff, *ib.*, 122637, 1898; F. Projahn, *ib.*, 136776, 1902; O. Simmersbach, *ib.*, 153931, 1904; E. Fleischer, *ib.*, 157582, 1902; W. Moore, *ib.*, 178183, 1906; F. von Siemens, *ib.*, 32309, 1884; O. Daube, *Eng. Min. Journ.*, **74.** 453, 1902.

² G. B. Waterhouse, *Mining Met.*, **11.** 34, 1930; *Iron Age*, **123.** 1143, 1929; O. Stromberg, *ib.*, **82.** 1868, 1908; Anon., *Iron Age*, **120.** 937, 1927; *Eng. Min. Journ.*, **122.** 14, 1926; *Echo Mines*, **51.** 424, 520, 1924; B. Kalling and G. Lilljequest, *Tek. Tids.*, **56.** 1, 6, 1926; E. Edwin, *ib.*, **56.** 41, 1926; P. M. Bonnerup, *Eng. Min. Journ.*, **121.** 889, 1926; C. E. Williams, E. P. Barrett and B. M. Larsen, *Iron Steel Canada*, **7.** 70, 76, 1924; *Iron Trade Rev.*, **76.** 344, 1925; *Bull. U.S. Bur. Mines*, 270, 1927; E. P. Barrett, *Bull. Canada Inst. Min. Met.*, 60, 1925; *Blast Furnace Steel Plant*, **17.** 1659, 1929; *Rep. Investigations Bur. Mines*, 2955, 1929; *Mining Met.*, **11.** 395, 1930; B. Stoughton, *Iron Age*, **125.** 790, 1930; N. K. G. Tholand, *ib.*, **120.** 1107, 1927; **121.** 1391, 1928; **124.** 108, 1929; **125.** 850, 1930; *Blast Furnace Steel Plant*, **17.** 1350, 1362, 1929; *Iron Steel Canada*, **11.** 210, 1928; H. Howe, *Eng. Min. Journ.*, **50.** 618, 1890; *The Metallurgy of Steel*, New York, **1.** 278, 1890; K. J. Smith, *Foundry Trade Journ.*, **29.** 232, 1924; *Iron Age*, **113.** 1003, 1924; E. Fornander, *Chem. Met. Engg.*, **30.** 864, 907, 1924; *Blad Bergshandt. Vänner*, **19.** 614, 1930; F. Sandelin, *Jernkontorets Ann.*, (2), **84.** 261, 1929; A. Johansson and A. Wahlberg, *Journ. Iron Steel Inst.*, **114.** ii, 51, 1926; A. Johansson, *Tek. Tids.*, **47.** 46, 1917; *Jernkontorets Ann.*, (2), **82.** 4, 1927; R. Akerman, *ib.*, (2), **23.** 264, 1868; (2), **25.** 1, 1870; G. Gröndal, *ib.*, (2), **67.** 158, 1912; C. Husgafvel, *ib.*, (2), **42.** 85, 1877; *Stahl Eisen*, **9.** 35, 121, 1889; A. F. Tigerstedt, *ib.*, **7.** 470, 1887; G. A. Aartovaara, *ib.*, **30.** 1117, 1910; F. Lürmann, *ib.*, **10.** 10, 194, 1890; I. L. Bell, *The Principles of the Manufacture of Iron and Steel*, London, 33, 1884; *Journ. Iron Steel Inst.*, **8.** 80, 1875; **38.** ii, 188, 406, 1890; T. Gibb, *ib.*, **8.** 246, 1875; M. Hougland, *ib.*, **23.** ii, 250, 1882; J. Ireland, *ib.*, **13.** i, 47, 1878; J. Wiborgh, *ib.*, 56. ii, 8, 1899; *Jernkontorets Ann.*, (2), **54.** 257, 1899; J. Percy, *Metallurgy—Iron Steel*, London, 335, 1864; C. Schinz, *Dingler's Journ.*, **193.** 222, 304, 1869; J. Reese, *Scient. Amer. Supp.*, **3.** 869, 1877; I. Rogers, *Scient. Amer.*, (2), **6.** 310, 1862; P. Longmuir, *Trans. Amer. Electrochem. Soc.*, **51.** 267, 1927; G. Westman, *Stahl Eisen*, **7.** 182, 1887; F. M. Grant, *Eng.*, **37.** 308, 1874; R. J. Traill and W. R. McClelland, *Canada Chem. Met.*, **13.** 265, 272, 1929; R. B. Marcy, *Génie Ind.*, **10.** 96, 1855; E. Liebermeister, *Berg. Hütt. Ztg.*, **20.** 137, 243, 253, 272, 1861; E. B. Wilson, *Rev. Univ. Mines*, **16.** 371, 1864; M. Velthuysen, *Zeit. Ver. deut. Ing.*, **14.** 344, 1870; H. Wedding and F. Ulrich, *Zeit. Berg. Hütt. Sal.*, **19.** 312, 1871; H. Wedding, *Verh. Gewerbfl.*, **86.** 212, 1907; *Zeit. Berg. Hütt. Sal.*, **24.** 481, 1876; *Stahl Eisen*, **11.** 112, 1891; *Ausführliches Handbuch der Eisenhüttenkunde*, Braunschweig, 1907; *Giesserei Ztg.*, **4.** 523, 550, 1907; C. Hofer, *ib.*, **4.** 430, 1907; C. Gilles, *ib.*, **23.** 587, 1926; P. von Tunner, *Oesterr. Zeit. Berg. Hütt.*, **21.** 49, 1873; H. M. Howe, *The Metallurgy of Steel*, New York, 259, 1890; A. Brand, *Verh. Gewerbfl.*, **79.** 197, 1900; C. Otto, *Eisen und Stahl unmittebar aus dem Erz*, Leipzig, 1916; *Verbesserung der Gasfeuerungen durch Einführung einer Verbrennung unter konstantem Volumen*, Berlin, 1893; *Oesterr. Zeit. Berg. Hütt.*, **49.** 61, 1901; *Tech. Rund.*, **18.** 7, 1904; *Berg. Hütt. Rund.*, **3.** 61, 211, 295, 1907; *Zeit. angew. Chem.*, **18.** 1014, 1905; **19.** 561, 1906; *Chem. Ztg.*, **26.** 181, 1902; **28.** 849, 1904; **29.** 139, 1905; *Feuerungstech.*, **3.** 93, 129, 1915; J. W. Evans, *Journ. Canada Min. Inst.*, **9.** 128, 1906; A. Stansfield, *ib.*, **13.** 151, 1910; *Fuels Furnaces*, **7.** 87, 251, 282, 1929; *The Electric Furnace for Iron*

and Steel, New York, 160, 1923; A. Grönwall, *Blad Bergshandt. Vänner*, **18**. 680, 1927; P. W. Uhlmann, *Chem. Ztg.*, **51**. 232, 1927; B. D. Saklatwalla, *Heat Treatment Forging*, **14**. 863, 1928; R. Freitag, *Kohle Erz*, **26**. 232, 1929; F. Kupelweiser, *Berg. Hütt. Jahrb.*, **24**. 238, 1876; *Oesterr. Zeit. Berg. Hütt.*, **22**. 488, 1874; **23**. 40, 1875; P. von Tunner, *Berg. Hütt. Jahrb.*, **8**. 151, 1858; **22**. 178, 432, 1874; *Zeit. Berg. Hütt. Steiermark*, **7**. 119, 175, 1875; *Oesterr. Zeit. Berg. Hütt.*, **4**. 415, 1856; **23**. 156, 1875; *Das Eisenhüttenwesen der Vereinigten Staaten von Nordamerika*, Wien, 58, 1877; *Bericht über die auf der Pariser Welt-Industrie-Ausstellung*, Wien, 46, 1855; G. Katzetl, *Oesterr. Zeit. Berg. Hütt.*, **22**. 475, 1874; F. W. Harbord and J. W. Hall, *The Metallurgy of Steel*, London, **1**. 295, 1923; A. E. Cassel, *Blad Bergshandt Vänner*, **18**. 798, 1927; C. A. B. Chenot, *Technologiste*, **17**. 65, 1856; *Oesterr. Zeit. Berg. Hütt.*, **4**. 148, 157, 1856; *Génie Ind.*, **31**. 117, 1866; F. Clerc, *ib.*, **25**. 283, 1863; G. von Viebahn and E. Schubarth, *Amtlicher Bericht über die Allgemeine Pariser Ausstellung im Jahre* 1855, Berlin, 69, 1856; C. T. A. Hartmann, *Die Fortschritte des Eisenhüttengewerbes in der neuern Zeit.*, Leipzig, 449, 1858; *Die Fortschritte des metallurgischen Hüttengewerbes im Jahre* 1859, Leipzig, 388, 1860; H. Hartmann, *Berg. Hütt. Ztg.*, **15**. 133, 1856; A. Thoma, *ib.*, **2**. 241, 1843; **4**. 161, 1845; **15**. 180, 1856; **32**. 335, 349, 1873; *Verh. Gewerbfl.*, **39**. 41, 81, 1860; J. Callon, *Ingénieur*, (2), **1**. 64, 1857; F. Grateau, *Rev. Univ. Mines*, (1), **6**. 1, 1859; J. Ziane, *ib.*, (1), **5**. 99, 1859; J. W. Neill, *Eng. Min. Journ.*, **123**. 243, 1927; M. Baills, *Ann. Mines*, (7), **15**. 209, 1879; M. Mussy, *ib.*, (6), **15**. 327, 1869; H. Margerin, *ib.*, (2), **3**. 73, 1828; D. Leo, *ib.*, **46**. 443, 453, 465, 1887; J. B. Duma, *Ann. Industrie*, **5**. 210, 1830; E. Euler, *Zeit. Ver. deut. Ing.*, **1**. 272, 1857; W. Lüders, *ib.*, **9**. 173, 1865; A. Gurlt, *ib.*, **7**. 595, 1863; *Berggeist*, **8**. 256, 1863; *Die Roheisenerzeugung mit Gas, oder die Verhüttung der Eisenerze mit indirecter Benutzung des Brennmateriales*, Freiberg, 1856; M. Ponsard, *Compt. Rend.*, **69**. 177, 1869; F. Wüst, *Stahl Eisen*, **47**. 905, 955, 963, 1927; *Rev. Tech. Luxembourgeoise*, **22**. 41, 1930; E. Sieurin, *Blad Bergshandt. Vänner*, **13**. 195, 1912; *Jernkontorets Ann.*, (2), **66**. 448, 1911; *Stahl Eisen*, **31**. 1391, 1518, 1921; **32**. 830, 1922; R. Durrer, *ib.*, **45**. 1533, 1925; W. Schidhammer, *ib.*, **6**. 465, 1886; J. O. Handy, *Proc. Eng. Soc. West. Pennsylvania*, **29**. 1, 1913; J. W. Hornsey, *Brit. Pat. No.* 306561, 1927; *German Pat.*, *D.R.P.* 466756, 1925; 467485, 1926; 494435, 1927; J. W. Hornsey and H. E. Coley, *Brit. Pat. No.* 284040, 1926; A. C. Blackall, *Iron Age*, **113**. 1867, 1924; G. Hooghwinkel, *Foundry Trade Journ.*, **32**. 215, 1925; H. Tholander and P. Harden, *Tek. Tids.*, **30**. 62, 1900; *Eisen Ztg.*, **22**. 870, 1901; F. Hodson and O. Smalley, *Trans. Amer. Electrochem. Soc.*, **51**. 225, 1927; F. Hodson, *Blast Furnace Steel Plant*, **15**. 329, 1927; J. Landin, *Tek. Tids.*, **30**. 60, 1900; **31**. 239, 1901; W. Heine, *Umschau*, **33**. 164, 1928; Aktieselskapet Norsk Staal, *Norwegian Pat. No.* 42213, 42290, 1924; *German Pat.*, *D.R.P.* 438558, 1925; M. Wiberg, *ib.*, 356762, 1919; *Brit. Pat. No.* 130334, 1919; *Stahl Eisen*, **47**. 1914, 1927; *Trans. Amer. Electrochem. Soc.*, **51**. 279, 1927; H. Pedersen, *Tek. Ukeblad*, **48**. 3, 1930; J. G. von Ehrenwerth, *Oesterr. Zeit. Berg. Hütt.*, **24**. 116, 1876; **25**. 520, 1877; **39**. 359, 456, 1891; *Stahl Eisen*, **11**. 354, 727, 978, 1891; *Zeit. Berg. Hütt. Steiermark*, **7**. 283, 1875; *Das Berg- und Hüttenwesen auf Weltausstellung in Chicago*, Wien, 81, 1895; E. de Billy, *Ann. Mines*, (9), **2**. 329, 1892; A. Brand, *Verh. Gewerbfl.*, **79**. 197, 1900; B. Kosmann, *ib.*, **65**. 132, 1886; T. S. Blair, *Trans. Amer. Inst. Min. Eng.*, **2**. 175, 1874; W. P. Ward, *ib.*, **12**. 522, 1884; A. Saltman and A. Homatsch, *ib.*, **23**. 3, 1893; A. E. Hunt, *ib.*, **16**. 693, 1888; W. E. C. Eustis, *ib.*, **9**. 274, 1881; L. F. Garrison, *ib.*, **16**. 334, 1888; *Journ. Iron Steel Inst.*, **34**. ii, 324, 1888; M. Ruthenburg, *Electrochem. Ind.*, **2**. 12, 1902.

³ J. D. Knox, *Iron Trade Rev.*, **84**. 382, 1929; L. Wickenden, *ib.*, **69**. 363, 1921; Anon., *ib.*, **68**. 1375, 1921; E. W. Davis, *ib.*, **80**. 133, 144, 197, 1927; K. Klöpper, *ib.*, **69**. 363, 1921; *Stahl Eisen*, **43**. 400, 1923; A. Ledebur, *ib.*, **4**. 249, 1884; **6**. 576, 1886; *Handbuch der Eisenhüttenkunde*, Leipzig, **3**. 173, 1908; C. Longenecker, *Blast Furnace Steel Plant*, **17**. 263, 1929; E. P. Barrett, *ib.*, **17**. 1659, 1929; *Iron Steel Canada*, **12**. 240, 1929; A. E. Bourcoud, *Yearbook Amer. Iron Steel Inst.*, ii, 355, 1921; *Blast Furnace Steel Plant*, **9**. 698, 1921; *Iron Trade Rev.*, **69**. 363, 1921; H. Groebler and P. Oberhoffer, *Stahl Eisen*, **47**. 1984, 1927; V. Lindt, *ib.*, **47**. 591, 1927; F. Wüst, *ib.*, **41**. 1841, 1921; **47**. 905, 955, 1927; *Iron Age*, **109**. 989, 1922; *Rev. Tech. Luxembourgeoise*, **22**. 36, 1930; *Proc. World's Eng. Congr. Tokyo*, **33**. 481, 1931; *Zeit. Ver. deut. Ing.*, **64**. 1011, 1920; *Mitt. Inst. Eisenforsch.*, **3**. 1, 1921; H. Stamm, *Continental Chem. Engg.*, **2**. 135, 1927; D. Perietzeanu, *Anal. Min. Romania*, 6, 1927; J. K. Smith, *Iron Age*, **113**. 1003, 1924; H. Lang, *ib.*, **107**. 1237, 1921; F. Lang, *Zeit. Berg. Hütt. Steiermark*, 175, 1875; W. F. Sutherland, *Iron Age*, **107**. 1450, 1921; T. T. Read, *ib.*, **108**. 451, 1921; P. H. Emmett, *Trans. Amer. Electrochem. Soc.*, **51**. 207, 1927; H. Kamura, *ib.*, **51**. 305, 1927; P. Longmuir, *ib.*, **51**. 267, 1927; F. Hodson and M. Sem, *Iron Age*, **113**. 1585, 1924; F. Hodson and O. Smalley, *ib.*, **51**. 225, 1927; F. Hodson, *Blast Furnace Steel Plant*, **15**. 329, 1927; *Iron Trade Rev.*, **69**. 1492, 1921; Anon., *Iron Age*, **119**. 498, 562, 1927; *Foundry Trade Journ.*, **35**. 235, 1927; H. Fleissner and F. Duftschmid, *Berg. Hütt. Jahrb.*, **74**. 42, 1926; H. Leobner, *Berg. Hütt. Jahrb.*, **50**. 1, 1902; *Jahrb. Eisenhüttenwesen*, **3**. 311, 1902; *Montan. Rund.*, **18**. 623, 1926; C. E. Williams, E. P. Barrett and B. M. Larsen, *Bull. U.S. Bur. Mines*, 270, 1927; R. H. Monk and R. J. Traill, *Canada Min. Journ.*, **47**. 671, 1926; R. J. Traill and W. R. McClelland, *Canada Dept. Mines*, 92, 1924; C. P. Perin, *Eng. Min. Journ.*, **122**. 372, 1926; J. A. Leffler, *Jernkontorets Ann.*, (2), **77**. 25, 1922; A. Gandini, *Giorn. Chim. Ind. Appl.*, **3**. 494, 1921; R. Whitfield, *Iron Coal Trades Rev.*, **105**. 84, 1922; **106**. 6, 1923; Anon., *Foundry Trade Journ.*, **28**. 185, 1923; *Iron Trades Rev.*, **74**. 1635, 1924; H. Harris, *Proc. South Staffs Iron Steel Inst.*, **38**. 42, 1923; A. Groenwalt, *Tek. Ukeblad*, **42**. 21, 1924; E. Fornander, *Blad. Bergshandt. Vänner*,

19. 416, 1930 ; *Chem. Met. Engg.*, 30. 864, 907, 1924 ; G. Hooghwinkel, *Foundry Trade Journ.*, 32. 215, 1925 ; *Iron Coal Trades Rev.*, 111. 326, 1925 ; R. E. Hore, *Canada Min. Journ.*, 41. 796, 1920 ; J. W. Moffat, *Iron Steel Canada*, 3. 271, 1920 ; N. Statham, *ib.*, 4. 91, 1921 ; E. Houbaer, *Rev. Univ. Mines*, 11. 45, 1921 ; T. Levoz, *Rass. Min.*, 54. 29, 1921 ; *Rev. Fond. Moderne*, 23. 521, 1929 ; A. Gurlt, *Eisenhüttenkunde*, 2. 596, 1857 ; *Die Roheisenerzeugung mit Gas oder die Verhüttung der Eisenerz mit inderecter Benutzung des Brennmaterials*, Freiberg, 1857 ; C. Husgafvel, *Jernkontorets Ann.*, 42. 85, 1887 ; J. W. Ramsay, *ib.*, 15. 93, 1860 ; G. Gröndal, *ib.*, 67. 158, 1912 ; S. E. Sieurin, *ib.*, 66. 448, 1911 ; *Brit. Pat. No.* 11807, 1910 ; J. G. Wiborgh, *Journ. Iron Steel Inst.*, 56. ii, 8, 1899 ; J. von Ehrenwerth, *Stahl Eisen*, 11. 978, 1891 ; *Oesterr. Zeit. Berg. Hütt.*, 30. 379, 1882 ; 31. 190, 1883 ; 39. 545, 1891 ; 40. 41, 53, 1892 ; *Stahl Eisen*, 12. 224, 275, 1892 ; H. H. Meyer, *Mitt. Eisenhüttenwesen*, 12. 1, 1930 ; K. Iwase, M. Fukusima and S. Mitsukuri, *Kinzoku no Kenkyu*, 7. 4, 12, 169, 269, 317, 1930 ; K. Iwase and M. Fukusima, *ib.*, 7. 524, 1930 ; K. Iwase and Y. Saito, *ib.*, 7. 4, 1930 ; C. E. Parsons, *Canada Min. Journ.*, 51. 242, 1930 ; *Iron Coal Trades Rev.*, 119. 916, 1929 ; B. Stålhane, *Jernkontorets Ann.*, (2), 113. 95, 1929 ; *Stahl Eisen*, 48. 798, 1928 ; 49. 1835, 1929 ; K. Dornhecker, *ib.*, 41. 1881, 1921 ; R. Durrer, *ib.*, 48. 798, 1928 ; E. G. T. Gustafsson, *Brit. Pat. No.* 262126, 1926 ; S. L. Madorsky, *U.S. Pat. No.* 1762622, 1925 ; *Journ. Ind. Eng. Chem.*, 23. 99, 1931 ; I. Moscicki, *Przemysl Chem.*, 6. 73, 1922 ; J. Percy, *Metallurgy—Iron and Steel*, London, 254, 1864 ; T. S. Blair, *Trans. Amer. Inst. Min. Eng.*, 2. 175, 1874 ; E. C. Harder, *ib.*, 50. 143, 1914 ; S. Croasdale, *ib.*, 49. 610, 1915 ; F. Laist and F. F. Frick, *ib.*, 49. 691, 1915 ; A. L. Holley, *ib.*, 8. 321, 1880 ; G. Lunge, *Dingler's Journ.*, 219. 323, 1876 ; P. Kupelweiser, *Berg. Hütt. Jahrb.*, 24. 238, 1876 ; R. C. Gosrow, *Chem. Met. Engg.*, 27. 490, 1922 ; E. Stassano, *ib.*, 6. 315, 1908 ; T. A. Rickard, *Eng. Min. Journ.*, 117. 15, 1924 ; F. W. Harboard and J. W. Hall, *The Metallurgy of Steel*, London, 1. 295, 1923 ; A. Bérard, *Compt. Rend.*, 60. 1352, 1865 ; J. Basset, *ib.*, 185. 343, 1927 ; L. P. Basset, *Brit. Pat. No.* 109452, 1916 ; 158523, 1918 ; 132262, 1919 ; 157398, 159475, 1921 ; *German Pat.*, *D.R.P.* 414494, 437912, 1920 ; 414381, 1921 ; 474784, 1924 ; *French Pat. No.* 488224, 1916 ; 503743, 510969, 1917 ; 501148, 1918 ; 22536, 1919 ; 523977, 1920 ; 558084, 1922 ; 594704, 1924 ; *U.S. Pat. No.* 1360711, 1920 ; F. Miltoun, *Iron Trade Rev.*, 67. 1335, 1920 ; A. E. White, *ib.*, 50. 655. 1912 ; D. H. Ross, *ib.*, 39. 12, 1906 ; O. H. Baker, *ib.*, 40. 987, 1907 ; A. Lissner, *Mitt. deut. Ing. Ver.*, 11. 25, 1922 ; H. M. Howe, *The Metallurgy of Steel*, New York, 1. 277, 1890 ; L. Katona, *Banyaszati es Kohaszati Lapok*, 38. 13, 1906 ; *Stahl Eisen*, 26, 56, 1906 ; A. Stansfield, *The Electric Furnace for Iron and Steel*, New York, 164, 1923 ; *Journ. Canada Min. Inst.*, 10. 129, 1907 ; E. Mills, *Journ. Iron Steel Inst.*, 1. 31, 1925 ; A. Johansson, *Jernkontorets Ann.*, (2), 82. 4, 1929 ; A. Johannson and A. Wahlberg, *Journ. Iron Steel Inst.*, 114. ii, 1926 ; D. Tschernoff, *ib.*, 55. i, 191, 1899 ; R. Catani, *ib.*, 84. ii, 215, 1911 ; E. Humbert and A. Hethey, *ib.*, 89. 378, 1914 ; R. A. Hadfield, *ib.*, 48. ii, 139, 1895 ; W. Colquhoun, *ib.*, 38. ii, 225, 1890 ; H. Flodin, *ib.*, 112. ii, 9, 1925 ; *Eng.*, 140. 263, 1925 ; *Brit. Pat. No.* 214655, 1924 ; 300637, 1928 ; *French Pat. No.* 580300, 1924 ; 660694, 662960, 1928 ; H. G. E. Cornelius, H. Flodin and E. G. Gustafsson, *ib.*, 592321, 606793, 1924 ; 603049, 606466, 1925 ; 625213, 1926 ; *Brit. Pat. No.* 227435, 243353, 243743, 1925 ; 252677, 262127, 1926 ; *German Pat.*, *D.R.P.* 461746, 1924 ; 483149, 483553, 487875, 1925 ; P. von Tunner, *Berg. Hütt. Jahrb.*, 8. 151, 1858 ; 22. 178, 1874 ; *Das Eisenhüttenwesen der Vereinigten Staaten von Nordamerika*, Wien, 63, 1877 ; *Zeit. Berg. Hütt. Steiermark*, 13. 253, 1881 ; F. Sandelin, *Jernkontorets Ann.*, (2), 84. 261, 1929 ; N. Lilienberg, *ib.*, (2), 36. 122, 1881 ; A. Smerling, *ib.*, (2), 36. 177, 1881 ; B. Kalling, *ib.*, (2), 82. 35, 1927 ; *Stahl Eisen*, 48. 798, 1928 ; F. Lürmann, *ib.*, 10. 10, 194, 1890 ; H. Wedding, *ib.*, 11. 111, 1891 ; *Ver. Gewerbfl.*, 86. 212, 1907 ; G. Günther, *Stahl Eisen*, 14. 614, 1894 ; C. A. Robak, *Journ. Ind. Eng. Chem. News*, 8. 7, 1930 ; A. Brand, *Verh Gewerbfl.*, 79. 197, 1900 ; W. F. Berner, *Stahl Eisen*, 17. 557, 1897 ; W. Schmidhammer, *ib.*, 6. 465, 1886 ; 28. 1680, 1908 ; *Zeit. Berg. Hütt.*, 56. 508, 1908 ; *Oesterr. Zeit. Berg. Hütt.*, 32. 111, 125, 1884 ; C. A. van Frey, *ib.*, 23. 120, 1875 ; W. Hupfeld, *ib.*, 17. 1882 ; C. Schinz, *Dingler's Journ.*, 193. 222, 304, 1869 ; J. Zeman, *ib.*, 209. 1, 1873 ; W. Siemens, *Ueber Gewinnung von Eisen und Stahl durch direkter Verfahren*, Berlin, 1874 ; *Eng.*, 26. 30, 1868 ; *Journ. Iron Steel Inst.*, 7. 37, 63, 1873 ; 11. i, 345, 1877 ; J. N. Whitman, *Bull. Amer. Iron Steel Assoc.*, 34, 1904 ; *Jahrb. Eisenhüttenwesen*, 5. 264, 1904 ; H. C. Bull, *Iron Age*, 30. 1, 1882 ; V. W. Jones, *ib.*, 30. 28, 1882 ; E. F. Cone, *ib.*, 110. 585, 1922 ; W. J. Miller, W. Metcalf, and M. Parkin, *ib.*, 21. 24, 1878 ; A. C. Dalton, *ib.*, 94. 877, 1914 ; 96. 1184, 1915 ; D. Danton, *Bull. Soc. Ind. Min.*, (3), 5. 311, 591, 1891 ; H. Harmet, *Compt. Rend. Soc. Ind. Min.*, 84, 115, 1902 ; R. M. Keeney, *Journ. Iron Steel Inst.—Carnegie Mem.*, 4. 108, 1912 ; *Trans. Amer. Inst. Min. Eng.*, 50. 161, 1915 ; R. M. Keeney and G. M. Lee, *Western Chem. Met.*, 66. 269, 323, 347, 1910 ; C. M. Dupuy, *Journ. Franklin Inst.*, 104. 377, 1877 ; 106. 404, 1878 ; 112. 1, 1881 ; E. J. Dittus and R. G. Bowman, *Trans. Amer. Electrochem. Soc.*, 20. 355, 1911 ; F. A. J. Fitzgerald, *ib.*, 14. 239, 1908 ; 15. 149, 1909 ; A. von Kerpely, *Eisen und Stahl auf der Weltausstellung in Paris, in Jahre* 1878, Leipzig, 178, 1879 ; *Berg. Hütt. Ztg.*, 33. 365, 373, 1874 ; I. L. Bell, *The Principles of the Manufacture of Iron and Steel*, London, 37, 1884 ; C. Hartmann, *Berg. Hütt. Ztg.*, 15. 410, 429, 1856 ; C. Otto, *Berg. Hütt. Rund.*, 3. 61, 295, 1907 ; *Chem. Ztg.*, 24. 1033, 1900 ; 29. 139, 1905 ; *Feuerungstech.*, 3. 129, 1915 ; *Verbesserungen der Gasfeuerungen durch Einführung einer Verbrennung unter Konstanten Volumen*, Berlin, 1893 ; *Stahl Eisen*, 16. 148, 1896 ; *Oesterr. Zeit. Berg. Hütt.*, 51. 128, 1903 ; *Iron Trade Rev.*, 57. 743, 764, 1915 ; A. E. Hunt, *Trans. Amer. Inst. Min. Eng.*, 16. 693, 1888 ; 17. 678, 1889 ; J. B. Nau, *ib.*, 20. 111, 1891 ; G. W. Maynard, *ib.*, 10. 173, 1882 ; J. T. Wainwright, *ib.*, 17. 132, 1889 ; F. de Billy, *Ann. Mines*, (9), 2. 329,

1892; J. W. Evans, *Trans. Canada Min. Inst.*, **15**. 123, 1912; A. Grönwall, *Tek. Ukeblad*, **41**. 53, 1923; **42**. 21, 1924; C. Svensson, *ib.*, **41**. 8, 1923; M. Ruthenberg, *Electrochem. Ind.*, **2**. 12, 1902; J. T. Jones, *Eng. Min. Journ.*, **87**. 168, 1900; R. J. Anderson, *ib.*, **32**. 431, 1881; J. Davis, *ib.*, **35**. 5, 1883; C. E. Edwards, *Iron Age*, **88**. 1305, 1911; *Mining World*, **32**. 654, 1911; M. Guédras, *Tech. Moderne*, **13**. 264, 1921; T. R. Loudon, *Appl. Science Toronto*, **8**. 219, 1914; G. Arnou, *Rev. Mét.*, **7**. 1190, 1910; W. Mason, *Elect. Rev.*, **93**. 190, 1923; E. F. Durre, *Eisen Ztg.*, **21**. 81, 1900; A. Michaelis, *ib.*, **25**. 378, 1904; G. Hofer, *Giesserei Ztg.*, **3**. 681, 1906; D. Reynolds, *Amer. Manf.*, **71**. 333, 1902; E. Bremer, *Foundry*, **58**. 51, 1930; O. Meyer and W. Eilender, *Arch. Eisenhüttenwesen*, **4**. 357, 1931; W. Baukloh and R. Durrer, *ib.*, **4**. 455, 1931; G. B. Waterhouse, *Iron Age*, **127**. 161, 1931.

⁴ Theophilus, also called Rugerus, *An Essay on Various Arts*, London, 214, 1047; J. W. Hall, *Eng.*, **144**. 689, 1927; *Trans. Newcomen Soc.*, **8**. 40, 1927; H. Powle, *Phil. Trans.*, **12**. 931, 1767; P. R. von Tunner, *Das Stabeisen und Stahbbereitung in Frischherden*, Grätz, 1846; Freiberg, 1858; A. Wigand, *Frischhüttenbetrieb, oder Fabrication des Staboder Schmiedesisens*, Berlin, 1837; J. Percy, *Metallurgy—Iron and Steel*, London, 579, 1864; F. Maresch, *Berg. Hütt. Ztg.*, **5**. 81, 1846; M. Stengel, *Karsten's Arch.*, (1), **18**. 332, 1829; (2), **18**. 200, 225, 260, 1844; M. Wachler, *ib.*, (2), **10**. 703, 1837; (2), **11**. 171, 1838; F. Overmann, *Ueber das Frischen des Roheisens*, Brünn, 1838; F. Botischeff, *Gorny Journ.*, **1**. 238, 1862; *Oesterr. Zeit. Berg. Hütt.*, **10**. 228, 1862; J. von Ehrenwerth, *ib.*, **34**. 621, 1885; R. Akerman, *Zeit. Berg. Hütt. Ver. Steiermark*, 120, 1877; E. Thirria, *Ann. Mines*, (3), **18**. 215, 1840; E. Audibert, *ib.*, (4), **1**. 613, 1842; S. Homfray, *Brit. Pat. No.* 988, 1771; C. A. Jacobssen, *Oester. Zeit. Berg. Hütt.*, **38**. 453, 1890; *Journ. Iron Steel Inst.*, **39**. i, 376, 1891; F. Korb and T. Turner, *Proc. South Staffs Inst. Iron Steel*, **1**. 50, 1890; G. Jars, *Voyages métallurgiques*, Paris, 1774.

⁵ H. Cort, *Brit. Pat. No.* 1351, 1783; 1420, 1784; R. Cort, *British Iron Manufacture*, London, 1855; *Petition to Parliament praying for more adequate reward for his father's Inventions*, London, 1857; *Observations showing the Real Value of Rolled Iron for Free Trade*, London, 1860; V. Couailhac, *Fers et aciers suivi du manuel pratique du puddleur*, Liége, 1860; L. Ansiaux and L. Masion, *Fabrication du fer et de l'acier puddlé*, Paris, 1865; J. M. Bineau, *Ann. Mines*, (3), **7**. 113, 241, 1835; C. Hartmann, *Der practische Puddel- und Walzmeister*, Weimar, 1861; J. V. St. Day, *On Certain Points in the Manufacture of Malleable Iron with Special Reference to the Richardson Process*, Glasgow, 1868; *Essay on the Puddling of Iron*, London, 1869; A. A. Fesquet, *Guide for Puddling Iron and Steel*, Philadelphia, 1868; J. J. Bodmer, *Mittheilungen über das mechanischen Puddeln nach Danks*, Wien, 1872; W. Yates, *Plans for Puddling Iron by Machinery*, Westminster, 1872; P. F. Nursey, *Mechanical Puddling*, London, 1874; C. Otto, *Sammlung Berg. Hütt. Abhand.*, **43**, 1909; *Chem. Ztg.*, **24**. 1033, 1900; *Oesterr. Zeit. Berg. Hütt.*, **49**. 61, 1901; C. H. Desch, *Iron Coal Trades Rev.*, **98**. 191, 229, 1919; *Journ. West Scotland Iron Steel Inst.*, **25**. 198, 1918; *Journ. Iron Steel Inst.*, **97**. i, 498, 1918; *Proc. Staffs Iron Steel Inst.*, **34**. 34, 1919; J. W. Hall, *ib.*, **34**. 32, 1917; J. von Langer, *Proc. Cleveland Inst. Eng.*, 61, 1891; *Industries*, **11**. 585, 1892; C. Rott, *Die Fabrikation des Schmiedbaren und Tempergusses*, Leipzig, 1892; T. Ashton, *Proc. South Staffs. Inst. Iron Steel Works Managers*, 76, 1894; J. Wilcock, *History, Progress, and Description of the Bowling Iron Works*, London, 1873; A. Gounot, *Bull. Soc. Ind. Min.*, **3**. 772, 1904; F. T. Sisco, *Trans. Amer. Soc. Steel Treating*, **7**. 640, 1925; T. and G. Granage, *Brit. Pat. No.* 851, 1766; P. Onions, *ib.*, 1370, 1783; J. Percy, *Metallurgy—Iron and Steel*, London, 621, 1864; H. Scrivenor, *A Comprehensive History of the Iron Trade throughout the World from the Earliest Records to the Present Time*, London, 289, 1841; I. L. Bell, *Principles of the Manufacture of Iron and Steel*, London, 360, 1884; *Journ. Iron Steel Inst.*, **13**. i, 17, 1878; E. Matheson, *Cassier's Mag.*, **18**. 179, 1900; W. Richards, *Journ. Iron Steel Inst.*, **43**. i, 22, 1893; J. Kitson, *ib.*, **35**. i, 14, 1889; T. Tscheuschner, *ib.*, **29**. i, 325, 1886; J. T. Jones, *Eng. Min. Journ.*, **87**. 168, 1909; J. A. Jones, *Journ. Iron Steel Inst.*, **4**. i, 278, 1872; T. R. Crampton, *ib.*, **7**. i, 384, 1874; E. F. Smith, *ib.*, **9**. i, 109, 1876; R. Howson, *ib.*, **4**. i, 332, 1872; **11**. i, 416, 1877; G. Allan, *ib.*, **4**. i, 140, 1893; H. A. Webb, *ib.*, **43**. i, 140, 1893; J. S. Jeans, *ib.*, **21**. i, 143, 1882; J. D. Denks, *Iron Age*, **80**. 1082, 1907; J. G. Danks, *Dingler's Journ.*, **253**. 120, 1884; *Eng. Min. Journ.*, **36**. 130, 1883; S. Danks, *Journ. Iron Steel Inst.*, **3**. ii, 258, 1871; **4**. i, 3, 1872; J. Lester, *ib.*, **4**. i, 286, 1872; A. Spencer, *ib.*, **4**. i, 318, 1872; F. A. Paget, *ib.*, **4**. i, 338, 1872; F. C. Calvert and R. Johnson, *On the Chemical Changes which Pig Iron undergoes during its Conversion into Wrought Iron*, Manchester, 1857; *Mem. Manchester Lit. Phil. Soc.*, **14**. 121, 1857; *Phil. Mag.*, (4), **2**. 165, 1857; B. Baylis, *On Puddling*, London, 1866; J. Head, *Proc. Inst. Mech. Eng.*, 266, 1876; *On the Newport Puddling Furnace*, London, 1872; *Journ. Iron Steel Inst.*, **4**. i, 220, 1872; **43**. i, 125, 1893; T. Turner, *ib.*, **39**. i, 119, 1891; *Varieties of Tap Cinder*, London, 1892; *The Metallurgy of Iron*, London, 350, 1915; *Journ. West Scotland Iron Steel Inst.*, **20**. 106, 1913; *Proc. South Staffs Iron Steel Inst.*, **1**. 138, 1890; **2**. 23, 1891; T. Turner and A. E. Barrows, *Journ. Chem. Soc.*, **61**. 351, 1892; L. Cubillo, *Journ. South Staffs Iron Steel Inst.*, **16**. 22, 1900; *Eng.*, **79**. 383, 1895; *Journ. Iron Steel Inst.*, **41**. i, 245, 1892; H. Louis, *ib.*, **15**. i, 219, 1879; H. Kirk, *ib.*, **10**. ii, 367, 1876; **11**. i, 140, 1877; *Proc. South Staffs Iron Steel Inst.*, **3**. 1, 1887; *Proc. Inst. Mech. Eng.*, **30**. 48, 1877; J. E. Stead, *Proc. Cleveland Inst. Eng.*, 132, 1877; 34, 1879; *Journ. Iron Steel Inst.*, **43**. i, 50, 1893; *Proc. South Staffs Iron Steel Inst.*, **1**. 1, 1884; A. E. Tucker, *ib.*, **3**. 1, 1887; **33**. i, 323, 1888; *Valuation of Pig Iron for Forge Purposes*, Smethwick, 1888; M. Düber, *Zeit. Berg. Hütt. Sal.*, **2**. 161, 1855; R. Beidermann, *Berg. Hütt. Jahrb. Leoben*, **6**. 242, 1857; G. A. C. Bremme, *Berg. Hütt. Ztg.*, **19**. 97, 1856; H. Fehland, *Stahl Eisen*, **6**. 224, 1886;

L. Beck in C. Matschoss, *Beiträge zur Geschichte der Technik und Industrie*, Berlin, **3**. 86, 1911 ;
R. Smith-Carson, *Journ. Iron Steel Inst.*, **25**. i, 60, 1884 ; F. Sauvage, *Ann. Mines*, (4), **6**. 461,
1844 ; C. D. af Uhr, *Karsten's Arch.*, **11**. 315, 1826 ; *Berättelse om de pa Bruks Societetens
Bekostand Aren* 1819–1922, Stockholm, 1825 ; W. von Gutmann and H. Esser, *Stahl Eisen*, **51**.
1193, 1931 ; H. S. Rawdon and S. Epstein, *Yearbook Amer. Iron Steel Inst.*, **16**. 117, 1926 ;
H. S. Rawdon and A. A. Knight, *Journ. Bur. Standards Research*, **3**. 953, 1929 ; *Metals Alloys*,
1. 46, 1929 ; *Symposium on Wrought Iron*, *ib.*, **15**. 117, 1925 ; N. E. MacCallum, *Trans. Amer.
Inst. Min. Eng.*, **44**. 250, 1912 ; H. F. Miller, *ib.*, **44**. 263, 1912 ; **45**. 346, 1913 ; E. W. Davis,
Brit. Pat. No. 315760, 316303, 1928 ; A. M. Byers, *ib.*, 170124, 1920 ; 224941, 1923 ; A. H. Beale,
H. A. Brassert and F. Wille, *ib.*, 315858, 1928 ; A. H. Beale and J. Aston, *ib.*, 315826, 1928 ;
E. C. Kreutzberg, *Iron Trade Rev.*, **85**. 133, 1929 ; G. A. Richardson, *ib.*, **84**. 317, 330, 1929 ;
Blast Furnace Steel Plant, **16**. 1566, 1928 ; E. W. Harvey, *Proc. South Staffs. Inst. Iron Steel
Works Managers*, 86, 1895 ; E. Bonehill, *ib.*, 2, 1895 ; *Journ. Iron Steel Inst.*, **48**. ii, 43, 1895 ;
J. Kerr, *Colliery Guardian*, **71**. 750, 1895 ; *Journ. West Scotland Iron Steel Inst.*, **3**. 206, 1896 ;
21. 61, 1914 ; F. A. Matthewman and A. Campion, *ib.*, **20**. 124, 1913 ; E. Laudron, *Rev.
Univ. Mines*, **33**. 22, 1896 ; (3), **45**. 36, 1899 ; J. Thieme, *Stahl Eisen*, **18**. 761, 803, 1898 ;
C. R. von Schwarz, *ib.*, **21**. 209, 277, 337, 391, 1901 ; A. Jung, *ib.*, **44**. 911, 1924 ; H. Bya, *Rev.
Univ. Mines*, **43**. 238, 1899 ; H. Leobner, *Berg. Hütt. Jahrb.*, **48**. 219, 1899 ; G. Hofer, *Giesserei
Ztg.*, **3**. 559, 1906 ; J. E. Fletcher, *Iron Steel Ind.*, **3**. 101, 133, 1930 ; J. S. Trinham, *ib.*, **3**. 83,
157, 223, 1929 ; P. M. Macnair, *Journ. Iron Steel Inst.—Carnegie Mem.*, **13**. 267, 1924 ; J. Vonka,
Geschmiedetes Eisen, Breslau, 1927 ; B. Kosmann, *Zeit. Berg. Hütt.*, **18**. 145, 1870 ; M. Drassdo,
ib., **11**. 170, 1863 ; D. E. Roberts, *Proc. South Staffs Iron Steel Inst.*, **28**. 185, 1913 ; P. Roberts,
Trans. Amer. Inst. Min. Eng., **8**. 355, 1880 ; A. Raze, *Rev. Univ. Mines*, (2), **1**. 196, 1877 ;
S. Jordan, *ib.*, (2), **3**. 100, 1878 ; E. Goedicke, *Stahl Eisen*, **9**. 554, 1889 ; E. Gouvy, *ib.*, **12**.
1001, 1892 ; O. Springer, *ib.*, **9**. 776, 1889 ; *German Pat.*, *D.R.P.* 19056, 1889 ; G. Pietzka,
German Pat., *D.R.P.* 40218, 42575, 1887 ; *Quadruple Puddling Furnace*, Leeds, 1890 ;
H. Wedding, *Glaser's Ann.*, **22**. 169, 1888 ; *Journ. Iron Steel Inst.*, **38**. ii, 491, 1890 ; **71**. iii,
264, 1906 ; *Yearbook Amer. Iron Steel Inst.*, 358, 1925 ; F. H. Dechant, *ib.*, 337, 1925 ;
J. Aston, *ib.*, 361, 1925 ; *Tech. Publ. Amer. Inst. Min. Eng.*, 228, 1929 ; *Blast Furnace Steel
Plant*, **18**. 291, 1930 ; J. P. Roe, *Trans. Amer. Inst. Min. Eng.*, **33**. 551, 1902 ; **36**. 203,
1905 ; *Iron Age*, **69**. 1, 1902 ; *Journ. Iron Steel Inst.*, **71**. iii, 264, 1906 ; A. le Play, *Ann.
Mines*, (5), **3**. 463, 1853 ; C. Lan, *Ann. Mines*, (5), **15**. 85, 1859 ; *Berg. Hütt. Ztg.*, **19**. 181,
1860 ; A. Schilling, *ib.*, **22**. 313, 1863 ; H. D. Hibbard, *Iron Age*, **110**. 1219, 1922 ; K. List,
Program. Gewerbschule Hagen, 4, 1860 ; *Zeit. Ver. deut. Ing.*, **9**. 380, 1865 ; **19**. 19, 1875 ;
J. Kollmann, *ib.*, **18**. 325, 1874 ; J. Hall, *Iron Scrap, or the Issue of an Old Shoe Heel,
being the Origin of the Discovery of Pig Boiling*, London, 1864 ; *The Iron Question : considered
in connection with Theory, Practice, and Experience with reference to the Bessemer Process*,
London, 27, 1857 ; S. B. Rogers, *An Elementary Treatise of Iron Metallurgy*, London, 1858 ;
R. Gardner, *Brit. Pat. No.* 1642, 1788 ; W. Taylor, *ib.*, 1966, 1793 ; D. S. Price and E. C. Nicholson, *ib.*, 2618, 2619, 1855 ; J. Payne, *ib.*, 505, 1728 ; J. Wood, *ib.*, 759, 1761 ; J. Goodyer, *ib.*,
1000, 1771 ; J. D. M. Stirling, *ib.*, 12288, 1848 ; T. Siemens, *ib.*, 2861, 1856 ; J. A. Detmold,
ib., 9911, 1843 ; H. de Simencourt and S. H. Blackwell, *ib.*, 1445, 1861 ; W. H. Tooth, *ib.*, 277,
1860 ; J. Nasmyth, *ib.*, 1001, 1854 ; T. Beddoes, *Phil. Trans.*, **82**. 257, 1792 ; C. W. von Siemens,
On Puddling Iron, London, 1868 ; *Sur l'application de four à gaz au puddlage du fer*, Paris, 1860 ;
B.A. Rep., 5, 1868 ; *Dingler's Journ.*, **190**. 203, 1869 ; A. Guenyveau, *Nouveaux procédés pour
fabriquer la fonte et le fer en barres*, Paris, 63, 1835 ; J. Gibbons, *Practical Remarks on the Use of
the Cinder Pig in the Puddling Furnace ; and on the Management of the Forge and Mill*, London,
21, 1844 ; L. E. Gruner, *Ann. Mines*, (5), **15**. 291, 1859 ; *Études sur les hauts fourneaux, suivies
d'une notice sur les appareils à air chaud*, Paris, 1872 ; *Studies of Blast Furnace Phenomena*,
London, 1873 ; H. Bauerman, *A Treatise on the Metallurgy of Iron*, London, 329, 1882 ;
F. L. Garrison, *Trans. Amer. Inst. Min. Eng.*, **16**. 334, 1888 ; *Supplementary Report on the Danks
Puddling Process*, Newcastle-on-Tyne, 1872 ; *Journ. Iron Steel Inst.*, **4**. i, 295, 1872 ; **32**. ii, 299,
1887 ; **34**. ii, 284, 1888 ; **35**. i, 325, 1889 ; O. Murisier, *ib.*, **30**. ii, 942, 1886 ; D. Mushet, *Papers
on Iron and Steel*, London, 1840 ; R. Richter, *Wagner's Jahresb.*, **7**. 33, 1861 ; *Berg. Hütt.
Jahrb.*, **10**. 505, 1861 ; G. Faller, *ib.*, **10**. 244, 1861 ; A. Mitinsky, *Hornicky Vestnik*, **13**. 145,
1931 ; *Chim. Ind.*, **26**. 834, 1931 ; H. von Jüptner, *Oester. Zeit. Berg. Hütt.*, **39**. 545, 1891 ;
G. J. Snelus, *Journ. Iron Steel Inst.*, **4**. i, 246, 1872 ; T. Gidlow, *ib.*, **13**. i, 240, 1878.

§ 6. The Manufacture of Steel

Steel is the mainspring of modern industry. The commercial importance of steel is
greater than that of gold, silver, zinc, copper, and lead combined, and, indeed, the trite
saying that this is an age of iron is well-founded.—W. M. JOHNSON.

As a first approximation, **steel** can be regarded as an iron-carbon alloy intermediate in composition between wrought and cast iron—*vide infra*, nomenclature.
The preparation of wrought iron has been considered from two aspects : (i) the

direct reduction of the metal from its ore in the form of blooms which are consolidated by forging, and (ii) the formation of cast iron, which is subsequently decarburized. The preparation of steel can be considered from four aspects : (i) the direct production of iron associated with carbon from iron ores ; (ii) the carburization of wrought iron ; (iii) the fusion of a mixture of wrought and cast iron ; and (iv) the partial decarburization of cast iron.

About 30 B.C., Diodorus Siculus, in his *Bibliotheca historica* (5. 33), and also Plutarch, in his *De garrulitate*, mentioned that the Celtiberians made steel of great hardness by burying plates of iron under the earth until the weaker part of the iron was consumed by rust, and using the part which remained for making their weapons. The process is mentioned by E. Swedenborg,[1] R. Watson, and J. Beckmann as a custom in use in Japan ; W. W. Campbell and E. E. Thum observed that some ancient specimens of Grecian iron were really steel.

The products of the bloomery furnaces must have frequently furnished mild steels (the processes indicated in connection with the history of the extraction of iron in India and Africa furnished steel) ; and steel was the product of the Catalan forge. Processes were described by S. Lucas,[2] D. Mushet, J. I. Hawkins, H. Larkin, H. Tholander and P. Hörden, E. Humbert and A. Hethey, and W. E. Newton for making steel by reducing ores rich in iron in crucibles, etc., along with carbonaceous matters. J. Percy said that more recent experiments on the subject often gave excellent products, but it was not found possible to ensure uniform results. According to R. Jenkins, the earliest definite reference to the production of steel in England occurs in the *Victoria County History of Sussex*, where it records that John Glade in 1513 held a tenement called *A Forge of Steel* in Ashdown Forest, Sussex. In 1525 this forge passed to John Bowley, who held it in 1548. M. Sudhoff said that the term *steel* first appears in the *Codex medicus Hertensis*—*ferrum quod stahal dicitur*— between the ninth and twelfth centuries. E. O. von Lippmann, and O. Schrader said that the word *steel* appears in all the German dialects—*Stahal* in Althochdeutsch ; *stahel, stachel,* or *stâl* in Mittelhochdeutsch ; *stál* in Altnordisch ; *steel* in English ; *stalle* in Lapland ; and *stalē* in Slavish.

Additional observations on the development of the steel industry were made by J. O. Arnold,[3] P. Barnes, M. Bazin, L. Beck, C. Benedicks, G. Bresson, G. Broling, H. H. Campbell, L. Campredon, F. L. von Canerin, C. Chômienne, L. von Crell, H. V. Collet-Descotils, R. M. Daelen, H. Damemme, J. H. Darby, E. Darmstaedter, A. Delesse, I. B. J. Dessoye, W. Eilender, O. Evenstadt, F. A. A. Eversmann, J. François, P. A. Gadd and G. Korsemann, E. Garuffa, L. E. Gruner, R. A. Hadfield, J. H. Hall, F. W. Harbord, F. W. Harbord and J. W. Hall, C. F. A. Hartmann, J. Heaton, H. M. Howe, B. F. J. Hermann, H. Horne, P. S. Ihlström, J. S. Jeans, C. J. B. Karsten, L. Knab, F. Kohn, E. F. Lake, C. Lan, H. C. Landrin, H. Leobner, D. Little, E. Marché, E. Matheson, J. A. Mathews, W. Metcalf, L. B. Guyton de Morveau, B. Neumann, M. W. Newfeld, H. Noble, F. Overman, C. Pälhem, W. Page, J. J. Perret, P. G. F. le Play, M. Rambourg, R. A. F. de Réaumur, J. Rosenreich-Diffrage, M. de Rozière, H. Rupe and F. Müller, H. Saemann, B. D. Saklatawalla, P. G. Salom, C. W. von Siemens, T. P. Smith, D. Tiselius, P. R. von Tunner, G. Turner, O. Vogel, J. B. Walker, T. Webster, K. Wittgenstein and A. Kurzwernhart.

For the direct production of steel in electric furnaces, *vide infra*. The old process of carburizing wrought iron by the cementation process has been practised from the Middle Ages up to the present time. The principles behind the process are described in a special section below. The bar-steel obtained by the cementation process was never homogeneous, and the same remark applies to steel made by several other processes. B. Huntsman found that homogeneous steel could be prepared by fusion in crucibles and subsequently casting the metal into ingots— **cast steel** or **crucible steel**. B. Huntsman's process was devised about 1700, and he melted blister-steel, cast it into ingots, and rolled it into bars. B. Huntsman's process was also described by P. G. F. le Play, and J. Percy. H. St. C. Deville and H. Caron reported on a process for melting the steel in reverberatory furnaces. One practical difficulty turns on preventing the metal changing its composition by contact with carbonaceous fuel. The manufacture of crucible steel or cast steel was improved by J. M. Heath, who introduced some manganese carbide, or a mixture of manganese oxide and carbonaceous matters, along with the blister-steel. The resulting cast steel could be welded. T. Webster has discussed some litigation in connection with the patent rights. W. Reynolds also patented the addition of manganese to cast iron, or to cast iron for its conversion into steel. The crucible process was discussed by J. Bischoff, A. Ledebur, F. T. Sisco, J. A. Coyle, H. G. Manning, J. J. Mahon, F. Wüst, J. M. Gledhill, R. H. Probert, G. Hofer, F. C. G. Müller, J. Henrotte, R. A. Hadfield, D. Flather, A. Stotzer, C. Otto, R. F. Böhler, A. Harpf, O. Thallner, A. Brand, J. B. Johnston, S. Johnson, C. Casper, H. Seebohm, P. Oestberg, M. Boeker, etc.

In 1722 R. A. F. de Réaumur [4] prepared steel by melting together a mixture of wrought iron and cast iron. He said :

It is, indeed, possible to fuse old scrap, points of nails, etc., in molten pig-iron. Such an addition of iron to the mixture causes it to lose its fusibility more quickly, and the period during which it remains in the molten state is shortened. A less quantity of the sulphurous constituents is evolved from the parts nearest to the surface. The iron takes up those which are given off by the fire, and the metal thus becomes converted into steel. By this means I have succeeded perfectly in making steel in an ordinary hearth by mixing sometimes one-quarter and sometimes one-third of iron with the pig-iron.

D. S. Price and E. C. Nicholson, G. Brown, and C. Attwood also patented processes for the same thing. M. Lister cited an obscure passage in Aristotle's Μετεωρολογικά referring to the conversion of iron into steel, and a process in which wrought iron is converted into steel by keeping it immersed in molten cast iron has been described by V. Biringuccio, G. Agricola, M. Lister, and others, as being well-known and practised in the sixteenth century ; and a reference in Pliny's *Historia naturalis* (**34**. 14) is taken to mean that the same process was in use at the beginning of our era. R. A. F. de Réaumur also described the same process.

There are several processes for the manufacture of steel by the decarburization of cast iron. In the old fining hearth the metal was heated with charcoal in a blast of air, while the cake of metal was covered with liquid cinder. With slight modifications the product may be either steel or wrought iron, as desired. The process as formerly conducted in Siegen, Carinthia, and Styria was described by P. R. von Tunner,[5] C. J. B. Karsten, and J. Percy. The decarburization of cast iron by cementation, that is, by heating it in contact with iron oxide, is discussed below ; while F. Uchatius proposed fusing the cast iron in contact with iron oxide or other substances capable of yielding oxygen. The operation more or less modified was described by J. and C. Wood, J. Wood, D. Mushet, M. de Rostaing, C. Peters, W. Spence, W. Spielfield, M. Lane, J. Paulis, etc. J. R. Bréant also, in 1824, said that he believed that it would be possible to produce steel in reverberatory furnaces by a process analogous to that of puddling. According to P. R. von Tunner, the process was employed in Styria for a short time. According to A. Delvaux de Fenffe, puddled steel was prepared in Bavaria, etc., about 1846. The process was also patented by E. Riepe, and described by C. Lan, G. Parry, W. W. Collins, B. Kerl, and J. Percy.

As in the case of puddling for wrought iron, various additions have been recommended with the idea of accelerating the process of decarburization. C. Schafhäutl's mixture of brown iron ore and common salt was discussed by P. R. von Tunner, and L. E. Gruner ; and J. Heaton's use of sodium nitrate for oxidizing the carbon was discussed by W. H. Miller, R. Mallet, D. Kirkaldy, W. Fairbairn, W. H. Williams, L. E. Gruner, and B. H. Paul. R. Mushet employed chromates or chromic oxide in place of manganese dioxide as an oxidizing agent ; J. E. Sherman, potassium iodide ; J. Henderson, fluorspar ; V. Gallet, a paste made of limestone, clay, resin, soot, charcoal, sodium carbonate and chloride, and manganese dioxide.

In 1855 J. G. Martin [6] obtained a patent for the manufacture of steel by the partial decarburization of cast iron by blowing air through the molten metal. W. Kelly, also, noticed that when cold air from the tuyères impinged on white-hot iron, the iron became hotter instead of colder, and in 1857, W. Kelly patented a process of purifying pig-iron by blowing atmospheric air through the molten metal. Meanwhile H. Bessemer developed a process for converting pig-iron into steel by blowing air through a crucible full of the molten metal. A. Galy-Cazalat, in his French patents between 1851 and 1858, mentioned the refining of pig-iron by blowing a current of steam through the molten metal, but he did not allude to the refining of the metal by a current of air, so that the claims that have been made that he anticipated this process have not been established. There has been a controversy on the origin of H. Bessemer's process—H. Bessemer, R. W. Hunt, J. N. Boucher, J. Cournot, S. Jordan, E. Riley, R. H. Thurston, J. D. Weeks, H. M. Howe, etc.—and this was summed up by the *Engineer* :

The Bessemer process is not a theory, it is an art. It is not one invention but fifty. W. Kelly's cupola did not anticipate the Bessemer converter as fully as Newcomen's engine did the modern triple-expansion engine. For Newcomen's engine could work ; it had an economical value ; it revolutionized the practice of mining.

The process of H. Bessemer was at first successful with Swedish pig-iron, which had a high proportion of manganese and a small proportion of phosphorus ; the process failed with English pig-iron, which was lower in manganese and higher in phosphorus. The product in the latter case was always red-short. The trouble was overcome by adding some spiegeleisen in accord with the patent of W. Reynolds, or of R. F. Mushet. It then became possible to manufacture low carbon steels—the so-called **Bessemer steels**—by the process. In **Bessemer's process,** 10 to 15 tons of molten pig-iron are run into a large egg-shaped vessel called the *converter*. The con-

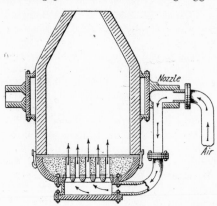

FIG. 35.—Section of the Bessemer's Converter.

verter can be tilted into any required position. It is provided with holes at the bottom through which a powerful blast of air can be blown. It is tilted horizontally while the molten metal is being poured in. The blast is turned on, and the converter is swung into a vertical position. The converter is made of wrought-iron plates, and lined with a suitable refractory material. A general idea of the structure of a converter can be gathered from Fig. 35, which gives a vertical section, showing the air nozzle leading to a wind-box from which a powerful blast of air in 150 to 200 fine jets passes through the mass of molten metal. The temp. rises owing to the heat evolved by the oxidation and com-

bustion of the impurities—the carbon, sulphur, and manganese. The carbon forms carbon monoxide, which burns at the mouth of the converter. The flame is accompanied by a brilliant spectacular shower of sparks. The other oxides form a slag with the furnace lining. Experience and the appearance of the flame tell the operator when to stop the blast. In about 10 or 15 mins. nearly all the carbon and most of the impurities are burnt out, and iron, equivalent to wrought iron, remains. The molten product is changed into steel by adding the right pro-portion of carbon, manganese, etc., as desired. Usually the right amount of spiegeleisen is then added to make a metal of definite composition. The blast is again turned on for a moment, and the metal is then cast into moulds to form blocks of Bessemer's steel.

The process was discussed by R. Akerman, H. Bansen, P. Barthel, M. Belman, G. Bergström, L. E. Boman, W. Borchers, F. G. Bremme, A. Brovot, H. H. Campbell, C. Canaris, W. M. Carr, F. J. R. Carulla, C. A. Casperson, W. J. Clapp and J. Griffiths, J. Cournot, R. M. Daelen, J. Deby, L. Delacuvellerie, E. Demenge, E. Faust, V. Firket,

J. Flohr, R. Frerich, H. van Gendt, F. Grassmann, C. Gonner, L. Hacha, J. Hardisty, A. P. Head, C. E. Heurteau, E. Heyrowsky, G. Hilgenstock, F. Hilton, O. von Hingenau, H. L. Hollis, E. Holz, H. M. Howe, R. W. Hunt, A. von Ihering, W. H. Jacques, A. Johansson, S. Jordan, O. von Keil, F. Kintzle, W. E. Koch, J. Lagerwall, E. Langhein-rich, F. Laur, K. Leo, L. Lewis, F. W. Lürmann, R. S. McCaffrey, C. Malz, P. N. Mathur, J. R. Miller, F. C. G. Müller, F. Munichsdorfer and E. A. Frey, J. B. Nau, S. Peters, C. Pixis, A. Pourcel and F. Valton, E. Priwoznik, A. W. Richards, A. de Riva-Berni, T. W. Robinson, C. Rott, H. J. van Royden, F. Schröder, E. Schrödter, J. Seigle, R. von Seth, A. Simonson, J. Smeysters, G. J. Snelus, K. Sorge, M. Stammschulte, W. Stercken, W. Stöckl, O. Thiel, J. Thieme, M. von Tittler, F. E. Thomson, R. H. Thurston, F. Toldt, A. Tropenas, L. Unckenbolt, B. Versen, O. Vogel, J. Wagner, G. B. Waterhouse, H. Wedding, J. D. Weeks, J. G. Wiborgh, and C. D. Wright.

In H. Bessemer's process the lining of the converter was made of siliceous material—say, ganister blocks with a bond of a mixture of fireclay and coke-dust. Owing to the acid character of the lining of the converter, this process is called the **acid Bessemer process**, to distinguish it from the so-called **basic Bessemer process**, in which the lining is of basic material—generally blocks made from well-burnt dolomite. The blow occupies about 12 mins. and three stages can be recognized : (i) The *sagging period* occupies about 4 mins. Most of the silicon burns to silica, forming a siliceous slag—$FeSiO_3$ and $MnSiO_3$. The flame is not very luminous, and it is attended by scintillating sparks. (ii) The *boiling period* occupies about 6 mins. The silicon continues to burn, and the carbon forms carbon monoxide, and molten metal boils violently. The flame is very luminous and is attended by showers of sparks. (iii) The *fining period* occupies about 2 mins. The carbon continues burning, and iron is oxidized. The flame becomes less luminous and drops, indicating the end of the blow.

The subject was investigated by T. Rowan, R. Akerman, R. Addie, E. Herzog, S. Jordan, P. Kupelwieser, F. C. G. Müller, A. von Kerpely, F. Kessler, W. J. Campbell, A. Tamm, E. Tschernoff, etc. According to G. J. Snelus, the composition of the gases during a 14-minutes blow was as follows (hydrogen by difference) :

	2	4	6	10	12	14 mins.
CO_2	9·12	8·57	8·05	3·58	2·38	1·34
O_2	0·92	0·00	0·00	0·00	0·00	0·00
CO	0·06	3·95	4·58	19·59	29·44	31·11
H_2	0·00	0·88	2·00	2·00	2·16	2·00
N_2	90·31	86·58	85·37	74·83	66·02	65·55

F. Kessler gave for the analyses of the metal at different stages of the blow :

	Pig-iron	After 4 mins.	Beginning 2nd period	Middle 2nd period	End before adding spiegel	Finished product
Free carbon	2·52	0·14	0·04	0·01	0·00	0·00
Combined C	1·06	3·65	3·53	2·47	0·29	0·45
Silicon	1·875	1·200	0·648	0·067	0·021	0·083
Phosphorus	0·100	0·106	0·096	0·097	0·109	0·104
Sulphur	0·372	0·069	0·061	0·077	0·113	0·080
Manganese	1·04	0·23	0·08	0·06	0·05	0·34

F. Kessler's results show that the amount of phosphorus in the steel decreases in the middle stage of the process, but increases both in the commencement of the blow—owing to the relatively greater oxidation of the other substances—as well as at the end, when it is, in part at least, taken up again from the slag. Sulphur decreases rapidly at first, but then increases in the middle stage, up to the addition of the spiegeleisen, for the reason that a portion of it which in the first stage went into the slag in the form of metallic sulphides was afterwards again taken up by the iron. So long as the manganese is being oxidized and removed from the iron the percentage of sulphur in the iron diminishes ; but as soon as the iron is free from manganese, it again takes up a portion of the sulphur contained in the slag. When the spiegeleisen is added and the blow recommenced, the sulphur again diminishes ; and if the first slag (which is sulphurous) could be removed, then it would be possible to use brands of iron which are known to contain sulphur for making Bessemer steel. The various analyses of the products at different stages of the blow show that there is an analogy between the chemical changes in the Bessemer process and in puddling, although the process of oxidation of silicon and carbon is not always the same. According to F. C. G. Müller,

It is probable that during the first few minutes of the blow, the silicon is consumed, raising the temp. of the bath 200°. This increase, however, impairs the affinity of silicon for oxygen, so that during the second period then following its elimination is of secondary importance only, while the oxidation of carbon, the formation of carbonic oxide, becomes the principal reaction, as the large flame and the splashing tend to show. The temperature remains constant. Without manganese the bath would cool, and thus the oxidation of silicon would be resumed. The burning manganese escapes as Mn_3O_4, in the shape of brown clouds ; it does not enter the slag, because little silica is forming. The oxidation takes place chiefly through the agency of oxide of iron, which is dissolved in the bath, the reaction being limited, however, to a low temperature. An entire cessation of the oxidation of silicon gives rise to the most violent splashing. The length of this period increases with an increase in the percentage of carbon, and therefore it is absurd to aim at a high percentage of carbon in the Bessemer process. As soon as the flame grows smaller and transparent, and the noise ceases, the third short period begins, during which, in consequence of a considerable increase in the amount of oxide in the bath, the silicon is again more energetically consumed. A slag is formed which is richer in iron, and which in colour approaches brown. A dip sample taken at this period serves as a good indicator for the state of the process. The silicon is consumed rapidly after the addition of spiegel, the cause being, perhaps, the cooling of the bath by the colder metal. Besides the large amount of silicon consumed during the last period, a slow combustion of the residual graphite takes place also. . . . The composition of the slag is SiO_2, 43·73 ; MnO, 45·41 ; FeO, 9·04 ; and Al_2O_3, 1·99. According to A. Ledebur, the slags formed before the addition of spiegeleisen in the acid Bessemer process have the composition :

Time	3	6	8 mins.
Silica	53·44	57·80	55·76
Alumina	1·84	1·94	1·58
Ferrous oxide	20·24	17·04	18·48
Manganous oxide	23·90	22·80	22·23
Earths	0·44	0·46	0·39

The theory and thermochemistry of the process were discussed by W. N. Hartley, H. Schenck, H. Hermann, R. von Seth, J. Sullivan, J. W. Haulman, B. Osann, R. S. McCaffrey, L. C. Glaser, G. K. Burgess, F. T. Sisco, J. W. Richards, G. Butz, H. Bansen, K. Thomas, and H. Pontière ; the temp. of the converter, by R. A. Hadfield, F. E. Bash, and A. Cornu-Thénard.

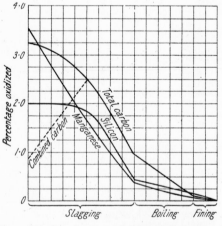

FIG. 36.—The Rates of Oxidation of Manganese, Silicon, and Carbon in the Bessemer Process.

F. Fischer showed that when atm. air is passed through the molten bath, all the substances which come in contact with oxygen will burn, so that primarily only direct combustion occurs. The oxides formed then interact with the other constituents of the bath.

There is first $C + CO_2 = 2CO - 3880$ Cals., which sensibly cools the bath. When pig-iron is fused with silica or silicates, silicon and carbon monoxide are formed : $2C + SiO_2 = 2CO + Si - 16,200$ Cals. This reaction requires, however, such a considerable amount of heat that it probably only takes place at very high temperatures. On the other hand, the reactions $Si + CO_2 = SiO_2 + C + 12,320$ Cals. and $Si + 2CO = SiO_2 + 2C + 16,200$ Cals. yield much heat and are consequently pronounced in their action. Manganese behaves similarly : $Mn + CO_2 = MnO + CO + 2680$ Cals. ; and $MnO + SiO_2 = MnSiO_3 +$ about 3500 Cals. The combustion of the manganese in carbon dioxide and its passage into the slag are therefore also accompanied by a considerable evolution of heat. The following reaction can also very readily take place :

$Mn + CO = MnO + C + 6560$ Cals. Silicon and manganese do not therefore protect the carbon from combustion, and they reduce again the products of combustion of carbon, and so cause the latter to pass again into the iron. The action of the iron itself is much weaker. At a red-heat : (1) $3Fe + 4CO_2 = Fe_3O_4 + 4CO - 810$ Cals. ; (2) $Fe_3O_4 + 4CO = 3Fe + 4CO_2 + 810$ Cals. ; and at a very high temperature (3) $Fe_3O_4 + 8CO = 3Fe + 2C + 6CO_2 - 10,710$ Cals. This last reaction is accompanied by such a large absorption of heat that it cannot be very pronounced.

The results of P. Kupelwieser with manganiferous pig-iron were summarized by W. N. Hartley, in a diagram resembling Fig. 36. The composition of the pig-iron was : 3·46, Mn ; 3·94, C ; and 1·96, Si. One of the first changes is the passage of free carbon to combined carbon, which is illustrated by the dotted line in the diagram. According to F. W. Harbord and J. W. Hall, the following may be regarded as typical analyses of acid Bessemer steel :

	Combined C	Si	S	P	Mn	As
Soft steel .	0·10–0·15	0·02–0·06	0·03–0·08	0·04–0·08	0·40–0·80	0·02–0·06 per cent.
Rail steel .	0·32–0·55	0·04–0·08	0·05–0·08	0·06–0·08	0·60–1·00	0·02–0·08 per cent.

By using specially selected pig-iron the phosphorus and sulphur may be reduced below these limits. The composition of the pig-iron used in the acid process is typically :

Combined C	Free C	Si	S	P	Mn	As
0·40	3·20	2·25	0·05	0·05	0·50	0·03 per cent.

The phosphorus, arsenic, and sulphur should be as low as possible and not exceed 0·06 per cent. ; while the manganese should not exceed 1 per cent. The carbon may be between 3·2 and 4 per cent. The silicon should be between 2·0 and 2·5 or 3·0 per cent. A. Ledebur found that the chromium and vanadium in pig-iron are thus affected by the Bessemer treatment :

	C	Mn	Cr	V
Before blow . .	2·518	0·792	0·073	0·072 per cent.
After blow . .	0·080	0·360	0·013	0·000 per cent.

H. Reuss discussed the liquation phenomena in a cast Bessemer steel roll weighing 7 tons.

The use of the spectroscope for fixing the end of the operation was discussed by E. Tschernoff, P. R. von Tunner, J. M. Silliman, T. Rowan, A. Greiner, etc. According to H. E. Roscoe, A. Lielegg, P. Kupelwieser, and J. S. Parker, the spectrum of the Bessemer flame is characterized by bands of carbon or carbon monoxide, while, according to R. Simmler, A. Greiner, J. Brunner, A. von Lichtenfeld, and H. Wedding, the spectrum is not due to carbon or carbon monoxide, but rather to manganese and other elements in pig-iron ; and M. Watts said that the spectrum is not due to carbon, carbon monoxide, or manganese, but rather to manganic oxide. According to M. Watts, the difference in the spectrum observed in different works is due to the temp. and the composition of the metal under treatment. In the first or slagging period the lines of the alkali metals—sodium, potassium, and lithium—were unreversed on a bright continuous spectrum of carbon monoxide ; the C-line and apparently the F-line of hydrogen were seen reversed during a snowstorm. In the second or boiling period bands of manganese overlying the continuous spectrum of carbon monoxide were prominent. There are lines of carbon monoxide, manganese, and iron, and also those of the alkali metals. In the third or fining period the lines of iron are not so strong as in the boiling stage and they are not so well-defined ; indeed, some of the short lines disappear. The lines of the alkali metals are visible. The bands of manganese oxide may be present ; if so, they are obscured by the continuous carbon monoxide spectrum. No absorption bands were seen, no nitrogen bands, nor bands of calcium and magnesium oxides, neither did the lines of these metals appear. There is no trace of cobalt, nickel, chromium, or copper ; certain carbon bands overlie those of manganese and are recognized by measurements of their edges. Some of the lines not identified by M. Watts were found to be iron lines, others belong to manganese. M. Watts observed the red line of hydrogen during wet weather. W. N. Hartley identified the spectral lines of calcium, rubidium, cæsium, copper, silver, thallium, and gallium in the flame of Bessemer's converter.

It will be observed that sulphur and particularly phosphorus are not removed by the acid Bessemer process. In 1878, S. G. Thomas showed that if the converter be lined with a basic material, say dolomite, and the blast be continued a little longer, the oxides of phosphorus, sulphur, and silicon which are formed are absorbed by the furnace lining. Some lime is put into the converter near the beginning of the blow to furnish the base necessary for the production of the slag, and to protect the basic lining of the converter from undue corrosion by slagging. Otherwise the operation is conducted as just indicated. S. G. Thomas developed the process in co-operation with P. C. Gilchrist, so that in England the process came to be called **Thomas-Gilchrist's process ;** in Germany it is called *Thomas's process*, and in America the *basic Bessemer process*. The process was discussed by H. Schulz and J. Schönava, A. Herberholz, C. W. Ljunggren, A. Brovot, V. Harbord, C. Longenecker, F. M. Feldhaus, E. Mathesius, F. Grassmann, F. Kintzle, J. von Ehrenwerth, G. Bresson, H. Schuphaus, A. Wasum, J. Massenez, G. Hilgenstock, A. Spannagel, etc. According to F. W. Harbord and J. W. Hall, the following may be regarded as typical analyses of basic Bessemer steel :

	Combined C	Si	S	P	Mn	As
Soft steel .	0·08–0·15	trace	0·03–0·08	0·04–0·08	0·40–0·80	0·02–0·06 per cent.
Rail steel .	0·32–0·55	0–0·02	0·05–0·08	0·06–0·08	0·60–0·100	0·02–0·06 per cent.

With special care in the selection of the pig-iron the impurities may be reduced below these limits, and vice versa. The pig-iron for the basic process has the typical analysis :

Combined C	Free C	Si	S	P	Mn	As
3·40	0·20	1·00	0·05	3·00	2·00	0·03 per cent.

Iron with over 1 per cent. silicon may be used, but the silicon is preferred low. The phosphorus may be between 2·5 and 3·5 per cent. The lower the sulphur and arsenic the better, and they should not exceed 0·06 per cent. A. Tamm made analyses of the gases at different stages of the blow ; C. Scheibler, E. Steinweg, G. Hilgenstock, and E. Schrödter discussed the slags—*vide* **3**. 24, 25, *et seq.* R. Finkener gave for the composition of the metal and of the corresponding slags at different stages of the basic Bessemer process and after the addition of spiegeleisen :

	Time	2' 46"	5' 21"	8' 5"	10' 45"	13' 28"	15' 13"	19' 14"	19' 49"	After spiegel
	SiO₂ .	41·15	36·30	34·41	31·94	16·64	14·65	12·94	11·71	22·77
	P₂O₅ .	0·80	3·12	2·99	4·02	7·15	11·60	18·83	18·15	16·92
	Al₂O₃ .	1·12	1·30	1·08	1·00	1·29	1·35	1·07	1·01	1·12
	Fe₂O₃ .	—	0·46	0·13	0·74	4·95	3·84	3·74	2·78	2·87
Slag	FeO .	2·40	3·97	3·60	4·23	8·42	7·15	5·84	7·19	5·94
	MnO .	9·03	11·02	10·72	9·94	8·51	7·39	4·25	4·05	4·80
	CaO .	41·27	39·50	42·80	43·12	44·37	46·63	47·76	48·19	47·87
	MgO .	4·13	3·36	3·35	4·01	7·34	6·34	6·00	6·38	6·75
	S .	0·25	0·10	0·13	0·05	0·13	0·12	0·07	0·09	0·05
	SO₃ .	0·06	0·05	0·09	0·05	0·12	0·15	0·07	0·05	0·13
	Si .	0·72	0·15	—	—	—	—	—	—	0·01
Metal	P .	2·15	2·22	2·16	2·10	2·05	1·91	0·23	0·09	0·14
	Mn .	0·71	0·05	0·18	0·16	0·14	0·01	0·01	—	0·48

According to W. N. Hartley and H. Ramage, the phenomena occurring during the blow in the basic Bessemer process differ considerably from those of the acid process. They said :

First, a flame is visible from the commencement of blowing, or as soon as the cloud of lime-dust has dispersed. We conclude that the immediate production of this flame is caused by carbonaceous matter in the lining of the vessel, that its luminosity is due partly to the volatilization of the alkalies, and to the incandescence of lime-dust carried out by the blast. Secondly, volatilization of metal occurs largely at an early period in the blow, and is due to the difference in composition of the metal blown, chiefly to the smaller quantity of silicon. There is practically no distinct period when siliceous slags are formed in the basic process, and metals are volatilized readily in the reducing atmosphere, rich in carbon monoxide. Thirdly, a very large amount of fume is formed towards the close of the second period. This arises from the oxidation of the metal and of phosphorus in the iron phosphide, being productive of a high temp., but little or no carbon remaining. The flame is comparatively short, and the metallic vapours carried up are burnt by the blast. Fourthly, the over-blow is characterized by a very powerful illumination from what appears to be a brilliant yellow flame : a dense fume is produced at this time composed of oxidized metallic vapours, chiefly iron. These particles are undoubtedly of very minute dimensions, as is proved by the fact that they scatter the light which falls on them, and the cloud casts a brown shadow, and, on a still day, ascends to a great height. The spectrum is continuous, but does not extend beyond wave-length 4000 A. This indicates that the source of light is at a comparatively low temp., approaching that of a yellowish-white heat. We conclude, therefore, that the light emanates from a torrent of very small particles, liquid or solid, at a yellowish-white heat. The " flame " can have but little reducing power at this stage, and this, together with its low temp., accounts for the very feeble lines of lithium, sodium, potassium, and manganese seen in the photographs or by eye observations. Fifthly, the spectra of flames from the first stage of the basic process differ from those of the acid process in several particulars. The manganese bands are relatively feeble, and lines of elements not usually associated with Bessemer metal are present. Both the charges of metal and of basic material contribute to these. Lithium, sodium, potassium, rubidium, and cæsium have been traced mainly to the lime ; manganese, copper, silver, and gallium to the metal. Other metals, such as vanadium and titanium, are not in evidence, because they do not yield flame spectra ; they, together with chromium, pass into the slag in an oxidized state.

In 1862, C. Attwood [7] patented a process for manufacturing steel from a mixture of wrought iron and cast iron with some spiegeleisen—*vide supra*. He employed a regenerative open-hearth or reverberatory furnace designed by C. W. von Siemens. The reverberatory furnace has a roof formed of silica bricks sloping towards the centre, with a shallow rectangular trough as hearth. The process was too costly. The process was also tried in France in 1863, at the works of P. and E. Martin, Sireuil, where steel was manufactured in the Siemens furnace by dissolving scrap wrought iron in a bath of cast iron with a suitable addition of manganese and carbon at the end of the operation. The process in this form assumed no commercial importance, but when C. W. von Siemens applied the regenerative furnace to the decarburization of cast iron by the use of iron ore, with or without the use of iron or steel scrap, the process developed rapidly as the **open-hearth process** or the **Siemens-Martin's process.** In the original process of C. W. von Siemens the oxide ore was added to the molten pig-iron, the so-called *pig and ore process* ; P. and E. Martin added scrap without ore to the molten pig-iron, the so-called *pig and scrap process*. E. Maurer and W. Bischof discussed the history of the open-hearth process.

According to L. Guillet, at Kladno, about 1830, successful attempts were made to dephosphorize iron by using a ferruginous lining with a puddling-furnace ; and in 1859, L. E. Gruner commented on the subject in connection with puddled steel. In 1869, E. Muller patented the use of magnesia linings for Bessemer converters and Martin's furnaces so as to eliminate sulphur. C. M. Tessié du Motay, in 1872, and A. Lencauchez, in 1875, reverted to the dephosphorizing effect of magnesia linings ; and in 1878, S. G. Thomas and P. C. Gilchrist announced the discovery of their basic process for the manufacture of steel.

Molten pig-iron is run directly into the furnace, or else a charge of, say, 5 tons· of pig-iron is put on the bed of the furnace, and when it is melted down iron ore broken to the size of ordinary road-metal is thrown in. This makes the molten metal " boil " vigorously ; more ore is added in successive portions so as to keep up a good " boil." It is then allowed to stand for a short time to permit as much as possible of the iron to work out of the slag. Broken limestone or quicklime may be added at intervals during the process to assist in separating the iron from the slag. The molten iron is maintained in a fluid condition to allow samples to be removed and tested. Additions of wrought scrap or pig-iron may be made to adjust the metal to the desired temper. Ferro-manganese or spiegeleisen is then added, and as soon as this is all melted the charge is tapped. A 5-ton furnace is a very small one; some hold up to 125 tons. The average capacity is about 70 tons per heat. The furnace is heated by producer gas. Both the gas and the secondary air for the combustion of the gas are pre-heated, so that a very high temperature can be obtained. A general idea of the process can be gathered from Fig. 37, which shows a section through the hearth. The gas and air burn on the left; the flue gases travel down the flue on the right and in doing so heat up two chambers below. The direction of the burning gas is then reversed. Gas and air pass separately through the hot chambers, and the flue gases heat up another pair of chambers below the hearth. The direction travelled by the burning gas is reversed about every half and in some cases every quarter of an hour, and the heat of the flue gases is utilized in warming-up chambers through which the unburnt gas and air will pass later on. The furnace is called *Siemens' regenerative furnace*.

If the bed of the furnace is made of siliceous materials—*acid open-hearth process*—the proportions of carbon, silicon, and manganese are reduced during the treatment, but the amounts of sulphur and phosphorus remain fairly constant. In the *basic*

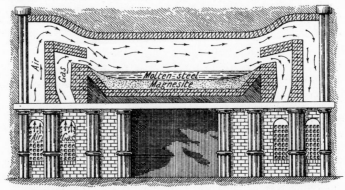

Regenerators
being cooled.

Regenerators
being heated.

FIG. 37.—Section through the Open-hearth Furnace.

open-hearth process the furnace is bedded with, say, dolomite, and there is a steady fall in the amount of phosphorus during the treatment, just as was the case with the basic Bessemer's process of S. G. Thomas and P. C. Gilchrist.

About 1908, the output of steel by the open-hearth process surpassed that produced by Bessemer's process; and although the former is slower, it permits a far greater control of the reactions involved and of the composition of the finished metal. It also allows a greater variety of phosphatic pig-irons to be treated.

The open-hearth process has been discussed by P. Acker, R. Akerman, W. Alberts, T. N. Armstrong, C. H. F. Bagley, H. Bansen, W. P. Barba and H. M. Howe, A. Barberot, W. J. Beck, R. Becker, A. Berglöf, F. Bernhardt, I. A. Billiar, E. Blau, C. Bohlin, A. Bosser, G. R. Boyd, H. Braune, J. A. Brinell, C. Brisker, G. B. Bruno and G. Delbart, A. Byström, J. W. Cabot, H. H. Campbell, C. Canaris, W. M. Carr, C. A. Casperson, S. Casson, W. P. Chandler, J. Christie, H. O. Chute, D. Clark, F. Clements, M. J. Conway, S. J. Cort, E. Cotel, C. C. de Coussergues, F. J. Crolius, H. Crowe, R. M. Daelen, R. M. Daelen and L. Pozczolka, J. Davis, B. Dawson, G. Desprit, C. Dichmann, A. M. Dick and C. S. Padley, A. N. Diehl, E. Diepschlag, J. von Ehrenwerth, H. de Estève, A. L. Field, F. Fiorelli, R. Frerich, R. Furness, L. Gautier, R. Genzer, M. L. Gerard, P. C. Gilchrist, H. Gille, A. Gouvy, F. Grassmann, H. G. Graves, J. A. de Grey, W. E. Griffiths and C. E. Meissner, H. Groeck, E. Günter, F. W. Harbord and J. W. Hall, J. Hartshorne, H. S. Hastings, A. Herberholz, H. Hermanns, C. H. Herty, C. H. Herty and co-workers, E. Herzog, H. D. Hibbard, N. F. Hindle, G. Hofer, O. Holz, J. K. Hoyt, H. Illies, E. J. Janitzky, E. R. Jette, R. Johannsson, A. Jung, P. Kahnert, W. Keen, R. T. Kent, E. Killing, C. D. King, C. L. Kinney, P. Klein, J. L. Klindworth, K. Köhler, F. Kofler, S. G. Koon, K. Kreiss, P. Kupelweiser, T. G. Kus, E. Langheinrich, B. M. Larsen, H. W. Lash, F. E. Lathe, M. Lencauchez, F. Lepersonne, W. Lister, E. de Loisy, E. Lubojatzky,

G. L. Luetscher, H. Macco, G. R. McDermott and C. L. Kinney, W. McFarlane, C. H. McMillan, A. McWilliam, A. McWilliam and W. H. Hatfield, E. von Maltitz, B. de Mare, G. Mars, E. Maurer and W. Bischof, E. Maurer and R. Schrödter, J. Meiser, A. Mignot, G. A. Milward, H. Monden, A. Monell, S. G. Moore, T. D. Morgan, E. Münker, T. Naske, B. Neuherz, G. Neumann, C. S. Nugent, E. G. Odelstjerna, F. W. Paul, M. A. Pavloff, O. Peterson, E. Piwowarsky, K. Poech, A. Ponthière, A. Pourcel, G. L. Prentiss, J. Puppe, W. J. Reagan, P. Rees, L. F. Reinartz, J. W. Richards, A. Riemer, J. Riley, G. A. V. Russell, F. Sandelin, E. H. Saniter, R. J. Sarjant, A. Sattmann, F. Sauerwald, A. Schack, W. Schdanoff, H. Schenck, W. Schmidhammer, R. Schöffel, K. Seaver, J. Seigle, W. Shaw, P. G. Shook, O. Simmersbach, R. P. Smith, W. Soltz, J. Sonnenfeld, E. Spetzler and co-workers, F. Springorum, F. Stein, I. L. Stevenson, C. Stöckl, B. Stoughton, T. D. Straub, C. Strobrawa, O. Stromborg, C. E. Stromeyer, S. Surzycki, W. Tafel, B. Talbot, O. Thiel, J. Thieme, F. Thomas, K. Thomas, B. H. Thwaite, C. W. Tideström, M. Tigerschiöld, M. von Tittler, G. Toppe, F. L. Toy, G. D. Tranter, W. Trinks, B. W. Turner, T. Turner, T. Twynam, H. C. Vacher and E. H. Hamilton, F. Valton, C. W. Veach, J. Wagner, Harbison Walker, C. Walrand, H. Wedding, J. Weeren, F. Weisgerber, S. T. Wellman, J. H. Whiteley and A. F. Hallimond, E. A. Whitworth, A. D. Williams, P. Williams, G. A. Wilson, V. Windett, H. C. Wood, M. von Zaykowsky, and E. von Zeipel, etc.

L. Cubillo followed the course of the acid open-hearth process by analyzing the slag periodically 1½ hrs. after the charge was completely melted, and the metal

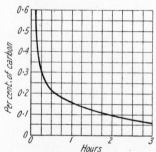

Fig. 38.—The Rate of Loss of Carbon in the Acid Open-hearth Process.

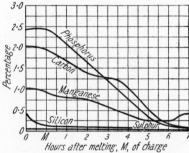

Fig. 39.—Rate of Loss of Impurities in the Basic Open-hearth Process.

half an hour after the charge was completely melted, *i.e.* at 12.30 p.m., with the addition of spiegeleisen at 4.40 p.m., and the metal was finished at 5.20 p.m. The following are the results :

		1.30	2.0	2.30	3.30	4.0	4.40 p.m.
Slag	SiO$_2$	53·11	48·05	49·40	50·16	52·21	50·90
	FeO	27·39	30·09	30·60	29·19	27·13	26·96
	MnO	13·39	14·14	12·65	10·60	11·17	11·905
	CaO	3·66	5·20	5·06	7·30	6·38	8·10
	MgO	2·45	2·52	2·23	2·66	3·08	2·42
	S	0·03	0·04	0·045	0·045	0·048	4·40

		12.30*†	1.30*	2.0*	2.30*	3.30†	4.0	4.40	5.20 p.m.
Metal	C	1·60	1·47	1·27	1·17	0·71	0·57	0·43	0·48
	Si	0·59	0·21	0·047	0·012	0·012	0·012	0·012	0·140
	S	0·075	0·079	0·079	0·079	0·079	0·079	0·079	0·080
	P	0·059	0·060	0·060	0·060	0·060	0·060	0·060	0·060
	Mn	0·34	0·17	—	—	—	—	—	0·43

The symbol * means that ore was added, and † that sand was added. During the melting period, when solid pig and scrap was used, the products of combustion— either as free oxygen or carbon dioxide—act on the metal to oxidize carbon, silicon, and manganese, but when the charge is completely melted and covered with a layer of molten slag, oxidation occurs through the abstraction of oxygen from some of the constituents of the slag. If the ferrous oxide becomes reduced by this means, the slag becomes too acidic and viscid, and it is necessary to add more ferric oxide in the form of iron ore. H. Allen represents the loss of carbon by the molten metal by a curve resembling Fig. 38 ; whilst the changes which take place during the working of a charge in a basic furnace are illustrated by Fig. 39.

Observations on the subject were made by H. H. Campbell, C. H. Herty and co-workers, F. Kollmann, G. Mehrtens, H. Schenck, F. Stille, H. Styri, and K. Thomas ; and in the basic furnace, by R. Back, H. Bansen, W. J. Beck, H. M. Boyston, W. D. Brown, G. K. Burgess, H. H. Campbell, W. P. Chandler, T. P. Colclough, S. Cornell, C. C. de Coussergues, A. S. Cushman, E. Damour, M. Deslandes, G. A. Dornin, J. B. Ferguson, A. L. Field, G. Fisk, R. Fornander, R. Furness, J. M. Gaines, K. Gierdziejewsky, M. Groume-Grjimailo, J. Guyot, F. W. Harbord, A. Harrison and R. V. Wheeler, W. Heil, W. M. Henry and T. J. McLoughlin, A. Herberholz, H. Hermanns, C. H. Herty, C. H. Herty and co-workers, E. Herzog, E. Houbaer, W. Hülsbruch, K. Huessener, E. R. Jette, A. Jung, E. Killing, C. L. Kinney and G. R. McDermott, S. P. Kinney, A. B. Kinzel and J. J. Egan, K. Köhler, B. M. Larsen, B. M. Larsen and J. W. Campbell, E. de Loisy, E. Lubojatzky, A. McCance, P. M. Macnair, G. Mars, R. Mather, F. A. Mathewman, F. A. Mathewman and A. Campion, E. Maurer and S. Schleicher, E. Mayer, G. Mehrtens, J. R. Miller, H. Monden, G. Neumann, E. Noaillon, P. Oberhoffer and co-workers, R. D. Pike, V. Polak, F. Sandelin, A. Schack, H. Schenck, S. Schleicher, W. Schmidhammer, H. Schmidt, H. Schmidt and W. Liesegang, C. Schwarz, H. See, H. W. Seldon, A. Silin, D. Sillars, F. T. Sisco, H. Styri, G. Tammann and co-workers, K. Thomas, M. Tigerschiöld, W. Trinks, C. W. Veach, G. B. Waterhouse, J. H. Whiteley, J. F. Wilson, J. T. Wright, F. Wüst, F. Wüst and J. Duhr, and B. Yaneske and co-workers. R. A. Hadfield measured the temp. of the furnace. S. Schleicher studied the composition of the bath at different depths.

According to F. W. Harbord and J. W. Hall, the following are typical analyses of open-hearth steels :

		Combined C	Si	S	P	Mn	As
Acid	Soft steel	0·12–0·20	0·04–0·08	0·02–0·06	0·02–0·06	0·40–0·60	0·02–0·06 per cent.
	Rail steel	0·20–1·50	0·04–0·35	0·02–0·06	0·02–0·06	0·40–1·00	0·02–0·06 per cent.
Basic	Soft steel	0·10–0·18	tr.	0·02–0·06	0·03–0·06	0·40–0·80	0·01–0·06 per cent.
	Rail steel	0·45–0·70	0·00–0·35	0·04–0·06	0·04–0·06	0·60–0·90	0·01–0·06 per cent.

By using special hæmatite pig-iron the phosphorus can be almost eliminated. Typical analyses of pig-iron for these processes are :

		Combined C	Free C	Si	S	P	Mn	As
Acid	.	0·40	3·20	2·00	0·04	0·04	0·60	0·03 per cent.
Basic	.	3·40	0·20	<1·00	0·05	<2·00	2·00	0·3 per cent.

The carbon for the acid process may vary from 3·2 to 4·0 per cent. ; the silicon should not exceed 2·50, and manganese, 1·00 ; and the lower the phosphorus, sulphur, and arsenic the better, but the percentage should not exceed 0·05 per cent. in each case. For the basic process the silicon should be less than 1 per cent., and the phosphorus below 2·00 per cent., but some is used with about 3 per cent. of phosphorus. If sulphur is low, the manganese may be less than 1 per cent., but if sulphur is high, more manganese may be necessary. H. Schenck studied the manganese and phosphorus reactions in the basic process ; H. Schenck, H. D. Hibbard, and A. S. Thomas, the silicon ; and S. Schleicher, E. H. Saniter, A. Riemer, F. E. Thompson, F. Stille, J. E. Stead, K. Gierdziejewsky, H. Gold-schmidt, W. G. Burman, J. Massenez, L. J. Ball and A. Wingham, etc., the sulphur. R. M. Keeney, W. S. Hamilton, H. J. Jones, H. L. Geiger, A. C. Dalton, and L. Goldmerstein discussed the use of fluorspar in steel-making.

Numerous modifications of the open-hearth process have been devised. In many of them the furnace is designed so that the hearth can be tilted and either metal or slag run off as desired. Modifications have been discussed by F. W. Harbord and J. W. Hall, H. Wedding, B. Talbot, L. Unckenbolt, S. Surzycki, O. Simmersbach, J. H. Darby and G. Hatton, A. P. Head, J. Head, P. Eyermann, R. M. Daelen and L. Pozczolka, H. Illies, O. Thiel, J. W. Cabot, A. Ledebur, H. M. Howe, A. E. Davies, etc. R. B. Carnahan, and A. S. Cushman developed a method for preparing iron of a high degree of purity. It has the trade-name **armco-iron**. It was discussed by A. Sauveur—vide infra.

The application of **electric furnaces** to the manufacture of steel has developed along two directions. Where electric power is cheap enough, electric heating has replaced the use of fuels like gas, so that ten years ago in Norway electric furnaces displaced open-hearth furnaces. In other cases it has been found advantageous to combine two operations, in which the steel is subjected to a preliminary treatment in the open-hearth furnace, and the liquid steel is then transferred to the electric furnace for the final purification—deoxidation, desulphurization, adjustment of carbon, and additions of other elements for the production of alloy steels. High-grade electric steel can be thus produced equivalent to high-grade crucible steels at a favourable cost. The use of a higher temp. and the maintenance of a clean reducing atmosphere are great advantages. With alloy steels the losses through oxidation are much less than in fuel-heated furnaces. Steel can be readily obtained from scrap metal without the use of pig-iron, and steel of a uniform and good quality can be produced from low-grade materials. The subject has been discussed by J. N. Pring,[8] etc.

One of the many forms of furnace designed by P. L. T. Héroult [9] is illustrated diagrammatically in Fig. 40. The furnace may be 16 ft. in diameter, and it has a plate-steel shell about an inch thick. It is lined for $4\frac{1}{2}$ ins. with firebrick; inside that is a lining of magnesite bricks, 9 to $13\frac{1}{2}$ ins. thick; and above that is a bed of burned magnesite, 13 ins. thick. The domed roof, 12 ins. thick, is of silica brick. The openings in the roof are for the three carbon electrodes, which are 20 ins. diam. and are carried by horizontal arms projecting over the furnace, and which can be adjusted by movable rods. Heavy copper cables and bars carry the current from the transformer. The bottom of the furnace is carried on toothed rockers and tracks so that the furnace can be tilted. The tilting gear is operated by a motor which tilts the furnace by means of a connecting-rod. The furnace is charged with, say, 25 tons of molten metal from the open-hearth or Bessemer furnace, and the current is switched on. The bottom of the electrode is adjusted with about three-quarters of an inch clearance from the surface of the slag. The alternating, 3-phase current has an amperage of about 6000

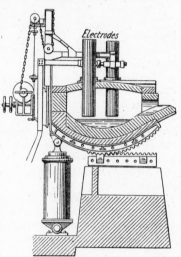

FIG. 40.—Héroult Electric Steel Furnace.

to 14,000 per phase, and a voltage of 110. The temp. rises from about 1510° with high-carbon steel to about 1650° with low-carbon steel. Limestone and iron oxide are added as desired. These materials form an oxidized slag for reducing the phosphorus down to about 0·008 per cent. The slag is then run off, and another mixture called a reducing slag is added. It consists of limestone, sand, fluorspar, and coke-dust. It deoxidizes and desulphurizes the metal. If desired, the proper amount of the alloy metals—manganese, nickel, chromium, or vanadium—is added, and the metal is ready for pouring after the slag has been run off. The whole operation occupies between 4 and 5 hrs. The reactions which occur in the basic process were discussed by F. T. Sisco, and W. E. Moore.

According to F. R. Eichoff, " it is impossible to heat a steel arc-furnace by utilizing the heat generated by the resistance of the thin layer of slag, or of the large cross-section of the bath. These resistances furnish only a few per cent. of the heat necessary in the furnace. . . . The heat cannot be obtained by the decreasing resistance offered by the slag as the temp. rises, or by utilizing the resistance of the bath. The slag layer is too thin, and the cross-section of the steel bath too large." The heat of the Héroult furnace is almost entirely derived from the heat of the arc formed between the electrodes and the bath. The ferric oxide added to the bath is reduced to ferrous oxide, and it distributes itself between the metal and the slag. The oxidizing slag contains about 40 per cent. CaO ; 26 to 29 per cent. FeO and MnO ; and up to about 4 per cent. P_2O_5. The oxidizing slag only affects the sulphur to a small extent. A little sulphur dioxide may be formed by the reaction $FeS+2FeO=3Fe+SO_2$. When the reducing slag is introduced, the ferrous sulphide which is formed is distributed between the slag and the metal in accord with the partition law ; and similarly also with the manganous sulphide. The reaction with the slag may proceed : $FeS+CaO \rightleftharpoons CaS+FeO$; but at the same time the ferrous oxide is reduced : $FeO+C \rightleftharpoons CO+Fe$. The subject was discussed by T. Geilenkirchen, and B. Osann. The carbon in the reducing slag may form silicon carbide, calcium silicide, and calcium carbide. The latter compound explains the smell of acetylene from a cooled sample. The calcium carbide in the slag may react with the ferrous sulphide : $2CaO+3FeS+CaC_2=3Fe+3CaS+2CO$. According to W. Fielding, some silicon sulphide may be formed : $2FeS+FeSi$ $=3Fe+SiS_2$. According to C. C. de Coussergues, hydrogen dissolved in the steel is attacked by the calcium carbide : $CaC_2+H_2=CaC_2H_2$.

The electric furnaces are usually classed as arc-furnaces and resistance furnaces. (1) *The arc-furnaces* may have (i) a direct heating arc (a) in series between the electrodes and the metal, as in P. L. T. Héroult's furnace just described. Other examples are the furnaces of W. E. Moore,[10] C. H. von Baur,[11] V. Stobie,[12] E. F. Russ,[13] and C. A. Keller.[14] Or (b) one or more electrodes may be imbedded in the hearth of the furnace so that the current arcs across from one set of electrodes to the steel, and thence out through the furnace bottom, as in the furnaces of P. Girod,[15] C. A. Keller,[16] F. T. Snyder,[17] The Electro-Metals Co.,[18] H. Nathusius,[19] and J. Härden.[20] W. K. Booth,[21] and J. L. Dixon[22] discussed the Greaves-Etchells furnace, which, according to C. E. Moore, is going out of use in the United States. The arc-furnaces may have (ii) an independent arc, as in the furnace of E. Stassano,[23] and I. Rennerfelt.[24] According to C. E. Moore, these two furnaces are not now used in the United States. There are (2) *the resistance furnaces*, which operate (i) by induction,[25] as in the furnaces of Z. de Ferranti,[26] F. A. Kjellin, O. Frick,[27] W. Rodenhauser,[28] A. Hiorth,[29] and E. F. Northrup.[30] The induction furnace proposed by C. Hering,[31] based on the so-called Pinch effect, has not been commercially successful. (ii) Resistance furnaces of the type proposed by G. Gin [32] have not proved satisfactory for steel refining.

REFERENCES.

[1] E. Swedenborg, *Regnum subterraneum sive minerale de ferro*, Dresden, 1. 194, 1734 ; R. Watson, *Chemical Essays*, Cambridge, 1. 220, 1781 ; J. Beckmann, *Beyträge zur Geschichte der Erfindungen*, Leipzig, 5. 88, 1805 ; W. W. Campbell and E. E. Thum, *Metal Progress*, 20. 43, 1931.
[2] S. Lucas, *Brit. Pat. No.* 1869, 1871 ; 1730, 1854 ; D. Mushet, *ib.*, 2447, 1800 ; J. I. Hawkins, *ib.*, 7142, 1836 ; W. E. Newton, *ib.*, 851, 1856 ; R. M. Daelen, *Stahl Eisen*, 17. 401, 1897 ; H. Tholander and P. Hörden, *Tek. Tids.*, 30. 60, 1900 ; E. Humbert and A. Hethey, *Journ. Iron Steel Inst.*, 89, i, 378, 1914 ; J. Percy, *Metallurgy—Iron and Steel*, London, 765, 1864 ; H. Larkin, *Journ. Roy. Soc. Arts*, 24. 86, 1875 ; *Van Nostrands Eng. Mag.*, 14. 250, 1876 ; R. Jenkins, *Eng.*, 134. 572, 1923 ; M. Sudhoff, *Arch. Geschichte Naturwiss.*, 10. 290, 1917 ; O. Schrader, *Sprachvergleichung und Urgeschichte*, Jena, 1906 ; E. O. von Lippmann, *Entstehung und Ausbreitung der Alchemie*, Berlin, 1919.
[3] H. Rupe and F. Müller, *Verh. Nat. Ges. Basel*, 27. 108, 1916 ; B. Neumann, *Stahl Eisen*, 39. 1105, 1919 ; F. Springorum, *ib.*, 44. 841, 1924 ; W. Eilender, *ib.*, 44. 1637, 1924 ; P. Oberhoffer, *ib.*, 45. 2074, 1925 ; H. Saemann, *ib.*, 46. 436, 1926 ; G. Turner, *Ironmonger*, 168. 93, 1919 ; J. A. Mathews, *Trans. Amer. Soc. Steel Treating*, 2. 990, 1922 ; M. W. Newfeld, *Mitt. Inst. Eisenforsch.*, 4. 1, 1922 ; E. Darmstaedter, *Tech. Ind.*, 11. 3, 1927 ; B. D. Saklatawalla, *Journ. Soc. Chem. Ind.*, 47. 195, T, 1928 ; J. B. Walker, *The Story of Steel*, New York, 1926 ; F. A. A. Eversmann, *Uebersicht der Eisen- und Stahl-Erzeugung auf Wasserwerken in den Ländern zwischen Lahn und Lippe*, Dortmund, 1804 ; G. Broling, *Anteckningar under en resa i England*, Stockholm, 1817 ; *Karsten's Arch.*, (1), 8. 342, 1824 ; H. Damemme, *Essai pratique sur l'emploi ou la manière de travailler l'acier*, Paris, 1835 ; J. François, *Ann. Mines*, (3), 12. 580, 1837 ; (3), 13. 535, 1838 ; P. G. F. le Play, *Mémoire sur la fabrication et le commerce des fers à aciers dans le nord de l'Europe*, Paris, 1846 ; *Ann. Mines*, (4), 3. 583, 1843 ; (4), 9. 113, 1846 ; C. Lan, *ib.*, (5), 15. 85, 1859 ; L. E. Gruner, *De l'acier et de sa fabrication*, Paris, 1867 ; New York, 1872 ; *Études sur l'acier*, Paris, 1869 ; *Ann. Mines*, (5), 15. 291, 1859 ; (6), 12. 207, 1867 ; C. Lan and L. E. Gruner, *ib.*, (5), 19. 131, 1861 ; A. Delesse, *Berg. Hütt. Ztg.*, 5. 513, 1846 ; F. Overman, *The Manufacture of*

Iron in all its Branches, Philadelphia, 1851 ; *The Manufacture of Steel*, Philadelphia, 1851 ;
C. J. B. Karsten, *Karsten's Arch.*, (2), **25**. 218, 1853 ; F. Kohn, *Iron and Steel Manufacture*,
London, 1869 ; J. S. Jeans, *Steel : Its History, Manufacture, Properties and Uses*, London, 1880 ;
C. W. von Siemens, *Journ. Iron Steel Inst.*, **6**. 37, 1873 ; **9**. i, 125, 138, 1877 ; K. Wittgenstein and
A. Kurzwernhart, *ib.*, **23**. ii, 451, 1882 ; J. H. Darby, *ib.*, **67**. i, 122, 1905 ; R. A. Hadfield, *ib.*,
46. ii, 224, 1894 ; P. R. von Tunner, *Oesterr. Zeit. Berg. Hütt.*, **30**. 447, 1882 ; H. Lcobner, *Berg.
Hütt. Jahrb. Leoben*, **48**. 219, 1900 ; *Stahl Eisen*, **46**. 1842, 1926 ; *Montana Rund.*, **18**. 623, 1926 ;
H. M. Howe, *The Metallurgy of Steel*, New York, 1890 ; C. Benedicks, *Jernkontorets Ann.*, (2),
62. 606, 1907 ; *Rev. Mét.*, **5**. 5, 1908 ; J. O. Arnold, *Engg.*, **45**. 162, 1913 ; R. A. F. de Réaumur,
L'art convertir le fer forgé en acier, Paris, 1722 ; *Nouvel art d'adoucir le fer fondu*, Paris, 1762 ;
An Essay on the Mystery of Tempering Steel, London, 1771 ; C. Pälhem, *Svenska Akad. Handl.*, **1**.
303, 437, 1840 ; D. Tiselius, *ib.*, **3**. 136, 1742 ; G. Lauraeus, *ib.*, **9**. 68, 1748 ; J. Rosenreich-
Diffrage, *Aus allen Eisen Stahl zu machen*, Nürnberg, 1760 ; O. Vogel, *Stahl Eisen*, **19**. 242, 1899 ;
33. 869, 1913 ; L. Beck, *ib.*, **26**. 1421, 1906 ; in C. Matschose, *Beiträge zur Geschichte der Technik
und Industrie*, Berlin, **3**. 86, 1911 ; P. A. Gadd and G. Korsemann, *Om Järnets förwandling till
stäl*, Abo, 1766 ; H. Horne, *Essays concerning Iron and Steel*, London, 1773 ; J. J. Perret,
Mémoire sur l'acier, Paris, 1779 ; Dresden, 1780 ; B. F. J. von Hermann, *Beschreibung der Methode
durch welche der Brescianer, Stahl verfertigt wird*, Wien, 1792 ; *Crell's Ann.*, i, 195, 1789 ; ii, 99,
1792 ; D. Little, *Mem. Amer. Acad.*, **1**. 525, 1785 ; *Crell's Ann.*, ii, 429, 1790 ; P. S. Ihlström,
ib., ii, 470, 1784 ; *Akademisk Afhandling om allmänna författningar vid Stal-Verken*, Upsala,
1783 ; F. L. von Cancrin, *Abhandlung von der Zubereitung des Roheisens in Schmiedereisen
auch des Stahleisens in Stahl*, Giessen, 1788 ; L. B. Guyton de Morveau, *Crell's Ann.*, i,
554, 1792 ; i, 75, 1799 ; i, 433, 1800 ; *Ann. Chim. Phys.*, (1), **27**. 186, 1798 ; (1), **31**. 328,
1799 ; (1), **32**. 62, 1799 ; *Nicholson's Journ.*, **3**. 353, 1800 ; *Phil. Mag.*, **5**. 353, 1800 ; *Phil.
Mag.*, **5**. 89, 1799 ; O. Evenstadt, *Praktische Abhandlung vom den Sumpf- und Morasteisen-
stein in Norwegen*, Göttingen, 1801 ; L. von Crell, *Crell's Ann.*, ii, 50, 1801 ; T. P. Smith,
Journ. Mines, **13**. 52, 1803 ; M. Rambourg, *ib.*, **13**. 194, 1803 ; **15**. 271, 380, 436, 1804 ;
H. V. Collet-Descotils, *ib.*, **13**. 421, 1803 ; M. de Rozière, *ib.*, **17**. 35, 225, 1805 ; M. Bazin,
Traité sur l'acier d'Alsace ou l'art de convertir le fer en fonte en acier, Strassburg, 1737 ; H. C. Landrin,
Traité de l'acier, Paris, 1859 ; Philadelphia, 1868 ; I. B. J. Dessoye, *Études sur les propriétés et
l'emploi de l'acier*, Paris, 1858 ; T. Webster, *The Case of J. M. Heath, Inventor of the Manufacture
of Welding Steel from British Iron*, London, 1856 ; C. F. A. Hartmann, *Praktische Handbuch der
Stahlfabrikation*, Weimar, 1861 ; J. Heaton, *The Process for the Treatment of Cast Iron and the
Manufacture of Steel*, London, 1869 ; E. Marché, *L'acier*, Paris, 1878 ; P. Barnes, *Bull. U.S. Geol.
Sur.*, 25, 1885 ; G. Bresson, *Les aciers : leurs propriétés, leur fabrication, leurs emplois*, Paris,
1886 ; E. Matheson, *Prop. Papers Corps of Roy. Eng.*, **12**. 159, 1886 ; L. Knab, *Fabrication et
emplois industriels de l'acier*, Paris, 1889 ; L. Campredon, *L'acier, historique, fabrication, emploi*,
Paris, 1890 ; H. H. Campbell, *The Manufacture and Properties of Structural Steel*, New York,
1896 ; C. Chômienne, *Fabrication de l'acier et procédés de forgeage de diverses pièces*, Paris, 1897 ;
F. W. Harbord, *The Metallurgy of Steel*, London, 1904 ; F. W. Harbord and J. W. Hall, *The
Metallurgy of Steel*, London, 1911 ; H. Noble, *Fabrication de l'acier*, Paris, 1905 ; E. F. Lake,
Composition and Heat Treatment of Steel, New York, 1911 ; P. G. Salom, *The Manufacture of Steel
Castings*, London, 1885 ; E. Garuffa, *La fonderia dell' acciaio produzione dell' acciaio senza
soffiature*, Milano, 1886 ; W. Metcalf, *Eng. Mag.*, **9**. 1072, 1895 ; *Steel : A Manual for Steel Users*,
New York, 1896 ; S. Kern, *Chem. News*, **74**. 5, 76, 1896 ; S. Johnson, *Journ. Amer. Foundrymen's
Assoc.*, **5**. 145, 1898 ; J. B. Johnston, *Amer. Manf.*, **68**. 242, 1901 ; C. Casper, *Stahl Eisen*, **19**.
277, 1899 ; D. Flather, *Proc. South Staffs Iron Steel Inst.*, **17**. 55, 1902 ; *Crucible Steel : its Manufacture and Treatment*, Brierley Hill, 1902 ; A. Stotzer, *Echo Mines*, **30**. 217, 1903 ; J. M. Gledhill,
Eng. Rev., **10**. 405, 497, 1904 ; H. G. Manning, *Eng. News*, **49**. 200, 1903 ; J. J. Mahon, *Iron Age*,
67. 12, 1903 ; G. Hofer, *ib.*, **79**. 1425, 1907 ; F. Wüst, *Stahl Eisen*, **23**. 1138, 1903 ; R. H. Probert,
Amer. Eng., **40**. 893, 1903 ; C. Otto, *Chem. Ztg.*, **29**. 139, 1905 ; W. Page, *The Victoria History
of the Counties of England (Sussex)*, London, 2. 241, 1907 ; R. F. Böhler, *School Mines Quart.*, **29**.
329, 1908 ; J. H. Hall, *Iron Trade Rev.*, **52**. 791, 849, 1913 ; F. T. Sisco, *Trans. Amer. Soc. Steel
Treating*, **7**. 640, 1925 ; W. R. Shimer, *ib.*, **1**. 423, 1921 ; J. A. Coyle, *Iron Trade Rev.*, **77**. 1457,
1592, 1925 ; **78**. 136, 261, 268, 397, 514, 636, 806, 929, 1057, 1062, 1926 ; J. F. Kayser, *Foundry
Trade Journ.*, **35**. 253, 268, 1927 ; *Iron Coal Trades Rev.*, **114**. 396, 438, 1927 ; R. M. Daelen,
Stahl Eisen, **17**. 401, 1897 ; B. Huntsman, in Anon., *The Useful Metals and their Alloys*, London,
346, 1857 ; J. Percy, *Metallurgy—Iron and Steel*, London, 828, 1864 ; H. St. C. Deville and
H. Caron, *Ann. Mines*, (6), **1**. 221, 1862 ; J. M. Heath, *Brit. Pat. No.* 8021, 1839 ; W. Reynolds,
ib., 2363, 1799 ; J. Bischoff, *Zeit. Ver. deut. Ing.*, **29**. 780, 1885 ; A. Ledebur, *Stahl Eisen*, **3**.
603, 1883 ; S. 370, 1885 ; **15**. 1, 1895 ; F. C. G. Müller, *ib.*, **5**. 180, 1885 ; **6**. 695, 1886 ; **8**. 375,
1888 ; J. Henrotte, *Rev. Univ. Mines*, (3), **3**. 190, 1888 ; *Trans. Amer. Inst. Min. Eng.*, **14**. 773,
1886 ; P. Oestberg, *ib.*, **14**. 773, 1886 ; O. Thallner, *Zeit. Ver. deut. Ing.*, **44**. 422, 1900 ; *Stahl
Eisen*, **19**. 868, 914, 1899 ; M. Boeker, *ib.*, **6**. 33, 1886 ; A. Brand, *Berg. Hütt. Ztg.*, **44**. 105,
1885 ; A. Harpf, *Oesterr. Zeit. Berg. Hütt.*, **20**. 253, 1899 ; H. Seebohm, *Journ. Iron Steel Inst.*,
24. ii, 372, 1883.

[4] R. A. F. de Réaumur, *L'art de convertir le fer forgé en acier et d'adoucir le fer fondu*, Paris,
256, 1722 ; *An Essay on the Mystery of Tempering Steel*, London, 1771 ; D. S. Price and
E. C. Nicholson, *Brit. Pat. No.* 2619, 1855 ; G. Brown, *ib.*, 205, 1856 ; C. Attwood, *ib.*, 1473,
1862 ; J. M. Heath, *ib.*, 8021, 1839 ; W. Reynolds, *ib.*, 2363, 1799 ; V. Biringuccio, *De la piro-*

technia, Venetia, 18, 1540 ; Paris, 48, 1556 ; G. Agricola, *De re metallica*, Basiliæ, 341, 1561 ;
M. Lister, *Phil. Trans.*, 17. 865, 1693 ; P. G. F. le Play, *Ann. Mines*, (4), 3. 638, 1848 ; H. St. C.
Deville and H. Caron, *ib.*, (6), 1. 221, 1862 ; J. Percy, *Metallurgy—Iron and Steel*, London, 828,
1864 ; B. Huntsman, in Anon., *The Useful Metals and their Alloys*, London, 346, 1857 ;
T. Webster, *The Case of Josiah Marshall Heath the Inventor and Introducer of the Manufacture of
Welding Cast Steel from British Iron*, London, 1856 ; J. Henrotte, *Rev. Univ. Mines*, (3), 3. 190,
1888 ; *Trans. Amer. Inst. Min. Eng.*, 14. 773, 1886 ; P. Oestberg, *ib.*, 14. 773, 1886 ; J. Bischoff,
Zeit. Ver. deut. Ing., 29. 780, 1885 ; O. Thallner, *ib.*, 44. 422, 1900 ; *Stahl Eisen*, 19. 868, 914,
1899 ; F. C. G. Müller, *ib.*, 5. 180, 1885 ; 6. 695, 1886 ; 8. 375, 1888 ; A. Ledebur, *ib.*, 3. 603,
1883 ; 5. 370, 1885 ; 15. 1, 1895 ; M. Boeker, *ib.*, 6. 33, 1886 ; A. Brand, *Berg. Hütt. Ztg.*, 44.
105, 1885 ; A. Harpf, *Oesterr. Zeit. Berg. Hütt.*, 20. 253, 1899 ; H. Seebohm, *Journ. Iron Steel Inst.*,
24. ii, 372, 1883 ; R. A. Hadfield, *Industries Iron*, 27. 191, 1899.

    [5] P. R. von Tunner, *Das Stabeisen und Stahlbereitung in Frischherden*, Freiberg, 2. 250, 1858 ;
Jahrb. Bergakad., 2. 180, 1852 ; 3. 281, 1853 ; C. J. B. Karsten, *Handbuch der Eisenhüttenkunde*,
Berlin, 4. 446, 1841 ; J. Percy, *Metallurgy—Iron and Steel*, London, 779, 1864 ; J. R. Bréant,
Ann. Mines, (1), 9. 327, 1824 ; C. Lan, *ib.*, (5), 15. 104, 1859 ; L. E. Gruner, *ib.*, (5), 15. 296, 1859 ;
(6), 16. 199, 1869 ; A. Delvaux de Fenffe, *Rev. Univ. Mines*, (1), 1. 59, 1857 ; M. de Rostaing, *ib.*,
(1), 6. 343, 1862 ; E. Riepe, *Brit. Pat. No.* 12950, 1850 ; W. W. Collins, *ib.*, 14033, 1852 ; C. Schafhäutl, *ib.*, 6837, 1835 ; F. Uchatius, *ib.*, 2189, 1855 ; J. Wood, *ib.*, 759, 1761 ; J. and C. Wood, *ib.*,
794, 1763 ; J. Heaton, *ib.*, 798, 1866 ; 1295, 1867 ; *Eng.*, 28. 321, 337, 341, 348, 1869 ; *Engg.*, 7. 95,
110, 1869 ; *Process for the Treatment of Cast Iron and the Manufacture of Steel*, London, 1869 ; B. Kerl,
Grundriss der Eisenhüttenkunde, Leipzig, 1. 875, 1861 ; W. Brauns, *Wagner's Jahresb.*, 75, 1861 ;
D. Mushet, *Papers on Iron and Steel*, London, 12, 1840 ; G. Parry, *Proc. South Wales Inst. Eng.*,
3. 75, 1863 ; W. Fairbairn, *Iron : Its History, Properties, and Manufacture*, Edinburgh, 1861 ;
W. H. Miller, *Chem. News*, 19. 85, 1869 ; R. Mallet, *ib.*, 19. 86, 1869 ; D. Kirkaldy, *ib.*, 19, 86, 1869 ;
W. M. Williams, *ib.*, 19. 95, 1869 ; B. H. Paul, *Journ. Chem. Soc.*, 22. 81, 1869 ; J. Paulis, *Brit.
Pat. No.* 2178, 1861 ; *Berg. Hütt. Ztg.*, 21. 344, 1862 ; R. Mushet, in W. Fairbairn, *Iron, its
History, Properties and Progresses of Manufacture*, Edinburgh, 181, 1861 ; J. E. Sherman, *Brit.
Pat. No.* 3323, 1873 ; J. Henderson, *ib.*, 554, 2318, 1873 ; V. Gallet, *ib.*, 1187, 2963, 1868 ;
W. Spence, *ib.*, 1048, 1859 ; W. Spielfield, *ib.*, 777, 1861 ; M. Lane, *U.S. Pat. No.* 33949, 1861 ;
C. Peters, *ib.*, 96479, 1869 ; *Scient. Amer.*, (2), 21. 334, 1869 ; D. Tschernoff, *Journ. Iron Steel
Inst.*, 55. i, 191, 1899 ; J. N. Boucher, *William Kelly : A True History of the so-called Bessemer
Process*, Greensburg, Pa., 1924 ; A. Galy-Cazalat, *French Pat. No.* 21099, 21594, 1858 ; J. Cour-
not, *Rev. Mét.*, 20. 695, 1923.

    J. G. Martin, *Brit. Pat. No.* 2082, 1855 ; W. Reynolds, *ib.*, 2363, 1799 ; R. F. Mushet, *The
Bessemer-Mushet Process, or the Manufacture of Cheap Steel*, Cheltenham, 1883 ; *Brit. Pat. No.*
2219, 1856 ; H. Bessemer, *ib.*, 2321, 2768, 1855 ; 356, 630, 1856 ; 275, 1861 ; *B.A. Rep.*, 162,
1856 ; 165, 1865 ; *Proc. Inst. Civil Eng.*, 18. 525, 548, 1859 ; *Iron and Steel Mag.*, 10. 481, 1905 ;
Journ. Iron Steel Inst., 30. ii, 638, 1886 ; *Stahl Eisen*, 6. 789, 1888 ; 16. 341, 1896 ; *Industries
Iron*, 20. 184, 372, 1896 ; *Eng.*, 81. 299, 1896 ; *Engg.*, 61. 367, 1896 ; *Iron Coal Trades Rev.*,
52. 417, 1896 ; *Iron Steel Trades Journ.*, 58. 373, 1896 ; *Iron Steel Trades Mech. Eng.*, 18. 455,
1897 ; *Autobiography*, London, 1905 ; E. Clibborn, *Proc. Roy. Irish Acad.*, 8. 164, 1864 ;
J. A. Mandelslo, *Travels into the Indies*, London, 160, 1669 ; W. Kelly, *U.S. Pat. No.* 17628,
18910, 1857 ; *Trans. Amer. Soc. Steel Treating*, 3. 162, 1922 ; H. M. Howe, *Eng. Min. Journ.*,
61. 227, 1896 ; 68. 276, 1899 ; *Journ. Iron Steel Inst.*, 37. ii, 95, 1890 ; *Mineral Ind.*, 365,
1894 ; Anon., *Eng.*, 81. 538, 545, 1896 ; *Engg.*, 61. 413, 1896 ; *Iron Coal Trades Rev.*, 52. 425,
1896 ; *Industries Iron*, 20. 191, 1896 ; *Iron Steel Trades Rev.*, 57. 368, 1896 ; *Stahl Eisen*, 16.
341, 1896 ; *Glückauf*, 32. 293, 1896 ; J. D. Weeks, *Eng. Min. Journ.*, 61. 180, 1896 ; *Trans.
Amer. Inst. Min. Eng.*, 25. 948, 1896 ; R. W. Hunt, *ib.*, 5. 201, 1875 ; *Journ. Franklin Inst.*,
127. 357, 1889 ; *Cassier's Mag.*, 21. 1, 1902 ; *Eng. Rec.*, 66. 655, 1912 ; C. Malz, *Stahl Eisen*, 17.
392, 1897 ; F. W. Lürmann, *ib.*, 23. 336, 1903 ; R. A. Hadfield, *Proc. Inst. Civil Eng.*, 138. 442,
1899 ; J. N. Boucher, *William Kelly : A True History of the so-called Bessemer Process*,
Greensburg, Pa., 1924 ; A. Ledebur, *Handbuch der Eisenhüttenkunde*, Leipzig, 3. 332, 1908 ;
Stahl Eisen, 14. 810, 1894 ; R. Finkener, *Mitt. Versuchsanst Berlin*, 31, 1883 ; R. Akerman,
Proc. Inst. Civil Eng., 43. 409, 1876 ; *Jernkontorets Ann.*, (2), 30. 85, 1875 ; *Allgem. deut. polyt.
Ztg.*, 6. 87, 1878 ; *Trans. Amer. Inst. Min. Eng.*, 22. 265, 1893 ; *Stahl Eisen*, 13. 920, 1893 ; *Journ.
Iron Steel Inst.*, 5. ii, 110, 1872 ; G. J. Snelus, *ib.*, 3. ii, 247, 1871 ; 15. i, 135, 1879 ; 45. i, 26, 1894 ;
Chem. News, 24. 159, 1871 ; *Rev. Univ. Mines*, (1), 30. 330, 1891 ; A. Pourcel and F. Valton, *ib.*,
(3), 13. 146, 1891 ; J. Smeysters, *ib.*, (3), 45. 36, 1899 ; *Ann. Mines Belg.*, 1. 97, 1896 ; S. Jordan,
Mem. Soc. Ing. Civils, 237, 1869 ; *Van Nostrand's Mag.*, 1. 1000, 1869 ; *Compt. Rend.*, 69. 539,
1869 ; *Engg.*, 2. 200, 1870 ; *Journ. Iron Steel Inst.*, 48. ii, 126, 1895 ; *Notes sur la fabrication de
l'acier Bessemer*, Paris, 1873 ; F. Kessler, *Oesterr. Zeit. Berg. Hütt.*, 19. 75, 1871 ; J. Brunner,
ib., 16. 227, 1868 ; P. Kupelwieser, *ib.*, 16. 59, 227, 1868 ; *Dingler's Journ.*, 185. 30, 1867 ;
191. 38, 1869 ; *Jahrb. österr. Bergakad.*, 21. 232, 1871 ; *Journ. Iron Steel Inst.*, 20. ii, 337, 1881 ;
F. J. R. Carulla, *ib.*, 65. i, 291, 1904 ; L. E. Boman, *Das Bessemern in Schweden in seiner jetzigen
Praxis*, Leipzig, 1864 ; F. Munichsdorfer and E. A. Frey, *Zwei Berichte über die Erzeugung und
Verarbeitung von Bessemerstahl*, Wien, 1865 ; O. von Hingenau, *Das Bessemern in Oesterreich*,
Wien, 1865 ; P. Barthel, *Deut. Ind. Ztg.*, 11. 315, 1872 ; J. Deby, *Journ. Iron Steel Inst.*, 8. 194,
1875 ; E. Priwoznik, *Oesterr. Zeit. Berg. Hütt.*, 62. 311, 1914 ; F. Toldt, *ib.*, 41. 198, 1893 ;
J. Cournot, *Rev. Mét.*, 20. 695, 1923 ; J. Wagner, *ib.*, 26. 287, 1929 ; P. N. Mathur, *Journ. Indian*

Chem. Soc., **6.** 353, 1929 ; L. Hacha, *Rev. Univ. Mines*, (8), **2.** 161, 1929 ; F. Hilton, *Iron Coal Trades Rev.*, **54.** 172, 262, 295, 473, 1897 ; T. W. Robinson, *Iron Age*, **44.** 674, 1889 ; F. E. Thomson, *ib.*, **56.** 1260, 1318, 1895 ; A. de Riva-Berni, *Portefeuille Écon. Machines*, **47.** 122, 1902 ; R. H. Thurston, *Cassier's Mag.*, **10.** 323, 435, 1896 ; W. H. Jacques, *Proc. U.S. Naval Inst.*, **15.** 4, 1890 ; F. Laur, *Echo des Mines*, **21.** 737, 1895 ; W. Stöckl, *Stahl Eisen*, **10.** 21, 1890 ; H. Schonwälder, *ib.*, **11.** 386, 1891 ; H. Reuss, *ib.*, **11.** 643, 1891 ; G. Hilgenstock, *ib.*, **3.** 498, 1883 ; **13.** 451, 1893 ; **29.** 1478, 1909 ; W. Borchers, *ib.*, **15.** 404, 1895 ; J. Thieme, *ib.*, **18.** 718, 766, 802, 1898 ; M. von Tittler, *ib.*, **21.** 519, 1901 ; E. Holz, *ib.*, **22.** 1, 50, 1902 ; O. Thiel, *ib.*, **21.** 1305, 1901 ; E. Langheinrich, *ib.*, **21.** 1101, 1901 ; J. Lagerwall, *Jernkontorets Ann.*, **49.** 281, 292, 1895 ; R. von Seth, *Iron Age*, **114.** 637, 1924 ; *Jernkontorets Ann.*, **79.** 1, 1924 ; E. G. Odelstjerna, *ib.*, **50.** 169, 1896 ; A. Johansson, *ib.*, **53.** 208, 1899 ; *Bihang Jernkontorets Ann.*, **3.** 197, 1902 ; **58.** 494, 1904 ; **115.** 239, 1931 ; G. Bergström, *ib.*, **49.** 373, 1895 ; J. B. Nau, *Iron Age*, **46.** 365, 1890 ; C. D. Wright, *ib.*, **46.** 179, 1890 ; G. Butz, *ib.*, **95.** 618, 1915 ; C. A. Casperson, *ib.*, **18.** ii, 599, 1880 ; **23.** i, 480, 1883 ; *Stahl Eisen*, **3.** 71, 1883 ; W. Stahl, *Berg. Hütt. Ztg.*, **49.** 439, 1890 ; E. Demenge, *Génie Civil*, **19.** 42, 1891 ; *Proc. Inst. Civil Eng.*, **106.** 402, 1891 ; H. J. van Royden, *Brit. Pat. No.* 282365, 282366, 1927 ; 295315, 1928 ; F. Tordeur, *Rev. Univ. Mines*, **20.** 1, 1893 ; O. Vogel, *Zeit. Ver. deut. Ing.*, **36.** 406, 1892 ; *Stahl Eisen*, **18.** 183, 1898 ; *Oesterr. Zeit. Berg. Hütt.*, **51.** 44, 57, 1893 ; F. Fischer, *ib.*, **50.** 433, 1902 ; J. Hartshorne, *Trans. Amer. Inst. Min. Eng.*, **21.** 743, 1892 ; H. L. Hollis, *ib.*, **26.** 134, 1896 ; E. Schrödter, *Stahl Eisen*, **14.** 1097, 1894 ; A. Knaff, *ib.*, **16.** 100, 1896 ; F. Grassmann, *ib.*, **16.** 57, 1896 ; A. Brovot, *ib.*, **16.** 50, 1896 ; R. M. Daelen, *ib.*, **8.** 433, 1888 ; **13.** 830, 1893 ; **16.** 704, 1896 ; **19.** 1173, 1899 ; F. G. Bremme, *ib.*, **16.** 762, 1896 ; K. Leo, *Zeit. Oberschles. Berg. Hütt. Ver.*, 323, 1902 ; E. Tschernoff, *Proc. Inst. Civil Eng.*, **55.** 418, 1879 ; *Amer. Met. Review*, 457, 1878 ; *Rev. Univ. Mines*, (2), **1.** 420, 1877 ; (2), **4.** 56, 1878 ; A. Tamm, *Iron*, **13.** 674, 707, 739, 771, 803, 1879 ; **14.** 2, 67, 98, 131, 1879 ; **16.** 23, 46, 310, 400, 418, 1880 ; **17.** 22, 58, 1881 ; *Jernkontorets Ann.*, **25.** 267, 1875 ; **30.** 257, 1880 ; *Berg. Hütt. Ztg.*, **34.** 437, 1875 ; F. C. G. Müller, *Zeit. Ver. deut. Ing.*, **22.** 386, 453, 1878 ; *Génie Civil*, **1.** 25, 1880 ; *Stahl Eisen*, **10.** 115, 1890 ; *Berg. Hütt. Ztg.*, **37.** 145, 1878 ; A. Bender, *ib.*, **31.** 261, 1872 ; A. von Kerpely, *ib.*, **30.** 438, 1871 ; H. Schuphaus, *Ueber die Herstellung und Bewertung von Thomasroheisen, sowie die Weiterderarbeitung des hergestellten Roheisens über Flusstahl zur Schiene*, Kattowitz, 1906 ; H. E. Roscoe, *Phil. Mag.*, (4), **34.** 487, 1867 ; *Proc. Manchester Lit. Phil. Soc.*, **3.** 57, 1862 ; *Chem. News*, **23.** 174, 182, 1871 ; *Journ. Iron Steel Inst.*, **3.** ii, 38, 1871 ; A. W. Richards, *ib.*, **73.** i, 104, 1907 ; W. J. Clapp and J. Griffiths, *Brit. Pat. No.* 1372, 1881 ; *L'age de l'acier*, Paris, 1883 ; *Stahl Eisen*, **6.** 172, 1886 ; E. Riley, *Iron Coal Trades Rev.*, **54.** 475, 1898 ; I. Powell and A. Tropénas, *Journ. Amer. Foundrymen's Assoc.*, **5.** 118, 1898 ; A. Tropenas, *The Tropenas Steel Process*, Detroit, 1898 ; *Engg.*, **65.** 43, 1898 ; S. R. Robinson, *Blast Furnace Steel Plant*, **10.** 282, 1922 ; C. Pixis, *Eng. Min. Journ.*, **63.** 425, 1897 ; G. Bresson, *Mémoire sur la fabrication et les emplois actuels de l'acier déphosphoré*, Liége, 1888 ; A. Wasum, *Verh. Ver. Beförd. Gewerbfleisses*, **63.** 104, 1884 ; H. Wedding, *ib.*, **84.** 259, 1905 ; *Basic Bessemer Process*, New York, 1884 ; *Die Darstellung des schmiedbaren Eisens*, Braunschweig, 1875 ; *Zeit. Berg. Hütt. Sal.*, **27.** 117, 1869 ; *Stahl Eisen*, **15.** 570, 574, 1895 ; A. Lielegg, *Dingler's Journ.*, **187.** 390, 1868 ; *Sitzber. Akad. Wien*, **55.** 153, 1867 ; **56.** 24, 1867 ; *Oesterr. Zeit. Berg. Hütt.*, **15.** 93, 381, 1867 ; *Phil. Mag.*, (4), **34.** 302, 1867 ; M. Watts, *ib.*, (4), **34.** 437, 1867 ; T. Rowan, *ib.*, (4), **41.** 1, 1871 ; *Proc. Glasgow Phil. Soc.*, **7.** 41, 1871 ; *Chem. News*, **19.** 170, 1868 ; J. S. Parker, *ib.*, **23.** 25, 1871 ; P. R. von Tunner, *Dingler's Journ.*, **178.** 465, 1865 ; A. von Lichtenfeld, *ib.*, **191.** 213, 1869 ; *Oesterr. Zeit. Berg. Hütt.*, **17.** 9, 1869 ; J. M. Silliman, *Proc. Amer. Assoc.*, **19.** 119, 1870 ; *Amer. Journ. Science*, (2), **50.** 297, 1870 ; *Phil. Mag.*, (4), **41.** 1, 1871 ; A. Greiner, *Rev. Univ. Mines*, (1), **35.** 623, 1874 ; *Dingler's Journ.*, **227.** 33, 1875 ; R. Simmler, *Zeit. anal. Chem.*, **1.** 353, 1862 ; *Pogg. Ann.*, **115.** 242, 425, 1862 ; C. E. Dutton, *Engg.*, **10.** 200, 1870 ; *Chem. News*, **23.** 51, 1871 ; *Amer. Chemist*, **1.** 131, 171, 1871 ; *Amer. Journ. Science*, (2), **50.** 432, 1870 ; S. G. Thomas, *Journ. Iron Steel Inst.*, **13.** i, 40, 1878 ; S. G. Thomas and P. C. Gilchrist, *ib.*, **20.** ii, 407, 1881 ; W. N. Hartley, *Proc. Roy. Soc.*, **56.** 192, 1894 ; *Phil. Trans.*, **185.** A, 199, 1894 ; *The Thermochemistry of the Bessemer Process*, London, 1898 ; *Journ. Iron Steel Inst.*, **48.** ii, 95, 1895 ; W. N. Hartley and H. Ramage, *ib.*, **60.** ii, 197, 1901 ; H. Ponthière, *Zeit. Ver. deut. Ing.*, **46.** 1006, 1902 ; *Journ. Iron Steel Inst.*, **52.** ii, 96, 1897 ; J. Hardisty, *ib.*, **30.** ii, 651, 1886 ; J. G. Wiborgh, *ib.*, **55.** i, 197, 1899 ; **56.** ii, 3, 1899 ; J. M. While, *ib.*, **59.** i, 299, 1901 ; H. Schulz and J. Schönava, *Stahl Eisen*, **25.** 396, 1905 ; H. van Gendt, *ib.*, **25.** 1446, 1905 ; **26.** 104, 1906 ; F. Kintzle, *ib.*, **17.** 381, 1897 ; *Zeit. Ver. deut. Ing.*, **34.** 713, 1890 ; H. Bansen, *Stahl Eisen*, **46.** 1277, 1926 ; **50.** 668, 1930 ; O. von Keil, *ib.*, **41.** 605, 1921 ; L. Unckenbolt, *ib.*, **23.** 988, 1227, 1903 ; **8.** 433, 1888 ; **13.** 830, 1893 ; **16.** 704, 1896 ; K. Sorge, *ib.*, **7.** 316, 1887 ; C. Wabrand, *ib.*, **7.** 390, 1887 ; B. Versen, *ib.*, **12.** 1089, 1893 ; **13.** 919, 1893 ; A. von Ihering, *ib.*, **14.** 250, 1894 ; M. Stammschulte, *ib.*, **20.** 357, 442, 1900 ; J. Massenez, *ib.*, **29.** 1465, 1909 ; A. Spannagel, *ib.*, **29.** 1483, 1909 ; W. Stercken, *Zeit. Ver. deut. Ing.*, **31.** 489, 1887 ; C. Rott, *Stahl Eisen*, **21.** 999, 1901 ; **23.** 1403, 1903 ; *Zeit. Ver. deut. Ing.*, **44.** 144, 1900 ; C. W. Ljunggren, *Jernkontorets Ann.*, **50.** 1, 1895 ; *Oesterr. Zeit. Berg. Hütt.*, **43.** 453, 1895 ; J. von Ehrenwerth, *ib.*, **27.** 599, 619, 629, 1879 ; **28.** 149, 163, 176, 191, 201, 217, 230, 243, 253, 268, 279, 533, 545, 559, 572, 583, 593, 615, 1880 ; **29.** 61, 81, 91, 102, 119, 134, 147, 159, 1881 ; *Abhandlungen über den Thomas-Gilchristprozess*, Leoben, 1879 ; *Studien über den Thomas-Gilchristprozess*, Wien, 1881 ; E. Heyrowsky, *Jahrb. Bergakad.*, **22.** 436, 1872 ; C. Scheibler, *Ber.*, **11.** 1883, 1886 ; E. Steinweg, *Die Konstitution des vierbasischer Kalkphosphates und seine Reduzierbarkeit durch*

Kohlenstoffhaltiges und reines Eisen, Halle a. S., 1911; F. W. Harbord and J. W. Hall, *The Metallurgy of Steel*, London, **1**. 231, 1918; A. P. Head, *Proc. South Staffs Inst. Iron Steel Works Managers*, **13**. 101, 1898; S. Peters, *Proc. Eng. Soc. West Pennsylvania*, **15**. 222, 1899; V. Firket, *Ann. Mines Belg.*, **7**. 279, 1902; L. Delacuvellerie, *ib.*, **9**. 560, 1904; C. E. Heurteau, *Ann. Mines*, (10), **6**. 111, 1904; C. Canaris, *Stahl Eisen*, **25**. 1125, 1905; F. Schröder, *ib.*, **28**. 1641, 1908; B. Osann, *ib.*, **39**. 677, 1919; L. C. Glaser, *ib.*, **40**. 73, 111, 188, 1930; E. Herzog, *ib.*, **41**. 781, 1921; J. Parry, *Iron Coal Trades Rev.*, **71**. 671, 1905; A. Simonson, *ib.*, **78**. 149, 1909; J. W. Richards, *Electrochem. Met. Ind.*, **4**. 446, 486, 1906; **5**. 11, 1907; H. Crowe, *Proc. Cleveland Inst. Eng.*, 234, 1906; M. Belmann, *Rev. Mét.*, **4**. 745, 1907; L. Lewis, *Eng. Min. Journ.*, **83**. 234, 1907; J. Flohr, *Engg.*, 65, 1908; *Rev. Univ. Mines*, **22**. 162, 1908; W. M. Carr, *Iron Trade Rev.*, **41**. 792, 951, 1908; H. Hermann, *ib.*, **73**. 1487, 1923; W. E. Koch, *El Paso Min. Journ.*, **1**. 8, 1908; J. R. Miller, *Blast Furnace Steel Plant*, **18**. 1602, 1930; J. W. Haulman, *ib.*, **9**. 658, 1921; G. K. Burgess, *Trans. Amer. Inst. Min. Eng.*, **56**. 432, 1917; W. J. Campbell, *Eng.*, **132**. 137, 1921; H. H. Campbell, *Iron Age*, **98**. 302, 1916; G. B. Waterhouse, *ib.*, **122**. 8, 1928; J. Sullivan, *Assoc. Iron Steel Elect. Eng.*, **3**. 85, 1921; F. T. Sisco, *Trans. Amer. Soc. Steel Treating*, **7**. 363, 1925; C. Gonner, *Rev. Tech. Luxembourgeoise*, **19**. 28, 1927; J. Seigle, *ib.*, **19**. 83, 1927; E. Faust, *Arch. Eisenhüttenwesen*, **1**. 119, 1927; H. Schenck, *ib.*, **1**. 483, 1927; *Stahl Eisen*, **48**. 199, 1928; R. Frerich, *ib.*, **48**. 1233, 1928; *Die Abhängigkeit des Frischvorganges in der Thomasbirne vom Temperaturverlauf*, Düsseldorf, 1928; V. Harbord, *Journ. Iron Steel Inst.*, **123**. i, 183, 1931; *Engg.*, **131**. 683, 1931; K. Thomas, *Stahl Eisen*, **50**. 1665, 1708, 1930; R. S. McCaffery, *Yearbook Amer. Iron Steel Inst.*, 351, 1931; *Blast Furnace Steel Plant*, **7**. 140, 1919; A. Galy-Cazalat, *French Pat. No.* 21099, 21594, 1858; J. Cournot, *Rev. Mét.*, **20**. 695, 1923; R. Addie, *Engg.*, **52**. 103, 1891; C. Longenecker, *Trans. Amer. Soc. Steel Treating*, **14**. 526, 1926; F. M. Feldhaus, *Tech. Ind.*, **2**. 93, 1915; E. Mathesius, *Verh. Gewerbefl.*, **91**. 35, 1912; A. Herberholz, *Arch. Eisenhüttenwesen*, **3**. 173, 1929; *Stahl Eisen*, **49**. 1579, 1929; A. Cornu-Thénard, *Compt. Rend.*, **157**. 319, 1913; F. E. Bash, *Trans. Amer. Inst. Min. Eng.*, **69**. 706, 1923.

⁷ P. Acker, *Congrès Internat. Liége*, **1**. 83, 1905; *Stahl Eisen*, **25**. 1091, 1905; R. Addie, *Engg.*, **52**. 103, 1891; R. Akerman, *Journ. Iron Steel Inst.*, **36**. i, 24, 1890; W. Alberts, *Stahl Eisen*, **49**. 977, 1929; **51**. 117, 1931; H. Allen, *Metallurgical Manual of Iron and Steel*, London, 1911; T. N. Armstrong, *Iron Age*, **127**. 864, 1931; C. Attwood, *Brit. Pat. No.* 1473, 1862; R. Back, *Stahl Eisen*, **51**. 317, 351, 1931; C. H. F. Bagley, *Journ. Iron Steel Inst.*, **98**. ii, 289, 1918; **99**. i, 143, 1919; L. J. Ball and A. Wingham, *ib.*, **42**. ii, 257, 1892; H. Bansen, *Iron Coal Trades Rev.*, **111**. 351, 774, 1925; *Arch. Eisenhüttenwesen*, **1**. 245, 1927; *Stahl Eisen*, **43**. 1031, 1923; **45**. 489, 702, 748, 789, 1925; **46**. 1277, 1926; **50**. 668, 1930; W. P. Barba and H. M. Howe, *Min. Met.*, **32**. 1922; A. Barberot, *Rev. Met.*, **20**. 1, 1923; *Fabrication de l'acier au four Martin*, Paris, 1923; W. J. Beck, *Yearbook Amer. Iron Steel Inst.*, 30, 1921; *Met. Chem. Engg.*, **24**. 968, 1921; R. Becker, *Stahl Eisen*, **33**. 465, 1913; M. Berek, *Zeit. Kryst.*, **77**. 1, 1931; A. Berglöf, *Jernkontorets Ann.*, **54**. 116, 1899; F. Bernhardt, *Stahl Eisen*, **46**. 1, 39, 73, 137, 1926; *Rev. Univ. Mines*, (7), **11**. 195, 1926; E. Bertrand, *Journ. Iron Steel Inst.*, **51**. i, 122, 1897; I. A. Billiar, *Iron Trade Rev.*, **70**. 1407, 1922; F. Blau, *Giesserei Ztg.*, **19**. 585, 1922; C. Bohlin, *Bihang Jernkontorets Ann.*, **3**. 1, 1902; A. Bosser, *Rev. Univ. Mines*, (6), **13**. 1, 1906; G. R. Boyd, *Iron Age*, **56**. 1166, 1895; H. M. Boyston, *Fuels Furnaces*, **4**. 289, 1926; H. Braune, *Jernkontorets Ann.*, **49**. 369, 1895; J. A. Brinell, *Tek. Tids.*, **34**. 250, 1904; C. Brisker, *Stahl Eisen*, **29**. 1139, 1909; W. D. Brown, *Journ. Iron Steel Inst.*, **13**. 236, 1925; G. B. Bruno, *Aciers Spéciaux*, **5**. 99, 1930; G. B. Bruno and G. Delbart, *Bull. Assoc. Tech. Fonderie*, **4**. 45, 1930; G. K. Burgess, *Trans. Amer. Inst. Min. Eng.*, **56**. 432, 1917; W. G. Burman, *Iron Coal Trades Rev.*, **66**. 94, 1903; R. W. Burnie, *Memoirs of Sidney Gilchrist Thomas, Inventor*, London, 1891; A. Byström, *Bihang Jernkontorets Ann.*, **7**. 118, 1906; *Stahl Eisen*, **23**. 1217, 1903; J. W. Cabot, *Iron Age*, **68**. 15, 1901; H. H. Campbell, *Trans. Amer. Inst. Min. Eng.*, **19**. 128, 1890; **20**. 229, 1891; **22**. 345, 440, 1893; *The Manufacture and Properties of Iron and Steel*, New York, 1907; *Min. Ind.*, **2**. 377, 1894; *Iron Age*, **98**. 448, 1916; C. Canaris, *Stahl Eisen*, **25**. 1125, 1905; R. B. Carnahan, *U.S. Pat. No.* 940784, 940785, 1909; 986359, 987549, 987857, 1911; 1035947, 1035948, 1912; W. M. Carr, *Open Hearth Steel Castings*, Cleveland, Ohio, 1907; *Iron Trade Rev.*, **40**. 376, 1907; *Trans. Amer. Foundrymen's Assoc.*, **28**. 217, 1909; C. A. Casperson, *Jernkontorets Ann.*, **51**. 319, 1897; S. Casson, *The Earl of Dudley's Round Oak Iron and Steel Works, with special reference to the Overhead Regenerative Furnace*, Brierley Hill, 1891; W. P. Chandler, *Fuels Furnaces*, **8**. 1069, 1105, 1930; *Proc. Eng. Soc. West. Pennsylvania*, **46**. 241, 1930; J. Christie, *Iron Age*, **67**. 21, 1902; H. O. Chute, *Iron Trade Rev.*, **42**. 221, 1907; D. Clark, *Iron Age. Foundrymen's Assoc.*, **1**. 22, 26, 1930; F. Clements, *Journ. Iron Steel Inst.*, **105**. i, 429, 192⁰; T. P. Colclough, *Trans. Faraday Soc.*, **21**. 202, 1925; M. J. Conway, *Fuel Economist*, **5**. 43, .05, 155, 193, 259, 1929; *Iron Steel Ind.*, **7**. 148, 1930; S. Cornell, *Met. Chem. Engg.*, **11**. 257, 1913; S. J. Cort, *Yearbook Amer. Iron Steel Inst.*, 149, 1926; E. Cotel, *Der Siemens-Martin Ofen*, Leipzig, 1927; C. C. de Coussergues, *Rev. Mét.*, **19**. 639, 1922; *Mém. Soc. Ing. Civils*, **54**. 116, 1899; F. J. Crolius, *Blast Furnace Steel Plant*, **13**. 42, 190, 1924; H. Crowe, *Proc. Cleveland Inst. Eng.*, 235, 1906; L. Cubillo, *Journ. Iron Steel Inst.*, **63**. i, 276, 1903; A. S. Cushman, *Trans. Amer. Soc. Testing Materials*, **11**. 100, 1911; *Iron Age*, **88**. 94, 1911; R. M. Daelen, *Iron Coal Trades Rev.*, **68**. 2030, 1904; *Zeit. Ver. deut. Ing.*, **35**. 122, 1891; *Stahl Eisen*, **11**. 93, 1891; **12**. 11, 1892; **18**. 89, 1898; **24**. 301, 507, 1904; R. M. Daelen and L. Pozczolka, *ib.*, **21**. 50, 1901; *Iron Coal Trades Rev.*, **62**. 68, 1901; A. C. Dalton, *Foundry Trade Journ.*, **28**. 271, 1923; E. Damour,

Chaleur Ind., **8.** 71, 1927 ; J. H. Darby and G. Hatton, *Journ. Iron Steel Inst.*, **67.** i, 122, 1905 ;
A. E. Davies, *Iron Coal Trades Rev.*, **96.** 612, 1918 ; *Foundry Trade Journ.*, **20.** 541, 1918 ;
J. Davis, *Colliery Guardian*, **61.** 103, 1891 ; *Proc. Cleveland Inst. Eng.*, 87, 1901 ; B. Dawson,
Iron Coal Trades Rev., **52.** 158, 1896 ; **54.** 166, 1897 ; *Proc. Cleveland Inst. Eng.*, 10, 1895 ;
M. Deslandes, *Rev. Mét.*, **3.** 321, 1906 ; G. Desprit, *Rev. Univ. Mines*, **11.** 246, 1891 ;
C. Dichmann, *Der basische Herdofenprozess—Eine Studie*, Berlin, 1910 ; *The Basic Open-hearth
Steel Process*, London, 1911 ; *Stahl Eisen*, **25.** 1337, 1429, 1905 ; **33.** 860, 939, 1913 ; A. M. Dick
and C. S. Padley, *Colliery Guardian*, **71.** 320, 1896 ; *Journ. West Scotland Iron Steel Inst.*, **3.**
172, 1896 ; A. N. Diehl, *Engg.*, **172.** 13, 1926 ; *Yearbook Amer. Iron Steel Inst.*, 54, 1926 ;
E. Diepschlag, *Zeit. Ver. deut. Ing.*, **68.** 1233, 1924 ; **75.** 1005, 1931 ; G. A. Dornin, *Trans.
Amer. Soc. Steel Treating*, **17.** 59, 1930 ; J. von Ehrenwerth, *Studien über den Thomas-
Gilchrist Process*, Wien, 1881 ; *Stahl Eisen*, **21.** 51, 1901 ; *Oesterr. Zeit. Berg. Hütt.*, **34.** 622,
1886 ; H. de Estève, *Revista Min.*, **59.** 58, 1908 ; P. Eyermann, *Journ. Iron Steel Inst.*, **61.** 1,
259, 1902 ; *Stahl Eisen*, **20.** 310, 1900 ; F. M. Feldhaus, *Tech. Ind.*, **2.** 93, 1915 ; J. B. Ferguson,
Trans. Faraday Soc., **21.** 240, 1925 ; A. L. Field, *ib.*, **21.** 255, 1925 ; *Tech. Publ. Amer. Inst.
Min. Eng.*, 111, 1928 ; 280, 1929 ; F. Fiorelli, *Met. Ital.*, **23.** 955, 1931 ; G. Fisk, *Iron Age*,
93. 732, 1914 ; A. Foniakoff, *Rev. Univ. Mines*, **31.** 40, 1895 ; R. Fornander, *Jernkontorets
Ann.*, **70.** 51, 1915 ; *Stahl Eisen*, **35.** 1255, 1915 ; R. Frerich, *Stahl Eisen*, **48.** 1233, 1928 ;
H. Frey, *Stahl Eisen*, **50.** 223, 1930 ; R. Furness, *Trans. Amer. Soc. Steel Treating*, **8.** 728,
1925 ; J. M. Gaines, *Blast Furnace Steel Plant*, **16.** 479, 1928 ; **18.** 102, 1930 ; L. Gautier,
Portefeuille Économique Machines, **47.** 36, 1902 ; H. L. Geiger, *Blast Furnace Steel Plant*, **19.**
412, 1931 ; R. Genzer, *Stahl Eisen*, **24.** 1418, 1904 ; M. L. Gerard, *Rev. Univ. Mines*, (4), **1.** 262,
1903 ; K. Gierdziejewsky, *Foundry Trade Journ.*, **40.** 465, 1929 ; P. C. Gilchrist, *Proc. Cleveland
Inst. Eng.*, 135, 143, 1896 ; H. Gille, *Giesserei Ztg.*, **4.** 452, 489, 1907 ; G. W. Goetz, *Trans. Amer.
Inst. Min. Eng.*, **19.** 59, 1891 ; L. Goldmerstein, *Iron Trade Rev.*, **55.** 167, 182, 1914 ;
H. Goldschmidt, *Electrochem. Met. Ind.*, **6.** 244, 1908 ; A. Gouvy, *Bull. Soc. Ind. Min.*, **8.** 333,
1895 ; F. Grassmann, *Stahl Eisen*, **21.** 1021, 1901 ; H. G. Graves, *Mineral Ind.*, **5.** 277, 1897 ;
J. A. de Grey, *Chim. Ind.*, **11.** 297, 1924 ; *Rev. Met.*, **21.** 338, 1924 ; *Chaleur Ind.*, **7.** 102, 1926 ;
W. E. Griffiths and C. E. Meissner, *Trans. Amer. Soc. Steel Treating*, **16.** 257, 1929 ; H. Groeck,
Zeit. Ver. deut. Ing., **52.** 91, 1908 ; M. Groume-Grjimailo, *Chaleur Ind.*, **5.** 511, 1924 ;
W. E. Groume-Grjimailo, *The Flow of Gases in Furnaces*, New York, 1923 ; L. E. Gruner, *Ann.
Mines*, (5), **15.** 291, 1859 ; (5), **18.** 555, 1860 ; E. Günter, *Continental Chem. Engg.*, **1.** 1, 1926 ;
L. Guillet, *Rev. Met.*, **14.** 1, 1917 ; J. Guyot, *ib.*, **22.** 515, 1925 ; R. A. Hadfield, *Proc. Inst.
Civil Eng.*, **138.** 442, 1899 ; J. Hall, *Iron Scrap, or the Issue of an Old Shoe Heel, being the Origin
of the Discovery of Pig Boiling*, London, 1864 ; W. S. Hamilton, *Met. Chem. Engg.*, **13.** 8, 1915 ;
F. W. Harbord, *Proc. Inst. Mech. Eng.*, i, 47, 1899 ; *Journ. Iron Steel Inst.*, **30.** ii, 700, 1886 ;
F. W. Harbord and J. W. Hall, *The Metallurgy of Steel*, London, **1.** 140a, 1918 ; A. Harrison and
R. V. Wheeler, *Journ. Iron Steel Inst.*, **78.** iii, 266, 1908 ; J. Hartshorne, *Trans. Amer. Inst.
Min. Eng.*, **28.** 254, 1896 ; **30.** 531, 1899 ; H. S. Hastings, *Iron Trade Rev.*, **44.** 411, 1908 ;
A. P. Head, *Iron Coal Trades Rev.*, **62.** 553, 1901 ; *Proc. South Staffs Inst. Iron Steel Workers*,
100, 1898 ; *Journ. Iron Steel Inst.*, **55.** i, 69, 1899 ; J. Head, *ib.*, **51.** i, 89, 1897 ; W. Heil,
Arch. Eisenhüttenwesen, **1.** 729, 1928 ; W. M. Henry and T. J. McLoughlin, *Blast Furnace Steel
Plant*, **19.** 828, 1931 ; A. Herberholz, *Arch. Eisenhüttenwesen*, **3.** 173, 1929 ; *Stahl Eisen*, **49.**
1579, 1929 ; H. Hermann, *The Planning, Erection and Operation of Modern Open-hearth Steel
Works*, London, 1924 ; *Iron Trade Rev.*, **73.** 1487, 1923 ; *Das Moderne Siemens-Martinstahlwerk*,
Halle, 1922 ; C. H. Herty, *Tech. Publ. Amer. Inst. Min. Eng.*, 229, 1929 ; *Metal Alloys*, **1.** 883,
1930 ; *Journ. Ind. Eng. Chem.*, **19.** 592, 1927 ; *Trans. Amer. Inst. Min. Eng.*, **73.** 1107, 1134,
1926 ; *Amer. Inst. Min. Eng.—Iron Steel*, 260, 1929 ; *Trans. Amer. Soc. Steel Treating*, **11.** 569,
1927 ; C. H. Herty, A. R. Belyea, E. H. Burkhart and C. C. Miller, *Trans. Amer. Inst. Min.
Eng.*, **71.** 512, 1925 ; C. H. Herty, C. F. Christopher and R. W. Stewart, *Bull. Min. Met. In-
vestigations Bur. Mines*, 38, 1930 ; C. H. Herty, G. B. Fitterer and J. M. Byrns, *ib.*, 46, 1930 ;
C. H. Herty, G. R. Fitterer and C. F. Christopher, *Tech. Paper U.S. Bur. Mines*, 492, 1931 ;
C. H. Herty and J. M. Gaines, *Bull. U.S. Bur. Mines*, 308, 1929 ; *Tech. Publ. Amer. Inst. Min.
Eng.*, 88, 1928 ; 165, 1929 ; E. Herzog, *Stahl Eisen*, **46.** 1631, 1777, 1926 ; **48.** 8, 1928 ; *Iron
Coal Trades Rev.*, **114.** 644, 1927 ; H. D. Hibbard, *Amer. Manf.*, **48.** 136, 1891 ; *Iron Age*, **48.**
4, 1891 ; **111.** 143, 211, 347, 1923 ; *Fuels Furnaces*, **9.** 1037, 1931 ; N. F. Hindle, *Foundry*,
57. 502, 568, 1929 ; G. Hofer, *Giesserei Ztg.*, **3.** 353, 1906 ; O. Holz, *Stahl Eisen*, **41.** 1285,
1921 ; E. Houbaer, *Journ. Iron Steel Inst.*, **88.** ii, 68, 1913 ; H. M. Howe, *Mineral Ind.*, **8.** 378,
1900 ; J. K. Hoyt, *Iron Steel Canada*, **12.** 28, 1929 ; W. Hülsbruch, *Stahl Eisen*, **45.** 1746, 1925 ;
K. Huessener, *Trans. Amer. Inst. Min. Eng.*, **73.** 1047, 1926 ; H. Illies, *Stahl Eisen*, **22.** 645, 713,
1902 ; *Feuerungstech.*, **18.** 229, 1930 ; E. J. Janitzky, *Iron Age*, **124.** 1235, 1929 ; *Blast Furnace Steel
Plant*, **17.** 1642, 1929 ; E. R. Jette, *Tech. Publ. Amer. Inst. Min. Eng.*, 380, 1931 ; R. Johannsson,
Oesterr. Zeit. Berg. Hütt., **46.** 675, 1898 ; *Jernkontorets Ann.*, **53.** 208, 1899 ; G. H. Jones, *Yearbook
Amer. Iron Steel Inst.*, 508, 1922 ; A. Jung, *Stahl Eisen*, **44.** 911, 1924 ; **49.** 1221, 1929 ; P. Kahnert,
Studien über die Durchführung des Roheisenerzprosses im Martinofen, Königshütte a. S., 1909 ;
W. Keen, *Iron Age*, **88.** 324, 1912 ; R. M. Keeney, *Min. Scient. Press*, **109.** 335, 1914 ; R. T. Kent,
Iron Trade Rev., **42.** 931, 1907 ; R. B. Kernohan, J. S. Lockhead and W. Trinks, *U.S. Pat. No.
1741025*, 1929 ; R. B. Kernohan and W. Trinks, *ib.*, 1741024, 1929 ; E. Killing, *Stahl Eisen*,
49. 527, 1121, 1929 ; F. A. King, *Yearbook Amer. Iron Steel Inst.*, 146, 1929 ; C. L. Kinney,
Trans. Amer. Inst. Min. Eng., **70.** 136, 1924 ; C. L. Kinney and G. R. McDermott, *Yearbook*

Amer. Iron Steel Inst., 464, 1922 ; S. P. Kinney, *Blast Furnace Steel Plant*, **13**. 243, 272, 1925 ; *Iron Age*, **116**, 466, 514, 1925 ; A. B. Kinzel and J. J. Egan, *Tech. Publ. Amer. Inst. Min. Eng.*, 230, 1929 ; P. Klein, *Riga Ind. Ztg.*, **23**. 237, 1898 ; J. L. Klindworth, *Stahl Eisen*, **22**. 106, 1902 ; K. Köhler, *ib.*, **50**. 1257, 1930 ; F. Kofler, *Grossversuche an einer zu Studien zwecken gebauten Siemens-Martin-Ofen-Regenerativ-kammer*, Aachen, 1929 ; F. Kollmann, *Verh. Ver. Beförd. Gewerbfleisses*, **59**. 221, 1880 ; S. G. Koon, *Trans. Amer. Soc. Testing Materials*, **125**. 35, 1930 ; K. Kreiss, *Stahl Eisen*, **10**. 771, 1890 ; S. Kriz and H. Kral, *ib.*, **50**. 221, 1930 ; P. Kupelweiser, *Oesterr. Zeit. Berg. Hütt.*, **38**. 261, 1890 ; T. G. Kus, *Proc. Eng. Soc. West Pennsylvania*, **47**. 391, 1931 ; E. Langheinrich, *Stahl Eisen*, **21**. 1168, 1901 ; B. M. Larsen, *Blast Furnace Steel Plant*, **15**. 10, 1927 ; B. M. Larsen and J. W. Campbell, *Trans. Amer. Inst. Min. Eng.*, **75**. 245, 1927 ; B. M. Larsen, F. W. Schroeder, E. N. Bauer and J. W. Campbell, *Feuerfeste Baustoffe in Siemens-Martin-Ofen*, Leipzig, 1929 ; H. W. Lash, *Iron Trade Rev.*, **66**. 14, 1901 ; F. E. Lathe, *Journ. Canada Min. Inst.*, **10**. 373, 1908 ; A. Ledebur, *Stahl Eisen*, **13**. 869, 1893 ; **19**. 438, 1899 ; **23**. 36, 1903 ; M. Lencauchez, *Mém. Soc. Ing. Civils*, **29**. 523, 1874 ; **54**. 116, 1899 ; *Rev. Scient.*, (3), **5**. 1023, 1875 ; F. Lepersonne, *Rev. Univ. Mines*, (7), **19**. 5, 109, 1928 ; (7), **20**. 5, 1928 ; W. Liesegang and W. Winkhaus, *Stahl Eisen*, **51**. 497, 1930 ; *Arch. Eisenhüttenwesen*, **4**. 421, 1931 ; W. Lister, *Metallurgia*, **2**. 140, 1930 ; E. de Loisy, *Bull. Soc. Nat. Ind.*, **101**. 572, 1901 ; *Rev. Mét.*, **23**. 369, 1926 ; C. Longenecker, *Trans. Amer. Soc. Steel Treating*, **14**. 526, 1926 ; E. Lubojatzky, *Montana Rund.*, **21**. 217, 1929 ; **22**. 27, 1930 ; *Feuerfest*, **4**. 20, 51, 65, 1928 ; F. W. Lürmann, *Rass. Min.*, **18**. 35, 1903 ; *Stahl Eisen*, **10**. 10, 194, 1890 ; **20**. 769, 1900 ; G. L. Luetscher, *Proc. Eng. Soc. Western Pennsylvania*, **21**. 93, 1905 ; A. McCance, *Trans. Faraday Soc.*, **21**. 176, 1925 ; *Journ. Met. Glasgow Univ.*, **4**. 4, 1925 ; H. Macco, *Stahl Eisen*, **24**. 151, 1904 ; W. McFarlane, *Iron Coal Trades Rev.*, **63**. 1326, 1901 ; **74**. 1127, 1907 ; W. McKee, *Trans. Amer. Foundrymen's Assoc.*, **30**. 324, 1922 ; C. H. MacMillan, *Proc. Cleveland Inst. Eng.*, 120, 1903 ; P. M. Macnair, *Journ. Iron Steel Inst.—Carnegie Mem.*, **13**. 267, 1924 ; *Trans. Faraday Soc.*, **21**. 243, 1925 ; A. McWilliam, *Journ. West Scotland Iron Steel Inst.*, **14**. 155, 1907 ; A. McWilliam and W. H. Hatfield, *Journ. Iron Steel Inst.*, **61**. i, 5, 1902 ; **66**. ii, 206, 1904 ; E. von Maltitz, *Iron Age*, **76**. 349, 1905 ; B. de Mare, *Mining Met.*, **10**. 417, 1929 ; *Arch. Eisenhüttenwesen*, **3**. 103, 1929 ; G. Mars, *ib.*, **3**. 249, 1929 ; J. Massenez, *Journ. Iron Steel Inst.*, **40**. ii, 76, 1891 ; P. N. Mather, *Journ. Indian Chem. Soc.*, **6**. 353, 1929 ; R. Mather, *Eng. Rev.*, **14**. 375, 1906 ; E. Mathesius, *Verh. Gewerbefl.*, **91**. 35, 1912 ; F. A. Matthewman, *Journ. West Scotland Iron Steel Inst.*, **27**. 34, 1920 ; F. A. Matthewman and A. Campion, *ib.*, **20**. 124, 1913 ; E. Maurer and W. Bischof, *Stahl Eisen*, **50**. 477, 1930 ; E. Maurer and S. Schleicher, *Mitt. Inst. Eisenforsch.*, **3**. 59, 1922 ; E. Maurer and R. Schrödter, *ib.*, **3**. 21, 1921 ; E. Mayer, *Stahl Eisen*, **28**. 717, 756, 802, 1908 ; G. Mehrtens, *ib.*, **19**. 709, 1899 ; J. Meiser, *ib.*, **47**. 446, 1927 ; A. Mignot, *Compt. Rend. Soc. Ind. Min.*, 108, 1906 ; J. R. Miller, *Iron Age*, **125**. 1223, 1930 ; G. A. Milward, *On the Manufacture of Basic Steel by the Open-hearth Process, with special reference to some furnaces employed*, London, 1891 ; H. Monden, *Stahl Eisen*, **43**. 745, 782, 1923 ; A. Monell, *Journ. Iron Steel Inst.*, **57**. i, 75, 1900 ; *Iron Trade Rev.*, **66**. 39, 1901 ; S. G. Moore, *Board Trade Journ.*, **60**. 498, 1908 ; T. D. Morgan, *Iron Age*, **83**. 386, 1908 ; T. D. Morgan and F. Rogers, *Journ. Iron Steel Inst.*, **96**. ii, 209, 1917 ; E. Münker, *Zeit. Ver. deut. Ing.*, **46**. 1049, 1902 ; E. Muller, *French Pat. No.* 84735, 1869 ; A. Nahoczay, *Mitt. Berg. Hütt.*, 150, 1929 ; T. Naske, *Stahl Eisen*, **27**. 157, 191, 229, 265, 1907 ; B. Neuherz, *Bany. Koh. Lapok.*, **36**. 125, 1903 ; **38**. 81, 1904 ; G. Neumann, *Stahl Eisen*, **42**. 1641, 1922 ; **47**. 2222, 1927 ; *Arch. Eisenhüttenwesen*, **1**. 111, 1927 ; D. K. Nicholson, *Engg.*, **50**. 118, 1890 ; E. Noaillon, *Rev. Univ. Mines*, (8), **17**. 413, 1923 ; C. S. Nugent, *Iron Age*, **15**. 225, 1927 ; P. Oberhoffer and H. Schenck, *Stahl Eisen*, **47**. 1526, 1927 ; E. G. Odelstjerna, *Berg. Hütt. Ztg.*, (5), **55**. 417, 1896 ; *Stahl Eisen*, **14**. 697, 1894 ; *Jernkontorets Ann.*, **44**. 332, 1889 ; **50**. 169, 1896 ; *Trans. Amer. Inst. Min. Eng.*, **24**. 288, 1895 ; F. W. Paul, *Journ. Iron Steel Inst.*, **86**. ii, 91, 1912 ; M. A. Pavloff, *The Determination of the Dimensions of Blast Furnaces and Open-Hearth Furnaces*, Leningrad, 1925 ; *Album of Drawings relating to the Manufacture of Open-hearth Steel*, Ekaterinoslav, 1904 ; *Abmessungen von Hoch- und Martinöfen*, Leipzig, 1928 ; *Eng.*, **108**. 216, 1909 ; *Rev. Met.*, **20**. 607, 1923 ; **24**. 1, 1927 ; *Stahl Eisen*, **47**. 953, 1927 ; O. Peterson, *Iron Coal Trades Rev.*, **80**. 88, 123, 164, 210, 258, 1910 ; *Stahl Eisen*, **30**. 1, 58, 1910 ; R. D. Pike, *Journ. Ind. Eng. Chem.*, **20**. 1356, 1929 ; E. Piwowarsky, *Giesserei*, **16**. 685, 1929 ; K. Poech, *Stahl Eisen*, **18**. 476, 1898 ; **21**. 331, 1901 ; V. Polak, *Zeit. tech. Phys.*, **8**. 71, 1927 ; A. Ponthière, *Ann. Mines Belg.*, **13**. 457, 1908 ; A. Pourcel, *Mém. Soc. Ing. Civils*, **44**. 595, 1891 ; G. L. Prentiss, *Iron Age*, **107**. 1479, 1921 ; *Iron Trade Rev.*, **68**. 1586, 1921 ; J. Puppe, *Stahl Eisen*, **42**. 1, 46, 1922 ; *Iron Coal Trades Rev.*, **105**. 146, 1922 ; W. J. Reagan, *Tech. Publ. Amer. Inst. Min. Eng.*, 347, 1930 ; P. Rees, *Iron Coal Trades Rev.*, **65**. 852, 1902 ; L. F. Reinartz, *Blast Furnace Steel Plant*, **18**. 96, 1930 ; J. W. Richards, *Electrochem. Met. Ind.*, **5**. 44, 79, 1907 ; A. Riemer, *Stahl Eisen*, **22**. 269, 1357, 1902 ; J. Riley, *Journ. Iron Steel Inst.*, **57**. i, 22, 1900 ; *Iron Coal Trades Rev.*, **60**. 354, 1900 ; *Proc. Inst. Civil Eng.*, **154**. 115, 1903 ; G. Rivière, *Mem. Soc. Ing. Civils*, 373, 1906 ; F. Rogers, *Journ. Iron Steel Inst.*, **96**. ii, 181, 1917 ; J. Ruppe, *Stahl Eisen*, **42**. 1, 46, 1922 ; G. A. V. Russell, *Iron Coal Trades Rev.*, **109**. 197, 1924 ; F. Sandelin, *Metals Alloys*, **1**. 475, 1930 ; *Jernkontorets Ann.*, **113**. 519, 1930 ; **115**. 519, 1931 ; E. H. Saniter, *ib.*, **50**. 632, 1895 ; **54**. 175, 1897 ; *Eng.*, **80**. 13, 1895 ; *Journ. Iron Steel Inst.*, **41**. ii, 216, 1892 ; **43**. i, 73, 1893 ; R. J. Sarjant, *Fuel Econ. Rev.*, **2**. 15, 1922 ; A. Sattmann, *Stahl Eisen*, **19**. 956, 1899 ; **21**. 572, 1901 ; F. Sauerwald, *Arch. Eisenhüttenwesen*, **4**. 361, 1931 ; A. Sauveur, *Rev. Mét.*, **22**. 297, 1925 ; A. Schack, *Arch. Eisenhüttenwesen*, **3**. 7, 1929 ; W. Schdanoff, *Stahl Eisen*, **29**. 1930, 1987, 1909 ; H. Schenck, *Stahl Eisen*, **48**. 199, 407,

1928; **50**. 953, 1930; **51**. 197, 292, 1931; *Krupp's Monatsh.*, **11**. 1, 29, 39, 101, 1930; **12**. 63, 1931; *Arch. Eisenhüttenwesen*, **1**. 483, 1927; **3**. 57, 505, 571, 685, 1930; .4. 320, 1931; *Metals Alloys*, **1**. 674, 1930; *Metallbörse*, **20**. 1547, 1930; S. Schleicher, *Arch. Eisenhüttenwesen*, **4**. 239, 1930; *Stahl Eisen*, **41**. 285, 357, 1921; **49**. 458, 1929; **50**. 1049, 1778, 1930; A. Schlüter, *Wärmederluste und Haltbarkeit des Siemens-Martin-Ofengewölbes während einer Ofenreise*, Düsseldorf, 1930; W. Schmidhammer, *Oesterr. Zeit. Berg. Hütt.*, **41**. 33, 1893; *Stahl Eisen*, **11**. 546, 1891; **14**. 751, 1894; **17**. 775, 1897; **22**. 651, 1902; H. Schmidt, *Arch. Eisenhüttenwesen*, **2**. 293, 1928; H. Schmidt and W. Liesegang, *Mitt. Inst. Eisenforsch.*, **10**. 71, 1928; *Arch. Eisenhüttenwesen*, **1**. 677, 1927; R. Schöffel, *Oesterr. Zeit. Berg. Hütt.*, **39**. 212, 225, 1891; F. Schuster, *Journ. Iron Steel Inst.*, **89**. i, 51, 1914; C. Schwarz, *Arch. Eisenhüttenwesen*, **1**. 33, 273, 525, 1927; K. Seaver, *Trans. Amer. Inst. Min. Eng.*, **52**. 849, 1913; H. See, *Iron Coal Trades Rev.*, **91**. 41, 1915; J. Seigle, *Tech. Moderne*, **19**. 641, 1927; H. W. Seldon, *Blast Furnace Steel Plant*, **9**. 229, 422, 521, 1921; W. Shaw, *Proc. Cleveland Inst. Eng.*, **71**, 1893; P. G. Shook, *Proc. Alabama Ind. Scient. Soc.*, **6**. 24, 1897; C. W. von Siemens, *Journ. Chem. Soc.*, **21**. 283, 1868; *De l'application du four à gaz et à chaleur régénérée à la production de l'acier fondu*, Paris, 1869; A. Silin, *Proc. Russ. Met. Soc.*, 102, 1929; D. Sillers, *Journ. West Scotland Iron Steel Inst.*, **32**. 52, 1924; O. Simmersbach, *Berg. Hütt. Rund.*, **2**. 93, 1906; *Iron Age*, **77**. 45, 1906; *Stahl Eisen*, **23**. 829, 1903; **25**. 569, 769, 1905; F. T. Sisco, *Trans. Amer. Soc. Steel Treating*, **7**. 494, 1925; R. P. Smith, *Journ. Met. Glasgow Univ.*, **4**. 18, 1925; W. Soltz, *Oesterr. Zeit. Berg. Hütt.*, **41**. 1, 1893; J. Sonnenfeld, *Giesserei Ztg.*, **7**. 244, 269, 1910; E. Spetzler, *Stahl Eisen*, **43**. 1315, 1923; E. Spetzler and H. Spitzer, *ib.*, **52**. 233, 1932; F. Springorum, *ib.*, **17**. 396, 1897; **30**. 396, 1910; J. E. Stead, *Journ. Iron Steel Inst.*, **42**. ii, 260, 1892; O. H. Steel, *Blast Furnace Steel Plant*, **18**. 114, 1930; F. Stein, *Iron Age*, **17**. 409, 1929; I. L. Stevenson, *ib.*, **54**. 181, 1894; F. Stille, *Stahl Eisen*, **19**. 325, 1899; *Oesterr. Zeit. Berg. Hütt.*, **47**. 246, 1899; C. Stöckl, *Stahl Eisen*, **10**. 21, 1890; B. Stoughton, *Journ. Franklin Inst.*, **168**. 470, 1910; *Eng. Mag.*, **34**. 49, 1907; *Trans. Amer. Foundrymen's Assoc.*, **28**. 31, 1909; T. D. Straub, *Iron Age*, **87**. 201, 1911; C. Strobrawa, *Stahl Eisen*, **25**. 30, 1905; O. Stromborg, *Iron Age*, **78**. 680, 1907; C. E. Stromeyer, *Trans. Inst. Eng. Shipbuilders Scotland*, **41**. 227, 1898; H. Styri, *Chem. Met. Engg.*, **20**. 478, 1919; *Journ. Iron Steel Inst.*, **108**. ii, 189, 1923; S. Surzycki, *Stahl Eisen*, **23**. 170, 1903; **24**. 163, 1904; *Iron Coal Trades Rev.*, **68**. 752, 1904; *Journ. Iron Steel Inst.*, **67**. i, 112, 1905; W. Tafel, *Stahl Eisen*, **39**. 1280, 1919; B. Talbot, *Journ. Iron Steel Inst.*, **57**. i, 90, 1900; **63**. i, 57, 1903; **88**. ii, 232, 1913; **117**. i, 33, 1928; G. Tammann, *Arch. Eisenhüttenwesen*, **5**. 71, 1931; G. Tammann and W. Oelsen, *ib.*, **5**. 75, 1931; C. M. Tessié du Motay, *French Pat. No.* 96452, 1872; *Journ. Iron Steel Inst.*, **6**. 494, 1873; **7**. 232, 1874; O. Thiel, *Oesterr. Zeit. Berg. Hütt.*, **45**. 15, 73, 1897; *Stahl Eisen*, **17**. 403, 733, 1897; **18**. 86, 146, 1898; **21**. 1305, 1901; **24**. 458, 1904; J. Thieme, *ib.*, **18**. 714, 761, 802, 805, 1898; A. S. Thomas, *Journ. Iron Steel Inst.*, **72**. iv, 576, 1906; F. Thomas, *Stahl Eisen*, **41**. 185, 223, 1921; *Feuerungstechnik*, **7**. 165, 1919; K. Thomas, *Stahl Eisen*, **50**. 1665, 1708, 1930; *Untersuchungen über die Vorgänge beim Thomasverfahren*, Düsseldorf, 1930; S. G. Thomas, *Journ. Iron Steel Inst.*, **13**. i, 40, 1878; S. G. Thomas and P. C. Gilchrist, *ib.*, **20**. ii, 407, 1811; F. E. Thompson, *Iron Age*, **57**. 810, 1896; B. H. Thwaite, *The Theoretic Rationale of an Improved Design of an Open-hearth Furnace*, London, 1891; *Eng.*, **83**. 160, 1897; *Colliery Guardian*, **61**. 280, 1891; *Proc. S. Staffs Inst. Iron Steel*, 32, 1901; C. W. Tideström, *Bihang Jernkontorets Ann.*, **4**. 351, 389, 1903; M. Tigerschiöld, *ib.*, **112**. 71, 1928; *Stahl Eisen*, **49**. 851, 1929; M. von Tittler, *ib.*, **21**. 519, 1901; F. Toldt, *Berg. Hütt. Jahrb.*, **41**. 289, 1893; *Ueber Details von Siemens-Martinofen*, Leipzig, 1894; G. Toppe, *Stahl Eisen*, **16**. 141, 1896; F. L. Toy, *Yearbook Amer. Iron Steel Inst.*, 319, 1920; G. D. Tranter, *Iron Age*, **17**. 69, 80, 1929; S. Treverton, *U.S. Pat. No.* 1741666, 1929; W. Trinks, *Fuels Furnaces*, **5**. 33, 307, 477, 1927; *U.S. Pat. No.* 1741002, 1741024, 1929; *Blast Furnace Steel Plant*, **10**. 451, 1923; B. W. Turner, *Iron Coal Trades Rev.*, **63**. 1211, 1901; T. Turner, *Journ. West Scotland Iron Steel Inst.*, **7**. 121, 1900; T. Twynam, *Proc. Cleveland Inst. Eng.*, 87, 1907; L. Unckenbolt, *Iron Coal Trades Rev.*, **69**. 1804, 1904; *Stahl Eisen*, **23**. 1275, 1903; H. C. Vacher and E. H. Hamilton, *Tech. Publ. Amer. Inst. Min. Eng.*, 409, 1931; F. Valton, *Étude sur la validité des brevets Martin*, Paris, 1879; C. W. Veach, *Iron Age*, **15**. 278, 323, 1927; *Rolling Mill Journ.*, **5**. 335, 350, 407, 467, 490, 527, 587, 647, 658, 1931; J. Wagner, *Rev. Mét.*, **26**. 287, 1929; Harbison Walker, *A Study of the Open Hearth*, Pittsburg, 1911; C. Walrand, *Eng. Min. Journ.*, **59**. 606, 1895; G. B. Waterhouse, *Yearbook Amer. Iron Steel Inst.*, **28**. C, 133, 1928; *Iron Age*, **121**. 1529, 1928; *Trans. Amer. Inst. Min. Eng.—Iron Steel*, **28**. C, 113, 1928; H. Wedding, *Vech. Ver. Beförd Gewerbfleisses*, **83**. 329, 1904; *Glaser's Ann.*, **38**. 166, 1897; *Berg. Hütt. Ztg.*, **56**. 21, 1897; *Stahl Eisen*, **24**. 918, 1904; J. Weeren, *Dingler's Journ.*, **307**. 108, 1898; F. Weisgerber, *Stahl Eisen*, **50**. 1489, 1930; S. T. Wellman, *Iron Age*, **57**. 13, 1896; F. Wesemann, *Stahl Eisen*, **49**. 1853, 1929; J. H. Whiteley, *Rev. Ind. Min.*, 369, 1926; *Trans. Faraday Soc.*, **21**. 249, 1925; J. H. Whiteley and A. F. Hallimond, *Journ. Iron Steel Inst.*, **99**. i, 199, 1919; E. A. Whitworth, *Trans. Amer. Soc. Steel Treating*, **8**. 739, 1925; A. D. Williams, *Iron Age*, **76**. 1532, 1905; **109**. 1075, 1279, 1922; **105**. 35, 119, 317, 475, 805, 1225, 1510, 1920; P. Williams, *Proc. Lincoln. Iron Steel Inst.*, **1**. 1, 58, 1920; G. A. Wilson, *Journ. West Scotland Iron Steel Inst.*, **11**. 52, 75, 1904; **13**. 75, 85, 90, 1906; J. F. Wilson, *Journ. Iron Steel Inst.*, **101**. i, 266, 1920; V. Windett, *The Open Hearth; its Relation to the Steel Industry; its Design and Operation*, New York, 1920; H. C. Wood, *Iron Steel Canada*, **13**. 194, 213, 215, 1930; *Iron Age*, **126**. 1299, 1930; *Engg.*, **130**. 373, 447, 1930; *Journ. Iron Steel Inst.*, **122**. ii, 111, 1930; J. T. Wright, *Proc. Cleveland Inst. Eng.*, 121, 1923; F. Wüst, *Mitt. Inst. Eisenforsch.*, **4**. 95, 1922;

F. Wüst and J.,Duhr, *ib.*, **2**. 39, 1921; B. Yaneske, *Journ. Iron Steel Inst.*, **99**. i, 255, 1919; B. Yaneske and G. A. Wood, *ib.*, **101**. i, 287, 1919; M. von Zaykowsky, *Stahl Eisen*, **18**. 810, 1898; E. von Zeipel, *Oesterr. Zeit. Berg. Hütt.*, **48**. 442, 1900.

⁸ W. Alberts, *Stahl Eisen*, **49**. 977, 1929; A. J. Allmand, *The Principles of Applied Electrochemistry*, London, 1912; R. Amberg, *Electrochem. Met. Ind.*, **7**. 115, 1909; *Stahl Eisen*, **29**. 176, 1929; G. Arnou, *Rev. Mét.*, **7**. 1190, 1910; L. T. Aronoff, *Iron Trade Rev.*, **80**. 193, 1927; *Foundry*, **54**. 980, 1927; T. F. Baily, *Electrochem. Met. Ind.*, **29**. 1062, 1923; A. I. Balandin, *Journ. Russ. Met. Soc.*, 228, 1929; G. Batty, *Foundry*, **58**. 100, 1930; C. H. vom Baur, *Iron Age*, **92**. 612, 1913; *Trans. Amer. Electrochem. Soc.*, **33**. 237, 1918; *Iron Coal Trades Rev.*, **94**. 689, 1917; V. D. I. Belani, *Montan. Rund.*, **21**. 479, 1929; P. McN. Bennie, *Eng. Min. Journ.*, **88**. 84, 1909; *Iron Age*, **85**. 216, 1910; M. Bergsman, *Tek. Tids.*, **37**. 90, 1907; J. Bibby, *Iron Coal Trades Rev.*, **96**. 165, 1918; *Trans. Faraday Soc.*, **14**. 79, 1918; W. Borchers, *Zeit. Ver. deut. Ing.*, **49**. 966, 1905; *Stahl Eisen*, **25**. 631, 1905; *Elektrometallurgie*, Leipzig, 1902; *Electric Furnaces*, London, 1908; P. H. Brace, *Journ. Amer. Inst. Elect. Eng.*, **44**. 992, 1925; J. Brown, *Zeit. Metallkunde*, **18**. 333, 1926; *Metallurgist*, 191, 1926; C. A. Buck, *Iron Coal Trades Rev.*, **94**. 688, 1917; *Trans. Amer. Electrochem. Soc.*, **31**. 81, 1917; G. Bulle, *Arch. Eisenhüttenwesen*, **1**. 205, 313, 1927; G. de Burlet, *Rev. Mét.*, **7**. 93, 1925; W. E. Cahill, *Min. Scient. Press.*, **122**, 535, 1921; D. F. Campbell, *Journ. Iron Steel Inst.*, **112**. ii, 69, 1925; **122**. ii, 85, 1930; *Trans. Faraday Soc.*, **7**. 195, 1911; L. Campredon, *Mining World*, **81**. 749, 1907; **82**. 229, 1907; C. G. Carlisle, *Journ. Iron Steel Inst.*, **102**. ii, 115, 1920; O. Casperson, *Swedish Pat. No.* 66560, 1929; R. Catani, *Met. Ital.*, **3**. 222, 1911; G. Charpy, *Rev. Mét.*, **8**. 305, 1911; G. H. Clamer, *Journ. Franklin Inst.*, **190**. 473, 1920; E. B. Clark, *Mech. Eng.*, **33**. 445, 1914; E. F. Cone, *Iron Age*, **100**. 488, 1917; C. C. de Coussergues, *Rev. Mét.*, **6**. 589, 1909; *L'électrosiderurgie*, Paris, 1923; *Mém. Soc. Ing. Civils*, 423, 1923; A. Coutagne, *Rev. Mét.*, **17**. 450, 1920; W. N. Crafts, *Iron Age*, **93**. 1066, 1914; N. R. Davis, *Foundry Trade Journ.*, **41**. 437, 1930; E. Decherf, *Rev. Univ. Mines*, (7), **14**. 58, 105, 1927; E. Dieudonne, *Age de Fer*, **37**. 1026, 1921; J. A. Edgerton, *Commonwealth Eng.*, **9**. 44, 1921; B. Egelberg, *Trans. Amer. Soc. Steel Treating*, **10**. 395, 1926; E. R. Eichhoff, *Iron Age*, **84**. 388, 1909; F. R. Eichhoff, *Stahl Eisen*, **27**. 41, 1907; W. Eilender, *ib.*, **33**. 585, 1913; C. F. Elwell, *Proc. Amer. Inst. Elect. Eng.*, **30**. 621, 1911; *Iron Age*, **87**. 961, 1911; V. Engelhardt, *Herstellung von Stahl im elektrischen Ofen*, Wien, 1905; *Schrift. Ver. Verbreit. Naturw. Kenntnisse*, **45**. 455, 1905; *Oesterr. Zeit. Berg. Hütt.*, **53**. 399, 419, 431, 444, 461, 470, 1905; *Zeit. oesterr. Ing. Arch. Ver.*, **61**. 749, 765, 781, 1910; *Elektrotech. Zeit.*, **14**. 1051, 1084, 1104, 1124, 1907; *Stahl Eisen*, **30**. 633, 1910; J. Escard, *L'électrosiderurgie*, Paris, 1908; *Rev. Gén. Sciences*, **29**. 401, 1918; *Les fours électriques industriels et les fabrications électriques*, Paris, 1919; H. C. Estep, *Iron Coal Trades Rev.*, **94**. 663, 1917; G. E. Evréinoff and S. Y. Telny, *Rev. Mét.*, **24**. 57, 1927; A. V. Farr, *Iron Age*, **102**. 74, 1918; W. Fielding, *Trans. Faraday Soc.*, **5**. 110, 1909; G. I. Finch, *Journ. Soc. Arts*, **47**. 1081, 1108, 1927; F. A. J. Fitzgerald, *Electrochem. Met. Ind.*, **6**. 493, 1908; **7**. 10, 268, 1909; **8**. 317, 1910; *Trans. Amer. Electrochem. Soc.*, **14**. 239, 1908; **15**. 149, 1909; J. A. Fleming, *Journ. Soc. Arts*, **59**. 883, 857, 870, 885, 1911; E. Fornander, *Bihang Jernkontorets Ann.*, 291, 1909; O. Frick, *Journ. Iron Steel Inst.*, **88**. ii, 296, 1913; J. W. Galvin and C. N. Ring, *Trans. Amer. Foundrymen's Assoc.*, **67**. 1130, 1920; W. S. Gifford, *Electrician*, **85**. 528, 1920; **91**. 603, 1923; **95**. 617, 627, 1925; G. Gin, *Trans. Amer. Electrochem. Soc.*, **12**. 97, 1908; M. Gobillot, *Rev. Ind. Min.*, 27, 1922; R. C. Gosrow, *Met. Chem. Engg.*, **21**. 235, 1919; C. C. Gow, *The Electrometallurgy of Steel*, London, 1921; J. H. Gray, *Met. Chem. Engg.*, **13**. 656, 1915; H. A. Greaves, *Iron Coal Trades Rev.*, **98**. 621, 1919; A. Grönwall, *Oesterr. Zeit. Berg. Hütt.*, **14**. 256, 1907; *Lihang Jernkontorets Ann.*, 409, 1909; *Electrochem. Met. Ind.*, **8**. 34, 1910; A. Grönwall, A. Lindblad and O. Stålhane, *Bihang Jernkontorets Ann.*, 296, 1907; E. Guarini, *L'état actuel de l'électrometallurgie du fer et de l'acier*, Paris, 1905; M. Guédras, *Aciers Spéciaux*, **4**. 274, 1929; *Tech. Moderne*, **13**. 497, 1921; V. Guillerman and M. Gillot, *Journ. Four. Élect.*, **30**. 38, 1921; L. Guillet, *Mém. Soc. Ing. Civils*, 391, 1907; *Génie Civil*, **50**. 89, 105, 124, 140, 156, 174, 1907; *Houilla Blanche*, **6**. 97, 1907; E. Haanel, *Iron Trade Rev.*, **45**. 616, 1910; *Electrothermic Processes for the Smelting of Iron Ores and the Making of Steel in Operation in Europe*, Ottawa, 1904; J. Härden, *Electrochem. Met. Ind.*, **7**. 320, 1909; **9**. 595, 1911; *Trans. Faraday Soc.*, **4**. 120, 1908; **7**. 183, 1911; *Elect. Eng.*, **45**. 270, 1910; *Electrician*, **70**. 436, 1912; *Iron Coal Trades Rev.*, **81**. 907, 1910; C. A. Hansen, *Electrochem. Met. Ind.*, **7**. 206, 1909; F. W. Harbord, *Journ. West Scotland Iron Steel Inst.*, **16**. 173, 212, 1909; C. Hering, *Electrochem. Met. Ind.*, **11**. 183, 1913; *Journ. Franklin Inst.*, **172**. 55, 1911; J. Hess, *Zeit. Elektrochem.*, **12**. 25, 1906; H. D. Hibbard, *Electrochem. Met. Ind.*, **7**. 265, 1909; A. Hiorth, *Berg. Hütt. Runds.*, 272, 1906; *Trans. Amer. Electrochem. Soc.*, **20**. 293, 1911; *Iron Trade Rev.*, **49**. 699, 1911; G. Hooghwinkel, *Iron Coal Trades Rev.*, **80**. 371, 1910; H. M. Howe, *Eng. Min. Journ.*, **88**. 400, 1909; R. S. Hutton, *Journ. Soc. Chem. Ind.*, **24**. 589, 1905; *Electrochem. Met. Ind.*, **5**. 9, 1907; H. Illies, *Zeit. Giessereipraxis*, **51**. 54, 1930; C. Irresberger, *Chem. Ztg.*, **38**. 90, 1918; J. Izart, *L'Ind. Élect.*, **13**. 304, 1905; J. R. Jackson, *Iron Trade Rev.*, **79**. 644, 1926; W. McA. Johnson and G. N. Seiger, *Met. Chem. Engg.*, **11**. 41, 504, 563, 643, 683, 1913; L. Katona, *Bany. Koh. Lapok*, **41**. 193, 257, 321, 1908; R. M. Keeney, *Met. Chem. Engg.*, **23**. 980, 1920; O. von Keil and K. Hess, *Stahl Eisen*, **45**. 1134, 1925; A. Keller, *Journ. Iron Steel Inst.*, **63**. 161, 1903; K. von Kerpely, *Giesserei Ztg.*, **24**. 98, 1927; **27**. 101, 1930; *Giesserei*, **16**. 1030, 1929; J. B. C. Kershaw, *The Electric Furnace in Iron and Steel Production*, London, 1907; *Technics*, **2**. 132, 1904; *Iron Coal Trades Rev.*, **101**. 638, 1928; *Electrician*, **87**. 636, 1921; *Elect. World*, **51**. 856, 1908; *Cassier's Mag.*, **36**. 237, 1904; *Iron Trade Rev.*, **46**.

76, 1910 ; **51**. 959, 1007, 1067, 1105, 1169, 1912 ; **52**. 197, 1913 ; *Elect. Times*, **44**. 58, 85, 108, 1913 ; F. Körber, F. Wever and H. Neuhauss, *Stahl Eisen*, **46**. 1641, 1926 ; M. H. Kraemer, *Metallurgist*, **4**. 170, 1929 ; *Stahl Eisen*, **48**. 1120, 1928 ; *Giesserei*, **16**. 1092, 1929 ; M. Kreuzkam, *Erzbergbau*, 132, 1911 ; S. Kriz, *Arch. Eisenhüttenwesen*, **1**. 413, 1927 ; *Stahl Eisen*, **49**. 417, 1929 ; S. Kriz and H. Kral, *ib.*, **50**. 221, 1930 ; E. C. Kroutzberg, *Iron Trade Rev.*, **80**. 139, 1927 ; A. M. Kuhlmann and A. D. Spillman, *Trans. Amer. Electrochem. Soc.*, **38**. 325, 1920 ; *Iron Trade Rev.*, **67**. 1546, 1920 ; W. Kunze, *Stahl Eisen*, **32**. 1089, 1136, 1181, 1912 ; B. Lacaze, *Rev. Ind.*, **60**. 277, 1930 ; G. P. de Laval, *Iron Trade Rev.*, **40**. 954, 1907 ; E. F. Law, *Electrician*, **70**. 433, 1912 ; A. Levasseur, *Arts Métiers*, **84**. 54, 1931 ; *Génie Civil*, **97**. 644, 1930 ; A. Lindblad and O. Stålhane, *Rass. Min.*, **26**. 153, 1907 ; L. B. Lindemuth, *Trans. Amer. Electrochem. Soc.*, **37**. 299, 1920 ; W. Lipin, *Met. Chem. Engg.*, **10**. 227, 1912 ; E. J. Ljungberg, *Journ. Iron Steel Inst.*, **80**. ii, 9, 1909 ; E. de Loïsy, *Rev. Mét.*, **23**. 253, 1926 ; J. Lonergan, *Met. Chem. Engg.*, **20**. 245, 1919 ; C. Louis, *Bull. Tech. Soc. École Nat. Arts Métiers*, 511, 1913 ; L. Lyche, *Stahl Eisen*, **43**. 110, 1923 ; T. Lyman, *Iron Age*, **87**. 322, 1911 ; *Chem. Eng.*, **13**. 250, 1911 ; C. C. Lynde, *Blast Furnace Steel Plant*, **5**. 214, 1917 ; D. A. Lyon and J. F. Cullen, *Bull. U.S. Bur. Mines*, 77, 1914 ; W. McClure, *Eng. News*, **11**. 335, 1904 ; A. McWilliam, *B.A. Rep.*, 83, 1911 ; M. Marantonio, *Journ. Four Élect.*, **30**. 53, 1921 ; P. Marthourey, *Rev. Mét.*, **28**. 101, 139, 1931 ; J. A. Mathews, *Trans. Amer. Electrochem. Soc.*, **31**. 49, 1917 ; *Met. Chem. Engg.*, **16**. 573, 1917 ; C. Matignon, *L'électrométallurgie des fontes, fers, et aciers*, Paris, 1906 ; F. A. Melmoth, *Elect. World*, **96**. 128, 1930 ; A. Minet, *Le four électrique*, Paris, 1905 ; F. J. Moffett, *Iron Staffs. Iron Steel Inst.*, **34**. 15, 1918 ; *The Electric Furnace*, London, 1921 ; W. von Molo, *Oesterr. Zeit. Berg. Hütt.*, **56**. 515, 1907 ; E. T. Moore, *Blast Furnace Steel Plant*, **11**. 153, 1923 ; *Iron Age*, **115**. 226, 1924 ; A. Müller-Hauff, *Stahl Eisen*, **46**. 213, 289, 1926 ; C. Myers, *Iron Coal Trades Rev*, **84**. 178, 1912 ; H. Nathusius, *Journ. Iron Steel Inst.*, **85**. i, 51, 1912 ; J. W. Naylor, *Electrician*, **83**. 363, 1920 ; A. Neuburger, *Sitzber. Ver. Beford. Gewerbfleisses*, **84**. 81, 1905 ; *Zeit. angew. Chem.*, **18**. 481, 1905 ; *Glaser's Ann.*, **58**. 103, 1906 ; *Zeit. angew. Chem.*, **20**. 97, 1907 ; H. Neuhass, *Stahl Eisen*, **49**. 689, 1929 ; B. Neumann, *ib.*, **30**. 1410, 1910 ; *Elektrometallurgie des Eisens*, Halle a. S., 1907 ; E. F. Northrup, *Met. Chem. Engg.*, **24**. 309, 1921 ; M. Oesterreich, *Stahl Eisen*, **33**. 303, 1913 ; E. Ommelange, *Ind. World*, 12, 1909 ; S. H. Ourbacher, *Journ. Amer. Inst. Elect. Eng.*, **39**. 1039, 1920 ; W. Pasckis, *Stahl Eisen*, **49**. 1685, 1929 ; C. Perkins, *Mining World*, **24**. 661, 691, 721, 1905 ; **25**. 494, 1906 ; F. Peters, *Glückauf*, **42**. 1384, 1419, 1443, 1469, 1519, 1552, 1582, 1619, 1644, 1906 ; **56**. 761, 1920 ; R. Pitaval, *Echo Mines*, **34**. 740, 1907 ; *Compt. Rend. Soc. Ind. Min.*, 88, 1907 ; G. A. Plummer, *Oesterr. Zeit. Berg. Hütt.*, **55**. 105, 125, 1907 ; J. N. Pring, *The Electric Furnace*, London, 1921 ; H. Prothière, *Traité d'électrométallurgie*, Paris, 1904 ; P. M. Pugsley, *Chem. Eng. Min. Rev.*, **21**. 131, 1929 ; J. M. Quinn, *Iron Age*, **111**. 1177, 1923 ; H. P. Rassbach, *Trans. Amer. Soc. Steel Treating*, **15**. 289, 1929 ; C. Reed, *Foundry*, **48**. 775, 1920 ; T. D. Robertson, *Electrician*, **70**. 501, 1912 ; *Journ. Inst. Elect. Eng.*, **53**. 533, 1915 ; *Engg.*, **99**. 176, 1915 ; A. G. Robiette, *Metallurgia*, **2**. 105, 1930 ; W. Rodenhauser, *Stahl Eisen*, **32**. 2127, 1912 ; *Chem. Ztg.*, **36**. 1294, 1912 ; W. Rodenhauser and J. Schoenawa, *Elektrische Oefen in der Eisenindustrie*, Leipzig, 1911 ; *Electric Furnaces in the Iron and Steel Industry*, New York, 1920 ; E. F. Roeber, *Met. Chem. Engg.*, **13**. 657, 1915 ; H. Roechling, *Stahl Eisen*, **27**. 81, 1907 ; M. Rossini, *Ind. Chimica*, **5**. 734, 1930 ; T. Rowlands, *Canadian Machinery*, 38, 1909 ; G. Ribaud, *Rev. Univ. Mines*, (6), **10**. 90, 1926 ; *Journ. Phys. Rad.*, (6), **8**. 250, 1926 ; *Tech. Moderne*, **21**. 225, 1929 ; J. W. Richards, *Iron Age*, **86**. 1206, 1910 ; *Trans. Amer. Electrochem. Soc.*, **18**. 191, 1911 ; *Iron Coal Trades Rev.*, **81**. 900, 1910 ; E. F. Russ, *Giesserei Ztg.*, **18**. 3, 1921 ; *Die Elektrostahlöfen*, Berlin, 1923 ; F. J. Ryan, E. E. McKee and W. D. Walker, *Iron Coal Trades Rev.*, **93**. 426, 1916 ; J. Saconney, *Bull. Soc. Ind. Min.*, **6**. 141, 1907 ; A. Sahlin, *Iron Coal Trades Rev.*, **98**. 609, 1919 ; A. Sailler, *Oesterr. Zeit. Berg. Hütt.*, **57**. 775, 1910 ; S. Schey, *Giesserei Ztg.*, **26**. 583, 1929 ; E. Schmelz, *Oesterr. Zeit. Berg. Hütt.*, **59**. 295, 313, 325, 341, 1911 ; *Foundry Trade Journ.*, **17**. 151, 1915 ; E. K. Scott, *Iron Coal Trades Rev.*, **95**. 7, 1917 ; W. Scott, *ib.*, **105**. 538, 1922 ; J. A. Seede, *Gen. Elect. Rev.*, **24**. 833, 1921 ; *Iron Age*, **114**. 128, 1924 ; J. Seigle, *Rev. Ind. Min.*, 104, 1927 ; R. Sevin, *Journ. Four. Élect.*, **37**. 137, 335, 1928 ; F. A. de Silva and C. G. Carlisle, *U.S. Pat. No.* 1745360, 1930 ; G. L. Simpson, *Trans. Amer. Electrochem. Soc.*, **57**. 435, 1930 ; F. T. Sisco, *The Manufacture of Electric Steel*, New York, 1924 ; *Trans. Faraday Soc.*, **21**. 224, 1925 ; *Fuels Furnaces*, **6**. 589, 1928 ; F. T. Snyder, *Trans. Amer. Electrochem. Soc.*, **19**. 198, 317, 1911 ; *Eng. Mag.*, **51**. 488, 1911 ; *Iron Coal Trades Rev.*, **95**. 280, 1917 ; F. Sommer, *Stahl Eisen*, **44**. 490, 526, 553, 1924 ; **46**. 909, 1926 ; J. H. Stansbie, *Foundry Trade Journ.*, **14**. 430, 1912 ; **21**. 703, 1919 ; A. Stansfield, *Trans. Canada Soc. Civil Eng.*, **18**. 72, 1906 ; *Blast Furnace Steel Plant*, **87**. 636, 1921 ; *Zeit. Ver. deut. Ing.*, **49**. 966, 1905 ; *Stahl Eisen*, **25**. 631, 1905 ; *The Electric Furnace*, Toronto, 1907 ; H. G. A. Stedman, *Proc. Cleveland Inst. Eng.*, 78, 1912 ; C. H. Stevenson, *Forging Heat Treating*, **13**. 222, 1927 ; A. Stewart, *Eng. Rev.*, **14**. 219, 1906 ; V. Stobie, *Iron Coal Trades Rev.*, **98**. 618, 1919 ; B. Stoughton, *Journ. Franklin Inst.*, **167**. 73, 1910 ; J. A. Sucrop, *Metal Progress*, **18**. 40, 1930 ; E. A. Suverkrop, *Met. Chem. Engg.*, **18**. 371, 1918 ; R. Sylvany, *Iron Trade Rev.*, **71**. 33, 1922 ; M. Tama, *Stahl Eisen*, **49**. 399, 1929 ; R. Taussig, *Electrochem. Met. Ind.*, **7**. 478, 1909 ; G. E. Taylor, *Elect. Rev.*, **97**. 285, 327, 1925 ; H. Thieme, *Elektrotech. Zeit.*, **31**. 903, 1910 ; R. D. Thomas, *Journ. Amer. Inst. Elect. Eng.*, **39**. 1038, 1920 ; P. Thompson, *Electrochem. Met. Ind.*, **4**. 265, 1906 ; *Eng. Min. Journ.*, **82**. 24, 1906 ; H. Verdinne, *Rev. Univ. Mines*, (6), **5**. 5, 1920 ; D. T. Waby, *Journ. Western Soc. Eng.*, **34**. 339, 1929 ; L. Waldo, *Eng. Min. Journ.*, **80**. 968, 1905 ; C. J. West, *Trans. Amer. Electrochem. Soc.*, **38**. 365, 1920 ; F. Wever, *Stahl Eisen*, **46**. 533, 1926 ; F. Wever and W. Fischer, *Mitt. Inst. Eisenforsch.*, **8**. 149, 1926 ; F. Wever and G. Hindrichs, *Stahl Eisen*, **48**. 11, 1928 ; *Metallurgist*, **6**, 1928 ; *Arch. Eisenhüttenwesen*, **1**. 345, 1927 ; F. Wever and G. Neuhauss, *Iron Age*, **121**. 1073, 1928 ; *Mitt. Inst. Eisenforsch.*, **8**. 171, 1926 ; D. Wilcox, *Trans. Amer. Foundrymen's Assoc.*, **33**. 206, 1925 ; J. Wright, *Electric Furnaces and their Industrial Applications*, London, 1904 ; J. L. M. Yardley, *Blast Furnace Steel Plant*, **12**. 532, 1924 ; **13**. 20, 1925 ; D. Zuege, *Elect. World*, **94**. 880, 1929.

⁹ P. L. T. Héroult, *Electrochem. Ind.*, **1**. 63, 287, 449, 467, 1903 ; **2**. 408, 1904 ; **3**. 56, 1905 ; **4**. 30, 84, 125, 152, 1906 ; **7**. 261, 1909 ; *Chem. Met. Eng.*, **8**. 179, 1910 ; *Electrician*, **81**. 588, 1918 ; *Zeit. Elektrochem.*, **9**. 556, 655, 1903 ; *Elektrotech. Zeit.*, **10**. 17, 123, 170, 1903 ; *Stahl Eisen*, **24**. 682, 761, 821, 883, 944, 1904 ; *Iron Age*, **77**. 690, 1906 ; **80**. 1884, 1907 ; *Iron Coal Trades Rev.*, **85**. 986, 1912 ; *Internat. Cong. Appl. Chem.*, **8**. xxi, 59, 1912 ; *Journ. Électrolyse*, **104**. 91, 1900 ; **114**. 1, 1901 ; **130**. 1, 1901 ; **131**. 1, 1901 ; **133**. 1, 1902 ; **150**. 17, 1902 ; **175**. 2, 1903 ; *Eng. Min. Journ.*, **75**. 524, 1903 ; *Elect. World and Eng.*, **37**. 874, 1901 ; *Brit. Pat. No.* 16293, 1900 ; 14486, 14576, 14643, 1901 ; 3912, 6950, 1902 ; 7027, 1903 ; *Eng. News*, **45**. 321, 1902 ; N. Wark, *Arch. Eisenhüttenwesen*, **2**. 145, 1928 ; H. Klinar, O. Reinhold and N. Wark, *ib.*, **2**. 151, 1928 ; E. de Mulinen, *Génie Civil*, **93**. 143, 1928 ; *Journ. Four Élect.*, **38**. 9, 1928 ; L. Lyche and H. Neuhauss, *Stahl Eisen*, **46**. 780, 1926 ; O. Thallner, *ib.*, **27**. 1677, 1712, 1907 ; H. Hollis, *Electrician*, **77**. 243, 1916 ; J. A. Mathews, *Trans. Amer. Inst. Min. Eng.*, **53**. 304, 1916 ; *Iron Age*, **97**. 1327, 1916 ; D. D. McGuffie, *Iron Coal Trades Rev.*, **95**. 609, 1917 ; F. T. Sisco, *Chem. Met. Engg.*, **26**. 17, 1922 ; *Trans. Faraday Soc.*, **21**. 224, 1925 ; K. Kerpely, *Giesserei Ztg.*, **19**. 487, 509, 1922 ; **21**. 242, 277, 320, 1924 ; D. A. Lyon and R. M. Keeney, *Bull. U.S. Bur. Mines*, 67, 1913 ; R. M. Keeney, *Chem. Met. Engg.*, **23**. 980, 1920 ; *Journ. Soc. Chem. Ind.*, **40**. 24, 1921 ; C. Combes, *Rev. Mét.*, **2**. 1, 1905 ; J. H. Gray, *Iron Age*, **96**. 1238, 1915 ; J. B. C. Kershaw, *Iron Trade Rev.*, **51**. 865, 1912 ; W. S. Gifford, *Electrician*, **70**. 444, 1912 ; T. W. Robinson, *Yearbook Amer. Iron Steel Inst.*, **8**. 115, 1918 ; *Chem. Met. Engg.*, **19**. 15, 1918 ; R. Turnbull, *ib.*, **7**. 260, 1909 ; *Trans. Amer. Electrochem. Soc.*, **15**. 139, 1909 ; W. H. Wills and A. H. Schuyler, *ib.*, **28**. 207, 1915 ; C. G. Osborne, *ib.*, **19**. 205, 1911 ; *Iron Age*, **87**. 262, 1911 ; J. J. Barton, *ib.*, **108**. 581, 1921 ; F. R. Eichoff, *Stahl Eisen*, **29**. 843, 1909 ; **27**. 41, 1907 ; H. Roechling, *ib.*, **27**. 81, 1907 ; F. Doubs, *ib.*, **31**. 589, 1911 ; W. Fielding, *Trans. Faraday Soc.*, **5**. 110, 1909 ; C. C. de Coussergues, *Rev. Mét.*, **6**. 589, 1909 ; T. Geilenkirchen, *Stahl Eisen*, **28**. 873, 1180, 1507, 1908 ; B. Osann, *ib.*, **28**. 654, 1017, 1908 ; M. H. Schmid, *Elect. World*, **77**. 605, 1921 ; E. G. Odelstjerna, *Bihang Jernkontorets Ann.*, 378, 1906 ; W. E. Moore, *Trans. Amer. Electrochem. Soc.*, **60**. 165, 1931.

¹⁰ A. W. Gregg and N. R. Knox, *Trans. Amer. Foundrymen's Assoc.*, **33**. 669, 1925 ; W. E. Moore, *U.S. Pat. No.* 1304350, 1923 ; 1532599, 1925.

¹¹ C. H. von Baur, *Chem. Met. Engg.*, **20**. 488, 1919 ; *Trans. Amer. Electrochem. Soc.*, **33**. 237, 1918 ; E. F. Cone, *Iron Age*, **100**. 485, 1917.

¹² V. Stobie, *Iron Coal Trades Rev.*, **96**. 402, 1918 ; *Brit. Pat. No.* 6741, 1911 ; 2081, 1912.

¹³ E. F. Russ, *Giesserei Ztg.*, **18**. 3, 1921 ; *Elektrotech. Zeit.*, **42**. 34, 1921 ; *Engg.*, **131**. 479, 1931.

¹⁴ C. A. Keller, *Trans. Amer. Electrochem. Soc.*, **15**. 87, 1909 ; **37**. 189, 1920 ; *Zeit. Electrochem.*, **9**. 516, 555, 1903 ; *Elektrotech. Zeit.*, **18**. 156, 1901 ; **9**. 20, 1902 ; **10**. 92, 126, 1903 ; *Zeit. angew. Chem.*, **17**. 131, 1904 ; *Electrochem. Ind.*, **1**. 162, 420, 1903 ; **2**. 150, 808, 1904 ; **3**. 433, 1905 ; **4**. 167, 1906 ; *Journ. Iron Steel Inst.*, **63**. i, 161, 1903 ; *Brit. Pat. No.* 22584, 1900 ; 24234, 24235, 1901 ; 15271, 1902 ; *French Pat. No.* 300630, 1900 ; 322700, 1902 ; 329013, 1903 ; 387461, 393740, 1907 ; 399643, 400461, 400655, 1908 ; *Trans. Faraday Soc.*, **5**. 113, 1909.

¹⁵ P. Girod, *Trans. Faraday Soc.*, **6**. 172, 1910 ; *Elect. Eng.*, **46**. 36, 1910 ; *Journ. Four Élect.*, **29**. 19, 1920 ; *Chem. Met. Engg.*, **6**. 452, 1908 ; **7**. 259, 1909 ; **9**. 581, 1911 ; **10**. 663, 1912 ; *French Pat. No.* 350524, 350802, 1905 ; 388614, 1907 ; 402758, 416927, 422717, 1910 ; *Iron Age*, **97**. 1194, 1916 ; *Trans. Amer. Electrochem. Soc.*, **15**. 127, 1909 ; C. A. Buck, *ib.*, **31**. 81, 1917 ; J. W. Richards, *Electrochem. Met. Ind.*, **7**. 9, 1909 ; J. A. Seager, *Iron Trade Rev.*, **44**. 1027, 1909 ; W. Borchers, *Stahl Eisen*, **29**. 1761, 1909 ; *Journ. Iron Steel Inst.*, **81**. i, 141, 1910 ; *Eng. Min. Journ.*, **88**. 1113, 1909 ; A. Müller, *Stahl Eisen*, **31**. 1165, 1258, 1911 ; J. B. C. Kershaw, *Iron Trade Rev.*, **51**. 1007, 1912 ; A. Stansfield, *Blast Furnace Steel Plant*, **9**. 550, 1921 ; C. E. Moore, *Trans. Amer. Electrochem. Soc.*, **60**. 165, 1931.

¹⁶ C. A. Keller, *Electrochem. Met. Ind.*, **7**. 255, 1909 ; *Trans. Amer. Electrochem. Soc.*, **15**. 97, 1909 ; *Trans. Faraday Soc.*, **5**. 113, 1909 ; *Iron Coal Trades Rev.*, **72**. 1237, 1906 ; J. B. C. Kershaw, *Iron Trade Rev.*, **51**. 1105, 1912.

¹⁷ F. T. Snyder, *Chem. Met. Engg.*, **13**. 336, 1915 ; *Trans. Amer. Electrochem. Soc.*, **19**. 185, 1911 ; **28**. 221, 1915 ; C. E. Moore, *ib.*, **60**. 165, 1931 ; H. B. Smith, *Foundry Trade Journ.*, **31**. 264, 1925.

¹⁸ The Electro-Metals Co., *Cassier's Mag.*, **52**. 51, 1917 ; *Elect. Rev.*, **73**. 155, 1913 ; T. D. Robertson, *Chem. Met. Engg.*, **9**. 573, 1911 ; D. A. Lyon and R. M. Keeney, *Bull. U.S. Bur. Mines*, 67, 1914 ; *Iron Age*, **98**. 517, 1916 ; J. Bibby, *Journ. Inst. Elect. Eng.*, **57**. 231, 1919 ; *Trans. Faraday Soc.*, **14**. 79, 1919 ; *Engg.*, **107**. 649, 1919 ; J. A. Crowley, *Trans. Amer. Foundrymen's Assoc.*, **25**. 359, 1916 ; J. L. Dixon, *Trans. Amer. Electrochem. Soc.*, **31**. 53, 1917.

¹⁹ F. Bitter, *Stahl Eisen*, **37**. 49, 1917 ; E. Blau, *Chem. Ztg.*, **50**. 6, 26, 1926 ; H. Nathusius, *Foundry Trade Journ.*, **24**. 71, 1921 ; *Stahl Eisen*, **30**. 1410, 1910 ; W. Kunze, *Zeit. Ver. deut. Ing.*, **58**. 256, 1914 ; J. B. C. Kershaw, *Iron Trade Rev.*, **52**. 197, 1913 ; *Elect. Times*, **44**. 58, 85, 108, 1913.

20 J. Härden, *Brit. Pat. No.* 26251, 1909 ; 3739, 1910 ; *Chem. Met. Engg.*, **9**. 595, 1911 ; *Trans. Faraday Soc.*, **7**. 183, 1912.

21 W. K. Booth, *Trans. Amer. Electrochem. Soc.*, **33**. 247, 1919 ; J. B. C. Kershaw, *Iron Coal Trades Rev.*, **101**. 638, 1920.

22 *Elect. Rev.*, **80**. 395, 1917 ; E. T. Moore, *Chem. Met. Engg.*, **23**. 825, 1920 ; *Electrician*, **83**. 438, 1919 ; *Elect. World*, **75**. 224, 1920 ; F. J. Cleary, *Journ. Amer. Soc. Naval Eng.*, **32**. 24, 1920 ; J. B. Kershaw, *Iron Coal Trades Rev.*, **101**. 638, 1920 ; F. Hodson, *Elect. Furnace Ind.*, **77**. 167, 1920 ; *Iron Age*, **106**. 1686, 1920 ; J. L. Dixon, *Brit. Pat. No.* 4742, 1914 ; 106626, 111103, 111104, 1916 ; 118233, 121563, 1918 ; H. Etchells, *Trans. Faraday Soc.*, **14**. 71, 1919 ; *Journ. West Scotland Iron Steel Inst.*, **29**. 2, 1922 ; F. W. Brooke, *Journ. Amer. Inst. Elect. Eng.*, **39**. 1036, 1920 ; C. E. Moore, *Trans. Amer. Electrochem. Soc.*, **60**. 165, 1931.

23 E. Stassano, *U.S. Pat. No.* 707776, 1902 ; 721703, 733040, 1903 ; *Brit. Pat. No.* 11604, 1898 ; *Italian Pat. No.* 47476, 1898 ; *Trans. Amer. Electrochem. Soc.*, **15**. 63, 1909 ; *Rev. Mét.*, **5**. 575, 1908 ; *Atti Congresso Internaz. Chim. Appl.*, **2**. 362, 1907 ; *Zeit. Elektrochem.*, **5**. 379, 1899 ; **6**. 221, 1900 ; **8**. 61, 852, 1902 ; **9**. 555, 1903 ; *Elektrochem. Zeit.*, **8**. 16, 1901 ; **10**. 123, 168, 1903 ; *Electrochem. Met. Ind.*, **7**. 247, 254, 1909 ; *Elektrotech. Zeit.*, **4**. 65, 1905 ; *Elektrotech. Rund.*, **20**. 103, 136, 1902 ; *Trans. Faraday Soc.*, **2**. 150, 1906 ; *Iron Coal Trades Rev.*, **72**. 1233, 1906 ; *Chem. News*, **93**. 221, 1907 ; *Zeit. angew. Chem.*, **12**. 104, 1904 ; *Journ. Soc. Chem. Ind.*, **20**. 816, 1902 ; *Stahl Eisen*, **19**. 727, 1899 ; **24**. 682, 761, 821, 883, 944, 1904 ; *Eng. Min. Journ.*, **75**. 524, 1903 ; **83**. 1135, 1907 ; *L'Électrochim.*, **8**. 121, 1899 ; *Chim. Ind.*, **4**. 114, 131, 145, 1902 ; *L'Ind. Électrochim.*, 29, 1901 ; 1, 1902 ; 27, 1903 ; *Brit. Pat. No.* 11604, 1898 ; 8288, 1902 ; *Chem. Met. Engg.*, **6**. 315, 1908 ; H. Goldschmidt, *ib.*, **1**. 247, 461, 1903 ; E. M. Schmelz, *Iron Age*, **92**. 856, 1913 ; *Chem. Met. Engg.*, **11**. 709, 1913 ; **12**. 216, 1914 ; R. Catani, *ib.*, **9**. 642, 1911 ; *Journ. Iron Steel Inst.*, **106**. ii, 215, 1922 ; F. C. Perkins, *Mines Minerals*, **29**. 277, 1909 ; J. B. C. Kershaw, *Iron Trade Rev.*, **51**. 959, 1912 ; C. E. Moore, *Trans. Amer. Electrochem. Soc.*, **60**. 165, 1931.

24 G. Muntz and I. Rennerfelt, *Chem. Met. Engg.*, **12**. 379, 581, 1914 ; **13**. 108, 1915 ; C. H. vom Baur, *ib.*, **14**. 479, 1916 ; **16**. 580, 1917 ; *Trans. Amer. Electrochem. Soc.*, **29**. 497, 1916 ; **31**. 87, 1917 ; I. Rennerfelt, *Brit. Pat. No.* 7367, 1912 ; 25171, 1913 ; A. Sahlin, *Iron Coal Trades Rev.*, **87**. 950, 1913 ; J. B. C. Kershaw, *ib.*, **101**. 638, 1920 ; C. E. Moore, *Trans. Amer. Electrochem. Soc.*, **60**. 165, 1931.

25 N. Broglio, *Stahl Eisen*, **51**. 605, 635, 1931 ; F. Gölzguter, *ib.*, **51**. 513, 1931 ; M. Mathieu, *Arts Métiers*, **84**. 199, 1931 ; E. F. Northrup, *Iron Age*, **127**. 228, 318, 367, 395, 447, 1931 ; *Fuels Furnaces*, **9**. 473, 603, 711, 833, 923, 1067, 1931 ; A. G. Robiette, *Iron Steel Ind.*, **4**. 125, 1931 ; M. Lacroix, *Rev. Mét.*, **28**. 151, 1931 ; J. A. Succop, *Metal Progress*, **18**. 40, 1930 ; W. Hessenberg, *Mitt. Inst. Eisenforsch.*, **13**. 169, 1931 ; R. Perrin and V. Sorrel, *Rev. Mét.*, **28**. 448, 1931 ; R. A. Hadfield and R. J. Sarjant, *Fuel Econ. Rev.*, **10**. 71, 1931 ; W. Esmarch, *Wiss. Veröffent. Siemens-Konzern*, **10**. 172, 1931 ; H. G. Bigge, *Steel*, **88**. 39, 57, 1931 ; R. B. Radulet, *Zur Theorie der eisenlosen Induktionsöfen*, Timisora, 1931.

26 Z. de Ferranti, *Brit. Pat. No.* 700, 1887 ; J. B. C. Kershaw, *Iron Trade Rev.*, **51**. 1067, 1912 ; *Electrician*, **58**. 812, 1907 ; F. A. Kjellin, *Trans. Amer. Electrochem. Soc.*, **15**. 173, 1909 ; *Tek. Tids.*, **35**. 260, 1905 ; *Jernkontorets Ann.*, **57**. 289, 1902 ; *Trans. Amer. Inst. Min. Eng.*, **34**. 742, 1903 ; *Zeit. Elektrochem.*, **8**. 710, 1902 ; **9**. 517, 658, 1903 ; *Elektrotech. Zeit.*, **10**. 122, 1903 ; *Electrochem. Met. Ind.*, **1**. 162, 376, 576, 1903 ; **3**. 433, 1905 ; **7**. 265, 269, 1909 ; *Eng. Min. Journ.*, **74**. 78, 1902 ; **75**. 524, 1903 ; *Zeit. angew. Chem.*, **17**. 133, 1904 ; *Brit. Pat. No.* 18921, 1900 ; R. Catani, *Journ. Iron Steel Inst.*, **84**. ii, 227, 1911 ; G. H. Stanley and W. Buchanan, *Chem. Met. Engg.*, **18**. 349, 416, 1918 ; V. Engelhardt, *Elektrotech. Zeit.*, **14**. 211, 256, 1907 ; **15**. 14, 1908 ; *Oesterr. Zeit. Berg. Hütt.*, **53**. 399, 419, 431, 444, 461, 470, 1905 ; *Stahl Eisen*, **25**. 148, 205, 272, 1905 ; *Zeit. Oesterr. Ing. Arch. Ver.*, **57**. 173, 1905 ; H. Wedding, *Stahl Eisen*, **27**. 1605, 1907 ; A. Schmid, *ib.*, **27**. 1613, 1907 ; W. von Rüdiger, *Giesserei Ztg.*, **3**. 385, 1906 ; H. Becker, *L'Ind. Électrochim.*, 7, 1903 ; A. Neuburger, *Berg. Hütt. Ztg.*, **62**. 481, 493, 1903 ; *Zeit. angew. Chem.*, **17**. 104, 129, 1904 ; F. C. Perkins, *Electrochem. Ind.*, **1**. 576, 1903 ; M. Saladin, *Rev. Mét.*, **2**. 20, 1905 ; E. C. Ibbotson, *Journ. Iron Steel Inst.*, **71**. iii, 397, 1906 ; J. A. Rawlins, *Iron Age*, **79**. 1136, 1907 ; J. Härden, *Elect. World*, **48**. 1140, 1907 ; *Elektrotech. Maschinenbau*, **17**, 1907 ; M. Dumuis, *Rev. Mét.*, **5**. 758, 1908 ; T. Rowlands, *Trans. Amer. Electrochem. Soc.*, **17**. 103, 1910 ; *Iron Age*, **85**. 1136, 1910.

27 O. Frick, *Journ. Iron Steel Inst.*, **88**. ii, 296, 1913 ; *Brit. Pat. No.* 4866, 1904.

28 W. Rodenhauser, *Journ. Iron Steel Inst.*, **79**. i, 261, 1909 ; *Elek. Kraftbetriebe Bahnen*, 381, 1911 ; *Giesserei Ztg.*, **7**. 17, 80, 112, 142, 174, 1910 ; *Zeit. angew. Chem.*, **24**. 2289, 1911 ; *Chem. Met. Engg.*, **6**. 10, 143, 458, 1908 ; *Stahl Eisen*, **28**. 1605, 1908 ; *Trans. Faraday Soc.*, **4**. 120, 1908 ; J. B. C. Kershaw, *Iron Trade Rev.*, **51**. 1067, 1912 ; A. Gradenwitz, *Eng. Min. Journ.*, **87**. 364, 1909 ; C. H. von Bauer, *Iron Age*, **97**. 1052, 1916 ; *Met. Chem. Engg.*, **11**. 113, 1913 ; O. von Kerl and W. Rohland, *Stahl Eisen*, **43**. 1095, 1923 ; H. Illies, *Blast Furnace Steel Plant*, **13**. 70, 1925 ; N. R. Stansel and E. F. Northrup, *Heat Treating Forging*, **14**. 663, 668, 787, 794, 1928.

29 A. Hiorth, *Some Remarks on Iron Smelting*, Kristiania, 1912 ; *Zeit. Elektrochem.*, **11**. 913, 1905 ; *Electrochem. Ind.*, **2**. 283, 323, 1904 ; **3**. 156, 1905 ; *Brit. Pat. No.* 7338, 1901 ; 28805, 1903 ; *Tek. Ukeblad*, 92, 1907 ; *Eng. Times*, **16**. 196, 1907 ; *Norsk. Tids. Haandwoerk*, **13**. 82, 1907 ; *Trans. Amer. Electrochem. Soc.*, **20**. 293, 1911 ; J. W. Richards, *ib.*, **18**. 191, 1910 ; A. Hiorth and F. A. Fitzgerald, *Met. Chem. Engg.*, **10**. 71, 1912 ; J. B. C. Kershaw, *Iron Trade Rev.*, **51**. 1169, 1912.

³⁰ E. F. Northrup, *Trans. Amer. Electrochem. Soc.*, **52**. 317, 1927 ; *U.S. Pat. No.* 1551766, 1925 ; *Trans. Faraday Soc.*, **13**. 212, 1917 ; *Journ. Franklin Inst.*, **201**. 221, 1926.
³¹ C. Hering, *Trans. Amer. Electrochem. Soc.*, **19**. 255, 1911 ; **39**. 313, 1921 ; **41**. 303, 1922 ; *Journ. Franklin Inst.*, **192**. 599, 1921 ; *Engg.*, **92**. 325, 1911 ; E. K. Scott, *Trans. Faraday Soc.*, **7**. 202, 1911 ; *Electrochem. Met. Ind.*, **7**. 266, 1909 ; **8**. 471, 1910 ; J. Härden, *ib.*, **7**. 478, 1909 ; **11**. 429, 1913 ; E. F. Russ, *Arch. Eisenhüttenwesen*, **4**. 277, 1930 ; *Giesserei*, **18**. 165, 1931.
³² G. Gin, *Bull. Tech.*, 566, 1065, 1904 ; *Congrès Internat. Liége*, **1**. 301, 1905 ; *Chem. Ztg.*, **31**. 739, 1907 ; *Electrician*, **60**. 295, 1908 ; *Trans. Faraday Soc.*, **5**. 137, 1909 ; *Foundry Trade Journ.*, **12**. 403, 1910 ; *Trans. Amer. Electrochem. Soc.*, **8**. 105, 1905 ; **11**. 291, 1907 ; **15**. 205, 1907 ; *Chem. Met. Engg.*, **3**. 372, 1905 ; **5**. 226, 1907 ; *Eng. Min. Journ.*, **80**. 875, 1905 ; *French Pat. No.* 263783, 1897 ; *The Electrical Manufacture of Steel*, Ottawa, 1904 ; J. L. Gages, *Rev. d'Artillerie*, **62**. 361, 1903 ; P. M. Bennie, *Electrochem. Ind.*, **2**. 20, 1903 ; G. Dary, *Électricien*, **30**. 305, 1905.

§ 7. The Annealing, Hardening, and Tempering of Steel

Theories of heat treatment are really theories of the effect of time on the changes represented in terms of temperature and composition by the iron-carbon equilibrium diagram.—J. M. ROBERTSON.

In the mechanical working of steel ingots by rolling and forging, if the work is performed above the A_1-arrest it is called **hot-working.** The hot-working of steel, said A. Sauveur,[1] (i) closes blow-holes and promotes soundness ; (ii) it at first increases the density by closing the blow-holes, and then decreases it ; (iii) it destroys the pre-existing coarse crystallization, and produces a grain which when other things are equal is smaller the nearer the finishing temp. is to the critical range —hence the operation is known as the *mechanical refinement* of steel ; (iv) it causes a deformation of the dendritic segregation, which results in a banded structure and directional properties ; and (v) it at first increases tensile strength and ductility, both longitudinally and transversely, but on further refinement, while it may continue to increase the elongation and reduction of area longitudinally, it produces a decided decrease in those properties transversely. It also increases resistance to shock longitudinally, but decreases it transversely. These results are the more marked the more impure the steel or the more intense is its dendritic segregation— *vide infra*, heterogeneous alloys.

When the mechanical work—*e.g.* cold-drawings, rolling, or twisting—causing a permanent change of shape is performed below the A_1-arrest, the process is called **cold-working.** According to R. Job, A. Sauveur, and S. S. Martin, if the work is sufficiently vigorous to affect all parts of the mass, no crystallization takes place while the steel is being worked ; and H. M. Howe found that hot-work has no direct action on the structure of the steel, but, as it retards crystallization until a lower temp. is reached, it may influence the structure in this way. According to A. Sauveur, the cold-working of steel (i) causes a permanent deformation of the components—ferrite, cementite, and pearlite—resulting in an increase in the hardness, tensile strength, and elastic limit, and a decrease in ductility ; (ii) decreases the density, magnetic permeability, and remanence, and increases the coercive force ; (iii) slightly increases the electrical resistance ; and (iv) decreases the resistance to corrosion and to the action of acids. Cold-work distorts the grain, or flattens and elongates the crystals in the direction of rolling ; and the lower the temp. the more pronounced the effects of cold-work. S. Sekito found the internal stresses in quenched steel due to the expansion of the lattice to be of the same order of magnitude as the tensile strength—*vide supra*, sp. gr.

P. Bardenhauer, C. F. Brush, G. K. Burgess and G. W. Quick, G. K. Burgess and R. W. Woodward, P. Chevenard, E. G. Coker, E. Crepaz, G. Delanghe, F. C. Edwards, J. H. Edwards and co-workers, H. Favre, E. W. Fell, C. F. Flolliott, A. Fry, R. L. Geruso, H. Giersberg, A. F. Golovin, G. W. Green, O. V. Greene, T. W. Greene, J. N. Greenwood, W. H. Hatfield, P. Heymans, E. Heyn, H. D. Hibbard, K. Honda and co-workers, B. Hopkinson, J. E. Howard, H. M. Howe and E. C. Goesbeck, S. L. Hoyt, J. C. W. Humfrey, T. M. Jasper, Z. Jeffries and R. S. Archer, J. D. Jevons, R. S. Johnston, J. A. Jones, W. Kerr, A. L. Kimball, F. Körber and E. Siebel, H. K. Landis, T. Leitner, P. Ludwik,

R. Mailänder, H. Malzacher, E. Marcotte, G. Masing, E. Maurer, E. Murata, A. Nadei and co-workers, A. Ono, B. Osann, A. J. S. Pippard and C. V. Miller, H. Poellein, E. P. Polushkin, A. Pomp and H. Poellein, A. M. Portevin, H. S. Rawdon, P. Régnauld, R. T. Rolfe, W. Rosenhain, P. A. Russell, G. Sachs, H. Scott, J. Seigle, S. Sekito, E. Siebel and A. Pomp, J. M. Snodgrass and F. H. Guldner, J. B. Sommerville, F. Stäblein, A. H. Stang and T. W. Greene, B. Strauss and A. Fry, W. Tafel, I. Takaba and K. Okuda, A. le Thomas, C. A. Trask, T. H. Turner and J. D. Jevons, A. W. Whitney, H. V. Wille, A. Wingham, and K. Yuasa studied the internal stresses in steel and iron.

T. Baker and T. F. Russell discussed the potential energy of cold-worked steel, and they assumed that the work done on the test-piece is $\int P.de$, where P denotes the applied load, and e the extension; and that the whole of that work is converted into heat excepting the quantity $\int \sigma (l+e)^{-1}de$, where σ denotes the load at the elastic limit; $(l+e)^{-1}$ denotes the area; and $\sigma(l+e)^{-1}$, the load. The subject was also discussed by G. M. Brown. T. F. Russell worked on the assumption that the increase in potential energy is accompanied by a change of phase—crystalline to amorphous or vitreous (q.v.). C. Barus calculated the energy potentialized in strained steel. If r_s and r_h denote the radii of wires before and after straining, P the stretching force, and $\delta l/l$ the longitudinal extension, then the work done per centimetre of length is $E=p\delta l/l$. If σ denotes the observed increment of temp., then E_θ/E will denote the part of the applied energy which is converted into heat, and the remainder $(E-E_\theta)/E$ represents the energy potentialized in virtue of the strain. For iron, $2r_s$=0·1362; $2r_h$=0·1310; P=50,000; $\delta l/l$=0·0875; $P\delta l/l$=4·37; θ=3·9°; and E_θ/E=0·48, so that 52 per cent. of the applied energy remains as potential energy. C. Barus was unable to detect any influence of mechanical strain on the state of the combined carbon in steel, but he did find that the rate of dissolution of steel wires hardened by drawing is greater than with the soft metal; and W. Rohn obtained a similar result. H. Hort estimated that the potential energy is of the order of 5 to 15 per cent. of the total work done on the test-piece. W. S. Farren and G. I. Taylor measured the energy stored in a metal during cold-working in terms of the difference between the heat evolved during deformation and the total work of deformation, and obtained 0·144 cal. per gram of metal with a 14 per cent. reduction; T. F. Russell obtained 2·27 cals. per gram. W. Spring made some estimates based on the difference of electrolytic potential of annealed and cold-worked metals. The subject was discussed by C. H. Desch, V. N. Krivobok, S. Sato, and T. Andrews—vide infra, electromotive force and tempering.

According to C. Barus, the density of white cast iron is of the order 7·6 and that of grey cast iron is 6·9; consequently, the density increases in a marked degree the greater the proportion of combined carbon in the metal. With steel the density decreases as the total carbon is more and more nearly combined, and the allotropic expansion produced by quenching steel is about 0·005. J. D. Everett found the vol. resilience of steel amounts to 2×10^{12}, so that if p be the value of the stress per sq. cm. for the given expansion, p=10$\times10^9$ dynes for steel. The tenacity of steel is 8×10^9 dynes per sq. cm., so that the approximate ratio of stress to tenacity is about 1·3 for steel; similarly, for glass the ratio is 3·3. In both cases stress is in excess. In the case of Rupert's drops it is probable that rupture would occur on quenching were it not for the favourable symmetrical structure of the globule. J. M. Batchelder observed that of twelve massive pieces of quenched steel, eight subsequently cracked, and one actually exploded—vide infra, sp. gr.

According to H. Wedding, the individual grains of malleable iron are ductile, and the malleability of the mass depends on the ductility of the separate grains. When press. is exerted on a single grain in the direction of one axis, as occurs, for example, when a piece of iron is hammered on an anvil, a scale is formed from the polyhedral grain. If, however, the press. acts in the direction of two axes, either at the same time, as in the case of rolling with a diagonal groove, or at different times, as in the case of hammering an ingot or rolling a bar, turning it round 90° after every passage through the rolls, the grain is converted into a column which is termed a fibre. Sections cut parallel to the fibres when examined under the microscope show a fibrous structure in which the separate fibres can be clearly followed, while sections cut at right angles to the fibres show a granular structure. A fibre cannot extend to any possible length without breaking up under the right conditions into granules. If the carbon attains or exceeds 0·5 per cent., the fibres split into grains with even a slight stretching. The same effect is produced with a low percentage of carbon by a small proportion of phosphorus, a large amount of silicon, or a moderate amount of sulphur.

Steels rich in carbon, and fine-grained iron usually form no fibres, but where steel ingots, after solidification, are made up of closely interlocking dendrites (Fig. 41), the dendritic segregation persists even when the dendrites have undergone granulation on cooling. When such steels are forged or rolled, the portions rich in the segregating elements or the fillings of the dendrites—*vide supra*—as well as those poor in those elements—the axes—are elongated in the direction of the work. Hot-worked steel thus acquires a laminated appearance (Figs. 42, 43, and 44), for it seems to be composed of parallel bands. Figs. 41 to 44 are due to G. Charpy.

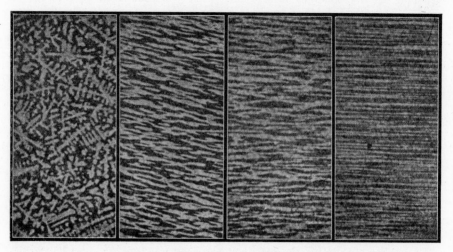

Figs. 41 to 44.—The Dendritic Structure of a Steel Ingot Before and After Cold-Working.

Fig. 41 shows the dendritic structure of a steel ingot ; Fig. 42, the same after being reduced to one-fifth of its original cross-section by hot-working ; Fig. 43, the same after being reduced to one-thirtieth; and Fig. 44, after being reduced to a hundred-and-fiftieth of its original cross-section. According to K. Nagasawa, the fibrous structure in forged or rolled steels is a deformed structure of dendrite, in which the segregation of impurities is present. Phosphorus is the impurity which chiefly causes the fibrous structure. The fibrous structure is not completely removed by an annealing below 1300°. The mechanical properties of forged or rolled steels are superior in the direction of the fibres to what they are in the direction perpendicular to them, and this directional difference is hardly reduced by a subsequent heating below 1300°. The direction of the fibres has an intimate relation to the lines of quenching cracks in steel.

M. Ettisch and co-workers observed that the crystallites in soft wires are arranged irregularly, but in hard wires they are regularly arranged to give a fibrous structure. E. H. Schulz and J. Goebel, and J. D. Gat studied the fibrous fracture of steel ; C. O. Bannister, S. G. Smith, A. N. Farfourine, W. Rosenhain and D. Hanson, F. Jansen, M. Hamasumi, K. Hübers, H. Pinsl, A. Wagner, G. M. Enos, and F. Rogers, the fractures of iron and steel ; and J. Descolas and

E. Prétet, A. le Thomas, I. Iitaka, K. Nagasawa, W. Claus and R. Hensel,
P. Oberhoffer and A. Heger, and M. Moreillon, the effect of mechanical treatment
on the texture of iron and steel. G. Tammann and A. Heinzel, H. G. Keshian,
B. Buffet and H. Thyssen, H. H. Meyer, A. Pomp and W. E. Schmid, A. Pomp
and H. Poellein, P. Oberhoffer, W. F. Durfee, and F. Wever and E. Schmid studied
the alterations in the orientation of the crystals produced by rolling ; E. F. Cone,
G. Tammann and co-workers, T. M. Service, A. Campion, T. Matuschka,
A. M. Portevin, F. C. Nix and E. Schmid, E. Schmid, F. Leitner, M. G. Yatsevitch, the structure acquired by casting ; E. Pitois, H. Wedding, and E. Schmid
the texture of cold-worked metals ; and N. P. Goss, the X-radiograms of plastic
deformation, when it was found that in the early stages of grain fragmentation there
was no orientation of the crystal *débris* until the grains are all broken into particles
of submicroscopic dimensions.

In the **heat treatment**—*Wärmebehandlung*—of iron and steel the attempt is
made to impart certain desired physical properties to the metal through the agency
of heat, chiefly by regulating the speed of cooling the metal in the austenitic
condition so that it is converted into martensite, troostite, sorbite, or pearlite,
or into aggregates of these constituents. The various forms in which the heat
treatment is applied include annealing, normalizing, hardening, and tempering.
In view of the predominant constituent present when particular qualities are
desired, hardening can also be called *martensitizing* ; softening as *pearlitizing* ;
and strengthening as *troostitizing* or *sorbitizing*. The structural changes due to cold-
work can be altered by heat treatment up to or over the A_1-arrest. The process
of **annealing**—*Glühen*—is often applied to counteract the hardening produced by
cold-work, so as to make the metal soft and ductile by the release of internal strains
and deformation produced by cold-work, the release of strains through the formation
of pearlite, and grain refinement. In annealing, the metal is heated past its critical
range so that on subsequent slow cooling it may be pearlitic and fine-grained. If
the metal is heated below the critical range, no structural
change occurs, except in the case of cold-worked hypoeutectic steel, where distorted ferrite may assume its
normal crystalline form. If the steel be heated to too high
a temp., the structure of the metal may be coarsened—
vide supra. The annealing temp. varies with the carbon
content, since the position of the critical range, or rather
its width, varies in the same way. The Heat Treatment
Committee of the American Society for Testing Materials
recommended 875° to 925° for steels with less than 0·12
per cent. carbon ; 840° to 870° for steels with 0·12 to
0·29 per cent. carbon ; 815° to 840° for steels with 0·30
to 0·49 per cent. carbon ; and 790° to 815° for steels with
0·50 to 1·00 per cent. carbon. The results are summarized in Fig. 45. The object
to be annealed must be kept in a given zone of temp. long enough to enable it to
acquire that temp. in all its parts. Hypoeutectoidal steels suffer no change until
the Ac_1-arrest is reached, when pearlite becomes austenite, and as the temp. rises
the free ferrite is gradually absorbed and the iron is changed to γ-iron ; beyond
the Ac_3-arrest the absorption of γ-iron is complete, and a homogeneous solid soln.
of carbon or iron carbide in γ-iron is produced—to wit, austenite.

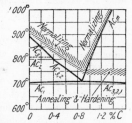

FIG. 45.—Diagrammatic
Representation of Heat
Treatment Zone.

M. Brés, D. Ewen, P. Galy-Aché, P. Galy-Aché and M. Charbonnier, P. Goerens,
L. Guillet, M. Hanriot, A. M. Portevin, F. Robin, A. Sauveur, A. Stadeler, H. P. Tiemann,
J. F. Tinsley discussed the influence of annealing on the microstructure, and the per-
sistency of the internal crystalline structure of steel which has been strained by local
deformation. The annealing of steels was discussed by A. T. Adam, H. Brearley,
A. Campion, H. Fay and S. Badlam, P. Goerens, N. P. Goss, R. Hohage and R. Rollett,
H. M. Howe and A. G. Levy, R. Hugues, E. Marke, J. Muir, R. Schäfer, O. Sirovich,
O. G. Styrie, C. D. Young and co-workers, and E. Zingg and co-workers, etc. ; and the
annealing of malleable and cast iron, by H. Bornstein, W. Campbell, R. Carrick, P. Cheve-

nard and A. M. Portevin, F. B. Coyle, J. V. Emmons, E. Houdremont and co-workers, H. M. Howe and co-workers, O. F. Hudson, E. L. Leasman, E. E. Marbaker, J. E. Stead and A. W. Richards, and O. W. Storey.

According to Z. Jeffries, an austenitic steel with a coarse grain structure at atm. temp. and heated through the transformation temp. will have a larger austenitic grain than one with a smaller grain size. If the cooling is slow enough, these changes are reversed and the free ferrite may form distinct grains ; if the cooling is faster, the rejection of ferrite may be complete, but the time may be too short for the ferrite to collect in grains ; while if the cooling is still faster, only part of the liberated ferrite can be recognized ; while with a still faster cooling, only part of the rejected ferrite collects at the grain boundaries, and part remains as a kind of emulsion in the pearlite. Eutectoidal steels have only one critical temp., the $A_{3,2,1}$-arrest. Above that temp. austenite is formed, and below that temp. pearlite. Very slow cooling furnishes laminated pearlite, or the cementite may be more or less balled-up to furnish the structure known as divorced pearlite ; with faster cooling the pearlite laminations may be curly, or so fine as to be scarcely recognizable—the so-called granular pearlite—and with still faster cooling, the system seems emulsified, for no laminated structure or ferrite can be detected microscopically. This is the sorbite structure—or hardenite. The subject was discussed by J. O. Arnold. With hypereutectoidal steels—say, one with 1·20 per cent. carbon or 94·6 per cent. of pearlite and 5·4 per cent. excess cementite—cooling through the $A_{3,2,1}$-arrest gives laminated, granular, or divorced pearlite according to the rate of cooling ; the excess cementite is scarcely affected, since it was deposited above the zone of temp. now under discussion—*vide supra*. Consequently, the cooling should be slow if maximum softening and ductility are desired, since the steel then becomes pearlitic ; but if greater hardness, strength, and elasticity are desired, at the expense of some ductility, the cooling should be faster. As a rule, the lower the carbon content of the metal the more rapidly it may be cooled from the annealing temp. without seriously interfering with the ductility of the metal. H. C. Jones compared the effects of annealing in an atm. of nitrogen, or hydrocarbons, or in air.

The cooling of steel—*Normalglühen*—from the annealing temp. in air with the object of obtaining a uniform structure is usually called **normalizing** the steel. In normalizing, the steel is heated uniformly to a temp. exceeding its upper critical point, the Ac_3-arrest, by about 50°, and then cooled in air only ; but hypereutectoidal steels are heated high enough to break up and dissolve the brittle network and needles of cementite, and cooled fast enough to keep the excess cementite in soln. at atm. temp. The most favourable condition for producing uniformity in structure is to keep the solid metal at high temp. for a long enough time. In practice, however, such a treatment may modify the grain-size or crystalline structure so as to affect deleteriously the physical properties, and the steel may become one of the states previously described as over-heated or burnt. In any case, a considerable grain-growth may occur during the normalizing process, and the treatment also tends to equalize the grain-size. Hence, in order to produce a more or less homogeneous, soft, and ductile steel containing a minimum of hard and brittle cementite the normalizing must be followed by annealing just above the $Ac_{3,2,1}$-arrest, in order to produce a smaller grain-size and change hard sorbite or troostic sorbite into soft and more ductile pearlite. The annealing may be conducted very near to the $A_{3,2,1}$-arrest with the object of spheroidizing the steel, whereby the cementite is converted into rounded particles or spheroids instead of lamellæ as in ordinary annealing—*vide supra*. Spheroidizing usually follows the normalizing process. It increases the machining qualities and the toughness of steel, and makes it more amenable to hardening processes. The subject was discussed by W. Parker, E. Houdremont and H. Müller, S. Epstein and H. S. Rawdon, F. G. Sefing, C. H. Herty and co-workers, O. E. Harder and co-workers, R. Whitfield, B. M. Larsen and A. W. Sykes,

J. D. Gat, A. M. Portevin and P. Chevenard, O. Sirovich, A. Pomp, and W. E. Woodward.

According to E. W. Ehn,[2] a coarse-grained structure in the case or core of carburized steel with large crystals of pearlite, and clean-cut cementite at grain boundaries in network in the hypereutectoidal zone are signs of good or **normal steel** ; while curly cementite, disintegrated pearlite in hypereutectoidal zone, and fine grained structure with rounded pearlite areas in the gradation zone and core of carburized steel are signs of an **abnormal steel.** In case-hardening, an abnormal steel has a tendency to give a thin case of high carbon-content and to form soft troostitic spots on hardening. The observations of H. W. McQuaid and E. W. Ehn, and of E. W. Ehn show that the abnormal structure is due to the presence in the steel of an excess of oxides, probably in the colloidal state. The particles of oxide act as centres of crystallization in the solidification of the steel. In normal steel comparatively few well-developed crystals are formed, while in an abnormal steel a large number of crystals interfere with the growth and development of one another. The original structure of solidification persists through the different stages of conversion and heat treatment. Hence, grain size with angular or triangular outlines of the pearlite is larger in normal steel than is the case with the more rounded areas of pearlite in abnormal steels. The particles of oxide retain their mutual position in the steel, and later on arrange the crystals in accord with the secondary crystallization of the steel. Observations were made by J. D. Gat, and S. Epstein and H. S. Rawdon. According to O. E. Harder and co-workers, the lattice dimensions of abnormal steel are greater than those of normal steels, indicating the presence of foreign material, probably oxide, in solid soln. in the ferrite—otherwise expressed, the oxygen goes into the space-lattice of the iron, and there exercises some bonding valencies with the adjacent iron atoms. Heating abnormal steel at the carburizing temp. in vacuo had no effect on the normality ; heating normal steel in nitrogen at about 940° did not change its carburizing qualities—presumably because nitrides are not formed at this temp. ; heating normal steel in oxygen at about 940° produced an abnormal steel—presumably owing to the formation and dissolution of oxides in the steel ; and heating normal steel in carbon dioxide at about 940° produced abnormal steel—presumably owing to the oxidizing action of the gas. When normal steel is heated in contact with various oxides at the carburizing temp., abnormal steels are produced by the dissolution of oxides. The depth of penetration of the oxides is proportional to the time of heating. Of the various oxides tried—Fe_3O_4, Fe_2O_3, Al_2O_3, and slag—ferric oxide penetrates the most rapidly and produces the most abnormal steel for a given time of heating. The rate of penetration of the oxide or oxygen, as determined by the formation of an abnormal carburizing zone, is exceedingly slow as compared with carbon penetration. The carbon is able to penetrate through a surface of abnormal steel and then produce a normal hypereutectoid zone. The more rapid penetration of the carbon, as compared with that of the oxygen, is probably attributable mostly to the relative affinities of oxygen and carbon for iron—or to state the same relation in another way, the relative stabilities of iron carbide and iron oxide compounds. In addition, the carbon atom is smaller than the oxygen atom and should for that reason diffuse more rapidly. Melting abnormal steel in vacuo in alundum or magnesite crucibles decreased the abnormality, and a normal steel under similar conditions became more or less abnormal. Melting normal steel in an alundum crucible in nitrogen or carbon monoxide produced more or less abnormality.

It is often said that civilization, directly or indirectly, owes to **the hardening properties** of steel very many advances which have been made. The hardening—*Härten*—of steel is effected by heating the metal above its critical temp., say to bright redness, and cooling relatively quickly, say by **quenching**—*Abschrecken*—it in a relatively cold liquid or in air. This fact has been known and utilized for ages. H. C. H. Carpenter and J. M. Robertson [3] observed that samples of ancient implements dating from about 1200 B.C. showed that the Egyptians were acquainted with the hardening, carburizing, and heat treatment of iron ; and N. T. Belaiew considered that the evidence showed that the Egyptians learned the art after the battle of Kadesh, when they came into contact with the Hittites and other peoples of Asia ; and that the art probably originated in Asia Minor, possibly Anatolia—*vide supra*, the history of iron. According to F. M. Feldhaus, St. J. V. Day, P. Jordan, O. Vogel, L. Beck, and B. Neumann, the Greeks knew at an early date that iron could be hardened by quenching the hot metal in water or in oil. Thus Homer, in his *Odyssey* (**9.** 93), related that when Ulysses plunged a stake into Cyclop's eye, the tumult was like that produced

> When the armourer tempers in the ford
> The keen-edged pole-axe, or the shining sword,
> The red-hot metal hisses in the lake.

It is said that the Chinese *Shoo King*, 2500 B.C., mentioned hardened iron. In Sophocles' *Ajax* (720) there is a comparison of being hardened like immersed iron ; Lucretius, in his *De rerum natura* (6. 148), may possibly have had in mind the hardening of steel by quenching. M. Lister discussed the passages bearing on this subject in Aristotle's Μετεωρολογικά (4. 6), and in Pliny's *Historia naturalis* (34. 14). According to H. Hanemann, a metallographic examination of some Celtic implements from Steinsburg, Thuringia, showed that the art of hardening steel was practised in Thuringia before the Germans settled there ; B. Neumann likewise examined some specimens, dating from the beginning of this era, and inferred that the carburization of iron was known in 200 A.D., but the specimens gave no evidence of quenching. In 1689, C. Salmasius described the process used for hardening iron in India. In the first century of our era, Pliny, in his *Historia naturalis* (34. 14 ; 39. 41), said that :

There is a very great difference when glowing iron is immersed in water. . . . It is used to quench thin pieces of iron in oil, for water would make them so hard as to be brittle. . . . The main difference in the steel prepared in different places results from the quality of the water into which the red-hot metal is plunged. The water is in some places—*e.g.* Bilbilis (Bambola near Calatayud), Tariasso (Tarragona), and Comum in Italy—better for this purpose than in others, and consequently some localities have become quite celebrated for the excellence of their steel even though no iron mines occur in these localities.

In consequence, attention was focused on the liquid employed for quenching ; it was believed that something passed from the liquid into the steel ; and some curious solutions and fantastic nostrums were recommended for this purpose during the period extending up to the sixteenth century, and even up to the present day. In the Middle Ages Justin, in his *Historiœ Philippicœ* (44. 4), referred to the subject ; and the hardening of steel was discussed by J. J. Becker, J. le Bègue, M. Eraclius, J. R. Glauber, R. A. F. de Réaumur, J. J. Wecker, etc. Even as late as 1810, in an anonymous book of trade secrets, it is said that steel will be hardened if quenched in an infusion of the roots of blue lilies or in urine ; and it will become as soft as lead if quenched in a decoction of common beans. The subject was discussed by B. Neumann, E. Grateau, etc. M. von Eulenspiegel found the remains of the workshop of an ancient armourer amongst the ruins of ancient Tyre. The "find" included a parchment describing in Syriac characters the hardening of Damascus sword blades. He thus translates :

Let the high dignitary furnish an Ethiopian of fair frame, and let him be bound down, shoulders upward, upon the block of the God Bal-hal, his arms fastened underneath with thongs ; a strap of goatskin over his back, and wound twice round the block ; his feet close together lashed to a dowel of wood, and his head and neck projecting over and beyond the end of the block. . . . Then let the master workman, having cold-hammered the blade to a smooth and thin edge, thrust it into the fire of the cedarwood charcoal, in and out, the while reciting the prayer to the God Bal-hal, until the steel be of the colour of the red of the rising sun when he comes up over the desert toward the East, and then with a quick motion pass the same from the heel thereof to the point, six times through the most fleshy portion of the slave's back and thighs, when it shall have become the colour of the purple of the king. Then, if with one swing and one stroke of the right arm of the master workman it severs the head of the slave from his body, and display not nick nor crack along the edge, and the blade may be bent round about the body of a man and break not, it shall be accepted as a perfect weapon, sacred to the service of the God Bal-hal, and the owner thereof may thrust it into a scabbard of asses' skin, brazen with brass, and hung to a girdle of camel's wool dyed in royal purple.

R. Theophilus towards the end of the eleventh century said that in order to harden tools for cutting glass and stone a he-goat, three years old, should be made to starve for three days, and then nourished with fern for two days, during which time the urine should be collected and used for hardening tools. He also said that the urine from a red-haired boy exerts a stronger action than does ordinary water. In the sixteenth century H. Cardanus said :

Steel is nobler than iron ; the best is that with small white cores. . . . If it is well cleaned, and then, while red-hot, quenched three or four times in a mixture of radish juice and water from earthworms, it will cut iron as if it were lead.

J. Ferguson pointed out that a sixteenth-century anonymous book on trade secrets advocated that the right use of alchemy is to apply chemical knowledge to industry, and the following quaint recipes were given for hardening steel :

Take snayles and first drawn water of a red die of which water being taken in the two first months of harvest when it raynes, boil it with the snayles, then heate your iron red hot, and quench it therein, and it shall be hard as steele. . . . Ye may do the like with the blood of a man of XXX years of age and of a sanquine complexion, being of a merry nature and pleasant, distilled in the middst of May.

The old workers, after all, may not have been so very far from the truth in assuming that special virtues resided in the liquid employed for quenching, since J. A. Brinell found the hardness of a steel with 0·45 per cent. C ; 0·27, Si ; 0·45, Mn ; 0·018, S ; and 0·028, P, which before hardening had a Brinell's hardness of 202 after quenching from 780°, had a Brinell's hardness of 217 using boiling water as the quenching liquid ; 223, using bitter milk at 20° to 25° ; 235, using wood-tar at 80° ; 241, using lead at 360° ; 248, using petroleum at 20° to 25° ; 255, using tallow at 80° ; 293, using skimmed milk at 20° to 25° ; 302, using sweet milk at 20° to 25° ; 402, using sulphuric acid, sp. gr. 1·837, at 20° to 25° ; 555, using whey at 20° to 25° ; 600, using soapy water (1 : 10) at 20° to 25° ; 627, using a sat. soln. of sodium chloride at 20° to 25° ; and 652, using soda-water at 20° to 25°. K. Honda and K. Iwase stated that the fact observed by J. A. Mathews that, in the case of alloy steels, more austenite is produced by oil-quenching than by water-quenching is valid only for thick plates or rods in which the internal stress caused by rapid cooling is fairly large and can be explained as an effect of stress—*vide supra*, martensite.

When steel is hardened, it is first heated above the A_1-arrest, Fig. 46, and then more or less abruptly cooled. Very little, if any, increase in hardness occurs if the steel be heated to a temp. lower than the critical range. This means that before quenching the metal must be in the condition of a solid soln. of iron and carbon or iron carbide, because the aggregate of ferrite and cementite formed on slow cooling through the critical range cannot be hardened by quenching. If the temp. be too high, the structure is coarsened without materially increasing its hardening power ; and quenching from too high a temp. increases the risk of warping and cracking the objects in the quenching. To produce the maximum hardness combined with the finest possible texture the metal should be heated just beyond the critical range, and cooled as soon as it emerges from the critical range of temp. Abrupt cooling or quenching arrests the change of martensite into soft pearlite ; so that quenching more or less fixes the constitution the steel possessed just before quenching. Quenching arrests the transformation of austenite into pearlite at the martensite stage. H. C. Boynton found the hardness of the different stages in the transformation to be as follows (ferrite unity) :

Austenite→Martensite→Troostite→Sorbite→Pearlite
104·0   239·0   88·0   52·0   4·3

Rapid cooling hardens steel, provided the operation starts above the transformation range, but not if it starts below that range. If the cooling starts within the transformation range, the metal is hardened to an intermediate degree, dependent on the state of the metal. In any case, the proportion of martensite which escapes transformation into pearlite determines the hardness. The hardness of martensite increases with the carbon content. Other things being equal, J. O. Arnold showed that it does not matter much at what temp. the cooling begins, provided it is above the critical range, 720°. The heating of the steel should be slow enough to permit it gradually and evenly to acquire a uniform temp. C. Benedicks, and J. A. Mathews found that a higher initial temp. produces a quicker rate of cooling than a lower temp., so that large pieces, in general, are heated to a higher temp. than smaller pieces. A. M. Portevin emphasized the fact that the dissolution of cementite in the hardening process requires time, and that the objects should be heated at the hardening temp. until all is transformed into austenite. The zone or range of the critical temp. varies with different steels ; medium and low carbon steels require a higher quenching temp. than high carbon steels, because in order to acquire dull hardening power they must be heated past their Ac_3- or $Ac_{3,2}$-arrests as the case may be. The increase in hardness produced by quenching is greatest with eutectoidal steel ; actually, quenched hypereutectoidal steels are harder than quenched eutectoidal steels because of the presence in the former of free cementite or carburized martensite. The general behaviour of steel during cooling and quenching was studied by G. V. Luerssen, W. F. Chubb, H. J. French, F. Wever, and A. M. Portevin. H. le Chatelier thus summarized the effects of cooling on 0·8 per cent. carbon steel initially in the austenite stage :

Rate of cooling	Transformation	Final State
Slow . . .	Austenite→pearlite	Pearlite
Medium . .	Austenite→martensite→pearlite	Troostite
Rapid . . .	Austenite→martensite	Martensite
Very rapid . .	None	Austenite

F. Osmond, L. Demozay, P. Chevenard, P. Dejean, J. E. Hurst, H. le Chatelier, A. Lundgren, B. Strauss, and A. M. Portevin and M. Garvin have also shown that increasing the speed of cooling from above the critical range lowers the Ar_1-arrest ; this lowering is at first gradual, but becomes quite sudden for a certain cooling velocity—the critical speed of quench-ing, or the critical rate of cooling. The observations are summarized diagram-matically in Fig. 46. With a sufficiently slow rate of cooling the Ar_1-transforma-tion occurs at about 700°, and austenite is transformed into pearlite ; by increas-ing the rate of cooling the transforma-tion temp. is lowered and the steel becomes sorbitic ; as the rate of cooling increases the transformation temp. is depressed to about 650°, and troostite appears ; and at a slightly greater speed of cooling a second arrest abruptly appears at a much lower temp., and martensite appears ; while with a still

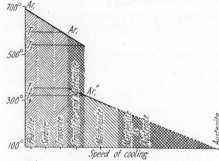

FIG. 46.—The Effect of the Speed of Cooling on the Ar_1-Critical Point, and the Micro-structure.

faster rate of cooling the upper Ar_1-arrest disappears, and the lower Ar_1''-arrest alone appears. When austenite is transformed at about 300°, martensite is formed. The appearance of the Ar_1''-arrest occurs at the so-called critical speed of quenching. If the transformation could be delayed by rapid enough cooling to ordinary temp., the steel would remain austenitic. This has been realized with manganese and nickel steels. A. M. Portevin found that when the cooling is fast enough to cause the trans-formation to occur at 300°, the hardening is only superficial—about 5 to 6 mms. thick ; and generally the greater the speed of cooling required to attain the critical speed, the more superficial the hardening. The intensity of the Ar_1'-arrest decreases as the temp. falls from T_1 to T_2, and at the same time the intensity of the Ar_1''-arrest increases as the temp. is lowered from T_3 to T_4. At the Ar_1'-arrest troostite seems to form around the corners of the austenite grains, and the central portions of the grains pass into martensite at the Ar_1''-arrest. K. Honda found that the doubling of the arrest can be studied better with nickel steels—· vide infra, manganese steels, Fig. 46 ; vide supra, the doubling of the Ar_1-arrest. K. Honda and T. Murakami called the Ar_1'- and the Ar_1''-arrests a stepped Ar_1-transformation—vide supra. H. Scott inferred that the Ar'-arrest involves the transformations $Ar_{3,2,1}$, and the Ar''-arrest the transformations $Ar_{3,2}$. The transformation Ar_2 is suppressed when Ar'' is observed, and it appears on a heating curve as an evolution of heat, and it is accompanied by the formation of troostite or a coarser condition of carbide. The maximum of the transformation $Ar_{1,2,3}$ occurs at a higher temp. when the previous cooling gives Ar' rather than when it gives Ar''. The subject was discussed by T. Murakami, T. Matsushita, T. Sutoki, P. Longmuir, H. de Nolly and co-workers, S. V. Bielznsky, H. Scott, etc.

H. Caron, and E. Hitzel discussed the quenching of steel in hot water. Observations on the effect of the rate of cooling, and on the cooling power of different liquids for quenching were made by J. A. Brinell, S. Haedicke, E. Jarolimek, L. Demozay, N. B. Pilling and T. D. Lynch, G. W. Pressell, P. Chevenard, H. V. Wille, C. D. Young, W. J. Merton, V. E. Hillman, J. Hébert, H. J. French and T. E. Hamill, R. Kühnel, C. Benedicks, J. Mercier and P. Michoulier, H. J. French and co-workers, E. Hitzel, D. Hattori, A. McCance, L. Grenet, J. A. Mathews and H. J. Stagg, S. E. Derby, J. B. Morey, W. G. Lottes, O. Smalley, A. M. Portevin, P. J. Haler, A. Mumper, R. M. Sandberg, B. H. de Long and F. R. Palmer, F. L. Wright, and K. Honda and K. Tamaru, J. H. Andrew, L. Roy, I. Obinata, H. Haedicke, E. Blass, P. Lejeune, W. J. Crook and co-workers, D. Uno, T. E. Hamill, F. B. Coyle, and J. Seigle; and H. le Chatelier, and J. A. Mathews found that (i) the rate of cooling in water remains constant up to a temp. of 37°; (ii) soln. of brine produce a faster rate of cooling, and retain their cooling power unimpaired so long as their temp. remains below 65°; and (iii) while oil-baths produce a slower rate of cooling, they can be heated to a much higher temp. without affecting seriously their cooling power. L. B. G. de Morveau mentioned the use of a water spray. R. A. F. de Réaumur used solid tin and solid lead as cooling agents; and also mercury; T. Gill, E. Lisbonne, and A. Evrard studied the use of lead baths; and L. A. Levat, phenol. C. Benedicks, and H. le Chatelier found that mercury is inferior to water; while C. Benedicks found methyl alcohol is superior to water as a cooling liquid. H. Scott, and G. Feodoséeff tried glycerol. C. Benedicks showed that the quenching power of a liquid depends largely on the latent heat of vaporization, and not on the initial temp. of the liquid or on its heat conductivity. H. le Chatelier also showed that sp. ht. rather than heat conductivity governs the speed of cooling. Mercury with a heat conductivity over ten times that of water is less effective as a cooling medium. A. M. Portevin and M. Garvin said that the rate of cooling is affected by (i) the temp. of the sample to be quenched; (ii) the mass form and dimensions of the sample; (iii) the position of a given point in the interior of the sample; (iv) the nature of the quenching bath, for the effect depends on the sp. ht., thermal conductivity, viscosity, and latent heat of vaporization of the medium; (v) the temp. of the bath, which may vary during the process of cooling; (vi) the agitation of the quenching liquid; (vii) the state of the surface of the sample; and (viii) the temp. of the liquid at the end of the cooling.

Hardened carbon steel contracts when it is kept for some time, and the process is accompanied by an evolution of heat. C. F. Brush and co-workers attributed the effects to the gradual relief of the strains produced during quenching—vide supra, martensite. The dilation of steel during quenching was studied by G. M. Eaton; the distribution of austenite in steel during quenching, by K. Honda and A. Osawa; C. Benedicks also showed that a certain amount of austenite is transformed into martensite at ordinary temp., but the transformation is opposed by the press. induced by the higher sp. vol. of the martensite. The separation of hard cementite is attended by a decrease in vol., and the transformation of γ- to α-iron, by an increase in vol. According to C. Benedicks, and Z. Jeffries and R. S. Archer, the separation of finely-divided cementite explains the tendency for a quenched steel to assume a greater hardness by ageing, even at ordinary temp. The subject was studied by C. E. Stromeyer, G. Sachs and W. Stenzel, R. F. Mehl, W. Köster, H. Lent and F. Kofler, G. Masing, L. B. Pfeil, F. Körber and A. Dreyer, W. P. Wood, W. P. Sykes and Z. Jeffries, J. Galibourg, A. Pomp, F. Nehl O. Bauer, E. Murata, F. S. Merrills, F. Sauerwald, A. Krüger, F. R. Hensel, A. Sauveur

K. Aders, W. Guertler, G. Sachs, P. Chevenard and A. M. Portevin, C. G. Heiby and G. Coles, L. C. Brant, W. H. Hatfield, H. J. French, H. Scott, B. F. Sheperd, G. V. Luerssen, G. Masing, W. Rosenhain, A. Michel and P. Benazet, H. Jungblüth, A. L. Bates, H. von Kroeckritz, J. Seigle, E. W. Ehn, S. S. Steinberg and W. Suboff, M. L. V. Gayler, F. Fettweis, K. Honda and S. Idei, G. A. Reinhardt and H. L. Cutter, and O. E. Harder and R. L. Dowdell. The spontaneous evolution of heat by hardened steel was noticed by C. F. Brush and co-workers. F. Cloup noted that the heating curves of quenched or cold-worked steels show evolution of heat at about 400°; the change is irreversible, and the cooling curves show no such phenomenon. K. Tamaru found that the density of steel consisting of β-martensite, at 200°, is less than that of annealed steel, but greater than that of quenched steel. T. Matsushita concluded that in the **seasoning or ageing of steel :** (i) Steels which are imperfectly hardened always exhibit a gradual elongation, or an elongation associated with a subsequent contraction. (ii) In steels which are well-hardened there is always a gradual contraction. (iii) The elongation is explained by the incomplete Ar_1-transformation, while the contraction is due to separation of unstable cementite from its solid soln.—the martensite. (iv) The complete separation of the first unstable cementite at room temp. requires several months or over one year, but by heating the steel to about 100° the same separation follows within two hours. (v) The separation of the unstable cementite does not affect the hardness of the steel appreciably, but the separation of the more stable cementite is associated with a loss of hardness. (vi) The electric resistance of a steel considerably increases by quenching, and decreases by tempering; this increase is due to the cementite in solid soln. (vii) The gradual elongation or contraction of quenched steel is always accompanied by an evolution of heat. This heat is the heat of transformation, but is not caused by yielding strain, as was generally supposed to be the case. P. Chevenard and A. M. Portevin studied the changes in the composition of the cementite during the ageing of the austenitic steels, by measuring the thermal expansion, hardness, electrical resistance, and remanent magnetism. Below 200° a carbide with a Curie point of 120° is precipitated and the iron returns from the γ- to the α-state at 200° to 225°, when another carbide with a Curie point of 170° is precipitated. Above 260° the transformation of the austenite to martensite and a carbide occurs, and the proportion of carbide becomes progressively less as the temp. rises. At 400° the steel is completely in the form of sorbite, and at higher temp., the precipitated carbide becomes richer in manganese at the expense of the ferrite. Observations were also made by M. Sauvageot; and W. Fraenkel and E. Heymann studied the kinetics of the operations—*vide supra.*

The early workers made several guesses in their attempt to explain how steel is hardened by quenching. According to E. Wiedemann, the Arabian Al Kâli early in the eleventh century said that iron exists in two forms, male and female; soft iron is the female, steel the male variety. In the thirteenth century Albertus Magnus said that water, the principle of fusibility, occurs in iron and gives it a certain softness, and if iron be made glowing hot, this most subtle, aqueous part distils away, and the remainder, in consequence, is hardened. Thomas Aquinas, A. Barba, and Basil Valentine held similar opinions. Robert Boyle, J. Locke, Isaac Newton, P. von Muschenbroek, and W. Nicholson referred hardness to the cohesion of the constituent particles. T. Hobbes, R. A. F. de Réaumur, and G. Agricola discussed the subject. O. Tachen said that when steel is quenched in water it acquires strength because " the light alcaly in the water is a true comforter of the light acid in the iron, and cutlers do strengthen it with the alcaly of animals "; and N. Lemery also mentioned that steel is produced by heating iron in the presence of horns of animals. G. Agricola, in 1546, seems to have regarded steel as purified iron—*ferrum sœpius liquefactum et a recrementis purgatum* ; A. Libavius, in 1606, compared the production of steel from iron with that of cement copper by iron; and, in 1779, J. Demeste regarded steel as iron free from what was then called zinc. G. E. Stahl said that steel is merely iron possessing, in virtue of its phlogiston, the characteristics of a metal in a higher degree than iron. A similar idea appeared in the works of J. F. Henkel, K. Neumann, J. A. Cramer, C. E. Gellert, S. Rinman, R. Kirwan, and P. J. Macquer. T. Bergman also held the phlogiston theory with respect to steel, although by oxidizing wrought iron, steel, and cast iron he showed that the percentage amounts of carbon in these materials were respectively 0·05 to 0·20, 0·20 to 0·80, and 1·00 to 3·00. J. Black attributed the hardness of steel to the extrication of latent heat ; and the abatement of the hardness by temper, to the restoration of a part of that heat. The observations of L. B. G. de Morveau, in 1786, and of J. R. Bréant, in 1823, have been previously discussed. R. A. F. de Réaumur experimented on the subject and concluded that " since the hardening of steel is due neither to the intervention of a new substance, nor to the expulsion of air, it remains to seek its cause in the changes occurring in its substance." When steel is heated, the " sulphurs and salts " are driven from the molecules into the interstitial spaces ; when the metal is abruptly quenched, the " sulphurs and salts " have not time to return to the molecules, but remain firmly cemented in the interstitial space., and hard, rigid steel is formed. In tempering, the " sulphurs and salts " partially return to the molecules, and the metal becomes proportionally soft.

The hardening, annealing, and tempering of steel, etc., are described in many textbooks and the general subject was discussed by R. R. Abbott, A. T. Adam, J. Adamson, J. H. Andrew, W. R. Angell, H. H. Ashdown, E. C. Bain and W. S. N. Waring, J. H. Baker, O. Bauer, O. M. Becker, A. E. Bellis, C. M. Bigger, H. Birnbaum, J. W. Bolton, H. M. Boylston, S. N. Brayshaw, H. Brearley, H. Busch, E. D. Campbell, W. Campbell, A. Campion, F. Camus, G. Charpy, P. Chevenard, E. F. Cone, J. Cournot, W. J. Crook, J. J. Curran, H. Damemme, E. F. Davis, G. Delbart, C. H. Desch, J. Durand, G. M. Eaton, G. Ede, B. Egeberg, W. Eilender, H. Esser and W. Eilender, E. W. Esslinger, G. S. Evans, H. Fay, R. B. Fehr, G. Franche, H. J. French, L. H. Fry, C. H. Fulton and co-workers, L. de Gerando, R. L. Geruso, F. Giolitti, N. P. Goss, L. Grenet, E. Greulich, M. A. Grossmann, L. Guillet and co-workers, P. J. Haler, J. H. Hall, H. Hanemann and co-workers, J. F. Harper and R. S. MacPherran, J. W. Harsche, D. Hattori, R. Hay and R. Higgins, R. A. Hayward, W. Heike and W. Brenscheidt, A. Heller, C. T. Hewitt, E. Heyn, E. Heyn and O. Bauer, H. D. Hibbard, O. Hoffmann, K. Honda, K. Honda and A. Osawa, H. M. Howe and A. G. Levy, W. P. Ishewsky, C. M. Johnson, B. E. Jones, A. Jung, H. Kalpers, M. Kawakami, H. C. Knerr, H. B. Knowlton, F. Körber, W. Köster, J. B. Kommers, E. F. Lake, F. C. A. H. Lantsberry, E. L. Leasman, P. Lejeune, P. Longmuir, H. Lüpfert, G. V. Luerssen, J. Lund, D. J. McAdam, A. McCance, G. W. McKee, P. E. McKinney, E. E. Marbaker, E. Marke, E. R. Markham, J. A. Mathews and H. J. Stagg, T. Matsushita and K. Nagasawa, E. Maurer, A. Merz and C. Pfannenschmidt, A. Michel and P. Bénazet, E. C. Miller, E. Müncker, P. Murnoch, P. Oberhoffer and co-workers, F. Osmond, C. Otto, E. Piwowarsky, C. H. Plant, A. Pomp, A. M. Portevin and co-workers, A. Poucholle, F. Rapatz and H. Pollack, F. Reiser, R. Rimbach, W. C. Roberts-Austen, J. M. Robertson, F. Robin and P. Gartner, P. Rohland, E. Ryd, G. Sachs, S. Sato, M. Sauvageot and H. Delmas, A. Schack, A. Schleicher, E. Schüz, H. Scott, R. M. Sherry, F. T. Sisco, E. K. Smith, J. E. Stead, S. S. Steinberg, B. Stoughton, C. E. Stromeyer, H. Styrie, K. Tamaru, O. Thallner, C. Tronson du Coudray, D. K. Tschernoff, J. W. Urquhart, A. Vierendeel, C. M. Walter, A. Weber, H. Wedding, O. Wedemeyer, M. Weidig, F. Wever, J. H. Whiteley, S. G. Williams, J. K. Wood, W. P. Wood, J. V. Woodworth, F. Wrightson, and J. B. Zabé.

The phlogiston theory of the nature of steel was rejected by C. A. Vandermonde, C. L. Berthollet, and G. Mongé, who, in their *Mémoire sur le fer considéré dans ses différents états métalliques*, in agreement with T. Bergman, showed that the difference in the main varieties of iron is determined by variations in the proportions of carbon, and that steel must possess a definite proportion of carbon in order that it may possess definite qualities. This factor in *l'aciération* was confirmed by the experiments of L. Clouet, F. Margueritte, W. H. Pepys, and others indicated in connection with the iron carbides—**5**. 39, 20. Near the middle of the eighteenth century C. Linnæus, in his *Pluto Svecicus*, said that steel is devoid of sulphur, meaning by " sulphur " an inflammable substance (phlogiston) ; and another school regarded steel as iron containing an inflammable substance. These divergent views are accounted for by the approach to the metal being made in different ways.

In one case attention was concentrated on the extraction of iron from its ores, and in the other on the production of steel by cementation. The correct view, said C. Benedicks, was set forth in the anonymous French work *Traité sur l'acier d'Alsace, ou l'art de convertir le fer du fonte en acier*, published at Strasburg in 1737, probably by the brother of G. Bazin.

It is generally agreed that the hardening of steel by rapid cooling consists essentially in the martensitization of the metal through the suppression of the transformations which austenite normally undergoes when it changes into pearlite. The transformation is suspended while the alloy is in the form of hard martensite. It is, indeed, an example of an arrested reaction—4. 31, 20. The martensite, so to speak, is trapped by the abrupt cooling. If some austenite has escaped transformation, it will not be so hard as if it had been completely martensitized, because austenite is softer than martensite; similarly, if some martensite has passed into the pearlite stage, the product is still softer. In fine, the degree of hardness of a steel quenched from above the transformation range is roughly a measure of the proportion of metal caught in transit in the martensite stage. The transformation of the martensite at ordinary temp., under ordinary conditions, is too slow to be of any consequence. According to H. M. Howe and co-workers, the suppression of the transformation of austenite before it passes beyond the martensite stage, that is, martensitization, is produced by (i) cooling carbon steels rapidly from the austenite stage; (ii) by the addition of a small proportion of an element, like nickel or manganese, which introduces a kind of lag, hysteresis, or passive resistance, hindering or obstructing the transformation beyond the martensite stage; (iii) by the super-cooling of cold austenitic steel in, say, liquid air; (iv) by overstraining austenitic steel by cold deformation, for this enables the austenite to pass into hard martensite; (v) by a reheating of austenitic steels to such a temp. that the austenite can pass into martensite; and (vi) by subjecting the metal to plastic deformation—*vide infra*, hardness.

Hardness in a general way may be regarded as a resistance offered to permanent deformation. Metals owe their resistance to deformation to attractive and repulsive forces between the atoms. A permanent deformation, therefore, involves changes in the relative positions of some of the atoms and the rupture of some interatomic bonds. Rupture takes place by degrees—*vide supra*, slip bands—so that the breaking of the atomic bonds does not proceed simultaneously. The different hypotheses which have been suggested are not necessarily mutually exclusive.

In one group of hypotheses the hardness of the martensite is referred to some peculiarity of the iron—say β-iron. This means that the cohesive forces of the atoms of this allotrope are assumed to offer a greater resistance to deformation than do the cohesive forces of the other allotropic forms of iron. In the so-called **allotropic iron theories of hardening,** expounded by F. Osmond,[4] and mainly of historical interest, it is supposed that hardened steel consists of a soln. of iron carbide or carbon in β-iron. The mixture is supposed to contain some α-iron in order to account for the magnetic properties. F. Osmond said :

Hardened steel is a steel in which the iron and carbon have preserved more or less completely in the cold the condition which it possessed at high temp. The heat of the change that has not been affected remains disposable in the metal, and may be termed the latent heat of hardening. We conclude that hardened steel owes its properties principally to the presence of β-iron, which is hard and brittle by itself at the ordinary temp. Carbon in the state of hardening carbon maintains iron in the condition during slow cooling up to a temp. which is in inverse proportion to the amount of carbon contained in the metal. . . . The influence of carbon is of the same character as that of the rate of cooling, and both combine to produce the final result. The rate of cooling alone is not sufficient under ordinary conditions in which hardening is effected to maintain an appreciable fraction of the iron in the β-condition. But as, under the same conditions, it is easy to maintain the carbon in the state of hardening carbon, and as the hardening carbon imparts stability to β-iron, it is evident in what manner β-iron may be successfully preserved up to the ordinary temp. by the aid of carbon. The more rapid the cooling, the more incomplete are the changes and the harder is the hardened metal.

The β-iron hypothesis has been previously discussed, and the β-iron hypothesis of hardening is dependent on the assumed properties of that allotrope. The equilibrium diagram shows that steels with up to 0·45 per cent. of carbon when quenched from between 900° and 750° would consist of β-iron and γ-solid soln. ; while steels with up to 0·85 per cent. of carbon quenched from between 750° and 700° consist of α-iron and γ-solid soln. Consequently, C. A. Edwards said that β-iron does not enter into the constitution of steels containing more than 0·45 per cent. of carbon. H. le Chatelier, and L. Guillet deny the existence of β-iron, and hold that the A_2-arrest does not represent an allotropic change. They also believe that the soln. is that of a carbide in α-iron, and that the hardness is due to the internal pressure caused (i) by the contraction of the red-hot material, and (ii) by the change in volume which attends the partial or complete change of austenite to martensite. Instead of β-iron, it has also been assumed that the iron of martensite is a soln. of γ-iron in α-iron. Indeed, all the possible changes have been rung in attempting to explain the hardness of martensite by assuming that it is due to the condition of the iron—α-, β-, or γ-iron and the possible combinations of these. As a result, C. A. Edwards could say that it is legitimate to infer that none of these allotropic forms of iron, as such, is an adequate cause of the hardening of carbon steels quenched from above the critical points. The subject was discussed by E. Maurer—vide supra, the allotropes of iron. G. Sirovich and R. Ariano invented another form of α-iron to explain hardness. G. Charpy said that the hardening produced in the cold metal by a permanent deformation by strain and that produced by quenching from a high temp. are similar states.

G. T. Beilby's theory of amorphous iron (q.v.) previously discussed has been adapted to explain the hardness of steel—the **amorphous state theories of hardening.** The hard structure is supposed to be due to the formation of an amorphous soln. of carbide in α-iron during the change from one allotropic form to another. The sudden lowering of the temp. prevents the viscous mass from crystallizing in a new state, so that the metastable, amorphous state is retained in the cold. This hypothesis was advocated by J. C. W. Humfrey. The interstratal movements caused by the dilation which accompanies the γ-iron→α-iron or the austenite→pearlite transformation are supposed to break up the crystalline condition of the iron and make it amorphous, and if the cooling is fast enough, this iron does not crystallize, but is trapped, so to speak, while it is in the hard and amorphous state. W. E. Williams found that the X-radiograms of hardened steel agree with the assumption that the hardness of martensite is due to the presence of amorphous material which crystallizes out in the tempering process. W. Rosenhain supposed that the amorphous iron is formed during the rapid cooling from a state in which every grain is encased in a thin, amorphous envelope ; in cooling there is not enough time for the growth of the grains of α-iron, and, in consequence, the grain-size is very small, while the amorphous envelopes are proportionally increased. The retardation produced by carbon is taken to represent the time needed by the nascent α-ferrite to transfer carbon to the surrounding untransformed austenite. Carbon is readily soluble in austenite, but sparingly soluble in ferrite, so that the transformation of a given particle from austenite to ferrite cannot occur until it has succeeded in expelling the carbon to the surrounding untransformed austenite. This hypothesis was discussed by H. M. Howe, R. J. Anderson and J. T. Norton, F. Osmond, A. Sauveur, J. O. Arnold, F. W. Harbord and T. Twynam, C. H. Desch, and Z. Jeffries and R. S. Archer. In the production of amorphous metal it was supposed by C. A. Edwards and H. C. H. Carpenter that during the quenching the mass undergoes an internal straining on the slip or gliding planes which produces a twinning of the crystals ; and that hard, amorphous or vitreous layers, formed during the internal slipping or twinning, are retained by quick cooling. C. Benedicks contended that the hypothesis that surface colours and that hardness are produced by amorphous metals in the plastic state is not in accord with metallographic facts.

It is generally held that the carbon in martensite is held in soln. either as carbon atoms or as carbide. The general opinion is that the carbide is present as the tritacarbide, Fe_3C, but J. O. Arnold postulated the existence of a subcarbide, $Fe_{24}C$—**subcarbide hypothesis of hardening**—because that corresponds with the eutectoidal proportion of carbon, viz. 0·89 per cent., and because some maxima in the physical properties—e.g. evolution of heat, and magnetic retentivity—are obtained with that proportion of carbon. It is assumed (i) that above the critical temp. the carbon of steel forms a subcarbide, the excess of iron separating as free iron, and the excess of carbon as cementite ; (ii) that by abrupt cooling this condition is preserved, so that hardened steel consists of and owes its properties to the subcarbide in the form of hardenite (q.v.) ; and (iii) that by slow cooling the excess of free iron and cementite persists, while the subcarbide is resolved into a mixture of ferrite and cementite, which, under favourable conditions, is interstratified to form pearlite. It is shown elsewhere that there is probably no such chemical individual as is here postulated, although H. Hanemann and A. Schrader also assume that the hardness is due to the presence of some such carbide. A rather vague hypothesis refers the hardening of steel to the assumption that carbon exists in the steel in two states—hardening carbon and cement carbon—vide supra, A. Ledebur. This is the so-called **carbon hypothesis of hardening.** Between 620° and 720° carbon passes spontaneously from the normal state of cement carbon to a special condition called hardening carbon ; the reverse change occurs during slow cooling. The cause of hardening by sudden cooling is attributed to the retention of carbon in the hardening state. It is generally recognized, as F. Osmond expressed it, that carbon presents, in its relations with iron, a certain number of peculiarities which are inseparable from its presence ; and a variation of the allotropic iron hypothesis was suggested by H. M. Howe, who assumed that the hardening of suddenly-cooled steel is due to the presence of hard carbides of γ- and β-iron, which are decomposed at the critical points only when the steel is cooled slowly. The carbides are supposed to have the properties needed to agree with the observed phenomena. This hypothesis was called the **carbo-allotropic hypothesis of hardening.**

C. Benedicks showed that in general solid soln. are much harder than the metals themselves—**solid solution hypothesis of hardening.** This was confirmed by N. S. Kurnakoff and S. F. Schemtschuschny. For small proportions of the element B dissolved in the solvent element A the coeff. of hardness, H, may be written $\delta h = H . \delta C$, where h denotes the hardness and C the at. percentage concentration of B. The more nearly similar, chemically, A is to B, the less the hardness coeff. H. The ready substitution of A by B generally means that the solubility of B in A is large, and conversely. Hence, when the solubility of B in A is large, the hardness coeff. H is small ; and when the stability of B in A is small, the hardness coeff. is large. If the added element B is very dissimilar to A, it must necessarily cause an essential change or distortion of the space-lattice of A, or it may interfere with the probably synchronous vibrations occurring in solid crystals. C. Benedicks inferred : In order that a metal A be hardened on quenching it is a necessary and sufficient condition that a substance B occurs which is but little soluble in A at temp. below a definite temp. T, but which is easily dissolved at a higher temp., and that it is impossible on sudden cooling from a temp. exceeding T to preserve the solid soln. AB at ordinary temp. On slightly reheating to a temp. less than T, a partial segregation of the solid soln. AB into a mixture A+B occurs, and the metal is tempered. This view is supported by L. Guillet, and A. M. Portevin. E. Maurer assumed that the hardness is due to the forced soln. of carbon—supersaturated soln.—which causes an appreciable increase in vol., and consequently a distortion of the crystal structure. Z. Jeffries and R. S. Archer said that solid soln. are harder than the solvent metal because slip is interfered with by the greater attraction between unlike than between like atoms, and by the roughening of the slip-planes due to solute atoms of different effective size than the solvent atoms.

Intermetallic compounds are hard and brittle because of the great attractive forces between the combining atoms, the non-interchangeability of positions of unlike atoms in the space-lattice, and the low crystalline symmetry of the space-lattice. The presence in an aggregate of any constituent having a high specific hardness interferes with slip in the surrounding material and thereby increases the hardness of the aggregate. This agrees with C. Benedicks' statement that every foreign atom by its frictional or locking effect retards the slipping action along a surface in the same way as a grain of sand retards the moving surface of a machine. C. Benedicks showed that while solid soln. are harder than the pure metals, the greatest increase in hardness is shown by supersaturated solid soln.; supercooled solid soln. are not so hard. The partial splitting up of a supersaturated solid soln., such as occurs on tempering steel, results in a decrease in the hardness of the metal. Austenite is regarded as a supercooled solid soln., and martensite as a supersaturated solid soln. The subject was discussed by H. Styri. J. O. Arnold's hardenite, 21Fe.Fe$_3$C, formed from pearlite, is a solid soln. which has the hardness characteristic of an amorphous solid soln. On tempering, a desired proportion of the carbide is precipitated from the solid soln. P. Chevenard suggested a modification of these hypotheses.

A. McCance suggested an **interstrain hypothesis of hardening**. He concluded that in a quenched and uniformly hardened steel the carbon is in solution, and it retains a portion of the iron in the γ-state; the greater the percentage of carbon the greater the proportion retained in solution. Most of the iron, however, is in the α-state, but owing to the restricted mobility during quenching, the crystalline units are not homogeneously orientated. In other words, owing to the rapidity of the cooling process the crystals of α-iron have not time to assume homogeneous orientation. At quenching, the crystal grains have the symmetry of γ-iron, and any γ-iron retained in the cold will have that symmetry, but the rest will be changed to α-iron, although lack of time, internal friction, and the obstruction caused by the crystals of γ-iron will prevent the crystals of α-iron arranging themselves homogeneously. The interstrain so induced by the α-iron makes the material very hard. W. von Möllendorff objected to the term amorphous when applied to metals with broken space-lattices, since it is not in accord with the mechanical properties of plastic materials. He attributed the hardness to a disturbed orientation and vectorial shape distortion of the crystalline molecules. H. Hanemann and A. Schrader attribute the hardness of martensite to a definite arrangement of iron and carbon atoms in a definite iron carbide. The actual bearer of the martensitic hardness is attributed to η-martensite—*vide supra*.

Z. Jeffries and R. S. Archer described what they called the **slip interference hypothesis of hardening** in the following words:

Metals are crystalline and are built up of atoms arranged in definite and repeating patterns. The regularity of atomic arrangement gives rise to certain planes of weakness, or low resistance to shearing stress. When an external load produces a shearing stress on such a plane, which exceeds the resistance of the crystal to shear on that particular plane, fracture of the crystal takes place. The fragments formed may or may not adhere to each other. If they do not, the failure of the crystal is complete, and it is said to be brittle. The plane of weakness is then known as a " cleavage plane." More generally; in the useful metals, the crystal fragments adhere and merely glide or " slip " over each other. The result of such slip, repeated on many planes, is a measurable permanent deformation. The crystal is ductile, and the planes of weakness are called " slip planes." The first appreciable formation of slip-planes marks the beginning of plastic deformation and, therefore, the passing of the elastic limit. The resistance to permanent deformation, which is a general measure of hardness and strength, represents resistance to the beginning and propagation of slip. Anything that serves to hinder slip is a source of strength and hardness.

In applying the hypothesis that *the hardening and strengthening of metals by any of the known methods may be considered as due principally to interference with slip*, Z. Jeffries and R. S. Archer say that the hardness of amorphous metals is attributed to the absence of planes of weakness characteristic of crystalline metals.

The increased hardness and strength of pearlite over pure iron are attributed largely to the increased resistance to slip in the ferrite grains offered by the hard cementite. The increased hardness of sorbite and troostite over pearlite is due to the refinement of the ferrite grains and the greater dispersion of the cementite particles. The increased hardness of martensite over troostite is attributed to the greater refinement of the ferrite grains, and, in cases of maximum hardness, to the critical dispersion of the cementite particles. The carbon in soln. or in a state of atomic dispersion in the ferrite of martensite makes it harder than the ferrite of pure iron. Carbon is less soluble in α-iron than in γ-iron; the α-iron of freshly-formed martensite contains carbon atoms in a state of atomic dispersion, so that it is supersaturated with respect to carbon; equilibrium is brought about by the precipitation of carbon as cementite. The carbon dispersed in α-iron at room temp. diffuses more rapidly as the temp. is increased. The carbide therefore precipitates slowly at room temp. and more rapidly with rising temp. The increase in hardness of freshly-quenched martensite on standing or after a mild tempering is attributed to the precipitation of hard cementite, which hinders movement on the slip-planes of the ferrite grains. Heating softens martensite by producing a growth of the ferrite grains. Heating produces changes in the carbide which tend to harden the steel until the critical dispersion of the carbide particles is produced; further heating softens the martensite. The growth of the carbide particles occurs as a result of the slight solubility of carbon in α-iron, which is greater the smaller the size of the cementite particles with which the soln. is in contact. The α-iron should reach approximately its equilibrium value before the growth of the particles begins, so that the carbide must be nearly completely precipitated at an early stage of the tempering. The more rapid the cooling of austenite, the lower the temp. of its transformation into ferrite and cementite. When the transformation occurs at or above 600°, both ferrite and cementite are formed as pearlite, sorbite, or troostite. If the austenite is preserved below about 600°, it seems relatively stable until a temp. of about 300° is obtained on cooling. When the austenite transformation is suppressed to about 300° or less, the allotropic transformation of iron occurs independently of the carbide formation. The composition of the steel may be such that by rapid cooling the austenite is preserved at room temp., but not so with slow cooling. The transformation of this austenite to martensite or another product on ageing or tempering results in an increase in hardness, which is also attended by an increase in volume. R. F. Mehl and B. J. Mair consider that the identity of the compressibility coeff. of quenched and annealed eutectoidal steel shows that the structural units and the binding forces between the atoms are not greatly different, and consequently that the hardness, as in the slip interference theory, is produced only by differences in the mechanical arrangement of the structural units. R. Vondracek attributed the hardness to the altered structure of the metal during crystallization. K. Honda, E. C. Bain, E. Heyn, A. Westgren, P. D. Merica, F. T. Sisco, M. G. Corson, O. E. Harder and R. L. Dowdell, and D. J. McAdam made observations on this subject—*vide supra*, martensite.

Another hypothesis, due to F. Reiser, refers the hardening of steel by rapid cooling—**stress hypothesis of hardening**—to the internal stresses which arise owing to the rapid contraction of red-hot material owing to (i) the shrinkage of the outer skin, and (ii) the increase in volume during the complete or partial change of austenite to martensite. C. Barus and V. Strouhal said that in steel there is a limited interchange of the atoms between the molecules under stress, which must be a property common to solids, if solids are made up of configurations in all degrees of molecular stability. In hardened steel the strain applied to the steel is locked up in the metal in virtue of its viscosity; tempering is the release of the molecular strain by heat. The hypothesis was discussed by O. Thallner, and W. Tafel. The stress hypothesis was discussed by R. Akerman, A. le Chatelier, W. Metcalfe, G. Charpy, L. Guillet, and H. M. Howe. The hypothesis does not explain why steel quenched from just below the Ac_1-arrest is soft, and when quenched from above that temp. is hard; why the hardness produced by quenching steel is so much greater than is the case with other alloys; and why quenched materials do not have the greatest hardness at the centre of the mass, where the internal press. is a maximum. Cold-work sets up a certain amount of strain and produces a slight increase in the hardness, a definite loss in ductility, and an increase in the elastic limit.

C. A. Edwards and H. C. H. Carpenter assume that austenite and martensite are constitutionally identical; the latter alone exhibits twinning. The hardness of martensite is attributed to the formation of amorphous material at the surfaces of slip on which twinning occurs. C. A. Edwards assumed that the hardness is due to the retention, by quenching, of the solid soln. of iron carbide in iron. The hardness depends on the fact that iron can exist in the γ-state and dissolve carbon; it is none the less dependent on the fact that the solid soln. decomposes with a slow rate of cooling into α-iron and iron carbide. Some energy must be absorbed in the quenching process in order to overcome the tendency for the Ar_1-inversion to occur. This energy acts in two ways: (i) by the sudden contraction of the outer envelope of the specimen; and (ii) by an internal mol. contraction of the mass which is related with the soln. press. or the osmotic press. of the dissolved carbide. The degree of hardness produced by quenching a given carbon steel will depend on the velocity and thermal magnitude of the suppressed inversion, *i.e.* on the amount of energy it is necessary to absorb in order to prevent the inversion taking place. This shows why the so-called austenitic, quenched, carbon steels are slightly softer than when the same steel is martensitic. The osmotic or soln. press. of carbon steels increases as the percentage of carbon increases from zero to 0·89, and then rapidly decreases as the percentage rises to 2·0, for, in general, the osmotic press. of soln. increases as the f.p. is lowered, as also the temp. at which the solid soln. deposits one of its constituents. The maximum osmotic press. in liquid soln. occurs with those having a eutectic composition, and in the analogous solid soln. with those having the eutectoidal composition. The maximum thermal change at the critical temp., indicated on the cooling curve, occurs with eutectoidal steel with 0·89 per cent. of carbon. Consequently, the maximum combined physical effect of iron and carbon occurs with steels having 0·89 per cent. of carbon; and since the hardening effect·is directly connected with the osmotic press., the thermal critical points, etc., it is to be anticipated that the maximum hardness should be obtained by quenching steels of that composition, and that austenitic steels should be a little softer than equivalent martensitic steels.

L. Grenet added that it is unnecessary to take the allotropic transformations of iron into consideration when discussing the hardness of steel. Quenching as compared with slow cooling may act (i) by changing the nature of the constituents, and notably by preventing, wholly or partly, the transformation on cooling. In this case, which is rare so far as steels are concerned, the quenched state and that obtained by slow cooling are really different states, and their properties cannot be foreseen. In a few cases the quenched state is softer than that obtained by slow cooling—*e.g.* J. H. Andrew's results with some copper-tin alloys. (ii) Quenching may also act by lowering the temp. of the transformation on cooling, and the quenched state is then always the harder. In general, "an alloy is the harder in proportion as the transformation which has given birth to its constituents at the time has taken place at a lower temp., has been more rapid, and as the maximum temp. reached since the last transformation has been at a lower temp. and has been maintained for a shorter period of time." The law also applied to pure metals. According to L. Grenet's hypothesis, hardness is not due to the complete suppression of the thermal transformation, but rather to its taking place at a lower temp.; quenching depresses but does not suppress the change. In consequence of the delayed transformation, the decomposition of the martensite furnishes products which are in a very fine state of subdivision, and the resulting fine state of aggregation accounts for the excessive hardness—**fine-grained hypothesis of hardening**—

vide infra, hardness. J. H. Andrew assumed that the hardness of a quenched steel largely depends on the transformation of austenite into martensite, and the formation of martensite as finely-divided free cementite embedded in a matrix of undecomposed austenite and α-iron. The hardness is thus attributed to the formation of a system with exceedingly hard, finely-divided cementite embedded in a relatively hard matrix of austenite, and α-iron. W. Rosenhain expressed his view of the hardening in the following words : "Hardening is due to the decomposition of a supersaturated or metastable solid soln. obtained by quenching, such decomposition resulting in the production of a very large number of crystallites of one or more phases, either constituting the whole of the hardened material, or scattered through a crystalline matrix." He added :

That a structure of this kind should possess, in some cases, an extreme degree of hardness is readily understood, since the softness and plasticity of metals in their ordinary condition are known to be due to the possibility of plastic deformation by a mechanism of internal slip in the crystals. Any disturbance of the regular crystalline arrangement results in a corresponding increase of resistance to slip, and therefore increase of hardness. If the disturbance of the structure be carried to the point where the slip mechanism is entirely destroyed or its functioning is eliminated, complete hardening results, and the degree of hardening in a given case will depend, in the first place, upon the exact extent to which the slip mechanism is disturbed, and, in the second place, upon the actual cohesive strength of the metal in question. In hardened steel, both factors operate to produce maximum hardness. Iron itself, although very soft and ductile when in the pure state, possesses a high degree of cohesion ; further, the simultaneous formation of α-iron and cementite during the decomposition of γ-iron, as a result of the allotropic transformation of the iron itself, brings about a structural arrangement most completely preventing the occurrence of plastic deformation by slip.

The relation of this hypothesis to the allotropic theory turns on the fact that the allotropic transformation gives rise to an abrupt change in the solid solubility ; it is related to the carbide hypothesis in that the presence of carbon is necessary to furnish one of the two decomposition products of the solid soln. ; and it is related to the amorphous hypothesis in that the kind of disturbance of the crystal structure of a solid soln. which is produced by the formation in it of minute crystallites of a deposited phase may be described as rendering the substance more or less completely amorphous in the immediate vicinity of each of these crystallites. One of the main features of the amorphous state is the very absence of slip mechanism, which in the present view is regarded as being essential to hardness. F. Osmond, however, inferred that the Ar_1-inversion is wholly or partly suppressed, because (i) the cooling curves taken during the quenching period show no signs of the evolution of heat ; (ii) the dissolution of soft and hard steels in a sat. soln. of ammonium cupric chloride shows that more heat is evolved by the hardened steel ; and (iii) the latent heat of hardening, so to speak, appears on the heating curves of hardened steel as accelerations. The subject was discussed by K. Scheel.

Modifications of this hypothesis—called the dispersion theory and the precipitation theory—have been discussed by Z. Jeffries and R. S. Archer, O. E. Harder, H. Esser and W. Eilender, W. Eilender and R. Wasmuht, and others. It is assumed that a metal may be effectively hardened by highly dispersed particles within the grains, such as may be precipitated from supersaturated soln. It is exemplified by the hardening of metals by heat treatment, in which the metal is cooled from a relatively high temp. into a region of supersaturation, and then by tempering or ageing to permit the formation of a fine precipitate. The precipitated granules tend to grow through a critical size, whereby a maximum hardness is attained ; any further growth is attended by a decrease in the hardness of the metal.

W. Rosenhain, W. L. Fink and K. R. van Horn, H. W. Gillett, S. Kimura, R. S. Dean and co-workers, G. Sachs, and K. Honda explained the hardness of martensite by the **distorted lattice hypothesis.** K. Honda said :

The distribution of the carbon atoms in the martensite has not yet been confirmed by X-ray analysis. These atoms cannot approach too near to iron atoms in virtue of the repulsive force coming into play between the two kinds of atoms when they approach very near together ; also they must take a symmetrical position in relation to the iron atoms. Hence in order to satisfy these two conditions, the carbon atoms in martensite may take positions in the centre of the face of an elementary cube, distributed here and there according to the law of probability. A local distortion of the lattice may of course result. These carbon atoms will send their lines of force toward six neighbouring atoms and themselves behave like diagonal supporters in square framework, thus giving to the lattice-building a great strength as a whole. From the above consideration the strength of martensite must increase with the concentration of carbon. This fact is confirmed by experiments as far as a medium carbon steel is concerned. In higher carbon con centrations the presence of austenite intermingled with martensite causes a decrease of hardness. Again, in a complete quenching, the size of the martensite crystals increases with carbon content and consequently causes a decrease of hardness in high carbon steels. It may be remarked that by quenching iron-nickel alloys containing about 15 to 30 per cent. of nickel from the austenitic region into water or liquid air, a martensitic structure is obtained, and the hardness greatly increases, though no appreciable content of carbon is present. This is also explained in the same way as in the case of carbon steels. Above the A_3-line iron atoms assume the distribution of a face-centred cube, some of them being replaced by nickel atoms according to the concentration, but below this line they take that of a body-centred cube ; the sides of the unit cubes in these two cases have a ratio of about 1·3. By quenching the alloys from the austenitic region into water or liquid air the lattice changes, as a whole, from the face-centred cube to the body-centred, but owing to the very rapid cooling, some of the nickel atoms may not have a sufficient time to assume their proper position and may remain in the centre of the face of the body-centred cube and play the part of carbon atoms in the martensite of carbon steels, thus giving to the alloys a great strength or great hardness.

The hardening or formation of martensite from austenite at the A_1-arrest involves a change from a solid soln. of carbon in γ-iron to ferrite and cementite. This involves the two independent transformations : (i) a change in the atomic configuration of iron from the face-centred to the body-centred lattice ; and (ii) the separation of carbon atoms as cementite from the interspace of the lattice. The change in the lattice configuration is attended by a great reduction in the solubility of carbon, and the formation of the α-iron lattice is attended by the precipitation of carbon as cementite. The A_1-transformation is a double process. With the slow cooling of carbon steels the austenite changes to martensite, and the lattice immediately forms pearlite ; but with very rapid cooling, or quenching, the change from austenite to martensite is retarded, and begins about 300°, and is virtually completed near room temp. The second change from martensite to pearlite cannot take place, because this change involves the diffusion of carbon atoms through iron and therefore the specimen will undergo a high resistance owing to its greater viscosity at room temperature. Thus the martensite is obtained by quenching the steel in water. Perfect quenching or hardening is obtained when the first half of the A_1-transformation—austenite to martensite— is completed, and the second half—martensite to pearlite—is suppressed. In the case of a less rapid cooling the first half of the transformation occurs at a temperature a little higher than in the above case, and therefore the second half partly takes place, resulting in a martensitic structure mixed with troostite. Troostite is a dispersed system, in which cementite is suspended in iron as very fine colloid-like particles, and hence is a mechanical mixture of cementite and iron and does not differ physically from pearlite. The hardness of martensite mixed with troostite is less than that of pure martensite. In this case there is an imperfect hardening. In the case of an extremely rapid cooling not only is the second half of the A_1-transformation completely suppressed, but also the first half is partially arrested ; there is thus formed a mixture of martensite and austenite the hardness of which is less than that of pure martensite. In this case there is a too severe quenching. L. Grenet pointed out that in quenching from, say, 1450° the α-phase, that is δ-iron, transforms to γ-iron with the evolution of heat ; but this transformation can be suppressed by quenching the metal in a bath at 850° : the iron then remains in the stable α-state without passing through the intermediate γ-state. Hence, quenching need not be attended by hardening.

R. F. Mehl and B. J. Mair consider that the identity of the compressibility coeff. of annealed and quenched eutectoidal steel shows that there is no marked alteration in the interatomic forces such as would have to be postulated by the lattice distortion hypothesis. H. Esser and W. Eilender concluded that the hardening of steel by quenching is controlled by the degree of dispersion of the precipitated iron carbide, and by the considerable distortion of the α-iron lattice produced by the separated carbide in the γ-α-transformation at a temp. at which the plasticity of the metal is very low. K. Heindlhofer and E. C. Bain added that the hardness of martensite must be explained on the basis of a strong interatomic bonding within the greatly supersaturated pseudo-solid soln. of carbon in ferrite, along with grain-size and distortion due to cold-work.

The different theories of hardening have been discussed by B. D. Enlund, W. T. Griffiths, etc. There is here a plurality of causes. O. E. Harder and R. L. Dowdell, and F. T. Sisco consider that hardness may be produced by (i) slip interference caused by the formation of martensite needles ; (ii) by grain refinement resulting from the recrystallization, as many small grains of α-iron are inherited from the parent austenite at a temp. below that at which normal recrystallization occurs ; (iii) the disturbance produced by stress distorting the lattice of α-iron and some residual γ-iron ; (iv) the saturation or supersaturation of the martensite with respect to the carbon atoms within the α-lattice; (v) the presence of numerous small particles of carbide which act as keys locking up the slip-planes, so that the hardness increases as the size of these particles up to a certain critical grain-size, after which it decreases as the particles of carbide grow larger ; and (vi) by the interatomic forces in the martensite. K. Honda also emphasized the probability that the cause of the great hardness is not due to any one condition, but rather to several. There is the hardness produced by fineness of grain, by internal strains, and by the presence of the carbon atoms within the lattice. He attempted a numerical estimate of these agencies in the case of the martensite of a 0·9 per cent. carbon steel with the Brinell's hardness of 680. The natural hardness of the steel is taken to be 280 ; the increase due to the fine-grained structure, 80 ; the increase due to interstrain, 150 ; and the increase due to the carbon atoms within the lattice, 230.

Heat treatment with the object of hardening the metal produces a fine-grained metal with the maximum hardness and tensile strength and the minimum ductility. The hardened metal, however, is usually too hard and too brittle, and it is also severely strained internally. W. R. Angell [5] found that the tensile strength and impact tests of steels quenched below the Ac_3- and above Ar_3-arrest are equally good, but the lower quenching temp. minimizes the quenching strains, and gives a more plastic material which can be handled without deformation. In order to relieve the quenching strains, to decrease the brittleness, and to restore the ductility without reducing the hardness and strength too much, the metal is tempered by heating it into a range of temp. extending from room temp. to a temp. below the Ac_1-arrest, and cooling it at any desired rate. The operation is called **tempering** —Anlassen—because it moderates, mitigates, relieves, or tempers the effects of the hardening process. An increase in toughness may be produced by a combination of hardening and tempering—Vergüten. In some cases the word "tempering" refers to the re-heating of hardened steel below 400°, and " drawing " or " drawing to the temper " for the re-heating of the steel above 400°. According to C. Barus and C. Strouhal, the tempering is accompanied by a chemical change even at temp. slightly above atmospheric. The mol. configuration of glass-hard steel is always in a state of incipient change, and a part of the change is permanent. If glass-hard steel be heated suddenly to 300°, it behaves almost like a viscous fluid. C. Barus added that the tempering may occur even at the ordinary temp., for the hardness of quenched steel, when kept at ordinary temp. for a few years, may be reduced as much as occurs if the steel be heated at 100° for a few hours. This phenomenon is rather different from the ageing to which reference has been made. This subject was discussed by F. Giolitti. A. Poucholle studied the variation in the length of steel rods as a function of the time of cooling after different heat treatments. He said that tempering is characterized by the absence of the transformation point Ar_1 at low temp. The transformation of γ-iron into α-iron only takes place at the point Ar_2, that is, at about 200°. Over the temp. range 650° to 200°, from the point Ar_1 to the point Ar_2, the curves do not show any angular point. However, invariably in this region, and only in this region, mechanical tensions appear, being manifested by sharp cracks and accompanied by the projection of the thin skin of oxide. The transformation point Ar_1 is lowered if the annealing observed follows a tempering. Similarly, the temp. at which tempering is obtained is lowered by successive temperings. The amplitude of the inflection Ar_1 diminishes (a) by rise in temp. until it becomes nil, (b) by the duration of the heating if the temp. remains constant. G. Kurdjumoff found by X-radiogram measurements that the tempering of hardened carbon steel takes place in three stages : (i) the breaking down of the tetragonal structure, which occurs at an appreciable velocity at 100° to 150°; (ii) the breaking down of the austenite at 250°; and (iii) the formation of an α-iron-cementite mixture, which occurs slowly at 300° to 400°.

Hardened steel is in an unstable or metastable condition ready to change to a more stable state as soon as the conditions are favourable—such as occurs, for instance, when the temp. is raised. Few pieces of structural metal are in a state of internal repose though not at the time acted upon by external forces. This subject was investigated by J. E. Howard. Internal strains up to the elastic limit may persist after all molecular flow has ceased. There is some stress above zero load which the metal will endure an indefinite time, whether this stress is the result of internal strains in some parts or is due to external forces. By annealing, the elastic limit is lowered as the temp. rises, and with a lowering of the elastic limit some of the strain is removed by an amount nearly proportional to the elastic limit. It is not strictly proportional, because the modulus of elasticity decreases as the temp. increases. The relief of the internal strains at ordinary temp. is hindered by the rigidity of the metal, but by raising the temp. a little the transformation can proceed at an appreciable rate. The speed of the transformation is faster the higher the temp. ; but in all cases it is a time reaction ; and hardening of steel is the result of an arrested reaction—4. 31, 33. C. Barus and V. Strouhal said that a transformation which occupies 3 hrs. at 100° is completed in a few seconds at 650°. E. Heyn and O. Bauer, and H. Hanemann also noted that the tempering may occupy only a few seconds when conducted at the right temp., where it does not proceed beyond the required stage during, say, 120 hrs. Hardened steel may contain a large proportion of martensite, as well as more or less austenite and troostite. If the steel is tempered with the idea of preserving its hardness, the operation is sometimes called *troostitizing*, because the steel is tempered in the range of temp. favourable to the growth of this constituent—between 100° and about 400° ; whereas if the steel is tempered for strength and ductility and retains the fine structure of martensite, the operation is sometimes called *sorbitizing;* the change occurs at a temp. between 400° and about 650° or even 700°. J. E. Stead and A. W. Richards, E. Marcotte, N. V. Kolokoloff, and N. N. Shadrin discussed this subject. G. Charpy and L. Grenet investigated the depth of the penetration of tempering.

The so-called *patenting of steel* is a process of heat treatment in which a structure verging on " over-heating " is imparted to rods or wire. In this process the temp. of the metal is raised steadily to a range dependent on the diameter of the wire, and well above the critical temp. of the steel ; this temp. is maintained for a period necessary to allow a complete diffusion of the carbon and the growth of the crystal grain to a maximum dependent on the sectional area of the wire. This metal is then rapidly cooled to retain the dispersed carbide in the state of sorbite. The process was discussed by J. S. G. Primrose, and J. D. Brunton.

H. Brearley gave 2499 for Brinell's hardness of a 1·1 per cent. carbon steel which had been heated to 760° and then quenched in water ; the hardness of the same steel after annealing at different temp. was as follows :

	50°	100°	200°	300°	400°	500°	600°
Hardness	2499	2490	2380	1190	917	770	358

H. C. Boynton stated that the decrease of hardness on tempering is gradual up to 350°, it is quite sudden between 350° and 550°, and zero above 550°. E. Heyn found the loss of hardness expressed as a percentage of the original increase produced by the hardening to be :

	100°	200°	300°	400°	500°	600°
Increased hardness	2·5	14·0	41·0	70·0	87·5	97·5 per cent.

K. Tamaru, and C. Grard noted an increase in Brinell's hardness of quenched 0·89 per cent. carbon steel from 661 to 683 when it is tempered at about 112° —*vide infra*, hardness. K. Tamaru found that the Rockwell hardnesses of armco and electrolytic iron, melted in vacuo, and of 0·2 per cent. carbon steel, melted in vacuo and in air, were :

	Annealed	Cold-worked	Tempered at 150°	300°	400°	600°	900°
Electrolytic in vacuo	58	86	84	83	80	56	43
Armco in vacuo	62	91	89	86	84	58	46
0·2 per cent. C {in vacuo	67·6	94	—	96	94	74·3	—
{in air	83	10·2	—	105	104	87	—

B. N. Enlund inferred that martensite is transformed into troostite at 100° to 200°, and that the reaction is most marked at about 110°, and that the retained austenite is decomposed at about 260°. This does not explain the initial hardening, for

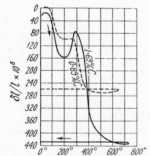

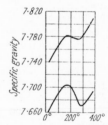

FIG. 47.—Dilation of Carbon Steel on Tempering.

FIG. 48.—The Effect of Tempering on the Specific Gravity.

troostite should cause a softening. K. Tamaru concluded that the initial hardening is due to the transformation of unconverted or retained austenite into martensite. The dilations $\delta l/l$ of 0·89 and 1·69 per cent. of carbon steels are shown in Fig. 47. These specimens do not show the expansion which should be caused by the transformation of retained austenite into martensite; rather do the specimens contract. This is because only a small proportion of austenite changes into martensite, and a considerable proportion of martensite changes into troostite. The latter change is attended by a contraction. The increased troostite does not have so marked an effect on the hardness. Near 240° the transformation of retained austenite into martensite produces an expansion, and that of martensite into troostite at 270°, a contraction. The sp. gr. determinations summarized in Fig. 48 show a maximum between 120° and 200°, and a minimum at about 270°, but not the effects of the expansion at 110°. These curves are similar to those obtained by E. Maurer—*vide infra*, sp. gr. K. Tamaru measured the sp. gr. of electrolytic and of armco iron, and of some carbon steels after cold-working and tempering at different temp. The selection from the results shows that the sp. gr. are as follow :

		Annealed	Cold-worked	Tempered at				
				150°	300°	400°	600°	900°
Electrolytic	in vacuo	7·883	7·881	7·880	7·879	7·881	7·880	7·882
	in air	7·834	7·835	7·834	7·838	7·837	7·840	7·840
Armco	in vacuo	7·878	7·875	7·875	7·875	7·874	7·875	7·877
	in air	7·808	7·807	7·806	7·809	7·806	7·811	7·817
0·1 per cent. C	as received	7·873	7·853	7·858	7·857	7·857	7·859	7·863
	in vacuo	7·861	7·855	—	7·853	7·853	7·856	—
	in air	7·820	7·801	—	7·803	7·803	7·807	7·814
0·2 per cent. C	as received	7·867	7·856	—	7·855	7·855	7·860	7·868
	in vacuo	7·844	7·831	—	7·830	7·832	7·837	—
	in air	7·822	7·811	—	7·813	7·815	7·820	—
0·4 per cent. C,	as received	7·840	7·828	—	7·830	7·829	7·837	7·845

The sp. gr. of armco iron is decreased by cold-work, and the sp. gr. attains a maximum with tempering at 150° and a minimum at 400°; the corresponding effects with steel are smaller. With armco and electrolytic iron remelted and solidified in vacuo, the change in sp. gr. produced by cold-work is slight; but if remelted in air, the sp. gr. is normally decreased by cold-work. L. Aitchison, M. G. Oknoff, E. H. Schulz, L. A. Lanning, M. A. Grossman, L. Aitchison and G. R. Woodvine, S. Sato, F. A. Livermore, W. Köhler, L. Traeger, A. M. Portevin and A. Sourdillon, C. M. Saeger and E. J. Ash, and G. M. Eaton also measured the change in the vol. or sp. gr. of iron and steel by heat treatment. Observations of the mechanical properties of steels tempered at different temp. were made by A. Jung, O. Thallner, O. Hoffmann, R. Kühnel, A. Michel and P. Bénazet, N. B. Pilling, M. A. Grossmann, G. Welter, A. T. Adam, R. Hay and R. Higgins, P. Goerens, H. Scott, H. Scott and H. G. Movius, W. P. Wood, L. Aitchison, H. Birnbaum, G. M. Eaton, R. Stotz and F. Henfling, M. G. Oknoff, H. I. Coe, M. Sauvageot and H. Delmas, F. T. Sisco, A. Bauschlicher, H. J. French, S. Curie, J. A. Mathews and H. J. Stagg, H. Bennek, E. Maurer, F. Giolitti, O. E. Harder and R. L. Dowdell, etc.; A. M. Portevin and co-workers, H. M. Howe and A. G. Levy, and C. R. Hayward and co-workers, the effect of time on tempering; S. L. Hoyt, and E. Murata, the effects of tempering on the internal stresses; W. Fraenkel and E. Heymann, the change in the sp. gr. and electrical resistance during tempering; W. P. Wood, and P. Chevenard, the volume changes; F. G. Sefing, the energy changes; W. Fraenkel and E. Heymann, the kinetics of tempering; A. M. Portevin, the relation of annealing to the phase rule and equilibrium diagram; and E. F. Law, K. W. Zimmerschied, R. C. Gosrow, W. B. Crowe, E. J. Janitzky, H. J. French and O. Z. Klopsch, J. A. Jones, and A. Schack, the influence of mass.

In the **Majorana effect**, observed by O. Majorana, two similar specimens of iron or steel are prepared, one is heated to orange redness, and the other remains untreated; the heated metal is then allowed to cool slowly; both specimens are polished; if now they be introduced into a very delicate thermostatic apparatus, the heat-treated specimen remains at a temp. 0·1° above the other for a few days. After some weeks, the temp. difference disappears. The effect is more pronounced with steel than with iron, and is of doubtful occurrence in lead or copper. M. A. Schirmann confirmed this result and suggested that the heating drives off dissolved gases and that these are gradually reabsorbed with evolution of heat. This is confirmed by H. Kleine's observations that the electrical resistance of vacuum-annealed iron (or platinum) increases practically linearly if it be allowed to stand in air over a period of five days. Similarly, when the gassed metal is reheated *in vacuo*, the resistance falls. E. D. Campbell and B. A. Soule observed similar effects.

According to E. Heyn, and O. Bauer, steel which had been hardened, but not tempered, showed well-developed martensite needles, which remained uncoloured after being immersed for 10 mins. in a 1 per cent. soln. of hydrochloric acid in alcohol. When tempered between 100° and 200° the martensitic structure was not changed, but it was coloured yellow or brown by treatment with the alcoholic hydrochloric acid. After tempering at 275° the acicular structure became coarser and behaved like mixtures of austenite and martensite, in that one constituent remained uncoloured while the other became dark. After tempering at 405° the martensitic needles disappeared and the sample appeared dark and mottled, suggesting a mixture of two relatively dark constituents—*viz.* troostite. After tempering at 500° the light-coloured areas became more abundant ; and after tempering at 600° irregular, rounded, light-coloured masses appeared which were surrounded by a darker network which was in relief. For theories of tempering, *vide supra*, theories of hardening.

P. Goerens said that hardened mild steel becomes soft at 520° ; and H. M. Howe found that the temp. required to release the internal strains or completely to soften steel hardened by various degrees of cold-working, measured by the reduction of area by cold-work, are :

Cold-work	4	8	12	15	25	50 per cent.
Temperature	750°	750°	650°	550°	550°	450°

J. H. Andrew and A. J. K. Honeyman found that the tempering of martensite begins at or below 150°, but is not complete at 360° in an hour. In a martensito-austenitic steel the austenite may be partially transferred at 150°, but below 260° the rate of change is very slow. It is complete below 370° in carbon steels. The tempering of a pure austenitic Ni-Cr-steel does not begin until near 300°, and is not complete in an hour at 360° to 370°. The presence of martensite thus appears to hasten the beginning of the austenitic transformation, but the pressure of the martensite thus produced inhibits the further tempering of austenite until more martensite is tempered. G. Tammann and E. Scheil found that martensite begins to pass into pearlite at about 100°, and austenite at about 250° ; H. Hanemann and L. Träger found that hardened steel is fundamentally changed when kept in boiling water for 14 hrs. R. Hay and R. Higgins discussed the low-temp. changes in quenched carbon steels. T. Matsushita and K. Nagasawa studied various physical properties of quenched carbon steels tempered at different temp., and concluded that the boundary temp. for martensite and troostite are produced between about 100° and 300° ; troostite at about 300° ; troostite and sorbite between about 300° and 400° ; sorbite (osmondite) at about 400° ; sorbite and granular pearlite between about 400° and 500° ; and granular pearlite from about 550° to the Ac_1-arrest. If the rate of heating be slower, the temp. here indicated should be lowered. They also said that when quenched steels are heated at the normal rate, a-martensite is formed on tempering between 100° and 170°, and β-martensite between 170° and 300°. The product of the decomposition of martensite on tempering is free carbon, not cementite ; and the precipitated carbon unites with iron, mainly between 300° and 400°, to form cementite. The subject was discussed by P. Chevenard and A. M. Portevin, H. Hanemann, A. Michel and P. Bénazet, G. Kurdjumoff, M. Godefroid, A. le Thomas, P. Roudié, and S. H. Rees.

W. Fraenkel and E. Heymann measured the electrical resistance and sp. gr. of various steels at different stages of the process of tempering at different temp., and they found that in quenched martensitic steels the change from martensite to osmondite will continue till completion at all temperatures between 100° and 400°, but below 200° the change takes several months. The rate at which the transformation takes place is a function of the temp., and the temp. coeff. is of the same order of magnitude as that of a chemical reaction in a homogeneous solid phase. The nature of the change that ensues in the structure of the metal during tempering between 100° and 400° can best be explained on the assumption that the dissolved carbon in the martensite reacts within the iron to form a metastable carbide, $FeC_{8\cdot10}$, and that an intimate mixture of this substance and iron constitutes osmondite. Further heating of the metal above 400° results in the gradual formation of cementite, followed by its agglomeration and crystallization to give with the excess iron the pearlite structure. The above theory is substantiated by an examination of the tempering curve as given by the change in electrical resistance ; this curve follows the kinetic law, $-dC/dt = KC^{10}$, where C is the amount of carbon in soln. after annealing for time, t. The velocity of the change from martensite to osmondite is independent of the quenching temp. within the range of the γ-phase, of the time of heating, and, within limits, of the carbon content of the steel. The sp. gr. of the samples shows that austenite changes first to martensite and then to osmondite during the process of tempering.

J. H. Andrew and co-workers studied the tempering of steels from the changes in their electrical resistance. The results show that the tempering involves a number of concurrent reactions, mutually dependent on one another. The process of tempering in martensitic steels may be divided into three reactions. The first of these is the separation of carbon from soln., accompanied by a fall in resistance proportional to the amount separating. The precipitated carbon is not removed from the system, but remains present as free carbide, the accumulation of which results in an increase of resistance proportional to the amount of carbon precipitated. This constitutes the second reaction. These two reactions proceed simultaneously,

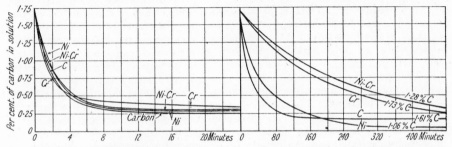

FIG. 49.—The Rate of Separation of Carbon from Martensitic Steel.

FIG. 50.—The Rate of Separation of Carbon from Austenitic Steel.

and give rise to an initial rapid fall of resistance. The state attained at the end of the primary rapid separation of carbon is not permanent, but the subsequent reaction is slower, and can be conveniently isolated. This final reaction is accompanied by a gradual fall of resistance, probably due to a gradual increase in the size of the precipitated particles. These three simple processes combine to give the experimentally determined curves. The rate at which carbon comes out of soln. was estimated by multiplying the fall in resistance per minute by a factor, 0·0334, expressing the ratio between the carbon in soln. and the resistance. The calculated rates of separation of carbon from martensitic steels are shown in Fig. 49, and from austenitic steels, in Fig. 50. The results show that martensitic steel tempers much more rapidly than austenitic steel, and that martensite cannot accumulate at the tempering temp. The martensite found in an austenitic chromium steel tempered for 3 hrs. at 250° must have been formed during the cooling. Austenite, indeed, can temper in two different ways : slowly at a constant temp., and more rapidly when the temp. is falling. At a constant temp. austenite appears in effect to temper directly to troostite ; martensite is only retained when the austenite is decomposed by cooling. The rapid breakdown during cooling is of the same nature as the lower change point designated Ar″, Fig. 46 ; the slow change at constant temp. is similar to that which occurs at the ordinary A_1- or A'-point. The resistance curves and the electrode potential curves indicate that the state attained by tempering at temp. below 650° is different from that obtained by annealing. At each temp. the steel attains a definite condition, retaining a certain amount of carbon in soln. in the ferrite, and this condition approaches closer to the annealed state, with progressive decrease in the amount of dissolved carbon, as the tempering temp. is raised. Between martensite and pearlite two states, troostite and sorbite, are generally recognized ; but it is clear that the transition from martensite to granular pearlite is progressive, and that troostite and sorbite are merely characteristic phases in the gradual change. Pearlite, sorbite, and troostite do not differ in state of division alone. They differ also in the amount of carbon in soln. in the ferrite, and to this may be attributed the remarkable difference in their properties, which is commonly ascribed to the state of division. A. Michel and P. Bénazet studied the effect of cobalt, nickel, chromium, and tungsten on the transformations.

The film of oxide formed on the smooth, bright surface of the metal varies in colour with the temp. of tempering. These **temper colours** are a guide to the workmen who temper tools, etc. They are discussed in connection with the tarnishing of iron. It is there shown that the time factor is ignored, since the same colour can be obtained by tempering for a given time at a given temp. or by tempering for a longer time at a lower temp. C. Barus and V. Strouhal found that each tempering temp. corresponds with a maximum tempering effect, which is more quickly reached the higher the temp. At 100°, for instance, the maximum effect was not obtained after one hour, and maintaining the steel two hours more at that temp. had little additional effect ; at 200°, the maximum effect was obtained in 10 mins. ; and at 300°, in one minute. E. G. de Cariolis and R. J. Cowan studied the heat treatment of metals in atmospheres of oxygen, nitrogen, and carbon monoxide ; and E. W. Esslinger, the effect of furnace atmospheres.

J. A. Mathews observed that three pieces of the same hardened steel when kept at 422° for 8, 20, and 40 mins., respectively, gave Brinell's hardness numbers of 425, 390, and 340. In general, the rate of cooling from the tempering temp. is immaterial, but after tempering for troostite the steel is generally quenched ; in tempering for sorbite slow cooling may make the metal more fragile under shock, a fault referred to as **temper brittleness** or *blue brittleness* (*q.v.*). The combined carbon of steel may occur as a soln. of carbon or cementite in iron—hardening carbon ; and as crystalline cementite—cement carbon. In tempering, the proportion of hardening carbon in martensite decreases and the proportion of cementite increases as the tempering temp. increases. E. Heyn thought that another form exists in hardened eutectoidal steel tempered below 400°, because of the carbon remaining as a residue on treatment with dil. sulphuric acid. F. Osmond regarded the residue in E. Heyn's experiment to be derived from finely-divided cementite which formed below 400° and which is decomposed by acid, whereas the cementite formed above 400° is coarser grained and more resistant to the acid. F. Osmond found more heat is liberated in the dissolution of hardened steel than is the case with unannealed steel —*vide supra*, cold-working ; E. Heyn also observed that the heat liberated on tempering hardened steel is a maximum at about 300° ; and H. Schottzky, that the evolution of heat when hardened steel is heated in water vapour indicates that some tempering occurs at 100°, and the evolution of heat increases with the proportion of carbon up to about 1·22 per cent., and then decreases. Hardened steel contracts at first when tempered, owing to the precipitation of some carbide, but the contraction is followed by an expansion, owing to the transformation of austenite into more bulky martensite.

Temper brittleness is exhibited mainly by alloy steels, although L. Grenet,[6] R. A. Hayward, F. Rogers, W. M. Carr, and others have reported it to occur with carbon steels. The temper brittleness is revealed by the notched bar or impact test, and not by the slow bending of plain bars or the tensile test. Hence, the stresses applied to the steel have to be localized to produce the brittle type of fracture represented by temper brittleness. The tough state appears when the steels are quenched from their tempering temp., and the brittle state when they are cooled slowly. Specimens subject to the disease that appear tough after water-quenching become brittle when cooled in the furnace. A sample of steel slowly cooled from 650° to

250° gave an impact test of 8 ft.-lbs., and when quenched from that temp. the test was 60 ft.-lbs. L. Grenet said that the embrittling effect is regularly observed with steels containing over 0·2 per cent. of carbon, over 0·2 per cent. manganese, 2 to 4 per cent. nickel, and 0·4 to 1·5 per cent. chromium, and that the effect is less regularly observed with steels containing a lower proportion of carbon. L. Grenet found the susceptibility to temper brittleness of acid open-hearth, electric furnace, and crucible steels to be in the ratio 4·7 : 2·2 : 1. Observations on this subject were also made by H. Brearley, R. H. Greaves and J. A. Jones, and Z. Jeffries. The microstructure shows no perceptible difference between the tough and brittle states in a given steel ; but G. d'Huart observed that the blue brittleness and ageing of steel are attended by a precipitation of cementite; H. P. Philpot, Z. Jeffries, and R. S. Archer hold that the fracture of the brittle steel is intercrystalline ; but W. Rosenhain said that it is practically impossible to recognize where the grain-boundaries are in oil-hardened and tempered nickel-chromium steel ; while W. H. Hatfield said that the fracture is not intercrystalline, but rather along the cleavage planes of the crystal grains ; a number of physical properties has been examined in order to find if any show marked differences between the brittle and the tough states.

R. H. Greaves and J. A. Jones found that the sp. gr. of tough steel was from 0·0004 to 0·0010 less than that of brittle steel, and when the tough steel was reheated to 200° the difference was greatly reduced. The difference due solely to toughness or brittleness is, at the most, one part in 20,000. When the effects of unequal tempering are eliminated they could detect no appreciable difference in Brinell's hardness of the two states. The electrical resistances of the two states were found to be the same within the limits of experimental error. The elastic limit of most steels in the brittle state is about 3 tons per sq. in. higher than the same steels in the quenched or tough condition, but with moderate rates of cooling, or when the tough, quenched steel is subjected to low-temp. annealing, the elastic limits in the two states are equalized. F. Rogers said that the brittle steel is softer than the tough steel, but he did not eliminate the effects of the extra-tempering of the brittle steel. F. Rogers, and R. H. Greaves and J. A. Jones obtained evidence that there may be an absorption of heat on heating and an evolution of heat on cooling through the brittle range. L. Guillet obtained no evidence of a difference in the brittle and tough conditions by observations on the thermal expansion or thermoelectric force. J. F. Kayser found that a steel subject to temper brittleness gave a 40 per cent. increase of magnetic remanence when slowly cooled. The phenomenon was studied by W. T. Griffiths, J. H. G. Monypenny, H. Kikkawa, H. P. Philpot, J. H. S. Dickenson, H. Brearley, L. Grenet, W. H. Hatfield, etc. The general results indicate that physical properties other than the notched bar test do show slight differences between tough and brittle specimens. Thus, J. H. Andrew and H. A. Dickie found the sp. vol. and hardness of tough specimens is rather greater than with brittle specimens ; K. Honda and R. Yamada found that the metal in the brittle stage is rather more magnetic than when in the tough stage. W. T. Griffiths discussed nitrogen as a possible factor in favouring the temper brittleness of steel. J. H. Andrew, G. W. Green, and R. H. Greaves and J. A. Jones noted the favourable effect of phosphorus on temper brittleness ; R. H. Greaves and J. A. Jones observed that manganese favours temper brittleness, and in the presence of phosphorus each element intensifies the action of the other one. R. H. Greaves and J. A. Jones observed that silicon favours temper brittleness ; vanadium has very little influence ; tungsten has no appreciable action ; molybdenum reduces or eliminates temper brittleness.

Z. Jeffries suggested that the phenomenon might be due to the existence of a low-temp. allotropic modification of iron, but there is no confirmatory evidence of this. J. H. S. Dickenson considered that the temper brittleness is connected with some alteration of the amorphous, intercrystalline cement, and is therefore confined to the layer, a few molecules thick, between the grains of sorbito-martensite. The

intercrystalline character of the fracture has not been established—*vide supra.*
W. H. Hatfield said that the fracture is transcrystalline.

On quenching from the tempering temp. the material has been trapped in a—from a
crystalline standpoint—metastable condition, that is, the atoms would not have had the
opportunity of·finally attaining their stable positions in the system of the crystals. If,
after tempering, the cooling be permitted to take place at a slow rate, resulting in a low
impact value, the atoms have had the necessary time and opportunity to take up their
stable situations in the crystal. The reason for the difference in manner in which the crack
is extended is to be found in the relative facility with which it can travel through the
diversely oriented crystals. In a perfect crystal, cleavage planes will offer planes of
weakness along which the crack may readily run, whilst in the unstable state, in which the
perfection of the arrangement is not attained, it is conceivable that the crack will not
travel with the same ease.

R. H. Greaves and J. A. Jones examined the hypothesis that temper brittleness is due to the presence of a chromium oxide in the steel, but did not find it
satisfactory ; nor did they agree with the hypothesis proposed by F. Rogers
attributing the phenomenon to the presence of carbides. He said :

On heating the steel to the dangerous zone, 450°, there is sufficient mobility of the
carbides to fall out of solution whilst the nature of the mixture still remains very intimate,
i.e. there is no microscopically visible aggregation of the constituents . . . at this stage
(with probably a minimum of true solid soln. in existence) there is a minimum toughness,
since the material is essentially but a mixture of carbides and solvent intimate enough to
have mechanical properties appreciably different from those of the solvent, but lacking
the toughness which it would have if infused throughout with a tough low concentration
soln.   Cooled in any manner from this condition, toughness is not regained, for there is no
solubility available to yield control below this temp.   Heated to the·(usual) higher zone,
in which there is a degree of solubility, toughness is produced, provided that the cooling
through the danger zone be rapid enough to prevent the dissociation of soln. so formed.

J. H. Andrew and H. A. Dickie assumed that the temper brittleness is caused
by the carbides separated on the grain-boundaries along the solubility line below
the A_1-arrest, and they demonstrated the presence of boundary carbides in brittle
specimens of nickel steel. The theory was advocated by K. Honda and R. Yamada,
who showed that the brittle metal is more magnetic than the tough metal, in agreement with the observation that carbide dissolved in ferrite diminishes its magnetizability ; and they also showed that the electrical resistance
on a rise of temp. is greater than on a falling temp. owing
to the dissolution of carbides. A nickel-chromium steel
becomes non-susceptible ·to temper brittleness when it is
free from carbon. The carbides here in question are
cementite and a complex iron-chromium carbide ; nickel
carbides are probably absent because of their instability,
and the nickel is present in solid soln. in the iron. As
R. Yamada has shown, with a carbon steel the solubility of
cementite below the A_1-point, Fig. 51, varies from 0·04 to
zero as the temp. falls to room temp., during which period

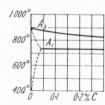

FIG. 51.—The Solu-
bility of Carbon in
Steel (diagrammatic).

cementite separates on the boundary of the ferrite grains. Nickel-chromium
steel will have a greater solubility than carbon steel for the carbides, and just
below the A_1-point this solubility decreases, at first rapidly and then gradually
as the temp. falls, until at room temp. the solubility of the carbides will be very
small or zero. If the specimen be cooled slowly from 650°, the carbides separate
on the boundary of the crystal grains and cause temper brittleness. K. Honda
and R. Yamada added :

The sorbite structure which is obtained by tempering a quenched steel consists of a fine
mixture of cementite and ferrite, and has a great resistance against the impact test as
compared with the pearlite ; while in a steel quenched, tempered, and slowly cooled the
carbides present on the boundaries of the sorbitic grains make the material very brittle,
so that the susceptible ratio of impact values in these two specimens becomes very large.
If the above view is correct, the sorbitic structure is not always necessary for the susceptibility, and the pearlitic nickel-chromium steel, when quenched from 600° to 650°, should

have a greater impact value than the same steel slowly cooled from the same temp.   But here the susceptibility ratio must be much smaller ; because the pearlite offers much less resistance than the sorbite to the impact test, while the grain boundary has the same strength as before.

REFERENCES.

[1] A. T. Adam, *Foundry Trade Journ.*, **16**. 227, 1914 ; T. Andrews, *Proc. Inst. Civil Eng.*, **118**. 356, 1894 ; J. O. Arnold, *ib.*, **123**. 127, 1896 ; T. Baker and T. F. Russell, *Journ. Iron Steel Inst.*, **101**. i, 341, 1920 ; C. O. Bannister, *ib.*, **69**. i, 161, 1906 ; P. Bardenhauer, *Stahl Eisen*, **45**. 1098, 1925 ; C. Barus, *Bull. U.S. Geol. Sur.*, 73, 1891 ; 94, 1892 ; *Amer. Journ. Science*, (3), **32**. 190, 1886 ; J. M. Batchelder, *Journ. Franklin Inst.*, **8**. 133, 1844 ; H. Bornstein, *Fuels Furnaces*, **7**. 1377, 1929; H. Brearley, *Foundry Trade Journ.*, **15**. 769, 1913; M. Brés, *Rev. Mét.*, **10**. 797, 1913 ; G. M. Brown, *Journ. Iron Steel Inst.*, **107**. i, 512, 1923 ; C. F. Brush, *Trans. Amer. Inst. Min. Eng.*, **62**. 17, 1919 ; B. Buffet and H. Thyssen, *Rev. Univ. Mines*, (7), **18**. 5, 1928 ; G. K. Burgess and G. W. Quick, *Tech. Paper Bur. Standards*, 235, 1923 ; G. K. Burgess and R. W. Woodward, *ib.*, 209, 1922 ; W. Campbell, *Journ. Iron Steel Inst.*, **64**. ii, 359, 1903 ; A. Campion, *Journ. West Scotland Iron Steel Inst.*, **7**, 72, 98, 1899 ; **8**. 23, 83, 1901 ; *Foundry Trade Journ.*, **42**. 88, 1930 ; R. Carrick, *Proc. Brit. Foundrymen's Assoc.*, 196, 1914 ; G. Charpy, *Journ. Iron Steel Inst.*, **98**. ii, 7, 1918 ; *Rev. Mét.*, **15**. 427, 1918 ; *Génie Civil*, **70**. 109, 1917 ; *Stahl Eisen*, **37**. 740, 1917 ; P. Chevenard, *Compt. Rend.*, **188**. 1670, 1929 ; P. Chevenard and A. M. Portevin, *Rev. Mét.*, **22**. 357, 1925 ; W. Claus and R. Hensel, *Giesserei*, **18**. 399, 437, 459, 476, 499, 1931 ; E. G. Coker, *Proc. Inst. Aeronautical Eng.*, 511, 1925 ; *Journ. Soc. Arts*, **75**. 1017, 1033, 1060, 1927 ; E. F. Cone, *Iron Age*, **96**. 1294, 1915 ; **97**, 1310, 1916 ; F. B. Coyle, *Trans. Amer. Soc. Steel Treating*, **12**. 446, 1929 ; E. Crepaz, *Atti Congresso Chim. Puro Appl.*, **3**. 380, 1930 ; G. Delanghe, *Génie Civil*, **91**, 243, 271, 297, 1927 ; C. H. Desch, *Proc. Roy. Soc.*, **125**. A, 628, 1929 ; J. Descolas and E. Prétet, *Rev. Mét.*, **20**. 597, 1923 ; W. F. Durfee, *Journ. Franklin Inst.*, **162**. 110, 1896 ; F. C. Edwards, *Foundry Trade Journ.*. **30**. 519, 1924 ; J. H. Edwards, H. L. Whitmore and A. H. Stang, *Journ. Research Bur. Standards*, **4**. 395, 1930 ; J. V. Emmons, *Iron Trade Rev.*, **50**. 450, 1912 ; G. M. Enos, *Metals Alloys*, **1**. 595, 1930 ; S. Epstein and H. S. Rawdon, *Trans. Amer. Soc. Steel Treating*, **12**. 337, 413, 1927 ; *Research Papers Bur. Standards*, 14, 1928 ; *Journ. Research Bur. Standards*, **1**. 423, 1928 ; M. Ettisch, M. Polyani and K. Weissenberg, *Zeit. phys. Chem.*, **99**. 332, 1921 ; J. D. Everett, *Phil. Trans.*, **156**. 369, 1866 ; D. Ewen, *Internat. Zeit. Metallog.*, **6**. 1, 1914 ; A. N. Farfourine, *Proc. Russ. Met. Soc.*, 91, 1928 ; *Rev. Mét.*, **27**. 220, 1930 ; W. S. Farren and G. I. Taylor, *Proc. Roy. Soc.*, **107**. A, 422, 1925 ; H. Favre, *Sur une nouvelle méthode optique de determination des tensions intérieures*, Paris, 1929 ; H. Fay and S. Badlam, *Metallographist*, **4**. 31, 1901 ; E. W. Fell, *Journ. Iron Steel Inst.—Carnegie Mem.*, **16**. 101, 1927 ; C. F. Flolliott, *Bull. Rensselaer Polyt. Inst.*, 17, 1927 ; A. Fry, *Stahl Eisen*, **41**. 1093, 1921 ; P. Galy-Aché, *Rev. Mét.*, **10**. 585, 1913 ; P. Galy-Aché and M. Charbonnier, *Mém. Artillerie Marine*, **28**. 39, 247, 1900 ; J. D. Gat, *Blast Furnace Steel Plant*, **15**. 173, 271, 279, 1927 ; *Trans. Amer. Soc. Steel Treating*, **12**. 337, 376, 1927 ; R. L. Geruso, *Heat Treating Forging*, **17**. 139, 1931 ; H. Giersberg, *Ueber Arbeitsverbranch, Kristallisation Verfestigung und ihre Temperaturabhängigkeit bei der Verformung der Metalle*, Breslau, 1927 ; P. Goerens, *Rev. Mét.*, **10**. 608, 1337, 1913 ; *Journ. Iron Steel Inst.—Carnegie Mem.*, **3**. 320, 1911 ; *Ferrum*, **10**. 226, 260, 1913 ; A. F. Golovin, *Proc. Russ. Met. Soc.*, 89, 1928 ; N. P. Goss, *Trans. Amer. Soc. Steel Treating*, **16**. 405, 1929 ; **17**. 241, 1930 ; G. W. Green, *Trans. Faraday Soc.*, **17**. 139, 1921 ; O. V. Greene, *Trans. Amer. Soc. Steel Treating*, **17**. 798, 1930 ; T. W. Greene, *Mech. Eng.*, **49**. 124, 1927 ; J. N. Greenwood, *Trans. Faraday Soc.*, **17**. 123, 1921 ; L. Guillet, *Rev. Mét.*, **10**. 665, 1913 ; M. Hamasumi, *Arch. Eisenhüttenwesen*, **1**. 157, 1927 ; M. Hanriot, *Rev. Mét.*, **10**. 595, 1913 ; O. E. Harder and W. S. Johnson, *Trans. Amer. Soc. Steel Treating*, **15**. 49, 1929 ; O. E. Harder, L. J. Weber and T. E. Jerabel, *ib.*, **13**. 961, 1928 ; W. H. Hatfield, *Trans. Faraday Soc.*, **17**. 36, 1921 ; C. H. Herty, J. M. Gaines, B. M. Larsen, W. A. Simpkins, P. L. Geruso and S. P. Watkins, *Bull. Carnegie Inst. Tech.*, 34, 1927 ; C. H. Herty, B. M. Larsen, Y. N. Krivonok, R. B. Norton, H. E. Wiley, A. W. Sykes, and J. E. Jacobs, *ib.*, 45, 1929 ; P. Heymans, *Rev. Univ. Mines*, (7), **6**. 207, 1925 ; E. Heyn, *Stahl Eisen*, **27**. 1309, 1347, 1907 ; **37**. 442, 474, 497, 1917 ; H. D. Hibbard, *Journ. Iron Steel Inst.*, **72**. 14, 608, 1906 ; R. Hohage and R. Rollett, *Arch. Eisenhüttenwesen*, **3**. 233, 1929 ; K. Honda, T. Matsushita and W. Idei, *Journ. Iron Steel Inst.*, **103**. i, 251, 1921 ; B. Hopkinson, *Proc. Roy. Soc.*, **74**. 498, 1904 ; H. Hort, *Mitt. Inst. Forschungsarb.*, 41, 1907 ; *Zeit. Ver. deut. Ing.*, **51**. 1831, 2100, 1907 ; E. Houdremont, H. Kallen and K. Thomsen, *Stahl Eisen*, **46**. 973, 1926 ; E. Houdremont and H. Müller, *ib.*, **50**. 1321, 1930 ; J. E. Howard, *Trans. Faraday Soc.*, **17**. 117, 1921 ; *Eng. News Rec.*, **80**. 812, 1918 ; H. M. Howe, *Iron, Steel, and other Alloys*, Boston, 263, 1903 ; H. M. Howe, F. B. Foley and J. Winlock, *Trans. Amer. Inst. Min. Eng.*, **69**. 702, 1923 ; H. M. Howe and E. C. Groesbeck, *Proc. Amer. Soc. Testing Materials*, **20**. ii, 37, 1920 ; H. M. Howe and A. G. Levy, *Proc. Cleveland Inst. Eng.*, 218, 1914 ; S. L. Hoyt, *Trans. Amer. Soc. Steel Treating*, **11**. 509, 658, 1926 ; O. F. Hudson, *B.A. Rep.*, 428, 1913 ; K. Hübers, *Rohrenindustrie*, **21**. 453, 473, 1928 ; R. Hugues, *Compt. Rend.*, **180**. 2043, 1925 ; J. C. W. Humfrey, *Trans. Faraday Soc.*, **17**. 47, 1921 ; I. Iitaka, *Proc. Acad. Tokyo*, **7**. 337, 1931 ; F. Jansen, *Arch. Eisenhüttenwesen*, **1**. 147, 1927 ; T. M. Jasper, *Engg.*, **118**. 343, 1924 ; Z. Jeffries, *Trans. Amer. Inst. Min. Eng.*, **58**. 669, 1917 ; Z. Jeffries and R. S. Archer, *Chem. Met. Engg.*, **27**. 833, 1922 ; J. D. Jevons, *Engg.*, **123**. 155, 221, 1927 ; *Journ. Iron Steel Inst.*, **111**. i, 191, 1925 ; R. Job, *Metallographist*, **5**. 177, 1902 ; R. S. Johnston, *Journ. Iron Steel Inst.*, **112**. ii, 341, 1925 ; H. C. Jones, *Engg. News*, **27**. 5, 1892 ; J. A. Jones, *Chem. Trade*

Journ., **70**. 323, 1922 ; W. Kerr, *Journ. Glasgow Tech. Coll.*, **2**. 230, 1930 ; H. G. Keshian, *Trans. Amer. Soc. Steel Treating*, **17**. 321, 1930 ; A. L. Kimball, *Amer. Machinist*, **63**. 7, 51, 1925 ; F. Körber and E. Siebel, *Mitt. Inst. Eisenforschung*, **10**. 15, 1928 ; V. N. Krivobok, *Trans. Amer. Soc. Steel Treating*, **8**. 703, 1925 ; H. K. Landis, *Amer. Manf.*, **59**. 908, 1897 ; B. M. Larsen and A. W. Sykes, *Trans. Amer. Soc. Steel Treating*, **14**. 355, 1928 ; E. L. Leasman, *Trans. Amer. Foundrymen's Assoc.*, **22**. 169, 1913 ; F. Leitner, *Stahl Eisen*, **50**. 1081, 1930 ; P. Ludwik, *Arch. Eisenhüttenwesen*, **1**. 537, 1928 ; R. Mailander, *Stahl Eisen*, **51**. 662, 1931 ; *Krupp's Monatsh.*, **12**. 139, 1931 ; H. Malzacher, *Stahl Eisen*, **47**. 2108, 1927 ; E. E. Marbaker, *Foundry Trade Journ.*, **41**. 153, 1929 ; E. Marcotte, *Arts Métiers*, **80**. 117, 170, 1927 ; E. Marke, *Arch. Eisenhüttenwesen*, **2**. 851, 1929 ; S. S. Martin, *Metallographist*, **5**. 191, 1902 ; G. Masing, *Stahl Eisen*, **45**. 1787, 1925 ; T. Matuschka, *Journ. Iron Steel Inst.*, **124**. ii, 361, 1931 ; T. Matsushita and S. Idei, *ib.*, **103**. i, 251, 1921 ; E. Maurer, *Stahl Eisen*, **48**. 225, 1928 ; H. H. Meyer, *Die Kristallitenorientierung im Kupfer und Eisen und ihre Bedeutung für den Walzvorgang*, Göttingen, 1926 ; M. Moreillon, *Bull. Soc. Mulhouse*, **61**. 629, 1892 ; *Génie Civil*, **21**. 365, 1892 ; J. Muir, *Phil. Trans.*, **198**. A, 1, 1902 ; E. Murata, *Kinzoku no Kenkyu*, **6**. 87, 1929 ; A. Nadei, R. V. Baud and A. M. Wahl, *Mech. Engg.*, **52**. 187, 1930 ; K. Nagasawa, *Science Rep. Tohoku Univ.*, **20**. 299, 1931 ; F. C. Nix and E. Schmid, *Zeit. Metallkunde*, **21**. 286, 1929 ; *Mitt. Materialprüfungsanst.*, 79, 1930 ; P. Oberhoffer, *Stahl Eisen*, **45**. 223, 1925 ; P. Oberhoffer and A. Heger, *ib.*, **43**. 1151, 1923 ; A. Ono, *Mem. Engg. Kyoto Univ.*, **3**. 267, 1925 ; B. Osann, *Stahl Eisen*, **33**. 2136, 1913 ; W. Parker, *Engg.*, **127**. 799, 1929 ; H. Pinsl, *Giesserei Ztg.*, **27**. 436, 1930 ; A. J. S. Pippard and C. V. Miller, *Proc. Inst. Mech. Eng.*, **2**. 1153, 1923 ; E. Pitois, *Le grain de l'acier*, Paris, 1926 ; H. Poellein, *Festigkeits- und Gefügeunterschungen an kaltgewalzten und geglühten Bandstählen verschiedener Vorbehandlung*, Düsseldorf, 1929 ; E. P. Polushkin, *Rep. Engg. Foundation*, 6, 1923 ; A. Pomp, *Stahl Eisen*, **40**. 1261, 1366, 1403, 1920 ; A. Pomp and H. Poellein, *Mitt. Inst. Eisenforschung*, **11**. 155, 1929 ; *Arch. Eisenhüttenwesen*, **3**. 223, 1929 ; A. Pomp and W. E. Schmid, *Mitt. Inst. Eisenforschung*, **11**. 109, 1929 ; A. M. Portevin, *Rev. Mét.*, **10**. 808, 1913 ; **21**. 729, 1924 ; **22**. 179, 1925 ; **26**. 68, 1929 ; *Journ. Iron Steel Inst.*, **108**. ii, 71, 1923 ; *Bull. Soc. Chim.*, (4), **41**. 961, 1927 ; *Compt. Rend.*, **167**. 531, 1918 ; A. M. Portevin and P. Chevenard, *ib.*, **188**. 1670, 1929 ; H. S. Rawdon, *Trans. Faraday Soc.*, **17**. 110, 1921 ; P. Régnauld, *Rev. Mét.*, **24**. 509, 1927 ; F. Robin, *ib.*, **11**. 489, 1914 ; **10**. 722, 1913 ; *Bull. Soc. Ing. Civils*, **64**, 1913 ; F. Rogers, *Journ. Iron Steel Inst.*, **85**. i, 379, 1912 ; W. Rohn, *Zeit. Metallkunde*, **18**. 387, 1926 ; R. T. Rolfe, *Metal Ind.*, **24**. 501, 525, 551, 1924 ; W. Rosenhain, *Metallurgist*, **4**. 168, 1928 ; *Trans. Faraday Soc.*, **17**. 2, 1921 ; W. Rosenhain and D. Hanson, *Journ. Iron Steel Inst.*, **102**. ii, 23, 1920 ; P. A. Russell, *Foundry Trade Journ.*, **38**. 55, 1928 ; T. F. Russell, *Journ. Iron Steel Inst.*, **107**. i, 497, 1923 ; G. Sachs, *Röhrenindustrie*, **21**. 453, 473, 1928 ; *Mitt. Materialprüfungsanst.*, 43, 1930 ; S. Sato, *Science Rep. Tohoku Univ.*, **20**. 140, 1931 ; A. Sauveur, *The Metallography and Heat Treatment of Iron and Steel*, Cambridge, Mass., 182, 1926 ; *Metallographist*, **5**. 197, 1902 ; *Journ. Franklin Inst.*, **177**. 501, 1914 ; R. Schäfer, *Giesserei Ztg.*, **11**. 249, 1914 ; E. Schmid, *Beiträge zur Kenntnis der Textur Kaltverformter Metalle*, Düsseldorf, 1929 ; *Mitt. Materialprüfungsanst.*, 26, 1930 ; E. H. Schulz and J. Goebel, *Stahl Eisen*, **40**. 1479, 1920 ; H. Scott, *Scient. Paper Bur. Standards*, 513, 1925 ; F. G. Sefing, *Bull. Eng. Exp. Station Michigan Univ.*, 13, 1927 ; J. Seigle, *Génie Civil*, **90**. 576, 1927 ; *Zeit. Metallkunde*, **19**. 352, 1927 ; *Rev. Ind. Min.*, 111, 149, 1930 ; S. Sekito, *Science Papers Tohuku Univ.*, **16**. 343, 1927 ; **17**. 679, 1227, 1928 ; *Zeit. Kryst.*, **67**. 285, 1928 ; T. M. Service, *Foundry Trade Journ.*, **42**. 266, 291, 1930 ; E. Siebel and A. Pomp. *Mitt. Inst. Eisenforschung*, **8**. 15, 1926 ; O. Sirovich, *Ital. Met.*, **22**. 555, 1930 ; S. G. Smith, *Foundry Trade Journ.*, **15**. 208, 1913 ; J. M. Snodgrass and F. H. Guldner, *Bull. Eng. Exp. Station Illinois Univ.*, 129, 1922 ; J. B. Sommerville, *Journ. Tech. Coll. Glasgow*, **1**. 22, 1926 ; W. Spring, *Bull. Acad. Belg.*, 1066, 1903 ; F. Stäblein, *Krupp's Monatsh.*, **12**. 93, 1931 ; A. Stadeler, *Ferrum*, **11**. 271, 1914 ; A. H. Stang and T. W. Greene, *Tech. Paper Bur. Standards*, 243, 1923 ; J. E. Stead and A. W. Richards, *Journ. Iron Steel Inst.*, **64**. ii, 119, 1903 ; O. W. Storey, *Trans. Amer. Foundrymen's Assoc.*, **23**. 460, 1914 ; B. Strauss and A. Fry, *Forging Heat Treating*, **8**. 225, 1922 ; *Stahl Eisen*, **41**. 1093, 1133, 1921 ; O. G. Styrie, *Die Wärmebehandlung des Stahles*, Berlin, 1929 ; W. Tafel, *Stahl Eisen*, **41**. 1321, 1921 ; I. Takaba and K. Okuda, *Arch. Eisenhüttenwesen*, **1**. 511, 1928 ; G. Tammann, *Zeit. tech. Phys.*, **7**. 531, 1926 ; *Zeit. Metallkunde*, **21**. 277, 1929 ; *Metals Alloys*, **1**. 392, 1930 ; G. Tammann and A. Heinzel, *Zeit. anorg. Chem.*, **167**. 173, 1927 ; *Arch. Eisenhüttenwesen*, **1**. 663, 1928 ; G. Tammann and H. H. Meyer, *Zeit. Metallkunde*, **18**. 339, 1926 ; A. le Thomas, *Foundry Trade Journ.*, **39**. 414, 1928 ; *Compt. Rend.*, **185**. 1595, 1927 ; *Mém. Soc. Ing. Civils*, **83**. 193, 1930 ; H. P. Tiemann, *Iron Age*, **93**. 956, 1914 ; J. F. Tinsley, *Yearbook Amer. Iron Steel Inst.*, 130, 1914 ; *Iron Age*, **93**. 1320, 1914 ; C. A. Trask, *Amer. Machinist*, **30**. 77, 1907 ; T. H. Turner and J. D. Jevons, *Journ. Iron Steel Inst.*, **111**. i, 169, 1925 ; A. Wagner, *Giesserei Ztg.*, **27**. 403, 1930 ; H. Wedding, *Journ. Iron Steel Inst.*, i, 187, 1885 ; *Stahl Eisen*, **11**. 879, 1891 ; F. Wever and E. Schmid, *Mitt. Inst. Eisenforschung.*, **11**. 109, 1929 ; R. Whitfield, *Metallurgia*, **4**. 29, 1931 ; A. W. Whitney, *Iron Trade Rev.*, **30**. 13, 1897 ; *Iron Age*, **59**. 12, 1897 ; *Journ. Franklin Inst.*, **163**. 267, 1897 ; H. V. Wille, *Proc. Amer. Soc. Testing Materials*, **15**. ii, 27, 1915 ; A. Wingham, *Journ. Iron Steel Inst.*, **60**. ii, 272, 1901 ; W. E. Woodward, *ib.*, **117**. i, 661, 1928 ; M. G. Yatsevitch, *Army Ordnance*, **11**. 297, 1931 ; C. D. Young, C. D. A. Pease and C. H. Strand, *Trans. Amer. Inst. Min., Eng.*, **48**. 424, 1914 ; K. Yuasa, *Journ. Eng. Tokyo Univ.*, **18**. 271, 1930 ; E. Zingg, P. Oberhoffer and E. Piwowarsky, *Stahl Eisen*, **49**. 721, 752, 1929.

² H. W. McQuaid and E. W. Ehn, *Trans. Amer. Inst. Min. Eng.*, **67**. 341, 1922 ; E. W. Ehn, *Journ. Iron Steel Inst.*, **105**. i, 158, 1922 ; *Trans. Amer. Soc. Steel Treating*, **2**. 1177, 1922 ; J. D. Gat, *ib.*, **12**. 376, 1927 ; S. Epstein and H. S. Rawdon, *Journ. Research Bur. Standards*, **1**. 423, 1928 ; *Trans. Amer. Soc. Steel Treating*, **12**. 337, 1927 ; O. E. Harder, L. J. Weber and T. E. Jerabek, *ib.*, **13**. 961, 1928.

³ R. R. Abbott, *Journ. Amer. Soc. Mech. Eng.*, **37**. 267, 1915 ; *Iron Age*, **89**. 1153, 1912 ; *Mech. Eng.*, **30**. 20, 1912 ; E. Abruzzese, *Metallografia a trattamenti termici dell'acciais*, Napoli, 1930 ; A. T. Adam, *Journ. Iron Steel Inst.—Carnegie Mem.*, **10**. 65, 1920 ; J. Adamson, *Trans. Inst. Marine Eng.*, **17**. 199, 1906 ; K. Aders, *Einfluss des Alterns auf das Verhalten weichen Stahles bei Schwingungs-beanspruchungen*, Berlin, 1930 ; G. Agricola, *De natura fossilium*, Basiliæ, 1546 ; *De re metallica*, Basiliæ, 117, 1553 ; London, 1912 ; J. H. Andrew, *Journ. Tech. Coll. Met. Club.*, **7**, 1928 ; *Iron Coal Trade Rev.*, **110**. 427, 1925 ; *Trans. North-East Coast Inst. Eng. Shipbuilders*, **36**. 355, 1920 ; W. R. Angell, *Trans. Amer. Soc. Steel Treating*, **17**. 262, 1930 ; Anon., *Rechter Gebrauch d'Alchimei*, Frankfurt a. M., 1531 ; *A profitable boke declaring dyuers approoved remedies*, London, 1583 ; *The Laboratory ; or, School of Arts*, London, 126, 1739 ; also 1810 ; Thomas Aquinas, *S. Thomæ Aquinatis, præclarissima commentaria in libros Aristotelis peri hermeniæ et posteriorum analyticorum*, Venetiis, 1562 ; *Physicorum*, Liber Quartus, Lectio XIX, pp. 66–67 ; J. O. Arnold, *Engg.*, **64**. 49, 1897 ; H. H. Ashdown, *Proc. Inst. Mech. Eng.*, 225, 1917 ; F. Bacon, *Sylva sylvarum*, London, 215, 1628 ; E. C. Bain and W. S. N. Waring, *Trans. Amer. Soc. Steel Treating*, **15**. 69, 1929 ; J. H. Baker, *Iron Age*, **78**. 858, 1906 ; A. Barba, *El arte de los metales*, Madrid, 1637 ; New York, 1923 ; A. L. Bates, *Compt. Rend.*, **193**. 35, 1931 ; *Trans. Amer. Soc. Steel Treating*, **19**. 449, 1931 ; O. Bauer, *Mitt. Materialprüfungsanst.*, **5**. 12, 1929 ; *Stahl Eisen*, **25**. 1245, 1905 ; H. C. Boynton, *Journ. Iron Steel Inst.*, **67**. i, 252, 1904 ; L. Beck, *Die Geschichte des Eisens*, Braunschweig, **1**. 401, 1891 ; J. J. Becker, *Physica subterranea*, Linsiæ, 452, 1703 ; O. M. Becker, *High Speed Steels*, New York, 1910 ; H. H. Beeny, *Foundry Trade Journ.*, **40**. 229, 251, 1929 ; N. T. Belaiew, *Journ. Iron Steel Inst.*, **121**. i, 449, 1930 ; A. E. Bellis, *Trans. Amer. Soc. Steel Treating*, **2**. 398, 1922 ; *Trans. Amer. Inst. Min. Eng.*, **58**. 696, 1918 ; C. Benedicks, *Rev. Mét.*, **5**. 5. 1908 ; *Metallographic Researches*, New York, 55, 1926 ; *Recherches physiques et physicochimiques sur l'acier au carbone*, Upsala, 1904 ; *Rev. Mét.*, **6**. 189, 1909 ; *Journ. Iron Steel Inst.*, **77**. ii, 153, 1908 ; **86**. ii, 261, 1921 ; **89**. i, 186, 1914 ; J. le Bègue, *Experimenta de coloribus, Bibliothèque Royal du Paris*, 1431 ; T. Bergman, *De analysi ferri*, Upsala, 1781 ; *Opuscula physica et chemica*, Upsala, **3**. 1, 1783 ; C. L. Berthollet and G. Mongé, *Mem. Acad.*, 132, 1786 ; *Histoire de l'Academie Royal des Sciences*, Paris, 132, 1788 ; S. V. Bielznsky, *Rev. Mét.*, **10**. 495, 1913 ; *Proc. Russ. Met. Soc.*, 396, 1912 ; C. M. Bigger, *Mech. Eng.*, **31**. 380, 1913 ; H. Birnbaum, *Die Anlassvorgänge im gehärteten Stahl und ihre Beeinflüssung durch Silizium und Nickel*, Düsseldorf, 1928 ; J. Black, *Lectures on the Elements of Chemistry*, Edinburgh, **2**. 505, 1803 ; E. Blass, *Stahl Eisen*, **24**. 1371, 1904 ; J. W. Bolton, *Iron Age*, **114**. 820, 1925 ; Robert Boyle, *History of Fluidity and Firmness*, London, 1660 ; *The Origin of Formes and Quantities*, Oxford, 35, 1667 ; H. M. Boylston, *Fuels Furnaces*, **4**. 1035, 1926 ; **5**. 297, 1927 ; L. C. Brant, *Phys. Rev.*, (1), **29**. 485, 1909 ; S. N. Brayshaw, *Engg. Production*, **8**. 99, 1925 ; *Engg.*, **119**. 382, 1925 ; *Trans. Liverpool Eng. Soc.*, **46**. 126, 1926 ; J. R. Breant, *Bull. Soc. Enc. Nat. Ind.*, (1), **22**. 222, 1823 ; *Quart. Journ. Science*, **18**. 386, 1825 ; *Ann. Mines*, (1), **9**. 319, 1824 ; *Ann. Phil.*, **8**. 267, 1824 ; *Ann. Chim. Phys.*, (2), **24**. 388, 1823 ; H. Brearley, *The Heat Treatment of Tool Steel*, London, 1911 ; *Proc. Brit. Foundrymen's Assoc.*, 237, 1912 ; J. A. Brinell, *Baumaterialienkunde*, **5**. 276, 294, 317, 364, 392, 416, 1900 ; **11**. 6, 1906 ; *Jernkontorets Ann.*, (2), **56**. 219, 1901 ; *Dingler's Journ.*, **317**. 419, 1902 ; *Mémoire sur les épreuves à bille en acier*, Paris, 1900 ; C. F. Brush, *Proc. Amer. Phil. Soc.*, **56**. 353, 1917 ; *Trans. Inst. Min. Eng.*, **62**. 17, 1919 ; C. F. Brush and R. A. Hadfield, *Proc. Roy. Soc.*, **93**. A, 188, 1917 ; C. F. Brush, R. A. Hadfield and S. A. Main, *ib.*, **95**. A, 120, 1918 ; H. Busch, *Sammlung Berg. Hütt. Abhand.*, 15, 1907 ; E. D. Campbell, *Journ. Iron Steel Inst.*, **92**. ii, 164, 1915 ; W. Campbell, *Proc. Amer. Soc. Testing Materials*, **10**. 193, 1910 ; A. Campion, *Mech. Eng.*, **28**. 172, 1911 ; F. Camus, *L'art de tremper les fers et les aciers*, Rocroi, 1846 ; H. Cardanus, *De substititate*, Lugduni Batavorum, 1580 ; H. Caron, *Compt. Rend.*, **77**. 836, 1873 ; H. C. H. Carpenter and J. M. Robertson, *Journ. Iron Steel Inst.*, **121**. i, 417, 1930 ; R. Chamley, *Traitement thermique et essais des métaux*, Paris, 1928 ; G. Charpy, *Bull. Soc. Chim.*, (4), **3**. i, 1908 ; *Compt. Rend.*, **151**. 399, 1910 ; H. le Chatelier, *Rev. Mét.*, **1**. 184, 303, 473, 1904 ; **2**. 25, 1905 ; *Compt. Rend.*, **165**. 172, 1917 ; P. Chevenard, *ib.*, **164**. 885, 1005, 1917 ; **165**. 59, 1917 ; **166**. 682, 1918 ; *Journ. Iron Steel Inst.*, **104**. ii, 117, 1921 ; *Rev. Ind. Min.*, 209, 1930 ; *Metallbörse*, **20**. 1828, 1930 ; *Rev. Mét.*, **16**. 17, 1919 ; **14**. 601, 1917 ; P. Chevenard and A. M. Portevin, *Rev. Mét.*, **18**. 428, 1921 ; **28**. 417, 503, 546, 1931 ; *Journ. Iron Steel Inst.*, **104**. ii, 116, 1921 ; *Génie Civil*, **99**. 172, 1931 ; *Compt. Rend.*, **188**. 167, 1929 ; **191**. 408, 523, 608, 1059, 1930 ; W. F. Chubb, *Heat Treating Forging*, **16**. 481, 1930 ; L. Clouet, *Journ. Mines*, **9**. 3, 1799 ; *Nicholson's Journ.*, **3**. 131, 1800 ; *Rapp. Inst. Nat. Paris*, (1), **2**. 81, 1798 ; *Ann. Chim. Phys.*, (1), **28**. 19, 1798 ; (1), **31**. 328, 1799 ; F. Cloup, *Compt. Rend.*, **166**. 415, 1918 ; F. H. Colvin and K. A. Juthe, *The Working of Steel Annealing Heat Treating and Hardening of Carbon and Alloy Steel*, New York, 1921 ; E. F. Cone, *Iron Age*, **91**. 1049, 1913 ; J. Cournot, *Compt. Rend.*, **171**. 170, 1920 ; *Rev. Mét.* **17**. 568, 1930 ; F. B. Coyle, *Metals Alloys*, **2**. 120, 1931 ; J. A. Cramer, *Elementa artis documasticæ*, Leyden, 1739 ; W. J. Crook, *Metal, Progress*, **18**. 47, 1830 ; W. J. Crook, D. J. Martin and J. W. Halley, *West. Mach. World*, **21**. 311, 1930 ; J. Curran, *Iron Age*, **121**. 134, 1928 ; H. Damemme, *Essai pratique sur l'emploi ou la*

manière de travailler l'acier, Paris, 1835 ; E. F. Davis, *Fuels Furnaces*, **9**, 153, 1931 ; St. J. V. Day, *The Prehistoric Use of Iron and Steel*, London, 134, 1877 ; P. Dejean, *Rev. Univ. Mines*, (6), **14**. 265, 1922 ; (6), **15**. 425, 1922 ; *Rev. Met.*, **18**. 419, 1921 ; *Compt. Rend.*, **165**. 334, 429, 1917 ; **169**. 1403, 1919 ; **171**. 791, 1920 ; G. Delbart, *ib.*, **180**. 934, 1925 ; J. Demeste, *Lettres sur la chymie*, Paris, 1779 ; L. Demozay, *Journ. Iron Steel Inst.*, **75**. iii, 144, 1907 ; S. E. Derby, *Iron Trade Rev.*, **69**. 674, 1921 ; C. H. Desch, *Trans. Faraday Soc.*, **10**. 255, 1915 ; J. Durand, *Compt. Rend.*, **175**. 522, 1922 ; G. M. Eaton, *Trans. Amer. Soc. Steel Treating*, **12**. 794, 1927 ; **16**. 819, 1929 ; G. Ede, *The Management of Steel*, London, 1866 ; B. Egeberg, *Trans. Amer. Soc. Steel Treating*, **12**. 46, 1927 ; E. W. Ehn, *Metal Progress*, **20**. 59, 1931 ; W. Eilender, *Metal Alloys*, **1**. 732, 1930 ; *Arch. Eisenhüttenwesen*, **3**. 659, 1930 ; M. Eraclius, *De coloribus et artibus Romanorum* (*c.* 1450) in R. E. Raspe, *A Critical Essay on Oil Painting*, London, 101, 1781 ; H. Esser and W. Eilender, *Arch. Eisenhüttenwesen*, **4**. 113, 1930 ; *Stahl Eisen*, **50**. 1616, 1930 ; E. W. Esslinger, *Metal Progress*, **17**. 60, 1930 ; M. von Eulenspiegel, *Journ. Iron Steel Inst.*, **47**. i, 452, 1895 ; G. S. Evans, *Foundry*, **43**. 219, 1915 ; A. Evrard, *Bull. Soc. Ind. Min.*, (3), **3**. 1063, 1889 ; H. Fay, *Proc. Amer. Soc. Testing Materials*, **11**. 422, 1911 ; *Iron Age*, **88**. 25, 1911 ; R. B. Fehr, *Bull. Pennsylvania State Coll.*, **11**. 84, 1917 ; F. M. Feldhaus, *Die Technik der Vorzeit.*, Leipzig, 515, 1914 ; G. Feodoséeff, *Brit. Pat. No.* 9457, 1888 ; J. Ferguson, *Proc. Glasgow Phil. Soc.* **17**. 206, 1886 ; **19**. 126, 1888 ; **25**. 224, 1894 ; F. Fettweis, *Stahl Eisen*, **39**. 1, 34, 1919 ; W. Fraenkel and E. Heymann, *Zeit. anorg. Chem.*, **134**. 137, 1924 ; G. Franche, *Traitement thermique de l'acier et ses essais*, Paris, 1926 ; H. J. French, *Chem. Met. Engg.*, **25**. 155, 1921 ; *Trans. Amer. Soc. Steel Treating*, **17**. 646, 798, 1930 ; H. J. French, G. S. Cook and T. E. Hamill, *ib.*, **15**. 217, 1929 ; H. J. French and T. E. Hamill, *ib.*, **16**. 711, 1930 ; *Journ. Research Bur. Standards*, **3**. 399, 1929 ; H. J. French and O. Z. Klopsch, *Tech. Paper Bur. Standards*, 295, 1926 ; 313, 1927 ; *Trans. Amer. Soc. Steel Treating*, **6**. 251, 1924 ; **9**. 33, 1926 ; L. H. Fry, *Journ. Iron Steel Inst.*, **95**. i, 119, 1917 ; C. H. Fulton, H. M. Henton and J. H. Knapp, *Iron Trade Rev.*, **73**. 943, 1099, 1240, 1369, 1483, 1493, 1603, 1728, 1923 ; **74**. 293, 300, 411, 551, 671, 799, 917, 1049, 1161, 1309, 1434, 1560, 1687, 1924 ; **75**. 355, 487, 595, 673, 807, 939, 1087, 1924 ; L. Gages, *Essai sur la théorie générale des aciers*, Paris, 1899 ; J. Galibourg, *Compt. Rend.*, **188**. 993, 1929 ; *Rev. Mét.*, **26**. 334, 1929 ; M. L. V. Gayler, *Metallurgist*, **91**, 1930 ; C. E. Gellert, *Anfangsründe der Metallurgischen Chymie*, Leipzig, 1750 ; L. de Gerando, *Les fers et les aciers modernes et leurs propriétés mécaniques et électriques*, Paris, 1884 ; R. L. Geruso, *Heat Treating Forging*, **17**. 139, 1931 ; T. Gill, *Ann. Phil.*, **12**. 58, 1818 ; F. Giolitti, *Chem. Met. Engg.*, **24**. 113, 161, 1921 ; J. R. Glauber, *Explicatio tractatuli*, Amstelodami, 43, 1656 ; N. P. Goss, *Trans. Amer. Soc. Steel Treating*, **16**. 405, 1929 ; **19**. 182, 1931 ; E. Grateau, *Génie Civil*, **2**. 238, 1863 ; L. Grenet, *Bull. Soc. Ind. Min.*, (4), **12**. 101, 191, 1911 ; (5), **8**. 237, 1915 ; *Journ. Iron Steel Inst.*, **84**. ii, 13, 1911 ; *Compt. Rend. Soc. Ind. Min.*, 401, 1913 ; *Généralities sur les traitements thermiques des alliages*, St. Étienne, 1916 ; *Trempe recuit, cémentation et conditions d'emploi des aciers*, Paris, 1911 ; E. Greulich, *Stahl Eisen*, **50**. 1397, 1930 ; M. A. Grossman, *Iron Trade Rev.*, **75**. 168, 215, 1924 ; W. Guertler, *Zeit. Metallkunde*, **22**. 78, 1930 ; L. Guillet, *Traitements thermiques des produits métallurgiques*, Paris, 1909 ; *Rev. Mét.*, **8**. 489, 1910 ; **10**. 665, 1913 ; **19**. 162, 1922 ; *Rev. Gén. Sciences*, **31**. 523, 564, 614, 1920 ; *La trempe et le revenu des produits métallurgiques*, Paris, 1921 ; *Chim. Ind.*, **7**. 211, 1922 ; L. Guillet, J. Galibourg and M. Ballay, *Compt. Rend.*, **191**. 538, 1930 ; L. Guillet and A. M. Portevin, *Rev. Mét.*, **22**. 52, 1925 ; H. Haedicke, *Stahl Eisen*, **17**. 900, 1897 ; S. Haedicke, *Stahl Eisen*, **24**. 1239, 1904 ; P. J. Haler, *Mech. Engg.*, **49**. 1187, 1927 ; *Heat Treating Forging*, **13**. 490, 1927 ; *Fuels Furnaces*, **8**. 1655, 1930 ; J. H. Hall, *Proc. Amer. Soc. Testing Materials*, **13**. 514, 1913 ; T. E. Hamill, *Metal Progress*, **20**. 55, 1931 ; *Journ. Research Bur. Standards*, **7**. 555, 1931 ; H. Hanemann, *Internat. Zeit. Metallog.*, **4**. 248, 1913 ; *Stahl Eisen*, **31**. 1365, 1911 ; H. Hanemann and R. Kühnel, *ib.*, **33**. 1686, 1913 ; H. Hanemann and A. Schrader, *ib.*, **51**. 645, 1931 ; *Arch. Eisenhüttenwesen*, **4**. 475, 1931 ; O. E. Harder and R. L. Dowdell, *The Decomposition of the Austenitic Structure in Steels*, Minneapolis, 1927 ; *Bull. Univ. Minnesota Met. Series*, **1**, 1927 ; *Trans. Amer. Soc. Steel Treating*, **11**. 217, 391, 583, 781, 939, 1927 ; **12**. 51, 1927 ; J. F. Harper and R. S. MacPherran, *Iron Age*, **110**. 1007, 1922 ; J. W. Harsch, *Heat Treating Forging*, **13**. 372, 1927 ; *Machinery*, **30**. 435, 1927 ; *Automobile Eng.*, **17**. 304, 1927 ; W. H. Hatfield, *Journ. Iron Steel Inst.*, **122**. ii, 215, 1930 ; D. Hattori, *Journ. Soc. Mech. Eng.*, **32**. 27, 1929 ; *Science Rep. Tohoku Univ.*, **18**. 665, 1929 ; R. Hay and R. Higgins, *Journ. Tech. Coll. Glasgow*, **4**. 62, 1927 ; **2**. 73, 1929 ; R. A. Hayward, *Chem. Met. Engg.*, **20**. 519, 1919 ; J. Hébert, *Tech. Moderne*, **18**. 65, 1926 ; C. G. Heiby and G. Coles, *Amer. Machinist*, **35**. 487, 1911 ; W. Heike and W. Brenscheidt, *Arch. Eisenhüttenwesen*, **4**. 99, 1930 ; A. Heller, *ib.*, **67**. 797, 903, 971, 1927 ; J. F. Henkel, *Pyritologia*, Leipzig, 1725 ; F. R. Hensel, *Tech. Publ. Amer. Inst. Min. Eng.*, 414, 419, 1931 ; C. T. Hewitt, *Iron Age*, **106**. 67, 1920 ; E. Heyn, *Berg. Hütt. Ztg.*, **63**. 317, 1904 ; E. Heyn and O. Bauer, *Mitt. Materialprüf*, **24**. 29, 1906 ; *Stahl Eisen*, **26**. 778, 915, 991, 1906 ; H. D. Hibbard, *Iron Age*, **110**. 1492, 1922 ; V. E. Hillman, *Forging Heat Treating*, **12**. 444, 450, 1926 ; *Trans. Amer. Soc. Steel Treating*, **1**. 161, 1921 ; E. Hitzel, *Rev. Mét.*, **12**. 584, 1915 ; T. Hobbes, *Dialogus physicus de natura aeris*, London, 1662 ; O. Hoffmann, *Qualitätsstähle*, Krefeld, 1907 ; K. Honda, *Science Rep. Tohoku Univ.*, **11**. 19, 1922 ; **14**. 165, 1925 ; *Trans. Amer. Soc. Steel Treating*, **4**. 450, 1923 ; K. Honda and S. Idei, *Science Rep. Tohoku Univ.*, **9**. 691, 1920 ; K. Honda and K. Iwase, *Trans. Amer. Soc. Steel Treating*, **11**. 399, 473, 1927 ; K. Honda and T. Murakami, *Science Rep. Tohoku Univ.*, **9**. 143, 1920 ; K! Honda and A. Osawa, *ib.*, **18**. 47, 1929 ; K. Honda and K. Tamaru, *Trans. Amer. Soc. Steel Treating*, **13**. 95, 125, 1928 ;

Science Rep. Tohoku Univ., **17**. 69, 1928 ; H. M. Howe and A. G. Levy, *Trans. Amer. Inst. Min. Eng.*, **47**. 587, 1913 ; J. E. Hurst, *Foundry Trade Journ.*, **43**. 385, 395, 1930 ; *Iron Steel Ind.*, **4**. 91, 1930 ; W. P. Ishewsky, *Internat. Zeit. Metallog.*, **6**. 199, 1914 ; E. Jarolimek, *Oesterr. Zeit. Berg. Hütt.*, **24**. 70, 1876 ; Z. Jeffries and R. S. Archer, *The Science of Metals*, New York, 425, 1924 ; *Chem. Met. Engg.*, **24**. 1057, 1921 ; *Trans. Amer. Soc. Steel Treating*, **4**. 263, 1923 ; C. M. Johnson, *Amer. Machinist*, **33**. 539, 1910 ; B. E. Jones, *Hardening and Tempering Steel*, London, 1911 ; P. Jordan, *Von Stahel und Eysen*, Maintz, 1802 ; A. Jung, *Studie über die Einwerkung thermischer Behandlung auf die Festigkeitseigenschaften und die Mikrostruktur hypereutektoides Stähle*, Berlin, 1911 ; H. Jungblüth, *Arch. Eisenhüttenwesen*, **4**. 533, 1931 ; *Krupp's Monatsh.*, **12**. 106, 1931 ; H. Kalpers, *Zentr. Europ. Giesserei Ztg.*, **2**. 9, 1929 ; M. Kawakami, *Kinzoku no Kenkyu*, **7**. 57, 1930 ; R. Kirwan, *Essay on Phlogiston and the Constitution of Acids*, London, 134, 1787 ; H. C. Knerr, *Forging and Heat Treating*, **10**. 319, 385, 419, 459, 1924 ; **11**. 18, 54, 95, 125, 166, 194, 243, 264, 283, 322, 361, 386, 420, 1925 ; **12**. 9, 52, 99, 127, 212, 275, 339, 392, 428, 451, 1927 ; **13**. 103, 144, 237, 379, 420, 1927 ; H. B. Knowlton, *Trans. Amer. Soc. Steel Treating*, **7**. 378, 1925 ; **8**. 484, 1925 ; **9**. 111, 615, 781, 954, 1926 ; **10**. 638, 971, 1926 ; **11**. 450, 790, 1927 ; **12**. 106, 479, 814, 1927 ; **13**. 142, 848, 1928 ; **14**. 127, 300, 414, 580, 1928 ; *Heat Treatment—Uses and Properties of Steel*, Cleveland, Ohio, 1929 ; F. Körber, *Stahl Eisen*, **45**. 217, 261, 1925 ; F. Körber and A. Dreyer, *Mitt. Inst. Eisenforsch.*, **2**. 59, 1921 ; W. Köster, *Arch. Eisenhüttenwesen*, **2**. 503, 1929 ; **3**. 553, 1930 ; *Metal Alloys*, **1**. 571, 1930 ; *Zeit. Metallkunde*, **22**. 289, 1930 ; J. B. Kommers, *Amer. Machinist*, **42**. 551, 1915 ; E. Kothny, *Stahl- und Temperguss.*, Berlin, 1926 ; H. von Kroeckritz, *Mitt. Eisenforsch. Inst.*, **2**. 193, 1932 ; A. Krüger, *Arch. Eisenhüttenwesen*, **3**. 721, 1930 ; *Stahl Eisen*, **50**. 768, 1930 ; R. Kühnel, *Internat. Zeit. Metallog.*, **3**. 225, 1913 ; E. F. Lake, *Compositions and Heat Treatment of Steel*, New York, 1911 ; *Amer. Machinist*, **30**. 152, 289, 1907 ; *Machinery*, **19**. 690, 1913 ; F. C. A. H. Lantsberry, *Amer. Machinist*, **33**. 109, 1919 ; E. L. Leasman, *Trans. Amer. Foundrymen's Assoc.*, **22**. 169, 1913 ; P. Lejeune, *Rev. Mét.*, **2**. 299, 1903 ; **3**. 394, 1906 ; N. Lemery, *Cours de chymie*, Paris, 1675 ; *A Course of Chemistry*, London, 131, 1686 ; H. Lent and F. Kofler, *Arch. Eisenhüttenwesen*, **2**. 173, 1928 ; L. A. Levat, *Compt. Rend.*, **123**. 945, 1896 ; A. Libavius, *Commentariorum alchemiæ*, Francofurti, 1606 ; E. Lisbonne, *Génie Civil*, **13**. 22, 1888 ; *Eng.*, **65**. 439, 1880 ; M. Lister, *Phil. Trans.*, **17**. 865, 1693 ; J. Locke, *Essay on Human Understanding*, London, 1689 ; B. H. de Long and F. R. Palmer, *Trans. Amer. Soc. Steel Treating*, **13**. 420, 1928 ; P. Longmuir, *Journ. Iron Steel Inst.*, **75**. iii, 137, 1907 ; W. G. Lottes, *Trans. Amer. Soc. Steel Treating*, **1**. 181, 1921 ; H. Lüpfert, *Vergleichende Untersuchungen über die Wärmebehandlung eingesetzter Stähle*, Cannstadt, 1929 ; G. V. Luerssen, *Trans. Amer. Soc. Steel Treating*, **17**. 161, 1930 ; J. Lund, *Amer. Machinist*, **42**. 505, 1915 ; A. Lundgren, *Journ. Iron Steel Inst.*, **114**. ii, 225, 1926 ; *Engg.*, **122**. 309, 1926 ; D. J. McAdam, *Chem. Met. Engg.*, **25**. 613, 1921 ; A. McCance, *Journ. Iron Steel Inst.*, **99**. i, 560, 1919 ; *Contribution à la théorie de la trempe*, Paris, 1916 ; G. W. McKee, *Page's Weekly*, **25**. 434, 1914 ; P. E. McKinney, *Trans. Amer. Soc. Steel Treating*, **6**. 51, 1924 ; P. J. Macquer, *Dictionnaire de chymie*, Paris, 1766 ; Albertus Magnus, *De mineralibus et rebus metallicis*, Coloniæ, 370, 1569 ; E. E. Marbaker, *Iron Age*, **122**. 282, 1928 ; F. Margueritte, *Recherches sur l'aciération action de l'oxyde de carbon et du carbon sur le fer*, Paris, 1865 ; *Ann. Chim. Phys.*, (4), **6**. 55, 1865 ; G. Maring, *Vergütbarkeit von Legierungen und neuartige Alterungreischeinungen beim Eisen*, Berlin, 1928 ; *Zeit. Metallkunde*, **22**. 90, 1930 ; E. Marke, *Arch. Eisenhüttenwesen*, **2**. 851, 1929 ; *Stahl Eisen*, **52**. 262, 1932 ; E. R. Markham, *The American Steel Worker*, New York, 1903 ; G. Masing, *Arch. Eisenhüttenwesen*, **2**. 185, 1928 ; *Stahl Eisen*, **48**. 1472, 1928 ; J. A. Mathews, *Journ. Iron Steel Inst.*, **112**. ii, 299, 1925 ; *Trans. Amer. Inst. Min. Eng.*, **71**. 568, 1925 ; *Proc. Amer. Inst. Testing Materials*, **14**. ii, 50, 1914 ; J. A. Mathews and H. J. Stagg, *Trans. Amer. Soc. Mech. Eng.*, **36**. 845, 1914 ; **37**. 141, 1915 ; T. Matsushita, *Science Rep. Tohoku Univ.*, **7**. 43, 1918 ; **8**. 79, 1919 ; T. Matsushita and K. Nagasawa, *ib.*, **16**. 639, 901, 1927 ; *Journ. Iron Steel Inst.*, **116**. ii, 311, 1927 ; E. Maurer, *Mét.*, **6**. 33, 1909 ; R. F. Mehl, *Iron Steel Canada*, **13**. 265, 287, 1930 ; E. Menzel, *Das Härten von Stahl und Eisen*, Berlin, 1927 ; J. Mercier and P. Michoulier, *Rev. Mét.*, **26**. 171, 1929 ; F. S. Merrills, *Iron Coal Trades Rev.*, **120**. 367, 1930 ; W. J. Merton, *Trans. Amer. Soc. Steel Treating*, **7**. 23, 1925 ; A. Merz and C. Pfannenschmidt, *Zeit. anorg. Chem.*, **167**. 241, 1927 ; W. Metcalf and J. W. Langley, *Trans. Amer. Soc. Civil Eng.*, **27**. 382, 1892 ; A. Michel and P. Bénazet, *Compt. Rend.*, **188**. 912, 1929 ; **192**. 163, 1931 ; E. C. Miller, *Heat Treating Forging*, **13**. 362, 1927 ; J. B. Morey, *Trans. Amer. Soc. Steel Treating*, **2**. 63, 1921 ; L. B. G. de Morveau, *Nouv. Mém. Dijon Acad.*, **6**. 406, 1785 ; *Encyclopédie méthodique*, Paris, **1**. 436, 1786 ; *An Essay on the Mystery of Tempering Steel*, London, 1771 ; E. Müncker, *Samm-lung Berg. Hütt. Abhand.*, 22, 1908 ; A. Mumper, *Heat Treating Forging*, **13**. 444, 1927 ; **16**. 460, 1930 ; T. Murakami, *Science Rep. Tohoku Univ.*, **7**. 217, 1918 ; E. Murata, *Kinzoku no Kenkyu*, **6**. 97, 1929 ; P. Murmoch, *Iron Coal Trades Rev.*, **72**. 458, 1906 ; P. von Muschen-broek, *Physicæ experimentales et geometricæ dissertations*, Lugduni Batavorum, 1729 ; F. Nehl, *Zeit. Bayerische Rev. Ver.*, **1**. 315, 324, 1928 ; *Stahl Eisen*, **49**. 472, 1929 ; B. Neumann, *Zeit. Elektrochem.*, **29**. 175, 1923 ; *Stahl Eisen*, **39**. 1105, 1919 ; K. Neumann, *Lectiones von vier subjectis chymicis*, Berlin, 1732 ; Isaac Newton, *Opticks*, London, 363, 1721 ; W. Nicholson, *Natural Philosophy*, London, 1782 ; H. de Nolly, *Bull. Soc. Ind. Min.*, (5), **4**. 371, 1913 ; H. de Nolly and L. Veyret, *Journ. Iron Steel Inst.*, **90**. ii, 165, 1914 ; P. Oberhoffer, *Stahl Eisen*, **33**. 891, 1913 ; P. Oberhoffer and F. Weisgerber, *ib.*, **40**. 1433, 1920 ; I. Obinata, *Mem. Ryojun Coll. Engg.*, **2**. 315, 1930 ; F. Osmond, *Transformation du fer et du carbone dan les fers, les aciers,* *et les fontes blanches*, Paris, 1888 ; *Journ. Iron Steel Inst.*, **37**. i, 38, 1890 ; C. Otto, *Sammlung Berg. Hütt. Abhand*, 37, 1909 ; W. H. Pepys, *Phil. Trans.*, **125**. 371, 1815 ; L. B. Pfeil, *Journ. Iron Steel Inst.*, **118**. ii, 167, 1928 ; N. B. Pilling and T. D. Lynch, *Trans. Amer. Inst. Min. Eng.*, **62**. 665, 1919 ; E. Piwowarsky, *Stahl Eisen*, **45**. 2001, 1925 ; C. H. Plant, *Iron Steel Ind.*, **1**. 85, 113, 159, 193, 250, 1927 ; A. Pomp, *Stahl Eisen*, **40**. 1261, 1365, 1405, 1920 ; **50**. 440, 1930 ; *Zeit. Bayerische Rev. Ver.*, **2**. 681, 1929 ; A. M. Portevin, *Compt. Rend.*, **175**. 959, 1922 ; *Mém. Artillerie Française*, 103, 1927 ; *Chem. Ind.*, **2**. 1139, 1919 ; *Bull. Soc. Enc. Nat. Ind.*, **132**. 198, 297, 1920 ; *Journ. Iron Steel Inst.*, **99**. i, 469, 1919 ; *Considérations générales relativement à nos connaissances concernant le trempe de l'acier et des alliages métalliques*, Liége, 1922 ; *Rev. Mét.*, **16**. 141, 1919 ; **19**. 267, 713, 1922 ; **20**. 521, 1923 ; *Mém. Rev. Ind. Min.*, 258, 1931 ; A. M. Portevin and M. Garvin, *Compt. Rend.*, **164**. 885, 1917 ; *Iron Coal Trade Rev.*, **98**. 599, 1919 ; A. M. Portevin and M. Sourdillon, *Rev. Mét.*, **28**. 348, 379, 1931 ; A. Poucholle, *Compt. Rend.*, **174**. 611, 1922 ; G. W. Pressell, *Amer. Drop Forger*, **4**. 273, 1918 ; F. Rapatz and H. Pollack, *Stahl Eisen*, **44**. 1698, 1924 ; R. E. Raspe, *A Critical Essay on Oil Painting*, London, 101, 1781 ; R. A. F. de Réaumur, *L'art de convertir le fer forgé en acier et d'adoucir le fer fondu*, Paris, 280, 351, 1722 ; *An Essay on the Mystery of Tempering Steel*, London, 1771 ; G. A. Reinhardt and H. L. Cutter, *Trans. Amer. Inst. Min. Eng.*, **62**. 420, 1919 ; F. Reiser, *Das Härten des Stahles*, Leipzig, 1881 ; London, 1903 ; R. Rimbach, *Forging Heat Treating*, **10**. 46, 1924 ; S. Rinman, *Anledning till Stahl- och Jernförüdlingen*, Stockholm, 1772 ; W. C. Roberts-Austen, *On the Hardening and Tempering of Steel*, London, 1889 ; *On the Heat Treatment of Steel*, London, 1904 ; J. M. Robertson, *Safety in Mines Research Board*, 59, 1930 ; F. Robin and P. Gartner, *Rev. Mécanique*, **28**. 4, 1911 ; P. Rohland, *Baumaterialienkunde*, **7**. 270, 1902 ; *Chem. Ztg.*, **28**. 569, 1904 ; W. Rosenhain, *Journ. Iron Steel Inst.*, **110**. ii, 85, 1924 ; L. Roy, *Aciers Spéciaux*, **4**. 75, 171, 1929 ; E. Ryd, *Tek Tids*, **57**. 52, 1927 ; G. Sachs, *Zeit. Metallkunde*, **17**. 85, 1925 ; *Trans. Amer. Inst. Min. Eng.*, **39**, 1931 ; G. Sachs and W. Stenzel, *Metallwirtschaft*, **9**. 959, 1930 ; *Mitt. Materialprüfungsanst.*, **48**. 38, 1931 ; C. Salmasius, *Exercitationes Plinianæ*, Lugduni Batavorum, 763, 1689 ; R. M. Sandberg, *Fuels Furnaces*, **6**. 53, 1928 ; S. Sato, *Science Rep. Tohoku Univ.*, **18**. 303, 1929 ; F. Sauerwald, *Arch. Eisenhüttenwesen*, **3**. 365, 1929 ; M. Sauvageot, *Compt. Rend.*, **173**. 297, 1921 ; M. Sauvageot and H. Delmas, *Rev. Mét.*, **30**. 777, 1923 ; *Compt. Rend.*, **176**. 1310, 1923 ; A. Sauveur, *Fuels Furnaces*, **9**. 1019, 1931 ; A. Schack, *Arch. Eisenhüttenwesen*, **2**. 287, 1928 ; A. Schleicher, *Rev. Mét.*, **24**. 293, 1927 ; E. Schüz, *Stahl Eisen*, **44**. 116, 1924 ; E. Schüz and R. Stotz, *Der Temperguss*, Berlin, 1930 ; H. Scott, *Scient. Paper U.S. Bur Standards*, 395, 1920 ; *Trans. Amer. Soc. Steel Treating*, **6**. 13, 1924 ; **9**. 277, 1926 ; *Trans. Amer. Inst. Min. Eng.*, **62**. 689, 1919 ; **67**. 100, 1919 ; *Scient. Paper U.S. Bur. Standards*, 335, 1919 ; J. Seigle, *Rev. Ind. Min.*, 256, 260, 1931 ; B. F. Sheperd, *Trans. Amer. Soc. Steel Treating*, **17**. 90, 1930 ; R. M. Sherry, *Met. Chem. Engg.*, **10**. 666, 1912 ; E. Simon, *Härten und Vergüten*, Berlin, 1924 ; F. T. Sisco, *Trans. Amer. Soc. Steel Treating*, **13**. 305, 659, 871, 1928 ; **14**. 859, 1928 ; **16**. 950, 1930 ; O. Smalley, *Foundry Trade Journ.*, **28**. 246, 1923 ; E. K. Smith, *Trans. Amer. Foundrymen's Assoc.*, **31**. 295, 1923 ; W. Smith, *Journ. Soc. Chem. Ind.*, **9**. 144, 1888 ; G. E. Stahl, *Fundamenta chymiæ dogmaticæ et experimentalis*, Norimbergæ, 1723 ; J. E. Stead, *Proc. Cleveland Inst. Eng.*, 79, 1916 ; *Journ. Iron Steel Inst.*, **53**. i, 145, 1898 ; **54**. ii, 137, 1898 ; S. S. Steinberg, *Proc. Russ. Met. Soc.*, 613, 1912 ; *Stahl Eisen*, **50**. 1164, 1930 ; *Rev. Mét.*, **10**. 502, 1913 ; S. S. Steinberg and W. Suboff, *Stahl Eisen*, **51**. 911, 1931 ; *Metallurgist*, **7**. 131, 1931 ; B. Stoughton, *Iron Age*, **113**. 15, 1924 ; *Chem. Met. Engg.*, **30**. 554, 1924 ; *Trans. Amer. Foundrymen's Assoc.*, **19**. 451, 1911 ; B. Strauss, *Krupp's Monatsh.*, **2**. 81, 1921 ; C. E. Stromeyer, *The Injurious Effect of a Blue Heat on Steel and Iron*, London, 1887 ; *Memorandum Manchester Steam Users' Assoc.*, 1, 1922 ; *Journ. Iron Steel Inst.*, **73**. i, 200, 1907 ; **75**. iii, 86, 1907 ; **79**. i, 404, 1909 ; H. Styrie, *Trans. Amer. Soc. Steel Treating*, **1**. 286, 1919 ; T. Sutoki, *Science Rep. Tohoku Univ.*, **10**. 93, 1921 ; W. P. Sykes and Z. Jeffries, *Trans. Amer. Soc. Steel Treating*, **12**. 871, 1927 ; O. Tachen, *Key to the Ancient Hippocratical Learning*, London, 68, 1690 ; K. Tamaru, *Bull. Japan. Inst. Phys. Chem. Research*, **7**. 1028, 1928 ; *Science Rep. Tohoku Univ.*, **18**. 473, 1930 ; G. Tammann, *Zeit. Metallkunde*, **22**. 368, 1930 ; O. Thallner, *Werkzeugstahl : die Behandlung desselben bei den Arbeiten des Schmiédens, Glühens, Härtens, etc.*, Freiberg, 1898 ; Philadelphia, 1902 ; R. Theophilus, *Mineralogia*, Franckfurt am Mayn, 1703 ; C. Tronson du Coudray, *Nouvelles expériences sur la fer*, Upsala, 1775 ; D. K. Tschernoff, *Note sur la Constitution et le travail de l'acier*, Paris, 1868 ; D. Uno, *Chikashige's Aniv. Vol.*, 215, 1930 ; J. W. Urquhart, *Machinery*, **24**. 230, 497, 649, 709, 1924 ; **22**. 566, 642, 786, 1923 ; **23**. 85, 198, 268, 446, 681, 707, 832, 1924 ; *Steel Thermal Treatment*, London, 1922 ; *Heat Treating Forging*, **17**. 672, 1931 ; Basil Valentine, *Chymische Schriften*, Hamburg, 506, 1717 ; *Letzte Testament*, Strassburg, 1. 34, 1651 ; London, 1671 ; C. A. Vandermonde, C. L. Berthollet and G. Monge, *Mém. Acad.*, 132, 1786 ; *Histoire de l'Académie Royal des Sciences*, Paris, 132, 1788 ; A. Vierendeel, *Génie Civil*, **84**. 630, 1924 ; H. V. Ville, *Proc. Amer. Soc. Testing Materials*, **15**. ii, 27, 1915 ; O. Vogel, *Stahl Eisen*, **19**. 242, 1899 ; C. M. Walter, *Forging Heat Treating*, **14**. 884, 1928 ; A. Weber, *Die natürliche und künstliche Alterung des gehärteten Stahles*, Berlin, 1926 ; J. J. Wecker, *De secretis*, Basileæ, 523, 1857 ; Lyon, 667, 1596 ; H. Wedding, *Verh. Ver. Beförd. Gewerbfl.*, 228, 1902 ; O. Wedemeyer, *Stahl Eisen*, **46**. 577, 1926 ; **41**. 1215, 1921 ; M. Weidig, *Verh. Ver. Beförd. Gewerbfleisses*, **90**. 455, 1911 ; F. Wever, *Naturwiss.*, **18**. 452, 1930 ; *Arch. Eisenhüttenwesen*, **5**. 367, 1932 ; J. H. Whiteley, *Journ. Iron Steel Inst.*, **106**. ii, 89, 1922 ; E. Wiedemann, *Ber. deut. phys. Ges.*, **9**. 364, 1907 ; *Beiträge Gesch Naturwiss. Arab.*, **3**. 330, 1904 ; H. V. Wille, *Proc. Amer. Soc. Testing Materials*, **15**. ii, 27, 1915 ; S. G. Williams, *Journ.*

Aeronautical Soc., **31**. 602, 1927; J. K. Wood, *Amer. Machinist*, **61**. 443, 791, 1925; W. P. Wood, *Chem. Met. Engg.*, **24**. 345, 1921; *Proc. Amer. Soc. Testing Materials*, **4**. 488, 1923; J. V. Woodworth, *Hardening, Tempering, Annealing, and Forging of Steel*, New York, 1903; F. L. Wright, *Trans. Amer. Soc. Steel Treating*, **13**. 282, 1928; F. Wrightson, *Proc. Inst. Civil Eng.*, **123**. 163, 1896; C. D. Young, *Proc. Amer. Soc. Testing Materials*, **16**. ii, 53, 1916; *Iron Age*, **97**. 1546, 1916; J. B. Zabé, *Traité pratique de l'art de tremper l'acier, le fer, la fonte, le cuivre, et le bronze*, Paris, 1903.

⁴ H. M. Howe, *The Metallography of Steel and Cast Iron*, New York, 176, 1916; *Eng. Min. Journ.*, **62**. 557, 1896; **64**. 367, 1897; *Metallographist*, **1**. 150, 259, 1898; *Trans. Faraday Soc.*, **10**. 265, 1914; *Proc. Inst. Civil Eng.*, **123**. 224, 1896; *The Metallurgy of Steel*, New York, 35, 1890; *Journ. Iron Steel Inst.*, **48**. ii, 258, 1895; **51**. i, 525, 1897; *Trans. Amer. Inst. Min. Eng.*, **28**. 624, 1895; **31**. 318, 1897; H. M. Howe and A. Sauveur, *ib.*, **49**. i, 170, 1896; F. Osmond, *ib.*, **37**. i, 38, 1890; **49**. i, 180, 1896; *Transformations du fer et du carbone dans les fers, les aciers et fontes blanches*, Paris, 1888; *Mém. Artillerie*, **24**. 573, 1887; *Metallographist*, **3**. 181, 275, 1900; *Bull. Soc. Enc. Nat. Ind.*, (4), **10**. 480, 1895; *Ann. Mines*, (8), **14**. 1, 1888; F. Osmond and J. Werth, *ib.*, (8), **8**. 5, 1885; *Compt. Rend.*, **100**. 450, 1885; S. Kimura, *Researches Electrotech. Lab. Tokyo*, 123, 1923; K. Honda, *Chem. Met. Engg.*, **25**. 1001, 1921; *Kinzoku no Kenkyu*, **1**. 1, 1926; *Arch. Eisenhüttenwesen*, **1**. 527, 1928; *Science Rep. Tohoku Univ.*, **14**. 165, 1925; **18**. 503, 1929; K. Honda and S. Sekito, *ib.*, **17**. 743, 1928; S. Sato, *ib.*, **20**. 260, 1931; S. Sekito, *ib.*, **18**. 69, 1929; H. C. H. Carpenter, *Proc. Roy. Inst.*, **22**. 481, 1919; C. A. Edwards, *The Physicochemical Properties of Steel*, London, 164, 1920; *Trans. Faraday Soc.*, **10**. 248, 1915; *Journ. Iron Steel Inst.*, **82**. ii, 147, 1910; C. A. Edwards and H. C. H. Carpenter, *ib.*, **89**. i, 138, 1914; L. Grenet, *Bull. Soc. Chim.*, (4), **5**. 758, 1909; *Rev. Mét.*, **22**. 472, 1925; *Compt. Rend. Soc. Ind. Min.*, 155, 1905; *Journ. Iron Steel Inst.*, **84**. ii, 13, 1911; A. Ledebur, *ib.*, **44**. ii, 53, 1893; *Stahl Eisen*, **14**. 523, 1894; **15**. 944, 1895; **17**. 302, 436, 618, 1897; G. T. Beilby, *B.A. Rep.*, 604, 1901; 557, 1903; *Engg.*, **72**. 543, 1901; **76**. 451, 1903; *Electrochemist Metallurgist*, **3**. 806, 1904; *Aggregation and Flow of Solids*, London, 1921; *Journ. Soc. Chem. Ind.*, **22**. 1166, 1903; *The Surface Structure of Solids*, Glasgow, 1903; *Trans. Faraday Soc.*, **10**. 212, 1914; R. F. Mehl and B. J. Mair, *Journ. Amer. Chem. Soc.*, **50**. 55, 1928; B. D. Enlund, *Jernkontorets Ann.*, (2), **83**. 374, 1929; *Journ. Iron Steel Inst.*, **113**. i, 305, 1926; *Värmlandska Bergsmanna Fören. Ann.*, 8, 1925; F. T. Sisco, *Trans. Amer. Soc. Steel Treating*, **14**. 767, 1928; **15**. 1027, 1929; K. Heindlhofer and E. C. Bain, *ib.*, **18**. 70, 1930; F. W. Harbord and T. Twynam, *Journ. West Scotland Iron Steel Inst.*, **5**. 193, 1898; F. Reiser, *Das Harten des Stahls in Theorie und Praxis*, Leipzig, 1881; O. Thallner, *Stahl Eisen*, **18**. 935, 1898; **19**. 318, 1899; W. Metcalfe, *Trans. Amer. Inst. Ming. Eng.*, **34**. 979, 1903; R. J. Anderson and J. T. Norton, *ib.*, **71**. 720, 1925; D. J. McAdam, *Chem. Met. Engg.*, **25**. 613, 1921; W. L. Fink and K. R. van Horn, *Journ. Inst. Metals*, **44**. 557, 1930; H. W. Gillett, *Metals Alloys*, **1**. 781, 1930; R. Vondracek, *Internat. Zeit. Metallog.*, **6**. 172, 1914; P. Chevenard, *Rev. Mét.*, **16**. 17, 1919; A. Sauveur, *The Metallography and Heat Treatment of Iron and Steel*, Cambridge, Mass., 251, 1926; *Trans. Amer. Inst. Min. Eng.*, **22**. 546, 1894; **26**. 863, 1896; **27**. 846, 1896; **73**. 859, 1926; *Eng. Min. Journ.*, **64**. 489, 1897; *Met. Chem. Engg.*, **13**. 655, 1915; **25**. 509, 1921; *Metallographist*, **2**. 264, 1899; *Journ. Iron Steel Inst.*, **88**. ii, 171, 1913; *Iron Trade Rev.*, **58**. 132, 1915; *Rev. Mét.*, **23**. 392, 446, 1926; A. le Chatelier, *Bull. Soc. Enc. Nat. Ind.*, (4), **10**. 1336, 1895; H. le Chatelier, *Rev. Gén. Sciences*, **8**. 11, 1897; *Bull. Soc. Chim.*, (2), **45**. 677, 1886; *Metallographist*, **1**. 52, 1898; *Compt. Rend.*, **108**. 1096, 1889; 109. 58, 1889; *Rev. Mét.*, (5), **6**. 661, 1900; L. Guillet, *Bull. Soc. Enc. Nat. Ind.*, **101**. 222, 1902; *Rev. Mét.*, **19**. 162, 1922; E. Maurer, *Mitt. Inst. Eisenforsch.*, **1**. 39, 1920; W. Tafel, *Ann. Physik*, (4), **78**. 465, 1925; J. O. Arnold, *Trans. Faraday Soc.*, **10**. 272, 1915; *Proc. Inst. Civil Eng.*, **123**. 127, 1896; *Eng. Min. Journ.*, **64**. 213, 1897; *Engg.*, **64**. 48, 592, 1897; *Journ. Iron Steel Inst.*, **45**. i, 107, 314, 1894; J. O. Arnold and A. McWilliam, *ib.*, **55**. i, 85, 1899; R. A. Hadfield, *ib.*, **55**. i, 156, 1894; H. C. H. Carpenter and C. A. Edwards, *ib.*, **89**. i, 138, 1914; E. C. Bain, *Chem. Met. Engg.*, **25**. 729, 1921; H. Styri, *ib.*, **25**. 313, 1921; A. Westgren, *ib.*, **25**. 641, 1921; E. Heyn, *ib.*, **25**. 728, 1921; P. D. Merica, *ib.*, **26**. 881, 1922; G. Sirovich and R. Ariano, *Met. Ital.*, **14**. 3, 37, 1922; H. Esser and W. Eilender, *Stahl Eisen*, **50**. 1616, 1930; *Arch. Eisenhüttenwesen*, **4**. 113, 1931; W. Eilender and R. Wasmuht, *ib.*, **3**. 659, 1930; *Metals Alloys*, **1**. 732, 1930; K. Scheel, *Arch. Eisenhüttenwesen*, **2**. 375, 1928; R. S. Dean and J. L. Gregg, *Trans. Amer. Inst. Min. Eng.—Metals Div.*, 368, 1927; R. S. Dean, *Chem. Met. Engg.*, **26**. 965, 1922; G. Sachs, *Mitt. Materialprufungsamt*, **64**. 99, 1926; *Zeit. Metallkunde*, **17**. 85, 1925; W. T. Griffiths, *Metallurgist*, **2**. 51, 72, 89, 1926; J. C. W. Humfrey, *Journ. Iron Steel Inst.—Carnegie Mem.*, **4**. 93, 1912; **5**. 86, 1913; *Trans. Faraday Soc.*, **10**. 240, 1915; W. Rosenhain and S. L. Archbutt, *Proc. Roy. Soc.*, **96**. A, 55, 1919; W. Rosenhain, *Trans. Faraday Soc.*, **10**. 286, 1915; *Proc. Roy. Soc.*, **99**. A, 196, 1921; *Metallurgist*, **1**. 102, 121, 136, 1925; *Journ. Iron Steel Inst.*, **110**. ii, 145, 1924; *Journ. Inst. Metals*, **30**. 3, 1923; *An Introduction to the Study of Physical Metallurgy*, London, 257, 1914; *Proc. Roy. Soc.*, **99**. A, 198, 1921; *Engg.*, **97**. 661, 1914; *Journ. Iron Steel Inst.*, **89**. i, 127, 1914; A. McCance, *ib.*, **89**. i, 192, 1914; *Trans. Faraday Soc.*, **10**. 257, 1915; C. H. Desch, *ib.*, **10**. 250, 255, 1914; R. Akerman, *Journ. Iron Steel Inst.*, **16**. ii, 504, 1879; C. Barus, *Wied. Ann.*, **7**. 383, 1879; *Amer. Journ. Science*, (3), **34**. 1, 175, 1887; *Phil. Mag.*, (5), **7**. 341, 1879; (5), **26**. 209, 1888; C. Barus and V. Strouhal, *Wied. Ann.*, **11**. 930, 1880; **20**. 525, 662, 1883; *Bull. U.S. Geol. Sur.*, 14, 1885; 19, 1886; 27, 35, 1886; 42, 1887; *Amer. Journ. Science*, (3), **31**. 181, 386, 439, 1886; (3), **32**. 20, 1887; G. Charpy, *Compt. Rend.*,

117. 850, 1893 ; **118.** 418, 1894 ; *Bull. Soc. Chim.*, (4), **3.** 1, 1908 ; J. H. Andrew, *Internat. Zeit. Metallog.*, **6.** 30, 1914 ; W. von Möllendorff, *ib.*, **6.** 45, 1914 ; C. Benedicks, *Metallographic Researches*, New York, 64, 1926 ; *Rev. Mét.*, **19.** 505, 1922 ; *Recherches physiques et physico-chimiques sur l'acier au carbone*, Upsala, 1904 ; *Jernkontorets Ann.*, **71.** 35, 1916 ; *Zeit. phys. Chem.*, **36.** 529, 1901 ; N. S. Kurnakoff and S. F. Schemtschuschny, *ib.*, **54.** 149, 1907 ; **60.** 1, 1908 ; *Jahrb. Rad. Elektron.*, **11.** 1, 1914 ; A. M. Portevin, *Considérations générales relative-ment à nos connaissances concernant la trempe de l'acier et des alliages métalliques*, Liége, 1922 ; Z. Jeffries, *Trans. Amer. Soc. Steel Treating*, **13.** 369, 1928 ; Z. Jeffries and R. S. Archer, *Trans. Amer. Soc. Steel Treating*, **10.** 718, 1926 ; *The Science of Metals*, New York, 405, 1924 ; *Chem. Met. Engg.*, **24.** 1057, 1921 ; **25.** 244, 671, 728, 1921 ; H. Hanemann, *Stahl Eisen*, **46.** 1585, 1926 ; H. Hanemann and A. Schrader, *Trans. Amer. Soc. Steel Testing*, **9.** 169, 1926 ; O. E. Harder and R. L. Dowdell, *ib.*, **11.** 217, 391, 583, 781, 959, 1927 ; **12.** 51, 1927 ; *Bull. Univ. Minnesota Met. Series*, 1, 1927 ; *The Decomposition of the Austenitic Structure in Steels*, Minneapolis, 1927 ; O. E. Harder, *Trans. Amer. Soc. Steel Treating*, **2.** 139, 1921 ; W. E. Williams, *Journ. Iron Steel Inst.—Carnegie Mem.*, **13.** 175, 1924 ; M. G. Corson, *Mining Met.*, **9.** 304, 1928 ; G. Kurdjumoff, *Zeit. Physik.* **55.** 187, 1929.

⁵ A. T. Adam, *Foundry Trade Journ.*, **10.** 65, 1899 ; L. Aitchison, *Trans. Amer. Soc. Steel Treating*, **1.** 734, 1921 ; *Metal. Ind.*, **19.** 486, 1921 ; **20.** 113, 1922 ; L. Aitchison and G. R. Woodvine, *Journ. Iron Steel Inst.*, **106.** ii, 125, 1922 ; J. H. Andrew and H. A. Dickie, *ib.*, **114.** ii, 359, 1926 ; J. H. Andrew, M. S. Fischer and J. M. Robertson, *Proc. Roy. Soc.*, **110.** A, 391, 1926 ; J. H. Andrew and A. J. K. Honeyman, *Journ. Iron Steel Inst.—Carnegie Mem.*, **13.** 253, 1924 ; W. R. Angell, *Trans. Amer. Soc. Steel Treating*, **17.** 262, 1930 ; C. Barus, *Wied. Ann.*, **7.** 383, 1879 ; *Phil. Mag.*, (5), **7.** 341, 1879 ; (5), **26.** 209, 1888 ; *Amer. Journ. Science*, (3), **34.** 1, 175, 1887 ; C. Barus and V. Strouhal, *ib.*, (3), **31.** 181, 386, 439, 1886 ; (3), **32.** 20, 1887 ; *Wied. Ann.*, **11.** 930, 1880 ; **20.** 525, 662, 1883 ; *Stahl Eisen*, **26.** 917, 1906 ; *Verh. phys. med. Ges. Würzburg*, (2), **15.** 123, 1881 ; *Bull. U.S. Geol. Sur.*, 14, 1885 ; 19, 1886 ; 27, 35, 1886 ; 42, 1887 ; O. Bauer, *Mitt. Materialprüfungsamt*, **5.** 12, 1929 ; *Stahl Eisen*, **25.** 1245, 1905 ; A. Bauschlicher, *Stahl Eisen*, **30.** 253, 1910 ; H. Bennek, *Wärme*, **54.** 300, 1931 ; H. Birnbaum, *Arch. Eisenhüttenwesen*, **2.** 41, 1928 ; *Stahl Eisen*, **48.** 1125, 1928 ; H. C. Boynton, *Journ. Iron Steel Inst.*, **70.** ii, 287, 1906 ; H. Brearley, *The Heat Treatment of Steel*, London, 1911 ; J. D. Brunton, *Wire*, **3.** 10, 1928 ; E. D. Campbell and B. A. Soule, *Blast Furnace Steel Plant*, **8.** 603, 1920 ; *Journ. Iron Steel Inst.*, **102.** ii, 281, 1920 ; W. M. Carr, *Metallographist*, **5.** 58, 1902 ; G. Charpy and L. Grenet, *Compt. Rend.*, **174.** 1273, 1922 ; P. Chevenard, *Rev. Ind. Minerale*, **10.** 209, 1930 ; P. Chevenard and A. M. Portevin, *Compt. Rend.*, **189.** 759, 1929 ; **191.** 408, 1059, 1930 ; H. I. Coe, *Journ. Birmingham Met. Soc.*, **7.** 583, 1921 ; W. B. Crowe, *Trans. Amer. Soc. Steel Treating*, **2.** 869, 1922 ; S. Curie, *Bull. Soc. Eng. Nat. Ind.*, (5), **3.** 36, 1898 ; G. M. Eaton, *Trans. Amer. Soc. Steel Treating*, **16.** 819, 1929 ; B. D. Enlund, *Journ. Iron Steel Inst.*, **111.** i, 305, 1925 ; E. W. Esslinger, *Metal Progress*, **18.** 60, 1930 ; W. Fraenkel and E. Heymann, *Zeit. anorg. Chem.*, **134.** 137, 1924 ; H. J. French, *Stahl Eisen*, **39.** 179, 1919 ; H. J. French and O. Z. Klopsch, *Trans. Amer. Soc. Steel Treating*, **9.** 33, 1926 ; *Tech. Paper Bur Standards*, 295, 1925 ; F. Giolitti, *Il trattamento termico preliminare degli acciai dolci e semi-duri per construzioni meccaniche*, Milano, 1918 ; *Heat Treatment of Soft and Medium Steels*, New York, 1921 ; M. Godefroid, *Fond. Moderne*, **23.** 293, 1929 ; P. Goerens, *Journ. Iron Steel Inst.—Carnegie Mem.*, **3.** 320, 1911 ; *Stahl Eisen*, **44.** 1645, 1924 ; R. C. Gosrow, *Forging Heat Treating*, **9.** 447, 1923 ; C. Grard, *Rev. Mét.*, **8.** 241, 1911 ; R. H. Greaves and J. A. Jones, *Journ. Iron. Steel Inst.*, **102.** ii, 171, 1920 ; **112.** ii, 123, 1925 ; L. Grenet, *Bull. Soc. Ind. Min.*, **12.** 101, 191, 1911 ; *Journ. Iron Steel Inst.*, **84.** ii, 13, 1911 ; *Trempe, recuit, cementation et conditions d'emploi des aciers*, Paris, 1911 ; M. A. Grossmann, *Trans. Amer. Soc. Steel Treating*, **2.** 691, 1922 ; *Met. Chem. Engg.*, **27.** 541, 1922 ; H. Hanemann, *Stahl Eisen*, **31.** 1365, 1911 ; **43.** 880, 1923 ; H. Hanemann and L. Träger, *ib.*, **46.** 1508, 1926 ; O. E. Harder and R. L. Dowdell, *The Decomposition of the Austenitic Structure in Steels*, Minneapolis 1927 ; *Bull. Univ. Minnesota Met. Series*, 1, 1927 ; *Trans. Amer. Soc. Steel Treating*, **11.** 217, 391, 583, 781, 959, 1927 ; **12.** 51, 1927 ; R. Hay and R. Higgins, *Journ. Tech. Coll. Glasgow*, **1.** 62, 113, 1927 ; C. R. Hayward, D. M. MacNeil and R. L. Presbrey, *Trans. Amer. Inst. Min. Eng.*, **67.** 82, 1922 ; C. R. Hayward and S. S. Raymond, *ib.*, **56.** 5170, 1917 ; E. Heyn, *Journ. Iron Steel Inst.*, **79.** i, 109, 1909 ; *Chem. Met. Engg.*, **25.** 728, 1921 ; *Handbuch der Materialienkunde*, Berlin, **2.** 301, 324, 1912 ; *Stahl Eisen*, **27.** 1309, 1347, 1907 ; **32.** 2097, 1912 ; **37.** 442, 497, 1917 ; **38.** 846, 853, 1918 ; E. Heyn and O. Bauer, *Mitt. Materialprüfungsamt Gross-Lichterfelde*, 529, 1906 ; *Internat. Zeit. Metallog.*, **1.** 16, 1911 ; *Stahl Eisen*, **29.** 736, 1909 ; **31.** 760, 1911 ; O. Hoffmann, *Qualitätstähl*, Krefeld, 1907 ; J. E. Howard, *Iron Age*, **46.** 248, 1890 ; H. M. Howe, *Trans. Amer. Inst. Min. Eng.*, **56.** 561, 1917 ; *Metallographist*, **3.** 43, 1900 ; H. M. Howe and A. G. Levy, *Proc. Amer. Soc. Testing Materials*, **16.** ii, 7, 1916 ; S. L. Hoyt, *Trans. Amer. Soc. Steel Treating*, **11.** 509, 658, 1926 ; E. J. Janitzky, *Iron Age*, **110.** 788, 1922 ; *Trans. Amer. Soc. Steel Treating*, **12.** 55, 377, 1921 ; J. A. Jones, *Metallurgist*, **4.** 70, 86, 1928 ; A. Jung, *Studie über die Einwirkung thermischer Behandlung auf die Festigkeitseigenschaften und die Mikrostruktur hypereutektoider Stähle*, Berlin, 1911 ; H. Kleine, *Zeit. Physik*, **33.** 391, 1925 ; W. Köhler, *Centrb. Hütt. Walzwerke*, **31.** 613, 1927 ; N. V. Kolokoloff, *Proc. Russ. Met. Soc.*, 1, 1928 ; R. Kühnel, *Das Verhalten gehärteter und angelassener untereutektischer Stähle*, Berlin, 1912 ; *Internat. Zeit. Metallog.*, **3.** 225, 1913 ; G. Kurdjumoff, *Zeit. Physik*, **55.** 187, 1929 ; *Stahl Eisen*, **49.** 1836, 1929 ; E. F. Law, *Journ. Iron Steel Inst.*, **97.** i, 333, 1917 ; L. A. Lanning, *Forging Heat Treating*, **7.** 610, 1921 ;

F. A. Livermore, *Automobile Eng.*, **15**. 142, 1925 ; O. Majorana, *Atti Accad. Lincei*, (6), **4**. 419, 1926 ; E. Marcotte, *Génie Civil*, **91**. 411, 1927 ; **96**. 241, 1930 ; G. Mars, *Stahl Eisen*, **39**. 1770, 1909 ; J. A. Mathews, *Journ. Iron Steel Inst.*, **112**. ii, 299, 1925 ; *Trans. Amer. Soc. Mech. Eng.*, **71**. 568, 1925 ; J. A. Mathews and H. J. Stagg, *ib.*, **37**. 141, 1914 ; T. Matsushita and K. Naga-sawa, *Kinzoku no Kenkyu*, **3**. 92, 1927 ; *Journ. Iron Steel Inst.*, **115**. i, 731, 1927 ; **116**. ii, 311, 1927 ; E. Maurer, *Untersuchungen über das Härten und Anlassen von Eisen und Stahl*, Halle a. S., 1909 ; *Met.*, **6**. 33, 1909 ; *Rev. Mét.*, **5**. 718, 1908 ; E. Maurer and R. Hohage, *Mitt. Inst. Eisenforsch*, **2**. 91, 1921 ; A. Michel and P. Bénazet, *Rev. Mét.*, **26**. 455, 1929 ; **27**. 501, 1930 ; E. Murata, *Kinzoku-no-Kenkyu*, **6**. 97, 1929 ; M. G. Oknoff, *Ferrum*, **11**. 1, 1914, *Rev. Mét.*, **14**. 85, 1917 ; *Met. Leningrad*, **5**. 1, 1930 ; F. Osmond, *Journ. Iron Steel Inst.*, **37**. i, 38, 1890 ; **49**. i, 180, 1896 ; *Ann. Mines*, (8), **14**. 1, 1888 ; *Mém. Artillerie*, **24**. 573, 1887 ; *Metallographist*, **3**. 181, 275, 1900 ; *Bull. Soc. Enc. Nat. Ind.*, (4), **10**. 480, 1895 ; *Transformations du fer et du carbone dans les fers, les aciers et fontes blanches*, Paris, 1888 ; N. B. Pilling, *Trans. Amer. Electrochem. Soc.*, **42**. 9, 1922 ; A. M. Portevin, *Compt. Rend.*, **175**. 959, 1922 ; *Rev. Mét.*, **10**. 677, 1913 ; **13**. 9, 1916 ; A. M. Portevin and A. Sourdillon, *ib.*, **24**. 215, 1927 ; A. Poucholle, *Compt. Rend.*, **174**. 611, 1922 ; J. S. G. Primrose, *Trans. Amer. Soc. Steel Treating*, **13**. 617, 1928 ; S. H. Rees, *Journ. Iron Steel Inst.*, **108**. ii, 273, 1923 ; P. Roudié, *Le contrôle de la dureté des métaux dans l'industrie*, Paris, 1930 ; N. M. Saeger and E. J. Ash, *Journ. Research Bur. Standards*, **8**. 37, 1932 ; S. Sato, *Science Rep. Tohoku Univ.*, **18**. 303, 1929 ; M. Sauvageot and H. Delmas, *Rev. Mét.*, **20**. 777, 1923 ; A. Schack, *Stahl Eisen*, **50**. 1289, 1930 ; M. A. Schirmann, *Phys. Zeit.*, **29**. 676, 1928 ; H. Schottzky, *Ferrum*, **10**. 274, 1913 ; E. H. Schulz, *Zeit. Ver. deut. Ing.*, **59**. 66, 1915 ; H. Scott, *Trans. Amer. Soc. Steel Treating*, **9**. 277, 1926 ; H. Scott and H. G. Movius, *ib.*, **1**. 758, 1921 ; *Scient. Papers Bur. Standards*, 396, 1920 ; F. G. Sefing, *Bull. Michigan Exp. Station*, **37**. 2, 1931 ; N. N. Shadrin, *Journ. Russ. Met. Soc.*, 83, 1929 ; F. T. Sisco, *Trans. Amer. Soc. Steel Treating*, **15**. 837, 1027, 1929 ; **16**. 155, 485, 626, 1929 ; J. E. Stead and A. W. Richards, *Journ. Iron Steel Inst.*, **108**. ii, 273, 1923 ; R. Stotz and F. Henfling, *Stahl Eisen*, **45**. 2137, 1925 ; G. Tammann and E. Scheil, *Zeit. anorg. Chem.*, **157**. 1, 1926 ; G. Tammann and G. Siebel, *ib.*, **148**. 297, 1925 ; K. Tamaru, *Science Papers Tohoku Univ.*, **15**. 829, 1926 ; **19**. 437, 1930 ; O. Thallner, *Werkzeugstahl*, Freiberg, 1898 ; *Tool Steel*, Philadelphia, 1902 ; A. le Thomas, *Compt. Rend.*, **189**. 629, 1929 ; L. Traeger, *Zeit. Ver. deut. Ing.*, **71**. 891, 1927 ; *Anlassvorgänge in abgeschrechten Kohlenstoffstählen*, Berlin, 1927 ; *Forschungsarb. Gebiete Ing.*, 294, 1927 ; G. Welter, *Stahl Eisen*, **43**. 1347, 1923 ; W. P. Wood, *Chem. Met. Engg.*, **24**. 345, 1921 ; K. W. Zimmerschied, *Proc. Amer. Soc. Testing Materials*, **13**. 510, 1913.

⁶ R. H. Greaves, *Journ. Iron Steel Inst.*, **100**. ii, 329, 1919 ; R. H. Greaves and J. A. Jones, *ib.*, **102**. ii, 171, 1920 ; **111**. i, 231, 1925 ; F. Rogers, *ib.*, **100**. ii, 325, 1919 ; **101**. i, 613, 1920 ; J. F. Kayser, *ib.*, **101**. i, 623, 1920 ; J. H. Andrew and H. A. Dickie, *ib.*, **114**. ii, 359, 1926 ; **115**. i, 647, 1927 ; J. H. Andrew, *ib.*, **101**. i, 621, 1920 ; G. W. Green, *ib.*, **102**. ii, 219, 1920 ; W. Rosenhain, *ib.*, **100**. ii, 385, 1919 ; H. Brearley, *ib.*, **101**. i, 619, 1920 ; W. T. Griffiths, **111**. i, 259, 1925 ; J. H. G. Monypenny, *ib.*, **100**. ii, 394, 1919 ; L. Guillet, *Compt. Rend.*, **182**. 249, 1926 ; R. Yamada, *Kinzoku no Kenkyu*, **5**. 294, 1926 ; K. Honda and R. Yamada, *Science Rep. Tohoku Univ.*, **16**. 307, 1927 ; L. Grenet, *Bull. Soc. Ind. Min.*, **15**. 339, 1919 ; *Journ. Iron Steel Inst.*, **95**. i, 107, 1917 ; J. H. S. Dickenson, *Journ. West Scotland Iron Steel Inst.*, **26**. 121, 1919 ; *Journ. Inst. Automobile Eng.*, **12**. 340, 1918 ; Z. Jeffries, *Trans. Amer. Inst. Min. Eng.*, **60**. 474, 1920 ; R. S. Archer, *ib.*, **62**. 754, 1919 ; W. H. Hatfield, *Proc. Inst. Mech. Eng.*, 347, 1919 ; *Journ. Inst. Automobile Eng.*, **12**. 347, 1918 ; H. P. Philpot, *Rev. Mét.*, **17**. 93, 1920 ; *Journ. Inst. Automobile Eng.*, **12**. 235, 1918 ; R. A. Hayward, *Chem. Met. Engg.*, **20**. 519, 1919 ; H. Kikkawa, *Tetsu to Hagane*, **11**. 723, 1924 ; G. d'Huart, *Science Ind.*, 559, 1929 ; H. Brearley, *The Heat Treatment of Steel*, London, 1911.

§ 8. The Nomenclature of Iron and Steel

SOCRATES : Why should we dispute about names when we have realities of such importance to consider ?

GLAUCON : Why indeed, when any name will do which expresses the thought of the mind with clearness ?—PLATO.

There is a difficulty in formulating precise definitions for the chief varieties of iron and steel—(i) wrought iron, (ii) steel, (iii) cast iron, and (iv) malleable cast iron. Universally-acceptable definitions of commercial iron and steel have not been devised. The various types have been classed in terms of *structure*—eutecti-ferous and non-eutectiferous ; *origin*—whether of molten or plastic origin ; *malle-ability*—whether usefully malleable, like steel, wrought iron, and malleable castings, or not usefully malleable, like cast iron ; *composition*—whether the metal owes its special qualities primarily to carbon or to elements other than carbon. H. M. Howe [1] commenced his discussion with the above quotation from Plato's *Republic*, and the subject has been taken up by many others—*e.g.* H. M. Howe and A. Sauveur.

A. Sauveur, A. Greiner, S. Jordan, E. Stassano, A. Semlitsch, J. W. Langley, C. Barus and V. Strouhal, W. F. Durfee, J. O. Arnold, C. H. Ridsdale, H. le Chatelier, K. Honda, J. A. Mathews, H. Scott, A. L. Holley, F. Prime, W. Metcalf, H. P. Tiemann, E. Schrödter, B. Osann, G. Mars, C. Geiger, E. Williams, V. Deshayes, H. Wedding, O. Thallner, K. Honda, J. Navarro, R. A. Bull, etc. *The Sixth Congress of the International Association for Testing Materials* (New York, 1912) discussed various definitions in the attempt to adopt a uniform nomenclature for iron and steel. There are anomalies in the best schemes yet devised. This is perhaps a necessary consequence when convenience and precision are antagonistic, and when arbitrary lines of demarcation have to be drawn in an ill-defined region where one variety merges into another. There are dictionaries of technical terms in the iron and steel industries by O. Thallner, H. P. Tiemann, A. Tolhausen, and W. Venator and C. Ross.

Iron containing varying percentages of silicon, phosphorus, etc., along with so much carbon that it is not usefully malleable at any temp. is called **cast iron**—*fonte* (French) ; *tackjern* or *gjutjern* (Swedish) ; *Roheisen* (German) if not remelted and *Gusseisen* if remelted ; and *ghisa* (Italian). K. Honda defined cast iron as an iron-carbon alloy with a content of carbon lying between 1·7 and 6·7 per cent. The lower limit represents the maximum solubility of carbon in iron at high temp., and the upper limit the case of pure cementite. Cast iron always contains a considerable proportion of carbon—usually from 2·5 to 4·5 per cent. of carbon—and in most cases an important percentage of silicon. The cast iron of commerce is reduced from the ore, usually in a blast-furnace, in direct contact with solid carbon. It is tapped in a molten state from the furnace. The three chief varieties were indicated by Dud Dudley in 1665 :

The first sort is Gray Iron, the second sort is called Motley Iron, of which one part of the Sowes of Piggs is gray, and the other part is white intermixt ; the third sort is called White Iron ; this is almost as white as Bell Mettle, but in the furnace is least fined, and the most terrestrial.

They are the same to-day : (i) **Grey cast iron**—*fonte grise* (French) ; *grätt tackjern* (Swedish) ; *graues Roheisen* (German) ; and *ghisa grigia* (Italian)—which is relatively soft, and characterized by the presence of sheetlets of graphite, often forming an irregular skeleton ; (ii) **White cast iron**—*fonte blanche* (French) ; *hwitt tackjern* (Swedish) ; *Weisses Roheisen* (German) ; and *ghisa bianca* (Italian)—is extremely hard and brittle. It is characterized by having all or nearly all its carbon in the combined state, and by its consequent lack of graphite. (iii) **Mottled cast iron**— *fonte truitée* (French) ; *halfhwitt* or *halfgrätt tackjern* (Swedish) ; *halbiertes Roheisen* (German) ; *ghisa trotata* (Italian)—is intermediate between grey and white cast iron. Emphasizing the high tensile strength of some modern cast irons—30 kgrms. per sq. mm.—A. Thum and H. Ude said that " cast iron is steel rendered impure by graphite."

Cast iron which has been cast direct from the blast or other furnace into moulds of varying sizes and shapes is called **pig-iron**—*fonte en gueuse* (French); *tackjern* (Swedish); *Gusseisen* or *Roheisen* (German) ; and *ghisa* (Italian). The iron solidifies in the slabs or *pigs* ; the moulds are called *pig-moulds*. The name is also applied loosely to molten cast iron which is about to be cast into pigs, or is in a condition in which it could be easily cast into pigs. Molten cast iron which has been passed into or through a metal mixer is called *mixer-metal*. Castings of cast iron are called *iron castings* ; they are usually made by pouring molten cast iron into moulds of designed shape or form, but other than in the shape of pigs or slabs. The molten cast iron is cast direct from blast-furnace, or from cast iron which has been remelted in a cupola, or other furnace, or in crucibles. *Hæmatite pig-iron* is pig-iron made from hæmatite ores containing so little phosphorus and sulphur that the product can be used directly for the acid Bessemer process. In *cinder pig-irons* a large proportion of tap cinder from the puddling-furnace is added to the blast-furnace charge ; the term *all mine pig-iron* is used to distinguish pig-iron from cinder pig-iron when no source of iron is used other than the ore ; *charcoal irons* are pig-irons made by the use of charcoal as a fuel ; *Swedish iron* is made from the magnetite ores of Sweden ; this iron is usually a charcoal iron of a high degree of purity with respect to sulphur and phosphorus ; and *Cleveland iron*, a phosphoric pig-iron made in North Yorkshire. Pig-iron containing so little silicon and sulphur that it is suitable for conversion into steel by the basic open-hearth process is sometimes called *basic pig-iron*. This metal contains no more than 1 per cent. silicon. The *Thomasroheisen* of Germany contains less than 0·5 per cent. silicon, and over 1·5 per cent. phosphorus ; and here, also, if the pig-iron for the basic Bessemer or basic open-hearth process has a composition outside these limits, and contains phosphorus, it is called *phosphoric pig-iron*. Similarly *Bessemer pig-iron* is pig-iron with so little phosphorus—say, not over 0·06 per cent. (in the United States 0·1 per cent.) phosphorus or sulphur—that it can be used for conversion into steel by the acid Bessemer process. The red-short metal made by purifying pig-iron in the Bessemer converter, without the subsequent removal of oxygen, is called *blown metal*. Molten cast iron from the blast-furnace before it has solidified is called *hot metal* or *direct metal*. Cast iron which has been freed from most of its silicon and phosphorus by rich ferruginous slags or their equivalent, without removing much of the carbon, so that it remains cast iron, is sometimes called *washed metal*—*fonte épurée* (French) ; *tvättad* (Swedish) ; *entphosphortes Roheisen* (German) ; and *metallo defosforato* (Italian). Cast iron which has had most of its silicon removed in a refinery furnace, but still contains so much carbon that it remains cast iron, is called *refined cast iron*—*fonte mazée* (French) ; *raffineradtjern* (Swedish) ; *gefeintes Eisen* (German) ; and *ghisa affinata* (Italian)—or *plate-iron* ; and cast iron which has had its silicon, and usually also phosphorus, removed in the charcoal hearth, but still contains so much carbon that it remains cast iron, is called *charcoal hearth cast iron*. *Bloomary* or *knobbled charcoal iron* is a high-grade iron used for boiler tubes. It is made by heating high-grade charcoal pig-iron in a charcoal knobbling furnace. The lump of iron is hammered into a bloom, and rolled into sinks. *Bushelled iron* is made by heating in a hearth furnace miscellaneous junk scrap iron, often mixed with iron and steel turnings. The heated metal like a puddled ball is squeezed and rolled. The product is irregular in quality. The comparatively rare *alloy cast irons* owe their special properties to the presence of an element or elements other than carbon—*vide infra*, ferro-alloys.

Iron which has been cast as brittle white cast iron into moulds and afterwards made more or less malleable without remelting is called **malleable cast iron**—*fonte malléable* (French) ; *aduceradtjern* (Swedish) ; *schmiedbares Gusseisen* (German) ; and *pezzi fusi dighisa malleabile* (Italian). The malleabilizing is effected by annealing the metal, usually in close contact with an oxidizing agent. As a result most of the contained carbon is converted from a state of cementite into that of temper graphite, and some is removed by the oxidation process. There are in commerce thus two classes of malleable cast iron : one owes its malleability to a large removal of carbon, and the other to a large removal of carbon from the outer part of the casting, and to the precipitation of most of the remaining carbon in the free or graphitic state. It is added that it is not in accord with good industrial usage to apply the name steel to the product of any of these malleabilizing processes. Malleable cast iron differs from steel (i) in containing more carbon, and (ii) in being cast into a mass which is not initially malleable. Malleable cast iron is not cast iron, but a product of cast iron, and it is distinct from wrought iron and steel, which are also products of cast iron.

The malleable casting has a white core—*white-heart malleable cast iron*—if cooled quickly enough, and if it be annealed at 625°–875°, graphite is precipitated to form *black-heart malleable cast iron*, so called because the fracture shows a black kernel with a steel-like skin. In the white-heart cast iron the steely rim may be regarded as extending to the centre—*vide infra*.

The term **wrought iron**—*fer soudé* (French) ; *smidesjern* (Swedish) ; *Schmiedeisen* or *Stabeisen* (German) ; and *ferro fucinato* or *ferro saldato* (Italian)—is applied to iron which has been produced at a temp. below its own m.p., and has been obtained either direct from iron ore or from cast iron ; wrought iron is obtained as a malleable mass from cast iron by the aggregation of pasty particles without subsequent fusion. It contains so little carbon that it does not usually harden when rapidly cooled, and it is soft and readily malleable within wide limits of temp., and always contains intermingled slag. The term weld-iron for wrought iron is obsolete.

The term **steel**—*acier* (French) ; *stähl* (Swedish) ; *Stahl* (German) ; and *acciaio* (Italian)—is sometimes applied to iron with less than 2·0 per cent. of carbon. The term is also applied to alloys to the left of the point E in the equilibrium diagram, and the term cast iron to alloys to the right of that point. C. J. B. Karsten regarded 2·3 per cent. as the limit between steel and cast iron. The fashionable definition of steel thus depends on an arbitrarily assigned limit. C. Barus and V. Strouhal tried to obtain a physical definition by defining steel as the iron-carbon alloy for which $\delta \log h$ is a maximum when h denotes the thermoelectric hardness taken in a special sense. This definition is not of practical use. According to J. W. Langley, commercial steels have the following composition :

		C	Si	S	P	Mn	O	gases
Steels	{Upper limits	1·50	0·30	0·10	0·10	1·00	(1·20)	little per cent.
	{Lower limits	0·30	0·02	0·005	0·01	0·08	traces	traces
Alloy steels	{Upper limits	2·25	1·50	0·10	0·30	—	2·0	0·25 per cent.
	{Lower limits	1·25	0·50	0·01	0·01	—	2·0	0·25 per cent.

The alloy steels also contain the alloying element—e.g. manganese, tungsten, chromium, nickel, etc. The International Association indicated above recommended applying the term steel to iron, alone or associated with other elements, which has been cast from a molten state, whether it hardens or not on rapid cooling from above its critical range, and, after solidification, is so usefully malleable that within some range of temp. it can be forged or rolled into merchant sections or shapes. The term is also applied to iron which has not been cast from a molten state, and contains sufficient carbon to cause it to harden usefully when rapidly cooled from above its critical range, and is so usefully malleable that within some range of temp. it can be forged or rolled into merchant sections or shapes. Otherwise expressed, there are :

(i) *Steels of plastic origin*, which are defined as iron which has not been cast from a molten state but has been aggregated from paste particles without subsequent fusion. It contains sufficient carbon—say 0·30 per cent. or more—to harden usefully when rapidly cooled from above its critical range, and is so usefully malleable that it can be forged or rolled, within some range of temp., into merchant shapes or sections.

The term *blister steel, cement bar*, or *converted bar* is a steel of plastic origin, made from high-class Swedish iron, or wrought-iron bar which has been subjected to a process of cementation, which process introduces carbon into the iron and usually develops blisters on the surface. The same steel when heated and worked into merchant sizes is also called blister steel. Cemented bar, blister bar, shear steel, and a few other high-carbon steels are the only commercial steels covered by this definition. Formerly blister bars were rolled or hammered at a yellow-heat to form the so-called *plated bars* or *bar steel* ; and springs were made from these bars, which were called *spring steel*. Blister bar or cemented bar which has been broken into suitable lengths, heated, and hammered out to confer some toughness and to flatten down the blisters is called *plated bar*. Steel made by piling and welding plated bars under a thin layer of suitable flux is called *shear steel*. If the welded steel has been drawn down the welded bars under a hammer into a faggot which is forged into merchant sizes, it is known as *single shear steel* ; and if single shear steel has been nicked, bent back on itself, the two parts heated, welded, and again hammered down, the resulting bloom is known as *double shear steel*. The merchant sizes forged from these blooms are also known as shear steel. The term *weld-steel—acier soudé* (French) ; *wällstähl* (Swedish) ; *Schweissstahl* (German) ; and *acciaio soldato* or *acciaio fucinato* (Italian)—is iron with a tensile strength of about 50 kgrms. per sq. mm. when annealed ; it contains some slag, because it is made by welding together pasty particles of metal in a bath of slag, as in puddling—hence called *puddled steel*—and it is not later freed from slag by melting.

(ii) *Steels of liquid origin*, which include iron alone or associated with other elements which has been cast from a molten state, whether it hardens or not on cooling from above its critical range, and after solidification is so usefully malleable that it can be forged or rolled, within some range of temp., into merchant shapes or sections.

The metal so defined is steel, whether it can be hardened or not, whether it contains much or little or even no carbon, and, for that matter, even if it be chemically pure iron. It is sometimes called *ingot metal*. With the exception of the comparatively unimportant steels of plastic origin, all steels of any present-day industrial importance are steels of liquid origin. The so-called *ingot iron* is steel with too little carbon to harden usefully on rapid cooling. The term is used in trade, but it is not considered advisable to use the term otherwise, because it is confusing to call a variety of steel " ingot iron." Steel with enough carbon—say 0·30 per cent. or more—to harden usefully on rapid cooling is called *ingot steel*. Steel made in a crucible is called *crucible steel—acier au creuset* (French) ; *Degelstähl*

(Swedish) ; *Tiegelflussstahl* (German) ; and *acciaio al crogiuolo* (Italian)—or *cast steel—acier au creuset* (French) ; *gjutstähl* (Swedish) ; *Gussstahl* (German) ; and *acciaio fuso* (Italian). When made in an electric furnace, *electric steel* ; when made by the Bessemer process, *Bessemer steel* ; when made by the open-hearth process, *open-hearth steel* ; when made by a basic process, *basic steel* ; and when made by the Bessemer process, *acid steel*. The term *semi-steel* is vaguely employed in the trade for various products near the border between cast iron and steel—*e.g.* low-carbon cast iron made in the air furnace or the cupola by adding steel scraps to the charge. It was discussed by J. E. Hurst. The term has also been applied to malleable castings.

K. Honda defines steel as an iron-carbon alloy with a content of carbon lying between 0·035 and 1·7 per cent. The lower limit is given by the solubility of carbon in iron at ordinary temp., and the upper limit is the maximum solubility of carbon in iron at high temp. The term **carbon steel** is sometimes applied to steel which owes its distinctive properties to carbon as distinct from other elements which it contains ; and **alloy steel,** or *special steel*, to steel which owes its distinctive properties to some element or elements other than carbon, or jointly to such other element and carbon. Although some of the alloy steels are but moderately malleable, among the carbon steels industrial usage confines the name steel to products malleable enough to be forged or rolled into merchant shapes. There is no agreement as to the line of demarcation between alloy steels and carbon steels. Some alloy steels gave 1·25 per cent. carbon. The term **ferro-alloys** is applied to iron so rich in some element or elements other than carbon that it is used primarily as a vehicle for introducing the alloying element or elements in the manufacture of iron or steel. The ferro-alloys are not usually usefully malleable, and they usually contain more of the alloying element than is desirable in an alloy steel. A substance may simultaneously be an alloy steel in the machine shop and a ferro-alloy in the steel mill. F. Wever discussed the classification of the ferro-alloys.

REFERENCES.

¹ Reports, *Journ. Iron Steel Inst.*, **61.** i, 90, 1902 ; **72.** iv, 699, 1906 ; **75.** iii, 216, 1907 ; Anon., *Chem. Met. Eng.*, **27.** 913, 1922 ; H. M. Howe, *The Metallography of Steel and Cast Iron*, New York, 36, 1916 ; *Metallurgy of Steel*, New York, 1, 1890 ; *Iron, Steel, and other Alloys*, Boston, 1903 ; *Eng. Min. Journ.*, **20.** 213, 1875 ; **91.** 327, 375, 1911 ; **92.** 550, 1911 ; *Rass. Min. Met. Chim.*, **34.** 135, 1911 ; *Trans. Amer. Inst. Min. Eng.*, **5.** 515, 1877 ; **52.** 928, 930, 1908 ; A. Sauveur, *Chem. Met. Engg.*, **30.** 782, 1924 ; H. M. Howe and A. Sauveur, *Iron Steel Mag.*, **8.** 133, 1905 ; *Rev. Mét.*, **22.** 355, 1925 ; *Proc. Amer. Soc. Testing Materials*, **6.** 11, 1912 ; E. Heyn, *ib.*, **6.** 2, 1912 ; *Handbuch der Materialenkunde*, Berlin, 1912 ; H. P. Tiemann, *Iron and Steel*, New York, 320, 1910 ; A. Tolhausen, *Dictionary of Technical Terms relating to Iron in German, English and French*, London, 1872 ; W. Venator and C. Ross, *Dictionary of the Metallurgy of Iron*, London, 1911 ; J. W. Bolton, *Proc. Amer. Soc. Testing Materials*, **29.** 35, 1929 ; E. Stassano, *Ann. Soc. Ing. Italiana*, 9, 1891 ; A. Semlitsch, *Oesterr. Zeit. Berg. Hütt.*, **51.** 2, 1893 ; C. Barus and V. Strouhal, *Bull. U.S. Geol. Sur.*, 14, 1885 ; *Abh. Böhm. Ges.*, **12.** 15, 1885 ; J. W. Langley, *Trans. Amer. Inst. Civil Eng.*, **27.** 385, 1892 ; W. F. Durfee, *Journ. Franklin Inst.*, **192.** 110, 1896 ; Dud Dudley, *Metallum martis*, London, 1665 ; *Journ. Iron Steel Inst.*, **5.** ii, 227, 1872 (reprint) ; J. O. Arnold, *ib.*, i, 185, 1910 ; **107.** i, 213, 1923 ; *Ironmonger*, **101.** 136, 1902 ; C. H. Ridsdale, *ib.*, **101.** 234, 1902 ; H. le Chatelier, *Rev. Mét.*, **1.** 513, 1904 ; J. W. Richards, *Met. Chem. Engg.*, **10.** 265, 1912 ; A. Hartman and H. D. Hibbard, *ib.*, **10.** 391, 1912 ; H. M. Boyston, *Fuels Furnaces*, **4.** 289, 1926 ; A. Greiner, *Rev. Univ. Mines*, **33.** 27, 1871 ; *Journ. Iron Steel Inst.*, **89.** i, 29, 1914 ; E. Williams, *ib.*, **156.** 1869 ; A. Thum and H. Ude, *Zeit. Ver. deut. Ing.*, **74.** 257, 1930 ; *Metallbörse*, **20.** 426, 482, 1930 ; S. Jordan, *Rev. Exposition Paris*, **4.** 280, 1870 ; A. L. Holley, *Journ. Franklin Inst.*, **94.** 252, 391, 1872 ; *Trans. Amer. Inst. Min. Eng.*, **4.** 138, 1876 ; F. Prime, *ib.*, **4.** 328, 1876 ; W. Metcalf, *ib.*, **5.** 355, 1877 ; H. Wedding, *Stahl Eisen*, **16.** 160, 1896 ; **27.** 775, 1907 ; V. Deshayes, *Classement et emploi des aciers*, Paris, 1880 ; E. Schrödter, *Gemeinfassliche Darstellung des Eisenhüttenwesens*, Düsseldorf, 4, 1912 ; B. Osann, *Lehrbuch der Eisen- und Stahlgiesserei*, Leipzig, 365, 1912 ; G. Mars, *Die Spezialstähle*, Stuttgart, 2, 1912 ; C. Geiger, *Handbuch der Eisen- und Stahlgiesserei*, Berlin, 1911 ; C. J. B. Karsten, *Sitzber. Akad. Berlin*, 315, 1846 ; *Journ. prakt. Chem.*, (1), **40.** 229, 1847 ; *Karsten's Arch.*, **21.** 500, 1847 ; O. Thallner, *Einleitung und Namenbeziehnung des Eisens*, Kattowitz, 1906 ; *Sammlung Berg. Hütt. Abhand.*, 7, 1907 ; *Berg. Hütt. Runds.*, **3.** 85, 106, 120, 1907 ; K. Honda, *Science Rep. Tohoku Univ.*, **13.** 187, 1924 ; *Bull. Inst. Phys. Chem. Research (Rikwagaku Kenkyujo Iho)*, **2.** 405, 1923 ; J. A. Mathews, *Trans. Amer. Soc. Steel Treating*, **2.** 980, 1922 ; H. Scott, *Chem. Met. Engg.*, **27.** 1156, 1922 ; J. E. Hurst, *Metal Ind.*, **30.** 295, 1927 ; F. Wever, *Proc. World's Eng. Congr. Tokyo*, **34.** 239, 1931 ; J. Navarro, *Anal. Soc. Fis. Quim.*, **29.** 443, 1931 ; R. A. Bull, *Trans. Amer. Foundrymen's Assoc.*, **2.** 257, 1931.

§ 9. Cast Iron

A. A. Inostzanzeff [1] reported a specimen of native iron from Vladivostock the composition of which was Fe, 93·87 ; C (combined), 0·33 ; C (free), 2·87 ; Al, 0·16 ; Mn, 0·66 ; Si, 1·55 ; and S, 0·04. The composition is thus identical with many artificial cast irons ; and similar remarks apply to its microscopic structure. There are bands of ferrite, granular cementite, a ground mass of pearlite, and some free graphite. This native cast iron is supposed to have been formed in the sedimentary rocks by the interaction of coal and iron ore induced by heat from an intruded igneous rock.

Excluding the ferro-alloys and the alloy steels, the various kinds of iron and steel form a continuous series ranging from the purest iron to the white cast irons. The series divides itself into two parts—graphitic (grey and mottled cast irons) and non-graphitic (white cast iron) ; for the graphitic cast irons can be regarded

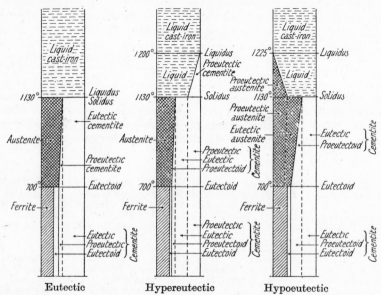

Eutectic Hypereutectic Hypoeutectic

FIGS. 52, 53, and 54.—A. Sauveur's Diagrammatic Representation of the Formation of the Constituents of Eutectic, Hypereutectic, and Hypoeutectic Cast Iron during Solidification and Cooling.

as white cast irons more or less graphitized. The purest obtainable electrolytic iron is soft and ductile ferrite, and the hardest white cast iron is in the extreme case mainly hard and brittle cementite. The intermediate series is continuous, so that only arbitrary lines of demarcation are possible. The carbon content of steels may range up to, say, 2·0 or 2·20 per cent., and of cast iron from, say, 2·20 to, say, 6·70 per cent. I. L. Bell said that the limit for the combined carbon in cast iron is 4·30 per cent. ; H. M. Howe reported cast irons with up to 4·82 per cent. of combined carbon. A further arbitrary subdivision of the steels is (i) *low carbon steels* with 0·00 to 0·20 per cent. of carbon ; (ii) *medium carbon steels* with 0·30 to 0·70 per cent. of carbon ; and (iii) *high carbon steels* with 0·80 to 2·20 per cent. of carbon. There is some overlapping, because the proportion of carbon in wrought iron may exceed that in some low carbon steels. Thus, J. Percy reported samples of wrought iron with 0·272 to 0·386 per cent. carbon ; L. Cubillo, a sample with 0·24 per cent. ; H. M. Howe, samples with 0·212 to 0·512 per cent. ; and E. Riley, a sample with 0·171 per cent. On the other hand, some low carbon steels—e.g. tube steel—have 0·06 to 0·07 per cent. of carbon. There is a similar overlapping in the proportion of carbon in the region between steels and cast iron. Thus, H. M. Howe reported cast irons with about 1·61 per cent. of carbon. W. E. Dennison, and J. L. Francis represented the composition of cast iron by volume. The proximate structure of any member of the series between iron and the **white cast irons** can be approximately determined by a consideration of one of the equilibrium diagrams for the iron-carbon alloys—Figs. 61 to 63. Thus, in percentages :

			Total carbon.	Total pearlite.	Excess ferrite.	Excess cementite.	Primary austenite.	Eutectic.	Eutectic austenite.	Eutectic cementite.	Primary cementite.	Total ferrite.	Total cementite.
Carbon Series	Steels	Hypoeutectoidal	0·20	22	78	0	—	0	0	0	0	97·0	3·0
		Eutectoidal .	0·90	100	0	0	100	0	0	0	0	86·5	13·5
		Hypereutectoidal	2·20	77	0	12·5	81	19	9	10	0	67·0	33·0
	White cast irons	Hypoeutectic .	2·30	76	0	12·2	77	23	11	12	0	65·5	34·5
		Eutectic . .	4·30	41	0	6·6	0	100	48	52	0	35·5	64·5
		Hypereutectic .	6·67	0	0	0	0	0	0	0	100	0·0	100·0

The formation of the different constituents during the solidification and slow cooling of eutectic (ledeburite), hypereutectic, and hypoeutectic cast iron was illustrated by A. Sauveur by diagrams analogous to Figs. 52, 53, and 54, for the case where no graphitization occurs. In all cases, after cooling below the pearlitic transformation at about 700°, the ultimate constituents are ferrite and cementite. Fig. 55 represents the microscopic appearance of white cast iron; the dark areas represent ferrite and the white areas cementite. H. A. Schwartz and A. N. Hird said that during the solidification of molten cast iron, equilibrium is attained when the silicon has all passed into the liquid phase, and austenite free from silicon is able to separate. The whole of the silicon is associated with the eutectic cementite, probably as a silico-cementite. The austenite contains the non-sulphide manganese, and on passing through the A_1-arrest the manganese is equally soluble in the ferrite and the eutectoid cementite. About 93 per cent. of the phosphorus is found with the cementite. A. Mittinsky, and B. Osann discussed properties of the eutectic.

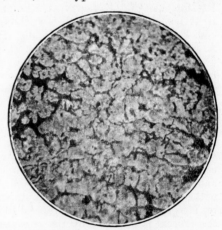

Fig. 55.—Structure of White Cast Iron (F. Popplewell).

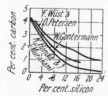

Fig. 56.—The Effect of Silicon on the Carbon Content of the Eutectic.

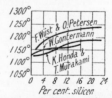

Fig. 57.—The Effect of Silicon on the Temperature of the Eutectic.

F. Wüst and O. Petersen showed that the eutectic composition is lowered from 4·3 to 4 per cent. when a little more than 1 per cent. of silicon is present.

Observations were also made by K. Honda and T. Murakami, J. G. Pearce, H. Pinal, A. Wagner, F. Yamada, A. Sauveur, and W. Gontermann—*vide infra*, iron-silicon alloys. The observed results showing the effect of silicon in lowering the proportion of carbon in the eutectic and in raising the eutectic temp. are summarized in Fig. 57. The general behaviour of silicon-iron·alloys is discussed

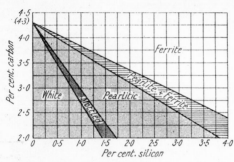

FIG. 58.—The Constitution of Cast Iron.

above. E. Maurer represented the constitution of cast iron by the diagram, Fig. 58. E. Maurer and P. Holtzhaussen, D. Hanson, E. Scheil, J. E. Hurst, E. Piwowarsky, L. Piedbœuf, J. Challansonnet, H. Tanimura, A. L. Norbury, R. Kühnel, and F. B. Coyle also studied the subject — *vide infra*, Fig. 212, Vol. XIII, tensile strength. The so-called *pearlitic cast iron* was discussed by K. Emmel, L. E. Gilmore, O. Bauer, A. Diefenthaler, H. J. Young, C. Irresberger, J. E. Hurst, J. E. Fletcher, L. Piedbœuf, J. A. Smeaton, H. J. Young, G. Gilles, A. E. M. Smith, G. Meyersberg, A. le Thomas, A. M. Portevin, E. Zimmermann, P. Kleiber, R. Moldenke, E. J. Lowry, K. Emmel, B. Osann, R. T. Rolfe, A. Mittinsky, R. P. Lemoine, E. E. Marbaker, F. D. Corbin, M. Lincke, G. Sulzer, A. G. Lambert and F. M. Robbins, A. J. Grindle, H. R. Hiscott, W. West, F. K. Neath, A. Logan, S. G. Werner, A. B. Everest, and C. Sipp.

As pointed out by J. E. Stead, grey cast iron, no matter how grey, in its passage from the commencement of solidification to the cold condition, always commences as white cast iron, and gradually becomes grey during cooling owing to the decomposition of the iron carbide, which has a white fracture. The **graphitization** of the cementite in iron-carbon alloys has previously been discussed in connection with the equilibrium diagram. Graphitization is more likely to occur during and after solidification with increasing difficulty in the following order : (i) proeutectic cementite, (ii) eutectic cementite, (iii) proeutectoidal cementite, and (iv) eutectoidal cementite. In the solidification of hypoeutectic alloys austenite is first formed, and at the eutectic temp. cementite falls out of soln. The high temp. of formation of the eutectic cementite favours its graphitization. As the alloy cools, the austenite rejects proeutectoidal cementite, and its graphitization proceeds more slowly, but the process is favoured by the pre-existing nuclei of graphite from the eutectic cementite. The eutectoidal cementite is graphitized with difficulty because of the low temp. If the graphitization of the proeutectoidal cementite is incomplete, the cast iron will have a hypereutectoidal matrix ; if the graphitization of the proeutectoidal cementite is complete, but that of the eutectoidal cementite incomplete, the cast iron will have a hypoeutectoidal matrix ; and if the graphitization of the proeutectoidal cementite is complete and no eutectoidal cementite is graphitized, the cast iron will have a eutectoidal matrix. Fig. 59 (×250) shows the graphite needles in a cast sample of grey cast iron containing 0·97 per cent. of combined carbon, 3·21 per cent. of graphite, and 2·29 per cent. of silicon. There is a ground mass of almost pure pearlite in which the black needles of graphite are embedded. Fig. 60 (×250) shows another sample of cast iron containing 3·391 per cent. of combined carbon, 2·727 per cent. of graphite, and 2·354 per cent. of silicon. The ground mass of pearlite occurs in rounded cells, the white fields in the diagram represent ferrite, and black needles of graphite are embedded in the ferrite. Both specimens are etched with a soln. of hydrochloric acid in amyl alcohol. The case of the graphitization of eutectic alloys needs no special consideration ; and, in the case of hypereutectic alloys, the proeutectic cementite is particularly liable to graphitization, and kish may be formed — *vide supra*. A. L. Norbury and

L. W. Bolton, J. W. Bolton, and H. Pinsl discussed the form of the graphite which separates from iron—*vide supra*; H. Jungbluth, and E. Maurer, the so-called *black fracture* due to the growth of graphite nuclei in steel subjected to abnormal heat treatment; and J. L. Francis, the volume composition of cast iron.

H. Sawamura observed that when chill-cast white cast iron with about 3·4 per cent. carbon, and about 2 per cent. silicon, is heated at a constant rate in vacuo to the end of graphitization and then quenched in water, the proportions of combined carbon after quenching from different temp. are :

Quenching .	1000°	950°	900°	860°	840°	800°
Comb. carbon	0·30	0·21	0·10	0·06	0·02	0·02 per cent.

M. Hamasumi observed that the strength of cast iron increases with the velocity of cooling owing to the more uniform distribution of the curved plates of graphite.

P. D. Merica and L. J. Gurevich found that (i) the greater the carbon content, the narrower the zone of complete graphitization; (ii) more graphite was found in a specimen cooled from 1000° than when cooled from 1100°, and this is taken to mean that the graphite separated from solid soln. on cooling when its nuclei

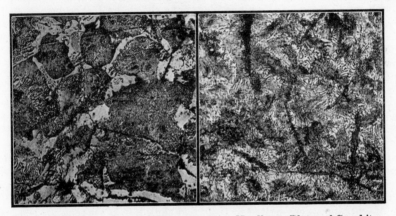

FIGS. 59 and 60.—Grey Cast Iron containing Needles or Plates of Graphite.

were already present; and (iii) that only 0·2 per cent. of combined carbon was found in some slowly cooled specimens, and this was taken to indicate that the graphite was formed from pearlite at temp. directly below that of its formation, or else the graphite eutectoid occurs at lower values than is generally supposed. R. S. Archer showed that graphitization can be initiated and completed below the A_1-arrest, and that complete graphitization is possible only at or below a point close to or identical with the A_1-arrest. A. Phillips and E. S. Davenport also suggested that temper carbon is derived from areas of solid soln., not from massive cementite; and they found that the areas of temper carbon produced at lower temp. were more compact and sharply outlined than when produced at higher temp. H. A. Schwartz and co-workers assumed that a stable solid soln. of graphite is formed, which they called boydenite—*vide supra*—and the separation of graphite about graphite nuclei may begin at 900° to 1000°. C. J. McNamara and C. H. Lorig thought that the continued slow cooling below the critical point is not necessary for graphitization. The chemistry of cast iron was studied by A. H. Hiorns, L. Houghton, and E. Adamson; and the effect of the melting conditions on the microstructure and mechanical strength, as well as on the distribution of carbon and silicon, by A. L. Norbury and E. Morgan. As a result of the observations of O. Ruff, H. Hanemann, and H. P. Tiemann, H. M. Howe raised the question whether in the absence of manganese and maybe certain other impurities it is possible to obtain hypereutectic iron, that is, white cast iron containing more than 4·30 per cent. of combined carbon.

O. von Keil found that when the m.p. and f.p. of cast iron are both low, say 1145°, the iron solidifies as white iron, but if both the m.p. and f.p. are high, needle-like graphite is formed ; and if the m.p. is high and the f.p. low, graphite is formed in a finely-dispersed condition. The needle-like graphite separates directly from the fused mass, and the finely-dispersed graphite separates from the decomposition of a metastable solid. Pig-iron separates first as white iron, then, with a high carbon content, the ledeburite first formed decomposes rapidly, with the separation of fine graphite, but in the neighbourhood of the eutectic composition needle-like graphite separates from the liquid phase owing to the retardation of the cooling. For iron of a given composition there is a critical rate of cooling, above which the metal freezes in the metastable state, and below which needle-like graphite separates from the liquid. Overheating reduces the critical rate of cooling to a low value, so that even after slow cooling the metal solidifies in the metastable state. Repeated melting the overheated metal does not cause it to revert to the normal state. As indicated in connection with the equilibrium diagram of the iron-carbon alloys, if cementite be regarded as a metastable phase, there are two equilibrium diagrams, one with cementite and one with graphite. As shown by L. Forquignon, in 1881, the hard iron carbide or cementite is metastable at an elevated temp., and is liable to dissociate. O. Ruff, for instance, estimated that the time required to graphitize half the cementite is decreased by half for every 10° rise of temp. just below 1135°, being 16 secs. at 1105°, 8 secs. at 1115°, and 2 secs. at 1135°. The fact is also evidenced by the slighter graphitization of steel than of cast iron, and of hypoeutectic than hypereutectic cast iron. In both these cases graphitization is favoured by the higher temp. of solidification—vide infra. The higher the temp. at which cementite is formed, the more readily will it dissociate into graphite : $Fe_3C=3Fe+C_{graphite}$. The simultaneous production of ferrite and graphite is illustrated microscopically by the frequent juxtaposition of these products—e.g. Fig. 64. It will be observed that the low sp. gr. of graphite in comparison with the cementite and ferrite is such that the sectional area of the ferrite from the parent cementite should be about four times that of its twin brother graphite. E. H. Saniter found that when cementite is heated to 800° and slowly cooled, it yields 0·40 per cent. of graphite ; when heated to 1000° and chilled, 0·56 per cent. ; when heated to 1000° and slowly cooled, 2·45 per cent. ; and when fused at 1400° and slowly cooled, 3·05 per cent. F. Mylius and co-workers also observed the decomposition of cementite when fused. A. Lodin pointed out that the dissociation of cementite is accompanied by an expansion, so that the formation of cementite will be favoured by compression such as is exercised by the outer zones on the internal zones in cases of rapid cooling ; and from this point of view slow cooling would thus favour the dissociation of the cementite. W. H. Hatfield added that in cast iron the free cementite is broken up into free carbon and free iron between 800° and 900° ; and that the carbide resulting from the resolution of the hardenite decomposes between 650° and 700°, i.e. immediately after or during the hardenite→pearlite change. K. Honda and T. Murakami concluded that graphite in fine cast iron is produced by the decomposition of cementite during cooling, and that graphitization is an indirect process. H. P. Evans and A. Hayes inferred that below 700° and above 850° cementite is metastable in iron-carbon alloys ; and H. A. Schwartz added that as the stable A_3-point in these alloys approaches the A_2-point, the concentration of the element promoting graphitization decreases, and he concluded that the stable A_3-point is below the metastable A_3-point. The subject was discussed by I. R. Valentine, H. Nishimura, H. R. Pitt, A. le Thomas, E. Schülz, and A. M. Portevin and P. Chévenard. A. Allison considered that sulphide inclusions in cast iron served as nuclei for the precipitation of graphite. C. J. McNamara and C. H. Lorig, and H. Sawamura made analogous observations; while L. Northcott found that the free carbon liberated above 1000° tends to become flaky, and if below 1000° it tends to take on the typical rounded form of annealing or tender carbon. The more compact the granules of carbon, the greater the malleability of the casting. The slower the rate of cooling, the greater the graphitization. This is exemplified by comparing the smaller proportion of graphite in the exterior of chilled castings of grey cast iron with that in the interior. J. E. Fletcher studied the structural relation between the original pig-iron and the derived cast iron, wrought iron, malleable iron, or steel; and W. Bruch, the isotropy of cast iron.

A. Achenbach, E. Adamson, A. Allison, J. H. Andrews, R. S. Archer, P. Bardenheuer and co-workers, O. Bauer, H. H. Beeny, P. F. Blackwood, J. W. Bolton, G. Charpy, E. J. Cook, F. Diepschlag, J. W. Donaldson, E. Dübi, Y. A. Dyer, F. Erbreich, H. P. Evans and A. Hayes, A. B. Everest, H. Field, J. E. Fletcher, W. Gahl, K. Glinz, P. Goerens, P. Goerens and N. Gütowsky, C. Gresty, F. Grotts, M. Hamasumi, H. Hanemann, W. H. Hatfield, A. Hayes and co-workers, W. Heike and G. May, N. Hekker, E. Heyn, J. A. Holden, P. Holtzhaussen, K. Honda and T. Murakami, J. E. Hurst, J. E. Johnson, T. Kase, O. von Keil, O. von Keil and R. Mitsche, R. R. Kennedy and G. J. Oswald, K. von Kerpely, E. Kirk, C. Kluijtmans, O. Kröhnke, R. Kühnel, R. Kühnel and E. Nesemann, F. C. A. H. Lantsberry, J. A. Leffler, D. M. Levy, A. McCance, G. May, P. D. Merica and L. J. Gurevich, W. J. Merten, A. Merz and H. Schuster, E. Meyer, J. W. Miller, R. Moldenke, E. Namba, F. K. Neath, G. Neumann, L. Northcott, B. Osann, J. G. Pearce, T. F. Pearson, B. H. Pinsel, H. R. Pitt, E. Piwowarsky, A. M. Portevin and co-workers, O. W. Potter, H. S. Rawdon and S. Epstein, R. T. Rolfe, P. Ropsy, E. L. Roth, F. W. Rowe, E. Scheil, R. Schmitt, E. Schülz, H. A. Schwartz and co-workers, J. Seigle, J. Shaw, F. T. Sisco, O. Smalley, A. Stadeler, B. Stoughton, H. Tanimura, A. le Thomas, H. P. Tiemann, A. C. Timmins, E. Touceda, T. Turner, G. B. Upton, W. R. Webster, O. Wedemeyer, T. D. West, F. White and R. S. Archer, F. White and H. E. Gladhill, F. Wüst and co-workers, F. Wüst and E. Leuenberger, and E. Zimmermann have studied the micro-structure, texture, properties, and the progress of the graphitization of cast iron, etc., with time.

P. Bardenheuer and co-workers, and G. Neumann found that the form and degree of fineness of the graphite are the dominant factors in determining the tensile strength, bending strength, and resistance to shock. The results of these investigations show that the graphitizing reaction is not an erratic phenomenon, but it occurs through the operation of definite natural laws, but the physical constants involved are functions of so many variables that their application is distinctly complex. H. A. Schwartz found that the graphitization curves are all alike when plotted so as to show the graphite formation as a percentage of the possible total at different intervals of the time required to complete half the total reaction. Graphitization proceeds by an increase in the size rather than in the number of carbon nodules. The rate of graphitization is determined by the rate of migration of carbon, in some form, through solid soln. or through ferrite. Either the form in which carbon migrates is always the same, or carbon in all its forms migrates in iron at the same rate. Equal increments in temp. multiply the rate of graphitization by equal amounts. In the initial stages of graphitization the speed is the same above and below the A_1-arrest; and the temp. coeff. of the reaction is of the same order of magnitude. There is no perceptible discontinuity in the speed of graphitization at the critical temp. There is no reason to assume that graphitization does not progress at all temp., no matter how low. P. Chevenard studied the volume changes which occur during graphitization. B. W. Winder found that graphite is formed during the rolling at a dull red-heat of steel with over 0·90 per cent. of carbon; and A. Ledebur said that hammering produces a similar result.

K. Tawara and G. Asahara consider that carbon exists as cementite in molten iron-carbon alloys, and that there is some dissociation, though possibly a small proportion, of the cementite in the soln. into carbon and iron. The free carbon atom may serve as nuclei for the graphitization when the conditions are favourable. When an alloy containing over 2 per cent. and less than 4·3 per cent. of carbon is allowed to cool sufficiently slowly, the primary austenite crystallizes out along the liquidus AB, Fig. 67, and the mother-liquor reaches the eutectic composition B.

At this point, when the cooling is sufficiently slow to maintain the equilibrium, since there are a number of the nuclei already present, graphite will crystallize together with austenite, forming the eutectic. As a general rule the deposition of the dissociated carbon from the molten system will bring about a further dissociation of the molten cementite, in order to re-establish equilibrium. This process is repeated and graphite crystals are developed. On the other hand, the residual molten alloy is diluted all the time by the ferrite, which is the contemporaneous product of the dissociation, and finally it will attain the composition A, which corresponds with that of sat. austenite having 2 per cent. carbon. Consequently, in the final state, there is a eutectic of graphite and sat. austenite, and the whole regulus consists only of graphite and austenite, the latter, of course, resolving into pearlite and needle-shaped cementite when cooled. If the favourable conditions for the solidification of this eutectic of graphite and austenite cease—for example, if the rate of the cooling of the melt becomes greater over a certain range—that process will no longer take place, and cementite will crystallize out of the molten alloy. The separation of cementite at the point B does not represent a true equilibrium ; it is a transitional and metastable condition. When the solidification of the alloy is not retarded sufficiently until the whole becomes solid, mottled cast iron will be obtained—*vide supra*.

H. A. Schwartz and co-workers assumed that the solid soln. of carbon in iron, boydenite, is a different phase from austenite, the solid soln. of cementite in iron— *vide supra* ; and they explain graphitization as follows :

The process is initiated by the separation of a graphite nucleus, possibly due to carbon precipitated out by some local conversion of austenite into boydenite and excess carbon. The bulk of the solid soln., however, remains austenitic and maintains its carbon concentration by dissolving cementite. More carbon precipitates and more cementite dissolves until the latter is used up.

H. Sawamura said that at a temp. below the A_1-arrest only one process can occur, namely, the decomposition of cementite, but above that temp. the following processes may occur consecutively or concurrently : (i) the cementite is first decomposed to iron and annealing carbon, and then the former absorbs the latter to secure stable equilibrium ; and (ii) the cementite is first dissolved in austenite, and the excess carbon in austenite is precipitated as annealing carbon to secure stable equilibrium. This subject has been previously discussed. H. J. Young described the manufacture of so-called pearlitic cast iron. A. M. Portevin and P. Chevenard, and A. le Thomas discussed the influence of structure on the annealing of cast iron. W. H. Hatfield did not agree with D. M. Levy's statement that the cementite balls up or spheroidizes before dissociation.

As previously indicated, the graphitization of cementite is favoured by the presence of *silicon*. This was noticed by G. Charpy and L. Grenet, H. Sawamura, F. Wüst and P. Schlösser, A. Hayes and H. E. Flanders, D. Hanson, E. Piwowarsky, A. M. Portevin and P. Chevenard, J. H. Küster and C. Pfannenschmidt, F. Roll, G. M. Thrasher, C. James, A. Allinson, D. G. Anderson and G. R. Bessmer, G. Takahashi, A. L. Norbury and E. Morgan, G. P. Royston, and A. Lissner. K. Honda and T. Murakami explained the favourable influence by assuming that (i) a non-magnetic, unstable silicocarbide is formed ; (ii) silicon diminishes the solubility of carbon in austenite ; and (iii) silicon raises the eutectic and eutectoidal temp. H. A. Schwartz found that equal increments of silicon multiply the rate of graphitization by equal amounts ; and the presence of silicon decreases the temp. coeff. of the speed of graphitization ; this has not yet been determined, but it approximates to the rule that the logarithm of the temp. coeff. is a linear function of the concentration of the silicon. T. F. Pearson observed that with iron containing 2·5 per cent. of carbon, over 0·75 per cent. of silicon must be present to produce complete graphitization. The effect of silicon has been discussed in connection with Figs. 61 to 63, and also in connection with the silicon-iron alloys. T. F. Pearson represented the effect of silicon on the graphitization in vacuo by Figs. 61 to 63; and the effect of oxygen was to shift the phase fields more to the right of the temperature axis. E. Piwowarsky, and H. Sawamura found that *titanium* also favours graphitization. The favourable action of *aluminium* on graphitization was observed by W. J. Keep, P. Longmuir, F. Roll, E. Piwowarsky, T. W. Hogg, G. Melland and H. W. Waldron, and H. Sawamura.

The effects of *sulphur* and *manganese* under most conditions are to hinder the formation of graphite. The retarding influence of sulphur and manganese on the graphitization of cast iron was discussed by E. R. Taylor, W. Heike and G. May, B. Osann, E. Leuenberger, F. Roll, A. Hayes and H. E. Flanders, W. P. Putman, O. von Keil and R. Mitsche, F. Wüst, A. L. Norbury, F. Wüst and P. Schlösser, D. M. Levy, R. T. Rolfe, W. H. Hatfield, and H. Sawamura—*vide infra*, iron and sulphur compounds. H. P. Tiemann found that with the proportion of silicon very low, or with proportions of sulphur or manganese proportionally high, graphitization is relatively slow even at 1050°. G. Charpy and A. Cornu-Thenard observed that with 0·14 to 0·40 per cent. of carbon no graphite is formed in the presence of 2·20 per cent. of silicon, but with 4 per cent. of silicon graphitization is complete in 3 hrs. at 800°, and nearly complete in an hour. A. Lissner found that the cementite in white cast iron with 0·4 per cent. of silicon and 0·15 per cent. of sulphur commenced to decompose at 765°, and, at the decomposition temp., rose with increasing proportions of sulphur until it attained 1020° with 1·24 per cent. of

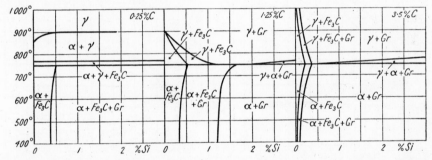

FIGS. 61, 62, 63.—The Effect of Silicon on the Graphitization of Iron-Carbon Alloys.

sulphur. F. Wüst and P. Schlösser said that up to 0·5 per cent. of manganese is indifferent, and F. Wüst and H. Meissner, that its retarding effect does not appear until 2·5 per cent. is present; and H. Sawamura, that the retardation appears when over 1 per cent. has been added. The retarding influence of manganese is attributed to the formation of exothermic Mn_3C, which is more stable than Fe_3C. C. Benedicks, and H. M. Howe discussed the re-solution of the graphite by the austenite as the temp. rises to 900°, and its subsequent reprecipitation on cooling. W. H. Hatfield concluded from his observations on the effects of silicon, sulphur, and manganese on the carbide in cast iron: (i) the silicon is not uniformly distributed through the cast iron, but that the carbide, while not containing so much silicon as the matrix, still contains appreciable quantities; (ii) the manganese is in combination with the carbide to the exclusion of the silicon; and (iii) the proportion of silicon in the carbide is low with high sulphur irons, and the sulphur is in some way responsible for the comparative absence of silicon. T. F. Pearson observed that in the presence of 0·03 to 0·04 per cent. of sulphur complete graphitization was prevented in cast iron with approximately 3·5 per cent. of carbon. E. F. Diepschlag and L. Treuheit studied the effect of lime and of alumina in the slag.

L. Guillet, W. H. Hatfield, M. Waehlert, O. Bauer and co-workers, G. Takahashi, A. B. Everest, E. Piwowarsky and K. Ebbefeld, F. Roll, H. Sawamura, and J. Challansonnet found that *nickel* favours graphitization; H. A. Schwartz, that

nickel hinders the work of silicon as an accelerator of graphitization; and
G. Brodsky, that nickel gives castings free from blow-holes and sponginess.
O. Bauer and H. Sieglerschmidt, W. Lipin, and M. Hamasumi said that copper is
indifferent, but H. Sawamura, and F. Roll found that up to 2 per cent. favours
graphitization; O. Bauer and E. Piwowarsky said that *cobalt* is unfavourable, but
H. Sawamura said that the effect is favourable though feeble. E. Piwowarsky,
and H. Sawamura found that *gold* and *platinum* favour graphitization; and
T. F. Jennings, H. Sawamura, and F. Roll, that *chromium, molybdenum* and
tungsten hinder graphitization. W. H. Hatfield, J. E. Hurst, F. Roll, E. Piwowarsky, and J. Challansonnet, said that *vanadium* hinders graphitization; and
P. Oberhoffer doubted this; but H. Sawamura showed that the unfavourable
effect is very marked.   J. E. Hurst discussed the effect of *titanium.*   J. E. Stead,
F. Wüst, and P. Goerens and O. Dobbelstein found that *phosphorus* prevents
combined carbon existing in forms other than cementite.   F. Wüst and P. Schlösser
said that up to about 0·5 per cent. of phosphorus has no appreciable effect on
graphitization; while M. Hamasumi, F. Roll, and H. Sawamura said that it
favours graphitization.   The subject was discussed by O. von Keil and R. Mitsche.

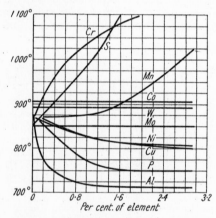

FIG. 64.—Relation of the Beginning
Temperature of Graphitization to the
Proportion of added Element.

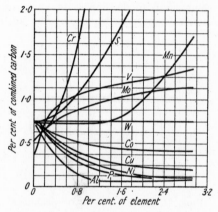

FIG. 65.—The Relation between the
Proportion of Combined Carbon in the
Annealed Alloys and the Proportion
of Added Element.

F. Roll said that vanadium, chromium, and manganese preserve the carbide;
cobalt, nickel, copper, and zinc decompose the carbide; tungsten, uranium, and
lead favour the formation of graphite; whilst tin produces grey cast iron,
and molybdenum, boron, aluminium, silicon, germanium, phosphorus, oxygen,
and sulphur partly preserve and partly decompose the carbide. D. Saito and
K. Nishihara found that manganese favours graphitization.

H. Sawamura summarized his results in Fig. 64, representing the effect of
different proportions of the elements on the temp. at which graphitization begins,
and in Fig. 65 representing the percentage amount of combined carbon in the
annealed alloy with different proportions of the added element. H. Sawamura
showed that the elements which favour the graphitization of white cast iron are in
the order of their decreasing strength Si, Al, (Ti), Ni, Cu, Co, and P. Platinum
and gold also favour the action, while the elements which hinder graphitization
in the order of increasing strength are W, Mo, V, Cr, and S. Most of the elements
which favour graphitization crystallize in a face-centred, cubic lattice, and most
of those which hinder graphitization crystallize in a body-centred, cubic lattice. He
showed that most of the elements which favour the graphitization of cast iron have
a limit in their effect on the starting temp. for the graphitization of white cast iron.

White cast irons having a high content of some elements (*e.g.* Si, Al, Ti, P) begin to graphitize at temp. lower than their Ac_1. The stability of the cementite in the cast irons with silicon or aluminium changes with the content of carbon and the added element, and the cementite in some of the alloys directly decomposes at temp. lower than their Ac_1 by annealing. These facts probably hold in other cases. In white cast iron alloyed with some elements a part or all of the carbon may exist in a combined form different from cementite. The stability of the combination, of course, influences the graphitization of the mother white cast iron, *e.g.* alloys with silicon or aluminium. In white cast irons which rapidly graphitize by annealing— that is, alloys containing a high proportion of silicon, aluminium, titanium, or nickel—the form of the temper-carbon produced is always governed by the form of the cementite and in most cases is flaky. Both the number of particles and the grain-size of the temper-carbon are also governed by those of the cementite in the alloys. In white cast iron which slowly graphitizes by annealing—that is, alloys with a low proportion of silicon, aluminium, titanium, or nickel; or containing cobalt, copper, phosphorus, molybdenum, or other elements having an unfavourable effect on graphitization—the form of the temper-carbon is different from that of the cementite and is always nodular. Generally speaking, the grain-size of the nodular temper-carbon is far larger and the number of the grains is far smaller than expected from the structure of the alloys in the cast state. The mechanism of the formation of temper-carbon is of the same nature as that of the formation of graphite in cast iron during cooling, and consequently the effect of the elements on the formation of graphite in cast iron can be approximately inferred.

By annealing specimens in atmospheres of carbon monoxide and dioxide, under press., at 927°, A. Hayes and G. C. Scott showed that the rate of absorption of free carbide was increased nearly 100 per cent. ; and at the critical range graphitization was inhibited by the gas mixture. H. Sawamura studied the effect of gases on the graphitization of cast iron, and found that the action is retarded by hydrogen, ammonia, and methane ; carbon monoxide and dioxide have a moderate retarding effect ; and nitrogen, oxygen, and air are indifferent. The action with malleable cast iron is rapid in carbon dioxide, and it is retarded by hydrogen, ammonia, and methane. T. F. Pearson observed that whilst sulphur and oxygen separately tend to inhibit graphitization, together they counterbalance one another to some extent. The general effect of oxygen is to push the phase fields to the right of the temp. axis.

H. Sawamura [2] discussed the effect of *the rate of solidification* of white cast iron containing silicon, and found that the effect on the graphitization is remarkable. A given white cast iron graphitizes more easily the faster it has been solidified, and the increase in vol. due to complete graphitization is far greater with the rapidly solidified metal than it is with the same metal more slowly solidified. The effect of *the temperature of casting* on the properties of the metal has been examined. Apart from the regular mechanical defects in castings produced at too low or too high a temp., the mechanical properties of cast iron or steel are to some extent determined by the initial temp. at which the molten metal enters the mould. T. Turner observed that cast iron is perhaps not so sensitive to the effect of variations due to pouring temp. as are some other metals, and herein lies one of its great advantages, in that castings are not so readily spoiled by inattention. R. A. Hadfield said that steel cast too hot has a peculiar crystalline fracture, which disappears on reheating, but the metal is never quite satisfactory ; and if the metal is cast too cold, the metal is unsatisfactory in mill and forge. J. O. Arnold also found a difference in the mechanical properties of steel which had been cast at different temp. G. M. Thrasher found that by varying the pouring temp. it is possible to pour a test of mottled cast iron and of grey cast iron from the same ladle of iron. P. Oberhoffer and H. Stein considered 1240° to be the optimum temp. for casting ordinary iron from a cupola. G. Hailstone obtained the best results between 1428° and 1386°. A. McWilliam found that with special crucible steels the metal should be cast as cold as possible consistent with the last drop being liquid and falling into a thoroughly liquid bath. A. le Thomas discussed the effect of the speed of cooling and said that the strength of the metal depends on a kind of heredity, *i.e.* on the structure imposed on the metal during solidification. Observations were made by F. Beitter, H. H. Campbell, A. Sauveur, E. Piwowarsky, C. Schreiber and H. Menking, J. E. Hurst, A. McCance, H. A. Schwartz, E. J. Lowry, A. Ledebur, W. J. Keep, E. Deny, E. F. Dürre, J. Kollmann, T. Turner, F. Busse, F. J. Cook, K. Honda and T. Murakami, H. Hanemann, E. Meyer, T. Klingenstein, P. Bardenheuer and co-workers, H. M. Howe, and R. Hohage.

W. H. Hatfield observed that the temp. of casting influences the proportion of combined and free carbon. The higher the casting temp., the greater the proportion of combined carbon. G. Hailstone also said that as the casting temp. falls, the proportion of combined carbon is reduced. P. Bardenheuer and K. L. Zeyen also observed that the higher the temp. at which cast iron is heated in the molten state, the smaller is the amount of graphite which separates on cooling. F. Sauerwald and A. Koreny found that the rate of dissolution of graphite in cast iron at 1255° and 1350° follows the regular law, being proportional to the degree of saturation of the molten metal, the form of the graphite particles, the temp., and the time of contact. The amount of graphite dissolved in a given time increases rapidly with temp., and that dissolved at a given temp. at first increases rapidly with time and then proceeds more slowly and the results furnish a hyperbolic curve.

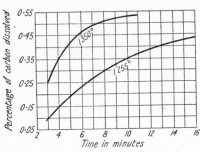

Fig. 66.—The Dissolution of Graphite in Molten Iron.

G. Charpy, speaking generally, observed that the size of the crystals varies with the speed of solidification; the slower the rate of solidification, the more the crystals are developed. Generally the size of the grain is increased by casting at a high temp. and in warm moulds, or in cooling slowly. On pouring at a low temp., in metallic moulds so as to ensure rapid cooling, a fine crystallization will result. As the conditions of pouring modify equally the mechanical properties corresponding with a given composition, one can form an idea of the properties of a cast metal from the size of the grain, as has been done by A. Sauveur in the case of steel. P. Longmuir found that in general bars of cast iron are dry and open in fracture with a high casting temp.; close and uniform with a medium casting temp.; and open with a low casting temp. Bars cast at a medium temp. were sounder than those cast at a high or at a low temp. The sp. gr. of cast iron is, as a rule, increased by lowering the temp. of casting. A sample of cast iron with 3·35 per cent. of combined carbon, cast at 1440° and 1299° respectively, gave tensile strengths of 9·4 and 12·1 tons per sq. in. Again, a steel with 0·52 per cent. combined carbon, 3·4 graphite, 1·78 Si, 0·28 Mn, 0·04 S, and 0·28 P, when cast at 1400°, 1350°, and 1245° gave tensile strengths of 9·7, 14·1, and 10·6 tons per sq. in. respectively. In general, with both cast iron and steel, the tensile strengths, elastic limits, and elongations were better when cast at the intermediate temp., and this also applied when the cast metal was heated to 1000° and slowly cooled, or annealed, or quenched from 940°. E. Piwowarsky, and E. Schüz discussed the annealing of cast iron. W. H. Hatfield, however, observed that there is a great variation in the strength of cast iron of the same composition and that the variation does not appear to follow any recognizable rule with regard to the temp. of the casting operations; that a difference in mechanical tests is generally accompanied by a difference of microstructure; and that the inequalities of the metal can be annulled by a judicious heat treatment; that is, under certain conditions, the irregularity need not persist after heat treatment.

C. Benedicks and H. Löfquist thus described the constitution of grey cast iron. Structurally, grey cast iron contains (i) A ground-mass of iron, generally containing in soln. a considerable amount of silicon (silico-ferrite) and also some manganese. (ii) Graphite, occurring partly in the form of large lamellæ precipitated during solidification, partly as smaller particles precipitated in the solid state (temper carbon); its total amount is generally about 3 per cent. (iii) A certain amount of combined carbon, occurring generally as pearlite. If the manganese is high and the silicon low, the carbon may also be present as free cementite, formed during the solidification. Further, impurities occur, such as phosphorus and sulphur. The most characteristic feature of the cast iron may be said to be its high degree of heterogeneity, due to the soft graphite lamellæ. Their considerable quantity and extent cause a low tensile strength, unusual for metallic materials; as a matter of fact, the graphite lamellæ act as notches, inducing cracks.

W. H. Hatfield regarded grey cast iron as a matrix of ferrite or of silicoferrite strengthened by pearlite which is cut up and weakened by numerous plates of graphite and possibly also of phosphides. If the proportion of silicon is low, or if other favourable conditions exist, a cementite network is formed, and this strengthens the material under compression. **Annealing** relieves the internal strains set up during the solidification of the iron, and it also softens the casting. A short annealing of grey cast iron between 750° and 800° breaks down the cementite network to form graphite and ferrite. *Mutatis mutandis*, the grey cast irons, indeed, are structurally similar to carbon steels, but the cast iron is weakened by the presence of the graphite flakes, just as would be the case if the steel were weakened by a number of indiscriminate cracks. Thus, P. Longmuir found that grey cast iron with 0·52 per cent. of combined carbon and 3·4 per cent. of graphitic carbon, cast at 1350°, had a tensile strength of 14·1 tons per sq. in., and when annealed at 940° and cooled slowly, the tensile strength fell to 9·9, and when cooled by quenching, to 3·0 tons per sq. in. W. H. Hatfield observed that the weakening of the metal by annealing is connected with the way the graphite segregates during the heat treatment. A. Campion and J. W. Donaldson found that the strength is improved by heat treatment up to 400°, and is not seriously modified up to 700°. F. Graziani, R. T. Rolfe, and W. H. Hatfield observed that annealing below 500° reduces the initial strains set up during the solidification of the metal, without at the same time materially affecting the mechanical strength; and J. E. Hurst observed that the combined carbon is not quite stable at 575° to 600°, for annealing at these temp. generally reduces the hardness and tensile strength. The weakening or embrittling action produced by the graphitization of cast iron was also confirmed by the work of W. J. Keep, W. A. Jenkins, G. Jüngst, G. R. Johnson, E. Gridley, G. L. Norris, W. P. Putman, S. B. Chadsey, B. Osann, etc. The softening of grey cast iron is affected by annealing for 6 to 12 hrs. at 650°, or by cooling slowly from 800° to 900°. H. Sawamura represented the speed of graphitization by $V=at^n$, or $V=ak^n\theta^n$, where a and k denote constants, and V denotes the speed, t the time, and θ the temp.; while n is probably a constant and independent of the chemical composition, or else is equal to 2, and a variable. It was observed that the speed of solidification of cast irons with silicon as an impurity is independent of n and a, but the speed of graphitization at the eutectic temp. of quickly solidified cast iron is greater than that of slowly solidified cast iron of the same composition. The amount of cementite remaining undecomposed in cast iron depends on the product of the speed of graphitization of cast iron at its eutectic temp. and the time occupied in cooling from the eutectic temp. to the temp. at which graphitization begins. Hence, the degree of graphitization of white cast iron greatly depends on the temp. at which graphitization begins and the speed of graphitization. H. A. Schwartz and co-workers also discussed the mechanism of the reaction. There is nothing to show that graphitization does not occur very slowly at low temp. The curves furnished an equation which, by extrapolation at 20°, indicated that white cast iron, after the lapse of 20 years, should contain about 0·0001 per cent. of graphite. The thermal coeff. of the reaction indicated that a rise of 20° multiplied the velocity by 1·229. W. Fraenkel and E. Heymann discussed the kinetics of the process of annealing—*vide supra*.

Observations on the annealing and heat treatment of cast iron and steel were reported by E. Piwowarsky, E. Schüz, O. W. Potter, A. Pomp and co-workers, R. Stotz, F. Wüst and E. Leuenberger, E. Leuenberger, H. E. Diller, P. Chevenard, E. Touceda, J. E. Stead, H. R. Stanford, R. A. Hadfield, G. P. Royston, C. James, N. Hekker, V. V. Usoff and N. N. Pustuimikoff, E. H. Putman, G. C. Davis, A. Hayes and co-workers, H. Fay and S. Badlam, Y. Watanabe, etc. G. Charpy and L. Grenet summarized their observations as follows : (i) free carbon separates at a lower temp. when the proportion of silicon is high ; (ii) the separation of free carbon once begun continues at temp. below those which inhibit the reaction ; (iii) at a constant temp. the separation of carbon is effected progressively more freely as the temp. is lower and the proportion of silicon is less ; (iv) the amount of combined carbon which corresponds with a state of equilibrium at a given temp. diminishes with an increase in the silicon content ; (v) the amount of combined carbon corresponding with a state of equilibrium diminishes as the temp. decreases ; (vi) the structure of the temper-carbon varies with the temp. at which it is produced ; (vii) the precipitation of carbon is more complete in certain regions, and proceeds from various centres ; and (viii) the ultimate stable phases are ferrite and free carbon. A. Hayes and G. C. Scott studied the effect of annealing in an atm. of carbon monoxide and dioxide under press.

According to W. H. Hatfield, a small casting of cast iron is brittle and will not resist shock ; small steel castings cannot be made cheaply because of the comparative difficulty in attaining a sufficiently high temp. to make small castings satisfactorily. Cast iron can be melted with ease and cast into the smallest and most intricate shapes. Hence, the discovery that the annealing of some kinds of iron furnishes a product almost as tough and ductile as wrought iron became of great industrial value. In 1722, R. A. F. de Réaumur softened cast iron and rendered it malleable to a certain extent by exposing it to a high temp. with excess of air while embedded in hæmatite—*safran de Mars* ; he found that the red oxide of iron gave better results than chalk, bone-ash, etc. S. Lucas obtained a patent for a similar process in 1804. About 1732, C. Neumann also noted that :

Cast iron surrounded by animal ashes, and exposed to a fire not sufficient to melt it, becomes in a shorter or longer time, according to the strength of the fire and thickness of the metal, so soft that ornaments or utensils made of it, however hard before, may now be easily cut, filed, embellished, or freed from their superfluities. The gradual changes produced in this process are pretty remarkable.

In 1769, J. Ashton obtained a patent for softening cast iron by the heat of a slow fire ; and in 1783, G. Matthews obtained another patent for softening large castings such as guns, etc., by a similar process ; and J. E. Beauvalet, still another in 1852. The subject is here connected with the decarburization of cast iron—*vide infra*. The product of processes based on that of R. A. F. de Réaumur is sometimes called **European** or **Réaumur's malleable cast iron.** It will be observed that rapid cooling of cast iron favours the formation of cementite at the expense of the graphite, and it also yields the graphite in smaller granules. When the graphite is generated in cast iron at the high temp. of solidification, 1135°, and immediately below, the mobility is great enough to allow the graphite to assemble in long flakes, which break up the continuity of the mass so as seriously to interfere with its mechanical properties. If, however, the graphite be generated at a lower temp., say at 730° for 60 hrs., it forms an impalpable powder filling the interstices between a skeleton of ferrite and pearlite, as shown in Fig. 58. The continuity of the mass in consequence is not so seriously broken. The purpose of **black-heart malleabilizing** is to break up the hard and brittle cementite so as to avoid the development of the graphite during and immediately after solidification, but to induce its formation at about 730°, when it is in a condition to do least harm. The product of this operation is sometimes called **American malleable cast iron** because of its development in American foundries. It is also called **black-heart,** and that produced by the Réaumur's process **white-heart.** It gives higher mechanical tests than the Réaumur malleable cast iron.

The manufacture of malleable cast iron was discussed by G. A. Ackerlind, E. Adamson, E. Adamson and J. E. Fletcher, R. D. Allen, J. H. Anderson, P. Bardenheuer, W. R. Bean and co-workers, A. J. Beck, G. A. Blume, E. C. Boehringer, S. Bolland, A. Boussu, O. Brauer, E. Bremer, J. Bronn, C. Busquet, A. Cairnes, E. F. Cone, F. J. Cook, M. Dalifol, R. W. Davenport, G. C. Davis, J. D. Deisher, W. J. Diederichs and H. E. Flanders, H. E. Diller, R. L. Dowell and J. T. Gow, E. F. Dürre, M. Epstein, F. Erbreich, G. A. Evans, W. T. Evans and A. E. Peace, S. J. Felton, H. Field, B. Finney, E. P. Fischer, D. P. Forbes, L. Forquignon, R. Gailly, L. E. Gilmore, N. G. Girschowitsch and E. C. Widin, M. Guedras, A. Harley, W. H. Hatfield, A. Hayes and co-workers, N. Hekker, H. Hemenway, C. C. Hermann, G. Hofer, F. H. Hurren, H. W. Hyde, C. James, A. T. Jeffrey, T. Kikuta, F. R. King, C. Kluijtmans, C. E. Kluijtmans and W. H. W. Proctor, B. Kranz, G. L. Lacher, M. Lamla, E. H. Leasman, M. Leroyer, T. Levoz, O. M. Levy, A. Lissner, T. D. Lynch and W. J. Merten, M. M. Marcus, L. H. Marshall, C. J. McNamara and C. H. Lorig, F. A. Melmoth, A. W. Merrick, R. Moldenke, J. V. Murray, E. Namba, R. Namias, J. B. Nealey, S. S. Nekryti, P. Oberhoffer and J. Welter, P. Oberhoffer and E. Zingg, E. C. Ongley, B. Osann, S. J. Parsons, P. A. Paulson, A. E. Peace, J. P. Pero, J. P. Pero and J. C. Nulsen, A. Phillips and E. S. Davenport, E. Piwowarsky, C. H. Plant, A. L. Pollard, W. H. Poole, E. H. Putman, W. P. Putman, R. N. Richardson, P. Rodigin, G. P. Royston, D. Saito and H. Sawamura, U. Savoia, O. Schliewiensky, W. Schneider, E. Schömann, E. Schüz, H. A. Schwartz, G. R. Shotton and R. G. Hall, R. H. Smith, H. R. Stanford, O. W. Storey, R. Stotz, B. Stoughton, C. L. Sullivan, E. R. Taylor, J. H. Teng, A. le Thomas, G. M. Thrasher, E. Touceda, T. Turner, I. R. Valentine, P. Vidor, A. Wahlberg, H. Wedding, E. C. Wheeler, A. E. White, A. E. White and R. S. Archer, D. Wilkinson, F. Wüst, and F. Wüst and E. Leuenberger. The properties of malleable cast iron were discussed by A. G. Ashcroft, P. Aubie, H. Bornstein, E. Chamberlain, A. T. Child and W. P. Heincken, F. B. Coyle, H. E. Diller, H. Field, M. Gailly, C. H. Gale, L. E. Gilmore, W. H. Hatfield, F. Henfling, G. Hofer, F. H. Hurren, D. H. Ingall and H. Field, E. E. Marbaker, L. H. Marshall, A. Mertens, R. Moldenke, W. J. Molineux, J. V. Murray, E. Namba, A. E. Outerbridge, A. Phillips and E. S. Davenport, J. Piers, H. Pinsl, W. P. Putman, O. Quadrat and J. Koritta, E. Schüz, H. A. Schwartz, E. K. Smith, E. K. Smith and W. Barr, J. K. Smithson, H. R. Stanford, J. E. Stead, R. Stotz, C. L. Sullivan, E. R. Taylor, E. Touceda, E. C. Wheeler, W. Valentin, and I. R. Valentine.

The following are some books and monographs on malleable irons :

H. W. Craver, *Bibliography of Articles on Malleable Cast Iron since 1894*, Pittsburg, 1895 ; *Bull. Brit. Cast Iron Research Assoc.*, 1, 1923 ; W. H. Hatfield, *Cast Iron in the Light of Recent Research*, London, 1912 ; H. M. Howe, *Iron, Steel, and other Alloys*, Boston, 1903 ; *Metallography of Steel and Cast Iron*, New York, 1916 ; R. Moldenke, *The Production of Malleable Castings*, Cleveland, Ohio, 1921 ; S. J. Parsons, *Malleable Cast Iron*, New York, 1919 ; E. Schüz and R. Stotz, *Der Temperguss*, Berlin, 1930 ; H. A. Schwartz, *American Malleable Cast Iron*, Cleveland, U.S.A., 1922 ; T. Turner, *Metallurgy of Iron*, London, 1915.

J. E. Johnson induced a **spheroidization of the graphite** by first bessemerizing the iron at a low temp., and when the iron is remelted with some silicon, the required degree of graphitization is obtained, for the spheroidized characteristic persists during the remelting. J. E. Johnson's idea is that the oxygen introduced during the bessemerizing lowers the temp. of graphitization relatively to that of solidification, so that the rigidity of the mass prevents the graphite spreading out into broad flakes.

In the process employed by R. A. F. de Réaumur[3] for malleabilizing cast iron the iron is embedded in red oxide of iron, so that in addition to the transformation of hard cementite into graphite and soft ferrite, a process of decarburization, or **decarburization** by the oxidation of the carbon, is at work ; and J. J. Berzelius said that when iron rich in carbon is heated in air—*e.g.* in converting cast iron into wrought iron—the air does not come into contact with all the particles, but carbon travels from within outwards until equilibrium is established. This is a reversal of the process of cementation (*q.v.*), in which, according to A. C. Becquerel, the atoms of iron at the surface which have combined with carbon turn half-round, give up their carbon to the iron atoms immediately within, take up another portion at the surface, and so on until the two substances have penetrated one another completely.

At a red-heat the iron is sufficiently soft to allow this rotation of the atoms. A. F. E. Degen admitted that this is possible, though the hypothesis has too much imagination and too little fact to be accepted in detail at the present day. According to A. Ledebur, the decarburization is not confined to the surface of the glowing piece of iron, but it also penetrates to the inmost parts. As long as the heating is sufficiently prolonged and the temp. is high enough a circulation of carbon takes place. When the carbon at the surface of the iron is oxidized, the carbon flows, so to speak, from within outwards, so that the concentration of the carbon in each part approaches uniformity. As soon as one part has a less proportion of carbon than another, the carbon may be imagined as passing from one molecule to another. F. Wüst did not accept the diffusion hypothesis of A. Ledebur, and he said that the process of diffusion can occur where carbon is in soln. ; free carbon can in no way travel from mol. to mol. in solid iron. It has been shown above that the successful production of malleable cast iron depends largely upon the precipitation of carbon, so that the malleabilization involves the elimination of the carbon by oxidation and the precipitation of annealing carbon. F. Wüst said :

The oxidation of the annealing carbon can take place not only at the points of contact between the iron oxide and the heated iron, but it also must distribute itself throughout the mass of metal. The carbon, he said, does not move towards the oxidizing agent, but conversely, the oxidizing agent beginning its activity at the surface, gradually penetrates the metal, and in this way reaches the annealing carbon not yet oxidized. Accordingly, the oxidizing agent can only be a gas giving off oxygen, and the iron oxide used to carry on the process of elimination effects only indirectly the conversion of carbon into gas.

F. Wüst showed that the elimination of carbon is confined to the free annealing carbon, since analyses show that only that form of carbon diminishes, while the combined carbon remains constant. The gas which actually effects the elimination is carbon dioxide, for that gas decreases and carbon monoxide increases during the decarburization. The ferric oxide begins to give off oxygen at about 600°, and this oxygen combining with the free annealing carbon produces carbon dioxide ; as soon as the oxygen has been used up, the process is kept up by the carbon dioxide, which unites with the annealing carbon to form carbon monoxide ; that carbon monoxide then reacts with the iron oxide, reducing it to metallic iron and ferrous oxide, whereby carbon dioxide is again generated. The ratio $CO_2 : CO$ in the gas thus depends upon the proportion of ferric oxide to the cast iron being decarburized. The rise of press. reaches its maximum, temp. constant, when a state of equilibrium is established between the partial press. of the oxygen and the dissociated press. of the iron oxide. If there is a lack of oxygen from the bed of ferric oxide, the carbon dioxide is not regenerated and the proportion of carbon monoxide in the mixture can increase to such an extent that the process of decarburization becomes one of cementation. Under these conditions a microscopic examination of a polished and etched section shows that :

The metal being decarburized has a surface of ferrite, below that is a layer of pearlite, and in the middle is a layer of ferrite and annealing carbon. The band of pearlite is supposed to have been formed by a reversal of the annealing process into a cementation process. The carbon monoxide increases to such an extent that it can neither have an oxidizing action nor remain neutral, but, acting in accord with $3Fe+2CO=Fe_3C+CO_2$, it produces an increase of carbon in the metal, for the iron takes up carbon from the carbon monoxide.

P. Goerens accepted F. Wüst's theory of the process of decarburization ; but W. H. Hatfield did not agree with the assumption that carbon must be precipitated from solid soln. before it is oxidized, because the separation of carbon from white cast iron occurs throughout the mass, and hence, in F. Wüst's experiments, if the carbon in the interior is in the combined state, the outer decarburized layer does not contain free carbon. He therefore represented the process of decarburization : $2Fe_3C+2CO_2=6Fe+4CO$; $2CO+O_2=2CO_2$; $2CO_2+2Fe_3C=6Fe+4CO$; and so on ; and not as F. Wüst did : $Fe_3C=3Fe+C$; $C+CO_2=2CO$; $2CO+O_2=2CO_2$; $C+CO_2=2CO$; and so on. W. H. Hatfield also said that the surface of the billet or ingot in any mill or forge has a tendency to be decarburized by furnace gases, and this with steels free from combined carbon ; and that at 960°, the temp. employed by F. Wüst, much of the annealing carbon would re-combine with the iron. This is in accord with observations by W. H. Hatfield, R. A. Hadfield, T. Murakami and H. Sekiguchi, J. O. Arnold and A. McWilliam, E. H. Schulz and P. Niemeyer, E. H. Saniter, G. P. Royston, G. Charpy, C. Benedicks, M. Winter and P. B. Crocker, and H. F. Rugan and H. C. H. Carpenter. F. Giolitti, in opposition to F. Wüst, said that in producing malleable iron decarburization does not occur until the carbon of the cementite has separated in the form of temper-carbon, and that the oxidation of the carbon in the interior of cast iron is due exclusively to the penetration of the heated metal by oxidizing gases. Besides the temper-carbon, the carbon dissolved in the iron is oxidized directly ; and in addition to the penetration of the heated metal by the oxidizing gases, the dissolved carbon migrates towards the surface of the iron owing to differences of concentration in the inner and outer portions of the metal. W. H. Hatfield thus summarizes his interpretation of the decarburization :

The carbon is eliminated while still in combination with the iron. At the comparatively low temp. of 750° C. this reaction begins to take place between the carbide of iron and the oxidizing medium. The activity of the elimination gradually becomes greater with the increase in temp. until a temp. is reached at which, according to the composition of the iron, the precipitation of annealing carbon takes place, until equilibrium for that temp. is established. Previous to this precipitation the iron consists of a decarburized exterior, with the interior still retaining the original quantity of combined carbon. After precipitation the decarburized exterior is still present, but in the centre there is a composition equal to saturated or slightly supersaturated steel, in which the precipitated temper-carbon is contained. The carbon now in soln. would appear to diffuse outwardly to the skin to replace the already eliminated carbon. As in this manner further combined carbon is removed from the iron, so is the equilibrium maintained by the absorption and soln. of more temper-carbon to fill its place. The effect of a diffusion or absorption of temper-carbon in this manner is shown by the fact that on the completion of the softening of this material considerable quantities of annealing carbon remained.

E. D. Campbell and co-workers, and J. Cischina studied the decarburization of steel by hydrogen ; J. V. Emmons, by hydrogen, steam, carbon dioxide, oxygen, and air ; and W. E. Jominy, and G. Belloc, by occluded gases. For the decarburization of steel by hydrogen and nitrogen, *vide infra*, chemical properties of iron. No decarburization occurred below the Ac_1-arrest. It was inferred that the carbon must form a solid soln. with iron to permit of its oxidation, and the depth of oxidation is dependent on the speed of diffusion of the carbon. Steam had the strongest action, then carbon dioxide, and finally air and oxygen. No action at all was observed with hydrogen. J. V. Emmons also noted that steel is decarburized if heated in charcoal at 780°, and H. C. Greenwood obtained a similar result, and also noted a decarburization when the metal is heated in a lead bath containing a little oxide. H. Scott observed that in air there is scarcely any decarburization, owing to the fact that scale formation proceeds at the same rate as decarburization. Heating half an hour at 1060° gives the same depth of decarburization as an hour at 970°, but less ferrite is formed than at the higher temp. E. H. Schulz and P. Niemeyer found that in air no difference was observed with planed, ground, and polished surfaces ; for a constant period of time the decarburization is proportional to the temp. ; at the same temp. the speed of decarburization is greatest at the beginning of the heating ; in a eutectoidal steel incipient decarburization appears after 2 hrs.' heating at 700° ; eutectoidal steel decarburizes deepest, and a hypoeutectoidal steel decarburizes deeper than a hypereutectoidal steel below 1000°, but at 1100° the reverse is the case ; silicon and tungsten steels show distinct decarburization at 800°, but chromium and manganese steels show no trace of decarburization at 900° ; at 1000°, chromium steel showed a decarburization of 0·06 mm. ; manganese steel, 0·2 mm. ; silicon and carbon steel, 0·3 mm. ; and tungsten steel, 0·4 mm. ; and at 1100°, decarburization is fastest with chromium steel. Hence tungsten should promote decarburization, chromium and manganese should reduce it, and silicon should have no influence.

A. Johansson and R. von Seth showed that the main reactions concerned in the carburization and decarburization of iron by mixtures of carbon monoxide and dioxide are $Fe_3C \rightleftharpoons 3Fe + C$ and $2CO \rightleftharpoons C + CO_2$, on the assumption that carbon has a small but definite vap. press. which is constant for a given form of carbon at any assigned temp., but is variable for different modifications of carbon. Let the concentration of carbon dioxide, carbon monoxide, and carbon vapour be respectively denoted by [CO], [CO$_2$], and [C$_3$]; then, for equilibrium, $[CO]^2 = K_3'[CO_2][C_3]$, but since the vap. press. of carbon is constant, $[CO]^2 = K_3[CO_2]$, where K_3', [C$_3$], and K_3 are functions of the temp. only. Let [C$_1$] denote the vap. press. of the carbon of cementite, and [C$_2$] that of the carbon of the solid soln. of carbon in iron, then [C$_2$], unlike [C$_3$], is a function of the concentration of the carbon in solid soln. as well as of the temp. For the reaction $3Fe + 2CO \rightleftharpoons CO_2 + Fe_3C$, $[CO]^2 = K_1'[C_1][CO_2]$, where $K_1' = K_3'$, the dissociation constant of carbon monoxide, and $[C_1] = [C_2]$. Consequently $K_3'[C_2] = K_1'[C_1] = K_1$, and $[CO]^2 = K_1[CO_2]$. Hence,

$$\frac{K_1}{K_3} = \frac{[C_2]}{[C_3]} \quad \cdots \cdots \cdots \quad (1)$$

or the equilibrium constants of the reactions $3Fe + 2CO \rightleftharpoons Fe_3C + CO_2$ and $2CO \rightleftharpoons C + CO_2$ stand in the same relation as the carbon press. of cementite and elementary carbon. Fig. 67a represents part of the iron-carbon equilibrium diagram.

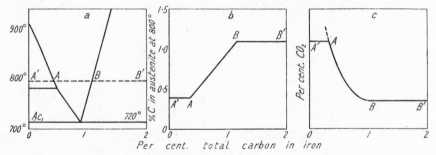

FIG. 67.—The Carburization and Decarburization of Iron.

Below the Ac$_1$-arrest, at about 720°, ferrite and cementite appear; above that temp. the system contains one or two solid phases. Between A' and A (0 to 0·35 per cent. carbon) the system at, say, 800° contains ferrite and austenite; between A and B (0·35 to 1·05 per cent. carbon), austenite only; whilst between B and B' it contains austenite and cementite. The variation in the proportion of carbon in austenite, at 800°, is shown in Fig. 67b. The proportion is constant below A (about 0·35 per cent. carbon), though the qualities of ferrite and austenite vary with the proportion of total carbon, but the austenite does not hold less than 0·35 per cent. carbon. Between A and B, where austenite alone is present, the proportion of carbon in the austenite is the same as in the alloy. At and above B the austenite is saturated with carbon, so that its composition is constant. A higher proportion of carbon alters only the relative proportions of cementite and saturated austenite.

The reaction $3Fe + 2CO \rightleftharpoons Fe_3C + CO_2$ represents a bivariant system in the presence of two solid phases, and tervariant in the presence of one solid phase between A and B, the additional variable being the carbon vap. press. of the austenite. Consequently, the proportion of carbon dioxide in the stable gas ought to vary with the proportion of carbon in the alloy, as shown diagrammatically in Fig. 67c. If more carbon dioxide is present, the carbon press. is lower along AA'; an equilibrium is established between the gas and ferrite and austenite of the lowest concentration. The same will occur from A to B, between the gas and austenite; the percentage of the carbon of the austenite rises between A and B. Likewise, an equilibrium prevails along BB' between the gas and cementite and saturated austenite. If it were possible for austenite at 800° to have a lower proportion of carbon than 0·35 per cent., the curve AB would continue to rise as indicated by the dotted line. This does not occur, so that the curve AB will be intersected by AA' at A, which gives the carbon content of the alloy whose A_3-arrest is saturated at 800°.

M. L. Becker found that the composition of the gas in equilibrium with graphite varies over a range of temp. from 650° to 1000° in accord with the measurements of A. Johansson and R. von Seth, and others. The gas in equilibrium with iron carbide plus a saturated solid soln. is richer in carbon monoxide than that in equilibrium with graphite at the same temp. The carbon vap. press. of iron carbide, between 650° and 1000°, must in consequence be higher than that of carbon alone. Graphite is therefore stable with respect to iron carbide over this range of temp., and this conclusion is not in agreement with that of A. Matsubara, and A. Johansson and R. von Seth, who inferred that the vap. press. of the carbon of the carbide is lower than that of graphite at temp. exceeding 800°. M. L. Becker observed that the presence of silicon raised the ratio $CO : CO_2$ for steels of a given carbon content;

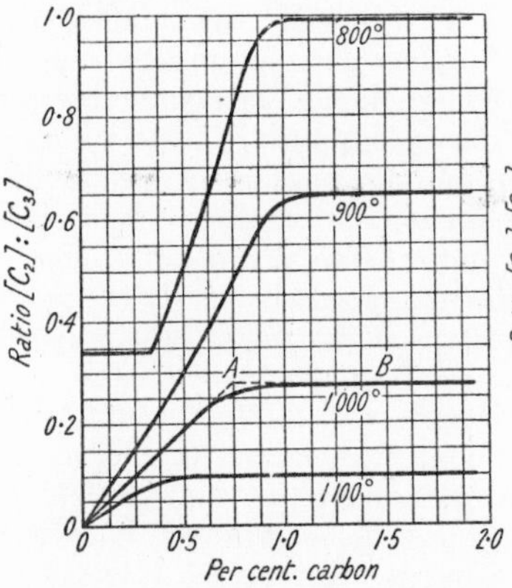

FIG. 68.—The Carbon Pressure as a Function of the Carbon Content of the Solid Phase.

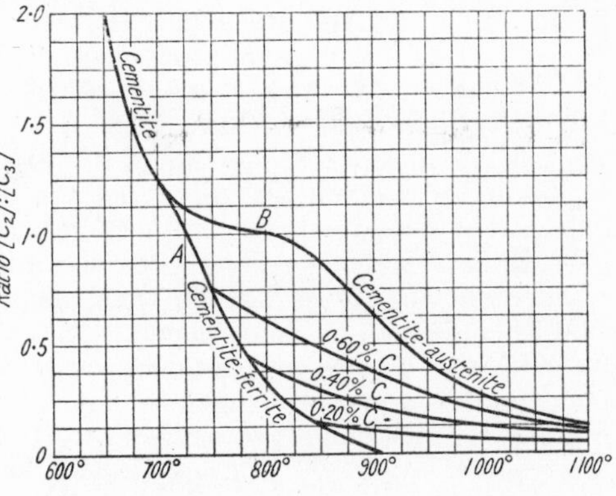

FIG. 69.—The Carbon Pressure as a Function of the Temperature.

manganese and nickel had no perceptible effect on the gaseous equilibrium; and chromium lowered the carbon vap. press. of a solid soln.

Observations on the constants of the reactions were discussed in connection with the reactions in the blast-furnace; and since K_1 and K_3 are known, it follows from (1) that the carbon press. of cementite and solid soln. can also be calculated, since these stand in the same relation to the press. of elementary carbon as $K_1 : K_3$. Continuing, A. Johansson and R. von Seth observed that the isotherms of the carbon press. as functions of the carbon content of the solid phase are shown in Fig. 68, where $[C_3]$ is a constant for each temp., so that the curves represent $[C_2]$ as a function of the carbon content at each temp. respectively. This function is almost rectilinear for solid soln., meaning that the carbon press. of austenite increases proportionally with its carbon content, and thus follows the same law as the osmotic press. of a dil. soln. The carbon press. of cementite does not increase with increasing temp. as rapidly as that of austenite, and it follows that the higher the temp. the lower the carbon content of austenite. An equal carbon press. is not attained until the austenite is saturated with carbon. For instance, the isotherm at 1000°, where the curve of the carbon press. of austenite bends before the point A is reached, and passes into the cementite line at B. The relation between the carbon press. and temp. is shown in Fig. 69. Below the line 1·0, the carbon press. of cementite and solid soln. is less than that of carbon ; above 1·0 per cent. of carbon, it is greater than that of carbon.   An atm. of carbon monoxide and dioxide in equilibrium with elementary carbon is therefore unable to carburize the iron until about 735° (*A*, Fig. 69) is attained, when austenite with about 0·7 per cent. of carbon is formed. The carbon content of austenite is increased with a rising temp., but no free cementite is formed until about 790° (*B*, Fig. 69).   Below 735°, decarburization always occurs in such an atmosphere.   A steel with an excess of cementite is decarburized at 790°.   This shows the risk of surface decarburization in the annealing of steel.   In the surface decarburization of steel by dry carbon dioxide and monoxide, mixed with 60 per cent. nitrogen, as well as by dry air—at 750°, 800°, 900°, and 1100°—the results, in general, can be represented by Fig. 70, showing the depths of carburization in mm. and the carbon content of the layer in percentages.   The stippled area shows the amount of decarburization below a plane surface, and is represented as the degree of decarburization—per cent. mm.   When the degree of decarburization is represented as a function of the proportion of carbon dioxide in the gas, the curve rises at first very rapidly, with an increasing content of carbon dioxide, reaching its highest value with 10 per cent. carbon dioxide for the hypoeutectoid steels and with 15 per cent. carbon dioxide for the hypereutectoid steels.   It then remains nearly constant for higher percentages of carbon dioxide, although the speed of the reaction ought to have increased.   The maximum degree of decarburization may possibly be determined by the speed of diffusion of the carbon ; but it ought to be observed that the formation of oxide-scale on the surface of the specimen sets in at the breaks in the curves.   It is therefore also possible that the oxide-scale in some way represses the decarburization, presumably by protecting the underlying surface of the steel from the influence of the gases, thus rendering the diffusion of the gas more difficult.   The results are similar at 900° : the hypoeutectoid steel reaches its maximum decarburization with 15 per cent. carbon dioxide, and with the hypereutectoid not until about 25 per cent. carbon dioxide is attained.   The formation of oxide-scale sets in with about the same percentages of carbon dioxide.   At 800°, the formation of the oxide-scale has so great an influence on the degree of decarburization that the latter, after having reached its maximum with about 25 per cent. carbon dioxide, decreases considerably with higher proportions.   The hypoeutectoid steel here decarburizes more than the hypereutectoid steel, while the contrary is the case at 900° and 1100°.   A somewhat stronger decarburization is obtained in air than in gases containing 40 per cent. carbon dioxide.   No decarburization occurs at 750°, 710°, and 650°.   Practical use has also been made of this circumstance, but the explanation generally suggested— namely, that the formation of oxide-scale should proceed *pari passu* with the decarburization, no surface decarburization thus taking place—seems to be wrong. The oxide layer is much too thin to be able to act in this way.   Instead, as at higher temp., it appears simply to form a protective layer against the influence of the gases.

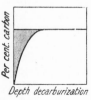

Depth decarburization

Fig. 70.—Decarburization Curve.

The phenomenon was also studied by E. Zingg and co-workers, H. Schenck, C. R. Austin, P. Oberhoffer and J. Welter, H. C. Greenwood, R. G. Guthrie, J. J. Curran and J. H. G. Williams, E. Leuenberger, J. G. Ayres, A. Bramley and K. F. Allen, A. Seuthe, etc.   L. Hackspill and E. Schwarz, and A. M. Portevin and V. Bernard observed that at 1000° the chlorides and carbonates of the alkali and alkaline-earth metals effect the superficial decarburization of cast iron and steel ; and that in 2 to 3 hrs. the carbon is almost completely removed from hypoeutectoidal steels to a depth of about 1 mm.   They suggest that the active agent in this reaction is the alkali or alkaline-earth metal liberated from its salt by the iron.   Calcium rapidly removes carbon and phosphorus almost completely from cast iron 1 to 2 mm. thick at 1000°, forming calcium carbide and phosphide.

Lithium behaves similarly above 450°, but sodium and potassium above 800° act much more slowly, as the carbides formed are relatively unstable at the ordinary press. Sodium carbide has been made by direct union of the elements under press. at 1100°.

REFERENCES.

[1] J. Percy, *Metallurgy—Iron and Steel*, London, 738, 1864 ; L. Cubillo, *Proc. South Staffs Iron Steel Inst.*, **16**. 22, 1901 ; *Journ. Iron Steel Inst.*, **59**. i, 452, 1901 ; E. Riley, *ib.*, **41**. i, 93, 1892 ; E. H. Saniter, *ib.*, **52**. ii, 115, 1897 ; D. M. Levy, *Foundry Trade Journ.*, **13**. 321, 1911 ; *Journ. Iron Steel Inst.*, **77**. ii, 33, 1908 ; **81**. i, 403, 1910 ; A. Lodin, *ib.*, **68**. ii, 74, 1906 ; G. Charpy and A. Cornu-Thenard, *ib.*, **91**. i, 276, 1915 ; *Compt. Rend.*, **156**. 1616, 1913 ; **157**. 319, 901, 1913 ; *Bull. Soc. Chim.*, (4), **15**. 497, 1914 ; *Rev. Mét.*, **12**. 493, 1915 ; A. Achenbach, *Giesserei*, **14**. 724, 1927 ; E. Adamson, *Trans. Manchester Eng. Assoc.*, 125, 1923 ; *Journ. West Scotland Iron Steel Inst.*, **14**. 38, 65, 1907 ; *Foundry Trade Journ.*, **28**. 252, 1923 ; *Foundry*, **51**. 732, 1923 ; *Journ. Iron Steel Inst.*, **84**. ii, 86, 1911 ; A. Allison, *Foundry Trade Journ.*, **43**. 417, 1930 ; **35**. 397, 1927 ; F. G. Allison and M. M. Rock, *Chem. Met. Engg.*, **23**. 383, 1920 ; D. G. Anderson and G. R. Bessmer, *Trans. Amer. Foundrymen's Assoc.*, **36**. 453, 1928 ; J. H. Andrews, *Foundry Trade Journ.*, **22**. 690, 1920 ; Anon., *Metal Ind.*, **27**. 189, 219, 315, 1925 ; *Machinery*, **26**. 299, 1925 ; R. S. Archer, *Trans. Amer. Inst. Min. Eng.*, **67**. 445, 1920 ; P. Bardenheuer, *Stahl Eisen*, **47**. 857, 1927 ; P. Bardenheuer and K. Ludwig, *Giesserei*, **15**. 354, 385, 1928 ; P. Bardenheuer and K. L. Zeyen, *ib.*, **16**. 733, 1929 ; *Metallurgist*, **5**. 141, 1929 ; *Mitt. Inst. Eisenforsch.*, **9**. 215, 1927 ; **10**. 23, 1928 ; **11**. 225, 1929 ; *Stahl Eisen*, **48**. 515, 1928 ; O. Bauer, *ib.*, **553**, 1923 ; *Foundry Trade Journ.*, **27**. 454, 1923 ; O. Bauer and H. Siegleschmidt, *Mitt. Materialprüfungsamt*, **48**. 110, 1930 ; O. Baur and E. Piwowarsky, *Stahl Eisen*, **40**. 1300, 1920 ; W. R. Bean, H. W. Highriter and E. S. Davenport, *Trans. Amer. Foundrymen's Assoc.*, **29**. 306, 1921 ; H. H. Beeny, *Foundry Trade Journ.*, **24**. 333, 1924 ; F. Beitter, *Stahl Eisen*, **48**. 577, 1928 ; I. L. Bell, *The Principles of the Manufacture of Iron and Steel*, London, 157, 1884 ; C. Benedicks, *Met.*, **5**. 41, 1908 ; C. Benedicks and H. Löfquist, *Journ. Iron Steel Inst.*, **115**. i, 603, 1927 ; P. F. Blackwood, *Trans. Amer. Foundrymen's Assoc.*, **23**. 358, 1915 ; J. W. Bolton, *ib.*, **35**. 386, 1927 ; L. W. Bolton, *Iron Age*, **113**. 47, 155, 1924 ; **114**. 685, 1924 ; *Foundry*, **50**. 53, 109, 436, 1922 ; **51**. 405, 658, 699, 1923 ; **52**. 628, 1924 ; G. Brodsky, *Journ. Scient. Instr.*, **6**. 168, 1929 ; F. Busse, *Metal Ind.*, **41**. 57, 1929 ; J. Challansonnet, *Compt. Rend.*, **190**. 939, 1930 ; **194**. 283, 1932 ; G. Charpy, *Compt. Rend.*, **148**. 1767, 1909 ; G. Charpy and L. Grenet, *Engg.*, **73**. 626, 1902 ; *Bull. Soc. Enc. Nat. Ind.*, **102**. 398, 1902 ; P. Chevenard, *Rev. Ind. Minerale*, **10**. 209, 1930 ; E. J. Cook, *Foundry Trade Journ.*, **16**. 43, 1914 ; F. D. Corbin, *ib.*, **40**. 83, 94, 1929 ; F. B. Coyle, *Trans. Amer. Soc. Testing Materials*, **29**. ii, 87, 1929 ; *Comm. Internat. Assoc. Testing Materials*, **1**. 35, 1930 ; S. E. Dawson, *Metal Ind.*, **28**. 277, 303, 327, 351, 1926 ; W. E. Dennison, *Foundry Trade Journ.*, **38**. 224, 230, 1928 ; A. Diefenthaler, *Brit. Pat. No.* 147933, 1923 ; *Foundry Trade Journ.*, **28**. 186, 1923 ; E. F. Diepschlag, *Giesserei Ztg.*, **24**. 418, 1927 ; *Giesserei*, **16**. 822, 1929 ; *Foundry Trade Journ.*, **41**. 23, 1929 ; E. F. Diepschlag and L. Treuheit, *Giesserei*, **18**. 705, 1931 ; J. W. Donaldson, *Journ. West Scotland Iron Steel Inst.*, **31**. 54, 1924 ; *Rev. Met.*, **26**. 78, 1929 ; *Foundry Trade Journ.*, **31**. 517, 1925 ; **39**. 299, 315, 1928 ; E. Dübi, *Comm. Internat. Assoc. Testing Materials*, **1**. 10, 1930 ; Y. A. Dyer, *Iron Age*, **20**. 333, 1922 ; K. Emmel, *Stahl Eisen*, **44**. 330, 1924 ; *Giesserei*, **16**. 605, 1929 ; *Foundry Trade Journ.*, **41**. 295, 1929 ; F. Erbreich, *Giesserei Ztg.*, **10**. 561, 603, 628, 695, 1913 ; H. P. Evans and A. Hayes, *Trans. Amer. Soc. Steel Treating*, **11**. 691, 1927 ; A. B. Everest, *Foundry Trade Journ.*, **39**. 223, 1928 ; **41**. 61, 67, 1929 ; **44**. 355, 1931 ; *Giesserei Ztg.*, **26**. 137, 1929 ; H. Field, *Foundry Trade Journ.*, **29**. 353, 1923 ; J. E. Fletcher, *Foundry*, **53**. 878, 890, 929, 1925 ; *Proc. S. Staffs Iron Steel Inst.*, **29**. 163, 1914 ; *Iron Coal Trades Rev.*, **111**. 694, 736, 777, 1925 ; *Foundry Trade Journ.*, **36**. 69, 89, 1927 ; L. Forquignon, *Ann. Chim. Phys.*, (5), **23**. 433, 1881 ; *Compt. Rend.*, **91**. 817, 1881 ; *Recherches sur la fonte malleable et sur le recuit des aciers*, Paris, 1881 ; J. L. Francis, *Iron Steel Inst.*, **1**. 31, 87, 1927 ; *Metal Ind.*, **28**. 85, 1926 ; W. Gahl, *Stahl Eisen*, **28**. 225, 1908 ; G. Gilles, *Foundry Trade Journ.*, **34**. 70, 1926 ; *Giesserei Ztg.*, **23**. 203, 1926 ; H. Pinal, *ib.*, **27**. 436, 1930 ; A. Wagner, *ib.*, **27**. 403, 1930 ; L. E. Gilmore, *Foundry*, **55**. 734, 1927 ; K. Glinz, *Stahl Eisen*, **19**. 1061, 1899 ; **20**. 38, 1900 ; P. Goerens, *ib.*, **45**. 137, 1925 ; P. Goerens and O. Dobbelstein, *Met.*, **5**. 516, 1908 ; P. Goerens and N. Gutowsky, *ib.*, **5**. 137, 1908 ; W. Gontermann, *Zeit. anorg. Chem.*, **59**. 373, 1908 ; *Journ. Iron Steel Inst.*, **83**. i, 421, 1911 ; C. Gresty, *Foundry Trade Journ.*, **27**. 273, 1923 ; A. J. Grindle, *Foundry*, **56**. 139, 1928 ; F. Grotts, *Trans. Amer. Soc. Steel Treating*, **7**. 735, 1925 ; L. Guillet, *Rev. Mét.*, **5**. 306, 1908 ; M. Hamasumi, *Science Rep. Tohoku Univ.*, **13**. 133, 157, 169, 1924 ; H. Hanemann, *Stahl Eisen*, **31**. 333, 1911 ; **47**. 693, 1927 ; **51**. 966, 1931 ; *Centrb. Hütt. Walzwerke*, **31**. 273, 1927 ; D. Hanson, *Journ. Iron Steel Inst.*, **116**. ii, 129, 1927 ; W. H. Hatfield, *Cast Iron in the Light of Recent Research*, London, 210, 1926 ; *Rev. Mét.*, **10**. 937, 1913 ; *Proc. Roy. Soc.*, **85**. A, 1, 1911 ; *Journ. Iron Steel Inst.*, **70**. ii, 157, 1906 ; **74**. ii, 79, 1907 ; A. Hayes and W. J. Diederichs, *Bull. Iowa State College Eng.*, 71, 1924 ; *Trans. Amer. Soc. Steel Treating*, **8**. 918, 1923 ; A. Hayes, W. J. Diederichs and H. E. Flanders, *Trans. Amer. Foundrymen's Assoc.*, **32**. 601, 1924 ; A. Hayes and H. E. Flanders, *ib.*, **33**. 634, 1925 ; A. Hayes, H. E. Flanders and E. E. Moore, *Trans. Amer. Soc. Steel Treating*, **5**. 183, 1924 ; A. Hayes and G. C. Scott, *Trans. Amer. Foundrymen's Assoc.*, **33**. 574, 1925 ; A. Hayes and H. U. Wakefield, *Trans. Amer. Soc. Steel Treating*, **9**. 430, 1925 ; **10**. 214, 1926 ; W. Heike and G. May, *Giesserei*, **16**. 625, 645, 1929 ; N. Hekker,

Giesserei, **18.** 14, 39, 1931; E. Heyn, *Zeit. Ver. deut. Ing.*, **44.** 433, 503, 1900; *Stahl Eisen*, **20.** 37, 1900; A. H. Hiorns, *Proc. South Staffs Iron Steel Inst.*, **22.** 18, 1906; H. R. Hiscott, *Gas World*, **87.** 110, 1927; *Gas Journ.*, **179.** 109, 1929; T. W. Hogg, *Journ. Iron Steel Inst.*, **46.** ii, 104, 1894; R. Hohage, *Krupp's Monatsh.*, **7.** 101, 1926; J. A. Holden, *Iron Coal Trades Rev.*, **98.** 479, 1919; P. Holtzhaussen, *Das Gusseisendiagram von Maurer bei verschiedenen Abkählungs-geschwindigkeiten*, Düsseldorf, 1927; K. Honda and T. Murakami, *Journ. Iron Steel Inst.*, **102.** ii, 287, 1920; *Science Rep. Tohoku Univ.*, **10.** 273, 1921; **12.** 287, 1924; L. Houghton, *Centr. Eisenhüttenwesen*, **1.** 766, 1906; *Foundry*, **29.** 109, 1907; H. M. Howe, *The Metallography of Steel and Cast Iron*, New York, 61, 1916; *Trans. Amer. Inst. Min. Eng.*, **44.** 470, 1912; *Eng. Min. Journ.*, **86.** 943, 1909; *Journ. Iron Steel Inst.*, **86.** ii, 291, 1912; J. E. Hurst, *Engg.*, **108.** 1, 1919; **121.** 583, 1926; *Iron Steel Ind.*, **2.** 385, 1929; **3.** 3, 1929; *Foundry Trade Journ.*, **30.** 327, 1924; **31.** 326, 353, 545, 1925; **32.** 31, 101, 108, 1925; **38.** 226, 1928; **41.** 173, 1929; **43.** 351, 1930; **45.** 237, 1931; *Journ. Iron Steel Inst.*, **96.** ii, 121, 1918; A. A. Inostzanzeff, *Trav. Soc. Nat. St. Petersburg*, **35.** 21, 1907; *Zeit. Kryst.*, **50.** 61, 1911; C. Irresberger, *Stahl Eisen*, **37.** 621, 1917; **38.** 487, 1918; C. James, *Journ. Franklin Inst.*, **144.** 80, 1897; **148.** 482, 1899; **150.** 227, 1900; Z. Jeffries and R. S. Archer, *Chem. Met. Engg.*, **24.** 1057, 1921; T. F. Jennings, *Amer. Metal Market*, **37.** 126, 1930; J. E. Johnson, *Journ. Franklin Inst.*, **179.** 59, 1915; *Met. Chem. Engg.*, **15.** 530, 589, 1916; H. Jungbluth, *Krupp's Monatsh.*, **4.** 180, 1923; T. Kase, *Science Rep. Tohoku Univ.*, **19.** 17, 1930; W. J. Keep, *Trans. Amer. Inst. Min. Eng.*, **18.** 102, 1890; *Journ. Iron Steel Inst.*, **48.** ii, 227, 1895; O. von Keil, *Arch. Eisenhütten-wesen*, **4.** 245, 1931; *Stahl Eisen*, **50.** 1718, 1930; O. von Keil and R. Mitsche, *ib.*, **49.** 1041, 1929; R. R. Kennedy and G. J. Oswald, *Trans. Amer. Foundrymen's Assoc.*, **34.** 871, 1926; K. von Kerpely, *Giesserei Ztg.*, **23.** 435, 1926; *Die metallurgischen und metallographischen Grundlagen des Gusseisens*, Halle (Scale), 1928; E. Kirk, *Iron Trade Rev.*, **32.** 7, 1900; P. Kleiber, *Krupp's Monatsh.*, **8.** 109, 1927; C. Kluijtmans, *Foundry Trade Journ.*, **34.** 123, 133, 1926; O. Kröhnke, *Met.*, **7.** 674, 1910; R. Kühnel, *Stahl Eisen*, **45.** 1461, 1925; R. Kühnel and E. Nesemann, *ib.*, **44.** 1042, 1924; J. H. Küster and C. Pfannenschmidt, *Giesserei*, **16.** 969, 1929; A. G. Lambert and F. M. Robbins, *Canada Foundryman*, **21.** 14, 1930; F. C. A. H. Lantsberry, *Foundry Trade Journ.*, **22.** 377, 1920; A. Ledebur, *Stahl Eisen*, **16.** 116, 1896; J. A. Leffler, *Jernkontorets Ann.*, (2), **79.** 149, 1924; R. P. Lemoine, *Trans. Amer. Soc. Foundrymen's Assoc.*, **37.** 259, 1929; E. Leuenberger, *Stahl Eisen*, **41.** 285, 1921; M. Lincke, *Giesserei Ztg.*, **26.** 104, 1929; W. Lipin, *Stahl Eisen*, **20.** 536, 1900; A. Lissner, *Ferrum*, **10.** 52, 1912; **11.** 44, 1913; A. Logan, *Metal Ind.*, **26.** 163, 189, 218, 1925; P. Longmuir, *Trans. Amer. Foundrymen's Assoc.*, **11.** 61, 1902; E. J. Lowry, *Trans. Amer. Soc. Steel Treating*, **17.** 538, 1929; A. McCance, *Journ. Iron Steel Inst.*, **99.** i, 437, 1919; C. J. McNamara and C. H. Lorig, *Trans. Amer. Foundrymen's Assoc.*, **33.** 624, 1925; E. E. Marbaker, *ib.*, **37.** 71, 1929; *Foundry*, **56.** 979, 1005, 1928; **57.** 10, 1929; E. Maurer, *Krupp's Monatsh.*, **4.** 117, 1923; **5.** 115, 1924; E. Maurer and P. Holtz-haussen, *Stahl Eisen*, **47.** 1805, 1977, 1927; *Foundry Trade Journ.*, **37.** 222, 1927; H. L. Max-well and A. Hayes, *Journ. Amer. Chem. Soc.*, **48.** 584, 1926; G. May, *Ueber die Bildung des Graphits insbesondere des eutektischen, im Gusseisen*, Düsseldorf, 1929; G. Melland and H. W. Waldron, *Journ. Iron Steel Inst.*, **58.** ii, 244, 1900; P. D. Merica and L. J. Gurevich, *Trans. Amer. Inst. Min. Eng.*, **62.** 509, 1919; *Tech. Paper Bur. Standards*, 129, 1919; W. J. Merten, *Trans. Amer. Soc. Steel Treating*, **9.** 907, 1926; A. Merz and H. Schuster, *Giesserei*, **13.** 496, 1931; E. Meyer, *Stahl Eisen*, **47.** 294, 1927; G. Meyersberg, *Arch. Wärmewirtschaft*, **8.** 340, 1927; *Zeit. Ver. deut. Ing.*, **71.** 1427, 1927; J. W. Miller, *Journ. Iron Steel Inst.*, **56.** ii, 160, 1899; A. Mittinsky, *Rev. Met.*, **26.** 84, 1929; R. Moldenke, *Iron Age*, **121.** 1241, 1928; *Iron Steel Canada*, **14.** 1, 17, 1931; *Foundry Trade Journ.*, **26.** 367, 1922; F. Mylius, F. Förster and G. Schöne, *Ber.*, **29.** 2991, 1896; *Zeit. anorg. Chem.*, **13.** 38, 1896; E. Namba, *Kinzoku no Kenkyu*, **6.** 416, 1929; F. K. Neath, *Bull. Brit. Cast Iron Research*, 29, 1930; 38, 1931; G. Neumann, *Stahl Eisen*, **47.** 1606, 1927; H. Nishimura, *Suiyokaishi (Japan)*, **5.** 763, 1929; A. L. Norbury, *Journ. Iron Steel Inst.*, **119.** i, 443, 1929; *Foundry Trade Journ.*, **41.** 79, 1929; A. L. Norbury and L. W. Bolton, *Bull. Brit. Cast Iron Research Assoc.*, 22, 1928; A. L. Norbury and E. Morgan, *Journ. Iron Steel Inst.*, **121.** i, 367, 1930; L. Northcott, *Foundry Trade Journ.*, **29.** 515, 1924; P. Oberhoffer, *Das technische Eisen*, Berlin, 130, 1925; B. Osann, *Foundry Trade Journ.*, **39.** 448, 456, 1928; *Maschinenbau*, **8.** 284, 314, 1929; *Giesserei*, **16.** 565, 1929; **18.** 373, 1931; J. G. Pearce, *Comm. Internat. Assoc. Testing Materials*, **1.** 1, 1930; *Metallurgist*, **4.** 25, 39, 1925; *Foundry Trade Journ.*, **38.** 201, 1928; T. F. Pearson, *Journ. Iron Steel Inst.*— *Carnegie Mem.*, **18.** 73, 1929; A. Phillips and E. S. Davenport, *Trans. Amer. Inst. Min. Eng.*, **67.** 466, 1922; L. Piedbœuf, *Foundry Trade Journ.*, **33.** 496, 1926; *Rev. Univ. Mines*, (6), **12.** 2, 1926; B. H. Pinsel, *Continental Chem. Engg.*, **2.** 35, 67, 1927; H. Pinsl, *Stahl Eisen*, **48.** 473, 1928; H. R. Pitt, *Foundry Trade Journ.*, **41.** 351, 1930; E. Piwowarsky, *Stahl Eisen*, **43.** 1491, 1923; **45.** 289, 457, 1455, 1925; **50.** 966, 1930; *Comm. Internat. Assoc. Testing Materials*, **1.** 5, 1930; *Giesserei*, **16.** 318, 1929; *Trans. Amer. Foundrymen's Assoc.*, **34.** 914, 1926; *Foundry Trade Journ.*, **31.** 331, 345, 1925; **32.** 317, 1925; E. Piwowarsky and K. Ebbefeld, *Stahl Eisen*, **43.** 967, 1923; A. M. Portevin, *Rev. Mét.*, **19.** 227, 1922; *Bull. Assoc. Tech. Fonderie*, **1.** 1927; A. M. Portevin and P. Chévenard, *Compt. Rend.*, **183.** 1283, 1926; **189.** 759, 1929; **193.** 169, 1931; A. M. Portevin and M. Garvin, *Journ. Iron Steel Inst.*, **99.** i, 469, 1915; O. W. Potter, *Trans. Amer. Foundrymen's Assoc.*, **33.** 294, 1925; *Foundry Trade Journ.*, **35.** 371, 413, 1927; W. P. Putman, *Trans. Amer. Foundrymen's Assoc.*, **19.** 363, 1911; H. S. Rawdon and S. Epstein, *Chem. Met. Engg.*, **27.** 650, 1922; R. T. Rolfe, *Iron Steel Ind.*, **2.** 283, 377, 1929; F. Roll, *Giesserei*, **16.** 933,

1929; P. Ropsy, *Foundry Trade Journ.*, **36**. 199, 1927; E. L. Roth, *Trans. Amer. Soc. Steel Treating*, **12**. 27, 1927; F. W. Rowe, *Metal Ind.*, **21**. 563, 583, 1922; G. P. Royston, *Journ. Iron Steel Inst.*, **51**. i, 154, 166, 1897; O. Ruff, *Met.*, **8**. 462, 507, 1911; D. Saito and K. Nishihara, *Suiyokai Shi*, **6**. 535, 1931; F. Sauerwald and A. Koreny, *Stahl Eisen*, **48**. 537, 1928; A. Sauveur, *The Metallography and Heat Treatment of Iron and Steel*, Cambridge, Mass., 377, 1926; *Trans. Amer. Inst. Min. Eng.*, **45**. 367, 1913; H. Sawamura, *Mem. Coll. Engg. Kyoto Univ.*, **4**. 159, 1926; *Iron and Steel*, **14**. 741, 1928; E. Scheil, *Giesserei*, **15**. 1086, 1928; R. Schmitt, *Zeit. ges. Giess.*, **51**. 25, 1930; *Chim. Ind.*, **25**. 81, 1931; E. Schülz, *Stahl Eisen*, **42**. 1135, 1345, 1485, 1922; **45**. 144, 1925; *Giesserei*, **15**. 73, 102, 1928; **16**. 1185, 1929; H. A. Schwartz, *Foundry*, **56**. 871, 918, 1928; *Trans. Amer. Soc. Steel Treating*, **9**. 883, 1926; **10**. 55, 1926; **11**. 277, 767, 1927; **15**. 957, 1929; H. A. Schwartz and C. M. Guiler, *Trans. Amer. Foundrymen's Assoc.*, **33**. 639, 1925; H. A. Schwartz and A. N. Hird, *Trans. Amer. Inst. Min. Eng.*, **69**. 470, 1925; H. A. Schwartz and H. H. Johnson, *Trans. Amer. Soc. Steel Treating*, **10**. 965, 1926; H. A. Schwartz, H. H. Johnson and C. H. Junge, *ib.*, **17**. 383, 1930; H. A. Schwartz, H. R. Payne, and A. F. Gorton, *Trans. Amer. Inst. Min. Eng.*, **69**. 791, 1923; H. A. Schwartz, H. R. Payne, A. F. Gorton and M. M. Austin, *ib.*, **68**. 212, 916, 1923; J. Seigle, *Foundry Trade Journ.*, **27**. 484, 1923; *Rev. Ind. Min.*, 427, 1928; J. Shaw, *Foundry Trade Journ.*, **39**. 377, 395, 1928; C. Sipp, *Foundry*, **51**. 986, 1923; F. T. Sisco, *Trans. Amer. Soc. Steel Treating*, **11**. 986, 1927; **12**. 279, 651, 1927; **13**. 1043, 1928; O. Smalley, *Engg.*, **114**. 277, 1922; J. A. Smeaton, *Foundry Trade Journ.*, **34**. 10, 1926; A. E. M. Smith, *ib.*, **34**. 13, 1926; A. Stadeler, *Stahl Eisen*, **36**. 933, 1034, 1916; J. E. Stead, *Foundry Trade Journ.*, **17**. 144, 1915; *Journ. Iron Steel Inst.*, **58**. ii, 60, 1900; **91**. i, 176, 1915; B. Stoughton, *Foundry*, **32**. 41, 1908; G. Sulzer, *Comm. Internat. Assoc. Testing Materials*, **1**. 49, 1930; G. Takahashi, *Kinzoku no Kenkyu*, **8**. 102, 1931; H. Tanimura, *Mem. Coll. Kyushu*, **6**. 115, 1931; K. Tawara and G. Asahara, *Journ. Coll. Engg. Tohoku Univ.*, **9**. 196, 1918; E. R. Taylor, *Journ. Iron Steel Inst.—Carnegie Mem.*, **14**. 131, 1925; **15**. 281, 1926; A. le Thomas, *Mem. Soc. Ing. Civils*, **83**. 193, 1930; *Compt. Rend.*, **189**. 639, 1929; *Bull. Assoc. Tech. Fonderie*, **5**. 46, 1931; *Rev. Industrielle*, **58**. 16, 1928; G. M. Thrasher, *Chem. Met. Engg.*, **13**. 39, 1915; H. P. Tiemann, *Metallographist*, **4**. 313, 319, 322, 1901; A. C. Timmins, *Foundry Trade Journ.*, **22**. 436, 1920; E. Touceda, *Iron Trade Rev.*, **74**. 1244, 1924; T. Turner, *Foundry Trade Journ.*, **28**. 121, 1923; *Proc. Cleveland Inst. Eng.*, 219, 1924; G. P. Upton, *Journ. Phys. Chem.*, **12**. 507, 1908; I. R. Valentine, *Metals Alloys*, **1**. 233, 1929; M. Waehlert, *Giesserei*, **17**. 57, 1930; W. R. Webster, *Proc. Amer. Soc. Testing Materials*, **22**. ii, 217, 1922; O. Wedemeyer, *Stahl Eisen*, **46**. 557, 1926; *Foundry Trade Journ.*, **33**. 411, 1926; S. G. Werner, *Metal Ind.*, **26**. 89, 111, 1925; T. D. West, *Iron Trade Rev.*, **32**. 11, 1900; W. West, *Metallurgia*, **4**. 187, 1931; F. White and R. S. Archer, *Trans. Amer. Foundrymen's Assoc.*, **27**. 351, 1919; F. White and H. E. Gladhill, *ib.*, **30**. 413, 1922; *Rev. Met.*, **20**. 148, 1923; B. W. Winder, *Proc. Inst. Civil Eng.*, **123**. 258, 1896; F. Wüst, *Met.*, **3**. 189, 201, 1906; **5**. 86, 1908; **5**. 86, 1908; F. Wüst and P. Bardenhauer, *Foundry Trade Journ.*, **28**. 410, 1923; F. Wüst and E. Leuenberger, *Ferrum*, **13**. 161, 1916; F. Wüst and H. Meissner, *ib.*, **11**. 91, 1913; F. Wüst and O. Petersen, *Met.*, **3**. 811, 1906; F. Wüst and P. Schlösser, *Stahl Eisen*, **24**. 1120, 1904; F. Yamada, *Journ. Iron Steel Inst. Japan*, **15**. 184, 1929; H. J. Young, *Foundry Trade Journ.*, **31**. 503, 1925; **32**. 294, 1925; **39**. 408, 1928; *Iron Steel Ind.*, **3**. 167, 1930; E. Zimmermann, *Zeit. Ges. Giess.*, **49**. 2, 17, 28, 38, 48, 54, 64, 71, 78, 91, 104, 111, 159, 166, 175, 1928; W. Bruch, *Versuche über die Isotropie von Flusseisen*, Danzig, 1924.

² E. Adamson, *Proc. Brit. Foundrymen's Assoc.*, 223, 1918; *Proc. South Staffs Iron Steel Inst.*, **33**. 56, 1918; E. Adamson and J. E. Fletcher, *Journ. Iron Steel Inst.*, **96**. ii, 327, 1917; G. A. Ackerlind, *Foundry*, **30**. 154, 1907; R. D. Allen, *Trans. Amer. Soc. Steel Treating*, **10**. 630, 1926; J. H. Anderson, *Foundry*, **49**. 592, 1921; J. O. Arnold, *Journ. Iron Steel Inst.*, **59**. i, 175, 1901; A. G. Ashcroft, *Proc. Inst. Civil Eng.*, **117**. 322, 1893; J. Ashton, *Brit. Pat. No.* 938, 1769; P. Aubie, *Fond. Moderus*, 8, 1911; P. Bardenheuer, *Stahl Eisen*, **41**. 569, 719, 1921; *Giesserei*, **15**. 1169, 1928; P. Bardenheuer and K. L. Zeyen, *Mitt. Ind. Eisenforsch. Düsseldorf*, **10**. 23, 1928; *Stahl Eisen*, **48**. 515, 1928; K. L. Zeyen, *Beiträge zur Kenntnis des Graphite in graien Gusseisen und seines Einflusses auf die Festigkeit*, Düsseldorf, 1928; W. R. Bean, *Iron Age*, **104**. 497, 1919; W. R. Bean, H. W. Highriter, and E. S. Davenport, *Foundry*, **49**. 557, 1921; *Trans. Amer. Foundrymen's Assoc.*, **29**. 306, 1920; J. E. Beauvalet, *Brit. Pat. No.* 2703, 1852; A. J. Beck, *Foundry Trade Journ.*, **38**. 7, 1928; F. Beitter, *Stahl Eisen*, **48**. 577, 1928; C. Benedicks and H. Löfquist, *Journ. Iron Steel Inst.*, **115**. i, 613, 1927; G. A. Blume, *Proc. Brit. Foundrymen's Assoc.*, 148, 1910; *Trans. Amer. Foundrymen's Assoc.*, **21**. 431, 1912; E. C. Boehringer, *Foundry*, **52**. 521, 533, 1924; *Iron Trade Rev.*, **75**. 29, 1924; S. Bolland, *Amer. Machinist*, **16**. 2, 1893; H. Bornstein, *Fuels Furnaces*, **7**. 1377, 1929; A. Boussu, *Tech. Zentr. Berg. Hütt. Maschinenwesen*, 2, 1908; O. Brauer, *Zeit. gesamte Giess. Praxis*, **51**. 70, 1930; E. Bremer, *Iron Trade Rev.*, **78**. 992, 998, 1926; J. Bronn, *Stahl Eisen*, **26**. 881, 1921; C. Busquet, *La fabrication de la fonte malléable*, Paris, 1929; F. Busse, *Ueber den Einfluss der Giesstemperatur beim Hartguss*, Düsseldorf, 1929; *Giesserei*, **16**. 169, 1929; A. Cairnes, *Iron Trade Rev.*, **31**. 10, 1898; H. H. Campbell, *Trans. Amer. Inst. Min. Eng.*, **14**. 345, 1893; A. Campion, *Foundry Trade Journ.*, **31**. 67, 1925; A. Campion and J. W. Donaldson, *Proc. Brit. Foundrymen's Assoc.*, **15**. 211, 1922; *Journ. West Scotland Iron Steel Inst.*, **31**. 54, 1924; *Foundry Trade Journ.*, **31**. 517, 1925; **32**. 553, 1925; S. B. Chadsey, *Foundry*, **38**. 51, 1911; E. Chamberlain, *Engg. News*, **38**. 253, 1897; G. Charpy, *Bull. Soc. Enc. Nat. Ind.*, (5), **1**. 178, 564, 925, 1896; G. Charpy and L. Grenet, *Engg.*, **73**. 626, 1902; *Bull. Soc. Enc. Nat. Ind.*, **102**. 399, 1902; P. Chevenard,

734 INORGANIC AND THEORETICAL CHEMISTRY

Compt. Rend., **169**. 712, 1919; A. T. Child and W. P. Heincken, *Trans. Amer. Inst. Min. Eng.*, **30**. 734, 1900; E. F. Cone, *Iron Age*, **124**. 1364, 1930; F. J. Cook, *Proc. South Staffs Iron Steel Inst.*, **25**. 102, 1910; *Foundry Trade Journ.*, **30**. 116, 1922; F. B. Coyle, *Trans. Amer. Soc. Testing Materials*, **29**. ii, 138, 1929; M. Dalifol, *La fonte malléable*, in E. Lacroix, *Études sur l'exposition de 1878*, Paris, 1878; S. J. E. Dangerfield, T. Johnson and E. R. Taylor, *Journ. Iron Steel Inst.—Carnegie Mem.*, **19**. 1, 1930; R. W. Davenport, *Amer. Journ. Science*, (3), **4**. 270, 1872; G. C. Davis, *Proc. Amer. Foundrymen's Assoc.*, **5**. 263, 1898; **8**. 1, 1900; *Iron Trade Rev.*, **33**. 19, 1900; J. D. Deisher, *Trans. Amer. Foundrymen's Assoc.*, **26**. 403, 1917; E. Deny, *Études sur la fonderie*, Paris, 1886; H. E. Diller, *Trans. Amer. Foundrymen's Assoc.*, **27**. 404, 1918; **28**. 261, 1919; *Iron Trade Rev.*, **63**. 1414, 1918; R. L. Dowell and J. T. Gow, *ib.*, **83**. 570, 578, 1928; E. F. Dürre, *Ueber die Constitution des Roheisens*, Leipzig, 1868; *Stahl Eisen*, **17**. 967, 1897; M. Epstein, *Iron Trade Rev.*, **76**. 383, 1925; F. Erbreich, *Stahl Eisen*, **35**. 549, 652, 1915; G. A. Evans, *Foundry*, **43**. 219, 1915; W. T. Evans and A. E. Peace, *Foundry Trade Journ.*, **38**. 423, 454, 478, 1928; H. Fay and S. Badlam, *Tech. Quart.*, **13**. 295, 1900; S. J. Felton, *Iron Age*, **115**. 489, 1925; H. Field, *Proc. South Staffs Iron Steel Inst.*, **43**. 21, 1928; *Foundry Trade Journ.*, **35**. 249, 271, 291, 1927; B. Finney, *Iron Age*, **121**. 1209, 1928; E. P. Fischer, *Trans. Amer. Foundrymen's Assoc.*, **30**. 395, 1922; D. P. Forbes, *ib.*, **37**. 397, 1929; H. Ford, *Proc. Brit. Foundrymen's Assoc.*, 173, 1913; L. Forquignon, *Recherches sur la fonte malléable et sur la recuit des aciers*, Paris, 1881; *Ann. Chim. Phys.*, (5), **23**. 433, 1881; *Compt. Rend.*, **91**. 817, 1880; *Jernkontorets Ann.*, **37**. 229, 1882; W. Fraenkel and E. Heymann, *Zeit. anorg. Chem.*, **134**. 137, 1924; R. Gailly, *Foundry Trade Journ.*, **28**. 267, 1923; **43**. 255, 1930; C. H. Gale, *Trans. Amer. Foundrymen's Assoc.*, **20**. 271, 1911; **21**. 252, 1912; L. E. Gilmore, *Foundry*, **44**. 181, 1916; **56**. 529, 1928; *Trans. Amer. Foundrymen's Assoc.*, **24**. 233, 1915; **36**. 287, 1928; N. G. Girschowitsch and E. C. Widin, *The Theory of the Malleablizing Process*, Moscow, 1929; *Vestnik Metallopromuishlennusti*, 11, 1929; *Trans. Inst. Met. Moscow*, 4, 1929; *Trans. U.S.S.R. Inst. Metals*, 4, 1929; *Proc. Russ. Met. Soc.*, 312, 1929; F. Graziani, *Giorn. Chim. Ind. Appl.*, **4**. 56, 1922; E. Gridley, *Trans. Amer. Inst. Min. Eng.*, **17**. 472, 1889; M. Guedras, *Rev. Fond. Moderne*, **21**. 30, 1927; R. A. Hadfield, *Proc. Inst. Civil Eng.*, **138**. 442, 1899; *Journ. Iron Steel Inst.*, **45**. i, 156, 1894; G. Hailstone, *Journ. Iron Steel Inst.—Carnegie Mem.*, **5**. 51, 1913; **7**. 55, 1916; H. Hanemann, *Monatsbl. Bezirkver. deut. Ing.*, 4, 1926; *Stahl Eisen*, **47**. 693, 1927; *Centr. Hütt. walz.*, **31**. 273, 1927; A. Harley, *Proc. Brit. Foundrymen's Assoc.*, 176, 1918; W. H. Hatfield, *Cast Iron in the Light of Recent Research*, London, 1928; *Proc. Royal Aero. Soc.*, **7**. 169, 1917; *Journ. Inst. Eng. Shipbuilders Scotland*, **51**. 398, 1908; *Proc. Roy. Soc.*, **85**. A, 1, 1911; *Journ. Iron Steel Inst.*, **70**. ii, 157, 1906; **74**. ii, 79, 1907; **79**. i, 262, 1909; **96**. ii, 307, 1917; *Foundry Trade Journ.*, **17**. 248, 1915; *Met.*, **6**. 358, 1909; *Proc. Brit. Foundrymen's Assoc.*, 194, 1914; A. Hayes and W. J. Diederichs, *Trans. Amer. Soc. Steel Treating*, **3**. 624, 1923; **6**. 491, 1924; A. Hayes and H. E. Flanders, *Trans. Amer. Foundrymen's Assoc.*, **33**. 634, 1925; A. Hayes, E. L. Henderson and G. R. Bessmer, *Trans. Amer. Foundrymen's Assoc.*, **33**. 646, 1925; *Foundry Trade Journ.*, **32**. 387, 1925; A. Hayes and G. C. Scott, *Trans. Amer. Foundrymen's Assoc.*, **33**. 574, 1925; N. Hekker, *Giesserei*, **18**. 14, 39, 1931; H. Hemenway, *ib.*, **23**. 413, 1914; F. Henfling, *Giesserei*, **15**. 534, 1928; C. C. Hermann, *Foundry*, **50**. 952, 1922; G. Hofer, *Giesserei Ztg.*, **3**. 681, 1906; **4**. 481, 677, 1907; R. Hohage, *Krupp's Monatsh.*, **7**. 101, 1926; K. Honda and T. Murakami, *Journ. Iron Steel Inst.*, **102**. ii, 287, 1920; *Science Rep. Tohoku Univ.*, **10**. 273, 1921; **12**. 287, 1924; H. M. Howe, *Trans. Amer. Inst. Min. Eng.*, **31**. 318, 1901; F. H. Hurren, *Foundry Trade Journ.*, **23**. 125, 1921; **38**. 301, 1928; **31**. 499, 526, 1925; **40**. 33, 1929; *Proc. Inst. British Foundrymen*, **18**. 148, 1925; *Iron Coal Trades Rev.*, **81**. 283, 1910; J. E. Hurst, *Engg.*, **108**. 1, 1919; H. W. Hyde, *Foundry*, **58**. 104, 109, 1930; D. H. Ingall and H. Field, *Journ. Iron Steel Inst.*, **111**. i, 265, 1925; C. James, *Journ. Franklin Inst.*, **144**. 80, 1897; **148**. 482, 1899; **150**. 227, 1900; A. T. Jeffrey, *Trans. Amer. Foundrymen's Assoc.*, **26**. 383, 1917; W. A. Jenkins, *Iron Age*, **81**. 1926, 1908; G. R. Johnson, *Journ. Iron Steel Inst.*, **54**. ii, 203, 1898; J. E. Johnson, *Trans. Amer. Inst. Min. Eng.*, **44**. 314, 1912; **50**. 344, 1914; *Iron Age*, **89**. 1206, 1912; **90**. 1375, 1912; G. Jungst, *Beiträge zur Untersuchungen des Gusseisens und des Stahleisens*, Düsseldorf, 1913; W. J. Keep, *Cast Iron*, New York, 136, 1902; *Foundry*, **31**. 160, 1907; F. R. King, *Page's Weekly*, **13**. 183, 1908; T. Kikuta, *Science Rep. Tohoku Univ.*, **15**. 115, 1926; *Kinzoku no Kenkyu*, **7**. 487, 1930; T. Klingenstein, *Giesserei Ztg.*, **24**. 335, 1927; C. Kluijtmans, *Foundry Trade Journ.*, **23**. 447, 1921; **34**. 123, 133, 550, 1926; C. E. Kluijtmans and W. H. W. Procter, *Brit. Pat. No.* 288980, 1928; J. Kollmann, *Verh. Ver. Beförd. Gewerbfleisses*, **59**. 211, 1880; B. Kranz, *Trans. Amer. Foundrymen's Assoc.*, **25**. 501, 1916; G. L. Lacher, *Iron Age*, **113**. 921, 1924; **114**. 5, 1924; M. Lamla, *Giesserei Ztg.*, **8**. 197, 233, 268, 300, 335, 408, 1911; E. H. Leasman, *Trans. Amer. Foundrymen's Assoc.*, **22**. 169, 1913; A. Ledebur, *Das Roheisen in Bezung auf seine Verwendung zur Eisengiesserei*, Leipzig, 1872; *Das Roheisen mit besonders Berücksicht seiner Verwendung für die Eisengiesserei*, Leipzig, 1891; M. Leroyer, *Rev. Fond. Moderne*, **21**. 101, 149, 1927; E. Leuenberger, *Stahl Eisen*, **37**. 513, 601, 1917; T. Levoz, *Fonderie Moderne*, 169, 1922; *Trans. Amer. Foundrymen's Assoc.*, **30**. 420, 1922; *Foundry Trade Journ.*, **30**. 175, 1924; D. M. Levy, *Journ. Iron Steel Inst.*, **77**. ii, 33, 1908; O. M. Levy, *Proc. Brit. Foundrymen's Assoc.*, 200, 1911; A. Lissner, *Ferrum*, **10**. 44, 1912; P Longmuir, *Journ. Iron Steel Inst.*, **63**. i, 457, 1903; **65**. i, 420, 1904; E. J. Loury, *Foundry*, **57**. 228, 1929; S. Lucas, *Brit. Pat. No.* 2767, 1804; T. D. Lynch and W. J. Merten, *Trans. Amer. Soc. Steel Treating*, **3**. 833, 1923; A. McCance, *Foundry Trade Journ.*, **39**. 465, 1928; **40**. 25, 1929; A. McWilliam, *Journ. Iron Steel Inst.*, **65**. i, 435, 1904; A. McWilliam and J. Barnes, *ib.*, **81.** i, 246, 1910 ; E. E. Marbaker, *Foundry Trade Journ.*, **41.** 153, 1929 ; M. M. Marcus, *Foundry*, **50.** 994, 1922 ; L. H. Marshall, *Tech. Paper Bur. Standards*, 245, 1923 ; *Trans. Amer. Inst. Min. Eng.—Min. Met.*, 264, 1926 ; G. Matthews, *Brit. Pat. No.* 1360, 1783 ; F. A. Melmoth, *Proc. Inst. Brit. Foundrymen*, **19.** 222, 1926 ; *Foundry Trade Journ.*, **32.** 325, 1925 ; A. W. Merrick, *Trans. Amer. Foundrymen's Assoc.*, **28.** 322, 1919 ; A. Mertens, *Mitt. Tech. Versuchsanst*, **6.** 815, 1886 ; E. Meyer, *Stahl Eisen*, **47.** 294, 1927 ; R. Moldenke, *The Production of Malleable Castings*, Cleveland, Ohio, 1910 ; *Iron Trade Rev.*, **42.** 333, 416, 803, 993, 475, 1907 ; **43.** 353, 1908 ; **48.** 275, 1911 ; **55.** 857, 911, 930, 1914 ; *Trans. Amer. Foundrymen's Assoc.*, **22.** 251, 1913 ; *Cassier's Mag.*, **31.** 211, 1907 ; *Proc. Amer. Soc. Testing Materials*, **3.** 204, 1903 ; **12.** ii, 43, 1912 ; W. J. Molineux, *Metallurgie*, **1.** 242, 1930 ; **2.** 7, 1930 ; G. L. Norris, *Iron Age*, **87.** 1399, 1911 ; J. V. Murray, *Metallurgie*, **1.** 107, 161, 1930 ; **2.** 215, 1930 ; E. Namba, *Kinzoku no Kenkyu*, **6.** 416, 1929 ; C. J. McNamera and C. H. Lorig, *Trans. Amer. Foundrymen's Assoc.*, **33.** 627, 1925 ; R. Namias, *Proc. Internat. Congr. Appl. Chem.*, **7.** iii, 29, 1909 ; J. B. Nealey, *Foundry*, **57.** 582, 1929 ; S. S. Nekryti, *Vestnik Metalloprom.*, **10.** 78, 1930 ; *Chim. Ind.*, **25.** 353, 1931 ; C. Neumann, *Lectiones con vier subjectis chymicis*, Berlin, 1732 ; *Chemical Works*, London, 77, 1759 ; A. Numais, *Rass. Min.*, **29.** 113, 1908 ; P. Oberhoffer and H. Stein, *Die Giesserei*, **10.** 423, 431, 1923 ; P. Oberhoffer and J. Welter, *Giesserei*, **43.** 105, 301, 1923 ; *Foundry Trade Journ.*, **28.** 59, 76, 1923 ; *Stahl Eisen*, **43.** 105, 301, 1923 ; P. Oberhoffer and E. Zingg, *Foundry Trade Journ.*, **44.** 1197, 1924 ; E. C. Ongley, *Journ. West Scotland Iron Steel Inst.*, **15.** 13, 1908 ; B. Osann, *Stahl Eisen*, **23.** 22, 1903 ; **24.** 719, 1904 ; *Maschinenbau*, **8.** 785, 832, 1929 ; *Iron Age*, **125.** 1285, 1930 ; A. E. Outerbridge, *Proc. Amer. Soc. Testing Materials*, **2.** 229, 1902 ; S. J. Parsons, *Malleable Cast Iron*, New York, 1919 ; London, 1909 ; P. A. Paulson, *Trans. Amer. Foundrymen's Assoc.*, **27.** 425, 1918 ; A. E. Peace, *Foundry Trade Journ.*, **34.** 460, 1926 ; J. Piers, *Mét.*, **3.** 786, 1906 ; J. P. Pero, *Trans. Amer. Foundrymen's Assoc.*, **23.** 451, 1914 ; J. P. Pero and J. C. Nulsen, *ib.*, **24.** 222, 1915 ; A. Phillips and E. S. Davenport, *Trans. Amer. Inst. Min. Eng.*, **67.** 466, 1922 ; H. Pinsl, *Giesserei*, **13.** 365, 1926 ; E. Piwowarsky, *Ber. Werkstoffausch. Eisenhütt*, 63, 1925 ; *Hochwertiger Grauguss*, Berlin, 1929 ; *Giesserei*, **18.** 19, 1931 ; *Giesserei Ztg.*, **22.** 813, 833, 1925 ; **23.** 379, 1926 ; **24.** 253, 273, 290, 1927 ; *Stahl Eisen*, **42.** 1481, 1922 ; **45.** 1455, 2001, 1925 ; **47.** 308, 1927 ; C. H. Plant, *Iron Steel Ind.*, **1.** 381, 1928 ; **2.** 22, 53, 89, 117, 151, 175, 211, 333, 1928 ; **3.** 25, 1929 ; A. L. Pollard, *Trans. Amer. Foundrymen's Assoc.*, **23.** 460, 1914 ; **24.** 437, 1915 ; A. Pomp and H. Poellein, *Arch. Eisenhüttenwesen*, **3.** 223, 1929 ; *Mitt. Inst. Eisenforschung. Düsseldorf*, **11.** 155, 1929 ; A. Pomp and A. Walther, *Arch. Eisenhüttenwesen*, **2.** 859, 1929 ; W. H. Poole, *Foundry Trade Journ.*, **27.** 309, 329, 1923 ; O. W. Potter, *Trans. Amer. Foundrymen's Assoc.*, **33.** 294, 1925 ; E. H. Putman, *Iron Trade Rev.*, **32.** 15, 18, 1899 ; **33.** 11, 1900 ; W. P. Putman, *Foundry*, **39.** 66, 1911 ; *Trans. Amer. Foundrymen's Assoc.*, **20.** 363, 1911 ; **28.** 257, 1919 ; O. Quadrat and J. Koritta, *Foundry Trade Journ.*, **34.** 306, 1926 ; **38.** 191, 1928 ; *Trans. Amer. Foundrymen's Assoc.*, **34.** 1081, 1926 ; *Giesserei*, **14.** 849, 1927 ; R. A. F. de Réaumur, *L'art de convertir le fer forgé en acier et l'art d'adoucir le fer fondu*, Paris, 472, 1722 ; R. N. Richardson, *Engg. Production*, **7.** 311, 1924 ; P. Rodigin, *Trans. Amer. Foundrymen's Assoc.*, **22.** 201, 1913 ; R. T. Rolfe, *Proc. Royal Aero. Soc.*, **7.** 169, 1917 ; G. P. Royston, *Journ. Iron Steel Inst.*, **51.** i, 154, 166, 1897 ; D. Saito and H. Sawamura, *Mem. Coll. Engg. Kyoto*, **5.** 1, 1927 ; E. H. Saniter, *Journ. Iron Steel Inst.*, **52.** ii, 115, 1897 ; F. Sauerwald and A. Koreny, *Stahl Eisen*, **48.** 537, 1928 ; A. Sauveur, *Metallographist*, **3.** 154, 1900 ; U. Savoia, *Proc. Internat. Congr. Appl. Chem.*, **7.** iii, 37, 1909 ; H. Sawamura, *Mem. Coll. Engg. Kyoto Univ.*, **4.** 159, 1926 ; C. Scheiber and H. Menking, *Zeit. Metallkunde*, **21.** 297, 1929 ; W. Schneider, *Giesserei Ztg.*, **22.** 381, 1925 ; E. Schömann, *Stahl Eisen*, **29.** 593, 1909 ; E. Schüz, *ib.*, **42.** 1345, 1484, 1922 ; **44.** 116, 1924 ; **45.** 1189, 1925 ; *Giesserei*, **16.** 1185, 1930 ; H. A. Schwartz, *Trans. Amer. Soc. Steel Treating*, **9.** 883, 1926 ; **10.** 55, 1926 ; **11.** 767, 1927 ; *Mech. Engg.*, **47.** 623, 1925 ; *Foundry*, **47.** 462, 1919 ; *Eng. News*, **83.** 132, 1919 ; *Iron Age*, **104.** 495, 1919 ; *American Malleable Cast Iron*, Cleveland, Ohio, 1922 ; *Trans. Amer. Foundrymen's Assoc.*, **27.** 373, 1918 ; **29.** 342, 1920 ; **32.** i, 643, 1924 ; **34.** 1049, 1926 ; **37.** 205, 1929 ; **50.** 210, 1930 ; *Iron Trade Rev.* **67.** 1536, 1920 ; **68.** 213, 353, 361, 485, 490, 628, 633, 770, 901, 1038, 1175, 1317, 1453, 1662, 1792, 1921 ; **69.** 98, 233, 354, 371, 496, 611, 626, 813, 1921 ; *Proc. Amer. Soc. Testing Materials*, **19.** ii, 247, 1919 ; **20.** ii, 70, 1920 ; *Fuels Furnaces*, **7.** 187, 1929 ; *Forging Stamping Heat Treatment*, **12.** 413, 1926 ; *Metals Alloys*, **2.** 143, 1931 ; H. A. Schwartz and H. H. Johnson, *Trans. Amer. Soc. Steel Treating*, **10.** 965, 1926 ; G. R. Shotton and R. G. Hall, *Foundry Trade Journ.*, **42.** 399, 1930 ; E. K. Smith, *Trans. Amer. Foundrymen's Assoc.*, **31.** 295, 1923 ; R. H. Smith, *Journ. Iron Steel Inst.*, **92.** ii, 141, 1915 ; E. K. Smith and W. Barr, *Trans. Amer. Foundrymen's Assoc.*, **28.** 330, 1919 ; J. K. Smithson, *Foundry Trade Journ.*, **44.** 110, 1931 ; H. R. Stanford, *Trans. Amer. Soc. Civil Eng.*, **34.** 1, 1895 ; J. E. Stead, *Proc. Cleveland Inst. Eng.*, 79, 1895 ; O. W. Storey, *Met. Chem. Engg.*, **12.** 383, 1914 ; *Trans. Amer. Foundrymen's Assoc.*, **23.** 460, 1914 ; R. Stotz, *Stahl Eisen*, **36.** 501, 1916 ; **40.** 997, 1920 ; *Zeit. Giess. Praxis*, **51.** 261, 1930 ; *Foundry*, **50.** 286, 1922 ; *Betrieb*, 631, 1921 ; *Giesserei Ztg.*, **17.** 305, 356, 373, 1920 ; **19.** 301, 319, 1922 ; *Giesserei*, **15.** 145, 248, 905, 1928 ; **16.** 839, 1209, 1929 ; **18.** 1, 1931 ; *Foundry Trade Journ.*, **14.** 286, 1929 ; B. Stoughton, *School Mines Quart.*, **29.** 54, 1908 ; C. L. Sullivan, *Iron Trade Rev.*, **31.** 16, 17, 1898 ; E. R. Taylor, *Journ. Iron Steel Inst.—Carnegie Mem.*, **15.** 381, 1926 ; *Bull. Brit. Cast Iron Research*, 22, 1928 ; *Foundry Trade Journ.*, **36.** 23, 41, 1927 ; J. H. Teng, *Journ. Iron Steel Inst.*, **98.** ii, 349, 1918 ; A. le Thomas, *Rev. Fond. Moderne*, **21.** 33, 1927 ; G. M. Thrasher, *Chem. Met. Engg.*, **13.** 39, 1915 ; *Trans. Amer. Inst. Min. Eng.*, **53.** 189, 1916 ; E. Touceda, *Trans. Amer. Foundrymen's Assoc.*, **25.**

506, 1916; **26.** 375, 1917; **27.** 438, 1918; **29.** 356, 1920; **34.** 1072, 1926; **23.** 440, 1914; *Foundry Trade Journ.,* **26.** 50, 75, 102, 122, 142, 1922; **24.** 357, 1921; *Mech. Eng.,* **42.** 431, 1920; *Metals Alloys,* **1.** 815, 1930; *Trans. Amer. Inst. Min. Eng.,* **67.** 457, 527, 1922; *Tech. Publ. Amer. Inst. Min. Eng.,* 11, 1927; *Iron Age,* **91.** 1426, 1913; *Trans. Amer. Foundrymen's Assoc.,* **34.** 1072, 1926; *Journ. Amer. Soc. Mech. Eng.,* **41.** 593, 1919; *Proc. Inst. British Foundrymen,* **15.** 120, 1922; T. Turner, *Journ. West Scotland Iron Steel Inst.,* **25.** 285, 1918; *Journ. Iron Steel Inst.,* **69.** i, 48, 1906; V. V. Usoff and N. N. Pustuimikoff, *Vestnik Metalloprom.,* **10.** 97, 1930; *Chim. Ind.,* **25.** 352, 1931; W. Valentin, *Giesserei Ztg.,* **27.** 617, 1930; I. R. Valentine, *Brit. Pat. No.* 315724, 1928; *Metals Alloys,* **1.** 233, 1929; *Heat Treating Forging,* **15.** 1344, 1929; P. Vidor, *Giesserei,* **18.** 8, 1931; A. Wahlberg, *Baumaterialienkunde,* **2.** 141, 1898; Y. Watanabe, *Stahl Eisen,* **17.** 628, 1897; H. Wedding, *ib.,* **14.** 465, 528, 1894; E. C. Wheeler, *Iron Age,* **63.** 2, 1899; **64.** 4, 1899; A. E. White, *Trans. Amer. Soc. Steel Treating,* **11.** 245, 1926; A. E. White and R. S. Archer, *Trans. Amer. Foundrymen's Assoc.,* **27.** 331, 1918; D. Wilkinson, *Foundry Trade Journ.,* **31.** 28, 1925; *Metal Ind.,* **26.** 112, 141, 1925; F. Wüst, *Mét.,* **5.** 7, 1908; *Stahl Eisen,* **24.** 305, 1904; F. Wüst and E. Leuenberger, *Ferrum,* **13.** 161, 1916; O. Schliewiensky, *Giesserei,* **16.** 267, 1929.

³ R. A. F. de Réaumur, *L'art de convertir le fer forgé en acier, et l'art d'adoucir le fer fondu,* Paris, 1722; *An Essay on the Mystery of Tempering Steel,* London, 1771; P. Goerens, *Einführung in die Metallographie,* Halle a. S., 1906; F. Wüst, *Met.* **3.** 1, 1906; **5.** 7, 1908; *Stahl Eisen,* **33.** 1136, 1913; H. Schenck, *Arch. Eisenhüttenwesen,* **3.** 505, 571, 685, 1930; W. H. Hatfield, *Cast Iron in the Light of Recent Research,* London, 254, 1928; *Journ. Iron Steel Inst.,* **70.** ii, 157, 1906; **79.** i, 242, 1909; J. O. Arnold and A. McWilliam, *ib.,* **68.** ii, 27, 1905; H. F. Rugan and H. C. H. Carpenter, *ib.,* **80.** ii, 29, 1909; M. L. Becker, *ib.,* **112.** ii, 239, 1925; **121.** i, 337, 1930; E. D. Campbell, *ib.,* **100.** ii, 407, 1919; E. D. Campbell, J. F. Ross and W. L. Fink, *ib.,* **108.** ii, 373, 179, 1923; H. C. Greenwood, *ib.,* **89.** i, 508, 1914; C. R. Austin, *ib.,* **105.** i, 93, 1922; J. H. Whiteley, *ib.,* **102.** ii, 143, 1920; E. H. Saniter, *ib.,* **52.** ii, 115, 1898; R. A. Hadfield, *ib.,* **45.** i, 157, 1894; G. P. Royston, *ib.,* **51.** i, 154, 166, 1897; A. Johansson and R. von Seth, *ib.,* **114.** ii, 295, 1926; E. R. Taylor, *Journ. Iron Steel Inst.—Carnegie Mem.,* **14.** 131, 1925; **15.** 281, 1926; F. Giolitti, *Rend. Soc. Chim. Roma,* **6.** 388, 1908; G. Charpy, *Rev. Mét.,* **5.** 41, 1908; C. Benedicks, *ib.,* **5.** 77, 1908; J. J. Berzelius, *Jahresber.,* **18.** 160, 1839; E. Leuenberger, *Stahl Eisen,* **41.** 285, 1921; P. Oberhoffer and J. Welter, *ib.,* **43.** 105, 301, 1923; E. Zingg, P. Oberhoffer and E. Piwowarsky, *ib.,* **49.** 721, 762, 1929; P. Oberhoffer, and A. Heger, *ib.,* **43.** 1417, 1923; A. Ledebur, *Handbuch der Eisen- und Stahlgiesserei,* Leipzig, 385, 1901; *Stahl Eisen,* **17.** 628, 1897; G. Belloc, *Compt. Rend.,* **136.** 500, 1321, 1903; A. C. Becquerel, *Ann. Chim. Phys.,* (2), **49.** 134, 1832; A. F. E. Degen, *Liebig's Ann.,* **29.** 261, 1839; H. Scott, *Chem. Met. Engg.,* **25.** 72, 1921; E. H. Schulz and W. Hülsbruch, *Stahl Eisen,* **47.** 1694, 1927; *Arch. Eisenhüttenwesen,* **1.** 225, 1927; *Metallurgist,* **4.** 164, 1927; E. H. Schulz and P. Niemeyer, *Mitt. Versuchanst., Dortmunder,* 110, 1923; J. V. Emmons, *Trans. Amer. Inst. Min. Eng.,* **50.** 405, 1914; A. Matsubara, *ib.,* **67.** 3, 1922; *Zeit. anorg. Chem.,* **124.** 39, 1922; *Stahl Eisen,* **43.** 241, 1923; J. G. Ayres, *Proc. Amer. Soc. Testing Materials,* **15.** ii, 80, 1915; L. Hackspill and E. Schwarz, *Ann. Chim. Phys.,* (10), **13.** 5, 1930; A. M. Portevin and V. Bernard, *Chim. Ind.,* 243, 1930; J. J. Curran and J. H. G. Williams, *Trans. Amer. Soc. Steel Treating,* **14.** 809, 1928; R. G. Guthrie, *ib.,* **15.** 96, 1929; T. Murakami and H. Sekiguchi, *Journ. Japan Iron Steel Inst.,* **16.** 1015, 1930; A. Seuthe and E. H. Schulz, *Mitt. Forsch. Inst. Dortmund,* **2.** 61, 1931; *Stahl Eisen,* **51.** 791, 1931; W. E. Jominy, *Bull. Univ. Michigan Eng.,* 18, 1931; J. Ciochina, *Stahl Eisen,* **51.** 1024, 1931; M. Winter and P. B. Crocker, *Heat Treating Forging,* **16.** 1450, 1930; *Fuels Furnaces,* **8.** 1547, 1930; A. Bromley and K. F. Allen, *Engg.,* **133.** 92, 123, 229, 305, 1932.

§ 10. The Cementation of Iron and Steel

One of the oldest commercial methods of making steel is by what is now known as the cementation process. The purpose of **cementation** is partially or totally to carburize iron or steel without fusing the metal, and in such a way that the carburized metal shall possess the structure and properties of a true steel. This is done by heating wrought-iron bars packed in boxes made from a fireclay. Each bar is surrounded by broken charcoal, heated to 950° or 1000°, and kept at this temp. until the desired percentage of carbon has been absorbed from the charcoal. The carburizing agent may be solid—*e.g.* wood-charcoal, lampblack, and various organic substances like hoofs, hides, dung, etc.; it may be liquid—*e.g.* fused cyanides or ferrocyanides, urine, or molten cast iron; or it may be gaseous—*e.g.* volatile hydrocarbons or carbon monoxide.

Mixtures and methods have been discussed by R. R. Abbott,[1] A. A. Ackermann, F. André, F. G. Bates, C. Binks, G. F. Hinkens, J. F. J. A. Boullet, P. W. Brennan, H. L. Heathcote, R. A. Millholland, S. A. Teschenko-Tschopiwsky, V. Grönquist,

J. Herbert, G. Takahashi, J. S. Ayling, P. W. Döhmer, J. W. Urquhart, S. Tour, R. A. Brooman, G. B. Cattaneo and A. Faggian, M. F. Coomes and A. W. Hyde, F. Cowden, V. H. E. Gallot, J. Holland, J. B. Jenkins, N. Kimball, M. B. Messimer and E. F. Carter, W. Nelson, S. P. Rockwell, E. C. Moffett, T. Langer, C. Lamargese, J. Lecarme, and G. C. Thomas, R. A. Ragatz and O. L. Kowalke, G. M. Enos, and by numerous others. The Cyanide-Gesellschaft proposed to use cyanamide or one of its compounds with the alkalies or alkaline earths ; and E. Engels, carbon silicide. J. C. Olsen and W. S. Weissenbach observed that the relative carburizing action of carbon monoxide, acetylene, and methane is in the order named. *H. Caron's cement* is a mixture of 60 parts of carbon (wood-charcoal) and 40 parts of barium carbonate ; *F. Giolitti's cement* is carbon assisted by carbon monoxide. C. Macintosh, and G. Vismara obtained steel by the action of hydrocarbons at a white-heat ; but D. Mushet found that the difficulties in keeping the containing vessels air-tight at the high temp. were insuperable.

The time of heating depends on the thickness of the desired coating, the temp. of the furnace, and the nature of the carburizing agent. In certain cases where a metal with a tough interior and a hard working surface is required the piece is made from a mild steel with about 0·14 per cent. of carbon. The piece is then subjected to the cementation process, so that its carbon content is raised to about 0·9 per cent. The piece is then quenched from a red-heat, say 800°, whereby the outer surface is hardened without affecting very much the mild steel core. In the case where all or part of the surface of a steel or iron object is carburized and subsequently hardened, the operation is called **case-hardening.** If a particular part of the surface is not to be carburized, it is protected by some inert material— fire-clay, electrodeposited copper, etc. The technology of case-hardening and cementation is discussed in special books :

H. Brearley, *The Case-Hardening of Steel*, London, 1921 ; F. W. Harbord, *The Metallurgy of Steel*, **1.** 241, 1916 ; F. Giolitti, *La cementazione dell'acciajo*, Torino, 1912 ; *La cémentation de l'acier*, Paris, 1914 ; *The Cementation of Iron and Steel*, New York, 1915 ; F. W. Rowe, *Iron Steel Ind.*, **3.** 77, 116, 1930 ; J. W. Urquhart, *Steel Thermal Treatment*, London, 1922 ; A. M. Portevin, *Pyrométrie et cémentation*, Paris, 1920 ; E. Menzel, *Das Härten, Schweissen und Löten von Stahl und Eisen nebst vielen Rezepten zur Herstellung praktischer Helfsmittel*, Berlin, 1921.

J. Beckmann said that he was not able to find any reference to the manufacture of steel by cementation in any of the ancient writings, and that the obscure reference in Pliny's *Historia naturalis* (**34.** 41) does not refer to this process. Towards the end of the eleventh century, P. Theophilus described the hardening of files by carburization ; and the old process was described by V. Biringuccio in 1540 ; by G. Agricola in 1561 ; by G. J. Löhneyss in 1617 ; by M. Lister in 1693 ; and in later years, by J. Buttery, J. R. Bréant, H. Damemme, L. B. G. de Morveau, G. Vismara, and P. C. J. B. Tronson du Coudray.

Attempts to trace the origin of the cementation process of steel manufacture have not been successful. R. Jenkins supposed that the process was invented by W. Ellyott and M. Meysey, as indicated in their patents of 1614 and 1617. The older writers, C. J. B. Karsten, A. L. Landrin, J. Franquoy, etc., state emphatically that the cementation process was invented on the Continent and not in England. D. Brownlie examined the claims of W. Ellyott and M. Meysey and showed that a strong protest against the patent monopoly was made at the time by the iron and steel manufacturers, and that the patented process would not furnish cementation steel. The reference of R. Plot to the manufacture of cementation steel at Bromley, Staffordshire, shows that in 1686 he regarded the process as new and unusual. J. Franquoy stated in 1861 that the two armourers P. du Coudraye and J. van Buhl of Liége made steel out of iron by the cementation process at the beginning of the seventeenth century. After examining the original documents, Baron de Laveleye concluded that there is nothing to show that the cementation process was here employed, although, about this period, the cementation process seems to have been employed in the principality of Liége for making steel from iron. Baron de Laveleye, and D. Brownlie therefore conclude that how or when the cementation process was invented remains unknown.

As indicated above, the phlogiston chemists—T. Bergman, and C. W. Scheele—believed that steel is a compound of iron with variable proportions of plumbago ; and that plumbago is a compound of fixed air and phlogiston. R. A. F. de Réaumur showed that the transformation proceeds from the surface towards the interior of the mass ; and that the foreign substance which penetrates into the iron and increases its weight is contained in the powders used as *cement*. He wrongly inferred that the substances which penetrate the iron during the cementation are sulphur and volatile salts. C. A. van der Monde, C. L. Berthollet and G. Monge, however, inferred that the foreign substance which combines with pure iron to form steel is no other than the element carbon. They showed that, as already observed by R. A. F. de Réaumur, iron is transformed into steel by merely heating it with wood-charcoal alone and protected from contact with air or moisture. The transformation is attended by an increase in weight owing to the gradual absorption of carbon by the iron.

To the early observers it appeared that in cementation solid carbon can readily penetrate the pores of solid iron when dilated by heat. The phenomenon was said to be *une opération inexpliquée, mystérieuse, présentait le carbone comme un corps anormal*, because it seemed to contradict what was thought to be a law of nature—*corpora non agunt nisi soluta*. The process was therefore regarded as obscure and mysterious. A. Laurent suggested the improbable hypothesis—the *carbon vapour hypothesis*—that it is the vapour of carbon itself which penetrates the iron during the cementation. P. G. F. Leplay attempted to explain the carburizing action of wood-charcoal by assuming that the oxygen of the air contained in the cementation boxes reacts with the carbon, forming carbon dioxide and subsequently carbon monoxide. The latter penetrates the iron, depositing half its carbon to form carbon dioxide. This is again reduced to carbon monoxide by the carbon of the cementing agent. The carbon monoxide—in the *carbon monoxide catalyst hypothesis*—thus acts as a carrier of oxygen by a cycle of reactions continued indefinitely. The hypothesis was favoured by A. Laurent, and H. Behrens and A. R. von Linge ; and a modification of this hypothesis—*vide infra*—is the one now generally accepted. J. L. Gay-Lussac emphasized that there is no need to accept in *une foi aveugle* the ancient principle, because solids, liquids, and gases can act on one another, though the solid state is the least favourable to the exercise of chemical affinity. J. L. Gay-Lussac's hypothesis—the *diffusion of solid carbon hypothesis*—reduces the phenomenon to the assumption that solid carbon can diffuse into solid iron and at the same time carburize the iron.

W. H. Pepys proved that iron can be directly carburized by heating an iron wire in contact with diamond dust ; analogous observations were made by L. Clouet, D. Mushet, G. S. MacKenzie, L. B. G. de Morveau, P. A. Dufrénoy, and F. Margueritte ; while W. C. Roberts-Austen repeated the experiment by heating electrically a strip of iron while in contact with small diamonds at a temp. far below the m.p. of iron, and in vacuo, so as to preclude the presence or influence of occluded gas. W. Hempel heated the iron in contact with different forms of carbon in an atmosphere of nitrogen. He said that the lowest temp. at which the diamond carburizes is 1160° ; and that amorphous carbon, between 1385° and 1420°, forms grey cast iron. F. Osmond observed that at 1035° to 1065° iron is carburized by diamonds about the points of contact ; and at 1085° to 1125°, with diamonds in the proportion of 4 per cent., the diamonds dissolve in the iron to form white cast iron ; and with diamonds in the proportion of 8 per cent. fused grey cast iron is formed to which adheres a graphitic patina containing iron. The diamond itself does not cement iron until it has undergone a molecular transformation into graphite. While the carbon diffuses into iron, the iron also diffuses into the transformed diamond.

W. C. Roberts-Austen studied the rate of diffusion of carbon in solid iron. He represented the variation in the concentration of the carbon in successive layers of the carburized zone in a cemented steel containing originally 0·26 per cent. of carbon. Observations on the diffusion of carbon were reported by G. Tammann.

and K. Schönert, J. H. Hruska, E. G. Mahin and co-workers, E. Zingg, J. Parry, A. Fry, F. Abel, I. Runge, F. Osmond, and J. E. Stead ; and on diffusion in solid soln. in general, by H. Braune and H. Hellweg, J. H. Hruska, and C. H. Desch.

G. J. Snelus regarded the direct union of carbon with iron as analogous with a process of solution rather than of chemical combination. J. O. Arnold thought that the carbon diffused in the form of the two carbides Fe_3C and $Fe_{24}C$; the former begins at about 950° and the latter at 750°. W. C. Roberts-Austen supposed that the carbon diffused in iron as salt does in water until the saturation point is attained. There is nothing very definite to show whether it diffuses as carbon or as carbide.

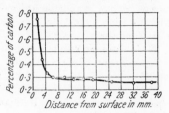

Fig. 71.—The Depth of Penetration of Iron by Carbon.

A. Colson emphasized the reciprocal nature of the process of diffusion—while carbon diffuses into iron, the iron diffuses into carbon. The phenomenon is manifest at 250°, when the diffusion of iron into carbon is predominant ; at higher temp. the reciprocal process prevails and cementation occurs. L. Forquignon also noted the decarburization of cast iron when it is ignited with powdered charcoal and subjected to the same conditions as would carburize steel. A. Gautier, A. F. E. Degen, R. Mannesmann, and I. L. Bell also noted that when cast iron in contact with wrought iron is heated, carbon passes from the former to the latter—maybe by diffusion, maybe by the intervention of gases, say carbon monoxide. G. P. Royston found that no diffusion occurred at 900° in vacuo when two bars of soft steel with 0·15 per cent. of carbon were kept in contact with a bar containing 0·95 per cent. of steel, but if a more highly carburized bar was employed, the proportion of carbon in the bars of mild steel rose from 0·15 to 0·29 per cent., and the proportion in the highly carburized bar fell to 0·42 per cent. This shows that carbon diffuses into iron by simple difference of concentration, without the intervention of gases. J. O. Arnold and A. McWilliam obtained an analogous result.

C. R. Austin observed that the diffusion of carbon proceeds until the concentration and pressure of the diffusing substance attain a constant value, and the constant of diffusion—that is, the amount of carbon which would diffuse across unit area under a concentration gradient of unity in unit time (say one day), if the rate were constant during that time—was estimated to be 0·005 at 650°, and 0·05 at 850°. A round steel bar containing 1·27 per cent. of carbon was decarburized by moist hydrogen at 680° for 100 hrs. so as to furnish a layer of ferrite and an unchanged core. Pieces of the bar were heated in vacuo. The diffusion of carbon was very slow below the Ac_3-arrest ; at 920° the core was freed from cementite and carbon had passed halfway to the surface ; at 1000° only a very narrow layer was free from carbon ; and at 1100°, in 30 mins., the carbon had passed halfway to the surface, while some cementite still remained in the core. I. Runge determined the rate of diffusion of carbon into iron by measuring the change in the resistance of iron wire in a current of gaseous hydrocarbon at a high temp. Illuminating gas diluted with hydrogen had little or no action ; toluene diluted with nitrogen reacted slowly, more quickly when diluted with hydrogen ; whilst a rapid action was shown by mixtures of benzene with nitrogen, high petroleum (b.p. 90°–100°) with hydrogen, and hexane with nitrogen or hydrogen. The time-resistance curves were similar to those obtained on the assumption that the diffusion of carbon follows the diffusion law. At 900°, the diffusion coeff. of carbon in iron is about 2×10^{-7} cm. per sec. With an active gas, at 930°, 0·6 mgrm. of carbon passes through 1 sq. cm. of surface in the first three minutes. The resistance change due to 1 per cent. of carbon is 5·7 per cent. at 920°, 7 per cent. at 830°, and 40 per cent. at 18° of the resistance at the corresponding temp. The velocity of cementation falls off rapidly with temperature and is inappreciable at 700°. When cementation takes place above 900°, γ-mixed crystals are formed, and the product is found to consist of cementite and pearlite. At 800° the β-iron takes up carbon to form an equilibrium mixture of γ-mixed crystals containing about 0·3 per cent. of carbon and β-iron. Whether diffusion takes place in the gaseous form or as carbon cannot be affirmed, but the marked influence of hydrogen on the rate of diffusion points to the former. The subject was studied by N. Agéeff and M. Zamotorin.

G. Tammann' and K. Schönert gave for the diffusion coeff. of carbon in iron with 0·07 per cent. of carbon 3×10^{-7} at 925°, and $19\cdot3\times10^{-7}$ at 1000°; and for iron with 0·26 per cent. carbon, $11\cdot2\times10^{-7}$ at 1000°. I. Runge gave for electrolytic iron $1\cdot15\times10^{-7}$ at 925°. A. Bramley and A. J. Jinkings also found for iron with 0·02 per cent. carbon, $1\cdot7\times10^{-8}$ at 850°; $3\cdot8\times10^{-8}$ at 900°; $9\cdot0\times10^{-8}$ at 950°; and 20×10^{-8} at 1000°. Different results were obtained by varying the rate of flow of the carburizing gases, and with steels containing different proportions of carbon. A. Bramley and co-workers found that the diffusion of carbon follows the law :

$$C=\frac{H}{2\sqrt{\pi Kt}}e^{-\frac{x^2}{4Kt}}$$

where C denotes the concentration of carbon above that initially present in the steel at a depth x cm. below the surface ; t denotes the time of diffusion in seconds ; H, a numerical constant ; and k, the diffusivity constant. For armco iron at 1000°, $H=0\cdot312$ to $0\cdot320$, and $k=13\cdot0\times10^{-8}$ to $15\cdot0\times10^{-8}$; whilst for Swedish iron at 1000°, $H=0\cdot310$ to $0\cdot320$, and $k=18\times10^{-8}$. T. Ishiwara said that the rate of diffusion, V, of carbon in iron increases rapidly with rise of temp., $\theta-\theta_1$, so that between 950° and 1300°, $V=e^{a(\theta-\theta_1)}$ cm. per second, where a is a constant—in one case $a=0\cdot00986$, and $\theta_1=2220°$; and

	1300°	1200°	1100°	1000°	950°
$V\times10^6$ . .	111·00	43·19	16·20	5·981	3·616

The work of F. Osmond, also, has demonstrated the great molecular mobility of solid iron at a temp. at least 600° below its m.p.—*vide infra*, the decarburization of cast iron.

F. Margueritte, C. E. Jullien, R. Mannesmann, A. Ledebur, and R. S. Marsden favoured the opinion that cementation can take place by simple contact ; J. Percy, and L. Guillet held the contrary opinion. R. Mannesmann said that the maximum concentration of carbon, 4·76 per cent., which iron can take up by direct contact in the process of cementation is the same as that obtained by the diffusion process. It is therefore necessary to admit the molecular migration of carbon by diffusion into the mass of solid iron. These two processes must therefore play a part in the practice of cementation. Iron at the temp. of cementation is said to behave as a very viscous liquid in which the mobility of the molecules is shown by the tendency to form a coarsely crystalline structure when the iron is heated for a long time at a high enough temp. Carbon has a tendency to migrate from more highly carburized zones to less carburized zones. This agrees with the observations of J. B. J. D. Boussingault on the molecular migration of other elements—sulphur, phosphorus, silicon, and arsenic—in iron and steel. The movements of carbon in steel were discussed by W. E. Day, and W. Metcalf and J. W. Langley, and F. W. Adams. T. H. Byron showed that the carbide is formed by the action of blast-furnace gases ; and H. C. H. Carpenter and C. C. Smith, that a carbide, probably Fe_3C, is formed by the action of carbon monoxide on iron at about 650°. The formation of this carbide is hindered by the presence of carbon dioxide, and favoured by the presence of hydrogen. M. L. Becker studied the carburization of iron by the gaseous carbon oxides.

J. Garnier in a memoir, *Action de l'électricité sur la carburation du fer par cémenta-tion*, reported that he had placed a bar of steel containing only 0·1 per cent. of carbon, and a rod of gas carbon, end to end in a refractory tube and the two were well insulated. The tube was then heated at 900° to 1000°, and a current of

55 ampères and 7 volts was passed from the carbon to the steel.   After three hours it was found that that part of the iron opposed to the carbon cut glass easily, and a section showed that cementation had taken place to a depth of about 10 mm., whilst the carbon was corroded at the surface of contact.   Two bars of steel were then packed side by side in wood-charcoal with a space of 10 mm. between them, and were heated at 900° to 1000° for three hours, a current of 55 ampères and 2·5 volts being passed from one to the other.   It was found that the bar which served as the anode was practically unaffected, whilst in that which played the part of the cathode cementation had occurred to a considerable depth.   It would seem, therefore, that at about 1000° the cementation of iron takes place with very great rapidity under the influence of a comparatively weak electric current.   Attempts to accelerate cementation by means of an electric current, applied independently of its heating effect, were made by R. K. Boyle, G. Mars, and A. Hillairet.

G. P. Royston stated that below the Ar_1-arrest carbon has no tendency to diffuse into iron.   The limit of saturation at 700° corresponds with 6·9 per cent. of carbon, and, according to E. H. Saniter, the limit at 900° is 2·95 per cent.   F. Osmond pointed out that the limit of carburization of solid iron at a given temp. represents the solubility of cementite at that temp.; and at about 670°, the recalescence temp., this limit is 0·9 per cent., and this increases with a rise of temp.   The limits of solubility do not represent definite compounds $Fe_{14}C$, $Fe_{24}C$, etc., otherwise there would be an indefinitely large number of such compounds.   One of J. O. Arnold's micrographs shows an abrupt variation in the concentration of the strata corresponding with the surface of contact of the hypereutectoidal and eutectoidal steel— vide infra, Fig. 70.   He supposed that the diffusion of carbon takes place in two ways: the first begins at about 750°, the Ar_2-arrest, between iron and the alleged subcarbide, $Fe_{24}C$, whilst the second takes place above 950° between the normal carbide, Fe_3C, and the subcarbide, $Fe_{24}C$.   This shows how, at 800°, it is not possible to increase cementation beyond 0·9 per cent. carbon, the proportion in $Fe_{24}C$, and why the cementation must be conducted at higher temp. if a more highly carburized steel is required.   J. O. Arnold and A. McWilliam reported that when pure iron at 950° to 1050° is in contact with iron containing 1·5 per cent. of copper, aluminium, silicon, arsenic, chromium, and tungsten, no diffusion of these elements occurred in 10 hrs., but with carbon the percentage diffusion was 0·50 ; with sulphur, 0·10 ; with phosphorus, 0·095 ; and with nickel, 0·11.   For the effect of various elements on the velocity of cementation, vide infra.   S. C. Spalding, and J. Sorenson compared the rate of penetration in various kinds of carbon and alloy steels. G. Takahashi studied the relation between the quantity and depth of carburization.

F. W. Harbord, A. S. Stansfield, E. H. Saniter, and A. Ledebur doubt the hypothesis of diffusion involving the dubious subcarbide, particularly when the phenomena can be explained simply by the passage of carbon from molecules richer in it to those containing a smaller amount, by a process entirely analogous to that of diffusion in saline soln.   G. Takahashi concluded that the carburization of steel is not due to the diffusion of carbon monoxide, but to the direct diffusion of nascent carbon atoms produced by the decomposition of that gas.   H. Louis suggested that the diffusion of nickel into solid iron may be due to the formation of a nickel carbonyl.

In conformity with a suggestion of H. W. Stein, H. Caron tried to establish the hypothesis that the process of industrial cementation is always due to the action of volatile cyanides—volatile cyanides hypothesis—the cyanides acting as carriers of carbon to the iron.   The work of H. Caron was discussed by P. Nicolardot.   H. Caron obtained no cementation when iron is heated with carbon in the presence of hydrogen, carbon dioxide, nitrogen, and air.   In this H. Caron went wrong.   He attributed the carburization he obtained with ammonia gas to the preliminary formation of ammonium cyanide and he found that ammonium cyanide alone is a powerful cementing agent.   He also found that with carbon in the presence of alkalies and alkaline earths which can form cyanides in air cementation occurs.   The favourable effects obtained with a mixture of barium carbonate and carbon were attributed to the preliminary formation of barium cyanide. Wood-charcoal was supposed to act in virtue of its forming cyanides by the action of carbon and the nitrogen from the air on the ashes of the carbon. C. Binks also concluded that in order to carburize iron it is necessary for nitrogen (*e.g.* ammonia) and carbon (*e.g.* ethylene) to act simultaneously; no cementation occurred with carbon, carbon monoxide, ammonia, or ethylene alone. H. Caron emphasized that the more easily the carburizing agent is decomposed the greater is the concentration of the carbon in the cemented iron ; thus ammonium cyanide is the most effective cementing agent among the cyanides, and is the one most easily decomposed. L. Cailletet did not find cyanogen or cyanides in his analysis of the gases present in the cementation boxes.

E. Frémy considered that nitrogen is a necessary constituent of steel—*nitrogen hypothesis*—since the gas has been always found to be occluded in steel ; he went so far as to say that iron is converted into steel (*acière*) by absorbing nitrogen (*azotant*) in the presence of carbon, and that steel is changed to iron (*désacière*) by removing its nitrogen (*désazotant*) by hydrogen ; the function of nitrogen is not only that of forming cyanides, which carry the carbon in a state of combination into the pores of the iron, where the iron absorbs the carbon in the nascent state, but also that of serving as a vehicle for the penetration of the carbon into the iron, and taking part directly in the formation of steel, since it forms a kind of cyanogen compound which is an essential constituent of steel. He regarded steel not as a simple carbide but as a nitrogenized iron carbide. E. Frémy's hypothesis excited some interest, but H. Caron's experiments on the cementation of iron by hydrocarbons showed that the nitrogen hypothesis is untenable. H. Caron, however, not only disproved E. Frémy's hypothesis, but he also considerably weakened his own. For instance, in cementations obtained with purified methane and other hydrocarbons cyanides are absent. He therefore said that hydrocarbons, on account of their too easy decomposability, carburize the iron too much, transforming it into cast iron instead of steel ; and added that the alkali cyanides are the only compounds capable of producing a true cementation under industrial conditions. F. Margueritte in a controversy with H. Caron showed that cementation can occur (i) by simple contact without the intervention of nitrogen ; and (ii) by the action of carbon monoxide. H. Caron said that charcoal, under industrial conditions, becomes exhausted with use, and is then incapable of carburizing iron. This is not likely to be the case if, as F. Margueritte supposed, carbon and carbon monoxide are the most active agents in industrial cementation. H. Caron attributed the decreased efficiency of used charcoal to the loss by volatilization of alkalies, for the charcoal can be rendered inactive by washing it with acid to remove at least some of the alkali ; the activity of the charcoal can be restored by the addition of alkali ; and the varieties of charcoal richest in alkali are the most efficacious. F. Margueritte attributed the exhaustion to its acquiring a more compact atomic structure by the prolonged heating, a view favoured by R. Mannesmann. H. Caron admitted that carbon monoxide can produce a slight cementation, but he said that it is not produced at a red-heat, but rather during the cooling, when the decomposition of carbon monoxide is possible. C. E. Jullien said that carbon alone can carburize iron, but carbon monoxide does not do so under industrial conditions. J. Percy, on the other hand, found that purified sugar charcoal, freed from occluded gases, cannot carburize iron, except at a temp. high enough to melt the product. There is thus one school which assumes that a gas is necessary for the continued diffusion of carbon—*gaseous diffusion theory*—and another school which believes that the carbon penetrates the metal without the intervention of a gas—*solid diffusion theory.*

R. Mannesmann showed that the *concentration* of the carbon in the cemented crust and the *velocity* of penetration of the carbon vary with the progress of the cementation. He showed that the variation in the gradual increase in the velocity of penetration agrees rather with the hypothesis that the action is mainly due to the molecular migration of carbon, and is not due solely to the action of gases, for in this case the cementation should proceed with increasing slowness as the deeper layers of the mass are reached. When the cementation is not effected by free carbon, but by a compound of carbon, the degree of carburization is proportional to the difference between the affinity of carbon for iron and the affinity of carbon for the substances with which it is combined. Hence, at a given temp., free carbon can give a higher carburization than when the contact is sufficiently prolonged. The cyanides are specially suited for obtaining thin, superficial cemented layers, and to cases where it is desired to work at low temp., where the molecular migration of carbon is slow ; solid carbon is best for producing deep, highly carburized cementations. He found wood-charcoal does its work faster than graphite. The velocity of cementation was found to be smaller the greater is the initial concentration of carbon in the steel to be cemented ; but with an equal velocity of cementation the work of cementation required for saturation is less the greater is the proportion of carbon in the sample to be treated. Owing to the lowering softening temp. with increasing proportions of carbon in steel, and since an increased mobility facilitates the migration of the carbon, the cementation is effected more rapidly the harder the steel, and steel is cemented more rapidly than iron. In general, it is considered that the gases formed in the cementation boxes containing carbon are so dil. as to render negligible their carburizing action, even if some of them—*e.g.* carbon monoxide— have a stronger carburizing action when sufficiently concentrated. The carburization produced by the penetration of gases into the iron plays but a small part in the process of cementation, and is limited to a superficial zone of small depth. The main work is done by the molecular migration of carbon into the deeper layers of iron—*vide infra.*

G. Charpy showed that by heating filings of soft iron in fused potassium cyanide at about 650° for about 86 hrs. it is possible to transform the metal completely into iron carbide containing 6·67 per cent. of carbon. At higher temp. the iron carbide decomposes, giving graphite. Thus steel heated in a current of coal gas for 64 hrs. at 1000° gives a product with 8·32 per cent. of carbon, of which 7·66 per cent. is graphite ; and with carbon monoxide for 36 hrs. at 1000° the product has 9·27 per cent. of carbon, of which 8·27 per cent. is graphite. Hence, added G. Charpy, the cementation is not limited by the solubility of carbon in iron. It is possible to obtain either the transformation of iron into the carbide or the indefinite transformation of carbon into graphite. G. Charpy heated iron in a slow current of purified carbon monoxide, and observed that cementation occurs at 560° ; in 8 hrs. a deposit of carbon was formed at 560°, 600°, and 715° ; while in 2 to 3 hrs.' heating the following relative weights of carbon were fixed by the metal :

	825°	935°	1025°	1085°	1125°	1175°	1185°	1190°
Carbon .	0·60	0·60	0·58	0·58	0·47	0·51	0·47	0·33

Hence, above 750° no deposit of carbon is formed and the cemented metal remains polished and bright ; the velocity of cementation (not penetration) does not increase appreciably above 900°. The cementation is limited if instead of working in a current of gas the steel is heated in a limited quantity of carbon monoxide, for in that case cementation ceases when the proportion of carbon dioxide formed reaches a certain limiting value : $2CO \rightleftharpoons C + CO_2$. He inferred that the cementation can be conducted in such a way that the quantity of carbon absorbed is automatically regulated by using as cementing substance a continuous current of a gaseous mixture containing definite proportions of carbon monoxide and dioxide, cyanogen and nitrogen, or hydrocarbons and hydrogen. F. Giolitti could not truly cement low-carbon steels below 780°. It is here necessary to distinguish different meanings of the term carburization. With cementation proper there is a cemented zone which not only contains an increased proportion of carbon (carburization), but possesses the characteristic structure of steel having a high carbon content. This structure results from the segregation in iron during the cooling of a solid soln. of carbon to a state of cementite, and this soln. cannot be formed below 780°. This temp. therefore represents the lower limit at which true cementation can occur.

L. Guillet stated that cements composed of carbon alone—*e.g.* sugar carbon, wood-charcoal, or graphite—cannot act by a simple soln. of the carbon by the iron in contact with it, for pure carbon does not cement iron in vacuo—*vide supra*. The subject was discussed by O. Bauer. L. Guillet, and R. Bruch observed that the velocity of penetration varies greatly with the temp. In some cases a difference of 100° can double the velocity of penetration. F. Giolitti measured the depth of the cemented zones at different temp. for different periods of time when soft steel is cemented by a mixture of ground wood-charcoal, potassium ferrocyanide, and barium carbonate. The results are summarized in Fig. 72. Other curves show how the temp. of cementation and the time occupied by the operation greatly influence the form of the curves representing the distribution of carbon in the cemented zones. L. Guillet showed that a cement containing carbon can act by means of carbon monoxide formed by the action of air in the cementation boxes ; but carbon monoxide acts slowly in virtue of the reaction $2CO \rightleftharpoons C + CO_2$; carbon dioxide has a decomposing action. R. Bruch said that the cementing action of carbon dioxide is nil. L. Guillet classified cements into (i) those whose activity is due to carbon monoxide ; (ii) those whose activity is due to the presence of a cyanide ; and (iii) those whose activity is due to hydrocarbons. The cyanogen group when decomposed liberates carbon ; and the hydrocarbons act by dissociation. As a rule, at 1000° the velocity of penetration of carbon is about the same for all cements, but at the beginning the velocity varies widely from cement to cement. L. Guillet believed that the active agent in every industrial cementation is a cyanide or a carbide, and not carbon alone ; on the contrary, A. Ledebur maintained that the active agent is carbon—*vide supra*. L. Guillet concluded that the velocity of penetration of carbon is independent of the initial proportion of carbon in hypo-eutectic steels ; it varies with different cements, but reaches the same limit with different cements after acting for 8 hrs. at 1000°. Both H. Caron, and L. Guillet attribute the increased efficiency of wood-charcoal produced by the addition of about 5 per cent. of potassium carbonate to the formation of potassium cyanide in the cementation boxes. In agreement with L. Cailletet, G. Charpy observed no evidence that cyanides are formed during cementation with wood-charcoal, with a mixture of wood-charcoal and barium carbonate, and with animal-charcoal ; only at about 1050° are cyanides formed with the mixture of charcoal and barium carbonate, but cementation occurs between 900° and 1000°. Cyanides are not necessary for cementation ; the observations of H. Caron on the influence of alkalies on cementation by wood-charcoal are explained as readily by the intervention of carbon monoxide as of cyanides. I. Musatti and M. Croce said that the presence of nitrogen in steel or of nitrogen compounds in the cementation gases accelerates carburization by carbon monoxide. According to W. P. Fishel and J. F. Wooddell, the reaction $3Fe + 2CO \rightleftharpoons Fe_3C + CO_2$ sets in between 800° and 1100°, and the depth of penetration increases with temp., whilst the maximum carbon in the outer " case " decreases even though the total carbon increases ; both carbon monoxide and dioxide penetrate iron very slowly at 950° and 1100°, and this at a rate which does not explain the depth of the case produced by carbon monoxide.

By cementing a fine wire of soft steel at 1100° L. Guillet obtained a concentration of 1·9 per cent. of carbon. The structure was uniform and was characterized by the network of cementite usually found in highly carburized steel. A repetition of the cementation resulted in the agglomeration of the cementite network and a re-absorption of carbon. With steel containing over 7 per cent. of nickel it is possible to obtain by cementation a zone with over 0·8 per cent. of carbon and with the characteristic structure of tempered carbon steel, while the external, untempered

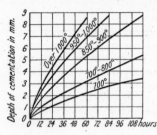

FIG. 72.—The Distribution of Carbon in Iron during Cementation.

layer has the martensite structure and hardness of tempered steel. Steels with over 30 per cent. of nickel have the γ-structure, and are cemented at lower temp. than carbon steels. Indeed, a γ-iron steel can be cemented by fused potassium cyanide at 450°. The diffusion of carbon into γ-iron occurs even at ordinary temp. Thus, such a steel cemented at 1000° contained at the surface 1·22 to 1·35 per cent. of carbon, and after 6 months, 0·85 to 0·92 per cent. This showed that the carbon in the periphery continued dissolving in the mass. L. Guillet measured the influence of various elements on the velocity of penetration of carbon, under identical conditions, into steels with 1·5 per cent. of carbon. The carbon showed a velocity of penetration of 0·9 mm. in a given time. With 2 and 5 per cent. nickel the velocity of penetration was respectively 0·7 and 0·5 mm.; with 0·5 to 1·0 per cent. manganese, 1·1 and 1·2 mm.; with 1·0 and 2·0 per cent. chromium, 1·0 and 1·1 mm.; with 0·5, 1·0, and 2·0 per cent. tungsten, 0·9, 0·9, and 2·0 mm.; with 1·0 and 2·0 per cent. molybdenum, 0·9 and 1·1 mm.; with 1·0 and 2·0 per cent. titanium, 0·8 and 0·7 mm.; with 0·5, 1·0, 2·0, and 5·0 per cent. silicon, 0·6, 0·5, 0·4, and 0·0 mm.; and with 1·0 and 3·0 per cent. aluminium, 0·4 and 0·2 mm. Hence, the substances which retard cementation are those which dissolve in the iron—e.g. silicon, titanium, aluminium, and nickel—while those which accelerate cementation form complex carbides—e.g. chromium, molybdenum, tungsten, and manganese. There was a discussion between L. Guillet, and A. Ledebur on some of these results; and H. le Chatelier added that it can be regarded as certain that in cementation many gaseous substances permit the rapid transport of carbon to the iron without direct contact of these two substances, and that the diffusion of carbon in contact with iron is also possible. The disappearance of temper-carbon on heating, for instance, is a proof of it, and the only point open to a difference of opinion is whether carbon penetrates directly into iron in the industrial process of cementation.

F. Margueritte observed that most of the common elements exert some influence on carburization, but usually the effect is small. A. Sauveur, and W. J. Merten inferred from L. Guillet's work that elements which form double carbides usually accelerate carbon absorption, whilst those elements which remain in solid soln. with ferrite have the opposite effect. G. Tammann observed that molybdenum, tungsten, nickel, manganese, and cobalt favoured the penetration of carbon up to a certain maximum, and the effect then diminished. Antimony, and vanadium retarded penetration; whilst aluminium made no appreciable difference. S. C. Spalding found that high percentages of phosphorus and sulphur retarded carbon penetration, but chromium had the opposite effect. B. F. Shepherd also found that chromium-vanadium steels carburize more readily than carbon steels.

J. Lecarme showed that the brittleness of cemented steel is not due to the heating which accompanies cementation; and that the cementation which occurs at the surface is accompanied by a chemical transformation of the middle of the mass which appears homogeneous throughout. H. Braune, J. Kirner, and A. Petrén and J. Grabe studied the effect of nitrogen on the mechanical properties of cemented steel—vide infra, action of nitrogen on steel. R. Bruch concluded that cementation is a process of diffusion or solution of the carbon which results in a continuous and uniform increase in the carbon content in passing from the nucleus to the periphery. J. O. Arnold found the process discontinuous—vide supra; and R. Bruch's own diagram, Fig. 73 (×10 and then reduced to one-fourth), shows that with a steel cemented by acetylene, at 1050° for 7 hrs., there is an abrupt transition from the external hypereutectoidal zone, rich in cementite, to an intermediate eutectoidal zone of pearlite and a hypoeutectoidal nucleus. F. Giolitti observed cases in which the outer or hypereutectoidal layer is characterized by cementite and pearlite, and has 1·27 to 1·33 per cent. of carbon; the second or eutectoidal layer contains pearlite alone, and has about 0·9 per cent. of carbon; and the third or hypoeutectoidal layer is characterized by the presence of ferrite and pearlite. J. Kirner reported that with nitrogenous cements a special constituent is present in proportions which increase with increasing amount of nitrogen. He called it **flavite,** and said that it behaves like a solid soln. in steels etched with picric acid, and it then has a yellowish-brown colour and stands out in clear contrast to the other constituents. It disappears when the steels are hardened. B. Strauss showed that flavite can

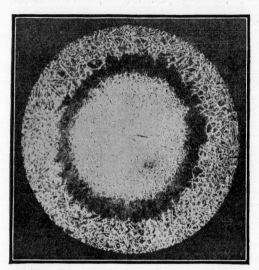

be distinguished by heat tinting. A. Fry inferred that the composition of the eutectoid is 1·5 per cent. nitrogen, and the eutectoidal temp., 580°. He called the eutectoid *braunite.* A. Bramley and F. W. Haywood found that the iron-iron nitride eutectoid has 2 per cent. of nitrogen, and that the eutectoid temp. is 608°. All the structures characteristic of the iron-iron carbide system can be obtained with the iron-iron nitride system, but they are finer in texture. As emphasized by H. Fay, and G. R. Brophy and S. B. Leiter, case-hardening is partly a nitrogenizing and partly a carburizing process. G. F. Hinkens, and S. Satoh studied the cementation of steel with nitrogen or nitrogenous materials—*vide infra,* the action of nitrogen on iron.

Fig. 73.—Three Zones in a Section of Cemented Steel Wire (R. Bruch).

The structural changes which occur in steel during cementation, etc., were discussed by H. Brearley, J. Sorenson, C. H. Herty and co-workers, and C. W. Bildt ; and observations on the cementation process, by M. Partiot, H. Braune, E. F. Lake, J. F. Springer, O. M. Becker, E. F. Davis, S. A. Grayson, L. Grenet, H. A. Vanvught, E. R. Markham, H. de Nolly and L. Veyret, A. Sauveur and G. A. Reinhardt, G. S. McFarland, H. M. Crawford, L. Aitchison, T. G. Selleck, R. M. P. Hamilton, T. Murakami and H. Sekiguchi, C. Kluytmans, H. Schagrin, G. S. Scott, C. J. G. Malmberg, W. T. Griffiths, J. Cournot, A. Jaeschke, F. W. Rowe, E. G. Mahin and R. C. Spencer, W. E. Day, P. Henry, D. Uno, W. J. Merten, H. Müller, H. Weiss, B. F. Shepherd, F. Hodson, F. Kurek, F. Robin, H. L. Heathcote, T. Baker, H. Neuhauss, H. Rodman, J. D. Gat, H. Swain, C. O. Bannister and W. J. Lambert, S. A. Grayson, J. Kirner, S. Epstein and H. S. Rawdon, A. C. Sladky and A. F. Schultz, A. M. Portevin, J. C. Olsen and W. S. Wiessenbach, R. G. Guthrie, A. J. Lindberg, D. A. Holt, I. Musatti and L. Dainelli, H. B. Northrup, F. Hebler, F. Rapatz, R. G. Roshong, M. T. Lothrop, and J. H. Nead and J. N. Bourg.

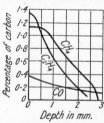

Fig. 74.—The Concentration of Carbon in the Successive Zones Cemented respectively by Ethylene, Methane, and Carbon Monoxide.

F. Giolitti's observations on the percentage of carbon in successive layers 0·5 mm. thick when steel at 1000° is cemented in a current of ethylene, methane, and carbon monoxide are summarized in Fig. 74. With carbon monoxide the conc. of the carbon does not attain the eutectoidal value 0·9 per cent., and it decreases uniformly and slowly from the surface inwards. Here the conc. of the carbon in the deeper layers varies so little from that in the external layers that it is doubtful if the carbon has simply diffused into the deeper layers ; the cementation has been effected by the penetration of the gas into the steel in co-operation with diffusion. With methane and ethylene the external layer is highly carburized, for it attains a value exceeding 0·9 per cent., and as in the case of carbon alone, the distribution of the carbon is characteristic of diffusion by difference of con-centration. In general, other things being equal, the conc. of the carbon in the cemented zone is smaller the higher is the temp., for the reaction is exothermic ; the conc. of carbon in the cemented zone is smaller the lower is the press. of the gas, because the reaction $2CO \rightleftharpoons CO_2 + C$ is attended by a decrease in volume ; and the conc. of the carbon in the cemented zone increases with an increase in the quantity of carbon monoxide which comes in contact with unit surface of steel. The reaction occurs under such conditions that no carbon is deposited, so that the free carbon formed in the reaction $2CO \rightleftharpoons CO_2 + C$ dissolves entirely in the γ-iron. This means that the speed at which carbon is formed is less than the speed at which carbon dissolves in the γ-iron. The carbon dissolves in γ-iron until it has attained a state of equilibrium. The velocity of penetration of carbon by soln. in the γ-iron and the penetration of carbon monoxide into the metallic mass are favoured by increasing the quantity of carbon monoxide which comes in contact with the surface in a given time. F. Eisenstecken studied the cementation of iron by methane.

Hard, homogeneous, quenched steels have a characteristic fracture ; but soft steels, carburized by cementation in a more or less deep surface layer, after being subjected to a hardening treatment, present a totally different fracture. The steel breaks along a surface almost parallel to the external surface of the cemented steel, and instead of lenticular masses detaching themselves as in homogeneous steels, the whole surface yields layers more or less thick according to the depth of the cementation. The phenomenon is called *expoliation*. The surface along which the steel expoliates corresponds with zones possessing a different structure or grain. The expoliation was shown by F. Giolitti to be due to sudden variations in the concentration of the carbon. To avoid as much as possible the formation of these layers the cementation should be carried out in the presence of carbon monoxide. The use of cements which furnish carbon monoxide also hinders the formation of hypereutectoidal zones with their dangerous brittleness. These facts also show how the different effects are produced by the so-called gradual or mild cements and by the violent cements.

G. Charpy found that cementation is rather more intense when wood-charcoal is used as a cement in an atmosphere of carbon monoxide than when it is employed in the presence of its own occluded air. F. Giolitti and L. Astorri concluded that the reports by L. Guillet and others that solid carbon does not cement iron are due to lack of sufficiently intimate contact between iron and carbon, for γ-iron dissolves and is cemented by solid carbon. An increase in the pressure of the carbon on the iron, by favouring closer contact, gives an increased cementation. F. Weyl, L. Guillet and C. Griffiths, and F. Giolitti and L. Astorri showed that the direct action of carbon on iron is very small ; G. Charpy and S. Bonnerot found that the action is nil. In either case, contrary to the opinions of R. Mannes-mann, W. C. Roberts-Austen, and A. Ledebur, the direct action of carbon in industrial cementation must be negligibly small. The preponderating effect is produced by the simultaneous action of carbon and gaseous cementing agents. With wood-charcoal without carbon monoxide, at 100° for 4 hrs., the hyper-eutectoidal layer was 0·7 mm. thick, the eutectoidal layer was 0·6 mm. thick, and the hypoeutectoidal layer, 0·2 mm. thick, whereas when assisted by carbon monoxide no hypereutectoidal layer was observed, while the eutectoidal and hypoeutectoidal layers were respectively 1·0 and 0·7 mm. thick. Working with six litres of carbon monoxide mixed with the following proportions of liquid benzene, at 1000° for 4 hrs., the thicknesses of the different layers were found to be respec-tively :

Benzene . . .	1	1·5	2	15	38 c.c.
Depth { Hypereutectoid	0	0·2	0·2	0·7	0·7
Eutectoid .	0·7	0·6	0·6	0·4	0·4
Hypoeutectoid	0·5	0·2	0·2	0·4	0·4

No deposit of carbon was observed in the first experiment, but in the other cases the deposition of carbon became greater as the proportion of benzene increased. It is therefore possible to regulate the concentration of carbon in the external layer from the minimum obtained with carbon monoxide alone to the maximum obtained with hydrocarbon vapour alone. The results show that it is possible to graduate the concentration of carbon in the cemented zones. With carbon in an atm. of nitrogen the results resemble those obtained with carbon in contact with carbon monoxide. J. Kirner showed that with some nitrogenous cements considerable proportions of nitrogen diffuse into the steel, and that nitrogen exercises a marked influence on the cementation. Experiments on the equalizing action of carbon monoxide in the cementation of iron in contact with carbon were made by F. Giolitti and G. Tavanti. The results also agree with the observations of A. M. Portevin and H. Berjot. F. Giolitti also showed that by carburizing the metal in the usual way so as to produce a high concentration of carbon near the surface, and subsequently treating the metal with carbon monoxide alone, the carbon will be distributed more uniformly and the dangerous effects of a hypereutectoidal zone minimized.

F. Giolitti and F. Carnevali found that by increasing the press. of the gaseous medium—carbon monoxide, ethylene, and methane—the velocity of cementation, and the concentration of the carbon in the cemented zones are increased. They also devised a process of cementation by compressed carbon monoxide and free carbon. A superficial oxidation of the case-hardened steel was sometimes observed. G. Charpy studied the action of carbon monoxide at 1000° on chromium, manganese, and various chromium steels and chromium-nickel steels, and concluded that with the various steels in the form of filings the chromium decomposes the carbon monoxide, and there is a simultaneous oxidation of the chromium and a carburiza-into of the iron; the two elements behave as if they were isolated. If, instead of working with filings, pieces of tolerable dimensions are employed, the same phenomena do not recur; the oxidation of the chromium is restricted to the surface layer, beneath which cementation proceeds regularly by diffusion. At 1000° carbon monoxide carburizes iron, tungsten, and possibly also nickel, but it oxidizes chromium and manganese. F. Giolitti and F. Carnevali, however, have shown that the phenomena are more readily explained in the light of R. Schenck's diagram, Fig. 31, discussed in connection with the reduction of iron oxides (q.v.). In the case of cementation with carbon monoxide and dioxide in the presence of wood-charcoal, it follows that at press. above those corresponding with O—the point of intersection of the curves 4 and 5—the simultaneous formation of ferrosic oxide and a solid soln. occurs in the presence of wood-charcoal, where the solid soln. has a concentration of carbon in equilibrium with $2CO \rightleftharpoons CO_2 + C$. At press. ranging between those corresponding with O and Q—the point of intersection of curves 3 and 5—there is a simultaneous formation of ferrous oxide and of the solid soln., also in the presence of wood charcoal. At press. lower than those corresponding with Q the solid soln. is formed alone, also in the presence of wood-charcoal. Only at press. lower than those corresponding with Q can the cementa-tion take place unaccompanied by the oxidation of the metal. Hence, if the press. of the gas is large enough, phenomena analogous to those observed by G. Charpy with chromium steels will also occur with pure iron or with carbon steels, without assuming the selective action implied in G. Charpy's words. G. Takahashi, S. Matsubara, and F. Giolitti discussed the chemical equilibria between the iron, carbon, and oxygen during cementation—vide supra, reactions in the blast-furnace.

The general results of the work of F. Giolitti and co-workers show that (i) the direct action of carbon is exceedingly slight, and it is negligibly small under industrial conditions. (ii) The cyanides, ferrocyanides, etc., exercise on iron a specific carburizing action, but the activity of cements containing free carbon and alkali or alkaline earth carbonate is not due to the formation of volatile cyanides by the action of atm. nitrogen, but to the formation of carbon monoxide by the action of carbon on carbon dioxide produced by the dissociation of the carbonates. (iii) The carburizing action of nitrogen in the presence of carbon is negligibly small under industrial conditions. (iv) Hydrocarbons exert a direct carburization of iron, but the carburizing action of the finely-divided carbon deposited by decomposing hydrocarbons on the surface of iron has not been established. (v) Carbon monoxide carburizes iron directly at the temp. of the cementation. (vi) The specific action of carbon monoxide is intensified when the gas acts on iron in the presence of free carbon. This specific action—modified by other carburizing substances present, e.g. hydrocarbons and cyanides—preponderates enormously above all other in all cements in which carbon monoxide is present or can be formed. F. Giolitti and G. Tavanti reported that in the cementation of steel by gases, say ethylene at 1050°, the curves showing the concentration of carbon at different depths below the surface of the metal show a step with about 1·2 per cent. of carbon, and the phenomena was regarded as an effect of liquation. A. Bramley and co-workers were unable to verify this observation.

H. Caron observed that besides barium carbonate other carbonates, e.g. those of strontium, lithium, sodium, potassium, etc., favour the cementation of iron and steel. F. Hebler found that no better results were obtained by wood-charcoal than with other carbonaceous materials, and that the degree of cementation is scarcely affected by the addition of chalk to the carbon, but the thickness of the hardened layer progressively increases by the use of the carbonates of sodium, strontium, and barium. The subject was studied by J. Herbert. The explanation of F. Giolitti, A. R. Page, J. F. Shadgen, and J. Tetschenko-Tschopiwsky assumes that the effect is due to the decomposition of the carbonate and the conversion of the carbon dioxide into the monoxide. H. Rodman, however, thought that the carbon monoxide so produced is less important than the residual oxide. G. Takahashi found the carburization of iron or steel in the presence of carbon is more energetic in the presence of the carbonate than it is in the presence of a brisk current of carbon monoxide ; that the carbonate may accelerate the action even when it has not suffered dissociation ; that in a current of carbon monoxide the carbonate accelerates the carburization process even in the absence of solid carbon ; and that the formation of carbon monoxide by the direct reaction between the carbonate and solid carbon is not the main factor involved in the process. He assumed that the carbonate separates carbon from carbon monoxide ; that the velocity of carburization increases as the amount of separated carbon coming in contact with the surface of iron or steel increases ; and that any substance which favours the separation of carbon from carbon monoxide accelerates the speed of carburization. The carbon liberated from carbon monoxide easily reacts with carbon dioxide. The carbonates do not energize the process of carburization if no carbon monoxide is present. The active carbon liberated from carbon monoxide diffuses readily into iron and steel. The energizing action of the carbonates is therefore due to the separation of active carbon by a reaction between the carbonates and carbon monoxide and the subsequent diffusion of this carbon into the iron or steel.

H. W. B. Roozeboom used the phenomenon of the formation of free cementite in the direct carburization of cementite against the hypothesis that cementite is metastable at the temp. of cementation; but G. Charpy and P. Pingault found that the cementite is relatively stable—vide infra—and F. Osmond, G. Charpy, and C. Benedicks showed that the cementite may be formed by the oscillations of temp. which are inevitable during industrial cementation. The cementite separates during the cooling alternation of temp. The results were confirmed by F. Giolitti and G. Scavia. They showed that there is a difference in the rate of the dissolution of cementite in γ-iron and the rate at which carbon dissolves in iron by cementation. The iron carbide set free during the cooling is in a form best adapted for rapid dissolution in the iron. In the heating phase carbon is dissolved—as cementite—by cementation, and cementite also passes into soln.

In the cooling phase cementite separates out again. As a result, when there is an oscillation of the temp., there is an increase in the carbon present in the cemented zone above the value corresponding with the conditions of equilibrium realized when the temp. is constant. The phenomenon is complicated by the speed of dissociation of carbon monoxide during the lowering of the temp., the speed of diffusion of the gases in iron at different temp., the speed of the reaction of the carbon of the solid soln. on the mixtures of carbon monoxide and dioxide, at various concentrations and temperatures, etc.

A. Bramley and A. J. Jinkings showed that in the cementation of iron and steel with carbon monoxide the rate of flow of the gas affects the weight of carbon introduced, but not the depth of penetration of the carbon. The period of carburization affects the weight of carbon introduced, and if the carburizing period increases in geometrical progression, the depth of penetration also increases in this way, but with a different common ratio. The amount of carbon absorbed increases continuously with a rise of temp. between 800° and 1000°; the depth of penetration also varies, increasing in a linear manner with rise of temp. The concentration-depth curves are steeper the lower the temp. The weight of carbon introduced diminishes uniformly with an increase in the original conc. of the carbon. A steel with 1·54 per cent. of carbon cannot be further carburized by carbon monoxide at 950°. The concentration-depth curves are flatter the higher is the initial conc. of the carbon in the steel. The depth of penetration of the carbon being independent of the rate of flow of the gas and of the initial conc. of the carbon, the depth to which the carbon penetrates at constant temp. and press. is independent of the gradient of the carbon concentration.

A. Bramley and G. H. Beeby likewise studied the cementation of steel with the nitrogenous vapours of pyridine or methyl cyanide in a current of carbon monoxide. The efficiency of methyl cyanide increased progressively up to 1100°, but pyridine became less efficient above 1000°. The conc. of carbon in the cemented zone when methyl cyanide was used, was increased by a rise of temp., but the conc. of nitrogen was decreased. In the case of pyridine, an increase of either the period or temp. of cementation causes the conc. of both nitrogen and carbon to rise to a maximum and then fall again. The maximum with nitrogen was attained at a lower temp. than with carbon.

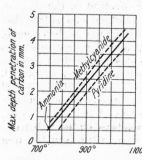

FIG. 75.—Depth of Penetrations of Carbon with Carbon Monoxide associated with Pyridine, Ammonia, and Methyl Cyanide.

A. Bramley and G. Turner obtained results analogous to those obtained with pyridine by adding ammonia to the carbon dioxide. A comparison of the results is shown in Fig. 75. They found that the carburizing action of the mixtures of carbon monoxide and different proportions of ammonia is much greater than that of carbon monoxide alone. The stimulating action of ammonia is attributed partly to the formation of cyanides and partly to the influence of the hydrogen formed by the decomposition of the ammonia on the carbon monoxide and carbon dioxide equilibrium. The distribution of nitrogen in the cemented zones resembles closely that which results from cementations made with mixtures of carbon monoxide and methyl cyanide, but the way in which the carbon is distributed resembles more the effect produced by pyridine. Mixtures of carbon monoxide and hydrogen have stronger carburizing properties than carbon monoxide itself, but not so intense as the corresponding mixtures containing ammonia.

A. Bramley and G. Lawton studied the carburization of steel with the vapours of hydrocarbons—xylene, toluene, benzene, and petrol—along with carbon monoxide or nitrogen. They found that the depth of penetration of the carbon increased according to a linear law as the temp. of cementation was raised; as the

period of cementation was increased in geometrical progression, the depth of penetration increased in the same way, but with a different common ratio ; the depth
of penetration was not much affected by the rate at which the carburizing gas mixture
was passed through the furnace, but it appeared to be slightly greater the stronger
the cementing agent used. This is not in agreement with A. Bramley and
A. J. Jinkings's experiment, where the hydrocarbon was carried into the cementation chamber by means of nitrogen ; it was found that uneven carburization was
produced under the same conditions as yielded uniformity when carbon monoxide
was used as the vehicle for introducing the hydrocarbon vapour. A. W. Machlet
cemented steel with propane and air under press.

A. Bramley and H. D. Lord showed that after bars of the same steel, carburized
to the same extent initially, had been reheated for a definite period at the same
temp., but in atmospheres differing greatly from one another, the redistribution
of carbon was the same in all cases. This result is taken to support the solid
diffusion theory, and to be incompatible with the gaseous diffusion theory.
A slight loss of carbon occurred in all cases when the carburized steels were
reheated.

The cementation of iron with the gas under pressure was studied by F. C. Langen-
berg ; with cyanogen, by W. J. Merten, and E. Pérot ; with cyanamide, by
P. W. Shimer, E. Pérot, and H. Fay ; with cyanides, by E. F. Davis, B. Jousset,
A. H. d'Arcambal, V. E. Hillman, F. Rapatz, H. B. Northrup, and G. R. Brophy
and S. B. Leiter—vide infra, nitridization of iron ; with ammonium formate, by
H. Reininger ; with fused sodium carbonate, by W. A. Jayme ; with methane,
or a mixture of hydrogen and methane or natural gas, by W. P. Sykes, and
F. Eisenstecken ; with blast-furnace gases, by T. H. Byron ; and with coal gas,
by W. Rohland, O. J. Wilbor and J. A. Comstock, and R. G. Guthrie and O. Wozasek.
P. Pingault observed that sodium cyanide does not cement iron at temp. up to
900° when air is absent, whilst grey cast iron heated with sodium cyanide at 675°
shows an outer zone from which all the carbon has been burned away. If fused
sodium cyanide be electrolyzed at 650° with soft steel electrodes, the anode with
a high enough current density gives indication of cementation. The effect of
dissolved or included oxides was studied by E. W. Ehn, and S. P. Rockwell and
F. Downes, H. W. McQuaid and E. W. Ehn.

The observations of P. Oberhoffer and E. Piwowarsky, A. Vita, E. Mauer, and
K. Iwase show that the amount of gas which can be absorbed by iron and steel
is very small, being only 0·05 grm. per 100 grms. at 1000°. This, said G. Takahashi,
is far too small to explain the observed rate of penetration of carbon into iron, and
he favours the hypothesis that the carbon monoxide, hydrocarbons, and cyanide
do their work by decomposing on the surface of the iron, and the principal
mechanism of carbon penetration is attributed to the diffusion of the nascent
carbon atoms into the body of the metal. If the carburization be effected by an
agent of the carbon monoxide system, or of the hydrocarbon system under the
same conditions, the distribution of the carbon is the same with different agents
irrespective of their difference in efficiency.

L. Guillet studied the cementation of **nickel-steels,** and, as previously indicated,
he measured the speed of penetration of carbon, and showed that when 7 per cent.
of nickel is present it is possible to obtain at the periphery a superficial zone with
over 1 per cent. of carbon, which, when not tempered, but allowed to cool slowly,
possesses the martensite structure and the hardness characteristic of tempered
steels. By prolonging the carburization until the periphery has 1·5 per cent. of
carbon, there is formed on the martensitic zone a superficial layer containing
γ-iron, which can be polished without loss. F. Giolitti and F. Carnevali also
studied this subject, and found that, other things being equal, (i) the course of
the cementation with steels containing 2 to 3 per cent. of nickel is virtually the
same as that of carbon steels ; (ii) when the proportion of nickel exceeds 3 per
cent., the maximum concentration of carbon in the cemented zones decreases

with an increase in the proportion of nickel in the steel; (iii) the variations in the concentration of carbon in the cemented zones are more uniform in nickel steels than in carbon steels, and the phenomenon of liquation in the solid soln. is less intense than with carbon steels; (iv) in pearlitic nickel steels the region of transition from the hypereutectoidal to the eutectoidal layer in the cemented zone corresponds to a carbon content of 0·60 to 0·65 per cent., which is lower than the corresponding eutectoidal zone of cemented carbon steels with 0·9 per cent. of carbon; (v) the specific action of carbon monoxide in the cementation of nickel steels is the same as it is with carbon steels; and (vi) the speed of cementation, that is, the depth attained by the carburized zone in a given time with carbon and carbon monoxide, is slightly higher for nickel steels than it is for carbon steels. W. T. Griffiths, J. N. Greenwood, J. G. R. Woodvine, and S. C. Spalding discussed the cementation of nickel steels.

L. Guillet measured the speed of penetration of carbon in the cementation of **manganese steels**—*vide supra*. In general, manganese steels behave like nickel steels, except that on cementing a steel with, say, 5 per cent. of manganese, so that the external layer contains 1 per cent. of carbon, a pearlitic core is obtained, then a little martensite, and the periphery is characterized by a great abundance of troostite. It is not therefore as hard as steel with 7 per cent. of nickel. S. C. Spalding, and A. A. Blue also made observations on the subject. L. Guillet, and S. C. Spalding measured the rate of penetration of carbon in **chromium steels**—*vide supra*. When a steel with 5 per cent. of chromium is cemented, a martensitic steel can be obtained, and, by sufficiently extending the operation, there is formed in the surface layer a complex iron-chromium carbide. G. Charpy's observations, supplemented by those of F. Giolitti and F. Carnevali, are indicated above. F. Giolitti and F. Carnevali also found that the cementation of a steel with 2·33 per cent. of chromium, with ethylene, carbon monoxide, or carbon and carbon monoxide, is similar to that with carbon steel. In general, however, the presence of chromium tends to increase the maximum concentration of the carbon in the cemented zones. L. Guillet, and S. C. Spalding measured the rate of penetration of carbon in **molybdenum steels,** and also in **tungsten steels** —*vide supra*. The cementation of tungsten steels produces the double carbide, or increases the proportion in which it already exists. L. Guillet, and S. C. Spalding measured the rate of penetration of carbon in **silicon steels**—*vide supra*. Steels with over 7 per cent. of silicon, or those with a smaller proportion if heated a sufficiently long time, contain all the carbon in the state of graphite, and they cannot be cemented. L. Guillet measured the rate of penetration of carbon in **titanium steels,** and also in **aluminium steels**—*vide supra*. E. W. Ehn studied the action of dissolved oxides on the case-hardening of steels; H. Lüpfert, the heat treatment of case-hardened steels.

Experienced workmen accustomed to particular types of steel and to a particular process of cementation can arrange bars of cemented steel into groups roughly in accord with their carbon contents. Their judgment is based on the appearance of the fracture. The bars of cemented wrought iron do not have the metallic appearance and the uniformity presented by the original bars. They are rather coarsely opaque, brown in colour, and covered with bubbles, blisters, or beads varying in size from a pea to a walnut. It is considered a good sign when the blisters are small, regular, and uniformly distributed over the surface of the bars and do not accumulate along definite lines. The characteristic blisters have given rise to the name applied to the cemented bar—**blister steel,** *acier poule*, and *Blasenstahl*. H. M. Howe and A. Sauveur, for instance, say that blister steel is defined as steel obtained by carburizing wrought iron, or steel of low carbon content, by heating it in contact with substances rich in carbon; and they apply the term to steel obtained by cementation whether or not it shows the characteristic blisters. Another characteristic is the variation in structure from the periphery to the centre of the mass. This gives an indication of the approximate progress of the cementa-

tion.   Analyses were reported by J. O. Arnold, H. Wedding, A. Ledebur,
O. Thallner, J. Percy, C. W. Bildt, etc.   The blistering does not generally appear
in the partial cementation of cast-steel objects—*e.g.* case-hardening.   J. Percy
first suggested that the blisters are formed by the local evolution of carbon monoxide
formed when carbon diffuses into iron containing oxides and slags.   If carbon
monoxide and not the diffusion of carbon is responsible for the carburization of
iron, this hypothesis requires modification.   J. Percy later showed that if slag
is not present in the iron, the blisters are not produced, although cementation
proceeds as usual.   The slag is therefore responsible for the blisters.   W. Siemens
also observed no blistering in the cementation of mild steel.   T. H. Henry supposed
that the blisters are produced by carbon disulphide formed by the action of carbon
on the sulphides in the metal.

The manufacture of **cement steel**—*acier cémenté* (French), *acciaio cementato*
(Italian), *acero cementado* (Spanish), *Cementstäl* (Swedish), and *Zementstahl*
(German)—by fusing in crucibles—**crucible steel**—wrought iron which had been
first carburized by cementation was inaugurated in Sheffield about 1740 by
B. Huntsman.[2]   This furnished a sounder and more homogeneous product than
had previously been obtained.   This process gave a strong impetus to the manufacture of crucible steel.   On account of the relatively large expenditure of time
and fuel in preparing crucible steel from carburized wrought iron, other methods
have been proposed.   The processes of S. Lucas,[3] W. E. Newton, A. Chenot, etc.,
were discussed by J. Percy, E. Grateau, S. Kern, and W. Metcalf.

According to F. Giolitti,[4] the steel obtained by fusing wrought iron, carburized
by cementation, is superior to the crucible steel now made by directly carburizing
wrought iron during the fusion of wrought iron melted in covered crucibles in
which the desired amount of carbon is placed on the charge or the mixture is
heated in the electric furnace ; or the steel obtained by cementing the best Bessemer
or Siemens-Martin soft steels and melting the product in a crucible.

F. G. Bates,[5] A. A. Ackermann, and J. Lecarme tried to produce alloy steels
by mixing a compound of the required metal with the cementation powder.
F. Giolitti added that the technology of the direct manufacture of special steels
by means of the so-called processes of *metallic cementation* is in its infancy and has
not yet given satisfactory practical results.   H. Moissan attempted to cement
iron with *silver* and *chromium* ; and J. Cournot, and A. Folliet and N. Sainderichin,
with *aluminium*.   J. Laissus embedded steel in powdered ferrochromium and
obtained, at carburizing temp., a thin coat of high chromium steel; and similarly
in the presence of ammonium chloride he obtained, at 800° to 1200°, another case
or layer of high *molybdenum, tungsten,* or *tantalum steel.*   T. Miyaguchi embedded
the iron or steel in a mixture of carbon and boric oxide, and obtained a hard, tough
layer of borized metal ; *boron* was also examined from this point of view by
N. Tschischewsky, T. P. Campbell and H. Fay, M. Fesczenko-Czopowse, and
J. Fetschenko-Tschopiwsky ; and aluminium by A. B. Kinzel.   H. Moissan found
that if soft iron be embedded in *silicon* and heated sufficiently, the metal is silicized.
J. E. Stead obtained no silicon penetration at 1125° to 1175°, and fusion occurred
at 1300° to 1350°.   W. E. Thomson obtained no penetration with silicon at 1100°,
superficial penetration between 1100° and 1350°, and fusion at higher temp.
P. Lebeau observed a penetration of silicon in reduced iron at 950°.   A. Sanfourche
studied the silico-cementation of steel by silicon chloride ; and W. E. Vawter
obtained a coating of silicon on iron heated in silicane at 400° to 600°.   The coating
easily flaked off.   R. T. Haslam and L. E. Carlsmith obtained silicon penetration
by heating the metal in ferrosilicon between 800° and 1200°, where fusion
generally occurred.   Confirmatory results were obtained by A. Fry, L. Guillet,
and E. G. Mahin and co-workers.   W. van Drunen obtained surface films
of chromium-nickel-iron by the simultaneous diffusion of chromium and nickel
into iron.

REFERENCES.

[1] P. Theophilus, *Mineralogia*, Franckfurt am Mayne, 1703 ; V. Biringuccio, *De la pirotechnia*, Venetia, 18, 1540 ; Paris, 48, 1556 ; G. Agricola, *De la metallica*, Basileæ, 341, 1556 ; M. Lister, *Phil. Trans.*, **17**. 765, 1693 ; J. Percy, *Metallurgy—Iron and Steel*, London, 102, 807, 1864 ; *Journ. Iron Steel Inst.*, **13**. i, 116, 1878 ; G. J. Löhneyss, *Bericht vom Bergkwerck*, Zellerfeldt, 1617 ; G. Vismara, *Della cementazione e della fusione dell'acciajo*, Milano, 1825 ; *Giorn. Fis. Chim.*, (2), **8**. 190, 1825 ; T. Bergman, *De analysi ferri*, Upsala, 1781 ; *Opuscula physica et chemica*, Upsala, **3**. 1, 1783 ; C. A. van der Monde, C. L. Berthollet and G. Monge, *Mém. Acad.*, 430, 1786 ; *Histoire de l'Académie Royal des Sciences*, Paris, 132, 1788 ; C. W. Scheele, *Konig. Acad. Handl. Stockholm*, **1**, 1779 ; J. Beckmann, *Beiträge zur Geschichte der Erfindungen*, Leipzig, **5**. 86, 1805 ; London, **2**. 327, 1846 ; A. L. Landrin, *A Treatise on Steel*, New York, 1868 ; H. Landrin, *Manual complet du maître de forges*, Paris, 1829 ; R. Jenkins, *Trans. Newcomen Soc.*, **3**. 16, 1923 ; W. Ellyott and M. Meysey, *Pat. Roll*, 12, 1614 ; 14, 1617 ; J. Franquoy, *Des progrès de la fabrication du fer dans le pays de Liége*, Liége, 1861 ; C. J. B. Karsten, *Grundriss der Metallurgie und des metallurgischen Hüttenkunde*, Berlin, 1818 ; R. Plot, *The Natural History of Staffordshire*, London, 1686 ; R. A. F. de Réaumur, *L'art de convertir le fer forgé en acier et d'adoucir le fer fondu*, Paris, 1722 ; *An Essay on the Mystery of Tempering Steel*, London, 1771 ; F. Margueritte, *Recherches sur l'aciération : action de l'oxyde de carbone et du charbon sur le fer*, Paris, 1865 ; *Compt. Rend.*, **59**. 139, 185, 376, 518, 726, 821, 1043, 1864 ; *Ann. Chim. Phys.*, (4), **6**. 55, 1865 ; J. L. Gay-Lussac, *ib.*, (3), **17**. 221, 1846 ; L. Forquignon, *ib.*, (5), **23**. 433, 1881 ; J. B. J. D. Boussingault, *Compt. Rend.*, **78**. 1458, 1874 ; *Étude sur la transformation du fer en acier par la cementation*, Paris, 1875 ; *Ann. Chim. Phys.*, (5), **5**. 145, 1875 ; L. Clouet, *Journ. Mines*, **9**. 3, 1799 ; *Nicholson's Journ.*, **3**. 131, 1800 ; *Rapp. Inst. Nat. Paris*, (1), **2**. 81, 1798 ; *Ann. Chim. Phys.*, (1), **28**. 19, 1798 ; (1), **31**. 328, 1799 ; A. Laurent, *ib.*, (2), **65**. 417, 1837 ; P. G. F. Leplay and A. Laurent, *ib.*, (2), **65**. 403, 1837 ; P. G. F. Leplay, *Ann. Mines*, (5), **19**. 267, 1841 ; P. A. Dufrénoy, *ib.*, (5), **5**. 171, 1834 ; F. Camus, *L'art de tremper les fers et les aciers*, Rocroi, 1846 ; H. Damemme, *Essai pratique sur l'emploi ou la manière de travailler l'acier*, Paris, 1835 ; P. C. J. B. Tronson du Coudray, *Nouvelles expériences sur le fer*, Upsala, 1775 ; A. Colson, *Ann. Chim. Phys.*, (3), **60**. 210, 1860 ; *Chem. News*, **3**. 20, 373, 1861 ; *Mém. Acad. Bruxelles*, **32**. 1, 1865 ; *Compt. Rend.*, **93**..1074, 1881 ; **94**. 26, 1882 ; *Rev. Mét.*, **6**. 505, 1909 ; *Mém. Soc. Ing. Civils*, (6), **57**. 177, 1904 ; G. Charpy, *Iron Steel Mag.*, **8**. 309, 1904; *Rev. Mét.*, **6**. 505, 1909 ; *Compt. Rend.*, **136**. 1000, 1903 ; **137**. 120, 1903 ; G. Charpy and S. Bonnerot, *ib.*, **150**. 173, 1910 ; **151**. 644, 1911 ; **153**. 671, 1912 ; G. Charpy and P. Pingault, *ib.*, **187**. 554, 1928 ; P. Pingault, *ib.*, **191**. 1007, 1930 ; H. Caron, *ib.*, **51**. 564, 930, 1860 ; **52**. 635, 677, 960, 1063, 1190, 1246, 1861 ; **59**. 333, 613, 819, 953, 1864 ; **62**. 891, 1866 ; C. E. Jullien, *ib.*, **59**. 915, 1864 ; L. Cailletet, *ib.*, **60**. 344, 564, 1865 ; F. Osmond, *Journ. Iron Steel Inst.*, **52**. ii, 142, 1897 ; *Trans. Amer. Inst. Min. Eng.*, **27**. 786, 1897 ; *Compt. Rend.*, **112**. 578, 1891 ; L. Grenet, *ib.*, **150**. 921, 1910 ; J. Cournot, *ib.*, **185**. 990, 1927 ; J. Garnier, *ib.*, **116**. 1449, 1893 ; L. Guillet, *ib.*, **136**. 1319, 1903 ; **138**. 1600, 1904 ; *Génie Civil*, **59**. 158, 183, 203, 226, 241, 266, 286, 1912 ; *Mém. Soc. Ing. Civils*, (6), **57**. 2, 177, 1904 ; *Ann. Assoc. Ing. École Speciale Gand*, (5), **16**. 181, 1926 ; *Rev. Mét.*, **3**. 227, 1906 ; **7**. 496, 1910 ; L. Guillet and C. Griffiths, *ib.*, **6**. 1013, 1909 ; *Compt. Rend.*, **149**. 125, 1910 ; L. Guillet and V. Bernard, *Rev. Mét.*, **11**. 752, 1914 ; H. de Nolly and L. Veyret, *ib.*, **9**. 53, 1912 ; W. C. Roberts-Austen, *Phil. Trans.*, **187**. A, 383, 1896 ; *Nature*, **41**. 14, 1889 ; *Journ. Iron Steel Inst.*, **37**. i, 81, 91, 1890 ; **49**. i, 139, 1896 ; **54**. ii, 195, 1898 ; G. P. Royston, *ib.*, **51**. i, 166, 1897 ; E. H. Saniter, *ib.*, **52**. ii, 115, 1897 ; **55**. i, 127, 1899 ; J. O. Arnold, *ib.*, **54**. ii, 185, 1898 ; J. O. Arnold and A. McWilliam, *ib.*, **55**. i, 85, 1899 ; W. Hempel, *Ber.*, **18**. 998, 1885 ; W. E. Day, *Trans. Amer. Soc. Steel Treating*, **9**. 247, 1926 ; R. S. Marsden, *Journ. Chem. Soc.*, **39**. 149, 1881 ; J. Lecarme, *French Pat. No.* 327984, 1902 ; *Rev. Mét.*, **2**. 516, 720, 1905 ; M. Partiot, *ib.*, **3**. 400, 1906 ; C. Benedicks, *ib.*, **3**. 41, 1906 ; S. Satoh, *ib.*, **26**. 248, 1929 ; A. M. Portevin and H. Berjot, *ib.*, **7**. 61, 1910 ; A. M. Portevin, *Compt. Rend.*, **163**. 1025, 1914 ; **165**. 180, 1917 ; *Bull. Soc. Ing. Civils*, 139, 772, 1913 ; *Rev. Mét.*, **7**. 859, 1910 ; P. Nicolardot, *ib.*, **6**. 1, 1909 ; H. le Chatelier, *ib.*, **3**. 154, 1906 ; F. Schmitz, *Stahl Eisen*, **39**. 313, 406, 1919 ; B. Strauss, *ib.*, **34**. 1814, 1914 ; A. Vita, *ib.*, **42**. 455, 1922 ; P. Oberhoffer and E. Piwowarsky, *ib.*, **42**. 801, 1922 ; E. Zingg, *ib.*, **46**. 776, 1926 ; E. Zingg, P. Oberhoffer and E. Piwowarsky, *ib.*, **49**. 721, 762, 1929 ; E. Mauer, *ib.*, **42**. 447, 1922 ; H. Braune, *Stahl Eisen*, **27**. 75, 1907 ; *Bihang Jernkontorets Ann.*, **8**. 191, 1907 ; C. J. G. Malmberg, *ib.*, **8**. 432, 1907 ; A. Petrén and J. Grabe, *Jernkontorets Ann.*, **60**. 1, 1906 ; G. S. Scott, *Journ. Iron Steel Inst.*, **75**. iii, 120, 1907 ; C. O. Bannister and W. J. Lambert, *ib.*, **75**. iii, 114, 1907 ; S. A. Grayson, *ib.*, **81**. i, 287, 1910 ; G. J. Snelus, *ib.*, **37**. i, 91, 1890 ; I. L. Bell, *ib.*, **37**. i, 93, 1890 ; H. W. B. Roozeboom, *ib.*, **65**. i, 257, 1904 ; F. Robin, *Rev. Mécanique*, **33**. 409, 1913 ; T. H. Henry in J. Percy, *Metallurgy—Iron and Steel*, London, 773, 1864 ; R. Mannesmann, *Verh. Ver. Beförd. Gewerbefl.*, **58**. 31, 1879 ; H. W. Stein, *Journ. prakt. Chem.*, (1), **53**. 491, 1851 ; *Berg. Hütt. Ztg.*, **10**. 673, 1851 ; *Dingler's Journ.*, **121**. 279, 1851 ; W. H. Pepys, *Phil. Trans.*, **105**. 371, 1815 ; E. Frémy, *Compt. Rend.*, **61**. 567, 1860 ; **62**. 321, 415, 626, 998, 1162, 1861 ; *Chem. News*, **2**. 256, 1860 ; **3**. 276, 320, 331, 344, 361, 375, 1861 ; *Journ. Pharm. Chim.*, (3), **38**. 347, 1860 ; (3), **39**. 241, 321, 1861 ; C. Binks, *ib.*, (3), **36**. 310, 1859 ; *Journ. Soc. Arts*, **5**. 410, 1857 ; *Brit. Pat. No.* 2695, 2711, 1856 ; A. A. Ackermann, *German Pat.*, *D.R.P.* 79429, 1895 ; F. G. Bates, *ib.*, 57729, 1891 ; 83093, 1895 ; G. Mars, *ib.*, 37948, 1887 ; R. K. Boyle, *ib.*, 46200, 1888 ; *Brit. Pat. No.* 9782, 1887 ; V. Grönquist, *ib.*, 210870, 1922 ; T. Langer, *German Pat.*,

D.R.P. 55544, 1891 ; F. W. Harbord, *Journ. Iron Steel Inst.*, **55**. i, 111, 1899 ; A. S. Stansfield, *ib.*, **55**. i, 113, 1899 ; H. Louis, *ib.*, **55**. i, 117, 1899 ; W. Siemens, *ib.*, **13**. i, 122, 1878 ; C. R. Austin, *ib.*, **105**. i, 93, 1922 ; H. L. Heathcote, *ib.*, **89**. i, 342, 1914 ; F. W. Adams, *ib.*, **91**. i, 255, 1915 ; P. W. Döhmer, *Chem. Ztg.*, **51**. 725, 1927 ; J. S. Ayling, *Trans. Amer. Soc. Steel Treating*, **13**. 1039, 1928 ; E. G. Mahin and R. C. Spencer, *ib.*, **15**. 117, 1929 ; O. J. Wilbor and J. A. Comstock, *ib.*, **122**. ii, 537 ; 1930 ; G. Takahashi, *Kinzoku no Kenkyu*, **4**. 432, 1927 ; **6**. 186, 1929 ; *Science Rep. Tohoku Univ.*, **15**. 157, 1926 ; **17**. 761, 883, 1135, 1928 ; T. Ishiwara, *ib.*, **12**. 309, 1924 ; K. Iwase, *ib.*, **15**. 531, 1926 ; J. W. Urquhart, *Heat Treating Forging*, **14**. 505, 1928 ; S. Tour, *Fuels Furnaces*, **6**. 883, 1928 ; W. P. Sykes, *ib.*, **6**. 913, 1928 ; *Trans. Amer. Soc. Steel Treating*, **12**. 137, 1927 ; J. Sorensen, *Fuels Furnaces*, **8**. 41, 1930 ; V. E. Hillman, *ib.*, **7**. 31, 1929 ; *Trans. Amer. Soc. Steel Treating*, **2**. 296, 1922 ; *Iron Age*, **114**. 611, 1924 ; F. Eisenstecken, *Ueber die Zementierung des Eisens durch Methan und die dabei auftretenden Gleichgewichte* (480°–720°), Dortmund, 1928 ; A. Jaeschke, *Zeit. gesamte Giessereipraxis*, **50**. 135, 1929 ; W. T. Griffiths, *Aciers Spéciaux*, **5**. 146, 1930 ; F. W. Rowe, *Iron Steel Ind.*, **3**. 77, 116, 1929 ; A. Fry, *Ueber die Diffusion der Begleitelemente des technischen Eisens in festes Eisen*, Berlin, 1922 ; *Krupp's Monatsh.*, **4**. 137, 1923 ; F. Giolitti, *La Cementazione dell'Acciajo*, Torino, 1912 ; *La cémentation de l'acier*, Paris, 1914 ; *The Cementation of Iron and Steel*, New York, 184, 263, 1915 ; *Met. Chem. Engg.*, **13**. 656, 1915 ; **25**. 312, 1921 ; *Met. Ital.*, **3**. 578, 1911 ; *Rend. Soc. Chim. Roma*, **6**. 337, 354, 1908 ; *Rass. Min. Met. Chim.*, **35**. 101, 125, 141, 1911 : *Journ. Iron Steel Inst.*, **84**. ii, 307, 1911 ; *Gazz. Chim. Ital.*, **38**. ii, 352, 1908 ; F. Giolitti and F. Carnevali, *Rend. Soc. Chim. Roma*, **6**. 359, 1908 ; *Atti Accad. Lincei*, (5), **17**. ii, 748, 1908 ; *Atti Accad. Torino*, **45**. 337, 376, 1910 ; **46**. 409, 558, 1911 ; *Journ. Iron Steel Inst.*, **84**. ii, 331, 1911 ; *Gazz. Chim. Ital.*, **38**. ii, 1, 309, 1908 ; F. Giolitti and G. Tavanti, *ib.*, **38**. ii, 1, 1908 ; **39**. ii, 1, 1909 ; *Atti Accad. Torino*, **45**. 539, 1910 ; *Rass. Min. Met. Chim.*, **34**. 259, 1911 ; F. Giolitti, F. Carnevali and G. Tavanti, *ib.*, **33**. 97, 118, 129, 149, 162, 1910 ; F. Giolitti and L. Astorri, *Gazz. Chim. Ital.*, **40**. i, 1, 1910 ; *Rass. Min. Met. Chim.*, **34**. 259, 1911 ; F. Giolitti and G. Scavia, *Met. Ital.*, **3**. 332, 403, 1911 ; F. Giolitti, and F. Carnevali and G. Gherardi, *Atti Accad. Lincei*, (5), **17**. ii, 662, 1908 ; F. Giolitti, J. Galibourg, and P. Beuret, *Rev. Mét.*, **18**. 213, 1921 (I am indebted to Prof. Giolitti for permission to use Fig. 72) ; A. R. Page, *Metal Ind.*, **26**. 297, 321, 345, 1925 ; J. F. Schadgen, *Trans. Amer. Inst. Steel Treating*, **2**. 333, 1922 ; H. Rodman, *ib.*, **7**. 535, 1925 ; S. C. Spalding, *ib.*, **2**. 950, 1922 ; S. A. Tetschenko-Tschopiwsky, *Rev. Mét.*, **12**. 518, 1915 ; **23**. 267, 1926 ; *Journ. Russ. Met. Soc.*, 245, 1914 ; *Stahl Eisen*, **47**. 229, 1927 ; G. Tammann, *ib.*, **42**. 654, 1922 ; A. Sauveur, *The Metallography and Heat Treatment of Iron and Steel*, Cambridge, Mass., 294, 1926 ; L. B. Guyton de Morveau, *Ann. Chim. Phys.*, (1), **31**. 328, 1799 ; H. Lüpfert, *Stahl Eisen*, **49**. 1717, 1929 ; C. H. Herty, B. M. Larsen, V. N. Krivobok, R. B. Morton, R. E. Wiley, A. W. Sikes and J. E. Jacobs, *Bull. U.S. Bur. Min. Advisory Board*, 45, 1929 ; R. E. Guthrie, *ib.*, **7**. 1345, 1929 ; R. G. Roshong, *ib.*, **7**. 1393, 1909 ; A. W. Machlet, *U.S. Pat. No.* 1745104, 1930 ; H. Swain, *Automobile Eng.*, **19**. 226, 377, 1929 ; F. Hebler, *Chem. Ztg.*, **52**. 775, 1928 ; F. Rapatz, *Iron Steel Ind.*, **2**. 241, 251, 1929 ; *Stahl Eisen*, **49**. 427, 1929 ; G. J. Pitt, *Proc. South Staffs Iron Steel Works Managers*, **13**. 148, 1898 ; D. Brownlie, *Journ. Iron Steel Inst.*, **121**. i, 455, 1930 ; B. de Laveleye, *ib.*, **88**. ii, 8, 1913 ; **121**. i, 465, 1930 ; *Proc. Inst. Mech. Eng.*, 339, 1883 ; J. Herbert, *Tech. Moderne*, **18**. 481, 525, 1926 ; J. Parry, *Nature*, **46**. 283, 1892 ; S. Epstein and H. S. Rawdon, *U.S. Bur. Standards Journ. Research*, **1**. 423, 1928 ; A. Hillairet, *Industries Iron*, **15**. 182, 1893 ; M. B. Messimer and E. F. Carter, *ib.*, **27**. 284, 1900 ; H. Behrens and A. R. van Linge, *Rec. Trav. Chim. Pays-Bas*, **13**. 155, 1894 ; *Zeit. anal. Chem.*, **33**. 513, 1894; *Oesterr. Zeit. Berg. Hütt.*, **43**. 190, 1895 ; G. F. Hinkens, *Machinery*, **13**. 75, 1907 ; *Iron Trade Rev.*, **64**. 11, 1899 ; F. Weyl, *Met.*, **7**. 440, 1910 ; J. Kirner, *ib.*, **8**. 72, 1911 ; R. Bruch, *ib.*, **3**. 123, 1906 ; H. Brearley, *The Case-Hardening of Steel*, London, 8, 1921 ; A. C. Sladky and A. F. Schultz, *Bull. Wisconsin Univ.—Eng. Series*, 8, 1910 ; D. Mushet, *Papers on Iron and Steel*, London, 671, 1840 ; *Phil. Mag.*, **5**. 201, 1799 ; **9**. 289, 1801 ; **12**. 27, 97, 1802 ; V. H. E. Gallet, *U.S. Pat. No.* 146330, 1874 ; J. B. Jenkins, *ib.*, 490660, 1898 ; E. Engels, *French Pat. No.* 337154, 1903 ; F. André, *Brit. Pat. No.* 1356, 1906 ; M. F. Coomes and A. W. Hyde, *ib.*, 2981, 1890 ; C. Lamargese, *ib.*, 25986, 1903 ; Cyanid-Gesellschaft, *ib.*, 16412, 1904 ; F. Cowden, *ib.*, 13761, 1904 ; G. B. Cattaneo and A. Faggian, *ib.*, 13931, 1906 ; C. Macintosh, *Journ. prakt. Chem.*, (2), **333**. 1834 ; *Brit. Pat. No.* 5173, 1825 ; R. A. Brooman, *ib.*, 359, 1856 ; G. C. Thomas, *ib.*, 2039, 1856 ; J. F. J. A. Boullet, *ib.*, 2174, 1854 ; J. Holland, *ib.*, 12705, 1849 ; N. Kimball, *ib.*, 5263, 1825 ; H. M. Howe and A. Sauveur, *Proc. Amer. Assoc. Testing Materials*, **6**. xi, 4, 1912 ; L. B. G. de Morveau, *Rapport sur les résultats des expériences de Clouet sur les différens états du fer et pour la conversion du fer en acier fondu*, Paris, 1798 ; F. Kurek, *Beiträge zur Kenntis der Zementation des Eisens mittels Gasen*, Düsseldorf, 1911 ; *Stahl Eisen*, **32**. 1780, 1912 ; H. Wedding, *Handbuch der Eisenhüttenkunde*, Braunschweig, 1891 ; A. Ledebur, *Handbuch der Eisenhüttenkunde*, Leipzig, **3**. 401, 1908 ; *Rev. Mét.*, **3**. 222, 1906 ; *Stahl Eisen*, **26**. 72, 478, 1906 ; O. Bauer, *ib.*, **24**. 1058, 1904 ; O. Thallner, *ib.*, **19**. 914, 1899 ; A. Bauschlicher, *ib.*, **30**. 253, 1910 ; C. W. Bildt, *ib.*, **22**. 438, 1902 ; *Jernkontorets Ann.*, **56**. 242, 1901 ; W. Metcalf and J. W. Langley, *Trans. Amer. Inst. Min. Eng.*, **9**. 385, 1883 ; **27**. 382, 1893 ; J. C. Olsen and W. S. Weissenbach, *Iron Age*, **84**. 120, 1909 ; *Amer. Machinist*, **32**. 156, 1909 ; *Trans. Amer. Inst. Chem. Eng.*, **2** 194, 1909 ; J. E. Stead, *Proc. Cleveland Inst. Eng.*, 54 1895 ; F. Abel, *Proc. Inst. Mech. Eng.*, 56, 1883 ; 30, 1885; G. Tammann and K. Schönert, *Stahl Eisen*, **42**. 654, 1922 ; *Zeit. anorg. Chem.*, **122**. 27, 1922 ; I. Runge, *ib.*, **115**. 293, 1921 ; *Ueber die Diffusiongeschwindigkeit von Kohlenstoff in Eisen*, Göttingen, 1921 ; *Chem. Trade Journ.*, **69**. 245, 1921 ;

G. S. MacKenzie, *Scherer's Journ.*, **5**. 366, 1800 ; *Nicholson's Journ.*, **4**. 103, 1801 ; A. Gautier, *Journ. Pharm. Chim.*, (1), **13**. 18, 1827 ; A. F. E. Degen, *Liebig's Ann.*, **29**. 261, 1839 ; J. Buttery, *Schweigger's Journ.*, **35**. 339, 1822 ; A. Ure, *A Dictionary of Chemistry*, London, 1821 ; J. R. Bréant, *Ann. Chim. Phys.*, (2), **24**. 388, 1823 ; *Ann. Mines*, (1), **9**. 319, 1824 ; *Quart. Journ. Science*, **18**. 386, 1825 ; *Ann. Phil.*, **8**. 267, 1824 ; A. Bramley and A. J. Jinkings, *Journ. Iron Steel Inst.—Carnegie Mem.*, **15**. 17, 127, 1926 ; A. Bramley and H. D. Lord, *ib.*, **18**. 1, 1929 ; A. Bramley and G. Lawton, *ib.*, **16**. 35, 1927 ; A. Bramley and G. H. Beeby, *ib.*, **15**. 71, 1926 ; A. Bramley, *ib.*, **15**. 155, 1926 ; A. Bramley and G. Turner, *ib.*, **17**. 23, 1928 ; A. Bramley and F. W. Haywood, *ib.*, **17**. 65, 1928 ; H. Reininger, *Werkzeng-maschine*, **34**. 133, 1930 ; I. Musatti and M. Croce, *Ann. Chim. Applicata*, **14**. 18, 1924 ; *Rev. Mét.*, **21**. 340, 1924 ; E. F. Lake, *Iron Age*, **89**. 81, 1912 ; *Amer. Machinist*, **31**. 331, 1908 ; O. M. Becker, *Eng. Mag.*, **35**. 728, 1908 ; *Amer. Machinist*, **31**. 519, 1908 ; J. F. Springer, *Cassier's Mag.*, **34**. 137, 1908 ; *Iron Age*, **81**. 1688, 1908 ; J. H. Nead and J. N. Bourg, *ib.*, **90**. 904, 1912 ; E. F. Davis, *Steel*, **87**. 43, 60, 1930 ; H. A. Vanvught, *Iron Coal Trades Rev.*, **81**. 90, 1910 ; E. R. Markham, *Mech. Eng.*, **25**. 688, 1910 ; T. Turner, *ib.*, **26**. 775, 1911 ; T. Baker, *ib.*, **39**. 134, 1917 ; D. Uno, *Mem. Coll. Kyoto*, **7**. 108, 1924 ; P. Henry, *Rev. Gén. Sciences*, **37**. 431, 1926 ; R. R. Abbott, *Trans. Amer. Inst. Min. Eng.*, **46**. 371, 1912 ; **47**. 467, 1913 ; A. Sauveur and G. A. Reinhardt, *ib.*, **46**. 422, 1912 ; P. W. Brennan, *Brass World*, **8**. 310, 1912 ; *Foundry Trade Journ.*, **19**. 545, 1916 ; M. T. Lothrop, *Journ. Amer. Soc. Mech. Eng.*, **34**. 1995, 1912 ; H. Neuhauss, *Stahl Eisen*, **44**. 1664, 1924 ; W. Rohland, *ib.*, **47**. 52, 1927 ; T. H. Byron, *Journ. Iron Steel Inst.*, **92**. ii, 106, 1915 ; M. L. Becker, *ib.*, **121**. i, 337, 1930 ; F. C. Langenberg, *ib.*, **95**. i, 129, 1917 ; H. C. H. Carpenter and C. C. Smith, *ib.*, **98**. ii, 139, 1918 ; E. W. Ehn, *ib.*, **105**. i, 157, 1922 ; *Trans. Amer. Soc. Steel Treating*, **2**. 1177, 1922 ; R. A. Millholland, *Iron Age*, **96**. 1041, 1111, 1166, 1915 ; H. W. McQuaid and E. W. Ehn, *Trans. Amer. Inst. Min. Eng.*, **67**. 341, 1922 ; E. Pérot, *Rev. Mét.*, **24**. 23, 72, 1927 ; *Compt. Rend.*, **183**. 1108, 1926 ; H. Braune and H. Hellweg, *Zeit. phys. Chem.*, **110**. 147, 1904 ; E. G. Mahin, R. C. Spencer and C. R. Hayner, *Proc. Indiana Acad.*, **34**. 177, 1925 ; H. Fay, *Chem. Met. Engg.*, **24**. 289, 1921 ; F. Hodson, *ib.*, **28**. 308, 1923 ; H. M. Crawford, *Gas Age*, **46**. 204, 1920 ; R. G. Guthrie, *Metal Progress*, **20**. 50, 1931 ; S. P. Rockwell, *Iron Age*, **127**. 1009, 1065, 1931 ; W. J. Merton, *Amer. Drop Forger*, **6**. 481, 1920 ; *Trans. Amer. Soc. Steel Treating*, **1**. 270, 1920 ; **2**. 950, 1922 ; R. G. Guthrie and O. Wozasek, *ib.*, **12**. 853, 1927 ; S. P. Rockwell and F. Downes, *ib.*, **5**. 285, 1924 ; A. H. d'Arcambal, *ib.*, **2**. 1111, 1922 ; G. R. Brophy and S. B. Leiter, *ib.*, **1**. 330, 1920 ; W. P. Fishel and J. F. Wooddell, *ib.*, **11**. 730, 1927 ; G. S. MacFarland, *ib.*, **1**. 297, 1920 ; H. Schagrin, *ib.*, **2**. 331, 1922 ; T. G. Selleck, *ib.*, **1**. 383, 1921 ; **2**. 705, 1922 ; H. B. Northrup, *Trans. Amer. Electrochem Soc.*, **60**. 49, 1913 ; *Fuels Furnaces*, **6**. 61, 1928 ; *Trans. Amer. Soc. Steel Treating*, **12**. 470, 1927 ; H. B. Knowlton, *ib.*, **1**. 689, 1920 ; **4**. 494, 1923 ; **16**. 607, 1929 ; *Heat Treating Forging*, **7**. 543, 590, 1921 ; W. A. Jayme, *ib.*, **7**. 567, 1921 ; J. D. Gat, *ib.*, **13**. 393, 1927 ; S. Matsubara, *Trans. Amer. Inst. Min. Eng.*, **67**. 3, 1922 ; L. Aitchison, *Iron Coal Trades Rev.*, **102**. 728, 1921 ; A. A. Blue, *Heat Treating Forging*, **7**. 413, 1921 ; C. Kluytmans, *Foundry Trade Journ.*, **24**. 29, 1921 ; P. W. Shimer, *U.S. Pat. No.* 1279457, 1279458, 1918 ; P. W. and E. B. Shimer, *Trans. Amer. Soc. Steel Treating*, **2**. 403, 1922 ; B. F. Shepherd, *ib.*, **4**. 171, 1923 ; **5**. 485, 1924 ; **6**. 606, 1924 ; C. H. Desch, *B.A. Rep.*, 348, 1912 ; J. N. Greenwood, *Journ. Birmingham Met. Soc.*, **8**. 243, 1922 ; *Iron Coal Trades Rev.*, **104**. 77, 1922 ; H. Weiss, *Introduction à l'étude de la cémentation métallique*, Paris, 1923 ; *Rev. Mét.*, **21**. 18, 1924 ; T. Murakami and H. Sekiguchi, *Journ. Japan Iron Steel Inst.*, **16**. 1015, 1930 ; J. H. Hruska, *Heat Treating Forging*, **16**. 1397, 1530, 1930 ; **17**. 35, 1931 ; N. Agéeff and M. Zamotorin, *Ann. Inst. Polyt. Leningrad*, **31**. 15, 1928 ; H. Müller, *Arch. Eisenhüttenwesen*, **5**. 57, 1931 ; R. M. P. Hamilton, *Eng. Min. Journ.*, **132**. 809, 1931 ; A. J. Lindberg, *Metals Alloys*, **2**. 106, 1931 ; D. A. Holt, *Metal Progress*, **20**. 68, 1931 ; F. C. Thompson and W. H. Dearden, *Trans. Faraday Soc.*, **20**. 84, 1924 ; I. Musatti and L. Dainelli, *Met. Ital.*, **23**. 1015, 1931 ; R. A. Ragatz and O. L. Kowalke, *Metals Alloys*, **2**. 290, 343, 1931 ; E. C. Moffett, *Steel*, **88**. 38, 1931 ; *Iron Age*, **127**. 1388, 1931 ; W. Henninger and H. Jurich, *Engg. Progress*, **11**. 297, 1930 ; W. Nelson, *Metallurgist*, **7**. 21, 1931 ; G. M. Enos, *Trans. Amer. Soc. Steel Treating*, —, 1931 ; R. J. Cowan, *Tech. Publ. Amer. Inst. Min. Eng.*, 439, 1931 ; J. G. R. Woodvine, *Journ. Iron Steel Inst.—Carnegie Mem.*, **20**. 125, 1931.

² P. G. F. Leplay, *Ann. Mines*, (4), **3**. 638, 1843 ; J. Percy, *Metallurgy—Iron and Steel*, London, 828, 1864 ; B. Huntsman, in Anon., *The Useful Metals and their Alloys*, London, 346, 1857 ; H. Horne, *Essays concerning Iron and Steel*, London, 165, 1773.

³ S. Lucas, *Brit. Pat. No.* 1730, 1854 ; W. E. Newton, *ib.*, 851, 1856 ; J. I. Hawkins, *ib.*, 7142, 1836 ; S. Kern, *Chem. News*, **65**. 133, 158, 170, 1892 ; **74**. 5, 76, 1896 ; W. Metcalf, *Steel : A Manual for Steel Users*, New York, 1896 ; A. Chenot, *Compt. Rend.*, **38**. 685, 1854 ; *French Pat. No.* 7826, 1852 ; E. Grateau, *Rev. Univ.*, (1), **6**. 40, 1859 ; J. Percy, *Metallurgy—Iron and Steel*, London, 766, 1864.

⁴ F. Giolitti, *La Cementazione dell'Acciajo*, Torino, 1912 ; *La cémentation de l'acier*, Paris, 1914 ; *The Cementation of Iron and Steel*, New York, 201, 1915.

⁵ J. Laissus, *Rev. Mét.*, **23**. 233, 1926 ; *Compt. Rend.*, **180**. 2040, 1925 ; **182**. 465, 1154, 1926 ; H. Moissan, *ib.*, **121**. 621, 1895 ; J. Cournot, *ib.*, **182**. 696, 1926 ; *Rev. Mét.*, **23**. 219, 1926 ; A. Sanfourche, *Compt. Rend.*, **183**. 791, 1926 ; L. Guillet, *ib.*, **182**. 1588, 1926 ; T. Miyaguchi, *Brit. Pat. No.* 193917, 1921 ; A. B. Kinzel, *U.S. Pat. No.* 1736919, 1736920, 1929 ; N. Tschischewsky, *Journ. Iron Steel Inst.*, **95**. i, 185, 1917 ; J. E. Stead, *ib.*, **63**. i, 271, 1903 ; T. P. Campbell and H. Fay, *Journ. Ind. Eng. Chem.*, **16**. 719, 1924 ; R. T. Haslam

and L. E. Carlsmith, *ib.*, **16**. 1110, 1924 ; W. E. Vawter, *ib.*, **9**. 580, 1917 ; J. Fetschenko-
Tschopiwsky, *Stahl Eisen*, **47**, 229, 1927 ; *Rev. Mét.*, **23**. 267, 1926 ; P. Lebeau, *Bull. Soc.
Chim.*, (4), **27**. 3, 1920 ; A. Fry, *Stahl Eisen*, **43**. 1041, 1923 ; W. E. Thomson, *Rep.
Research Lab. applied Chem.*, May, 1909 ; E. G. Mahin, R. C. Spencer and C. R. Hayner,
Proc. Indiana Acad., **34**. 117, 1925 ; *Trans. Amer. Soc. Steel Treating*, **15**. 117, 1929 ;
G. Grube and K. Schneider, *Zeit. anorg. Chem.*, **168**. 17, 1927 ; F. G. Bates, *German
Pat.*, *D.R.P.* 57729, 1891 ; 83093, 1895 ; A. A. Ackermann, *ib.*, 79429, 1895 ; J. Lecarme, *French
Pat. No.* 327984, 1902 ; *Rev. Mét.*, **2**. 516, 720, 1905 ; F. Giolitti, *La Cementazione dell'Acciajo*,
Torino, 1912 ; *La cémentation de l'acier*, Paris, 1914 ; *The Cementation of Iron and Steel*, New
York, 184, 263, 1915 ; *Met. Ital.*, **3**. 578, 1911 ; *Rend. Soc. Chim. Roma*, **6**. 337, 354, 1908 ;
Rass. Min. Met. Chim., **35**. 101, 125, 141, 1911 ; *Journ. Iron Steel Inst.*, **24**. ii, 307, 1911 ; *Gazz.
Chim. Ital.*, **38**. ii, 352, 1908 ; W. van Drunen, *Ueber die Diffusion von Eisen mit Kobalt, Nickel,
und Chrom in festen Zustande*, Stuttgart, 1928 ; M. Fesczenko-Czopowse, *Trav. Mines Cracovie*,
5, 1925 ; A. Folliet and N. Sainderichin, *Brit. Pat. No.* 337562, 337635, 1929.

§ 11. The Preparation of Purified Iron

The term iron is applied not only to the element supposed to be chemically
pure, but it is also employed generally for various forms of technical iron and even
for steel—*vide supra*, nomenclature. In speaking of iron, therefore, it is often
necessary to designate the particular kind of iron to which reference is made. A
close approximation has been made to chemically pure iron, but it is doubtful
if strictly pure iron has ever been made *en masse*. Some investigators of the
magnetic properties of iron are dissatisfied with iron of the highest degree of purity
that they have been able to prepare. A great many determinations of the properties
of iron have been made with Swedish charcoal iron, since this iron was for a long
time one of the purest forms of iron in commerce. O. Ruff and E. Gersten found
that it approximated to the following analysis :

Fe	C	Mn	Si	P	S	Cu
99·745	0·085	0·090	0·020	0·046	0·004	0·010 per cent.

Iron of a high degree of purity is manufactured by the open-hearth process for
steel as modified by R. B. Carnahan.[1] The product, prepared by the American
Rolling Mill Co., is known commercially as *armco iron*. W. J. Beck gave the first
of the following analyses, and R. L. Keynon the second :

Fe	C	Mn	Si	P	S
99·865	0·013	0·021	trace	0·005	0·035 per cent.
(99·941)	0·013	0·017	trace	0·005	0·025 per cent.

so that, as pointed out by A. Sauveur, it rivals electrolytic iron in its degree of
purity, and it is much cheaper. The subject was discussed by A. S. Cushman,
R. L. Keynon, E. L. Dupuy, W. J. Beck, and J. A. Aupperle. The process of
manufacture is thus described by R. B. Carnahan :

The basic open-hearth furnace is charged with low carbon or steel scrap. Lime or
limestone is added to the charge to reduce the sulphur and phosphorus, these agents being
preferably charged prior to charging the metal. The charge is then refined, as in making
soft steel, by the employment of ore or agitation, or both, but recarburization at this stage
is not necessary in case the charge melts to a product specially low in carbon. Carbon,
manganese, sulphur, and phosphorus are thereby reduced. This refining operation is
carried out for a much longer time, from one to four hours more, than is usually employed
in making high-grade soft steel ; naturally, while the carbon is being more and more
reduced, the m.p. of the iron bath rises and the temp. must be gradually raised, until it is
finally at least 1565°. The refining operation is finished when the bath contains not over
0·14 per cent. of sulphur, phosphorus, carbon, manganese, and silicon taken in the aggregate.
For the best results it is desirable and practicable to reduce this aggregate to less than one-
half the percentage named, and to have neither carbon nor manganese over 0·02 per cent.
The refined metal is poured into moulds while still at a high temp. ; and, while still molten,
it is deoxidized and degasified by the addition of aluminium to the molten metal—say
2½ lbs. per ton. If this operation be conducted in the furnace, aluminium pig-iron is
employed. Aluminium may be economized by partially deoxidizing the bath by employing
pig-iron—say 2 to 8 per cent. of the charge. The degasifying and deoxidizing agents must,
of course, not be such as to lessen the above-mentioned purity of the ultimate product.
The slag is floated off in tapping the metal.

Iron of a high degree of purity—*ferrum reductum*—has been prepared in the laboratory by reducing the purified ferrous or ferric oxides or salts. The reduction of the oxides by hydrogen has been discussed in a previous section, and the metal was obtained in this way by J. J. Berzelius,[2] A. Thibierge, E. Soubeiran and J. B. Dublanc, A. M. B. Burin du Buisson, H. F. Gaultier de Claubry, S. de Luca, M. H. Deschamps, and L. Dusart. H. Moissan, and F. Glaser thought that the reduction occurs in definite stages, but S. Hilpert, L. Mathesius, and K. Hofmann showed that this is not the case, for there is a continuous gradation in the composition of the solid phase between oxide and metal. F. Wüst and P. Rütten observed that the reduction can be observed at as low a temp. as 350°, but S. Hilpert, with artificial ferric oxide, and F. Wüst and P. Rütten, with the natural oxide, found that the temp. at which reduction begins depends on the previous history of the oxide. F. Wüst and P. Rütten also showed that the speed of reduction depends on the porosity and gas permeability of the oxide. G. P. Baxter and C. R. Hoover showed that in order to obtain iron of a high degree of purity, a much higher temp., 900°, is needed for the reduction than that at which the reduction begins. H. Moissan stated that the reduction is completed in 36 hrs. at 350°, in 12 hrs. at 440°, and at 500° the reaction proceeds very quickly. The equilibrium conditions are discussed elsewhere. F. Wöhler reduced crystalline ferric oxide prepared by heating a mixture of one part of ferrous sulphate and 2 or 3 parts of sodium chloride and leaching the product with water ; while A. Matthiessen and S. P. Szczepanovsky heated a mixture of equal parts of ferrous sulphate and dehydrated sodium sulphate to redness in a platinum crucible until sulphurous fumes were no longer evolved, extracted the mass with water, reduced the oxide with hydrogen, and fused it to a regulus in a lime crucible in the oxyhydrogen flame.

According to L. Jordan and co-workers, crucibles made from commercial fused oxides, alumina, zirconia, and magnesia, were unsuitable for melting pure iron, the alumina and zirconia because of the contamination of the melt by silicon and the magnesia because of sulphur. Strong and dense crucibles can be made from calcined, chemically pure magnesia mixed with 2 per cent. of magnesium chloride and about 10 per cent. of water, and such crucibles fired to about 1600° enable pure melts to be obtained. Magnesia crucibles bonded with shellac and alcohol are also satisfactory, and materials found suitable for melting pure iron were satisfactory also for nickel.

With the idea of removing traces of sulphur, phosphorus, silicon, and occluded hydrogen, M. Crolas removed sulphates from ferric chloride by barium chloride, purified the chloride by recrystallization, and then converted the chloride to oxide for reduction with hydrogen. H. Kreusler converted purified Mohr's salt to oxalate, converted the oxalate to oxide by heating it over an ether flame, and reduced the oxide in a hard glass tube with purified electrolytic hydrogen. A. Sanfourche, L. C. Turnock, N. Parravano and P. de Cesaris, Vereinigten Stahlwerke, and O. Ruff and E. Gersten also purified the oxide before reducing it with hydrogen. T. W. Richards and G. P. Baxter dissolved electrolytic iron in purified conc. nitric acid, and after recrystallizing the nitrate a few times, treated the soln. with aq. ammonia. The washed and dried hydroxide was heated in a porcelain tube at 900° in a current of purified electrolytic hydrogen for 20 hrs. F. K. Bell and W. A. Patrick recommended heating the nitrate in hydrogen at 600° for 7 hrs. and then one hour at 1000° ; and G. P. Baxter and C. R. Hoover recommended heating the nitrate in air at 1000°, until its weight is constant, and then reducing the oxide in hydrogen at 1100° to 1150°. The process was also used by T. W. Richards and co-workers, and G. P. Baxter and co-workers. T. W. Richards and G. P. Baxter recommended the following process :

A soln. of commercial " chemically pure " ferrous chloride was treated with an excess of hydrogen sulphide, and the resulting sulphides and sulphur were removed by filtration. From the filtrate, after oxidation with nitric acid, the iron was precipitated with an excess of aq. ammonia and the precipitate was thoroughly washed by decantation. In this process traces of a number of metals which might have been present must have been removed. The precipitate was dissolved in sulphuric acid, and by cautious addition of aq. ammonia basic ferric sulphate was thrown down ; a precipitate which is more easily washed than ferric hydrate, but which was re-dissolved in sulphuric acid with considerable difficulty. In order to reduce to the ferrous state the ferric sulphate thus formed, the soln. was next subjected to the action of a galvanic current of several ampères. The soln. was contained in a large platinum dish which served as the negative electrode, the positive electrode being a flat spiral of platinum wire. Since the soln. was very conc. and contained a considerable excess of sulphuric acid, the greater part of the ferrous sulphate crystallized out when the soln. was allowed to cool. By alternately electrolyzing and cooling, almost all of the iron was eventually obtained as ferrous sulphate. The ferrous sulphate was then mixed with purified ammonium oxalate and the soln. electrolyzed—aluminium remains in soln., and manganese is deposited as peroxide on the anode. The iron was then dissolved in nitric acid and treated as before.

E. Péligot reduced ferrous chloride at a red-heat in hydrogen and obtained crystals of iron—for crystals, *vide infra*. W. Spring added that crystals of iron are formed if the reduction occurs at a high enough temp. F. Schmitz found that at 300° to 400° the reduced metal is pulverulent ; and H. Wolfram observed that the reduction is very slow at 220°, and the black product contains chlorine. A. B. Bagdasarian showed that the reduction of ferric chloride occurs in two stages : $FeCl_3 \rightarrow FeCl_2 \rightarrow Fe$. The reaction was studied by K. Jellinek and R. Koop. For the equilibrium conditions, etc., *vide infra*, ferrous chloride. F. Wöhler, G. Dragendorff, L. Mond and C. Langer, and D. Guicciardi similarly reduced dried ferrous oxalate in hydrogen ; and C. Stahlschmidt, iron nitride. The reduction of the complex cyanides—used as catalysts in formation of ammonia from a mixture of hydrogen and nitrogen at 360° to 430° and 80 to 95 atm. press.—to form α-iron was observed by A. Mittasch and E. Kuss ; and R. Brill and H. Mark, and A. Mittasch and co-workers showed that ferrous cyanide is probably formed as an intermediate stage in the reduction.

B. Lambert and J. C. Thomson heated ferric nitrate in an iridium boat so as to form ferric oxide or a basic nitrate. The product was placed in a vitreous silica tube, and heated just above 1000° in a current of hydrogen obtained by the electrolysis of a soln. of barium hydroxide. T. W. Richards and G. P. Baxter tried an analogous process, and said that when the nitrate is heated in platinum vessels, the metal always contained a trace of platinum, which remained as a residue when the product was dissolved in acid. According to F. Sauerwald, commercial ferrum reductum is usually contaminated with foreign matter. The impurities in iron prepared by reducing the purified oxide or chloride are oxide and occluded hydrogen. G. P. Baxter said that the hydrogen can be removed by melting the iron in vacuo ; and H. Kreusler added that one fusion in vacuo is not sufficient. A. Sieverts said that only 0·0002 per cent. of hydrogen is occluded at 800° ; and G. P. Baxter and C. R. Hoover showed that even if the metal is cooled in hydrogen, the occluded hydrogen is not sufficient to affect appreciably the value obtained for the at. wt. T. W. Richards and G. P. Baxter observed that small quantities of oxygen are present in iron reduced from the oxide in hydrogen at 900°. The presence of the oxide was also noted by F. Mylius, R. Schenck and T. Dingmann, and R. Ruer and J. Kuschmann—*vide infra*, ferrous oxide. Iron oxide can also be reduced to the metal by using carbon monoxide in place of hydrogen. As shown by R. Akerman and C. G. Särnström, L. Gruner, A. Guntz, S. Hilpert, H. Moissan, and K. Stammer, the product is liable to be more or less carburized—*vide supra*. A. Ledebur, L. Mathesius, and R. Schenck and T. Dingmann showed that the reduction must be conducted at a low temp., since carburization is to be avoided. The reactions are then symbolized : $Fe_3O_4 + CO \rightleftharpoons 3FeO + CO_2$; and $FeO + CO \rightleftharpoons Fe + CO_2$.

Iron pentacarbonyl, prepared by L. Mond and co-workers, was shown by M. Berthelot and G. André, and A. Stoffel to decompose when passed through a hot glass tube, depositing a thin film of iron as a mirror on the glass. A. Mittasch observed that the decomposition of the pentacarbonyl begins at about 60°, **and,** at ordinary press., is completed at 200°. The subject was studied by H. Freundlich and co-workers, the Farbenindustrie A.G., and A. Curs—*vide* **5**. 39, 27. A. Mittasch showed that it is possible to prepare iron from the carbonyl spectro-scopically free from sulphur, phosphorus, and arsenic, copper, zinc, silicon, manganese, nickel, and cobalt ; and that carbon and oxygen are alone present as impurities—possibly in the form of ferrous oxide and iron tritacarbide—*vide infra*, pyrophoric iron. A. E. van Arkel observed that metals which form an easily-dissociated compound can be obtained in a coherent form by heating a filament of the metal in an atm. of the vapour of the compound.

A. Hiorth observed that the oxide is reduced by heating it in sodium vapour ; and F. Ephraim, that the oxide or phosphate is reduced to metal by heating it with sodium amide. J. A. Poumarède reduced ferrous chloride by heating it in the vapour of zinc. F. M. Perkin and L. Pratt found that iron oxide is reduced to the metal when it is heated with calcium or calcium hydride at a bright red-heat. Z. Roussin found that magnesium precipitates iron from slightly acid soln. of ferrous and ferric salts ; some hydrogen is also evolved. A. Commaille found that magnesium precipitates hydrated ferrous oxide from a neutral soln. of ferrous sulphate, and iron from an acidified soln. H. Goldschmidt also observed that the oxide is reduced to metal by heating it with aluminium as in the alumino-thermite process ; and L. Weiss and O. Aichel, that the oxide is similarly reduced by misch-metal. According to H. Capitaine, and G. E. Davis, boiling aq. soln. of ferrous salts are reduced by zinc, yielding finely-divided iron. According to N. W. Fischer, and J. A. Poumarède, if zinc be immersed in a neutral soln. of ferrous chloride or sulphate, in a stoppered bottle, iron contaminated with much oxide is precipitated, but E. F. Anthon added that he obtained only flakes of hydrated ferrosic oxide—presumably air had access to the soln. in the latter case. H. Capitaine found that when a plate of zinc and copper, soldered together, is immersed in a neutral soln. of ferrous chloride, a friable mass of iron is deposited on the copper, and it becomes tough when heated in hydrogen. O. Prelinger observed that powdered manganese reduces iron from a soln. of ferrous sulphate. G. Gore found that a neutral soln. of ferrous sulphate deposited no iron on copper, silver, gold, brass, tin, lead, antimony, bismuth, nickel, german silver, or platinum. J. H. Gladstone and A. Tribe observed that a platinum-iron couple reduces ferric to ferrous salts more rapidly than does iron alone ; platinum alone has no action. F. M. Raoult observed no precipitation of metal from acidic or neutral, cold or hot soln. of salts of iron by a gold-iron couple. W. Ipatieff and W. Werchowsky found that if soln. of iron salts be heated in hydrogen under press., oxide and a basic salt are deposited, but with a 0·1*N*-soln. of iron acetate at 400°, in hydrogen at 420 atm. press., a small proportion of spongy iron separates out.

M. Zängerle, and W. Engelhardt obtained the metal by heating ferrous oxalate with a mixture of potassium ferrocyanide and carbonate, and extracting the product with water ; and A. Brochet, by heating ferrous formate in a closed vessel. C. Broling tried to purify iron by melting iron filings with a quarter of their weight of smithy scales under a layer of green glass in a luted crucible at a high temp. ; and L. Troost, by heating iron in a lime crucible by means of an oxyhydrogen flame, finishing off with the flame strengthened with oxygen—the oxidized impurities are absorbed by the crucible.

According to A. C. Becquerel [3] the electrolysis of a conc. soln. of ferrous sulphate or chloride results in the deposition of small granules of iron on the negative platinum ; with sodium chloride, separated from the soln. of ferrous salt by moist clay, glittering crystals of iron are deposited, and they exhibit magnetic polarity. R. Böttger in 1846 also described the electrodeposition of iron, and later on observations were made by H. Krämer, and F. Varrentrapp. In 1846, M. Boch-Buschmann and M. Liet prepared plates 2 mm. thick, and H. Meidinger in 1867 and H. Bouilhet in 1868 prepared plates and galvanoplastic moulds of iron by processes which, according to L. Guillet, were secret. In 1868, E. Klein and H. Jacobi prepared iron electrodes for printing bank-notes in Russia. D. Belcher, S. O. Cowper-Coles, L. Guillet, W. E. Hughes, D. R. Kellog, and W. A. Macfadyen discussed the application of the electrodeposition of iron to the production of finished iron sheets and tubes in one operation, and the repair of worn parts of machinery.

According to F. Förster, neutral soln. of ferrous sulphate do not give good results as electrolyte for the electrodeposition of iron, since at ordinary temp. the resistance is high and disturbances are caused by the liberation of hydrogen at the cathode. The need for the employment of high current densities favours the liberation of hydrogen at the cathode. This makes the deposit brittle and hard. With low current densities, at low temp., the deposition is slow, but the contamination with occluded hydrogen is relatively small. These conclusions were established by the work of H. Lee, S. Maximowitsch, A. Müller, and A. Ryss and A. Bogomolny. A. Watt observed that the results are better if the temp. of the bath be raised to 60° or 70°. F. Förster said that with the simple sulphate the best working temp. is 80°; A. Pfaff gave 70°; and W. A. Macfadyen found 65° gave the best results with Mohr's salt—ammonium ferrous sulphate. The increased temp. lessens contamination with occluded hydrogen and enables high current densities to be employed. Observations were also made by M. Schlötter, and G. Tischtschenko and H. Plauson. The electrolysis of neutral soln. was discussed by E. F. Kern, S. Pagliani, and A. Skrabal. According to G. Langbein, if the bath tends to become acid, a few linen bags containing magnesium carbonate can be suspended in the liquid; and if the bath becomes alkaline, the deposit acquires a matt appearance and is liable to peel off—in that case a few drops of dil. sulphuric acid or, better, citric acid will restore neutrality. The subject was discussed by N. H. M. Dekker, O. Mustad, F. Förster, S. Maximowitsch, A. S. Ramage, and C. J. Reed. F. Förster added that better results are obtained by working with a bath slightly acid. This prevents the hydrolysis of the electrolyte, and lessens the contamination of the cathode deposit with occluded hydrogen, which makes the iron brittle and hard. Acetic or oxalic acid gives satisfactory results. A. Skrabal used dil. sulphuric acid in a bath of ammonium ferrous oxalate; A. Pfaff, and H. Lee, dil. sulphuric acid in a bath of ferrous sulphate free from ferric salt; F. Förster, and O. Mustad, boric acid in a soln. of ferrous sulphate; T. Moore, metaphosphoric acid in a soln. of ferric sulphate and an excess of ammonium carbonate.

The use of ferrous sulphate alone is not usually recommended, since the bath is liable to become turbid soon after it has been in use. F. Varrentrapp therefore recommended the addition of ammonium salts to the electrolyte. This, said F. Förster, keeps down the conc. of the OH'-ions in the vicinity of the cathode and thus prevents the deposition of ferrous hydroxide. K. Arndt, T. P. Thomas, A. Pfaff, and H. Lee recommended the addition of ammonium sulphate; and A. Hiorns, A. Skrabal, R. Amberg, A. Müller, E. Klein and H. Jacobi, C. F. Burgess and C. Hambüchen, W. C. McWilliams, A. Neuberger, A. Ryss and A. Bogomolny, C. H. Desch and E. M. Vellan, W. H. Gee, D. Belcher, W. E. Hughes, G. Gore, W. H. Walenn, and S. A. Tucker and E. Schramm recommended using ammonium ferrous sulphate. W. A. Macfadyen found that thick, adherent deposits of iron on a steel base could be readily obtained from dil. soln. of ferrous ammonium sulphate at ordinary temp., but the deposition proceeds slowly. With conc. soln. equally good results were produced at about seven times the speed obtained with dil. soln. The deposits were very sensitive to the acidity of the soln.; an acidity of $0.005N$-H_2SO_4 gave the best results. With a temp. of 50° deposition from a conc. soln. occurred about fifty times as rapidly as with a cold, dil. soln. The yield is 90 to 95 per cent. of the theoretical with a soln. containing 50 to 100 grms. of Mohr's salt per litre and acidified to $0.005N$-H_2SO_4, using a current density of 0.86 to 2.48 amps. per sq. dm. The purification of iron by electrodeposition from a bath of Mohr's salt was described by R. Amberg, S. O. Cowper-Coles, W. M. Johnson, H. Lovelock, A. Müller, and W. Palmaer and J. A. Brinell.

The addition of ammonium chloride to the ferrous sulphate bath—say 1 : 2—

has been recommended by R. Böttger, C. F. Burgess, A. Hiorns, E. Klein and H. Jacobi, H. Krämer, R. Lenz, G. F. McMahon, W. Pfanhauser, N. B. Pilling, F. A. Shepherd, B. Speed and G. W. Elmen, B. Stoughton, F. Varrentrapp, and T. D. Yensen. The addition of sodium sulphate to the ferrous sulphate bath in order to increase the conductivity of the soln. was recommended by M. Schlötter, and E. F. Kern; P. A. Govaerts and P. M. Wenmaekers added sodium thiosulphate and enough organic acid to produce an incipient decomposition of the thiosulphate. Small potential differences may be used and thick, strongly adherent deposits of iron obtained. Langbein-Pfanhauser Werke, and F. Fischer added sodium chloride to the ferrous sulphate bath; and A. Boucher, and Société de Fer Grenoble, ferrous chloride—O. P. Watts and M. H. Li used a mixture of ferrous sulphate and ferrous chloride (150 : 75 grms.) and 6 grms. of ammonium oxalate (or 0·6 grm. of hexamethylene tetramine) per litre. C. Kadota recommended a soln. of ferrous chloride equivalent to 10 to 15 per cent. Fe; 12 per cent. sodium chloride; and 0·005 to 0·008N-HCl; and a current density of 3 to 7 amps. per sq. dm. at 85°.

The use of complex salts hinders the separation of iron hydroxide and raises the conductivity of the soln. This method was adopted by F. Varrentrapp in 1868. According to S. Maximowitsch, a very good method of preparing electrolytic iron is to make a soln. containing 20 per cent. of ferrous sulphate, $FeSO_4,7H_2O$, and 5 per cent. of magnesium sulphate, $MgSO_4,7H_2O$; and 25 grms. of sodium hydrocarbonate were dissolved in this soln. The skin of ferric hydroxide which forms on the surface protects the bath from further oxidation. The precipitate is allowed to settle to the bottom and to remain undisturbed; a wrought-iron anode and a copper cathode (thinly silvered and iodized) are used. The bath is kept continuously at work, and 20 to 25 grms. of sodium hydrocarbonate are added about twice a week. The iron formed improves in quality as time goes on, finally reaching a strength of 1580 kgrms. per sq. cm., and being so soft that it can be bent at a sharp angle without breaking. The best current density was found to be 0·3 amp. per sq. dm., and the current efficiency, 97 to 99 per cent. The brittleness commonly found with electrolytic iron is here absent, and this is attributed to the low acidity of the bath, which does not favour the occlusion of hydrogen. A. Ryss and A. Bogomolny found that both the magnesium sulphate and sodium hydrocarbonate are essential constituents of the bath, and that the best conditions are : current density, with a rotating cathode, 0·003 amp. per sq. cm. ; and an electrolytic bath of 200 grms. of ferrous ammonium sulphate or ferrous chloride, 50 grms. of magnesium sulphate, and 5 grms. of sodium hydrocarbonate per litre of water at a temp. of 15° to 18°. During the electrolysis, 4 to 5 grms. of sodium hydrocarbonate per litre are added at intervals of 3 days. The effects of various additions were tried, but no improvement in the deposit was observed. The addition of magnesium sulphate to enhance the conductivity of the ferrous sulphate soln. was favoured by E. Klein and H. Jacobi, W. C. Roberts-Austen, W. C. McWilliams, F. Haber, R. Amberg, C. F. Burgess and C. Hambüchen, W. Pfanhauser, O. Mustad, and V. Kohlschütter and H. Stäger. H. D. Hineline studied the electrodeposition of iron from a bath of iron sulphite and calcium sulphite.

According to A. Skrabal, iron of a high degree of purity is produced by using iron deposited electrolytically on platinum as the anode in a soln. of purified ferrous sulphate, as recommended by C. Stammer, or ferrous ammonium sulphate, as used by R. Böttger, H. Meidinger, etc., with a platinum foil as cathode and an e.m.f. of 0·4 volt. According to R. Amberg, and A. Müller, iron deposited from sulphate soln. is contaminated with sulphates—0·0050 to 0·0099 per cent. sulphur was found in iron from a sulphate bath, and 0·0024 to 0·0029 per cent. in iron from a chloride bath. When iron of a high degree of purity is to be prepared electrolytically, care must be taken to have an electrolyte of a high degree of purity. On the other hand, C. F. Burgess and C. Hambüchen, W. M. Hicks and L. T. O'Shea, H. Lee, and A. Skrabal observed virtually no sulphur in electrolytic iron; and with a conc., feebly acidic soln. of ferrous sulphate, at 70°, a current density of 2 amps. per sq. dm., and agitating the electrolyte by a current of gas, A. Pfaff observed only traces of sulphur in the electrodeposited iron ; for instance, with soln. acidified with 6, 12, and 13 per cent. of acid, the respective proportions of sulphur averaged 0·00030, 0·00065, and 0·00065 ; C. F. Burgess and C. Hambüchen obtained only 0·00018 per cent. of sulphur in electrodeposited iron ; W. C. Roberts-Austen, 0·005 ; J. O. Arnold, 0·15 ; O. W. Storey, 0·001 ; L. Guillet, 0·006 ; T. D. Yensen, 0·003 ; J. Billiter, 0·016 ; A. Vosmaer, 0·006 ; G. P. Fuller, 0·004 ; N. B. Pilling, 0·005 ; A. Bouchayer, 0·0048 ; and J. Escard, traces. According to A. Müller, the soluble anodes employed in the purification of iron should be as free from sulphur and carbon as practicable. L. Houllevigue found that with an anode of steel rapidly cooled from 900° the iron deposited on the cathode contained only 0·003 per cent. of carbon, whereas when the steel anode was slowly cooled, the cathodic iron had 0·033 to 0·035 per cent. of carbon. The subject was discussed by N. H. M. Dekker, H. Gerdien, W. A. Macfadyen, G. Masing, K. Oma, W. Pfanhauser, A. S. Ramage, and C. Tschappet. W. M. Hicks and L. T. O'Shea enclosed the anode of Swedish iron in a porous pot, to prevent the spongy carbon which separates from the anode reaching the cathode and interfering with the deposition. Any ferric hydroxide suspended in the electrolyte might interfere with the adhesion of the deposit if it settled on the cathode. Hence, in practice, deep tanks are used for the baths to allow the sediment to settle. A. Bouchayer, British Thomson-Houston Co., S. O. Cowper-Coles, F. Exner, and the Société Anonyme des Aciéries Firminy considered the rotation or oscillation of the anode during the electrolysis. E. Duhme prepared iron of 99·994 per cent. purity by the electrolysis of a cold sat. soln. of ferrous chloride containing magnesium chloride and free acid eq. to less than 0·01N. The anode may consist of steel or even cast iron. The cathode is rotated inside a stationary auxiliary cathode on which a small secondary alternating current (of which the negative component is greater than the positive) is superposed. A porous earthenware U-tube is arranged round the cathode and a current of air is blown through the tube. At the bottom of the cell a number of permanent magnets sealed into thin glass tubes serve to collect the particles of carbide and silicide that fall from the anode. V. Kohlschütter and F. Jakober found that the effect of superposing an alternating on the direct current is to lessen the percentage current-yield.

The electrodeposition of iron from soln. of ferrous or ferric chloride was studied by H. Buff, A. Geuther, W. Hittorf, H. Krämer, and J. Thiele. According to A. Ryss and A. Bogomolny, if ferrous chloride is electrolyzed—equal weights of water and of the salt—the temp. of the bath should be 60° to 70° ; the current density at the cathode should not exceed 0·004 amp. per sq. cm. ; rapid rotation of the cathode improves the quality of the deposit. E. Kelsen used a mixture of ferrous chloride, 122·5 grms. ; calcium chloride, 109 grms. ; potassium chloride, 110 grms. ; and water, 525 grms. Observations were also made by R. Amberg, D. Belcher, A. Boucher, C. T. Thomas and W. Blum, Chemische Fabrik Griesheim-Elektron, J. R. Cain and co-workers, T. P. McCutcheon and E. F. Smith, W. E. Hughes, H. Lee, S. I. Levy and G. W. Gray, E. Merck, R. H. Monk and R. J. Traill, A. Müller, A. Pfaff, A. Pertsch, W. Pip, A. S. Ramage, J. H. Paterson, M. Schlötter, O. Spinzig and A. Wannag, and G. Vié. According to W. A. Noyes, the minimum potential required for the electrolysis of an aq. soln. of ferrous salt is 0·66 volt at 20° when electrodes of electrolytic iron are employed ; this value decreases with a rise of temp., attaining a minimum at 110° ; a further rise of temp. is attended by an increased voltage. W. M. Hicks and L. T. O'Shea used a 5 per cent. soln. of ferrous chloride with enough ammonium chloride to make up the ratio $FeCl_2 : NH_4Cl = 1 : 2$. A clean copper plate was used as cathode, and a plate of Swedish iron in a porous cell as anode. A current density of 0·08 to 0·2 amp. per sq. dm. and 0·7 volt was used. The iron content of the bath should not fall below 4 per cent. $FeCl_2$. M. L. V. Gayler recommended the process for the preparation of iron of a high degree of purity. The contamination of the deposited iron with chlorides was discussed by R. Amberg, G. F. McMahon, W. Sontag, and A. Müller. In C. F. Burgess and C. Hambüchen's process for the electrolytic purification of iron the electrolyte, at 30°, consists of a soln. of ferrous chloride mixed with ammonium chloride or sulphate ; the cathode current density is 0·7 to 1·1 amp. per sq. dm. The anode consists of wrought iron or steel. The current yield is 90 to 100 per cent. The process was discussed by G. F. McMahon, and B. Speed and G. W. Elmen. As an example, the anode of iron to be purified contained 0·06 per cent. C, 0·05 P, 0·23 Si, 0·3 to 0·5 Mn, and 0·10 S ; whilst the cathodic deposit of electrolytic iron contained 0·014 per cent. C, 0·013 P, 0·028 Si, 0·029 Mn, and 0·003 S. Société de Fer Grenoble, A. Boucher, and A. Bouchayer developed a process for purifying pig-iron by using it as a rotating anode in a bath of ferrous chloride or sulphate, or a mixture of both. The process was examined by D. Belcher, J. Escard, L. Guillet, and B. Stoughton. H. Krämer, and H. Meidinger observed that with a soln. of ammonium chloride and ferrous sulphate as electrolyte the iron obtained contained both chloride and nitride.

According to A. T. C. Estelle, iron can be obtained by electrodeposition from a suspension of ferric oxide in a hot conc. soln. of sodium hydroxide. The process was examined by S. J. Lloyd, who found that the current efficiency is high, and the estimated power consumption is 3000 to 3300 kw.-hrs. per ton of iron. C. P. Perin and F. A. Eustis proposed to obtain electrolytic iron from sulphide ores by first grinding the ore to a pulp with spent electrolyte—a mixture of ferric and ferrous chlorides. There is a reaction : $2FeCl_3+FeS=3FeCl_2+S$, which is nearly complete with pyrrhotite and about 60 per cent. completion with pyrite. Any copper which passes into soln. is precipitated by metallic iron. The soln. is then electrolyzed in a diaphragm cell with graphite anodes. Iron is deposited in the cathode compartment, and ferric chloride is formed in the anode compartment. The electrolyte is kept in circulation, and its concentration does not exceed 70 grms. per litre of $FeCl_3$, and about the same with $FeCl_2$. When conditions are right, iron is deposited at high current efficiency, exceeding 95 per cent. That is to say, 1 grm. of iron may be had per ampère-hour. The amount per kilowatt-hour depends, of course, on the resistance of the cell, which in turn depends upon the composition and temp. of the electrolyte, but more particularly on the current density. For instance, other conditions being equal, a current density of 20 ampères per sq. foot requires 1 volt, 40 ampères 2 volts, and 160 ampères 4 volts. Modifications of the process for titanium ores were made by R. H. Monk and R. J. Traill ; somewhat similar principles were applied by W. Pip, R. D. Pike and co-workers, R. J. Traill and W. R. McClelland, and A. J. Moxham. F. Förster, and O. Mustad obtained good results by additions of boric acid to the bath of ferric chloride ; E. F. Kern, S. A. Tucker and E. Schramm, J. R. Cain and co-workers, F. Fischer, Langbein-Pfanhauser Werke, C. Arzano and G. Clerici, F. Förster, H. Plauson and G. Tischtschenko, G. Vié, A. Nodon and A. Lecandre, W. C. McWilliams, H. Lee, Allgemeine Elektrizitäts-Gesellschaft, A. Pfaff, and G. F. McMahon used additions of sodium or ammonium chloride ; and F. Fischer, H. D. Hineline, W. E. Hughes, and Langbein-Pfanhausen Werke used additions of calcium or magnesium chloride. H. D. Hineline also recommended a bath of 200 grms. each of $FeCl_2$ and $CaCl_2$, 20 grms. of chromous chloride, and 5 grms. of hydroquinone per litre at 30°, with a current density of 2·7 to 8 amps. per sq. dm.

E. F. Kern obtained a deposit of brittle, dark grey iron contaminated with some silica by the electrolysis of a sat. soln. of iron in 31 per cent. hydrofluosilicic acid, using a current density of 1 to 2 amps. per sq. dm. and 0·9 to 1·2 volts at 20°, or 0·51 to 0·70 volt at 60°. E. F. K. Harbeck obtained good results with additions of alkali or alkaline earth sulphates, chlorides, or fluorides. H. Oettinger used a soln. containing some free hydrofluoric acid ; and H. Plauson and G. Tischtschenko, soln. of fluosilicates or fluoborosilicates. M. Schlötter electrolyzed soln. of ferrous perchlorate—say 100 grms. $FeCl_2$, 200 grms. $Fe(ClO_4)_2$, and 2 grms. perchloric acid in a litre of water—and obtained a deposit with a very fine-grained crystalline structure. A. Brand electrolyzed an ammoniacal soln. of sodium ferrous or ferric pyrophosphate ; T. Moore, a soln. containing ferric sulphate, metaphosphoric acid, and ammonium carbonate ; G. Gore, and R. Böttinger, a soln. of potassium ferrocyanide ; and G. Gore, a soln. of potassium ferrate. The general subject was discussed by G. Fuseya and co-workers.

G. Vortmann used as electrolyte a soln. of a ferrous salt mixed with an alkali tartrate and hydroxide, and A. K. Balls and C. C. McDonnell used a similar soln. with the alkali hydroxide in considerable excess. A. T. C. Estelle found that iron can be obtained by the electrolysis of the slime obtained by the action of alkali hydroxide or carbonate on iron oxide at a high temp. Iron alloys were also obtained by using a mixture of oxides instead of iron oxide alone. F. K. Bezzenberger obtained iron by the electrolysis of a soln. of ferrous sulphate containing in suspension precipitated iron hydroxide. A. Simon electrolyzed soln. of ferric oxide in molten calcium fluoride, when phosphorus and silicon if present are liberated from the anode as fluorides. Carbon electrodes and a current density of 600 to 700 amps. per sq. dm. were employed.

R. H. Aiken electrolyzed molten ferrous silicate containing lime or magnesia and iron oxide in soln. The electrodeposition of iron from molten electrolytes was discussed by J. W. Beckman, G. Hofer, F. Sauerwald, and F. Sauerwald and G. Neuendorff. E. M. Chance employed an anode of fused sulphide, and with fused sodium metasilicate as electrolyte and a steel cathode. He found that copper, nickel, and iron could be separately deposited, in the order named, by raising the current density. Sulphur, arsenic, and antimony volatilized at the anode. R. H. Aiken found that when a molten sulphide is electrolyzed, copper and nickel, if present, are first deposited and iron sulphide remains. By increasing the current density iron is deposited. The subject was studied by T. D. Yensen, and R. D. Pike and co-workers.

W. Hampe, and A. H. W. Aten and co-workers obtained iron by the electrolysis of the fused chloride. F. Krupp proposed to refine cast iron by using it as anode in molten halides. S. Grünauer found that in the electrolysis of a mixture of fused zinc and ferric chlorides the iron deposited on the cathode before the zinc ; and H. J. Blikslager obtained a similar result with a fused mixture of ferrous and manganous chlorides at 470°. F. Andersen showed that the electrolysis of a mixture of ferrous chloride and a fused eutectic mixture of potassium and lithium chlorides gives iron of a high degree of purity.

Iron can be readily deposited from soln. where the iron is present as a complex salt of organic acids. Thus A. Neuburger, and K. Schild used an electrolyte of ferrous sulphate mixed with ammonium oxalate ; F. Exner, and W. Fischer, a soln. of ammonium ferric sulphate and ammonium oxalate ; and A. Classen and co-workers, G. Parodi and A. Mascazzini, A. Skrabal, S. Avery and B. Dales, W. Sontag, H. Verwer and F. Groll, and J. Früh, ferric or ferrous sulphate or chloride and ammonium oxalate. Platinum foil was often used as cathode and a platinum wire as anode, with a current density of 0·01 amp. per sq. cm. at 20°. Salts of other acids, carbonates, formates, acetates, succinates, tartrates, and citrates have also been tried by S. Avery and B. Dales, R. Ehrenfeld, P. K. Frölich, A. Skrabal, J. Früh, M. Heidenreich, G. Luckow, R. Kremann and co-workers, O. Orlandi, H. Schmidt, E. F. Smith, and H. Verwer. The addition of other organic substances has been tried. A. Ryss and A. Bogomolny observed no particular advantage to attend the addition of various alcohols, organic acids, esters, aldehydes, or ketones ; and O. P. Watts and N. H. Li, the addition of phenols, bases, sugar, and colloids, although formaldehyde and hexamethylenetetramine exerted a favourable influence. R. Kremann and co-workers tried additions of glycerol ; M. Schlötter, glycol, chlorhydrin, and dichlorhydrin ; E. H. Archibald and L. A. Pignet, soln. of ferric chloride in acetone, ethyl alcohol, and mixtures of acetone with water or alcohol. W. A. Macfadyen obtained poor results with glue, gelatin, and β-naphthol ; and

S. O. Cowper-Coles, creosol and sulphuric acid. S. O. Cowper-Coles' process was examined by E. H. Archibald and L. A. Pignet, D. Belcher, W. Heyn, and B. Neumann.

The contamination of iron with carbon when the metal is deposited from electrolytes containing organic acids has been observed. E. F. Smith and F. Muhr said that tartrates give a variable proportion of carbon; G. Parodi and A. Mascazzini, that oxalate soln. gave a deposit with 0·5 per cent. of carbon— S. Avery and B. Dales, 0·21 to 0·42 per cent.; E. F. Smith, that citrate soln. gave a deposit with 0·5 per cent. These results are high, and much smaller proportions were observed by H. Verwer and F. Groll. The subject was also discussed by E. H. Archibald and L. A. Pignet, L. Balbiano and A. Alessi, F. Förster, P. K. Frölich, A. Glazunoff and A. Rozmus, A. Müller, G. Lambris, C. P. Madsen, H. Schmidt, A. Skrabal, W. Sontag, J. Tafel and G. Friedrichs, and H. Verwer. With electrolytic iron obtained by other processes J. Billiter reported 0·06 per cent. of carbon; A. Bouchayer, 0·029; C. F. Burgess and C. Hambuechen, 0·013; O. W. Storey, 0·012; T. D. Yensen, 0·010; J. Escard, 0·008; G. P. Fuller, 0·006; N. B. Pilling, 0·005; A. Vosmaer, 0·004; and E. Duhme, 0·002. W. C. Roberts-Austen prepared electrolytic iron from a soln. of ferrous and magnesium sulphates of so high a degree of purity that the metal contained only 0·007 per cent. of carbon and 0·005 per cent. of sulphur. K. Oma found that iron deposited from ammonium ferrous sulphate baths may contain 0·001 per cent. of sulphur as sulphide derived from the anode material, and 0·02 to 0·03 per cent. as sulphate derived from the electrolyte. At high temp. the sulphate may be reduced to sulphide and then to hydrogen sulphide. The rate of desulphurization by hydrogen above 800° is a function of time, temp., and grain-size.

Iron has also been deposited from soln. of its salts in non-aqueous solvents by electrolysis between platinum electrodes. Thus J. Timmermans used a soln. of ferric chloride in methyl chloride; H. E. Patten and W. R. Mott, a soln. of ferric chloride in acetone at ordinary temp. and with a large current density; and E. H. Archibald and L. A. Pignet, a soln. of ferric chloride in acetone, ethyl alcohol, and mixtures of the two. The iron is free from carbon when deposited from the acetone soln. At low voltages the iron is in the metallic state, but at higher voltages the deposit is red. The iron deposited from the acetone-alcohol soln. is contaminated with carbon. H. Röhler obtained no electrodeposit from soln. of iron salts in formamide; L. F. Audrieth and L. F. Yntema, and H. S. Booth and M. Merlub-Sobel obtained a similar result with soln. in liquid ammonia. H. E. Williams electrolyzed a soln. of ferric chloride in ether, and found that with high current densities and conc. soln. iron is deposited, but with dil. soln. and low current densities ferrous chloride is formed. R. Müller and co-workers found that a soln. of ferrous bromide in pyridine at ordinary temp. furnishes deposits of grey, passive iron. G. Fuseya and co-workers examined the effect of glycerol on the electrolyte to find if it enters the electrodeposit and influences the grain-size.

Analyses of electrolytic iron have been reported by J. Billiter, A. Bouchayer, C. F. Burgess and C. Hambüchen, E. Duhme, J. Escard, G. P. Fuller, L. Guillet, N. B. Pilling, O. W. Storey, and T. D. Yensen. The proportion of iron ranges from 99·963 to 99·971 per cent. The proportion of carbon—*vide supra*—ranges from 0·002 to 0·060 per cent.; and that of sulphur—*vide supra*—from mere traces to 0·016 per cent. The proportion of phosphorus ranges from 0·0001 to 0·041 per cent., and observations on the subject were also made by S. Avery and B. Dales, E. Duhme, L. Guillet and A. Portevin, and T. Moore. The silicon content ranges from 0·001 to 0·11 per cent. The manganese content was discussed by A. Pfaff; the copper, by G. P. Fuller; the lead, by G. Tammann; 0·004 per cent. of arsenic was reported by J. Billiter; and the oxygen or oxide content, by E. F. K. Harbeck, E. F. Kern, and A. Skrabal; for the chloride content, *vide supra*; and for the proportion of occluded gases, *vide infra*, the chemical properties of iron.

T. D. Yensen recommended fusing electrodeposited iron in vacuo in order to reduce the proportion of impurities, and he found that the metal so obtained had a permeability two or three times greater than that previously obtained for the iron of the highest degree of purity. G. K. Burgess, E. Duhme, and O. W. Storey discussed the preparation of iron of a higher degree of purity.

Electrolytic iron is not homogeneous, since it contains gas pores, occluded gases, and foreign inclusions, and L. Schäfer emphasized the fact that it is liable to have a lamellar structure. A. Skrabal's observations on two forms of electrolytic iron are discussed below. V. Kohlschütter said that the crystalline character of electro-deposited iron is determined by the mode of arrangement of the individual crystals to form the aggregate, as well as the form, habit, and size of the individual crystals. As in other crystallization processes, growth of existing crystals and formation of new nuclei are differently affected by changing conditions, and wide variations in the character of such deposits are possible. C. Marie and N. Thon discussed the subject.

Numerous factors may operate in determining the character of the cathodic deposit, for the growth of the deposit is affected not only by the forces of crystalliza-tion but also probably by the forces in soln. A. K. Graham, G. Eger, R. Glocker and E. Kaupp, R. H. Greaves, and R. Audubert discussed the structure of electro-lytic iron, and of the factors concerned in the production of symmetrical, columnar, fibrous, and powdery deposits. For V. Kohlschütter and E. Vuilleumier's observa-tions on the formation of a colloidal, highly dispersed layer on the cathode in the first stages of the electrolysis, vide nickel. According to W. Blum and H. S. Rawdon, the cathodic discharge of metal-ions and the formation of crystals constitute one and the same process, and any given ion is discharged at the point at which the lowest discharge potential is required. The discharge potential is a function of the soln. press. of the metal and the " effective " metal-ion concentration adjacent to it. The single potential and solution pressure of a metal are the resultant of the " primary single potential," which is defined in terms of the solution pressure of a single unorientated atom, and the " orientation potential," which is a measure of the diminution in solution pressure and corresponding algebraic increase in single metal potential caused by the orientation of the adjacent metal atoms. A higher potential is required to discharge an ion in a position unrelated to those of previously discharged atoms than on an existing crystal, and similarly a higher potential is required to discharge an ion on a small crystal than on a large one. There are three main types of structure : (i) those in which all, or practically all, the initial nuclei continue to grow ; (ii) those in which only part of the initial nuclei continues to grow ; and (iii) those in which none of the initial nuclei continue to grow.

According to V. Kohlschütter and F. Jakober, the superposition of an alternating current on the direct current during the electrolysis tends to make the crystalline structure coarse-grained. The orientation of the crystals was discussed by R. Audubert, A. Müller, R. M. Bozorth, F. Förster, W. E. Hughes, W. A. Macfadyen, L. B. Hunt, and O. W. Storey. According to O. W. Storey, electrolytic iron changes to the usual fine-grained structure at the A_3-arrest, and no change was observed when this form of iron was heated at a lower temp. The manufacture of electrolytic iron has been described by F. Sauerwald and G. Neuendorff, S. J. Lloyd, C. Hambüchen, G. P. Fuller, T. Johnston, F. A. Eustis and C. P. Perrin, A. Bouchayer, E. C. Kreutzberg, T. W. S. Huchins, F. N. Budgen, D. Belcher, R. H. Monk and R. J. Traill, W. A. Noyes, W. E. Hughes, A. Levasseur, D. R. Kellogg, G. F. McMahon, N. B. Pilling, R. P. Neville and J. R. Cain, B. Stoughton, H. D. Hineline, M. L. V. Gayler, and R. Dupuis.

In some of the old bloomery processes for extracting iron from its ores, the metal was obtained as a more or less spongy mass. The product furnished by A. Chenot's [4] process is in the form of **spongy iron**—*éponge métallique*. Spongy iron was extracted in Sweden, before the 1914–18 war, and exported for use in the open-hearth process. Alternate layers of iron ore and coal were heated by producer gas at a temp. between 1050° and 1200°. According to J. O. Handy, the spongy iron has 96 to 97 per cent. Fe ; 0·01 to 0·02, S ; 0·012, P ; and 1·4, Si. E. P. Barrett described the production

of spongy iron and the absorption of sulphur by that form of metal.   The subject
was discussed by B. Stoughton, E. P. Barrett, F. Wüst, W. Rohland, A. Adams,
G. Mars, J. von Ehrenwerth, S. E. Sieurin, E. de Billy, C. E. Williams and co-workers,
C. A. Keller, A. E. Bourcoud, F. Krupp, M. Wiberg, W. W. Percy, J. Y. Johnson,
N. K. G. Tholand, B. Britton, and P. Longmuir—*vide supra*.   P. Longmuir
found the iron contents varied from 90 to 97 per cent., and, in addition, contained
4 per cent. of oxygen ; 1·3, C ; 5·2, Si and slag ; 0·2, P, Mn, etc.   As shown by
F. Hatton, spongy iron can be used as a reducing agent in organic chemistry.   By
its aid combined nitrogen is reduced to free nitrogen, and in some cases methane is
produced.

G. Magnus [5] obtained powdered and **pyrophoric iron** by reducing many
compounds of iron in a current of hydrogen at a relatively low temp.—between 360°
and 420°.   L. Troost and P. Hautefeuille also obtained it from ferric oxide ;
F. Wöhler, M. Zängerle, F. Göbel, A. Vogel, S. Birnie, and G. S. Newth also obtained
it by reducing the oxide, carbonate, or oxalate with hydrogen or carbon dioxide.
F. Wüst and P. Rütten observed that the minette ore gives pyrophoric iron when
reduced in hydrogen.   H. Moissan obtained it by heating the oxalate at about
440° ;   A. Smits and co-workers, from ferrous tartrate, citrate, chloride, or oxide at
about 350° ;   T. G. Finzel, from hydrated ferric oxide free from chlorides ;   C. J. Sims
and E. W. J. Mardles, and A. Mittasch and co-workers, by the decomposition of iron
pentacarbonyl ;   and A. Job and R. Reich, by the action of ethyl magnesium
bromide on ferrous iodide.   H. Moissan observed that the reduction of ferric
oxide is very slow at 435°, and 96 hrs. were needed to obtain iron free from ferrous
oxide ;   the reduction proceeds rapidly at 600°, but the product is not pyrophoric.
G. Magnus observed that pyrophoric iron prepared from a mixture of ferric oxide
and alumina retains its pyrophoric quality after heating to redness, but S. Birnie
found that when prepared from the oxalate it loses its pyrophoric quality at 470°,
but not when heated in nitrogen or hydrogen at 430° to 440°.   G. Tammann and
N. Nikitin observed that iron obtained by reducing the oxide in hydrogen at 370°
to 530° is pyrophoric, but above 530° it is not pyrophoric ;   and A. Smits and
G. Wallach were able to obtain pyrophoric iron by reducing the oxide at 600°,
and found that its activity decreased steadily as the temp. was raised to 710°,
beyond which the iron was no longer pyrophoric.   The reduction occupied an hour
and a half, and thoroughly dried hydrogen was employed.   The best temp. was
found to be 450°, when the reduction occupied 5 hrs.   M. Siewert stated that the
iron loses its pyrophoric qualities if kept in hydrogen for 12 hrs., but this has not
been confirmed ;   A. Smits and co-workers found that the pyrophoric quality is
lost when the iron is heated in a high vacuum at 300°, and there is a marked decrease
in the pyrophoric quality when heated to 650° in purified dry hydrogen.   F. Wüst
and P. Rütten found that the pyrophoric iron from minette ore loses its pyrophoric
quality if heated in hydrogen at 700° ;   and K. Hofmann found that natural ferric
oxide is pyrophoric when reduced below 600° for less than 45 mins., but if heated for
a longer time the reduced iron is no longer pyrophoric.   T. G. Finzel observed that
the pyrophoric quality is retained in dry air at −78°.

The general idea is that the temp. of the reduction employed in the preparation
of pyrophoric iron is so low that a skeleton framework of iron atoms remains where
the iron oxide molecule was present, and that the thermal movement of the atoms of
iron at the low temp. is too sluggish to allow of their orientation into the dense
and more compact crystalline state which is the stable form at that temp.   In
consequence, pyrophoric iron is wholly or partly in the colloidal state, pseudomorphous after iron oxide.   G. Magnus attributed the pyrophoric quality to the
extremely finely-divided state of the product of the low-temperature reduction, and
if the reduction occurs at a higher temp., the product is coarser grained.   The
absorption of oxygen by the fine-grained powder is enough to raise the temp. to the
ignition point.   The oxidation of occluded hydrogen by the metal was also thought
by G. Magnus, and L. Troost and P. Hautefeuille to have some influence on the

result. S. Birnie added that the presence of finely-divided carbon has no positive influence on the pyrophoric quality. F. Stromeyer, and J. W. Gilles considered that the presence of lower oxides which have escaped reduction favours the pyrophoric quality. B. Osann, K. Hofmann, F. Sauerwald and G. Elsner, and G. Tammann and co-workers agree that the pyrophoric quality depends on the extent of the free surface exposed by the powder to air ; but A. Smits and co-workers could detect no difference in the sizes of the particles of pyrophoric and non-pyrophoric iron, and they conclude that the pyrophoric quality is due to the metal being in a metastable state. W. Frankenburger and K. Mayrhofer heated a spiral of iron in an atm. of nitrogen at 0·1 to 0·01 mm. press., while the vessel was cooled in liquid nitrogen. They thus obtained finely divided or " atomized " iron.

In 1787, M. van Marum [6] obtained deposits of thin films, the so-called **iron mirrors,** of iron on glass by passing an oscillating electric discharge through a thin iron wire. M. Faraday also obtained thin films by cathodic spluttering in hydrogen. K. Lauch and W. Ruppert obtained a film on a polished crystal of rock salt by means of cathodic spluttering, and then removed the salt with water. This furnished a thin, elastic film of the metal. A. W. Wright emphasized the importance of preparing the films in an atmosphere free from oxygen and moisture. The results are good when the spluttering occurs either in vacuo or in an atmosphere of hydrogen gas ; B. Dessau said that an atm. of hydrogen at 1 mm. press. gives good results. Observations were also made by F. Braun, H. Freundlich and co-workers, J. de Kowalsky, A. Kundt, L. R. Ingersoll, J. Moser, A. Skinner and A. Q. Tool, J. Strong and C. H. Cartwright, W. W. Nicholas, A. Ungerer, G. P. Thomson, J. Y. Johnson, and S. Procopiu. J. Y. Johnson, and H. Freundlich and co-workers obtained a mirror by the thermal decomposition of iron pentacarbonyl in an evacuated glass vessel. According to R. Brill, the grain-size of iron liberated by the thermal decomposition of iron carbonyl is 10^{-6} cm. W. Frankenburger and K. Mayrhofer, and G. W. C. Kaye and D. Ewen obtained a mirror which was not homogeneous by the sublimation of iron in vacuo ; A. Knocke also obtained a mirror by heating iron powder in an evacuated tube at 755° ; F. H. Constable, by heating a paste made of ferrous oxalate or ferric oxide in oleic acid ; E. Tiede and E. Birnbräuer, by heating iron in vacuo ; and the Maschinebauanstalt Humboldt, by direct heating, or by an electric arc formed with one of the electrodes of iron. G. Belloc, J. H. Howey, L. Houllevigue, P. Lambert and A. Andant, A. J. Sorensen, and J. C. Steinberg also prepared iron mirrors in analogous ways. A. Kundt prepared a mirror by electrolysis, and likewise also E. Breuning and O. Schneider, and C. Müller. Ž. Debinska found thin metallic films obtained by vacuum distillation exhibit orientation of the micro-crystals. G. F. Taylor made **thin filaments** by drawing out the molten metal enclosed in a suitable glass tube and removing the glass with hydrofluoric acid.

The **aerosols** of iron were described by J. Fischer.[7] According to H. Freundlich, and T. Svedberg, the disperse phase obtained by spluttering iron under water, **colloidal iron,** contains more or less hydrated ferric oxide. This form of iron was produced by F. Ehrenhaft by G. Bredig's method—**3.** 23, 10—using an arc from iron wire electrodes under water. G. Bredig did not have much success with this process, but a similar one was successfully used by E. F. Burton, P. N. Pavloff, T. Malarsky, O. Scarpa, and D. Zavrieff. J. Billiter used zinc wires on which a film of iron had been deposited electrolytically. T. Svedberg obtained a colloidal soln. of iron in ether by allowing sparks to pass between iron wire chippings immersed in that liquid and connected with an induction coil. R. Gans studied the optical properties and the absorption spectrum of the colloidal soln. and as a result inferred that the particles are not disc-shaped.

The **hydrosol** of iron is not very stable, and A. Schmauss found this defect mollified by the use of gelatine as protective colloid. The colloid can also be obtained by chemical methods ; thus, E. Richter obtained the hydrosol by treating a 2·5 per cent. soln. of ferric sulphate with 1 to 3 drops of a soln. of dimethylparaphenylenediamine (1 : 4000) ; H. Crookes and L. Stroud, by treating a mixture of a 1 per cent. soln. of ferrous chloride, free from alkali, and a neutral soln. of peptone containing 9·5 grms. per litre, with a small quantity of phenol ; and H. H. Franck, by reducing a dil. soln. of an iron salt in the presence of a protective colloid—like gum arabic, gelatin, gum tragancath, and saponin. B. C. Soyenkoff made sols of iron soaps in benzene. According to C. Serono, when a soln. of gelatin and a dil. soln. of an alkali chloride or sulphate is electrolyzed between iron electrodes, a colloidal soln. of iron is obtained mixed with some colloidal ferrous hydroxide and a ferric salt. The metal is positively charged. The Chemische Fabrik von Heyden also prepared the colloid by electrical spluttering under a soln. containing a reducing agent and a protective colloid—for instance, 0·75 grm. of pyrocatechol and 1 grm. of albumose or albumen in a litre of water. P. von Mutzenbecher used paraglobulin as protective colloid.

M. Traube-Mengarini and A. Scala thought that some colloidal iron is spontaneously formed by cold or boiling water in contact with iron, but H. Nordenson showed that this is not the case. What actually occurs is the formation of colloidal hydroxide when air has access to iron. E. F. Burton and P. Phillips' observations on the magnetic susceptibility of colloidal soln. of iron agree with the assumption that the particles of iron are surrounded by a film of hydroxide. F. Fischer and F. Schröter observed no colloid is formed in the direct current arc with iron electrodes under liquid argon.

G. Bredig did not obtain a stable **ethersol** by forming a direct current arc under ether, and G. Bredig's process was found by T. Svedberg not to be applicable to the formation of organosols of iron, because of the decomposition of the organic medium, but he did obtain an ethersol by the oscillating discharge—**3.** 23, 10— between iron electrodes under ether in the presence of the finely-divided metal. T. Svedberg also prepared **alcoholsols** with propyl and *iso*butyl alcohol, and **acetonosol** with acetone. H. B. Weiser and G. L. Mack obtained alcoholsols, etc.; E. Berl and co-workers, various organosols using rubber as a protective colloid when the dispersion medium is a hydrocarbon ; F. Haurowitz obtained **benzenesols**; and E. F. Burton, a sol with methyl alcohol. H. Nordenson obtained no alcoholsol by boiling ethyl alcohol in the presence of iron, nor by exposing an iron plate in contact with methyl or ethyl alcohol to X-rays or to ultra-violet rays. F. Haurowitz prepared by T. Svedberg's method benzenesol with benzene as dispersion medium and non-vulcanized caoutchouc as protective colloid. C. J. Sims and E. W. J. Mardles obtained a petroleum sol from a soln. of iron pentacarbonyl in petroleum, **naphthalene sol** from a soln. of the same substance in naphthalene, and **bromonaphthalene sol** by using bromonaphthalene as solvent. A. Cotton and H. Mouton obtained a **glycerol sol** by arcing iron under glycerol; some of the medium is decomposed. C. Benedicks observed that when the conditions are such that arc discharge takes place for a very short interval of time, as may easily be arranged if the current is furnished by an induction coil and a Leyden jar placed in parallel with the discharge gap, the surfaces of the electrodes exhibit well-formed eruptive craters, which are attributed to the melting of the metal under the influence of the discharge. When the discharge ceases, the surrounding liquid comes in contact with the hot metal, and this is supposed to be directly responsible for the disintegration of the electrodes. Ultra-microscopic observations show that the particles are spherical and have a diameter varying over a wide range, with an upper limit of about 5μ. D. C. Bahl studied the flocculation of the sol.

REFERENCES.

[1] R. B. Carnahan, *U.S. Pat. No.* 940748, 940785, 1909 ; *Chem. Met. Engg.*, **8.** 98, 1910 ; J. A. Aupperle, *ib.*, **8.** 263, 1910 ; W. J. Beck, *ib.*, **24.** 965, 1921 ; *Iron Age*, **107.** 1462, 1921 ; E. L. Dupuy, *Rev. Mét.*, **25.** 637, 1928 ; A. S. Cushman, *Proc. Amer. Soc. Testing Materials*, **11.** 96, 1911 ; A. Sauveur, *Rev. Mét.*, **22.** 397, 1925 ; R. L. Keynon, *Trans. Amer. Soc. Steel Treating*, **13.** 242, 435, 1928 ; O. Ruff and E. Gersten, *Ber.*, **45.** 69, 1912.

² H. F. Gaultier de Claubry, *Bull. Soc. Enc. Nat. Ind.*, (2), **5**. 633, 1858 ; A. Thibierge, *Journ. Pharm. Chim.*, (3), **8**. 132, 1845 ; G. Dragendorff, *ib.*, (3), **2**. 988, 1872 ; E. Soubeiran and J. B. Dublanc, *ib.*, (3), **8**. 187, 1845 ; M. H. Deschamps, *ib.*, (3), **38**. 250, 1860 ; *Chem. News*, **2**. 268, 1860 ; L. Dusart, *Journ. Pharm. Chim.*, (3), **39**. 415, 1861 ; A. C. Becquerel, *Ann. Chim. Phys.*, (2), **48**. 346, 1831 ; C. Broling, *Anteknigar under en resa i England*, Stockholm, 1817 ; F. Wöhler, *Liebig's Ann.*, **94**. 125, 1855 ; **95**. 192, 1855 ; L. Weiss and O. Aichel, *ib.*, **337**. 376, 1904 ; H. Goldschmidt, *ib.*, **301**, 19, 1898 ; *Zeit. Elektrochem.*, **4**. 494, 1898 ; A. Sieverts, *ib.*, **16**. 707, 1910 ; A. Matthiessen and S. P. Szczepanovsky, *B.A. Rep.*, 342, 1868 ; 82, 1869 ; *Chem. News.*, **18**. 114, 1868 ; **20**. 101, 1869 ; G. E. Davis, *ib.*, **30**. 292, 1874 ; D. Guicciardi, *Répert. Chim. Appl.*, **2**. 126, 1860 ; *Repert. Pharm.*, **16**. 212, 1859 ; F. Glaser, *Zeit. anorg. Chem.*, **36**. 21, 1903 ; W. Spring, *ib.*, **1**. 242, 1892 ; A. Stoffel, *ib.*, **84**. 59, 1914 ; F. Ephraim, *ib.*, **44**. 193, 1905 ; S. Hilpert, *Ber.*, **42**. 4575, 1909 ; O. Ruff and E. Gersten, *ib.*, **45**. 69, 1912 ; W. Ipatieff, *ib.*, **59**. 1420, 1926 ; W. Ipatieff and W. Werchowsky, *ib.*, **42**. 2086, 1909 ; L. Mond and F. Quincke, *ib.*, **24**. 2248, 1891 ; *Chem. News*, **23**. 301, 1891 ; L. Mond and C. Langer, *ib.*, **59**. 1090, 1891 ; L. Mathesius, *Studie über die Reduzierbarkeit von eisenerzen in stromenden Gazen*, Berlin, 1913 ; *Stahl Eisen*, **34**. 872, 1914 ; K. Hofmann, *Zeit. angew. Chem.*, **38**. 715, 1928 ; A. Mittasch, *ib.*, **41**. 831, 1914 ; A. Mittasch and E. Kuss, *Zeit. Elektrochem.*, **34**. 159, 1928 ; A. Mittasch, E. Kuss and O. Emert, *Zeit. anorg. Chem.*, **170**. 195, 1928 ; F. Wüst and P. Rütten, *Mitt. Inst. Eisenforsch.*, **5**. 6, 1924 ; L. C. Turnock, *Chem. Met. Engg.*, **15**. 260, 1916 ; N. Parravano and P. de Cesaris, *Gazz. Chim. Ital.*, **47**. 144, 1917 ; H. Kreusler, *Verh. deut. phys. Ges.*, **10**. 344, 1908 ; R. Akerman and C. G. Särnström, *Jernkontorets Ann.*, (2), **37**. 329, 1882 ; A. Ledebur, *Handbuch der Eisenhüttenkunde*, Leipzig, **1**. 360, 1923 ; F. M. Perkin and L. Pratt, *Trans. Faraday Soc.*, **3**. 181, 1908 ; O. Prelinger, *Monatsh.*, **14**. 368, 1893 ; H. Wolfram, *Die Verbindungen des Stickstoffs mit reinem und technischen eisen*, Dresden, 1913 ; F. Schmitz, *Untersuchungen über die Gesetzmässigkeit der chemischen Einwirkungen der Gase auf Eisen und seine Verbindungen mit Nichtmetallen bei höheren Temperaturen*, Aachen, 1915 ; Farbenindustrie A.G., *French Pat. No.* 609204, 1925 ; 629521, 1927 ; *U.S. Pat. No.* 1663916, 1926 ; *Brit. Pat. No.* 262938, 1925 ; 269345, 269677, 1926 ; 284082, 1927 ; Vereinigten Stahlwerke, *ib.*, 284991, 1928 ; A. Curs, *German Pat.*, *D.R.P.* 452630, 1926 ; A. Hiorth, *Norway Pat. No.* 18750, 1908 ; W. Engelhardt, *Zeit. Chem.*, (2), **4**. 238, 1861 ; C. Stahlschmidt, *Pogg. Ann.*, **125**. 37, 43, 53, 1865 ; K. Stammer, *ib.*, **82**. 138, 1852 ; N. W. Fischer, *ib.*, **9**. 266, 1827 ; M. Zängerle, *Repert. Pharm.*, **6**. 27, 1857 ; E. F. Anthon, *ib.*, **77**. 121, 1842 ; H. F. Gaultier de Claubry, *Bull. Soc. Enc. Nat. Ind.*, (2), **5**. 633, 1858 ; A. M. B. Burin de Buisson, *ib.*, (2), **5**. 633, 1858 ; E. Péligot, *Compt. Rend.*, **19**. 670, 1844 ; A. Guntz, *ib.*, **114**. 115, 1892 ; M. Crolas, *ib.*, **78**. 977, 1874 ; H. Moissan, *ib.*, **84**. 1298, 1877 ; *Ann. Chim. Phys.* (5), **21**. 201, 1880 ; L. Gruner, *ib.*, (4), **26**. 8, 1872 ; *Dingler's Journ.*, **202**. 160, 1871 ; S. de Luca, *Nuovo Cimento*, (2), **11**. 137, 1860 ; *Journ. Pharm. Chim.*, (3), **38**. 275, 1860 ; *Compt. Rend.*, **51**. 333, 1860 ; **52**. 202, 1862 ; J. A. Poumarède, *ib.*, **29**. 518, 1849 ; H. Capitaine, *ib.*, **9**. 737, 1839 ; *Ann. Chim. Phys.*, (3), **2**. 126, 1841 ; L. Troost, *Bull. Soc. Enc. Nat. Ind.*, (2), **15**. 548, 1867 ; *Bull. Soc. Chim.*, (2), **9**. 250, 1867 ; M. Berthelot and G. André, *ib.*, (3), **7**. 435, 1892 ; A. Brochet, *ib.*, (4), **27**. 898, 1920 ; M. Berthelot, *Compt. Rend.*, **112**. 1343, 1891 ; *Ann. Chim. Phys.*, (6), **26**. 572, 1892 ; A. Sanfourche, *Rev. Mét.*, **16**. 218, 1919 ; A. B. Bagdasarian, *Trans. Amer. Electrochem. Soc.*, **51**. 484, 1927 ; T. W. Richards and G. P. Baxter, *Proc. Amer. Acad.*, **35**. 253, 1900 ; **39**. 245, 1903 ; *Chem. News*, **81**. 174, 1900 ; *Zeit. anorg. Chem.*, **23**. 247, 1900 ; **38**. 237, 1904 ; T. W. Richards and G. E. Behr, *Zeit. phys. Chem.*, **58**. 303, 1907 ; T. W. Richards, *Journ. Amer. Chem. Soc.*, **46**. 92, 1924 ; G. P. Baxter and C. R. Hoover, *ib.*, **34**. 1657, 1912 ; *Zeit. anorg. Chem.*, **80**. 204, 1913 ; G. P. Baxter, *ib.*, **38**. 237, 1904 ; *Proc. Amer. Acad.*, **39**. 245, 1902 ; *Amer. Chem. Journ.*, **22**. 363, 1899 ; G. P. Baxter, T. Thorvaldson and V. Cobb, *Journ. Amer. Chem. Soc.*, **33**. 319, 1911 ; *Zeit. anorg. Chem.*, **80**. 204, 1913 ; F. K. Bell and W. A. Patrick, *Journ. Amer. Chem. Soc.*, **43**. 453, 1921 ; B. Lambert and J. C. Thomson, *Journ. Chem. Soc.*, **97**. 2429, 1910 ; R. Schenck and T. Dingmann, *Zeit. anorg. Chem.*, **166**. 146, 1927 ; R. Ruer and J. Kuschmann, *ib.*, **173**. 244, 1928 ; F. Sauerwald, *ib.*, **122**. 278, 1922 ; H. Freundlich, G. Patscheke and H. Zocher, *Zeit. phys. Chem.*, **128**. 321, 1927 ; **130**. 290, 1927 ; A. Brill and H. Mark, *ib.*, **133**. 443, 1928 ; T. Mylius, *Naturwiss.*, **5**. 409, 1917 ; K. Jellinek and R. Koop, *Zeit. phys. Chem.*, **145**. 305, 1929 ; A. E. van Arkel, *Chem. Weekbl.*, **24**. 90, 1927 ; J. H. Gladstone and A. Tribe, *Phil. Mag.*, (4), **49**. 425, 1875 ; F. M. Raoult, *Compt. Rend.*, **75**. 1103, 1873 ; Z. Roussin, *Journ. Pharm. Chim.*, (4), **3**. 413, 1866 ; *Chem. News*, **14**. 27, 1866 ; A. Commaille, *ib.*, **14**. 188, 1866 ; *Compt. Rend.*, **63**. 556, 1866 ; G. Gore, *Electrochemistry*, London, 93, 1906 ; L. Jordan, A. A. Peterson and L. H. Phelps, *Trans. Amer. Electrochem. Soc.*, **50**. 115, 1926 ; J. J. Berzelius, *Lehrbuch der Chemie*, Dresden, **2**. i, 376, 1826.

³ A. C. Becquerel, *Ann. Chim. Phys.*, (2), **48**. 346, 1831 ; R. Böttger, *Versuche für chemische und physikalische Vorlesungen*, Frankfurt, 17, 1846 ; *Pogg. Ann.*, **67**. 117, 1846 ; W. Hittorf, *ib.*, **106**. 386, 1859 ; F. Varrentrapp, *Dingler's Journ.*, **187**. 152, 1858 ; C. Stammer, *ib.*, **190**. 116, 256, 1868 ; H. Meidinger, *Jahrb. prakt. Pharm.*, **16**. 295, 1862 ; *Dingler's Journ.*, **163**. 283, 1862 ; H. Krämer, *ib.*, **160**. 284, 444, 1861 ; H. Bouilhet, *ib.*, **189**. 476, 1868 ; *Bull. Soc. Enc. Nat. Ind.*, (2), **15**. 278, 1868 ; M. Boch-Buschmann and M. Liet, *ib.*, (1), **45**. 96, 1846 ; *Dingler's Journ.*, **100**. 75, 1846 ; B. H. Thomas, *Iron Coal Trades Rev.*, **100**. 685, 1920 ; A. Müller, *Ueber die Darstellung des Elektrolyteisens, dessen Zusammensetzung und thermische Eigenschaften*, Halle a. S., 1909 ; *Stahl Eisen*, **29**. 919, 1909 ; *Met.*, **6**. 145, 1909 ; F. Andersen, *Ueber die Darstellung einiger Schwermetalle und Liegerungen durch elektrolyse im Schmelzfluss*, Darmstadt, 1916 ; *Zeit. angew. Chem.*, **30**. 298, 1917 ; O. Mustad, *Abscheidungspontential des Eisens aus seinen Sulfat- und*

Chlorürlösungen bei verscheidenen Temperaturen, Dresden, 1908 ; J. Früh, *Ueber die Abscheidung von Eisen und Nickel aus Komplexen Oxalat- und Laktatlösungen*, Dresden, 1911 ; W. C. Mc-Williams, *Trans. Amer. Electrochem. Soc.*, **4**. 251, 1899 ; D. Belcher, *Swiss Pat. No.* 58030, 1911 ; *Trans. Amer. Electrochem. Soc.*, **45**. 455, 1924 ; *Chem. Trade Journ.*, **74**. 589, 1924 ; N. B. Pilling, *Trans. Amer. Electrochem. Soc.*, **42**. 6, 1922 ; H. D. Hineline, *ib.*, **43**. 119, 1923 ; G. P. Fuller, *ib.*, **50**. 371, 1926 ; P. K. Frölich, *ib.*, **46**. 100, 1924 ; C. P. Madsen, *ib.*, **45**. 249, 1924 ; A. H. W. Aten, H. J. den Hertog and L. Westenberg, *ib.*, **46**. 323, 1927 ; E. M. Chance, *ib.*, **17**. 235, 1910 ; W. Blum and H. S. Rawdon, *ib.*, **44**. 305, 1923 ; W. H. Gee, *Chem. Met. Engg.*, **2**. 319, 1904 ; W. Palmaer and J. A. Brinell, *ib.*, **11**. 196, 1913 ; G. F. McMahon, *ib.*, **26**. 639, 1922 ; S. A. Tucker and E. Schramm, *Chem. News*, **102**. 16, 1910 ; *Journ. Ind. Eng. Chem.*, **2**. 237, 1910 ; A. K. Balls and C. C. McDonnell, *ib.*, **7**. 26, 1915 ; J. R. Cain, E. Schramm and H. E. Cleaves, *Journ. Franklin Inst.*, **181**. 408, 1916 ; *Scient. Paper Bur. Standards*, 266, 1916 ; W. A. Macfadyen, *Trans. Faraday Soc.*, **15**. 102, 116, 1920 ; C. H. Desch and E. M. Vellan, *ib.*, **21**. 17, 1925 ; D. R. Kellog, *Min. Met.*, **3**. 61, 1922 ; G. Luckow, *Zeit. anal. Chem.*, **19**. 18, 1880 ; B. Speed and G. W. Elmen, *Journ. Amer. Inst. Elect. Eng.*, **40**. 596, 1921 ; B. Stoughton, *Iron Age*, **109**. 32, 1922 ; *Chem. Met. Engg.*, **26**. 128, 1922 ; *The Metallurgy of Iron and Steel*, New York, 200, 1923 ; W. C. Roberts-Austen, *Journ. Iron Steel Inst.*, **31**. i, 71, 1887 ; J. O. Arnold, *ib.*, **45**. i, 107, 1894 ; G. Vié, *Ann. Chim. Anal.*, (2), **1**. 175, 1919 ; E. Merck, *Zeit. angew. Chem.*, **15**. 36, 1902 ; *German Pat., D.R.P.* 126839, 1900 ; O. Spinzig and A. Wannag, *ib.*, 255454, 1911 ; W. Pip, *ib.*, 316597, 1918 ; A. Pertsch, *ib.*, 66185, 1892 ; E. F. K. Harbeck, *ib.*, 288660, 1914 ; *Zeit. Elektrotech.*, **22**. 428, 1916 ; R. H. Monk and R. J. Traill, *Canadian Chem. Met.*, **10**. 137, 1926 ; R. J. Traill and W. R. McClelland, *Canada Dept. Mines*, 670, 1925 ; L. Houllevigue, *Journ. Phys.*, (3), **7**. 708, 1898 ; A. Vosmaer, *Chem. Weekbl.*, **16**. 417, 1919 ; J. Escard, *Génie Civil*, **75**. 165, 199, 225, 1919 ; G. Vortmann, *Monatsh.*, **14**. 536, 1893 ; F. Sauerwald and G. Neuendorff, *Zeit. Elektrochem.*, **31**. 643, 1925 ; F. Sauerwald, *ib.*, **38**. 76, 1932 ; H. Schmidt, *ib.*, **32**. 33, 1926 ; W. Sontag, *ib.*, **30**. 333, 1924 ; G. Lambris, *ib.*, **15**. 973, 1909 ; R. H. Aiken, *Chem. Met. Engg.*, **4**. 191, 1906 ; *U.S. Pat. No.* 816142, 873648, 1903 ; J. W. Beckman, *ib.*, 973336, 1910 ; *Chem. Met. Engg.*, **9**. 274, 1911 ; F. Exner, *Journ. Amer. Chem. Soc.*, **25**. 903, 1903 ; H. E. Williams, *ib.*, **34**. 1014, 1912 ; K. Schild, *Ann. Physik*, (4), **25**. 588, 1908 ; G. Eger, *Zeit. Metallkunde*, **16**. 134, 1924 ; A. Bouchayer, *U.S. Pat. No.* 1516326, 1921 ; *Rev. Mét.*, **20**. 434, 1923 ; *Mem. Soc. Ing. Civils*, 557, 1923 ; W. Hampe, *Chem. Ztg.*, **12**. 171, 1888 ; C. Tschappet, *Swiss. Pat. No.* 121383, 1926 ; L. Schäfer, *Zeit. Dampfkessel*, **42**. 30, 1919 ; V. Kohlschütter and H. Stäger, *Helvetica Chim. Acta*, **4**. 833, 1921 ; V. Kohlschütter, *Trans. Amer. Electrochem. Soc.*, **45**. 229, 1924 ; *Zeit. Elektrochem.*, **33**. 272, 1927 ; V. Kohlschütter and F. Jakober, *ib.*, **33**. 290, 1927 ; V. Kohlschütter and E. Vuilleumier, *ib.*, **24**. 304, 1918 ; R. Müller, E. Hönig and A. Konetschnigg, *Monatsh.*, **44**. 244, 1923 ; J. Timmermans, *Bull. Soc. Chim. Belg.*, **20**. 305, 1906 ; H. E. Patten and W. R. Mott, *Chem. News*, **100**. 319, 1909 ; *Trans. Amer. Electrochem. Soc.*, **15**. 529, 1909 ; P. Ferchland and P. Rehländer, *Die elektrochemischen deutschen Reichspatente*, Halle a. S., 1906 ; P. Ferchland, *Die neuesten elektrischemischen Patente*, Halle a. S., 1907–1913 ; P. Jenisch, *Handbuch für alle galvanostegischen und galvanoplastischen Arbeiten*, Leipzig, 185, 1905 ; M. le Blanc, *Die Darstellung des Chroms*, Halle a. S., 31, 1902 ; Easton, Pa., 1907 ; P. Askenasy, *Einführung in die technische Elektrochemie*, Braunschweig, 1916 ; W. Guertler, *Die metallische Werkstoff*, Leipzig, 3. 62, 1927 ; G. Buchner, *Die elektrolytischen Metallabscheidungen*, Berlin, 265, 1922 ; J. Billiter, *Elektrometallurgie wässriger Losungen*, Halle a. S., 235, 1923 ; *Technische Elektrochemie*, Halle a. S., **1**. 238, 1923 ; H. Steiner and G. Buchner, *Die galvanischen Metallniederschläge*, Berlin, 131, 1923 ; H. Krause, *Galvanotechnik*, Leipzig, 153, 1928 ; F. Michel, *Metallniederschläge und Metallfärbungen*, Berlin, 133, 1927 ; A. Classen and H. Danneel, *Quantitative Analyse durch Elektrolyse*, Berlin, 301, 1927 ; A. Classen, *Zeit. Elektrochem.*, **1**. 288, 1895 ; *German Pat., D.R.P.* 17864, 1881 ; *Ber.*, **15**. 1096, 1882 ; A. Classen and M. A. von Reis, *ib.*, **14**. 1625, 1881 ; R. Ehrenfeld, *ib.*, **38**. 4139, 1905 ; M. Heidenreich, *ib.*, **29**. 1585, 1896 ; J. Tafel and G. Friedrichs, *ib.*, **37**. 3187, 1904 ; A. Schleicher, *Elektroanalytische Schnellmethoden*, Stuttgart, 1926 ; W. Fischer, *Elektroanalytische Schnellmethoden*, Stuttgart, 158, 1908 ; F. Fischer, *U.S. Pat. No.* 992951, 992952, 1910 ; S. Pagliani, *Atti 1st Veneto*, (6), **5**. 1181, 1887 ; C. J. Reed, *German Pat., D.R.P.* 269927, 1912 ; 1055652, 1911 ; N. H. M. Dekker, *Swiss Pat. No.* 65381, 1913 ; 76764, 1917 ; *Brit. Pat. No.* 7328, 1912 ; *U.S. Pat. No.* 1101620, 1913 ; W. M. Johnson, *ib.*, 780191, 1902 ; A. Boucher, *ib.*, 28746, 1910 ; 1086132, 1913 ; A. S. Ramage, *ib.*, 1007388, 1911 ; *Swiss Pat. No.* 51148, 1909 ; H. Oettinger, *Zeit. Elektrochem.*, **22**. 136, 1916 ; *German Pat., D.R.P.* 284608, 1912 ; 366149, 1919 ; 388549, 1920 ; M. Schlötter, *Galvanostegie*, Halle a. S., 91, 1912 ; *German Pat., D.R.P.* 252875, 1912 ; 305156, 308543, 309116, 309271, 310043, 1917 ; P. A. Govaerts and P. M. Wenmaekers, *ib.*, 384284, 1921 ; *Brit. Pat. No.* 190500, 1922 ; F. A. Shepherd, *ib.*, 119200, 1918 ; Allgemeine Elektrizitäts Gesellschaft, *German Pat., D.R.P.* 316748, 1916 ; H. Plauson and G. Tischtschenko, *Brit. Pat. No.* 10882, 1912 ; *German Pat., D.R.P.* 252875, 1911 ; E. Wilke-Dörfurt, *ib.*, 401110, 1918 ; Chemische Fabrik Griesheim-Elektron, *ib.*, 390648, 1917 ; *U.S. Pat. No.* 1444887, 1922 ; Société de Fer Grenoble, *French Pat. No.* 44614, 1911 ; 458294, 1912 ; A. Nodon and A. Lecandre, *ib.*, 450065, 1912 ; Société Anonyme des Aciéries Firminy, *ib.*, 586314, 1913 ; A. T. C. Estelle, *German Pat., D.R.P.* 298339, 1914 ; 299835, 1916 ; *Brit. Pat. No.* 159906, 1918 ; *U.S. Pat. No.* 1275161, 1918 ; A. J. Moxham, *ib.*, 1420127, 1420128, 1420129, 1919 ; F. K. Bezzenberger, *ib.*, 1729607, 1929 ; A. Simon, *ib.*, 704393, 1901 ; *German Pat., D.R.P.* 131414, 1900 ; H. Gerdien, *ib.*, 481139, 1925 ; G. Masing, *ib.*, 413148, 1923 ; E. Duhme, *Wiss. Veröffentl. Siemens-Konzern*, **3**. 41,

1924 ; *German Pat., D.R.P.* 416082, 1923 ; G. Hofer, *Giesserei Ztg.*, **4**. 140, 1907 ; H. J. Blikslager, *Rec. Trav. Chim. Pays-Bas*, **46** 323, 1927 ; S. Grünauer, *Zeit. anorg. Chem.*, **39**. 461, 1904 ; E. Krupp, *German Pat., D.R.P.* 81225, 1893 ; Langbein-Pfanhauser Werke, *ib.*, 212994, 1908 ; 228893, 230876, 233722, 1909 ; 283670, 1913 ; 355306, 1921 ; *Brit. Pat. No.* 24841, 1909 ; 22204, 25092, 25969, 1910 ; *U.S. Pat. No.* 987318, 1001770, 1910 ; C. P. Perin and F. A. Eustis, *ib.*, 1377822, 1412174, 143554, 1920 ; F. A. Eustis, *Brit. Pat. No.* 194638, 194639, 196334, 1921 ; *Chem. Met. Engg.*, **27**. 684, 1922 ; C. P. Perin and D. Belcher, *Min. Met.*, **2**. 17, 1921 ; E. Kelsen, *Brit. Pat. No.* 306151, 1929 ; T. P. McCutcheon and E. F. Smith, *Journ. Amer. Chem. Soc.*, **29**. 1463, 1907 ; J. H. Paterson, *Proc. Durham Phil. Soc.*, **4**. 187, 1912 ; *Journ. Soc. Chem. Ind.*, **31**. 1040, 1912 ; O. Orlandi, *Belg. Pat. No.* 360116, 360634, 1929 ; R. D. Pike, G. H. West, L. V. Steck, R. Cummings and B. P. Little, *Tech. Publ. Amer. Inst. Min. Eng.*, 268, 1930 ; R. D. Pike, *U.S. Pat. No.* 1751099, 1930 ; T. D. Yensen, *Min. Met.*, **11**. 212, 1930 ; *Trans. Amer. Electrochem. Soc.*, **32**. 170, 1918 ; *Trans. Amer. Inst. Min. Eng.*, **53**. 214, 1916 ; *Magnetic and other Properties of Iron-Silicon Alloys melted in Vacuo*, London, 1916 ; *Foundry Trade Journ.*, **18**. 491, 1916 ; G. K. Burgess, *Journ. Franklin Inst.*, **182**. 19, 1916 ; G. Fuseya, K. Murata and R. Yomoto, *Tech. Rept. Tohoku Univ.*, **9**. 33, 1929 ; G. Gore, *Electrochemistry*, London, 92, 1906 ; *Telegr. Journ.*, **2**. 128, 1870 ; *Chem. News*, **18**. 133, 1868 ; **21**. 137, 1870 ; W. H. Walenn, *ib.*, **17**. 170, 1868 ; R. Böttinger, *ib.*, **36**. 11, 1877 ; K. Oma, *Bull. Inst. Phys. Chem. Research Tokyo*, **8**. 126, 1929 ; A. Glazunoff and A. Rozmus, *Chem. Obzor.*, **5**. 4, 59, 96, 1930 ; T. P. Thomas, *Metal Cleaning*, 464, 1929 ; *Metals Alloys*, **1**. 474, 1929 ; R. Lenz, *Journ. prakt. Chem.*, (1), **108**. 438, 1869 ; *Pogg. Ann. Ergbd.*, **5**. 242, 1871 ; *Bull. Soc. Chim.*, (2), **13**. 551, 1870 ; *Bull. Acad. St. Petersburg*, (3), **14**. 337, 1870 ; E. Klein and H. Jacobi, *ib.*, (3), **13**. 40, 1868 ; (3), **14**. 337, 1870 ; *Russ. Pat. No.* 2456, 1869 ; *Bull. Soc. Enc. Nat. Ind.*, (2), **15**. 286, 1868 ; H. Jacobi, *ib.*, (2), **15**. 286, 1868 ; *Bull. Acad. St. Petersburg*, (3), **18**. 11, 1873 ; *Pogg. Ann.*, **149**. 341, 1873 ; *Ann. Chim. Phys.*, (4), **28**. 252, 1873 ; S. Maximowitsch, *Zeit. Elektrochem.*, **11**. 52, 1905 ; A. Neuberger, *Electrotech. Zeit.*, **11**. 77, 1904 ; W. Heyn, *Zeit. Electrochem.*, **16**. 77, 1909 ; K. Arndt, *ib.*, **18**. 233, 1912 ; F. Förster, *Elektrochemie wässeriger Lösungen*, Leipzig, 1922 ; *Beiträge zur Kenntnis des elektrochemischen Verhaltens des Eisens*, Halle a. S., 1909 ; *Zeit. Elektrochem.*, **4**. 163, 1897 ; **13**. 566, 1907 ; G. Neuendorff and F. Sauerwald, *ib.*, **34**. 199, 1928 ; A. Ryss and A. Bogomolny, *ib.*, **12**. 697, 1906 ; A. Pfaff, *ib.*, **16**. 217, 1910 ; R. Amberg, *ib.*, **14**. 326, 1908 ; **16**. 125, 1910 ; H. Röhler, *ib.*, **16**. 419, 1910 ; F. Haber, *ib.*, **4**. 411, 1898 ; A. Skrabal, *ib.*, **10**. 749, 1904 ; *Zeit. anal. Chem.*, **42**. 395, 1903 ; *Ber.*, **35**. 3404, 1902 ; S. Avery and B. Dales, *ib.*, **32**. 64, 2233, 1899 ; H. Verwer and F. Groll, *ib.*, **32**. 806, 1899 ; H. Verwer, *ib.*, **25**. 792, 1901 ; W. M. Hicks and L. T. O'Shea, *Journ. Chem. Soc.*, **72**. 374, 1897 ; *Electrician*, **35**. 843, 1895 ; *Zeit. Elektrochem.*, **2**. 406, 1895 ; *B.A. Rep.*, 634, 1895 ; A. Watt, *Electrician*, **20**. 6, 50, 135, 156, 185, 241, 1888 ; O. P. Watts and M. H. Li, *Chem. Met. Engg.*, **12**. 343, 1914 ; *Trans. Amer. Electrochem. Soc.*, **25**. 529, 1914 ; A. K. Graham, *ib.*, **44**. 427, 1923 ; C. T. Thomas and W. Blum, *ib.*, **57**. 59, 1930 ; C. F. Burgess and O. P. Watts, *ib.*, **9**. 229, 1905 ; C. F. Burgess and C. Hambüchen, *ib.*, **5**. 201, 1904 ; *Electrochem. Ind.*, **2**. 184, 1904 ; *Electrochem. Zeit.*, **10**. 76, 1904 ; C. F. Burgess, *Trans. Amer. Electrochem. Soc.*, **19**. 181, 1911 ; *Iron Age*, **87**. 268, 1911 ; L. F. Audreith and L. F. Yntema, *Journ. Phys. Chem.*, **34**. 1903, 1930 ; O. W. Storey, *Met. Chem. Engg.*, **14**. 534, 1916 ; *Mech. Engg.*, **37**. 484, 1916 ; *Trans. Amer. Electrochem. Soc.*, **25**. 489, 1914 ; **29**. 357, 1916 ; S. J. Lloyd, *ib.*, **55**. 305, 1929 ; C. Hambüchen, *ib.*, **51**. 81, 1927 ; W. A. Noyes, *Trans. Amer. Electrochem. Soc.*, **39**. 451, 1921 ; *Compt. Rend.*, **169**. 971, 1919 ; S. Field and A. D. Weill, *Electroplating*, London, 1930 ; R. Audubert, *Rev. Mét.*, **21**. 567, 1924 ; Anon., *Foundry Trade Journ.*, **38**. 118, 1928 ; *Engg.*, **125**. 339, 1928 ; T. Johnston, *Metal Ind.*, **30**. 241, 1927 ; F. A. Eustis and C. P. Perrin, *Met. Chem. Engg.*, **27**. 684, 1922 ; E. C. Kreutzberg, *Iron Trade Rev.*, **73**. 595, 1923 ; T. W. S. Huchins, *Iron Coal Trades Rev.*, **109**. 117, 1924 ; *World Power*, **2**. 341, 1924 ; R. Dupuis, *Metallbörse*, **20**. 1829, 1930 ; R. M. Bozorth, *Phys. Rev.*, (2), **26**. 390, 1925 ; F. N. Budgen, *Engg. Production*, **8**. 98, 1925 ; W. Couldson, *Trans. Amer. Electrochem. Soc.*, **32**. 238, 1917 ; A. Hiorns, *ib.*, **2**. 648, 1895 ; *Brit. Pat. No.* 4660, 1895 ; H. Lee, *Abhand. deut. Bunsen Ges.*, 2, 1909 ; *Ueber den Wasserstoffgehalt des Elektrolyteisens*, Dresden, 1906 ; R. Kremann and H. Breymesser, *Monatsh.*, **38**. 359, 1917 ; R. Kremann, R. Schadinger, and R. Kropsch, *ib.*, **38**. 91, 1917 ; R. Kremann and J. Lorber, *ib.*, **35**. 1387, 1914 ; R. Kremann, C. T. Suchy and R. Maas, *Sitzber. Akad. Wien*, **122**. 1023, 1913 ; L. Guillet and A. Portevin, *Compt. Rend.*, **156**. 702, 1913 ; L. Guillet, *Engg.*, **130**. 350, 1920 ; W. E. Hughes, *Chem. Met. Engg.*, **26**. 268, 1922 ; **29**. 536, 1925 ; *Electrician*, **87**. 640, 1921 ; *Chem. Age*, **5**. 521, 1921 ; *Amer. Metal. Ind.*, **19**. 405, 1921 ; *The Electrodeposition of Iron*, London, 1921 ; *Trans. Amer. Electrochem. Soc.*, **40**. 185, 1921 ; *Journ. Iron Steel Inst.*, **101**. i, 321, 1920 ; S. O. Cowper-Coles, *ib.*, **78**. iii, 134, 1908 ; *Brit. Pat. No.* 20990, 21081, 21082, 28897, 29300, 1906 ; 10367, 12747, 22311, 22312, 1907 ; 3160, 1908 ; 3626, 9082, 10655, 28592, 1910 ; E. H. Archibald and L. A. Pignet, *Trans. Roy. Soc. Canada*, (3), **11**. 107, 1918 ; W. Pfanhauser, *Elektroplatierung Galvanoplastik, und Metallpolirung*, Wien, 499, 1900 ; *German Pat., D.R.P.* 402078, 1923 ; *Die Herstellung von Metallgegenständen auf elektrolytischen Wege*, Halle a. S., 1903 ; *Die Galvanoplastik*, Halle a. S., 1904 ; *Galvanotechnik*, Berlin, 1928 ; *L'électrodeposition des métaux*, Paris, 1930 ; G. Langbein and A. Friessner, *Galvanoplastik und Galvanostegie*, Leipzig, 213, 1904 ; G. Langbein, *Handbuch der elektrolytischen (galvanischen) Metallniederschläge*, Leipzig, 1906 ; London, 1920 ; B. Neumann, *Theorie und Praxis der analytischen Elektrolyse der Metalle*, Halle a. S., 113, 1897 ; *Zeit. Elektrochem.*, **15**. 454, 1909 ; E. F. Smith, *Electroanalysis*, Philadelphia, 142, 1907 ; E. F. Smith and F. Muhr, *Journ. Anal. Chem.*, **5**. 488, 1891 ; W. Ostwald, *Grundlinien der anorganischen Chemie*, Leipzig,

253, 1900; G. Parodi and A. Mascazzini, *Gazz. Chim. Ital.*, **8**. 169, 1878; L. Balbiano and A. Alessi, *ib.*, **12**. 190, 1882; J. Thiele, *Liebig's Ann.*, **265**. 58, 1891; H. Buff, *ib.*, **92**. 117, 1854; **94**. 22, 1855; **110**. 274, 1859; *Ann. Chim. Phys.*, (3), **59**. 121, 1860; *Arch. Sciences Genève*, (1), **29**. 129, 1855; *Phil. Mag.*, (4), **9**. 139, 1855; *Journ. Pharm. Chim.*, (3), **27**. 154, 1855; A. Geuther, *Liebig's Ann.*, **99**. 326, 1856; T. Moore, *Chem. News*, **53**. 209, 1886; E. F. Kern, *Trans. Amer. Electrochem. Soc.*, **13**. 103, 1908; *Electrochem. Met. Ind.*, **6**. 242, 1908; A. Brand, *Zeit. anal. Chem.*, **28**. 581, 1889; S. I. Levy, *U.S. Pat. No.* 1752348, 1930; S. I. Levy and G. W. Gray, *Brit. Pat. No.* 304053, 1928; H. Lovelock, *ib.*, 165535, 1920; C. Arzano and G. Clerici, *ib.*, 114305, 1918; British Thomson-Houston Co., *ib.*, 1179675, 1921; M. L. V. Gayler, *Metallbörse*, **9**. 677, 1930; R. P. Neville and J. R. Cain, *Scient. Paper U.S. Bur. Standards*, 453, 1922; L. B. Hunt, *Journ. Phys. Chem.*, **36**. 1006, 1932; L. E. Stout and C. L. Faust, *Trans. Amer. Chem. Soc.*, **61**. 1, 1932; H. S. Booth and M. Merlub-Sobel, *Journ. Phys. Chem.*, **35**. 3303, 1931; C. Kadota, *Proc. World's Congr. Eng. Tokyo*, **33**. 127, 1931; F. Krupp, *Gluckauf*, **47**. 114, 160, 201, 1910; A. Levasseur, *Les métallurgies électrolytiques et leurs applications*, Paris, 1921; R. Glocker, *Zeit. Metallkunde*, **16**. 180, 1924; R. Glocker and E. Kaupp, *Zeit. Physik*, **24**. 121, 1924; R. H. Greaves, *Metallurgist*, **1**. 141, 1925; C. Marie and N. Thon, *Journ. Chim. Phys.*, **29**. 11, 1932.

[4] A. Chenot, *Brit. Pat. No.* 1587, 1588, 1589, 1590, 1856; J. O. Handy, *Proc. Eng. Soc. Western Pennsylvania*, **29**. 1, 1913; Anon., *Stahl Eisen*, **32**. 830, 1912; F. Hatton, *Journ. Chem. Soc.*, **39**. 258, 1881; J. von Ehrenwerth, *Stahl Eisen*, **11**. 727, 1891; *Oesterr. Zeit. Berg. Hütt.*, **39**. 456, 545, 1892; *Iron Age*, **49**. 162, 1892; A. Adams, *ib.*, **46**. 448, 855, 1890; W. Rohland, *Stahl Eisen*, **49**. 1477, 1929; E. P. Barrett, *Rep. Investigations U.S. Bur. Mines*, 2955, 1929; *Mining Met.*, **11**. 395, 1930; *Blast Furnace Steel Plant*, **17**. 1659, 1929; *Canada Iron Steel*, **12**. 240, 1929; C. E. Williams and A. E. Anderson, *Journ. Ind. Eng. Chem.*, **14**. 1057, 1922; C. E. Williams, E. P. Barrett and B. M. Larsen, *Bull. U.S. Bur. Mines*, 270, 1927; S. E. Sieurin, *Brit. Pat. No.* 296235, 1927; E. de Billy, *Ann. Mines*, (9), **2**. 329, 1892; F. Wüst, *Stahl Eisen*, **47**. 905, 955, 1927; W. W. Percy, *U.S. Pat. No.* 1645968, 1927; G. Mars, *German Pat.*, *D.R.P.* 390936, 1922; J. Y. Johnson, *Brit. Pat. No.* 278167, 1926; B. Britton, *Berg. Hütt. Ztg.*, **41**. 413, 1882; P. Longmuir, *Trans. Amer. Electrochem. Soc.*, **51**. 267, 1927; N. K. G. Tholand, *Iron Age*, **125**. 850, 1930; *ib.*, **55**. 5, 1929; M. Wiberg, *ib.*, **51**. 279, 1927; B. Stoughton, *Bull. Canadian Min. Met.*, 215, 1930; *Iron Age*, **125**. 790, 1930; C. A. Keller, *Journ. Iron Steel Inst.*, **100**. ii, 139, 1900; *Iron Trade Rev.*, 381, 1920; A. E. Bourcoud, *Yearbook Amer. Iron Steel Inst.*, **11**. 355, 1921.

[5] G. Magnus, *Pogg. Ann.*, **3**. 84, 1825; **6**. 509, 1826; F. Stromeyer, *ib.*, **6**. 471, 1826; F. Wöhler, *Liebig's Ann.*, **95**. 192, 1855; A. Smits, A. Kettner and A. L. W. de Gee, *Versl. Akad, Amsterdam*, **22**. 990, 1914; *Proc. Acad. Amsterdam*, **16**. 999, 1914; A. Smits and G. Wallach, *Rec. Trav. Chim. Pays-Bas*, **44**. 130, 1925; S. Birnie, *ib.*, **2**. 273, 1883; M. Zängerle, *Repert. Pharm.*, **6**. 27, 1857; G. Tammann and N. Nikitin, *Zeit. anorg. Chem.*, **135**. 201, 1924; G. Tammann and Q. A. Mansuri, *ib.*, **126**. 119, 1922; G. S. Newth, *Chemical Lecture Experiments*, London, 1910; F. Wüst and P. Rütten, *Mitt. Inst. Eisenforsch.*, **5**. 8, 1924; L. Troost and P. Hautefeuille, *Compt. Rend.*, **80**. 791, 1875; A. Job and R. Reich, *ib.*, **177**. 1439, 1923; H. Moissan, *ib.*, **84**. 1298, 1877; *Ann. Chim. Phys.*, (5), **21**. 199, 1880; A. Mittasch, C. Müller and E. Linckh, *U.S. Pat. No.* 1759659, 1759660, 1759658, 1930; T. G. Finzel, *Journ. Amer. Chem. Soc.*, **52**. 142, 150, 1930; W. Frankenburger and K. Mayrhofer, *Zeit. Elektrochem.*, **35**. 590, 1929; F. Göbel, *Journ. prakt. Chem.*, (1), **6**. 387, 1835; C. J. Sims and E. W. J. Mardles, *Trans. Faraday Soc.*, **22**. 364, 1926; K. Hofmann, *Stahl Eisen*, **46**. 917, 1926; B. Osann, *ib.*, **43**. 467, 1923; J. W. Gilles, *ib.*, **42**. 884, 1922; M. Siewert, *Zeit. Ges. Naturwiss.*, **23**. 3, 1864; F. Sauerwald, *Metall Erz.*, **21**. 117, 1924; F. Sauerwald and G. Elsner, *Zeit. Elektrochem.*, **31**. 18, 1925; A. Vogel, *Journ. Pharm. Chim.*, (3), **26**. 32, 1854; *Journ. prakt. Chem.*, (1), **63**. 187, 1854; A. Mittasch, *German Pat. No.* 422269, 1924.

[6] M. van Marum, *Verh. Teyler's Genootsch.*, **4**. 1, 1787; W. Frankenburger and K. Mayrhofer, *Zeit. Elektrochem.*, **35**. 590, 1929; M. Faraday, *Phil. Trans.*, **147**. 154, 1857; A. W. Wright, *Amer. Journ. Science*, (3), **13**. 49, 169, 1877; *Chem. News*, **36**. 170, 1877; J. Y. Johnson, *Brit. Pat. No.* 324363, 325526, 1928; G. Belloc, *Thermoélectricité du fer et des aciers*, Paris, 62, 1903; L. Houllevigue, *Journ. Phys.*, (4), **4**. 409, 1905; *Ann. Chim. Phys.*, (8), **20**. 138, 1910; *Compt. Rend.*, **149**. 1368, 1909; P. Lambert and A. Andant, *ib.*, **175**. 154, 1922; H. Moissan, *ib.*, **116**. 1929, 1893; *Bull. Soc. Chim.*, (3), **11**. 826, 1894; J. Strong and C. H. Cartwright, *Phys. Rev.*, (2), **37**. 228, 1931; H. Freundlich, G. Patschke and H. Zocher, *Zeit. phys. Chem.*, **128**. 321, 1927; **130**. 290, 1927; A. Skinner and A. Q. Tool, *Phil. Mag.*, (6), **16**. 833, 1908; L. R. Ingersoll, *ib.*, (6), **18**. 81, 91, 1909; J. Moser, *Wied. Ann.*, **42**. 638, 1891; B. Dessau, *ib.*, **29**. 353, 1880; A. Kundt, *ib.*, **23**. 228, 1884; **27**. 59, 1886; *Sitzber. Akad. Berlin*, 761, 1884; C. Müller, *ib.*, 464, 1925; W. W. Nicholas, *Circular U.S. Bur. Standards*, 389, 1931; R. Brill, *Metallwirt*, **8**. 699, 1929; S. Procopiu, *Compt. Rend.*, **169**. 1030, 1919; A. Ungerer, *Ann. Physik*, (4), **46**. 138, 1915; F. Braun, *ib.*, (4), **16**. 5, 1905; J. de Kowalsky, *Arch. Sciences Genève*, (4), **32**. 468, 1911; Maschinebauanstalt Humboldt, *German Pat.*, *D.R.P.* 419758, 1923; E. Breuning and O. Schneider, *Brit. Pat. No.* 275221, 1927; E. Tiede and E. Birnbräuer, *Zeit. anorg. Chem.*, **87**. 154, 1914; K. Lauch and W. Ruppert, *Phys. Zeit.*, **27**. 452, 1926; G. W. C. Kaye and D. Ewen, *Proc. Roy. Soc.*, **89**. A, 58, 1914; F. H. Constable, *ib.*, **117**. A, 376, 1927; G. P. Thomson, *ib.*, **125**. A, 352, 1929; A. Knocke, *Ber.*, **42**. 210, 1909; J. C. Steinberg, *Phys. Rev.*, (2), **21**. 23, 1923; A. J. Sorensen, *ib.*, (2), **24**. 658, 1924; G. F. Taylor, *ib.*, (2), **23**. 655, 1924; J. H. Howey, *ib.*, (2), **34**. 1440, 1929; Z. Debinska, *Spraw. Prace Polsk. Towarz Fizyea*, **4**. 59, 1929.

⁷ C. Serono, *Arch. Farm. Sperim.*, **9**. 152, 1910 ; R. Gans, *Contribucion Fis. Mat. Univ. La Plata*, **1**. 161, 1915 ; J. Fischer, *Die Zerstäubungserscheinungen bei' Metallen unter besonderer Berücksichtigung der mechanisch-thermischen Zerstäubung und der elektrischen Stossverdampfung*, Berlin, 1927 ; T. Svedberg, *Ber.*, **38**. 3616, 1905 ; **39**. 1707, 1712, 1906 ; *Nova Acta Upsala*, (4), **2**. 1, 1911 ; *Die Methoden zur Herstellung kolloider Lösungen anorganischer Stoffe*, Dresden, 413, 1909 ; H. Freundlich, *Kapillarchemie*, Leipzig, 536, 1923 ; G. Bredig, *Anorganische Fermente*, Leipzig, 34, 1901 ; *Zeit. Elektrochem.*, **4**. 514, 1898 ; *Zeit. angew. Chem.*, **11**. 951, 1898 ; *Zeit. phys. Chem.*, **32**. 127, 1900 ; E. Berl, K. Barth and K. Winnacker, *ib.*, **145**. 298, 1929 ; D. Zavrieff, *ib.*, **87**. 507, 1914 ; E. F. Burton, *Phil. Mag.*, (6), **11**. 441, 1906 ; E. F. Burton and P. Phillips, *Proc. Cambridge Phil. Soc.*, **13**. 260, 1906 ; J. Billiter, *Ber.*, **35**. 1933, 1902 ; F. Fischer and F. Schröter, *ib.*, **43**. 1453, 1910 ; A. Schmauss, *Phys. Zeit.*, **6**. 506, 1905 ; F. Ehrenhaft, *Anz. Akad. Wien*, **39**. 241, 1902 ; O. Scarpa, *Nuovo Cimento*, (5), **11**. 178, 1906 ; A. Cotton and H. Mouton, *Ann. Chim. Phys.*, (8), **11**. 194, 1907 ; *Compt. Rend.*, **141**. 350, 1905 ; C. Benedicks, *Arkiv. Mat. Fys.*, **8**. 7, 1912 ; *Koll. Beihefte*, **4**. 236, 1913 ; H. Nordenson, *ib.*, **7**. 102, 1915 ; M. Traube-Mengarini and A. Scala, *Atti Accad. Lincei*, (5), **19**. ii, 505, 1910 ; *Koll. Zeit.*, **10**. 113, 1912 ; T. Malarsky, *ib.*, **23**. 114, 1918 ; F. Haurowitz, *ib.*, **40**. 139, 1926 ; E. Richter, *German Pat.*, *D.R.P.* 342212, 1919 ; H. H. Franck, *ib.*, 412167, 1922 ; Chemische Fabrik von Heyden, *ib.*, 326655, 1919 ; H. Crookes and L. Stroud, *ib.*, 320796, 1913 ; *Brit. Pat. No.* 28776, 1912 ; C. J. Sims and E. W. J. Mardles, *Trans. Faraday Soc.*, **22**. 366, 1926 ; P. N. Pavloff, *Koll. Zeit.*, **34**. 100, 1924 ; H. B. Weiser and G. L. Mack, *Journ. Phys. Chem.*, **34**. 86, 1930 ; B. C. Soyenkoff, *ib.*, **34**. 2519, 1930 ; P. von Mutzenbecher, *Biochem. Zeit.*, **243**. 113, 1931 ; D. C. Bahl, *Koll. Zeit.*, **59**. 60, 1932.

§ 12. The Allotropes of Iron

L'utile bien considéré a toujours du curieux et il est rare que le curieux bien suivi ne mène pas à l'utile.—R. A. F. DE RÉAUMUR.

The first recorded observation on the discontinuity in the properties of iron and steel was made at the beginning of the seventeenth century by W. Gilbert,[1] in his *De magnete* (London, 1600). He found that when a magnet is heated to redness, it loses all traces of magnetization. About half a century later, T. Brown, in his *Pseudodoxia epidemica* (London, 1650), also said that the magnetization of iron is affected by temp., for he observed that " by the fire, iron abandons whatsoever it has received from the loadstone." In developing his *théorie de la trempe*, C. E. Jullien seems to have had a notion that iron can exist in allotropic forms. About 1820, J. Cumming noted that the thermoelectric current between iron and other metals is reversed at a red-heat. In 1869, G. Gore pointed out that when a bar of iron is heated to redness, a whole series of changes occurs in its molecular structure, as shown by observations on its magnetism, its dimensions, its cohesive power, its sp. ht., its thermoelectric capacity, and its electrical conductivity. Thus, on cooling a red-hot iron wire a sudden dilation occurs while the iron is still at a red-heat, and at this temp. the iron suddenly becomes magnetic. In 1873, W. F. Barrett observed that if a piece of steel be heated to redness and allowed to cool, it progressively becomes darker and darker until a certain temp. is attained, when there is a sudden evolution of heat, which is sufficient to raise the temp. of the mass and render it perceptibly brighter. The phenomenon is called *recalescence*. The facts were confirmed by the observations of M. Aliamet, C. Barus, C. Bauer, C. Benedicks, F. G. A. Berson, J. H. Brinell, W. Broniewsky, H. L. Callendar, H. le Chatelier, G. Chrystal, J. Coffin, G. Forbes, G. Heim, E. Heyn, J. Hopkinson, H. Hort, H. M. Howe, A. Ledebur, C. G. Knott, W. Kohlrausch, P. H. Ledeboer, H. F. Newall, R. Norris, R. C. Gale, A. Nouel, J. E. N. Pionchon, H. W. B. Rozeboom, E. Saladin, H. Scott, C. M. Smith and co-workers, A. Stadler, P. G. Tait, A. Schulze, and H. Tomlinson. A. Mallock noted that as the proportion of carbon in the iron is increased the temp. at which recalescence occurs is lowered—*vide infra*. W. Metcalf, and J. O. Arnold raised the question whether or not the recalescence in· steel is due to a change from the plastic to the crystalline state ; and the subject was discussed by F. Osmond, and J. O. Arnold. The hypothesis was sterile.

In 1887, F. Osmond showed that if an iron bar be cooled from its m.p. to 0°, the time-temperature cooling curve shows three breaks or arrests. The arrests are due to the evolution of a small amount of heat, whereby the rate of cooling is

retarded.   The evolution of heat is produced by some internal change in the metal ;
these changes are reversible, because the heating curve of iron shows three breaks.
The arrests on the heating curve occur at a slightly higher temp. than those on the
cooling curve.   The difference in the temp. obtained by the heating and cooling
curves is due to a certain amount of hysteresis, lag, inertia, or resistance to change ;
the resulting lag tends to lower the temp. of the arrest during the cooling, and to
raise it during the heating.   D. K. Tschernoff, and F. Osmond represented the discontinuities by the symbol A, from the initial letter of the French word *arrestation*,
or arrest, and the arrests on the cooling curve were symbolized Ar, where r
is the initial letter of the word *refroidissement*, cooling ; and those on the heating
curve were represented by Ac, where c is the initial letter of the French word
chauffage, heating.   The approximate temp. at which the breaks occur in the cooling
and heating curves are :

Heating	.	.	Ac_4, 1404°	Ac_3, 910°	Ac_2, 770°
Cooling	.	.	Ar_4, 1400°	Ar_3, 890°	Ar_2, 760°
Average	.	.	A_4, 1400°	A_3, 906°	A_2, 768°

J. O. Arnold, W. Reinders and P. van Groningen, and E. Colver-Glauert showed
that with the iron of a very high degree of purity the Ar_2-arrest may show as a
double or twinned arrest.   The subject was discussed by J. Driesen, A. E. Oxley,
P. N. Laschtschenko, A. I. Brodsky, M. Oknoff, and M. Temnikoff.   Breaks
also occur in the curves relating the temp. with other physical properties—
sp. gr., tensile strength, sp. ht., electrical resistance, magnetic susceptibility,
thermo-electric force, etc.   There are several possible explanations of these
critical temperatures.   F. Osmond suggested that they represent changes from
one allotropic form to another.   This means that there are four **allotropic states**
of iron.   The form stable at ordinary temp. and up to about 769°—*i.e.* A_2—is
called α-**ferrite,** or α-**iron ;** that form stable between 769° and 906° is called β-**ferrite,**
or β-**iron ;** and that between 906° and 1404°, γ-**ferrite,** or γ-**iron.**   Owing to
hysteresis or lag these arrests are not necessarily sharply defined, but represent
regions or zones within which the assumed allotropic changes occur.   K. Honda
and S. Miura, and G. K. Burgess and co-workers, for example, found that with a
cooling or heating rate of 2° per minute the A_3-arrest for purified iron begins at
860° and ends at 850°.   These intervals may be widened if other elements be
present—*e.g.* nickel (*vide infra*).   The ranges of stability of the four phases are :
α-iron up to 768° ; β-iron between 768° and 906° ; γ-iron between 906° and 1400° ;
and δ-iron between 1400° and the m.p.   If with L. Cammen, C. H. Desch,
W. Guertler, K. Honda, R. Ruer, F. Sauerwald, G. Tammann, F. Wever, and
others, the β-phase be considered as a non-magnetic form of the α-phase, and the
definition of an allotropic phase be phrased to exclude the inclusion of non-magnetic
forms as true allotropes, the ranges of stability of the three phases will be : α-iron
up to 906° ; γ-iron between 906° and 1400° ; and δ-iron between 1400° and the
m.p.   F. Wever, H. Hanemann and A. Schrader, and P. Oberhoffer observed that
the polished and etched surfaces of α- and β-ferrite appear as irregular grains ; and
γ-iron shows twinned crystals.   A. Perrier and F. Wolfers reported a break in the
heating curve at 1130°.

   E. J. Ball first observed the A_4-arrest at about 1300° with iron containing 0·12
per cent. carbon ; and this probably represents the transformation of δ- into
γ-ferrite, subsequently observed by R. Ruer and F. Goerens, when allowance is
made for the lowering of the transition temp. by carbon.   With purified iron
R. Ruer and F. Goerens observed that the temp. between 1404° and the m.p.,
1505°, represents the zone of stability of δ-**ferrite,** or δ-**iron.**   These temp. were
given by R. Ruer and F. Goerens as the best representative values.   The idea is
illustrated diagrammatically in Fig. 76.   At the critical temp. two forms are in
equilibrium with one another.

   The X-radiograms of the different forms of iron (*vide infra*) show that the

crystals of δ-ferrite have a body-centred cubic lattice ; those of γ-ferrite have a
face-centred cubic lattice ; whilst those of β- and α-ferrite have an identical body-
centred cubic lattice. The change from β- to α-ferrite at
about 770° is not connected with any change in crystal form,
but it happens that at this temp. the magnetic permeability
of the iron increases very rapidly, and the arrest is accordingly sometimes termed the temp. of *magnetic transformation*.
Thus, R. Ruer and K. Kaneko regarded the change as a
transformation of a non-magnetic crystalline form into a
ferromagnetic one.

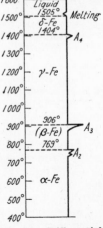

FIG. 76.—Differential
Cooling Curve of Iron
(Diagrammatic).

A. Smits distinguishes between what he calls heterogeneous and homogeneous allotropy, and believes that in the
case of heterogeneous liquids or solids two different forms or
phases co-exist in equilibrium. The relative proportions of
the two forms vary with temperature. At the so-called
transition point there is a sudden disturbance in the conditions of equilibrium. Otherwise expressed, the equilibrium
condition is a discontinuous function of temp. This is supported by the fact that the f.p. of sulphur, phosphorus, tin,
etc., vary with the temp. at which equilibrium has been
attained. Mercury is homogeneous and the f.p. is independent
of its previous thermal treatment. The transformation corresponding with the change in some property may be abrupt,
as in I, Fig. 77. Again, one—II or III, Fig. 77—or both—IV or V, Fig. 77—
modifications may be soluble in the other and the curve may show all degrees of
continuity, and there will then be a range of temp. within which the transformation takes place—V, Fig. 77. The allotropic transformation then involves the
splitting up of a homogeneous solid soln. of two modifications or phases. The
subject was discussed by C. Benedicks, H. M. Howe, H. C. H. Carpenter, A. Holt,
E. Cohen and G. de Bruin, and A. Smits. According to K. Honda and H. Takagi,
the β→α transformation extends over a small interval of temp., and the interval
with both the β→α and the γ→α transformations increases as the proportion
of carbon contained in steels is augmented—*cf.* Fig. 76.

The A₂-point.—Although A. Kroll, and W. Rosenhain and J. C. W. Humfrey
reported a difference in the *microstructure* of α- and β-phases, they could not
satisfy themselves that there is a real difference ; nor could E. H. Saniter,

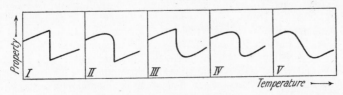

FIG. 77.—Abrupt and Graded Transformation Points.

J. E. Stead and H. C. H. Carpenter, and O. W. Storey detect any difference.
The observations of F. Wever on the X-radiograms of the metal in the α- and
β-states revealed no difference in the *space-lattices*, although R. Bach reported a
discontinuity in the lattice constant between 750° and 860°. Observations by
G. Charpy, and W. Rosenhain and J. C. W. Humfrey indicated an increase in the
hardness as the metal passed through the A₂-arrest.

W. Rosenhain and J. C. W. Humfrey heated one end of a rod of purified iron in vacuo
and simultaneously subjected the rod to strain. Three zones appeared : in the α-range
the iron became weaker and softer as the temp. was raised ; in the β-range the iron was
harder and stronger ; whilst in the γ-range the material developed a sharply defined
crystalline structure and its strength was reduced. A. Sauveur heated bars of iron in the

middle whilst the ends were cold. Pure irons always broke in the central hottest portion when they were twisted ; but if the centre of the bar was above the A_3-arrest, the greatest twist occurred at two points along the rods corresponding with the A_3-arrest. This shows that iron is more plastic whilst passing through the A_3-transformation. Again, F. Wever and P. Giani heated one end of a thin strip of iron in vacuo and observed that coarse crystals of δ-iron appeared where the temp. was over 1400° ; below that temp. finer crystals of γ-iron appeared ; and below 906°, α-iron formed crystals larger than γ-iron, but rather smaller than δ-iron.

The *heating and cooling* curves of purified iron by G. K. Burgess and co-workers, J. F. T. Berliner, and F. Wever gave 763° for the A_2-arrest ; R. Ruer and co-workers found 769° ; F. C. Thompson, $Ac_2=765°$; P. Bardenhauer gave $Ac_2=773°$ and $Ar_2=771°$; W. C. Roberts-Austen, $Ar_2=766°$; W. Gontermann, and G. Charpy and L. Grenet, $A_2=770°$; A. Müller, and W. Rosenhain and J. C. W. Humfrey, $Ac_2=770°$ and $Ar_2=763°$. Observations were also made by J. O. Arnold, G. Belloc, W. Broniewsky, H. C. H. Carpenter and B. F. E. Keeling, P. Oberhoffer, A. Perrier and F. Wolfers, and A. Sanfourche. According to G. K. Burgess and J. J. Crowe, and E. Maurer, the A_2-arrest does not show hysteresis phenomena ; the Ar_2-arrest, for instance, remains at 770° whether the rate of cooling is at the rate of 15 or 250 degrees per minute. G. Tammann also found that the A_2-arrest is not affected by pressures up to 12,000 kgrms. per sq. cm.—*cf.* Fig. 92. H. C. H. Carpenter found that the A_2-arrest is almost obliterated when electrolytic iron is repeatedly heated in vacuo so as to remove the occluded hydrogen. L. Guillet and A. M. Portevin observed that the presence or absence of adsorbed hydrogen had no particular influence on the A_2-arrest ; and A. Sauveur found that the position of the A_2-arrest is influenced by the previous thermal history of the metal ; thus, on a first heating to 1000° the Ac_2-arrest occurred at 725° ; on the eighth heating, at 769° ; on the ninth heating, at 781° ; on the tenth heating, at 783° ; and on the eleventh heating, at 783°. This shows that by previous heatings and coolings there is a gradual drift of the A_2-point towards a constant value. K. Honda observed that whilst the A_2-arrest represents a gradual change in which the equilibrium condition is a continuous function of the temp., the A_3- and A_4-arrests take place at definite temp. G. Sirovich supposed that there are two forms of α-iron, namely $α_1$-ferrite, stable at ordinary temp., and $α_2$-ferrite, stable above 370°. He suggested that the former is hard and magnetic, and forms solid soln. with cementite ; whilst the latter is soft and magnetic, and not capable of holding carbon in solid soln. The *specific heat* by P. Weiss and P. N. Beck gave for the at. ht., C_p, a peak at 753° when $C_p=17\cdot64$; F. Wüst and co-workers, 755° when $C_p=21\cdot00$; P. Weiss and co-workers, 784° when $C_p=17\cdot03$ to $17\cdot26$; P. Oberhoffer and W. Grosse, 785° when $C_p=27\cdot90$; S. Umino, 825° when $C_p=14\cdot53$ for steel, and 820° when $C_p=19\cdot00$ for armco iron ; H. Lecher observed a singular point in the sp. ht. curve at 740° ; P. N. Laschtschenko, one at 730° ; A. Meuthen, one at 780° ; W. Winkler, between 780° and 840° ; R. Durrer, between 725° and 780° ; and P. Oberhoffer, between 750° and 760°. Observations were also made by J. Maydel—*vide infra.* C. Benedicks observed a very slight deflection in the *thermal expansion* curves at 760° to 775°, and another small deflection at 830°. These very mild singularities are thought to be connected with magnetostriction. Observations were also made by G. Charpy and L. Grenet, H. le Chatelier, P. Chevenard, J. Driesen, H. Esser, and E. Maurer. The *electrical resistance* curves of G. K. Burgess and I. N. Kellberg showed a decided cusp at 757° ; and those of K. Honda and Y. Ogura, one at 798°. Similarly, I. Iitaka gave $A_2=790$; A. Somerville, 785° ; W. Broniewsky, 750° to 850° ; A. R. Meyer, 700° ; P. Fournel, and O. Boudouard, 775°. These singularities are supposed by F. Osmond to be connected with the A_2-arrest. The subject was studied by P. Saldau. The *thermoelectric force* curves by W. Broniewsky found a discontinuity at about 795° ; G. K. Burgess and H. Scott, and J. F. T. Berliner, one at 768°. Observations on the subject were also made by C. Benedicks, and W. Geiss and J. A. M. van Liempt. The *magnetic susceptibility* curve was found by H. le Chatelier, P. Curie, P. G. Tait, A. Regner, R. B. Fehr, and P. H. Ledeboer to show singularities near the A_2-arrest corresponding with the temp. of magnetic transformation. In this way J. Hopkinson, E. M. Terry, and T. D. Yensen found the Ar_2-arrest is near 785°; D. K. Morris, R. L. Wills, and K. Honda and H. Takagi gave $Ar_2=770°$ and $Ac_2=870°$; P. Curie, $Ac_2=745°$ and $Ar_2=741°$; P. Weiss and P. N. Beck, 753°; P. Weiss, 756°; K. Honda and Y. Ogura, 796°; S. Sato, $Ac_2=790°$ and $Ar_2=786°$; and T. Ishiwara, 780° to 800° with purified iron, and this was lowered to 790° with low-carbon steels, and to 780° with high-carbon steels. K. Honda's observations are discussed in connection with the magnetic properties of iron; he gave 790° for the Curie point of purified iron, and for carbon alloys, 770°; and he regarded 770° as the Curie point of austenite, which he proposed designating the A_2'-point to show its relationship with the A_2-point of iron. P. Weiss and G. Foëx thought that their curves indicated the existence of two forms of β-iron, which they called respectively β_1-iron and β_2-iron; but E. M. Terry showed that the supposed breaks were illusionary. P. Curie found that for stronger fields there is a tendency for the inversion to extend over a wider range of temp.; K. Honda observed that variations in the field strength had no effect on the inversion, but K. Renger found a difference with different field strengths. The magnetic inversion—*vide infra*—was discussed by P. Dejean, G. Eger, S. Hilpert, K. Honda and co-workers, A. Perrier and F. Wolfers, G. Rümelin and R. Maire, R. Ruer and co-workers, F. C. Thompson, and P. Weiss and co-workers. A. B. Bagdasarian observed a break in the *equilibrium constant* of the reaction $FeCl_2+H_2 \rightleftharpoons 2HCl+Fe$ at different temp.

The effect of alloying elements on the A_2-arrest has not been closely investigated. It is lowered from 780° to 690° by 21 per cent. of titanium; and it is also known to be lowered by carbon, nitrogen, chromium, and nickel, but raised by cobalt.

The A_2-arrest is reversible, and ferromagnetic α-iron does not show the phenomenon of superheating, nor does the paramagnetic β-iron show the phenomenon of under-cooling. The ultimate molecular or atomic particles concerned in ferromagnetism, even though they are in an intense magnetic field, acquire more and more violent thermal oscillations as the temp. rises. This destroys the orientations of these particles imposed by the magnetic field. The most rapid loss in magnetic susceptibility or permeability occurs at about 768°, the A_2-arrest, and thereafter the ferromagnetism continues to decrease, so that the last detectable traces have vanished completely at about 790°. Energy must be expended in breaking up the orientation of the molecular or atomic magnets, so that there is a marked change in the heat content or sp. ht. at the A_2-arrest. There is also a change in the thermoelectric power and electrical resistance at the A_2-arrest. There is also a slight expansion at this temp., possibly associated with magnetostriction. The fact that the principal physical properties which are changed at the A_2-arrest are magnetic and electrical led M. Geiss and J. A. M. van Liempt to suggest that the changes in the space-lattice are electronic not atomic; but from a study of the K-emission spectra F. Wever could not detect any difference in the electronic configuration of the outer shell of magnetic and non-magnetic iron atoms. D. Jones, and F. Wever also discussed the electronic structure of the two phases.

The A_3-point.—O. L. Roberts and W. P. Davey considered 907° to 910° to be best representative value for this temp. The mean temp. between the Ac_3- and the Ar_3-arrests represents the point above which iron exists in the γ-form, and below which it exists in the paramagnetic α-form, *i.e.* the β-form. A. Sauveur found that the A_3-arrest depends on the previous thermal history of the specimen, for the Ac_3-point on a first heating was 850°, and on the eleventh heating, 919°; E. Maurer, that the Ar_3-arrest is lowered from 865° to 830° when the rate of cooling is increased from 15 to 280 degrees per minute; and R. Ruer and F. Goerens, that it is lowered from 900° to 892° when the rate of cooling is increased from 1 to 12 degrees per minute. Analogous results were obtained by F. Wever and N. Engel. O. L. Roberts found that with purified iron the face-centred cubic lattice persists at 921°. A. M. Portevin and M. Garvin, W. Schneider, F. Wever and A. Heinzel, and F. Wever and N. Engel studied the subject.   S. Sato's results for the Ar_3- and Ac_3-arrests are summarized in Fig. 78.   G. Tammann observed that the A_3-arrest is lowered by press.—*cf.* Fig. 78.   The effect of pressure on the A_3-arrest was calculated from R. Clausius and E. Clapeyron's equation (**1**. 9, 4), $dT/dp=Tdv/dQ$,

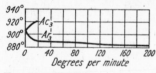

by F. C. Thompson; he thus showed that the temp. is lowered $1°$ by the application of 136 atm. press.   O. C. Ralston calculated that the Ac_3-arrest is lowered $-0.00482°$ per atm., or $1°$ per 208 atm., by the use of more recent data, $T=1179°$, $dQ=370$ cals., $dv=-0.0625$ c.c., and $dp=$unity.   The change in the *microstructure* of iron as it passes through the A_3-arrest was studied by T. Andrews, H. C. H. Carpenter, B. A. Rogers, D. Ewen, H. Hanemann, J. C. W. Humfrey, A. Kroll, P. Oberhoffer and A. Heger, H. S. Rawdon and co-workers, W. C. Roberts-Austen, W. Rosenhain and co-workers, E. H. Saniter, F. Sauerwald and co-workers, A. Sauveur and C. H. Chou, J. E. Stead and co-workers, O. W. Storey, F. Wever, and T. D. Yensen.   B. A. Rogers said that the change in microstructure which takes place at the A_3-arrest, between $899°$ and $912°$, occurs as an eruption wave which passes quickly over the surface and leaves it completely changed in appearance.   No change in the microstructure of armco iron and of electrolytic iron which has been melted in vacuo occurs below the A_3-point.   The nature of the *crystalline change* in passing through the A_3-arrest was first studied by F. Osmond, and F. Osmond and G. Cartaud, and it is discussed in a special section below.   The changes in the *mechanical properties* at the A_3-arrest were discussed by J. C. W. Humfrey, F. C. Lea, W. Rosenhain, W. Rosenhain and J. C. W. Humfrey, and J. E. Stead—*vide infra.*   F. Sauerwald and T. Sperling found that the Ac_3-arrest can be lowered $4°$ and the Ar_3-arrest raised $4°$ by mechanical strain.   Numerous observations have been made on the location of the A_3-arrest by *heating and cooling* curves, by F. Osmond, J. O. Arnold, G. Belloc, W. Broniewsky, G. Charpy, G. Charpy and L. Grenet, W. Gontermann, E. Heyn, P. Oberhoffer, W. C. Roberts-Austen, and W. Rosenhain and J. C. W. Humfrey.   R. Ruer and K. Bode place the Ar_3-arrest at $875°$ and the Ac_3-arrest at $880°$; R. Ruer and K. Fick gave $875°$ for the Ar-arrest, R. Ruer and F. Goerens gave $906°$ for the A_3-arrest; K. Honda and H. Takagi gave $916°$ for the Ac_3-arrest and $890°$ for the Ar_3-arrest; and H. Masumoto gave $908°$ for the Ac_3-arrest and $888°$ for the Ar_3-arrest; F. Wever and K. Apel gave $905°$ for the Ac_3-arrest, and $855°$ for the Ar_3-arrest; A. Perrier and F. Wolfers gave $A_3=900°$; A. Sanfourche, $Ac_3=959°$ and $Ar_3=877°$; P. Bardenheuer, $Ac_3=911°$ and $Ar_3=886°$; F. C. Thompson, $Ac_3=920°$; A. Müller, $Ac_3=917°$ and $Ar_3=984°$; H. C. H. Carpenter and B. F. E. Keeling, $Ac_3=908°$ and $Ar_3=901°$; J. E. Stead and H. C. H. Carpenter, $Ac_3=920°$ and $Ar_3=887°$; and A. Sauveur, $Ac_3=915°$ and $Ar_3=983°$.   G. K. Burgess and J. J. Crowe obtained by extrapolation from the results with different rates of heating $Ac_3=909°$ and $Ar_3=898°$—mean$=903.5°$. K. Honda and S. Miura observed that the transformation takes place through a range of temp. and is not to be regarded as a point—*vide infra.*   H. Quinney found that the difference in the fall of temp. between single crystals and polycrystals at the Ac_3-arrest is about $4°$, and the result is explained by the existence of surface energy at the crystal faces of polycrystalline iron.   Indeed, it was found that mechanical overstrain, which leads to a breaking up of the crystals, reduces the heat absorption at the critical point, owing to an increase in the surface area of the crystals.   J. E. N. Pionchon, J. Maydel, and F. K. Bailey also observed breaks corresponding with the A_3-arrest on the *specific heat* curves.   F. Wüst and co-workers showed with electrolytic iron that the Ac_3-break occurs at $919°$ and the Ar_3-break at $911°$; J. A. Harker observed a break at $900°$; A. Meuthen, one at $890°$; P. N. Laschtschenko, one at $895°$; and P. Oberhoffer and W. Grosse, and S. Umino, a break at $906°$.   W. Broniewsky, G. Charpy, P. Chevenard, J. Driesen.

Fig. 78.—The Effect of Rate of Heating or Cooling on the A_3-arrests.

and J. E. Stead and L. Grenet observed singularities corresponding with the A_3-arrest in the *thermal expansion* curve; that of C. Benedicks gave a marked change in vol. for Ac_3-arrest at 903° to 906°. These changes may be due to the relief of strains which attend recrystallization; the sharpness of the transformation made C. Benedicks assume that α- or β-iron is insoluble in γ-iron, but P. Chevenard found that there is an interval of temp. indicating that β-iron is soluble in γ-iron. H. Esser obtained results in agreement with $Ac_3 = 906°$ and $Ar_3 = 897°$; S. Konno, $Ac_3 = 903°$; and S. Sato, $Ac_3 = 895°$ and $Ar_3 = 885°$—or eliminating the effects of the rate of cooling, $A_3 = 903°$. K. Honda and S. Miura found that the Ac_3-arrest of armco iron occurs at 860° to 905°, and the Ar_2-arrest, at 889° to 850°. Observations by O. Boudouard, W. Broniewsky, H. le Chatelier, P. Fournel, A. R. Meyer, and D. K. Morris showed that there are discontinuities in the *electrical resistance* curve corresponding with the Ac_3-arrest. G. K. Burgess and I. N. Kellberg found singularities corresponding with the Ac_3-arrest between 900° and 911°, and with the Ar_3-arrest between 887° and 872°; and I. Iitaka, for $Ac_3 = 950°$ and $Ar_3 = 910°$. Singularities were observed by P. Saldau, G. Belloc, C. Benedicks, W. Broniewsky, R. Durrer, and E. B. Harrison in the curve for the *thermoelectric force*. G. K. Burgess and H. Scott found singularities corresponding with the Ac_3-arrest between 906° to 916°, and with the Ar_3-arrest between 900° and 896°; P. Oberhoffer, with $Ac_3 = 909°$ and $Ar_3 = 895°$; whilst A. Goetz observed singularities in the range 900° to 910°. J. F. T. Berliner obtained similar results. Irregularities were observed by P. Curie, K. Honda and co-workers, and P. Weiss and co-workers in the *magnetic susceptibility* curves. K. Honda and H. Takagi found singularities corresponding with the Ac_3-arrest at 908° to 911°, and for the Ar_3-arrest, 889° to 898°; T. Ishiwara similarly obtained singularities for the Ac_3-point at 898° and for the Ar_3-point at 890°; T. D. Yensen, Ar_3 at 894°; and E. M. Terry, at 918° for the Ac_3-point and at 903° for the Ar_3-point. G. Belloc, A. Sieverts, and E. Jurisch observed singularities in the *solubility of hydrogen* in iron corresponding with the A_3-arrest; P. van Groningen, in the *equilibrium constant* of the system α—Fe—FeO—γ—Fe—gas; and A. B. Bagdasarian, in the equilibrium constant of the reaction: $FeCl_2 + H_2 \rightleftharpoons 2HCl + Fe$.

A. E. Oxley, G. Mars, L. Grenet, and T. D. Yensen inferred that if iron could be completely purified, it would be found to exist only in the α-form. It is assumed that pure iron, below the m.p., has no allotropic forms, and its characteristic lattice structure is the body-centred cube; it is further assumed that the A_3- and A_4-transformations are caused by the entrance of carbon and other " stranger " atoms in the interstitial spaces of the lattice; and when their amount exceeds the solubility in α-iron at the particular temp., they cause the iron to modify its structure in order to accommodate them. The γ-phase is suppressed in the iron-silicon alloys when the proportion of silicon exceeds 1·5 to 2·5 per cent., and this amount of silicon represents what is required to deoxidize the iron; otherwise silicon is not an interstitial element so far as the space-lattice is concerned, rather is it a substitution element. Similarly with the alloys with chromium (*q.v.*). The subject was discussed by F. C. Thompson, R. A. Hadfield, J. E. Stead and H. C. H. Carpenter, and G. K. Burgess and I. N. Kellberg.

The A_4-point.—This corresponds with the appearance of a new phase called δ-iron. As indicated above, this transition point was discovered by E. J. Ball; and it was discussed by F. Wever, P. Weiss, J. O. Arnold, W. Rosenhain, F. Osmond, R. Ruer and co-workers, M. Copisarow, H. Bredmeier, K. Honda, and H. le Chatelier. The effect of pressure on the A_4-arrest, calculated as in the case of the A_3-arrest, is to raise the Ac_4-point 0·00557° per atm. or 1° per 180 atm. when $T = 1673°$, $dQ = 140$ cals., $dv = 0·0192$ c.c.; $dp =$ unity. The change in the *microstructure* was examined by F. Wever, F. Sauerwald and co-workers, and H. S. Rawdon and T. Berglund. E. J. Ball, and F. Osmond observed by the *heating and cooling* curves that the Ar_4-arrest occurs at about 1300°, and more accurate observations by W. Gontermann gave 1411°; R. Ruer and K. Fick, and R. Ruer and K. Kaneko observed 1420°;

R. Ruer and R. Klesper, 1401° ; and D. Hanson and J. R. Freeman, 1400°. The subject was also studied by W. C. Roberts-Austen, H. Harkort, A. Müller, and A. Sanfourche. The *specific heat* curves of F. Wüst and co-workers showed a singularity at 1404·5° ; and those of P. Oberhoffer and W. Grosse, at 1401°. J. Maydel made observations on the subject. S. Sato, and P. Chevenard examined the *thermal expansion* curves and found a break corresponding with $A_4 = 1400°$. S. Sato said that the expansion curve of δ-iron is continuous with that of α-iron, and hence inferred that α- and δ-irons are the same allotrope. P. Oberhoffer found a discontinuity in the curve for the *thermoelectric force* at 1403°, and A. Goetz, one at 1400°. The *magnetic susceptibility* curves of P. Curie gave the transition at about 1390° ; P. Weiss and G. Foëx observed a singularity at 1395° ; T. Ishiwara, at 1390° ; and E. M. Terry, at 1406°. A. Sanfourche observed 1360° on the heating and 1310° on the cooling curves. A. Goetz observed a change in the *emission of electrons* between 1400° and 1500° ; and A. B. Bagdasarian, a change in the *equilibrium constant* for the reaction $FeCl_2 + H_2 \rightleftharpoons 2HCl + Fe$.

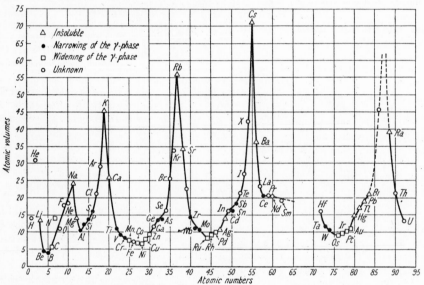

FIG. 79.—The Effect of the Atomic Volume of the Alloying Element on the γ-Phase.

Most elements have an opposite effect on the A_4- and A_3-arrests. Thus, the addition of chromium lowers the A_4-arrest and raises the A_3-arrest, so that the range of stability of the γ-phase becomes smaller and smaller, until it finally disappears. This occurs with about 14 per cent. of chromium. The curves for the A_3-, A_4-arrests meet at 1075°, and γ-iron does not exist in alloys with more chromium. The A_3- and A_4-arrests are suppressed. Similar results are obtained with about 6 per cent. of tungsten, or 1·85 per cent. of silicon, or 2 per cent. of tin, or 2·5 per cent. of vanadium ; and aluminium, molybdenum, and phosphorus act similarly and narrow the field of stability of γ-iron. On the other hand, the reverse effect is produced by carbon, copper, and nickel. These elements thus enlarge the field of stability of γ-iron. The A_4-arrest is raised from 1400° to 1477° by 8 per cent. of copper, and the A_3-arrest is lowered 833° by 3 per cent. of copper ; the A_4-arrest is raised to 1502° by 3·2 per cent. of nickel, and the A_3-arrest is lowered to room temp. by 36 per cent. of nickel ; whilst the A_4-arrest is raised to 1486° by 0·38 per cent. of carbon, and the A_3-arrest is lowered to 730° by 0·9 per cent. of carbon. Cobalt is peculiar in that it does not produce opposite effects on the A_4- and A_3-arrests. Thus the presence of 22 per cent. of cobalt raises the A_4-arrest to 1492°, and the

A_3-arrest is raised to 990° by 45 per cent. of cobalt. F. Wever showed that the elements Mn, Ni, Co, Ru, Rh, Pd, Os, Ir, and Pt enlarge the temp. range of stability of the γ-phase, whilst the elements Be, Al, Si, P, Ti, V, Cr, Ge, As, Cb, Mo, Sn, Sb, Ta, and W narrow the range of stability of the γ-phase. All this is in accord with F. Osmond's rule that elements with a small at. vol. tend to produce in iron that form which has the smallest at. vol.—*i.e.* γ-iron. Boron and beryllium are exceptional. J. O. Arnold, and H. von Jüptner thought that the alleged allotropic changes were largely due to the presence of impurities—notably hydrogen. The effect of hydrogen on the A_3-arrest was examined by H. le Chatelier ; and L. Guillet and A. M. Portevin could detect no marked influence of hydrogen on the A_3-arrest. For the effect of hydrogen on the A_2-arrest, *vide supra*. The effect of elements of different at. vol. in relation to the at. number is shown in F. Wever's tables, Fig. 79, where ▲ denotes that the element is virtually insoluble; ●, that the element narrows the range of the γ-phase ; and ■, that the element widens the range of the γ-phase. An analogous curve is produced by plotting the at. radius and at. number. The relation between the effects produced by elements and their position in the periodic

	I a	I b	II a	II b	III a	III b	IV a	IV b	V a	V b	VI a	VI b	VII a	VII b	VIII a	VIII b
I													1H			2He
II	3Li ▲		4Be ●		5B ●		6C ■		7N ■		8O		9F			10Ne
III	11Na ▲		12Mg ▲		13Al ●		14Si ●		15P ●		16S ●		17Cl			18Ar
IV	19K ▲		20Ca ▲		21Sc		22Ti ●		23V ●		24Cr ●		25Mn ■		26Fe ■ 27Co ■ 28Ni	
		29Cu ■		30Zn ■		31Ga ●		32Ge ●		33As ●		34Se		35Br		36Kr
V	37Rb ▲		38Sr ▲		39Y		40Zr ●		41Nb ●		42Mo ●		43Ma		44Ru ■ 45Rh ■ 46Pd ■	
		47Ag ▲		48Cd ▲		49In		50Sn ●		51Sb ●		52Te		53I		54X
VI	55Cs ▲		56Ba ▲		58Ce ●		72Hf		73Ta ●		74W ●		75Re		76Os ■ 77Ir ■ 78Pt ■	
		79Au ■		80Hg ▲		81Tl ▲		82Pb ▲		83Bi ▲		84Po		85–		86Em
VII	87–		88Ra ▲		89Ac		90Th		91Pa		92U					

Fig. 80.—The Effect produced by Different Elements Grouped in Accord with the Periodic Table.

table is indicated in Fig. 80. A. Merz found that chromium lowers the A_3-arrest, tungsten raises the temp., silicon, and nickel broaden the γ-field, and manganese has little effect.

The X-radiograms of A. W. Hull, and A. Westgren show that the α- and δ-forms of iron have the same body-centred cubic lattice, whilst the γ-form of iron has a face-centred cubic lattice. Observations on the temp. coeff. of the thermoelectric force by W. Schneider, A. Goetz, and G. K. Burgess, the magnetic susceptibility by P. Weiss and G. Foëx, and the sp. ht. by P. Oberhoffer and W. Grosse show that the curves for the α- and δ-forms of iron would be continuous were they not disturbed by the intervention of the γ-phase ; and, as just indicated, this phase can be suppressed. F. Wever therefore suggested that α- and δ-iron are one and the same phase.

At first sight it seems thermodynamically improbable that at one temp. an allotrope A should pass into an allotrope B with the evolution of heat, and that at a higher temp. the allotrope B should return to the original allotrope A, again with an evolution of heat. H. Bredemeier showed that there may be a thermodynamic reason for this strange phenomenon. He said that if it were possible to plot the thermodynamic potential ζ, or free energy of one form, and compare it with that of the other, the two curves would present the appearance of those in Fig. 81 (ζ, arbitrary scale). The curve ab would be the isobaric curve of the thermodynamic potential of α- and δ-iron, and cd, the same for γ-iron. Their intersections at 906° and 1400° are the transition temp. The form of iron with the smallest potential is the most stable, and this is the case for γ-iron between 906° and 1400°. Thermodynamic potential ζ is a measure for the stability of a phase, and it can be represented as a function of the free energy, E, and the entropy, S, so that $\zeta = E - TS + pv$, where p, v, and T respectively denote the press., vol., and temp. The entropy is the first derivative of the free energy, so that $S = d\zeta/dT$, whilst the second derivative is a function of the sp. ht., so that $d^2\zeta/dT^2 = -C_p/T$. By comparing the slopes, $d\zeta/dT$, of the curves at 906° and 1400°, Fig. 81, it follows that at 906° the thermodynamic potential of α-iron is greater than that of γ-iron, whilst at 1400° the thermodynamic potential of γ-iron is greater than that of δ-iron. The energy contents of the two forms of iron can be compared at these two temp., and it follows that in passing from α- to γ-iron the heat of transformation is positive, as is also the case in passing from γ- to δ-iron. The curvature $d^2\zeta/dT^2$ of the curve for γ-iron is less than is that of the α-, δ-iron curve, and this would mean that the sp. ht. of γ-iron is the smaller. The sp. ht. data available do not show this, for while the sp. ht. of γ-iron is less than that of α-iron, it is greater than is that of δ-iron. The sp. ht. data of F. Wüst, however, make the sp. ht. of γ-iron smaller than of both the α- and δ-forms of iron. E. Rengard discussed the theory of cooling curves; and F. H. Jeffery, and Y. Chu-Phay, the thermodynamics of the system; and U. Dehlinger, the changes in the electronic systems in passing from one allotropic form to another.

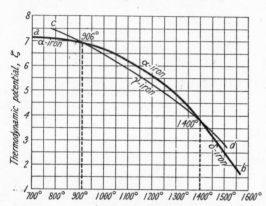

FIG. 81.—The Thermodynamic Potential of Iron (Diagrammatic).

There is a general agreement that the A_4- and A_3-arrests represent allotropic changes, but there is a difference of opinion about the existence of β-ferrite as an allotropic form of iron. It may represent (i) a veritable allotropic change from a β- to an α-allotrope of iron ; (ii) it may not be an independent phase, but rather a solid soln. of α- and γ-ferrites ; or (iii) it may represent an intermolecular, not an allotropic change, taking place within a considerable range of temp. in the α-phase.

G. K. Burgess thus compared the evidence for the existence of allotropic transformations of purified iron at the A_2- and A_3-points :

	A_2-arrest	A_3-arrest
Heat evolution or absorption	Present ; $Ar_2 = Ac_2$	Present ; $Ar_3 < Ac_3$
Specific heat	Present ; $Ar_2 = Ac_2$	Present
Electrical resistance . .	Marked ; $Ar_2 = Ac_2$	Present
Magnetic susceptibility .	Marked ; $Ar_2 = Ac_2$	Very feeble
Other magnetic properties .	Most are well-marked	Most are feeble
Mechanical properties .	Probable	Marked
Expansion	Present	Marked
Crystalline structure (X-rays) .	Body-centred cube	Face-centred cube

and in Table IX A. Sauveur summarized the chief properties of three of the allotropes of iron, for iron containing carbon. According to F. Osmond :

TABLE IX.—A COMPARISON OF SOME PROPERTIES OF ALLOTROPES OF IRON.

	γ-iron	(β-iron)	α-iron
Metallurgical name .	Austenite	β-ferrite	Ferrite ; α-ferrite ; or pearlite ferrite
Stability range . .	Over A_3, $A_{3,2}$ or $A_{3,2,1}$ for excess ferrite ; over A_1 or $A_{3,2,1}$ for eutectoid ferrite	Between A_3 and A_2	$A_{3,2,1}$
Crystallization system .	Cubic	Cubic	Cubic
Habit	Octahedra	Cubes	Cubes
Space-lattice . .	Face-centred	Body-centred	Body-centred
Twinning . . .	Frequent	None	None
Sp. gr. . . .	$>β$- or α-iron	$>α$-iron	$<γ$- and β-iron
Electrical conductivity .	$<α$-iron	$>γ$-iron	$>β$-iron
Magnetic property . .	Non-magnetic	Feebly magnetic	Strongly magnetic
Hardness . . .	$<β$-iron, $>α$-iron	Very hard	Soft

It is difficult to say whether A_2 is an allotropic modification of iron, or whether it is simply the end of the A_3-transformation retarded by the presence of a little carbon.

The main arguments against the assumption that there is no formation of an allotropic β-iron at the Ar_2-arrests are thus summarized by A. Sauveur :

(i) C. Benedicks, and H. C. H. Carpenter said that the Ac_2-point does not occur with purified iron, but G. K. Burgess and J. J. Crowe do not agree. (ii) H. le Chatelier, and C. Benedicks held that the A_2-arrest does not represent an allotropic change because of the absence of hysteresis between the Ac_2- and Ar_2-arrests. This involves the unjustified assumption that the absence of this phenomenon proves that no allotrope is formed. (iii) No crystallographic change can be detected at the A_2-arrest. This involves the unjustified assumption that no two allotropes can have the same crystallographic form. (iv) The absence of dilation as iron cools through the Ar_2-arrest is supposed by G. Charpy and L. Grenet, and by C. Benedicks to prove the absence of a β-allotrope. This assumes that allotropic changes must be accompanied by changes in vol., and that the measurements so far made are decisive. This is by no means the case ; indeed, W. Rosenhain and J. C. W. Humfrey reported a dilation to occur. (v) Although a marked change in the magnetic properties occurs at the A_2-arrest, H. le Chatelier, P. Weiss, K. Honda, C. Benedicks, etc., hold that the A_2-change is not sufficiently abrupt to agree with an allotropic transformation, and that magnetic transformations do not generally indicate allotropic changes. It is argued that the Ac_2-arrest marks the end of a progressive transformation, and that the Ar_2-arrest indicates the beginning of the reverse change. On the other hand, the beginning and end points of a progressive transformation are not likely to be accompanied by an abrupt evolution or absorption of heat. Whilst a magnetic transformation starts below the A_2-arrest, the marked heat evolution at this temp. indicates a sharp break in the continuity of the process, and this suggests allotropy. (vi) No discontinuity in any of the properties of iron has been observed at the Ar_2-arrest, and therefore the transformation cannot be an allotropic one. The curve of the thermoelectric force of iron and carbon does not exhibit any distinct break at the A_2-arrest. On the other hand, the existence of the Ar_2-arrest indicates a sharp discontinuity in the internal energy ; a discontinuity in the magnetic properties does occur about this temp.; W. Rosenhain and J. C. W. Humfrey noted a discontinuity in the dilation, although others have denied this ; the same observers noted a discontinuity in the tensile strength; P. Weiss and co-workers, and F. Wüst and co-workers noted a discontinuity in the sp. ht. ; and G. K. Burgess and I. N. Kellberg, a discontinuity in the electrical resistance.

C. Benedicks attempted to explain the existence of the A_2-arrest in impure iron, without recourse to allotropy, by assuming that highly purified iron will give no A_2-arrest (*vide supra*), that the A_2-arrest indicates the end of the A_3-change, and that some γ-iron remains untransformed below Ar_3 because the impurities enable a kind of under-cooling to occur. This means that the alleged β-iron is in reality a metastable solid soln. of γ-iron in α-iron, and in consequence, unless the cooling be very slow, the Ar_2- and the Ac_2-arrests might occur in pure iron without disproving the hypothesis. A similar hypothesis was made by M. Copisarow ; P. Curie thought that some γ-iron is present in β-iron. H. le Chatelier showed that there is no need for these hypotheses ; and K. Honda added that the phenomenon at the A_2-arrest is purely a thermomagnetic effect.

K. Honda also tried to explain the nature of the progressive change in the A_2-transformation, as follows :

It is not a change of atomic configuration, as is the case with an allotropic change, but very probably a gradual change of energy in atoms accompanying the rise of temp. According to the theory of K. Honda and J. Okubo, the gradual diminution of magnetization with rise of temp. is due to the increasing velocity of rotation of the atoms about their magnetic axes. The angular velocity of this rotation is assumed to be comparatively small at room temp., and the gyrostatic resistance to the turning of the magnetic axes of the atoms in the direction of the field is very small. But as the temp. is continuously increased to a very high degree, the angular velocity, by virtue of thermal impact among atoms, always becomes greater, and hence the gyrostatic action of the atoms rapidly increases, the substance becoming thereby less and less magnetizable, till magnetization vanishes. Here it is to be assumed that when the field ceases to act, the direction of the magnetic axes takes a distribution uniform in all directions by virtue of thermal impact. Thus, according to this theory, the A_2-transformation is of the progressive nature and the change will obviously be a definite function of temp., as actually observed. The heat absorbed during the Ac_2-transformation is the energy required to increase the angular velocity of the atoms, while the heat evolved during the Ar_2-transformation is the energy of rotation liberated. F. Osmond later gave up this hypothesis, for he said that β-iron is hard and brittle at ordinary temp., while α-iron is soft ; and since the A_2-arrest, and not the A_3-arrest, corresponds with the loss of magnetism, it follows that there are at least three distinct allotropic forms of iron, namely α-, β-, and γ-ferrites with ranges respectively from 0° to 760° ; 760° to 900° ; and 900° to 1505°.

G. Tammann, G. K. Burgess and H. Scott, H. M. Howe, F. Osmond, W. Rosenhain and J. C. W. Humfrey, R. Ruer, R. Ruer and K. Bode, and A. Sauveur also favoured that assumption that β-ferrite is an allotropic form of iron. J. E. Stead and H. C. H. Carpenter said that the phenomena attending the recrystallization of electrodeposited iron are more readily explained by assuming that at the Ar_2-arrest iron changes directly from the γ- to the α-state. According to C. Benedicks, β-ferrite is really a solid soln. of γ-ferrite in α-ferrite, so that as iron cools beyond the A_3-arrest γ-ferrite passes into α-ferrite, but the change is not complete, a certain proportion of γ-ferrite persists in solid soln. in α-ferrite until the A_2-arrest is reached when the change into α-ferrite is completed. H. C. H. Carpenter showed that the A_2-point become less and less marked as the degree of purity of the iron is increased, until a sample with 99·967 per cent. Fe, and 0·008 per cent. C, showed the A_2-point only faintly. A. Müller, G. K. Burgess and J. J. Crowe, J. O. Arnold, and A. Sauveur observed that the Ar_2- and Ac_2-points persist even with iron of an exceptionally high degree of purity. J. O. Arnold found that the Ar_3-point occurs within narrower limits of temp., and more sharply when hydrogen and other occluded gases are absent. In no case, however, has it been possible to eliminate the Ar_3- and Ar_2-points by heating iron of a high degree of purity in vacuo. He inferred that the Ar_3-temp. is not connected with the Ar_2-arrest ; and that the Ar_3-temp. represents the physical change of hot iron from the plastic to the crystalline state.

It is very clear that the A_2-arrest represents the temp. of magnetic transformation where ferromagnetic iron becomes paramagnetic. This temp. is often called *Curie's point*. Consequently, β-iron can be regarded as non-magnetic α-iron, ordinary α-iron being magnetic. It is very well established that both paramagnetic and ferromagnetic α-iron have the same crystalline structure—a body-centred, cubic space-lattice—whilst there is a break in the continuity of some physical properties as the metal passes through the A_2-arrest. The fact that the A_2-transformation occurs not so much at a definite and sharply-defined temp. as within a certain range of temp. is of no significance when it is remembered that K. Honda and S. Miura, and G. K. Burgess and co-workers proved that the same phenomenon is characteristic of the A_3-arrest—*vide* nickel-iron alloys. It has been suggested that since no crystalline change occurs at the temp. of magnetic transformation the term allotropic change should not be employed. Thus, H. le Chatelier said :

Le phénomène tout-à-fait différent des transformations allotropiques ordinaires. Je suis de plus en plus convaincu que la différence entre le fer α et le fer β n'est pas une différence d'état allotropique, comme entre le fer γ et les variétés stables à froid. Tous les corps magnétiques, sans aucune exception, présentent, à une certaine température, le même chute progressive des propriétés magnétiques. C'est un phénomène caractéristique des corps magnétiques et seulement de ceux-là.

P. Weiss, from magnetic considerations, thought that the α- and β-states are not different phases ; K. Honda and Y. Okura obtained a pronounced break in the resistance-temperature curve, but even then did not consider the A_2-arrest to be the seat of an allotropic transformation ; and a similar conclusion was drawn by L. Grenet, C. A. Edwards, L. Guillet and A. M. Portevin, K. Honda and co-workers, R. A. Hadfield, F. Wüst and co-workers, T. Ishiwara, F. Wever, H. le Chatelier, P. Weiss, A. E. Oxley, E. Maurer, H. C. H. Carpenter, and C. Benedicks. The attempt is made to evade the definition which commonly applies the word *allotropy* to the various states of an element or compound possessing different physical properties. It is objected that the term " different physical properties " is vague ; and that is certainly the case if it implies the right to include one or more physical properties so as to make any given phase an allotrope of the same element or compound. Consequently, to ignore isomorphism, and use the term polymorphism in place of allotropy, does not answer the real question behind the words : " Is β-iron an allotropic modification of iron ? " or " Does the A_2-arrest indicate that the iron is undergoing an allotropic change ? " We are quite at liberty to make any definition we please, so as to be able to affirm or deny that β-iron is an allotropic form of iron. The subject was discussed by M. Copisarow, K. Honda, C. Benedicks, C. H. Desch, A. E. Oxley, F. C. Thompson, A. Sauveur, etc. We are in quite a similar predicament in answering the question : Are solutions chemical compounds ? (**1**. 2, 9 ; and **1**. 9, 5). Indeed, we are frequently perplexed with a similar type of question. F. Wever and P. Giani said a change of phase can be characterized by a discontinuous change in suitable physical properties, but not necessarily by all physical properties of the substance involved. A polymorphic change or transformation applies only to crystalline substances and is characterized by a discontinuous change in the space-lattice which can now be realized without difficulty. A change in crystalline form is usually accompanied by changes in physical properties so that a polymorphic change is always a change of phase. O. C. Ralston inquired : Is a change of phase always a polymorphic change ? and added that β-iron, or non-magnetic α-iron, has enough difference in physical properties and internal energy to deserve recognition even though there is no satisfactory word or definition to express the difference. In any case, β-iron or β-ferrite can be understood to mean that particular phase of iron which exists between the A_2- and A_3-arrests.

P. G. Tait inferred that iron becomes as it were a different metal on being raised above a certain temp., and he said that this may possibly have some connection with the *ferricum* and *ferrosum* of the chemists. J. N. von Fuchs said there are two species of iron, and he suggested that malleable iron consists of cubic crystals, and cast iron of rhombohedral crystals. He thus foreshadowed the assumption that iron exists in allotropic forms, although his reasons for assuming these varieties were utterly inadequate. A. Baudrimont's *Observations sur la constitution intime du fer* were to the same effect as those of J. N. von Fuchs. Now for the world of speculation. P. Weiss suggested that the molecules of δ-ferrite are monatomic ; those of γ-ferrite, diatomic ; and those of β-ferrite, triatomic. K. Honda and H. Takagi, however, do not agree. A. E. Oxley referred the differences in the allotropic forms of iron to differences in the grouping of the atoms ; M. Copisarow, to differences in the number of atoms in the molecule ; and D. Jones, to changes in the atoms of iron.

REFERENCES.

¹ G. Charpy and L. Grenet, *Metallographist*, **6**. 238, 1903 ; *Bull. Soc. Enc. Nat. Ind.*, **104**. 464, 882, 1903 ; *Compt. Rend.*, **134**. 549, 598, 1902 ; G. Charpy, *ib.*, **108**. 1069, 1889 ; **117**. 850, 1893 ; **118**. 418, 868, 1258, 1894 ; **119**. 735, 1894 ; **129**. 279, 331, 1899 ; *Internat. Zeit. Metallog.*, **3**. 254, 1913 ; *Bull. Soc. Enc. Nat. Ind.*, **94**. 660, 1895; *Metallographist*, **3**. 38, 152, 1900; *Stahl*

Eiscn, **15**. 459, 1895 ; A. Ledebur, *ib.*, **6**. 374, 1886 ; **7**. 447, 1887 ; **15**. 745, 1895 ; L. Grenet, *Journ. Iron Steel Inst.*, **84**. ii, 13, 1911 ; *Bull. Soc. Ind. Min.*, (4), **13**. 101, 1901 ; J. Coffin, *Trans. Amer. Soc. Civil Eng.*, **16**. 324, 1887 ; C. Barus, *Nature*, **41**. 369, 1890 ; G. Gore, *Proc. Roy. Soc.*, **17**. 260, 1869 ; *Phil. Mag.*, (4), **38**. 59, 1869 ; (4), **40**. 177, 1870 ; W. F. Barrett, *ib.*, (4), **46**. 472, 1873 ; *B.A. Rep.*, 259, 1875 ; 476, 1882 ; *Pharm. Journ.*, (3), **4**. 127, 1874 ; F. Osmond and J. Werth, *Compt. Rend.*, **99**. 848, 1884 ; **100**. 450, 1885 ; *Ann. Mines*, (8), **8**. 5, 1885 ; F. Osmond, *Mém. Artillerie*, **24**. 573, 1887 ; *Journ. Iron Steel Inst.*, **37**. i, 38, 102, 1890 ; **39**. i, 117, 1891 ; **45**. i, 149, 1894 ; **49**. i, 180, 1896 ; *Bull. Soc. Enc. Nat. Ind.*, **94**. 480, 1895 ; *Rev. Mét.*, **3**. 411, 1906 ; *Ann. Mines*, (8), **14**. 1, 1888 ; (9), **17**. 110, 1900 ; *Contributions à l'étude des alliages*, Paris, 1901 ; *Metallographist*, **1**. 5, 27, 1898 ; **2**. 169, 1899 ; **3**. 181, 275, 1900 ; *Engg.*, **53**. 50, 331, 1892 ; *Transformation du fer et du carbone dans les fers, aciers et fontes blanches*, Paris, 1888 ; *Compt. Rend.*, **103**. 743, 1135, 1886 ; **104**. 985, 1887 ; **110**. 346, 1890 ; F. Osmond and G. Cartaud, *ib.*, **71**. iii, 444, 1906 ; *Ann. Mines*, (9), **18**. 113, 1900 ; *Trans. Amer. Inst. Min. Eng.*, **37**. 813, 1906 ; *Rev. Mét.*, **3**. 491, 1906 ; *Met.*, **3**. 522, 1906 ; *Stahl Eisen*, **26**. 1074, 1906 ; *Zeit. Kryst.*, **35**. 658, 1902 ; **44**. 541, 1908 ; *Metallographist*, **4**. 119, 236, 1901 ; C. A. Edwards, *Journ. Iron Steel Inst.*, **82**. ii, 147, 1910 ; R. B. Fehr, *ib.*, **95**, i, 203, 1917 ; D. K. Tschernoff, *Metallographist*, **2**. 74, 1899 ; *Proc. Inst. Mech. Eng.*, 152, 286, 1880 ; *Rev. Univ. Mines*, (2), **1**. 396, 1868 ; R. Ruer, *Metallographie in elementar Darstellung*, Leipzig, 1922 ; *Phys. Zeit.*, **21**. 108, 1920 ; *Zeit. anorg. Chem.*, **165**. 142, 1927 ; R. Klesper, *Die δγ-Umwandlung des reinen Eisens und ihre Beeinflussung durch Kohlenstoff, Silizium, Kobalt und Kupfer*, Aachen, 1915 ; R. Ruer and R. Klesper, *Ferrum*, **11**. 257, 1914 ; R. Ruer and K. Fick, *ib.*, **11**. 39, 1914 ; R. Ruer and F. Goerens, *ib.*, **13**. 1, 1915 ; R. Ruer and K. Bode, *Stahl Eisen*, **45**. 1184, 1925 ; R. Ruer and K. Kaneko, *Phys. Zeit.*, **15**. 17, 1914 ; *Ferrum*, **11**. 33, 1914 ; J. Driesen, *ib.*, **11**. 129, 161, 1914 ; **13**. 27, 1916 ; *Mitt. Eisenhütt. Inst. Aachen*, **6**. 158, 1915 ; A. Smits, *Zeit. phys. Chem.*, **76**. 421, 1911 ; **88**. 743, 1914 ; A. Smits and S. C. Bokhorst, *ib.*, **88**. 608, 1914 ; C. Benedicks, K. G. Land and W. H. Dearden, *Trans. Amer. Soc. Steel Treating*, **7**. 445, 1925 ; C. Benedicks, *Metallographic Researches*, New York, 1926 ; *Jahrb. Rad. Elektron.*, **13**. 56, 1916 ; *Recherches physiques et physicochemiques sur l'acier au carbone*, Uppsala, 1904 ; *Rev. Mét.*, **5**. 167, 1908 ; **10**. 11, 1913 ; **12**. 990, 1915 ; *Stahl Eisen*, **32**. 1704, 1912 ; **34**. 1177, 1914 ; *Ferrum*, **13**. 40, 1916 ; *Scient. Amer. Suppl.*, **82**. 362, 1916 ; *Internat. Congress Appl. Chem.*, **8**. xii, 13, 1912 ; *Compt. Rend.*, **162**. 297, 1916 ; *Journ. Iron Steel Inst.*, **77**. 11, 153, 1908 ; **86**. ii, 242, 1912 ; **87**. i, 333, 1913 ; **88**. ii, 171, 1913 ; **89**. i, 407, 1914 ; **93**. i, 211, 1916 ; H. C. H. Carpenter and B. F. E. Keeling, *ib.*, **65**. i, 224, 1904 ; H. C. H. Carpenter, *ib.*, **87**. i, 315, 1913 ; **88**. ii, 119, 1913 ; *Engg.*, **105**. 392, 426, 452, 1918 ; F. C. Lea, *ib.*, **113**. 829, 1923 ; A. Sauveur and C. H. Chou, *Fuels Furnaces*, **7**. 535, 1929 ; A. Sauveur, *The Metallography and Heat Treatment of Iron and Steel*, Cambridge, Mass., 142, 1926 ; *Trans. Amer. Inst. Min. Eng.*, **26**. 863, 1896 ; **50**. 501, 1914 ; **70**. 3, 1924 ; *Rev. Mét.*, **12**. 990, 1915 ; *Ferrum*, **11**. 349, 1914 ; *Engg.*, **96**. 353, 1913 ; *Metallographist*, **2**. 264, 1899 ; *Journ. Iron Steel Inst.*, **88**. ii, 171, 1913 ; J. E. Stead and L. Grenet, *Metallographist*, **6**. 238, 1903 ; *Compt. Rend.*, **134**. 540, 598, 1902 ; W. Broniewsky, *ib.*, **156**. 699, 1983, 1913 ; **162**. 917, 1916 ; *Chim. Ind.*, **1**. 55, 1918 ; J. E. Stead and H. C. H. Carpenter, *Ferrum*, **11**. 133, 1914 ; *Journ. Iron Steel Inst.*, **88**. ii, 119, 1913 ; J. E. Stead, *Metallographist*, **1**. 289, 1898 ; **2**. 85, 1899 ; *Bull. Soc. Enc. Nat. Ind.*, (5), **4**. 127, 1347, 1899 ; *Journ. Iron Steel Inst.*, **53**. i, 145, 1898 ; **54**. ii, 137, 1898 ; **88**. ii, 399, 1913 ; E. J. Ball, *ib.*, **37**. i, 85, 1890 ; D. Hanson and J. R. Freeman, *ib.*, **107**. i, 301, 1923 ; E. Colver-Glauert, *ib.*, **82**. ii, 180, 1910 ; **87**. i, 275, 1913 ; A. Regner, *ib.*, **122**. ii, 343, 1930 ; J. O. Arnold and A. McWilliam, *ib.*, **68**. ii, 27, 1905 ; J. O. Arnold, *ib.*, **45**. i, 110, 1894 ; **82**. ii, 166, 1910 ; **87**. i, 272, 1913 ; *Proc. Inst. Civil Eng.*, **123**. 127, 1896 ; *Proc. Inst. Mech. Eng.*, 543, 1891 ; 102, 1893 ; 35, 1899 ; *Internat. Zeit. Metallog.*, **1**. 192, 1911 ; *Nature*, **41**. 11, 32, 1890 ; *Metallographist*, **2**. 186, 1890 ; *Engg.*, **53**. 214, 1892 ; *Eng.*, **113**. 129, 1912 ; *B.A. Rep.*, 562, 1910 ; W. C. Roberts-Austen, *ib.*, 35, 1899 ; *Stahl Eisen*, **20**. 625, 1900 ; A. E. Oxley, *Chem. News*, **112**. 205, 1915 ; *Phil. Trans.*, **214**. A, 109, 1914 ; **215**. A, 79, 1915 ; *Engg.*, **100**. 425, 1915 ; *Trans. Faraday Soc.*, **11**. 129, 1916 ; L. Guillet and A. M. Portevin, *Compt. Rend.*, **156**. 699, 1913 ; A. M. Portevin and M. Garvin, *ib.*, **164**. 783, 885, 1917 ; A. M. Portevin and V. Bernard, *Rev. Mét.*, **16**. 175, 1919 ; H. L. Callendar, *Phil. Trans.*, **178**. A, 161, 1887 ; E. Heyn, *Verh. Gewerbefl.*, **83**. 355, 1904 ; *Mitt. Internat. Verband. Materialprüf. Tech.*, **2**. ii, 1, 1913 ; *Stahl Eisen*, **20**. 625, 1900 ; A. Stadler, *ib.*, **37**. 112, 1917 ; H. Esser, *ib.*, **47**. 338, 1927 ; L. Heunrich, *Baumaterialkunde*, **2**. 53, 1898 ; *Metallographist*, **1**. 5, 27, 1898 ; H. Hort, *Zeit. Ver. deut. Ing.*, **50**. 1831, 1906 ; *Mitt. Forschungarb Ingenieurwesens*, 41, 1907 ; G. E. Svedelius, *Phil. Mag.*, (5), **46**. 173, 1898 ; *Om Järnets kritiska Länzd-och Temperaturförändringer*, Uppsala, 1896 ; H. W. B. Roozeboom, *Zeit. phys. Chem.*, **34**. 437, 1900 ; H. Hanemann and A. Schrader, *Atlas Metallographicus*, Berlin, 1928 ; P. Oberhoffer, *Das technische Eisen*, Berlin, 1925 ; *Met.*, **4**. 427, 448, 486, 1907 ; *Mitt. Eisenhütt. Inst. Aachen*, **2**. 76, 1908 ; *Stahl Eisen*, **27**. 1764, 1907 ; P. Oberhoffer and A. Heger, *ib.*, **43**. 1322, 1923 ; P. Oberhoffer and W. Grosse, *ib.*, **47**. 576, 1927 ; P. van Groningen, *Evenwichten in de Stelsels Ijzer-Koolstof-Zuurstof, en Ijzer-Waterstof-Zuurstof*, Delft, 1921 ; G. Belloc, *Ann. Chim. Phys.*, (7), **30**. 42, 1903 ; *Bull. Soc. Enc. Nat. Ind.*, **110**. 492, 1908 ; *Stahl Eisen*, **28**. 1116, 1908 ; E. Jurisch, *ib.*, **34**. 252, 1914 ; *Studien über die Löslichkeit von Gasen in festen Metallen und Legierungen*, Leipzig, 1912 ; A. Sieverts, *Zeit. phys. Chem.*, **77**. 591, 1911 ; A. Perrier and F. Wolfers, *Arch. Sciences Genève*, (5), **2**. 272, 1920 ; *Rev. Mét.*, **18**. 111, 1921 ; A. Sanfourche, *Compt. Rend.*, **167**. 683, 1918 ; *Rev. Mét.*, **16**. 217, 1919 ; E. Rengard, *ib.*, **7**. 89, 1910 ; P. Chevenard, *ib.*, **14**. 610, 1917 ; *Trav. Mem. Bur. Internat. Poids Mesures*, **17**. ii, 59, 1927 ; *Journ. Inst. Metals*, **37**. 471, 1927 ; *Journ. Phys. Rad.*, (6), **6**. 264, 1925 ; *Rev.*

Univ. Mines, (7), **7**. 235, 1925; *Compt. Rend.*, **164**. 916, 1917; P. Dejean, *ib.*, **173**. 141, 412, 1921; P. Curie, *ib.*, **118**. 796, 859, 1894; *Séances Soc. Franc. Phys.*, 167, 1894; *Chim. Ind.*, **2**. 654, 888, 1923; *Journ. Phys.*, (3), **4**. 263, 1895; *Ann. Chim. Phys.*, (7), **5**. 289, 1895; *Bull. Soc. Enc. Nat. Ind.*, **97**. 36, 1898; *Propriétés magnétiques des corps à divers températures*, Paris, 1895; G. Mars, *Die Spezialstähle*, Stuttgart, 102, 1922; H. von Jüptner, *Ber.*, **39**. 2376, 1906; *Grundzüge der Siderologie*, Leipzig, **2**. 79, 1901; *Phys. Zeit.*, **9**. 358, 1908; *Mitt. Internat. Verb. Materialprüf. Tech.*, **1**. vii, 2, 1910; *Trans. Faraday Soc.*, **8**. 153, 1912; *Ann. Physik*, (4), **31**. 5, 1911; *Rev. Mét.*, **6**. 601, 1909; *Internat. Verb. Materialprüfung Copenhagen*, **7**. ii, 11, 1909; *Arch. Sciences Genève*, (4), **27**. 1, 1909; P. Weiss, *Compt. Rend.*, **143**. 1136, 1906; **144**. 25, 1907; **145**. 1417, 1907; P. Weiss, A. Piccard and A. Carrard, *ib.*, (4), **42**. 378, 1916; (4), **43**. 22, 113, 199, 1917; P. Weiss and P. N. Beck, *ib.*, (4), **25**. 529, 1908; (4), **31**. 5, 89, 1911; *Journ. Phys.*, (4), **7**. 249, 1908; P. Weiss and G. Foëx, *Phys. Zeit.*, **9**. 362, 1908; **12**. 935, 1911; *Arch. Sciences Genève*, (4), **31**. 5, 89, 1911; *Journ. Phys.*, (5), **1**. 744, 1911; *Rev. Mét.*, **6**. 680, 1909; *Compt. Rend.*, **145**. 1417, 1907; K. Honda and S. Miura, *Trans. Amer. Soc. Steel Treating*, **13**. 270, 1928; K. Honda and H. Takagi, *Journ. Iron Steel Inst.*, **92**. ii, 181, 1915; *Rev. Mét.*, **10**. 1326, 1913; *Proc. Phys. Math. Soc. Tokyo*, (2), **6**. 314, 1911; *Science Rep. Tohoku Univ.*, **1**. 207, 1912; **2**. 203, 1913; **4**. 261, 1915; K. Honda, *ib.*, **2**. 69, 1913; **4**. 169, 261, 1915; **5**. 285, 1916; **6**. 213, 1917; **10**. 433, 1921; **11**. 119, 1922; **13**. 1, 363, 1924; **15**. 247, 1926; *Phys. Zeit.*, **15**. 705, 1914; *Trans. Amer. Soc. Steel Treating*, **6**. 187, 1924; *Journ. Iron Steel Inst.*, **91**. i, 199, 1915; **99**. i, 457, 1919; **105**. i, 381, 1922; **112**. ii, 345, 1925; K. Honda and Y. Ogura, *Proc. Phys. Math. Soc. Tokyo*, (2), **7**. 231, 1914; *Science Rep. Tohoku Univ.*, **3**. 113, 1914; K. Honda and J. Okubo, *ib.*, **6**. 153, 1917; T. Ishiwara, *Proc. Phys. Math. Soc. Tokyo*, (2), **9**. 107, 1917; (3), **3**. 91, 1920; *Science Rep. Tohoku Univ.*, **6**. 133, 1917; **9**. 401, 1920; S. Konno, *ib.*, **12**. 127, 1923; T. Kikuta, *ib.*, **11**. 1, 1922; I. Iitaka, *ib.*, **7**. 172, 1918; S. Umino, *ib.*, **15**. 567, 1926; H. Masumoto, *ib.*, **15**. 449, 1926; S. Sato, *ib.*, **14**. 513, 1925; *Tech. Rep. Tohoku*, **8**. 27, 1928; *Kinzoku no Kenkyu*, **6**. 53, 1929; *Phil. Mag.*, (7), **1**. 996, 1926; F. Wüst, A. Meuthen and R. Durrer, *Forsch. Arb. Ver. deut. Ing.*, 204, 1918; *Stahl Eisen*, **38**. 777, 1918; R. Durrer, *Kalorimetrische Bestimmung der Temperatur-Wärmeinhaltskurve von reinen Eisen*, Aachen, 1915; *Stahl Eisen*, **37**. 430, 1917; A. Meuthen, *Kalorimetrische Untersuchung des Systems Eisen-Kohlenstoff*, Aachen, 1912; *Ferrum*, **10**. 1, 1913; *Mitt. Eisenhütt. Inst. Aachen*, **5**. 134, 1913; A. F. Angerstein, *Hushällning's Journ.*, 35, 1778; M. Oknoff, *Ferrum*, **11**. 1, 1913; M. Copisarow, *Journ. Amer. Chem. Soc.*, **43**. 1870; 1921; O. C. Ralston, *Iron Oxide Reduction Equilibria*, Washington, 134, 1929; J. Maydel, *ib.*, **178**. 123, 1929; H. Bredmeier, W. Gontermann, *Zeit. anorg. Chem.*, **59**. 378, 1908; J. Maydel, *ib.*, **178**. 123, 1929; H. Bredmeier, *ib.*, **151**. 109, 1926; S. Rinman, *Hushällning's Journ.*, 38, 1778; A. Grabe, *En Bergsbok*, Stockholm, 263, 1921; G. K. Burgess and I. N. Kellberg, *Bull. Bur. Standards*, **11**. 457, 1915; *Ferrum*, **13**. 84, 1916; *Journ. Washington Acad.*, **4**. 436, 1914; G. K. Burgess and J. J. Crowe, *Trans. Amer. Inst. Min. Eng.*, **47**. 665, 1913; *Stahl Eisen*, **34**. 726, 1914; *Bull. Bur. Standards*, **10**. 315, 1914; *Journ. Iron Steel Inst.*, **87**. i, 335, 1913; *Phys. Rev.*, (2), **2**. 404, 1913; *Journ. Washington Acad.*, **3**. 329, 1913; G. K. Burgess and H. Scott, *ib.*, **6**. 650, 1916; *Bull. Bur. Standards*, **14**. 15, 1918; *Compt. Rend.*, **163**. 30, 1916; *Journ. Iron Steel Inst.*, **94**. ii, 258, 1916; *Engg.*, **102**. 391, 1916; H. S. Rawdon and T. Berglund, *Scient. Paper Bur. Standards*, **22**. 649, 1928; H. S. Rawdon and H. Scott, *Trans. Amer. Inst. Min. Eng.*, **67**. 414, 1922; H. S. Rawdon and P. Hidnert, *Phys. Rev.*, (2), **25**. 898, 1925; J. F. T. Berliner, *ib.*, 484, 1924; *Scient. Papers Bur. Standards*, 213, 1914; G. K. Burgess, *ib.*, **14**. 5, 1918; *Journ. Iron Steel Inst.*, **89**. i, 444, 1914; **94**. ii, 258, 1916; *Trans. Faraday Soc.*, **11**. 152, 1916; G. Sirovich, *Met. Ital.*, **16**. 3, 1922; *Gazz. Chim. Ital.*, **53**. 674, 1923; A. Baudrimont, *Mém. Soc. Bordeaux*, **8**. 124, 1870; C. H. Desch, *Metallography*, London, 1910; *Trans. Faraday Soc.*, **11**. 142, 1916; F. C. Thompson, *ib.*, **11**. 134, 1916; C. E. Jullien, *Introduction à l'étude de la métallurgie du fer*, Paris, 1873; J. Forbes, *Proc. Roy. Soc. Edin.*, **8**. 363, 1875; C. M. Smith, C. G. Knott and A. MacFarlane, *ib.*, **8**. 629, 1875; C. G. Knott, *ib.*, **33**. 187, 1886; P. G. Tait, *ib.*, **27**. 125, 1874; *Nature*, **8**. 86, 122, 1873; R. Norris, *Proc. Roy. Soc.*, **26**. 127, 1877; *Phil. Mag.*, (5), **4**. 389, 1877; J. N. von Fuchs, *Abhand. Bayr. Akad.*, **7**. 1, 1853; *Dingler's Journ.*, **124**. 346, 1852; *Schweiz. Gewerbefl.*, **11**. 264, 1852; *Chem. Gaz.*, **11**. 94, 1853; G. Heim, *Untersuchungen über die Gore'schen Phänomene*, Münich, 1885; F. G. A. Berson, *De l'influence de la température sur l'aimantation*, Paris, 1886; *Ann. Chim. Phys.*, (6), **8**. 433, 1886; R. A. Hadfield, *Trans. Amer. Inst. Min. Eng.*, **47**. 513, 1914; *Trans. Faraday Soc.*, **8**. 208, 1912; **11**. 125, 1916; F. Robin, *Proc. Internat. Congress Testing Materials*, **6**. ii, 5, 1912; D. Jones, *Trans. Amer. Soc. Steel Treating*, **14**. 199, 1928; W. Reinders and P. van Groningen, *Rec. Trav. Chim. Pays-Bas*, **40**. 701, 1921; H. Tomlinson, *Proc. Phys. Soc.*, **8**. 171, 1887; *Phil. Mag.*, (5), **24**. 256, 1887; (5), **25**. 45, 103, 372, 1887; (5), **26**. 18, 1888; H. F. Newall, *ib.*, (5), **24**. 435, 1887; (5), **25**. 510, 1888; K. Daeves, *Stahl Eisen*, **45**. 427, 1925; H. le Chatelier, *Rev. Mét.*, **1**. 134, 213, 301, 1904; **5**. 167, 1908; **12**. 990, 1915; *Journ. Chim. Phys.*, **1**. 490, 1903; *Journ. Phys.*, (2), **10**. 369, 1891; *Bull. Soc. Enc. Nat. Ind.*, (5), **6**. 661, 1900; *Séances Soc. Franç. Phys.*, 167, 1894; *Internat. Zeit. Metallog.*, **3**. 38, 1900; *Bull. Soc. Chim.*, (2), **45**. 677, 1886; *Compt. Rend.*, **108**. 1096, 1889; **109**. 58, 1889; **110**. 283, 1890; **129**. 279, 331, 1899; J. E. N. Pionchon, *ib.*, **102**. 677, 1454, 1886; **103**. 1122, 1886; *Journ. Phys.*, (2), **6**. 269, 1887; *Recherches calorimétriques sur les chaleurs spécifiques et les changements d'état aux températures élevées*, Paris, 1886; *Ann. Chim. Phys.*, (6), **11**. 33, 1887; M. Temnikoff, *Gorny Journ.*, i, 308, 1887; *Proc. Inst. Civil Eng.*, **91**. 545, 1888; A. Nouel, *Génie Civil*, **10**. 495, 1887; G. Chrystal, *Nature*, **22**.

303, 1880 ; A. Mallock, *ib.*, **113**. 566, 1924 ; H. Quinney, *Proc. Roy. Soc.*, **124**. A, 591, 1929 ; P. N. Laschtschenko, *Journ. Russ. Phys. Chem. Soc.*, **46**. 311, 1914 ; M. Geiss and J. A. M. van Liempt, *Zeit. Metallkunde*, **18**. 216, 1926 ; H. Bredemeier, *Zeit. anorg. Chem.*, **151**. 109, 1926 ; W. Schneider, *Einfluss der Abkühlungsgeschwindigkeit auf die Lage der Umwandlungspunkte,* Breslau, 1920 ; *Stahl Eisen,* **42**. 1577, 1922 ; A. Goetz, *Phys. Zeit.*, **25**. 562, 1924 ; E. M. Terry, *Phys. Rev.*, (1), **30**, 133, 1910 ; (2), **9**. 394, 1917 ; A. Somerville, *ib.*, (1), **31**. 261, 1910 ; F. K. Bailey, *ib.*, (1), **24**. 129, 1907 ; A. W. Hull, *ib.*, (2), **9**. 84, 1917 ; A. Merz, *Arch. Eisenhüttenwesen,* **3**. 587, 1929 ; *Stahl Eisen,* **50**. 518, 1930 ; *Dilatometrische Untersuchungen über den Einfluss verschiedener Legierungenselemente auf die Kritischen Punkte von Kohlenstoffstahl mit einem verbesserten Dilatometer,* Dusseldorf, 1928 ; B. A. Rogers, *Tech. Publ. Amer. Min. Eng.*, 218, 1929 ; O. L. Roberts, *Phys. Rev.*, (2), **35**. 1426, 1930 ; G. F. Fitzgerald, H. F. Newall, F. Trouton, and W. F. Barrett, *B.A. Rep.*, 145, 1890 ; J. Cumming, *Trans. Cambridge Phil. Soc.*, **2**. 47, 1823 ; *Ann. Phil.*, **5**. 427, 1823 ; **6**. 177, 321, 1823 ; W. Metcalf, *Engg.*, **53**. 50, 1892 ; E. Saladin, *Metallographist,* **7**. 237, 1903 ; M. Aliamet, *L'électricien,* (2), **26**. 49, 131, 1903 ; C. Bauer, *Wied. Ann.*, **11**. 394, 1880 ; F. Auerbach, *ib.*, **5**. 289, 1878 ; W. Kohlrausch, *ib.*, **33**. 42, 1888 ; J. H. Brinell, *Jernkontorets Ann.*, **40**. 9, 1885 ; *Stahl Eisen,* **5**. 611, 1885 ; H. M. Howe, *Tech. Quart.*, **2**. 136, 1888 ; *Metallographist,* **2**. 257, 1900 ; *Trans. Amer. Inst. Min. Eng.*, **47**. 650, 720, 1913 ; H. M. Howe and A. G. Levy, *ib.*, **47**. 587, 1913 ; J. Hopkinson, *Phil. Trans.*, **180**. 443, 1889 ; *Proc. Roy. Soc.*, **45**. 318, 455, 1889 ; T. Andrews, *ib.*, **58**. 59, 1895 ; W. Rosenhain and J. C. W. Humfrey, *ib.*, **83**. A. 200, 1909 ; *Journ. Iron Steel Inst.*, **87**. i, 219, 1913 ; *Stahl Eisen,* **33**. 1370, 1913 ; W. Rosenhain, *B.A. Rep.*, 567, 1910 ; *Proc. Inst. Mech. Eng.*, 243, 1911 ; *Engg.*, **93**. 181, 1912 ; *Zeit. Kryst.*, **52**. 417, 1913 ; **53**. 304, 1914 ; *Phys. Zeit.*, **11**. 1156, 1910 ; *Chem. Met. Engg.*, **9**. 104, 1911 ; J. C. W. Humfrey, *Journ. Iron Steel Inst.—Carnegie Mem.*, **4**. 80, 1912 ; P. Saldau, *ib.*, **7**. 195, 1916 ; P. H. Ledeboer, *Lumière Élect.*, **27**. 61, 1888 ; *Compt. Rend.*, **106**. 129, 1889 ; G. Tammann, *Lehrbuch der Metallurgie,* Leipzig, 1923 ; *Zeit. phys. Chem.*, **65**. 79, 1908 ; A. Westgren, *Journ. Iron Steel Inst.*, **103**. i, 303, 1921 ; **105**. i, 241, 1922 ; A. Westgren and A. E. Linder, *ib.*, **98**. 181, 1921 ; F. Wever, *Stahl Eisen,* **45**. 1208, 1787, 1925 ; **49**. 839, 1929 ; *Metallurgist,* **6**. 27, 1930 ; *Zeit. anorg. Chem.*, **154**. 294, 1926 ; **162**. 193, 1927 ; **168**. 327, 1928 ; *Naturwiss.*, **12**. 1106, 1924 ; **14**. 1217, 1926 ; **17**. 304, 1929 ; *Arch. Eisenhüttenwesen,* **2**. 54, 739, 1929 ; *Mitt. Inst. Eisenforschung.*, **9**. 151, 1927 ; **13**. 183, 1931 ; *Zeit. Elektrochem.*, **30**. 376, 1924 ; *Phys. Zeit.*, **26**. 698, 1925 ; *Zeit. tech. Phys.*, **6**. 474, 682, 1925 ; *Mitt. Inst. Eisenforsch.*, **3**. 45, 1921 ; *Ueber den Einfluss von Legierungselementen auf die polymorphen Umwandlungen des Eisens,* Düsseldorf, 1913 ; F. Wever and A. Heinzel, *Zwei Beispiele von Dreistoffsystemen des Eisens mit geschlossenem γ-Raum,* Düsseldorf, 1931 ; F. Wever and K. Apel, *Mitt. Inst. Eisenforsch.*, **4**. 87, 1922 ; F. Wever and W. Reincken, *ib.*, **7**. 69, 1925 ; F. Wever and P. Giani, *ib.*, **7**. 59, 1925 ; F. Wever and N. Engel, *ib.*, **12**. 93, 1930 ; *Stahl Eisen,* **50**. 1308, 1930 ; N. Engel, *Ueber den Einfluss der Abkühlungsgeschwindigkeit auf die Temperatur der Umwandlungen, das Gefüge und den Feinbau der Eisen-Kohlenstoff-Legierungen,* Düsseldorf, 1930 ; T. D. Yensen, *Science,* (2), **68**. 376, 1928 ; *Tech. Publ. Amer. Inst. Min. Eng.*, 185, 1929 ; *Proc. Amer. Inst. Elect. Eng.*, **34**. 237, 1914 ; *Bull. Univ. Illinois Eng.*, 72, 1914 ; *Stahl Eisen,* **34**. 1637, 1914 ; *Trans. Amer. Inst. Min. Eng.*, **77**. 320, 1929 ; R. Bach, *Helvetica Phys. Acta,* **2**. 95, 1929 ; F. Sauerwald, W. Schultze and G. Jackwirth, *Zeit. anorg. Chem.*, **140**. 384, 1924 ; F. Sauerwald and T. Sperling, *Zeit. Physik,* **56**. 544, 1929 ; F. Sauerwald, *Lehrbuch der Metallkunde des Eisens und der Nichtersenmetalle,* Berlin, 291, 1929 ; W. Guertler, *Metallurgie,* Berlin, **1**. ii, 38, 1912 ; L. Cammen, *Mech. Engg.*, **47**. 339, 1925 ; E. Maurer, *Mitt. Inst. Eisenforschung.* **1**. 30, 1920 ; *Stahl Eisen,* **41**. 1696, 1921 ; P. Bardenhauer, *Ferrum,* **14**. 129, 1917 ; *Mitt. Eisenhütt. Inst. Aachen,* **8**. 115, 1917 ; A. Müller, *ib.*, **3**. 72, 1909 ; *Met.*, **6**. 145, 1909 ; H. Harkort, *ib.*, **4**. 639, 1907 ; H. Lecher, *Verh. deut. phys. Ges.*, (2), **9**. 647, 1907 ; A. R. Meyer, *ib.*, (2), **13**. 680, 1911 ; *Ueber die Aenderung des elektrischen Widerstandes reinem Eisens mit der Temperatur in dem Bereiche 0° bis 1000° C.,* Greisswald, 1911 ; R. L. Wills, *Rev. Mét.*, **10**. 146, 1913 ; *Mitt. Internat. Verband. Materialprüf. Tech.*, **2**. ix, 4, 1913 ; *Phil. Mag.*, (5), **50**. i, 1900 ; J. A. Harker, *ib.*, (6), **10**. 430, 1905 ; E. B. Harrison, *ib.*, (6), **3**. 177, 1902 ; K. Renger, *Die anfänglich Suszeptibilität von Eisen und Magnetit in Abhängigkeit von der Temperatur,* Zürich, 1913 ; S. Hilpert, *Zeit. Elektrochem.*, **16**. 390, 1910 ; G. Rümelin and H. Maire, *Mitt. Eisenhütt. Inst. Aachen,* **7**. 56, 1916 ; *Ferrum,* **12**. 141, 1915 ; G. Eger, *Internat. Zeit. Metallog.*, **9**. 15, 1918 ; D. Ewen, *ib.*, **6**. 1, 1914 ; H. Hanemann, *ib.*, **3**. 176, 1912 ; O. Boudouard, *Bull. Soc. Enc. Nat. Ind.*, **102**. 447, 1903 ; *Compt. Rend.*, **137**. 1054, 1902 ; *Journ. Iron Steel Inst.*, **63**. i, 299, 1903 ; E. H. Saniter, *ib.*, **53**. i, 206, 1898 ; *Internat. Zeit. Metallog.*, **1**. 251, 1898 ; P. Fournel, *Mét.*, **3**. 802, 1906 ; *Rev. Mét.*, **3**. 411, 1906 ; *Compt. Rend.*, **143**. 46, 285, 1906 ; J. E. Storey, *Machinery,* **16**. 136, 1910 ; O. W. Storey, *Trans. Amer. Electrochem. Soc.*, **25**. 489, 1914 ; A. B. Bagdasarian, *ib.*, **51**. 482, 1927 ; A. Kroll, *Journ. Iron Steel Inst.*, **81**. i, 304, 1910 ; A. Holt, *Journ. Soc. Chem. Ind.*, **34**. 693, 1915 ; E. Cohen and G. de Bruin, *Proc. Akad. Amsterdam,* **17**. 926, 1915 ; A. I. Brodsky, *Journ. Russ. Met. Soc.*, 7, 1926 ; R. C. Gale, *Journ. Scient. Instr.*, **7**. 165, 1930 ; O. L. Roberts and W. P. Davey, *Metals Alloys,* **1**. 648, 1930 ; H. Scott, *Comm. Internat. Assoc. Testing Materials,* **1**. 339, 1930 ; Y. Chu-Phay, *Trans. Faraday Soc.*, **27**. 777, 790, 1931 ; F. H. Jeffery, *ib.*, **27**. 751, 1931 ; **28**. 98, 1932 ; U. Dehlinger, *Zeit. Physik,* **68**. 535, 1931 ; A. Schulze, *Zeit. Ver. deut. Ing.*, **76**. 108, 1932 ; W. Gilbert, *De magnete,* London, 1600 ; D. K. Morris, *Phil. Mag.*, (5), **44**. 213, 1897 ; W. Winkler, *Dissertation,* Aachen, 1924 ; G. Tammann, *Zeit. anorg. Chem.*, **37**. 448, 1903.

§ 13. The Microstructure of Iron and Steel

Numerous examples of the microstructure of iron and steel are indicated below. The history of the subject of *metallography*, the study of the minute structure of metals, commenced seriously after the work of H. C. Sorby [1] on the microstructure of steel. His idea was that a close analogy obtains between the constitution of steel and of a crystalline igneous rock : " Steel," said he, " must be regarded as an artificial crystalline rock, and to get a complete knowledge of it, it must be regarded as such." The general subject has been discussed by C. H. Desch, L. Guillet, and others. Many papers and books have also been written on the preparation of specimens for microscopic examination. For example :

H. Behrens, *Das mikroskopische Gefüge der Metalle und Legierungen*, Hamburg, 1894 ; A. H. Hiorns, *Metallography*, London, 1902 ; U. le Verrier, *Ann. Conservatoire Arts Métiers*, (2), **9.** 121, 1896 ; J. T. Milton, *Trans. Inst. Marine Eng.*, **14.** 101, 1902 ; E. Heyn, *Verh. Ver. Beförd. Gewerbefleisses*, **83.** 355, 1904 ; H. Wedding, *ib.*, **65.** 203, 1886 ; R. K. B. Wild, *Prof. Papers Roy. Eng.*, **30.** 207, 1904 ; O. Boudouard, *Bull. Soc. Chim.*, (3), **1**, 1906 ; R. Ruer, *Metallographie in elementarer Darstellung*, Hamburg, 1907 ; P. Goerens, *Einführung in die Metallographie*, Halle a. S., 1922 ; London, 1908 ; W. Guertler, *Metallographie*, Berlin, 1909 ; *Metallurgie*, Berlin, 1923 ; C. H. Desch, *Metallography*, London, 1910 ; L. Révillon, *La métallographie microscopique*, Paris, 1910 ; F. Robin, *Traité de métallographie*, Paris, 1912 ; W. T. Hall and R. S. Williams, *The Chemical and Metallographic Examination of Iron, Steel, and Brass*, New York, 1921 ; W. Fraenkel, *Leitfaden der Metallurgie mit besonderer Berück sichtigung der physikalisch-chemischen Grundlagen*, Dresden, 1922 ; L. Guillet, *Les méthodes d'études des alliages métalliques*, Paris, 1922 ; L. Guillet and A. M. Portevin, *Précis de métallographie microscopique et de macrographie*, Paris, 1923 ; F. L. Garrison, *The Microscopic Structure of Iron and Steel*, London, 1886 ; F. Osmond, *Sur la cristallographie du fer*, Paris, 1900 ; London, 1904 ; *Ann. Mines*, (9), **17.** 110, 1900 ; *Ordnance Bur. U.S. War Dept.*, 68, 1893 ; *Microscopic Metallurgy*, London, 1893 ; S. A. Houghton, *Trans. Inst. Marine Eng.*, **14.** 101, 1902 ; H. von Jüpter, *Ver. Verbreit. Naturw. Kenntnisse*, **45.** 113, 1904 ; H. Savoia, *Metallografia applicata ai prodotti siderurgici*, Milano, 1909 ; London, 1910 ; O. Kröhnke, *Kurze Einführung in den innern Gefügeaufbau der Eisenkohlenstofflegierungen*, Berlin, 1911 ; A. Martens, *Stahl Eisen*, **12.** 672, 1892 ; **15.** 954, 1895 ; *Mitt. tech. Versuchanst.*, **11.** 347, 1894 ; *Verh. Ver. Eisenbahnkunde*, 67, 1892 ; A. Sauveur, *The Metallography and Heat Treatment of Iron and Steel*, Cambridge, Mass., 1926 ; H. M. Howe, *The Metallography of Steel and Cast Iron*, New York, 1916.

In developing the structure of a heterogeneous solid for microscopic examination, the differences in the constituents can be emphasized by taking advantage of the fact that some are harder than others, so that when the surface is polished, the softer constituents are worn away to a greater depth, and the harder constituents appear in relief when the polished surface is viewed by oblique illumination. The polishing may be varied by using a suitable liquid which acts preferentially on some constituents more than others. The process is referred to as the **polish-attack** or **polish etching.** F. Osmond rubbed the surface on a piece of stretched parchment soaked in an aq. extract of liquorice and calcium sulphate ; and later, F. Osmond and G. Cartaud used a 2 per cent. aq. soln. of ammonium nitrate. If the surface be heated in a suitable atmosphere—say air—the rate of oxidation of the different constituents varies, so that films of different thicknesses and colorations are produced. These exhibit characteristic effects under the microscope. This method of developing the structure is called **heat tinting,** or **heat relief.** It was employed by F. Osmond, W. C. Roberts-Austen, C. Benedicks, N. Gutowsky, P. Breuil, P. Oberhoffer and co-workers, F. Sauerwald and co-workers, P. Goerens and co-workers, J. E. Stead, G. Tammann and G. Siebel, F. Robin, J. Czochralsky, F. Reiser, L. Löwenherz, T. Turner, and H. Haedicke.

Chemical methods of **etching** are more frequently employed. Here the different constituents are attacked by suitable reagents at different rates—*vide* Table X.

TABLE X.—THE ETCHING OF THE CONSTITUENTS OF IRON-CARBON ALLOYS

Constituent	Polish attack	Iodine	Nitric acid	Remarks
Ferrite .	Granular	Colourless	Polygonal structure	Softer than other constituents ; coloured by nitric acid, while cementite is not.
Cementite .	Nil	White	No action in 40 sec. with 20 per cent. acid	Harder than other constituents ; not coloured by nitric acid, while ferrite is.
Martensite .	Intersecting needles appear	Coloured slowly	Yellowish	Unlike pearlite, has straight intersecting fibres.
Pearlite .	Curved lamellæ	Dark	Dark	Unlike martensite, fibres are curved and never intersecting.
Troostite .	Yellow brown to blue bands	Coloured faster than martensite	Dark yellow	Accompanies martensite, and is coloured more slowly than sorbite.
Sorbite .	Coloured	Coloured faster then troostite	Dark	Accompanies pearlite, and is coloured more quickly than troostite.
Austenite .	Nil	Coloured	Lighter yellow than martensite	Martensite goes yellow, brown, and black when treated by eléctrochemical attack.

The rate of attack was studied by L. Loskiewicz. In 1772, J. J. Perret proposed testing Damascus steel by etching ; in 1781, T. Bergman distinguished iron from steel by etching with sulphuric acid ; in 1850, E. Clark used etching to distinguish between hand and machine riveting ; in 1872, M. van Ruth tested the character of iron by etching ; in 1873, F. Kick used etching to show the structure of welded iron ; in 1878, A. R. von Kerpely studied the structure of iron and steel by the etching process ; and later A. Ledebur, O. F. Hudson, S. Stein, H. Wedding, and A. Martens discussed the subject. L. von Tetmajer, W. C. Roberts-Austen, and O. Wawrziniok emphasized the importance of etching tests for rail-steel. General observations were made by W. Campbell, H. S. Rawdon, E. C. Groesbeck, W. Guertler, W. Ast, C. Frémont, etc. Many reagents have been recommended for special alloys.

Hydrochloric acid—H. le Chatelier, F. Osmond, F. Osmond and J. E. Stead, N. M. von Wittorf, W. Ast, C. Frémont, C. F. Comstock, F. P. Gilligan and J. J. Curran, A. Fry, B. Strauss and A. Fry, E. Heyn, O. Ruff and W. Martin, A. Jung, and P. Goerens and K. Ellingen. F. Osmond recommended a 10 per cent. aq. soln. of hydrochloric acid. E. Heyn and A. Martens employed a soln. of 1 c.c. of hydrochloric acid of sp. gr. 1·19 in 120 c.c. of absolute alcohol. H. le Chatelier used a soln. of hydrochloric acid in glycerol ; and F. W. Spiller recommended a gram of nitric acid of sp. gr. 1·42 in 9·9 grms. of glycerol. A. Baykoff exposed the hot steel to the action of hydrogen chloride gas. **Sulphuric acid**— N. M. von Wittorf, W. Ast, and C. Frémont. F. W. Rowe used a hot, dil. mixture of sulphuric and hydrochloric acids. J. E. Stead recommended 20 per cent. sulphuric acid followed by a cleaning with nitric acid. **Sulphurous acid**—S. Hilpert and E. Colver-Glauert employed a 3 to 4 per cent. sat. aq. or alcoholic soln. of sulphurous acid. **Nitric acid**—H. Bell, F. Osmond and G. Cartaud, F. Rinne, N. Parravano, W. C. Roberts-Austen, F. Osmond, J. E. Stead, H. C. Sorby, W. Ast, J. P. Gill and L. D. Bowman, C. Frémont, A. Sauveur, J. O. Arnold, N. M. von Wittorf, W. Campbell, E. Maurer, O. Ruff and W. Martin, O. Mezger and co-workers, and P. Goerens and K. Ellingen. A. Martens used a soln. of 4 c.c. of nitric acid of sp. gr. 1·14 in 100 c.c. of absolute alcohol. H. le Chatelier used a soln. of nitric acid in glycerol. W. J. Kurbatoff recommended a soln. of 20 per cent. nitric acid in 4 parts of amyl alcohol, and this was used with good results by P. Goerens and H. Meyer. W. J. Kurbatoff's reagent A was a 1 per cent. soln. of nitric acid in a mixture of methyl, ethyl and isoamyl alcohols with some acetic anhydride. A mixture of nitric and hydrochloric acids—aqua regia—was employed by F. Osmond and W. C. Roberts-Austen.

and C. Frémont. C. Benedicks and P. Sederholm used an alcoholic soln. of 0·1 per cent. nitric acid. N. B. Pilling used a soln. of nitric acid and methyl alcohol in nitrobenzene for etching carbides in silicon steels. J. R. Vilella used a soln. of **aqua regia** in glycerol for chromium-iron alloys. **Hydrofluoric acid**—L. Baraduc-Müller used a mixture of one part of hydrofluoric acid and two parts of alcohol for silicon alloys ; and it was also employed by F. Dörinckel, and H. le Chatelier. **Iodine solution**—say 10 grms. of iodine, 20 grms. of potassium iodide, and 100 c.c. of water—was used by K. Friedrich, W. C. Roberts-Austen, P. Oberhoffer, E. Heyn, V. N. Svetchnikoff, F. Osmond, H. C. Boynton, C. Benedicks, L. von Tetmajer, W. Ast, and C. Frémont. K. Friedrich also recommended a **solution of bromine** and potassium iodide for dealing with iron and sulphur alloys. O. Ruff and W. Martin used a soln. of 1 c.c. of bromine in 1 c.c. of 8 per cent. hydrochloric acid. H. B. Pulsifer used **chloric acid**.

Orthonitrophenol—four parts in a sat. soln. was mixed with one part of a 4 per cent. soln. of nitric acid as W. J. Kurbatoff's reagent D. An alcoholic soln. was employed by N. T. Belaiew, E. Maurer, and J. Guillemin. *Meta*nitrobenzenesulphonic acid in 4 to 5 per cent. alcoholic soln. was employed by C. Benedicks. **Picric acid** was introduced as W. P. Ischewsky's reagent in 1902, and it is in common use in about 5 per cent. alcoholic soln. The reagent was used by N. Baar, F. Osmond and G. Cartaud, M. Levin and G. Tammann, S. Hilpert, N. Parravano, E. Isaac and G. Tammann, H. le Chatelier, H. le Chatelier and A. Ziegler, F. Robin, J. Kirner, W. Campbell, E. Maurer, G. Röhl, N. M. von Wittorf, L. Guillet, F. Robin and P. Gartner, J. P. Gill and L. D. Bowman, P. Goerens and K. Ellingen, and J. E. Stead. A soln. in acetone was employed by F. Osmond and G. Cartaud for iron-nickel meteorites. H. le Chatelier employed a soln of picric acid in glycerol. A soln. of **sodium picrate** was recommended for cementite by H. le Chatelier, M. Matweieff, W. J. Kurbatoff, and A. Sauveur and V. N. Krivobok used a hot, 3 per cent. soln. of sodium picrate in an excess of soda-lye. An alcoholic soln. of **salicylic acid** was recommended for pearlite by V. N. Svechnikoff.

Alkali hydroxide was employed by U. Raydt and G. Tammann, and H. le Chatelier, who also recommended a boiling soln. of alkali hydroxide with a small proportion of an oxidizing agent—nitrate, iodate, plumbate, or picrate. H. le Chatelier employed an aq. soln. of potassium hydrotartrate ; or a mixture of equal parts of a 50 per cent. aq. soln. of sodium carbonate and a 10 per cent. aq. soln. of lead nitrate. **Hydrogen dioxide** in ammoniacal soln. was recommended by R. Sahmen, and J. P. Gill and L. D. Bowman. M. Yatsevitch used 10 c.c. of commercial hydrogen dioxide, and 20 c.c. of a 10 per cent. soln. of sodium hydroxide for high-speed tool steels. **Ammonium persulphate** was recommended by J. Czochralsky, and H. S. Rawdon. G. Tammann and co-workers used a 10 per cent. soln. of the salt. F. C. Thompson and E. Whitehead found that a soln. of **ammonium molybdate** will darken cementite.

Ammonium nitrate soln. was used by C. Benedicks and F. Osmond—*vide supra*. **Calcium chloride**—E. H. Saniter recommended immersion in molten calcium chloride. An alcoholic soln. of **potassium ferricyanide** mixed with nitric acid was recommended by G. Gallo, T. F. Russell, T. Murakami and K. Someya, F. C. Thompson and E. Whitehead, C. E. McQuigg, and P. Oberhoffer and co-workers. For chromium and tungsten steels, K. Daeves used a soln. of potassium ferricyanide, 20 grms. ; sodium hydroxide, 10 grms. ; water, 100 grms. T. Murakami recommended a soln. of 10 grms. potassium ferricyanide, 10 grms. of potassium hydroxide, and 100 c.c. of water for the identification of the complex carbides of iron and chromium. **Mercuric chloride** soln., five grams in 100 c.c. of water, was used by C. Frémont. **Copper sulphate** soln. was used by U. Raydt and G. Tammann, G. Tammann and W. Treitschke, A. von Vegesack, W. Guertler, N. M. von Wittorf, and M. Chikashige and T. Hiki. **Ammonium cuprous chloride** in 8 per cent. soln. was used by F. Osmond and G. Cartaud, E. Isaac and G. Tammann, and E. Heyn. **Ammonium cupric chloride**—say 10 per cent. soln.--was used by E. Isaac and G. Tammann, A. M. Portevin, E. Heyn and O. Bauer, O. Bauer and E. Deiss, E. Heyn and A. Martens, G. Preuss, F. Osmond, F. Osmond and J. E. Stead, J. C. W. Humfrey, A. von Dormus, G. Haufe, W. Ast, and C. Frémont. **Cupric chloride**—a soln. of cupric chloride appears in many forms. J. E. Stead used CuCl₂, 10 grms. ; MgCl₂, 40 grms. ; hydrochloric acid, 10 c.c. ; water, 20 c.c. ; and alcohol to 1000 c.c. The soln. was used by G. F. Comstock, A. Hultgren, and H. le Chatelier and B. Bogitch. H. le Chatelier and J. Lemoine used a similar soln., but with hydrochloric acid, 20 c.c., and water, 180 c.c. P. Oberhoffer used CuCl₂, 1·0 grm. ; FeCl₃, 20 grms. ; SnCl₂, 0·5 grm. ; hydrochloric acid, 50 c.c. ; water, 500 c.c. ; ethyl alcohol, 500 c.c. J. H. S. Dickenson recommended CuCl₂, 3 grms. ; FeCl₃, 40 grms. ; hydrochloric acid, 40 c.c. ; and water, 500 c.c. W. Rosenhain and J. L. Haughton recommended CuCl₂, 10 grms. ; FeCl₃, 30 grms. ; SnCl₂, 0·5 grm. ; hydrochloric acid, 100 c.c. ; water, 1000 c.c. H. le Chatelier and E. L. Dupuy recommended CuCl₂, 1 grm. ; picric acid, 0·5 grm. ; ethyl alcohol, 100 c.c. ; water, 10 c.c. ; and conc. hydrochloric acid, 1·3 to 2·5 c.c. ; A. Fry, crystalline copper chloride, 5 grms. ; conc. hydrochloric acid, 40 c.c. ; water, 30 c.c. ; and ethyl alcohol, 25 c.c. ; and B. Kalling, 5 grms. CuCl₂, and 100 c.c. each of hydrochloric acid, alcohol and water. J. H. Whiteley used a soln. of 0·04 grm. of cupric oxide in 6 c.c. of conc. nitric acid made up to 200 c.c. with methylated spirit for etching iron-phosphorus alloys. O. Hengstenberg and F. Bornefeld used for nitrogenized steels a soln. of a gram of mercurous chloride in 20 c.c. of conc. hydrochloric acid, and 80 c.c. of alcohol followed by a soln. of 10 grms. of magnesium chloride and a gram of cupric chloride in 40 c.c. of conc. hydrochloric acid and 100 c.c. of alcohol. F. C. Thompson and E. Whitehead found a soln. of **potassium copper cyanide** of assistance in discriminating different forms of cementite. **Silver nitrate**—M. Künkele dissolved 5 grms. of gelatin in 20 c.c. of water, then added 20 c.c. of glycerol, and 2 c.c. of sulphuric acid, and finally 0·8 grm. of silver nitrate dissolved in water. The liquid was used for sulphur inclusions. **Chromic acid**—G. d'Huart used a soln. of 40 grms. chromic acid ; 16 grms. NiCl₂ ; distilled water, 100 c.c. ; and conc. hydrochloric acid, 100 c.c. for mild steels, cast irons, and copper alloys. The soln. does not keep. **Ferric chloride** in acid— say 10 per cent. soln.—was recommended by H. le Chatelier, W. Ast, C. Frémont, N. Parravano, and A. M. Portevin ; L. Baraduc-Müller used a soln. of 100 c.c. nitric acid, 150 c.c. hydrochloric acid, and 500 c.c. of a soln. of ferric chloride. A. Hultgren used 100 grms. FeCl₃ ; 5 c.c. of conc. hydrochloric acid, and 250 c.c. each of water and alcohol ; and P. Oberhoffer, and K. Harneker and E. Rassow used distilled water, 500 c.c. ; ethyl alcohol, 500 c.c. ; stannous chloride, 0·5 grm. ; cupric chloride, 1·0 grm. ; ferric chloride, 30 grms. ; and conc. hydrochloric acid, 50 c.c. **Molten zinc**—J. L. Jones recommended immersing the specimen in molten zinc and afterwards removing the zinc or dross mechanically, or by dil. sulphuric acid.

The etching may be done electrically—**electrolytic etching**—by making the specimen the anode with a feeble current ; the cathode is a strip of platinum or a platinum dish ; and E. Heyn and A. Martens used 1 c.c. of hydrochloric acid in 500 c.c. of water as electrolyte. The subject was discussed by A. H. Sirks, and V. Velguth, W. Rosenhain and J. L. Haughton developed a *deposition method* in which the specimen is placed in a soln. of 30 grms. ferric chloride ; 100 c.c. of conc. hydrochloric acid ; one gram of cupric chloride ; 0·5 grm. of stannous chloride ; and a litre of water. The thickness and coloration of the copper films produced vary with the different constituents.

REFERENCES.

[1] H. C. Sorby, *B.A. Rep.*, 189, 1864 ; 139, 1865 ; *Journ. Iron Steel Inst.*, **29**. i, 140, 1886 ; **33**. i, 255, 1888 ; C. H. Desch, *Journ. West Scotland Iron Steel Inst.*, **29**. 62, 1922 ; L. Loskiewicz, *Rev. Mét.*, **19**. 681, 1922 ; O. Wawrziniok, *Handbuch des Materialprüfungswesens*, Berlin, 545, 1908 ; M. van Ruth, *Berg. Hütt. Ztg.*, **31**. 355, 1872 ; *Journ. Iron Steel Inst.*, **4**. i, 370, 1872 ; O. F. Hudson, *Journ. Inst. Metals*, **13**. 193, 1915 ; F. Kick, *Dingler's Journ.*, **212**. 40, 1873 ; A. R. von Kerpely, *Oesterr. Zeit. Berg. Hütt.*, **25**. 209, 219, 232, 1877 ; *Zeit. Berg. Ver. Kärnten*, **9**. 185, 1877 ; A. Ledebur, *Journ. Iron Steel Inst.*, **35**. i, 386, 1889 ; **44**. ii, 52, 1893 ; *Stahl Eisen*, **11**. 294, 1891 ; S. Stein, *ib.*, **7**. 94, 1887 ; **10**. 821, 1890 ; H. Wedding, *Verh. Ver. Beförd. Gewerbefleisses*, **65**. 203, 1886 ; *Journ. U.S. Assoc. Charcoal Iron Workers*, **7**. 120, 1887 ; *Stahl Eisen*, **7**. 82, 1887 ; L. von Tetmajer, *Mitt. Ver. Eisenbahnkunde*, 15, 1881 ; E. Clark, *The Britannia and Conway Tubular Bridges*, London, 632, 1850 ; W. Ast, *Proc. Internat. Assoc. Testing Materials*, 36, 1906 ; *Met.*, **4**. 123, 1907 ; G. Preuss, *Die praktische Nutzanwendung der Prufung des Eisens durch Aetzverfahren und mit Hilfe des Mikroskops*, Berlin, 1913 ; J. J. Perret, *Mém. Acad.*, **22**. 1772 ; T. Bergman, *De causa fragilitatis ferri frigidi*, Upsala, 1781 ; G. Röhl, *Beiträge zur Kenntnis der sulfidischen Einschlüsse in Eisen und Stahl*, Freiberg, 1913 ; E. Heyn, *Stahl Eisen*, **19**. 709, 768, 1899 ; **20**. 37, 1900 ; **26**. 8, 580, 1295, 1386, 1906 ; *Zeit. Ver. deut. Ing.*, **44**. 137, 175, 1900 ; *Met.*, **4**. 119, 1907 ; *Verh. Ver. Beförd. Gewerbefleisses*, **83**. 355, 1904 ; *Mitt. Materialprüfungsamt*, **24**. 253, 1906 ; *Mitt. tech. Versuchanst.*, **16**. 310, 1899 ; A. Martens, *ib.*, **11**. 247, 1894 ; *Mitt. Ver. Eisenbahnkunde*, 67, 1892 ; *Stahl Eisen*, **7**. 235, 1887 ; **12**. 672, 1892 ; **15**. 954, 1895 ; E. Heyn and A. Martens, *Verh. Ver. Beförd. Gewerbefleisses*, **83**. 355, 1904 ; E. Heyn and O. Bauer, *Metallographie*, Leipzig, **1**. 21, 1909 ; *Mitt. Materialprüfungsamt*, **26**. 29, 1906 ; *Stahl Eisen*, **26**. 778, 915, 991, 1906 ; **32**. 402, 1912 ; O. Bauer and E. Deiss, *Probenahme und Analyse von Eisen und Stahl*, Berlin, 1912 ; F. Osmond and J. E. Stead, *Microscopic Analysis of Metals*, London, 1904 ; F. Osmond and W. C. Roberts-Austen, *Proc. Roy. Soc.*, **60**. 148, 1896 ; F. Osmond and G. Cartaud, *Metallographist*, **3**. 1, 1900 ; *Rev. Gén. Sciences*, **16**. 51, 1904 ; *Rev. Mét.*, **1**. 78, 1904 ; F. Osmond, *ib.*, **1**. 199, 1904 ; **6**. 1363, 1910 ; *Contribution à l'étude des alliages*, Paris, 277, 1901 ; *Bull. Soc. Enc. Nat. Ind.*, (4), **10**. 480, 1896 ; *Metallographist*, **3**. 181, 275, 1900 ; *Ann. Mines*, (9), **17**. 110, 1900 ; J. E. Stead, *Proc. Cleveland Inst. Eng.*, 97, 1900 ; *Journ. Soc. Chem. Ind.*, **22**. 340, 1903 ; *Metallographist*, **3**. 261, 1900 ; **4**. 89, 199, 332, 1901 ; *Journ. Iron Steel Inst.*, **58**. ii, 60, 1900 ; **91**. i, 173, 1915 ; **97**. i, 408, 1918 ; W. C. Roberts-Austen, *Proc. Inst. Mech. Eng.*, 35, 1899 ; *Committee appointed by the Board of Trade to inquire into the Loss of Strength of Steel Rails through Use on Railways*, London, 1900 ; H. le Chatelier and A. Ziegler, *Bull. Soc. Enc. Nat. Ind.*, **103**. ii, 368, 1902 ; H. le Chatelier, *ib.*, (4), **10**. 1336, 1896 ; *Contributions à l'étude des alliages*, Paris, 67, 1901 ; *Rev. Mét.*, **1**. 207, 1904 ; **5**. 167, 1908 ; **8**. 367, 1911 ; H. le Chatelier and J. Lemoine, *ib.*, **12**. 649, 1915 ; H. le Chatelier and E. L. Dupuy, *Compt. Rend.*, **165**. 349,

1917; *Rev. Mét.*, **15.** 127, 1918; H. le Chatelier and B. Bogitch, *ib.*, **16.** 129, 1919; F. Robin and P. Gartner, *ib.*, **8.** 224, 1911; C. Frémont, *ib.*, **5.** 649, 1908; M. Matweieff, *ib.*, **7.** 447, 1910; A. Baykoff, *ib.*, **6.** 829, 1909; M. Yatsevitch, *ib.*, **15.** 65, 1918; G. d'Huart, *ib.*, **26.** 300, 1929; *Metallurgist*, **5.** 142, 1929; A. M. Portevin, *Rev. Mét.*, **6.** 951, 1909; L. Baraduc-Müller, *ib.*, **7.** 687, 1910; J. Guillemin, *ib.*, **6.** 946, 1909; N. T. Belaiew, *ib.*, **9.** 321, 1912; *Journ. Inst. Aeronautical Eng.*, **1.** 14, 1920; *On the Structure and Crystallization of Steel on Slow Cooling*, Petrograd, 1909; L. Guillet, *Mém. Soc. Ing. Civils*, 31, 1903; *Rev. Univ. Mines*, (6), **14.** 7, 1922; *Journ. Iron Steel Inst.*, **64.** ii, 98, 1903; J. C. W. Humfrey, *ib.*, **99.** i, 273, 1919; C. Benedicks, *ib.*, **68.** ii, 352, 1905; *Met.*, **5.** 41, 1908; J. H. S. Dickenson, *Journ. Iron Steel Inst.*, **99.** i, 294, 1919; H. Bell, *ib.*, **85.** i, 118, 1912; J. H. Whiteley, *ib.*, **101.** i, 359, 1920; **103.** i, 277, 1921; **116.** ii, 293, 1927; W. Campbell, *ib.*, **64.** ii, 359, 1903; *Iron Age*, **66.** 23, 1904; *School Mines Quart.*, **25.** 390, 1904; *Journ. Amer. Chem. Soc.*, **28.** 1304, 1906; *Met.*, **3.** 741, 1906; *Proc. Amer. Soc. Testing Materials*, **15.** ii, 96, 1915; J. L. Jones, *ib.*, **15.** ii, 90, 1915; A. H. Sirks, *On the Advantage of Metal-etching by means of the Electric Current*, Amsterdam, 1902; *Proc. Akad. Amsterdam*, **5.** 219, 1902; G. Haufe, *Krupp's Monatsh.*, **7.** 66, 1926; F. P. Gilligan and J. Curran, *Trans. Amer. Soc. Steel Treating*, **10.** 9, 1926; J. P. Gill and L. D. Bowman, *ib.*, **2.** 184, 1921; V. Velguth, *Chem. Met. Engg.*, **25.** 567, 1921; F. C. Thompson and E. Whitehead, *Trans. Faraday Soc.*, **19.** 152, 1923; N. B. Pilling, *Trans. Amer. Inst. Min. Eng.*, **69.** 780, 1924; J. R. Vilella, *Iron Age*, **117.** 761, 834, 903, 1926; T. Murakami and K. Someya, *Science Rep. Tohoku Univ.*, **16.** 245, 1927; H. H. Shepherd, *Foundry*, **56.** 785, 1928; F. W. Rowe, *Iron Steel Inst.*, **2.** 37, 1928; C. Benedicks and P. Sederholm, *Zeit. phys. Chem.*, **138.** 123, 1928; V. N. Svetchnikoff, *Proc. Russ. Met. Soc.*, 105, 1928; *Rev. Mét.*, **27.** 407, 1930; H. B. Pulsifer, *Tech. Paper Amer. Inst. Min. Eng.*, 137, 1929; O. Hengstenberg and F. Bornefeld, *Krupp's Monatsh.*, **12.** 265, 1930; F. Robin, *Bull. Soc. Enc. Nat. Ind.*, **118.** 210, 1912; T. Turner, *Proc. Birmingham Phil. Soc.*, **6.** 296, 1889; *Chem. News*, **60.** 190, 1889; L. Löwenherz, *Zeit. Instrkd.*, **9.** 316, 1889; H. Haedicke, *ib.*, **7.** 144, 1887; F. Reiser, *Das Härten des Stahles in Theorie und Praxis*, Leipzig, 103, 1919; S. Hilpert and E. Colver-Clauert, *ib.*, **82.** ii, 54, 1910; *Zeit. anorg. Chem.*, **68.** 63, 1910; S. Hilpert, *Zeit. Elektrochem.*, **16.** 390, 1910; T. F. Russell, *Journ. Iron Steel Inst.*, **104.** ii, 247, 1921; W. Rosenhain, *B.A. Rep.*, 510, 1914; W. Rosenhain and J. L. Haughton, *ib.*, **89.** i, 515, 1914; A. Hultgren, *ib.*, **120.** ii, 112, 1929; E. H. Saniter, *ib.*, **53.** ii, 115, 1897; *Metallographist*, **1.** 72, 1898; F. W. Spiller, *ib.*, **6.** 264, 1903; A. Sauveur, *ib.*, **3.** 231, 1900; *Eng. Mag.*, **17.** 977, 1899; A. Sauveur and V. N. Krivobok, *Trans. Amer. Inst. Min. Eng.*, **70.** 239, 1924; J. O. Arnold, *Nature*, **63.** 613, 1901; B. Kalling, *Jernkontorets Ann.*, **82.** 612, 1927; T. Murakami, *Science Rep. Tohoku Univ.*, **7.** 217, 1918; C. E. McQuigg, *Trans. Amer. Inst. Min. Eng.*, **69.** 831, 1923; G. F. Comstock, *Chem. Met. Engg.*, **23.** 1081, 1920; *Trans. Amer. Inst. Min. Eng.*, **70.** 251, 1924; H. S. Rawdon, *Chem. Met. Engg.*, **24.** 207, 385, 475, 1921; *Circular Bur. Standards*, 113, 1922; *Science Paper Bur. Standards*, 402, 1920; E. C. Groesbeck, *ib.*, 518, 1925; H. S. Rawdon and S. Epstein, *Tech. Paper Bur. Standards*, 156, 1920; E. Maurer, *Compt. Rend.*, **146.** 822, 1908; F. Rinne, *Neues Jahrb. Min.*, i, 115, 1910; A. Jung, *Internat. Zeit. Metallog.*, **1.** 209, 1911; W. P. Ischewsky, *ib.*, **6.** 199, 1914; *Journ. Russ. Met. Soc.*, 196, 1910; *Met.*, **8.** 701, 1911; W. Guertler, *Zeit. phys. Chem.*, **74.** 428, 1911; *Internat. Zeit. Metallog.*, **8.** 228, 1916; G. Gallo, *Rass. Min.*, **32.** 72, 1910; N. Parravano, *Gazz. Chim. Ital.*, **42.** ii, 367, 385, 513, 589, 1912; G. Tammann and A. A. Botschwar, *Zeit. anorg. Chem.*, **175.** 121, 1928; R. Vogel and G. Tammann, *ib.*, **58.** 73, 1908; M. Levin and G. Tammann, *ib.*, **47.** 136, 1905; U. Raydt and G. Tammann, *ib.*, **83.** 257, 1913; G. Tammann and W. Salge, *ib.*, **176.** 152, 1928; G. Tammann and G. Siebel, *ib.*, **148.** 297, 1925; G. Tammann and W. Treitschke, *ib.*, **49.** 320, 1906; **55.** 402, 1907; E. Isaac and G. Tammann, *ib.*, **53.** 281, 1907; **55.** 58, 63, 1907; R. Sahmen, *ib.*, **57.** 1, 1908; F. Heinrich and W. Voigt, *ib.*, **153.** 209, 1926; F. Dörinckel, *ib.*, **48.** 185, 1906; **50.** 117, 1906; N. S. Konstantinoff, *ib.*, **60.** 410, 1908; **64.** 209, 1910; *Journ. Russ. Phys. Chem. Soc.*, **40.** 763, 1908; **41.** 1220, 1909; N. M. von Wittorf, *ib.*, **43.** 1613, 1911; *Rev. Mét.*, **9.** 600, 1912; *Zeit. anorg. Chem.*, **79.** 1, 1903; A. von Vegesack, *ib.*, **52.** 30, 1907; M. Chikashige and T. Hiki, *ib.*, **77.** 197, 1912; N. Baar, *ib.*, **70.** 352, 1911; F. Sauerwald, W. Schultze and G. Jackworth, *ib.*, **140.** 384, 1924; K. Daeves, *ib.*, **118.** 55, 1921; *Stahl Eisen*, **41.** 1262, 1921; P. Oberhoffer and A. Heger, *ib.*, **43.** 1322, 1923; P. Oberhoffer, K. Daeves and F. Rapatz, *ib.*, **44.** 432, 1924; P. Oberhoffer, *Das technische Eisen*, Berlin, 486, 1925; *Zeit. anorg. Chem.*, **81.** 156, 1913; *Stahl Eisen*, **36.** 798, 1916; **46.** 1191, 1926; K. Harneker and E. Rassow, *ib.*, **38.** 1079, 1918; A. von Dormus, *ib.*, **29.** 907, 1909; B. Strauss and A. Fry, *ib.*, **41.** 1133, 1921; *Forging Heat Treating*, **8.** 225, 1922; A. Fry, *Chem. Met. Engg.*, **27.** 349, 1922; *Stahl Eisen*, **40.** 622, 1920; **41.** 1093, 1921; J. Czochralski, *ib.*, **35.** 1073, 1915; W. J. Kurbatoff, *ib.*, **25.** 543, 1905; *Rev. Mét.*, **2.** 169, 1905; *Journ. Russ. Phys. Chem. Soc.*, **36.** 1524, 1905; *Met.*, **5.** 721, 1908; P. Goerens, *Einführung in die Metallographie*, Halle a. S., 1915; P. Goerens and K. Ellingen, *Met.*, **7.** 72, 1910; P. Goerens and H. Meyer, *ib.*, **7.** 307, 1910; O. Ruff and W. Martin, *ib.*, **9.** 143, 1912; J. Kirner, *ib.*, **8.** 72, 1911; K. Friedrich, *ib.*, **4.** 129, 1907; N. Gutowsky, *ib.*, **5.** 463; 1908; P. Breuil, *ib.*, **5.** 59, 96, 105, 1908; *Bull. Soc. Ind. Min.*, (4), **6.** 3, 1907; H. C. Boynton, *Iron Steel Mag.*, **7.** 470, 1904; M. Künkele, *Ber. Werkstoff. Ver. deut. Eisenhüttenleute*, 75, 1925; H. Hanemann and A. Schrader, *Arch. Eisenhüttenwesen*, **4.** 475, 1931; *Stahl Eisen*, **51.** 645, 1931; O. Mezger, B. Schöninger and E. Elben, *Zeit. angew. Chem.*, **44.** 651, 1931; V. N. Svechnikoff, *Trans. Russ. Central Board Labour*, **1.** 31, 1930.

§ 14. The Equilibrium Diagram of the Iron-Carbon System

W. C. Roberts-Austen [1] showed that in addition to the Ar_3- and Ar_2-arrests with purified iron, two evolutions of heat occur at 487° and at 261°. These two points were observed with iron which had been heated in vacuo at 1300° for three successive periods. After repeated treatment, however, the two points become so feeble that they cannot be identified with certainty. Hence it is inferred that they are connected with the presence of hydrogen in iron. It was also observed that the presence of hydrogen increased the magnitude of the Ar_2- and Ar_3-arrests. The A_4-point at 1401° was found by R. Ruer and R. Klesper to be gradually lowered by silicon until it attained 1335° with 1·2 per cent.; the addition of up to 0·29 per cent. of carbon raised it to 1482°; likewise with up to 22 per cent. of cobalt it was raised to 1492°; and with 11 per cent. of copper, to 1477°. H. W. Gillett discussed the action of oxygen and nitrogen on the iron-carbon system; and F. Yamada, the effect of chemical composition on the liquidus curve of cast iron.

Carbon readily dissolves in γ-ferrite; it is slightly soluble in β-ferrite; and almost insoluble in α-ferrite. F. Osmond showed that if iron contains even a small proportion of carbon, an entirely new critical point occurs at approximately 690° or 710° on the cooling curve. This is called the Ar_1-arrest. It is inferred that the carbon is held in solid soln. by the iron at a temp. above the Ar_1-arrest, but at that temp. the carbon separates from solid soln. in the form of iron tritacarbide, Fe_3C, the so-called *cementite*, and the arrest is sometimes called the temp. of the *carbide transformation*. F. Osmond also observed that as

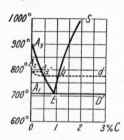

FIG. 82.—The Influence of Carbon on the Critical Points of Iron.

the proportion of carbon increases, the Ar_3-arrest is rapidly lowered and joins up with the Ar_2-point at a, Fig. 82; the double $Ar_{2,3}$-point then descends and finally coincides with the Ar_1-point, at E, when the proportion of carbon has attained 0·8 to 0·9 per cent. Such steels have one arrest, Ar_1, and it is sometimes called the $Ar_{3,2,1}$-point. The fact may be expressed other ways: Carbon retards the transformation of hard γ-iron into soft α-iron, and therefore increases the stability of hard γ-iron. The abrupt cooling or quenching of the iron-carbon alloy may result in hard γ-iron persisting at ordinary temp. when the transformation of γ- to α-iron is indefinitely slow. Alloying the iron with, say, manganese, nickel, chromium, tungsten, etc., considerably lowers the temp. of the Ar_1-arrest, so that the hard γ-iron may persist when the iron is cooled in air down to ordinary temp.—*vide infra*, air-hardening or self-hardening steels, and high-speed or rapid-cutting steels. F. Osmond found that the effect of foreign elements on the critical temp. when ranged in the order of their at. vols. is as follows: C, 3·6; B, 4·1; Ni, 6·7; Mn, 6·9; and Cu, 7·1. These elements with a smaller at. vol. than that of iron, *viz.* 7·2, delay the β→α change as well as that of hardening carbon into carbide carbon. On the other hand, elements with a larger at. vol. than that of iron—*viz.* Cr, 7·7; W, 9·6; Si, 11·2; As, 13·2; P, 13·5; and S, 15·7—either raise or else maintain the β→α change normal, and usually hasten the change of hardening carbon to carbide carbon. The subject was discussed by A. Sauveur, H. le Chatelier, K. W. Zimmerschied, A. Stansfield, H. M. Howe and co-workers, and G. K. Burgess and co-workers.

The work of K. Honda, K. Honda and H. Takagi, I. Iitaka, and T. Ishiwara showed that the A_2-point falls slightly at first with increasing proportions of carbon. It is also inferred that the A_2-point does not represent a change of phase, and that β-iron does not exist. The line ES represents the solubility of cementite, Fe_3C, in the solid soln. of austenite. The portion of the A_2abd line for the A_2-arrest represented by bd corresponds with austenite of concentration b, which changes from a weakly magnetic to a paramagnetic substance; in the portion ab the concentration of the austenite changes from a to b, but no variation of the A_2-arrest occurs; hence, steels with a concentration between A_2 and a'

consist of a mixture of ferrite and austenite of concentration a'. It is therefore inferred that the A_2a-line consists of two horizontal lines about 20° apart. As pure ferrite is approached, its quantity increases at the expense of the austenite ; on the other hand, as the austenite is approached, the quantity of austenite increases while that of ferrite decreases.

According to A. Grabe, and C. Benedicks, the A_1-critical point was first noted in Sweden by A. F. Angerstein, in 1777, in a paper afterwards discussed by S. Rinman. A. F. Angerstein said that when steel is heated, there is " a kind of twinkling, or, so to speak, a fluttering, flitting like a fog or vague shadow on the glowing steel " ; and this is taken to mean that on heating a piece of steel a slight cooling sets in at a definite temp., which was considered to indicate the right moment for quenching to produce the best hardening effect, and the finest grain. It was not until nearly a century later that D. K. Tschernoff noticed the connection between the critical point and the hardening of steel. This was followed by the work of F. Osmond just indicated.

Observations on the allotropic forms of iron have been largely concerned with iron associated with small proportions of other elements which inhibit or retard their transformation during cooling into the form or forms normally stable at ordinary temp. Most observations have been made with iron associated with carbon ; and the forms stable at higher temp. have been cooled or quenched before the metal has had time to pass into a state of equilibrium. At the lower temp. the speed of transformation into the state of equilibrium is often indefinitely slow. In some cases the presence of another element may reduce the transition temp. so that a state which is stable, in its absence, only at a high temp., is stable at a low temp. when it is present. For the doubling and tripling of the Ar_1-arrest, *vide infra*. A. Hultgren, G. W. Sargent, P. Goerens and H. Meyer, G. Goldberg, J. O. Arnold, J. E. Storey, A. Sauveur, and J. H. Andrew and H. A. Dickie studied the A_1- and the other transformations.

The work on the iron carbides—**5. 39, 20**—shows that in all probability molten carburized iron is a soln. of carbon or of iron tritacarbide in iron. The solidified mass is a solid soln. or a mixture of solid soln. with or without iron, *i.e.* **ferrite ;** and iron tritacarbide, *i.e.* **cementite.** In 1806 J. L. Proust in his paper *Fonte de fer* regarded carburized iron or steel as a solidified soln. of carburetted cast iron in an excess of iron ; and he added that this is but one example of a multitude of cases of solution of a compound by one or other of its elements, or even by other compounds. In 1863 A. Matthiessen suggested that the metal alloys can be regarded as solutions of metals or metal compounds in one another. The application of the laws of dil. soln. to the molten carburized iron was made by B. Pawlewsky, W. Campbell, J. A. Mathews, A. Stansfield, E. Heyn, E. D. Campbell, T. T. Read, J. H. Stansbie, G. Quincke, A. M. Portevin, C. A. Edwards, E. Nusbaumer, F. Rosendahl, G. J. Snelus, J. Parry, and H. von Jüptner ; and the phase rule, by H. W. B. Roozeboom, H. le Chatelier, O. E. Harder and F. Gonzalez, T. K. Rose, E. L. Dupuy, Z. Jeffries, Z. Jeffries and R. S. Archer, F. Osmond, N. T. Belaiew, L. Grenet, C. A. Edwards, C. Benedicks, E. Frasenster, W. Broniewsky, W. Rosenhain, A. Linder, F. T. Sisco, and F. J. Brislee. N. H. Aall studied the diagrams for the binary and ternary systems ; and T. F. Russell, P. Oberhoffer and co-workers, R. Vogel, K. Fishbeck, P. Goerens, and A. von Vegesack, the use of triangular and space diagrams for representing the equilibrium conditions of ternary iron-carbon alloys. F. Wever, Y. Chu-Phay, and F. H. Jeffery discussed the thermodynamics of the transformations.

In 1879 R. Mannesmann represented some relations between carbon and iron by means of a diagram ; and a few years later W. C. Roberts-Austen depicted the thermal transformations of the iron-carbon system in one diagram. This was improved by H. W. B. Roozeboom, and made to include data obtained by F. Osmond. Even then the relations were admittedly tentative. The diagram is illustrated by Fig. 83 and the dots represent the thermal data obtained by H. C. H. Carpenter

and B. F. E. Keeling. The observed results represented by dots in Fig. 83 confirm
H. W. B. Roozeboom's diagram ; but AC is slightly convex upwards ; EC rises
slightly from E to C ; SE can be represented as well by a straight line as by a

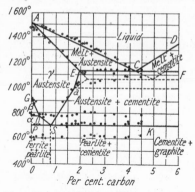

curve ; and PK rises in passing from P to K.
In addition, (i) a small thermal change
occurred at about 790° for alloys with 0·8 to
4·5 per cent. carbon ; (ii) a slow thermal
change occurred at about 600° with all the
alloys ; and (iii) evolutions of heat at about
900° occurred in two of the alloys. The
liquidus curve, AC, Fig. 83, shows how the
f.p. is influenced by the amount of carbon
present, there being a continuous drop from
the m.p. of iron, 1505°, to 1130°, the eutectic
temp. for a mixture with about 4·3 per cent.
carbon. The solidus line Aa represents temp.
below which the whole mass is solid.

Fig. 83.—Equilibrium Diagram of the
Iron-Carbon Alloys.

N. Gutowsky found that the solidus line Aa
for mixtures with less than 2 per cent. carbon
is convex downwards as indicated in Fig. 83 ;
and G. Asahara obtained for the solidus a position intermediate between the
curves of N. Gutowsky, and H. C. H. Carpenter and B. F. E. Keeling. The
liquidus and solidus curves were discussed by O. W. Ellis. The solid which separates
from the cooling liquid along AC is a solid soln. to which the name **austenite** has
been applied—after W. C. Roberts-Austen. Solid alloys with less than 2 per cent.
of carbon contain iron carbide held in solid soln. by γ-iron. The alloys with up to
2 per cent. carbon persist as a homogeneous soln. of tritacarbide in γ-iron down to
temp. denoted by the lines $GOSE$. The mixture represented by the point S—0·9
per cent. carbon—is called the *eutectoid* or eutectic steel ; mixtures with a smaller
proportion of carbon are called *hypoeutectoids*, and mixtures with 0·9 to 2·0 per cent.
carbon, *hypereutectoids*.

H. M. Howe considered that the term eutectic steel may lead to confusion, and proposed the term *bonmutic steel* for the steel with the lowest transformation temp., but later
preferred *æolic steel*. The term has not been adopted. The subject was discussed by
B. H. Brough, A. Sauveur, J. O. Arnold, and A. Stansfield.

The hypoeutectoidal mixtures to the left of S, on passing the temp. represented
by GO, yield β-iron, and on passing the temp. represented by OS, α-iron. On
reaching the temp. represented by PS, the Ar_1-arrest, the remaining alloy is eutectoidal and it passes into a mixture of α-ferrite and cementite. During the cooling
of the hypereutectoidal alloys, with between 0·9 and 2·0 per cent. of carbon, to the
right of S, the curve SE is reached ; this represents the limit of saturation of the
solid soln. of tritacarbide or cementite in γ-iron, so that as the temp. falls, the
austenite is resolved along the line ES into γ-iron and cementite, until the eutectoidal
mixture is attained. J. H. Andrew and D. Binnie found that the liquidus and
solidus curves of commercial carbon steels conform with Fig. 84, provided the proportion of manganese is below 0·45 per cent. K. Honda and H. Endo found that
the solidus line lies between that of H. C. H. Carpenter and B. F. E. Keeling, and
N. Gutowsky, and nearly coincides with that obtained by G. Asahara, and by
S. Kaya. O. W. Ellis discussed the solidus curve ; and G. Gesaro, the liquidus
curve.

The line GOS thus represents the effect of carbon on the critical temp. of iron.
With about 0·45 per cent. of carbon the Ar_3-arrest is practically coincident with
the Ar_2-arrest ; and with 0·9 per cent. of carbon the Ar_3-, Ar_2-, and Ar_1-arrests
coincide. The line PSK represents the temp. at which the solid soln. of carbide
separates into cementite and α-ferrite. The eutectoidal mixture has 0·9 per cent.
of carbon. The eutectoidal mixture, roughly six parts of ferrite to one of cementite,

is called **pearlite,** owing to the fact that it can be made to show the rainbow tints of mother-of-pearl. The eutectoidal line *PSK* was found by H. C. H. Carpenter and B. F. E. Keeling to have a slight upward slope beyond the eutectoidal point *S* ; but it is usually drawn horizontal, because, in the observation of critical temp. on cooling curves, the observed results may be affected by under-cooling. Observations on the transformations associated with the zone *GOSP*, Fig. 83, have been considered in connection with the allotropic forms of iron ; and in addition, by R. Ruer and F. Goerens, P. Bardenheuer, H. M. Howe, P. Goerens and P. Saldau, M. Levin and H. Schottsky, O. F. Hudson, W. J. Foster, H. Hanemann, R. Ruer and co-workers, W. H. Hatfield, A. Meuthen, J. Driesen, G. Rümelin and R. Maire, P. Curie, A. Merz, F. Stahlein, H. Esser, and S. Hilpert.

In constructing his equilibrium diagram, H. W. B. Roozeboom assumed that graphite forms the more stable system at the higher temp., and this view was favoured by A. Stansfield, and H. Le Chatelier, and E. Heyn. This means that the equilibrium diagram includes two systems—a metastable system free from graphite, and a stable system free from carbide. The metastable carbide system is supposed to be in a state of undercooling. E. Heyn added that if the proportion of carbon exceeds a certain limiting value, undercooling is prevented, and that occluded gases may favour the transformation of the metastable into the stable system. G. Charpy inferred that the system produced depends on the rate of cooling during solidification, and he assumed, but did not prove, that the graphite-iron eutectic is 10° to 15° above the carbide-iron eutectic.

F. Osmond inferred from his observations on the quenching of grey cast iron that the graphite is produced in the solidified metal. F. Wüst obtained only one eutectic for both systems ; he regarded this as the carbide-iron eutectic ; and inferred that graphite is not a primary product at all, but rather a secondary product being produced by the decomposition of the carbide—the yield of graphite being greater the longer the alloy is maintained in the region of solidification. E. Heyn and O. Bauer found that some alloys with silicon can be solidified without the separation of graphite, and that the graphite is formed in the solidified metal within 30° or 40° below the m.p. Quite a number of observers agreed that graphite is not a direct product of the freezing of the iron-carbon alloy, but is rather formed by the decomposition of the carbide, cementite=graphite+pearlite, soon after its solidification from the molten state. A similar view of the process of graphite formation was taken by P. Goerens, P. Goerens and N. Gutowsky, A. M. Portevin, J. E. Stead, K. Honda and T. Murakami, K. Honda and H. Endo, L. Northcott, M. Hamasumi, and J. E. Hurst. E. Mauer and P. Holtzhaussen, and E. Schüz concluded that only the eutectic graphite is formed by direct separation from the alloy, but that the other graphite is produced by the secondary decomposition of the carbide.

On the other hand, C. Benedicks argued that graphite can separate directly from the freezing liquid, and this view was supposed by H. M. Howe, H. Hanemann, W. Guertler, J. E. Johnson, R. Ruer and F. Goerens, O. Ruff and W. Bormann, K. Tawara and G. Asahara, P. Bardenheuer, A. Logan, K. von Kerpeley, and D. Hanson. The eutectic for the iron-carbon alloys occurs with 4·3 per cent. carbon ; alloys with 2 to 4·3 per cent. carbon are said to be *hypoeutectic*, and those with over 4·3 per cent. carbon, *hypereutectic*. The hypereutectic alloys deposit cementite as cooling occurs along the line *CD*. The eutectic line *ECF* corresponds with the formation of the eutectic mixture of cementite and austenite. The iron carbide in solid soln. under certain conditions may decompose into iron and graphite or free carbon—at first probably colloidal. Iron containing 4 per cent. of carbon in soln., if rapidly cooled from the liquid state, will contain all the carbon in solid soln. probably as carbide, but when slowly cooled most of the carbon will separate free. In 1881 L. Forquignon showed that hard carbides may be decomposed when the metal is annealed—*vide infra*, cast iron. The carbide present in rapidly cooled iron can be decomposed at about 1000°. Free carbon can be readily produced by annealing steels with over 9·0 per cent. carbon, and in steels with a lower percentage by a prolonged annealing just below 700°. This means that there are two equilibrium diagrams for the iron-carbide alloys, either a metastable diagram in which the carbide in solid soln. does not decompose into free carbon, etc., or a stable diagram in which the carbide is decomposed, or conversely. There are workers who believe that for true equilibrium no carbide will be present, and that iron carbides have no place in the true equilibrium diagram. E. Heyn, R. Ruer, and C. Benedicks suggested diagrams in which the graphite is represented as one of the constituents to separate from the eutectic if the cooling be slow enough, and if the cooling be fast enough iron carbide and not graphite is produced. According to K. Honda and H. Endo, if graphite be a decomposition product of cementite, and not a direct precipitation product from the solid soln., the double diagram is not a correct representation of the facts. C', Fig. 84, represents the *graphite eutectic*; and C, the *cementite eutectic*. F. Wüst called the eutectic mixture of austenite and cementite

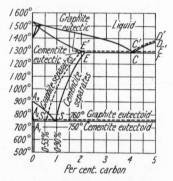

FIG. 84.—Stable and Metastable Equilibria Curves of the Iron-Carbon Alloys.

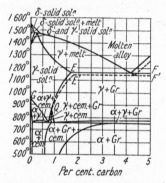

FIG. 85.—Equilibrium Diagram of the Iron-Carbon Alloys.

ledeburite—after A. Ledebur; and H. A. Schwartz and co-workers, solid soln. of iron and graphite boydenite—after S. Boyden—so that the term boydenite is used for a solid soln. of carbon in γ-iron in the same sense that austenite is used for a solid soln. of cementite in γ-iron—but *vide infra*. K. Daeves discussed the eutectic points in the iron-carbon system. According to R. Ruer and J. Biren, the eutectic with graphite is 1152° and 4·25 per cent. of carbon, but with cementite it is 1145° and 4·30 per cent. of carbon. Graphite can separate from molten hypereutectic alloys, and rising to the surface produce the so-called **kish**. Graphite or kish may thus be formed in the region $C'D'F'$, as cementite is formed in the region CDF. As shown by B. Osann, graphite is also formed in the slow cooling of iron-carbon below $E'C'D'$; and graphite or annealing carbon is formed after the prolonged annealing of other iron-carbon alloys, and it separates by the decomposition of austenite as the alloy is cooled through temp. represented by the line $S'E'$, just as under other conditions cementite separates along the line SE.

These conclusions on the transformation of combined carbon into graphite have been discussed by R. R. Abbott, P. Goerens, P. Goerens and N. Gutowsky, A. Hague and T. Turner, E. Adamson, J. Shaw, W. J. Foster, G. Phragmen, A. Merz and F. Fleischer, R. Ruer, K. Honda, A. A. Bates and co-workers, R. L. Dowdell, J. H. Andrew, A. Ledebur and G. Charpy, W. H. Hatfield, H. M. Howe, F. Wüst, F. Wüst and P. Schlösser, H. Hanemann, O. Ruff, O. Ruff and O. Goecke, N. M. von Wittorf, A. Smits, B. Osann, R. Horny, W. Guertler, E. H. Saniter, H. A. Schwartz and co-workers, P. D. Merica and L. J. Gurevich, R. S. Archer, A. E. White and R. S. Archer, A. Phillips and E. S. Davenport, R. W. Bean and co-workers, K. Tawara and G. Asahara, and G. Charpy and L. Grenet—*vide infra*, the graphitization of cast iron.

O. E. Harder and W. S. Johnson examined normal and abnormal steels respectively with 0·012 per cent. C; 0·021, Mn; 0·005, P; 0·038. S; 0·054, Cu;

and with 0·20, C ; 0·43, Mn ; 0·022, P ; 0·033, S, and found that the cementite solubility curve with normal steel is shifted to the left, so that the eutectoid comes at 0·75 per cent. carbon instead of 0·9 per cent. Similarly with abnormal steel, which is shifted still further to the left so as to cut the A_1-line at about 0·55 per cent. of carbon. N. J. Wark, L. Grenet, and E. Walldow studied the dissolution of cementite in α- and γ-iron; and J. O. Arnold and L. Aitchison, the solubility of cementite in hardenite —*vide infra*. O. E. Harder and co-workers also represented in Fig. 84 the results when iron oxide and alumina are present.

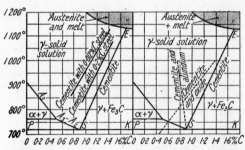

FIG. 86.—The Solubility of Carbide in Normal and Abnormal Steels.

FIG. 87.—The Solubility of Carbide in Steels with Iron Oxide and Alumina.

The results of R. Ruer and F. Goeren's, and of K. Honda's observations on δ-iron are included in the diagram. It also includes diagrammatically D. Hanson's assumptions based on his observations on the Fe–Si–C-system that the SE and $S'E'$ lines intersect so that graphite is the stable form at the higher temp., and carbide at the lower. It also shows how graphite can be the stable form for all alloys with over about 2 per cent. of carbon (and 0·4 per cent. of silicon—*q.v.*) ; and carbide is the stable form in steels. Intermediate zones are assumed to exist in which both forms have the appearance of being stable under ordinary conditions. Observations on this part of the equilibrium diagram were also made by G. Z. Nesselstrauss, K. Daeves, O. Ruff, O. Ruff and O. Goecke, O. Ruff and W. Bormann, I. Iitaka, L. Persoz, A. A. Bates and co-workers, S. Epstein, H. Hanemann, H. M. Howe, and R. B. Fehr. All these possibilities show how very imperfect is our knowledge of the equilibrium diagram of the iron-carbon system ; and this in spite of the extraordinary amount of work which has been done on the subject.

The line $S'E'$, Fig. 85, for the " graphite separation " does not necessarily mean that graphite as such is formed, since the separation may be temper carbon or annealing carbon and what has been called agraphitic carbon. H. A. Schwartz and co-workers said that they conceived the so-called graphitization to occur somewhat as follows :

At fairly high constant temp., say 900° to 1000°, the process is initiated by the separation of a graphite nucleus, possibly due to carbon precipitated out by some local conversion of austenite into boydenite and excess carbon. The bulk of the solid soln., however, remains austenitic and maintains its carbon conc. by dissolving cementite. More carbon precipitates and more cementite dissolves until the latter is used up, when there remains a matrix of austenite and grains of free carbon. This reaction is relatively rapid. Subsequently the austenite is graphitized into boydenite and free carbon, and reaction ceases when the solid soln. is boydenite of a carbon conc. corresponding to the saturation point at the temp. chosen. If the temp. falls slowly enough, carbon precipitates along the $S'E'$ line, the boydenite decreases in carbon content. Just above the Ar_1-arrest the solubility of carbon in boydenite is about 0·50. The agraphitic carbon becomes almost nil below Ar_1-stable and ferrite is formed, the remaining carbon precipitating as ferrite-carbon eutectoid. As a matter of fact, carbon is probably soluble in ferrite, so that the carbon concentration at the Ar_1-arrest has a small finite value ; in this case it was less than 0·03 per cent. If the temp. falls too rapidly to permit the boydenite to decrease its carbon content by precipitation, austenite will be formed, the metastable mix crystals having a higher carbon conc. than the stable. If the temp. falls somewhat rapidly below the Ac_1-arrest, metastable pearlite may form and graphitization will still proceed, though very slowly because of the slight carbon solubility at that temp. The ferrite ring around the temper carbon under these conditions, which is really a ring of boydenite of extremely low carbon content, suggests the rapid migration of carbon when dissolved as such. There is no evidence of the existence of the S'-eutectoid, and there may be a sharp inflection in the $E'S'$-curve so that it bends over to zero carbon at the A_1-arrest.

The relative portions of the $S'E'$ and SE-lines have not been precisely determined. In C. Benedicks', and N. M. von Wittorf's diagrams, these curves agree with the assumption that with slow cooling the iron carbide in soln. should break down into iron and carbon, since the carbon solubility line lies wholly to the left of the cementite solubility line. On the other hand, on O. Ruff's diagram, the curve $S'E'$ approaches and possibly intersects SE before the $A_{2,3}$- or the A_3-arrest is reached. $E'S'$ intersects ES at a point Q; this would mean that graphite is the stable phase at the higher temp., above the point of intersection, and cementite, at the lower temp., below Q. Analogous diagrams can be constructed to show the carbide stable at the higher temp., and graphite at the lower temp. These possibilities were discussed by D. Hanson, Fig. 88. Whether the alloy graphitized or not then depends on whether $S'E'$ intersects the A_3- or $A_{3,2}$-lines on the one hand or the SE-line on the

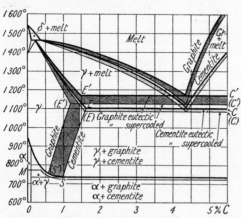

FIG. 88.—Constitutional Diagram of Carbon-Iron Alloys with no Silicon.

other hand. In the former case α-iron, carbon, and solid soln., sat. with carbon, would be in equilibrium, and the extraction of heat at the temp. of intersection should make the solid soln. break down into α-iron and carbon. If the $S'E'$-line intersects the SE-line, carbon, cementite, and solid soln., sat. with carbon, would be in equilibrium, and the extraction of heat would produce cementite from carbon and solid soln. The relative slopes of the $S'E'$ and SE lines, near 700°, are determined by the relative values of the heats of soln. of carbon and cementite in the sat. solid soln. if the difference between the solubilities of carbon from carbon and from cementite is not great. If the formation of cementite is accompanied by the evolution of much heat, the slope of the $S'E'$-line will be less than that of the SE-line, as in C. Benedicks' diagram, and if the formation of cementite is attended by the absorption of much heat, the line $S'E'$ will have the greater slope, as in O. Ruff's diagram. These considerations led H. L. Maxwell and A. Hayes to determine the heats of formation and free energy of cementite between 650° and 700°. It was found that for 3α–Fe$+$C graphite$=$Fe$_3$C the heats of formation at 650° and 700° are respectively $+3138$ cals. and 2281 cals., and the free energies 19,163 cals. Determinations of the course of the cementite line, SE, have been made by W. C. Roberts-Austen, E. Heyn, H. C. H. Carpenter and B. F. E. Keeling, N. J. Wark, P. Goerens and P. Saldau, S. Epstein, N. Gutowsky, N. Tschischewsky and N. Schulgin, and H. M. Howe and A. S. Levy.

A. L. Norbury has studied the constitutional diagram for cast irons and steels, and observed that in one type of iron the graphite may occur in a finely-divided form which has been called *supercooled graphite*; and in the other type of iron the graphite, occurring in relatively coarse flakes, has been called *normal graphite*. All intermediate stages between these two types have been prepared. When the silicon content is below 3 per cent., there is a tendency for the fine graphite to associate with ferrite in the matrix. The fine, supercooled graphite has been obtained by E. Piwowarsky, H. Hanemann, and P. Bardenheuer and K. L. Zeyen by superheating the melt; and they assume that the refining of the grain-size of graphite is due to the destruction of graphite nuclei in the melt. E. Schüz obtained the fine form of graphite by casting "iron" with 3·5 per cent. silicon in chill-moulds; and C. Irresberger, by jolting molten cast iron which had been melted with additions of steel. The fine graphite structure has frequently been reported—*e.g.* by

A. Hague and T. Turner, and H. I. Coe. A. L. Norbury represented the phase boundaries of iron-carbon alloys with 0, 2, and 4 per cent. silicon by Figs. 88 to 90. These diagrams show both the austenite-cementite and austenite-graphite for normal and supercooled systems. A. L. Norbury said that the grey irons have been assumed to crystallize according to the normal graphite-austenite system when graphite nuclei are present in the melt. Such irons contain coarse graphite flakes and tend to be pearlitic. Conversely, when graphite nuclei are absent, supercooling occurs, and the graphite is deposited in the form of exceedingly fine flakes which tend to be associated with ferrite. In the case of white iron it has been assumed that nuclei cause the precipitation of small amounts of graphite eutectic, which in turn cause the precipitation of white iron eutectic at the maximum possible temperature and with consequent coalescence. In grey irons the tendency for coarse graphite to be associated with pearlite, and fine graphite with ferrite, has been explained by assuming that the γ-solid soln. adjacent to the graphite flakes holds carbon in solid soln. according to the (lower) solid solubility of graphite, while that away from the graphite flakes holds carbon in solid soln. according to the (higher) solid solubility of cementite. Consequently, the coarser and the fewer the graphite flakes, the higher the percentage of carbon in solid soln. The lowering of the change points in steels

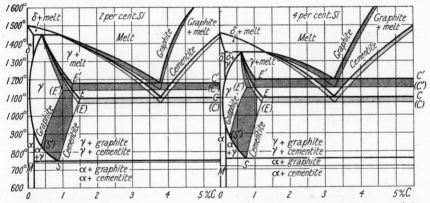

FIG. 89.—Constitutional Diagram of Carbon-Iron Alloys with 2 per cent. of Silicon.

FIG. 90.—Constitutional Diagram of Carbon-Iron Alloys with 4 per cent. of Silicon.

due to quenching has also been represented in a constitutional diagram as a form of supercooling. In the three diagrams the positions assigned to them are only approximately correct. $E'C'$ represents the eutectic temp. for normal graphite, and $(E')(C')$ the eutectic line for supercooled graphite. The work of F. Wüst and O. Petersen, and A. Hague and T. Turner indicates that the one line is about 20° higher than the other. The results of W. Gontermann, D. Hanson, and K. Honda and T. Murakami refer to intermediate temp. Similarly for the normal cementite eutectic EC, at 1110° in Fig. 88, at 1105° in Fig. 89, and at 1100° in Fig. 90, the coarse graphite eutectic is placed at 4·3, 3·75, and 3·25 per cent. carbon respectively for 0, 2, and 4 per cent. silicon alloys. The liquidus lines joining the four eutectics are shown in the diagram, and similarly with the solidus lines. The solubility curves for graphite are represented by $(S')(E')$, and for cementite by SE. The curves involving the $\delta = \gamma = \alpha$-allotropic changes are based on the observations of R. Ruer and R. Klesper, F. Wever and P. Giani, and A. Sanfourche. The suppression of the γ-phase with high proportions of silicon was demonstrated by F. Wever and P. Giani and predicted by P. Oberhoffer. K. Tamaru supposed that the solid solubility curve of carbon in δ-iron is a continuation at high temp. of the solubility curve of carbon in α-iron. The lowering of the temp. of magnetic change, M, from 768° was demonstrated by the work of T. Baker, E. Gumlich, F. Wever and P. Giani, and K. Honda and T. Murakami. E. Scheil did not agree with D. Hanson that the double diagram is at variance with the phase rule. C. P. Yap studied the thermodynamics of the system.

The effect of pressure on the iron-carbon equilibrium diagram has not been closely studied. G. Tammann's results for the effect of variations of pressure show that the A_2-arrest remains constant, whilst the A_3-arrest is lowered by pressure. Hence there are indications of a triple point. G. Charpy observed that the separation of graphite is favoured by press. When a white cast iron, containing 3 per cent. carbon and 4 per cent. nickel, or one containing 3 per cent. carbon and 2 per cent. nickel, is heated at 1100° under a press. of 150 kgrms. per sq. mm. until no further decrease in vol. occurs, graphite occurs in the cold product. The longer the heating, the greater the proportion of graphite formed. Similar results were obtained with cementite. The quantitative estimate of E. Scheil and E. H. Schulz is summarized in Fig. 91. C. Benedicks inferred that mechanical stress may cause a partial conversion of γ- into α-iron.

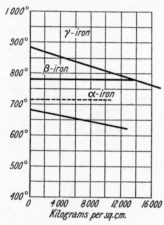

FIG. 91.—The Effect of Variation of Pressure on the Critical Points.

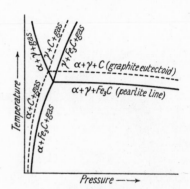

FIG. 92.—The Effect of Pressure and Temperature on the Iron-Carbon System (Diagrammatic).

O. Ruff and O. Goecke studied the relations between iron and carbon at higher temp. and higher concentrations than those now under consideration; for this, *vide* **5.** 39, 20 (Fig. 31). R. Ruer and J. Biren found that the solubility curve of graphite in molten iron is almost linear between 1152° and 1700°, and after that is slightly concave towards the concentration axis. The data for the percentage solubility, S, are :

	1152°	1200°	1400°	1600°	1800°	2000°	2200°	2400°	2500°
S .	4·25	4·37	4·85	5·37	6·00	6·78	7·72	8·88	9·54

H. A. Schwartz and co-workers suggested that the solid soln. of graphite—called boydenite—is not the same as the so-called metastable solid soln. of carbide—called ledeburite ; and they concluded that the presence of some silicon is necessary for the existence of the boydenite. This is another way of saying that the graphitic solid soln. is less stable than the carbide solid soln. E. Schüz observed that a structure having the appearance of the graphite eutectic can be observed in cast iron only when it contains a high proportion of silicon and when it has been rapidly chilled from the molten state. The alleged graphite eutectic consists of a mass of finely divided plates of graphite evenly dispersed in a ground-mass of austenite, or its derived products. J. E. Hurst observed that when a sample of hypoeutectic pig-iron was melted and allowed to cool in air, the part which cooled slowest had finely-divided graphite plates evenly dispersed in a matrix of ferrite and pearlite. Another sample showed a mass of dendrites of austenite free from graphite, with graphite in the intermediate spaces, and this part had all the appearance of a eutectic—Fig. 93 (×75). Of course, the mere fact that a structure has the appearance of a eutectic is not a sufficient proof that the structure is really eutectic, when it has not been shown that the alleged eutectic is produced at a definite temp., and that it has a constant composition. The fact that the final solidification of these alloys furnishes the austenite-cementite eutectic is assumed to be due to undercooling. The phenomenon occurs, however, even when the alloy is seeded with graphite—*e.g.* (i) when samples are melted while surrounded by graphite, and (ii) when hypereutectic alloys which liberate graphite still give as a result of the supposed undercooling the austenite-cementite eutectic. The supposed graphite eutectic structure can be produced by annealing at 1050°, when the structure is not eutectic because it has been produced below the final solidification temp. Hence, E. Schulz admitted that it has not been possible to find why the solidification of molten iron in adjacent parts should proceed at one time so as to furnish the graphite system, and at another time, the cementite system ; and still less so why the white and

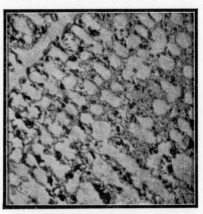

FIG. 93.—Hypoeutectic Iron with the Appearance of a Graphite Eutectic mixed with Dendrites of Austenite (J. E. Hurst).

grey patches are formed not regularly on the outside or in the middle of the drops, but quite irregularly throughout the mass. The general conclusion is that carbon exists in the molten alloy as carbide, and that the available evidence does not favour the assumption of a graphite-austenite eutectic. W. H. Hatfield, H. le Chatelier, A. Baykoff, and A. I. Krynitsky have discussed this subject.

According to J. E. Hurst, the possibility of obtaining the alleged graphite structure by the heat treatment of the solid, and the fact that quenching the alloy containing graphite from the vicinity of its final solidification temp. furnishes the austenite-cementite eutectic, make it probable that the carbon is dissolved as carbide in liquid iron, and that the existence of an austenite-cementite eutectic is not proven. The alleged graphitic eutectic is a kind of transitional stage in the appearance of the separated graphite and is formed within certain limiting conditions of cooling and composition. The formation of the austenite-cementite structure with no free carbon during the rapid quenching of the molten alloys from all temp. down to the final solidification temp., is taken to mean that the cementite is the stable phase down to temp. slightly below the final solidification temp., and is not necessarily a result of undercooling. The subsequent appearance of graphite is attributed to the breaking down of the austenite or austenite-cementite structures at lower temp. The production of kish in the liquid hypereutectic is attributed to the presence of silicon or of some other impurity—a subject discussed by W. H. Hatfield, and J. E. Stead. It is assumed by W. Gontermann, J. E. Stead, J. H. Andrew, and C. A. Edwards that with the hypoeutectic alloys it is primary austenite which separates from the cooling liquid, and with hypereutectic alloys, cementite ; the cementite is the stable phase down to temp. a little below the eutectic temp. According to J. E. Stead, when hypoeutectic alloys low in silicon solidify, nearly all the silicon separates out with the primary austenite, and by gradually increasing the carbon so as to reduce the quantity of primary austenite, the austenite is gradually enriched in silicon up to the point of saturation ; and when that point is reached, the excess silicon crystallizes out with a portion of the iron carbide to form an iron silicocarbide. In eutectic and hypereutectic alloys no primary austenite can form, and the silicon crystallizes out with the carbide. The primary carbosilicides are very unstable, and they are the first to decompose into graphite and silicoaustenite. In the absence of all but traces of phosphorus, two cementites form and crystallize as a eutectic mixture—one is silicocarbide-cementite, and the other a carbide-cementite. The unstable silicocarbides are responsible for the greyness of commercial irons rich in silicon and low in sulphur. When white iron is heated to 1000° with iron silicide, it decomposes into graphite and iron. Hence the silicon of hypoeutectic alloys crystallizes out with the primary austenite ; and after the carbide has solidified a diffusion of the silicide occurs, and this leads to the decomposition of the iron carbide into graphite and iron.

N. M. von Wittorf's diagram is shown in Fig. 94, where the assumption is made that different iron carbides are formed—*vide* 5. 39, 20. M denotes molten alloy ; I, austenite (γ-iron) ; II, β-iron ; III, α-iron ; IV, graphite ; V, Fe₄C ; VI, Fe₃C or cementite ; VII, FeC₂. It illustrates how very uncertain is the state of our knowledge of the details of the binary system : Fe–C. H. M. Howe, B. Stoughton, N. N. Ljubavin, G. Auchy, A. Smits, and O. Ruff discussed these different carbides—*vide* 5. 39, 20.

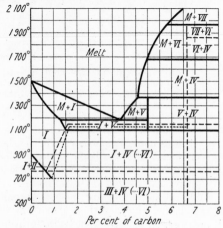

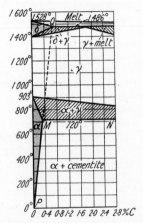

FIG. 94.—N. M. von Wittorf's Equilibrium Diagram of the Iron-Carbon Alloys.

FIG. 95.—Portion of Equilibrium Diagram of the Iron-Carbon System Associated with Small Proportions of Carbon.

C. A. Edwards explained the formation of kish by assuming an upper limit of stability of cementite-carbide as indicated by *MN*, Fig. 95, so that at temp. and conc. a little in excess of those of the eutectic alloy, the cementite-carbide is stable, and crystallizes from the molten metal. The break at *M* in the liquidus curve corresponds with the reaction Fe₃C=Graphite+Melt. No such break, however, was observed by O. Ruff and O. Goecke, and H. Hanemann in their studies of the hypereutectic alloys. G. B. Upton also made an attempt to deal with the formation of graphite by assuming the existence of a number of complex carbides. There is no definite arrest on the cooling curves corresponding with the separation of graphite, for the graphite may separate continuously over a considerable range of temp. below the solidification temp. of the eutectic. Several other modified equilibrium diagrams have been proposed—*e.g.* by G. B. Upton, A. Vinogradoff, etc.

J. H. Andrew said that the formation of graphite commences between 1150° and 1100° ; K. Honda and T. Murakami, between 1150° and 1130° ; and L. Northcott, between 1145° and 1000° with ordinary grey cast irons. The assumption that graphite begins to be formed at least 5° or 10° below the solidification temp. of the eutectic is in agreement with the observations of J. O. Arnold, C. A. Edwards, W. Gontermann, and G. Cesaro. Unlike R. Ruer and F. Goerens, K. Honda and

T. Murakami concluded that graphite is not directly precipitated from the molten soln. of iron and carbon, but is a secondary product of the decomposition of the solidified cementite. Consequently, the graphite system is not an integral part of the iron-carbon equilibrium diagram. The conclusion is based on these facts :

(i) If a specimen of cast iron is quenched from 1130°, when it has just solidified, no graphite is observable, provided the alloy is hypoeutectic ; while in specimens quenched between 1050° and 1000°, a considerable amount of graphite is found in the microstructure. Moreover, in specimens very slowly cooled through the solidifying range, the graphitization is very small. If the graphite were a direct product from the melt, it should be found in specimens which have just solidified and been quenched from 1130°, or slowly cooled through the solidifying range ; but this is not the case. (ii) If the graphite were a product directly precipitated from the melt, it must be found in a greater quantity round a graphite rod dipped in it, because a new phase easily appears when a nucleus of the same phase exists. But this conclusion is not confirmed by experiments. (iii) Flaky graphite, which is similar to that produced during cooling from the melt, is also obtained by heating solidified alloys containing cementite from 1000° to 1100°. This fact clearly shows that cementite can graphitize and form flakes at a temp. below the eutectic point. (iv) K. Honda and H. Endo found that the contraction which occurs when cast iron solidifies is 3·5 per cent., provided no cementite decomposes. If graphite be a decomposition product of cementite, the change in vol., $\delta v/v$, on solidification will be $\delta v/v = -3\cdot6+$ the vol. change due to the decomposition of the cementite. The observed and calculated results agree.

The general conclusion of O. Ruff and W. Bormann, R. Ruer and F. Goerens, G. Charpy, F. Wüst, K. Honda and co-workers, T. Kase, and H. Sawamura is that graphite is produced by the dissociation of the primarily formed carbide as it cools below the solidification of the austentite-cementite eutectic. It is simplest to suppose that the carbide dissociates $Fe_3C = 3Fe + C_{graphite}$. Assuming that cementite is the metastable phase, and graphite the stable phase, the formation of the metastable intermediate phase anterior to the appearance of the stable one is in general agreement with the observations of W. Ostwald on the transition of substances from one state to another. On the other hand, K. Honda suggested that graphite is formed by a strictly chemical process, namely the catalytic action of free carbon dioxide on the cementite : $Fe_3C + CO_2 = 2CO + 3Fe$; followed by $2CO = CO_2 + C_{graphite}$, and the resulting carbon dioxide maintains the continuity of the cycle. According to these hypotheses, free ferrite must occur along with the graphite, but this has not been observed. Hence it is assumed that the cementite-carbide dissociates into graphite and a solid soln. of carbon in iron ; $Fe_3C = C_{graphite} + $ solid soln. of carbon in iron. The solidification of a cooling soln. of carbide in molten iron furnishes a mixture of austenite and the austenite-cementite. This is stable down to about 1100°, when the primary cementite of the eutectic may furnish graphite and a solid soln. As the austenite cools down it becomes saturated with respect to carbide, and needles of secondary cementite are deposited. The line SE represents the solubility of cementite in the solid soln. The secondary cementite can presumably dissociate into graphite and solid soln. T. Kase's observations on the cooling curves, the microstructure of cast iron cooled under various conditions, and the change of electrical resistance near the eutectic temp. favour the interpretation that graphite is a secondary product. The two-stepped thermal change observed by R. Ruer and F. Goerens with the austenite-cementite and the austenite-graphite eutectics does not prove that graphite is a primary product ; T. Kase said that the phenomenon is due to the difference in the velocity of the mutual dissolution of cementite and austenite, and graphite and austenite, respectively. No evidence of the presence of two eutectic temp. could be observed ; for the two eutectic horizontals sometimes observed are attributed to the difference in the speed of melting of the austenite-cementite and austenite-graphite systems. The so-called eutectic graphite—boydenite—is a decomposition product of the eutectic cementite.

P. D. Merica and L. J. Gurevich, D. Hanson, R. S. Archer, K. Tawara and G. Asahara, A. Phillips and E. S. Davenport, A. Hayes and co-workers, A. Smits, and M. S. Fischer and J. M. Robertson hold that the graphite or free carbon is not produced by the dissociation of the carbide *per se*, but rather separates directly from solid soln. R. A. Hadfield, W. H. Hatfield, J. E. Hurst, H. M. Howe, R. S. Archer, P. D. Merica, G. S. Scott, E. Heyn and O. Bauer, and G. P. Royston showed that in the reverse process graphite can redissolve when cast iron is heated, without the intervention of the free carbide stage, to form, presumably, a solid soln. Similarly, also, it is not improbable that the solid soln. can deposit graphite directly. Free ferrite can thus be formed by the reduction in the conc. of the solid soln. as it deposits graphite, and by the resolution of the solid soln. into ferrite and pearlite as it passes through the pearlite transformation.

R. Ruer and R. Klesper showed that δ-iron dissolves about 0·07 per cent. of carbon at the peritectic temp. 1486°. T. D. Yensen observed that iron with 0·003 per cent. of carbon at ordinary temp. contains a trace of cementite. Hence the solubility of carbon in α-iron is very low, but not zero. H. Scott observed that with iron containing less than 0·03 per cent. of carbon no break can be observed corresponding with the A_1-arrest; and F. Yamada showed that no eutectoidal mixture is formed when less than 0·034 per cent. of carbon is present, but appears as an intercrystalline film in slowly-cooled specimens. K. Tamaru, acting on the assumption that the solubility of carbon in α-iron at the A_1-arrest is 0·034 per cent., inferred that since α-iron and δ-iron have a similar space-lattice, the solubility of carbon in δ-iron lies on a continuation of the solubility curve of carbon in α-iron *PMO*, Fig. 95. *MN* denotes the eutectoidal horizontal. Fig. 95 then represents the position of the equilibrium curves at the extreme left of the equilibrium diagram of the iron-carbon alloys.

A. Sauveur and V. N. Krivobok said that the **solubility of carbon** in α-ferrite, slowly cooled, is about 0·06 per cent. of carbon in soln. at ordinary temp.; A. Sauveur, basing his statement on the non-observance of cementite in certain carbon steels, said that ferrite or α-iron can dissolve 0·06 per cent. of carbon; C. Benedicks gave 0·27 per cent.; whilst W. H. Hatfield gave 0·04 to 0·05 per cent. These numbers are doubtless too high for ordinary temp. F. Yamada gave 0·01 per cent.; T. D. Yensen, 0·006 to 0·008 per cent.; H. Scott, <0·03 per cent.; J. H. Whiteley, 0·03 per cent.; N. B. Pilling, 0·015 per cent.; K. Tamaru gave 0·034 per cent.; and A. Bramley and F. W. Haywood, 0·04 per cent. The subject was also discussed by F. Wever, H. A. Dickie, K. Daeves, N. J. Wark, G. Charpy and A. Cornu-Thénard, J. A. Holden, I. Iitaka, and N. Seljakoff and co-workers. According to J. H. Whiteley, carbon is soluble in α-iron at temp. exceeding 630°; and it can be retained in solid soln. by quenching. On tempering at or below 250° the precipitation of cementite occurs in the ferrite grains, and as the temp. rises the minute particles migrate to the boundaries of the grains. The speed of movement is rapid at 550°. Above 630° the solubility of carbon in ferrite gradually increases with temp., and at 720°, 0·03 per cent. is dissolved. As the purity of the ferrite is diminished, the initial temp. for soln. rises a little, and at the same time the solubility of carbon is, in all probability, correspondingly reduced. Carbon is not insoluble in iron, even at ordinary temp., and T. D. Yensen stated that up to about 0·008 per cent. is retained in soln. O. C. Ralston gave 0·003 per cent. for the solubility of carbon in α-ferrite at ordinary temp., and S. Tamura observed 0·034 per cent. at about 720°; the maximum solubility in δ-iron at about 1482° is 0·07 per cent. W. Köster gave the curves, Fig. 96, for the solubility of carbon in α-iron. R. Ruer and J. Biren observed that the solubility of graphite in molten iron rises linearly with temp. from 1152° to 1700°; it then bends away from the concentration axis, slightly at first, and then more strongly as the temp. rises. The concentration at the graphite eutectic, 1152°, is 4·25 per cent. of carbon, and at the cementite eutectic, 1145°, it is 4·30

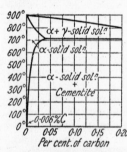

Fig. 96.—The Solubility of Carbon in α-Iron.

per cent.—*vide* **5**. 39, 20.   K. Schichtel and E. Piwowarsky found that phosphorus, silicon, and nickel lower the solubility of carbon in iron.   With over 2·5 per cent. of phosphorus, 3 per cent. of silicon, and 15 per cent. of nickel, the effect on carbon ceases.   At 1200°, 0·29 part of carbon is thrown out for every one part of phosphorus, 0·28 part of carbon for one part of silicon, and 0·045 part of carbon for one part of nickel ; at 1700° the corresponding parts of carbon separated are 0·42, 0·40, and 0·045 respectively—*vide* the chemical properties of iron, and the alloys of silicon, and nickel.   E. M. Wise, and H. L. Maxwell and A. Hayes discussed the solubility in austenite of carbon from the element, and from carbide ; and

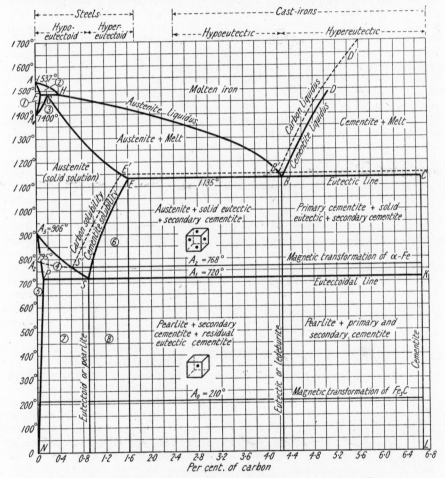

FIG. 97.—Conventional Phase Diagram of the System : Carbon-Iron.

G. Charpy, C. Benedicks, and S. Konobejewsky, the solubility of iron in graphite. G. Sirovich supposed that there are two ferrites, one stable below and the other stable above 370° ; the former dissolves cementite or carbon, and the latter not so.

The rate of diffusion of the dissolved carbon (*vide infra*) is very rapid at the A_1-point.   During slow cooling the dissolved carbide is deposited on the existing crystals, so that slowly cooled ferrite in ordinary steels contains very little, if any, carbon in solid soln.   The presence of dissolved carbon in α-iron increases its Brinell's hardness to a small, but definite, extent.   Thus, untreated steel and steel quenched from 550°, 680°, and 980° had the respective hardnesses, 89, 91, and

105. F. Sauerwald and A. Koreny discussed the rate of dissolution of graphite in molten iron.

Fig. 97 can be taken as the conventional phase equilibrium diagram of the carbon-iron system. The diagram, however, has not yet assumed its final form ; and it must be understood that it leaves for discussion many anomalies whose significance has not yet been interpreted. Results obtained with commercial irons do not always fit the diagram, and this is taken to mean that in many cases equilibrium conditions have not been attained. The steels include the alloys with up to about 1·7 per cent. of carbon, and the cast irons begin with about 2·2 per cent. of carbon. There is a more or less ill-defined border-land in between, and the upper limit for cast irons is more or less indefinite and is probably near that of the composition of cementite, namely 6·67 per cent. of carbon. Area (1) includes δ-ferrite with a maximum carbon solubility of 0·07 per cent.—the point F ; area (2) includes δ-ferrite and the molten alloy ; area (3), δ-ferrite and austenite ; area (4), α-ferrite and austenite ; area (5), α-ferrite with a maximum carbon solubility of 0·034 per cent. ; area (6), austenite and proeutectoid cementite ; area (7), proeutectoid α-ferrite and pearlite ; and area (8), proeutectoid cementite and pearlite. The temp. of the magnetic transformation of cementite, A_0, is 210°, and the temp. of magnetic transformation of α-ferrite, A_2, is 795°. The temp. of the A_1-arrest, where the eutectoid of solid austenite splits into α-ferrite and cementite, is 720°. The temp. of the A_4-arrest, where δ-ferrite is transformed into γ-ferrite, is 1400°. The m.p. of iron is taken as 1535°. The point N representing the solubility of carbon, as cementite, at room temp., corresponds with 0·003 per cent. of carbon, and NP represents the solubility curve with a rise of temp. The composition of the α-ferrite crystals which separate from austenite is represented by A_3P ; whilst that of austenite in equilibrium follows along A_3S. The temp. of the peritectic FH is 1486°, and the peritectic G corresponds with 0·18 per cent. of carbon—K. Honda gave 0·38 per cent. The curve A_4E is where δ-ferrite separates from the alloy, and A_4G where austenite solid soln. separate out. The eutectic mixture of cementite and austenite, B, is ledeburite, and the eutectic B' refers to the mixture of graphite and austenite ; SE is the solubility curve of cementite, and $S'E'$ that of carbon in austenite. E. Scheil worked out a tentative equilibrium diagram varying both temp. and press. Observational data, however, are too meagre to make this much more than a speculation.

T. D. Yensen argued that pure iron has never been examined. Electrolytic iron contains 0·005 per cent. of carbon, and up to about 0·4 per cent. of oxygen. Carbon, oxygen, and nitrogen here act as interstitial elements in that they occupy the open spaces between the solvent atoms. The effect of these elements is to favour the change from the body-centred to the face-centred cube. These interstitial elements are more soluble in the γ-iron with its face-centred cube than in α-iron with its body-centred cube. As a result, it is inferred that if all the elements whose atoms enter the lattice of the solvent occupy the open spaces, the iron would not change into the γ-form. The corresponding change necessary in the equilibrium diagram is illustrated by Fig. 98, where the dotted lines indicate the effect of this hypothesis on the conventional equilibrium diagram.

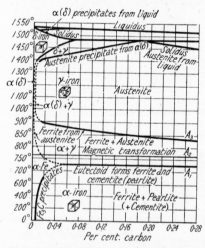

FIG. 98.—Constitutional Diagram of the Iron-Carbon Alloys—Low Carbon.

The critical temperatures of the iron-carbon alloys.—The m.p. of purified iron is somewhere between 1528° and 1537°. The presence of carbon lowers the m.p. down to the eutectic at about 1135°.

The A$_4$-point.—According to S. Tamura, the A$_4$-arrest of iron is raised from 1400° to 1486° by the dissolution of 0·07 per cent. of carbon ; whilst K. Honda said that only the iron-carbon alloys with less than 0·38 per cent. of carbon can exhibit the A$_4$-arrest. With more carbon δ-iron passes into γ-iron, that is, the solid soln. of carbon in δ-iron passes into a solid soln. of carbon in γ-iron.

The A$_3$-point.—R. H. Harrington and W. H. Wood said that there is about 6° difference in the A$_3$-transformation in heating and cooling ; the transformation seems to occur in two stages. H. M. Howe and A. S. Levy discussed the position of the A$_3$-arrest with carbon steel in a state of equilibrium. He took 917° as the normal value for this arrest, and gave for the temp. T of the A$_3$-arrest with C per cent. of combined carbon, $T°=917-306C$. The subject was discussed by G. K. Burgess and co-workers, A. Stansfield, K. W. Zimmerschied, H. le Chatelier, A. Sauveur, and P. Bardenheuer. Carbon raises the A$_4$-arrest, and lowers the temp. of the A$_3$-arrest of iron from its normal value, 906°. The lowering which the A$_3$-point undergoes with increasing proportions of carbon is represented by the curve A_3S, where S represents the eutectic between α-iron and cementite. With higher proportions of carbon, the A$_3$-arrest coincides with the A$_1$-arrest. Those who regard β-iron as a definite allotrope, regard the A$_3$-arrest as the temp. or range of temp. within which γ-iron passes into β-iron, and the line where β-ferrite is liberated from the solid soln. of carbon in iron. The separation of β-iron continues down to the A$_1$-arrest. As the proportion of carbon increases, the A$_3$- and A$_2$-arrests merge into the A$_1$-arrest. The abrupt changes in physical properties which occur when the cooling alloy passes through the A$_3$-arrest become less marked as the proportion of carbon increases. The solvent power of the alloy for carbon is also reduced on cooling through this range of temp.

The A$_2$-point.—On passing the A$_2$-arrest, iron or steel with less than 0·35 per cent. of carbon suffers a transformation of α- to β-iron at about 768°. F. Osmond thought that α- and β-iron are isomorphous ; this is true if they are two distinct chemical individuals. In spite of the changes which occur in the physical properties as it passes through the A$_2$-arrest, it is generally held that no new allotrope is formed. The crystalline structure of the β-form is the same as that of the α-form. In any case, the A$_2$-arrest represents the temp. of magnetic transformation where ferromagnetic α-iron changes into paramagnetic α-iron on the heating curve, or conversely, on the cooling curve. The term paramagnetic α-iron is here used in place of β-iron— *vide supra*. The solvent power of iron for carbon is also reduced on passing through this range of temp.

The A$_{3,2}$-arrest.—The Ar$_3$-arrest merges into the Ar$_2$-arrest with steels containing between 0·35 and 0·85 per cent. of carbon. R. H. Harrington and W. H. Wood found that the merging of the A$_3$- and A$_2$-arrests occurs at 744° when the steel has 0·60 per cent. of carbon. The A$_{3,2}$-arrest marks the beginning of the liberation of iron which continues between the Ar$_{3,2}$- and the Ar$_1$-arrest, and it also marks the passage of iron from the β- to the alleged α-state, or directly from the γ- to the α-state. The changes as the alloy cools past the A$_{3,2}$-arrest are similar to those taking place with lower carbon steel at A$_3$- and the A$_2$-arrests, namely, liberation of α-ferrite, a change in the thermal expansion, in the tensile strength, sp. ht., electrical resistance, and magnetic susceptibility. There is also a loss in the solvent power for carbon.

The A$_1$-point.—H. M .Howe discussed the position of the A$_1$-arrest with carbon steel in a state of equilibrium. The recorded data vary from 700° to 731°, and he considered that the most reliable results fall between 715° and 723°. He gave 723° for the best representative value. S. W. J. Smith and J. Guild gave 735° for the Ac$_1$-arrest, and added that the value is the same for all steels. A. Hultgren said that the transformation which occurs in the Ac$_1$-range is influenced by (i) the presence of alloy elements ; (ii) the heterogeneity which occurs on solidification ;

and (iii) the slow rate of diffusion of carbon, and possibly other elements, present in the austenite. The arrest at about 723° occurs with hypoeutectoidal steels, or the **A$_{3,2,1}$-point** of hypereutectoidal and eutectoidal steels corresponds with the fairly sudden and spontaneous transformation of the residual solid soln. of austenite of eutectoidal composition into pearlite. The A$_1$-arrest is not generally associated with critical variations of the electrical, magnetic, and other properties of the alloy. On passing the A$_{3,2,1}$-arrest there is a marked thermal expansion which is a maximum with eutectoidal steel, a sudden decrease in electrical resistance, a sudden gain of magnetization, a loss in solvent power for carbon, and a temporary gain in malleability. The Ar_{cm}-*arrest* with hypereutectoidal steels indicates the beginning of the separation of cementite along the ES-line of the equilibrium diagram; and the Ar_G-arrest, the beginning of the separation of graphite along the $E'S'$-line. The PK-line in the equilibrium diagram is horizontal, but observations generally show an upward slope corresponding with a rise of 20°. This is thought to be an effect of silicon, which is usually present as an impurity and which is known to raise this point—whilst it is lowered by manganese. K. Tamaru showed that at this temp. a-iron has its greatest solvent power for carbon, for it dissolves 0·034 per cent. At this temp. γ-iron can dissolve 0·9 per cent. of carbon. K. Honda observed that with the rapid cooling of high-carbon steels through the A$_1$-arrest, the transformation occurs in two stages : (i) the conversion of γ- to a-iron ; and (ii) the separation of carbon from a supersaturated soln. in a-iron. The latter stage can be suppressed by sufficiently rapid cooling—*vide infra*. S. Konno, A. Hayes and W. J. Diederichs, J. A. Jones, and T. Murakami studied the effect of the rate of cooling, etc., on the A$_1$-arrest. B. Kjerrman found that in the absence of manganese, or other alloying element, the Ac$_1$-arrest occurred at a definite temp. or over a very small range. Anomalies were attributed to the presence of non-metallic inclusions—thus, manganese depressed the beginning of the pearlite interval, and widened the range ; silicon raised the interval and extended it. In a silicon manganese steel the interval was doubled. Heat treatment tending towards homogeneity of structure reduced the range caused by manganese, but did not affect the range caused by silicon. The effect of these two elements is explained on the assumption that at the same temp. manganese is more and silicon is less soluble in austenite than in ferrite. Phosphorus behaves like silicon.

The A$_0$-point.—This arrest does not occur with iron alone ; but it resembles in many respects the A$_2$-transformation with iron alone. It begins at 215° to 200° on the cooling curve and extends 50° to 60° downwards. It ends at 215° on the heating curve. Heat is evolved on cooling and absorbed on heating through this point. Above 205° cementite is paramagnetic. The A$_0$-arrest represents the beginning of the transformation of cementite from a paramagnetic to a ferromagnetic state, or conversely, S. Curie showed that this reversible transformation occurs at about 200° in iron-carbon alloys. No change was observed by F. Wever in the space-lattice of the crystals as the alloy passes through this critical temp. This A$_0$-arrest was observed by S. Wologdine, and studied by P. Dejean, S. W. J. Smith and J. Guild, P. Chevenard, and K. Honda and H. Takagi, who placed it at 210°, while T. Ishiwara, and I. Iitaka placed it at 215°. M. G. Morris and H. Scott found changes occurring in the sp. ht. in pearlitic and in high-carbon steels at this temp. The actual point depended on the rate of heating and the carbon content, both of which raised the thermal point; the Ac$_2$-arrest occurred at 191° to 207°, and the Ar$_0$-arrest, at 199° to 205°. I. Iitaka observed that with the electrical resistance, singularities occurred corresponding with the Ac$_0$-arrest at 195° to 212°, and the Ar$_0$-arrest at 192° to 200°. G. Tammann and K. Ewig found that the A$_0$-arrest occurs at room temp. when 0·5 per cent. of boron or 10 per cent. of manganese is present. Both these substances dissolve in the carbide, whereas substances like gold which dissolve in iron alone, but not in the carbide, do not affect the A$_0$-arrest of steels—*vide infra*, cementite. K. Tamaru found that the magnitude of the A_2-transformation, when observed magnetically, depends on the form of the cementite.

Other critical temperatures.—Quite a number of observers have reported critical changes in different physical properties of iron at temp. below 400°. For example, G. Borelius and F. Gunneson,[2] and G. Belloc observed critical temp. in the rate of removal of occluded hydrogen and nitrogen ; and W. C. Roberts-Austen noted an anomaly due to the presence of hydrogen ; J. H. Andrew and co-workers observed thermal changes at 60° to 150° ; and H. C. H. Carpenter and B. F. E. Keeling, an anomaly at 616°. G. Sirovich showed that at about 370° the A_0-arrest corresponds with a polymorphic transformation of a_1-iron ; a_1-Fe $\rightleftharpoons a_2$-Fe. Both forms of a-iron have a characteristic coefficient of expansion. The Bureau of Standards could not verify G. Sirovich's deductions other than to show that the X-radiograms indicated that near 370° there is a recrystallization of some amorphous metal ; and H. S. Rawdon and co-workers attributed the effect to the reducing action of hydrogen on the contained iron oxide, and the recrystallization of the fine-grained iron so obtained. As indicated below, there is a minimum in the torsional elastic limit at about 370°, and a peak in the electrical conductivity curves at about 350°. B. D. Enlund, G. E. Svedelius, P. Chévenard, T. Matsushita and K. Nagasawa, G. Charpy and L. Grenet, C. Grard, K. Honda, and K. Tamaru observed changes in the sp. vol. or sp. gr. at about 130° and about 280° ; J. H. Andrew and co-workers observed an expansion at 60° to 150°. F. Robin reported singular points in the hardness at 100° and 250° ; F. Fettweiss, and K. Tamaru, at about 600°. E. G. Herbert, D. Smith, and I. Hey, and S. S. Vanick and T. H. Wickenden observed critical points in the work-hardening of iron at different temp., and in the annealing temp. and hardness curves. M. Ishimoto measured the viscosity or internal friction of iron from the damping of vibrations at different temp., and found a minimum in the curve at 65°, a maximum at 170° to 183°, and a break at 260°. The hardness curves were found to be parallel with those of the internal fraction. C. E. Guye and S. Mintz found singularities in the viscosity of wires at 180° and 240° ; G. Wertheim, in the velocity of sound in wires at 100° ; and G. Chrystal, and F. Robin, in the acoustic properties at 120° and 250°. F. Robin suggested that the singularity in the acoustic tests of iron between 100° and 250° shows that a-iron really exists in two forms, a_1-iron and a_2-iron. As indicated above, the A_2-arrest sometimes shows a double peak on the curve. The cause is not clear. It is not to be confused with the splitting of the A_1-arrest discussed later. M. le Blant observed discontinuities in the tensile elastic limit at 100°, and between 250° and 300°—though F. Robin does not think this test of much importance, but he concluded that, in general, static stresses indicate a point of transformation between 100° and 250°, and dynamic stresses, between 300° and 450° ; F. C. Lea and O. H. Crowther, in the maximum tensile strength and yield point at 300° ; F. C. Lea, in the tensile strength of armco iron since there is a maximum at 230°, and in the elongation there is a maximum at 350° and a minimum in the tensile elastic limit at 230° ; and in mild steel, in the torsional rigidity modulus at 120° and 230°. O. Reinhold, H. J. French, Z. Jeffries, K. Honda, and T. Inokuty also observed a maximum between 200° and 300°. A. Goffey and F. C. Thompson found critical points in the torsional elastic limit at 70°, 120°, 170°, 230°, 290°, and 310° and 350°. E. L. Dupuy found that a maximum in the tensile strength occurs at 250° and a minimum in the reduction of area at 250° with 0·15 per cent. carbon steels, but this rises to 330° with 0·91 and 1·25 per cent. carbon—but in these two high-carbon steels no minimum was observed in the reduction of area ; G. Charpy, R. H. Greaves and J. A. Jones, and L. Guillet and L. P. M. Revillon noted one in the notched-bar brittleness at 100° to 150°.

K. Honda, and K. Honda and H. Takagi observed a thermal change between 130° and 215°, and between 220° and 280° ; K. Gebhard and co-workers, a break at 860° ; A. Perrier and F. Wolfers observed a break in the heating curve at 113° ;

and H. G. Movius and H. Scott, at 120°, 140°, 160°, and 200°; C. Benedicks observed a break in the thermal expansion curve at 830°; and he thought that this supported the singularity observed by P. Weiss and G. Foëx in the magnetic curves (q.v.). F. C. Thompson, J. H. Andrews and co-workers observed an expansion between 60° and 150°; and R. Ariano, A. Nouel, F. Robin, G. Sirovich, and J. Driesen also observed breaks in the expansion curve. The results were criticized by F. Rapatz, and H. S. Rawdon and co-workers. A. Perrier and F. Wolfers, and J. Maydel found many irregularities in the heat capacity curves —e.g. one at 800° and one at 1100°; J. A. Harker, and J. Pionchon, in the sp. ht. at 320°; P. Oberhoffer, at 320°; W. H. Dearden, at 115°; N. Stücker, at 200°, 250°, and 300°; and E. H. and E. Griffiths, at 66°.

P. Saldau observed breaks in the electrical resistance curves. W. Broniewsky found a slight bend in the electrical resistance curve at 850°, as well as at 750° and at 950°. B. D. Enlund, in the electrical resistance at about 100° and 250°; K. Honda, at about 130° and 280°; and J. H. Andrew and co-workers, between 60° and 150°; F. C. Thompson and E. Whitehead, in the electrical resistance and thermoelectric force against platinum at 55°, 100°, 120°, 140°, 220°, 245°, etc.; A. Goffey and F. C. Thompson, in the electrical resistance at 70°, 120°, 170°, 230°, 290°, 310°, and 350°; G. Borelius and F. Gunneson, G. Borelius, G. Belloc, and W. Heræus, in the thermoelectric force (q.v.); D. K. Morris, in the magnetic properties at 150°; K. Honda, at about 130° and 280°; W. H. Dearden and C. Benedicks, at 120°; J. H. Andrew and co-workers, between 50° and 150°; C. Maurain, at 180° and 300°; and S. R. Roget, at 135°; F. C. Thompson, at 830°; and S. W. J. Smith, and K. Honda and H. Takagi, in the magnetic permeability of white and grey cast iron and high-carbon steel—a change commenced at about 160° and was completed at 215° on heating, and on cooling it started at 215° and finished at 160°; the magnitude of the change was roughly proportional to the percentage of free cementite; the temp. of 160° varied with the strength of the magnetizing field. R. Forrer and J. Schneider observed that the forms of iron produced by annealing the quenched metal at 200° to 400°, and at 450° to 900°, have different magnetic properties, and he accordingly supposed that iron exists in two forms, both stable at ordinary temp.

The cause of these low temp. changes is unknown; C. Benedicks, and Z. Jeffries suggested that they are due to allotropic transformations, although C. Benedicks showed that a definite temp. may not be necessary for one element to change into another, and he assumed that an allotropic change begins at about 100° and extends up to about 400°. It is, however, not clear whether a number of distinct changes occur, or whether the phenomena are the result of one long continuous process. Changes at 160° and 200° are due to the carbide or cementite, because they are not present when carbide is absent—vide supra. The magnetic transformations are discussed in connection with magnetism—vide infra. K. Honda attributed the change at about 130° to the decomposition of martensite whereby cementite is precipitated, but later showed that it is more probably due to the change of α- into β-martensite; the precipitation of cementite from martensite occurs between 220° and 280°. A satisfactory explanation for the other singular points on the curves is not known; some of the singularities are due to secondary actions—vide supra for effects due to occluded gases.

G. Borelius and F. Gunneson obtained such a number of singular points that they arranged them in groups about a central one—e.g. the Z-changes included the singularities $Z_3, Z_4, Z_5, \ldots$ They considered that there is a periodicity about these points, and they give an expression connecting the temp., T, with the numerical suffix, n, of the point; thus, for iron, $T_n = 97_n$, where n ranges from 3 to 12. It is assumed that the Z-changes occur when the number of atoms, r^{-1}, bearing a number of energy quanta equal to or greater than the numerical suffix of the change, n, is one-fourth of the total. When one-fourth the atoms have their respective number of quanta increased by one, a Z-change occurs. The hypothesis is arbitrary, and is not based on known facts. G. Auchy attempted to explain the different properties of the iron-carbon alloys on the assumption that different ferrated carbides are involved in the various states.

A. Goffey and F. C. Thompson consider that the changes are intra- not inter-atomic or inter-molecular; and that they are produced by alterations in the arrangements or movement of the electrons about the positive nucleus of the atom, and are closely connected with the characteristic vibration frequency of the atom. Indeed, it can be shown that a decrease in the frequency of vibration of the iron atom in the neighbourhood of 300° can bring about (i) an abrupt rise in the electrical resistance, (ii) a fall in the bulk and rigidity modulus, and (iii) an abrupt rise in the sp. ht. at constant vol. If the effects are due to changes in the structure of the iron atom, it follows that the iron atom must be in a very unstable state. The magnetic property of iron may be due to a peculiar electronic arrangement which is very unstable with respect to changes of temp.

REFERENCES.

[1] J. L. Proust, *Journ. Phys.*, **68**. 463, 1806; *Nicholson's Journ.*, **17**. 185, 1807; A. Matthiessen, *B.A. Rep.*, 37, 1863; A. Stansfield, *Trans. Amer. Inst. Min. Eng.*, **47**. 649, 721, 1913; *Eng. Min. Journ.*, **75**. 360, 1902; *Metallographist*, **3**. 24, 300, 1900; *Journ. Iron Steel Inst.*, **56**. ii, 169, 1899; **58**. ii, 317, 1900; H. W. B. Roozeboom, *Berg. Hütt. Ztg.*, **63**. 317, 1904; *Eng.*, **97**. 583, 1904; *Journ. Iron Steel Inst.*, **58**. ii, 311, 1900; **59**. i, 229, 1901; *Metallographist*, **3**. 293, 1900; *Bull. Soc. Enc. Nat. Ind.*, (5), **6**. 609, 1900; *Zeit. Elektrochem.*, **10**. 489, 1904; *Zeit. phys. Chem.*, **30**. 385, 1899; **34**. 437, 1900; H. von Jüptner, *Journ. Iron Steel Inst.*, **53**. i, 235, 1897; **54**. ii, 243, 1898; **55**. i, 204, 1899; **57**. i, 219, 1900; **58**. ii, 334, 1900; **59**. i, 229, 1901; **75**. iii, 59, 1907; *Oester. Zeit. Berg. Hütt.*, **44**. 211, 447, 1896; **48**. 15, 29, 46, 56, 72, 86, 1900; *Metallo-graphist*, **5**. 210, 1902; *Kohlenstoffformen in Eisen*, Stuttgart, 1896; *Stahl Eisen*, **19**. 23, 237, 278, 1899; **20**. 1205, 1269, 1900; **21**. 795, 1901; H. C. H. Carpenter and B. F. E. Keeling, *ib.*, **65**. i, 224, 1904; H. C. H. Carpenter, *Trans. Inst. Naval Arch.*, **60**. 83, 1918; *Journ. Iron Steel Inst.*, **67**. i, 433, 1905; E. H. Saniter, *ib.*, **53**. ii, 115, 1897; A. Hague and T. Turner, *ib.*, **82**. ii, 72, 1910; R. A. Hadfield, *ib.*, **47**. i, 156, 1894; E. J. Ball, *ib.*, **37**. i, 85, 1890; R. B. Fehr, *ib.*, **95**. i, 203, 1917; C. H. Ridsdale, *ib.*, **56**. ii, 102, 1899; W. Köster, *Zeit. Metallkunde*, **22**. 289, 1930; B. Pawlewsky, *Chem. Ztg.*, **23**. 68, 1899; W. H. Hatfield, *Cast Iron in the Light of Recent Research*, London, 43, 1912; *Trans. Faraday Soc.*, **21**. 272, 1925; *Mech. Eng.*, **26**. 818, 1910; **33**. 260, 1914; *Proc. Roy. Soc.*, **85**. A, 1, 1911; *Proc. Cleveland Inst. Eng.*, 135, 1916; *Journ. Iron Steel Inst.*, **70**. ii, 157, 1906; G. P. Royston, *ib.*, **52**. ii, 166, 1897; N. Tschieschewsky and N. Schulgin, *ib.*, **95**. i, 189, 1917; H. C. Sorby, *ib.*, **29**. i, 140, 1886; **33**. i, 255, 1888; *B.A. Rep.*, 189, 1864; 139, 1865; G. B. Upton, *Journ. Phys. Chem.*, **12**. 507, 1908; E. Heyn, *Journ. Iron Steel Inst.*, **67**. i, 50, 1905; *Eng.*, **95**. 609, 1903; *Die Theorie der Eisen-Kohlenstoff-Legierungen*, Berlin, 1923; *Mitt. Verb. Materialprüfung*, (1), **24**. 29, 1906; (2), **2**. 1, 1912; *Zeit. Elektrochem.*, **10**. 491, 1904; E. Heyn and O. Bauer, *Stahl Eisen*, **27**. 1565, 1907; F. Wüst and P. Schlösser, *ib.*, **24**. 1120, 1904; F. Wüst, *Wüllner's Festschrift*, 240, 1905; *Met.*, **3**. i, 757, 1906; **5**. 86, 1908; **6**. 512, 1909; *Zeit. Elektrochem.*, **15**. 577, 965, 1909; F. Wüst and O. Petersen, *Met.*, **3**. 811, 1906; H. Hanemann, *Zeit. anorg. Chem.*, **84**. 1, 1913; **90**. 67, 1914; *Stahl Eisen*, **31**. 333, 1911; **47**. 693, 1927; **51**. 647, 1931; *Arch. Eisenhüttenwesen*, **4**. 647, 1931; H. Hanemann and A. Schrader, *Trans. Amer. Soc. Steel Treating*, **9**. 169, 1926; *Stahl Eisen*, **51**. 645, 1931; *Arch. Eisenhüttenwesen*, **4**. 475, 1931; H. Hanemann, K. Herrmann, V. Hofmann and A. Schrader, *ib.*, **4**. 479, 1931; *Stahl Eisen*, **51**. 646, 1931; E. Schulz, *ib.*, **45**. 144, 1925; A. von Vegesack, *ib.*, **45**. 458, 1925; K. Fischbeck, *ib.*, **44**. 714, 1924; N. J. Wark, *Met.*, **8**. 704, 731, 1911; G. S. Scott, *Journ. Iron Steel Inst.*, **75**. iii, 120, 1907; *Stahl Eisen*, **27**. 1435, 1907; B. Osann, *ib.*, **27**. 1491, 1529, 1907; **34**. 183, 1914; R. Horny, *ib.*, **24**. 744, 1924; **45**. 22, 1925; *Ueber das System Eisenkarbid, Eisen, und Temperkohle bzw. Graphit*, Brünn, 1924; R. Horny and A. von Lissner, *Stahl Eisen*, **45**. 1297, 1925; C. Benedicks, *Recherches physiques et physico-chimiques sur l'acier au carbone*, Upsala, 1904; *Journ. Iron Steel Inst.*, **89**. i, 434, 1914; *Nature*, **115**. 230, 1924; *Zeit. phys. Chem.*, **40**. 545, 1902; **52**. 733, 1905; *Met.*, **3**. 470, 1906; **5**. 41, 1908; P. Goerens and P. Saldau, *Stahl Eisen*, **38**. 15, 1918; *Rev. Mét.*, **14**. 65, 1917; *Journ. Russ. Met. Soc.*, 789, 1914; P. Goerens and H. Meyer, *Met.*, **7**. 307, 1910; P. Goerens, *Mitt. Eisenhütt. Inst. Aachen*, **2**. 138, 1908; *Stahl Eisen*, **45**. 137, 1925; **34**. 282, 1914; *Met.*, **3**. 175, 1906; **4**. 137, 173, 1907; *Zeit. Elektrochem.*, **15**. 617, 1909; *Ferrum*, **11**. 226, 1913; P. Goerens and N. Gutowsky, *ib.*, **5**. 145, 1908; N. Gutowsky, *Zur Theorie des Schmelz- und Erstarrungs-prozesses der Eisen Kohlenstoff legierungen*, Halle a. S., 1910; *Ferrum*, **6**. 731, 737, 1909; R. Ruer and R. Klesper, *ib.*, **11**. 257, 1914; R. Ruer and F. Goerens, *ib.*, **13**. 1, 1915; **14**. 161, 1917; *Stahl Eisen*, **38**. 422, 1918; **39**. 1883, 1919; **46**. 918, 1926; R. Ruer and J. Biren, *Zeit. anorg. Chem.*, **113**. 98, 1920; R. Ruer and N. Iljin, *Met.*, **8**. 97, 1911; R. Ruer, *Stahl Eisen*, **46**. 918, 1928; **50**. 1062, 1930; *Zeit. anorg. Chem.*, **117**. 249, 1921; G. Tammann and K. Ewig, *ib.*, **167**.

385, 1927 ; E. Scheil, *ib.*, **139**. 81, 1924 ; **158**. 175, 1926 ; *Giesserei*, **15**. 1086, 1928 ; P. Bardenheuer and K. L. Zeyen, *Giesserei*, **15**. 354, 385, 1928 ; P. Bardenheuer, *Stahl Eisen*, **40**. 1141, 1920 ; **47**. 857, 1927 ; *Mitt. Inst. Eisenforsch.*, **9**. 215, 1927 ; *Ferrum*, **14**. 129, 145, 1917 ; **15**. 219, 1917 ; M. Levin and H. Schottsky, *ib.*, **10**. 193, 1912 ; A. Meuthen, *ib.*, **10**. 1, 1912 ; J. Driesen, *ib.*, **12**. 130, 1914 ; **14**. 27, 1916 ; G. Rümelin and R. Maire, *ib.*, **13**. 153, 1915 ; P. D. Merica, *Bull. Bur. Standards*, 129, 1919 ; H. M. Howe and A. S. Levy, *Trans. Amer. Inst. Min. Eng.*, **47**. `587, 1913 ; *Proc. Internat. Assoc. Testing Materials*, **6**. ii, 4, 1912 ; H. M. Howe, *Met.*, **6**. 65, 1909 ; *Eng. Min. Journ.*, **75**. 144, 588, 1903 ; **83**. 1087, 1907 ; *Trans. Amer. Inst. Min. Eng.*, **22**. 461, 1898 ; **31**. 318, 1901 ; **39**. 3, 1908 ; B. Stoughton, *ib.*, **46**. 478, 1913 ; G. K. Burgess, J. J. Crowe and H. S. Rawdon, *ib.*, **47**. 605, 1913 ; L. Grenet, *Compt. Rend.*, **175**. 1067, 1922 ; *Aciers Spéciaux*, **6**. 2, 1931 ; G. Charpy and L. Grenet, *Rev. Mét.*, **24**. 93, 1927 ; *Engg.*, **73**. 626, 1902 ; *Bull. Enc. Soc. Nat. Ind.*, **102**. 399, 1902 ; G. Charpy, *Rev. Mét.*, **5**. 75, 77, 1908 ; **6**. 983, 1909 ; *Compt. Rend.*, **141**. 948, 1905 ; **145**. 1277, 1907 ; **148**. 1707, 1909 ; G. Charpy and A. Cornu-Thénard, *ib.*, **157**. 319, 1913 ; A. Ledebur, *ib.*, **145**. 1173, 1907 ; R. Forrer and J. Schneider, *ib.*, **190**. 1391, 1930 ; P. Chevenard, **164**. 1005, 1917 ; S. Wologdine, *ib.*, **148**. 776, 1909 ; A. M. Portevin, *Rev. Mét.*, **4**. 915, 993, 1907 ; *Bull. Soc. Ing. Civils*, 806, 1913 ; *L'étude de la structure des métaux et alliages et ses conséquences*, Paris, 1921 ; *Journ. Iron Steel Inst.*, **108**. ii, 93, 1923 ; F. Osmond and J. Werth, *Compt. Rend.*, **100**. 450, 1885 ; *Ann. Mines*, (8), **8**. 5, 1885 ; F. Osmond, *Transformations du fer et du carbone dans les fers, les aciers, et fontes blanches*, Paris, 1888 ; *Journ. Iron Steel Inst.*, **37**. i, 38, 1890 ; *Compt. Rend.*, **100**. 1228, 1885 ; *Ann. Mines*, (8), **14**. 1, 1888 ; *Contribution à l'étude des alliages*, Paris, 277, 1901 ; *Metallographist*, **1**. 266, 1898 ; **2**. 136, 1899 ; **3**. 181, 1900 ; **4**. 150, 1901 ; F. Osmond and G. Cartaud, *Journ. Iron Steel Inst.*, **71**. iii, 444, 1906 ; H. le Chatelier, *Metallographist*, **3**. 290, 1900 ; **4**. 161, 1901 ; *Rev. Mét.*, **8**. 319, 1911 ; *Trans. Amer. Inst. Min. Eng.*, **47**. 27, 1913 ; *Bull. Soc. Enc. Nat. Ind.*, (5), **5**. 118, 1900 ; E. L. Dupuy, *Rev. Mét.*, **27**. 686, 1930 ; P. Curie, *Ann. Chim. Phys.*, (7), **5**. 289, 1895 ; *Propriétés magnétiques des corps à diverses températures*, Paris, 1895 ; W. C. Roberts-Austen, *Proc. Inst. Mech. Eng.*, 70, 90, 1897 ; 169, 1899 ; *Proc. Roy. Soc.*, **63**. 447, 1898 ; J. E. Stead, *B.A. Rep.*, 549, 1910 ; *Ferrum*, **12**. 25, 1914 ; *Trans. Northeast-Coast Inst. Eng. Shipbuilders*, **29**. 141, 1913 ; E. A. Sperry, *Chem. Met. Engg.*, **13**. 469, 1915 ; M. G. Morris and H. Scott, *ib.*, **22**. 1069, 1920 ; D. M. Levy, *ib.*, **8**. 531, 1910 ; *Journ. Iron Steel Inst.*, **81**. i, 403, 1910 ; G. Cesaro, *ib.*, **99**. i, 447, 1919 ; N. M. von Wittorf, *Zeit. anorg. Chem.*, **79**. 1, 1913 ; *Rev. Mét.*, **9**. 600, 1912 ; *Journ. Russ. Phys. Chem. Soc.*, **43**. 1613, 1911 ; N. N. Ljubavin, *ib.*, **44**. 609, 1912 ; S. Hilpert, *Zeit. Elektrochem.*, **16**. 390, 1910 ; J. E. Hurst, *Proc. Staffs Iron Steel Inst.*, **33**. 26, 1917 ; *Journ. Iron Steel Inst.*, **96**. ii, 121, 1917 ; **98**. ii, 199, 1918 ; *Engg.*, **106**. 217, 1918 ; **108**. 1, 1919 ; *Metallurgy of Cast Iron*, London, 47, 1926 ; (I am indebted to the Publishers for permission to use Fig. 82) ; *Eng.*, **122**. 549, 1916 ; *Foundry Trade Journ.*, **17**. 368, 1915 ; **31**. 326, 353, 1925 ; E. Adamson, *ib.*, **19**. 73, 140, 1917 ; *Journ. Brit. Foundrymen's Assoc.*, **12**. 223, 1917 ; J. Shaw, *ib.*, **12**. 20, 1917 ; W. J. Foster, *Journ. West Scotland Iron Steel Inst.*, **18**. 96, 1911 ; J. H. Andrew, *Journ. Tech. Coll. Glasgow*, **1**. 41, 1924 ; *Proc. Cleveland Inst. Eng.*, 99, 1926 ; *Journ. Iron Steel Inst.—Carnegie Mem.*, **3**. 236, 1911 ; **7**. 1, 1916 ; A. Bramley and F. W. Haywood, *ib.*, **17**. 67, 1928 ; W. Gontermann, *Journ. Iron Steel Inst.*, **83**. i, 421, 1911 ; *Zeit. anorg. Chem.*, **59**. 373, 1908 ; C. A. Edwards, *Journ. Inst. Metals*, **6**, 259, 1912 ; *Journ. Iron Steel Inst.*, **82**. ii, 147, 1910 ; *The Physicochemical Properties of Steel*, London, 48, 1916 ; O. Ruff and O. Goecke, *Met.*, **8**. 417, 1911 ; *Zeit. anorg. Chem.*, **84**. 1, 1914 ; *Met.*, **8**. 417, 1911 ; O. Ruff, *ib.*, **8**. 456, 497, 1911 ; *Ferrum*, **12**. 121, 1915 ; *Zeit. angew. Chem.*, **24**. 1134, 1911 ; *Zeit. anorg. Chem.*, **89**. 39, 1914 ; *Ber.*, **45**. 3143, 1912 ; *Zeit. Elektrochem.*, **18**. 761, 1912 ; **19**. 133, 1913 ; O. Ruff and W. Bormann, *Ferrum*, **12**. 124, 1915 ; *Zeit. anorg. Chem.*, **88**. 397, 1914 ; O. Ruff, W. Bormann and F. Keilig, *Ueber das Verhalten von Kohlenstoff gegen Mangan, Nickel, Eisen, und Kobalt*, Berlin, 1918 ; O. C. Ralston, *Iron Oxide Reduction Equilibria*, Washington, 1929 ; *Bull. U.S. Bur. Mines*, 296, 1928 ; E. Piwowarsky, *Trans. Amer. Foundrymen's Assoc.*, **34**. 914, 1926 ; A. L. Norbury, *Foundry Trade Journ.*, **41**. 79, 1929 ; *Journ. Iron Steel Inst.*, **119**. i, 443, 1929 ; J. A. Jones, *ib.*, **107**. i, 439, 1923 ; H. I. Coe, *ib.*, **87**. i, 361, 1913 ; T. Baker, *ib.*, **64**. ii, 312, 1903 ; E. Schüz, *Bull. Assoc. Tech. Fonderie*, 376, 1927 ; C. Irresberger, *Foundry Trade Journ.*, **34**. 184, 1926 ; E. Gumlich, *Wiss. Abh. Phys. Tech. Reichsanst*, **4**. 271, 330, 1918 ; J. O. Arnold, *Engg.*, **75**. 256, 1902 ; *Internat. Zeit. Metallog.*, **1**. 192, 1911 ; *Proc. Inst. Civil Eng.*, **123**. 127, 1896 ; **138**. 129, 1899 ; *B.A. Rep.*, 562, 1910 ; J. O. Arnold and L. Aitchison, *Journ. Iron Steel Inst.*, **85**. i, 235, 1912 ; B. H. Brough, *Eng. Min. Journ.*, **75**. 323, 1902 ; A. Sanfourche, *Rev. Mét.*, **16**. 217, 1922 ; O. E. Harder and F. Gonzalez, *Rev. Quim.*, **6**. 21, 1930 ; L. J. Weber and T. E. Jerabek, *Trans. Amer. Soc. Steel Treating*, **13**. 961, 1928 ; O. E. Harder and W. S. Johnson, *ib.*, **15**. 49, 1929 ; A. Hultgren, *ib.*, **16**. 227, 1929 ; B. Kjerrman, *ib.*, **9**. 430, 1926 ; H. W. Gillett, *Metals Alloys*, **1**. 237, 1929 ; S. Epstein, *ib.*, **1**. 559, 1930 ; E. Scheil and E. H. Schulz, *Zeit. anorg. Chem.*, **188**. 290, 1930 ; F. Yamada, *Tetsu-to-Hagané*, **15**. 184, 1929 ; A. Merz, *Arch. Eisenhüttenwesen*, **3**. 587, 1929 ; *Stahl Eisen*, **50**. 518, 1930 ; F. Stählein, *ib.*, **46**. 101, 1926 ; H. Esser, *ib.*, **47**. 337, 1927 ; K. Schichtel and E. Piwowarsky, *ib.*, **3**. 139, 1929 ; O. W. Ellis, *Metals Alloys*, **1**. 462, 1930 ; A. I. Krynitsky, *ib.*, **1**. 465, 1930 ; R. L. Dowdell, *ib.*, **1**. 515, 1930 ; J. Parry, *Nature*, **46**. 283, 1892 ; *Journ. Iron Steel Inst.*, **46**. ii, 469, 1894 ; *Proc. South Wales Inst. Eng.*, 19. 132, 1895 ; S. Konobejewsky, *Zeit. Kryst.*, **72**. 381, 1929 ; T. K. Rose, *Journ. Soc. Arts*, **49**. 846, 1901 ; J. A. Mathews, *Eng. Min. Journ.*, **72**. 819, 851, 1901 ; *Journ. Franklin Inst.*, **153**. 1, 119, 221, 1901 ; L. Northcott, *Proc. Inst. Brit. Foundrymen*, **17**. 94, 1924 ; *Foundry Trade Journ.*, **29**. 515, 548, 1924 ; W. Ostwald, *Lehrbuch der allgemeinen*

Chemie, Leipzig, **2.** ii, 444, 1902 ; T. D. Yensen, *Bull. Illinois Univ. Eng. Exp. Station*, 83, 1915 ; *Trans. Amer. Inst. Min. Eng.*, **77.** 320, 1929 ; *Science Paper Westinghouse*, 184, 1925 ; *Science*, (2), **68**, 376, 1928 ; *Chem. Met. Engg.*, **14.** 583, 1916 ; *Journ. Amer. Inst. Elect. Eng.*, **43**. 455, 1924 ; H. Scott, *ib.*, **43.** 1066, 1924 ; *Chem. Met. Engg.*, **27.** 1156, 1922 ; J. E. Johnson, *ib.*, **15**. 530, 588, 642, 1916 ; *Trans. Amer. Inst. Min. Eng.*, **47**. 267, 1914 ; W. Guertler, *Chem. Ztg.*, **31.** 495, 514, 1907 ; *Metallographie*, Berlin, **1.** ii, 175, 1913 ; *Stahl Eisen*, **34.** 520, 751, 1914 ; S. Tamura, *Journ. Iron Steel Inst.*, **115.** i, 750, 1927 ; G. J. Snelus, *ib.*, **37**. i, 91, 1890 ; A. Sauveur and V. N. Krivobok, *ib.*, **112.** ii, 313, 1925 ; A. Sauveur, *Eng. Min. Journ.*, **75**. 426, 1902 ; *The Metallography and Heat Treatment of Iron and Steel*, Cambridge, Mass., 1926 ; *Iron Trade Rev.*, **45.** 1053, 1909 ; *Trans. Amer. Inst. Min. Eng.*, **47**. 704, 1913 ; *Journ. Iron Steel Inst.*, **56.** ii, 195, 1899 ; **72.** iv, 493, 1906 ; **112.** ii, 313, 1925 ; J. H. Whiteley, *ib.*, **106.** ii, 89, 1922 ; **116.** ii, 293, 1927 ; A. F. Angerstein, *Hushällning's Journ.*, 35, 1778 ; S. Rinman, *ib.*, 38, 1778 ; A. Grabe, *En Bergsbok*, Stockholm, 263, 1921 ; D. K. Tschernoff, *Mém. Militaires*, **5.** 1, 1868 ; *Note sur la constitution et le travail de l'acier*, Paris, 1868 ; *Metallographist*, **2**. 74, 1899 ; *Proc. Inst. Mech. Eng.*, **152.** 286, 1880 ; *Rec. Univ. Mines*, (2), **1**. 396, 1868 ; K. Honda, *Journ. Iron Steel Inst.*, **105.** i, 381, 1922 ; **112.** ii, 345, 1925 ; *Nagaoka's Aniv. Vol.*, 95, 1925 ; *Trans. Amer. Soc. Steel Treating*, **16**. 183, 1929 ; *Science Rep. Tohoku Univ.*, **4**. 169, 1915 ; **5.** 285, 1916 ; **6.** 213, 1917 ; **8.** 181, 1919 ; **9.** 119, 1922 ; **11.** 105, 119, 487, 1922 ; **13.** 1, 1925 ; **14.** 165, 1925 ; **15.** 247, 1926 ; T. Ishiwara, *ib.*, **9.** 401, 1920 ; K. Honda and H. Takagi, *ib.*, **1.** 229, 1912 ; **2.** 203, 1913 ; K. Honda and H. Endo, *Kinzoku no Kenkyu*, **3**. 176, 1926 ; *Zeit. anorg. Chem.*, **154**. 238, 1926 ; *Science Rep. Tohoku Univ.*, **16.** 9, 1927 ; M. Hamasumi, *ib.*, **13**. 133, 1924 ; *Foundry Trade Journ.*, **32**. 71, 1925 ; I. Iitaka, *Science Rep. Tohoku Univ.*, **7**. 167, 1918 ; Y. Yamada, *ib.*, **15**. 851, 1926 ; T. Murakami, *ib.*, **7**. 212, 1918 ; *Osaka's Sexagint*, 171, 1927 ; K. Honda and T. Murakami, *ib.*, **10.** 273, 1921 ; **12.** 257, 1924 ; *Journ. Iron Steel Inst.*, **102.** ii, 287, 1920 ; **107.** i, 545, 1923 ; K. Honda, T. Kase and Y. Matsuyama, *Kinzoku no Kenkyu*, **6.** 273, 1929 ; *Science Rep. Tohoku Univ.*, **18.** 699, 1929 ; S. Konno, *ib.*, **12.** 127, 1923 ; T. Kase, *ib.*, **19.** 1, 1930 ; S. Kaya, *ib.*, **14.** 529, 1925 ; K. Tamaru, *ib.*, **18.** 473, 1930 ; K. W. Zimmerschied, *Trans. Amer. Inst. Min. Eng.*, **47.** 651, 1913 ; R. R. Abbott, *ib.*, **47.** 461, 1913 ; A. Vinogradoff, *Proc. Russ. Met. Soc.*, **234.** 1912 ; *Rev. Mét.*, **10.** 493, 1913 ; S. W. J. Smith and J. Guild, *Phil. Trans.*, **215**. A, 177, 1915 ; *Proc. Phys. Soc.*, **24.** 342, 1912 ; **25**. 77, 1912 ; A. Linder, *Zeit. Ver. deut. Ing.*, **60.** 41, 87, 1916 ; W. Broniewsky, *Chim. Ind.*, **1.** 55, 1918 ; J. A. Holden, *Foundry Trade Journ.*, **22.** 270, 1920 ; F. J. Brislee, *ib.*, **25**. 132, 1922 ; P. Oberhoffer, K. Daeves and F. Rapatz, *Stahl Eisen*, **44**. 432, 1924 ; F. Sauerwald and A. Koreny, *ib.*, **48.** 537, 1928 ; N. H. Aall, *Diagrammes d'équilibre de transformation des aciers spéciaux*, Paris, 1921 ; E. Frasenster, *Rev. Univ. Mines*, (6), **14.** 371, 1922 ; (6), **15.** 483, 1922 ; P. Dejean, *Compt. Rend.*, **165.** 334, 429, 1917 ; S. Curie, *Bull. Soc. Enc. Nat. Ind.*, (5), **3.** 47, 1898 ; H. J. French and O. Z. Klopsch, *Trans. Amer. Soc. Steel Treating*, **6.** 251, 1924 ; E. C. Bain, *ib.*, **9.** 9, 1926 ; H. Sawamura, *Mem. Coll. Eng. Kyoto*, **4.** 89, 1926 ; K. Tawara and G. Asahara, *ib.*, **9.** 196, 1918 ; *Iron Coal Trade Rev.*, **98.** 578, 1919 ; *Journ. Iron Steel Inst.*, **99.** i, 565, 1919 ; G. Asahara, *Rikwagaku Kenkyujo Iho*, **2.** 420, 1923 ; A. M. Portevin and M. Garvin, *Iron Coal Trade Rev.*, **98.** 599, 1919 ; *Journ. Iron Steel Inst.*, **99.** i, 559, 1919 ; E. D. Campbell, W. L. Fink and A. F. Gorton, *ib.*, **108.** ii, 173, 1923 ; E. D. Campbell, *ib.*, **56.** ii, 223, 1899 ; **78.** iii, 318, 1908 ; *Trans. Faraday Soc.*, **15**. 138, 1920 ; *Proc. Nat. Acad.*, **5.** 426, 1919 ; *Journ. Amer. Chem. Soc.*, **37**. 2039, 1915 ; W. Campbell, *Iron Age*, **69.** 23, 1904 ; R. Mannesmann, *Verh. Ver. Beförd. Gewerbfl.*, **58.** 31, 1879 ; P. Oberhoffer, *Stahl Eisen*, **44.** 979, 1924 ; K. Daeves, *Zeit. anorg. Chem.*, **115**. 290, 1921 ; *Stahl Eisen*, **45.** 427, 1925 ; E. Mauer and P. Holtzhaussen, *ib.*, **47**. 1805, 1977, 1927 ; A. Westgren and G. Phragmen, *Journ. Iron Steel Inst.*, **105**. i, 249, 1922 ; *Zeit. phys. Chem.*, **102.** 1, 1922 ; G. Phragmen, *Stahl Eisen*, **45.** 299, 1925 ; *Jernkontorets Ann.*, (2), **114**. 431, 1930 ; P. D. Merica and L. J. Gurevich, *Tech. Paper Bur. Standards*, 129, 1919 ; R. S. Archer, *Trans. Amer. Inst. Min. Eng.*, **62.** 509, 1920 ; **63.** 169, 1921 ; **67**. 73, 445, 496, 1922 ; A. Philips and E. S. Davenport, *ib.*, **67.** 466, 1922 ; N. B. Pilling, *ib.*, **70.** 254, 1924 ; A. Hayes, W. J. Diederichs and W. M. Dunlap, *Trans. Amer. Soc. Steel Treating*, **3.** 624, 1923 ; A. Hayes and W. J. Diederichs, *Trans. Amer. Soc. Steel Treating*, **3.** 918, 1923 ; A. Hayes, H. E. Flanders and E. E. Moore, *ib.*, **5.** 183, 1924 ; R. H. Harrington and W. P. Wood, *ib.*, **18.** 632, 1930 ; Z. Jeffries, *Trans. Amer. Inst. Min. Eng.*, **70.** 303, 1924 ; Z. Jeffries and R. S. Archer, *Chem. Met. Engg.*, **29**. 923, 965, 1923 ; C. P. Yap, *Tech. Publ. Amer. Inst. Min. Eng.*, 381, 382, 1931 ; L. Persoz, *Aciers Spéciaux*, **4.** 69, 1929 ; R. Vogel, *Arch. Eisenhüttenwesen*, **2.** 389, 1928 ; E. Walldow, *Journ. Iron Steel Inst.*, **122.** ii, 301, 1930 ; *Jernkontorets Ann.*, (2), **114**. 377, 1930 ; A. Merz and F. Fleischer, *Giesserei*, **17**. 817, 1930 ; M. S. Fischer and J. M. Robertson, *Journ. Roy. Tech. College Met. Club*, **4**. 23, 1925 ; L. Forquignon, *Ann. Chim. Phys.*, (5), **23**. 433, 1881 ; *Compt. Rend.*, **91.** 817, 1881 ; *Recherches sur les fontes malléables et sur le recuit des aciers*, Paris, 1881 ; G. Sirovich, *Gazz. Chim. Ital.*, **53.** 674, 1923 ; *Met. Ital.*, **16.** 3, 1922 ; A. Mallock, *Nature*, **113**. 566, 1924 ; A. F. Gorton and M. M. Austin, *Trans. Amer. Inst. Min. Eng.*, **68.** 916, 1923 ; H. A. Schwartz and H. H. Johnson, *ib.*, **10.** 965, 1926 ; H. A. Schwartz, H. R. Payne and A. F. Gorton, *ib.*, **69.** 791, 1923 ; H. A. Schwartz and A. N. Hird, *ib.*, **69.** 470, 1925 ; H. A. Schwartz, *Trans. Amer. Soc. Steel Treating*, **9.** 883, 1926 ; **10.** 55, 1926 ; **11.** 277, 767, 1927 ; **19.** 403, 1932 ; H. A. Schwartz, H. H. Johnson and C. H. Junge, *ib.*, **17.** 383, 1930 ; A. A. Bates, D. E. Lawson and H. A. Schwartz, *ib.*, **18.** 659, 1930 ; H. A. Schwartz and H. R. Payne, *Journ. Iron Steel Inst.*, **58.** ii, 330, 1900 ; **61.** i, 40, 1902 ; L. Dupuy, *Bull. Soc. Enc. Nat. Ind.*, **6.** 661, 1900 ; *Compt. Rend.*, **130.** 85, 1900 ; *Rev. Mét.*, **5.** 167, 1898 ; **27.** 686, 1930 ; A. Phillips and E. S. Davenport, *Trans. Amer. Inst. Min. Eng.*, **67**. 466, 1922 ;

3 G

Z. Jeffries and R. S. Archer, *Chem. Met. Engg.*, **24**. 1057, 1921 ; A. E. White and R. S. Archer, *Foundry*, **47**. 61, 1919 ; *Trans. Amer. Foundrymen's Assoc.*, **27**. 351, 1919 ; W. R. Bean, H. W. Highriter and E. S. Davenport, *ib.*, **29**. 306, 1921 ; H. L. Maxwell and A. Hayes, *Proc. Iowa Acad.*, **31**. 284, 1924 ; *Journ. Amer. Chem. Soc.*, **48**. 584, 1926 ; A. Hayes and H. E. Flanders, *Trans. Amer. Soc. Steel Treating*, **6**. 623, 1924 ; N. Seljakoff, G. Kurdjumoff and N. Goodtzoff, *Nature*, **119**. 494, 1927 ; *Rep. Leningrad Phys. Tech. Lab.*, 73, 1926 ; *Zeit. Physik*, **45**. 384, 1927 ; F. Wever, *Naturwiss.*, **13**. 49, 1925 ; *Zeit. Elektrochem.*, **30**. 376, 1924 ; *Mitt. Inst. Eisenforschung*, **4**. 67, 1922 ; **9**. 151, 1927 ; F. Wever and P. Giani, *ib.*, **7**. 59, 1925 ; A. Logan, *Foundry Trade Journ.*, **31**. 155, 1925 ; *Metal Ind.*, **26**. 163, 189, 218, 1925 ; K. von Kerpeley, *Giesserei Ztg.*, **23**. 435, 1926 ; D. Hanson, *Eng.-Metallurgist*, Feb. 27, 1925 ; *Foundry Trade Journ.*, **36**. 277, 1927 ; **37**. 7, 1927 ; *Journ. Iron Steel Inst.*, **116**. ii, 129, 1927 ; T. F. Russell, *ib.*, **104**. ii, 463, 1921 ; H. A. Dickie, *ib.*, **120**. ii, 161, 1929 ; P. Longmuir, *ib.*, **75**. iii, 137, 1907 ; J. H. Andrew and H. A. Dickie, *ib.*, **115**. i, 647, 1927 ; J. H. Andrew and D. Binnie, *ib.*, **119**. i, 307, 1929 ; L. Gruardet, *Rev. Artillerei*, **64**. 199, 1905 ; A. Smits, *Zeit. Elektrochem.*, **18**. 51, 362, 816, 1081, 1912 ; S. W. J. Smith, W. White and S. G. Barker, *Proc. Phys. Soc.*, **24**. 62, 1911 ; T. T. Read, *Iron Steel Mag.*, **11**. 96, 1906 ; J. H. Stansbie, *Engg.*, **81**. 29, 1906 ; G. Quincke, *Verh. Naturwiss. Ver. Heidelberg*, 355, 1907 ; J. E. Storey, *Machinery*, **16**. 136, 1910 ; G. W. Sargent, *Journ. Franklin Inst.*, **169**. 253, 1910 ; G. Goldberg, *Giesserei Ztg.*, **7**. 101, 133, 1910 ; O. F. Hudson, *Proc. Staffs Iron Steel Inst.*, **26**. 64, 1911 ; A. Baykoff, *Rev. Mét.*, **8**. 315, 1911 ; N. T. Belaiew, *Russ. Economist*, **2**. 2498, 1922 ; E. Nusbaumer, *Rev. Univ. Mines*, (4), **39**. 1, 1912 ; G. Auchy, *Iron Age*, **95**. 50, 1915 ; W. Rosenhain, *Foundry Trade Journ.*, **17**. 307, 1915 ; Y. Chu-Phay, *Tech. Publ. Amer. Inst. Min. Eng.*, 381, 382, 1931 ; *Trans. Faraday Soc.*, **27**. 777, 1931 ; F. H. Jeffery, *ib.*, **27**. 751, 1931 ; **28**. 98, 1932 ; F. Rosendahl, *Metallborse*, **21**. 963, 1011, 1059, 1931 ; E. M. Wise, *Mining Met.*, **12**. 270, 1931 ; F. T. Sisco, *Trans. Amer. Soc. Steel Treating*, **9**. 938, 1926 ; **10**. 189, 267, 457, 462, 800, 1926 ; **11**. 115, 284, 626, 651, 1927 ; G. Tammann, *Zeit. anorg. Chem.*, **37**. 448, 1903 ; G. Tammann and K. Ewig, *ib.*, **167**. 385, 1927 ; G. Z. Nesselstrauss, *Ann. Inst. Anal. Phys. Chem. Leningrad*, **2**. 484, 1924.

² L. Guillet and L. P. M. Revillon, *Rev. Mét.*, **6**. 1251, 1909 ; P. Chévenard, *ib.*, **14**. 610, 1917 ; G. Grard, *ib.*, **8**. 241, 1911 ; F. C. Thompson, *Trans. Faraday Soc.*, **11**. 134, 1916 ; F. C. Thompson and E. Whitehead, *Engg.*, **114**. 675, 1922 ; *Proc. Roy. Soc.*, **102**. A, 587, 1923 ; A. Goffey and F. C. Thompson, *Journ. Iron Steel Inst.*, **107**. i, 465, 1923 ; E. L. Dupuy, *ib.*, **104**. ii, 91, 1921 ; B. D. Enlund, *ib.*, **111**. i, 305, 1925 ; A. Sauveur and D. C. Lee, *ib.*, **111**. ii, 323, 1925 ; R. H. Greaves and J. A. Jones, *ib.*, **111**. ii, 123, 1925 ; H. C. H. Carpenter and B. F. E. Keeling, *ib.*, **65**. i, 224, 1904 ; C. Benedicks, *ib.*, **89**. i, 407, 1914 ; W. H. Dearden and C. Benedicks, *ib.*, **113**. i, 393, 1926 ; W. H. Dearden, *Journ. Iron Steel Inst.—Carnegie Mem.*, **17**. 89, 1926 ; P. Saldau, *ib.*, **7**. 195, 1916 ; F. Robin, *ib.*, **2**. 1, 1910 ; **3**. 125, 1911 ; *Rev. Mét.*, **5**. 893, 1908 ; *Proc. Amer. Assoc. Testing Materials*, **12**. i, 5, 1912 ; *Mitt. Internat. Verland. Materialprüf. Techn.*, **2**. ii, 5, 1913 ; *Compt. Rend.*, **150**. 780, 1910 ; W. C. Roberts-Austen, *Metallographist*, **2**. 186, 1899 ; *Proc. Inst. Mech. Eng.*, 35, 1899 ; J. Maydell, *Zeit. anorg. chem.*, **178**. 123, 1929 ; A. Nouel, *Génie Civil*, **10**. 406, 1887 ; H. S. Rawdon, P. Hidnert and W. A. Tucker, *Trans. Amer. Soc. Steel Treating*, **10**. 233, 1926 ; G. Belloc, *Bull. Soc. Enc. Nat. Ind.*, **107**. 492, 1908 ; *Ann. Chim. Phys.*, (7), **30**. 42, 1903 ; E. G. Herbert, *Proc. Inst. Mech. Eng.*, ii, 863, 1927 ; *Trans. Amer. Soc. Mech. Eng.*, **48**. 705, 1926 ; *Journ. Iron Steel Inst.*, **116**. ii, 265, 1927 ; **120**. ii, 239, 1929 ; *Trans. Amer. Soc. Steel Treating*, **16**. 77, 1929 ; D. Smith and I. Hey, *Trans. Manchester Assoc. Eng.*, 201, 1924 ; S. S. Vanick and T. H. Wickenden, *Trans. Amer. Soc. Steel Treating*, **11**. 551, 1927 ; A. Perrier and F. Wolfers, *Arch. Sciences Genève*, (5), **2**. 372, 1920 ; *Rev. Mét.*, **18**. 111, 1921 ; K. Gebhard, H. Hanemann and A. Schrader, *Arch. Eisenhüttenwesen*, **2**. 763, 1929 ; M. le Blant, *Bull. Internat. Railway Congress Assoc.*, **23**. 929, 1909 ; *Page's Weekly*, **15**. 1185, 1909 ; G. Chrystal, *Nature*, **22**. 303, 1880 ; G. Charpy, *Bull. Soc. Enc. Nat. Ind.*, (4), **4**. 191, 1899 ; G. Charpy and L. Grenet, *Compt. Rend.*, **136**. 92, 1903 ; R. Forrer and J. Schneider, *ib.*, **190**. 1391, 1930 ; C. E. Guye and S. Mintz, *Arch. Sciences Genève*, (4), **26**. 136, 263, 1908 ; (4), **29**. 474, 1910 ; P. Weiss and G. Foëx, *ib.*, (4), **31**. 5, 89, 1911 ; D. K. Morris, *Proc. Phys. Soc.*, **15**. 134, 1897 ; *Phil. Mag.*, (5), **44**. 213, 1897 ; G. E. Svedelius, *ib.*, (5), **46**. 173, 1898 ; *Om Järnets kritiska Länzd- och Temperaturförändringer*, Uppsala, 1896 ; C. Maurain, *Ann. Chim. Phys.*, (8), **20**. 353, 1910 ; J. Pionchon, *Compt. Rend.*, **103**. 1122, 1886 ; *Ann. Chim. Phys.*, (6), **11**. 33, 1887 ; G. Wertheim, *ib.*, (3), **12**. 385, 1844 ; S. R. Roget, *Electrician*, **41**. 182, 1898 ; *Proc. Roy. Soc.*, **63**. 258, 1898 ; S. W. J. Smith, *Proc. Phys. Soc.*, **23**. 63, 342, 1911 ; **24**. 77, 1912 ; J. A. Harker, *ib.*, **19**. 703, 1905 ; F. C. Lea, *Proc. Inst. Mech. Eng.*, i, 885, 1922 ; ii, 1053, 1924 ; *Engg.*, **113**. 829, 1922 ; F. C. Lea and O. H. Crowther, *ib.*, **98**. 487, 1914 ; P. Oberhoffer, *Met.*, **4**. 427, 447, 1907 ; *Stahl Eisen*, **27**. 1764, 1907 ; G. Borelius, *Nature*, **109**. 613, 1922 ; *Ann. Physik*, (4), **50**. 351, 1919 ; (4), **67**. 236, 1922 ; (4), **68**. 67, 1922 ; (4), **74**. 257, 1924 ; W. Heræus, *ib.*, (4), **73**. 554, 1924 ; G. Borelius and F. Gunneson, *ib.*, (4), **67**. 227, 1922 ; *Nature*, **113**. 82, 1923 ; T. Inokuty, *Kinzoku no Kenkyu*, **2**. 1087, 1925 ; K. Honda, *ib.*, **1**. 175, 1924 ; **18**. 503, 1929 ; K. Honda and H. Takagi, *Science Rep. Tohoku Univ.*, **2**. 203, 1913 ; **4**. 161, 261, 1915 ; **8**. 161, 1919 ; K. Tamaru, *ib.*, **15**. 829, 1926 ; H. G. Movius and H. Scott, *Chem. Met. Engg.*, **22**. 1069, 1920 ; E. H. and E. Griffiths, *Phil. Trans.*, **213**. A, 172, 1914 ; **214**. A, 348, 1914 ; N. Stücker, *Neue Bestimmungen des spezifischen Wärme einiger Metalle bei höheren Temperaturen*, Wien, 1905 ; F. A. Epps and E. O. Jones, *Chem. Met. Engg.*, **17**. 67, 1917 ; H. J. French, *ib.*, **26**. 1207, 1922 ; M. Ishimoto, *Proc. Math. Phys. Soc. Japan*, **1**. 267, 1919 ; W. Broniewsky, *Compt. Rend.*, **156**. 699, 1913 ; Bureau of Standards, *Iron Age*, **117**. 1720, 1926 ; F. Fettweiss, *Stahl Eisen*, **39**.

1, 1919; F. Rapatz, *ib.*, **44**. 319, 1924; O. Reinhold, *Ferrum*, **13**. 97, 1915; J. Driesen, *ib.*, **13**. 27, 1915; Z. Jeffries, *Trans. Amer. Inst. Min. Eng.*, **60**. 474, 1919; **67**. 509, 1920; T. Matsushita, *Science Rep. Tohoku Univ.*, **7**. 43, 1927; T. Matsushita and K. Nagasawa, *Journ. Iron Steel Inst.*, **116**. ii, 311, 1927; J. H. Andrew, J. E. Ripon, C. P. Miller and A. Wragg, *ib.*, **101**. i, 527, 1920; G. Auchy, *Iron Age*, **95**. 50, 1915; G. Sirovich, *Gazz. Chim. Ital.*, **53**. 674, 1923; *Met. Ital.*, **14**. 3, 37, 1921; *Giorn. Chim. Ind. Appl.*, **5**. 182, 1923; R. Ariano, *ib.*, **5**. 448, 1923.

§ 15. The Constituents of the Iron-Carbon Alloys

It was once postulated by chemists as axiomatic that " the particles of a solid are incapable of fundamental readjustment ; they are too rigidly braced together. Their mutual bonds are too close to permit the necessary shiftings." The converse proposition describes exactly an extraordinary variety of changes, dependent on atomic movements and rearrangements, which take place in the iron-carbon alloys while they are in the solid state. There are various forms of the solid soln. of carbide or cementite in iron, which can be more or less fixed at ordinary temp. by the abrupt chilling or quenching of the alloy from particular temp. J. M. Robertson [1] discussed the effect of variations in the rate of cooling on the structure of steel; and general observations on the microstructure were made by J. E. Howard, A. Sauveur and H. C. Boynton, J. J. Kessler, R. Adam, A. Bencke, G. Delbart, H. M. Boylston, E. A. Schott, J. Boiteux, J. Mitchell, and numerous others indicated below. Collections of photomicrographs were made by E. L. Reed, and H. Hanemann and A. Schrader.

As indicated above, a solid soln. of iron tritacarbide or cementite in γ-iron was called by F. Osmond **austenite**—after W. C. Roberts-Austen. C. Benedicks regarded austenite as a supercooled solid soln.; and the subject was discussed by O. E. Harder and R. L. Dowdell, and J. H. Whiteley. There are two opposing hypotheses as to the state of the carbon in solid soln. in austenite ; in one—Z. Jeffries and R. S. Archer—the solute is supposed to be carbon interstatically located in the face-centred lattice of γ-iron ; and in the other—A. Sauveur—a solid soln. of cementite, Fe_3C, in γ-iron. This agrees with C. P. Yap's thermodynamical study of the system, but an *experimentum crucis* has not been devised. The fact that cementite crystallizes directly from the austenite solid soln. when it is chilled does not prove that cementite existed previously, to any great extent, in the solid soln. J. M. Robertson, and Z. Jeffries and R. S. Archer hold that in austenite, cementite is not in soln. as such, and the evidence is based on the relation between the size of the cementite molecule and of the iron atom. It is known that carbon diffuses in austenite at an appreciable rate, and one school believes that it is not likely that with the relatively large molecules of cementite, where each atom of carbon is loaded with three atoms of iron, the carbon can diffuse easily through the lattice of γ-iron, whereas it is thought that the relatively small carbon atoms should be able to do it easily. Carbon diffusion, however, may be due to a small percentage dissociation of cementite when cementite carries the major portion of the carbon in austenite. Consequently, the general opinion based on the X-ray analysis, etc., by J. H. Andrew, A. Westgren, A. Westgren and G. Phragmen, Z. Jeffries and R. S. Archer, F. H. Jeffery, and E. C. Bain is that austenite is a solid soln. of carbon in γ-iron. On the other hand, H. A. Schwartz added that in view of G. Cesaro's statement that molten iron is a soln. of the tritacarbide in iron, and that cementite separates from the frozen soln. on further cooling, it is doubtful if austenite can be a soln. of free carbon as such. The X-radiograms of S. Shimura led him to conclude that the carbon is present in austenite in the form of neutral atoms—*vide infra*; and S. Sato concluded that the space-lattices of quenched steel and of carbon in soln. as carbon or as cementite are all the same. When a quenched steel is tempered at 300°, cementite is liberated and decomposed into iron and carbon. In hypereutectoid steels a similar decomposition of the carbide occurs above the Ac_1-arrest.

The equilibrium diagrams show that austenite may contain any proportion of carbon from a trace up to 1·7 or maybe 2·0 per cent. Austenite with the higher proportion is said to be saturated with carbon. Steels usually contain less than 1·7 per cent. of carbon, so that the austenite in such steels is unsaturated, but cast iron has generally more than 1·7 per cent. of carbon, and in such cases the austenite is always saturated. H. M. Howe called ? soln. of γ-iron with 1·7 per cent. of carbon *austenoid*. Austenite is stable within the region bounded by the lines GA_4A_3SE in the equilibrium diagram of the iron-carbon alloys, Fig. 97. As the alloy passes from the γ- to the α-state it deposits cementite, for the resulting α-iron dissolves only about 0·05 per cent. In consequence, as iron changes from γ-state to the β-α-state, the progressive lowering of the temp. of the transformation is represented by the line A_3S' as the proportion of carbon increases from a trace to 0·85 or 0·9 per cent., and with 0·85 to 1·70 per cent. carbon the temp. of the allotropic change is constant, and is represented by the line SK. In no case is the austenite stable below the temp. represented by SK, and it is therefore not stable at atm. temp., although it is possible to prevent almost the whole of the austenite from being transformed by a very rapid quenching of a high-carbon steel.

The austenite obtained by quenching iron-carbon steel is always accompanied by some martensite—*vide infra*. Thus, J. A. Mathews found that some austenite always escapes conversion to martensite in the hardening of medium or high-carbon steels ; and in the case of alloy steels, more escapes conversion after oil-quenching than after the water-quenching. H. Scott, A. Baykoff, L. Guillet, M. A. Grossmann, W. J. Kurbatoff, and K. Heindlhofer and F. L. Wright also observed that austenite persists in high-carbon steels, and B. D. Enlund, in low-carbon steels. The austenite that escapes conversion is called *retained austenite*. J. A. Mathews showed that the retained austenite is a contributing cause to the increased permanence of retentivity of permanent magnetic steels, and in many alloy steels not used for permanent magnets. When some metals are alloyed with the iron—say 14 per cent. of manganese or 25 per cent. of nickel—the transformation temp. of γ-iron is lowered to atm. temp. or less. Hence, austenite alone can be obtained under these conditions. As just indicated, austenite alone cannot be produced in carbon steels by quenching, but this structure can be obtained in the presence of a certain proportion of manganese. K. Tamaru gave Fig. 99 to show the relative proportions of carbon and manganese required to obtain the austenitic structure by quenching steel in water. When only a trace of carbon is present, over 16 per cent. of manganese is required, whereas with 2 per cent. of carbon, 5 per cent. of manganese suffices. Since austenite is paramagnetic and the other structures are ferromagnetic, the purity of austenite can be detected by a magnetometer. For the transformation of austenite to martensite, troostite, and pearlite—*vide infra*.

Fig. 99.—The Proportions of Manganese and Carbon required to produce Austenite by Water-quenching.

Under the microscope austenite appears as a mass of white, polyhedral grains. Fig. 100, by F. T. Sisco, represents a photograph of austenite. The carbon of austenite makes no lines in the X-radiogram, and this means that the carbon is present either in random positions scattered through the lattice, or else it displaces random iron atoms in the lattice. A. Westgren and co-workers observed that the X-radiogram of austenite, like that of γ-iron, corresponds with a face-centred cubic lattice : whilst the side of the cubic lattice of γ-iron is $a=3·60$ A. at 1100°, and 3·68 A. at 1425° ; the value of a for austenitic steel with 0·24 per cent. of carbon, quenched from 1000° in water, is 3·56 A., and with 1·18 per cent. carbon steel, 3·64 A. Consequently, unlike ferrite, the meshes of the γ-iron lattice of austenite are widened by the dissolved carbon. K. Honda and S. Sekito found the lattice constant $a=3·596$ A. for steel with 0·202 per cent. carbon ; 3·604 A. for 0·508 per cent. carbon ; and 3·607 A. for 1·075 per cent. carbon. It is inferred that the solid soln. is not formed by the simple substitution of the metal atoms in the lattice by carbon atoms, but that the carbon atoms are distributed according to the laws of probability within the lattice in the interstices between the metal atoms which occupy all the points of the face-centred lattice. This also agrees with F. Wever and P. Rüttens' studies on manganese steels, etc. O. E. Harder and R. L. Dowdell made observations on the X-radiograms of austenite.

N. Seljakoff and co-workers found the sp. vol. of austenite increased with increasing proportions of carbon ; and F. Wever made observations on this subject with manganese steels. K. Honda and S. Sekito represented the sp. vol. of austenite by $v=0·1257+0·0003C$, where C denotes the percentage amount of carbon. They observed for the sp. vol. :

Carbon .	0·202	0·396	0·508	0·602	0·73	0·895	1·04	1·075 per cent.
Sp. vol..	0·1257	0·1260	0·1259	0·1259	0·1259	0·1259	0·1260	0·1259

Austenite is comparatively soft, being but slightly harder than ferrite. According to H. C. Boynton, the hardness of austenite is 1·06 when that of ferrite

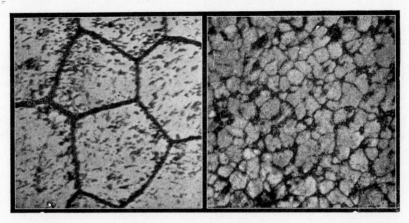

FIGS. 100 and 101.—Austenite Grains in Steel (× 500)—after F. T. Sisco ; and in Manganese Steel (× 50)—after A. Sauveur.

is unity—*vide infra*, hardness. K. Tamaru gave 155 for Brinell's hardness. Austenite is non-magnetic. H. Hanemann said that the austenite in steel is isotropic.

It has been shown—**1**. 11, 4—that as the molten metal solidifies, it first assumes a cellular structure. *La théorie cellulaire de l'acier* was discussed by F. Osmond and J. Werth. Crystallization starts about numerous nuclei, and the crystals grow in three dimensions until arrested by neighbouring growths. The growing crystals are so crowded that there is not sufficient space for them to develop their regular crystal form ; in consequence, a compact mass of irregularly shaped crystals is formed. The polyhedral crystalline grains, or simple grains, make the metal appear as if it had been built up in the form of a mosaic with irregularly shaped stones. No subsequent treatment is able to destroy this completely, because the impurities, which accumulated at the surfaces separating the grains as they are formed, always remain *in situ*. As indicated below, if the steel is held for a long period at a temp. above the critical range, the austenite grains grow in size. If two adjacent grains have the same orientation, the boundary may disappear, and the two grains may merge into one. W. J. Brooke and F. F. Hunting found that armco iron (99·84 per cent. Fe) or Swedish iron (0·04 per cent. C) on cooling passes through a brittle range between 900° and 800°, but not during heating. A eutectic or eutectoid structure appears in the metal quenched from between these temp., but is absent from metal quenched from above or below the brittle range. This constituent resembles pearlite in structure, but is not related to the carbon content, and is independent of the proportion of oxide in the iron.

J. O. Arnold criticized the existence of an austenite as defined above; and W. H. Hatfield proposed that the term austenite be employed for the saturated matrix on passing the Ac_1-arrest when a further absorption of the carbide of supersaturation has begun. The theory of labile and metastable soln.—1. 9, 6—was applied to the primary crystallization of austenite by A. F. Hallimond.

Austenite occurs in supersaturated iron-carbon alloys at high temp. in the constituent hardenite, sometimes named martensite, when it has, at high temp., increased its carbon percentage by its solvent action on the neighbouring carbide. It denominates that portion of a heat-treated mass which changes in composition with each variation in temp. above the point of diffusion of carbide in hardenite.

As previously indicated, H. A. Schwartz applied the term *boydenite* to stable solid soln. of carbon and iron in contradistinction to the term *austenite* for the metastable solid soln. of cementite or carbon in austenite, or the term may be used without implication as to the nature of the solute. In boydenite, the carbon atom is supposed to replace one of the iron atoms in the face-centred lattice, whereas in austenite the carbon atoms are supposed to be scattered in the interstices of the lattice. The evidence for the metallographic individuality of boydenite is not conclusive. H. A. Schwartz holds that the stable and metastable systems of boydenite and austenite differ in the maximum carbon concentration at a given temp., and also for a given conc. of carbon in their electrical resistance, and in the location of the A_1- and A_2-arrests. In view of A. Westgren and G. Phragmen's, and F. Wever's demonstrations (*vide infra*) that in austenite the carbon atom is located within the crystal cell or space-lattice and does not occupy any position normally belonging to the iron-atoms, H. A. Schwartz examined the hypothesis that in the solid soln. of carbon in iron known as austenite, the carbon is additive in the space-lattice, and substitutional in boydenite. With an altered lattice parameter, in the former case, the density of the austenitic solid soln. will increase, because the carbon atom will add to the mass of the soln. but not to the vol., whereas with the boydenite solid soln. the density will decrease with increasing carbon content, because the carbon atom is higher than the iron atom whose place it occupies. H. A. Schwartz made estimates from known data and calculated 7·535 for the sp. gr. of austenite, and 7·393 for that of boydenite at 900°.

The further discussion of austenite is associated with that of **martensite**, so named after A. Martens by F. Osmond. According to F. Osmond, martensite is best formed when a steel containing 0·2 to 0·8 per cent. of carbon is cooled from above the temp. of the A_3-arrest slowly to the A_2-arrest and then suddenly quenched in a freezing mixture at $-20°$, so as to prevent the splitting up of the austenite into pearlite, but not rapidly enough to preserve the austenite in its unchanged state. According to F. Osmond, and H. Hanemann, martensite can also be produced by immersing austenitic steel in liquid air. As indicated above, some austenite escapes conversion during quenching; thus K. Tamaru found that steel with 0·71 per cent. of carbon, quenched from 802°, retains 10 per cent. of austenite ; steel with 1·19 per cent. of carbon, quenched from 855°, retains 15 per cent. ; and steel with 1·48 per cent. of carbon, quenched from 980°, retains 20 per cent. of austenite. The subject was discussed by J. M. Robertson, and by O. E. Harder and R. L. Dowdell in their memoir : *The Decomposition of the Austenitic Structure in Steels* (Minneapolis, 1927).

The decomposition of austenite on quenching.—O. E. Harder and R. L. Dowdell found that in order to preserve a large proportion of austenite at room temp. a high-carbon steel, and preferably an alloy steel, should be used; an oil-quench from a high initial temp. will produce more austenite than a more drastic water-quench at the same temp. E. Scheil, for instance, obtained the results indicated in Fig. 102 with steels containing 0·93 and 1·05 per cent. of carbon respectively—*vide infra*, pearlite. The slower the cooling, the greater the proportion of retained austenite. This has also been established by the work of J. A. Mathews, W. J. Crook and H. S. Taylor, W. Ischewsky, D. J. McAdam, E. Hess, R. Ruer, A. Hayes and co-workers, O. E. Harder and R. L. Dowdell, E. C. Bain and W. N. S. Waring, J. M. Robertson, E. Scheil, K. Tamaru and S. Sekito, and K. Honda and A. Osawa. If large or small sections are quenched from a high temp., they will contain more austenite than if quenched from a lower temp. At high temp. larger austenite grains are produced. The larger austenite grains have a greater stability than the smaller ones, and it has been observed that the slip-lines or needles produced in a coarse-grained structure are longer and wider, which results in a coarser martensitic structure and gives the appearance of a smaller amount of martensite. The stability of the large grains produced at high temp. is further increased in steels containing an excess of carbides by the larger amount of carbon taken into soln. in the austenite. While the maximum temp. difference between the outside and the inside must be greater in quenching from the higher temp., and the resulting stress greater, the greater the stability of the more concentrated austenite and the larger grain-size. Also, a given amount of stress

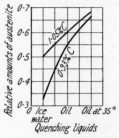

Fig. 102.—The Effect of the Quenching Temperature on the Proportion of Retained Austenite.

may be expected to produce fewer slip-lines in a coarse structure than in a fine-grained structure. E. Maurer observed that on cooling, austenite passes into martensite which is different from the martensite produced by tempering. H. Hanemann found that when a portion of a quenched 1·79 per cent. carbon steel with 0·6 per cent. manganese was immersed in liquid air and etched, some needles appeared darker and some lighter than the ground-mass of austenite, while the portion not submerged showed only dark needles. The dark needles were in a tempered condition, and they etched below the surface of the austenite, whilst the whitish, light blue needles were in relief in the light yellow ground-mass of austenite. The light-coloured needles of martensite formed by immersing austenite in liquid air are similar to those formed by ordinary quenching, because the martensite separates out in the Widmanstätten pattern along the octahedral slip planes of the austenite. There is a decrease of approximately 0·1 in the sp. gr. after various specimens had been immersed in liquid oxygen ; and the decrease in sp. gr. was attributed to the formation of martensite. When the martensite needles produced in liquid air are tempered, their carbon content is less than that of the mother austenite. When a steel with 1·5 per cent. of carbon and 0·3 per cent. of manganese is quenched from 1050° to 1200°, the martensite pre-dominates near the edges. K. Honda and A. Osawa found that the proportion of austenite retained in the outer layers of a specimen is greater than in the inner part by an amount which increases with rise of quenching temp. and with the proportion of carbon.

According to K. Schröter, a steel containing 1·89 per cent. of carbon and 2·22 per cent. of manganese on immersion in liquid air together with a small magnet is seized by the magnet shortly after immersion. Measurements of the magnetic saturation gave : 1070 gauss for a water-quenched specimen before immersion in liquid air, and 11,380 gauss after immersion ; while an oil-quenched specimen gave the respective values 2410 and 14,670 gauss. Similar results were obtained with a 25 per cent. nickel steel. G. Tammann and E. Scheil observed that in cooling hardened steel from 20° to −150° the austenite begins to change into martensite at about −20°, and the conversion continues down to −150°. The change is greater near the surface than within the mass, probably because high internal stresses exert a retarding influence.

D. Lewis observed that if a 0·8 per cent. carbon steel be quenched in a molten salt bath at 232°, austenite is produced, which is comparatively stable for, say, 5 mins., and which will convert to martensite on cooling. The cooling may be slow or rapid without affecting the final hardness—650 on Brinell's scale. When the austenite in a 0·8 per cent. carbon steel decomposes below 232°, the reaction is rapid, and the product is hard martensite; above this temp., up to, say, 316°, the decomposition is comparatively slow and it is not completed in 5 mins. The product has the appearance of martensite, and its hardness is low. It is thought that below 232° crystallization takes place from a labile state, and above that temp. from a metastable state— *vide* 1. 9, 6. E. S. Davenport and E. C. Bain found that the transformation of austenite in carbon steels is most rapid at about 540°; below this temp. the time required for the transformation increases rapidly. In the range from Ac_1 to 500° the time of transformation decreases with increasing or decreasing proportions of carbon, as the steel departs from the eutectoidal composition. The presence of manganese retards the transformation; and likewise also a small proportion of chromium. As a rule, the lower the temp. of transformation the greater the hardness. According to S. Shimura, the carbon in austenite is present as neutral atoms, but takes on the configuration of cementite with neighbouring ferrite atoms as the austenite changes to martensite, and segregates out as cementite at the A_1-transformation point. The metastable carbon in α-iron—with less than 0·03 per cent. carbon—also takes on the cementite arrangement.

K. Honda and S. Idei, C. Benedicks, and E. C. Bain reported the spontaneous formation of martensite from austenite at room temp.; and H. Hanemann and A. Schrader observed that after a rapidly quenched and polished steel with 1·52 per cent. carbon has stood at room temp. for a short time, martensite appeared here and there in relief on the specimen. C. F. Brush and co-workers observed that in the ageing of martensitic steels at room temp. there is a contraction of about 0·0848 per cent. by vol., and an evolution of heat which reaches a maximum in about 9 or 10 days after the water-quenching at the higher critical temp. A carbon steel quenched from the upper critical temp. gave off 404 cals. per gram during ageing at room temp.—*vide infra*. A. Meuthen found that the heat of the A_3-transformation is 5·6 cals. per gram, and N. Yamada, that for a eutectoidal steel the heat of the transformation from austenite to martensite is 5·7 cals. per gram. The heat of allotropic transformation of austenite to pearlite obtained by A. Meuthen, and the heat of transformation of austenite to martensite, and of martensite to pearlite obtained by N. Yamada, are as follow :

Carbon	0·38	0·52	0·65	0·70	1·30	1·74 per cent.
Aust. to pearlite	6·8	9·2	11·5	12·4	14·8	13·6 cals.
Aust. to martensite	2·4	3·3	4·1	4·4	5·3	4·8 cals.
Mart. to pearlite	4·4	5·9	7·4	8·0	9·5	8·8 cals.

The results show that the heats of the allotropic transformations increase linearly with the proportion of carbon—*vide infra*, the thermal properties of iron. K. Honda stated that the first change of the A_1-transformation is really the A_3-transformation, and hence the heat of the transformation of austenite to martensite must be equal to that of the A_3-transformation with pure iron, with a small allowance for the dissolved carbon atoms. A. Schneider, however, found that the heat change during the formation of martensite by quenching is less than that which occurs at the $Ar_{1,2,3}$-arrest. This is due to the fact that a residuum of austenite escapes conversion during quenching, and none of the exothermal reactions, at the $Ar_{1,2,3}$-transition temp., is completed. H. S. Rawdon and S. Epstein stated that the grain-size of martensite is almost entirely determined by the quenching temp.; and J. H. Whiteley added that the size of the martensite crystallites increases with the size of the grains from which they are formed.

P. Dejean, and P. Chévenard observed that the Ar_1-arrest is lowered to 300° or less when a high-carbon steel is rapidly quenched—*vide infra*. A. M. Portevin and M. Garvin called this the Ar″-arrest, and supposed that it represents the transformation of austenite to martensite, a change which is accompanied by an evolution of heat and an increase in vol. In the quenching of eutectoidal steels the rate of cooling required to retain the martensite is less drastic than is the case for hypo- or hypereutectoidal steels. The critical rate for a steel with 1·07 per cent. of carbon and 0·08 per cent. of manganese was found to be 6·9 seconds for cooling from 700° to 200°; with a slower rate of cooling a critical point, the Ar′-arrest, occurred at about 650°, and the core of specimens over 14 mm. diameter contained troostite; while with a faster rate of cooling the Ar″-arrest, smaller in magnitude than the Ar′-arrest, occurred at 300°, and the alloy contained coarse white needles of martensite in a matrix of austenite. J. A. Mathews observed that with a series of alloy steels the magnetic hardness or coercive force is greater after oil-quenching than after water-quenching, and conversely with the sleroscopic hardness. This indicates that more austenite is converted to martensite after water-quenching than after oil-quenching. The sp. gr., for instance, was smaller after water-quenching than after oil-quenching. H. Scott also noted that an increase in the proportion of austenite was observed by cooling the steel first in oil down to a little above the Ar″-arrest, and then in air to the room temp. K. Heindlhofer and F. L. Wright found that the sp. gr. of steels with 0·55 to 0·71 per cent. of chromium and 0·98 to 1·06 per cent. of carbon was lower with a quenching temp. of 915° to 950° than with a quenching temp. of 800° tc 865°. Also oil-quenchings from 865° to 950° gave products with the respective sp. gr. 7·790 and 7·766, while water-quenchings from 800° to 915° gave products with sp. gr. 7·755 and 7·745 respectively.

Various theories attribute the hardening of steel—*vide infra*—to the strains set up on quenching, and consequently some observations have been made on the effects of stress on the decomposition of austenite during quenching. C. Benedicks noticed that austenite is not formed near the surface of quenched specimens heated in graphite to prevent oxidation. During the quenching in liquid air the transformation of austenite to martensite cannot go beyond a certain limit where the increase of press. due to the formation of the specifically lighter martensite would prevent the further transformation of the austenite. If the outer edge of a quenched piece of 1·99 per cent. carbon steel is ground off so as to relieve the stress, the austenite decomposes spontaneously to martensite in a few hours. O. E. Harder and R. L. Dowdell showed that in the drastic quenching of small-sized pieces of metal, when martensite is produced at the edges, the result is probably due to the greater difference in temp. existing between the outside and the centre, which should produce a higher tensional stress. This favours martensite formation because of the increased vol. when martensite forms. During the first stage of quenching the outside of the section must be in tension, which will produce a compression on the inside and tend to retain the austenite by preventing its expansion to martensite. The absence of tensional stress is of more importance in the retention of austenite at room temp. than is the compressive stress. When quenched specimens are martensitic throughout, O. E. Harder and R. L. Dowdell said :

In the first part of the cooling operation the surface must be in tension and the core in compression, but as the cooling continues the tension zone progresses inward. As the outer zone produces martensite of a greater sp. vol. than the austenitic core it should lower the tension and gradually produce compression in the outer zone. The temp. of the core at the time the case changes to martensite on quenching must be considerably higher and as the core cools to ordinary temp. there is a shrinkage due to the normal decrease in vol. with decrease in temp. This must play an important part in producing tension in the core. At this time the outer compressive zone must be balanced by an equal tensional zone in the interior of the specimen which will promote the formation of martensite.

H. V. Wille cut three rings from a quenched steel with 0·41 per cent. of carbon and 0·55 per cent. manganese respectively 0·5, 1·625, and 2·75 ins. from the surface, and found that they were under compression in the original piece, because they expanded when cut off. He estimated that when the forging was quenched in water at 21°, the first ring was under a compression of 42,600 lbs. per sq. in., the second, 29,500, and the third, 16,500 ; and when quenched in oil, the first ring was under a compression of 42,300 lbs. per sq. in., the second, 16,800, and the third, 4500. Hence the internal stress developed by water-quenching is greater than with oil-quenching. W. Tafel said that owing to thermal changes, if a body of steel be heated to a high temp., the stresses will be small, but if it be quenched, the core, having a greater sp. vol. than the colder shell, will be under compression, while the shell is under tension ; as the interior cools to the same temp. as the shell it will shrink, but since the shell has assumed a greater sp. vol. than normal, owing to the formation of martensite, the stress gradient will reverse, leaving the shell in compression and the core in tension.   Observations were also made by T. McL. Jasper, H. Scott, H. J. French and co-workers, G. Tammann and E. Scheil, G. Kurdjumoff and E. Kaminsky, E. Maurer, W. H. Walker, F. Wever, and K. Honda and K. Iwase. Since the transformation of austenite to martensite is attended by an increase in volume, it follows, in accordance with H. le Chatelier's principle (**2.** 18, 4), that the change will be hindered by compression and favoured by tension.   This was established by C. Benedicks, J. Driesen, and E. Scheil.   According to E. H. Schulz, the surface layers are cooled more rapidly than the core and more martensite is formed than in the interior.   An increase in the sp. vol. attends the transformation of austenite to martensite, and the curve, Fig. 103, showing the decrease in the

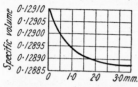

FIG. 103. — The Specific Volume at Different Distances from the Surface of a Block of Hard Steel with 1·72 per cent. of Carbon.

sp. vol. as the distance from the surface of a bar of hardened steel increases, shows that the compression in the chilling has hindered the formation of martensite in the interior.   O. E. Harder and R. L. Dowdell also observed that when austenite-martensitic steels are tempered under a transverse stress below their yield-point, at temp. between 100° and 200°, a permanent set results ; the bar is longer on the tension side, which indicates that tensional stress favours the change from the γ- to the α-state.   No difference in the microstructure on the tension and compression sides could be detected.   The production of martensite from austenite by hammering at room temp. could not be detected, but prominent slip-lines are developed which are characteristically different from martensite needles. Characteristic martensite has been produced from austenite at room temp. by tensile stress.   It is very probable that all martensite is formed by a similar process in the normal hardening of tool steels but at a much more sudden and higher tensional stress.   An austenitic specimen, which had been previously deformed in tension, was caused to transform to martensite at about —57°, while unstressed specimens were unchanged by this same treatment.   An austenitic specimen which had been deformed by hammering decomposed more readily on heating than an unstressed specimen.   Deformed austenite is rendered less stable on cooling or on heating.

The cold deformation of austenitic steels was shown by J. H. Hall and G. R. Hanks to favour the transformation to martensite.   The Brinell hardness of the surface of a steel with 11·0 per cent. manganese and 1·0 to 1·4 per cent. carbon increased from 190 to 450 during cold-working.   The abrasion of the steel produced by sawing also favours the γ- to α-inversion ; and this transformation along the slip-lines of manganese steel was discussed by H. M. Howe.   J. H. Whiteley also reported the formation of zig-zag needles of martensite from a high-carbon austenitic steel by impact at room temp. ; and when the needles were tempered at 200°, troostite was formed.   E. C. Bain also showed that cold-working greatly favoured the γ- to α-inversion.   K. Honda and K. Iwase observed that quenched austenite can be transformed into martensite by cold-working.   The internal stresses set up in a steel by quenching promote the transformation of austenite into martensite. Differences in the amount of austenite produced by oil- and water-quenching occur only with thick pieces and can be explained as an effect of internal stress.   On cooling quenched steels in liquid air, the retained austenite is transformed into martensite ; the amount of transformation is less the thinner the specimens.

The decomposition of austenite by tempering.—B. D. Enlund observed that when martensite is tempered at about 100°, there is a considerable decrease in the sp. vol., and when austenite is tempered, there is a large increase in the sp. vol. E. Scheil observed a break at 370° in the cooling curve of austenite corresponding with the formation of martensite. In the formation of martensite by the tempering of austenite, between 150° and 250°, E. Maurer observed that the martensite begins to transform first, but the progress of the change is slower than the transformation of austenite to troostite. H. Hanemann agreed that martensite changes more easily than austenite on tempering. H. Scott and H. G. Movius found that the beginning, maximum, and end of the Ac_0-arrest for a quenched 0·95 per cent. carbon steel are respectively 155°, 250°, and 260°, and that this arrest is raised by increasing the rate of heating. The Ac_0-arrest is the thermal effect observed in tempering quenched steels, and with carbon steels it usually occurs at about 200°. H. Hanemann observed that at 260° to 280° the austenite begins to change to troostite at the already decomposed needles, which act as inoculation centres, and the change then proceeds from the grain boundaries inwards. The carbon content of the crystals of martensite is less than that of the mother austenite. H. S. Rawdon and S. Epstein also noted that the plates of martensite contain a smaller proportion of carbon than the intervening matrix. With steels containing 0·07 to 1·12 per cent. of carbon, quenched between 750° and 1250°, the structural changes are slight when tempered below 250°, but above 250° the martensite and austenite, when present, are transformed, so that the steels assume a granular structure, and react vigorously when etched with dil. acid. No specimen tempered between 100° and 650° showed a scleroscopic hardness greater than the initial hardness produced by quenching. According to H. C. Boynton, the relative hardness of martensite is 2·39 when that of ferrite is unity—*vide infra*, hardness. J. H. Andrew and A. J. K. Honeyman observed that the change of martensite begins at 150°, and is not completed in an hour at 360°. H. von Jüptner gave 7·076 for the sp. gr. of saturated martensite. According to C. Benedicks, the work of F. Osmond, H. le Chatelier, and G. Charpy and L. Grenet shows that the passage from austenite to martensite is accompanied by a considerable increase in volume, and he added that the resulting press. which is developed will prevent the transformation proceeding beyond a certain limit, when the increase of press. corresponding with the increase in vol. will put a stop to the transformation of the γ-crystals. In consequence, these crystals will be preserved as austenite at ordinary temp. H. Scott measured the sp. gr. and hardness of 17·8 per cent. tungsten steels quenched from 900°, 1060°, 1220°, and 1300°, and tempered cumulatively at intervals of 200° for 15 mins. The sp. gr. of specimens quenched above 900° increased to a maximum between 200° and 400°, but specimens quenched at 1220° and 1300° showed a marked decrease on tempering at 600°. Both the scleroscopic and Brinell's hardnesses decreased at about 200°, and rapidly increased to a maximum at 600° ; above 600° the hardness decreased rapidly, probably owing to the coagulation of the carbide. The secondary hardness so developed is due to martensite produced by tempering the austenite. E. C. Bain and Z. Jeffries observed that when a quenched high-speed steel is tempered between 454° and 593°, the passage of austenite to martensite is accompanied by an expansion and an increase in hardness ; while above 593° the growths of ferrite grains and of the iron tungsten carbide particles rapidly produce a softening of the steel as is the case with carbon steels. The stability of the carbon at a red-heat is attributed to the presence of the tungsten atoms which, because of their large size, are prevented from diffusing into the space-lattice of ferrite until the temp. exceeds redness. E. C. Bain found that steels with 1·70 to 2·22 per cent. of carbon and 6·09 to 15·65 per cent. of chromium were quite soft and almost entirely austenitic when quenched from about 1150°, but on tempering at 482° to 593° the steels were martensitized and developed a hardness nearly equal to that produced by quenching from a lower temp. The tempered specimens did not show the structure of martensite, but rather that of troostite. E. C. Bain added that the cause of the easier retention of austenite in alloy steels is the stronger atomic bonding between unlike atoms which is necessary for any solid soln. Whether or not the product of the change of preserved austenite is martensite depends on the grain-growth in α-iron, and in the carbide. If the carbide precipitation precedes the allotropic change, as is usually the case, the product is very like troostite. O. E. Harder and R. L. Dowdell observed that the decomposition temp. for austenite is always higher than for martensite in the same specimen. The temp. range of the decomposition of austenite is as follows (the first ten results are due to E. C. Bain, and the remaining eight to O. E. Harder and R. L. Dowdell):

Steel				C	Mn	Cr	W	Range of decomposition
Carbon .	.	.	.	1·10	0·20	—	—	190° to 250°
Tungsten	.	.	.	1·40	—	0·50	4·0	205° to 280°
Tungsten	.	.	.	2·00	1·30	1·40	1·0	300° to 400°
Oil hardened .	.	.	.	0·90	1·70	—	—	205° to 287°
Oil hardened .	.	.	.	0·90	1·20	1·00	—	205° to 270°
Chrome magnet	.	.	.	0·85	0·40	2·60	—	205° to 260°
High chrome .	.	.	.	1·80	0·35	6·00	—	300° to 535°
High chrome .	.	.	.	2·20	0·35	10·00	—	448° to 535°
High-speed	.	.	.	0·70	—	0·40	18·0	538° to 650°
Manganese	.	.	.	1·20	12·00	—	—	413° to 620°
High nickel (graphitized) .		.	.	0·99	0·04	—	22·57 (Ni)	625° to 670°
Cobalt-chromium	.	.	.	0·86	0·13	9·31	13·66 (Co)	525° to 562°
High manganese	.	.	.	1·37	11·88	—	—	410° to 480°
Chromium	.	.	.	2·22	0·36	10·56	—	150° to 200°
High-speed	.	.	.	0·76	0·07	4·38	20·0	150° to 200°
High carbon .	.	.	.	1·35	0·24	—	—	150° to 200°
Tungsten	.	.	.	1·37	0·20	0·56	5·91	150° to 200°
High carbon .	.	.	.	2·66	0·22	—	—	150° to 200°

E. S. Davenport and E. C. Bain found that the transformation of austenite is most rapid at 540°, and in the range between the Ac_1-arrest and 500° the rate decreases with either increasing or decreasing carbon content as the eutectoid recedes. The presence of chromium or of manganese retards the transformation. At lower temp. both manganese and carbon decrease the rate of transformation. The decomposition of austenite during tempering was found by H. S. van Vleet and C. Upthegrove to follow the austenite→martensite→troostite→sorbite type of change, but at the temp. of liquid air the decomposition follows the austenite→ troostite type of change without the accompanying growth of cementite and ferrite.

O. E. Harder and R. L. Dowdell observed that with carbon steels the martensite needles, which are light-coloured and in relief, progressively darken at 100° as time increases, and the sp. gr. show that the precipitation of carbide particles takes place slowly until dark troostite is formed. The tempering at a higher temp., 200° to 270°, is attended by a coarsening of the structure, and this is followed by a decrease in hardness, probably caused by grain-growth in the ferrite, and the coalescence of the carbide to a size that can be recognized as a distinct phase. In alloy steels the martensite decomposes on tempering as in the case of carbon steels; the martensite needles darken, but they are more stable in alloy steels and require for their decomposition a higher temp. or a longer time, or both. Martensite needles can be produced by tempering chromium and manganese steels. It is possible that there is an overlapping of the ranges of stability of the austenite and the martensite of steels of certain compositions. Frequently dark needles (troostite) are produced in the tempering of austenitic steels. Nodular troostite usually forms on tempering austenite. Its common places of formation are at grain boundaries, along slip-planes, or along martensite, cementite, or troostite patches.

H. J. French and co-workers found that a high-speed steel—with 0·56 per cent. carbon ; 2·21, chromium ; 13·80, tungsten ; and 0·98, vanadium—quenched from about 1260° in oil, and in an air blast, and tempered cumulatively at intervals of about 93°, had a minimum contraction of approximately 0·0002 in. in 4 ins. at 482°, and it then rapidly expanded when tempered at about 593°. M. A. Grossmann and E. C. Bain observed that a tungsten steel—with 1·08 per cent. carbon ; 0·35, manganese ; 0·36, silicon ; 2·66, tungsten ; 0·50, chromium ; and 0·29, vanadium—quenched in oil from 871°, 927°, 982°, 1093°, and 1204°, underwent a maximum contraction at about 127°, a maximum expansion at about 260°, and a contraction at 649°. H. Scott obtained analogous results with a steel containing 1·10 per cent. of carbon and 1·10 per cent. of chromium. The ageing of the steel for an hour at 100° produced the same contraction as a natural ageing for six months. A maximum contraction occurred on tempering for an hour at 150° to 200° ; a maximum expansion at 260° ; and on tempering at higher temp., a continuous contraction occurred until the value for annealed steel was obtained. With a higher quenching temp., or with an oil-quenching to near the Ar''-arrest and then cooling in air, the initial contraction is lowered and the expansion at 260° is raised. This shows that more austenite is retained by oil-quenching owing to the development of a press. sufficient to retard the transformation at an earlier stage with slow cooling than with fast cooling because of the shrinkage of the matrix of martensite produced by the transient tempering which occurs when the metal is slowly cooled through the Ar''-arrest.

E. Maurer, and O. E. Harder observed that in the tempering of 0·70 to 1·18 per cent. carbon steels there is a rapid decrease of the remanent magnetic induction at about 100°, there is a break in the curve at about 260°, a maximum at about 500°, and subsequently a decrease at a slower rate. The results agree with observations on the sp. gr., changes in vol., and coercive force. The decrease in the remanent magnetic induction and tempering is attributed to the tempering of martensite, and the increase, to the α-iron formed in the tempering of the austenite. K. Heindlhofer and F. L. Wright observed two transformations in the tempering of quenched steels with a low proportion of chromium : (i) a transformation from a specifically light form to a denser form is attributed to a break-down of the martensite which proceeds over a wide range of temp. ; and (ii) a transformation from a specifically dense form to a lighter form occurring over a narrow range of temp., 200° to 260°, and attributed to the retained austenite changing to martensite. This was confirmed by the dilation curves of H. Styri. B. D. Enlund found that with carbon steels with between 0·21 and 1·57 per cent. of carbon, and tempered at various temp., the electrode potentials show that martensite is transformed into troostite at 100° to 200°, but the reaction is most marked at 110° ; that austenite is decomposed at about 260°, and at 270° the microstructure of the high-carbon steels is wholly troostitic. Even low-carbon steels retain a considerable proportion of austenite when quenched from ordinary quenching temp. The transformation of austenite was also discussed by A. M. Portevin and P. Chevenard, E. S. Davenport and E. C. Bain, N. Engel, and W. Brenscheidt. According to E. Walldow, the transformation of α-iron to γ-iron starts at the grain boundaries. U. Dehlinger studied the effect of grain-size on the rate of transformation.

O. E. Harder and R. L. Dowdell found that the austenite of different steels quenched and later submerged in liquid oxygen exhibits different stabilities.

The transformation to martensite is practically complete with plain carbon steels, while in the case of manganese and some high-speed steels little or no martensite is formed. The microstructures of martensite produced by ordinary quenching and by cooling with liquid oxygen are similar—white needles with a midrib structure when the orientation is suitable. The greater proportion of martensite produced at the interior than at the surface is attributed to the production of a compression on the outside and a tension on the inside, in which case the tensional stress favours the phase of greater vols.—that is, the martensite. The decomposition of austenite at liquid oxygen temp. is a recrystallization phenomenon which shows itself first along slip-planes, and is accompanied by an increase in hardness and decrease in sp. gr. In agreement with F. Osmond, and H. Hanemann, the formation of martensite from austenite in liquid oxygen probably takes place rapidly and almost immediately after immersion. However, this rate may be somewhat slower than when it forms on commercial quenching, owing to the decrease in the atomic mobility at the much lower temperature. Finally, the reaction does not go to completion, which may be influenced by the greater volume of the martensite which may relieve tensile stress and even produce compressive stress. The less stable structures, as in the carbon steels, go more nearly to completion. This is shown by the microstructures after long periods of time and by the changes in hardness.

E. Scheil showed that the change from austenite to martensite is favoured by tensile stresses and hindered by compressive stresses. The transformation of residual austenite which occurs below 0° is exposed to tensile stresses owing to the difference in the coeff. of expansion of austenite and martensite.

J. O. Arnold assumed that the Ar_1-arrest is connected with the formation and dissociation of an unstable carbide, $Fe_{24}C$, of intense hardness, and accordingly he called it **hardenite.** The microscopic appearance of hardenite in a specimen of hardened tool steel is shown in Fig. 104. The microstructure sometimes shows no

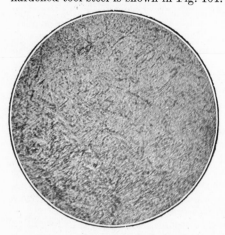

sign of crystallization. Hardenite is said to be the unsegregated eutectoid with its 0·8 to 0·9 per cent. of carbon, and, when annealed, it furnishes 100 per cent. pearlite, or $21Fe+Fe_3C$—J. O. Arnold called the product *true steel.* If J. O. Arnold meant that the eutectoid is a chemical individual, he reverted to the old cryohydrate theory which regarded eutectics as chemical compounds. In that case, hardenite is $Fe_3C.21Fe$, or cementite with " iron of crystallization." F. Osmond believed that hardenite is a saturated martensite which has a mesial rib that etches more deeply than the other parts. Martensite is not normally stable at any temp., and can be pre-

Fig. 104.—Structure of Hardenite (E. Heyn).

served in this unstable state only at comparatively low temp.—*vide infra,* tempering. For a steel of a given composition, it is distinguished from austenite by its greater magnetic permeability, and hardness. H. C. H. Carpenter and C. A. Edwards suggested as an hypothesis that martensite and austenite are constitutionally identical, and differ only in the repeatedly twinned structure of the martensite. C. H. Desch believed that the difference is more profound than is implied by this hypothesis. The subject was discussed by C. Benedicks and E. Walldow, H. Hanemann and J. H. Wiester, S. Steinberg, and M. Matweieff.

Martensite is sometimes considered to be responsible for the hardness of quenched carbon steels—*vide infra,* theories of hardening. According to W. Rosenhain, the alleged hardness of acicular martensite may be illusory, in that the hardness of such a structure is accidental rather than causative. The acicular martensite is not necessarily hard. Thus, steels of low carbon content, which undergo no appreciable degree of hardening when quenched, often show a well-developed martensite structure. It is possible that the acicular structure of martensite is associated primarily with the allotropic transformation of iron, and not with the hardening process itself.

Martensite is a solid soln. of carbon or iron carbide in iron—F. Osmond said that iron is partly in the α- and partly in the β-state ; H. le Chatelier, in the α-state ; and C. Benedicks, in the β-state ; but later he stated that what was formerly regarded as β-iron is a soln. of α- in γ-iron ; and added that the soln. is supersaturated, but not undercooled. Z. Jeffries and R. S. Archer believe that martensite consists of fine-grained α-iron in which carbon is atomically dispersed in the lattice of α-iron as a kind of supersaturated soln., for carbon is considered to be soluble in γ-iron, but almost insoluble in α-iron. Equilibrium is established by the precipitation of carbon. Under favourable conditions the martensite slowly changes and cementite is formed : $3Fe+C=Fe_3C$—*vide infra*, the hardening of steel. R. Ruer said that martensite is not a true soln. of carbon or cementite in α-iron. E. Maurer's hypothesis that martensite is a supersaturated soln. of carbon in α-iron was confirmed by E. Oehman.

J. O. Arnold argued that martensite is really structureless hardenite, $Fe_{24}C$; but this is rather a question of nomenclature. The term martensite usually refers to needle-like, microscopic structures, characteristic of quenched steels, which appear to be formed on the two sides of the incipient, octahedral cleavage planes of austenite. The structure of martensite is sometimes very like that of austenite, but it more frequently shows characteristic acicular markings, or interlacing needles, Fig. 105. This diagram represents a steel with 1·54 per cent. carbon heated for 15 mins: at 1350°, and then quenched in water at —5°. It has been etched with picric acid. It shows the needles of martensite in a matrix of austenite. F. Osmond observed that when etched, martensite is whiter than the matrix of austenite, which

Figs. 105 and 106.—Martensite in a Matrix of Austenite (Fig. 106, after F. F. Lucas).

usually etches a yellowish tint. C. Benedicks also said that the natural colour of the acicular or lanceolate martensite is slightly darker than when polished, and if the specimen be allowed to stand in air, the austenite rusts before the martensite is affected. Fig. 106 ($\times 2100$) represents martensite in austenite in a steel with 2·65 per cent. carbon and 0·07 per cent. manganese ; and etched with picric acid. Photographs of high magnification were also made by R. A. Hadfield and T. G. Elliott. H. Hanemann said that the martensite in steel, unlike austenite, is anisotropic. F. Osmond said that the martensitic structure appears to have three systems of fibres arranged parallel to the three sides of a triangle and crossing each other frequently, imparting the *fer de lance* structure ; the needle-like crystals assume various other forms—*vide* Figs. 105 and 106 ; and *vide infra*, Neumann's bands. The structure of martensite was discussed by A. Allison, K. Heindlhofer and E. C. Bain, and others—*vide infra*. F. Osmond and G. Cartaud refer to them as pseudomorphs of twinnings due to tension occurring in γ-iron, through the partial formation of the bulky β- and α-allotropes of iron. According to H. C. H. Carpenter and C. A. Edwards, the acicular markings of martensite are due to the twinning of the crystals of the solid soln. of carbon and γ-iron by the strains set up in the process of quenching—*vide infra*, Neumann's bands. J. E. Stead added that if martensite is twinned austenite the zigzag portions of what is considered to be martensite in austenite would not be of the same light or dark tint in any given microscopic field. They are always either all light on a dark ground or dark on a light ground, according to the method used in etching. When the zigzag structure is large enough to be examined under oblique light, there is no change in the appearance of the martensite during the rotation of the specimen. The magnetic properties and hardness do not increase with the proportion of martensite. *Ergo*, martensite is not twinned austenite, but is an independent substance. According to O. E. Harder and R. L. Dowdell, the so-called needles of martensite in a ground-mass of austenite, produced by the quenching of austenitic steels, are really plates formed by the octahedral slip-planes of the austenite, and they appear on a polished and etched surface either as narrow or wide plates which frequently form with one another an angle of 60° or 120° If the carbon steel has about 1·7 per cent. of carbon, and is quenched from about 1100°, the steel, at room temp., will contain roughly equal amounts of austenite and martensite, and the ground-mass will be the austenite. F. Sauerwald and co-workers found that the martensitic structure of steel is always oriented in the same way as the original grain boundaries, and that the slip-planes are similarly oriented. It is therefore assumed that the acicular structure of martensite is caused by slip phenomena induced by the hardening or quenching process ; it is also assumed that martensite is not a distinctive phase in the structure of steel.

F. F. Lucas inferred that a martensite needle is a decomposition product which first appears along the octahedral crystallographic planes of austenite, and it is confined to an area of uniformly oriented austenite, *i.e.* a needle never crosses a grain boundary or a twinning plane. Martensite needles darken with sodium picrate, an etching soln. which selects iron carbide. They also etch with nitric or picric acid, a reagent which does not stain or attack the carbide. Martensite needles have a mottled, granular appearance, and often a line structure is found, whilst occasionally needles are found which exhibit multiple twinning. A martensite needle is an aggregate and not a solid soln., and it indicates a decomposition of the austenite probably to α-iron and iron carbide highly dispersed. Later observations, taking precautions to prevent tempering during the preparation of the specimens, show that instead of the needles being mottled uniformly over the entire surface, they are either white or exhibit a delicate line structure traceable to the octahedral planes. Under high powers, avoiding surface tempering, the quenched steel does not give a felted mass of brown needles when the specimens are etched in the usual way, rather are the needles white, and it is the matrix in the interspaces between the needles which etches or dissolves away, so that the needle-like forms are more resistant to etching than the matrix in which they are found. Some needles are slightly mottled and some occasionally turn brown before the interspaces begin to develop. The white needles readily turn brown on tempering and develop a mottled structure, *i.e.* they start to precipitate carbide.

According to F. F. Lucas, and A. Sauveur, therefore, the needles of martensite are not made up of a single phase, but appear to be aggregates. The needles have a central mid-rib which is darker than the surrounding metal—Fig. 106. The mid-rib is supposed to be made up of troostite resulting from the transformation of austenite along its octahedral cleavage ; and the remainder of the needles is supposed to contain some troostite in a state too finely divided to be detected microscopically, but in sufficient quantity to darken the colour of the needles. A. Sauveur thus regarded martensite as an aggregate of solid soln. of iron carbide in γ-iron and of iron carbide in β-iron. An analogous hypothesis is held by H. C. Boynton, J. H. Andrew, L. Grenet, F. F. Lucas, and H. H. Lester. Here, the cooling of the austenite results in the more or less incomplete transformation of the iron into the β-state (A. Sauveur) or into the α-state (F. F. Lucas, and H. H. Lester). The austenite that is transformed becomes troostite, so that martensite is considered to be a mixture of retained austenite and troostite. A. Sauveur considers that troostite is first precipitated from the austenite. The troostite is unstable, and it may be α-iron with carbide in solid soln., or it may be an atomic aggregate of the two. He said that martensite is an aggregate of undercooled austenite and a supersaturated soln. of carbon in α-iron ; that the mechanism of the transformation of austenite to martensite is independent of the rate of cooling ; and that the change is brought about by an α-phase starting around the grain boundaries and along some of the crystallographic planes of the mother austenite ; this gives rise to a Widmanstätten structure on slow cooling, and a martensitic structure on rapid cooling. H. H. Lester regarded martensite as an aggregate of small distorted crystals of iron or of a solid soln. of iron and carbon. F. F. Lucas regarded martensite as an aggregate of ferrite or α-iron and cementite. H. Esser and W. Eilender likewise concluded that martensite is a heterogeneous mixture of α-iron and cementite, and not a solid soln. K. P. Grigorovich considered that the needle-like appearance and the zig-zag lines of martensite are optical effects produced by internal stresses. J. H. Andrew, and L. Grenet also considered martensite to be finely-divided cementite suspended in a matrix of undecomposed austenite and α-iron. Starting with steel in the austenitic condition, with all the carbides absorbed, on quenching quickly white needles are formed comprising a large proportion of the structure. J. A. Mathews, E. C. Bain, and B. D. Enlund have shown that some steels then consist of a mixture of (i) untransformed γ-iron, the original matrix ; (ii) iron carbide, which is formed as the γ-iron changes to α-iron ; and (iii) α-iron. J. Orland concluded that martensite is not a solid soln. of α-iron and carbon, but it occurs in at least two phases distinguishable by etching with nitric acid. K. Gebhard and co-workers also concluded that martensite contains two phases. The heterogeneity and structure of martensite were discussed by E. Oehman, and E. Maurer and G. Riedrich.

Z. Jeffries and R. S. Archer, E. C. Bain, C. Benedicks, P. Chévenard, A. M. Portevin, W. H. Hatfield, K. Honda, A. McCance, and O. E. Harder and R. L. Dowdell consider that when austenite, a solid soln. of carbon or iron carbide in γ-iron, is rapidly cooled, more or less γ-iron is transformed into α-iron, and carbon or iron carbide remains in a kind of supersaturated solid soln. K. Honda and K. Iwase assume that martensite is the first stage in the transformation of a solid soln. of carbon in γ-iron, and it is merely a solid soln. of carbon in α-iron. The solubility of carbon in α-iron is small, so that by rapid cooling the change is equivalent to the production of a supersaturated soln. Austenitic steels, as indicated below, can be converted at room temp. into martensitic steels by tensile stress, by hammering, and by the stresses set up when plunged into liquid air. K. Schröter showed by magnetic observations that the transformation occurs during the cooling and not during the subsequent restoration to ordinary temp. ; and A. Sauveur, and A. Sauveur and C. H. Chou, that when the γ-phase is converted into the α-phase by quenching, the α-phase first appears along the crystallographic planes of austenite and around the boundaries of the grains. According to K. Honda and K. Iwase, freshly-formed martensite hardens on standing for several hours at ordinary temp., or for a few minutes at 100°, so that a temp. in the vicinity of 0° is necessary to prevent the ageing or hardening of martensite. Otherwise expressed, the ordinary temp. of a room is near the limit which will permit the diffusion of carbon in steel, and at any lower temp. the austenite can be held indefinitely in a frozen, torpid condition. The formation of cementite is accompanied by a contraction, and the change from γ-iron to α-iron, by an expansion. The formation of martensite is attended by an expansion, so that, as emphasized by Z. Jeffries, the principal change involves the transformation of γ- to α-iron, and not the production of carbide. In the reheating of martensite the contraction which occurs is due to the formation of cementite. The austenitic, supercooled, solid soln. in γ-iron is unstable, but, at room temp., it changes only slowly into a solid soln. in α-iron. The solid soln. at room temp. is supersaturated with respect to either carbon or cementite, but the thermal agitation of the atoms is too slow to permit a rapid splitting of the martensite into its constituents. It is not clear whether carbon or cementite is the first stage of this transformation where troostite (*vide infra*) is formed.

Ageing or a slight tempering either causes a slight coagulation of the iron carbide into larger particles or else it results in a diffusion of the carbon atoms which form iron carbide, and on further tempering the iron carbide commences to coagulate. The very fine particles of carbide precipitated from the austenite during the quenching may be too minute to be visible microscopically. This is white martensite. With even a slight tempering the fine particles grow to microscopic dimensions. Z. Jeffries assumes that granules of α-iron are intimately associated with the white martensite ; the granules may or may not have carbide in solid soln. C. Benedicks said that there is not a single cause for assuming that martensite and austenite have a different empirical structure ; the difference in their properties on etching, etc., must be attributed to the different states of iron—γ-iron in austenite and β- or rather α-iron in martensite ; austenite is a supercooled solid soln., martensite, a supersaturated solid soln.

A. Westgren and co-workers found that the space-lattice of the iron in martensite corresponds with that of α-iron, and this is also the case with high-speed steel of ordinary composition and hardened at 1275°. A 1·98 per cent. carbon steel quenched in water from 1000° or 1100° had a lattice parameter $a = 2·90$ A., and when quenched from 760°, $a = 2·88$ A., indicating that the martensite contained α-iron. A 1·25 per cent. carbon steel, quenched in water from 760°, had $a = 2·88$ A., indicating that the lattice parameter depends on the amount of carbon in soln. and the quenching temp. When austenitic manganese and nickel steels were immersed in liquid oxygen, the manganese steel showed no change in the X-radiogram, but the nickel steel was changed so that the γ-lines still existed, but they were not sharp but diffuse, indicating that the steel had become extremely fine in crystalline structure ; the lattice parameter of the α-iron produced by this treatment had $a = 2·81$ A., while that of the γ-iron changed from 3·58 to 3·54 A. Only half the original austenitic structure was then changed to white, lanceolar needles. K. Heindlhofer also found that martensite has a body-centred cubic lattice-like α-iron, and inferred that it is spaced approximately 0·4 per cent. closer than the lattice of α-iron. Martensitic steel with 0·80 per cent. of carbon shows the same X-ray spectral lines as iron alone, but the lines are less intense, somewhat broader, and slightly shifted, the amount of shift being approximately the same for different carbon contents. The sp. gr. data show that a considerable part of the carbon present in martensite replaces iron atoms in the space-lattice. The carbon atoms are in the proportion 5 : 9 smaller in diameter than the iron atoms which they replace, and this causes considerable lattice distortion. In general, the results indicate that martensite is a mixture of two constituents, present in variable proportions ; one is a solid soln. of carbon in α-iron and the other is finely dispersed cementite. The solid soln. is unstable and some of the carbon gradually separates from the lattice even at room temp., so that it is difficult to keep more than a part of carbon in soln. Consequently, while austenite is a structure in which a face-centred cubic lattice of iron atoms also has carbon atoms in the interstices, martensite is a structure with a body-centred cubic lattice of iron atoms with carbon atoms in the interstices, as the iron in austenite passes from the γ- to the α-state when it is cooled below the Ac_1-arrest. The X-radiograms show that in addition to α-iron, some lines of γ-iron are always present in martensite, indicating that the transformation of the austenite is not complete. The unconverted austenite is called *retained austenite*. The solid soln. is unstable even at the ordinary temp. At 260° the lattice distortion of martensite largely disappears in 30 minutes, although only part of the carbon is precipitated, and the hardness is still far above that of the annealed state. The cementite also contributes to the hardness by reason of its fine-grained condition. R. F. Mehl and co-workers' observations on compressibility also agree with the assumption that martensite consists largely of ferrite and finely-divided cementite. J. Orland, and K. Gebhard and co-workers also agree that martensite consists of two phases involving a metastable system. W. Broniewsky regarded martensite as a transitional substance not deserving a place in the equilibrium diagram of the iron-carbon alloys.   S. Sekito studied the conversion of martensite to cementite (*q.v.*).

W. L. Fink and E. D. Campbell reported that in strongly-quenched, eutectoidal and hypereutectoidal carbon steels, the crystal structure seems to have a body-centred tetragonal lattice with $a=2\cdot85$ A., and $c=3\cdot02$ A., or an axial ratio $a:c$ $=1:1\cdot06$, so that the a-axis increased from $2\cdot55$ to $2\cdot85$ A., while the c-axis decreased from $3\cdot60$ to $3\cdot02$ A.   E. C. Bain, however, showed that in changing from the γ- to the a-lattice, the body-centred arrangement is at first tetragonal with an axial ratio $a:c=1:1\cdot414$; and suggested that the final condition in martensite is an incomplete transformation to the " perfectly cubically crystallized a-iron."

Z. Jeffries and R. S. Archer said that when the cooling rate of austenite is rapid enough to form martensite, the transformation of the γ-iron to a-iron is substantially complete, while the formation of cementite is not complete.   Martensite therefore consists principally of submicroscopic a-iron or ferrite grains containing carbon in soln.   The carbon of the mother austenite will strive to precipitate as particles of cementite, and the extent of the reaction will depend on the conditions of temperature and time during quenching, ageing, and tempering.   That the formation of martensite from austenite represents a change from γ- to a-iron is shown by : (i) the complete change in the microstructure of martensite, as compared with that observed when austenite is preserved by quenching, indicates a transformation of the γ-iron ; (ii) the magnetic susceptibility of martensite suggests the presence of a-iron ; and (iii) the X-radiograms show that a-iron is the principal constituent of martensite. Non-magnetic steels have face-centred cubic lattices characteristic of γ-iron, whereas magnetic, martensitic steels have the body-centred cubic lattice characteristic of a-iron.   A $1\cdot5$ per cent. carbon steel quenched in iced brine from above the critical point has both martensite and austenite and both body-centred and face-centred cubic lattices, whereas a $0\cdot35$ per cent. carbon steel quenched from above the Ac_1-arrest shows the presence of martensite only and only the body-centred lattice.   K. Heindlhofer and E. C. Bain observed that martensite is composed of characteristically distorted ferrite units or grains, not markedly different in size from those of the parent austenite.   The type of distortion is that developed by twisting or bending, so as to retain a moderate constancy of spacing between the (110)-planes, but at the same time to vary the orientation of some of the same planes through a considerable angle.   The ferrite units possess a marked random atomic irregularity of the solid soln. type—*vide infra*.

K. Honda, T. Matsushita, S. Sato, and K. Honda and S. Sekito showed that there are probably two martensites—a-**martensite,** which has a body-centred tetragonal lattice, with the axial ratio $c:a=1\cdot03$ to $1\cdot06$, is formed from austenite when the cooling is rapid ; and β-**martensite,** which has a body-centred cubic lattice.   When steel is quenched, the change of austenite to a-martensite is partly arrested and the change of a-martensite to β-martensite is completely hindered, so that in the outer layer, where the cooling is rapid, a-martensite with a little austenite is present ; but in the inner portion, where the cooling is slower, both changes occur almost completely, and β-martensite alone is found there—*vide infra*, hardening.   T. Matsushita, H. Hanemann and A. Schräder, and K. Honda showed that during the slow heating of a quenched high-carbon steel the heating curves indicate that the separation of carbon in the form of cementite occurs in two stages, one at 130° and the other at 280°.   This is taken to mean that there is an a-martensite and a β-martensite distinguishable by their degree of tempering.   Later K. Honda showed that it is more probable that the 130° breaks in the curves of magnetization, heating, electrical resistance and thermal expansion are not caused by the decomposition of martensite by the precipitation of cementite, but rather by the change of a- into β-martensite.   The change at 130° begins at about 100°, is very rapid at 230°, and is completed at 300°.   M. A. Grossmann found that a high-speed steel, quenched from a high temp., was softer when tempered at 482° than at 593°, and the result was explained on the basis of the a- and β-martensites.

T. Matsushita, and K. Honda attributed the hardness of quenched steels to the presence of β-martensite, not α-martensite. α-martensite is first formed in a cooling austenitic steel, and then β-martensite. The changes are reversed on heating pearlitic steels. The α-martensite is more easily etched by picric acid and more easily tempered by heating than β-martensite. W. L. Fink and E. D. Campbell, and N. Seljakoff and co-workers observed that in addition to the body-centred cubic lattice in quenched carbon steels there is also a body-centred tetragonal lattice with the axial ratio $c : a$ approximating 1·06. K. Honda and S. Sekito consider that the body-centred cubic lattice represents ordinary or β-martensite, and the body-centred tetragonal lattice, α-martensite—*vide infra*, ferrite, and also hardening. K. Honda and S. Sekito found that the parameter of the body-centred cubic lattice of β-martensite is lengthened with increasing proportions of carbon, thus :

Carbon	0·202	0·396	0·508	0·620	0·730	0·895	1·04 per cent.
A	2·860	2·863	2·864	2·864	2·867	2·870	2·866
Sp. vol.	0·1271	0·1275	0·1276	0·1276	0·1280	0·1284	0·1279

whilst for α-martensite with its body-centred tetragonal lattice :

Carbon	0·202	0·396	0·508	0·620	0·730	0·895	1·04	1·075 per cent.
A	2·839	2·838	2·836	2·832	2·834	2·837	2·838	2·839
$c : a$	1·068	1·073	1·072	1·073	1·072	1·066	1·066	1·055
Sp. vol.	0·1327	0·1332	0·1327	0·1324	0·1324	0·1321	0·1323	0·1313

A face-centred cubic lattice can be regarded as a body-centred tetragonal lattice with the axial ratio $c : a = \sqrt{2}$ (Fig. 107) ; and a body-centred cubic lattice as a body-centred tetragonal lattice with the axial ratio $c : a = 1$. Observations show that the axial ratio of the body-centred tetragonal lattice of α-martensite has the axial ratio $c : a = 1·03$ to 1·06. The alterations in the tetragonal lattices involve the change from austenite $(c : a = \sqrt{2})$ to α-martensite $(c : a = 1·03$ to 1·06) and to β-martensite $(c : a = 1)$. The successive changes involved in the transformation of the face-centred cubic lattice of austenite to the face-centred tetragonal lattice involve a uniform compression in the direction of the c-axis of the tetragonal lattice with $c : a = \sqrt{2}$, and at the same time a uniform expansion in a perpendicular direction ; when $c : a = \sqrt{2}$ has changed to 1·03 to 1·06, α-martensite is formed, and as the change continues until the ratio is unity, ordinary or β-martensite with its body-centred cubic lattice is formed. The fact that in martensite two tetragonal configurations (with $c : a = 1·06$ and 1) of the iron and carbon atoms are possible can be explained by the electron theory of atomic structure. The actual form of the atoms is far from being spherical, and hence it is quite probable that the orientation of the carbon atoms in relation to the iron

FIG. 107.—The Relationship of the Face-centred Cubic Lattice to the Body-centred Tetragonal Lattice.

atoms in the lattice may give rise to two or more metastable configurations. In the outer layer of a quenched steel, where cooling is very rapid, the first change of austenite to α-martensite goes on partially, and the second change of α-martensite to β-martensite is completely hindered, so that the outer layer must contain α-martensite mixed with a small amount of retained austenite ; while in the inner portion, where the cooling is less rapid, the first and the second changes will take place almost completely, so that the inner portion must contain almost pure β-martensite. The general result for single crystals was confirmed by G. Kurdjumoff and G. Sachs. The length of the c-axis increases, whilst that of the a-axis diminishes, with increasing carbon content. In a steel containing 1·03 per cent. C the ratio c/a is constant (1·041 to 1·045) for initial temp. of 900°, 1100°, and 1300° ; in a steel containing 0·91 per cent. C the diminution of the ratio commences at 850°. The non-homogeneity of the tetragonal structure causes diffusibility of the lines of the X-radiograms. K. Honda's β-martensite is probably a mixture of tetragonal crystals with different small ratios of the axes.

G. Kurdjumoff and E. Kaminsky found that in quenched steels containing 0·64 to 1·44 per cent. of carbon, the tetragonal structure exists not only at the surface, but also at a depth of 5 mm.   G. Kurdjumoff and co-workers found that the mixture of austenite and martensite in a chilled 1·5 per cent. carbon steel had the (011)-plane of the tetragonal crystallites parallel to the (111)-planes of austenite,

TABLE XI.—LATTICE DIMENSIONS OF TETRAGONAL MARTENSITE AND OF γ-IRON.

Carbon per cent.	Tetragonal Phase				γ-Iron	
	a	c	$a : c$	Vol.	a	Vol.
0·71	2·853	2·941	1 : 1·031	11·97	3·581	11·48
0·80	2·852	2·956	1 : 1·036	12·06	3·584	11·51
1·04	2·848	2·979	1 : 1·046	12·08	3·592	11·59
1·20	2·846	2·999	1 : 1·054	12·15	3·600	11·66
1·35	2·843	3·014	1 : 1·060	12·18	3·609	11·76
1·40	2·840	3·034	1 : 1·068	12·23	3·616	11·82

and the (111)-direction to the (101)-direction giving an 8° angle between the tetragonal and the austenite axis.   This position repeats itself 24-fold in agreement with the general cubical symmetry ; and it can be derived from a superposition of two simple slip motions.   E. Oehman measured the (101)-line in the X-radiogram of the tetragonal phase, and obtained the results indicated in Table XI for the linear dimensions of the tetragonal lattice in A-units and for the vol. per lattice point in A_3-units ; similarly also for the face-centred lattice of γ-iron.   The results are plotted in Fig. 108, and show the convergence of the curves for the axial dimensions converge to a point corresponding with the edge of the elementary cube of a-iron.   This is in agreement with the results of G. Kurdjumoff and E. Kaminsky, and with their assumption, confirmed by the thermal observations of E. Maurer and G. Riedrich, and the microscopic observations of F. Wever and N. Engel, that tetragonal martensite is a supersaturated soln. of carbon in a-iron ; and that tetragonal martensite and ferrite are one and the same phase.

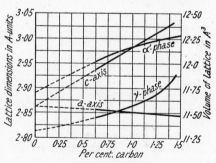

FIG. 108.—The Lattice Dimensions of the a'-Phase, and the Volumes per Lattice Point of the a'- and γ-Phases.

The two may be present in one specimen, and hence E. Oehman designates the tetragonal phase as the a'-phase.

Three hypotheses are available as to the disposition of the carbon atoms in the a'-phase.   (i) According to A. Westgren and G. Phragmen, the carbon atoms dissolved in γ-iron do not occupy points of the face-centred lattice, but are statistically distributed in the interstices between the iron atoms.   N. Seljakoff and co-workers suggested a similar arrangement for the a'-phase, and in order to explain the tetragonal deformation assumed that the carbon atoms are distributed at the centre of those faces which are perpendicular to the tetragonal axis. E. Oehman added that this arrangement is improbable, since the space available for the carbon is very small, and even if a carbon atom were located at one of the points where the distances to the surrounding iron atoms are greatest, the space available for the carbon atom would be much smaller than in the face-centred structure ; and as a consequence, the vol. of the body-centred lattice would increase more rapidly with the carbon content than would be the case with the face-centred lattice.   The curves for the a'- and γ-phrases, Fig. 108, show that the converse of this inference is true.   (ii) G. Hägg suggested that the carbon atoms may be so disposed that two carbon atoms replace one iron atom in the lattice, as was observed by M. von Stackelberg for many tetragonal carbides, and analogous with the tetragonal lattices of some hydrides observed by G. Hägg, where two hydrogen atoms occupy the place of one metal atom.   It is further assumed that the C_2-groups are oriented parallel with the tetragonal axis of martensite.   (iii) E. Oehman suggested that the carbon atoms are simply substituted for iron atoms in the lattice, and this explains the decrease in the lattice dimensions, since the carbon atoms are much smaller than the iron atoms.

E. Oehman found that when the a'- or tetragonal phase is produced by quenching steel containing 1·35 per cent. of carbon and allowing it to remain in liquid air for 48 hrs. the sp. gr. was 7·62.   The specimen contains both γ-iron and a'-iron, with the latter predominant.   The sp. gr. of austenite with 1·34 per cent. of carbon is 7·94 ;   the sp. gr. of a'-iron (i) with interstitial carbon atoms is 7·65 ;   (ii) with a substitution of doubled carbon atoms, 7·42 ;   and (iii) with a substitution of single carbon atoms, 7·19.   The observed sp. gr. does not agree with (i) ;   the observed sp. gr. would agree with 60 per cent. of a'-iron and 40 per cent. of γ-iron, which is in harmony with (ii) ; and the observed sp. gr. requires 57 per cent. of γ-iron and 43 per cent. of a-iron if the third assumption be valid, but this is not in conformity with the intensities of the X-ray lines, which show that the a'-phase is dominant.   Hence the only structure in agreement with the observed sp. gr., the increase in vol. with the carbon content, and the elongation of one of the crystallographic axes is that in the body-centred lattice C_2-groups of carbon atoms replace some iron atoms.   The carbon atoms are probably oriented in such a way that the axes of the C_2-groups are parallel to the tetragonal axis of the lattice.   The a'-phase is decomposed on tempering.

The sp. gr. of a-martensite is less than that of β-martensite.   The sp. vol. of a-martensite is represented by $v=0\cdot1335-0\cdot0018[C]$, and that of β-martensite by $v=0\cdot1267+0\cdot0017[C]$, where $[C]$ denotes the percentage of carbon.   The carbon atoms of β-martensite are assumed to be distributed in the centre of the face of the elementary cube, in accord with the laws of probability.   The atomic distances in a-martensite are a little greater than in β-martensite, in agreement with the greater hardness of β-martensite.   S. Sekito found that the axial ratio of the tetragonal lattice diminishes in magnitude from the surface to the interior, finally taking the value unity.   The axial ratio of the tetragonal lattice increases with the carbon content, as well as with the quenching temp.

The changes in the space-lattice which occur during the transformation of austenite into martensite were also discussed by A. E. van Arkel, S. Sato, K. Becker, O. E. Harder and R. L. Dowdell, F. C. Elder, U. Dehlinger, E. Scheil, G. Tammann and A. Heinzel, O. Mügge, K. Honda, A. Westgren, F. Wever, and A. Smekal. F. Wever represented the effect of carbon and manganese in austenitic steels on the parameter of the iron lattice by $3\cdot578+0\cdot0005[Mn]+0\cdot00645[C]$, where the bracketed symbols represent atomic percentages.   The lattice parameter of a-iron is increased from 2·861 A. to 2·875 A. in hardened steel, but is practically unchanged in annealed steels.   Hence carbon atoms fill spaces in the lattice of a-iron, and do not replace iron in the lattice structure.   The space-lattices are discussed below in connection with ferrite, and also in connection with hardening.   The marked broadening of the diffusion of the X-ray spectral lines of the martensites was explained by A. Westgren by assuming that each individual martensite crystal consists further of a very large number of minute crystals oriented at random, their linear dimensions containing only several hundreds of atoms.   K. Honda and S. Sekito said that this does not agree with the fact that martensite consists of well-defined acicular crystals, and they attributed the phenomenon to a continuously varying strain of the iron lattice caused by the carbon atoms in the interspaces.   N. Seljakoff and co-workers do not accept the inference that the axis of the lattice of tetragonal martensite is independent of the carbon content ;   the presence of carbon atoms in the lattice produces a decrease in the intensity, but not a broadening, of the spectral lines.

Both martensite and austenite are supposed to be unstable, and with a prolonged annealing their transformation into the stable phase will proceed to an end. The mechanism of tempering has been studied from different points of view—changes in microstructure by F. Osmond; solubility in acids by E. Heyn and O. Bauer; sp. gr. by E. Maurer; hardness, K. Honda and K. Tamaru; thermal expansion, T. Matsushita; X-ray spectrum, K. Heindlhofer; electrical resistance, B. D. Enlund; thermoelectric force, S. Sato; magnetization, S. Sato; and coercive force, E. Maurer. S. Sato showed that there is a small evolution of heat at about 150°, and this represents the change of α-martensite into β-martensite; a relatively large evolution of heat occurs in the range 260° to 300° due to the decomposition of β-martensite into troostite. Retained austenite decomposes into α- and β-martensites when it is cooled down to the temp. of liquid air, or more easily, when magnetically agitated in this cooled state. The retained austenite decomposes through α- and β-martensites into troostite when heated between 260° and 300°, and this is attended by a relatively large evolution of heat. K. Honda and T. Matsushita considered this thermal change to be due to the decomposition of β-martensite; and E. Maurer and G. Schilling, G. Tammann and E. Scheil, and A. Merz and

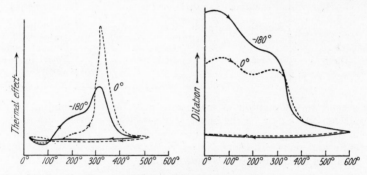

FIGS. 109 and 110.—The Thermal Effect and the Dilation of Hardened Steel when Annealed at Different Temperatures.

C. Pfannenschmidt regarded it as a result of the decomposition of austenite. According to S. Sato, there is a contraction in the range from 300° to 400°, and this is attended by a distinct evolution of heat. It is supposed to be produced by the lattice building of cementite particles or molecules. α-iron which has been mechanically strained during quenching begins to recrystallize between 450° and 600° and this is attended by a relatively small evolution of heat. The subject was discussed by S. Sato, K. Tamaru, and K. Kawakami.

G. Tammann and E. Scheil compared the thermal effect, Fig. 109, with the annealing of a steel hardened by cooling to 0°, and the same steel again cooled in liquid air at —180°. The steel had 1·72 per cent. of carbon. There are three critical points on the curves: (i) at about 100° there is a change due to the transformation of martensite; (ii) at about 250°, a change due to the transformation of austenite; and (iii) at about 300° there is a change which is not due to the transformation of austenite, because it is accentuated with the steel cooled in liquid air. It is thought to be due to a second transformation of the martensite. These changes were discussed by K. Honda, S. Sekito, and A. Merz and C. Pfannenschmidt; but T. Matsushita and K. Nagasawa supposed the transformation to be due not to a transformation of martensite, but to a change in the nature of the carbon associated with the iron. The properties of the structural constituents in these changes are summarized by E. Scheil in Table XII. K. Honda found that the specific properties X—hardness, electrical conductivity, and the intensity of magnetization—of austenite, β-martensite, and α-martensite are related as $X_{aus.} < X_{\alpha\text{-mar.}} < X_{\beta\text{-mar.}}$, and the sp. vol., v, as $v_{aus.} < v_{\beta\text{-mar.}} < v_{\alpha\text{ mar.}}$.

TABLE XII.—THE PROPERTIES OF THE CONSTITUENTS FORMED IN THE ANNEALING
OF HARDENED STEEL.

Property	First martensite transformation (about 100°)	Austenite transformation (about 250°)	Second martensite transformation (about 300°)
Volume . . .	Decrease	Increase	Decrease
Hardness . .	Initial increase, then decrease ; at higher temp. only decrease	Increase	With low carbon, initial feeble increase, then in all cases strong decrease
Acid attack . .	As with hardness	Increase	Initial increase, then decrease
Electric conductivity	Increase	Increase	Increase
Heat transformation	Feebly exothermal	Strongly exothermal	Feebly exothermal
Lattice change .	Tetragonal to cubic space - centred. Interference sharp	Face-centred cubic to space-centred cubic	Parameter changes. Interference sharper
Magnetic—			
Saturation . .	Small increase probable	Strong increase	Small increase probable
Remanence . .	—	Increase	Probable increase
Coercive force .	Decrease	Increase	Initial increase, then decrease

The second transformation of martensite may be a continuation of the first transformation, or it may be the result of some intermediate stages in the transformation of martensite to pearlite. The modification in the equilibrium diagram for austenite and martensite founded on E. Maurer's hypothesis that martensite is a solid soln. of carbon in α-iron is shown in Fig. 111. The equilibrium curve of

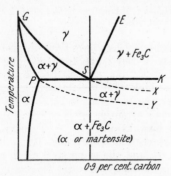

FIG. 111.—E. Maurer's Austenite-Martensite Diagram.

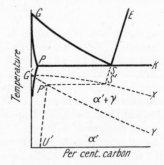

FIG. 112.—G. Tammann and E. Scheil's Austenite-Martensite Diagram.

austenite and martensite is represented by an extension of the lines GP and GS beyond the pearlite line PSK. If the martensite is a solid soln., its physical properties will change continuously with the carbon content, and this conclusion is in agreement with the measurements of E. Gumlich, E. Maurer, and C. Benedicks on the electrical conductivity, and with those of N. Seljakoff and co-workers, and W. L Fink on the change of the lattice parameter. The facts also fit the hypothesis of G. Tammann and E. Scheil that instead of α-iron a similar but unstable form α'-iron occurs as a phase in martensite. This renders the

modification indicated in Fig. 112 necessary, where the dotted lines refer to the
a'-martensite. In this case, it is supposed that at 100° carbon separates along
$P'U'$ in accord with its solubility in a'-iron, and at 300° there is a transformation
of the cementite-saturated a'-solid soln. into a-iron. If so, above the solubility
limits of the carbon, the transformation into a'-iron must be independent of the
carbon content.

There is also the hypothesis that the second martensite effect is the result of
the formation of an intermediate unstable carbide which possesses the required
properties. This hypothesis was explored by S. Hilpert and T. Dickmann,
E. D. Campbell, and H. Hanemann and L. Träger. There is also the hypothesis
that the second martensite transformation is a recrystallization of the martensite
—*vide supra* ; and the ϵ-η-hypothesis of H. Hanemann.

H. Hanemann observed that when austenite changes into martensite, *e.g.*
by quenching in liquid air, the crystals of martensite contain less carbon than the
adjacent austenite. According to H. Hanemann and A. Schrader, an examination
of the martensite of steels with 0·05
to 0·2 per cent. of carbon tempered
under various conditions shows that
in addition to phases involving a-
and γ-iron, there are also two phases
involving ϵ-iron, θ-iron, and η-iron.
The ϵ-**martensite** and η-**martensite**
are in metastable equilibrium with
austenite, and have the constitutional diagram, provisionally represented by Fig. 113 ; that is, they
form a peritectoid equilibrium. The
iron-cementite equilibrium diagram
was called, the metastable system
I, and the martensite system, the
metastable system II. The conc.
of the carbon at U is near 0·10 per
cent. ; at V, 0·89 per cent. ; and
at W, 1·40 per cent. The critical
temp., T, is near the A_3-point ; and
AVW, 325°. The critical temp. at
685° was observed with a 0·07 per
cent. carbon steel ; it is not a
delayed $\gamma{\to}a$ change, because the
difference is too large to be explained

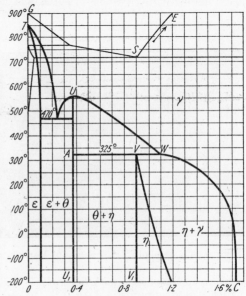

FIG. 113.—Supposed Phases in the Martensite
System.

as a super-cooling effect. They call T the Ar″ transformation. With rapid quenching
of steels with 1·40 per cent. of carbon in liquid air, the formation of cementite and of
troostite can be prevented, and the transformation of γ-**martensite** follows approximately the courses indicated by Fig. 113. TW, between 850° and 325°, represents
the line along which ϵ-martensite separates from γ-martensite, and AW, the line
along which ϵ-martensite reacts with γ-martensite to form either a mixture of
ϵ- and η-martensites or of η- and γ-martensites, depending on whether the proportion
of carbon is greater or less than 0·89 per cent. On quenching 0·89 per cent. carbon
steel, ϵ-martensite of 0·10 per cent. carbon reacts at 350° with γ-martensite of
1·4 per cent. carbon to form η-martensite with 0·89 per cent. of carbon. If the
carbon is between 1·40 and 1·70 per cent., the peritectoidal reaction just indicated
does not occur, and η-martensite separates from γ-martensite—*vide infra*, tempering.
The microsection, Fig. 114 ($\times$1200), shows ϵ-martensite in long narrow needles surrounded by darkly etched η-martensite which stands in relief. The specimen contained 0·13 per cent. of carbon, and 0·5 per cent. of manganese ; it was kept 45 mins.
at 1120°, cooled slowly to 920°, and then rapidly quenched in liquid air. Fig. 115

($\times 1200$) shows dark needles of ϵ- and η-martensite in a light ground-mass of austenite ; the specimen contained 1·23 per cent. of carbon and 0·41 per cent. of manganese ; it was held 30 mins. at 1100°, cooled to 960°, and then quenched in liquid air. Fig. 116 ($\times 150$) shows η-needles. The sample contained 1·75 per cent. carbon and 0·64 per cent. of manganese ; it was held 30 mins. at 1125°, tempered at 200°, cooled to −20°, and afterwards in liquid air. There are thus formed two sets of needles of η-martensite ; those formed by the liquid air quenching are etched lightly. The η-phase is J. O. Arnold's hardenite. The θ-phase, or θ-**martensite,** was demonstrated by K. Gebhard and co-workers, H. Birnbaum, and T. Matsushita. It was called **heynite,** after E. Heyn. It is found in hardened steel containing 0·3 to 0·4 per cent. of carbon. The subject was discussed by H. Hanemann and L. Träger, E. Maurer and G. Riedrich, and K. Gebhard and co-workers. J. Orland, and K. Gebhard and co-workers also agree that martensite consists of two phases involving a metastable system. In the metastable system ϵ-iron occurs in steels with up to about 0·1 per cent. of carbon ; in steels with from 0·1 to 0·37 per cent. of carbon martensite consists of ϵ-iron and heynite ; while in steels with 0·37 to 0·9 per cent. of carbon the constituents are heynite and hardenite ; and with steels with over 0·9 per cent. of carbon, hardenite and austenite. If equilibrium

Figs. 114, 115, and 116.—Forms of Martensite (H. Hanemann and A. Schrader).

is not completely established, heynite may occur with steels with over 0·9 per cent. of carbon, and austenite in steels with less carbon.

F. Osmond applied the term **troostite**—after L. Troost—to a transitional form of the solid soln. of carbide in iron between martensite and pearlite. It comes between martensite and sorbite, or martensite and osmondite, so that it is regarded as martensite arrested while changing into sorbite or osmondite—*vide infra,* tempering. Troostite is obtained by modifying the speed of quenching. F. Osmond, and H. le Chatelier obtained it in the cold by quenching steel with different proportions of carbon during the recalescence period, *i.e.* when martensite is changing to pearlite ; by a mild quenching of small pieces in oil or boiling water from a temp. above the critical point ; or by a mild tempering (*q.v.*) of martensite between 100° and 260°. The X-radiograms agree with the assumption that troostite, like sorbite and pearlite, is a mechanical mixture of ferrite and cementite. H. C. Boynton said that it is produced when a metal with 0·45 per cent. carbon is cooled down to the A_1-arrest and then quenched in water at atm. temp. It is formed by heating martensite or austenite to 400°, or by cooling the steel to the temp. of liquid air. B. D. Enlund observed that with quenched or martensitic steels the conversion of martensite to troostite occurs between 100° and 200°. The subject was discussed by A. E. Cameron and I. F. Morrison, O. V. Greene, D. K. Bullens, A. Schrader, and K. Tamaru—*vide infra,* tempering. H. le Chatelier obtained troostite by heating one end of a steel bar containing 0·9 per cent. of carbon, while the other end is free in air. There is thus a variation of temp. throughout the length of the bar. After quenching, the points of medium hardness are found by means of a file, and on suitably etching sections from these parts, untransformed pearlite will be found separated from completely transformed pearlite by a zone of troostite.

A. M. Portevin and M. Garvin observed that troostite formed in the neighbourhood of 600°, and martensite at 300°. L. Guillet found steels with 5 to 15 per cent. of chromium and over 0·5 per cent. of carbon have a structure of troostite mixed with martensite ; and steels with 3 to 12 per cent. of manganese and over 0·5 per cent. of carbon may consist of troostite above or admixed with martensite. H. le Chatelier, and H. von Jüptner observed that when troostite is formed by quenching from the recalescence period, there is a sudden contraction, indicating a molecular change in the metal. W. C. Roberts-Austen said that it is a modification of cementite ; and H. le Chatelier, a solid soln. of carbide in iron, differing from martensite and austenite in being magnetic at the temp. of its formation.

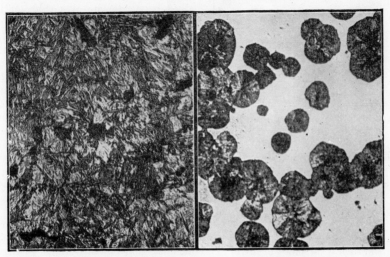

Fig. 117.—Small Cells of Troostite in Martensite.

Fig. 118.—Troostite in Martensite (F. F. Lucas).

H. M. Howe regarded it as a mixture of austenite, ferrite, and cementite in varying proportions. T. Matsushita and K. Nagasawa considered troostite, formed by tempering austenitic steels for 20 mins. at 100° to 300° and again cooling, is made up of α-iron with the elemental carbon precipitated in a highly dispersed form, so that it is nearly optically homogeneous. C. Benedicks added that the electrical resistance and sp. vol. of troostite behave like pearlite, that is, like a mechanical mixture of ferrite and cementite. Z. Jeffries and R. S. Archer observed that the tempering of martensite is attended by (i) the growth of ferrite and the precipitation of carbide, and (ii) the growth of cementite particles.

F. Osmond said that the microstructure of troostite can be resolved and recognized by polishing and etching with liquorice root, or ammonium nitrate, when it assumes a yellowish-brown colour, or blue bands merging into one another. When slightly etched with dil. tincture of iodine it appears as brown bands in the shape of needles resembling martensite but surrounding grains of hardenite—saturated martensite—and with ferrite between the grains. It can also be etched by dil. alcoholic soln. of nitric acid, hydrochloric acid, or picric acid, or by W. J. Kurbatoff's reagent—a four per cent. soln. of nitric acid in isoamyl alcohol. H. von

Jüptner referred to troostite as a jagged constituent between martensite and cementite. According to H. C. Boynton, the hardness of troostite is 88 when that of martensite is 239 and that of ferrite is unity—*vide infra*, hardness. The structure of troostite is illustrated by Fig. 117 (× 500), of a steel with 0·869 per cent. of carbon heated for an hour at 700°, 15 mins. at 800°, and quenched in water at 18° ; it was then etched with a soln. of hydrogen chloride in amyl alcohol. The small dark cells of troostite are embedded in paler cells of martensite : Fig. 118 (× 150) shows the dark troostite in steel with 1·5 per cent. of carbon ; and Fig. 119 (× 2400), by

FIG. 119.—Troostite in Martensite (F. F. Lucas).

F. F. Lucas, shows nodular troostite in a steel containing 2·65 per cent. of carbon and 0·07 per cent. of manganese, and etched with picric acid. Highly magnified photographs of troostite were also made by R. A. Hadfield and T. G. Elliott. Troostite thus appears as dark-coloured, irregular areas which represent sections through nodules ; it is generally accompanied by martensite or sorbite, or both, or else it appears as a membrane surrounding martensite grains. F. F. Lucas described two types of troostite ; one he called nodular, and the other floccular ; and J. H. Whiteley also considered two types of troostite, which he called *troostite-M*, and *troostite-A*. According to F. F. Lucas, in hypoeutectoidal steels the troostite is accompanied by ferrite, and in hypereutectoidal steels cementite, and even pearlite, may be present ; this, said A. Sauveur, indicates that the iron in troostite is capable of dissolving carbon as carbide up to the eutectoidal point, and hence he argued that the iron of troostite is in the β-state, because (i) α-iron can dissolve only about 0·05 per cent. of carbon and only carbide should be rejected by the cooling of troostite ; and (ii) the X-radiogram shows that it is not γ-iron.

H. C. Boynton adopted the hypothesis that troostite is a form of carbonless iron—ferrite—and since its properties, particularly its black colour on etching, differ so much from those of α-iron, he concluded that it was β-iron. F. Osmond originally thought that troostite is some transitory association of β-iron and carbon, but he abandoned the hypothesis. F. Rogers, W. J. Kurbatoff, and C. Benedicks regarded troostite as a soln. of elementary carbon, not carbide, in iron ; but C. Benedicks showed that this hypothesis is not probable ; rather is F. Osmond's opinion that troostite is an intermediate form between martensite and pearlite more likely. F. Osmond described troostite as being nearly amorphous, slightly granular, and mammillated. J. O. Arnold described what appears to have been F. Osmond's troostite as emulsified carbon present in an exceedingly fine state of subdivision in tempered steels ; and W. C. Roberts-Austen's definition of troostite was practically the same. C. Benedicks added that there is a continuous transition between troostite and pearlite, and that troostite is pearlite with ultramicroscopically small particles of cementite with the iron in the α- or β-state ; it is that part of martensite in which the cementite has just begun to form—incipient pearlite formation—but owing to the rapidity of cooling, the separate particles of cementite have not attained such a size that they can be distinguished microscopically. As observed by E. Heyn, in hypoeutectoid steels troostite occurs as a zone following the borders of the ferrite ; troostite has not been observed within the martensite where it is not in contact with ferrite ; while in hypereutectoid steel troostite occurs by preference in contact with cementite, and W. J. Kurbatoff, and C. Benedicks said that the centre of the patches of troostite generally contain cementite. In agreement with C. Benedicks' assumption that troostite is a colloidal soln. of cementite, that is, a pearlite with ultramicroscopically small particles of cementite, W. J. Kurbatoff said that there is no clear boundary limit between pearlite and troostite, so that it appears as if troostite is a pearlite composed of very thin laminæ—*vide infra*, sorbite. A. McCance also concluded that (i) troostite consists essentially of α-iron which is in the amorphous state and not as it is in the crystalline form of ferrite, and (ii) that troostite contains carbon in suspension, and not in soln. as iron carbide. The magnetic permeability of quenched or tempered steel is greater as the amount of contained troostite increases, and consequently the iron is present in the α- and not in the β-state. The growth of troostite was studied by S. Sato.

According to F. F. Lucas, in nodular troostite there is a crystalline growth about a nucleus, probably a result of the reorientation of freshly formed particles of α-iron about an inclusion or pore, or along a grain boundary of crystallographic plane. The carbide collects in very thin plates, forming a laminated or sandwich structure with the ferrite. Pearlite is formed under one set of conditions. The microscopic pattern which results is a visible manifestation of the way the transformation occurs. If rapid, the pattern is acicular; if less rapid, nodular. K. Honda believes that martensite forms first and troostite next. There is nothing to show that the needles are formed first and nodules second. If this were the case, nodules would sometimes appear with partially absorbed or transformed needles sticking out of their outlines, but none such has been seen. According to F. F. Lucas, the difference between martensite needles and troostite nodules does not lie in the ultimate constituents, for both seem to be composed of α-iron and iron carbide. The difference is the way in which the two structural forms have developed, and the grain-size of the particles of the carbide. There is a midrib in the martensitic needles indicating the plane along which decomposition first occurred. On each side of the midrib there is a tapering zone. These zones are not as fully transformed as the midrib, because the midrib etches out, forming a trough. The inner crystalline orientation of the needles appears in all cases to be the same as the orientation of the original austenite. In troostite, however, there is very definite evidence that the larger nodules develop about a nucleus, usually a pore or an inclusion, and they form into spheres. The nuclei at the centre of the nodules have grains radiating from them. A section of a troostitic nodule often looks like a wagon wheel in which the hub is the nucleus and the spokes are grain boundaries. In the case of troostite the freshly transformed α-iron appears to have been reoriented without following in all details the old austenite crystalline symmetry. The subject was discussed by N. T. Belaiew.

In the passage from martensite to pearlite, the colloidal theory of C. Benedicks assumed that martensite first changed into a colloidal soln. of cementite in ferrite, and that by the coalescence of the individual particles of ferrite and of cementite pearlite was produced. The nascent, unresolved pearlite was called troostite. Troostite thus differs from pearlite solely in its mechanical state of aggregation. According to the osmondite theory of E. Heyn and O. Bauer, it is assumed that a definite substance which they called **osmondite**—after F. Osmond—is formed as an intermediate stage in the passage of martensite to pearlite. The characteristics of osmondite are : (i) It is not cementite. (ii) It is more readily attacked by dil. sulphuric acid than martensite, ferrite, or cementite—*vide infra*, Fig. 131. The solubility curve shows a maximum with the formation of osmondite, and it diminishes in both directions towards martensite and towards pearlite. The transition stages between martensite and osmondite may therefore be denoted by the generic term troostite, and those between osmondite and pearlite, by sorbite. When dissolved in 10 per cent. sulphuric acid, out of contact with air, the troostites leave no carbon residue but a residue rich in carbon containing little or no iron. The whole carbon content of the residue does not dissolve in hot conc. hydrochloric acid, but all the iron is extracted by that solvent. The free carbon so obtained is distinct from the carbide carbon, which remains combined as carbide on dissolving steel in 10 per cent. sulphuric acid out of contact with air. This carbide is dissolved by hot conc. hydrochloric acid, giving off hydrocarbon gas, and leaves no carbon residue. This carbide first occurs in sorbites, and increases in quantity as the temp. of tempering increases up to the pearlite stage, the carbon of which is nearly all present as carbide. (iii) The colouring of all tempered steels in the presence of alcoholic hydrochloric acid, as well as the colouring of troostite and osmondite in hardened steels, is caused by the separation of free carbon. Osmondite contains the maximum amount of carbon, and is coloured darkest. (iv) When hardened or martensite steel is tempered, most of the heat is liberated below 400°. The transition from martensite to osmondite is therefore accompanied by the liberation of most of the heat, whereas the amount of heat liberated in the passage from osmondite to pearlite is very limited. (v) The segregation of one or more solids, x, from the solid soln. of martensite during its tempering up to about 400° may proceed ultramicroscopically or microscopically The x gives up the maximum amount of free carbon when treated with dil. sulphuric acid, and the amount of x therefore increases in passing in the troostites from martensite to osmondite, and decreases in passing in the sorbites from osmondite to pearlite. Osmondite was discussed by J. Calian, E. Maurer, and O. V. Greene.

J. O. Arnold noted that the passage of hardenite into normal carbide is accompanied by the evolution of heat; it commences at about 100°, the change is more rapid at 250°, reaches a maximum velocity at about 300°, and is complete at 400°. E. Heyn and O. Bauer observed the maximum evolution of heat at 360°. According to H. le Chatelier's hypothesis, the x is a carbide, and, according to C. Benedicks, a colloidal soln., which may be called *cementite-ferrosol*. H. le Chatelier's carbide shows reactions different from those of the normal carbide, and it is changed at 400° into stable carbide; and C. Benedicks' colloidal soln. is a metastable intermediate form which also passes into stable pearlite. W. Fränkel and E. Heymann inferred that an iron carbide of high carbon content, say $FeC_{8 \text{ to } 10}$, will be established; at present it is believed that osmondite and troostite contain the same carbide, Fe_3C. Osmondite is regarded as a state of steel exhibiting a maximum content of troostite, and thereby presenting a maximum speed of etching or dissolution in acids. Osmondite, said E. Heyn and O. Bauer, is characterized by: (1) a maximum degree of solubility; (2) a maximum yield of free carbon when treated with dil. sulphuric acid; (3) a maximum degree of dark colouring when etched with alcoholic hydrochloric acid; (4) a change in the direction of the curve for remanence and coercive force; and (5) a maximum sp. gr. The troostites contain carbon which remains as free carbon when treated with dil. acids, and also carbon which escapes during dissolution in 10 per cent. sulphuric acid; the sorbites contain in addition carbide carbon. The subject was discussed by H. M. Howe; and C. Benedicks, T. Matsushita and K. Nagasawa regard osmondite as a form of sorbite.

F. Osmond applied the term **sorbite**—after H. C. Sorby—to pearlite which has not segregated into the well-defined lamellar form. F. Osmond said that when the tempering is sufficient to efface the structure of martensite, it forms troostite; and sorbite is pearlite that has not succeeded in being segregated for want of time or some other reason. Hence sorbite is unsegregated pearlite, a kind of transitional form between martensite, osmondite or troostite and pearlite—*vide infra*, tempering. Sorbite is produced by tempering quenched martensite steels at 300° to 400° for 20 mins. and cooling. Sorbite has been regarded as ultramicroscopically fine-grained pearlite. W. D. Bancroft, J. Alexander, H. le Chatelier, V. Kohlschütter and K. Steck, and F. C. A. H. Lantsberry discussed the colloidal structure of steel. T. Matsushita and K. Nagasawa regard sorbite as a mixture of iron with highly dispersed cementite. Heating troostite to 300° or 400° makes the dispersed carbon of troostite form cementite. The mixture of troostite and sorbite formed by tempering at 300° to 400° has been called osmondite—*vide supra*. If sorbite be heated to 450° or 500°, it forms granular pearlite. Some consider *granular pearlite* or *granular cementite* to be sorbite. Hence it is also called *sorbitic pearlite*, and when referring to the contained carbon, *sorbitic carbide*. F. Körber and W. Köster studied the granular cementite ; and O. V. Greene, the structure of sorbite. Troostite of eutectoidal composition transforms into sorbite by forming α-iron ; hypoeutectoidal steel forms sorbite after rejecting excess ferrite ; and hypereutectoidal steel forms sorbite after rejecting excess cementite. In 1895 J. O. Arnold said that normal iron carbide exists in three distinct modifications, each one conferring upon the iron in which it is found particular mechanical properties : (i) emulsified carbide, present in an exceedingly fine state of subdivision in tempered steel ; (ii) diffused iron carbide, occurring in normal steels in the form of small, ill-defined striæ and granules ; and (iii) crystallized iron carbide, occurring as well-defined laminæ in annealed and in some normal steels. The first of these forms is presumably the so-called troostitic carbide, and the second, the so-called sorbitic carbide.

Consequently, sorbite cannot be properly called a constituent of hardened steel, but it can be regarded as a connecting link between annealed or pearlitic steels and hardened or troostitic or martensitic steels. The X-radiogram indicates

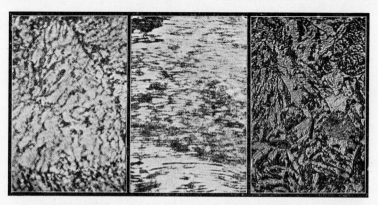

Fig. 120.—Granular Pearlite or Sorbite (E. Heyn).   Fig. 121.—Lamellar Sorbite (F. Osmond).   Fig. 122.—Sorbite (F. T. Sisco).

that sorbite, like troostite and pearlite, is a mechanical mixture of ferrite and cementite. N. Yamada found that at a given temp. the sp. hts. of troostite and sorbite are the same as that of pearlite. This agrees with the view that all three differ only in the degree of coagulation of the cementite particles and the mode of distribution. Sorbite is stronger, harder, and less ductile than pearlite, but softer and more ductile than troostite. H. C. Boynton represented the hardness of sorbite by 52 when that of troostite is 88, that of pearlite 4·3, and that of ferrite unity— *vide infra*, hardness. J. E. Stead and A. W. Richards discussed sorbitic steel for rails. H. C. Boynton found that the production of sorbite is favoured by : (i) a high temp. at which cooling commences ; (ii) a small sample ; (iii) keeping the sample a long time at a high temp. ; and (iv) rapid cooling. According to C. Benedicks, if martensite or austenite has begun transformation which ultimately results in pearlite, troostite is formed ; and if the martensite has not been completely resolved into pearlite, sorbite appears. Troostite is the first and sorbite is the last stage in the transformation of martensite to pearlite. Thus sorbite can be regarded as an uncoagulated mixture of the constituents of troostite and of pearlite. J. O. Arnold doubted the wisdom of applying definite terms to indefinite transition products like sorbite and troostite. The time-honoured Fig. 121 (×1500), representing lamellar sorbite, is due to F. Osmond ; and Fig. 120 (×1240), representing granular pearlite, or sorbite, from a forged bar of crucible steel with 0·92 per cent. of carbon, is due to E. Heyn. Fig. 122 (×500), by F. T. Sisco, represents the sorbite in a steel with 0·30 per cent. of carbon and etched with alcoholic nitric acid. Some highly magnified microphotographs were prepared by R. A. Hadfield and T. G. Elliott. Sorbite contains : (i) hardening carbon or cementite in soln., which makes it harder and stronger than pearlite ; (ii) α-iron, which makes it magnetic and relatively soft : and (iii) crystalline cementite. Sorbite is formed on tempering austenitic, martensitic, or troostitic steels. F. Osmond obtained sorbite by cooling steel slowly enough to allow the transformation to produce an imperfect separation of ferrite and cementite. This is done by the cooling in air of small samples, and then quenching in cold water or molten lead towards the end of the recalescence. Sorbite gives a brown colour when it is etched by polishing, or by iodine, or dil. acids. H. von Jüptner suggested that sorbite contains $(Fe_3C)_3$ in soln., but there is no trustworthy evidence in support of this. The subject was discussed by A. Schrader.

H. C. Sorby applied the term *pearly constituent of steel* to the material in steel which, when lightly etched, showed a peculiar play of colours suggestive of mother-

FIGS. 123, 124, and 125.—Structure of Pearlite.

of-pearl. The plates are rarely over 0·001 mm. in thickness, and the plates of carbide-cementite, being much harder than the ferrite plates, stand in relief after polishing. This results in an arrangement resembling a refraction grating which produces the appearance of mother-of-pearl, particularly with oblique illumination. H. M. Howe called it **pearlite.** H. C. Boynton found that its hardness is 4·3 when that of ferrite is unity and of cementite 272 ; but that, according to A. M. Portevin, the hardness of eutectics varies with the fineness, the shape, and the distribution of the eutectic particles. A. M. Portevin, and C. Benedicks studied the effect of an excess of one component of the eutectic in modifying its structure. F. L. Brady discussed the effect of the surface tension of the constituents on the eutectic structure. H. von Jüptner gave 7·74 for the sp. gr. of pearlite. Pearlite consists of alternating layers of cementite and ferrite or sorbite, or grains of cementite embedded in ferrite or sorbite. Fig. 123 (×500) shows the pearlite in rolled steel with 0·869 per cent. of carbon ; and Fig. 124 (×500), the pearlite in the same steel after heating to 1040° for 6 hrs. and then slowly cooling. Fig. 125 (×500) shows the pearlite in a steel with 1·3 per cent. of carbon, which had been heated for 12 days to 1100° in wood-charcoal. Some cells of cementite occur in the broad cells of pearlite. All three specimens were etched with a soln. of hydrogen chloride in amyl alcohol. Some highly magnified microphotographs were prepared by R. A. Hadfield and T. G. Elliott. Fig. 126 (×300) shows a photograph after F. T. Sisco in a steel with 0·90 per cent. of carbon and etched with alcoholic nitric acid. The plates of carbide-cementite remain bright, for they are not affected by the ordinary etching agents, while the ferrite plates appear dark, because (i) they are tarnished by the etching, and (ii) they are depressed owing to their greater softness, and they stand in the shadow of the plates of the cementite-carbide. M. Mikami raised the question whether the white or the dark parts in pearlite are cementite or ferrite, but was unable to satisfy himself with an answer, because in lamellar pearlite the top of the lamellar cementite in relief appears white, whilst the side faces are dark; and because the bottom of the lamellar ferrite between two consecutive lamellar cementites also appears white, whilst both edges are dark.

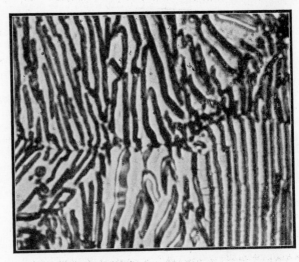

Fig. 126.—Minute Structure of Pearlite (after F. T. Sisco).

The pearlite may take on forms other than the lamellar arrangement; thus, it may appear granular—*vide supra*, sorbite. M. Oknof showed that pearlite forms a continuous connected network which is permeated throughout with cementite or ferrite grains. The percentage of carbon in pearlite is somewhere between 0·8 and 0·9 per cent., and this represents the composition of the eutectoid mixture, at the eutectic temp., corresponding with the A_1-arrest, Fig. 128. At this temp. the solid soln., austenite, martensite, or hardenite, is transformed into the pearlite aggregates of ferrite and cementite. This transformation implies the passage of γ-iron to β- and α-iron, or to α-iron directly; the crystallization of α-iron into parallel plates, or lamellæ; and the formation and crystallization or crystallization only of the cementite, Fe_3C, into parallel plates alternating with the plates of ferrite. W. E. Dalby said that steel containing about 0·9 per cent. of carbon is built up of blocks of pearlite, and that pearlite consists of alternating sheets of iron and cementite, packed closely together, 60,000 to the inch, and that these packed sheets are bent into shapes suggesting that their final forms have been developed by the complicated play of internal molecular forces. The structure of pearlite was discussed by H. E. Publow and co-workers, and H. Styri; and the effect of grain-size on the rate of formation of pearlite, by U. Dehlinger.

G. Tammann and E. Scheil said that the transformation of austenite into pearlite may take place at 100°. Pearlite so produced has a greater sp. vol. than the pearlite of soft steel, but the excess decreases with rise of temp., and vanishes at about 500°. The transformation of austenite and martensite to pearlite may be continuous or discontinuous, passing through intermediate stages represented by:

$$\text{Austenite} \rightleftharpoons \text{Martensite} \rightleftharpoons \text{Troostite} \rightleftharpoons \text{Sorbite} \rightleftharpoons \text{Pearlite} \begin{cases} \text{Ferrite} \\ \text{Cementite} \end{cases}$$

By suitably varying the rate of cooling, the alloy may be retained at ordinary temp. in any of these intermediate states. This depends on the fact that the change from austenite to pearlite is a time reaction, and if the time occupied in cooling through the critical range is less than that required for the complete transformation, one or other of the intermediate states persists. It is also assumed that the intermediate states are stages in a continuous change ; that the reaction which has been arrested by abrupt cooling will be resumed when the steel is reheated ; and that the results obtained by cooling at different rates or rapid cooling followed by reheating to different temp. are different means of attaining the same object—namely, arresting the austenite⇌pearlite transformation at an appropriate stage. As J. M. Robertson has shown, these assumptions are not quite right. The effect of speeding up the rate of cooling not only restricts the time taken to cool through the critical range, but it also lowers the temp. at which the transformation begins— *vide infra*, the doubling of the Ar_1-arrest.

K. Honda showed that since the Ar_1-arrest represents the change of soln. of carbon in γ-iron into a mixture of α-iron and cementite, the transformation of austenite into pearlite involves a sequence of consecutive reactions : (i) a change in the configuration of iron atoms from the face-centred to the body-centred lattice ; and (ii) the separation of carbon atoms from the interspaces of the lattice, (iii) to form cementite as they leave the lattice ; otherwise expressed, the Ar_1-transformation involves the changes : austenite→martensite→pearlite. With extremely rapid cooling a martensite mixed with some unchanged austenite is formed, and in some cases the troostite develops in a granular form about the boundary of the austenite. This does not mean that troostite is formed directly from austenite. X-radiograms show that troostite, sorbite, and pearlite are all mixtures of α-iron and cementite, hence the change from austenite to troostite necessarily involves a change in the configuration of the iron-lattice to form martensite, and the subsequent change of martensite into α-iron and cementite. K. Honda and A. Osawa also found that in quenched steels the amount of retained austenite is greater on the outer layer than in the inner one. For the same steel this difference increases as the quenching temp. is raised, and for the same quenching temp. it increases as the carbon content. M. Chikashige interpreted the A_1-transformation by the following scheme :

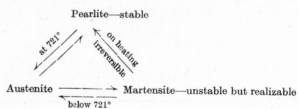

The subject was discussed by T. Murakami. The formation of cementite from austenite was discussed by H. Hanemann and O. Schroder, and R. H. Mehl and co-workers. The thermal value of the change austenite→pearlite at 700°, the Ar_1-arrest, was found by K. Honda to be 18·2 cals., in agreement with values by P. Weiss and N. Beck, and A. Meuthen. K. Honda gave for the transformation austenite→martensite 4·3 cals. ; so that the change martensite→pearlite approximates 13·9 cals., provided that the sp. hts. of pearlite and martensite are the same at 700°. The subject was also discussed by K. Honda and T. Kikuta, M. Chikashige, and E. Scheil. Immediately after the Ar_1-arrest and the α-iron and the tritacarbide or cementite have separated, the two constituents are in a very fine state of subdivision, so that if the mixture be kept in that state by abruptly cooling the mass, the intermediate stages appear, but if the mass be kept at a temp. just below the Ar_1-arrest, the fine particles of each constituent coalesce to form alternate layers or bands of ferrite and cementite. If, however, the time be prolonged, the plates become thicker, until finally the cementite becomes isolated in large patches surrounded by crystals of ferrite.

F. Osmond referred to the coalescence of the cementite in steels with less than 0·5 per cent. of carbon, where the pearlite areas become bounded by a belt of partly formed cementite with ragged edges which he termed *atolls* ; the phenomenon was not observed in eutectic and hypereutectic steels. The balling-up—spheroidization, or *coalescence*—of the cementite lamellæ into globules or spheroids is dependent on the extent of the annealing, and it is found in well-annealed steels, malleable cast irons, and in grey cast irons. The different appearances furnished by the balling-up of the constituents of the pearlite have been called different names— *e.g. globular pearlite* ; C. Benedicks thus recorded a bead-like variety—*beaded pearlite* or *necklace pearlite*. The strands of spherules represent a transition stage in the conversion of lamellar cementite into globules or spheroids. The **spheroidizing of the cementite,** particularly in high-carbon steels, is effected by heating the metal at or near the critical temp., followed by cooling slowly in the upper part of the cooling range. Fig. 127 ($\times 1000$), by R. S. MacPherran and J. F. Harper, represents a steel with 0·45 per cent. of carbon and 0·57 per cent. of manganese, which has been treated three times, each time for about 48 hrs., at about 670°, so as to spheroidize the pearlite. K. Honda and S. Saito found that if a quenched specimen be heated to below the Ac_1-arrest, sorbitic cementite spheroidizes ; if a hypereutectoid steel be heated above the Ac_1-arrest, but below the solubility line, and quenched, the supereutectoid cementite spheroidizes ; if a lamellar, pearlitic steel be heated just up to or a little above

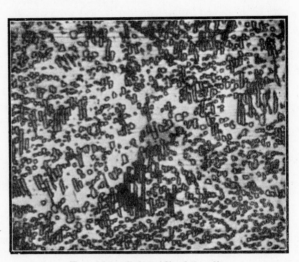

FIG. 127.—Spheroidized Pearlite.

the Ac_1-arrest for a certain interval, spheroidization occurs ; and if granular pearlite be heated below the Ac_1-arrest for a sufficient length of time, spheroidization occurs. If the Ac_1-point be not attained, the spheroidization of the lamellar cementite does not occur. If the maximum temp. exceeds a certain limit above the Ac_1-arrest, and the steel be cooled, the cementite forms lamellar pearlite. The temp. interval of spheroidization in low-carbon steels is very small, extending only to about 20° ; it increases rapidly with the content of carbon, and in high-carbon steels amounts to about 100°. A. Pomp and R. Wijkander found that spheroidal cementite dissolves more quickly than lamellar cementite, and consequently the latter form requires a more prolonged heating before the metal is quenched for hardening. The subject was studied by A. M. Portevin, D. Hanson, J. E. Stead, J. H. Andrew and H. A. Dickie, A. Schrader, H. C. Ihsen, A. M. Portevin and V. Bernard, H. Hanemann and F. Morawe, H. Hanemann and V. Lindt, H. M. Howe and A. G. Levy, A. Sauveur, A. L. Babochine, R. A. Thakore, A. E. White, C. H. Desch and A. T. Roberts, B. Stoughton and R. D. Billinger, M. Oknof, B. Kjerrman, A. Allison, N. G. Ilyne, J. H. Whiteley, J. O. Arnold, O. V. Greene, E. F. Lange, F. Osmond, P. Goerens, B. Ischewsky, N. T. Belaiew, and S. Kobayashi. T. Isihara studied the influence of various elements on the spheroidization of the carbides in steel. He observed that if manganese is present, the spheroidization interval of temp. above the

Ac_1-arrest is slightly increased proportionally with the manganese ; and the increase of the interval of temp. is much greater with the addition of chromium or copper.

By varying the conditions of time and temp., almost any degree of fineness can be obtained between balled-up cementite and ultra-microscopic grains. Usually the pearlite in hypoeutectoidal steels is finely laminated, while that in hypereutectoidal steels is coarser. According to J. H. Whiteley, the temp. of the formation of pearlite in steels at the Ar_1-arrest is not constant, but is lowered by increasing the rate of cooling. Again, the presence of nuclei of cementite within the γ-iron region induces the crystallization of cementite and ferrite as globular pearlite at a temp. much higher than that at which growth occurs in the absence of nuclei. When the growth of lamellar pearlite has started, it proceeds gradually, so that it is possible by quenching to obtain a specimen with intermixed areas of pearlite and martensite. This all shows that there is a lag in the transformation at the Ar_1-arrest. By analogy with supersaturated soln. it is inferred that lamellar pearlite is formed from supersaturated solid soln. The delayed crystallization, said A. F. Hallimond, may be hastened by violent mechanical working, which in solid soln. is equivalent to the agitation or stirring of a liquid to initial crystallization. J. H. Whiteley also proved that when steel is in a metastable state at the temp. of the Ar_1-arrest, the lag, or delay in crystallization, is abbreviated. G. Tammann and G. Siebel found that the rate of formation of pearlite remains constant in steels with 0·23 to 0·96 per cent. of carbon until the rate of cooling has fallen to a critical value, after which it falls off rapidly. The maximum linear speed of transformation of γ-iron to pearlite was 550 mm. per sec. The speed of transformation increases with increasing proportions of manganese ; and it is less in air than in hydrogen.

N. T. Belaiew studied the stereometry of pearlite grains. He found that the cementite lamellæ in a grain of pearlite are arranged roughly parallel to one another and to the crystallographic plane of the grain—presumably to one face of the cube. A secant plane perpendicular to that face will be normal to the lamellæ, and the angle of inclination, ω, for that plane will be zero. All the N lamellæ of the grain will appear on the normal plane ; and the distance, $\triangle$, between two lamellæ on such a plane will be the actual distance, $\triangle_0$. As the angle ω increases, the number of lamellæ, n, seen on a section of the same grain decreases, and the apparent distance, $\triangle_\omega$, between two lamellæ increases. Since $\cos \omega = n/N = \triangle_0/\triangle_\omega$, the graph of natural cosines will show the ratio of the decrease in the number of lamellæ, and of the increase in the distance between the lamellæ—$i.e.$ the coarseness of the structure of the lamellæ. Since $\triangle_0$ and $\triangle_\omega$ can be measured on a suitable microphotograph, the angle of inclination, ω, can be calculated from $\cos \omega = \triangle_0/\triangle_\omega$. When the angle of inclination, ω, approaches 80°, distance $\triangle_\omega$ between the lamellæ becomes five times greater than $\triangle_0$; ten times greater when $\omega = 84°$; and twenty times greater when $\omega = 87°$. Hence the change in the aspect of the pearlite in different sections. Imagine an idealized pearlite with a hundred cementite films of thickness $100\mu\mu$ packed in alternate layers with ferrite lamellæ $300\mu\mu$ thick. The thin, rigid films of cementite thus appear embedded in a matrix of ferrite.

As steel cools it contracts, in accord with the laws of cooling bodies, but in passing through the Ar_1-arrest there is a sudden dilation resulting from the change from γ-iron to α-iron. The expansion in passing from a face-centred to a body-centred lattice is about 9 per cent., and the linear expansion about 3 per cent. This arrest in the contraction is followed by the normal cooling contraction. As a result, pearlite, during and after its formation, is subjected to stresses, so that the cementite lamellæ get warped and twisted, giving rise to steps in the cleavages ; at the same time the ferrite lamellæ are split into a multitude of cubes. These deformations are in accord with C. G. Darwin's observations on the working and cracking of crystals. The dimensions of the ferrite cubes are of the order of magnitude of the wave-length of light. During the deformation of the cementite the ductile matrix of ferrite acts as a protective coating, and the brittle cementite films can be more or less bent and distorted to produce a curvature of the cementite lamellæ in the pearlite. True cementite particles are usually acicular and straight, and when the cementite lamellæ in pearlite are straight, they are close to free cementite, suggesting an earlier stage of crystallization. The structure of eutectics was discussed by C. Benedicks, A. M. Portevin, C. H. Green, and F. L. Brady ; and the theory of labile and metastable soln.—1. 9, 6—by A. F. Hallimond.

The Hindoo steel, **damascene** or **damascus steel,** called in Russia *poulad* or *bulat,* appeared in Western Europe during the Middle Ages. It often came via Damascus—hence the name. The same steel appeared on the European markets in the seventeenth century, as **wootz** or *wooz.* Various early writers have referred to the manufacture of this steel—J. Chardin, P. Anossoff, R. A. Hadfield, J. B. Tavernier, H. W. Voysey, P. Oberhoffer and co-workers, J. M. Heath, D. Mushet, D. Lardner, M. Bazin, G. Pearson, F. Buchanan, etc. Allusions to the famous sword blades of India are frequent in Arabic literature ; the *ondanique* of Marco Polo is considered to have been a fine steel resembling Indian steel—*vide supra,* hardening steel. The history was discussed by N. T. Belaiew. H. Wedding gave an analysis of wootz steel ; A. R. Roy described its manufacture in India ; B. Neumann, and W. Guertler discussed the structure and manufacture. One external characteristic of the steel is its patterned surface markings, or surface-watering. Hence the Persian term *poulad jauher der,* meaning steel with a watered surface. Fig. 128 will give an idea of the surface of damascene steel. It is a photo-

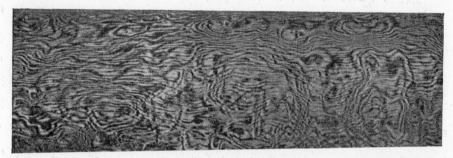

FIG. 128.—The Surface of Damascene Blade—Khozassan watering.

graph by Col. Belaiew, from a damascene blade in the Wallace Collection which appeared in his *Crystallization of Metals* (London, 1922). The quality of the Oriental sword blades made from the steel appears to have been judged by the pattern of the watered surface. The pattern changes according to the proportion of carbon present in the steel, and P. Anossoff said that it ranges from parallel stripes to wavy ones, then to mottled ones. As the proportion of carbon increases the chequered mottle grows bigger, forms grape-vine patterns, and finally extends over the whole breadth of the metal, dividing it into almost even and equally patterned vertebræ. This is the most prized variety, and forms the Persian *kirk narduban*—the forty steps of Mahomet's ladder. The steel is extremely ductile, so that P. Anossoff could say that a blade of good damascene steel cannot be broken by bending, but can yet be bent to such an extent as to lose its elasticity. When bent in the usual fashion the blade flies back and retains its original shape ; and when bent more forcibly, say at a right angle, it does not break or lose its original elasticity when straightened out again. D. K. Tschernoff considered this kind of steel to be " the best ever manufactured." Analyses reported by R. A. Hadfield, I. Ilimoff, and N. T. Belaiew show that the proportion of carbon usually ranges from 1·0 to 1·80 per cent. The variegated surface of the Oriental swords was at first attributed to the metal having been compounded of bars and wires of iron and steel welded and wrought together, and then twisted by forging in various directions. J. Stodart and M. Faraday experimented on alloys of iron with various metals with the idea

of discovering the origin of the watering.   J. R. Bréant assumed that the damask
effect is due to the irregular distribution of carbon in the metal, whereby two distinct
combinations are produced ;   the slower the cooling, the larger the damask veins.
The mode of manufacturing damascene steel was established by the experiments
of P. Anossoff, and N. T. Belaiew.   The conditions of annealing the hypereutectoidal
steel are similar to those employed by H. M. Howe and A. G. Levy, and J. E. Stead
for spheroidizing the cementite, and divorcing the eutectoidal pearlite so as to form
globulites of cementite.   Hence, said N. T. Belaiew :

> Bearing in mind that hypereutectoid steels spheroidize more readily than eutectoid,
> and that forging through the critical range facilitates the process very much, we must
> readily admit that structures such as those of the Oriental blades are usually arrived at
> without any additional tempering, but only through a very elaborate forging at com-
> paratively low temperature. . . . The heating should be but slightly in excess of the
> critical temperature, bringing the article only partially to the austenitic stage, so that the
> cementite pattern remains practically intact.   The hardening process then altered only
> the composition of the background, transforming it into a martensite stage, which finally,
> after annealing, was brought back to troostite.

In 1897, H. le Chatelier,[2] and in 1911, L. Grenet showed that the temp. at
which martensite changes to pearlite, the A_1-arrest, is lowered by quenching.
A. M. Portevin, A. M. Portevin and M. Garvin, H. Hanemann and co-workers,
P. Chévenard, P. Dejean, K. Honda, K. Honda and T. Kikuta, and A. F. Hallimond
found that with quenching, or very rapid rates of cooling, carbon steels give
transformation points in the vicinity of 300°.   M. Masloff emphasized the
importance of the effect of the rate of cooling on the Ar_1-arrest, and K. Daeves
illustrated the phenomenon by Fig. 129.   The Ar_1-arrest is depressed to Ar' by
increasing the speed of cooling to Oa ; and any
further increase in the rate of cooling depresses the
Ar_1-arrest still more, but simultaneously a second
arrest appears, Ar'', and troostite is formed.   When
the speed of cooling has increased to Ob, the Ar'-
arrest disappears, and the Ar''-arrest alone occurs,
with the formation of martensite—*vide supra*.   This
nomenclature is due to A. M. Portevin, who called the
arrest between 700° and 600° the Ar'-arrest, and that
between 500° and 250° the Ar''-arrest.   This splitting,
lowering, or **doubling of the Ar_1-arrest** was also
observed by F. Osmond, during his study of the

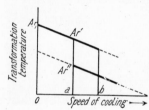

Fig. 129.—The Effect of the
Rate of Cooling on the Ar_1-
Arrest.

tungsten steels, in 1892 ; it is not to be confounded with the twinning of the
A_2-arrest—*vide supra*.   The phenomenon is fairly common with the alloy steels—
vide nickel steels.   Thus H. J. French and O. Z. Klopsch observed it during the
cooling of a 0·98 per cent. carbon steel at various rates from 875°.   It was also
observed by T. Kikuta, H. C. H. Carpenter, K. Honda, T. Murakami, etc.
K. Honda and T. Murakami, and A. Hultgren noted that the doubling of the
Ar_1-arrest occurs with tungsten steels, and A. Hultgren, with chromium steels
and nickel-chromium steels.   With tungsten steel, containing up to 1·29 per cent.
of carbon, the recalescence at Ar'' was identified with a separation of ferrite,
usually as needles, called *secondary ferrite*, sometimes, but not always, depending
upon subsequent rate of cooling.   This is followed by carbide formation, visible
as dark etching areas around the ferrite.   Furthermore, by keeping the specimen
during cooling at different temp. for varying lengths of time, followed by
quenching, it was found that the quantity of ferrite formed increased with temp.
and that it was a function of the temp. rather than of time.   In other words,
there appeared to be a metastable equilibrium between the ferrite and the
austenite, probably corresponding with the stable equilibrium curves extended to
lower temp.   This explains why such unexpectedly great quantities of ferrite
might be separated even in high-carbon alloy steels.   That carbide is not set free

at the same time was tentatively explained by assuming that in an alloy steel, stabilized by heating to high temp., the rate of separation of carbide out of soln. was slower than that of ferrite. The ferrite formed etched like ordinary ferrite, but might on prolonged etching assume a light brownish tint, the more so the lower the temp. of formation.

It is generally assumed that sorbite and troostite are formed from pearlite at the Ar'-arrest, and martensite at the Ar''-arrest ; and there are now two hypotheses : (i) The Ar''-change is the completion of the consecutive series of changes : austenite⇌martensite⇌troostite⇌sorbite⇌pearlite interrupted at the martensite stage. If so, then the discontinuity in the lowering of the change from Ar' to Ar'' remains unexplained, for if one change is alone involved, it would probably be depressed progressively by an increase in the rate of cooling. (ii) The Ar'-arrest is a direct change from austenite to pearlite, sorbite, or troostite, and the Ar''-arrest a direct change to martensite. In general, a transformation in a pure substance is gradually lowered as the rate of cooling increases. This phenomenon is an effect of hysteresis or lag, but with an alloy of two or more metals, as in the case of the Ar_1-transformation of steel, a stepped change occurs. T. Murakami explained the doubling of the arrest as an effect of a kind of supercooling of the austenite in the changes : austenite $\rightarrow$ martensite $\rightarrow$ (ferrite+cementite) — $vide$ $infra$. T. Murakami said that in chromium steels the doubling of the arrest is due to the presence of a chromium carbide, which, on passing into soln. at the Ac-arrest, dissociates into a simpler carbide and chromium, so that the chromium causes a doubling of the arrest on cooling. C. A. Edwards and co-workers concluded that the phenomenon was also dependent on the action of a chromium carbide, but gave the carbide a composition different from that found by T. Murakami. Both observers based their conclusion on the fact that the arrest is doubled only when the ratio of chromium to carbon exceeds a certain limit. W. T. Griffiths added that this does not agree with his observations that the percentage necessary to cause a complete depression of the Ar'-arrest depends not only on the proportion of carbon present, but also on that of nickel. A complete dispersion is also possible before the chromium : carbon ratio has attained the value necessary to give the carbide whose presence is considered necessary for the doubling of the arrest.

J. H. Andrew and co-workers said that a carbide expansion occurs above and during the Ac-arrest owing to the dissociation of a complex $(Fe_3C)_n$ into simpler molecules. This dissociation by increasing the mol. conc. in soln. causes a depression of the arrest. Chromium carbide also dissociated at high temp., the carbon remaining with the iron, and the chromium dissolving in the iron. Nickel and chromium act together in keeping the carbide in the dissociated state and thus assist one another in depressing the arrest. W. T. Griffiths added that increasing the carbon should give an increased tendency to the doubling of the point, since, with a given treatment, the conc. of the dissociated carbide molecules would then be likely to increase on soln. ; but this is not the case. If the hypothesis is correct, W. T. Griffiths also said that the temp. necessary to produce the conc. of dissociated molecules necessary to depress the point would be lower the higher the percentage of carbon. This is not in agreement with observation. Again, with either of the above hypotheses, it is necessary to assume that the carbides exist in solid soln. as such. Z. Jeffries and R. S. Archer hold that in austenite the carbide is dissolved as carbon atoms, not as carbide molecules, and this view is in agreement with the X-ray spectra observed by A. Westgren, A. Westgren and G. Phragmen, and E. C. Bain. The work of W. Rosenhain, and E. C. Bain also makes it difficult to assume the existence of large complex molecules of carbide in the space-lattice of γ-iron. A. M. Portevin and P. Chévenard, and K. Honda regard the doubling of the Ar-point as an effect of the special elements on the allotropic change ; and A. M. Portevin and P. Chévenard consider the lower point as one of labile equilibrium between a solid soln. of carbon in γ-iron (austenite) and a labile, solid soln. of carbon in α-iron. P. Dejean, and H. Scott regard the lower point to be the

$Ar_{3,2}$-arrest depressed by rapid cooling. H. Hanemann and A. Schrader proposed an explanation based on the existence of a new modification of iron.

W. T. Griffiths assumed that nickel and chromium exert a double effect in retarding the γ- to α-change and in keeping carbon in soln. In standard nickel-chromium steels the nickel is almost entirely in soln. in α-iron, the carbon is practically all present as carbide, and the chromium is almost entirely out of soln. as carbide. In agreement with C. A. Edwards and co-workers, in steels with higher proportions of chromium some will be in soln. in the α-iron. As the steel passes through the Ac-point, carbides pass slowly into soln., while the chromium and carbon diffuse outwards from the position of the carbide lattices. In agreement with the observations of W. Rosenhain, E. C. Bain, and E. A. Owen and G. D. Preston on solid soln., the nickel and chromium atoms replace some iron atoms in the γ-iron lattice, distorting the lattice to some extent. It is assumed that, owing to its small size, the carbon atom does not replace an iron atom, but is situated between the atoms of the face-centred lattice. The effect of the substitution of nickel and chromium atoms for iron is to make the position of the carbon atoms more stable, and, in turn, the carbon atoms would tend to hold the iron atoms in their high temp. arrangement.

W. T. Griffiths continued : If the heating is interrupted just above the Ac-point, where dissolution and allotropic change are completed, very little diffusion will take place, and on slowly cooling the reverse change will occur to give the higher Ar'-point and a structure of pearlite and ferrite or cementite or complex carbide. If the heating be continued, diffusion will proceed further. The rate of diffusion of the carbon will be higher than that of chromium, but not so high as in carbon steels, owing to the retarding effect of the nickel and chromium. As the chromium diffuses, the combined stabilizing effect of the chromium and nickel on the carbon will spread, and the effect will probably increase with rise of temp. Consequently, owing to the different rates of diffusion of carbon and chromium, the stability of the former will vary throughout the steel until a sufficiently high temp. or long period of soaking is employed. On cooling, a different condition obtains just above the Ar'-arrest, for if the above effect has occurred throughout the whole steel, a much slower rate of cooling will be necessary to allow the γ- to α-change and the precipitation of the carbide ; while if the rate of cooling be fast enough, the whole mass may pass through the Ar'-point without any nuclei being formed on which recrystallization may occur. E. W. Ehn discussed the effect of oxide and other impurities in providing nuclei for recrystallization. If the steel is not homogeneous, with certain rates of cooling, in some areas the allotropic change will occur and carbide come out of soln. Nuclei will thus be formed and recrystallization set in. Whether the recrystallization is completed or not will depend on the ratio of the rate of cooling to the velocity of crystallization, and the latter will also depend on the velocity of diffusion. Hence, the change will occur in some parts of the steel, while others pass through the crystallizing range without change. Hence, part of the recrystallization will occur at Ar', and the remainder completed at the lower temp. Ar''. Again, if throughout the mass the conc. of nickel and chromium is sufficient for the rate of cooling, the whole of the steel will pass through the upper point without change. Consequently, the proportions of carbon, nickel, and chromium required to depress the Ar-point are all interdependent ; so also are the effects of the initial temp., the time of soaking, and the rate of cooling.

W. T. Griffiths continued : If no recrystallization occurs at Ar' as the steel cools, the lattice will contract on itself, and the tendency to return to the more stable cube-centred lattice will increase. A. F. Hallimond likened this steel to the metastable condition of supersaturated soln. Finally, at a temp. depending on the proportions of nickel, chromium, and carbon, and on the rate of cooling, the lattice can no longer remain in the γ-state, and recrystallization will begin. The resulting product, as in the case of Ar', will depend on three factors—the temp. of the change, the rate of cooling, and the composition of the steel, for all these alter the rate of diffusion and the rate of crystallization. Provided the rate of cooling is not excessively high, the iron will almost entirely change into the α-lattice. The carbon, being only slightly, if at all, soluble in this, will tend to diffuse from the changing areas, while some atoms will probably combine with neighbouring atoms to give Fe_3C-molecules. The chances of a carbon atom having a suitable number of chromium atoms in its neighbourhood to give either of the known chromium carbides will be remote. Molecules of iron carbide will almost alone be formed, and hence J. H. Andrew and co-workers found no chromium in the carbide residues from steels with small proportions of that element. The remaining carbon will tend to diffuse towards these nuclei and carry on crystal growth. If the temp. is sufficiently high in those areas which are lower in chromium content, the carbon, provided the rate of cooling is slow enough, will be able to diffuse at a sufficiently rapid rate to feed the growing crystals of carbide. If this rate of diffusion is not high enough, either by the rate of cooling being too rapid, or by the retarding action of the nickel and chromium, the carbon atoms will be trapped in the changing iron and martensite will be produced. In any case, it is unlikely that the crystals of carbide will grow to any large extent, and the high dispersion characteristic of troostite will be usual.

Observations on the Ar′-, Ar″-, Ar‴-arrests show that these temp. can be all represented on one curve, and it is doubtful if the Ar‴-arrest can be regarded as being the Ar″-point depressed by the high carbon content of the steels which show the phenomenon. W. T. Griffiths showed that carbon is probably the determining factor in the production of the Ar‴-point—at least, in steels of the comparatively low nickel and chromium content used commercially. Once the steel has passed through the Ar′-arrest without recrystallization, the carbon tends to hold the lattice in the high temp. arrangement, and its effect is relatively great. Also, J. H. Andrew and co-workers have pointed out the difficulty of obtaining the Ar‴-arrest with steels containing less than a certain percentage of carbon. Nickel and chromium, though they very easily produce depression of the point to the Ar″-arrest, are not so effective in giving an Ar‴-point when the carbon is low. A. M. Portevin and P. Chévenard have suggested that the duplicating of the lower point is due to the slowness of diffusion of the carbon after going into soln. Though it is probable that the effect is due partly to this, it does not explain why the change from Ar″- to Ar‴-arrest is so sudden, unless it be assumed that there is an initial pronounced non-uniformity in the steel. If this assumption cannot be made, it is possible that when the requisite percentage of carbon is present, on raising the temp. sufficiently above Ac, there is a further pronounced effect on the lattice, making it still more stable on cooling. What that effect is and how it is brought about is not known ; it may be very tentatively suggested that if the carbon is initially in soln. in the way mentioned above, with higher carbon content and raised temp. some of the atoms may enter the γ-iron lattice and in this way produce a more stable arrangement. Initial temp. and time of soaking will affect the relative magnitudes of Ar″- and Ar‴-arrests in the same way as for Ar′- and the Ar″-arrests, that is, by regulating the amount of diffusion which will take place.

J. M. Robertson has made a study of the sequence of structures obtained when austenite is decomposed at progressively lower temp. He concluded that the ultimate composition of the decomposition products of austenite varies gradually as the temp. at which the transition takes place is lowered. When the transition takes place at the normal temp., the product consists of α-iron and cementite. As the temp. of the transition is lowered, more carbon is retained in soln. in α-iron, and less separates as cementite. The crystallographic form of the product of the decomposition of austenite depends on whether the decomposition is initiated by the allotropic change or by the formation of cementite. The Ar′-change is initiated by cementite, and the series of structures obtained at Ar′ is determined by this fact. The Ar″-transformation is initiated by the allotropic change, and the structures formed at this change point are related to the crystallographic planes of the austenite. The relations between the Ar'- and Ar'' points are determined by the fact that the allotropic change and the formation of cementite are differently affected by variations in the rate of cooling. The formation of cementite is slightly lowered, interrupted, and suppressed by a progressive increase in the rate of cooling. The allotropic change is progressively lowered as the rate of cooling is increased. The progressive lowering of the allotropic change cannot be realized in steels containing more than 0·2 per cent. of carbon, for in these steels, with certain rates of cooling, the decomposition of the austenite is initiated by the formation of cementite, and this change must be suppressed before the initiation of the transformation by the allotropic change can again be realized. In low-carbon steels, however, the structure passes directly from ferrite and pearlite to solid soln. structures, whose crystallographic form is similar to those produced when the Ar''-change in high-carbon steels takes place at a high temp. There are two series of structures produced by increasing the rate of cooling. Within each series the variation in structure is gradual. All structures formed at Ar'' may be tempered, and the tempered structure is related to the original structure, to the time, and to the temp. of tempering. The structures formed by cooling at different rates cannot be obtained by tempering other structures. So far as crystallographic form or structure is concerned, there is no relation between cooling at different rates and tempering at different temps. The same ultimate constitution may, however, be produced in either of two ways. When the α-solid soln. produced by very rapid cooling is reheated, carbon gradually separates from soln. and forms cementite. By reheating to different temp. all variations in constitution between solid soln. and ferrite-cementite aggregate may be obtained. Thus the globular structure, formed by tempering above 600°, may have the same ultimate constitution as the fan structure, but the crystallographic form and the general properties of these two structures are entirely different.

The dissolution of the pearlite by iron with a rising temp. was discussed by H. Jungbluth, etc. The sequence of changes which attends the cooling of iron or steel is more or less reversed as the temp. is raised—*vide supra*.

In 1786 L. B. G. de Morveau,[3] in his *Mémoire sur la conversion du fer en acier*, showed that *tout fer peut devenir acier* ; and he described his idea of the part played by carbon in converting iron into steel. He showed that carbon can exist in steel in two forms—*la plumbagine* (graphite) and *le charbon métallique* (iron carbide). J. R. Bréant also examined the steels microscopically, and classified steels into three groups according to the percentage of contained carbon. P. H. Berggren compiled a bibliography of the combinations of iron and carbon. As indicated in connection with the iron carbides—**5**. 39, 20—the finely-divided carbon which separates from white cast iron and certain steels during their prolonged annealing has some of the properties of graphite ; and, according to A. Ledebur, graphite is also formed by the rapid hammering of high-carbon steel at a red-heat. The graphite is insoluble in dil. acids. It is called **annealing** or **temper carbon**—or *carbon de recuit*—A. Ledebur's term, *Temperkohle, i.e. temper carbon,* is not so often used in England, because of the difference in meaning between the terms "tempering" and "annealing." The annealing or temper carbon in a sample of malleable cast iron is illustrated by J. E. Hurst's diagram, Fig. 130 (×200). There are three hypotheses as to the nature of annealing carbon : (i) C. James held that this carbon is a modification of graphite ; A. Lissner and R. Horny, that it is the same as iron graphite, since both forms have the same heat of combustion, but are in different states of subdivision ; and L. Northcott, that graphite and temper carbon are the same substance, but of different degrees of fineness ; (ii) A. Ledebur, that it is a carbide ; and F. Wüst, and H. von Jüptner, that it is amorphous carbon. F. Wüst and C. Geiger showed that chemically it behaves like graphite. J. W. Bolton recognized the following graphitic formations in cast irons : (i) broad, straight flakes ; (ii) rosettes or whorls ; (iii) dendritic striations ; (iv) grouped formations with clear, dendritic lakes and peninsulas

being filled with fine flakes ; and (v) rounded temper carbon. K. Iokibe concluded from the X-radiograms that the so-called graphitic carbon and temper carbon
occurring in cast iron are both the same substance as natural graphite—they give
the same X-radiogram. The conditions of the decomposition of cementite are
the same for both cast iron and steel, so that the temper carbon from carbon steels
is also graphite, and not amorphous carbon. This conclusion is supported by the
observations of G. Asahara, and F. Wever, and by other observations of L. Northcott, H. le Chatelier and S. Wologdine, A. Carnot and E. Goutal, G. Dillner,
A. Pourcel, F. C. G. Müller, E. Donath, H. Wedding, E. Maurer and F. Hartmann,
F. Mylius and co-workers, S. S. Knight, E. H. Campbell, H. Moissan, T. Turner,
J. W. Bolton, A. Lissner and R. Horny, and H. Sawamura. Temper or annealing
carbon usually occurs in the nodular form, while graphite is more or less flaky.
Free **graphite** separates from highly carburized molten iron in the act of solidification. T. Millner, and H. A. Schwartz and co-workers studied the dissolution of
cementite by acids. F. Wever found the particles of graphite from pig-iron,
grey cast iron, temper carbon, coke, and charcoal all have the same lattice structure,

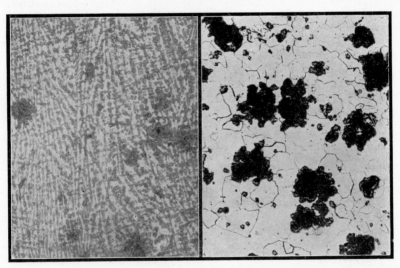

FIG. 130.—Annealing Carbon in   FIG. 131.—The Commencement of the
Malleable Cast Iron (J. E. Hurst).   Formation of Graphite at Several
                                         Centres in Cast Iron (J. E. Hurst).

showing that the carbon is the same allotropic form, but with different degrees of
dispersion. The average size of the crystals of graphite from grey iron is
100×10^{-8} cm. ; temper carbon, 30×10^{-8} to 50×10^{-8} cm. ; and coke and charcoal,
10×10^{-8} cm. The lamellæ of eutectic graphite are ultra-microscopic in size.
P. Debye and P. Scherrer said that the lattice of graphite is easily deformed by
mechanical stresses, but F. Wever did not find this to be the case.

J. E. Hurst's diagram, Fig. 131 ($\times 200$), shows the formation of graphite in
nuclei from the boundary of the chilled and grey portion of a sample of black-heart
cast iron. The free carbon which separates from masses of molten iron by the
dissociation of the carbide which separates in plates during the cooling of the
molten grey cast iron down to the temp. of solidification is called **kish**—*Garschaum-
graphit*—*vide supra*. B. Osann, and J. Freygang discussed the formation of kish
in cast iron.

As previously indicated—**5**. 39, 5—carbon in the form of *diamonds* has been
detected in some meteorites. L. Franck reported the formation of diamonds in
hardened steel, and A. Ludwig, A. Rossel, H. Moissan, D. C. Tschernoff, E. Demenge,

and R. von Hasslinger discussed the formation of graphite, boart, and diamonds when iron saturated with carbon at a high temp. is suddenly cooled; and H. Fleissner, and P. Neumann discussed the formation of diamonds in the blast-furnace slags. The artificial synthesis of diamonds under these conditions has been questioned—**5.** 39, 5.

The dissolved carbon which confers hardness to steel when quenched from above the Ar_1-arrest is called **hardening carbon**—*Härtungskohlenstoff*, or *carbon de trempe*. The carbon in hardened and tempered steel which does not give a coloration when the steel is dissolved in nitric acid of sp. gr. 1·20 is sometimes called *missing carbon—carbone manquant*. The condition of the carbon as it occurs in iron tritacarbide or cementite is called *carbide-carbon*, or **combined carbon.** The term is also used to embrace all the various carbides in steels containing manganese, chromium, etc. The term *cement carbon* was applied by S. Rinman to the tritacarbide which remains undissolved at ordinary temp. when annealed steel is digested with dil. sulphuric acid in the absence of air. Hence, H. M. Howe called the tritacarbide, Fe_3C, **cementite.** Its microscopic appearance was described by H. C. Sorby. In the presence of manganese the cementite may contain manganese carbide; and silicon, and sulphur (*q.v.*) may also dissolve therein. The subject was studied by L. G. Knowlton, P. Pingault, and J. H. Andrew. A. Ledebur heated test-pieces of malleable iron to a medium red-heat and found the distribution of the different forms of carbon to be after

Heating		0	4	5	6	7	8	10 days	
	Hardening	0·741	0·815	0·859	0·835	0·631	0·245	—	per cent.
Carbon {	Carbide .	2·597	2·246	2·073	1·874	0·430	0·492	0·656	per cent.
	Temper .	—	—	—	0·179	1·037	0·833	0·443	per cent.
Total carbon		3·338	3·061	2·932	2·888	2·098	1·570	1·099	per cent.

H. von Jüptner, and W. C. M. Lewis discussed the mol. wt. of the tritacarbide dissolved in iron. A. McCance calculated from the effect of carbon on the depression of the f.p. that the mol. wt. of the cementite in soln. is $(Fe_3C)_n$, where n is 2·03 at 1505° and 1·93 at 900°, so that the cementite between these temp. is dissolved as $(Fe_3C)_2$. A. Baykoff suggested that cementite is not really a definite compound, but rather a solid soln. This hypothesis is not supported by the available facts. The properties of the iron carbides are discussed **5.** 39, 20, and *vide supra*, pearlite. The thermal decomposition of cementite has been discussed above—*vide infra*, graphitization. Where ferrite and cementite are both present, the cementite is virtually unattacked by soln. of nitric or picric acid, tincture of iodine, etc., but it is darkly coloured by treatment with sodium picrate under conditions where pearlite remains bright.

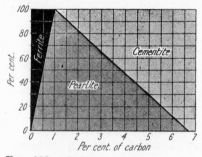

FIG. 132.—Relative Proportions of Ferrite, Cementite, and Pearlite in Steels with Different Proportions of Carbon.

The cementite in normal steel with its eutectoidal proportion, 0·85 per cent., of carbon is all pearlitic; and with 6·7 per cent. of carbon it would be all cementite. In hypoeutectoidal steels it is present as lamellar pearlite along with masses of ferrite, and in hypereutectoidal steels it is present as lamellar pearlite along with masses of cementite. The cementite in excess of that associated with the eutectoid pearlite is sometimes called free, surplus, excess, massive, or proeutectoidal cementite, and similarly with free, surplus, excess, massive, or proeutectoidal ferrite. The relative proportions of free ferrite, free cementite, and pearlite in steels with different proportions of carbon are illustrated by Fig. 132. Calculations on this subject were discussed by H. P. Tiemann. As shown by J. O. Arnold and J. Jefferson, T. Andrews, W. G. McMillan, and F. Osmond and W. C. Roberts-Austen, in general, during the solidification of a molten metal containing a trace of impurity, the particles of metal coalesce to form little islands of pure metal surrounded by a film of metal associated with impurity. In hypereutectic steels the pearlite behaves almost as if it were a pure metal, in that the excess of cementite may be rejected to the boundaries of the polyhedral grains so as to form a network of cementite with a ground-work of pearlite.

A. Sauveur measured by a planimeter the relative proportions of martensite, M, ferrite, F, and pearlite, P, in steels with 0·09, 0·21, 0·35, 0·80, 1·20, and 2·50 per cent. of carbon, quenched at different temp. Selecting the case of steel with 0·21 per cent. of carbon :

	880°	714°	698°	652°	620°	600°	559°	575°	200°
M .	100	97·2	70·2	35·2	30·0	4·0	2·0	0·0	0·0 per cent.
F .	0	2·8	29·8	64·8	68·4	78·5	75·8	78·9	21·1 per cent.
P .	0	0·0	0·0	0·0	1·6	17·5	22·2	76·4	23·6 per cent.

E. H. Saniter, K. Honda and T. Murakami, G. Tammann and K. Ewig, A. L. Babochine, R. Ruer, and H. Sawamura discussed the stability of cementite at high temp.—*vide* **5**. 39, 20. The dissociation of cementite above 600° was studied by R. Horny, and the subject has been previously discussed in connection with the equilibrium diagram. The A_0-arrest with cementite also has been previously discussed. K. Honda referred to the A_0-arrest, where paramagnetic cementite becomes ferromagnetic, in these words :

This is the transformation characteristic of cementite ; it is in its nature the same transformation as the A_2-transformation with iron. The transformation is progressive and extends from the lowest temp. to 215°, the change being a definite function of temp. During heating or cooling, the transformation terminates or commences at the same temp., the A_0-arrest at 215°. This point is observable for all alloys containing free cementite, and it always has the same value.

According to S. Sekito, by tempering quenched steels at a gradually increasing temp. martensite begins to decompose at 200° and its decomposition is completed at 300°. In this stage the precipitated cementite is in a molecular or colloidal state, and does not form the space-lattice characteristic of cementite ; hence its spectral lines are so much diffused that they cannot be observed, as we have already seen ; but as the temp. is further raised, fine particles of cementite gradually coagulate and build up its space-lattice. Thus the spectral lines of cementite begin to appear at 300° on the X-ray film and increase in intensity up to 600°. The changes in the e.m.f. of steels tempered at about 380° are attributed to the formation of the

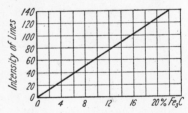

FIG. 133.—The Relation between the Proportion of Cementite and the Intensity of the X-Ray Spectral Lines.

cementite lattice from molecular or colloidal particles. The content of cementite can be roughly estimated from the intensity of the X-ray spectral lines, Fig. 133.

N. G. Ilyine discussed the forms in which cementite appears in hypereutectic steels ; M. Sauvageot, the retarded dissolution and premature precipitation of cementite in eutectic and hypereutectic steels ; A. M. Portevin, proeutectoid cementite ; and H. M. Howe and A. G. Levy, H. C. H. Carpenter, and I. Iitaka studied the separation of cementite in hypereutectoidal steels in cooling from, say, 1200°. The line *ES* in the equilibrium diagram, Fig. 83, represents the progressive generation or separation of the cementite ; and the commencement of the curve is represented by what was called above, the A_{cm}-arrest. The A_{cm}-arrest occurs in hypereutectoidal steels, and marks the beginning of the separation of free cementite from austenite as the metal cools from A_{cm} to $A_{1,2,3}$. Except for the structural change no other marked changes in properties of the alloy have been connected with the A_{cm}-arrest. The austenite was shown by F. Osmond and

G. Cartaud, N. J. Wark, and A. Baykoff to be strongly oriented, for it has a marked crystalline structure. The coalescence of the excess or proeutectoidal cementite into visible masses is slow. The result with a steel with 1·45 per cent. carbon heated to 1200° and cooled to 745° and quenched is shown in Fig. 83 ; and the same steel heated to 1000°, cooled to 800°, and quenched is shown in Fig. 83. The coalescence of the internal cementite is slower than that which accumulates at the walls of the cells. The quantity of visible internal cementite increases to a maximum and then decreases. The decrease is occasioned by a transfer of cementite from the interior to the network—possibly by solution and re-precipitation. The apparent proportion of internal cementite is greater than is theoretically possible. This is an optical illusion ; what is taken to be wholly cementite may be in part pearlite. Most of the internal cementite is probably distributed in the cleavages of the austenite in which it is born, and it records the position of those cleavages after the austenite has suffered metamorphosis. Many of the spines which shoot from the network into the interior of the grains may not represent the austenite cleavages, but the orientation of the minute crystals which collectively make up the network as a dendrite. Increasing the proportion of carbon in the steel accelerates the

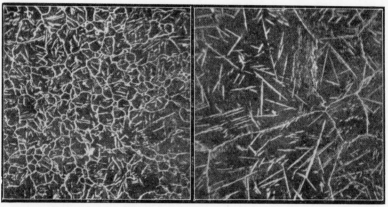

FIG. 134.—The Coalescence of Cementite   FIG. 135.—Pearlite with Cementite
(H. M. Howe and A. G. Levy).   Borders (H. M. Howe and A. G. Levy).

coalescence of the cementite. The coarseness of the network increases by raising the temp. and by increasing the proportion of carbon.

During the primary crystallization of the austenite foreign matter is rejected and driven to the surfaces of the crystals or collected along the cleavage planes. During the secondary crystallization of the grains of austenite free cementite, or free ferrite, is rejected, and as the pearlite grows it accumulates on the surface of the grains or along the cleavage planes. Hence, as observed by H. Brearley, the earlier formed slag may appear surrounded by the free ferrite or cementite which has been formed later. H. M. Howe pointed out that there is no need to assume that the common occurrence of slag in masses of ferrite is due to some attraction which the slag has for ferrite. H. M. Howe and A. G. Levy observed that if a hole is drilled in a block of hypoeutectoidal steel and closed to prevent the access of air, when the steel is heated above the transformation range and cooled slowly, the walls of the hole become covered with crystals of ferrite ; and with hypereutectoidal steel, with crystals of cementite. Analogous phenomena were observed by G. K. Burgess and co-workers. The expulsion of the excess ferrite or cementite in the pearlitic transformation of grains of austenite is paralleled by the presumed expulsion of graphite in making castings of malleable iron. For the metastability of cementite, *vide infra*, cementation. H. Kornfeld and G. Brieger studied the formation of cementite at the grain boundaries of mild steel.

A. Ledebur showed that the carbide existing in pearlite is chemically identical with that occurring as free cementite in the higher carbon alloys. P. Pingault obtained cementite of a high degree of purity by the action of sodium cyanide on electrolytic iron filings at 650°, and observed that the compound is stable in vacuo up to 1000° ; a slight decomposition occurs at 1075°, and complete decomposition at 1175°. G. Phragmen, however, said that general evidence indicates cementite to be more stable at elevated temp. than it is at lower temp. A. Westgren and G. Phragmen, S. Shigetaka, and F. Wever examined the X-radiograms of cementite and found that, like iron tritacarbide (*q.v.*), cementite crystallizes in the rhombic system, that four molecules are present in each space-lattice, and that the space-lattice has the dimensions $a=4\cdot518$ A., $b=5\cdot069$ A., and $c=6\cdot736$ A. The cementite of annealed steel, unannealed steel with lamellar pearlite, cast iron, spiegeleisen, and cohenite all gave the same X-radiogram. S. B. Hendricks studied the structure of the crystal lattice. For S. Shimura's observations, *vide supra*. T. Andrews gave 7·66 for the sp. gr. of cementite ; M. Levin and K. Dornhecker, 7·59 ; A. Westgren and G. Phragmen, 7·68 ; T. Ishigaki, 7·657 at 4° ; C. Benedicks, 7·74 and sp. vol. 0·1292 ; H. Moissan, 7·07 and sp. vol. 0·1414 ; and J. H. Andrew and A. J. K. Honeyman, 7·66 and sp. vol. 0·1306. A. Westgren and G. Phragmen gave 7·673 for the best representative value for the sp. gr., and 0·1304 for the sp. vol.— *vide* **5**. 39, 20. Cementite is extremely hard and brittle ; it is the hardest of all the constituents of iron and steel. H. C. Boynton gave 272 for the hardness of cementite when that of ferrite is unity and that of martensite is 239—*vide infra*, hardness. K. Tamaru gave 720 for the Brinell's hardness of martensite and 620 for that of cementite, but when the cementite is strained its hardness may rise to 820. On Moh's scale the hardness of cementite is about 6·5, since it scratches felspar and not quartz. G. Charpy and P. Pingault found that after the carburization of iron filings to cementite, by heating them in contact with hydrocarbons or alkali cyanides, the product scratched glass and left no trace of graphite when dissolved in nitric acid. The cementite was stable when heated to 1000° for 10 hrs. in vacuo, and the heating curves showed no marked critical point. E. Scheil studied the effect of press. on cementite. L. Troost and P. Hautefeuille gave for the heat of formation $-20\cdot48$ Cals. per mol. ; and T. Watase gave $3Fe+C=Fe_3C-4\cdot8$ Cals. at 20°, and for the heat of combustion, $Fe_3+C+3O_2=Fe_3O_4+CO_2+366\cdot3$ Cals. at 20°. Y. Chu Phary studied the surface tension of cementite.

The eutectic with molten alloys of carbon and iron consists of a solid soln. of γ-austenite and cementite, *vide supra* ; the cementite is unstable at this high temp., 1130° ; and just as the cementite-ferrite eutectoid at the lower temp. has received the name pearlite, so has the austenite-cementite eutectic at 1130° received the name **ledeburite**—*vide supra*. Fig. 136 illustrates the ledeburite in iron with 4·3 per cent. of carbon. This subject was discussed by B. Osann, and H. Jungbluth.

FIG. 136.—The Microstructure of Ledeburite (J. E. Hurst).

In 1863 H. C. Sorby observed the polyhedral grains of what he called *free iron* in wrought iron; and H. M. Howe proposed the term **ferrite** be applied to α-iron free from carbon or containing only a trace of carbon in solid soln., when present in iron or steel. The term includes iron containing silicon, manganese, nickel, etc., which form solid soln. with iron. Ferrite is the softest of all the constituents of iron or steel. Its microstructure is developed by etching with an alcoholic soln. of picric or nitric acid, when the outlines of the crystal aggregates appear to form polyhedral grains. The illustration of armco iron, Fig. 137 (×150 and reduced one-third), is due to W. J. Brooke and F. F. Hunting, and it shows that the ferrite is practically free from carbon and consequently also of pearlite. As indicated above, ferrite occurs in alternating layers with cementite in the pearlite of steels with 0·85 per cent. of carbon ; and any ferrite in excess of this is massive or free ferrite. Thus in Fig. 138 (×250), due to H. C. H. Carpenter, the polyhedral grains of the steel have here and there small, dark cells of pearlite. This steel had 0·048 per cent. of carbon, and was etched with a soln. of hydrochloric acid in amyl alcohol. When etched with nitric or picric acid, the ferrite of steels appears almost white. J. E. Stead reported crystals of ferrite 12·5 mm. across the major axis ; and A. Stadeler, crystals 7 mm. along the major axis, and they were visible to the naked eye. Observations on the structure and growth of ferrite crystals were made by H. S. Rawdon and H. Scott, C. Y. Clayton, E. Scheil, A. Hayes and H. E. Flanders, F. Giolitti and co-workers, N. T. Belaiew, and H. B. Pulsifer. V. N. Krivobok said that when cast hypoeutectoid steel is cooled and the temp.

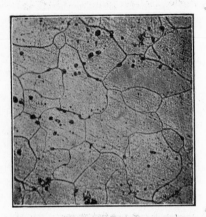

FIG. 137.—Polyhedral Grains of Ferrite in Armco Iron.

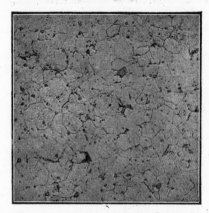

FIG. 138.—Grains of Ferrite with a few Dark Cells of Pearlite (×250).

reaches the Ar₁-arrest, the austenite is decomposed ; part of the ferrite is rejected and part remains in soln. The rejection of the ferrite is favoured at the boundaries between the grains, and the ferrite thus forms a continuous mesh-work structure enveloping the outlines of the original grains of austenite. The inner structure is sorbitic, containing more ferrite than is required for the production of pearlite. If the cooling is slower, more ferrite is rejected, and the ferrite at the grain boundaries stimulates the rejection of more ferrite near or at the peripheries of the grains. This ferrite may either (i) join the ferrite at the boundaries so as to thicken the needle-like crystals, or (ii) be located between the cleavage planes of the grain, forming the so-called " shoots " of excess ferrite. These shoots or lamellæ of ferrite gradually fade away as they approach the interior of the grain. If the cooling be still slower, the rejected ferrite will assume more nearly the perfected form and appear on polished sections as a cleavage of Widmanstätten structure—vide infra—and in the extreme case occupy the whole grain. Even under conditions of very long and slow cooling the cleavage character of the structure will still remain. The ultimate structure, when no spheroidizing of the cementite or graphitization occurs, is a cleavage structure rather than the network. C. A. Edwards and T. Yokoyama discussed the effect of strains and various annealing temp. on the growth of crystals of ferrite.

C. A. Edwards said that the dark boundaries of the grains may be explained in three ways : (i) a differential etching set up by the interpenetration of the crystal units at the crystal junctions ; (ii) a differential etching between adjacent crystals of varying orientation ; and (iii) a selective etching away of the amorphous cement surrounding the crystals. The ferrite of steels is assumed to be almost pure iron, but in all probability a small amount of carbon is held in solid soln. C. Benedicks' observations on the sp. gr. and magnetic properties of steels indicated that the ferrite of steels with more than 0·5 per cent. of carbon differs from the ferrite of steels with a lower proportion of carbon. In the former case the ferrite has about 0·27 per cent. of carbon in soln., and in the latter case much less is dissolved, and the actual amount probably varies with the percentage of carbon in the steels. He applied the term *ferronite* to the ferrite in steels with over 0·5 per cent. of carbon. The hypothesis, however, has not been established.

O. W. Storey observed that when electrolytic iron is heated to 910° to 915°, the crystalline structure of the deposit is converted into the grain structure of ordinary ferrite, the grain-size being large or small according as the original deposit was coarse or fine, but no change occurred below the A_3-arrest. Coarse-grained ferrite became finer grained with a prolonged annealing at the A_3-arrest, but not so fine as that resulting from a fine-grained deposit. The grains of electrolytic iron do not grow appreciably at 1150°. The ferrite grains of fused electrolytic iron were composed of smaller grains, the boundaries of the latter being merely shallow depressions, whereas those of the former were V-shaped grooves. There was a continuity of the inner grain structure between merging grains of similar crystal orientation, and this inner structure was destroyed only by several annealings above the Ac_3-point. The inner grains were supposed groups of similarly oriented iron crystals, the orientation in all the grains being alike throughout the ferrite grain ; and the large grains of γ-ferrite formed during the slow cooling of the molten metal contain numerous similarly oriented nuclei—not γ-ferrite—and are changed to this state without altering in size. The microstructure of rolled electrolytic iron consists of clean ferrite ; and that of the forged metal, of fine-grained ferrite containing a minimum of impurities.

A distinct sub-crystalline structure, or veining, has been detected in certain grains of ferrite, by T. Andrews, F. Robin, J. C. W. Humfrey, W. Rosenhain and J. C. W. Humfrey, F. Sauerwald and co-workers, G. K. Burgess and J. J. Crowe, F. S. Tritton, and F. S. Tritton and D. Hanson. H. S. Rawdon and T. Berglund observed that the etching of α-ferrite reveals three types: α-veining, γ-network, and δ-network. The α-veining appears within the grains, giving a veined appearance to the α-ferrite as if it were fine-grained. Ferrite, stressed or forged at a temp. close to the $\alpha\gamma$-transformation, shows the α-veining very well ; the presence of aluminium or manganese has no marked effect, but silicon suppresses this veining. The α-veining has no perceptible influence on the ordinary mechanical properties of ferrite. The γ- and δ-networks can usually be associated with tiny inclusions distributed in such a manner as to record the grain structure which existed in the high temp. allotropic states. The δ-network appears to be associated with the red-shortness of irons. E. Ammermann and H. Kornfeld found that the α-veining occurs throughout the ferrite grains of electrolytic iron only when the annealing temp. exceeds the A_3-point. Annealing between the A_1- and A_3-points produces local veining in those ferrite grains in close proximity to the cementite or pearlite fields, probably owing to a local reduction of the A_3-point by the segregation of the carbon. Deformation below the A_3-arrest does not produce veining unless the metal is subsequently annealed above this point, in which case the deformed metal has the veining more marked than is the case with metal which has been simply annealed without deformation.

According to C. O. Bannister and W. D. Jones, the veinage of α-ferrite grains is a manifestation of microscopical or sub-microscopical inclusions in the metal. In some cases, at a previous state of crystallization these inclusions would for the most part have been situated at the normal crystal boundaries, but following certain mechanical and thermal treatments, crystal growth has occurred, and the inclusions have not been of sufficient magnitude to prevent growth, although they have been sufficiently definite to be capable of being shown up by suitable etching operations. Summarizing the available evidence, C. O. Bannister and W. D. Jones say:

A.—The a-veining may be expected to be produced in iron and low carbon steel containing microscopical or sub-microscopical inclusions, or containing impurity in solid soln. which is liable under certain conditions to be precipitated as inclusions by any thermal treatment which (1) causes recrystallization or crystal growth; or (2) induces inclusions to segregate at boundaries, either as definite inclusions, or as inclusions in soln., which may be subsequently precipitated.

B.—The a-veining may be expected to be destroyed by treatment which (1) promotes the re-solution of the inclusions when soluble; or (2) causes the re-distribution of insoluble inclusions, as by (*a*) hot or cold-working, (*b*) recrystallization after heating to a high temp., or (*c*) quenching after certain heat treatments and from certain temp., depending on the nature of the inclusions.

C.—The a-veining may be expected to be absent in (1) very pure materials containing no non-metallic inclusions; (2) portions or definite crystals of a less pure material which are free from non-metallic inclusions; or (3) less pure materials in which the conditions have been such that any inclusions are held in solid soln.

REFERENCES.

[1] H. M. Howe, *Trans. Amer. Inst. Min. Eng.*, **24**. 829, 1901; **22**. 461, 1908; **51**. 886, 1915; *Journ. Iron Steel Inst.*, **79**. i, 230, 1909; *Met. Chem. Engg.*, **10**. 23, 1912; H. M. Howe and A. G. Levy, *Trans. Amer. Inst. Min. Eng.*, **50**. 542, 1914; *Journ. Iron Steel Inst.*, **94**. ii, 210, 1916; *Internat. Zeit. Metallog.*, **3**. 4, 1912; *Proc. Cleveland Inst. Eng.*, 218, 1914; F. T. Sisco, *Trans. Amer. Soc. Steel Treating*, **9**. 938, 1926; **10**. 109, 267, 457, 462, 800, 1926; **11**. 115, 284, 626, 651, 1927; **12**. 305, 1928; **13**. 305, 659, 1928; **15**. 155, 503, 1027, 1929 (I am indebted to Mr. F. T. Sisco for permission to use Figs. 100 and 117); F. F. Lucas, *ib.*, **6**. 669, 1924; **15**. 339, 1929; *Reprint Bell Telephone*, 454, B, 1930 (I am indebted to Mr. Lucas and to the Bell Telephone Laboratories, Inc., New York, for Figs. 106, 118, and 119); F. Osmond and G. Cartaud, *Journ. Iron Steel Inst.*, **71**. iii, 444, 1906; *Ann. Mines*, (9), **17**. 110, 1900; (9), **18**. 113, 1900; F. Osmond and J. Werth, *ib.*, (8), **8**. 5, 1885; F. Osmond, *ib.*, (8), **14**. 1, 1888; (9), **8**. 153, 1896; *Transformations du fer et du carbone dans les fers, les aciers, et fontes blanches*, Paris, 1888; *Contribution à l'étude des alliages*, Paris, 305, 1901; *Microscopic Analysis of Metals*, London, 1913; *Rev. Mét.*, **3**. 477, 1906; **4**. 819, 1907; *Metallographist*, **1**. 37, 1898; **2**. 235, 1899; **3**. 3, 1900; **4**. 23, 281, 1901; *Stahl Eisen*, **17**. 904, 1897; *Bull. Soc. Enc. Nat. Ind.*, (4), **10**. 476, 1895; C. Frémont and F. Osmond, *ib.*, **100**. 505, 1901; *Rev. Mét.*, **1**. 199, 349, 1904; *Journ. Iron Steel Inst.*, **37**. i, 38, 1890; F. Osmond, C. Frémont, and G. Cartaud, *Rev. Mét.*, **1**. 11, 1904; A. Baykoff, *ib.*, **6**. 829, 1909; J. O. Arnold and A. A. Read, *Journ. Chem. Soc.*, **65**. 788, 1894; J. O. Arnold, *Proc. Inst. Civil Eng.*, **123**. 127, 1896; *Mineral Ind.*, **5**. 697, 1897; *Ironmonger*, **126**. 274, 1909; *Metallographist*, **5**. 2, 1902; *Engg.*, **115**. 699, 1923; *Journ. Iron Steel Inst.*, **54**. ii, 185, 1898; **59**. i, 180, 1901; **68**. ii, 27, 1905; **81**. i, 185, 1910; **107**. i, 213, 1923; D. Lewis, *ib.*, **119**. i, 427, 1929; *Heat Treating and Forging*, **15**. 991, 1929; J. M. Robertson, *ib.*, **15**. 865, 1929; *Research Paper Safety in Mines*, 59, 1930; *Journ. Iron Steel Inst.*, **119**. i, 391, 1929; *Journ. Iron Steel Inst.—Carnegie Mem.*, **20**. 1, 1931; C. H. Desch, *Trans. Faraday Soc.*, **10**. 255, 1914; W. H. Hatfield, *ib.*, **81**. i, 203, 1910; *Cast Iron in the Light of Recent Research*, London, 227, 1912; C. A. Edwards, *The Physicochemical Properties of Steel*, London, 64, 1916; *Journ. Inst. Metals*, **5**. 150, 1911; *Journ. Iron Steel Inst.*, **82**. ii, 147, 1910; H. C. H. Carpenter and J. M. Robertson, *Iron Steel Ind.*, **4**. 273, 1931; *Journ. Iron Steel Inst.*, **123**. i, 345, 1931; **126**. i, —, 1932; H. C. H. Carpenter and C. A. Edwards, *ib.*, **89**. i, 138, 1914; H. C. Boynton, *ib.*, **67**. i, 262, 1904; *Iron Steel Mag.*, **7**. 470, 1904; E. Heyn and O. Bauer, *Mitt. Materialprüfungsamt.*, **24**. 29, 1906; *Stahl Eisen*, **26**. 782, 1906; *Rev. Mét.*, **8**. 417, 1911; *Journ. Iron Steel Inst.*, **79**. 1, 109, 1909; **61**. i, 160, 1902; J. H. Whiteley, *ib.*, **97**. i, 353, 1918; **105**. i, 339, 1922; **111**. i, 315, 1925; **112**. ii, 315, 1925; **116**. ii, 293, 1927; **120**. i, 147, 1929; *Proc. Cleveland Inst. Eng.*, 37, 1922; *Foundry Trade Journ.*, **41**. 203, 1929; J. A. Mathews, *Trans. Amer. Soc. Steel Treating*, **8**. 565, 1925; *Trans. Amer. Inst. Min. Eng.*, **71**. 568, 1925; *Proc. Amer. Soc. Testing Materials*, **14**. ii, 50, 1914; *Journ. Iron Steel Inst.*, **112**. ii, 299, 1925; B. D. Enlund, *ib.*, **111**. i, 305, 1925; W. J. Brooke and F. F. Hunting, *ib.*, **96**. ii, 233, 1917; F. Rogers, *ib.*, **67**. i, 484, 1905; L. Guillet, *Rev. Mét.*, **6**. 810, 1909; *Journ. Iron Steel Inst.*, **60**. ii, 1, 1906; D. Hanson, *ib.*, **105**. i, 354, 1922; J. E. Stead and A. W. Richards, *ib.*, **64**. ii, 119, 141, 1903; J. E. Stead, *ib.*, **61**. i, 172, 1902; **89**. i, 190, 1914; *Proc. Cleveland Inst. Eng.*, 53, 79, 1896; *Journ. Soc. Chem. Ind.*, **22**. 343, 1903; *Proc. Inst. Mech. Eng.*, 73, 1899; *Metallographist*, **1**. 329, 1898; **7**. 151, 1904; E. F. Lange, *ib.*, **6**. 9, 1903; A. Sauveur, *Trans. Amer. Soc. Steel Treating*, **17**. 199, 1930; *The Metallography and Heat Treatment of Iron and Steel*, Cambridge, Mass., 1926 (I am indebted to Prof. Sauveur for permission to use Fig. 101); *Metallographist*, **4**. 255, 1901; **6**. 13, 1903; *Journ. Iron Steel Inst.*, **72**. iv, 493, 1906; *Eng. Min. Journ.*, **63**. 662, 1896; **64**. 69, 215, 1897; *Trans. Amer. Inst. Min. Eng.*, **26**. 863, 1896; **73**.

902, 1926 ; *Heat Treating Forging*, **17**. 250, 1931 ; *Proc. Amer. Phil. Soc.*, **66**. 267, 1927 ; *Tech. Paper Amer. Inst. Min. Eng.*, 412, 1931 ; A. Sauveur and C. H. Chou, *ib.*, 169, 1929 ; A. Sauveur and H. C. Boynton, *Trans. Amer. Inst. Min. Eng.*, **34**. 150, 1903 ; C. Benedicks and E. Walldow, *Bihang Jernkontorets Ann.*, **16**. 219, 1918 ; C. Benedicks, *Koll. Zeit.*, **7**. 290, 1910 ; *Recherches physiques et physicochimiques sur l'acier au carbone*, Uppsala, 1904 ; *Nature*, **115**. 230, 1925 ; *Zeit. phys. Chem.*, **52**. 733, 1905 ; *Metallographic Researches*, New York, 73, 1926 ; *Internat. Zeit. Metallog.*, **1**. 184, 1911 ; *Rev. Mét.*, **6**. 567, 1909 ; *Journ. Iron Steel Inst.*, **68**. ii, 352, 1905 ; **76**. ii, 251, 1908 ; **77**. ii, 217, 1908 ; **79**. i, 229, 1909 ; **86**. ii, 242, 1912 ; **102**. ii, 153, 1920 ; A. Westgren, *Metal Progress*, **20**. 49, 1931 ; *Zeit. phys. Chem.*, **102**. 1, 1922 ; *Journ. Iron Steel Inst.*, **103**. i, 303, 362, 1921 ; **110**. i, 169, 1924 ; A. Westgren and G. Phragmen, *ib.*, **105**. i, 241, 1922 ; **109**. i, 159, 1924 ; A. Westgren and A. E. Lindh, *Zeit. phys. Chem.*, **98**. 181, 1921 ; H. Hanemann, *Arch. Eisenhüttenwesen*, **4**. 485, 1931 ; *Zeit. anorg. Chem.*, **88**. 265, 1914 ; *Internat. Zeit. Metallog.*, **3**. 127, 1913 ; *Stahl Eisen*, **32**. 1397, 1912 ; **43**. 880, 1923 ; **46**. 1585, 1926 ; **51**. 647, 1931 ; H. Hanemann and A. Schrader, *Trans. Amer. Soc. Steel Treating*, **9**. 169, 1926 (I am indebted to Dr. Hanemann for Figs. 114, 115, and 116) ; *Atlas Metallographicus*, Berlin, 1929 ; *Ber. Werkstoff. Ver. Eisenhüttenleute*, 61, 1925 ; *Ueber den Martensit*, Düsseldorf, 1926 ; *Stahl Eisen*, **51**. 645, 1931 ; *Arch. Eisenhüttenwesen*, **4**. 479, 1931 ; H. Hanemann, K. Heremann, U. Hofmann and A. Schrader, *ib.*, **4**. 479, 1931 ; *Stahl Eisen*, **51**. 646, 1931 ; H. Hanemann and F. Morawe, *ib.*, **23**. 1350, 1913 ; H. Hanemann and O. Schröder, *Zeit. Metallkunde*, **23**. 273, 297, 1931 ; H. Hanemann and V. Lindt, *Stahl Eisen*, **33**. 55, 1913 ; H. Hanemann and L. Träger, *ib.*, **46**. 1508, 1926 ; H. Hanemann and J. H. Wiester, *Arch. Eisenhüttenwesen*, **5**. 377, 1932 ; K. Gebhard, *Ueber das Martensitsystem*, Düsseldorf, 1929 ; K. Gebhard, H. Hanemann and A. Schrader, *Arch. Eisenhüttenwesen*, **2**. 763, 1929 ; *Stahl Eisen*, **49**. 940, 1929 ; A. Schrader, *ib.*, **44**. 309, 1924 ; E. L. Reed, *Photomicrographs of Iron and Steel*, New York, 1929 ; H. le Chatelier, *Contribution à l'étude des alliages*, Paris, 387, 1901 ; *Bull. Soc. Enc. Nat. Ind.*, (5), **6**. 661, 1900 ; *Metallographist*, **4**. 29, 1901 ; *Rev. Mét.*, **1**. 134, 222, 301, 473, 1904 ; **5**. 167, 640, 1908 ; *Trans. Amer. Inst. Min. Eng.*, **64**. 547, 1920 ; *Journ. Iron Steel Inst.*, **58**. ii, 330, 1900 ; **68**. ii, 364, 1905 ; *Compt. Rend.*, **129**. 331, 1899 ; **146**. 824, 1909 ; G. Charpy and L. Grenet, *ib.*, **134**. 549, 598, 1902 ; *Bull. Soc. Enc. Nat. Ind.*, **104**. 464, 882, 1903 ; W. C. Roberts-Austen, *Proc. Inst. Mech. Eng.*, 35, 1899 ; A. McCance, *ib.*, 1663, 1910 ; W. J. Kurbatoff, *Rev. Mét.*, **2**. 169, 1905 ; *Journ. Russ. Phys. Chem. Soc.*, **36**. 1524, 1905 ; *Stahl Eisen*, **25**. 543, 1905 ; *Met.*, **5**. 721, 1909 ; H. von Jüptner, *Metallographist*, **2**. 235, 1899 ; *Stahl Eisen*, **19**. 237, 278, 1899; *Grundzüge der Siderologie*, Leipzig, **2**. 137, 1902 ; A. M. Portevin and M. Garvin, *Iron Coal Trade Rev.*, **98**. 599, 1919 ; *Journ. Iron Steel Inst.*, **99**. i, 559, 1919 ; A. M. Portevin and P. Chévenard, *Compt. Rend.*, **171**. 350, 1920 ; **172**. 1490, 1921 ; **191**. 408, 523, 1059, 1930 ; A. M. Portevin, *L'étude de la structure des métaux et alliages et ses conséquences*, Paris, 1921 ; *Journ. Iron Steel Inst.*, **108**. ii, 93, 1923 ; *Engg.*, **115**. 477, 505, 1923 ; *Rev. Mét.*, **10**. 667, 1913 ; **16**. 141, 1919 ; *Rev. Ing.*, **28**. 165, 1921 ; *Bull. Soc. Enc. Nat. Ind.*, **121**. 207, 1914 ; *Journ. Inst. Metals*, **29**. 239, 1923 ; A. M. Portevin and V. Bernard, *ib.*, **12**. 147, 1915 ; *Journ. Iron Steel Inst.*, **90**. ii, 204, 1914 ; **104**. ii, 147, 1921 ; F. L. Brady, *Journ. Inst. Metals*, **28**. 369, 1922 ; H. C. Sorby, *B.A. Rep.*, 189, 1864 ; 139, 1865 ; *Journ. Iron Steel Inst.*, **29**. i, 140, 1886 ; K. Honda, *Arch. Eisenhüttenwesen*, **1**. 527, 1928 ; *Trans. Amer. Soc. Steel Treating*, **11**. 399, 473, 1922 ; **16**. 97, 1929 ; *Science Rep. Tohoku Univ.*, **6**. 203, 1917 ; **8**. 181, 1919 ; **11**. 19, 1922 ; **14**. 165, 1925 ; **16**. 279, 1927 ; **18**. 503, 1929 ; *Rev. Mét.*, **22**. 119, 1923 ; *Journ. Iron Steel Inst.*, **100**. ii, 417, 1919 ; **114**. ii, 417, 1926 ; K. Honda and S. Saito, *ib.*, **102**. ii, 261, 1920 ; *Science Rep. Tohoku Univ.*, **9**. 311, 1920 ; K. Honda and A. Osawa, *ib.*, **18**. 47, 1929 ; K. Honda and K. Tamaru, *ib.*, **17**. 69, 1928 ; K. Tamaru, *Bull. Inst. Phys. Chem. Research Japan*, **7**. 1028, 1928 ; *Science Rep. Tohoku Univ.*, **15**. 829, 1926 ; **18**. 473, 1929 ; K. Tamaru and S. Sekito, *Bull. Inst. Phys. Chem. Research*, **10**. 328, 1931 ; *Science Rep. Tohoku Univ.*, **20**. 377, 1931 ; M. Mikami, *Science Rep. Tohoku Univ.*, **22**. 681, 1931 ; N. Yamada, *ib.*, **10**. 453, 1921 ; *Journ. Iron Steel Inst.*, **105**. i, 409, 1922 ; T. Matsushita, *ib.*, **117**. i, 720, 1923 ; *Science Rep. Tohoku Univ.*, **7**. 43, 1918 ; **12**. 1, 1923 ; **16**. 901, 1927 ; T. Isihara, *ib.*, **14**. 377, 1925 ; S. Saito, *ib.*, **9**. 281, 1920 ; **18**. 303, 1929 ; **20**. 260, 1931 ; *Kinzoku no Kenkyu*, **5**. 174, 1928 ; K. Honda and S. Idei, *ib.*, **9**. 491, 1920 ; **14**. 165, 1925 ; S. Sekito, *ib.*, **18**. 69, 1929 ; **20**. 313, 369, 1931 ; K. Honda and S. Sekito, *Science Rep. Tohoku Univ.*, **17**. 743, 1928 ; *Nature*, **121**. 744, 1928 ; T. Matsushita and K. Nagasawa, *Kinzoku no Kenkyu*, **3**. 92, 1927 ; *Science Rep. Tohoku Univ.*, **16**. 901, 1927 ; *Journ. Iron Steel Inst.*, **115**. i, 721, 1927 ; **116**. ii, 311, 1927 ; K. Honda and T. Kikuta, *ib.*, **105**. i, 393, 1922 ; K. Honda and K. Iwase, *Science Rep. Tohoku Univ.*, **16**. 1, 1927 ; *Trans. Amer. Soc. Steel Treating*, **11**. 399, 473, 1927 ; K. Honda and T. Murakami, *ib.*, **6**. 23, 53, 1917 ; *Journ. Iron Steel Inst.*, **98**. ii, 385, 1918 ; T. Murakami, *Tech. Rep. Tohoku Univ.*, **8**. 119, 1929 ; K. Kawakami, *Kinzoku no Kenkyu*, **7**. 57, 1930 ; R. A. Hadfield and T. G. Elliott, *Microscope*, 156, 1920 ; C. F. Brush, *Trans. Amer. Inst. Min. Eng.*, **62**. 17. 1919 ; C. F. Brush, R. A. Hadfield and S. A. Main, *Proc. Roy. Soc.*, **95**. A, 120, 1918 ; C. F. Brush and R. A. Hadfield, *ib.*, **93**. A, 188, 1917 ; R. A. Hadfield, *History of the Metallurgy of Iron and Steel*, London, 1915 ; *Journ. Iron Steel Inst.*, **85**. i, 134, 1912 ; E. Hess, *ib.*, **77**. ii, 1, 1907 ; A. F. Hallimond, *Trans. Amer. Soc. Steel Treating*, **3**. 931, 1923 ; *Journ. Iron Steel Inst.*, **104**. ii, 359, 1922 ; **105**. i, 359, 1922 ; L. Grenet, *ib.*, **84**. ii, 13, 1911 ; G. Cesaro, *ib.*, **99**. i, 447, 1919 ; W. Rosenhain, *ib.*, **110**. ii, 145, 1924 ; A. L. Babochine, *Rev. Mét.*, **14**. 81, 1917 ; *Proc. Russ. Met. Soc.*, **3**. 561, 1915 ; N. G. Ilyne, *ib.*, **3**. 488, 1915 ; N. T. Belaiew, *ib.*, **2**. 445, 1914 ; *On the Bulat*, St. Petersburg, 1906 ; *The Structure, Crystallization, and Properties of Steel on Slow Cooling*, Petrograd, 1909 ; *Rev. Mét.*, **9**. 321, 1912 ; **26**. 424, 1929 ; **27**. 680,

1930 ; *Journ. Iron Steel Inst.*, **97**. i, 417, 1918 ; **104**. ii, 181, 1921 ; **105**. i, 201, 1922 ; **124**. ii, 195, 1931 ; *Chem. Met. Engg.*, **28**. 537, 1923 ; *Rev. Univ. Mines*, (6), **16**. 41, 1923 ; *Crystallization of Metals*, London, 130, 1922 (I am indebted to Col. Belaiew for permission to use Fig. 128) ; *Proc. Roy. Soc.*, **108**. A, 295, 1925 ; *Met.*, **8**. 449, 493, 699, 1911 ; B. Ischewsky, *Stahl Eisen*, **23**. 120, 1903 ; *Journ. Russ. Met. Soc.*, 196, 1910 ; *Mét.*, **8**. 701, 1911 ; P. Goerens, *ib.*, **3**. 175, 1906 ; 4. 137, 173, 182, 1907 ; M. Oknof, *ib.*, **8**. 138, 1911 ; R. S. MacPherran and J. F. Harper, *Trans. Amer. Soc. Steel Treating*, **6**. 341, 1924 ; J. R. Bréant, *Ann. Mines*, (1), **9**. 319, 1824 ; *Ann. Phil.*. **8**. 267, 1824 ; *Quart. Journ. Science*, **18**. 386, 1825 ; *Bull. Soc. Enc. Nat. Ind.*, (1), **22**. 222, 1823 ; *Ann. Chim. Phys.*, (2), **24**. 388, 1823 ; G. Pearson, *Phil. Trans.*, **17**. 322, 1795 ; J. Stodart and M. Faraday, *ib.*, **112**. 253, 1822 ; F. Buchanan, *A Journey from Madras through the Countries of Mysore, Canara, and Malabar*, London, **2**. 20, 1807 ; J. Chardin, *Voyages du Chevalier Chardin en Perse*, Paris, 355, 1811 ; J. Voysey, *Handbook of Indian Arms*, London, 27, 1880 ; C. von Schwarz, *Stahl Eisen*, **21**. 209, 1901 ; P. Anossoff, *O Bulatah*, St. Petersburg, 1841 ; *Ermann's Arch.*, **9**. 510, 1843 ; D. Lardner, *A Treatise on the Progressive Improvement in the Manufacture of Metal*, London, **1**. 254, 1842 ; M. Bazin, *Traité de l'acier*, Strassbourg, 1837 ; D. K. Tschernoff, *Metallography of Steel*, St. Petersburg, 1906 ; *Iron Trade Rev.*, **33**. 11, 1899 ; *Metallographist*, **2**. 255, 1899 ; *Proc. Russ. Imp. Tech. Soc.*, 399, 1868 ; W. Schneider, *Stahl Eisen*, **44**. 207, 1924 ; A. Schneider, *Ber. Ver. deut. Eisenhüttenleute*, 42, 1923 ; J. B. Tavernier, *Collection of the Travels through Turkey into Persia, and the East Indies*, London, 1684 ; *Les six voyages de J. B. Tavernier en Turquie, en Perse, et aux Indes*, Paris, 1676 ; H. W. Voysey, *Journ. Asiatic Soc. Bengal*, **1**. 245, 1832 ; R. A. F. de Réaumur, *L'art de convertir le fer forgé en acier*, Paris, 1722 ; *Nouvelle art d'adoucir le fer fondu*, Paris, 1782 ; *An Essay on the Mystery of Tempering Steel*, London, 1771 ; E. Scheil, *Arch. Eisenhüttenwesen*, **2**. 375, 1929 ; *Neuere Untersuchungen über die Theorie der Stahlhärtung*, Düsseldorf, 1928 ; *Stahl Eisen*, **48**. 1776, 1928 ; *Zeit. anorg. Chem.*, **183**. 98, 1929 ; E. H. Schulz, *Forschungsarb. Geb. Ingenieurw.*, 164, 1914 ; E. Gumlich, *Wiss. Abh. Phys. Tech. Reichsanst.*, **4**. 271, 1918 ; S. Hilpert and T. Dickmann, *Ber.*, **48**. 1281, 1915 ; Marco Polo, *Voyages and Travels*, London, **1**. 94, 1903 ; A. E. van Arkel, *Physica*, **5**. 208, 1925 ; K. Becker, *Zeit. Physik*, **42**. 226, 1927 ; U. Dehlinger, *Zeit. Kryst.*, **65**. 615, 1927 ; *Zeit. Physik*, **74**. 267, 1932 ; O. Mügge, *Neues Jahrb. Min.*, ii, 63, 1899 ; A. Smekal, *Zeit. tech. Phys.*, **7**. 535, 1926 ; F. Sauerwald and G. Jackwirth, *Zeit. anorg. Chem.*, **140**. 391, 1924 ; F. Sauerwald, W. Schultze and G. Jackwirth, *ib.*, **140**. 384, 1924 ; F. Wever and N. Engel, *Mitt. Inst. Eisenforschung*, **12**. 93, 1930 ; *Stahl Eisen*, **50**. 1308, 1930 ; N. Engel, *Ueber den Einfluss der Abkürhlgeschwindigkeit auf die thermischen Umwandlungen, das Gefüge und den Feinbau von Eisen-Kohlenstoff-Legierungen*, Düsseldorf, 1930 ; W. Brenscheidt, *Gefügeänderungen beim Glühen von weichem Stahl*, Düsseldorf, 1929 ; C. P. Yap, *Tech. Publ. Amer. Inst. Min. Eng.*, 381, 382, 1931 ; G. Delbart, *Aciers Spéciaux*, **5**. 254, 302, 1930 ; E. Walldow, *Engg.*, **131**. 27, 1931 ; A. Merz and C. Pfannenschmidt, *Zeit. anorg. Chem.*, **167**. 241, 1927 ; *Hütt. Walzwerke*, **32**. 391, 1928 ; D. J. McAdam, *Chem. Met. Engg.*, **25**. 613, 1921 ; R. Ruer, *Zeit. anorg. Chem.*, **117**. 249, 1921 ; *Zeit. phys. Chem.*, **121**. 484, 1926 ; *Stahl Eisen*, **46**. 918, 1926 ; J. E. Howard, *Iron Age*, **68**. 12, 1903 ; W. Campbell, *ib.*, **69**. 23, 1904 ; *Trans. Amer. Inst. Min. Eng.*, **44**. 489, 1912 ; *Journ. Amer. Chem. Soc.*, **28**. 1304, 1906 ; *Met.*, **3**. 741, 781, 1906 ; *Journ. Franklin Inst.*, **154**. 1, 131, 1902 ; **163**, 407, 1907 ; J. J. Kessler, *Journ. Assoc. Eng. Soc.*, **31**. 185, 1903 ; E. A. Schott, *Glückauf*, **40**. 36, 1903 ; J. Driesen, *Ferrum*, **12**. 29, 1914 ; I. Ilimoff, *Gorny Journ.*, 17, 1841 ; P. Oberhoffer, *Fortschr. Metallog.*, 1350, 1914 ; *Zeit. anorg. Chem.*, **81**. 156, 1913 ; *Stahl Eisen*, **33**. 1569, 1913 ; **35**. 140, 1915 ; **45**. 223, 1925 (I am indebted to the publishers of *Stahl und Eisen* for permission to use Fig. 153) ; P. Oberhoffer and H. Meyer, *Stahl Eisen*, **34**. 1241, 1914 ; P. Oberhoffer and P. Hartmann, *ib.*, **34**. 1245, 1914 ; W. Tafel, *ib.*, **41**. 1321, 1921 ; H. Scott and H. G. Movius, *Scient. Paper Bur. Standards*, 395, 396, 1920 ; H. Scott, *ib.*, 513, 1925 ; *Trans. Amer. Soc. Steel Treating*, **1**. 511, 1921 ; **3**. 593, 1923 ; **9**. 239, 275, 1929 ; M. Chikashige *Zeit. anorg. Chem.*, **124**. 59, 1922 ; P. Weiss and N. Beck, *Journ. Phys.*, (4), **7**. 249, 1908 ; A. Meuthen, *Ferrum*, **10**. 1, 1912 ; W. L. Fink, *ib.*, **9**. 717, 780, 1926 ; K. Heindlhofer, *Phys. Rev.*, (2), **20**. 221, 1922 ; (2), **24**. 426, 1924 ; K. Heindlhofer and F. L. Wright, *Trans. Amer. Soc. Steel Treating*, **7**. 34, 1925 ; K. Heindlhofer and E. C. Bain, *ib.*, **18**. 70, 1930 ; H. W. B. Roozeboom, *Zeit. phys. Chem.*, **34**. 437, 1900 ; J. H. Andrew and H. A. Dickie, *Journ. Iron Steel Inst.*, **114**. ii, 359, 1926 ; J. H. Andrew and A. J. K. Honeyman, *Journ. Iron Steel Inst.—Carnegie Mem.*, **13**. 253, 1924 ; J. H. Andrew, *Journ. Tech. Coll. Glasgow*, **1**. 41, 1924 ; **7**. 16, 1930 ; *Internat. Zeit. Metallog.*, **6**. 30, 1914 ; J. M. Heath, *Madras Journ. Literature Science*, **2**. 184, 1856 ; D. Mushet, *Papers on Iron and Steel*, London, 650, 1840 ; *Phil. Trans.*, **95**. 163, 1805 ; *Nicholson Journ.*, **11**. 221, 1805 ; K. Schröter, *Zeit. anorg. Chem.*, **169**. 157, 1928 ; E. Heymann, *ib.*, **134**. 137, 1924 ; G. Tammann and A. Heinzel, *ib.*, **167**. 173, 1927 ; G. Tammann and E. Scheil, *ib.*, **157**. 1, 1926 ; G. Tammann and G. Siebel, *Stahl Eisen*, **45**. 1202, 1925 ; G. Tammann, *ib.*, **42**. 654, 772, 1922 ; F. Wever, *Zeit. Elektrochem.*, **30**. 376, 1924 ; *Mitt. Inst. Eisenforsch.*, **3**. 45, 1921 ; **6**. 42, 1924 ; **9**. 151, 1927 ; *Arch. Eisenhüttenwesen*, **5**. 367, 1932 ; F. Wever and P. Rütten, *ib.*, **6**. 1, 1924 ; H. A. Schwartz, *Trans. Amer. Soc. Steel Treating*, **9**. 883, 1926 ; **11**. 277, 1927 ; H. A. Schwartz, H. A. Johnson and C. H. Junge, *ib.*, **17**. 383, 1930 ; W. L. Fink and E. D. Campbell, *ib.*, **9**. 717, 1926 ; K. Styri, *ib.*, **7**. 53, 1925 ; C. H. Green, *Trans. Amer. Inst. Min. Eng.*, **71**. 651, 1925 ; E. C. Bain, *ib.*, **68**. 685, 1924 ; *ib.*, **70**. 25, 1924 ; *Chem. Met. Engg.*, **26**. 543, 1922 ; *Trans. Amer. Soc. Steel Treating*, **5**. 89, 1924 ; **8**. 14, 1925 ; **9**. 754, 1926 ; **13**. 369, 1928 ; E. C. Bain and Z. Jeffries, *Iron Age*, **112**. 805, 1923 ; Z. Jeffries, *Trans. Amer. Inst. Min. Met.*, **73**. 863, 1926 ; *Trans. Amer. Soc. Steel Treating*, **13**. 369, 1928 ; Z. Jeffries and R. S. Archer, *The Science of*

Metals, New York, 425, 1924 ; *Chem. Met. Engg.*, **24**. 1057, 1921 ; R. Adam, *ib.*, **10**. 588, 1912 ; E. S. Davenport and E. C. Bain, *Tech. Publ. Amer. Inst. Min. Eng.*, 348, 1930 ; E. C. Bain and W. N. S. Waring, *Trans. Amer. Soc. Steel Treating*, **15**. 69, 1929 ; H. J. French, *ib.*, **6**. 251, 1924 ; H. J. French, J. Strauss and T. G. Digges, *ib.*, **4**. 353, 1923 ; M. A. Grossmann and E. C. Bain, *ib.*, **9**. 259, 1926 ; M. A. Grossmann, *ib.*, **2**. 691, 1001, 1920 ; *Iron Age*, **114**. 149, 1924 ; J. Mitchell, *Journ. West Scotland Iron Steel Inst.*, **28**. 38, 1921 ; O. E. Harder and R. L. Dowdell, *The Decomposition of the Austenitic Structure in Steels*, Minneapolis, 1927 ; *Bull. Univ. Minnesota Met. Series*, 1, 1927 ; *Trans. Amer. Soc. Steel Treating*, **11**. 17, 217, 391, 583, 781, 959, 975, 1927 ; **12**. 51, 1927 ; O. E. Harder, *ib.*, **5**. 27, 1924 ; E. D. Campbell, *Journ. Iron Steel Inst.*, **92**. ii, 164, 1915 ; E. Maurer and G. Schilling, *Stahl Eisen*, **45**. 1163, 1925 ; E. Maurer and G. Riedrich, *ib.*, **50**. 1431, 1930 ; *Arch. Eisenhüttenwesen*, **4**. 95, 1930 ; G. Riedrich, *Ueber die sogenannte Heterogenität des Martensits*, Düsseldorf, 1929 ; E. Maurer, *Untersuchungen über das Härten und Anlassen von Eisen und Stahl*, Halle a. S., 1909 ; *Compt. Rend.*, **146**. 822, 1908 ; *Stahl Eisen*, **44**. 622, 1924 ; *Rev. Mét.*, **5**. 715, 1908 ; *Met.*, **6**. 33, 1909 ; *Mitt. Inst. Eisenforschung*, **1**. 39, 1920 ; P. Dejean, *Compt. Rend.*, **165**. 334, 429, 1917 ; *Rev. Mét.*, **14**. 641, 1917 ; P. Chévenard (see A. M. Portevin), *ib.*, **16**. 17, 1919 ; O. V. Greene, *Iron Age*, **114**. 615, 670, 1924 ; E. Schiel, *Zeit. Elektrochem.*, **38**. 554, 1932 ; R. F. Mehl, *Tech. Publ. Amer. Inst. Min. Eng.*, 57, 1928 ; F. C. Elder, *Heat Treating Forging*, **15**. 717, 1929 ; S. Kobayashi, *Suiyokaishi (Japan)*, **5**. 807, 1929 ; J. Orland, *Anal. Association Ing.*, **8**. 28, 144, 1929 ; H. Birnbaum, *ib.*, **2**. 41, 1928 ; H. H. Lester, *Army Ordnance*, **5**. 455, 1924 ; W. J. Crook and H. S. Taylor, *Metals Alloys*, **1**. 539, 594, 1930 ; H. Wedding, *Stahl Eisen*, **15**. 506, 1895 ; A. Martens, *ib.*, **15**. 954, 1895 ; H. S. Rawdon, *Trans. Amer. Soc. Steel Treating*, **3**. 649, 1923 ; H. S. Rawdon, P. Hidnert and W. A. Tucker, *ib.*, **10**. 233, 1926 ; H. S. Rawdon and P. Hidnert, *Phys. Rev.*, (2), **25**. 898, 1925 ; H. S. Rawdon and S. Epstein, *Scient. Paper Bur. Standards*, 452, 1923 ; H. V. Wille, *Proc. Amer. Soc. Testing Materials*, **15**. 27, 1915 ; J. H. Hall and G. R. Hanks, *ib.*, **24**. 626, 1924 ; T. McL. Jasper, *Engg.*, **118**. 343, 1924 ; A. Hayes, W. J. Flanders and H. E. Moore, *ib.*, **5**. 183, 1924 ; G. Z. Nesselstrauss, *Chem. Trav. Tech. Science Russ.*, 12, 1923 ; *Rev. Mét.*, **21**. 317, 1924 ; *Zeit. Physik*, **64**. 325, 1930 ; N. Seljakoff, G. Kurdjumoff and N. T. Goodtzoff, *Nature*, **119**. 494, 1927 ; *Rev. Mét.*, **25**. 99, 222, 1928 ; *Zeit. Physik*, **45**. 384, 1927 ; G. Kurdjumoff and G. Sachs, *ib.*, **64**. 325, 1930 ; *Naturwiss.*, **18**. 534, 1930 ; G. Kurdjumoff and E. Kaminsky, *Zeit. Physik*, **53**. 696, 1929 ; *Nature*, **122**. 475, 1928 ; E. Oehman, *ib.* **127**. 270, 1931 ; S. Shimura, *Proc. Acad. Tokyo*, **6**. 269, 1930 ; F. C. A. H. Lantsberry, *Journ. Soc. Chem. Ind.*, **41**. 409, R, 1922 ; W. H. Walker, *Chem. Ztg.*, **31**. 739, 1907 ; H. S. van Vleet and C. Upthegrove, *Metal Progress*, **18**. 68, 1930 ; A. Bencke, *Oesterr. Zeit. Berg. Hütt.*, **57**. 43, 1909 ; B. Stoughton and R. D. Billinger, *Journ. Ind. Eng. Chem.*, **18**. 785, 1926 ; D. K. Bullens, *Met. Chem. Engg.*, **10**. 205, 1912 ; J. Calian, *Rev. Mét.*, **9**. 17, 1912 ; A. R. Roy, *Iron Age*, **90**. 764, 1912 ; A. Allison, *ib.*, **118**. 73, 1926 ; *Forging Heat Treating*, **14**. 624, 1928 ; J. Boiteux, *Fonderie Moderne*, **6**. 13, 1913 ; W. Guertler, *Internat. Zeit. Metallog.*, **5**. 5, 1914 ; R. A. Thakore, *Proc. Indian Science Congr.*, **15**. 92, 1928 ; W. E. Dalby, *Trans. Inst. Naval Arch.*, **59**. 75, 1917 ; M. Matweieff, *Proc. Russ. Met. Soc.*, **1**. 149, 1916 ; *Rev. Mét.*, **15**. 44, 1918 ; J. Alexander, *Trans. Amer. Inst. Min. Eng.*, **60**. 466, 1919 ; **64**. 524, 1920 ; *Chem. Met. Engg.*, **26**. 54, 119, 170, 201, 1922 ; G. Hägg, *Nature*, **127**. 271, 1931 ; *Zeit. phys. Chem.*, **8**. B, 455, 1930 ; M. von Stackelberg, *ib.*, **9**. B, 437, 1930 ; C. G. Darwin, *Phil. Mag.*, (6), **43**. 800, 1922 ; B. Kjerrman, *Stahl Eisen*, **42**. 697, 1922 ; H. Jungblüth, *ib.*, **45**. 1918, 1925 ; H. Esser and W. Eilender, *ib.*, **50**. 1616, 1930 ; *Arch. Eisenhüttenwesen*, **4**. 113, 1930 ; B. Neumann, *ib.*, **1**. 241, 1927 ; *Stahl Eisen*, **47**. 1695, 1927 ; H. C. Ihsen, *Forging Heat Treating*, **8**. 300, 1922 ; W. D. Bancroft, *Trans. Amer. Inst. Min. Eng.*, **68**. 604, 1922 ; A. E. White, *Trans. Amer. Soc. Steel Treating*, **3**. 396, 1923 ; C. H. Desch and A. T. Roberts, *Journ. Iron Steel Inst.*, **107**. i, 249, 1923 ; V. Kohlschütter and K. Steck, *Zeit. Elektrochem.*, **28**. 554, 1922 ; F. Körber and W. Köster, *Mitt. Inst. Eisenforsch.*, **5**. 145, 1924 ; A. Pomp and R. Wijkander, *ib.*, **8**. 2, 1926 ; K. P. Grigorovich, *Messager Tech. Russ.*, 127, 1923 ; *Rev. Mét.*, **21**. 319, 1924 ; H. M. Boylston, *Fuels Furnaces*, **5**. 433, 1927 ; A. E. Cameron and I. F. Morrison, *Trans. Roy. Soc. Canada*, (3), **22**. 289, 1928 ; S. Steinberg, *Arch. Eisenhüttenwesen*, **5**. 383, 1932 ; W. Broniewsky, *Compt. Rend.*, **156**. 699, 1983, 1913 ; F. H. Jeffrey, *Trans. Faraday Soc.*, **27**. 751, 1931 ; H. Styri, *Metal Progress*, **20**. 79, 1931 ; H. E. Publow and C. M. Heath, *Metals Alloys*, **2**. 155, 1931 ; H. E. Publow, C. M. Heath and M. E. Batchelor, *Bull. Michigan Eng. Exp. Station*, **41**. 3, 1931 ; R. F. Mehl and C. S. Barrett, *ib.*, **1**. 442, 1930 ; *Trans. Amer. Inst. Min. Eng.—Metals Div.*, **78**. 1, 1931 ; R. F. Mell and O. T. Marzke, *ib.*, **78**. 123, 1931 ; R. F. Mehl, C. S. Barrett and D. W. Smith, *Nature*, **129**. 313, 1932 ; P. Pingault, *Compt. Rend.*, **191**. 1007, 1930 ; J. M. Robertson, *Journ. Iron Steel Inst.—Carnegie Mem.*, **20**. 1, 1931.

² H. le Chatelier, *Rev. Gén. Sciences*, **8**. 18, 1897 ; M. Masloff, *Proc. Russ. Met. Soc.*, **1**. 495, 1916 ; A. M. Portevin and P. Chévenard, *Compt. Rend.*, **172**. 1490, 1921 ; *Rev. Mét.* **18**. 428, 1921 ; P. Chévenard *ib.*, **16**. 17, 1919 ; **19**. 546, 1922 ; *Compt. Rend.*, **165**. 59, 1917 ; **166**. 682, 1918 ; P. Dejean, *ib.*, **165**. 334, 429, 1917 ; *Rev. Mét.*, **18**. 419, 1921 ; A. M. Portevin, *ib.*, **14**. 707, 1917 ; A. M. Portevin and M. Garvin, *Journ. Iron Steel Inst.*, **99**. i, 469, 1919 ; L. Grenet, *ib.*, **84**. ii, 13, 1911 ; J. M. Robertson, *ib.*, **119**. i, 391, 1929 ; J. H. Andrew, J. Rippon, C. P. Miller and A. Wragg, *ib.*, **101**. i, 527, 1920 ; J. H. Andrew, J. N. Greenwood and G. W. Green, *ib.*, **100**. ii, 231, 1919 ; C. A. Edwards, J. N. Greenwood and H. Kikkawa, *ib.*, **93**. i, 114, 1916 ; C. A. Edwards, H. Sutton and G. Oishi, *ib.*, **101**. i, 403, 1920 ; C. A. Edwards and A. L. Norbury, *ib.*, **101**. i, 403, 1920 ; W. T. Griffiths, *ib.*, **108**. ii, 133, 1923 ; A. F. Hallimond, *ib.*, **105**. i, 359, 1922 ; E. W. Ehn, *ib.*, **105**. i, 157, 1922 ; A. Westgren, *ib.*, **103**. i, 303, 1921 ; A. Westgren and

G. Phragmen, *ib.*, **106**. ii, 241, 1922 ; K. Honda, *ib.*, **102**. ii, 417, 1919 ; K. Honda and T. Kikuta, *ib.*, **106**. ii, 392, 1922 ; T. Kikuta, *Science Rep. Tohoku Univ.*, **11**. 1, 1922 ; T. Murakami, *ib.*, **7**. 217, 1918 ; *Tech. Rep. Tohoku Univ.*, **8**. 119, 1929 ; *Osaka's Sexagint*, 171, 1927 ; T. Matsushita, *Journ. Iron Steel Inst.*, **107**. i, 723, 1923 ; H. C. H. Carpenter, *ib.*, **67**. i, 433, 1905 ; H. C. H. Carpenter and B. F. E. Keeling, *ib.*, **65**. i, 224, 1904 ; F. Osmond, *ib.*, **42**. ii, 115, 1892 ; *Rev. Mét.*, **1**. 348, 1904 ; P. Braesco, *Ann. Chim. Phys.*, (9), **14**. 5, 1920 ; H. Moore, *Proc. Inst. Mech. Eng.*, 51, 1921 ; W. Rosenhain, *Proc. Roy. Soc.*, **99**. A, 196, 1921 ; *Journ. Inst. Metals*, **13**. 160, 1915 ; **30**. 3, 1923 ; Z. Jeffries and R. S. Archer, *Chem. Met. Engg.*, **26**. 249, 1922 ; E. C. Bain, *ib.*, **28**. 21, 65, 1923 ; *Trans. Amer. Soc. Steel Treating*, **9**. 9, 1926 ; H. J. French and O. Z. Klopsch, *ib.*, **6**. 251, 1924 ; H. Hanemann and A. Schrader, *ib.*, **9**. 169, 1926 ; H. Hanemann, *Stahl Eisen*, **44**. 309, 1924 ; H. Hanemann and F. Morawe, *ib.*, **33**. 1350, 1913 ; H. Scott, *Scient. Paper Bur. Standards*, 335, 1919 ; K. Daeves, *Stahl Eisen*, **45**. 427, 1925 ; E. A. Owen and G. D. Preston, *Proc. Phys. Soc.*, **35**. 101, 1923 ; A. Hultgren, *A Metallographic Study on Tungsten Steels*, New York, 1920 ; *Journ. Iron Steel Inst.*, **104**. ii, 139, 1921 ; **108**. ii, 169, 1923 ; H. Jungb'uth, *Krupp's Monatsh.*, **5**. 95, 1924.

³ L. B. G. de Morveau, *Nouv. Mém. Dijon Acad.*, **6**. 406, 1785 ; J. R. Bréant, *Ann. Mines*, (1), **9**. 319, 1824 ; *Ann. Phil.*, **8**. 267, 1824 ; *Bull. Soc. Enc. Nat. Ind.*, (1), **22**. 222, 1823 ; *Quart. Journ. Science*, **18**. 386, 1825 ; *Ann. Chim. Phys.*, (2), **24**. 388, 1825 ; P. H. Berggren, *Bull. Amer. Inst. Min. Eng.*, 913, 1914 ; P. Debye and P. Scherrer, *Phys. Zeit.*, **18**. 291, 1917 ; *Engg.*, **104**. 17, 594, 1917 ; T. Millner, *Zeit. anorg. Chem.*, **164**. 186, 1927 ; H. A. Schwartz, H. H. Johnson and C. H. Junge, *Trans. Amer. Soc. Steel Treating*, **17**. 383, 1930 ; *Journ. Phys.*, **29**. 308, 1786 ; O. C. Ralston, *Iron Oxide Reduction Equilibria*, Washington, 227, 1929 ; *Bull. U.S. Bur. Mines*, 296, 1929 ; E. Ammermann and H. Kornfeld, *Stahl Eisen*, **49**. 1192, 1581, 1929 ; *Metallurgist*, **5**. 147, 1929 ; *Arch. Eisenhüttenwesen*, **3**. 307, 1929 ; J. O. Arnold, *Proc. Inst. Civil Eng.*, **123**. 127, 1896 ; E. Maurer and W. Bischof, *Stahl Eisen*, **48**. 15, 1928 ; E. Maurer and F. Hartmann, *Zeit. anorg. Chem.*, **136**. 75, 1924 ; E. Maurer and F. Stäblein, *ib.*, **137**. 115, 1924 ; F. Mylius, F. Förster and G. Schöne, *ib.*, **13**. 38, 1897 ; F. Sauerwald, H. Neudecker and J. Rudolph, *ib.*, **161**. 316, 1927 ; F. Sauerwald, W. Schultze and G. Jackwirth, *ib.*, **140**. 384, 1924 ; A. Pourcel, *Rev. Gén. Sciences*, **7**. 456, 510, 1896 ; S. S. Knight, *Foundry*, 1, 1896 ; E. H. Campbell, *Trans. Amer. Inst. Min. Eng.*, **27**. 869, 1897 ; E. Demenge, *Génie Civil*, **31**. 41, 1897 ; A. Carnot and E. Goutal, *Recherches sur la constitution chimique des fontes et des aciers*, Paris, 1900 ; *Ann. Mines*, (9), **18**. 263, 1900 ; G. Dillner, *Jernkontorets Ann.*, **57**. 97, 1902 ; F. C. Thompson and E. Whitehead, *Proc. Roy. Soc.*, **102**. A, 587. 1922 ; *Trans. Faraday Soc.*, **19**. 152, 1923 ; R. von Hasslinger, *Monatsh.*, **23**. 817, 1903 ; *Amer. Journ. Science*, (4), **15**. 153, 1903 ; S. Rinman, *Journ. prakt. Chem.*, (1), **100**. 33, 1867 ; *Försok til jäarnets historia med till ampning för slögder och handtwerk*, Stockholm, 1782 ; *Kongl. Vet. Akad.*, **35**. 3, 1774 ; *Crell's Ann.*, i, 276, 1786 ; A. Ledebur, *Stahl Eisen*, **8**. 742, 1888 ; **11**. 24, 1891 ; **14**. 523, 1894 ; **17**. 302, 436, 628, 1897 ; *Journ. Iron Steel Inst.* **44**. ii, 53, 1893 ; A. McCance, *ib.*, **92**. ii, 178, 1915 ; A. Sauveur, *Journ. Franklin Inst.*, **173**. 499, 1912 ; *Journ. Iron Steel Inst.*, **112**. ii, 313, 1925 ; J. H. Whiteley, *ib.*, **116**. ii, 293, 1927 ; E. H. Saniter, *ib.*, **52**. ii, 115, 1897 ; **53**. i, 206, 1898 ; K. Honda, *Science Rep. Tohoku Univ.*, **6**. 149, 1917 ; K. Honda and T. Murakami, *ib.*, **6**. 23, 53, 1917 ; *Journ. Iron Steel Inst.*, **98**. ii, 385, 1918 ; H. C. Boynton, *ib.*, 67, i, 262, 1904 ; H. C. Sorby, *ib.*, **29**. i, 140, 1886 ; **33**. i, 255, 1888 ; *B.A. Rep.*, 189, 1864 ; H. von Jüptner, *Stahl Eisen*, **19**. 237, 278, 1899 ; **20**. 1205, 1269, 1900 ; **21**. 795, 1901 ; *Baumaterialienkunde*, **2**. 84, 102, 1898 ; *Oesterr. Zeit. Berg. Hütt.*, **44**. 211, 447, 1896 ; **45**. 123, 1897 ; *Kohlenstoffermen in Eisen*, Stuttgart, 1896 ; *Journ. Iron Steel Inst.*, **53**. i, 235, 1897 ; **54**. ii, 243, 1898 ; **55**. i, 204, 1899 ; **57**. i, 219, 1900 ; H. M. Howe, *The Metallurgy of Steel*, New York, 1892 ; *Proc. Amer. Soc. Testing Materials*, **11**. 271, 295, 373, 375, 1911 ; *Trans. Amer. Inst. Min. Eng.*, **47**. 659, 1913 ; **58**. 487, 1917 ; H. M. Howe and A. G. Levy, *ib.*, **50**. 508, 1914 ; *Trans. Faraday Soc.*, **10**. 267, 1915 ; *Proc. Internat. Congress Testing Materials*, **6**. ii, 4, 1912 (I am indebted to the Secretary for permission to use Figs. 134 and 135 ; I am also indebted to Sir Harold Carpenter, F.R.S., for permission to use Fig. 130, 131, and 136 ; and to the Secretary of the Iron and Steel Institute for permission to use Fig. 138) ; W. J. Brooke and F. F. Hunting, *Journ. Iron Steel Inst.*, **95**. ii, 233, 1917 ; C. Benedicks, *Recherches physiques et physicochimiques sur l'acier au carbone*, Uppsala, 1904 ; *Journ. Iron Steel Inst.*, **77**. ii, 222, 1908 ; *Iron Steel Times*, **1**. 135, 1909 ; A. Baykoff, *Rev. Mét.*, **6**. 829, 1909 ; **8**. 315, 1911 ; D. C. Tschernoff, *ib.*, **5**. 79, 1908 ; J. E. Hurst, *Metallurgy of Cast Iron*, London, 73, 1926 (I am indebted to Mr. J. E. Hurst for permission to use Figs. 130, 131, and 136) ; H. P. Tiemann, *Metallographist*, **4**, 313, 1901 ; F. Wever, *Mitt. Kaiser Wilhelm Inst.*, **4**. 67, 81, 1922 ; N. J. Wark, *Mét.*, **8**. 704, 731, 1911 ; G. Phragmen, *Jernkontorets Ann.*, **114**. 431, 1930 ; A. Westgren and G. Phragmen, *Journ. Iron Steel Inst.*, **105**. i, 241, 1922 ; **109**. i, 159, 1924 ; **115**. i, 618, 1927 ; A. Westgren, *ib.*, **103**. i, 303, 1921 ; H. Brearley, *Proc. Sheffield Soc. Eng. Metallurgist*, 56, 1910 ; R. Horny, *Stahl Eisen*, **44**. 744, 1924 ; **45**. 22, 1925 ; *Ueber das System Eisenkarbid, Eisen, und Temperkohle bzw. Graphit*, Brünn, 1924 ; G. Tammann and K. Ewig, *Stahl Eisen*, **42**. 772, 1922 ; C. A. Edwards, *The Physicochemical Properties of Steel*, London, 52, 1920 ; C. A. Edwards and T. Yokoyama, *Journ. Iron Steel Inst.*, **118**. ii, 141, 1928 ; T. Andrews, *Proc. Roy. Soc.*, **58**. 59, 1895 ; H. S. Rawdon and T. Berglund, *Science Paper Bur. Standards*, 571, 1928 ; *Metallurgist*, **3**. 88, 1927 ; G. K. Burgess, J. J. Crowe and H. S. Rawdon, *Tech. Paper U.S. Bur. Standards*, **97**, 1917 ; *Engg.*, **105**. 77, 1918 ; *Trans. Amer. Inst. Min. Eng.*, **47**. 607, 1913 ; H. S. Rawdon and H. Scott, *ib.*, **67**. 414, 1920 ; F. Osmond and G. Cartaud, *Ann. Mines*,

(9), **17**. 110, 1900 ; (9), **18**. 113, 1900 ; H. le Chatelier and S. Wologdine, *Compt. Rend.*, **146**. 49, 1908 ; **148**. 1715, 1909 ; M. Sauvageot, *ib.*, **173**. 297, 1921 ; S. B. Hendricks, *Zeit. Kryst.*, **74**. 534, 1930 ; W. A. Roth, H. Umbach and P. Chall, *Arch. Eisenhüttenwesen*, **4**. 87, 1930 ; *Stahl Eisen*, **50**. 1331, 1930 ; H. C. H. Carpenter, *Nature*, **112**. 728, 1923 ; W. C. M. Lewis, *Zeit. Elektrochem.*, **18**. 158, 1912 ; J. E. Stead, *Journ. Iron Steel Inst.*, **49**. i, 486, 1896 ; **51**. i, 42, 1897 ; **53**. i, 145, 1898 ; **91**. i, 149, 1915 ; *Journ. West Scotland Iron Steel Inst.*, **4**. 23, 1897 ; *Proc. Cleveland Inst. Eng.*, **53**, 1895 ; 97, 1900 ; 164, 1906 ; 33, 1913 ; A. Stadeler, *Ferrum*, **10**. 376, 1913 ; F. Giolitti, *Chem. Met. Engg.*, **22**. 585, 737, 921, 1920 ; *Met. Ital.*, **5**. 193, 1913 ; F. Giolitti and N. Boyer, *ib.*, **5**. 360, 1913 ; N. T. Belaiew, *Journ. Iron Steel Inst.*, **87**. i, 679, 1913 ; H. B. Pulsifer, *Chem. Eng.*, **19**. 186, 1914 : O. W. Storey, *Trans. Amer. Electrochem. Soc.*, **25**. 489, 1914 ; A. L. Babochine, *Rev. Mét.*, **14**. 81, 1917 ; N. G. Ilyine, *ib.*, **14**. 83, 1917 ; P. Pingault, *Compt. Rend.*, **191**. 1007, 1930 ; G. Charpy and P. Pingault, *Compt. Rend.*, **187**. 554, 1928 ; *Génie Civil*, **93**. 361, 1928 ; C. Y. Clayton, *Trans. Amer. Inst. Min. Eng.*, **67**. 437, 1920 ; J. W. Bolton, *Foundry*, **51**. 658, 699, 1923 ; *Trans. Amer. Foundrymen's Assoc.*, **35**. 386, 1927 ; J. Freygang, *Giesserei Ztg.*, **22**. 70, 1925 ; V. N. Krivobok, *Trans. Amer. Soc. Steel Treating*, **7**. 457, 1925 ; A. Hayes and H. E. Flanders, *ib.*, **6**. 623, 1924 ; E. Scheil, *Zeit. anorg. Chem.*, **139**. 81, 1924 ; **158**. 175, 1926 ; H. Jungbluth, *Krupp's Monatsh.*, **5**. 95, 1924 ; T. Turner, *Foundry Trade Journ.*, **23**. 344, 1921 ; **28**. 127, 1923 ; W. H. Hatfield, *Trans. Faraday Soc.*, **21**. 272, 1925 ; L. Franck, *Stahl Eisen*, **16**. 585, 1896 ; **17**. 1063, 1897 ; A. Ludwig, *Chem. Ztg.*, **25**. 979, 1901 ; *Zeit. Elektrochem.*, **8**. 273, 1902 ; P. Neumann, *ib.*, **15**. 817, 1909 ; H. Moissan, *Compt. Rend.*, **100**. 1228, 1897 ; **116**. 218, 1893 ; **140**. 277, 1903 ; *Zeit. Elektrotech.*, **18**. 127, 1897 ; *Ann. Chim. Phys.*, (8), **5**. 174, 1905 ; *Bull. Soc. Chim.*, (3), **17**. 540, 1897 ; H. Fleissner, *Oesterr. Zeit. Berg. Hütt.*, **58**. 521, 539, 550, 570, 1910 ; F. Wüst, *Met.*, **5**. 86, 1908 ; **6**. 3, 1909 ; *Zeit. Elektrochem.*, **15**. 577, 1909 ; F. Wüst and C. Geiger, *Stahl Eisen*, **25**. 1134, 1196, 1905 ; A. Lissner and R. Horny, *ib.*, **45**. 1297, 1925 ; B. Osann, *ib.*, **46**. 1320, 1926 ; *Giesserei*, **16**. 565, 1929 ; H. Wedding, *Stahl Eisen*, **13**. 567, 1893 ; C. James, *Journ. Franklin Inst.*, **144**. 80, 1897 ; **148**. 482, 1899 ; **150**. 227, 1900 ; M. Levin and K. Dornhecker, *Ferrum*, **11**. 321, 1914 ; A. Rossel, *Compt. Rend.*, **123**. 113, 1896 ; J. H. Andrew and A. J. K. Honeyman, *Journ. Iron Steel Inst.—Carnegie Mem.*, **13**. 253, 1924 ; E. Donath, *Oesterr. Zeit. Berg. Hütt.*, **42**. 333, 348, 1894 ; J. Jermiloff, *Journ. Russ. Met. Soc.*, 357, 1911 ; *Stahl Eisen*, **32**. 65, 1912 ; O. Ruff and E. Gersten, *Ber.*, **45**. 63, 1912 ; **46**. 394, 1913 ; E. Gersten, *Ueber die Karbide des Eisens, Mangans, und Nickels*, Freiberg, 1912 ; L. Troost and P. Hautefeuille, *Compt. Rend.*, **80**. 964, 1875 ; E. D. Campbell, *Amer. Chem. Journ.*, **18**. 836, 1896 ; **20**. 78, 1898 ; **22**. 205, 1899 ; *Journ. Iron Steel Inst.*, **59**. i, 217, 1901 ; E. D. Campbell and M. B. Kennedy, *ib.*, **62**. ii, 288, 1902 ; L. Northcott, *ib.*, **107**. i, 491, 1923 ; A. M. Portevin, *ib.*, **108**. ii, 93, 1923 ; R. Schenck, J. Giesen and F. Walter, *Zeit. anorg. Chem.*, **127**. 101, 1923 ; **129**. 108, 1923 ; R. Ruer, *ib.*, **117**. 249, 1921 ; R. Schenck, *ib.*, **164**. 145, 1927 ; R. Schenck and R. Stenkhoff, *ib.*, **161**. 287, 1927 ; R. Schenck, H. Semiller and V. Falche, *Ber.*, **40**. 1704, 1907 ; H. L. Maxwell and A. Hayes, *Proc. Iowa Acad.*, **31**. 284, 1924 ; *Journ. Amer. Chem. Soc.*, **48**. 584, 1926 ; G. H. Brodie, W. H. Jennings and A. Hayes, *Trans. Amer. Soc. Steel Treating*, **10**. 615, 1926 ; T. Ishigaki, *Kinzoku no Kenkyu*, **3**. 169, 1926 ; *Science Rep. Tohoku Univ.*, **16**. 295, 1927 ; K. Iokibe, *Science Rep. Tohoku Univ.*, **9**. 275, 1920 ; S. Sekito, *ib.*, **20**. 313, 1931 ; K. Tamaru, *ib.*, **15**. 829, 1926 ; I. Iitaka, *ib.*, **8**. 167, 1918 ; M. Kawakami, *ib.*, **14**. 559, 1925 ; N. Yamada, *ib.*, **10**. 453, 1922 ; T. Watase, *ib.*, **17**. 1091, 1928 ; *Zeit. phys. Chem.*, **147**. 390, 1930 ; *Science Rep. Tohoku Univ.*, **17**. 1091, 1928 ; G. Asahara, *Bull. Japan Inst. Phys. Chem. Research*, **1**. 23, 1922 ; *Japan Journ. Chem.*, **1**. 35, 1922 ; H. Sawamura, *Mem. Coll. Engg. Kyoto Univ.*, **4**. 159, 1926 ; W. A. Roth, *Arch. Eisenhüttenwesen*, **3**. 339, 1929 ; *Stahl Eisen*, **49**. 1763, 1929 ; F. C. G. Müller, *ib.*, **14**. 849, 1894 ; S. Shimura, *Proc. Acad. Tokyo*, **6**. 269, 1930 ; S. Shigetaka, *Journ. Eng. Tokyo*, **20**. 1, 1931 ; L. G. Knowlton, *Journ. Phys. Chem.*, **32**. 1572, 1928 ; F. Osmond and W. C. Roberts-Austen, *Proc. Roy. Soc.*, **60**. 148, 1896 ; J. O. Arnold and J. Jefferson, *Engg.*, **61**. 140, 1896 ; W. G. McMillan, *Journ. Iron Steel Inst.*, **45**. ii, 157, 1894 ; Y. Chu-Phay, *Trans. Amer. Soc. Steel Treating*, Preprint 10, 1931 ; H. Kornfeld and G. Brieger, *Arch. Eisenhüttenwesen*, **5**. 315, 1931 ; J. H. Andrew, *Journ. Tech. Coll. Met. Club, Glasgow*, **7**. 16, 1930 ; C. O. Bannister and W. D. Jones, *Journ. Iron Steel Inst.*, **123**. i, 395, 1931 ; W. Rosenhain and J. C. W. Humfrey, *ib.*, **83**. 200, 1909 ; J. C. W. Humfrey, *Journ. Iron Steel Inst.—Carnegie Mem.*, **4**. 80, 1912 ; F. Robin, *Traité de métallurgie*, Paris, 169, 1912 ; G. K. Burgess and J. J. Crowe, *Scient. Paper U.S. Bur. Standards*, 213, 1914 ; F. S. Tritton and D. Hanson, *Journ. Iron Steel Inst.*, **110**. ii, 90, 1924 ; F. S. Tritton, *ib.*, **112**. ii, 233, 1925.

§ 16. Heterogeneous Alloys

T. W. Hogg [1] examined the metal taken from different parts of a mild steel ingot weighing about 11 tons, and found the impurities collect in the central core, where solidification is slowest. The phenomenon is similar to that observed in the freezing of water, where impurities are rejected by the first crystals of ice which are formed—1. 10, 2. M. Stevens found that, with cast iron from the blast-furnace, the silicon accumulates near the middle of the cast, amounting to 2·92 per cent. near the middle, 1·58 per cent. at the beginning, and 1·80 per cent. at the end of the cast. Phosphorus follows the silicon, but sulphur and manganese do not vary greatly.

A. Pourcel said that the average order of segregation during solidification in iron and steel is : carbon, phosphorus, sulphur, silicon, and manganese. Copper segregates quickly, but homogeneity is imparted by the addition of aluminium. Chromium and tungsten steels are liable to segregation, but not so with nickel steels. J. E. Stead said that sulphur segregates most, then phosphorus, and then carbon, whilst manganese and silicon do not segregate to any material extent ; and F. Wüst and H. L. Felser, that the tendency of sulphur and phosphorus to segregate is greater than that of carbon, copper, and manganese. H. Rubricius noted that silicon tends to accumulate near the bottom of the blast-furnace. W. Hampe found ferro-manganese from four levels in the furnace had 82·82, 81·97, 81·10, and 80·17 per cent. of manganese. E. Piwowarsky observed that samples of mild steel which had been deoxidized with aluminium or with ferrovanadium developed a structure on annealing in which the ferrite had segregated in wide-meshed networks enclosing areas of pearlite, and in some cases large ferrite areas were distributed irregularly through the specimens. Similar steels deoxidized with ferrosilicon and cast without a deoxidizing agent developed the usual dendritic ferrite structure on annealing.

B. Talbot, R. W. Hunt, and G. F. Comstock said that aluminium prevents segregation, but, according to N. Lilienberg, it does not prevent piping. G. B. Waterhouse observed that titanium retards the segregation of sulphur, phosphorus, and carbon ; and the subject was discussed by M. C. Smith, N. Petinot, and E. F. Lake. According to H. M. Wickhorst, silicon lessens segregation but increases piping. H. M. Boylston compared the effects with silicon, titanium, manganese, and aluminium ; T. Swinden, manganese, silicon, and aluminium ; G. K. Burgess and G. W. Quick, silicon and titanium ; and G. F. Comstock, aluminium and titanium. The Soret effect in alloys was observed by M. Ballay, A. W. Porter, and C. C. Tanner ; and segregation after solidification, by G. d'Huart, C. Benedicks, and A. Lundgren.

Segregation in steel castings was observed by L. Aitchison, J. H. Andrew and co-workers, T. Andrews, J. O. Arnold, P. Bardenheuer and co-workers, O. Bauer, O. Bauer and H. Arndt, G. Belloc, T. Berglund, R. Bolling, A. W. and H. Brearley, H. Brearley, A. Brüninghaus and F. Heinrich, R. H. Canfield, H. le Chatelier and co-workers, G. Charpy and S. Bonnerot, C. Y. Clayton and co-workers, J. J. Cohade, G. F. Comstock, M. Demole, J. Descolas and E. Pretet, M. T. Denne, W. Dinkler, T. M. Drown, P. H. Dudley, H. Fay, J. E. Fletcher, C. Frémont, J. D. Gat, F. P. Gilligan and J. J. Curran, F. Giolitti, R. A. Hadfield, H. Hanemann and O. Schröder, H. Harmet, J. Henderson, E. Heyn and O. Bauer, H. D. Hibbard, V. O. Homerberg, H. M. Howe and co-workers, H. G. Howorth, G. d'Huart, J. C. W. Humfrey, R. W. Hunt, C. L. Huston, K. Iokibe, J. E. Johnson, H. von Jüptner, E. F. Kenney, O. von Keil and A. Wimmer, S. S. Knight, W. E. Koch, A. Kriz, A. Ledebur, M. Levitzky, A. W. Lorenz, H. W. McQuaid and E. H. Ehn, E. G. Mahin and co-workers, A. Masing, A. Messerschmitt, H. Meyer, C. A. Müller, W. Oertel and L. A. Richter, P. Oberhoffer, B. Osann, F. Osmond, N. Petinot, L. Pichard, A. M. Portevin and co-workers, R. Powell, W. J. Priestley, H. B. Pulsifer, H. S. Rawdon, E. L. Reed, H. Reuss, J. Reimer, C. H. Ridsdale, A. Ruhfus, B. D. Saklatwalla, E. Scheur, E. H. Schulz and J. Goebel, F. Sommer and F. Rapatz, A. Stadeler and H. J. Thiele, J. E. Stead, H. Styri, P. Tabary, G. Taguéeff, B. Talbot, E. E. Thum, D. K. Tschernoff, T. H. Turner, M. Viteaux, A. Wåhlberg, E. Walldow, G. B. Waterhouse, W. R. Webster, P. Weiller, T. D. West, B. F. Weston, A. E. White, J. H. Whiteley, and F. Wüst and H. L. Felser. A. Schleicher, J. Hanny, P. Oberhoffer, J. J. Cohade, C. S. Crouse, E. H. Schulz and J. Goebel, F. Sommer and F. Rapatz, H. Styri, E. E. Thum, F. Giolitti, C. Y. Clayton and co-workers, and H. S. Rawdon discussed *flaky steel*, and *flaky fractures ;* F. C. Thompson and R. Willows, *banded steel.*

The *piping* of steel ingots was discussed by F. O. Beikirch,[2] H. Brearley, A. Brüninghaus and F. Heinrich, C. Canaris, G. Charpy, R. M. Daelen, A. Diefenthaler, P. H. Dudley, F. L. Enquist, G. Tammann and H. Bredemeier, J. E. Fletcher, J. D. Gat, H. M. Howe and co-workers, E. F. Kenney, W. Claus, H. Kusl, N. Lilienberg, B. Osann, D. K. Tschernoff, and H. Wedding.

The *inclusions* in iron and steel—slag, manganese, and iron sulphides, silicates, and oxides, phosphates or phosphides of calcium, magnesium, manganese, and iron, titanium nitride, alumina—were discussed by E. Ammann,[3] J. H. Andrew, T. Andrews, J. O. Arnold and G. R, Bolsover, A. Baikoff, O. Bauer, C. Benedicks and H. Löfquist, F. Bondolfi, H. Brearley, A. Campion, G. F. Comstock, E. J. Cook, J. H. S. Dickenson, J. W. Donaldson, W. Eilender and W. Oertel, H. Fay, F. Fischer, G. R. Fitterer, I. S. Gaieff, J. D. Gat, W. H. Gillet, F. Giolitti and co-workers, S. L. Goodale and P. H. Kutar, P. Goerens, L. E. Grant, W. H. Hatfield, F. Hartmann, C. H. Herty and co-workers, H. D. Hibbard,

H. G. Howorth, G. d'Huart, A. Hultgren, C. Johns, H. Kjerrman, J. N. Kilby, A. B. Kinzel
and W. Crafts, E. Kothny, S. Kriz and H. Kral, B. M. Larsen, E. F. Law, A. McCance,
E. G. Mahin, G. Mars, M. Matweieff, P. Oberhoffer and co-workers, F. Pacher, J. A. Pickard,
J. A. Pickard and F. M. Potter, W. J. Priestley, H. S. Rawdon, G. Röhl, A. Sauveur,
C. E. Sims and G. A. Lillieqvist, M. C. Smith, A. Stadeler, J. E. Stead, S. Steinberg,
L. Treuheit, J. H. Whiteley, A. Wimmer, C. R. Wohrmann, F. Wüst and N. Kirpach, and
W. Zieler. G. Tammann and W. Salge studied the residues left after treating the metal
with an acidified soln. of ammonium persulphate.

The *blowholes* in iron and steel ingots due to the escape of occluded gases were dis-
cussed by T. Andrews,[4] T. Baker, G. Belloc, H. Brearley, G. Charpy, J. W. Donaldson,
C. H. Desch, W. Eichholz and J. Mehovar, J. Goebel, P. Goerens and J. Paquet, E. Goutal,
P. L. T. Hérault, H. D. Hibbard, H. M. Howe, K. Iwase, O. von Keil and A. Wimmer,
P. Klinger, W. Kusl, A. G. Lobley and C. L. Betts, E. von Maltitz, P. Oberhoffer and
co-workers, N. Parravano and A. Scortecci, A. Ruhfus, J. E. Stead, T. C. Sutton and
H. R. Ambler, K. G. Troubine, D. K. Tschernoff, H. Wedding, and A. Wimmer.

REFERENCES.

[1] Bibliography on segregation, *Journ. Iron Steel Inst.*, **113**. i, 116 1926 ; **117**. i 401, 1928 ;
119. i 305, 1929 ; **126**. i, —, 1932 ; H. von Jüptner, *Oesterr. Zeit. Berg. Hütt.*, **44**. 159, 1896 ;
H. Fay, *Metallographist*, **4**. 115, 1901 ; R. Bolling, *Journ. Amer. Chem. Soc.*, **22**. 798, 1900 ;
T. Andrews, *Trans. Soc. Eng.*, 209, 1902 ; *Eng.*, **74**. 653, 687, 724, 1902 ; C. H. Ridsdale, *ib.*, **74**.
684, 1902 ; B. F. Weston, *Iron Age*, **69**. 28, 1904 ; A. Messerschmitt, *Stahl Eisen*, **25**. 895, 1905 ;
H. B. Pulsifer, *Metal Progress*, **18**. 85, 1930 ; J. F. Springer, *Cassier's Mag.*, **35**. 426, 1909 ;
G. Taguéeff, *Journ. Iron Steel Inst.*, **81**. i, 467, 1910 ; F. Wüst and H. L. Felser, *Met.*, **7**. 363,
1910 ; G. B. Waterhouse, *Mech. Eng.*, **26**. 167, 1910 ; *Proc. Amer. Soc. Testing Materials*, **10**.
201, 804, 1910 ; R. A. Hadfield, *Rev. Mét.*, **7**. 1133, 1910 ; N. Petinot, *Met. Chem. Engg.*, **11**.
231, 1913 ; M. Demole, *Compt. Rend. Soc. Ind. Min.*, 329, 1913 ; B. Osann, *Stahl Eisen*, **31**.
673, 1911 ; C. Y. Clayton, F. B. Foley and F. B. Laney, *Trans. Amer. Inst. Min. Eng.*, **62**. 211,
1919 ; F. Giolitti, *Chem. Met. Engg.*, **20**. 271, 1918 ; **23**. 149, 1920 ; H. Styri, *ib.*, **20**. 342, 478,
1919 ; E. E. Thum, *ib.*, **21**. 145, 1919 ; C. S. Crouse, *ib.*, **23**. 329, 1920 ; L. Pichard, *Génie Civil*,
92. 132, 1928 ; M. Viteaux, *ib.*, **92**. 333, 1928 ; G. d'Huart, *Rev. Mét.*, **26**. 532, 1929 ; M. Stevens,
Eng. Min. Journ., **54**. 558, 1893 ; W. Hampe, *Chem. Ztg.*, **17**. 99, 1893 ; D. K. Tschernoff, *Rev.
Mét.*, **12**. 840, 1915 ; H. le Chatelier and J. Lemoine, *ib.*, **12**. 649, 1915 ; H. le Chatelier and
E. L. Dupuy, *ib.*, **15**. 127, 1918 ; H. le Chatelier and E. Bogitch, *Compt. Rend.*, **167**. 472, 1918 ;
Rev. Mét., **16**. 129, 1919 ; A. M. Portevin, *Journ. Iron Steel Inst.*, **100**. ii, 203, 1919 ; A. M. Portevin
and V. Bernard, *Rev. Mét.*, **15**. 273, 1918 ; T. W. Hogg, *Journ. Soc. Chem. Ind.*, **12**. 236, 1893 ;
14. 245, 1895 ; J. E. Stead, *ib.*, **22**. 340, 1903 ; *Iron Steel Metallurgist*, **7**. 139, 258, 1903 ; *Iron
Coal Trades Rev.*, **71**. 1689, 1906 ; *Proc. Cleveland Inst. Eng.*, 163, 1906 ; 33, 1913 ; *Engg.
Congress Inst. Civil Eng.*, iv. 94, 1907 ; H. Reuss, *Journ. Iron Steel Inst.*, **40**. ii, 299, 1891 ;
B. Talbot, *ib.*, **68**. ii, 204, 1905 ; A. Wahlberg, *ib.*, **60**. ii, 29, 1901 ; H. G. Howorth, *ib.*, **68**. ii,
301, 1905 ; A. W. and H. Brearley, *Ingots and Ingot Moulds*, London, 1918 ; *Journ. Iron Steel
Inst.*, **94**. ii, 137, 1916 ; J. C. W. Humfrey, *ib.*, **99**. i, 273, 1919 ; J. J. Cohade, *ib.*, **100**. ii, 187,
1919 ; E. Scheuer, *Zeit. Metallkunde*, **23**. 237, 1931 ; J. H. Andrew, *Journ. Roy. Tech. Coll.*,
2. 613, 1932 ; J. H. Andrew and D. D. Howat, *ib.*, **2**. 608, 1932 ; J. H. Andrew, J. N. Greenwood
and G. W. Green, *Journ. Iron Steel Inst.*, **101**. ii, 231, 1919 ; C. Benedicks, *ib.*, **117**. i, 557, 1928 ;
Metallographic Researches, New York, 108, 1926 ; W. E. Koch, *Proc. Eng. Soc. Western Pennsylvania*, **9**. 23, 1893 ; E. Piwowarsky, *Stahl Eisen*, **48**. 1665, 1928 ; P. Oberhoffer, *ib.*, **40**. 705, 872,
1920 ; E. H. Schulz and J. Goebel, *ib.*, **40**. 1479, 1920 ; A. Brüninghaus and F. Heinrich, *ib.*,
41. 497, 1921 ; A. Pourcel, *Trans. Amer. Inst. Min. Eng.*, **22**. 105, 1893 ; J. E. Johnson, *ib.*,
46. 368, 1913 ; H. M. Howe, *Yearbook Amer. Iron Steel Inst.*, 446, 1915 ; *Iron Age*, **96**. 995,
1915 ; *Proc. Amer. Soc. Testing Materials*, **9**. 327, 1909 ; *Eng. Min. Journ.*, **84**. 1011, 1907 ;
Trans. Amer. Inst. Min. Eng., **23**. 576, 1893 ; **24**. 839, 1894 ; **38**. 3, 1907 ; **39**. 829, 1908 ; **45**.
502, 1908 ; **51**. 876, 1910 ; H. M. Howe and B. Stoughton, *ib.*, **38**. 109, 1907 ; T. M. Drown,
ib., **17**. 543, 1891 ; P. H. Dudley, *ib.*, **39**. 818, 1908 ; N. Lilienberg, *ib.*, **37**. 238, 1906 ;
H. W. McQuaid and E. H. Ehn, *ib.*, **67**. 341, 1922 ; H. S. Rawdon, *Chem. Met. Engg.*, **24**. 385,
1921 ; *Trans. Amer. Inst. Min. Eng.*, **62**. 246, 1919 ; W. J. Priestley, *ib.*, **67**. 317, 1922 ;
W. R. Webster, *ib.*, **21**. 766, 999, 1893 ; **23**. 113, 1894 ; **28**. 618, 876, 1899 ; **51**. 876, 1925 ;
H. W. Hixon, *ib.*, **39**. 829, 1908 ; W. Campbell, *ib.*, **39**. 843, 1908 ; A. A. Stevenson, *ib.*, **39**. 830,
1908 ; J. Reimer, *Zeit. Ver. deut. Ing.*, **47**. 1675, 1903 ; *Stahl Eisen*, **23**. 1196, 1903 ; **26**. 185,
1906 ; A. Ledebur, *ib.*, **16**. 116, 1896 ; A. Ruhfus, *ib.*, **17**. 41, 1897 ; E. Heyn and O. Bauer, *ib.*,
32. 402, 1912 ; *Mitt. Materialprüfungsamt*, **30**. 1, 1912 ; O. Bauer, *ib.*, **40**. 71, 1922 ; C. L. Huston,
Iron Age, **78**. 1, 1906 ; *Proc. Amer. Soc. Testing Materials*, **6**. 182, 1906 ; J. O. Arnold, *Trans.
Inst. Naval Architects*, **5**. 260, 1908 ; S. S. Knight, *Iron Trade Rev.*, **46**. 475, 926, 1910 ;
H. M. Wickhorst, *ib.*, **52**. 801, 1913 ; *Iron Age*, **88**. 1306, 1911 ; **83**. 1073, 1914 ; *Proc. Amer.
Soc. Testing Materials*, **13**. 582, 1913 ; E. F. Lake, *Chem. Met. Engg.*, **11**. 144, 1913 ; A. W. Lorenz,
ib., **21**. 203, 1919 ; G. Charpy and S. Bonnerot, *Rev. Mét.*, **15**. 132, 1918 ; *Compt. Rend.*, **165**.
536, 1917 ; F. Osmond, *ib.*, **121**. 684, 1896 ; M. Levitzky, *Rev. Univ. Mines*, **49**. 65, 1899 ;
E. F. Kenney, *Yearbook Amer. Iron Steel Inst.*, 464, 1915 ; H. D. Hibbard, *ib.*, 93, 1919 ;
R. W. Hunt, *Bull. Amer. Railway Eng. Assoc.*, **17**. 27, 1915 ; H. M. Boylston, *Journ. Iron Steel*

Inst.—Carnegie Mem., **7**. 102, 1916 ; L. Aitchison, *Chem. Met. Engg.*, **23**. 280, 1920 ; H. Brearley, *Journ. West Scotland Iron Steel Inst.*, **27**. 63, 1920 ; *Journ. Iron Steel Inst.*, **103**. i, 27, 1921 ; A. Lundgren, *Rolling Mill Journ.*, **4**. 107, 1930 ; E. G. Mahin and E. H. Hartwig, *Journ. Ind. Eng. Chem.*, **12**. 1090, 1920 ; E. G. Mahin and H. J. Dillon, *Trans. Amer. Soc. Steel Treating*, **12**. 905, 1927 ; G. Mahin and G. B. Wilson, *ib.*, **15**. 829, 1923 ; E. G. Mahin and G. E. Brewer, *ib.*, **12**. 1095, 1920 ; E. G. Mahin and H. W. Botts, *Chem. Met. Engg.*, **27**. 980, 1922 ; M. C. Smith, *Iron Age*, **105**. 1426, 1920 ; B. D. Saklatwalla, *ib.*, **112**. 815, 1923 ; G. F. Comstock, *ib.*, **114**. 1477, 1924 ; *Journ. Iron Steel Inst.*, **114**. ii, 405, 1926 ; E. Walldow, *ib.*, **122**. ii, 301, 1930 ; T. Swinden, *Proc. Staffs Iron Steel Inst.*, **37**. 80, 1923 ; T. H. Turner, *Engg.*, **114**. 662, 1922 ; *Proc. Staffs Iron Steel Inst.*, **38**. 17, 1923 ; T. D. West, *ib.*, **48**. ii, 249, 1895 ; *Iron Age*, **56**. 1210, 1895 ; J. Descolas and E. Pretet, *Rev. Mét.*, **20**. 597, 1923 ; T. Berglund, *Jernkontorets Ann.*, (2), **78**. 149, 1923 ; W. Oertel and L. A. Richter, *Glockenstahlwerke Remscheid*, 3, 4, 1924 ; V. O. Homerberg, *Trans. Amer. Soc. Steel Treating*, **6**. 294, 1924 ; A. Sauveur, *ib.*, **4**. 12, 83, 1923 ; F. P. Gilligan and J. J. Curran, *ib.*, **10**. 9, 1926 ; A. Sauveur and V. N. Krivobok, *Trans. Amer. Inst. Min. Eng.*, **70**. 239, 1924 ; *Journ. Iron Steel Inst.*, **112**. ii, 313, 1925 ; A. Kriz, *ib.*, **122**. ii, 13, 1930 ; **126**. i, —, 1932 ; J. Henderson, *ib.*, **73**. i, 286, 1907 ; H. Harmet, *ib.*, **72**. ii, 146, 1902 ; J. H. Whiteley, *ib.*, **103**. i, 213, 1926 ; J. D. Gat, *Forging, Stamping, Heat Treating*, **13**. 38, 79, 124, 1927 ; *Blast Furnace Steel Plant*, **15**. 207, 1927 ; P. Bardenheuer, *Mitt. Inst. Eisenforschung*, **7**. 1, 1925 ; P. Bardenheuer and C. A. Müller, *ib.*, **11**. 255, 273, 1929 ; C. Frémont, *Génie Civil*, **87**. 349, 1925 ; G. Belloc, *ib.*, **44**. 16, 1903 ; W. Rogers, *Foundry Trade Journ.*, **33**. 119, 1926 ; M. Ballay, *Compt. Rend.*, **183**. 603, 1926 ; A. W. Porter, *Trans. Faraday Soc.*, **23**. 314, 1927 ; C. C. Tanner, *ib.*, **23**. 75, 1927 ; H. Rubricius, *Chem. Ztg.*, **18**. 1005, 1894 ; P. Tabary, *Rev. Univ. Mines*, **28**. 98, 1895 ; J. E. Fletcher, *Proc. Staffs Iron Steel Inst.*, **23**. 43, 1907 ; P. Weiller, *Chem. Ztg.*, **37**. 724, 1913 ; R. Powell, *Iron Steel Ind.*, **3**. 369, 1930 ; **4**. 29, 1930 ; G. Masing, *Zeit. Metallkunde*, **17**. 251, 1925 ; W. Dinkler, *Giesserei Ztg.*, **23**. 531, 1926 ; E. H. Schulz and J. Goebel, *Stahl Eisen*, **40**. 1679, 1920 ; H. Meyer, *ib.*, **48**. 506, 1928 ; F. Sommer and F. Rapatz, *ib.*, **42**. 1708, 1922 ; F. Rapatz, *ib.*, **43**. 1199, 1923 ; A. Schleicher, *ib.*, **43**. 1449, 1923 ; O. von Keil and A. Wimmer, *ib.*, **45**. 835, 1925 ; J. Hanny, *ib.*, **41**. 1298, 1921 ; A. E. White, *Trans. Amer. Soc. Steel Treating*, **3**. 386, 1923 ; R. H. Canfield, *Chem. Met. Engg.*, **30**. 470, 1924 ; E. L. Reed, *Journ. Iron Steel Inst.—Carnegie Mem.*, **14**. 91, 1925 ; C. A. Müller, *Untersuchungen über die Seigerung der Begleitelemente des Eisens, insbesondere des Sauerstoffs, in Flusstahlblöcken*, Düsseldorf, 1929 ; A. Stadeler and H. J. Thiele, *Stahl Eisen*, **51**. 449, 1931 ; H. Hanemann and O. Schröder, *Zeit. Metallkunde*, **23**. 269, 1931 ; F. C. Thompson and R. Willows, *Journ. Iron Steel Inst.*, **124**. ii, 151, 1931 ; O. Bauer and H. Arndt, *Zeit. Metallkunde*, **13**. 497, 559, 1921 ; K. Iokibe, *Science Rep. Tohoku Univ.*, **20**. 608, 1931 ; G. K. Burgess and G. W. Quick, *Tech. Paper Bur. Standards*, 241, 1923 ; M. T. Denne, *Journ. Roy. Microscopic Soc.*, 157, 1923.

² N. Lilienberg, *Trans. Amer. Inst. Min. Eng.*, **37**. 238, 1906 ; H. M. Howe, *Yearbook Amer. Iron Steel Inst.*, 446, 1915 ; *Trans. Amer. Inst. Min. Eng.*, **38**. 3, 1907 ; H. M. Howe and B. Stroughton, *ib.*, **38**. 109, 1907 ; H. M. Howe, W. Campbell and W. L. Token, *Proc. Amer. Soc. Testing Materials*, **8**. 185, 1908 ; P. H. Dudley, *Trans. Amer. Soc. Min. Eng.*, **39**. 818, 1908 ; *Proc. Amer. Soc. Testing Materials*, **9**. 98, 1909 ; H. Kusl, *Oesterr. Zeit. Berg. Hütt.*, **54**. 593, 610, 1906 ; F. L. Enquist, *Tek Tids.*, **22**. 275, 1892 ; G. Tammann and H. Bredemeier, *Zeit. anorg. Chem.*, **142**. 54, 1925 ; *Stahl Eisen*, **45**. 1211, 1925 ; B. Osann, *ib.*, **31**. 673, 1911 ; C. Canaris, *ib.*, **32**. 1174, 1264, 1912 ; A. Diefenthaler, *ib.*, **32**. 1813, 1912 ; A. Brüninghaus and F. Heinrich, *ib.*, **41**. 497, 1921 ; G. Charpy, *Génie Civil*, **67**. 7, 1915 ; E. F. Kenney, *Yearbook Amer. Iron Steel Inst.*, 464, 1915 ; D. K. Tschernoff, *Rev. Mét.*, **12**. 840, 1915 ; L. Guillet, J. Gallibourg and M. Ballay, *ib.*, **22**. 253, 1925 ; J. E. Fletcher, *Journ. Iron Steel Inst.*, **98**. ii, 231, 1918 ; H. Brearley, *ib.*, **103**. i, 27, 1921 ; *Journ. West Scotland Iron Steel Inst.*, **27**. 63, 1920 ; J. D. Gat, *Forging, Stamping, Heat Treating*, **13**. 38, 79, 124, 1927 ; *Blast Furnace Steel Plant*, **15**. 207, 1927 ; F. O. Beikirch, *Zeit. Ver. deut. Ing.*, **49**. 1342, 1905 ; R. M. Daelen, *Stahl Eisen*, **25**. 923, 1905 ; H. Wedding, *ib.*, **25**. 832, 1905 ; W. Claus, *Giesserei*, **17**. 449, 1930.

³ A. Stadeler, *Stahl Eisen*, **37**. 40, 1917 ; *Rev. Mét.*, **15**. 292, 1918 ; C. Benedicks and H. Löfquist, *Non-metallic Inclusions in Iron and Steel*, London, 1930 ; *Comm. Internat. Assoc. Testing Materials*, **1**. 345, 1930 ; G. Tammann and W. Salge, *Zeit. anorg. Chem.*, **176**. 152, 1928 ; E. Ammann, *Beitrag zur Bestimmung oxydischer Einschlüsse in Roheisen und Stahl*, Düsseldorf, 1927 ; L. Treuheit, *Giesserei*, **15**. 585, 1928 ; C. R. Wohrman, *Trans. Amer. Soc. Steel Treating*, **14**. 81, 255, 385, 539, 1928 ; C. H. Herty and G. P. Fitterer, *Bull. Carnegie Inst. Pittsburg—Min. Met.*, 36, 1928 ; *Proc. Amer. Soc. Testing Materials*, **28**. ii, 23, 1928 ; G. R. Fitterer, *Tech. Publ. Amer. Inst. Min. Eng.*, 440, 1931 ; C. H. Herty and J. E. Jacobs, *Foundry*, **59**. 40, 44, 1931 ; *Trans. Amer. Soc. Steel Treating*, **19**. 271, 1932 ; *Blast Furnace Steel Plant*, **19**. 553, 683, 1931 ; F. Hartmann, *Arch. Eisenhüttenwesen*, **4**. 601, 1931 ; S. Kriz and H. Kral, *Stahl Eisen*, **49**. 880, 1929 ; A. Hultgren, *Journ. Iron Steel Inst.*, **120**. i, 69, 1929 ; H. Kjerrman, *Jernkontorets Ann.*, (2), **113**. 181, 1929 ; T. Andrews, *Engg.*, **78**. 737, 778, 810, 1904 ; **79**. 563, 1905 ; **80**. 235, 1905 ; **81**. 331, 1906 ; J. E. Stead, *Journ. Iron Steel Mag.*, **9**. 105, 1905 ; *Journ. Iron Steel Inst.*, **97**. i, 287, 1918 ; **103**. i, 271, 1921 ; J. N. Kilby, *ib.*, **97**. i, 365, 1918 ; H. G. Howorth, *ib.*, **68**. ii, 301, 1905 ; E. F. Law, *ib.*, **74**. ii, 94, 1907 ; J. O. Arnold, *Proc. Inst. Mech. Eng.*, ii, 653, 1915 ; J. O. Arnold and G. R. Bolsover, *Journ. Iron Steel Inst.*, **89**. i, 396, 1914 ; **91**. i, 271, 1915 ; J. A. Pickard and F. M. Potter, *ib.*, **90**. ii, 181, 1914 ; W. H. Hatfield, *ib.*, **92**. ii, 122, 1915 ; E. Walldow, *ib.*, **122**. ii, 301, 1930 ; W. Rosenhain, *ib.*, **80**. ii, 290, 1909 ; J. W. Donaldson, *ib.*, **113**. i, 620, 1926 ; J. H. Whiteley, *Proc. Cleveland Inst. Eng.*, 36, 1923 ; *Journ. Iron Steel*

Inst., **101**. i, 359, 1920 , **103**. i, 278, 1921 ; **113**. i, 213, 1926 ; H. Brearley, *ib.*, **103**. i, 27, 1921 ; *Journ. West Scotland Iron Steel Inst.*, **27**. 63, 1920 ; G. Röhl, *Journ. Iron Steel Inst.—Carnegie Mem.*, **4**. 28, 1912 ; J. A. Pickard, *ib.*, **7**. 68, 1916 ; H. Fay, *Proc. Amer. Soc. Testing Materials*, **8**. 74, 1908 ; G. Auchy, *Iron Age*, **85**. 108, 1910 ; M. Matweiff, *Rev. Mét.*, **7**. 848, 1910 ; **15**. 44, 1920 ; H. D. Hibbard, *Yearbook Amer. Iron Steel Inst.*, 93, 1919 ; *Iron Age*, **103**. 1427, 1919 ; *Trans. Amer. Inst. Min. Eng.*, **41**. 803, 1910 ; W. J. Priestley, *ib.*, **67**. 317, 1922 ; F. Pacher, *Stahl Eisen*, **32**. 1647, 1912 ; G. Mars, *ib.*, **32**. 1557, 1912 ; F. Fischer, *ib.*, **32**. 1563, 1912 ; E. Kothny, *ib.*, **40**. 41, 1920 ; A. Wimmer, *ib.*, **47**. 781, 1927 ; G. d'Huart, *Science Ind.*, **14**. 364, 1930 ; G. F. Comstock, *Trans. Amer. Inst. Min. Eng.*, **56**. 553, 1917 ; *Chem. Met. Engg.*, **12**. 577, 1914 ; **13**. 891, 1915 ; *Comm. Internat. Assoc. Testing Materials*, **1**. 348, 1930 ; *Iron Trade Rev.*, **57**. 894, 920, 1916 ; A. Sauveur, *ib.*, **15**. 149, 1916 ; H. S. Rawdon, *ib.*, **24**. 385, 1921 ; F. Giolitti and G. Tavanti, *Ann. Chim. Applicata*, **2**. 360, 1914 ; F. Giolitti and S. Zublena, *Internat. Zeit. Metallog.*, **7**. 35, 1914 ; F. Bondolfi, *Met. Ital.*, **8**. 165, 1916 ; A. McCance, *Journ. West Scotland Iron Steel Inst.*, **24**. 55, 1917 ; *Journ. Iron Steel Inst.*, **97**. i, 239, 1918 ; J. H. S. Dickenson, *ib.*, **113**. i, 177, 1925 ; C. Johns, *Journ. Soc. Chem. Ind.*, **37**. R, 145, 1918 ; E. G. Mahin, *Journ. Ind. Eng. Chem.*, **11**. 739, 1919 ; E. G. Mahin and G. B. Wilson, *ib.*, **15**. 829, 1923 ; E. G. Mahin and H. W. Botts, *Chem. Met. Engg.*, **27**. 980, 1922 ; M. C. Smith, *Iron Age*, **105**. 1426, 1920 ; J. H. Andrew, *Trans. North-East Coast Inst. Eng. Shipbuilders*, **36**. 355, 1920 ; *Journ. West Scotland Iron Steel Inst.*, **28**. 28, 1921 ; O. Bauer, *Mitt. Materialprüfungsamt*, **40**. 71, 1922 ; F. Wüst and N. Kirpach, *Mitt. Inst. Eisenforschung*, **1**. 31, 1920 ; S. L. Goodale and P. H. Kutar, *Forging, Stamping, Heat Treating*, **12**. 68, 1926 ; P. Goerens, *Krupp's Monatsh.*, **8**. 1, 25, 1927 ; P. Oberhoffer and H. Meyer, *Stahl Eisen*, **34**. 1241, 1914 ; P. Oberhoffer and P. Hartmann, *ib.*, **34**. 1245, 1914 ; P. Oberhoffer, *Rev. Tech. Luxembourg*, **19**. 99, 1927 ; *Zeit. Ver. deut. Ing.*, **71**. 4569, 1927 ; P. Oberhoffer, H. J. Schiffler and W. Hessenbruch, *Arch. Eisen-hüttenwesen*, **1**. 57, 1927 ; *Stahl Eisen*, **47**. 1540, 1927 ; P. Oberhoffer and E. Ammann, *ib.*, **47**. 1536, 1927 ; P. Oberhoffer and K. d'Huart, *ib.*, **39**. 165, 196, 1919 ; W. Eilender and W. Oertel, *ib.*, **47**. 1558, 1927 ; C. H. Herty, *Proc. Eng. Soc. West. Pennsylvania*, **44**. 259, 1928 ; *Metal Progress*, **20**. 37, 1931 ; *Trans. Amer. Soc. Steel Treating*, **19**. 1, 1931 ; H. D. Hibbard, *Yearbook Amer. Iron Steel Inst.*, **11**. 93, 1919 ; *Iron Age*, **103**. 1427, 1919 ; J. D. Gat, *ib.*, **119**. 1142, 1927 ; *Blast Furnace Steel Plant*, **15**. 271, 279, 1927 ; *Trans. Amer. Soc. Steel Treating*, **15**. 271, 279, 1927 ; S. Steinberg, *Proc. Russ. Met. Soc.*, **1**. 514, 1913 ; B. M. Larsen, *Metals Alloys*, **1**. 763, 1930 ; A. Campion, *Mech. Eng.*, **29**. 314, 1912 ; A. Baikoff, *Comm. Internat. Assoc. Testing Materials*, **1**. 355, 1930 ; A. B. Kinzel and W. Crafts, *Tech. Publ. Amer. Inst. Min. Eng.*, 436, 1931 ; E. J. Cook, *Foundry Trade Journ.*, **44**. 335, 345, 1931 ; L. E. Grant, *Trans. Amer. Soc. Steel Treating*, **19**. 165, 1931 ; C. E. Sims and G. A. Lillieqvist, *Tech. Publ. Amer. Inst. Min. Eng.*, 453, 1932 ; I. S. Gaieff, *Russ. Metallurgist*, **3**. 369, 1929 ; W. Zieler, *Arch. Eisenhüttenwesen*, **5**. 299, 1932.

⁴ H. Wedding, *Stahl Eisen*, **25**. 923, 1905 ; A. Ruhfus, *ib.*, **26**. 775, 1906 ; J. E. Stead, *Proc. Cleveland Inst. Eng.*, 33, 1913 ; W. Kusl, *Oesterr. Zeit. Berg. Hütt.*, **54**. 593, 610, 1906 ; E. von Maltitz, *Trans. Amer. Inst. Min. Eng.*, **38**. 412, 1907 ; H. M. Howe, *ib.*, **38**. 3, 1907 ; **40**. 644, 1909 ; *B.A. Rep.*, 563, 1910 ; *Proc. Amer. Soc. Testing Materials*, **9**. 327, 1909 ; **10**. 167, 1910 ; L. Jordan, *ib.*, **23**. ii, 7, 1923 ; G. Belloc, *Compt. Rend.*, **145**. 1280, 1908 ; *Rev. Mét.*, **5**. 469, 571, 1908 ; E. Goutal, *ib.*, **7**. 6, 1910 ; K. G. Troubine, *ib.*, **9**. 127, 1912 ; **21**. 288, 1924 ; T. Baker, *Journ. Iron Steel Inst.—Carnegie Mem.*, **1**. 219, 1909 ; L. Baraduc-Muller, *ib.*, **6**. 216, 1914 ; J. W. Donaldson, *ib.*, **7**. 41, 1916 ; *Trans. Faraday Soc.*, **15**. 238, 1920 ; P. L. T. Hérault, *Trans. Amer. Electrochem. Soc.*, **17**. 135, 1910 ; *Iron Age*, **85**. 1170, 1910 ; D. K. Tschernoff, *Rev. Mét.*, **12**. 840, 1915 ; P. Goerens and J. Paquet, *Ferrum*, **12**. 57, 73, 1915 ; **13**. 145, 1916 ; H. D. Hibbard, *Iron Age*, **114**. 565, 599, 631, 1924 ; **116**. 1511, 1605, 1671, 1925 ; *Trans. Amer. Inst. Min. Eng.*, **62**. 160, 1919 ; P. Oberhoffer and A. Beuttel, *Stahl Eisen*, **39**. 1584, 1919 ; P. Oberhoffer and E. Piwowarsky, *ib.*, **42**. 801, 1922 ; O. von Keil and A. Wimmer, *ib.*, **45**. 835, 1925 ; A. Wimmer, *ib.*, **47**. 781, 1927 ; G. Charpy, *Compt. Rend.*, **170**. 306, 1920 ; C. H. Desch, *Journ. West Scotland Iron Steel Inst.*, **32**. 40, 1925 ; H. Brearley, *ib.*, **27**. 63, 1920 ; *Journ. Iron Steel Inst.*, **103**. i, 27, 1921 ; A. G. Lobley and C. L. Betts, *ib.*, **111**. 215, 1925 ; N. Parravano and A. Scortecci, *Ann. Chim. Applicata*, **14**. 3, 1924 ; *Rev. Mét.*, **21**. 340, 1924 ; P. Klinger, *Krupp's Monatsh.*, **6**. 11, 1925 ; T. C. Sutton and H. R. Ambler, *Trans. Faraday Soc.*, **22**. 406, 1926 ; K. Iwase, *Kinzoku no Kenku*, **3**. 119, 1926 ; *Science Rep. Tohoku Univ.*, **15**. 531, 1926 ; T. Andrews, *Microscopic Internal Flaws in Steel Rails and Propeller Shafts*, London, 1897 ; J. Goebel, *Zeit. geramte Giessereipraxis*, **50**. 215, 1929 ; W. Eichholz and J. Mehovar, *Arch. Eisenhüttenwesen*, **5**. 449, 1932.

§ 17. The Crystallization of Iron and the Iron-Carbon Alloys

The formation of the first germs of crystallization is one of the most important' phenomena among the many occurring during the solidification of molten alloys. The properties characteristic of the solid alloy depend to a very large degree upon the number of centres of crystallization and the cause of their formation. So strongly, in fact, does this state of affairs impress itself on the metal, that the vestiges remain even after all the heat treatment and mechanical work to which it will be afterwards subjected.—F. GIOLITTI.

The polyhedral—πολύεδρος, with many sides—network, meshed or cellular structure of iron, Figs. 137 and 138, bears no relation to its internal symmetry, and, as pointed out by C. H. Desch,[1] it represents a compromise between the opposing forces of crystallization and surface tension in the later stages of the solidification of the metal. The study of the homogeneous partitioning of space to form cells with the minimum superficial area furnished E. Fedoroff with a cubo-octahedron which he called a heptaparallelhedron ; and Lord Kelvin, with a similar cell which he called the tetrakaidecahedron. The actual shape of the cell produced by the crystallization of a molten metal is, of course, modified by the crowding of the growths. The space needed for the development of one crystal may be already occupied by other crystals. Crystals which have taken the shape imposed on them by their environment are called **allotrimorphic crystals**— ἀλλόντρος, strange ; μορφή, form—whereas those which have developed their characteristic external form are called **idiomorphic crystals**—ἴδιος, peculiar ; μορφή, form. This subject was also discussed by V. M. Goldschmidt, N. T. Belaiew, L. Cammen, L. Gruardet, and L. Baclé.

The early workers noticed that iron has a crystalline structure. F. Wöhler obtained cubic crystals by breaking plates of cast iron which had been exposed to a white-heat in the brickwork of an iron smelting-furnace, and he also obtained octahedral crystals in the cavities of a large cast iron roll. M. Augustin also reported cubic crystals on the fractured surfaces of gun-barrels which had been long in use. J. Percy also found cleavage planes of crystals arranged perpendicularly to the surface of an iron bar which had been standing for a long time in molten glass ; while W. H. Miller said that iron prepared by the Bessemer process is an aggregate of small cubic crystals. The crystals are very imperfect in consequence of their not having room to develop their faces. Some of them have measurable angles, approximating 90°. The amount of impurity present was considered too small to be likely to have affected the crystalline structure. W. H. Hatfield showed that the structure of steel ingots after solidification results in (i) a thin external zone with a very fine, almost amorphous, crystalline structure which acts as an outer envelope of the ingot, and it is formed by the abrupt cooling, during the pouring of the steel, by contact with the cold walls of the mould ; (ii) an intermediate zone consisting of elongated dendrites having their axes perpendicular to the walls of the mould ; and (iii) a central zone consisting of globular crystals having equal perpendicular axes. The crystallization of cooling ingots was studied by W. H. Hatfield, B. Matuschka, and C. Schwarz. V. N. Krivobok and O. E. Romig noted the absence of any relation between the surface structure of cast metals and the internal crystalline structure.

G. Tammann and A. A. Botschwar observed that when a fine ray of light is passed through a pin-hole in a piece of photographic paper on to an etching pit in a deeply etched crystal surface of copper or iron a light figure is reflected on to the paper in a form characteristic of the orientation of the crystal and of the angle of incidence of the light. When the incident ray is perpendicular to the reflecting surface an octahedral plane produces a figure composed of three intersecting lines of equal length at an angle of 120° to one another, a cube plane gives a " webbed " cross, and a rhombic dodecahedral plane a straight line.

G. W. A. Kahlbaum obtained microscopic hexahedral crystals by sublimation ; and A. C. Becquerel, by electrolysis, as indicated in connection with the preparation of iron. J. A. Poumarède prepared dendritic iron frequently in the form of hollow tetrahedra, by reducing ferrous chloride by zinc vapour ; and E. Péligot obtained octahedral crystals and W. Haidinger, hexahedral crystals by reducing ferrous chloride in hydrogen. E. F. Lange described the so-called furnace crystals of carbonless or almost carbonless iron occasionally found in furnace hearths or slag masses. The analysis of crystals from the pocket in the hearth of a steel furnace gave no combined carbon or manganese, a trace of silicon, 0·02 per cent. sulphur, 0·36 per cent. phosphorus, and 99·62 per cent. iron. The external appearance of the metal resembled a mass of crystal surfaces, mostly pentagonal, with smooth, flat faces, some being of considerable size. Their formation is due to the constant growth of the granules under the combined influence of time and heat; and the effects of expansion and contraction upon groups of such granules in their plastic condition produce the forms of pentagonal dodecahedra such as are produced by the compression of plastic spheroids. This would be helped by the liquation of the more fusible phosphide of iron between their cleavage planes. On breaking up the mass when cold, the lines of fracture would be along the brittle films of the phosphide, thus clearly revealing the formation produced under the above circumstances.

References to the crystalline structure and the metallography of iron and steel were also made by T. Andrews, W. Armstrong, J. O. Arnold, J. A. Aupperle, C. O. Bannister and W. D. Jones, A. Beardsley, H. Behrens, C. Benedicks, G. V. Bianchetti, H. Braune, P. Breuil, R. von Carnall, A. T. Child and W. P. Heineken, W. Crookes, J. Czochralsky, M. Desfosses, G. Dillner, E. F. Dürre, J. A. Ewing, K. Faller, H. Fay and co-workers, T. B. Focke, C. W. C. Fuchs, J. N. von Fuchs, F. Giolitti, R. Glocker, P. Goerens, L. Gruardet, A. Greiner, P. C. Grignon, J. Grone, L. Guillet, E. F. Gurlt, J. F. L. Hausmann, W. Heike and W. Brenscheidt, F. Hermann, E. Heyn, S. A. Houghton, H. M. Howe, O. F. Hudson, O. W. Huntington, C. L. Huston, Z. Jeffries, J. H. B. Jenkins and D. G. Riddick, J. E. Johnson, L. M. Jordan, H. von Jüptner, F. Kerdyk, S. S. Knight, C. Kohn, M. Kralupper, A. Kroll, R. Kühnel, C. F. Lan, P. Lejeune, G. E. Linck, N. N. Ljamin, P. Longmuir, W. von Möllendorff and J. Czochralsky, R. Moldenke, L. B. G. de Morveau, D. Mushet, J. J. Nöggerath, J. Parry, P. M. Partsch, A. M. Portevin, M. A. F. Prestel, F. S. Rice, C. H. Ridsdale, J. B. L. Romé de l'Isle, W. von Rüdiger, A. Sadebeck, A. Sauveur, J. von Siemachko, W. C. Smeaton, A. Stansfield, S. Stein, J. von Sternberg, B. Stoughton, F. Ulrich, and H. Wedding. A. L. Colby compiled a bibliography of the subject. For the structure of electrodeposited metal, vide supra.

The granular structure of steel, as evidenced by the formation of irregularly-shaped, polygonal masses, devoid of any definite crystalline form, was discussed by D. K. Tschernoff, J. A. Brinell, H. C. Sorby, A. Martens, J. O. Arnold, T. Andrews, J. E. Stead, U. Savoia, A. Sauveur, P. Kreuzpointer, A. E. Seaton, W. E. W. Millington and F. C. Thompson, L. Baclé, L. Gruardet, etc. F. Leitner found that the size of the primary crystallites is dependent on the fluidity and casting temp. of the metal. F. Osmond said :

Iron is a mass of globules, more or less welded, which present an apparent tendency to group themselves in margarites and layers. Its mass is subdivided into jointed polyhedrons. When the temperature has not been too high, these forms are regular enough, and one can easily recognize in them those of the pentagonal dodecahedron. Are the polyhedrons in question crystals or grains ? Are their surfaces of contact cleavages or joints ? The answer does not appear to me to be doubtful. The mass may be crystalline, but the envelopes are not. Forms exactly similar are obtained by synthesis, by compressing plastic spheroids in a mould. The desiccation of damp pastes and the solidification of melted materials equally produce analogous divisions.

H. Wedding said that other things being equal, the size of the grains increases with the slowness of the cooling, but with the same kind of cooling and with proportions of carbon up to 2 per cent., the size of the grain decreases. Above this amount the size of the grains increases. Silicon, sulphur, small proportions of manganese, titanium, chromium, and tungsten favour small grains, while phosphorus increases their size. R. M. Bozorth discussed the orientation of the electrodeposited crystals.

J. E. Stead observed that when steel is heated in lime for a few hours at 700° or 800°, the metal is partially decarburized, and the crystal grains assume a columnar formation ; and a similar phenomenon was observed in the decarburization of malleable cast iron, for the crystal grains were found to be arranged in columns radiated inwards from the exterior. C. R. Austin found that in the decarburization of steel by hydrogen the columnar formation appeared. He concluded that carbon-free iron does not form the columnar structure by any simple heat treatment ; this structure is not developed if the steel is annealed in a non-oxidizing environment ; nor is it developed by the diffusion of carbon from a high-carbon steel to pure iron when the two are brought in contact and annealed together. It is developed only when the carbon is removed by oxidizing agents from the surface at a temp. below 850°.

J. E. Stead and H. C. H. Carpenter found that when electrodeposited iron of a high degree of purity—0·008 per cent. carbon and 99·967 per cent. iron—is heated above the Ac₃-arrest and then cooled below the Ac₃-arrest, it furnishes a coarsely crystalline structure with the crystals sometimes equiaxial and sometimes radial, or both. They are both probably α-iron. These effects are produced with plates with a thickness between 0·009 and 0·012 inch. The coarse crystals are destroyed by cold mechanical work ; by heating above the Ac₃-arrest and quenching ; or by a prolonged heating above this temp. followed by slow cooling. The heat treatment that produces coarse crystals in electrodeposited iron refines wrought iron and very mild steel that have been rendered coarsely crystalline by close-annealing between 700° and 800° ; but annealing at 700° to 800° has no effect in coarsening the structure of electrodeposited iron which has been refined by cold mechanical work.

C. A. Edwards and L. B. Pfeil studied the conditions under which large single crystals can be obtained, and, by modifying H. C. H. Carpenter and C. F. Elam's process for aluminium, produced single crystals by annealing deformed crystals of purified iron just below the Ac₃-arrest. E. Sütter found that large crystals could be obtained by electrolysis ; and that crystals could be grown on iron or tungsten wires heated to redness in the vapour of ferric chloride. Observations on this subject were made by W. Gerlach, E. Dussler and W. Gerlach, K. Honda and co-workers, W. L. Webster, E. B. Wedmore, J. A. M. van Liempt, E. Sütter, M. Privault, J. Seigle, P. W. Bridgman, W. E. Ruder, H. Griess, H. Griess and H. Esser, C. F. Elam, R. Glocker, and N. A. Ziegler. L. B. Pfeil, F. Wever, G. Tammann and A. Müller, and L. W. McKeehan prepared long single crystals of iron by allowing an electrically heated portion, at 1400°, to move along the wire. Irregular tension and torsional stresses result in twinning.

F. Osmond and co-workers reduced ferrous chloride by hydrogen and by zinc vapour, at different temp., and concluded that all three allotropic forms of iron— α-, β-, and γ-iron—crystallize in the cubic system. The crystals were all small, but there was an element of uncertainty, for H. le Chatelier suggested that the results for γ-iron might be explained by the assumption that the crystals are rhombohedra simulating a cube. H. Wedding stated that the presence of over 2 per cent. of manganese changes the regular crystal form of iron containing carbon into crystals belonging to some system other than the cubic—probably rhombic ; but H. Bauerman did not accept this statement, in view of A. Erman's observation that the ferromanganese of the Urals is cubic with a rhombic habit, and E. Mallard's observation that 11 to 52 per cent. ferromanganese crystallizes in the tabular form, with a prism of about 112°, and with more manganese the structure becomes acicular owing to the aggregation of six-sided prisms of about 120°. In confirmation of the cubic form, J. E. Stead showed that by strongly etching purified iron, or iron containing much phosphorus, crystals apparently in the form of square plates are readily developed—*vide* Fig. 14, **1**. 11, 4. In mechanical tests with micro-sections, such of the grains as are built up of crystals with cleavages at right angles to the surface break up and fracture in two directions at right angles to one another, in agreement with the assumption that the crystals are cubic. Cubical

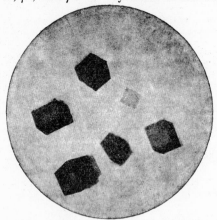

Fig. 139.—Cubic Crystals of α-iron (J. E. Stead).

forms obtained by splitting up a large granule of phosphoretic iron through the cleavage planes are shown in Fig. 139 ($\times$ 5). In general, iron forms cubic, octahedral, or trapezohedral crystals. The cube is the characteristic form of α-iron or ferrite. This is shown by the strongly marked cleavage ; by the course of Neumann's bands and slip-bands—*vide infra* ; and by the cleavages of some meteoric iron. The octahedron is the characteristic form of γ-iron and austenite. This is shown by the twinning planes, the slip-planes, and the Widmanstätten figures. The trapezohedron is revealed by the course of the Neumann bands and the slip-bands. The crystalline forms of the different known varieties of iron have been definitely settled by the X-radiograms. A. Westgren and co-workers showed that the X-radiograms of α-, β-, and δ-iron correspond with a body-centred cubic lattice, whilst the X-radiogram of γ-iron corresponds with a face-centred cubic lattice. Observations on the X-radiograms and on the atomic structure of the crystals of iron and steel were made by G. Tammann and A. A. Botschwar, K. Heindlhofer, D. H. Killeffer, R. Schenck, E. Schmid, R. Berthold, F. Rinne, H. Shoji, O. L. Roberts, A. Smekal, G. L. Clark and co-workers, J. H. Andrew, K. Weissenberg, O. Mügge, F. Roll, A. Karlsson, W. Rosenhain, R. Bach, F. Kirchner, and R. W. G. Wyckoff. W. E. Williams discussed the structures of hardened and tempered steels obtained by X-radiograms. M. C. Neuburger has a monograph : *Röntgenographie des Eisens und seiner Legierungen* (Stuttgart, 1928). W. Hume-Rothery discussed the relations amongst the lattice constants of iron and other elements ; and W. L. Fink and E. D. Campbell, the effect of heat treatment and carbon content on the lattice. J. Forrest discussed the magnetic lattice ; and U. Dehlinger, the electron entropy of the transition forms of iron.

R. Bach emphasized the fact that from room temp. up to the m.p. there are really only two allotropic forms of iron, (i) with the body-centred lattice and including the α-, β-, and δ-varieties, and (ii) the face-centred lattice or γ-iron. He measured the effect of temp. on the lattice constant, a, of 99·46 per cent. iron, and found for the percentage values da/a at

	730°	785°	830°	860°	885°	900°	1370°	1400°
a .	2·9004	2·882	2·9071	2·9043	3·653*	3·655*	3·688*	2·9347 A.
da/a .	1·06	1·02	1·29	1·19	1·02	1·08	2·01	2·25 per cent.

The results are plotted in Fig. 140. The * denotes γ-iron. A. E. van Arkel and W. G. Burgers observed that the lattice constant, a, for the purified oxide reduced by hydrogen is 2·8614 A. ; for electrolytic iron, 2·8614 A. ; for cast steel, 2·8623 A. ; and for steels with 1, 12, and 25 per cent. of chromium, respectively 2·8635, 2·8666, and 2·8675 A. The α- and δ-varieties are considered to be the same owing to the continuity of the thermal expansion curves. In the interval between 900° and 1400° the expansion curve of γ-iron runs parallel to the continuation of the curve for

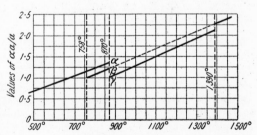

FIG. 140.—The Effect of Temperature on the Lattice Constants of Iron.

β-iron. The contraction represented by the passage of α- to β-iron is greater than that which can be attributed to the disappearance of spontaneous magnetization, and it is doubtful if the α-state can be distinguished from the β-state uniquely by magnetic differences. P. P. Ewald and C. Hermann summarized the data as in Table XIII.

A. W. Hull found that the space-lattice of α-iron is a body-centred cube with side $a = 2·86$ A., and W. P. Davey gave $a = 2·858$ A. for the lattice constant of purified iron, and 2·585 for iron with 0·020 per cent. of carbon, 0·017 of sulphur, and 0·021

TABLE XIII.—LATTICE CONSTANTS OF IRON CRYSTALS.

Lattice		Temperature	Parameter a	Shortest distance between atoms	Atomic volume
α-iron	Body-centred	16°	2·86 A.	2·477 A.	11·7
β-iron	Body-centred	800°	2·90 A.	2·513 A.	12·2
γ-iron	Face-centred	1100°	3·63 A.	2·57 A.	12·0
δ-iron	Body-centred	1425°	2·93 A.	2·538 A.	12·6

of silicon; he also gave $2·472 \times 10^{-8}$ cm. for the closest approach of the atoms. F. Wever showed that the α-lattices for electrolytic iron and for annealed steels with 0·07, 0·56, and 0·86 per cent. carbon all gave the same lattice parameter, $a = 2·863 \times 10^{-8}$ cm.; E. A. Owen and G. D. Preston gave $a = 2·869$ A. for the body-centred cubic lattice; L. W. McKeehan, $a = 2·872$ A.; G. Mayer found for α-iron obtained from iron carbonyl, $a = 2·86106$ A. at 22°; A. Osawa, $a = 2·865$ A. at 15°; A. Westgren and A. E. Lindh, 2·87 A. for α-iron, and 2·92 A. for β-iron; A. Westgren and G. Phragmen, 2·87 A. for α-iron at 16°; 2·90 A. for β-iron at 800°; and 2·93 A. for δ-iron at 1425°; F. C. Blake, 2·8603 A.; R. Brill and H. Mark, and O. Eisenhut and E. Kaupp, 2·863 A. The shortest distance apart of the atoms of α-iron was estimated by A. Goetz to be 2·512 A., when $a = 2·90$ at 900°. H. Perlitz discussed the subject.

A. Westgren and A. E. Lindh found the parameter a of the space-lattice of γ-iron at 1000° to be 3·60 A.; A. Westgren and G. Phragmen gave at 1100°, $a = 3·63$ and at 1425°, 3·68 A.; F. Wever, 3·56 to 3·60 A.; and A. Goetz, $a = 3·59$, and the shortest distance of the atoms apart is 2·539 A. For austenitic steel with 25·2 per cent. of nickel, A. Westgren and A. E. Lindh gave $a = 3·58$ A.; for austenitic steel with 12·1 per cent. of manganese, $a = 3·61$ A., and A. Westgren and G. Phragmen gave 3·61 A. for the 12·1 per cent. manganese steel. E. Oehman gave $a = 3·562$, and for the shortest distance apart of the atoms, 2·52 A.—vide infra, the iron-manganese alloys. F. Wever gave for austenitic steel cooled in liquid air $a = 3·565$ A., for the same steel partially converted into martensite, $a = 2·849$ A., and for the same steel after cold-working, $a = 2·839$ A.; and F. Wever and P. Rütten observed that the lattice constant for γ-iron containing carbon in solid soln. expands linearly 0·006 to 0·007 A. per atom of carbon; and A. Osawa obtained a similar result with nickel steels. A. Westgren and G. Phragmen gave for the γ-iron lattice for carbon steel quenched from 1000° and 1100°:

Quenched from				1000°			1100°	
Carbon	.	.	.	0·24	1·18	1·98	0	1·98 per cent.
a	.	.	.	3·56	3·64	3·64	3·63	3·65

According to F. Wever, the lattice parameter for α-iron is 2·861 A., and it is not affected by the presence of carbon in the annealed alloy, and there is only a slight increase in the hardened alloy. This all shows that the carbon here is mainly occupied in filling spaces in the lattice. On the other hand, the lattice parameter for γ-iron in austenitic steels increases directly with the carbon content and the manganese content in accord with $3·578 + 0·0005[Mn] + 0·00645[C]$, where the bracketed symbols represent atomic percentages. This is taken to mean that these elements replace iron in the lattice.

K. Honda and S. Sekito consider that in the case of austenite the carbon atoms are distributed according to the law of probability at the centre of an elementary cube; whilst in the case of martensite the carbon atoms are distributed according to the law of probability in the centre of the face of an elementary cube. The observations of W. L. Fink and E. D. Campbell, M. Majima and S. Togino, N. Seljakoff and co-workers, G. Kurdjumoff and E. Kaminsky, K. Honda and co-workers showed that in quenched steel the surface layer contains a body-centred tetragonal lattice with the axial ratio $c : a = 1.06$, as well as a small quantity of retained austenite with a face-centred lattice. K. Honda and S. Sekito identify this with α-martensite—*vide supra*, martensite ; and *vide infra*, hardening.

A. Osawa noticed that the edge-length of a unit cell of α-iron increases with temp. as iron expands on heating. A. Westgren and co-workers observed that while $a = 2.87$ A. at 800°, it becomes 2.90 A. at 1425°. It was also found that the so-called β-iron, between 800° and 830°, has the iron atoms oriented in exactly the same way

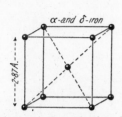

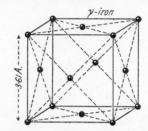

Fig. 141.—Space-lattice of α- and δ-irons.

Fig. 142.—Space-lattice of γ-iron.

as those of α-iron : and hence, on the assumption that allotropy and polymorphy are synonymous terms, it was inferred that β-iron is not truly a definite modification of iron—*vide supra*. It was also found that γ-iron, at 1100°, has a face-centred cubic lattice with sides $a = 3.61$ A. The results are summarized in Figs. 141 and 142. Assuming that the crystals are made up of spherical atoms, an imitation of the body-centred packing is given in Fig. 143, and of the face-centred packing in Fig. 144. Since δ-iron at 1400° has a body-centred cubic lattice, it follows that

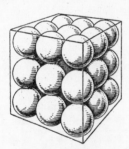

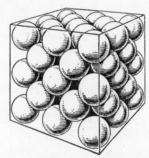

Fig. 143.—The Body-centred Cubic Packing.

Fig. 144.—The Face-centred Cubic Packing.

the transformation which occurs at 900°, or the A_3-arrest, is reversed at 1400°, the A_4-arrest. S. Sato thus summarized the data derived from the X-radiograms, and plotted the results in Fig. 145 :

	Body-centred cube			Face-centred cube		
	20°	800°	1450°	1000°	1100°	1425°
a-edge . . .	2·86	2·89	2·93	3·65	3·66	3·68 A.

E. C. Bain, H. Shoji, and E. J. Janitzky studied the mechanism of the transformation from body-centred α-iron to face-centred γ-iron ; and for K. Honda and S. Sekito's observations on this subject, *vide* martensite, and the theories of hardening.

A. Westgren and G. Phragmen studied the X-radiogram of cementite and concluded that the crystals are rhombic, with the axial ratio $a : b : c = 0.891 : 1 : 1.329$. The dimensions of unit structure containing $4Fe_3C$ are $a = 4.518$ A., $b = 5.069$ A., and $c = 6.736$ A. The sp. gr. is 7·662 ; the vol. of unit cell is 154.3×10^{-24} c.c. ;

and the mol. vol.=23·43 c.c.   S. B. Hendricks has worked out the structure, which he says is of the co-ordination type with octahedra of iron atoms around central carbon atoms, as indicated in Fig. 146. The assumed structure explains the observed absence of the formation of solid soln. in the iron-carbon system between cementite and phases containing more or less carbon ; the hardness of cementite ; and the lack of metallographic characteristics that would require similarity of arrangement of iron atoms in some plane of cementite compared with a specific plane of α-iron.

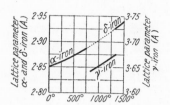

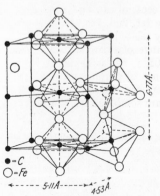

FIG. 145.—The Lattice Constant of Iron at Different Temperatures.

FIG. 146.—Structure of the Cementite with Octahedra of Iron about Central Carbon Atoms.

The work on X-radiograms has shown that **solid solutions** are of two kinds : (i) Those in which the solute is a *substitution element, i.e.* one in which the atoms enter the space-lattice of the solvent and occupy the place previously occupied by the solvent atoms—for instance, nickel or silicon in solid soln. with iron. This is illustrated by F. Wever's diagram, Fig. 147, where the black spots represent nickel atoms, and the others atoms of γ-iron. (ii) Those in which the solute is an *interstitial element—die vagabundierenden Atomen—i.e.* one on which the atoms enter the space-lattice of the solvent and occupy open spaces between the solvent atoms—

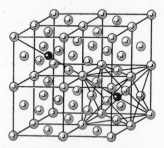

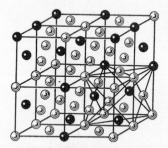

FIG. 147.—Lattice of γ-Iron-Nickel Alloys—Substitution Element.

FIG. 148.—Lattice of γ-Iron-Carbon Alloys—Interstitial Element.

for example, carbon, nitrogen, and oxygen. This is illustrated by F. Wever's diagram Fig. 148, where the black spots represent carbon atoms, the others atoms of γ-iron. T. D. Yensen pointed out that the interstitial elements may enter the iron lattice in small amounts and so produce a condition which makes the lattice tend to change from the body-centred to the face-centred lattice when the solubility of the interstitial elements is greater. All the interstitial elements have a low solubility. Thus the solubility of carbon at 1475° in iron with the body-centred lattice corresponds with one carbon atom to every 125 unit cubes. At that high temp.

the thermal agitation of the atoms is very large, so that a carbon atom may travel from cube to cube with a high velocity. At low concentrations the carbon atoms may slip through the α- (body-centred) lattice without permanent distortion, but as the concentration is increased a point will be reached, depending on the temp., where the visits of the carbon atoms to the α-lattice are too frequent, and accommodation is provided by a change from the α-lattice to the γ-lattice. S. Sekito found that the variation in the lattice parameter is equivalent to 0·45 per cent. for every 1 per cent. of carbon—*vide supra*, martensite. A. Heinzel observed that elements of the 1st, 2nd, 7th, and 8th groups of the periodic system, if soluble in iron, and closely related to iron physically and chemically—*e.g.* manganese—generally widen the range of existence of the face-centred structure, which is normally from 906° to 1401°; whilst elements from the 3rd to the 6th group narrow the range of existence of γ-iron, and finally make it disappear—*e.g.* with vanadium exceeding 1·1 per cent. there is no γ-phase. These elements are not related to iron even if they are soluble in it. Carbon and nitrogen are exceptions. All elements of large

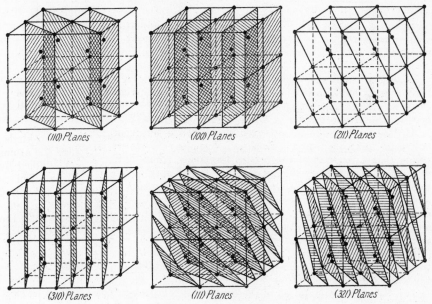

(110) Planes   *(100) Planes*   *(211) Planes*

(310) Planes   *(111) Planes*   *(321) Planes*

Fig. 149.—Systems of Atomic Planes.

atomic radius—*e.g.* the metals of the alkalies and alkaline earths, mercury, lead, thallium, bismuth, silver, and cadmium—are insoluble in iron. With still higher concentrations of carbon even the γ-lattice is insufficient, and the compound Fe_3C is formed. Interstitial atoms like oxygen and nitrogen may be too large to be able to pass freely from lattice to lattice as readily as does the carbon atom, so that it becomes permanently attached to the regularly spaced unit cubes. The stranger atom may displace the central iron atom, and this in turn displaces its neighbour, and so on until a number of the displaced atoms meet to form a face-centred cube. This action upsets the regularity of the whole lattice, the neighbouring central iron atoms are displaced, and as more stranger atoms enter, more and more γ- (face-centred) cubes are formed, until the entire α-lattice breaks down, and the γ-lattice is formed with stranger atoms in the centres at regular intervals. T. D. Yensen also inferred that if no stranger atoms (impurities) be present, there will be no change from the face-centred to the body-centred lattice, and that pure iron would not appear in forms other than that of α(δ)-iron. The subject was discussed by F. Bitter, and K. Heindlhofer.

Owing to the definite geometric arrangement of the crystal units, the atoms fall into a series of parallel planes inclined at different angles to the sides of the cube, and each system of planes includes every atom of the body-centred cube. These planes are illustrated diagrammatically in Fig. 149 by H. H. Lester and R. H. Aborn. A. W. Hull, and R. W. G. Wyckoff discussed this subject. Each set of planes may be regarded as a space-grating for the X-radiations ; for the equally-spaced reflecting planes are of such an order of spacing that interference phenomena in the reflections are possible. The grating constant, d, is the distance between the planes. An incident beam of X-rays passing through a mixture of small crystals may be arranged to give reflections from each of the possible systems of planes, and with a suitable arrangement — 1. 11, 8 — the spectral lines can be represented as the envelope of a series of circles with their centres in a straight line. Fig. 150, by H. H. Lester and R. H. Aborn, represents a portion of the two crystal spectra (i) for unstressed iron, and (ii) for iron subjected to a tensile stress. If the beam of X-rays is monochromatic, the lines are single.

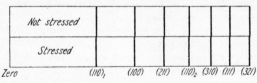

FIG. 150.—Portion X-ray Film for Stressed and Unstressed Iron (Diagrammatic).

M. Ettisch and co-workers found that in hard-drawn wires of metals with a body-centred cubic lattice only a single lattice plane, (110), lies in the section of the wire. The arrangement of the crystallites imparts a fibrous structure, so called because the arrangement was first observed in natural fibres like ramie and silk. E. C. Bain and Z. Jeffries observed that when a very coarse-grained metal with only a few grains is rolled it develops a complete assortment of orientations, indicating that a rotation of the crystal fragments occurs during deformation. The rotation of the microcrystals as a result of cold-working has been proved by the work of H. C. Burger, G. Tammann, F. Wever, C. Nusbaum, C. F. Elam, G. I. Taylor and C. F. Elam, A. Smekal, A. Ono, K. Becker and co-workers, F. Wever and co-workers, F. Körber, W. P. Davey and co-workers, R. Glocker, and G. Sachs and E. Schiebold. The resulting orientation depends on the nature of the metal and on the kind of cold-working. In iron, with its body-centred cubic lattice, the (110)-axis takes the axial direction of the bar, whilst with copper and aluminium, with their face-centred cubic lattices, the (111)-axis takes the axial direction of the bar along which the metals are stretched or drawn. According to G. Kurdjumoff and G. Sachs, the orientation of the crystals of rolled electrolytic iron, as revealed by the X-radiograms, and the stenographic projection of the polar sphere of the directions of reflection, for the (110)- and (200)-faces, show that S. T. Konobejewsky's single orientation is not satisfactory, but that three simultaneous orientations are required. The (100)-, (112)-, and (111)-faces are respectively parallel to the plane of rolling, and the (011)-, (110)-, and (112)-directions are parallel to the direction of rolling. The character of the polar figures for the (200)- and (110)-faces of iron recrystallized between 550° and 840° can also only be explained by a similar triple orientation. The orientations in the rolled and recrystallized iron are so related that two orientations in the recrystallized metal are obtained from those of the rolled metal by rotation through an angle of 15° in the plane of rolling, whilst the third orientation is the same in both cases. The relative intensities of various orientations are different in both cases. The structure of the metal recrystallized above the $\alpha \rightarrow \gamma$-transition temp. is similar to that of recrystallized α-iron, showing that in the change from α- to γ-iron the two modifications take up a definite relative orientation. P. W. Bridgman studied the relation between the orientation of the crystal and Young's modulus (q.v.) for tungsten.

A. Ono found that the X-ray diffraction pattern of α-iron strained in extension, compression, and torsion shows that there are two kinds of symmetry in the strained lattice. In the first kind the rotation of the lattice during strain takes place about one of the axes in a definite direction, and in the second kind the lattice rotates about an axis which may occupy any position in a definite plane. In α-iron strained in extension the symmetry is of the second kind, with the axis (110) more or less parallel to the direction of extension, whereas in the same metal strained by compression the symmetry may be of the first kind with the axis (111) in the direction of compression, or of the second kind with the axis of rotation (011) lying in the cross-sectional plane. In twisted α-iron the second kind of symmetry exists with the plane (110), and probably also the plane (211), in the horizontal position. The mechanism of the crystal arrangement of a strained metal is explained on the assumption that slip and rotation are the causes of distortion, and that the direction of slip is constant for each kind of lattice. The resistance to slip of a metal increases with a diminution in the grain-size, and this agrees with the fact that fine-grained metals are usually much harder and stronger than those in which the crystals are relatively large.

W. E. Williams studied the X-radiograms of hardened steel, and concluded that when a carbon steel is quenched from above the transformation point, all or part of the γ-iron is changed into α-iron, but the α-iron grains do not grow from independent centres. In the tempered state the radical pattern is not altered, and hence tempering does not produce a recrystallization of the distorted crystals. Consequently, the extreme hardness of martensite is not to be ascribed to this distortion. A. E. van Arkel and P. Koets observed that the number of crystals of γ-iron in mechanically deformed strips of steel is approximately proportional to the number of crystals of α-iron in the undeformed strips. S. Sekito found that the maximum distortion of the space-lattice is $\delta a/a=0.004$ with cold-drawn wire reduced 0.2326 in diameter—*cf.* Fig. 151. If the modulus of elasticity is $E=21\times10^3$ kgrms. per sq. mm., when the maximum internal stress $P=E\times\delta a/a$, or $P=84$ kgrms. per sq. mm., this is a little less than the tensile strength, 88 kgrms. per sq. mm. for the cold-drawn wire. The values of $\delta a/a$ for 0.1, 0.3, and 0.5 per cent. carbon steels annealed at different temp. are shown in Fig. 151. Most of the internal stress is

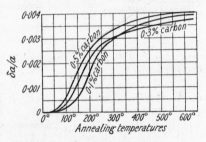

Fig. 151.—The Effect of Annealing on the Lattice Distortion of Steel by Cold-work.

relieved by annealing at 400°. F. C. Elder, M. Ettisch and co-workers, S. T. Konobejewsky, M. Polanyi and K. Weissenberg, and G. Kurdjumoff and E. Kaminsky also studied the effect of cold-work, tempering, and composition on the lattice of carbon steels.

When a metal passes from the liquid to the solid state, nuclei are first formed, and crystals begin to grow about the nuclei. In the case of iron, if the crystallizing forces had free play, the crystals would assume regular geometrical forms, cubes or octahedra. The crystals, however, grow more rapidly in favoured directions to form elongated crystals called **dendrites.** The dendrites are often described in terms of their imagined resemblance to some better-known object—*e.g.* fir-tree crystals. H. Capitaine prepared dendritic crystals with branches parallel to the cubic axes. Dendrites are sometimes found in the cavities or pipes of large ingots, hanging like stalactites from the roof. The dendrite of ferrite illustrated by Fig. 152 —a so-called pine-tree crystal—was found by D. K. Tschernoff formed in a cavity in an ingot of cast steel as the retreating liquid left the incompleted form. In 1775, P. C. Grignon described similar crystals formed in cavities in cast iron ; he said that under a magnifying glass the dendrites had " the appearance of a small metallic forest made up of trees with quaternary branches." E. F. Lange found pine-tree crystals encrusting a cavity in a pipe of a large steel casting. The crystals in some

cases were 14 to 15 inches long.   They are kept in the museum of the Manchester
Literary and Philosophical Society.   E. F. Lange's analysis of drillings from the

crystal gave : 0·43 per cent. of combined carbon; 0·191 Si ;
1·05 Mn ; 0·101 S ; and 0·098 P ; and an analysis of the steel
outside the crystal area was : 0·345 per cent. combined carbon ;
0·16 Si ; 1·02 Mn ; 0·08 S ; and 0·076 P.   J. S. G. Primrose
obtained a fir-tree crystal 19 inches long and 3 lbs. in weight
from a pipe-cavity in a 50-ton steel ingot.   F. C. G. Müller,
and H. M. Howe poured the liquid metal out of the interior
of partially frozen ingots at various stages of solidification,
but invariably found the interior surfaces smooth and without
any surface protrusion of crystal growths.

It is generally assumed that the primary axis forms first,
and that the secondary axes are then quickly developed ; then
follow the ternary axes and so on all in rapid succession.   The
branches thicken and elongate to form a branched structure
or **crystal skeleton.**   As H. Wedding puts it :

> In commercially pure iron the crystals show the form of an
> incomplete regular octahedron, that is to say, the external form
> corresponds to the octahedron ; the mass of the crystal, however, is
> not filled up, but is replaced by branches which run in a direction
> parallel to the axes of the octahedron, and consequently correspond
> to the position of the faces of the fundamental cube.   Such branches
> have, as a rule, side branches standing at right angles to the main
> branches ; these also again often have perpendicular branches of the
> third degree, so that the whole is only the skeleton of an octahedron,
> and has an external form recalling that of the pine-tree.

Fig. 152.—Pine-tree
Crystal of Ferrite
(D. Tschernoff).

The formation of skeleton or dendritic crystals during the solidification of metals
was described by F. G. Allison and M. M. Rock, A. W. and H. Brearley, H. G. Carter,
C. H. Desch, J. A. Ewing and W. Rosenhain, A. L. Feild, J. D. Gat, F. P. Gilligan
and J. J. Curran, A. Glazunoff, F. von Goeler and G. Sachs, W. H. Hatfield,
C. T. Heycock and F. H. Neville, H. M. Howe and co-workers, T. Ishiwara,
H. G. Keshian, V. N. Krivobok, N. M. H. Lightfoot, G. Masing, A. M. Portevin
and V. Bernard, J. S. G. Primrose, W. Rosenhain, A. Sauveur, A. Sauveur and
C. H. Chou, A. Sauveur and V. N. Krivobok, J. E. Stead, B. Stoughton and
F. J. G. Duck, and R. Vogel.

P. C. Grignon said that when grey cast iron is in a perfect condition, it gives a
very regular crystallization, every crystal being distinct and isolated.   He described
skeleton forms built up on the rectangular axes of the cubic system.   The axes
grow and thicken by the gradual deposition of particles of solid, until the interstices
between the axes are filled up and the dendrite is formed.   Its external shape is
influenced by contact with neighbouring growths, and occasionally the boundary
lines between the different growths can be detected.   Solidified masses of iron or
steel are composed of closely interlocked masses of dendrites—cf. Fig. 13, 1. 11, 4.
The dendritic structure is revealed by suitably polishing and etching the surface—
cf. Figs. 41 to 44.   Fig. 153 (×4), by P. Oberhoffer, shows the unetched surface
of steel with 0·4 per cent. of carbon, after fusion and solidification in vacuo.   It
shows the crystallization nuclei enclosed by cell-like boundaries—vide 1. 11, 4.

The dendrites are intermediary forms between crystal skeletons and fully
developed crystals.   The dendritic structure of iron or steel is sometimes called
the *primary structure,* and the colonies of grains each enclosing the dendrites within
its boundaries are called *primary grains.*   If only one metal is under consideration,
the dendrite will be chemically homogeneous ; but if the metal is associated with
another element, the crystal axes which are the first to solidify contain more of the
constituent with the highest m.p., and the portion last to solidify between the crystal
axes will contain more of the constituent with the lowest m.p.   The segregation of
the molten alloy to form dendrites which are chemically homogeneous is called

dendritic segregation, or **intercrystalline segregation.** A. le Thomas, and L. Guillet discussed what they called the *heredity* of iron castings. The primary crystallization of binary, ternary, and more complex systems was discussed by F. Giolitti. The tendency of a metal to migrate from parts where it is highly concentrated to parts where it is less concentrated by the process of diffusion tends to make the metal homogeneous and to undo the state produced by dendritic segregation. This diffusion was discussed by F. Giolitti. It continues in the cooling metal after it has solidified, and it is promoted by slow solidification, by a prolonged heating of the solid at a high temp., and by slowly cooling the solid. J. E. Stead suggested that the presence of phosphorus, sulphur, and silicon in iron and steel favours dendritic segregation—*vide supra.* H. le Chatelier supposed that oxygen acts in a similar manner; and H. le Chatelier and J. Lemoine, manganese, silicon, nickel, and chromium. The subject was discussed by H. M. Howe, etc. A. Sauveur and V. N. Krivobok

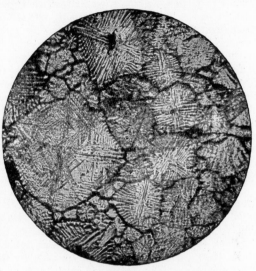

Fig. 153.—Crystallization Nuclei in Cells of 0·4 per cent. Carbon Steel (P. Oberhoffer).

said that oxygen alone in pure iron or in iron with carbon or phosphorus or both does not produce persistent dendritic segregation; phosphorus can produce dendritic segregation in iron alone, as well as in iron-carbon alloys, and it causes the separation of carbon from steel with 0·17 per cent. carbon. Carbon and iron alone can produce dendritic segregation provided the solidification is fast enough. Crystallization was studied by A. Hultgren, C. H. Desch, A. W. and H. Brearley, N. T. Belaiew, C. A. Müller, P. Bardenheuer and C. A. Müller, and H. G. Keshian—*vide infra,* cast iron. A. Wingham discussed the internal strains set up in iron and steel during crystallization.

N. T. Belaiew showed that at least three types of crystallization occur in the production of steel. There are: (i) the *primary crystallization* which occurs in a liquid or mush and which furnishes dendrites; (ii) the *granulation* which occurs in a completely solidified alloy and involves a rearrangement of the crystals to form grains of various sizes and dimensions; each grain has its own crystallographic orientation and is a distinct crystallographic unit. The result is to give a polyhedral structure to the solid soln. of austenite. (iii) The *secondary crystallization* takes place in the solidified and granulated metal and it results in the formation of the usual pearlitic structure. Consequently, the properties of the finished alloy are to be traced back to the dendrites of the primary crystallization and to their unavoidable heterogeneous composition; then to the granules—number, dimensions, cohesion, etc.; and then to the secondary crystallization or pearlitic structure. F. Giolitti discussed the secondary crystallization of homogeneous and non-homogeneous austenite; and the morphological relationships between the primary and secondary crystallization systems. N. T. Belaiew showed that the process of secondary crystallization or chemical decomposition starts at some point in each polyhedral grain, and ceases when it reaches the boundary of the grain. There is a neutral zone between two adjacent grains when the crystalline matter cannot assume the orientation of either of the grains. As the cooling alloy approaches the eutectoidal temp., the excess ferrite or cementite will accumulate about the periphery of the grains ; so that if the cooling proceeds slowly enough, the whole of the excess ferrite or cementite will form a membrane or shell more or less thick, leaving the while the interior forms eutectoidal pearlite. On a plane section the resulting structure appears to have a **cellular** or **network structure**—*vide supra*, Figs. 137 and 138. Hence the iron with 1·29 per cent. of carbon shows a network of white lines of excess cementite surrounding the grains of pearlite. If the secondary crystallization proceeds rather rapidly by quick cooling, a certain amount of excess element will crystallize where it is formed, in the middle of the grain, and not at the boundary. The lines of separation will follow the crystallographic planes of the crystalline grains. The γ-iron, with its face-centred lattice, has four pairs of octahedral planes, and the separation of the excess ferrite or cementite will follow these planes. On a secant plane such octahedral sections will then appear as **Widmanstätten figures,** which bear a distinct character in each grain. The combination of the meshes with these figures can be called the **Widmanstätten structure.** Still a third type of structure—*the structure of large crystals*—might be anticipated where the conditions are such that granulation does not occur, and the deposit from the secondary crystallization arranges itself parallel to the dendritic axes. Such a structure usually occurs in isolated crystals ; thus N. T. Belaiew observed it in the D. K. Tschernoff's crystal, Fig. 152, which contained 0·60 per cent. of carbon. The subject was studied by N. T. Belaiew, F. Berwerth, O. W. Ellis, F. B. Foley, F. Giolitti, H. Hanemann, K. Harnecker, T. Kase, V. N. Krivobok, A. M. Portevin and V. Bernard, A. Sauveur, E. E. Thum, J. Young, and B. Zschokke. T. Kase obtained the Widmanstätten structure in hypoeutectoid steels by annealing them above 1000° ; or by heating them until partly fused and cooling in air from above the Ar_3-arrest. Hypereutectoid steels must be cooled from above the A_{cm}-arrest ; quenching them is not an effective process, and cooling slowly through the A_1-arrest destroys the characteristic structure. The structure is produced in nickel steels by long annealing at the Ac_3-arrest, and then quenching in water, so that meteorites may have acquired the structure by a prolonged exposure to a very high temp. and subsequent rapid cooling. For the observations of C. Benedicks, *vide* the iron-nickel alloys. A. Sauveur and C. H. Chou observed that there is a close relation between the martensitic and the Widmanstätten structures. A. M. Portevin showed that when the carbon is homogeneously distributed the cementite may separate between the grains (*a*) in the network of the junctures of the grains, or (*b*) it may become isolated in the interior of the grains themselves and its distribution there is governed more or less by the directive influence of the crystalline forces. This includes intergranular distribution, Widmanstätten figures, and imprisoned cementite. There may be also a pseudodendritic distribution arising from the irregular concentration of the solid soln., for the concentration is highest in the interaxial spaces of the dendrites formed during the primary crystallization. The diffusion of the carbon may make the steel homogeneous. To summarize :

SECONDARY DEPOSITS			STRUCTURES
Secondary Structures {	At outlines of grains		Network
	In crystal structures {	parallel cleavage planes	Widmanstätten
		parallel to crystal axes	Large crystals

According to N. T. Belaiew, a steel with 1·80 per cent. of carbon furnishes the structure of large crystals ; one with 0·60 per cent. carbon, the network structure with large meshes ; and one with 0·55 per cent. gave the well-developed Widmanstätten structure shown in Fig. 154 ($\times$6) and Fig. 155 ($\times$ 6). The Widmanstätten figures were observed on a meteorite by A. de Widmanstätten in 1808, but no publication was made. The figures attracted some attention, and they soon came to be known by their present name. It was thought for a time that the figures were peculiar to meteorites, but they were found to develop on various metal alloys—*e.g.* the alloys of platinum and antimony by M. Chouriguine. In 1900, F. Osmond observed on a steel ingot equilateral triangular markings which " recalled the Widmanstätten

figures which are known to belong to the regular octahedral system "; and
J. O. Arnold and A. McWilliam also observed them on carbon steels. The subject
was discussed by A. Sauveur, and A. Sauveur and C. H. Chou.

The fundamental conditions for the production of Widmanstätten's figures are
that the alloy (i) crystallizes with the face-centred cubic lattice ; (ii) is subject to
secondary crystallization ; (iii) is in the granulated state when secondary crystallization occurs ; and (iv) is cooled through the secondary crystallization so as to
favour the deposition of the excess element, not at the boundaries only, but also
inside the grains. The markings or lines on the surface of each grain are peculiar
to itself. The interpretation of the lines requires a knowledge of the geometry of
the regular octahedron. If such a solid be built of lamellæ lying parallel to the
outer faces of the solid, there will be four sets of such lamellæ, since the regular
octahedron has four pairs of parallel surfaces. Any sectional plane through the
solid will show four sets of lines, each set of lines corresponding to the intersection
of the cutting or secant plane and one of the sets of lamellæ, except when the secant
plane lies parallel to any one of the faces of the solid, and therefore parallel to the
corresponding set of lamellæ, in which case only three sets of lines will be produced.
The majority of the grains show four distinct sets of lines. N. T. Belaiew studied

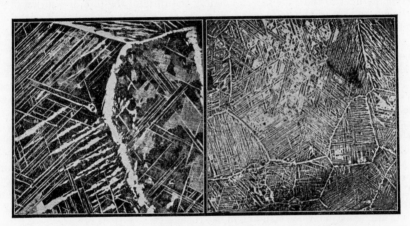

FIGS. 154 and 155.—Widmanstätten Structure (N. T. Belaiew).

this subject in some detail. H. Wilkinson, A. M. Portevin, F. Giolitti, and
S. V. Bielyansky discussed the morphology of proeutectoidal or excess cementite—
vide supra.

According to T. Kase, a hypoeutectoid steel gives the Widmanstätten structure
on annealing above 1000° or on heating it to partial melting and cooling in air from
a temp. above the Ar_3-point. Hypereutectoid steel must be cooled from above the
A_{cm}-point. Quenching is not an effective method and cooling slowly through the
A_1-transformation point destroys the characteristic structure. The Widmanstätten
structure is obtained in iron-nickel alloys by a long annealing above the Ac_3-point
and then quenching in water, and the formation of this structure in meteorites may
be due to a long exposure to a very high temp. and subsequent rapid cooling.

The **corrosion figures** of iron are cubical, although J. A. Ewing and W. Rosenhain [2] did not find it easy to obtain a good development of the geometrically etched
figures. The polygonal boundaries of the grains divide a polished and etched
surface into a number of areas—Fig. 137 ; each area represents a section of a
crystal grain. Each grain is built up of a large number of what T. Andrews called
secondary crystals, which have different orientations in different grains. This was
shown by J. E. Stead in the case of a steel with 4·5 per cent. of silicon. A fractured
ingot exhibits large crystals ; and by deeply etching a polished surface he obtained

a fine development of regularly oriented elements of which the crystal grains are built up—Fig. 14, **1**. 11, 4. As F. Osmond and W. C. Roberts-Austen express it, the general orientation of these secondary crystals remains constant in the area of each grain. Each grain has grown from a nucleus ; each grain is built up of similarly oriented parts, but the orientation changes from grain to grain. According to E. Heyn, and J. E. Stead, the corrosion figures of α-iron occurring on the (001)-face are squares parallel to the edges of the cube face. They were also observed by F. Osmond and G. Cartaud. Some of the corrosion figures or etched pits may appear like triangular wedges when the section cuts the crystal grain at certain angles. H. H. Potter and W. Sucksmith showed that the etch-planes of iron in a 10 per cent. alcoholic soln. of nitric acid are (100). C. A. Edwards and L. B. Pfeil observed that square etching pits are sometimes obtained with a diagonal of a large crystal in the direction of straining. C. F. Elam showed that when the cube face lies in the plane of the specimen, cubic etching pits are obtained in that and in no other position. J. E. Stead also observed that the different faces are attacked at different rates by dil. nitric acid. If a cube face of iron be pricked by a needle and then strongly etched by the acid, the hole, originally round, becomes square, because the sides of the hole are dissolved away at different rates. The sides of the square become parallel to the cube face. Possibly the ratio of the rate of solution of the (001)-face to that of the (011)-face is equal to the ratio of the length of one of the square sides of a right-angled triangle to the length of the hypotenuse, or about $1 : \sqrt{2}$. Sections of the same crystal of iron cut parallel to and at an angle to the cube face, when immersed in acid and connected by wires to a galvanometer, give an electric current, proving that the cube face is electro-negative to the other face. F. Osmond and G. Cartaud observed that the corrosion figures on the alleged β-iron are similar to those on α-iron ; and with γ-iron the lines of corrosion on the (001)-face are neither so continuous nor so soft as those on α-iron. Etching figures were obtained on manganese steel with a soln. of ammonium copper chloride, or by 10 per cent. nitric acid ; and on nickel-chromium steel, by a dil. hydrochloric acid soln. of ferric chloride. The etching is irregular, and even after deformation followed by annealing at 1300° shows the primary crystals very clearly. G. Tammann and co-workers, P. Oberhoffer and A. Heger, J. Czochralsky, V. N. Svechnikoff, J. C. W. Humfrey, and K. Harnecker and E. Rassow studied the corrosion figures of iron. H. S. George said that the etching figures on ferrite generally assumed to be pits are really pyramids standing in bas-relief.

F. Osmond and G. Cartaud observed that when a crystal of iron with a polished cube face is introduced in a bath of molten boric acid at 800°, needles of boric acid congealed at first on the polished face and preserved it provisionally from attack. Instead of the crystals arranging themselves in their natural order, they follow the direction of the system of iron crystals to form **synchronous crystallization figures.** F. Osmond and G. Cartaud also found that in a sample of crude manganese steel, little, hard nuclei have segregated to form **segregation figures.** The principal planes of segregation of γ-iron are the (111)-planes ; but secondary planes, (001), (011), (012), and (122), may exist. G. Rose, and G. Tschermak also observed that the rhabdite, $(Fe,Ni)_3P$, of some cubic meteoric irons is oriented in accord with the three cube faces ; and G. F. Kunz and E. Weinschenk noted that in one case the rhabdite is arranged parallel to the Neumann's bands.

According to H. O'Neil,[3] the cubical **cleavage** is perfect, and, according to O. W. Huntington, meteoric iron shows in addition octahedral and dodecahedral cleavages. This subject was discussed by A. Breithaupt, J. Cornuel, and H. von Dechen. F. Sauerwald and co-workers found that at low temp. cleavage takes place along the cubic planes of single crystals of iron. E. Sütter obtained **overgrowths** on tungsten. According to A. Sadebeck, there are **gliding planes** about the (211)-face—*vide infra*, slip-bands, discussed by O. Mügge, G. Tammann and A. Müller, W. Schwinning and E. Strobel, H. O'Neil, S. T. Konobejewsky, F. Wever, and J. A. Ewing and W. Rosenhain. H. Gough found that α-iron has three crystallographically different slip-planes, namely, (110), (112), and (123), whilst other metals usually have one kind of slip-plane. The **pressure figures**—*vide infra,* Neumann's bands—were discussed by G. Tammann and A. Müller, who found that if an indentation be made in a crystallite of a polished surface by means of a gramophone needle, the slip-lines are regularly oriented around the impression if there are no inclusions in the crystallites ; but in the presence of such impurities the slip-lines are curved around the inclusion. Stress figures were studied by W. Köster, and H. Jungbluth. F. Osmond and G. Cartaud reported the following results :

	a-iron	β-iron	γ-iron
Planes of translation parallel to (111) .	Difficult	Unknown	Easy
Folds	Dominant	Exclusive	Absent
Mechanical (twinning planes . . .	(111)	Unknown	(111)
twinning (planes of junction	(112)	Unknown	(111)
Annealing (twinning planes . . .	Unknown	Unknown	(111)
twinning (planes of junction . .	Unknown	Unknown	(111)
Face of maximum hardness . . .	(111)	—	(011)
Planes of easiest etching . . .	(001)	(001)	(001)

Both terrestrial and meteoric iron occur in solid masses which in some cases consist of one crystal individual and in other cases of several individuals. Some specimens have a scaly structure. **Twinning** occurs about the (111)-plane ; and in some cases there are lamellar intergrowths about the (211)-plane. This subject was discussed by A. Sadebeck, C. H. Mathewson and G. H. Edmunds, C. H. Mathewson, K. Harnecker and E. Rassow, L. W. McKeehan, G. I. Taylor and C. F. Elam, H. O'Neil, W. E. Hughes, O. Mügge, S. Tamura, V. N. Svetchnikoff, and G. E. Linck. Twinning produced during the solidification of the molten alloy is called **congenital twinning** by F. Osmond and G. Cartaud. In the plastic deformation of metals certain crystal units may form *macles* or twin crystals instead of slipping, owing to the crystal units rotating into a new position symmetrical with their initial orientation. J. A. Ewing said that the nature of twinning is perhaps most easily intelligible if the crystals are considered to be built up of layers of brickbats, and after one layer has been completed the next layer has all the bricks turned round through an angle of 180°. The result would be a twin formation. According to H. M. Howe, a twin or macle can be recognized in a polished section of a metal (i) by the presence of re-entering angles ; (ii) as a parallel-sided area within a given grain. It differs from the metal on both sides of it in the directions of the slip-bands, which zigzag on entering and leaving it. A twin can also be recognized (iii) in strength of the contrast between the treads and rises of the slip-bands ; (iv) in the tint to which it etches ; and (v) in the shape of its corrosion figures. Broad annealing twins are common in γ-iron and austenite, but they are rare in a-iron or ferrite. **Annealing twinning** does not occur on deformation but on annealing after deformation. Presumably the plastic deformation produces a stress in certain rows of crystal units which is not sufficient to cause them to rotate into the twinned position until the high temp. of annealing has made the metal mobile enough to allow the particles to move in obedience to the stress. Secondary or postgenital twinning is usually multiple or polysynthetic ; and it may be formed mechanically by the deformation, or it may be produced by annealing at a suitable temp. after deformation. According to W. Rosenhain and D. Ewen, the slight deformation produced by the saw used in cutting a section for microscopic examination, by blow-holes, or by polishing, may be sufficient to produce twinning when the metal is subsequently annealed. C. A. Edwards and H. C. H. Carpenter found that twinning occurs in a marked degree when steels are quenched, and they assume that martensite is twinned austenite—*vide supra* ; and C. A. Edwards discussed the formation of twinned crystals by direct mechanical strain. W. Rosenhain doubted the twinning of steel during quenching. According to J. E. Stead, the twinning observed in steel hardened by quenching from 1000° is always of the prismatic type, and the martensite of which the twins consist is oriented differently from the martensite grains in which they are embedded. H. C. H. Carpenter and

S. Tamura observed that annealing twins in metals are structures which are in a relatively stable state. C. A. Edwards and H. C. H. Carpenter assume that the twinning of crystals, which occurs when a steel is quenched, is attended by the production of amorphous metal. W. Rosenhain, J. E. Stead, and H. M. Howe did not accept this hypothesis. Most cases of artificial twinning are produced by annealing after deformation. Annealing twins are so rare in α-iron or ferrite that the few cases reported are suspected by some to be mechanical twins. H. M. Howe, E. Heyn, A. Baykoff, and O. Mügge said that α-iron may form twins ; and W. Rosenhain observed twinning with a steel with 1·94 per cent. of carbon and traces of manganese. F. C. Thompson and W. E. W. Millington attempted to produce annealing twins in ferrite without satisfactory results ; but V. N. Krivobok annealed electrolytic iron at 593° for 30 mins. and obtained a structure having the appearance of twinning, but which was shown to be a result of progressive crystallization along the deformation lamellæ. When annealed after being strained, unlike α-iron or ferrite, γ-iron and austenite readily form twins. This behaviour is probably connected with the arrangement of the atoms in the space-lattice. In general, twinning occurs readily with metals having the face-centred lattice—*e.g.* α-iron, and austenite—but twinning seldom, if ever, occurs with metals having the body-centred cubic lattice—*e.g.* ferrite or α-iron. S. Tamura observed what appeared to be a twin in specimens of wrought iron and mild steel ; only one twin-like crystal appeared within an individual crystal of ferrite, and the twin never exceeded 0·08 mm. in length. Hence it was doubted if the structures were true annealing twins, and he called them *pseudo-twins*. W. Rosenhain also observed a case where what appeared to be a twin was not really so, because slip-bands cross it without deflection. H. O'Neil, and G. I. Taylor and C. F. Elam discussed the distortion of iron crystals.

In 1848, J. G. Neumann observed that a sample of meteoric iron from Braunau, described by C. C. Beinert, showed in addition to the cubic cleavage planes other lines in the direction of the triakisoctahedral or (221)-face. The fine etching lines or bands were supposed to be produced by thin flakes in twin-formation, which were less attacked than the main mass. M. A. F. Prestel also observed these bands in artificial iron ; and they were called by A. Brezina **Neumann's bands,** or *Neumann's lines*, or *Neumann's lamellæ*, or *Neumann's figures*. They are narrow straight bands running in definite directions. They appear black under vertical illumination, and white when illuminated obliquely. They represent thin, mechanically twinned lamellæ or strata which are produced in iron, and some other metals, by deformation, and most readily by shock, impact, or explosion. If the suddenly applied dynamic stress has caused the rupture of the metal, the bands will generally be found near the seat of the fracture. M. Matweieff said that in polishing with emery, twinning occurs when the direction of rubbing coincides with a cleavage plane ; but A. M. Portevin and J. Durand consider that the lines so produced are not Neumann's lines, but they originate from the scratches of the polishing powder producing inter-strain in the layers beneath, and this interstrain is relieved by the etching. Deep etching makes them disappear. F. Osmond and G. Cartaud found that when a crystal of iron is cleaved, Neumann's bands appear in abundance on both sides of this cleavage face. The bands are more easily produced by shock at low temp. ; they are readily obtained by shock at ordinary temp., but they are not formed at a blue temper heat or a higher temp. ; and R. A. Hadfield found that they appear when iron is ruptured by tension at the temp. of liquid air. F. Robin was unable to produce them by moderate shock in wrought iron or very ductile steels except at −185°, yet he found them in 0·07 per cent. carbon steels which had been struck by a projectile moving at the rate of 380 metres per sec. In very brittle steels with 1 per cent. of phosphorus he produced the bands by shock at 20° up to 600°, but not at 700°. F. B. Foley obtained Neumann's bands as ridges and furrows when mild steel discs are subjected to the impulse from the action of explosives. T. E. Stanton and L. Bairstow found that the bands were developed by breaking ductile Swedish iron by a single severe blow or by a small number of moderate blows, but not by a large number of light blows.   The Neumann bands are more or less parallel and follow the orientation of the grains, so that the lines on a cleavage face are parallel either to the diagonals of the square or to the lines which join the angles as the centres of the opposite edges.   The appearance of Neumann's bands in a sample of wrought iron is given in Fig. 156 ($\times$150) from a photograph by H. C. H. Carpenter. Fig. 157 ($\times$250) represents Neumann's lamellæ with indentations assumed by F. Osmond and G. Cartaud to be connected with the formation of another system of lamellæ.   The specimen was etched with picric acid.   The bands are sometimes visible to the naked eye.   After polishing to low relief they may appear as slight depressions on the faces of the cube, or they may be in relief.   A. M. Portevin and J. Durand do not agree with M. Matweieff that the Neumann bands stand out in relief.   Alcoholic picric acid or dil. nitric acid (1 : 500) are convenient reagents. The lamellæ may have a uniform thickness, or they may be more or less indented. The subject was also discussed by F. B. Foley and co-workers, P. von Jeremejeff, H. von Jüptner, G. E. Linck, L. W. McKeehan, O. Mügge, H. O'Neil, F. Osmond and G. Cartaud, J. Seigle, G. Tammann and H. H. Meyer, etc.

According to M. Matweieff, Neumann's bands are always parallel to the Widman-

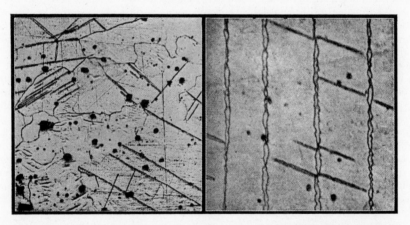

FIG. 156.—Neumann's Bands   FIG. 157.—Indented Neumann's Bands
     (H. C. H. Carpenter).   (F. Osmond and G. Cartaud).

stätten figures, but H. M. Howe said that they are only so in the majority of cases. F. Robin found that the Neumann bands develop normally to the direction of impact of a projectile, but H. M. Howe observed that in silicon steel, when formed by blows, the bands run preferentially 45° with the direction of impact.   The contacts between Neumann's bands and the enclosing metal are assumed to be planes of low cohesion, because F. Osmond and co-workers showed that fracture follows Neumann's bands.   J. E. Stead, and C. H. Desch showed that there is no evidence that Neumann's bands do not affect the hardness of the metal.   According to F. Berwerth and G. Tammann, Neumann's bands are obliterated on rapidly heating meteoric iron to 800°, and with a slower rise of temp. they disappear at a lower temp.   H. M. Howe said that they do not disappear at 800°, but they do so at 950°.   This means that at the A_3-arrest, when α-iron passes into γ-iron or austenite, the bands are affected, and that in the presence of nickel the transformation temp. is lowered from 900° to 800°.   According to F. Osmond and co-workers, the formation of a Neumann's band at an angle to one already formed may produce a displacement analogous to a fault.

The Neumann bands are oriented differently from the crystal, and are considered to be a fine form of twinning.   Both J. G. Neumann, and G. Tschermak consider that the Neumann bands are produced by a fluorspar twinning, where the octahedral face is the plane of twinning, and the ternary axis, the axis of twinning. There are four ternary axes ; and the 24 faces of the four sub-elements, identified with the planes of Neumann, are consequently parallel to the triakisoctahedra or (122)-faces. G. Rose could not decide whether the bands are parallel to the (122)- or (112)-faces. A. Sadebeck observed on the cleavage face of a dominant cube that the faces terminal to those of the bands, which make an angle of 45° with the sides of the square, make an angle of $144\frac{3}{4}°$ with the plane of the face of the cube. Supposing that these terminal faces are the cleavages of the sub-elements, he concluded that the plan of twinning was triakisoctahedral—the axis of twinning is then perpendicular to a face of the triakisoctahedron. Hence, in the case of the two elements twinned in accord with the law of association, when two faces of the twinned cubes cut one another in the direction of a common diagonal, the faces of one of these cubes is the face of the trapezohedron (112) of the other, and at the same time the octahedral face of the dominant cube is the rhombododecahedral face of the secondary cube. Like J. G. Neumann, and G. Tschermak, G. E. Linck assumed that the law of fluorspar twinning applies, but he considered that the junction faces should be (112) and not (122). The planes of junction then have the same rotation for the two unit elements twinned ; and (112)-planes are at the same time the planes of translation. He thus showed that Neumann's lines are due to lamellar twinning with gliding on the planes of the icositetrahedron (211). F. Osmond and G. Cartaud found that G. E. Linck's theory best fitted their observations on the bands parallel to the (112)-planes. S. W. J. Smith and co-workers showed that Neumann's bands are due to lamellar twinning, and that they are of secondary origin due to strain ; lamellar twinning by shearing is possible on the (211)-planes of a body-centred cubic lattice—e.g. kamacite, α-iron taenite, and γ-iron have a face-centred cubic lattice. H. C. H. Carpenter and S. Tamura have suggested that Neumann's bands of the kamacite or meteoric irons were produced by the shock of impact when the meteorite struck the earth's surface. C. H. Mathewson and G. H. Edmunds showed that X-radiograms indicate that the inner structure of the bands is that required to produce the observed twinning of the body-centred cubic lattice. The mechanism of the formation of Neumann's bands was discussed by W. E. W. Millington and F. C. Thompson. G. Tschermak thought that the bands are congenital twinned crystals, but F. Osmond and G. Cartaud said that if so, the twins should have the same magnitude as the crystals from which they are derived, since the development of the two twinned elements has been simultaneous ; on the contrary, the Neumann twins are extremely small, and they are frequently inflected and thrust aside by meeting lamellæ of another system. It is therefore inferred that the Neumann bands are mechanical twins in α-iron. This is in agreement with H. le Chatelier, A. M. Portevin and J. Durand, T. B. Focke, O. A. Derby, G. T. Prior, L. J. Spencer, F. Osmond and co-workers, etc. W. Rosenhain and J. McMinn added that the bands are sections through lamellæ or plates, and not thin rods ; they believe that they are not the nature of mechanical twins, but result from localized deformation brought about by the rapid application of a heavy stress. After slowly straining a sample of iron, and causing numerous slip-bands to ap ear, the subsequent abrupt application of a stress fails to produce Neumann's bands, but the additional deformation under impact takes place by a further slip of some of the slip-bands previously developed by the slow plastic strain.

F. Osmond and G. Cartaud continue : there are no known twins in β-iron due to mechanical twinning ; and with γ-iron a slight deformation produces effaceable lines of translation, but more severe deformation produces mechanical twins. The twinning which occurs when γ-iron in cast nickel-chromium steel is deformed cold and then annealed at 1300° is the same as the mechanical twinning with (111) as the plane of twinning and the plane of junction. The transformation of γ-iron into α-iron starts below 400° in the case of sudden quenching and causes considerable stresses. These stresses involve a more or less complete formation of an infinity of twins parallel in each grain to the four pairs of octahedral faces, hence the frequency of squares and equilateral triangular figures on a chance section. Hence the structure of martensite is peculiar to γ-iron, even though the iron is not for the most part present in the γ-state. Even after tempering, when all the iron has resumed the α-state, if the temp. and duration have been sufficiently controlled to prevent the reconstitution of equiaxial grains which characterize α-iron, the pseudomorphous α-iron may be retained on the martensite structure of γ-iron. The grains are in this way cut up by an infinite number of extremely thin lamellæ parallel to four different planes. The continuity of the (001)-cleavages is broken, and the natural fragility of α-iron due to these cleavages is evaded. Hence the parts played by quenching and tempering in the manufacture of different varieties of mild steels. The structure of martensite is that of the octahedral meteoric irons on a reduced scale. These irons are formed of comparatively thick lamellæ parallel to the four pairs of regular octahedral faces. The structure of γ-iron is preserved by the iron in the α-state, because in the presence of nickel the A_3-transformation is lowered to such an extent that the α-iron cannot resume its natural structure of equiaxial grains. The position is that of martensite tempered at a moderate temp. The α-iron remains crystallized on the axes of the γ-iron. G. E. Linck said that the

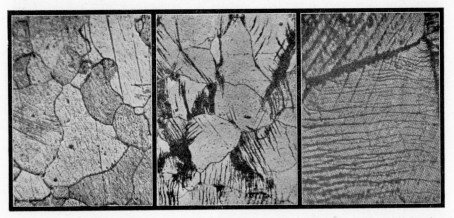

Fig. 158.—Slip-bands appear   Fig. 159.—Slip-bands multi-   Fig. 160.—Slip-bands (J. A.
   (J. A. Ewing and J. C. W.   ply (J. A. Ewing and   Ewing and J. C. W. Hum-
   Humfrey).   J. C. W. Humfrey).   frey)

octahedral meteoric irons are polysynthetic aggregates of four twinned cubic sub-elements with a dominant cube following the ordinary law : (111)-plane of twinning and plane of junction. F. Osmond and G. Cartaud found this in agreement with their observations on pressure figures ; and in accord with G. E. Linck's theory, a (001)-face of the dominant cube cuts the associated four twinned secondary cubes on the (122)-planes ; and every pressure-figure on such a face of the dominant cube is characteristic either of a (001)-plane or of four (122)-planes variously oriented. No other figure is formed.

The deformation of some metals produces lines on the polished faces of some crystals. In 1895, O. Mügge [4] showed that with ice, cyanite, etc., the lines are due to a translation and not twinning, and, in 1899, he made a similar observation with respect to metals. He called the markings *translation-banding—Translations-streifung*. The subject was discussed by E. Heyn in 1900. Independently, about the same time, J. A. Ewing and W. Rosenhain described a similar phenomenon, and they called the translation bands **slip-bands**. F. Osmond and G. Cartaud called them *lines of translation*, and F. Robin, *lignes de glissement*. According to J. A. Ewing and W. Rosenhain, if a metal be strained past its yielding-point, the elastic limit, the faces of the crystals show fine black lines (Fig. 158), which increase in number as the strain increases (Fig. 159). The lines first appear on certain crystals nearly transverse to the pull ; but as the strain increases, lines appear on other grains. Intersecting lines then make their appearance. Such a strained surface is illustrated by Fig. 159. As J. Muir has shown, a piece of iron strained beyond its elastic limit will recover its original elasticity if it be allowed to rest for some time or if it be heated to 100°. The dark lines do not disappear, but they do disappear if the surface be lightly polished in the usual manner. If, however, the deformation has been severe, as, for instance, in the vicinity of a fracture, when the surface is repolished and simply etched traces of the old slip-bands may reappear. Ordinary slip-bands produced by a moderate deformation are unlike bands produced by twinning and Neumann's bands, in that they disappear when the surface is repolished. The slip-bands are not actual cracks in the surface, but rather slips along cleavage planes or gliding planes of the crystals. These slips produce steps, so to speak, on the polished surface. W. Rosenhain observed that the smallest displacement is not more than $0·00002$ in., or of the order of wave-length of light, and when the deformation has not been severe, a displacement of $0·0001$ in. is observed. Other things being equal the greater the number of steps, the smaller their depth ; and with progressive deformation a given step breaks up into a number of steplets. The angle of the steps changes on passing from grain to grain. The uplift of the grains was demonstrated by W. Rosenhain, W. Rosenhain and J. C. W. Humfrey, G. I. Taylor and C. F. Elam, H. O'Neil, H. F. Moore and T. Ver, H. M. Howe and A. G. Levy, C. Frémont, P. Gaby-Aché, and F. Osmond and co-workers. The bands may appear in almost parallel lines, or the lines may deviate independently. J. C. W. Humfrey observed that with tension the first slip-bands are confined almost entirely to the central parts of the crystals, and spread only gradually towards the boundaries as the straining becomes severe ; whereas H. M. Howe found that with a compression the slip-bands start more frequently at or near a grain boundary. Those which propagate from one grain into a neighbouring one enter the new grain via the grain boundary. When the slip-bands pass through a zone of twinned crystals, they may be obliterated, or they may continue with a change of direction into the twin and so form a series of zigzag lines. The zigzagging of the slip-bands has been used to demonstrate the presence of twinned crystals. J. A. Ewing and W. Rosenhain, and F. Osmond and G. Cartaud agree that the slip-bands in ferrite follow octahedral directions ; and the former workers also observed them to follow cubic directions. H. C. H. Carpenter and C. A. Edwards showed that the twinning of the crystals of some metals can be produced by direct mechanical deformation ; and C. A. Edwards inferred that since mechanical deformation is not always accompanied by slipping alone, but may produce fine twinned lamellæ, it may be that what are now regarded as slip-bands are really extremely fine twinned lamellæ far beyond the resolving power of the ordinary microscope. According to J. E. Stead, the tensile strain in iron is the sum of two factors—internal and external slips. F. C. Thompson and W. E. W. Millington inferred that in a single crystal of iron, or in a coarse aggregate, the dodecahedron (110) is the first plane of movement under stress, and in this case the elastic limit is low. In normal iron or mild steel the elastic limit is reached when the cube or (100)-face movement is initiated. Under higher stresses some movement on the dodecahedral face accompanies the deformation on the cube face.

The production of slip-bands by repeated stresses was discussed by W. E. W. Millington and F. C. Thompson, J. A. Ewing and J. C. W. Humfrey, F. Rogers, W. Rosenhain, and T. E. Stanton and L. Bairstow. The former workers subjected Swedish iron with a breaking stress of 23·6 tons per sq. in. to a series of alternating stresses, 9 tons per sq. in., repeated 400 times per min. On examination it was found that fine slip-bands appeared in a few crystals after a few—say 5,000 per min.—reversals of stress, as shown in Figs. 158 to 160. With a greater number of reversals—say 40,000 per min.—the slip-bands increase in number, and those which first appeared broaden and develop into small cracks, as shown in Fig. 161.

If the specimen be repolished, so as to clear off the slip-bands, the cracks alone become visible, as at A, Fig. 161. The crack or flaw gradually creeps right across the specimen when the number of alternations is still further increased, as shown in Fig. 162. Finally the specimen breaks. Quoting J. A. Ewing and J. C. W. Humfrey's own words :

Whatever the selective action of the stress is due to, the experiments demonstrate that in repeated reversals of stress certain crystals are attacked, and yield by slipping, as in other cases of non-elastic strain. Then, as the reversals proceed, the surfaces upon which the slipping has occurred continue to be surfaces of weakness. The parts of the crystal lying on the two sides of each such surface continue to slide back and forth over one another. The effect of this repeated sliding or grinding is seen at the polished surface of the specimen by the production of a burr or rough and jagged irregular edge, broadening the slip-band, and suggesting the accumulation of débris. Within the crystal this repeated grinding tends to destroy the cohesion of the metal across the surface of the slip, and in certain cases this develops into a crack. Once the crack is formed, it quickly grows in a well-known manner, by tearing at the edges, in consequence of the concentration of stress which results from lack of continuity. The experiments throw light on the known fact that fracture, by repeated reversals or alternations of stress, resembles, in its abruptness, fracture resulting from creeping flaw, in the absence of local drawing-out, or other deformation of shape.

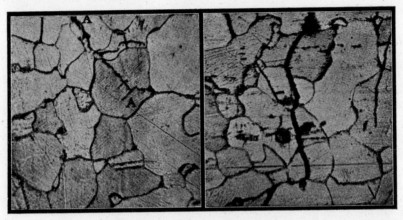

FIGS. 161 and 162.—The Passage of Slip-bands into Cracks. Polished Surfaces with Small Cracks and with a Large Crack respectively.

J. C. W. Humfrey [5] observed that the surface of the crystals of electrodeposited iron, after etching, showed peculiar wavy markings and numerous cavities filled with electrolyte. W. E. Hughes found that the lines of a fibrous deposit on a cylindrical cathode appear as wavy annular rings, but if the deposit is not of the fibrous type, the lines have no regular relation in passing from grain to grain, but on individual grains the herring-bone structure may appear. Increasing the depth of etching broadens the lines, and with high magnifications and deep etching the staircase structure may appear. The lines are common to deposits from chloride and sulphate soln. ; they are formed with high and low current densities ; the formation of the lines is not much affected by temp. ; the lines are found in deposits of various thicknesses—0·005 to 0·015 in. ; and the lines do not appear in deposits containing a large proportion of foreign matter—e.g. oxide, or, according to W. A. Macfadyen, carbon. J. A. Ewing and W. Rosenhain proved that slip-bands have been shown to be the result of a stress—mediately or immediately ; and E. J. Mills showed that when metals are deposited electrolytically, a press. is produced owing to the contraction of the deposit. He called the pressure *electrostriction*. Observations on electrostriction were made by E. Bouty, G. C. Stoney, H. Stäger, V. Kohlschütter and E. Vuilleumier, O. Faust, and F. Credner. E. J. Mills considered that the press. of electrostriction may amount to 109 atm., and E. Bouty, to 350 atm. According to W. E. Hughes, the lines in electrodeposited iron are slip-bands produced by electrostriction.

The path of the plastic deformation of a metal is internal, and when rupture occurs, the fracture is itself a path of deformation. When rupture does not occur, the internal path of deformation may show itself as a disturbance on the outer surface. With a slaty substance the path of deformation follows the parallel planes of lamination ; in a jointed substance, like brickwork, the path is along the joints ; in a fibrous substance, like wrought iron or wood it follows the fibre ; and in a crystalline substance, like mica or unburnt steel, it follows the crystal planes. Geometrical lines or lines of preferential deformation—**lines of flow**—produced by moderate deformations and occurring on polished surfaces were described by W. Lüders [6] in 1860, and by L. Hartmann in 1896. They are hence called **Lüders' lines** or *Hartmann's lines*. According to P. Breuil, in the bending of a plain bar

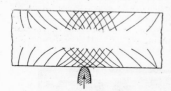

(Fig. 163) two systems of lines start under the knife-edge on opposite sides of the bar. The lines cut one another at the same angle ; the two groups of lines are symmetrical ; and they do not unite at first, but spread rapidly from one part to another of the bent surface, leaving a central space as a kind of neutral zone without lines. The lines then disappear, the neutral zone is deformed, and finally rupture occurs. L. Hartmann and A. Nadai showed that the lines form families of isogonal cycloids. E. Heyn said that Lüders' lines appear earlier than slip-bands when polished test-pieces are subjected to a tensile stress. The production of these lines was also discussed by P. Breuil, C. H. Carus-Wilson, C. Chappell, C. Frémont, G. H. Gulliver, E. Heyn, H. M. Howe, J. E. Howers, J. B. Johnson, W. Mason, M. Matweieff, P. Oberhoffer and M. Toussaint, F. Osmond and co-workers, A. M. Portevin and J. Durand, H. S. Rawdon, F. Robin, J. Seigle, and S. W. J. Smith and co-workers. B. C. Laws and A. O. Allen studied the lines of maximum stresses in steel plates. C. Chappell suggested a connection between Lüders' lines and brittleness ; H. Fowler studied the hardness in the vicinity of Lüders' lines.

FIG. 163.—Lüders' or Hartmann's Lines produced in the Deformation of a Plain Iron Bar.

It has just been shown that the plastic strain or deformation of metals is not a homogeneous shear such as is the case with a viscous liquid, but is rather the resultant effect of a limited number of separate slips. When a stress is great enough to cause a crystalline plate to rupture, the resistance to shearing offered by the cohesion of the crystalline particles is not greater before than after the slip has taken place. Indeed, the cohesion between the particles seems to increase progressively as the slip or deformation increases in magnitude. Once slip has occurred the deformation does not continue when the deforming stress is again applied ; a greater stress is needed to produce further deformation. The cohesion of the deformed metal increases during the test. The explanation of the phenomenon offered by G. T. Beilby [7] involves the assumption that iron, and other metals can exist in an amorphous state—**amorphous iron.** The term "amorphous" is contrasted with the term " crystalline " ; and it is intended to connote a state in which the orientation or regular, orderly arrangement of the constituent parts characteristic of the crystalline state is absent. An ordinary liquid is in the amorphous state. When a liquid is cooled without undergoing any critical change or crystallization, it forms an undercooled liquid, and when the viscosity is great enough, an amorphous solid. Ordinary glass is an example of a congealed liquid or an amorphous solid—*vide* 1. 9, 6. G. T. Beilby said :

In the operation of polishing, a true skin is formed over the polished surface. This skin gives unmistakable signs that it has passed through a state in which it must have possessed the perfect mobility of a liquid. In its final state it possesses distinctive qualities which differentiate its substance very clearly from that of the unaltered substance beneath. It is, for instance, much harder, and, even when formed on the surface of a crystal on which the hardness varies in different directions, its hardness is the same in all directions. The discovery that layers of a solid many hundreds of molecules in thickness can have the mobility of the liquid state conferred upon them by purely mechanical movement opens up a new field of inquiry into the internal structure of metals which have been hardened by cold-working. A theory of hard and soft states is suggested in which hardening results from the formation at all the surfaces of slip or shear of mobile layers similar to those produced on the outer surface of polishing. These layers retain their mobility for a very brief period, and then solidify in a vitreous amorphous state, thus forming a cementing material at all surfaces of slip or shear throughout the mass. The term " vitreous " here employed narrows the field to amorphous substances which in some degree resemble the glass-like form assumed by the silicates when they are solidified from the molten state. . . . The transient existence of the mobile phase makes slip and movement among the lamellæ possible and easy, and it is the sudden resolidification of these mobile layers into a non-crystalline, vitreous condition which arrests deformation under a given deforming stress. The original surfaces of any slip are now cemented together by the more rigid material, and new surfaces of slip are developed only by higher stresses. The plasticity of the crystalline state is thus gradually used up, and the aggregate as a whole becomes more and more rigid. When this has reached a certain stage, further increase of stress leads, not to plasticity flow, but to disruption.

The general effect of mechanical cold-work is to lower the electrical conductivity (A. Michels) ; to change the magnetic susceptibility (K. Honda and Y. Shimizu) ; to distort the lattice structure (A. F. Joffé) ; to modify the sliding friction (R. B. Dow) ; to modify the contact potential (W. Ende) ; to modify the photoelectric current (R. F. Hanstock) ; to modify the triboelectric effect (R. F. Hanstock) ; etc.

F. Osmond pointed out that in the **crystal boundaries** between adjacent crystals, differently oriented, there must be many pockets so small that no crystal unit can fit into them.

When two grains possessing different orientation touch one another, their respective reticular systems cannot interlock, and there are strong reasons for the belief that there exists between the two grains a sort of amorphous envelope, the average thickness of which is of the same order as that of the crystalline molecule. If it be assumed, as it is admissible to do, that in the case of hardened steel the average diameter of the actual grain—invisible under the microscope—is also of the same order of size, the idea might be entertained that in hardened steel the iron might be amorphous.

G. D. Bengough suggested that the reason why rupture usually avoids the crystal boundaries is because these are stronger than the crystals themselves, since they are filled with an **intercrystalline cement** of amorphous metal. J. E. Sears also explained some of the anomalies in the elastic properties of metals by supposing them to consist of crystalline grains held together by an amorphous cement. The idea was developed by W. Rosenhain and D. Ewen. W. Rosenhain assumes that the intercrystalline cement is amorphous iron like G. T. Beilby's strong, hard, and brittle amorphous iron. The latter is produced by the severe straining of the crystalline metal, the former, by the solidification of liquid layers enclosed in such narrow spaces that they cannot assume a crystalline orientation. Some circumstantial evidence is quoted in support of the hypothesis : (i) the widening of the grain boundaries by etching ; (ii) the greater loss by volatilization when fine-grained metals are heated in vacuo than when coarse-grained metals are similarly treated ; (iii) the embrittling of silver by prolonged heating in vacuo is attributed to the loss of intercrystalline cohesion by the volatilization of the bond ; and (iv) the intergranular fracture which occurs when metals under stress are heated just below their m.p. It is assumed that the solution and vapour pressures of the amorphous material then are those of the crystalline metal. H. M. Howe considers this evidence extremely weak, because the facts quoted can be explained in other ways. W. Rosenhain and J. C. W. Humfrey observed (v) that as the temp. rises and the rate of straining decreases, rupture in ferrite tends to become intergranular rather than intercrystalline. The amorphous intercrystalline cement, behaving like ordinary undercooled solids, becomes a viscous liquid as the temp. is raised, and thus offers less and less resistance, until it yields to the stress. The brittleness which accompanies coarseness of grain is explained by assuming that slip occurs simultaneously along the whole of any one plane, and this creates a weak mobile state along the whole of that plane; so that with coarse crystals, where the length and breadth of each plane is relatively large, the metal becomes relatively weak and rupture occurs. Thus, F. Osmond and co-workers found that a chisel-blow along one of the cubic cleavages of an isolated crystal of ferrite split it easily without deformation, whereas a similar blow at an angle of 45° to the cleavage plane cut the crystal without breaking it. F. C. Thompson developed a theory that the intercrystalline strength will be greatest when the intercrystalline film is thinnest.

G. T. Beilby showed that amorphous iron is probably brittle and hard like other vitreous, amorphous substances—e.g. glass. R. J. Anderson and J. T. Norton failed to find X-ray evidence of an amorphous phase; they said that the polished surfaces of metals give a radiogram of the same pattern as severely cold-worked metals, and inferred that the surface layer consists of innumerable submicroscopic crystalline fragments, and not of amorphous metal, which should give black bands in the diffraction pattern. L. Cammen suggested that the crystals do not have an intermediate amorphous cement, but rather a matrix of extremely fine crystalline matter in which are embedded visible crystals, presumably of the same composition as the matrix. F. B. Foley also said that the growth of crystals in the freezing metal takes place atom by atom, and not cube by cube. This is taken to mean that no amorphous cement exists at the grain boundaries. The intercrystalline fracture at high temp. is due to a weakness of the structure of the boundaries, for the atoms at the boundaries are only loosely held, having become detached from the lattice of the crystal, and are consumed in the process of crystal growth, not having finally settled into the lattice of the growing crystals. When ferrite separates from austenite, the ferrite is not formed within the crystals and rejected at the boundaries; rather does the ferrite form at the boundaries of the austenite crystals. Atoms at the crystal boundaries are freer to assume new orientations; they possess energy in excess of that necessary for maintaining their positions in the lattice. The subject was discussed by F. Hargreaves and R. J. Hills.

C. A. Edwards and H. C. H. Carpenter assumed that when steel is quenched, a pronounced twinning of the crystals occurs, and that the hard, amorphous, vitreous layers, formed on the gliding planes during the internal slipping or twinning, are retained by quick cooling. This hypothesis brings the hardening by cold-working and hardening by quenching into close relationship; both are due to the formation of amorphous layers by intercrystalline movement or slip, although the agencies producing the slipping are different. This is in agreement with F. Osmond's statement: If it be assumed, as is permissible, that in the case of hardened steel the average diameter of the actual grain, invisible under the microscope, is of the same size as the crystal molecule, the idea might be entertained that in hardened steel the iron might be amorphous. In order to agree with the observation that all carbon steels are magnetic, no matter how quickly they are quenched from a high temp., it is supposed that the amorphous layers—decrystallized γ-iron—are magnetic. According to W. E. Ruder, the intergranular cement in iron containing 4 per cent. silicon may be completely removed by making the alloy an anode in a soln. of potassium dichromate; or by heating the alloy in hydrogen at a temp. just below the m.p.

W. D. Bancroft objected to the amorphous film theory that its advocates have taken whatever properties they needed and have assigned them arbitrarily to the hypothetical amorphous phase. G. Tammann suggested that the amorphous film theory violates the phase rule—1. 9, 5—which shows that the liquid of a pure metal can exist in contact and in equilibrium with its own solid only at one definite temp.—press. constant. W. Rosenhain, however, showed that the deductions from the phase rule make no stipulation as to the time necessary for an unstable phase to pass into a stable phase. The phase rule gives no indication whether an indefinitely large number of years or a movement is needed for the change. G. Tammann, and M. Hasselblatt also showed that since the crystalline state is more stable than the amorphous or undercooled liquid state, the amorphous phase should tend to become crystalline and not conversely. This objection does not allow for internal pressure. Again, the amorphous phase is bulkier than the crystalline phase, so that the effect of press. should convert the amorphous into the crystalline solid—*vide* **1**. 9, 4—but only when the liquid phase is free to escape—*vide* **1**. 13, 18. E. Heyn assumes that the contact films differ from the undeformed metal, but are not amorphous. The difference is due to surface tension. The total surface tension of the films with a fine-grained metal is greater than when the metal is coarse-grained; as a result the small grains have a tendency to unite and become large; while deformed grains have a tendency to become equiaxial, and, as observed in other cases by O. Lehmann, to combine into a single homogeneous crystal. The variation in surface energy is supposed to explain the changes in physical properties which are produced by plastic deformation; but H. M. Howe said that it does not explain the phenomena attending slip—*vide supra*. The subject was discussed by J. H. Andrew.

G. Tammann inferred that the hardening, etc., during plastic deformation is due to the crystal grains being subdivided into an increasing number of polyhedra or lamellæ through the formation of gliding planes, and without any destruction of the true crystalline arrangement. The increase in the energy on deformation, observed by G. Tammann, and H. Schottky, is absorbed owing to the formation of so many new boundary surfaces, and this reappears in the hardened metal as an increased soln. press., etc. Hence, a worked metal differs from an unworked metal in having its crystals definitely oriented owing to the development of cleavage lamellæ and twinning. C. Chappell modified the hypothesis in some directions. He assumed that deformation does not in the first instance destroy the continuity of the molecules across the cleavage or gliding planes, but produces between them at those points a condition of high tension. By further deformation along one of these planes the tension becomes greater than molecular cohesion, the molecular continuity is broken, and the deformation along this plane becomes permanent. By the simple grinding together of these two surfaces, by further deformation, a layer of débris is produced between them, as would be the case if two stones were rubbed together. This layer of powdered ferrite retains its crystalline character, and can be regarded as being in a *metacrystalline state* likely to possess a very low crystallization temp. It is probable that the parallel markings observed in severely deformed ferrite crystals at 350° to 500° are the result of the recrystallization of this material and of the severely deformed adjacent parts. The decrease in density which accompanies plastic deformation is due to the crystalline débris along the cleavage planes occupying a greater vol. in its irregularly arranged condition than when fitted accurately together in the crystalline mass, just as an irregular heap of bricks occupies a greater volume than when the bricks are built into a wall. C. Chappell's metacrystalline state recalls W. Guertler's assumption that the intercrystalline matter is in a *paracrystalline state,* or *weniger stabil orientiert.* According to J. C. W. Humfrey, the slow contraction of tensile test-pieces on releasing the stress after plastic deformation and the decreased elastic limit in compression after plastic tensile-strain are due to the elastic skin enclosing the crystals. According to C. Chappell, the slow contraction after plastic tensile strain is simply due to the condition of high molecular tension existing on the planes of slip, in consequence of which the crystals seek to return to their previous shape, like springs in tension. Rise of temp., by decreasing the frictional resistance of the material, accelerates this contraction. The restoration of elastic properties by heating at very low temp., as also the disappearance of slip-bands on heating, may be attributed to this same effect, whereby rise of temp. facilitates the release of the condition of internal molecular tension, thus restoring normal conditions within the crystals. It is also evident that the molecular tension produced on the cleavage planes by plastic tensile strain will assist a force subsequently applied in the opposite direction, thus aiding compression after previously applied tension.

There are other hypotheses as to the nature of the intercrystalline boundaries, which experiment has shown to be the seat of cohesive forces so powerful that fracture, as a rule, runs across the grains themselves rather than follow the intercrystalline boundaries—*vide infra*, tensile strength. F. Hargreaves and R. J. Hills postulated the existence of a transition zone between two orientations, so that the intercrystalline phase is not amorphous material, because for the same two orientations and the same relative position of the boundary, the same pattern of atomic arrangement is always found on the unstressed metal. J. O. Arnold referred to the interlocking of the crystals across their boundaries, presumably due to the dendritic interlacing of adjoining crystals. W. Rosenhain also suggested that the strength of intercrystalline cohesion is partly due to the interlocking of the skeleton arms which the crystals develop during their first formation. Owing to the dendritic branching of the crystals at the boundaries, the boundaries may be more or less jagged or saw-toothed. The intercrystalline boundaries are thus considered to be regions of mixed orientation, which offer greater resistance to slip than regions of uniform orientation. Some branches of the dendrites follow the orientation of a grain on the right and others the orientation of the grain on the left of the boundary. The intercrystalline boundaries form a network of cells upon which the true resistance of the metal depends. Plastic deformation occurs when the cell-walls begin to give way and in doing so they carry with them the less resisting masses of the crystalline grains. This agrees with the observed relations between the slip-bands and the intercrystalline boundaries. F. Osmond and co-workers also observed the frequent doubling of the intercrystalline boundaries of the crystal grains of ferrite in purified iron.

W. Barlow suggested that surrounding each growing crystal there is a layer of molecules which, although not held together in the rigid solid condition, yet are tending to a regular formation such as exists within the crystal itself. According to J. C. W. Humfrey, when two crystals are gradually growing towards one another, each will endeavour to marshal the surrounding molecules of the liquid to its own orientation. If equilibrium could be established before the temp. fell below that at which crystallization becomes difficult, there would be formed between two crystals a layer of matter in which the molecules are so arranged as to pass by small displacements from the orientation of one crystal to that of the other. If the cooling be rapid enough, before the state of equilibrium can be attained the layer of liquid between two crystals would become so viscous as to remain in the amorphous, undercooled state. In such a case the amorphous layer would be connected to each crystal by molecules whose distribution gradually approached that of the crystal nearest them. Subsequent annealing would tend to reduce the layer of undercooled liquid and bring about the gradual and continuous change representing complete equilibrium. When the system is in equilibrium, in any particular plane of the region between two crystals in which displacement from the orientation of either occurs, the thickness will depend on the relative difference of orientations in this plane. The greater the difference of orientation, the more adjustment is required and the greater thickness necessary to complete it. No displacement of either orientation will be required in passing from one crystal to an adjacent crystal similarly oriented ; and if this plane be also one of gliding or cleavage, these properties should be continuous between two crystals. This is in agreement with the microscopic study of strain phenomena. J. C. W. Humfrey offered as evidence of the existence of some such boundary the curvature and forking of slip-bands in ferrite as they approach the boundaries. This curvature, however, was regarded by H. M. Howe as facilitating the propagation of slip along the slip-planes of the grain on the other side of the boundaries.

H. M. Howe was unable to confirm the existence of a region of mixed orientation. He considered that surface tension opposes the crystallizing force, thus tending to straighten and smooth the grain boundaries and efface the initial dendritic interlocking. It is also difficult to suppose that such a state of things at the boundaries of the grains can survive the obliteration and regeneration of grain boundaries which must occur during the various transformations which steel undergoes during the mechanical kneading which attends rolling, forging, wire-drawing, and annealing. Grain-growth would also tend to efface the interlocking or mixed orientation assumed to exist between adjoining crystals. H. M. Howe does not consider that the theories of interlocking and of mixed orientation explain adequately how deformation and rupture avoid the grain boundaries and preferentially cross the grains themselves. Nor does he consider that the amorphous cement filling can explain this, because an intergranular layer at once discontinuous and approximately of molecular thickness is not likely to offer sufficient resistance to a shearing stress. He prefers to modify the amorphous film theory by assuming that there is a progressive accumulation of amorphous metal about the crystal boundaries owing to the breaking up of crystalline metal caused by the discontinuity of the slip-planes in adjoining crystal grains. The generation of the amorphous metal in the disturbed region would add to the discontinuity in opposing the propagation of slip past the grain boundaries. Once such a layer is formed along the grain boundaries, any further slip has to overcome (i) the resistance which this amorphous material opposes to slip because of the absence of slip-planes, planes of low cohesion ; and (ii) any increase in the strength of the grain boundary regions.

The **grain-size of the crystals** of metals is affected by the rate of cooling during solidification, so that a large casting will have an average grain-size different from that of a small casting cast at the same temp., because of the different rates of cooling. As a rule, with slow solidification, crystallization proceeds from a relatively small number of nuclei, and the final grain-size will be relatively large ; on the other hand, with rapid solidification, crystallization proceeds from a relatively large number of centres, and the final grain-size is relatively small. If metals be exposed to a high enough temp., there is a tendency for the crystal grains to enlarge, but it is doubtful if the grain-growth will take place below the m.p. unless the metal has been previously strained, or unless, as in the case of iron, allotropic transformations occur. When the deformed metals are heated—annealed—a rearrangement of the crystals—a **recrystallization** or **grain-growth**—occurs, tending to remove the strain of distortion produced by cold-working and to produce equiaxial grains. G. Tammann and W. Crone observed that quenched electrolytic iron had 3·4 crystals per sq. mm., and slowly cooled iron, 1·8 crystals per sq. mm.—the numbers of crystals after recrystallization at 880° were respectively 163·6 and 107·7 per sq. mm. Z. Jeffries and R. S. Archer [8] gave 450° for the temp. of recrystallization ; and the theory of the subject was discussed by J. A. M. van Liempt. H. Altreter supposed that grain-growth and recrystallization are the result of thermodynamic instability, and that the energy changes which accompany cold-working are partly reversible and partly irreversible. According to Z. Jeffries and R. S. Archer, grain-growth in solids can occur with (i) worked metals, (ii) compressed powders, (iii) electrodeposited metals, (iv) when a metal changes its allotropic form, and (v) when a new phase is formed in the solid state. According to A. Sauveur, the dimensions of the grains so produced will be dependent on (i) the nature of the metal, (ii) the amount of deformation or mechanical work, (iii) the size of the distorted grains, (iv) the temp. of deformation, (v) the annealing temp., (vi) the duration of the annealing, and (vii) the rate of cooling from the initial temp.

H. M. Howe called the temp. at which the recrystallization or grain-growth begins the *germinative temperature* ; the range of temp. below the germinative temp., the *inert range* ; and the range of temp. above the germinating temp., the *growth range*. According to Z. Jeffries and R. S. Archer, certain conditions of non-uniformity—grain-size contrast, strain gradients, concentration gradients, and obstruction gradients—may result in the formation of abnormally large grains. The presence of foreign matter or of a second phase introduces mechanical obstruction to grain-growth ; and resistance increases as the proportion of foreign matter or other phase increases, and as the grain-size diminishes.

The presence of a certain amount of obstructive matter may promote germination. The higher the germinative temp., the coarser the grain-size and the quicker the growth. The more rapid the rise of temp. through the germinative temp. range, within certain limits, the finer the grain-size.

Z. Jeffries and R. S. Archer showed that the grain-size in any given metal after complete recrystallization is normally smaller the lower the recrystallization temp. Above this temp. the grain-size is normally greater the higher the temp. and the longer the exposure. The higher the temp., the more rapid the grain-growth. At a temp. near the m.p. a few seconds may suffice to produce grains which do not change on a prolonged exposure. They said :

The grain-size in cast metals is usually small in proportion to the rate of solidification. In such metals as undergo no phase change in the solid state grain-size cannot be appreciably

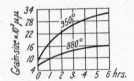

FIG. 164.—The Effect of Time on the Grain-size.

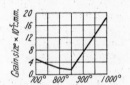

FIG. 165.—The Effect of Temperature on the Grain-size.

changed by heating below the melting point. Grain-growth in the solid state may occur under various conditions, as when iron changes its allotropic form, and in alloys when a new phase is formed in the solid state. Deformation, smallness of grain, purity, low temp. deformation, and long heating lower recrystallization temp. Grain-size after complete recrystallization is normally smaller the lower the recrystallization temp. High temp. increases grain-size. The higher the temp. the more rapid the grain-growth. The formation of abnormally large grains (germination) is sometimes due to non-uniform conditions. Such conditions are grain-size contrast and strain, temp., concentration and obstruction " gradients." Presence of foreign matter or of a second phase introduces mechanical obstruction to grain-growth. A certain amount of obstruction promotes germination. The higher the germinative temp., the larger grains and the more rapid their growth. The more rapid the heating through the germinative temp. range (within limits), the finer the grain-size.

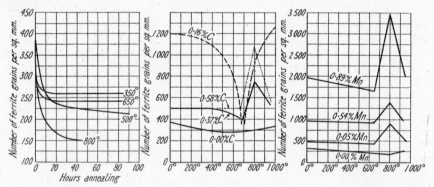

FIG. 166.—Grain-growth in Armco Iron.

FIG. 167.—The Effect of Carbon on the Grain-size.

FIG. 168.—The Effect of Manganese on the Grain-size.

P. Oberhoffer's curves for the effect of time on the grain-size of ferrite are shown in Fig. 164 ; and his curve for the effect of temp. on the grain-size of cast steel with 0·27 per cent. of carbon, in Fig. 165. Observations on this subject were also made by L. E. Benson and F. C. Thompson, some of whose results are indicated in Figs. 166, 167, and 168. The ordinates in all cases represent the number of grains per sq. mm., so that the greater the number the smaller the grain-size. Fig. 166 shows the effect with armco iron ; the results with pearlite are similar. Fig. 167 shows the influence of carbon on the grain-size after annealing for an hour; and Fig. 168, the effect of manganese on the grain-size after annealing for an hour. R. Johnson found that the temp. at which recrystallization begins and ends are higher the higher the proportion of carbon. Observations on grain-growth were made by C. Agte and K. Becker, R. J. Anderson, A. E. van Arkel and co-workers, J. O. Arnold, E. J. Ball, P. Beck and M. Polanyi, A. A. Blue, A. A. Botschwar, H. Brandes, J. A. Brinell, E. R. Brophy and R. H. Harrington, Y. Chu-Phay, W. J. Crook, J. Czochralsky, K. Daeves, F. S. Dodd, C. A. Edwards and L. B. Pfeil, H. Fay and S. Badlam, P. Fischer, W. Fraenkel, J. R. Freeman, H. Giersberg, L. Grenet, D. Hanson, W. Heike and F. Westerholt, E. Heyn, V. E. Hillman and F. L. Coonan, O. F. Hudson, H. von Jüptner, F. Körber, V. N. Krivobok, R. Kühnel, J. A. M. van Liempt, H. Lüpfert, C. H. Mathewson and A. Philips, R. G. Morse, C. H. Risdale, F. Sauerwald, A. Sauveur, E. Scheil, W. Schneider and E. Houdremont, H. Schottky and H. Jungbluth, M. von Schwarz, W. Tafel and co-workers, G. Tammann and W. Salze, D. Tschernoff, G. W. Walker, H. C. Wang, etc. In a general way, with eutectoidal steels which have been previously deformed or strained, the higher the temp. above the Ac_1-arrest from

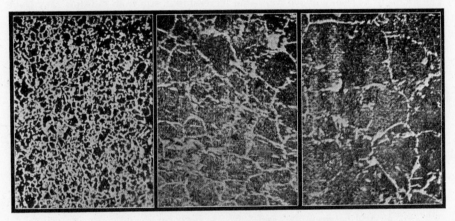

FIGS. 169, 170, and 171.—The Grain-size acquired at 966°, 1212°, and 1339° (W. Campbell).

which the steel cools, the larger the size of the crystal grains; while if the Ac_1-arrest is the highest temp. attained, then the steel will have the finest grain structure it can assume. H. M. Howe and A. Sauveur, indeed, found empirically for one sample that if θ denotes the highest temp. in the annealing furnace, and A the average area of the grain in sq. mm., $\theta=680+281250A$. The results of W. Campbell's observations on the grain-size at 966°, 1212°, and 1339° are illustrated by Figs. 169 to 171 ($\times$33). If hardened or unhardened eutectoidal or hypereutectoidal steels be heated above the Ac_1-arrest, all previous crystalline structure is obliterated and replaced by the finest possible structure the metal can assume at the given temp. The breaking up and obliteration of the old structure may not be complete with some hypoeutectoidal steels. According to K. Daeves, iron containing a small proportion of carbon acquires a new structure when heated to 1125°, owing to the separation of ferrite and pearlite in certain directions which are oriented crystallographically. J. E. Stead studied the recrystallization of mechanically deformed iron and steel, and found:

In practically carbonless iron, and steels of fine grain produced by forging, the grains increase slowly in size at 500°, and more rapidly between 600° and 750°; and it is possible by heating for a few hours at about 700° to develop granular masses of exceeding coarseness. When iron is made coarsely granular, by long heating at a dull red-heat, and heated between 750° and 870°, the structure is as a rule not altered to any material extent, but as soon as the temp. rises to about 900°, the granules again become small. . . . Elongated crystals of ferrite, produced by severe cold deformation, usually split up on recrystallization into smaller crystals whose diameter in each direction corresponds approximately with the breadth of the original elongated ones.

H. C. H. Carpenter and C. F. Elam concluded that in the recrystallization of metals : (i) growth may take place either by a large crystal growing into a smaller one or conversely, *i.e.* growth is independent of the size of crystals—*vide* **1.** 10, 1 ; (ii) the relative orientation of the crystal being grown into and that which is growing does not affect the growth ; (iii) a crystal being invaded by one crystal may at the same time grow at the expense of another ; (iv) the rate of growth is not constant for a given time at any particular temp. ; and (v) the change of orientation is accompanied by a difference of level of the surface, which is the boundary marking observed.

A. Pomp and S. Weichert noticed that the recrystallization of cold-rolled, low-carbon steel was first noticeable at 600°. The results of J. E. Stead on hypo-eutectoidal steel are represented graphically in Fig. 172, along with H. M. Howe's observations on a eutectoidal steel. The dotted continuation of A indicates that the grains of austenite above Ac_1 begin increasing in size from the time they begin to form as soon as the temp. rises above Ac_1. In both steels refining occurs on passing the Ac_1-arrest, but with low-carbon steel there is a coarsening and consequent embrittling as the temp. approaches the Ac_1-arrest. The brittleness caused by over-heating high-carbon steel, and that due to the long exposure of

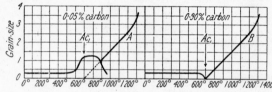

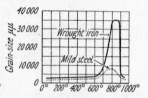

FIG. 172.—The Effect of Temperature on the Grain-size of Steel.

FIG. 173.—The Effect of Temperature on the Grain-size of Iron.

low-carbon steel between 500° and 700°, are both cured and the metal refined by heating it beyond the Ac_1-arrest. As the temp. approaches the Ac_3-arrest, the free ferrite becomes progressively less owing to its absorption by the austenite, but its position does not appear to change, for its grain-size does not alter. On passing the Ac_3-arrest, however, the absorption of the ferrite is completed, and the coarse granulation and brittleness also disappear. The different behaviour of the two steels as the temp. approaches 700° is connected with their constitution. The high-carbon steel consists of a ground mass of pearlite penetrated by a thin network of ferrite, whereas with the low-carbon steel the pearlite is present in scattered masses in an excess of ferrite. Hence, the coarsening of the grain of the low-carbon steel as the temp. approaches 700° is due to a coarsening of ferrite rather than to a change in the pearlite. The observations of C. Chappell on the recrystallization of Swedish wrought iron and mild steel at different temp. are summarized in Fig. 173. The average grain-sizes of the two materials are similar at about 650°, but at 850° the crystal grains of wrought iron have six times the average diameter of those of the mild steel.

H. Lüpfert studied the effect of time, annealing temperature, and speed of cooling on the grain-size of steel with 0·196 per cent. of carbon, and the results are summarized in Figs. 174 and 175. Similarly with the results on chrome-nickel steel, containing 4·0 per cent. nickel, 0·7 per cent. chromium, and 0·1 per cent. carbon, which are summarized in Figs. 176 and 177. B. Jonsen found that with steels containing 0·60 to 1·15 per cent. of carbon, the temp. at which crystallization begins and ends are the higher the higher is the proportion of carbon. The optimum temp.

lies between 650° and the Ac_1-point. W. Crone, and F. Wever and N. Engel also studied the effect of the rate of cooling on the structure of the carbon-iron alloys.

According to P. Goerens, the ferrite in cold-drawn iron and steel recrystallizes at temp. between 520° and 580° ; the elongated ferrite crystals are then replaced by ordinary polyhedral or allotrimorphic shapes. H. O'Neil found that recrystallization commences at the grain boundaries and at etch bands where the metal is

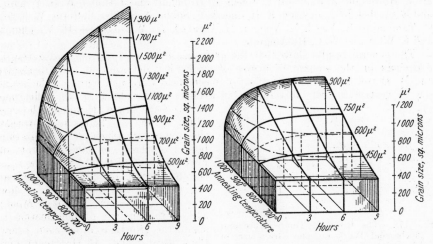

FIG. 174.—The Effect of Annealing Temperature and Time on the Grain-size of Steel cooled in the Kiln.

FIG. 175.—The Effect of Annealing Temperature and Time on the Grain-size of Steel cooled in Air.

hardest. H. le Chatelier, and G. Charpy showed that in the annealing of a metal which had suffered a local deformation, abnormally large crystals developed, but only in the deformed area. A. Sauveur also observed that this remarkable growth of crystals takes place only when the iron has been subjected to an intermediate degree of deformation, such that when stressed beyond this critical range no growth takes place on annealing at 650°. F. Robin found that in very soft steel which had been

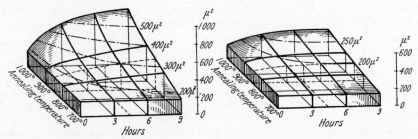

FIG. 176.—The Effect of Annealing Temperature and Time on the Grain-size of Chrome-Nickel Steel cooled in Kiln.

FIG. 177.—The Effect of Annealing Temperature and Time on the Grain-size of Chrome-Nickel Steel cooled in Air.

deformed in the cold the crystal size reaches a maximum between 700° and 750°, and decreases slightly with a rise of temp. to 900°, where the gross crystallization is destroyed.

Observations on the recrystallization of cold-worked and other forms of iron and other metals were also made by R. P. Ahrell, H. Allen, A. E. van Arkel, J. Bauschinger, P. Beck, R. Becker, J. D. Brunton, G. Charpy, E. O. Courtman, K. Daeves, U. Dehlinger, A. N. Dovrovidoff and Y. V. Grdina, O. W. Ellis,

J. R. Freeman, O. Fuchs, N. P. Goss, L. Grenet, H. Hanemann, H. Hanemann and C. Lind, E. Heyn, E. Heyn and O. Bauer, H. M. Howe, A. Joisten, T. von Karman, O. von Keil, G. L. Kelley, F. Körber, P. Longmuir, H. Lüpfert, D. J. McAdam, G. Masing, E. Maurer, K. Neu, P. Oberhoffer and co-workers, A. Pomp, A. M. Portevin, E. Preuss, H. E. Publow and co-workers, H. Puppe, E. Rasch, O. Reinhold, F. Riedel, W. Rosenhain, M. Rudeloff, W. E. Ruder, K. Rummel, A. Sauveur, H. M. Howe and A. Sauveur, E. Scheil, E. H. Schulz and J. Göbel, W. Schwinning and E. Strobel, K. A. Seyrich, R. H. Sherry, C. Sobbe, A. Stadler, C. Sutor, W. Tafel, G. Tammann, R. Vogel, M. Volmer, H. Wald, J. H. Whiteley, M. H. Wickhorst, and F. Wüst and W. C. Huntington.

The general results show that the grain-size developed on recrystallization is dependent on the amount or degree of mechanical deformation. P. Oberhoffer and W. Oertel represented the effect of mechanical work and temp. on the grain-size of electrolytic iron, in terms of an average crystal, by Fig. 178, a diagram analogous to that employed for the case of tin—7. 46, 4. The results show that the temp. at which recrystallization begins depends on the amount of previous deformation, being lower as the amount is increased; if the deformation is severe, the grain-growth is slow up to 700°, and above that it is rapid; and if the amount of deformation is slight, the growth is rapid even below the critical range. H. Hanemann and co-workers observed that the curve showing the relation between the grain-size and degree of deformation and that showing the relation between the deformation and the temp. of recrystallization are hyperbolic. The parameter of the hyperbola for the grain-size of steel is a linear function of the crystallization temp. If θ is the minimum temp. at which crystallization occurs; v, the degree of deformation; ϕ, the grain-size; and θ, the temp. of recrystallization, then $2v\phi^2 = a^2(\theta - \theta_r)$, where a is a constant, and $\theta_r = 620°$. The subject was discussed by P. Oberhoffer and W. Oertel, and W. Riede—*vide infra*, alternating stress tests. The subject was also studied by H. E. Publow and S. E. Sinclair, and M. von Moos, P. Oberhoffer and W. Oertel. According to F. C. Kelley, rapid grain-growth results from diffusion, when the direction of the grains is parallel to that of the diffusion. G. Tammann said :

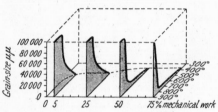

Fig. 178.—The Effect of Temperature and Mechanical Work on the Grain-size of Electrolytic Iron.

Two contiguous crystals can be in equilibrium with one another only when the crystallographic equilibrium lattice planes of both crystals lie together in the same plane at the surface of contact, that is, when the space-lattices of both crystals form a single lattice, or when the plane of contact is a twinning plane. If one or the other of these conditions is not fulfilled, then when the temp. is raised sufficiently to allow of a certain amount of change in the position of the atoms or molecules in the lattice, new lattices of mean orientation to the surface of contact will be formed, that is, a recrystallization will take place.

Abnormal crystallization does not occur if the deformation be above or below ; there is a maximum and minimum limit of straining required to develop the abnormal crystals. C. Chappell demonstrated this by heating a broken test-bar of wrought iron to 870°. The crystals were found to be normal at both ends and very large in the middle. He also found that when iron of a high degree of purity is strained, large crystals are always produced, provided the temp. at which the material is deformed is not above 900°. C. Chappell also showed that in suitably deformed iron crystal growth between 850° and 870° is extremely rapid. The less the strain, the higher the annealing temp. necessary to obtain very large crystals, and the larger these crystals will be, provided a certain minimum strain be exceeded. The correct degree of plastic deformation applied at any temp. up to 900° will cause the production of abnormally large crystals on annealing. The presence of carbon reduces the size of the largest crystals and makes a greater strain necessary to induce their growth. When carbon is present, as in the mild steels, the abnormal growth is prevented by the solid soln. of carbide in iron, which separates the various crystals from one another—*vide supra*, germinative temp. C. Chappell gave two explanations of the rôle of plastic deformation in promoting the union of the ferrite crystals : (i) If identity of orientation is the only condition necessary for the union of adjacent crystals, plastic deformation may be supposed to act by increasing the potential energy of the crystals, enabling them to bring about this rotation of their axes parallel to each other with greater ease and rapidity when the temp. is raised. (ii) The union of ferrite crystals may be considered to be analogous with the welding of two pieces of iron in which work is necessary to break up any separating layer of oxide or flux and establish molecular contact. An intercrystalline cement, acting as a separating layer, is penetrated by plastic deformation, and two crystals are brought in contact so that on reaching a high enough temp. they weld together directly.

Z. Jeffries studied what he called the effect of inheritance on the grain-size of iron and of carbon steels, and the results were summarized as follows :

(i) The ferrite grain-size in pure iron, the ferrite and pearlite grain-size in hypoeutectoid steel, the pearlite grain-size in eutectoid steel, and the cementite and pearlite grain-size of hypereutectoid steel are not inherited from the grain-size of the mother-austenite. (ii) The only structural feature that is generally inherited from the austenite of hypo- and hypereutectoid steels, on cooling through their transformation ranges, is the position of the excess ferrite or cementite at the austenite grain boundaries, sometimes causing complete and sometimes incomplete networks, which outline the old austenite grain boundaries. Rapid cooling through the transformation range will prevent the inheritance of this structural (network) feature. (iii) The austenite grain boundaries themselves are nearly always effaced in all steels and also in pure iron during the Ar_1-transformations. (iv) The grain-size refining of steel and iron is brought about by the combined effects of non-inheritance of the transformation products on either heating or cooling, *i.e.* the austenite transformation products do not inherit their grain-size from the austenite on cooling through the transformation range, nor does austenite inherit its grain-size from the structure which forms austenite on heating. (v) In general, both in iron and in carbon steels, the larger the austenite grain-size, the larger will be the grain-size of the transformation products on cooling. This, of course, assumes all other conditions constant except the austenite grain-size. Iron of a high degree of purity, such as electrolytic iron, is an exception to this general rule. In this instance small austenite grains may form very large ferrite grains on cooling throughout the Ar_3-arrest. (vi) In iron and steel, the larger the ferrite, cementite, or pearlite grain-size, the larger will be the austenite grain-size on heating above the Ac-transformations. (vii) The faster the rate of cooling of iron and steel through the Ar_1-transformation range, the smaller will be the grain-size of the transformation products. (viii) The faster the rate of heating of iron and steel, other conditions remaining the same, the smaller will be the austenite grain-size. (ix) The greater the temp. gradient during the transformations in iron and steel on heating or cooling, the larger will be the grain-size. (x) If the grain-size of a transformation product in iron and steel immediately after the transformation is smaller than the equilibrium grain-size of that product under the existing conditions, the equilibrium grain-size will be established in accordance with the known laws of grain-growth. (xi) A single grain of any constituent in iron or steel (austenite, ferrite, pearlite), when caused by thermal treatment to undergo one of the polymorphic transformations, must transform from at least one nucleus, but may, and nearly always does, transform from more than one nucleus.

C. A. Edwards and L. B. Pfeil studied the conditions under which large crystals can be obtained. They found that a grain-size approximately 120 grains per sq. mm. can be obtained by decarburizing iron by heating at 950° for 48 hrs., followed by slow cooling—12 hrs. from 950° to 100°. The carbon can be all removed if hydrogen is passed through the furnace while the metal is being heated. They also found that the orientation of the large crystals seems to bear a relation to the direction of straining and to the surface of the strips. The critical strain required to produce very large crystal growth on subsequent annealing varies with the initial size of the grain. A greater strain is needed as the grain-size increases. With very large crystals sufficient strain cannot be applied, owing to the recrystallization at the boundaries of the crystal. Surface crystals of the original finely crystalline aggregate behave differently from the interior ones, for they require a greater tensile strain before they disappear. The subject was discussed by E. Sutter. C. A. Edwards and L. B. Pfeil found that the deformation of single crystals occurs by a process of slip causing little change in the crystal lattice. They added :

If, however, two crystals in contact are deformed, interference with slip will occur, owing to the change in the direction of the slip-planes in passing from one crystal to another. Under these circumstances some other kind of movement occurs during deformation ; this second kind of movement will be most intense at and near the crystal boundaries, and less so as the distance from the boundaries increases. X-ray analysis does not indicate any difference between the lattice constants of cold-worked and of annealed metals, but shows a relation in the former between the directions of the crystallographic axes and the direction of straining. The second type of deformation (caused by interference with slip) is interpreted, therefore, as a rotation of the crystallographic axes accompanied by elastic strains (the latter not being detected by X-ray analysis). The depth to which this change penetrates from the boundaries depends upon the degree of deformation. With small crystals but little deformation will cause the depth to correspond with the radius of the crystals. The larger the crystals, the greater will be the deformation necessary to cause the change to reach the centres of the crystals. When this second type of deformation has penetrated to the crystal centres (and the strain at the crystal boundaries has not exceeded a certain value), and the degree of axial alignment due to rotation has proceeded to such an extent that, on annealing, it is more easy for the atoms to form a single crystal than to revert to their original orientations. With very large crystals, however, before the second type of deformation has penetrated to the centres, the strain set up at and near the crystal boundaries has become so great that, on annealing, it is more easy for the atoms in these highly strained regions to form new crystals (i.e. recrystallization) than for a process of perfectly uniform and stable alignment to occur. For equal amounts of tensile deformation, a surface crystal, not being subjected to interference with slip on all sides, is not affected to the same degree as an interior crystal, so far as the second type of movement is concerned. A greater degree of deformation is in consequence required before the change in surface crystals will be sufficiently complete to permit of growth or absorption during annealing. When, however, the critical degree of strain is caused by rolling, and the freedom of the surface crystals is thus at least partly removed, growth or absorption of the surface crystals can occur.

The Report of the Iron and Steel Institute on the nomenclature of metallography [9] defined **burnt steel** as follows :

The term " burnt " is applied to metal which is brittle in consequence of an alteration in its mass caused by excessive heating. A so-called burnt steel is not necessarily oxidized in its mass. Near to the external surface, if carbon is low or absent, intergranular layers of oxide of iron may sometimes be detected. The chemical composition is not necessarily altered by the so-called burning. Steel may, on heating to a very high temp. in an inert atmosphere, develop, after cooling, many of the properties of burnt steel. Burnt steel is generally coarsely granular and is easily fractured.

It also said that **overheated steel** is a term applied to steel that has been heated to excess, but not burnt. Oxidized membranes are often found surrounding some of the grains of burnt steel, and in that case the original state cannot be restored by forging, since the films of oxide would prevent the welding of adjacent grains. H. M. Howe said that steel known as overheated has a coarse structure which may be removed more or less completely by reheating or careful forging. If the overheating has been extreme, the cohesion between the adjacent grains becomes so feeble that they are forced apart to a certain extent by gas evolved from within. Part at least of this gas is carbon monoxide formed by the union of infiltering atm. oxygen with the carbon of the steel, although other gases, like hydrogen and nitrogen, may also contribute, as they are thrown out of soln. by a rise of temp. Burnt steel is red-short as well as cold-short, and brittle ; it can be forged and welded only with care ; it has a low tensile strength ; and its fracture is coarse and even flaky, crystalline, with brilliant facets. Excessively long or strong overheating produces burnt steel ; and the coarseness and brittleness due to burning are removed with greater difficulty and much less completely than those due to overheating. J. E. Stead said overheating occurs when the steel is heated at any point below that which produces incipient disintegration, and results in the formation of large crystals ; and burning occurs when the steel is heated at or above the point at which the disintegration occurs. Burnt steel is nearly always coarsely crystalline.

J. E. Stead added that the coarse crystalline structure of overheated steel, with 0·20 to 0·50 per cent. of carbon, exhibits triangular arrangements of ferrite and pearlite ; and that of steel with 0·50 to 0·70 per cent. of carbon exhibits large ferrite cell-walls with offshoots of ferrite penetrating the pearlite. A. S. Stansfield regarded the overheated steel as a steel that has been heated to the point of incipient fusion. J. E. Stead described this theory, and rejected the oxidizing gas hypothesis. In other words, it is assumed that the steel has been heated to a temp. between the liquidus and solidus curves, *i.e.* between AC and AE, Fig. 83. If this is the only reason, it follows that carbonless iron cannot be burnt, and that the higher the proportion of carbon, the greater the danger of burning. Thus, with a steel with 0·50 per cent. of carbon, the burning zone extends from about 1400° to 1450° ; with 1·0 per cent. carbon it extends from 1310° to 1410° ; and with 1·50 per cent. carbon, from 1210° to 1360°. The carbon increases the tendency to burning by lowering the m.p. and by widening the solidification zone, which is also the burning zone. An overheated steel has been heated close to but below the solidus curve, Fig. 83. A. W. Richards and J. E. Stead added that when steel is burnt by heating to incipient fusion, fusible globules or envelopes, rich in phosphorus, are formed round the crystals, and their presence or absence is regarded as a proof whether or not the steel has been burnt. If these red-short globular specks rich in phosphorus are absent, it may be concluded that a red-short steel has not been burnt, but is naturally red-short. J. H. Andrew said that the over-heating of a mild steel occurs only when the temp. is sufficiently high to bring about a dissociation and diffusion of the carbide which, until this temp. is attained, forms as a conc. phase around the ferrite grains. The subject was also discussed by L. Aisenstein and co-workers, P. Bardenheuer and K. L. Zeyen, W. Campbell, W. H. Cathcart, K. F. Göransson, E. Heyn, H. M. Howe, W. E. Jominy, J. V. McCrae and co-workers, E. Pohl and co-workers, W. Rosenhain, J. E. Stead, L. W. Wild, and K. W. Zimmerschied, as well as in numerous books on the heat treatment of steels. H. Hanemann discussed the theory of over-heating grey cast iron.

REFERENCES.

[1] F. G. Allison and M. M. Rock, *Chem. Met. Engg.*, **23**. 383, 1920 ; J. H. Andrew, *Journ. Tech. Coll. Glasgow*, **1**. 9, 63, 1925 ; T. Andrews, *Proc. Roy. Soc.*, **58**. 59, 1895 ; *Engg.*, **61**. 91, 1896 ; **63**. 266, 499, 841, 1897 ; **64**. 99, 249, 298, 455, 611, 1897 ; **65**. 201, 451, 617, 1898 ; **78**. 737, 778, 810, 1904 ; **79**. 563, 1905 ; **80**. 235, 1906 ; **81**. 331, 1906 ; *Industries Iron*, **22**. 167, 1897 ; A. E. van Arkel and W. G. Burgers, *Zeit. Metallkunde*, **23**. 149, 1931 ; A. E. van Arkel *Physica*, **5**. 208, 1925 ; *Naturwiss.*, **13**. 662, 1925 ; A. E. van Arkel and P. Koets', *Zeit. Physik*, **41**. 701, 1927 ; W. Armstrong, *Polyt. Notizbl.*, 45, 1881 ; J. O. Arnold, *Engg.*, **81**. 278, 1906 ; *Eng.*, **100**. 158, 1906 ; *B.A. Rep.*, 684, 1900 ; *Mineral Ind.*, **5**. 697, 1897 ; *Journ. Iron Steel Inst.*, **45**. i, 107, 1894 ; *Iron Coal Trades Rev.*, **62**. 765, 1901 ; *Ironmonger*, **94**. 611, 1901 ; **122**. 249, 1908 ; *Mining Journ.*, **71**. 421, 1901 ; J. O. Arnold and A. McWilliam, *Journ. Iron Steel Inst.*, **61**. i, 120, 1902 ; **68**. ii, 35, 1905 ; *Nature*, **71**. 32, 1904 ; M. Augustin, *Ber. Mitt. Freund. Naturwiss. Wien*, **3**. 82, 1847 ; J. A. Aupperle, *Eng. News*, **45**. 162, 1901 ; C. R. Austin, *Ingots and Ingot Moulds*, London, **105**. i, 93, 1922 ; R. Bach, *Contribution à l'étude roentgenographique de l'état cristallin du fer*, Bâle, 1929 ; *Helvetica Phys. Acta.*, **2**. 95, 1929 ; L. Baclé, *Génie Civil*, **21**. 71, 198, 1892 ; *Rev. Univ. Mines*, **31**. 18, 1891 ; **35**. 121, 1895 ; **39**. 25, 1897 ; E. C. Bain, *Trans. Amer. Inst. Min. Eng.*, **68**. 625, 1922 ; *Journ. Ind. Eng. Chem.*, **16**. 692, 1924 ; *Chem. Met. Engg.*, **25**. 657, 1922 ; **26**. 543, 1922 ; E. C. Bain and Z. Jeffries, *ib.*, **25**. 775, 1921 ; C. O. Bannister, *Journ. Iron Steel Inst.*, **69**. i, 161, 1906 ; C. O. Bannister and W. D. Jones, *ib.*, **123**. i, 395, 1931 ; *Iron Steel Ind.*, **4**. 299, 1931 ; P. Bardenheuer and C. A. Müller, *Mitt. Inst. Eisenforschung, Düsseldorf*, **11**. 255, 273, 1929 ; H. Bauermann, *Ingots and Ingot Moulds*, **27**. i, 203, 1885 ; A. Beardsley, *Min. Mag.*, **2**. 223, 261, 1879 ; K. Becker, R. O. Herzog, W. Jancke and M. Polanyi, *Zeit. Physik*, **5**. 61, 1922 ; A. C. Becquerel, *Ann. Chim. Phys.*, (2), **48**. 346, 1831 ; H. Behrens, *Das mikroskopische Gefüge der Metalle und Legierungen*, Hamburg, 1894 ; *Rec. Trav. Chim. Pays-Bas*, **13**. 155, 1894 ; C. C. Beinert, *Der Meteorit von Braunau*, Breslau, 1848 ; N. T. Belaiew, *Crystallization of Metals*, London, 1923 ; *The Structure, Crystallization, and Properties of Steel on Slow Cooling*, Petrograd, 1909 ; *Rev. Mét.*, **7**. 510, 1910 ; **9**. 321, 647, 1912 ; **11**. 221, 1914 ; *Journ. Inst. Aeronautical Eng.*, **1**. 14, 1920 ; *Chem. Met. Eng.*, **28**. 537, 1923 ; *Stahl Eisen*, 32, 1272, 1912 ; *Journ. Russ. Phys. Chem. Soc.*, **39**. 399, 1907 ; *Trans. Amer. Soc. Steel Treating*, **5**. 214, 549, 1924 ; *Metal Ind.*, **20**. 54, 1922 ; *Proc. Russ. Min. Soc.*, (2), **47**. 209, 1909 ; *Min. Mag.*, **20**. 379, 1923 ; *Journ. Inst. Metals*, **12**. 45, 1914 ; **29**. 379, 1923 (1

am indebted to Col. N. T. Belaiew for permission to use Figs. 154 and 155); *Journ. Iron Steel Inst.*, **97**. i, 417, 1918 ; **104**. ii, 187, 1922 ; *Journ. Russ. Met. Soc.*, **2**. 21, 1910 ; *Chem. Met. Engg.*, **28**. 537, 1923 ; C. Benedicks, *Koll. Zeit.*, **7**. 290, 1910 ; *Internat. Zeit. Metallog.*, **1**. 184, 1911 ; *Journ. Iron Steel Inst.*, **117**. i, 557, 1928 ; Metallographic Researches, New York, 108, 1926 ; *Bihang Jernkontorets Ann.*, 293, 1903 ; R. Berthold, *Zeit. Metallkunde*, **20**. 378, 1928 ; F. Berwerth, *Journ. Iron Steel Inst.*, **75**. iii, 37, 1907 ; G. V. Bianchetti, *Rass. Min.*, **26**. 69, 1907 ; S. V. Bielyansky, *Proc. Russ. Met. Soc.*, 396, 1912 ; F. Bitter, *Phys. Rev.*, (2), **37**. 1527, 1931 ; F. C. Blake, *ib.*, (2),. **26**. 60, 1925 ; R. M. Bozorth, *ib.*, (2), **23**. 764, 1924 ; W. H. Bragg, *Journ. Iron Steel Inst.*, **103**. i, 327, 1921 ; H. Braune, *Bihang Jernkontorets Ann.*, 533, 1906 ; A. W. and H. Brearley, *Journ. Iron Steel Inst.*, **94**. ii, 137, 1916 ; Ingots and Ingot Moulds, London, 1918 ; H. Brearley, *Journ. Iron Steel Inst.*, **113**. i, 157, 1926 ; L. Breguet, *Chem. News*, **6**. 261, 1862 ; *Proc. Manchester Lit. Phil. Soc.*, (3), **3**. 10, 1862 ; P. Breuil, *Recherches sur les constituents des aciers trempés*, Paris, 1907 ; *Bull. Soc. Ind. Min.*, **6**. 553, 1907 ; P. W. Bridgman, *Proc. Amer. Acad.*, **58**. 265, 1923 ; **60**. 305, 329, 1925 ; R. Brill and H. Mark, *Zeit. phys. Chem.*, **133**. 453, 1928 ; J. A. Brinell, *Jernkontorets Ann.*, **40**. 9, 1885 ; *Stahl Eisen*, **5**. 611, 1885 ; H. C. Burger, *Phys. Zeit.*, **23**. 14, 1922 ; L. Cammen, *Trans. Amer. Soc. Steel Treating*, **17**. 563, 1930 ; H. Capitaine, *Compt. Rend.*, **9**. 737, 1839 ; *Ann. Chim. Phys.*, (3), **2**. 126, 1841 ; R. von Carnall, *Zeit. deut. geol. Ges.*, **10**. 230, 1858 ; H. C. H. Carpenter, *Journ. Iron Steel Inst.*, **107**. i, 175, 1923 ; *Nature*, **126**. Suppl., 1930 ; *Proc. Roy. Inst.*, **26**. 267, 1930 ; *Chem. News*, **141**. 97, 113, 1930 ; H. C. H. Carpenter and C. F. Elam, *Proc. Roy. Soc.*, **100**. A, 329, 1922 ; *Journ. Inst. Metals*, **24**. 83, 1920 ; **35**. 409, 1926 ; H. G. Carter, *Trans. Amer. Soc. Steel Treating*, **1**. 56, 1920 ; H. le Chatelier, *Rev. Mét.*, **11**. 766, 1914 ; *Bull. Soc. Enc. Nat. Ind.*, **104**. 212, 1905 ; *Congrès Internat. Liége*, **1**. 255, 1906 ; *Metallographist*, **4**. 1, 1901 ; H. le Chatelier and J. Lemoine, *Compt. Rend.*, **161**. 373, 1915 ; A. T. Child and W. P. Heineken, *Trans. Amer. Inst. Min. Eng.*, **30**. 734, 1901 ; M. Chouriguine, *Rev. Mét.*, **8**. 935, 1912 ; *Compt. Rend.*, **155**. 156, 1912 ; G. L. Clark, E. W. Brugmann and S. D. Heath, *Journ. Ind. Eng. Chem.*, **17**. 1142, 1925 ; A. L. Colby, *Iron Age*, **61**. 4, 1897 ; W. Crookes, *Chem. News*, **19**. 136, 1869 ; J. Czochralsky, *Internat. Zeit. Metallog.*, **8**. 36, 1916 ; *Zeit. Metallkunde*, **15**. 60, 126, 1923 ; W. P. Davey, *Phys. Rev.*, (2), **23**. 292, 1924 ; (2), **25**. 753, 1925 ; *Trans. Amer. Soc. Steel Treating*, **6**. 375, 1924 ; *Journ. Amer. Opt. Soc.*, **5**. 479, 1921 ; *Zeit. Kryst.*, **63**. 316, 1926 ; *Gen. Elect. Rev.*, **25**. 565, 1922 ; *Mech. Eng.*, **50**. 213, 1928 ; *Journ. Franklin Inst.*, **205**. 221, 1928 ; W. P. Davey, C. C. Nitchie and M. L. Fuller, *Tech. Publ. Amer. Inst. Min. Eng.*, 243, 1929 ; U. Dehlinger, *Zeit. Physik*, **68**. 535, 1931 ; C. H. Desch, *Foundry Trade Journ.*, **13**. 530, 1911 ; *Mech. Eng.*, **28**. 699, 1911 ; *Nature*, **117**. 694, 1926 ; *Trans. Amer. Inst. Min. Eng.*, **75**. 128, 526, 1927 ; *Journ. Inst. Metals*, **22**. 276, 1919 ; M. Desfosses, *Journ. Pharm. Chim.*, (3), **16**. 81, 1849 ; G. Dillner, *Jernkontorets Ann.*, **57**. 97, 1902 ; E. F. Dürre, *Ueber die Constitution des Roheisens*, Leipzig, 58, 1868 ; P. F. Dujardin, *Stahl Eisen*, **26**. 522, 732, 1906 ; E. Dussler and W. Gerlach, *Zeit. Physik*, **44**. 279, 1927 ; C. A. Edwards, *Journ. Inst. Metals*, **5**. 150, 1911 ; C. A. Edwards and L. B. Pfeil, *Journ. Iron Steel Inst.*, **108**. ii, 263, 1923 ; **109**. 1, 129, 1924 ; **112**. ii, 72, 1925 ; *Engg.*, **116**. 416, 1924 ; *Iron Coal Trades Rev.*, **108**. 779, 834, 1924 ; *Nature*, **114**. 15, 1924 ; **116**. 593, 1925 ; O. Eisenhut and E. Kaupp, *Zeit. phys. Chem.*, **133**. 457, 1928 ; C. F. Elam, *Phil. Mag.*, (6), **50**. 517, 1925 ; *Journ. Iron Steel Inst.*, **112**. ii, 111, 1925 ; F. C. Elder, *Heat Treating Forging*, **15**. 717, 1929 ; O. W. Ellis, *Trans. Amer. Soc. Steel Treating*, **5**. 209, 1924 ; A. Erman, *Erman's Russ. Arch.*, **1**. 314, 713, 1841 ; M. Ettisch, M. Polanyi and K. Weissenberg, *Zeit. phys. Chem.*, **99**. 332, 1921 ; *Phys. Zeit.*, **22**. 646, 1921 ; *Zeit. Physik*, **7**. 181, 1921 ; P. P. Ewald and C. Hermann, *Strukturbericht Zeit. Kryst.*, **66**. 13, 1928 ; J. A. Ewing, *Engg.*, **71**. 82, 1901 ; *Proc. Roy. Inst.*, **16**. 419, 1901 ; J. A. Ewing and W. Rosenhain, *Proc. Roy. Soc.*, **65**. A, 85, 1899 ; *Phil. Trans.*, **193**. A, 353, 1900 ; **195**. A, 279, 1901 ; *Bull. Soc. Min.*, **23**. 228, 1901 ; K. Faller, *Bany. Koh. Lapok*, **36**. 687, 1903 ; A. N. Farfourine, *Proc. Soc. Russ. Metal*, **91**. 1928 ; *Rev. Mét.*, **27**. 220, 1930 ; H. Fay, A. W. Higgins and F. W. Coburn, *Tech. Quart.*, **16**. 4, 1903 ; E. Fedoroff, *Gorny Journ.*, 4, 1885 ; 3, 12, 1886 ; 4, 1887 ; *Proc. Russ. Min. Soc.*, (2), **21**. 1, 1885 ; A. L. Feild, *Trans. Amer. Soc. Steel Treating*, **11**. 264, 338, 1927 ; W. L. Fink and E. D. Campbell, *ib.*, **9**. 717, 1926 ; T. B. Focke, *Étude de quelques propriétés des très gros cristaux de fer*, Nancy, 1928 ; F. B. Foley, *Trans. Amer. Inst. Min. Eng.*, **73**. 850, 1925 ; J. Forrest, *Trans. Roy. Soc. Edin.*, **54**. 601, 1926 ; C. W. C. Fuchs, *Die Künstlich dargestellten Mineralien nach Roses System geordnet*, Haarlem, 18, 1872 ; J. N. von Fuchs, *Schweiz Gewerbebl.*, **11**. 264, 1852 ; *Chem. Gaz.*, **11**. 94, 1853 ; J. D. Gat, *Forging, Stamping, Heat Treating*, **13**. 38, 79, 124, 1927 ; *Blast Furnace Steel Plant*, **15**. 207, 1927 ; W. Gerlach, *Phys. Zeit.*, **26**. 914, 1925 ; **58**. 828, 1926 ; *Verh. deut. phys. Ges.*, (3), **7**. 24, 327, 1926 ; *Heraeus' Festschrift*, 27, 1930 ; F. P. Gilligan and J. J. Curann, *Trans. Amer. Soc. Steel Treating*, **10**. 9, 1926 ; F. Giolitti, *Il trattamente termico preliminaire degli acciai dolci e semi-duri per construzioni meccanche*, Milano, 1918 ; *Le traitement thermique préliminaire des aciers*, Paris, 1920 ; The Heat Treatment of Soft and Medium Steel, New York, 1921 ; *Gazz. Chim. Ital.*, **36**. 142, 1906 ; *Rass. Min.*, **27**. 257, 1908 ; *Chem. Met. Engg.*, **22**. 585, 1920 ; A. Glazunoff, *Foundry Trade Journ.*, **41**. 117, 131, 1929 ; R. Glocker, *Zeit. Metallkunde*, **16**. 180, 182, 1924 ; *Zeit. Physik*, **31**. 386, 1925 ; F. von Goeler and G. Sachs, *Zeit. Ver. deut. Ing.*, **71**. 1353, 1927 ; P. Goerens, *ib.*, **49**. 1871, 1905 ; *Stahl Eisen*, **26**. 397, 1906 ; *Met.*, **5**. 19, 1908 ; A. Goetz, *Phys. Zeit.*, **26**. 260, 1925 ; V. M. Goldschmidt, *Zeit. Metallkunde*, **13**. 449, 1921 ; A. Greiner, *Rev. Univ. Mines*, **42**. 145, 1898 ; H. Griess, *Ueber Einkristalle aus Eisen*, Aachen, 1930 ; H. Griess and H. Esser, *Metallurgist*, **5**. 111, 1929 ; *Stahl Eisen*, **49**. 879, 1929 ; *Arch. Eisenhüttenwesen*, **2**. 145, 749, 1929 ; P. C. Grignon, *Mémoires de physiques sur l'art de fabriquer le fer*, Paris, 1775 ; J. Grone, *Gorny Journ.*, 1, 1907 ; L. Gruardet,

Rev. Artillerie, **64**. 199, 1905 ; *Théorie moléculaire de la constitution des aciers*, Paris, 1905 ; L. Guillet, *Mém. Soc. Ing. Civils*, 31, 1903 ; *Rev. Gén. Sciences*, **17**. 586, 630, 1906 ; *Bull. Soc. Min. Ind.*, **7**. 115, 1907 ; *Rev. Mét.*, **4**. 1027, 1907 ; *Compt. Rend.*, **185**, 1598, 1927 ; E. F. Gurlt, *Dingler's Journ.*, **160**. 131, 1861 ; W. Haidinger, *Sitzber. Akad. Wien*, **15**. 354, 1855 ; *Jahrb. Geol. Reichsanst.*, **1**. 151, 1850 ; H. Hanemann, *Zeit. Metallkunde*, **22**. 404, 1930 ; K. Harnecker, *Stahl Eisen*, **44**. 1409, 1924 ; W. H. Hatfield, *Journ. Iron Steel Inst.*, **118**. i, 39, 1926 ; *Proc. South Wales Inst. Eng.*, **45**. 523, 1930 ; *Proc. Lincoln Iron Steel Inst.*, **2**. 167, 1930 ; J. F. L. Hausmann, *Gött. Nachr.*, **101**. 1817 ; 143, 1855 ; *Handbuch der Mineralogie*, Göttingen, **38**. 1847 ; W. Heike and W. Brenscheidt, *Stahl Eisen*, **50**. 1362, 1930 ; K. Heindlhofer, *Phys. Rev.*, (2), **24**. 426, 1924 ; A. Heinzel, *Zeit. tech. Phys.*, **10**. 136, 1929 ; S. B. Hendricks, *Zeit. Kryst.*, **74**. 534, 1930 ; F. Hermann, *Giesserei Ztg.*, **4**. 641, 1908 ; C. T. Heycock and F. H. Neville, *Phil. Trans.*, **202**. A, 1, 1903 ; E. Heyn, *Mitt. tech. Versuchsanst. Berlin*, **16**. 310, 1898 ; **18**. 191, 1900 ; *Stahl Eisen*, **19**. 709, 768, 1899 ; **20**. 36, 1900 ; **21**. 977, 1901 ; **26**. 8, 580, 1295, 1396, 1906 ; *Zeit. Ver. deut. Ing.*, **44**. 137, 175, 1900 ; *Amer. Machinist*, **30**. 806, 1908 ; E. Heyn and O. Bauer, *Mitt. Materialprüf.*, **24**. 117, 1906 ; *Stahl Eisen*, **27**. 1565, 1621, 1907 ; K. Honda and S. Kaya, *Science Rep. Tohoku Univ.*, **15**. 721, 1926 ; K. Honda, S. Kaya and Y. Masuyama, *Nature*, **117**. 753, 1926 ; K. Honda and Y. Masuyama, *Science Rep. Tohoku Univ.*, **15**. 755, 1926 ; K. Honda and S. Sekito, *ib.*, **17**. 743, 1928 ; S. A. Houghton, *Mech. Eng.*, **9**. 617, 1901 ; *Iron Coal Trades Rev.*, **64**. 1064, 1901 ; *The Internal Structure of Iron and Steel, with Special Reference to Defective Material*, London, 1902 ; H. M. Howe, *Metallographist*, **6**. 19, 1903 ; *Trans. Amer. Inst. Min. Eng.*, **47**. 621, 1913 ; *Proc. Amer. Soc. Testing Materials*, **11**. 362, 1911 ; *Internat. Zeit. Metallog.*, **2**. 11, 1912 ; *Chem. Met. Eng.*, **15**. 623, 1916 ; *Iron, Steel, and Other Alloys*, Boston, 85, 1903 ; *The Metallography of Steel and Cast Iron*, New York, 135, 1916 ; H. M. Howe and E. Groesbeck, *Trans. Amer. Inst. Min. Eng.*, **62**. 341, 1919 ; H. M. Howe and B. Stoughton, *ib.*, **38**. 109, 1907 ; G. d'Huart, *Rev. Mét.*, **26**. 532, 1929 ; O. F. Hudson, *Proc. South Staffs Iron Steel Inst.*, **20**. 118, 1905 ; A. W. Hull, *Journ. Franklin Inst.*, **193**. 189, 1922 ; *Phys. Rev.*, (2), **9**. 83, 1917 ; (2), **10**. 661, 1917 ; A. Hultgren, *Journ. Iron Steel Inst.*, **120**. ii, 69, 1929 ; W. Hume-Rothery, *Phil. Mag.*, (7), **10**. 217, 1930 ; O. W. Huntington, *Amer. Journ. Science*, (3), **32**. 284, 1886 ; C. L. Huston, *Journ. Franklin Inst.*, **165**. 371, 1908 ; T. Ishiwara, *Science Rep. Tohoku Univ.*, **12**. 309, 1924 ; E. J. Janitzky, *Trans. Amer. Assoc. Steel Treating*, **2**. 377, 1922 ; **6**. 728, 1924 ; Z. Jeffries, *Journ. Inst. Metals*, **20**. 109, 1918 ; Z. Jeffries and R. S. Archer, *Ueber Einkristalle aus Eisen*, Aachen, **24**. 771, 1921 ; *Rev. Univ. Mines*, **11**. 65, 1921 ; Z. Jeffries and E. C. Bain, *Chem. Met. Engg.*, 779, 1921 ; J. H. B. Jenkins and D. G. Riddick, *Analyst*, **30**. 2, 1905 ; P. von Jeremejeff, *Proc. Russ. Min. Soc.*, (2), **34**. 37, 1906 ; *Zeit. Kryst.*, **30**. 387, 1899 ; J. E. Johnson, *Metallographist*, **6**. 14, 1903 ; L. M. Jordan, *Heat Treating and Forging*, **15**. 1441, 1929 ; H. von Jüptner, *Verh. Ver. Beförd. Gewerbfl.*, 194, 1901 ; *Tschermak's Mitt.*, (2), **23**. 197, 1904 ; *Oesterr. Zeit. Berg. Hütt.*, **55**. 161, 177, 1907 ; G. W. A. Kahlbaum, *Verh. Nat. Ges. Basel*, **12**. 221, 1900 ; A. Karlsson, *Arkiv. Mat. Astron. Fys.*, **22**. A, 9, 1930 ; T. Kase, *Science Rep. Tohoku Univ.*, **14**. 537, 1925 ; Lord Kelvin (W. Thomson), *Phil. Mag.*, (5), **24**. 503, 1887 ; *Proc. Roy. Soc.*, **55**. 1, 1894 ; *The Molecular Tactics of a Crystal*, Oxford, 1894 ; F. Kerdyk, *Dingler's Journ.*, **322**. 683, 1908 ; H. G. Keshian, *Trans. Amer. Soc. Steel Treating*, **17**. 321, 1930 ; D. H. Killeffer, *Journ. Ind. Eng. Chem.*, **18**. 577, 1926 ; F. Kirchner, *Ann. Physik*, (4), **69**. 59, 1922 ; S. S. Knight, *Journ. Amer. Foundrymen's Assoc.*, **5**. 92, 1898 ; F. Körber, *Stahl Eisen*, **45**. 217, 261, 1925 ; C. Kohn, *Sitzber. Akad. Wien*, **6**. 149, 1851 ; *Repert. Chim. Appl.*, **1**. 55, 1858 ; S. T. Konobejewsky, *Zeit. Physik*, **39**. 415, 1926 ; M. Kralupper, *Oesterr. Zeit. Berg. Hütt.*, **54**. 162, 177, 190, 1906 ; P. Kreuzpointer, *Iron Age*, **49**. 1224, 1892 ; V. N. Krivobok, *Trans. Amer. Soc. Steel Treating*, **7**. 457, 1925 ; **10**. 758, 1926 ; V. N. Krivobok and O. E. Romig, *ib.*, **6**. 66, 1924 ; A. Kroll, *Journ. Iron Steel Inst.*, **81**. i, 304, 1910 ; *La système fer-carbone au point de vue de la cristallization*, Paris, 1912 ; *Rev. Univ. Mines*, (4), **37**. i, 1912 ; R. Kühnel, *Zeit. Metallkunde*, **22**. 53, 1930 ; G. Kurdjumoff, *Zeit. Physik*, **55**. 187, 1929 ; G. Kurdjumoff, and E. Kaminsky, *Nature*, **122**. 475, 1928 ; *Zeit. Physik*, **53**. 696, 1929 ; G. Kurdjumoff and G. Sachs, *ib.*, **52**. 592, 1930 ; E. F. Lange, *Mem. Manchester Lit. Phil. Soc.*, **55**. 24, 1911 ; F. C. Lan, *Metallographist*, **3**. 244, 1900 ; **4**. 261, 1901 ; F. Leitner, *Stahl Eisen*, **46**. 525, 1926 ; P. Lejeune, *Trans. Amer. Inst. Min. Eng.*, **3**. 312, 1906 ; H. H. Lester and R. H. Aborn, *Army Ordnance*, **5**. 455, 1924 ; **6**. 120, 1925 ; J. A. M. van Liempt, *Tech. Publ. Amer. Inst. Min. Eng.*, **15**. 1927 ; N. M. H. Lightfoot, *Journ. Iron Steel Inst.*, **119**. i, 364, 1929 ; G. E. Linck, *Ann. Hofmuseum Wien*, **8**. 113, 1893 ; *Stahl Eisen*, **13**. 243, 1893 ; *Zeit. Kryst.*, **20**. 214, 1892 ; N. N. Ljamin, *Zap. Imp. Russ. Tech. Obschtsch.*, 1, 1897 ; *Baumaterialienkunde*, **3**. 105, 1899 ; P. Longmuir, *Journ. Amer. Foundrymen's Assoc.*, **12**. 95, 1903 ; *Page's Mag.*, **3**. 99, 1903 ; A. Lundgren, *Rolling Mill Journ.*, **4**. 107, 1930 ; L. W. McKeehan, *Nature*, **119**. 705, 1927 ; *Proc. Inst. Min. Mat. Eng.*, 453, 1928 ; *Stahl Eisen*, **48**. 1799, 1928 ; *Phys. Rev.*, (2), **21**. 402, 1923 ; (2), **29**. 920, 1927 ; *Popular Science Monthly*, **25**. 272, 1927 ; M. Majima and S. Togino, *Science Papers Inst. Tohoku*, **7**. 75, 259, 1927 ; *Science Papers Inst. Phys. Chem. Research*, **7**. 259, 1927 ; E. Mallard, *Neues Jahrb. Min.*, 617, 1879 ; A. Martens, *Mitt. tech. Versuchsanst.*, **11**. 247, 1894 ; *Verh. Ver. Eisenbahnkunde*, 67, 1892 ; *Mitt. tech. Versuchsanst.*, 2, 1892 ; *Stahl Eisen*, **12**. 672, 1892 ; **15**. 538, 1895 ; *Zeit. Ver. deut. Ing.*, **21**. 205, 1878 ; *Trans. Amer. Inst. Min. Eng.*, **22**. 1895 ; G. Masing, *Zeit. Metallkunde*, **21**. 282, 1929 ; B. Matuschka, *Journ. Iron Steel Inst.*, **124**. ii, 361, 1931 ; *Arch. Eisenhüttenwesen*, **5**. 335, 1932 ; G. Mayer, *Zeit. Kryst.*, **70**. 383, 1929 ; W. H. Miller, *Metallurgy—Iron and Steel*, **4**. 1864 ; W. E. W. Millington and F. C. Thompson, *Trans. Manchester Assoc. Eng.*, 45, 1925 ; W. von Möllendorff and J. Czochralsky, *Zeit. Ver. deut. Ing.*, **57**. 931, 1014, 1913 ; R. Moldenke,

Iron Trade Rev., **30**. 19, 1897 ; L. B. G. de Morveau, *Mém. Acad.*, 513, 1775 ; O. Mügge, *Neues Jahrb. Min. B.B.*, **14**. 314, 1901 ; *Zeit. anorg. Chem.*, **121**. 68, 1921 ; *Neues Jahrb. Min.*, ii, 67, 1899 ; *Gött. Nachr.*, 108, 1922 ; C. A. Müller, *Untersuchungen über die Seigerung der Begleit-elemente des Eisens, insbesondere der Sauerstoffs, in Flusstahl-blöcken*, Düsseldorf, 1929 ; F. C. G. Müller, *Glaser's Ann.*, 138, 1880 ; *Stahl Eisen*, **2**. 531, 1882 ; *Iron*, **21**. 17, 51, 115, 1883 ; D. Mushet, *Phil. Mag.*, **61**. 22, 83, 1823 ; M. C. Neuburger, *Röntgenographie des Eisens et seiner Legierungen*, Stuttgart, 1928 ; J. G. Neumann, *Haidinger's Abhand.*, **3**. ii, 45, 1849 ; J. J. Nöggerath, *Schweigger's Journ.*, **44**. 251, 1825 ; C. Nusbaum, *Phys. Rev.*, (2), **37**. 458, 1931 ; P. Oberhoffer, *Das technische Eisen*, Berlin, 295, 1925 (I am indebted to the publishers for permission to use Fig. 153) ; *Stahl Eisen*, **45**. 223, 1925 ; E. Oehman, *Zeit. phys. Chem.*, **8**. B, 81, 1930 ; H. O'Neil, *Journ. Iron Steel Inst.*, **117**. i, 689, 1928 ; **123**. i, 445, 1931 ; A. Ono, *Mem. Coll. Kyushu Univ.*, **3**. 267, 1925 ; *Mem. Coll. Eng. Kyushu*, **3**. 195, 267, 287, 1925 ; A. Osawa, *Science Rep. Tohoku Univ.*, **15**. 387, 619, 1926 ; *Journ. Iron Steel Inst.*, **113**. i, 447, 1926 ; F. Osmond, *Trans. Amer. Inst. Min. Eng.*, **22**. 243, 1893 ; *Eng.*, **78**. 171, 1894 ; *Stahl Eisen*, **17**. 904, 1897 ; *Metallographist*, **3**. 181, 1900 ; **4**. 23, 1901 ; *Sur la cristallographie du fer*, Paris, 1900 ; *Compt. Rend.*, **103**. 743, 1135, 1886 ; **104**. 980, 1887 ; **118**. 807, 1894 ; **119**. 329, 1894 ; *Bull. Soc. Enc. Nat. Ind.*, (6), **10**. 476, 1895 ; *Transformations du fer et du carbone dans les fers, aciers et fontes blanches*, Paris, 1888 ; *Mém. d'artillerie*, 573, 1887 ; *Stahl Eisen*, **7**. 447, 1887 ; **8**. 364, 1888 ; **11**. 634, 1891 ; *Ann. Mines*, (8), **14**. 5, 1888 ; (9), **17**. 110, 1899 ; (9), **18**. 13, 1901 ; *Journ. Iron Steel Inst.*, **47**. i, 456, 1895 ; F. Osmond and G. Cartaud, *ib.*, **71**. iii, 444, 1906 ; *Ann. Mines*, (9), **17**. 110, 1900 ; *Compt. Rend.*, **141**. 122, 1905 ; **142**. 1530, 1906 ; *Rev. Gén. Sciences*, **16**. 51, 1905 ; *Sur la cristallographie du fer*, Paris, 1901 ; *Metallographist*, **3**. 181, 275, 1901 ; **4**. 119, 236, 1901 ; *Met.*, **3**. 522, 1906 ; *Rev. Mét.*, **2**. 811, 1905 ; *Bull. Soc. Min.*, **28**. 305, 1905 ; *Trans. Amer. Inst. Min. Eng.*, **37**. 813, 1906 ; F. Osmond and C. Fremont, *Rev. Mét.*, **1**. 11, 1904 ; E. A. Owen and G. D. Preston, *Proc. Phys. Soc.*, **35**. 101, 1923 ; J. Parry, *Proc. South Wales Inst. Eng.*, **21**. 30, 1898 ; P. M. Partsch, *Die Meteoriten oder vom Himmel gefallenen Steine und Eisenmessen im k.k. Hofmineralien Cabinets*, Wien, 1843 ; E. Péligot, *Compt. Rend.*, **19**. 670, 1844 ; J. Percy, *Metallurgy—Iron and Steel*, London, 3, 1864 ; H. Perlitz, *Trans. Faraday Soc.*, **28**. 515, 1932 ; L. B. Pfeil, *Journ. Iron Steel Inst.—Carnegie Mem.*, **15**. 319, 1926 ; M. Polanyi and K. Weissenberg, *Zeit. tech. Phys.*, **4**. 199, 1923 ; A. M. Portevin, *Compt. Rend.*, **160**. 344, 1915 ; **171**. 350, 1920 ; *Journ. Iron Steel Inst.*, **108**. ii, 93, 1923 ; A. M. Portevin and V. Bernard, *La microstructure de l'acier*, Paris, 1918 ; *Rev. Mét.*, **9**. 544, 1912 ; **15**. 273, 1918 ; J. A. Poumarède, *Compt. Rend.*, **29**. 518, 1849 ; M. A. F. Prestel, *Jahrb. Geol. Reichsanst.*, **5**. 866, 1854 ; *Dingler's Journ.*, **148**. 157, 1858 ; J. S. G. Primrose, *Trans. Amer. Soc. Steel Treating*, **8**. 30, 1925 ; **11**. 763, 1927 ; M. Privault, *Rev. Gén. Sciences*, **39**. 363, 1928 ; H. S. Rawdon and T. Berglund, *Scient. Papers U.S. Bur. Standards*, 571, 1928 ; F. S. Rice, *Eng. News*, **38**. 274, 1897 ; F. Rinne, *Zeit. Metallkunde*, **18**. 37, 1926 ; C. H. Risdale, *Journ. Iron Steel Inst.*, **56**. ii, 102, 1899 ; O. L. Roberts, *Phys. Rev.*, (2), **35**. 1425, 1931 ; F. Roll, *Zeit. Kryst.*, **65**. 119, 1927 ; J. B. L. Romé de l'Isle, *Cristallographie*, Paris, **3**. 169, 1783 ; G. Rose, *Abhand. Akad. Berlin*, 43, 1863 ; W. Rosenhain, *Proc. Roy. Inst.*, **24**. 361, 1925 ; *Journ. Soc. Arts.*, **73**. 1000, 1022, 1039, 1925 ; *Journ. Iron Steel Inst.*, i, 335, 1904 ; W. Rosenhain and D. Hanson, *ib.*, **102**. ii, 23, 1920 ; W. E. Ruder, *Trans. Amer. Soc. Steel Treating*, **8**. 23, 1925 ; W. von Rüdiger, *Giesserei Ztg.*, **3**. 593, 677, 1906 ; G. Sachs and E. Schiebold, *Zeit. Ver. deut. Ing.*, **69**. 1557, 1925 ; *Mitt. Inst. Metallforschung*, **2**. 211, 1926 ; A. Sadebeck, *Pogg. Ann.*, **156**. 554, 1875 ; S. Sato, *Science Rep. Tohoku Univ.*, **14**. 513, 1925 ; F. Sauerwald, B. Schmidt and H. Dienenthal, *Zeit. Physik*, **61**. 153, 1930 ; A. Sauveur, *Stahl Eisen*, **15**. 537, 1895 ; *Metallographist*, **3**. 154, 1900 ; **4**. 252, 261, 1901 ; *Mineral Ind.*, **9**. 701, 1900 ; *Proc. Amer. Phil. Soc.*, **66**. 267, 1928 ; *Trans. Amer. Inst. Min. Eng.*, **22**. 546, 1893 ; *Journ. Iron Steel Inst.*, **44**. ii, 488, 1893 ; *Electrochem. Met. Ind.*, **5**. 119, 1907 ; *Journ. Franklin Inst.*, **155**. 273, 1903 ; *Journ. Amer. Foundrymen's Assoc.*, **11**. 69, 1902 ; *Iron Steel Mag.*, **10**. 309, 1905 ; **11**. 119, 1906 ; *Eng. Mag.*, **17**. 977, 1899 ; *Eng. Min. Journ.*, **63**. 662, 1896 ; **64**. 69, 215, 517, 611, 1897 ; *Trans. Amer. Soc. Steel Treating*, **4**. 12, 83, 1923 ; A. Sauveur and C. H. Chou, *Tech. Paper Amer. Inst. Min. Eng.*, 169, 1929 ; 299, 1930 ; A. Sauveur and V. N. Krivobok, *Trans. Amer. Inst. Min. Eng.*, **70**. 239, 1924 ; *Journ. Iron Steel Inst.*, **112**. ii, 313, 1925 ; U. Savoia, *Metallografia applicata ai prodotti siderurgici*, Milano, 1909 ; London, 1910 ; R. Schenck, *Zeit. Metallkunde*, **20**. 93, 1928 ; E. Schiebold, *Mitt. Material-prüfungsamt*, 61, 1926 ; *Zeit. Metallkunde*, **16**. 417, 462, 1924 ; E. Schmid, *ib.*, **20**. 370, 1928 ; C. Schwarz, *Arch. Eisenhüttenwesen*, **5**. 139, 177, 1931 ; A. E. Seaton, *Trans. Inst. Naval Arch.*, **37**. 210, 1896 ; J. Seigle, *Tech. Moderne*, **20**. 665, 1928 ; S. Sekito, *Journ. Study Metals*, **5**. 380, 1928 ; *Zeit. Kryst.*, **67**. 563, 1928 ; *Science Rep. Tohoku Univ.*, **17**. 679, 1227, 1928 ; **18**. 69, 1929 ; **20**. 313, 1931 ; N. Seljakoff, G. Kurdjumoff and N. Goodtsoff, *Rev. Met.*, **25**. 99, 1928 ; *Nature*, **119**. 494, 1927 ; *Zeit. Physik*, **45**. 384, 1927 ; *Rep. Leningrad Phys. Tech. Lab.*, 73, 1926 ; H. Shoji, *Kinzoku-no-Kenkyu*, **6**. 127, 1929 ; *Zeit. Kryst.*, **77**. 381, 1931 ; *Bull. Inst. Phys. Chem. Research, Tokyo*, **10**. 909, 1931 ; J. von Siemachko, *Tschermak's Mitt. Westinghouse*, 184, 1925 ; *Science*, (2), **68**. 276, 1928 ; *Trans. Amer. Inst. Min. Eng.*, **77**. 320, 1924 ; W. C. Smeaton, *Iron Steel Mag.*, **9**. 222, 1904 ; A. Smekal, *Stahl Eisen*, **45**. 1786, 1925 ; *Zeit. Ver. deut. Ing.*, **72**. 667, 1928 ; *Metallurgist*, **4**. 121, 1928 ; S. G. Smith, *Foundry Trade Journ.*, **15**. 208, 1913 ; H. C. Sorby, *Industries*, **13**. 466, 1892 ; *Journ. Iron Steel Inst.*, **31**. i, 225, 1887 ; A. Stansfield, *Railroad Gaz.*, **36**. 207, 1904 ; J. E. Stead, *Journ. Iron Steel Inst.*, **49**. i, 486, 1896 ; **51**. i, 42, 1897 ; **53**. i, 145, 1898 ; **91**. i, 149, 1915 ; *Journ. West. Scotland Iron Steel Inst.*, **4**. 23, 1897 ; *Proc. Cleveland Inst. Eng.*, 53, 1895 ; 97, 1900 ; 164, 1906 ; 33, 1913 ;

J. E. Stead and H. C. H. Carpenter, *Journ. Iron Steel Inst.*, **88**. ii, 119, 1913 ; S. Stein, *Stahl Eisen*, **10**. 821, 1890 ; J. von Sternberg, *Versuch über das vortjeilhafteste Ausschmelzen des Roheisens aus seinen Erzen*, Prag, 19, 1796 ; B. Stoughton, *Eng.*, **98**. 537, 1904 ; B. Stoughton and F. J. G. Duck, *Trans. Amer. Soc. Steel Treating*, **10**. 31, 1926 ; E. Sütter, *Die Entstehung von Eisen-kristallen und ihre Wachstumsbedingungen mit Berücksichtigung der Vorgänge bei der allotropen umwandlung*, Greisswald, 1927 ; G. Tammann, *Journ. Inst. Metals*, **44**. 29, 1930 ; G. Tammann and A. A. Botschwar, *Zeit. anorg. Chem.*, **175**. 121, 1928 ; G. Tammann and H. Meyer, *Zeit. Metallkunde*, **19**. 85, 1927 ; G. Tammann and A. Müller, *ib.*, **18**. 69, 1926 ; G. I. Taylor and C. F. Elam, *Proc. Roy. Soc.*, **112**. A, 337, 1926 ; A. le Thomas, *Compt. Rend.*, **185**. 1595, 1927 ; E. E. Thum, *Chem. Met. Engg.*, **21**. 145, 1919 ; R. H. Thurston, *Iron and Steel*, New York, 581, 1885 ; G. Tschermak, *Sitzber. Akad. Wien*, **70**. 443, 1874 ; D. K. Tschernoff, *Proc. Inst. Mech. Eng.*, 152, 225, 1880 ; *Metallographist*, **2**. 74, 1899 ; *Rev. Univ. Mines*, (2), **7**. 129, 1880 ; F. Ulrich, *Neues Jahrb. Min.*, 666, 1856 ; R. Vogel, *Zeit. anorg. Chem.*, **116**. 21, 1921 ; W. L. Webster, *Proc. Roy. Soc.*, **107**. A, 496, 1925 ; **109**. A, 570, 1925 ; **114**. A. 611, 1927 ; *Nature*, **117**. 859, 1926 ; H. Wedding, *Stahl Eisen*, **7**. 82, 1887 ; **9**. 263, 1889 ; **13**. 974, 1893 ; **15**. 507, 1895 ; **26**. 456, 1906 ; *Das Kleinegefüge das Eisens*, Berlin, 1891 ; *Journ. Iron Steel Inst.*, **27**. i, 187, 1885 ; E. B. Wedmore, *Nature*, **118**. 14, 1926 ; K. Weissenberg, *Zeit. Kryst.*, **61**. 58, 1924 ; A. Westgren, *Engg.*, **111**. 727, 757, 1921 ; *Zeit. Metallkunde*, **22**. 368, 1930 ; *Jernkontorets Ann.*, (2), **75**. 101, 1920 ; (2), **78**. 121, 1923 ; *Phys. Ber.*, 935, 1921 ; *Journ. Iron Steel Inst.*, **103**. i, 302, 1921 ; A. Westgren and A. E. Lindh, *Zeit. phys. Chem.*, **98**. 181, 1921 ; A. Westgren and G. Phragmen, *Journ. Iron Steel Inst.*, **105**. i, 241, 1922 ; **109**. i, 159, 1924 ; *Nature*, **113**. 122, 1924 ; *Iron Coal Trades Rev.*, **108**. 784, 1924 ; *Jernkontorets Ann.*, (2), **78**. 449, 1923 ; *Phys. Ber.*, 1233, 1922 ; *Engg.*, **113**. 630, 1922 ; *Zeit. phys. Chem.*, **102**. 1, 1922 ; F. Wever, *Zeit. Elektrochem.*, **30**. 376, 1924 ; *Zeit. tech. Phys.*, **6**. 682, 1925 ; *Arch. Eisenhüttenwesen*, **2**. 58, 1929 ; *Stahl Eisen*, **44**. 51, 1924 ; *Naturwiss.*, **12**. 1106, 1924 ; *Zeit. physik*, **28**. 69, 1924 ; *Zeit. Metallkunde*, **20**. 363, 1928 ; *Mitt. Inst. Eisenforschung*, **3**. 45, 1921 ; **5**. 69, 1924 ; F. Wever and P. Rütten, *ib.*, **6**. 1, 1924 ; F. Wever and W. E. Schmid, *Zeit. Metallkunde*, **22**. 133, 1930 ; H. Wilkinson, *Journ. Asiatic Soc.*, **4**. 187, 1837 ; W. E. Williams, *Journ. Iron Steel Inst.—Carnegie Mem.*, **13**. 175, 1924 ; A. Wingham, *Journ. Iron Steel Inst.*, **60**. ii, 272, 1901 ; F. Wöhler, *Liebig's Ann.*, **94**. 125, 1855 ; **95**. 192, 1855 ; *Pogg. Ann.*, **26**. 182, 1832 ; R. W. G. Wyckoff, *The Structure of Crystals*, New York, 47, 1924 ; *Journ. Franklin Inst.*, **195**. 183, 1923 ; T. D. Yensen, *Trans. Amer. Electrochem. Soc.*, **56**. 215, 1929 ; J. Young, *Proc. Roy. Soc.*, **112**. A, 630, 1926 ; N. A. Ziegler, *Rev. Mét.*, **8**. 655, 1911 ; *Tech. Publ. Amer. Inst. Min. Eng.*, 273, 1930 ; B. Zschokke, *Rev. Mét.*, **21**. 635, 1924.

² H. S. George, *Trans. Amer. Inst. Min. Eng.*, **70**. 259, 1924 ; E. Heyn, *Zeit. Ver. deut. Ing.*, **44**. 433, 1900 ; *Stahl Eisen*, **8**. 82, 1887 ; J. A. Ewing and W. Rosenhain, *Proc. Roy. Soc.*, **65**. A, 85, 1899 ; *Phil. Trans.*, **193**. A, 353, 1899 ; **195**. A, 279, 1900 ; F. Osmond and W. C. Roberts-Austen, *ib.*, **187**. A, 424, 1896 ; K. Harnecker and E. Rassow, *Zeit. Metallkunde*, **16**. 312, 1924 ; J. C. W. Humfrey, *Engg.*, **71**. 360, 1901 ; V. N. Svechnikoff, *Rev. Mét.*, **27**. 404, 512, 1930 ; F. Osmond and G. Cartaud, *Journ. Iron Steel Inst.*, **71**. iii, 444, 1906 ; J. E. Stead, *ib.*, **53**. i, 145, 1898 ; **93**. i, 93, 1916 ; T. Andrews, *ib.*, **48**. ii, 542, 1895 ; *Proc. Roy. Soc.*, **58**. 59, 1895 ; W. Schwinning and E. Strobel, *Zeit. Metallkunde*, **22**. 402, 1930 ; G. Tammann and A. Müller, *ib.*, **18**. 69, 1926 ; G. Tammann and W. Krings, *Zeit. anorg. chem.*, **146**. 420, 1925 ; J. Czochralsky, *Stahl Eisen*, **35**. 1073, 1915 ; P. Oberhoffer and A. Heger, *ib.*, **43**. 1322, 1923 ; G. F. Kunz and E. Weinschenk, *Tschermak's Mitt.*, (2), **12**. 183, 1921 ; C. A. Edwards, *Journ. Inst. Metals*, **14**. 116, 1915 ; C. A. Edwards and L. B. Pfeil, *Journ. Iron Steel Inst.*, **109**. i, 129, 1924 ; C. F. Elam, *ib.*, **112**. ii, 111, 1925 ; H. H. Potter and W. Sucksmith, *Nature*, **119**. 924, 1927 ; W. Köster, *Arch. Eisenhüttenwesen*, **3**. 649, 1930 ; H. Jungbluth, *ib.*, **4**. 533, 1931 ; G. Rose, *Abhand. Akad. Berlin*, 43, 1863 ; G. Tschermak, *Sitzber. Akad. Wien*, **70**. 443, 1874.

³ A. Baykoff, *Rev. Mét.*, **6**. 832, 1909 ; C. C. Beinert, *Der Meteorit von Braunau*, Breslau, 1848 ; C. Benedicks, *Journ. Iron Steel Inst.*, **77**. ii, 237, 1908 ; F. Berwerth and G. Tammann, *Zeit. anorg. Chem.*, **75**. 145, 1912 ; A. Breithaupt, *Journ. prakt. Chem.*, (1), **4**. 245, 1835 ; A. Brezina, *Jahrb. Geol. Reichsanst.*, **35**. 199, 1885 ; H. C. H. Carpenter and S. Tamura, *Proc. Roy. Soc.*, **113**. A, 161, 1926 ; *Trans. Inst. Min. Met.*, **37**. 381, 1928 ; H. le Chatelier, *Rev. Mét.*, **11**. 766, 1914 ; J. Cornuel, *Compt. Rend.*, **35**. 961, 1852 ; H. von Dechen, *Ber. Niederrh. Ges. Bonn*, 51, 1861 ; O. A. Derby, *Arch. Museum Nacional Rio de Janeiro*, **9**. 153, 1896 ; C. H. Desch, *Trans. Faraday Soc.*, **10**. 255, 1915 ; C. A. Edwards, *Journ. Inst. Metals*, **14**. 116, 1913 ; (I am indebted to Prof. H. C. H. Carpenter, F.R.S., for Fig. 156) ; C. A. Edwards and H. C. H. Carpenter, *Journ. Iron Steel Inst.*, **89**. i, 138, 1914 ; J. A. Ewing, *Journ. Inst. Metals*, **8**. 1, 1912 ; J. A. Ewing and W. Rosenhain, *Phil. Trans.*, **193**. A, 353, 1899 ; **195**. A, 279, 1900 ; *Proc. Roy. Soc.*, **65**. A, 85, 1899 ; T. B. Focke, *Étude de quelques propriétés de très gros cristaux de fer*, Nancy, 1928 ; F. B. Foley, *Trans. Amer. Inst. Min. Eng.*, **68**. 891, 1923 ; F. B. Foley and J. E. Crawshaw, *ib.*, **73**. 948, 1926 ; F. B. Foley and S. P. Howell, *ib.*, **68**. 891, 1923 ; H. Gough, *Proc. Roy. Soc.*, **118**. A, 498, 1928 ; R. A. Hadfield, *Journ. Iron Steel Inst.*, **67**. i, 248, 1905 ; K. Harnecker and E. Rassow, *Zeit. Metallkunde*, **16**. 312, 1924 ; E. Heyn, *Zeit. Ver. deut. Ing.*, **44**. 443, 1900 ; *Stahl Eisen*, **8**. 82, 1888 ; *Journ. Iron Steel Inst.*, **65**. i, 377, 1904 ; H. M. Howe, *The Metallography of Steel and Cast Iron*, New York, 400, 1916 ; W. E. Hughes, *Proc. Roy. Soc.*, **103**. i, 355, 1921 ; O. W. Huntington, *Amer. Journ. Science*, (3), **32**. 284, 1886 ; P. von Jeremejeff, *Proc. Russ. Min. Soc.*, (2), **34**. 37, 1896 ; *Zeit. Kryst.*, **30**. 387, 1899 ; H. von Jüptner, *Tschermak's Mitt.*, (2), **23**. 197, 1904 ; H. Jungbluth, *Arch. Eisenhüttenwesen*, **4**. 533, 1931 ; W. Köster, *ib.*, **3**. 649, 1930 ;

S. T. Konobejewsky, *Zeit. Physik*, **39**. 415, 1926; V. N. Krivobok, *Trans. Amer. Soc. Steel Treating*, **8**. 703, 1926; G. E. Linck, *Zeit. Kryst.*, **20**. 214, 1892; L. W. McKeehan, *Trans. Amer. Inst. Min. Eng.—Metals Division*, 453, 1928; *Tech. Publ. Amer. Inst. Min. Eng.*, **29**, 1927; *Nature*, **119**. 705, 1927; C. H. Mathewson, *Trans. Amer. Inst. Min. Eng.*, **76**. 554, 1928; C. H. Mathewson and G. H. Edmunds, *Tech. Paper Amer. Inst. Min. Eng.*, **139**, 1928; M. Matweieff, *Rev. Mét.*, **11**. 766, 1914; W. E. W. Millington and F. C. Thompson, *Journ. Inst. Metals*, **31**. 81, 1924; O. Mügge, *Neues Jahrb. Min.*, ii, 55, 1899; *Neues Jahrb. Min. B.B.*, **14**. 314, 1901; *Zeit. anorg. Chem.*, **121**. 68, 1922; J. G. Neumann, *Haidinger's Ber.*, **4**. 86, 1838; *Haidinger's Abhandl.*, **3**. ii, 45, 1850; H. O'Neil, *Journ. Iron Steel Inst.*, **113**. i, 417, 1926; **117**. i, 689, 1928; F. Osmond and G. Cartaud, *Met.*, **3**. 536, 1906; *Trans. Amer. Inst. Min. Eng.*, **37**. 838, 1906; *Journ. Iron Steel Inst.*, **71**. iii, 444, 1906; F. Osmond, C. Frémont and G. Cartaud, *Rev. Mét.*, **1**. 25, 1904; (I am indebted to the Secretary of the Iron and Steel Institute for permission to use Fig. 157); A. M. Portevin and J. Durand, *ib.*, **11**. 771, 1914; M. A. F. Prestel, *Sitzber. Akad. Wien*, **15**. 355, 1855; C. W. Preston, *Nature*, **119**. 600, 1927; G. T. Prior, *Min. Mag.*, **21**. 189, 1929; F. Robin, *Rev. Mét.*, **8**. 444, 1911; G. Rose, *Sitzber. Akad. Berlin*, 45, 1863; W. Rosenhain, *Journ. Iron Steel Inst.*, **65**. i, 354, 1904; **89**. i, 180, 1914; *Engg.*, **96**. 510, 1913; W. Rosenhain and D. Ewen, *Journ. Inst. Metals*, **8**. 168, 1912; W. Rosenhain and J. McMinn, *Proc. Roy. Soc.*, **108**. A, 231, 1925; A. Sadebeck, *Pogg. Ann.*, **156**. 554, 1875; F. Sauerwald, B. Schmidt and H. Dienenthal, *Zeit. Physik*, **61**. 153, 1930; W. Schwinning and E. Strobel, *Zeit. Metallkunde*, **22**. 402, 1930; J. Seigle, *Tech. Moderne*, **20**. 665, 1928; S. W. J. Smith, A. A. Dee and J. Young, *Proc. Roy. Soc.*, **121**. A, 477, 1928; L. J. Spencer, *Min. Mag.*, **22**. 271, 1930; T. E. Stanton and L. Bairstow, *Engg.*, **86**. 731, 1908; *Proc. Inst. Mech. Eng.*, 889, 1908; J. E. Stead, *Trans. Faraday Soc.*, **10**. 275, 1915; *Journ. Iron Steel Inst.*, **89**. i, 190, 1914; E. Sütter, *Die Entstehung von Eisenkristallen und ihre Wachstumsbedingungen mit Berücksichtigung der Vorgänge bei der allotropen umwandlung*, Greisswald, 1927; V. N. Svetchnikoff, *Rev. Mét.*, **27**. 404, 512, 1930; G. Tammann, *Lehrbuch der Metallurgie*, Leipzig, 129, 1914; G. Tammann and H. H. Meyer, *Zeit. Metallkunde*, **19**. 85, 1927; G. Tammann and A. Müller, *ib.*, **18**. 69, 1926; S. Tamura, *Proc. Roy. Soc.*, **113**. A, 161, 1926; *Journ. Iron Steel Inst.*, **115**. i, 747, 1927; G. I. Taylor and C. F. Elam, *Proc. Roy. Soc.*, **112**. A, 337, 1926; F. C. Thompson and W. E. W. Millington, *Journ. Iron Steel Inst.*, **109**. i, 67, 1924; G. Tschermak, *Sitzber. Akad. Wien*, **70**. 443, 1875; F. Wever, *Zeit. Elektrochem.*, **30**. 376, 1924; *Zeit. tech. phys.*, **6**. 682, 1925; *Arch. Eisenhüttenwesen*, **2**. 58, 1929; *Stahl Eisen*, **44**. 51, 1924; *Naturwiss.*, **12**. 1106, 1924; *Zeit. Physik*, **28**. 69, 1924; *Zeit. Metallkunde*, **20**. 363, 1928; *Mitt. Inst. Eisenforschung*, **3**. 45, 1921; **5**. 69, 1924.

⁴ H. C. H. Carpenter and C. A. Edwards, *Journ. Iron Steel Inst.*, **89**. i, 138, 1914; C. A. Edwards, *The Physico-chemical Properties of Steel*, London, 131, 1920; J. A. Ewing, *Proc. Roy. Inst.*, **16**. 419, 1901; *Eng. Mag.*, **32**. 113, 1906; *Elect. Eng.*, **38**. 154, 196; *Journ. Inst. Metals*, **8**. 1, 1912; J. A. Ewing and J. C. W. Humfrey, *Phil. Trans.*, **200**. A, 241, 1902; J. A. Ewing and W. Rosenhain, *Proc. Roy. Soc.*, **65**. A, 85, 1899; *Phil. Trans.*, **193**. A, 353, 1899; **195**. A, 279, 1900 (I am indebted to Prof. Ewing for permission to use Figs. 158 to 162); C. Frémont, *Bull. Soc. Enc. Nat. Ind.*, **102**. ii, 357, 1903; P. Gaby-Aché, *Rev. Mét.*, **10**. 588, 1913; E. Heyn, *Mikroskopische Untersuchungen an tiefgeätzen Eisenschliffen*, Berlin, 1908; *Journ. Iron Steel Inst.*, **65**. i, 378, 1904; *Zeit. Ver. deut. Ing.*, **44**. 435, 503, 1900; E. Heyn and A. Martens, *Handbuch der Materialenkunde*, Berlin, 219, 1912; H. M. Howe, *The Metallography of Steel and Cast-Iron*, New York, 295, 1916; H. M. Howe and A. G. Levy, *Trans. Amer. Inst. Min. Eng.*, **50**. 536, 1914; J. C. W. Humfrey, *Journ. Iron Steel Inst.—Carnegie Mem.*, **5**. 91, 1913; W. E. W. Millington and F. C. Thompson, *Journ. Inst. Metals*, **31**. 81, 1924; H. F. Moore and T. Ver, *Bull. Eng. Univ. Illinois*, 208, 1930; O. Mügge, *Neues Jahrb. Min.*, ii, 211, 1895; i, 71, 1898; ii, 55, 1899; J. Muir, *Phil. Trans.*, **193**. A, 1, 1900; *Proc. Roy. Soc.*, **67**. A, 461, 1900; H. O'Neil, *Journ. Iron Steel Inst.*, **113**. i, 417, 1926; F. Osmond and G. Cartaud, *ib.*, **71**. iii, 444, 447, 1906; F. Osmond, C. Frémont and G. Cartaud, *Rev. Mét.*, **1**. 1, 1904; F. Robin, *Traité de Metallographie*, Paris, 153, 1912; F. Rogers, *Journ. Roy. Micro. Soc.*, (2), **27**. 14, 1907; W. Rosenhain, *ib.*, (2), **27**. 119, 1907; *Journ. Iron Steel Inst.*, **67**. i, 335, 1904; **70**. ii, 195, 1906; W. Rosenhain and J. C. W. Humfrey, *ib.*, **87**. i, 261, 1913; T. E. Stanton and L. Bairstow, *Proc. Inst. Civil Eng.*, **166**. 78, 1906; *Proc. Inst. Mech. Eng.*, 889, 1908; *Engg.*, **86**. 731, 1908; J. E. Stead, *Journ. Iron Steel Inst.*, **107**. i, 377, 1923; G. I. Taylor and C. F. Elam, *Proc. Roy. Soc.*, **112**. A, 337, 1926; F. C. Thompson and W. E. W. Millington, *Journ. Iron Steel Inst.*, **109**. i, 67, 1924.

⁵ J. C. W. Humfrey, *Journ. Iron Steel Inst.—Carnegie Mem.*, **4**. 80, 1912; W. E. Hughes, *Journ. Iron Steel Inst.*, **103**. i, 355, 1921; W. A. Macfadyen, *Trans. Faraday Soc.*, **15**. 98, 1920; J. A. Ewing and W. Rosenhain, *Phil. Trans.*, **193**. A, 353, 1900; *Proc. Roy. Soc.*, **65**. A, 85, 1899; E. J. Mills, *ib.*, **26**. 504, 1877; G. C. Stoney, *ib.*, **82**. A, 172, 1909; E. Bouty, *Compt. Rend.*, **88**. 714, 1879; **89**. 146, 1879; **90**. 987, 1880; **92**. 868, 1881; H. Stäger, *Helvetica Chim. Acta*, **5**. 584, 1920; V. Kohlschütter and E. Vuilleumier, *Zeit. Elektrochem.*, **24**. 300, 1918; O. Faust, *Zeit. anorg. Chem.*, **78**. 20, 1912; F. Credner, *Zeit. phys. Chem.*, **82**. 457, 1913.

⁶ P. Breuil, *Journ. Iron Steel Inst.*, **65**. 63, 1904; C. H. Carus-Wilson, *Phil. Mag.*, (5), **29**. 200, 503, 1890; *Proc. Phys. Soc.*, **10**. 331, 388, 1890; *Proc. Roy. Soc.*, **20**. 243, 1891; C. Chappell, *Journ. Iron Steel Inst.*, **89**. i, 492, 1914; C. Frémont, *Bull. Soc. Enc. Nat. Ind.*, (5), **1**. 1218, 1896; **102**. ii, 357, 1903; *Génie Civil*, **90**. 41, 453, 1927; **91**. 10, 1927; G. H. Gulliver, *Proc. Inst. Mech. Eng.*, **141**. 1905; L. Hartmann, *Compt. Rend.*, **118**. 520, 738, 1894; **152**. 1005, 1084, 1911; *Dis-*

tribution des déformations dans les métaux soumis à des efforts, Paris, 1896 ; *Congrès Internat., Methodes d'essai*, **1**. 95, 1901 ; *Bull. Soc. Enc. Nat. Ind.*, (5), **2**. 103, 1897 ; E. Heyn, *Handbuch der Materialenkunde*, Berlin, 223, 1912 ; J. E. Howard, *Eng. Record*, **67**. 332, 1913 ; H. M. Howe, *The Metallography of Steel and Cast-Iron*, New York, 298, 1916 ; J. B. Johnson, *The Materials of Construction*, New York, 241, 1897 ; B. C. Laws and A. O. Allen, *Phil. Mag.*, (7), **1**. 1039, 1926 ; W. Lüders, *Dingler's Journ.*, **155**. 18, 1860 ; W. Mason, *Chem. News*, **103**. 309, 1911 ; *Proc. Phys. Soc.*, **23**. 305, 1911 ; *Proc. Inst. Mech. Eng.*, 1205, 1909 ; M. Matweieff, *Rev. Mét.*, **11**. 766, 1914 ; P. Oberhoffer and M. Toussaint, *Stahl Eisen*, **44**. 1330, 1924 ; F. Osmond, *Compt. Rend.*, **118**. 650, 1894 ; F. Osmond, C. Frémont and G. Cartaud, *Rev. Mét.*, **1**. 11, 1904 ; *Génie Civil*, **44**. 76, 1903 ; A. M. Portevin and J. Durand, *Rev. Mét.*, **11**. 771, 1914 ; H. S. Rawdon, *U.S. Bur. Standards Journ. Research*, **1**. 467, 1928 ; F. Robin, *Rev. Mét.*, **8**. 454, 1911 ; J. Seigle, *Génie Civil*, **88**. 315, 332, 357, 1926 ; S. W. J. Smith, A. A. Dee and J. Young, *Proc. Roy. Soc.*, **121**. A, 477, 487, 501, 1928 ; H. Fowler, *Engg.*, **132**. 299, 1931 ; A. Nadai, *Proc. Amer. Soc. Testing Materials*, **31**. ii, 11, 1931 ; *Plasticity—A Mechanics of the Plastic State of Matter*, New York, 1931.

[7] R. J. Anderson and J. T. Norton, *Trans. Amer. Inst. Min. Eng.*, **71**. 720, 1925 ; J. H. Andrew, *Journ. Tech. Coll. Glasgow*, **1**. 63, 1925 ; R. S. Archer, *Trans. Amer. Inst. Min. Eng.*, **62**. 754, 1919 ; J. O. Arnold, *Journ. Iron Steel Inst.*, **59**. i, 175, 1901 ; *Proc. Inst. Civil Eng.*, **123**. 123, 1895 ; J. O. Arnold and J. Jefferson, *Engg.*, **61**. 177, 1896 ; W. D. Bancroft, *Trans. Amer. Inst. Min. Eng.*, **68**. 604, 1923 ; W. Barlow, *Scient. Proc. Roy. Dublin Soc.*, (2), **8**. 527, 1897 ; G. T. Beilby, *B.A. Rep.*, 604, 1901 ; 557, 1903 ; 449, 1904 ; 351, 1905 ; *Proc. Roy. Soc.*, **72**. A, 218, 226, 1903 ; **79**. A, 463, 1907 ; **82**. A, 599, 1909 ; **89**. A, 593, 1914 ; *Journ. Soc. Chem. Ind.*, **22**. 1166, 1903 ; *Proc. Faraday Soc.*, **3**. 827, 1904 ; **10**. 212, 1915 ; *Journ. Inst. Metals*, **6**. 5, 1911 ; *Phil. Mag.*, (6), **8**. 258, 1904 ; *Journ. Iron Steel Inst.*, **89**. i, 178, 1914 ; *Aggregation and Flow of Solids*, London, 1921 ; *Trans. Optical Soc.*, 22, 1908 ; G. T. and H. N. Beilby, *Proc. Roy. Soc.*, **76**. A, 462, 1905 ; G. D. Bengough, *Journ. Inst. Metals*, **7**. 167, 1912 ; **8**. 180, 1912 ; L. Cammen, *Trans. Amer. Soc. Steel Treating*, **17**. 563, 1930 ; C. Chappell, *Journ. Iron Steel Inst.*, **89**. i, 460, 1914 ; C. A. Edwards and H. C. H. Carpenter, *ib.*, **89**. i, 138, 1914 ; W. Ende, *Phys. Zeit.*, **30**. 477, 1929 ; F. B. Foley, *Trans. Amer. Inst. Min. Eng.*, **73**. 850, 1925 ; W. Guertler, *Internat. Zeit. Metallog.*, **5**. 312, 1914 ; R. F. Hanstock, *Phil. Mag.*, (7), **10**. 937, 1930 ; (7), **13**. 81, 1932 ; F. Hargreaves and R. J. Hills, *Journ. Inst. Metals*, **41**. 257, 1929 ; M. Hasselblatt, *Zeit. anorg. Chem.*, **93**. 75, 1915 ; E. Heyn, *Proc. Internat. Assoc. Testing Materials*, **6**. ii, 43, 1912 ; E. Heyn and A. Martens, *Handbuch der Materialenkunde*, Berlin, 1912 ; K. Honda and Y. Shimizu, *Nature*, **126**. 990, 1930 ; H. M. Howe, *The Metallography of Steel and Cast-Iron*, New York, 501, 1916 ; J. C. W. Humfrey, *Journ. Iron Steel Inst.*, **65**. i, 360, 1904 ; *Journ. Iron Steel Inst.—Carnegie Mem.*, **4**. 93, 1912 ; **5**. 86, 1913 ; *Trans. Faraday Soc.*, **10**. 240, 1915 ; Z. Jeffries, *Trans. Amer. Inst. Min. Eng.*, **56**. 571, 1918 ; **58**. 669, 1919 ; **60**. 474, 1919 ; Z. Jeffries and R. S. Archer, *Chem. Met. Engg.*, **25**. 697, 1921 ; A. F. Joffé, *The Physics of Crystals*, London, 1928 ; O. Lehmann, *Flüssige Kristalle*, Leipzig, 14, 1904 ; A. Michels, *Ann. Physik*, (4), **85**. 6, 1927 ; F. Osmond, *Journ. Iron Steel Inst.*, **84**. ii, 61, 1911 ; F. Osmond, C. Frémont and G. Cartaud, *Rev. Mét.*, **1**. 45, 1904 ; W. Rosenhain, *Trans. Faraday Soc.*, **10**. 290, 1915 ; *Engg.*, **96**. 509, 1913 ; *An Introduction to the Study of Physical Metallurgy*, London, 246, 1914 ; *Journ. Iron Steel Inst.*, **65**. i, 335, 1904 ; **70**. ii, 212, 1906 ; *Journ. Inst. Metals*, **8**. 179, 1912 ; W. Rosenhain and D. Ewen, *ib.*, **8**. 149, 1912 ; W. Rosenhain and J. C. W. Humfrey, *Journ. Iron Steel Inst.*, **87**. i, 256, 1913 ; W. E. Ruder, *Journ. Ind. Eng. Chem.*, **5**. 452, 1913 ; H. Schottky, *Nachr. Gött.*, 480, 1912 ; J. E. Sears, *Trans. Cambridge Phil. Soc.*, **21**. 105, 1912 ; G. Tammann, *Zeit. Elektrochem.*, **18**. 584, 1912 ; *Zeit. anorg. Chem.*, **92**. 37, 1915 ; G. Tammann and W. Crone, *ib.*, **187**. 289, 1930 ; F. C. Thompson, *Trans. Faraday Soc.*, **71**. 104, 1915 ; *Journ. Iron Steel Inst.*, **93**. i, 155, 1916 ; **95**. i, 155, 1917.

[8] A. T. Adam, *Journ. Iron Steel Inst.—Carnegie Mem.*, **10**. 65, 1920 ; C. Agte and K. Becker, *Phys. Zeit.*, **32**. 65, 1931 ; R. P. Ahrell, *Jernkontorets Ann.*, (2), **83**. 288, 1928 ; H. Allen, *Proc. Inst. Civil Eng.*, **94**. 235, 1888 ; H. Altpeter, *Stahl Eisen*, **35**. 362, 1915 ; *Beiträge zur Kenntnis des Einflusses des Drahtziehens auf die Eigenschaften von Flusseisendrähten, speziell auf deren Fedtigkeit und Biegbarkeit*, Düsseldorf, 1914 ; R. J. Anderson, *Journ. Inst. Metals*, **20**. 203, 1918 ; A. E. van Arkel, *Zeit. Metallkunde*, **22**. 217, 1930 ; A. E. van Arkel and P. Koets, *Zeit. Physik*, **41**. 701, 1927 ; J. O. Arnold, *Proc. Inst. Civil Eng.*, **123**. 127, 1895 ; E. J. Ball, *Journ. Iron Steel Inst.*, **37**. i, 85, 1890 ; **39**. i, 103, 1891 ; O. Bauer, *Mitt. Materialprüfungsamt Gross-Lichterfelde*, **7**, 1915 ; J. Bauschinger, *Civilingeneur*, 289, 1881 ; *Mitt. Mech. Tech. Lab. Hochschule Münchem*, 13, 1886 ; P. Beck, *Technika*, **11**. 151, 1930 ; P. Beck and M. Polanyi, *Zeit. Elektrochem.*, **37**. 521, 1931 ; R. Becker, *Zeit. tech. Phys.*, **7**. 547, 1926 ; L. E. Benson and F. C. Thompson, *Journ. Iron Steel Inst.*, **107**. i, 525, 1923 ; A. A. Blue, *Iron Age*, **113**. 716, 1271, 1924 ; A. A. Botschwar, *Zeit. anorg. Chem.*, **164**. 189, 1927 ; H. Brandes, *Zeit. phys. Chem.*, **126**. 196, 1927 ; J. A. Brinell, *Metallographist*, **2**. 129, 1899 ; *Journ. Iron Steel Inst.*, **29**. i, 365, 1886 ; G. R. Brophy and R. H. Harrington, *Trans. Amer. Soc. Steel Treating*, **19**. 385, 1931 ; J. D. Brunton, *ib.*, **62**. ii, 142, 1902 ; W. Campbell, *Journ. Franklin Inst.*, **154**. 1, 131, 201, 1902 (I am indebted to Mr. Campbell for permission to use Figs. 169 to 171) ; *Metallographist*, **5**. 286, 1902 ; *Trans. Amer. Foundrymen's Assoc.*, **23**. 582, 1914 ; *Met.*, **8**. 772, 1911 ; *Journ. Iron Steel Inst.*, **59**. i, 211, 1901 ; **64**. ii, 359, 1903 ; H. C. H. Carpenter and C. F. Elam, *Proc. Roy. Soc.*, **100**. A, 329, 1922 ; *Journ. Inst. Metals*, **24**. 83, 1920 ; *Engg.*, **110**. 385, 424, 1920 ; C. Chappell, *Journ. Iron Steel Inst.*, **89**. i, 460, 1914 ; G. Charpy, *Rev. Mét.*, **7**. 655, 1910 ; *Compt. Rend.*, **158**. 311, 1914 ; **155**. 585, 1912 ; H. le Chatelier, *Rev. Mét.*, **8**. 367, 1911 ; Y. Chu-Phay, *Trans. Amer. Soc. Steel*

Treating, **12.** 601, 1927 ; E. O. Courtman, *Bull. Brit. Non-ferrous Metals Research Assoc.*, 6, 1923 ; W. Crone, *Zur Rekristallisation der Metalle*, Göttingen, 1930 ; *Zeit. anorg. Chem.*, **187.** 289, 1930; W. J. Crook, *Iron Trade Rev.*, **75.** 1365, 1924; J. Czochralsky, *Zeit. Metallkunde*, **19.** 316, 1927 ; K. Daeves, *Zeit. anorg. Chem.*, **125.** 167, 1922 ; U. Dehlinger, *Zeit. Metallkunde*, **22.** 221, 1930 ; F. S. Dodd, *Proc. Staffs Iron Steel Inst.*, **40.** 12, 1924 ; A. N. Dovrovidoff and Y. V. Grdina, *Proc. Siberian Inst. Tomsk*, **1.** 34, 1926 ; *Trans. Amer. Soc. Steel Treating*, **10.** 820, 1926 ; C. A. Edwards and L. B. Pfeil, *Journ. Iron Steel Inst.*, **109.** i, 129, 1924 ; **112.** ii, 79, 1925 ; O. W. Ellis, *Journ. Inst. Metals*, **21.** 319, 1919 ; H. Fay and S. Badlam, *Metallographist*, **4.** 31, 1901 ; P. Fischer, *Krupp's Monatsh.*, **4.** 77, 1923 ; W. Fraenkel, *Zeit. Metallkunde*, **13.** 148, 1921 ; J. R. Freeman, *Trans. Amer. Soc. Steel Treating*, **10.** 67, 1926 ; O. Fuchs, *Zeit. deut. Ing.*, **59.** 915, 1916 ; H. Giersberg, *Ueber Arbeite verbrauch, Kristallisation, Verfestigung und ihre Temperaturabhängigkeit bei der Verformung der Metalle*, Breslau, 1927 ; P. Goerens, *Journ. Iron Steel Inst.—Carnegie Mem.*, **3.** 320, 1911 ; N. P. Goss, *Trans. Amer. Soc. Steel Treating*, **16.** 405, 1929 ; L. Grenet, *Bull. Soc. Ind. Min.*, **4.** 13, 123, 1910 ; *Compt. Rend.*, **183.** 600, 1926 ; C. Hambüchen, *Electromet. Electrochem.*, **1.** 73, 1891 ; *Zeit. Elektrochem.*, **8.** 226, 1891 ; H. Hanemann, *Zeit. Metallkunde*, **17.** 316, 1925 ; **18.** 16, 1926 ; *Stahl Eisen*, **31.** 1365, 1911 ; **47.** 481, 1927 ; H. Hanemann and C. Lind, *ib.*, **33.** 551, 1913 ; H. Hanemann and F. Lucke, *ib.*, **45.** 1117, 1925 ; H. Hanemann and A. Schneider, *ib.*, **49.** 7, 1929 ; D. Hanson, *Journ. Inst. Metals*, **20.** 141, 1918 ; W. Heike and F. Westerholt, *Zeit. anorg. Chem.*, **174.** 244, 1928 ; E. Heyn, *Journ. Iron Steel Inst.*, **62.** ii, 73, 1902 ; *Zeit. ver. deut. Ing.*, **44.** 433, 503, 1900 ; E. Heyn and O. Bauer, *Internat. Zeit. Metallog.*, **1.** 16, 1911 ; *Mitt. Materialprüfungsamt Gross-Lichterfelde*, 529, 1906 ; E. Heyn and A. Martens, *Handbuch der Materialienkunde*, Berlin, **2.** 219, 258, 1912 ; V. E. Hillman and F. L. Coonan, *Trans. Amer. Soc. Steel Treating*, **4.** 162, 1923 ; H. M. Howe, *Iron, Steel and Other Alloys*, New York, 256, 1906 ; *Chem. Met. Engg.*, **15.** 623, 1916 ; *Trans. Amer. Inst. Min. Eng.*, **37.** 404, 1906 ; **40.** 327, 1909 ; **41.** 167, 1910 ; **45.** 414, 1913 ; **47.** 585, 1913 ; **54.** 551, 1916 ; **56.** 582, 1916 ; **58.** 487, 1917 ; H. M. Howe and A. Sauveur, *ib.*, **22.** 546, 1893 ; *Eng. Min. Journ.*, **60.** 537, 1895 ; *Journ. Iron Steel Inst.*, **56.** ii, 195, 1899 ; *Metallographist*, **2.** 264, 1899 ; O. F. Hudson, *B.A. Rep.*, 428, 1913 ; Z. Jeffries, *Chem. Met. Engg.*, **18.** 185, 1918 ; *Trans. Amer. Inst. Min. Eng.*, **54.** 558, 1916 ; **56.** 571, 1916 ; **58.** 669, 1917 ; *Journ. Inst. Metals*, **20.** 109, 1918 ; *Trans. Faraday Soc.*, **12.** 40, 1916 ; Z. Jeffries and R. S. Archer, *The Science of Metals*, New York, 86, 117, 1924 ; *Chem. Met. Engg.*, **26.** 343, 402, 449, 1922 ; **27.** 747, 789, 1922 ; Z. Jeffries, A. H. Kline and E. B. Zimmer, *Trans. Amer. Inst. Min. Eng.*, **54.** 594, 1915 ; R. Johnson, *Jernkontorets Ann.*, **113.** 207, 1929 ; A. Joisten, *Met.*, **7.** 456, 1910 ; *Ber. Internat. Kongr. Bergbau Hüttenwesen*, 127, 1910 ; *Stahl Eisen*, **30.** 1562, 1910 ; *Einfluss der thermischen Behrandlung auf die Korngrösse und die Festigkeitseigenschaften des Eisens*, 1911 ; Aachen, 1911 ; B. Jonsen, *Jernkontorets Ann.*, (2), **82.** 207, 1927 ; H. von Jüptner, *Stahl Eisen*, **19.** 237, 278, 1899 ; *Metallographist*, **2.** 222, 1899 ; T. von Karman, *Zeit. Ver. deut. Ing.*, **55.** 1756, 1911 ; *Stahl Eisen*, **36.** 863, 1916 ; O. von Keil, *Des Oxydationsvorgänge im Thomas verfahren*, Breslau, 1919 ; F. C. Kelley, *Trans. Amer. Inst. Min. Eng.*, **76.** 390, 1928 ; G. L. Kelley, *U.S. Pat. No.* 1581269, 1926 ; *Trans. Amer. Soc. Steel Treating*, **10.** 133, 1926 ; G. L. Kelley and J. Winlock, *Journ. Franklin Inst.*, **201.** 71, 1926 ; F. Körber, *Stahl Eisen*, **38.** 877, 1918 ; **45.** 217, 261, 1925 ; V. N. Krivobok, *Trans. Amer. Soc. Steel Treating*, **8.** 703, 1925 ; R. Kühnel, *Zeit. Elektrochem.*, **22.** 53, 1930 ; J. A. M. van Liempt, *Zeit. anorg. Chem.*, **195.** 366, 1930 ; P. Longmuir, *Journ. Iron Steel Inst.*, **86.** ii, 188, 1912 ; **87.** i, 93, 1913 ; H. Lüpfert, *Vergleichende Untersuchungen über die Wärmebehandlung eingesetzter Stähle*, Dresden, 1929 ; *Stahl Eisen*, **49.** 1717, 1929 ; D. J. McAdam, *Tech. Paper Amer. Soc. Testing Materials*, **17.** ii, 58, 1917 ; **18.** ii, 446, 1916 ; G. Masing, *Naturwiss.*, **11.** 413, 1923 ; C. H. Mathewson and A. Philips, *Trans. Amer. Inst. Min. Eng.*, **54.** 608, 1916 ; E. Maurer, *Untersuchungen über das Härten und Anlassen von Eisen und Stahl*, Halle a. S., 1909 ; *Met.*, **6.** 33, 1909 ; *Rev. Mét.*, **5.** 711, 1908 ; E. Meyer, *Stahl Eisen*, **47.** 294, 1927 ; N. von Moos, P. Oberhoffer and W. Oertel, *ib.*, **48.** 393, 1928 ; R. G. Morse, *Metallographist*, **3.** 130, 1900 ; *Trans. Amer. Min. Eng.*, **29.** 729, 1900 ; K. Neu, *Stahl Eisen*, **32.** 397, 1363, 1912 ; P. Oberhoffer, *Zeit. anorg. Chem.*, **81.** 156, 1913 ; *Das schmiedbare Eisen*, Berlin, 217, 1920 ; *Stahl Eisen*, **33.** 1507, 1564, 1913 ; **36.** 798, 1916 ; P. Oberhoffer and P. Hartmann, *ib.*, **34.** 1245, 1914 ; P. Oberhoffer and W. Jungbluth, *ib.*, **42.** 1513, 1922 ; P. Oberhoffer, L. Lauber and H. Hammel, *ib.*, **36.** 234, 1916 ; P. Oberhoffer and H. Meyer, *ib.*, **34.** 1241, 1914 ; P. Oberhoffer and W. Oertel, *ib.*, **39.** 1061, 1919 ; **44.** 500, 1924 ; H. O'Neil, *Journ. Iron Steel Inst.—Carnegie Mem.*, **15.** 233, 1926 ; **17.** 109, 1928 ; A. Pomp, *Ferrum*, **13.** 49, 65, 1916 ; *Stahl Eisen*, **40.** 1261, 1366, 1403, 1723, 1920 ; *Zeit. Ver. deut. Ing.*, **62.** 1100, 1919 ; A. Pomp and E. Holweg, *Mitt. Inst. Eisenforschung*, **13.** i, 1930 ; *Röhrenind.*, **24.** 133, 148, 172, 184, 1931 ; A. Pomp and S. Weichert, *Mitt. Materialprüfungsamt.*, **10.** 301, 1928 ; A. M. Portevin, *Rev. Mét.*, **10.** 677, 1913 ; *Bull. Soc. Enc. Nat. Ind.*, **113.** ii, 207, 1914 ; *Internat. Zeit. Metallog.*, **6.** 58, 1914 ; E. Preuss, *Stahl Eisen*, **34.** 1370, 1914 ; H. E. Publow and S. E. Sinclair, *Bull. Michigan Exp. Station*, 29, 1930 ; H. E. Publow and L. J. Waldron, *ib.*, 9, 14, 1927 ; K. Puppe, *Stahl Eisen*, **35.** 706, 1915 ; **36.** 1185, 1916 ; E. Rasch, *Sitzber. Akad. Berlin*, 210, 1908 ; O. Reinhold, *Mitt. Eisenhütt. Inst. Aachen*, 47, 1919 ; W. Riede, *Stahl Eisen*, **44.** 880, 1924 ; F. Riedel, *ib.*, **34.** 19, 1914 ; C. H. Risdale, *Journ. Iron Steel Inst.*, **53.** i, 220, 1898 ; **56.** 102, 1899 ; *Metallographist*, **3.** 64, 1900 ; F. Robin, *Rev. Mét.*, **10.** 722, 752, 758, 1913 ; W. Rosenhain, *Journ. Inst. Metals*, **21.** 354, 1919 ; M. Rudeloff, *Mitt. tech. Versuchsanst Berlin*, **1.** 1, 1910 ; W. E. Ruder, *Trans. Amer. Inst. Min. Eng.*, **47.** 569, 1913 ; *Journ. Ind. Eng. Chem.*, **5.** 452, 1913 ; *Trans. Amer. Soc. Mech.*

Eng., **47**. 569, 1913 ; K. Rummel, *Stahl Eisen*, **39**. 237, 285, 1919 ; F. Sauerwald, *Zeit. anorg. Chem.*, **122**. 277, 1922 ; *Zeit. Elektrochem.*, **29**. 79, 1923 ; A. Sauveur, *Iron Age*, **91**. 258, 1913 ; *Proc. Internat. Assoc. Testing Materials*, **6**. ii, 6, 1912 ; *The Metallography and Heat Treatment of Iron and Steel*, Cambridge, Mass., 17, 1926 ; *Trans. Amer. Inst. Min. Eng.*, **26**. 863, 1896 ; E. Scheil, *Zeit. anorg. Chem.*, **139**. 81, 1924 ; E. Scheuer, *Zeit. Metallkunde*, **23**. 237, 1931 ; W. Schneider and E. Houdremont, *Stahl Eisen*, **44**. 1681, 1924 ; H. Schottky and H. Jungbluth, *Krupp's Monatsh.*, **4**. 197, 1923 ; E. H. Schulz and J. Göbel, *Stahl Eisen*, **40**. 1479, 1920 ; M. von Schwarz, *Zeit. Metallkunde*, **19**. 321, 1927 ; W. Schwinning and E. Strobel, *ib.*, **22**. 402, 1930 ; K. A. Seyrich, *Ueber die Einwirkung des Ziehprozesses und die wichtigstentechnischen Eigenschaften des Stahles*, Dresden, 1911 ; R. H. Sherry, *Iron Age*, **97**. 76, 1916 ; *Chem. Met. Engg.*, **10**. 666, 1912 ; *Chem. News*, **115**. 3, 15, 1917 ; *Trans. Faraday Soc.*, **12**. 284, 1917 ; C. Sobbe, *Stahl Eisen*, **33**. 1154, 1913 ; **34**. 19, 1914 ; A. Stadler, *Ferrum*, **11**. 271, 1914 ; *Stahl Eisen*, **34**. 1741, 1914 ; J. E. Stead, *Metallographist*, **1**. 289, 1898 ; **2**. 85, 1899 ; *Journ. Iron Steel Inst.*, **53**. i, 145, 1898 ; **54**. ii, 137, 1898 ; **83**. i, 54, 1911 ; **85**. i, 104, 1912 ; **88**. ii, 399, 1913 ; J. E. Stead and H. C. H. Carpenter, *ib.*, **88**. ii, 119, 1913 ; C. Sutor, *Stahl Eisen*, **37**. 740, 1917 ; E. Sutter, *Die Entstehung von Eisenkristallen und ihre Wachstumsbedingungen mit Berück-sichtigung der Voränge bei der Allotropen Umwandlung*, Greisswald, 1927 ; W. Tafel, *Zeit. Metall-kunde*, **21**. 265, 1929 ; *Stahl Eisen*, **34**. 481, 578, 1914 ; W. Tafel, H. Hanemann and A. Schneider, *ib.*, **49**. 7, 1929 ; G. Tammann, *Zeit. Elektrochem.*, **37**. 429, 1931 ; *Zeit. Metallkunde*, **22**. 224, 1930 ; *Gött. Nachr.*, 321, 332, 251, 1918 ; *Zeit. anorg. Chem.*, **113**. 163, 1920 ; **157**. 321, 1926 ; **185**. 1, 1929 ; G. Tammann and Q. A. Mansuri, *ib.*, **126**. 119, 1923 ; G. Tammann and H. H. Meyer, *Zeit. Metallkunde*, **18**. 339, 1926 ; G. Tammann and W. Salze, *ib.*, **19**. 187, 1927 ; D. Tschernoff, *Proc. Inst. Mach. Eng.*, **152**. 286, 1880 ; *Metallographist*, **2**. 74, 1899 ; R. Vogel, *Zeit. Elektrochem.*, **29**. 301, 1923 ; M. Volmer, *Zeit. phys. Chem.*, **102**. 267, 1922 ; H. Wald, *Stahl Eisen*, **34**. 1705, 1914 ; G. W. Walker, *Trans. Amer. Soc. Steel Treating*, **11**. 619, 1927 ; H. C. Wang, *Journ. Iron Steel Inst.*, **108**. ii, 285, 1923 ; F. Wever and N. Engel, *Ueber den Einfluss der Abkühlungschwin-digkeit auf die Temperatur der Umwandlungen, das Gefüge und den Feinbau der Eisen-Kohlenstoff-Legierungen*, Düsseldorf, 1930 ; *Mitt. Inst. Eisenforsch.*, **12**. 93, 1930 ; *Stahl Eisen*, **50**. 1308, 1930 ; J. H. Whiteley, *Journ. Iron Steel Inst.*, **98**. ii, 211, 1918 ; M. H. Wickhorst, *Proc. Railway Eng. Assoc.*, **13**. 753, 797, 1912 ; F. Wüst and W. C. Huntington, *Stahl Eisen*, **37**. 820, 1917.

[9] L. Aisenstein, *Rev. Univ. Mines*, (7), **13**. 106, 1927 ; L. Aisenstein and E. Decherf, *ib.*, (7), **8**. 330, 1925 ; J. H. Andrew, *Journ. Tech. Coll. Glasgow*, 93, 1926 ; P. Bardenheuer and K. L. Zeyen, *Mitt. Inst. Eisenforschung. Düsseldorf*, **11**. 225, 1929 ; *Giesserei*, **16**. 733, 1929 ; *Metallurgist*, **5**. 141, 1929 ; W. Campbell, *Journ. Iron Steel Inst.*, **64**. ii, 359, 1903 ; W. H. Cath-cart, *Proc. Cleveland Inst. Eng.*, 39, 1918 ; K. F. Göransson, *Jernkontorets Ann.*, **57**. 170, 1902 ; H. Hanemann, *Stahl Eisen*, **47**. 693, 1927 ; E. Heyn, *ib.*, **22**. 1227, 1902 ; *Journ. Iron Steel Inst.*, **62**. ii, 73, 1902 ; H. M. Howe, *Iron, Steel, and Other Alloys*, New York, 257, 1906 ; *Trans. Amer. Inst. Min. Eng.*, **47**. 456, 1913 ; *The Metallography of Steel and Cast Iron*, New York, 141, 202, 490, 1916 ; W. E. Jominy, *Trans. Amer. Soc. Steel Treating*, **16**. 298, 372, 893, 1929 ; J. V. McCrae and R. L. Dowdell, *Journ. Research Bur. Standards*, **5**. 265, 1930 ; J. V. McCrae, R. L. Dowdell, and L. Jordan, *ib.*, **5**. 1123, 1930 ; E. Pohl, E. Krieger and F. Sauerwald, *Stahl Eisen*, **51**. 324, 1931 ; *Report on the Nomenclature of Metallography*, *Metallography*, **5**. 145, 1902 ; *Journ. Iron Steel Inst.*, **61**. i, 90, 1902 ; A. W. Richards and J. E. Stead, *ib.*, **68**. ii, 84, 1905 ; W. Rosenhain, *Automobile Eng.*, **2**. 42, 71, 164, 1912 ; A. S. Stansfield, *Journ. Iron Steel Inst.*, **64**. ii, 433, 1903 ; J. E. Stead, *ib.*, **91**. i, 400, 1915 ; *Trans. North-East Inst. Eng. Shipbuilders*, **29**. 142, 1913 ; *Engg.*, **99**. 564, 1915 ; L. W. Wild, *Blast Furnace Steel Plant*, **9**. 541, 1921 ; K. W. Zimmerschied, *Trans. Amer. Inst. Min. Eng.*, **47**. 653, 1913.

INDEX

A

END OF VOL. XII